NON-LEAGUE
DIRECTORY
1994

PUBLISHER: TONY WILLIAMS

EDITOR: JAMES WRIGHT

ASSISTANT EDITOR: MIKE WILLIAMS

Published by:

Tony Williams

Copyright in this edition:

Tony Williams

ISBN 1-869833-51-1

Typeset by:

L'Hibou

Printed by:

BPCC Wheatons Ltd, Exeter

Distributed by:

Little Red Witch Book Distribution, 24a Queen Square, North Curry, Taunton TA3 6LE. Tel: 0823 491 069. Fax: 0823 490 281.

Cover photograph:

Yeovil Town's Jeff Sherwood is first to the ball on this occasion against Ian Wright, Arsenal's hat-trick hero in last year's third round FA Cup tie at Huish Park. Photo: Colorsport.

EDITORIAL PREFACE

Welcome to the sixteenth edition of the 'Non-League Club Directory'. A record 300 Leagues are now covered - coverage ranges from 150 pages devoted to the G.M.V. Conference to the tables of top divisions of parks' leagues. Likewise, 2,500 clubs are included in the book, and again the focus varies from six-page sections for each Conference club to one-line minor club entries.

The time flies past so quickly! I can hardly believe that this is the fourth Directory I have been involved with - it seems like only yesterday that I first came to North Curry to lend a hand with the 1991 edition. Whilst time between Directories seems to shorten, it fairly whizzes past during the hectic summer months when the 1000 page target is daunting to say the least. Well, we got there in the end, and I hope that the great amount of effort that has been invested by the hundreds of contributors, as well as ourselves, is reflected in the following pages.

James Wright

PUBLISHER:
Tony Williams

EDITOR:
James Wright

ASSISTANT EDITOR:
Michael Williams

EDITORIAL ASSISTANTS:
Steve Whitney, Greg Tesser, Daniel Wyrill

EDITORIAL ADDRESS:
**Football Directories, 24a Queen Square, North Curry, TAUNTON, Somerset
TA3 6LE
(Tel: 0823 490469.   Fax: 0823 490281)**

PHOTOGRAPHIC TEAM:

Eric Marsh, Colin Stevens, Dennis Nicholson, Dave West, Gavin Ellis-Neville, Mick Cheney, Francis Short, Paul Dennis, Roger Turner, Ged Rule, Keith Gillard, Ian Morseman, Alan Coomes, David Collins, Victor Robertson, Neil Whittington, Nick Robinson, Steve Daniels, Martin Wray, Elaine Sarjeant, Keith Clayton, Richard Brock, Don Fowler, Paul Barber, Derrick Kinsey, Alan Watson, Barry Lockwood, Rob Ruddock, John Diamond, Alan Monument, Tim Lancaster.

CONTRIBUTORS:

Mike Ford - 'Bureau of Non-League Football' (League Tables & County Cup Results), Paul Marsh (Statistics), Peter Hunter (GMV Conference), Nick Robinson (Diadora League), Dennis Strudwick (Beazer Homes League), Duncan Bayley (Northern Premier League), Malcolm Stammers (Welsh Football), Wally Goss (Amateur Football Alliance), Dave West (Women's Football), Mike Simmonds (Schools Football), Jeremy Biggs, Trevor Bailey (Sunday Football), Bob Morrison - 'First XI Sports Agency', Dudley Jackson, Stewart Davidson, Bill Berry - 'Non-League Traveller' (League & Club Addresses), Robert Errington, Gareth Davies (North Wales Football), Rob Kelly, Peter Bentley, Paul Bates, Basil Stallard, Mike Wilson (Diadora statistics), Kerry Miller, Leslie G Moore (Ten Year Records), Richard Ralph, Andy Molden, P Dridge, Steve Layzell, G E Andrews, P R Shelton, Steve Durham, Graham Showell, Julian Pugh, F P Wye, David Robinson, Richard Grey, Steve Farmery, Brian Byles, Paul Clayton, Trevor Perry, Kevin Motley, David Walton.

All League Secretaries & Officials - names accompany relevant pieces

All Club Secretaries & Officials who completed questionnaires

Welcome to Lucozade Sport

Lucozade Sport, the UK's No.1 Sport drink and Official Sport drink of the FA Premier League, is pleased to announce its link with non-League Football. With 95% of all football being played at this level, it gives us great pleasure to be involved with the many club activists up and down the country, whose ceaseless efforts keep the clubs going.

To this end, Lucozade Sport, in partnership with Team Talk magazine, is pleased to be involved in the Team Talk monthly awards, which recognise hard work and dedication to the sport at grass roots level. Sponsorship of this Non-League Club Directory, the game's well respected 'bible' in its sixteenth year, and its annual awards is also an important part of Lucozade Sport's overall contribution to British sport. This partnership also recognises the valuable role that Lucozade Sport, the UK's No.1 Sport drink, can play in enhancing the performance of full-time and part-time sportsmen alike.

On behalf of Lucozade Sport, may I take this opportunity to wish everyone involved in non-League football every success for the forthcoming season.

Andy Armstrong (Marketing Director - S.B. Consumer Drinks U.K.)

Acknowledgements

League Secretaries:
In my three years years compiling the Directory I have been very impressed with the efficency and enthusiasm of the Pyramid Leagues. Information has flowed into the office all summer, and as usual the problem has been finding the time to type it all rather than to gather it in the first place. This year I also wrote to the secretaries of many junior and Sunday leagues requesting tables. This was treading new ground somewhat as, unlike Pyramid Leagues, these competitions are unused to requests for information. The response was again heartening for example 106 Sunday leagues replied out of around 120 contacted. We are aware that summer brings many administrative chores for league officials, so thank you for taking the time to help publicise your competitions.

Club Secretaries:
In May questionnaires were sent to the secretaries of around 600 clubs, and so a warm thank you goes to those that replied.

Character Graphics (Taunton):
This summer sees the Directory technologically move into a new era. Gone are the dark ages when having run out a page we would unsheath the scalpal and spend ten minutes trimming and pasting bromides. We now just send the pages and photos to Character and they scan them to film. This makes our job simpler, and the finished product better. Our thanks go to Graham and the team.

Photographers:
Photographs are an absolute must to break up a statistical tome like this. The fact that whenever I needed a relevant picture of a championship or cup- winning side one was to hand, speaks volumes of the amount of work accomplished by the 'team'. They have travelled farther and wider this season in pursuit of the action, and the hundreds of photos scattered throughout this book bear testimony to this.

The Football Association:
In sixteen years the Football Association have been unwavering in their support of the Directory. The three F.A. Competitions provide, as always, the first major section of the book, and thanks go to Steve Clark and the Competitions Department for supplying information.

CONTENTS

For an index for all the individual leagues in this book, see overleaf (page 6).

LEAGUE INDEX

All leagues featured in this Directory are listed below with their appropriate page numbers. 'S.L.' denotes Sunday League, 'W.L.' denotes Women's League. For leagues that run to more than one page, the page listed is the front page. The League names listed are the original titles with sponsors names omitted - this is to ease reference only. League sponsors' receive due recognition on the relevant pages.

INTRODUCTION

So what will the 1992-93 season be remembered for? Certainly not the Conference title 'race' in which most runners found themselves 'lapped' by a Wycombe Wanderers side who were not to be denied after their near-miss twelve months earlier. The First Round of the F.A. Cup provided some cheer as six non-League sides captured Football League scalps, but things went a lttle flat after that with only one further victory, by Yeovil at Hereford, being registered.

After the most catastrophic summer ever for club closures (famous names such as Dartford, Alvechurch, Hythe and North Shields fell by the wayside), it was very heartening to note the successful return of reformed/rejuvenated clubs. Alvechurch, Hythe and North Shields all picked themselves up, dusted themselves down, and recommenced under a new guise at lower levels (Dartford will be looking to do likewise in the Winstonlead Kent League this season), but the real success stories were to be found at Aldershot Town, Oxford City, Romford, Bedford Town - the list goes.

I haven't yet had much time to dwell on what 1993-94 might have in store, so frantic has the summer been compiling this publication. Compilation of the Directory began in late May with a massive 'mail out'. Nearly a thousand letters were dispatched to league and club Secretaries and Press Officers. The responses soon began to flood back, and the past three months have seen myself and Mike slavishly trying to arrange them into a finished product. The aim, as in previous years, was to provide a comprehensive statistical review of the season past and informative companion to 1993-94.

I must confess that there has been many an occasion over the past summer when I regretted having contacted so many leagues and clubs, so swollen was my mail bag, and indeed my typing finger. But almost imperceptibly, the bulging folders containing tables, grids, reviews, questionnaires, photos etc have been emptied and the sixteenth 'Non-League Club Directory' is on its way to the printers.

As I write these notes on the final morning of the Directory's production, it looks as though 99% of the material submitted has been included, but even with 1088 pages to play with it has been an incredible cram. I think the book has now reached its optimum size, and in future editions we shall be concentrating more on improving the lay-out and standardising comparable sections rather than seeking to expand further.

My thanks again go to the hundreds of contributors. Most are active league and club officials, and this book should serve as a tribute to their season's work.

James Wright

LUCOZADE SPORT SPONSORSHIP

1989
* John Barnes first appeared on TV endorsing Lucozade Sport

1990
* Lucozade Sport was announced as the Official Sport Drink of British Athletics

1991
* Lucozade Sport was announced as the Official Sponsors of:
  - The Chafford Hundred Athletic Club
  - Team Solent
  - Motherwell Athletic Club
    * Most of the top British athletes now endorse the product

1992
* The Lucozade Games held at Sheffield's Don Valley Stadium heralded the return of our Olympic Champions

* Announcement of Sponsorship of Middlesex County Cricket Club

* Major Sponsorship with the FA Premier League as Official Sport Drink

* The Official Sport Drink of 19 Premier League Clubs

* Endorsed and used by the players - as seen in the 1992-93 FA Cup Final

1993
* Continued sponsorship of:
  - British Athletics (includes club sponsorship)
  - FA Carling Premiership (now endorsed by all 22 Premier League Clubs)
  - Middlesex County Cricket Club

"LUCOZADE SPORT" LINK WITH "TEAM TALK" IN UNIQUE PYRAMID FOOTBALL PARTNERSHIP

Britian's only National non-League Football monthly magazine "Team Talk" recently celebrated its second birthday with a new and novel tie-up with the UK's leading sports drink brand name **Lucozade Sport**, The Official Sport drink of the FA Premier League.

Determined that the many dedicated people who work so tirelessly to keep even the humblest of clubs buzzing with confidence - the unsung heroes - should be honoured for their days, weeks and months of ceaseless effort, "**Lucozade Sport**" and "Team Talk" have come up with an idea of making regional monthly awards to non-League club activists who go beyond the call of duty.

The awards, which will of course be announced and publicised through the pages of "Team Talk", cover all aspects of the daily bread and butter life of every club North, East, South and West. **The smartest looking ground; The most attractive club bar; The best value-for-money programme; The most impressive club shop.** All these categories will come under the microscope of the "**Lucozade Sport**"/"**Team Talk**" panel, with the monthly winners guaranteed extensive local media attention via the press and radio.

Both "**Lucozade Sport**" and "**Team Talk**" believe that the feedback obtained from such an award scheme will prove, if proof were necessary, that the dedicated amateur can still be the life blood of even such a money-conscious sport as football.

This partnership also recognises the valuable role that **Lucozade Sport, the UK's No.1 Sport drink**, can play in enhancing the performance of professional and amateur alike.

PUBLISHER'S FOREWARD

Its sixteen years since our first little non-League Football Annual was published and the game has certainly seen some major changes since Leatherhead visited Spennymoor United in that FA Trophy Semi-Final second leg, which gave us our first cover photo! I bumped into John Doyle, the featured Leatherhead player, in a Kingston pub last season and he still watches non-League football in the Surrey area. The differing fortunes of those two clubs underline the opportunities presented by the superb non-League Pyramid that The Football Association and the senior league officials gradually pieced together.

Leatherhead have sadly slipped down to Diadora Division Two since their glory days at of the Seventies Wembley while Spennymoor United are steadily moving up to join the senior northern clubs once again.

It was the initiative of the whole non-League world that provided the 'Pyramid' set up after many a wrangle, much loss of pride and a lot of persuasive debate, that put the pressure on the Football League to offer automatic promotion to our champions - the top team in The Alliance - now the GM Vauxhall Conference.

Lincoln City, Darlington and Colchester United (after two seasons) have been relegated from the Football League and have quickly returned in a blaze of glory having boosted their support, revitalised their administration and lifted club morale. They all said they had never enjoyed their football so much and hopefully the atmosphere they sampled in the Conference was taken back to be introduced to Division Three or Four.

Sadly our representatives haven't benefitted in the same way. Scarborough weathered their financial 'storm', have consolidated and enjoyed some exciting cup results, but Maidstone United and Barnet, who spent liberally in their determined efforts to leave the non-League world, then found that the necessary solid foundations were just not in place and tragically Maidstone disappeared while Barnet, at the time of writing, are battling to survive.

The Football League quite understandably have now tightened up the criteria needed for a Conference club to obtain an 'A' grading for entry into Division Three. It will be interesting to see first how many clubs will now be deemed fit to move up and sadly we may find that if only a couple do qualify, it could be a long time before someone actually wins promotion as champions.

So we have come a long way and got our pyramid in place. The days' when non-League clubs were frozen out of the 'old network' ensuring League clubs were always re-elected, came to an end and we had automatic promotion. It's our own fault we may now have 'blown it' but now our standards must go up again. Facilities, financial stability and quality of play will all improve if Conference clubs are seriously ambitious - I wonder how many really are?

In the last two years James Wright has worked incredibly hard on the Directory while Steve Whitney has ensured the progress made with our monthy non-League magazine 'Team Talk'. We have a very compact team on these publications with Michael Williams organising production, supervising layout and design and typesetting, Greg Tesser in charge of promotion, club sales, advertising and publicity and George Brown supervising all accounts and distribution.

The fact that a famous name in the world of advertising and sponsorship such as 'Lucozade Sport' is now involved with The Directory, Team Talk Awards, and non-League football in general, is a good compliment to the standing that our level of the game now has in the sporting world.

Yes, we have all come a long way in the last sixteen years. A great many of you have supported us all the way and we are also pleased to be making more and more new friends as the years go by.

Thanks to you all for the support, and lets hope that we will be able to publicise non-League football continuing to keep its unique friendly, but positive, atmosphere, while improving its standards on and off the field in the seasons ahead.   **Tony Williams**

Non-League Players Fact File

The definitive non-League football Who's Who containing detailed pen-pictures of some 3000 players from outside the Premier and Football Leagues. Literally every player from the GM Vauxhall Conference, Beazer Homes, Diadora and Northern Premier Leagues is included.

Edited by Steve Whitney
(Editor of Team Talk Magazine)

Price: £9.99

Orders should be sent to:

Non-League Players (NLD),
24a Queen Square, North Curry, Taunton TA3 6LE.
Cheques made payable to 'Non-League Publications'.
You can also pay by credit card by phoning our sales hot-line on 0823 490 080.

THE LUCOZADE SEMI-PROFESSIONAL FOOTBALL AWARDS 1992-93

PLAYER OF THE YEAR

Steve Guppy

* * * * *

INDIVIDUAL MERIT AWARDS

David Leworthy
Martin O'Neill
Brian Ross
Hedley Steele

* * * * *

REGIONAL CLUB AWARDS

NORTH EAST	Whitby Town
NORTH WEST	Southport
MIDLANDS	Nuneaton Borough
EAST of ENGLAND	Canvey Island
HOME COUNTIES NORTH	Chesham United
HOME COUNTIES SOUTH	Peacehaven & Tels.
WEST of ENGLAND	Clevedon Town
WALES	Cwmbran Town
F.A. CUP	Yeovil Town

PLAYER OF THE YEAR

Steve Guppy
(Wycombe Wanderers)

Wycombe Wanderers proved to be a quality team last season and one of their real 'gems' was Steve Guppy, whose every involvement with play gave the impression of sheer class. He was selected for the England Semi-Professional team and was followed by senior club scouts throughout the season. His manager Martin O'Neill was far too sensible to sell his most naturally gifted player, however, as Steve is not only a match-winner, as Gateshead found out in the last minute of the FA Trophy tie at Wycombe, but also a supplier of superb crosses and a tireless ninety minute worker, both in attack and defence. Good luck to our 'player of the year' in The Endsleigh Football League and hopefully there will be many more honours ahead.

INDIVIDUAL MERIT AWARDS 1992-93

David Leworthy (Farnborough Town)

David Leworthy proved to be one of those very rare talents that looked and was a class above the standard of football in which he was playing. He scored a super tally of 32 goals for Farnborough Town although his club suffered relegation, and he won his place in the England semi-professional team and of course scored! How Reading could release this natural goalscorer is difficult to understand, but the pleasure he gave in the Conference with his sharpness and natural eye for an opening will be remembered by those who saw last seaons 'goal machine' at work, and will doubtless be appreciated by Dover fans this season.

Martin O'Neill (Manager, Wycombe Wanderers)

Martin O'Neill certainly did it his way! In a charming and relaxed manner where there was always a twinkle in the eye and a smile, he sent out a relaxed but determined Wycombe Wanderers side whose football did its own talking. When in with a chance of the Nottingham Forest manager's job he surprised nearly everyone by announcing he would be taking Wycombe Wanderers into The League. The whole of non-League football wishes him well.

There will be new and more difficult hurdles to clear, but with sensible support throughout the club during the difficult periods, Martin's Wanderers should be able to give us all a lot of reflected glory as 'our champions' represent us in a manner of which we will be mighty proud.

Brian Ross (Marine)

When the Northern Premier League take on an FA XI they really want to win! So it wasn't surprising that Marine's Brian Ross played 'out of his skin' to help give his manager, Roly Howard, a 3-2 victory in the annual representative game last season. Neither was it a surprise when Brian was then selected for an FA XI himself and after another good preformance he became one of very few players outside the Conference to win England Semi-Professional Internationals caps. Marine of course had another great Cup season with Brian contributing vital goals and no doubt the 'Marine Machine' will be prominent again in the season ahead.

Hedley Steele (Tiverton Town)

It may appear that many of the better players in the West of England move from club to club following the available cash and winning the local medals. However Hedley Steele has stood out like a beacon from the mercenaries as he has given superb loyal service to Dorchester Town, Weymouth and Gloucester City since his early days with Exeter City. He has represented the Great Mills League and FA XIs with equal enthusiasm and his obvious love of the game saw him once again skipper the superb Tiverton Town team, who last season reached the FA Vase Final at Wembley, beat champions Clevedon 5-1 in the Les Phillips (League) Cup, and all this at the age of 39.

REGIONAL CLUB AWARDS 1992-93

North East - Whitby Town

The well-supported Whitby Town emerged champions after a very exciting battle at the top of the Northern League. Incredibly, it was the club's first title although they have been runners-up on five occasions. The whole town was looking forward to the club's promotion to the Northern Premier League under the Northern Pyramid, but this elevation was blocked by their league who are unhappy with current arrangements.

North West - Southport

Having noted the excellent performance in non-League football of three of the four clubs demoted from the Football League since automatic promotion/relegation was introduced, it is interesting to see how the last club to be voted out of the Fourth Division have fared. Since failing to gain re-election at the end of the 1977-78 season, Southport have been on a downward spiral with attendances slumping and the ground decaying. However, there has been a steady improvement on the field in recent years - the Northern Premier League Presidents Cup was won twice in the late Eighties, the League Cup followed in 1991 (a year in which the club also reached the final of the now disbanded national Premier Inter-League Cup), and finally this Spring Brian Kettle's talented side brought the championship to Haig Avenue. And the fans have returned - four figure gates are once again the norm. And the club accomplished a mammoth amount of ground improvements in a limited time to ensure that Haig Avenue was fit for the Conference. It may have taken them a little longer than Lincoln and Darlington, but who would bet against Southport returning to the League?

Midlands - Nuneaton Borough

The Beazer Homes League Midland Division was very competitive this season with a number of excellent sides around, but Nuneaton Borough proved themselves to be the best of the bunch. This is another case of a famous club returning from the brink of disaster. The Borough finished as high as second in the Gola League during the mid-Eighties, but suffered two consecutive relegations and found themselves on the verge of extinction. But club's with large popular support are rarely allowed to die, and Borough's many friends rallied around to save her. After a couple of season's consolidation, Nuneaton Borough, with Paul Culpin rattling in the goals again, are heading back in the right direction and the fans are following in droves.

East of England - Canvey Island

With an experienced and talented side, Canvey Island stormed to the Essex Senior League title remaining undefeated until well into the New Year. To round off a memorable season, they completed a League and Cup 'double' by beating Sawbridgeworth in the League Cup final, but their season will be perhaps best remembered for a fabulous run in the F.A. Vase that took them to the brink of Wembley. Teams from all of the country travelled to the compact 'inferno' of Park Lane and left defeated; even Tiverton Town who were to spoil Canvey's dreams of the Twin Towers. A fantastic season for a fantastic team.

Home Counties North - Chesham United

Chesham's very talented team, brilliantly managed by Gerald Aplin, were favourites to lift the Diadora League title from very early in the season, and they did not disappoint despite a spirited late challenge from St Albans City. However, before the season had been completed, the club had made it known that they would not be seeking promotion to the Conference because the amount of work needed to achieve that goal was prohibitive. Recent non-League history is littered with the corpses of clubs who died because they over-reached, and therefore Chesham should be applauded for their realism rather than panned for lack of ambition. Hopefully players and fans will remain loyal to this well-run club and more championships will be celebrated at Meadow Park.

Home Counties South - Peacehaven & Telscombe

Over the past couple of seasons, Peacehaven & Telscombe have been virtually unstoppable in the Unjet Sussex County League. To win a League and Cup 'double' is a worthy achievement, to win two consecutively is staggering. The club also had a fine run in the F.A. Vase, bowing out by the only goal at Gresley Rovers in the last sixteen after grabbing the headlines with a Fourth Round 4-1 walloping of Sittingbourne. In the year at Piddinghoe Avenue, manager Alan Pook has certainly worked wonders, and the success will probably continue now he has moved on.

West of England - Clevedon Town

Title favourites Clevedon were surprisingly pipped for the Great Mills League championship two years ago by neighbours and rivals Weston-super-Mare, but this meant that when their turn came it would be celebrated in the magnificent 'Hand Stadium', the plush new ground built on the outskirts of the seaside town during the summer of 1992. When you have strikers of the quality of Andy Perrett and John Durham, who bagged a hundred goals between them, you can hardly fail. Terry Rowles' team went through the entire league season undefeated, failing to win just four times, and excelled in all other competitons; in the F.A. Cup and F.A. Vase they enjoyed their longest ever runs, in the League Cup they were finalists for the first time losing only to Vase heroes Tiverton, and in the county cup they recorded a win over Yeovil's full Conference side.

Wales - Cwmbran Town

When the Konica League of Wales was inaugurated at the start of the season, Cwmbran Town were certainly not among the favourites to become its first champions. However, Tony Wilcox's side, based on a misely defence, slowly edged its way into contention and when early-season leaders Inter Cardiff were roundly defeated at Cwmbran Stadium on a February Friday in front of the new league's first four-figure crowd, the title became a real possibility. Inter Cardiff never gave up the chase, but Cwmbran hung on doggedly to become the Principality's first representatives in the European Champions Cup. And, as these notes are written, they have made a winning start in the first leg against Ireland's Cork City, so the dreams of playing A.C. Milan or Manchester United are still alive. It is on dreams like these that the League of Wales must thrive if it is to prosper.

F.A. CUP
TEAM OF THE YEAR

As we all appreciate it's often easier to raise one's game when you are the underdogs. However Yeovil Town's FA Cup record unfortunately deprives them of this advantage as they are now often favoured to win FA Cup ties against League Clubs. So last season's Cup run of Crawley Town (away) 2-1, Torquay United (away) 5-2, Hereford United (home) 0-0, (away) 2-1 and Arsenal (home) 1-3 was all the more praiseworthy.

Added to their 1-0 win at Walsall in 1991-92, The Glovers have now acheived three straight away wins at League grounds, but unfortunately they faced the might of Arsenal's Alan Smith and Ian Wright without centre-halves Mark Shail and Steve Rutter. However, their performances on the field and indeed the quality of interviews in the media did non-League football a power of good.

PREVIOUS AWARD WINNERS

Player of the Year

1983-84	Brian Thompson (Maidstone United)
1984-85	Alan Cordice (Wealdstone)
1985-86	Jeff Johnson (Altrincham)
1986-87	Mark Carter (Runcorn)
1987-88	David Howell (Enfield)
1988-89	Steve Butler (Maidstone United)
1989-90	Phil Gridelet (Barnet)
1990-91	Mark West (Wycombe Wanderers)
1991-92	Tommy Killick (Wimborne Town)

Individual Merit Awards

1978-79

Jim Arnold (Stafford Rangers)
Tony Jennings (Enfield)
Bily Kellock (Kettering)
Chris Tudor (Almondsbury Greenway)
Howard Wilkinson (England S-Pro Manager)

1979-80

Ted Hardy (Manager of Enfield)
Leo Skeete (Stamford)
Mark Newsom (Maidstone Utd)
Dave Ryan (Northwich Victoria)

1980-81

Tony Sanders (Manager of Altrincham)
Larry Pritchard (Sutton Utd)
Terry Moore (Bishop's Stortford)
Colin Williams (Northwich Victoria)
Keith Wright (England S-Pro Manager)

1981-82

Mickey Burns (Forest Green Rovers)
Barry Howard (Altrincham)
John Williams (Manager of Runcorn)
Keith Barrett (Enfield)
Graham Bennett (Bangor City)

1982-83

John Watson (Maidstone Utd)
John Davison (Altrincham)
John Barley (Maidstone Utd)
Ken Jones (Northwich Victoria)
Tommy Dixon (Blyth Spartans)
Bill Dellow (Secretary of Southern League)

1983-84

Paul Culpin (Nuneaton Borough)
Tommy Robson (Stamford)
Mark Newsom (Maidstone Utd)
Dave Ryan (Northwich Victoria)

1984-85

Paul Culpin (Nuneaton Borough)
David Howells (Enfield)
Paul & Lee Joinson (Halesowen Town)

1985-86
Kim Casey (Kidderminster H)
Paul Shirtliff (Frickley Athletic)
Cyril Whiteside (Chairman of Clitheroe FC)
Barrie Williams (Manager of Sutton Utd)

1986-87
Paul Davies (Kidderminster H)
Barry Fry (Manager of Barnet)
Peter Hunter (Secretary of GMV Conference)
Jim Thompson (Chairman of Maidstone Utd)
(Special 'Pyramid' creation award)

1987-88
Kevin Verity (England S-Pro Manager)
Steve Burr (Macclesfield)
Bill McCullough (Chairman of Barrow)

1988-89
Barrie Williams (Manager of Sutton Utd)
Stan Storton (Manager of Telford Utd)
Mickey Roberts (Macclesfield Town)
Nigel Ransom (Welling United)

1989-90
Gary Wager (Merthyr Tydfil)
Ray Wilkie (Manager of Barrow)
Gordon Bartlett (Manager of Yeading)
Gary Simpson (Altrincham)

1990-91
Dereck Brown (Woking)
Frank Northwood (Manager of Gresley Rovers)
Ted Pearce (Manager of Farnborough Town)
Noel White (Liverpool and The Football Association)

1991-92
David Leworthy (Farnborough Town)
Martin O'Neill (Wycombe Wanderers)
Brian Ross (Marine)
Hedley Steele (Tiverton Town)

PAST CLUB AWARDS

1977-1978

Team of the Year: Blyth Spartans
Special Merit Award: Enfield
FA Cup Award: Blyth Spartans
FA Vase Merit Award: Barton Rovers

1978-1979

Team of the Year: Barking
Special Merit Award: Worcester City
FA Cup Award: Altrincham
FA Vase Merit Award: Billericay Town

1979-1980

Team of the Year: Dagenham
Special Merit Awards: Altrincham &
Stamford
FA Cup Award: Harlow Town
FA Vase Merit Award: Guisborough
Town

1980-1981

Team of the Year: Altrincham
Special Merit Awards: Bishop's
Stortford, Runcorn & Slough
FA Cup Award: Enfield
FA Vase Merit Award: Willenhall

1981-1982

Team of the Year: Leytonstone &
Ilford
Special Merit Awards: Shepshed
Charterhouse, Enfield, Runcorn &
Wealdstone
FA Cup Award: Altrincham
FA Vase Merit Award: Rainworth MW

1982-1983

Team of the Year: England Semi-Pro
team
Special Merit Awards: Enfield, Sutton
Utd, Gateshead & Harrow Borough
FA Cup Award: Bishop's Stortford
FA Vase Merit Award: Harry Rudge
(Sec. Halesowen)

1983-1984

North East: Whitby Town
North West: South Liverpool
Midlands: Shepshed Charterhouse
East of England: Stansted
Home Counties: Maidstone Utd
West & Wales: Exmouth Town

1984-1985

North East: Bishop Auckland
North West: Fleetwood Town
Midlands: Telford United
East of England: Boston United
Home Counties: Wealdstone
West & Wales: Exmouth Town

1985-1986

North East: Gateshead
North West: Altrincham
Midlands: Kidderminster Harriers
East of England: Wisbech Town
Home Counties: Enfield
West & Wales: Barry Town

1986-1987

North East: Scarborough
North West: Macclesfield
Midlands: Burton Albion

East of England: Fareham Town
Home Counties: Barnet
West & Wales: Merthyr Tydfil

1987-1988

North East: Blyth Spartans
North West: Colne Dynamoes
Midlands: Kettering
East of England: Lincoln City
Home Counties: Bashley & Barnet
West & Wales: Yeovil Town

1988-1989

North East: Bishop Auckland
North West: Hyde United
Midlands: Tamworth
East of England: Kettering Town
Home Counties North: Leytonstone-Ilford
Home Counties South: Maidstone United
West & Wales: Merthyr Tydfil

1989-1990

North East: Darlington
North West: Colne Dynamoes
Midlands: Leek Town
East of England: Wivenhoe Town
Home Counties North: Barnet
Home Counties South: Welling United
West & Wales: Newport AFC
FA Cup Team of the Year: Whitley Bay

1990-1991

North East: Guiseley
North West: Witton Albion
Midlands: Stourbridge
East of England: Colchester United
Home Counties North: Barnet
Home Counties South: Littlehampton Town
West of England: Gloucester City
FA Cup Team of the Year: Woking

1991-1992

North East: Blyth Spartans
North West: Stalybridge Celtic
Midlands: Bromsgrove Rovers
East of England: Colchester United
Home Counties North: Stevenage Borough
Home Counties South: Hastings Town
West of England: Wimborne Town
FA Cup Team of the Year: Farnborough Town

THE FOOTBALL ASSOCIATION CHALLENGE CUP

REVIEW 1992-93

Featuring Non-League Clubs.

Group Results

(Attendances in brackets)

SECTION 1

Preliminary Round (29-August-92)

Hebburn 1 v 1 Annfield Plain (142)
r: Annfield Plain 5 v 1 Hebburn (90)
Easington Colliery 2 v 1 Shotton Com. (322)
Newcastle Blue Star 0 v 0 Whickham (47)
r: Whickham 0 v 2 Newcastle B.S. (75)
Workington 3 v 2 West Auckland (161)

First Qualifying Round (12-Sept.-92)

Annfield Plain 0 v 1 Newcastle B.S. (96)
Durham City 1 v 1 Bishop Auck. (301)
r: Bishop Auckland 5 v 2 Durham City (236)
Penrith 1 v 2 Blyth Spartans (185)
Easington Colliery 1 v 1 Workington (53)
r: Workington 1 v 0 Easington (239)

Second Qualifying Round (26-Sept.-92)

Newcastle Blue Star 0 v 1 Bishop Auck. (132)
Blyth Spartans 6 v 0 Workington (409)

Third Qualifying Round (10-October-92)

Bishop Auckland 1 v 3 Blyth Sp. (503)

SECTION 2

Preliminary Round (29-August-92)

Bamber Bridge 4 v 0 Prudhoe E.E. (275)
Shildon 2 v 0 Blackpool R. (107)
Peterlee Newtown 1 v 0 Evenwood T. (42)
Willington 1 v 5 Whitby Town (52)
Ferryhill Athletic 2 v 3 Spennymoor (232)

First Qualifying Round (12-Sept.-92)

Bamber Bridge 1 v 1 Peterlee N. (380)
r: Peterlee N. 0 v 2 Bamber B. (101)
Spennymoor United 4 v 0 Gretna (181)
Gateshead 3 v 1 Billingham S. (173)
Shildon 0 v 2 Whitby Town (157)

Second Qualifying Round (26-Sept.-92)

Bamber Bridge 0 v 4 Spennymoor (590)
Gateshead 5 v 2 Whitby Town (237)

Third Qualifying Round (10-October-92)

Spennymoor United 0 v 7 Gateshead (647)

SECTION 3

Preliminary Round (29-August-92)

Esh Winning 0 v 0 Alnwick T. (40)
r: Alnwick T. 2 v 1 Esh Winning (70)
Armthorpe Welfare 2 v 0 Brandon Utd (54)
Darlington CB 0 v 1 Consett (62)
Chester-le-Street T. 0 v 1 Billington T. (109)

First Qualifying Round (12-Sept.-92)

Alnwick Town 0 v 0 Consett (52)
r: Consett 2 v 0 Alnwick (72)
Ossett Albion 1 v 3 Netherfield (99)
Murton 1 v 2 Guisborough (60)
Armthorpe Welfare 2 v 2 Billingham T. (66)
r: Billingham Town 2 v 0 Armthorpe (128)

Second Qualifying Round (26-Sept.-92)

Consett 1 v 1 Netherfield (91)
(abandoned due to fog, 58 mins)
Consett 3 v 4 Netherfield (106)
Guisborough Town 3 v 0 Billingham T. (154)

Third Qualifying Round (10-October-92)

Netherfield 4 v 1 Guisborough (199)

SECTION 4

Preliminary Round (29-August-92)

Ossett Town 1 v 2 Dunston F.B. (132)
Horden Colliery Wf. 1 v 1 Darwen (39)
r: Darwen 5 v 0 Horden C.W. (131)
Crook Town 0 v 3 Norton & S.A. (36)
Northallerton Town 6 v 1 Langley Park (88)
South Bank 5 v 0 Bedlington Ter. (46)

First Qualifying Round (12-Sept.-92)

Dunston Fed. B. 7 v 0 Norton & S. (68)
South Bank *w/o - N. Shields w'drawn*
Fleetwood Town 3 v 2 Guiseley (288)
Darwen 1 v 6 Northallerton (182)

Second Qualifying Round (26-Sept.-92)

Dunston Feds 2 v 0 South Bank (79)
Fleetwood Town 1 v 2 Northallerton (239)

Third Qualifying Round (10-October-92)

Dunston Feds 0 v 3 Northallerton (165)

SECTION 5

Preliminary Round (29-August-92)

Yorkshire Amateur 1 v 3 Seaham Red S. (84)
St Helens Town 3 v 2 Tow Law Town (64)
Eccleshill United 3 v 2 Harworth C.I. (60)
Washington 1 v 3 Stockton (29)
(Played at Stockton)

First Qualifying Round (12-Sept.-92)

Seaham Red Star 3 v 2 Eccleshill (110)
Maine Road 2 v 1 Morecambe (108)
Chorley 1 v 1 Knowsley U. (232)
r: Knowsley Utd 2 v 1 Chorley (133)
St Helens Town 3 v 4 Stockton (79)

Second Qualifying Round (26-Sept.-92)

Seaham Red Star 1 v 1 Maine Rd (118)
r: Maine Road 1 v 1 Seaham R.S. (143)
r: Maine Road 0 v 5 Seaham R.S. (251)
Knowsley United 0 v 2 Stockton (100)

Third Qualifying Round (10-October-92)

Seaham Red Star 1 v 2 Stockton (195)

SECTION 6

Preliminary Round (29-August-92)

Salford City 0 v 1 Nth Ferriby U. (69)
Chadderton 2 v 1 Lancaster C. (173)
Ashton United 1 v 2 Garforth T. (154)
Formby 1 v 2 Bootle (90)

First Qualifying Round (12-Sept.-92)

Nth Ferriby Utd 1 v 0 Garforth T. (146)
Brigg Town 2 v 1 Bridlington (151)
Southport 0 v 0 Buxton (432)
r: Buxton 1 v 2 Southport (316)
Chadderton 3 v 0 Bootle (130)

Second Qualifying Round (26-Sept.-92)

Nth Ferriby Utd 0 v 2 Brigg Town (235)
Southport 2 v 0 Chadderton (542)

Third Qualifying Round (10-October-92)

Brigg Town 0 v 1 Southport (324)

SECTION 7

Preliminary Round (29-August-92)

Irlam Town 1 v 2 Atherton L.R. (30)
Sheffield 2 v 2 Rossendale U. (247)
(Played at Rossendale)
r: Rossendale Utd 1 v 2 Sheffield (250) *AET*
Gt Harwood Town 2 v 1 Prescot (87)
Thackley 2 v 1 Radcliffe B. (81)

First Qualifying Round (12-Sept.-92)

Atherton L.R. 1 v 1 Gt Harwood (150)
r: Gt Harwood T. 1 v 2 Atherton L.R. (117)
Caernarfon Town 1 v 4 Colwyn Bay (116)
Altrincham 3 v 0 Curzon Ash. (594)
Sheffield 3 v 1 Thackley (120)
(Played at Thackley)

Second Qualifying Round (26-Sept.-92)

Atherton L. Rovers 1 v 2 Colwyn Bay (300)
Altrincham 3 v 1 Sheffield (578)

Third Qualifying Round (10-October-92)

Colwyn Bay 3 v 3 Altrincham (601)
r: Altrincham 1 v 1 Colwyn Bay (784)
r: Altrincham 3 v 1 Colwyn Bay (805)

SECTION 8

Preliminary Round (29-August-92)

Harrogate Town 4 v 3 Louth Utd (171)
Bradford Pk Ave. 1 v 1 Burscough (142)
(Played at Burscough)

Durham's Mark Taylor outpaces Bishop Auckland's Mark Warrior in the 1-1 derby draw. Photo - Alan Watson.

A piece of juggling as Bishop Auckland win in the Second Qualifying Round at Blue Star. Photo - John Diamond.

Donald Peattie scores as Blyth demolish Workington 6-0 at Croft Park. Photo - Colin Stevens.

r: Burscough 1 v 2 Bradford (146) *AET*

Burscough	1 v 2 Bradford (146) *AET*
Warrington Town	6 v 1 Skelmersdale (145)
Mickleover R.B.L.	0 v 2 Belper Town (125)

r: before Burscough.

First Qualifying Round (12-Sept.-92)

Harrogate Town	1 v 2 Warrington (227)
Stocksbridge Pk S.	0 v 4 Stalybridge (501)
Hyde United	1 v 5 Accrington S. (333)
Bradford Pk Avenue	2 v 0 Belper Town (161)

Second Qualifying Round (26-Sept.-92)

Warrington	0 v 3 Stalybridge (638)
Accrington Stanley	2 v 0 Bradford P.A. (707)

Third Qualifying Round (10-October-92)

Stalybridge Celtic 1 v 2 Accrington (1323)

SECTION 9

Preliminary Round (29-August-92)

Clitheroe	2 v 1 Immingham T. (114)
Flixton	1 v 1 Worksop T. (155)
Worksop Town	3 v 0 Flixton (462)
Hucknall Town	2 v 1 Grantham T. (481)
Arnold Town	4 v 0 Liversedge (96)

r: before Worksop Town.

(Played at Kimberley Town)

First Qualifying Round (12-Sept.-92)

Clitheroe	1 v 3 Hucknall T. (240)
Glossop	0 v 1 Macclesfield (815)
Goole Town	0 v 1 Horwich RMI (163)
Worksop Town	5 v 3 Arnold T. (448)

Second Qualifying Round (26-Sept.-92)

Hucknall Town	1 v 1 Macclesfield (1305)
Macclesfield Town	3 v 1 Hucknall (635)
Horwich RMI	1 v 1 Worksop T. (147)
Worksop Town	1 v 5 Horwich (475)

r: before Macclesfield Town and Worksop Town.

Third Qualifying Round (10-October-92)

Macclesfield Town 1 v 0 Horwich (789)

SECTION 10

Preliminary Round (29-August-92)

Congleton Town	2 v 0 Eastwood T. (151)
Denaby United	2 v 5 Heanor Town (111)
Nantwich Town	1 v 1 Maltby M.W. (140)
Maltby M.W.	2 v 3 Nantwich (120) *AET*
Ilkeston Town	7 v 0 Harrogate R.A. (585)

r: before Maltby M.W.

First Qualifying Round (12-Sept.-92)

Congleton Town	0 v 0 Nantwich T. (190)
Nantwich Town	2 v 1 Congleton (283)
Blakenall	4 v 3 Droylsden (143)
Marine	5 v 0 Emley (341)
Heanor Town	2 v 1 Ilkeston T. (658)

r: before Nantwich Town.

Second Qualifying Round (26-Sept.-92)

Nantwich Town	1 v 0 Blakenall (269)
Marine	2 v 0 Heanor T. (306)

Third Qualifying Round (10-October-92)

Nantwich Town 0 v 1 Marine (382)

SECTION 11

Preliminary Round (29-August-92)

West Mids Police	5 v 2 Bridgnorth T. (76)
Halesowen Harriers	2 v 2 Wednesfield (110)
Wednesfield	2 v 3 Halesowen H. (115)
Bedworth United	1 v 0 Walsall Wood (110)
Lye Town	1 v 1 Barwell (82)

r: before Wednesfield.

(Played at Dudley Town FC)

Barwell	1 v 3 Lye Town (102)
Alfreton Town	2 v 1 Oakham Utd (163)

r: before Barwell.

First Qualifying Round (12-Sept.-92)

West Mids Police	1 v 2 Bedworth T. (114)
Alfreton Town	0 v 0 Stafford R. (381)
Stafford Rgrs	3 v 0 Alfreton (750)
Frickley Athletic	0 v 0 Lincoln U. (229)
Lincoln Utd	0 v 1 Frickley (334)
Halesowen Harriers	2 v 1 Lye Town (190)

r: before Stafford Rgrs and Lincoln Utd.

Second Qualifying Round (26-Sept.-92)

Bedworth United	1 v 1 Stafford R. (301)
Stafford Rangers	1 v 0 Bedworth (762)
Frickley Athletic	8 v 2 Halesowen H. (263)

r: before Stafford Rangers.

Third Qualifying Round (10-October-92)

Stafford Rangers 3 v 0 Frickley (814)

SECTION 12

Preliminary Round (29-August-92)

Bilston Town 1 v 3 Newcastle T. (85)

Pelsall Villa	0 v 0 Oldbury Utd (352)
Oldbury Utd	4 v 4 Pelsall Villa (209)
Pelsall	1 v 0 Oldbury (465) *AET*
Gresley Rovers	4 v 2 Highgate Utd (441)
Hinckley Town	1 v 1 Willenhall T. (67)
Willenhall T.	2 v 1 Hinckley Town (110)

r: before Oldbury Utd, Pelsall, and Willenhall T.

First Qualifying Round (12-Sept.-92)

Newcastle Town	0 v 1 Gresley R. (315)
Paget Rangers	1 v 3 Gainsborough (124)
Mossley	0 v 0 Borrowash (240)
Borrowash Vics	0 v 1 Mossley (130)
Pelsall Villa	1 v 0 Willenhall (347)

r: before Borrowash Vics.

Second Qualifying Round (26-Sept.-92)

Gresley Rovers	1 v 4 Gainsborough (748)
Mossley	1 v 2 Pelsall V. (290)

Third Qualifying Round (10-October-92)

Gainsborough Trin. 4 v 2 Pelsall V. (289)

SECTION 13

Preliminary Round (29-August-92)

Nuneaton Borough	2 v 1 Boldmere S. (515)
Raunds Town	2 v 2 Rocester (85)
Rocester	3 v 4 Raunds Town (162)
Leicester United	3 v 0 Dudley Town (132)
Stratford Town	6 v 2 Hinckley Ath. (142)

First Qualifying Round (12-Sept.-92)

Nuneaton Borough	3 v 1 Leicester U. (742)
Rothwell Town	0 v 2 Matlock T. (157)
Northwich Victoria	4 v 1 Winsford (1154)
Raunds Town	0 v 0 Stratford (83)
Stratford Town	1 v 2 Raunds T. (164)

r: before Stratford Town.

Second Qualifying Round (26-Sept.-92)

Nuneaton Borough	2 v 1 Matlock T. (846)
Northwich Victoria	0 v 2 Raunds Town (685)

Third Qualifying Round (10-October-92)

Nuneaton Borough 4 v 0 Raunds T. (1206)

SECTION 14

Preliminary Round (29-August-92)

Stewart & Lloyds	4 v 2 Evesham Utd (47)
N'hampton Spencer	1 v 1 Rushall O. (83)
Rushall	3 v 2 N'ton Sp. (108) *AET*
Sutton Coldfield	0 v 0 West Brom. T. (164)
West Brom. Town	0 v 2 Sutton C'field (164)
Sandwell Borough	4 v 0 Malvern Town (18)

r: before Rushall and West Brom. Town.

First Qualifying Round (12-Sept.-92)

Stewart & Lloyds	1 v 3 Sutton C'field (58)
Racing Club Warwick	0 v 2 Eastwood H. (108)
Leek Town	3 v 2 Burton A. (636)
Rushall Olympic	3 v 0 Sandwell B. (80)

Second Qualifying Round (26-Sept.-92)

Sutton Coldfield	2 v 1 Eastwood H. (156)
Leek Town	0 v 1 Rushall O. (418)

Third Qualifying Round (10-October-92)

Sutton Coldfield	0 v 0 Rushall O. (255)
Rushall Olympic	0 v 0 Sutton C'field (280)
Rushall Olympic	1 v 2 Sutton C'field (323)

r: before Rushall Olympic (both).

SECTION 15

Preliminary Round (29-August-92)

Boston	4 v 1 Banbury Utd (109)
Histon	1 v 2 Long Buckby (72)
Stourport Swifts	0 v 5 Stourbridge (273)
Rushden & Diamonds	2 v 0 Desborough (301)

First Qualifying Round (12-Sept.-92)

Boston	3 v 4 Stourbridge (45)
Arlesey Town	0 v 1 Shepshed A. (118)
Hednesford Town	1 v 1 Tamworth (1277)
Tamworth	2 v 4 Hednesford (1347)
Long Buckby	0 v 1 Rushden & D. (105)

r: before Tamworth.

Second Qualifying Round (26-Sept.-92)

Stourbridge	0 v 0 Shepshed A. (272)
Shepshed Albion	4 v 2 Stourbridge (272)
Hednesford Town	4 v 1 Rushden & D. (685)

r: before Shepshed Albion.

Third Qualifying Round (10-October-92)

Shepshed Albion 1 v 2 Hednesford (404)

SECTION 16

Preliminary Round (29-August-92)

Bourne Town	4 v 3 Peterboro. C. (93)
Hitchin Town	3 v 1 Chatteris T. (276)

Eynesbury Rovers 4 v 5 Milton K. Boro. (118)
Wisbech Town 10 v 0 Wellingboro. (403)

First Qualifying Round (12-Sept.-92)
Bourne Town 3 v 2 Milton K.B. (119)
Barton Rovers 2 v 3 Moor Green (141)
V.S. Rugby w/o Alvechurch w'drew
Hitchin Town 4 v 2 Wisbech T. (370)

Second Qualifying Round (26-Sept.-92)
Bourne Town 4 v 8 Moor Green (210)
V.S. Rugby 3 v 0 Hitchin T. (470)

Third Qualifying Round (10-October-92)
Moor Green 1 v 2 V.S. Rugby (428)

SECTION 17

Preliminary Round (29-August-92)
Cheshunt 0 v 0 Spalding Utd (75)
r: Spalding 0 v 5 Cheshunt (162)
Letchworth G.C. 1 v 1 Haverhill Rvrs (63)
r: Haverhill 3 v 4 L'worth (106) AET
Chalfont St Peter 1 v 0 Hoddesdon T. (106)
March Town Utd 1 v 3 Braintree T. (252)

First Qualifying Round (12-Sept.-92)
Cheshunt 1 v 0 Chalfont S.P. (80)
Hemel Hempstead 1 v 2 Solihull B. (88)
Chasetown 1 v 0 Redditch U. (110)
Letchworth Garden C. 0 v 4 Braintree (126)

Second Qualifying Round (26-Sept.-92)
Cheshunt 0 v 0 Solihull (115)

Solihull Borough 4 v 0 Cheshunt (125)
Chasetown 0 v 2 Braintree (181)

Third Qualifying Round (11-October-92)
Solihull Borough 4 v 1 Braintree (291)
(Played 11-10-92)

SECTION 18

Preliminary Round (29-August-92)
Purfleet 4 v 1 Gt Yarmouth T. (85)
Harwich & P'ston 3 v 3 Leighton T. (205)
r: Leighton 2 v 1 Harwich & P. (525)
Watton United 1 v 0 Burnham Rblrs (88)
Brook House 1 v 1 Aveley (89)
Rainham Town 2 v 0 Mirrlees B. (98)
(Played at Purfleet, 30/8/92)

First Qualifying Round (12-Sept.-92)
Purfleet 6 v 1 Watton U. (73)
Rainham Town 0 v 1 Corby Town (130)
(Played at Purfleet, 13/9/92)
Boston United 2 v 1 King's Lynn (1013)
Leighton Town 2 v 4 Aveley (463)

Second Qualifying Round (26-Sept.-92)
Purfleet 2 v 2 Corby T. (155)
r: Corby Town 1 v 0 Purfleet (261)
Boston United 1 v 2 Aveley (882)

Third Qualifying Round (10-October-92)
Corby Town 4 v 1 Aveley (321)

Tony Hemmings dives in as Northwich race to a four goal lead in 17 minutes v. Winsford. Photo - Colin Stevens.

Aveley defender Chris Bulgen brings the ball clear shadowed by Mark Day of Brook House. Photo - Francis Short.

SECTION 19

Preliminary Round (29-August-92)
Haringey Borough 5 v 2 Bury Town (32)
Norwich United 1 v 0 Edgware T. (79)
Gorleston 5 v 2 Clapton (139)
Biggleswade Town 1 v 3 Barking (61)
(Played at Langford)
Leyton 5 v 4 Felixstowe (100)
First Qualifying Round (12-Sept.-92)
Haringey Borough 0 v 0 Gorleston (30)
r: Gorleston 1 v 0 Haringey (266)
Leyton 4 v 2 Lowestoft (128)
Heybridge Swifts 2 v 4 Cambridge C. (132)
Norwich United 2 v 1 Barking (96)
Second Qualifying Round (26-Sept.-92)
Gorleston 1 v 2 Leyton (184)
Cambridge City 6 v 1 Norwich U. (311)
Third Qualifying Round (10-October-92)
Leyton 3 v 0 Cambridge C. (303)

SECTION 20

Preliminary Round (29-August-92)
Tilbury 3 v 2 Collier R. (60)
Sudbury Town 6 v 1 Saffron Wal. (416)
Newmarket Town 4 v 0 Langford (86)
Royston Town 1 v 2 Potton Utd (143)
Waltham Abbey 1 v 1 Halstead (100)
(Played at Halstead)
r: Halstead Town 3 v 4 Waltham A. (140)
First Qualifying Round (12-Sept.-92)
Tilbury 1 v 1 Newmarket (73)
Waltham Abbey 2 v 3 Baldock (178)
(at Baldock Town)
Chelmsford City 0 v 0 Grays Ath. (761)
r: Grays Athletic 2 v 1 Chelmsford (454)
Sudbury Town 3 v 2 Potton Utd (430)
Second Qualifying Round (26-Sept.-92)
Newmarket Town 2 v 2 Baldock T. (196)
r: Baldock Town 2 v 6 Newmarket (278)
Grays Athletic 1 v 0 Sudbury T. (398)
Third Qualifying Round (10-October-92)
Newmarket Town 1 v 0 Grays Ath. (350)

SECTION 21

Preliminary Round (29-August-92)
Wealdstone 2 v 1 Tiptree Utd (379)
(Played 30-8-92)
Flackwell Heath 2 v 0 Walt'stow P. (50)
Witham Town 4 v 3 Wingate & F. (118)
Ware 1 v 2 Stowmarket (91)
First Qualifying Round (12-Sept.-92)
Wealdstone 2 v 1 Witham T. (355)
(Played 13-9-92)
Kempston Rovers 3 v 4 Wivenhoe T. (128)
Dagenham & Redb. 1 v 1 Billericay (963)
r: Billericay Town 1 v 0 Dagenham (1018)
Flackwell Heath 0 v 5 Stowmarket (68)
Second Qualifying Round (26-Sept.-92)
Wealdstone 1 v 1 Wivenhoe T. (356)
(Played 27-9-92)
r: Wivenhoe Town 0 v 2 Wealdstone (302)
Dagenham & Redb. 6 v 1 Stowmarket (868)
Third Qualifying Round (10-October-92)
Wealdstone 1 v 6 Dagenham
(Played 11-10-92)

SECTION 22

Preliminary Round (29-August-92)
Ruislip Manor 1 v 0 Hornchurch (141)
Rayners Lane 2 v 2 Ashford (Mx) (70)
rAshford Town (Middx) 0 v 1 Rayners L. (117)
Basildon United 1 v 0 Tring T. (62)
Uxbridge 4 v 2 Southall (136)
Fisher Athletic 2 v 1 Bright'sea (114)
(Played at Brightlingsea United)
First Qualifying Round (12-Sept.-92)
Ruislip Manor 3 v 1 Basildon (159)
Fisher Athletic 1 v 7 Stevenage (569)
(Played at Stevenage Borough)
St Albans City 3 v 1 Brimsdown (440)
Rayners Lane 1 v 1 Uxbridge (122)
r: Uxbridge 0 v 1 Rayners Lane (156)
Second Qualifying Round (26-Sept.-92)
Ruislip Manor 1 v 3 Stevenage (437)

St Albans City 5 v 1 Rayners L. (681)
Third Qualifying Round (10-October-92)
Stevenage Borough 3 v 3 St Albans (1561)
r: St Albans City 2 v 1 Stevenage (1781)

SECTION 23

Preliminary Round (29-August-92)
Harefield Utd 0 v 1 Barkingside (16)
Burnham 1 v 0 Canvey Island (86)
(Played at Windsor & Eton FC)
Wembley 5 v 0 Welwyn G.C. (74)
Viking Sports 0 v 1 B. Stortford (140)
First Qualifying Round (12-Sept.-92)
Barkingside 1 v 3 Wembley (95)
Slade Green w/o Harlow T. (w'drawn)
Hertford Town 2 v 0 Hendon (188)
Burnham 3 v 2 B. Stortford (128)
(Played at Windsor & Eton F.C.)
Second Qualifying Round (26-Sept.-92)
Wembley 3 v 2 Slade Green (92)
Hendon 6 v 0 Burnham (338)
Third Qualifying Round (10-October-92)
Wembley 1 v 0 Hendon (421)

SECTION 24

Preliminary Round (29-August-92)
Molesey 3 v 1 Northwood (80)
Kingsbury Town 4 v 3 Oakwood (41)
East Thurrock U. 1 v 0 Chipstead (127)
Beckenham Town 2 v 0 Feltham & H. (50)
Redhill 1 v 5 Boreham Wd (115)
First Qualifying Round (12-Sept.-92)
Molesey 4 v 2 E Thurrock (63)
Boreham Wood 2 v 2 Chesham U. (272)
r: Chesham United 9 v 1 Boreham Wd (454)
Harrow Borough 0 v 2 Berkhamsted (261)
Kingsbury Town 2 v 3 Beckenham (65)
Second Qualifying Round (26-Sept.-92)
Molesey 0 v 4 Chesham U. (222)
Berkhamsted Town 0 v 0 Beckenham (162)
r: Beckenham Town 0 v 1 Berkhamsted (340)
Third Qualifying Round (10-October-92)
Chesham United 3 v 0 Berkhamsted (764)

SECTION 25

Preliminary Round (29-August-92)
Metropolitan Police 0 v 0 Ford Utd (50)
r: Ford United 0 v 2 Met. Pol. (80)
Three Bridges 0 v 3 Alma Swanley (111)
Lewes 1 v 0 Leatherhead (132)
Haywards Hth Town 0 v 1 Bedfont (101)
First Qualifying Round (12-Sept.-92)
Met. Police 2 v 1 Lewes (75)
Corinthian-Casuals 1 v 1 Slough T. (264)
r: Slough Town 4 v 3 C.-Casuals (518)
Staines Town 0 v 3 Yeading (239)
Alma Swanley 1 v 0 Bedfont (70)
Second Qualifying Round (26-Sept.-92)
Metropolitan Police 0 v 1 Slough T. (340)
Yeading 7 v 1 Alma Swan. (142)
Third Qualifying Round (10-October-92)
Slough Town 2 v 1 Yeading (930)

SECTION 26

Preliminary Round (29-August-92)
Wick 1 v 1 Ashford T. (150)
r: Ashford Town 3 v 1 Wick (246)
Deal Town 3 v 0 Epsom & E. (260)
Portfield 2 v 4 Faversham (60)
Merstham 0 v 0 Malden V. (60)
r: Malden Vale 3 v 1 Merstham (124)
Whyteleafe 5 v 1 Pagham (88)
First Qualifying Round (12-Sept.-92)
Ashford Town 1 v 1 Faversham (311)
r: Faversham Town 0 v 2 Ashford Town (391)
Whyteleafe 1 v 3 Windsor & E. (137)
Horsham w/o Dartford (w-drawn)
Deal Town 4 v 0 Malden V. (215)
Second Qualifying Round (26-Sept.-92)
Ashford Town 2 v 2 Windsor & E. (325)
r: Windsor & Eton 2 v 3 Ashford Town (234)
Horsham 1 v 6 Deal Town (275)

Paul Cavell (left) shrugs off Neil Cordice of Wealdstone as Dagenham & Redbridge win 6-1. Photo - Paul Dennis.

Jimmy King sells a dummy as St Albans avenge their 91-92 cup defeat against Brimsdown. Photo - John Sherwood.

Berkhamsted 'keeper Carlton Humphreys punches clear, but his side lose 0-3 at Chesham. Photo - Paul Dennis.

Third Qualifying Round (10-October-92)
Ashford Town 3 v 1 Deal Town (606)

SECTION 27

Preliminary Round (29-August-92)
Croydon Athletic 7 v 3 Arundel (31)
Banstead Athletic 2 v 1 Eastbourne U. (31)
Dorking w/o Hythe T. (w'drew)
Herne Bay 3 v 3 Camberley (134)
r: Camberley Town 2 v 3 Herne B. (76) AET
Walton & Hersham 2 v 1 Peacehaven (132)
First Qualifying Round (12-Sept.-92)
Croydon Athletic 1 v 2 Dorking (64)
Walton & Hersham 2 v 0 Wokingham (216)
Tonbridge A.F.C. 0 v 0 Dover Ath. (1012)
Dover Athletic 2 v 1 Tonbr. (1127) AET
Banstead Athletic 4 v 1 Herne Bay (56)
Second Qualifying Round (26-Sept.-92)
Dorking 4 v 2 Walton & H. (253)
Dover Athletic 0 v 0 Banstead (928)
r: Banstead Athletic 1 v 2 Dover Ath. (370)
Third Qualifying Round (10-October-92)
Dorking 1 v 0 Dover Athletic

SECTION 28

Preliminary Round (29-August-92)
Egham Town 2 v 1 Selsey (94)
Sheppey United 0 v 1 Croydon (77)
Worthing 8 v 0 Chatham T. (190)
Canterbury City 4 v 1 Bracknell (65)
Hailsham Town 3 v 1 Steyning T. (300)
First Qualifying Round (12-Sept.-92)
Egham Town 1 v 1 Worthing (140)
Worthing 7 v 1 Egham T. (276)
Hailsham Town 2 v 3 Bromley (487)
Burgess Hill Town 0 v 2 Hastings (306)
Croydon 0 v 0 Canterbury (25)
Canterbury City 2 v 1 Croydon (75)
Second Qualifying Round (26-Sept.-92)
Worthing 2 v 1 Bromley (267)
Hastings Town 1 v 2 Canterbury (419)
Third Qualifying Round (10-October-92)
Worthing 3 v 1 Canterbury (371)

SECTION 29

Preliminary Round (29-August-92)
Tunbridge Wells 0 v 4 Margate (251)
Worthing United 1 v 4 Langney S. (75)
Corinthian 1 v 0 Cove (26)
Lancing 2 v 3 Littlehampton (185)
First Qualifying Round (12-Sept.-92)
Margate 0 v 0 Corinthian (540)
r: Corinthian 1 v 1 Margate (137)
r: Corinthian 4 v 0 Margate (136)
Chertsey Town 3 v 2 Gravesend (287)
Kingstonian 4 v 0 Dulwich H. (535)
Langney Sports 3 v 1 Littlehampton (176)
Second Qualifying Round (26-Sept.-92)
Margate 1 v 4 Chertsey T. (565)
Kingstonian 2 v 2 Langney S. (431)
r: Langney Sports 1 v 1 Kingstonian (590)
r: Kingstonian 3 v 1 Langney (542) AET
Third Qualifying Round (10-October-92)
Chertsey Town 1 v 3 Kingstonian

SECTION 30

Preliminary Round (29-August-92)
Whitehawk 5 v 2 Chichester (71) AET
(replayed as ET should not have been played)
Chichester City 1 v 3 Whitehawk (100)
A.F.C. Totton 0 v 1 Havant T. (101)
Whitstable Town 1 v 2 Sittingbourne (391)
Horsham Y.M.C.A. 4 v 3 Eastbourne T. (67)
First Qualifying Round (12-Sept.-92)
Whitehawk 0 v 1 Sittingbourne (123)
Fareham Town 2 v 0 Tooting & M. (170)
Carshalton Athletic 1 v 0 Erith & B. (227)
Havant Town 2 v 1 Horsham YM (154)
Second Qualifying Round (26-Sept.-92)
Sittingbourne 3 v 2 Fareham T. (568)
Erith & Belvedere 1 v 1 Havant T. (245)
r: Havant Town 5 v 4 Erith & B. (240)

Third Qualifying Round (10-October-92)
Sittingbourne 3 v 2 Havant Town (682)

SECTION 31

Preliminary Round (29-August-92)
Ryde Sports 1 v 2 Southwick (104)
Poole Town 0 v 1 Abingdon Utd (145)
Shoreham 0 v 3 Witney T. (70)
Sholing Sports 1 v 2 Bemerton Hth (65)
Andover 5 v 0 Ringmer (147)
First Qualifying Round (12-Sept.-92)
Southwick 2 v 5 Witney T. (55)
Andover 0 v 6 Hampton (170)
Bognor Regis Town 9 v 2 Romsey Town (240)
Abingdon United 0 v 5 Bemerton Hth (42)
Second Qualifying Round (26-Sept.-92)
Witney Town 3 v 1 Hampton (261)
Bognor Regis Town 3 v 1 Bemerton Hth (245)
r: Bemerton Hth Harl. 2 v 2 Bognor R. (291)
r: Bognor Regis Town 1 v 1 Bemerton Hth (386)
r: Bemerton Hth Harl. 1 v 0 Bognor R. (429)
Third Qualifying Round (10-October-92)
Witney Town 1 v 0 Bemerton Hth (215)

SECTION 32

Preliminary Round (29-August-92)
Fleet Town 1 v 2 Abingdon T. (82)
Eastleigh 1 v 2 Newport I.W. (119)
Oxford City 2 v 3 Devizes T. (93)
Wimborne Town 1 v 1 Bournemouth (427)
r: Bournemouth 1 v 3 Wimborne (368)
First Qualifying Round (12-Sept.-92)
Abingdon Town 4 v 0 Devizes T. (145)
Buckingham Town 1 v 1 Maidenhead (181)
r: Maidenhead United 2 v 1 Buc'ham (187) AET
Thame United 2 v 3 Bashley (119)
Newport I.O.W. 2 v 3 Wimborne (296)
Second Qualifying Round (26-Sept.-92)
Abingdon Town 2 v 0 Maidenhead (241)
Bashley 3 v 1 Wimborne (826)
Third Qualifying Round (10-October-92)
Abingdon Town 4 v 2 Bashley (274)

SECTION 33

Preliminary Round (29-August-92)
Welton Rovers 4 v 1 Hungerford (81)
Petersfield Utd 0 v 1 Chippenham (70)
Gosport Borough 0 v 4 Calne Town (143)
Westbury United 0 v 5 Thatcham T. (121)
Shortwood Utd 0 v 4 Brockenhurst (75)
First Qualifying Round (12-Sept.-92)
Welton Rovers 1 v 4 Calne Town (63)
Brockenhurst 1 v 0 Basingstoke (302)
Salisbury 6 v 2 Trowbridge (425)
Chippenham Town 1 v 2 Thatcham T. (128)
Second Qualifying Round (26-Sept.-92)
Calne Town 0 v 1 Brockenhurst (103)
Salisbury 4 v 0 Thatcham T. (288)
Third Qualifying Round (10-October-92)
Brockenhurst 1 v 3 Salisbury (451)

SECTION 34

Preliminary Round (29-August-92)
Minehead 2 v 2 Lymington (120)
r: A.F.C. Lymington 2 v 1 Minehead (134)
Melksham Town 1 v 5 Swanage (80)
Paulton Rovers 0 v 2 Bristol M.F. (73)
Cinderford Town 3 v 0 Newbury T. (135)
First Qualifying Round (12-Sept.-92)
A.F.C. Lymington 3 v 3 Bristol M.F. (88)
r: Bristol Manor Farm 0 v 2 Lymington (80)
(at Keynsham Town F.C.)
Mangotsfield Utd 0 v 1 Dorchester (147)
Waterlooville 0 v 0 Cheltenham (204)
r: Cheltenham Town 2 v 0 Water'ville (541)
Swanage T. & H. 1 v 2 Cinderford (120)
Second Qualifying Round (26-Sept.-92)
A.F.C. Lymington 1 v 1 Dorchester (216)
r: Dorchester Town 2 v 4 Lymington (502)
Cheltenham Town 3 v 0 Cinderford (752)
Third Qualifying Round (10-October-92)
A.F.C. Lymington 0 v 1 Cheltenham (358)

Lloyd Hulme of Tonbridge just beats Corey Brown in the big Kent derby at Longmead. Photo - Alan Coomes.

Hailsham's Phil Comber holds off Paul Taylor, but the Sussex side lose narrowly to Bromley. Photo - Roger Turner.

Basingstoke suffered a shock defeat at Brockenhurst despite this surging run by Paul Odey. Photo - Jon Holloway.

SECTION 35

Preliminary Round (29-August-92)
Forest Green Rovers	4 v 2	Barnstaple (145)
Taunton Town	0 v 3	Barri (252)
Dawlish Town	0 v 3	Newport AFC (296)
Clevedon Town	4 v 1	Yate Town (346)

First Qualifying Round (12-Sept.-92)
Forest Green Rovers	1 v 2	Newport AFC (419)
Frome Town	1 v 2	Worcester (158)
Gloucester City	2 v 3	Weston-s-M. (509)
Barri	1 v 3	Clevedon T. (180)

Second Qualifying Round (26-Sept.-92)
Newport A.F.C.	3 v 0	Worcester (685)
Weston-super-Mare	0 v 4	Clevedon T. (695)

Third Qualifying Round (10-October-92)
Newport A.F.C.	1 v 1	Clevedon T. (723)
Clevedon Town	1 v 1	Newport (940)
Newport A.F.C.	4 v 2	Clevedon T. (599)

SECTION 36

Preliminary Round (29-August-92)
St Blazey	1 v 4	Falmouth T. (190)
Ilfracombe Town	3 v 4	Truro City (160)
Exmouth Town	1 v 2	Elmore (131)
Torrington	1 v 0	Bideford (220)

First Qualifying Round (12-Sept.-92)
Falmouth Town	2 v 0	Elmore (281)
Glastonbury	0 v 4	Bath City (422)
Weymouth	1 v 0	Saltash U. (750)
Truro City	2 v 0	Torrington (151)

Second Qualifying Round (26-Sept.-92)
Falmouth Town	0 v 3	Bath City (703)
Weymouth	3 v 2	Truro City (846)

Third Qualifying Round (10-October-92)
Bath City	2 v 0	Weymouth (890)

Bath's Paul Randall outjumps Dean Radford of Weymouth in City's 2-0 win. Photo - Alan P Casse.

Frank Sheriden uses his height well as Dorking start their magnificent run with a 2-1 win at Croydon Athletic. Photo - Dennis Nicholson.

Gary Donnellan crosses for Mark Xavier to score Hendon's first of six at home to Burnham. Photo - John Hutton.

Peter Shodeinde concludes a fine run to net Wembley's fifth and final goal against Welwyn. Photo - Paul Dennis.

Slough Town turn on the pressure in their win at Metropolitan Police. Photo - Mark Saunders, Slough Express.

Fourth Qual. Round

24th October 1992

Abingdon Town 0 v 0 **Merthyr Tydfil**
Att 800

Merthyr Tydfil 2 v 1 **Abingdon Town**
Webley 5, Rogers 79 868 Harvey-Lynch 85

Accrington Stanley 3 v 1 **Northallerton**
Burns 8, Beck 73, 1,159 McDonald 19
Lutkevitch 89

Ashford Town 1 v 2 **Slough Town**
McRobert 60 1,051 McKinnon 34
Stanley 46

Barrow 0 v 0 **Southport**
1,545

Southport 3 v 2 **Barrow**
Goulding 7, 2,082 Brady 16 30
McDonald 46,
Schofield 117

Blyth Spartans 1 v 1 **Stockton**
495

Stockton 1 v 2 **Blyth Spartans**
548

Cheltenham Town 3 v 2 **Worthing**
Owen 15, Irons 35, 891 Freeman 9 20
Howells 49

Enfield 0 v 0 **Aylesbury Utd**
940

Aylesbury Utd 2 v 1 **Enfield**
1,768

Farnborough Town 1 v 1 **Dorking**
Leworthy 3 1,023 Marriner 60

Dorking 2 v 0 **Farnborough**
Hanlon 32, Lunn 80 1,207

Gainsborough 0 v 2 **Altrincham**
805 Rudge 3,
Sidderley 50

Gateshead 3 v 0 **Whitley Bay**
Guthrie 12 75, 652
Cooke 69

Halesowen Town 1 v 2 **V.S. Rugby**
Massey 78 1,115 Green 3 13

Hednesford T. 1 v 3 **Dagenham & R.**
King 88 1,311 Cavell 34 49,
Broom 80

Kettering Town 2 v 1 **Corby Town**
Brown 66, 3,273 M Murphy 38(p)
F Murphy 76

Kidderminster 2 v 0 **Atherstone Utd**
Forsyth 24, 1,139
Hanson 83

Kingstonian 2 v 1 **Welling United**
Broderick 68, 861 Robbins 9
Cherry 88

Netherfield 1 v 1 **Macclesfield**
Ward 29 918 Leicester 19

Macclesfield 5 v 0 **Netherfield**
Kendall 18, 903
McMahon 53,
Sheppard 67,
Leicester 83,
Mitchell 85

Newmarket Town 0 v 2 **Hayes**
651

Newport A.F.C. 1 v 4 **Sutton United**
Lilygreen 60(p) 810 Thomas 44 49,
Brown 80, Scott 89

Runcorn 1 v 4 **Marine**
McCarty 39 749 Camden 14 27,
Ross 46 85

Sittingbourne 2 v 2 **Marlow**
Lillis 53, Emblem 89 1,259 Watkins 80
Blackman 83

Marlow 2 v 1 **Sittingbourne**
Lay 81 86(p) 450 Ross 41

Solihull Boro. 3 v 1 **Chesham United**
Burton 5 57, 618 Townsend 14
Carter 50

Stafford Rangers 3 v 0 **Bromsgrove**
Essex 35 44, Berry 88 1,274

Sutton Coldfield 6 v 1 **Leyton**
Richardson 23 31, 258 Frain 62
Alleyne 58,
Hunt 61 87,
Carroll 71

Telford United 1 v 2 **St Albans City**
Fergusson 69(p) 1,132 Cockram 30(p)
Clarke 86

Tiverton Town 0 v 0 **Bath City**
976

Bath City 2 v 1 **Tiverton Town**
Smart 3, Crowley 17 869 Short 83

Wembley 1 v 1 **Nuneaton Boro.**
Clark 25 828 Culpin 41

Nuneaton Borough 0 v 0 **Wembley**
2,512

Wembley 1 v 2 **Nuneaton Boro.**
Witter 74 384 Bullock 28,
Simpson 89

Witney Town 1 v 2 **Salisbury**
Clark 56 544 Bale 59,
Loveridge 86

Paul Burns (left) scrambles home Accrington's first goal against Northallerton. Photo - Colin Stevens.

Frankie Murphy nets Kettering's winner as they come from behind against local rivals Corby. Photo - Mick Cheney.

Adrian Blake saves spectacularly as his Kingstonian side surprisely beat Welling. Photo - Keith Gillard.

First Round Proper

14th November 1992

Accrington Stanley 3 (Beck 7 51 85)
Gateshead 2 (Lamb 9, Bell 75)
Att: 2,420
Accrington: Collings, Clark, Lampkin, Owen, Blackman, Hoskin, Collins, Cooper, Hughes, Beck, Lutkevitch. Sub: Burns.
Gateshead: Smith, Higgins, Halliday, Wrightson, McDowell, Elliott, Farrey, Cook, Bell, Askew, Lamb. Subs: Corner, Parnaby.

Blyth Spartans 1 (Howie 8)
Southport 2 (Haw 35, Withers 74)
Att: 2,300
Blyth: Gardiner, Liddle, Hayis, Mason, Ratcliffe, Teasdale, Plaskell, Howie, Peattie, Pyle, Muddleton. Subs: Walker, Nichol.
Southport: Moore, McDonald, Fuller, Mooney, Golding, Schofield, Senior, Brennan, Hall, Baines, Withers.

Bolton Wanderers 2 (Reeves 13, Walker 53)
Sutton Coldfield Town 1 (Gale 84)
Att: 5,345
Sutton: Elford, Ling, Sturgeon, Whittingham, Hadland, Carroll, Whitehouse, Hunt, Gale, Clarke, Biddle.

Brighton & Hove A. 2 (Kennedy 38, Codner 90)
Hayes 0
Att: 5,879
Hayes: Chatfield, W Kelly, Brown, Deer, Pedlar, Wingfield, Marshall, Walton, Pearce, Stevens, T Kelly. Subs: Cuffie, Baker.

Bury 2 (Knill 26(p), Robinson 81(p))
Witton Albion 0
Att: 2,682
Witton: Mason, Senior, Coathup, McNeilis, Connor, Lillis, Thomas, Rose, Gallagher, Burke, Adams. Sub: Alford.

Cardiff City 2 (Millar 26, Blake 36)
Bath City 3 (Withey 20, Gill 56, Vernon 70)
Att: 4,506
Bath: Mogg, Palmer, Dicks, Smart, Crowley, Cousins, Banks, Weston, Withey, Boyle, Gill. Sub: Vernon.

Chester City 1 (Ryan 34)
Altrincham 1 (Comstive 55(og))
Att: 2,420
Alty: Paladino, Woodhead, Freeman, France, Sidderley, Green, Saunders, Ogley, Harris, Carmody, Rudge. Sub: Bradshaw.

Altrincham 2 (Harris 69, Freeman 90)
Chester City 0
Played 25-11-92. Att: 3,000
Alty: Paladino, Woodhead, Freeman, France, Sidderley, Ogley, Saunders, Harris, Green, Carmody, Rudge. Sub: Bradshaw.

Colchester Utd 4 (Sorrell 17, Bennett 42 90, Ball 88)
Slough Town 0
Att: 3,858
Slough: Bunting, Whitby, Pluckrose, Briley, Forman, Anderson, Hazel, Scott, Sayer, McKinnon, Fiore.

Dagenham & Redbridge 4 (Broom 3, Connor 25, Butterworth 40, Cavell 79)
Leyton Orient 5 (Howard 37, Whitbread 45, Cooper 50 70, Jones 78)
Att: 5,300
Dagenham: McKenna, Shirtliff, Watts, Pamphlett, Connor, Broom, Owers, Butterworth, Cavell, Nuttell, Blackford. Subs: Kimble, Georgiou.

Dorking 2 (Grainger 21, Lunn 86)
Plymouth Argyle 3 (Dalton 31 65, Marshall 47)
15-11-92. Att: 3,200
Dorking: Orkney, Bird, Rains, Welch, Marriner, Tutt, Robson, Grainger, Lunn, Hanlan, Anderson. Sub: Thornton.

Exeter City 1 (Moran 7)
Kidderminster Harriers 0
Att: 3,082
Kidderminster: Steadman, Benton, McGrath, Weir, Brindley, Forsyth, Deakin, Grainger, Davies, Palmer, Hanson. Subs: Wilcox, Hadley.

Gillingham 3 (Clark 23, Crown 38, Forster 85)
Kettering Town 2 (Brown 18, Hill 69(p))
Att: 3,962
Kettering: Beasley, Reed, Gurnon, Nicol, Smalley, Stebbing, Brown, Donald, Riley, Murphy, Hill. Sub: Docker.

Kingstonian 1 (Russell 42)
Peterborough United 1 (Adcock 67)
Att: 3,826
Kingstonian: Blake, Finch, Cowler, Broderick, Russell, Kempton, Harlow, Parr, Barham, Vines, Cherry.

Peterborough United 9 (Philliskirk 8 26 66 89 90, Adcock 42 63, Cooper 82, Harlow 87(og))
Kingstonian 1 (Finch 74)
Played 25-11-92. Att: 5,307
Kingstonian: Blake, Finch, Lewis, Eriemo, Broderick, Kempton, Harlow, Barham, Cherry, Braithwaite, Parr. Subs: Shelford, Gbogindo.
Match declared void because Kingstonian goalkeeper, Adrian Blake, was injured by a coin thrown from the Peterborough supporters' end

Peterborough 1 (Sterling 68) **Kingstonian 0**
Played behind closed doors, 4-12-92
Kingstonian: Blake, Finch, Cowler, Eriemo, Broderick, Kempton, Harlow, Sheldrick (Cherry 56), Vines, Braithwaite, Parr. Unused sub: Lewis.

Lincoln City 0
Stafford Rangers 0
Att: 3,380
Stafford: Price, Pearson, Bradshaw, Simpson, Essex, Berry, Wood, Jones, Callaghan, Palgrave, Clayton.

Stafford Rangers 2 (Boughey 10, Bradshaw 62)
Lincoln City 1 (Costello 49)
Played 25-11-92. Att: 2,209
Stafford: Price, Circuit, Bradshaw, Wood, Essex, Berry, Boughey, Griffiths, Clayton, Palgrave, Callaghan. Sub: Jones.

Macclesfield Town 0
Chesterfield 0
Att: 3,063
Macc: S Farrelly, Sheppard, Bimson, Edwards, Kendall, Sorvel, Askey, Timmons, Lambert, Mitchell, Leicester.

Chesterfield 2 (Turnbull 20, Williams 107)
Macclesfield Town 2 (Mitchell 4 103)
Macclesfield won 3-2 on penalties
Played 25-11-92. Att: 4,143
Macc: S Farrelly, Sheppard, Bimson, Edwards, Kendall, McMahon, Askey, Timmons, Lambert, Mitchell, Leicester. Sub: M Farrelly.

A shot by Sutton scorer Simon Quail is charged by by Hereford player-manager Greg Downs. Photo - Francis Short.

Kidderminster's Paul Grainger slide-tackles Eamonn Collins of Exeter City. Photo. Photo - Paul Dennis.

Dorking's Steve Tutt battles it out with Plymouth's Warren Joyce at a rain-drenched Meadowbank. Photo - Dave West.

Marine 4 (Ward 30, Gautrey 38, Rowlands 40, Camden 60)
Halifax Town 1 (German 88)
Att: 1,892
Marine: O'Brien, Ward, Johnson, Roache, Draper, Gautrey, Murray, Rowlands, Ross, Camden, Dawson. Subs: McDonough, Grant.

Marlow 3 (Lay 19, Watkins 64, Glasgow 82)
Salisbury 3 (Loveridge 11, Sanders 30, Fletcher 53)
Att: 940
Marlow: Ellis, George, Mikurenda, Stone, Hubbick, Dell, Lay, Regan, Watkins, Davies, Glasgow. Subs: Blackman, Ferguson.
Salisbury: Simpkins, Payne, Green, Loveridge, Emms, Fletcher, Gommershall, Shaw, Sanders, Chalk, Bale.

Salisbury 2 (Chalk 40, Sanders 63)
Marlow 2 (Hannigan 49, Glasgow 62)
Played 5-12-92. Att: 1,854
Salisbury: Simpkins, Payne, Green, Loveridge, Emms, Fletcher, Hobson (Maskell 95), Shaw, Sanders, Chalk, Bale (Gommersall 44).
Marlow: Lester, Ferguson, Mikurenda, Stone (Glasgow 45), Hannigan, Hubbick, Lay, Regan, Watkins, Bushay (Francis 117), Caesar.

St Albans City 1 (Duffield 56(p))
Cheltenham Town 2 (Willetts 61(p), Purdie 72)
Att: 3,189
St Albans: Westwood, Smart, Risley, Dowie, Price, Cockram, Duffield, Gurney, Clark, Williams, King. Sub: Brett.
Cheltenham: Nicholls, Howells, Willetts, Brown, Vircavs, Tucker, Lovell, N Smith, J Smith, Bloomer, Hirons. Sub: Purdie.

Solihull Borough 2 (Canning 15, Carter 31)
V.S. Rugby 2 (Bufton 4, Green 80)
Att: 1,260
Solihull: Houghton, Byrne, Latchford, Boxall, Dyson, Ollis, Mulders, Tuohy, Canning, Carter, Burton. Sub: Hawker.
Rugby: Martin, Sweeney, Hardwick, Fitzpatrick, Olner, Redgate, Smith, Bradder, Bufton, Shearer, Green. Sub: Warner.

V.S. Rugby 2 (Green 49, Smith 93)
Solihull Borough 1 (Canning 45)
Att: 1,289
Rugby: Martin, Sweeney, T McGinty, Fitzpatrick, Olner, Redgate, Smith, Bradder, Carty, Shearer, Green. Sub: Hardwick.
Solihull: Houghton, Pinner, Latchford, Mulders, Dyson, Ollis, Hawker, Tuohy, Canning, Carter, Burton. Subs: Attwood, Bertschin.

Sutton United 1 (Quail 12)
Hereford United 2 (Pickard 19, Barton(og)) 77)
Att: 2,749
Sutton: Fearon, Gates, Barton, N Golley, Costello, M Golley, Byrne, Quail, Feltham, Thomas, Scott. Subs: Brown, Evans.

Torquay United 2 (Foster 83, Herd 89)
Yeovil Town 5 (Wilson 31 51, Batty 57(p) 77(p) 90)
Att: 3,453
Yeovil: Coles, Coates, Sherwood, Shail, Ferns, Cooper, Sanderson, Batty, Wilson, Spencer, Harrower. Subs: Wallace, Nevin.

West Bromwich Albion 8 (Donovan 22 37 87, McNally 34, Taylor 38, Raven 74, Hamilton 82)
Aylesbury United 0
Att: 12,337
Aylesbury: Garner, Day, Collins, Grenfell, Mason, Cassidy, Robinson, Ashby, Lawford, Sansom, Heath. Subs: Tomlinson, Jones.

Woking 3 (Clement 3, Biggins 80, Carroll 90)
Nuneaton Borough 2 (Bullock 2, Culpin 53)
Att: 3,280
Woking: Batty, Clement, L Wye, Nugent, Baron, S Wye, Fielder, Biggins, Senior, Puckett, Steele. Subs: Carroll, Fleming.
Nuneaton: Manuel, Wade, Tarry, Bullock, Ridding, Cotterill, Simpson, Culpin, Rosegreen, Mogford, Symons.

Wycombe 3 (Scott 12, Carroll 16, Stapleton 85)
Merthyr Tydfil 1 (Rogers 42)
Att: 4,322
Wycombe: Hyde, Cousins, Crossley, Kerr, Creaser, Hutchinson, Carroll, Casey, Stapleton, Scott, Guppy.
Merthyr: Morris, M Williams, James, Boyle, Abraham, Rogers, Beattie, Davies, D'Auria, Coates, C Williams.

Wycombe put up a good showing in their Second Round replay at West Bromwich before losing 0-1. Here Steve Thompson is outnumbered by defenders as he attacks a corner. Photo - Paul Dennis.

Second Round Proper

5th December 1992

Accrington Stanley 1 (Cooper 82)
Crewe Alexandra 6 (Carr 35, Naylor 40 84, Whalley 64 78, Clarkson 90)
At Blackburn Rovers. Att: 10,081
Accrington: Collings, Clark, Lampkin (Schofield 81), Owen, Johnstone, Burns (McCluskie 60), Collins, Cooper, Hughes, Beck, Hoskin.

Altrincham 1 (Dyson 83)
Port Vale 4 (Swan 16, Foyle 21, Taylor 79, Van der Laan 86)
Att: 4,000
Alty: Paladino, Woodhead, Freeman, France, Sidderley, Ogley, Saunders (Hayde 73), Harris, Bradshaw, Carmody, Rudge (Dyson 73).

Bath City 2 (Smart 59, Randall 82)
Northampton Town 2 (Mogg 59 (og), Chard 72)
Played 6-12-92. Att: 3,626
Bath: Mogg, Palmer (Singleton 74), Dicks, Gill, Crowley, Cousins, Banks, Weston (Randall 77), Withey, Smart, Vernon.

Northampton Town 3 (McParland 75, Wilkin 77, Bell 89)
Bath City 0
Played 15-12-92. Att: 2,420
Bath: Mogg, Palmer, Dicks, Ricketts (Vernon 65), Crowley, Cousins, Banks, Gill, Withey, Smart, Randall. Unused sub: Hedges.

Brighton 1 (Kennedy 18) **Woking 1** (S Wye 71)
Att: 9,208
Woking: Batty, Clement, L Wye, Nugent, Alexander, S Wye, Fleming, Staples, Senior, Puckett (Carroll 67), Fielder. Unused sub: Brown.

Woking 1 (Senior 8) **Brighton 2** (Codner 34, Crumplin 84)
Played 16-12-92. Att: 5,870
Woking: Batty, Fleming, K Brown, Fielder, Alexander, L Wye, S Wye, D Brown, Biggins, Puckett (Buzaglo 85), Senior. Unused subs: Steele.

Cheltenham Town 1 (Warren 83)
A.F.C. Bournemouth 1 (Shearer 12)
Att: 4,100
Cheltenham: Nicholls, Howells, Willetts, Brown, Vircavs, Tucker (Warren 70), Lovell, N Smith, J Smith, Purdie, Bloomer. Unused sub: Wring.

Bournemouth 3 (Mundee 19, McGorry 73, Morgan 86)
Cheltenham Town 0
Played 16-12-92. Att: 4,879
Cheltenham: Churchward, Howells, Willetts, Brown, Vircavs, Tucker, Lovell (Wring 82), N Smith, J Smith, Warren (Iddles 82), Bloomer.

Hartlepool United 4 (Peverall 60, Saville 65 77 85)
Southport 0
Played 6-12-92. Att: 4,171
Southport: Moore, McDonald, Fuller, Mooney, Goulding, Schofield, Walmsley (Baines 75), Brennan, Haw, Gamble (Senior 75), Withers.

Macclesfield Town 0
Stockport County 2 (Preece 2, Williams 54)
Att: 5,700
Macclesfield: S Farrelly, Sheppard, Bimson (M Farrelly 79), Edwards, Kendall, McMahon, Askey, Timmons, Lambert, Mitchell (Sorvel 6), Leicester.

Marine 3 (Murray 32 48, Gautrey 40)
Stafford Rangers 2 (Berry 70, Essex 87)
Att: 1,965
Marine: O'Brien, Ward, Johnson, Roche (McDonough 80), Draper, Gautrey, Murray, Rowlands, Ross, Camden (Grant 73), Dawson.
Stafford: Price, Circuit, Bradshaw, Henry, Essex, Berry, Boughey (Wood 49), Griffiths, Callaghan (Hemming 19), Palgrave, Clayton.

V.S. Rugby 0
Marlow 0
Played 9-12-92. Att: 2,258
Rugby: Martin, Sweeney, T McGinty, Fitzpatrick, Olner, Redgate, Smith, Bradder, Hardwick (Warner 78), Shearer, Green. Unused sub: Bufton.
Marlow: Lester, Ferguson, Mikurenda, Glasgow (Franks 80), Hubbick, Hannigan, Lay, Regan, Watkins, Bushay, Caesar (George 61).

Marlow 2 (Bushay 62, Watkins 78)
V.S. Rugby 0
Played 16-12-92. Att: 1,904
Marlow: Lester, Franks, Ferguson, Hubbick, Stone, Dell, Lay, Glasgow (Caesar 53), Watkins, Bushay (Regan 79), Hannigan.
Rugby: Martin, Sweeney, T McGinty, Fitzpatrick, Olner, Redgate, Smith (Warner 64), Bradder (Bufton 53), Hardwick, Shearer, Green.

Yeovil Town 0
Hereford United 0
Att: 8,085
Yeovil: Coles, Coates, Sherwood, Shail, Ferns, Batty, Sanderson (Hughes 71), Wallace, Wilson, Spencer (Nevin 90), Dobbins.

Hereford United 1 (Pickard 77)
Yeovil Town 2 (Sanderson 18, Coates 88)
Played 16-12-92. Att: 6,051
Yeovil: Coles, Dobbins, Sherwood, Shail, Ferns, Cooper (Coates 78), Sanderson, Batty, Wilson, Spencer, Harrower. Unused sub: Hughes.

Wycombe Wanderers 2 (Creaser 70, Thompson 85)
West Bromwich Albion 2 (Bradley 11, Taylor 42)
Played 6-12-92. Att: 6,904
Wycombe: Hyde, Cousins, Crossley, Hutchinson, Creaser, Thompson, Carroll, Casey (Greene 5), Stapleton, Scott, Guppy. Unused sub: Buckle.

W.B.A. 1 (Taylor 81)
Wycombe Wanderers 0
Played 15-12-92. Att: 17,640
Wycombe: Hyde, Cousins, Crossley, Kerr, Creaser, Thompson, Carroll, Buckle (Hutchinson 60), Stapleton, Scott, Guppy. Unused sub: Greene.

Bernie Hughes slips on the wet Ewood Park surface as Accrington run is ended by Crewe. Photo - Paul Dennis.

Laurence Batty leads the Woking players' salute to their 3,000 travelling fans at Brighton. Photo - Francis Short.

Hereford's Alan Judge makes a brilliant save to deny Yeovil's Paul Sanderson at Huish Park. Photo - Dave West.

Third Round

1st January 1993

Crewe Alexandra 3 (McKearney 2, Edwards 16, Clarkson 23)
Marine 1 (Johnson 58)
Played 12-1-93. Att: 4,036.
Marine: O'Brien, Ward, Johnson, Roche, Proctor, Gautrey, Murray (Grant 60), Rowlands, Ross, Camden, Dawson (McDonough).

Marlow 1 (Lay 70)
Tottenham Hotspur 5 (Sheringham 20, Barmby 41 90, Samways 50 71)
Played at Tottenham.
Marlow: Lester, Franks (Regan 55), Ferguson, Hubbick, Stone, Dell, Lay, Caesar (Glasgow 82), Watkins, Bushay, Hannigan.

Yeovil Town 1 (Batty 78 (pen))
Arsenal 3 (Wright 25 45 88)   Att: 8,612
Yeovil: Coles, Dobbins, Sherwood, Wallace, Ferns, Cooper (Coates 57), Sanderson, Batty, Wilson (Nevin 75), Spencer, Harrower.

It took took North London giants Tottenham Hotspur and Arsenal to see off Marlow and Yeovil Town in the Third Round. Above - Marlow's Colin Ferguson in action at White Hart Lane. Photo - Dennis Nicholson. Below - England defenders Tony Adams and Lee Dixon combine to shut out Yeovil's Paul Sanderson. Photo - Dave West.

F.A. CHALLENGE CUP

Reflections on 1992-93

The award for F.A. Cup 'Club of the Year' (see awards section earlier in the book) was really a straight choice between Marine and Yeovil Town, both of whom succumbed in the Third Round. Not far behind this duo were Marlow, who battled through three rounds to a meeting with Spurs at White Hart Lane, also in Round Three.

Marine's was the longest run in this season's competition. Unlike Marlow and Yeovil, both exempt to the final qualifying round, they had to fight their way right through from September. In the First Round they crushed Halifax to record their first win over a League club since 1975 when Barnsley were vanquished at Rossett Park. No lucrative tie was awaiting in the Second Round however; Roly Howard's men had to face Stafford Rangers, and almost squandered a three goal lead in a Crosby quagmire. Into the Third Round for the first time in their history - surely now the Mariners would get a big club! Out of the hat came Crewe. Away. A very difficult tie, and no glamour - Marine's run of 1993-94 was certainly not blessed with the luck it deserved.

Marlow had to survive three replayed ties en route to White Hart Lane. Sittingbourne, Salisbury (this tie was particularly nerve-wracking as they were two down late in the second-half at home and eventually came through a penalty shoot-out in the replay) and V.S. Rugby were beaten by Dave Russell's side.

Our award went to **Yeovil**, however, as they were the only non-Leaguers to manage two wins over League oppositon. After negotiating a tricky Fourth Qualifying Round trip to Crawley, Steve Rutter's side romped to a 5-2 win at Torquay in Round One. After they had been held to a goalless draw by Hereford in Round Two, the Glovers learned that victory in the replay at Edgar Street would bring mighty Arsenal to Somerset. It was a tense game, but a late winner by Neil Coates ensured that national media attention would be focused on Yeovil on 2nd January as the Arsenal, just as they had done in 1971, set out from the small market town on the road to F.A. Cup triumph.

On First Round day, only Yeovil, Marine and **Bath City** (with a superb win at Division Three champions-in-waiting Cardiff City) were victorious over League clubs. However, come the replays ten days later, this figure doubled. **Altrincham**, and Clive Freeman in particular with a stunning goal, delighted a television audience by beating Chester City 2-0, whilst Conference strugglers **Macclesfield Town** and **Stafford Rangers** recorded wins over Chesterfield and Lincoln City respectively. Macc's win earned its particular niche in Cup history being the first time a non-League side had beaten a Football League club on penalties.

Whilst the above stories made the back pages of all our newspapers, the bulk of the action in every F.A. Cup competition occurs in the two months between late August and late October. The qualifying competition enthralls us every season, and this campaign was no exception.

Two clubs appearing in the F.A. Cup for the very first time in their history, **Pelsall Villa** and **Bemerton Heath Harlequins**, managed to battle their way through three rounds. For Pelsall, of the Boddington's West Midlands League, the highlight was a 2-1 win away to H.F.S. Loans League Premier Division side **Mossley**. Bemerton's prize scalp was Diadora Premier side **Bognor Regis Town** in the longest running tie of this year's competion - they eventually won the fourth match at home less than 48 hours before travelling to **Witney Town** for the next round. Hereward Sports United Counties League side **Raunds Town** also made the Third Qualifying Round, in only their second season of participation in the Cup. In the Second Qualifying Round they created a major stir with a 2-0 win away to **Northwich Victoria** of the Conference.

For the first time since the old Football League club went under over thirty years ago, the name **Accrington Stanley** appeared in the First Round Proper. The reformed club have twice missed out in the final qualifying round, against Fleetwood two years ago and at Altrincham way back in 1974, but this time you sensed they were always going to make it from the moment they walloped **Hyde United** 5-1 away in the First Qualifying Round. A fine 2-1 win was recorded at Conference side **Stalybridge Celtic**, and I was fortunate enough to witness the joy at Accrington when they beat **Northallerton Town**, another side enjoying their best ever run, to clinch that long-sought after First Round place. In the Round One, 'Match of the Day' cameras captured Paul Beck's brilliant hat-trick that beat another Conference side an ex-Football League name, **Gateshead**. Then in the Second Round 10,000 flocked to Blackburn Rovers' ground to see the run finally ended by Crewe Alexandra.

But I think my best F.A. Cup memory of 1992-93 will be the First Round tie at **Dorking**'s tiny Meadowbank Ground. Dorking were another side to reach the Competition Proper for the first time, their run including superb wins over Beazer Homes League leaders **Dover Athletic,** and 1992 Cup heroes **Farnborough Town** of the G.M.V. Conference. Dorking 'bust a gut' to ensure they could stage their tie against **Plymouth Argyle**, and the thrilling game, and terrific atmosphere in the small Surrey town made one realise just what an extended F.A. Cup run can do for a small club.

James Wright

THE VAUXHALL F.A. CHALLENGE TROPHY

REVIEW 1992-93

FIRST QUAL. ROUND

(SAT. 19th SEPT. 1992)

(Attendances in brackets)

SPENNYMOOR UTD	4 v 3	BRANDON UTD (197)
ACCRINGTON S.	3 v 1	WHITLEY BAY (419)
NORTH SHIELDS *(withdrew)*		SHILDON *(w/o)*
PETERLEE NEWTOWN	2 v 1	GUISELEY (97)
CHORLEY	2 v 2	NEWCASTLE B.S. (175)
NEWCASTLE B.S.	3 v 1	CHORLEY (79)
LEICESTER UTD	1 v 1	WORKSOP TOWN (149)
WORKSOP TOWN	1 v 5	LEICESTER U. (310)
ALVECHURCH *(removed)*		HALESOWEN T. *(w/o)*
DROYLSDEN	0 v 2	WINSFORD UTD (256)
ALFRETON TOWN	2 v 4	EASTWOOD TOWN (205)
REDDITCH UTD	0 v 3	CAERNARFON T. (103)
SHEPSHED ALBION	1 v 0	BEDWORTH UTD (174)
CONGLETON TOWN	4 v 2	GRANTHAM T. (109)
MOSSLEY	6 v 2	DUDLEY TOWN (173)
GAINSBOROUGH TRIN.	1 v 1	SOLIHULL B. (270)
SOLIHULL	4 v 4	GAINSBOROUGH (142)
SOLIHULL	4 v 0	GAINSBOROUGH (168)
MOOR GREEN	1 v 1	COLWYN BAY (259)
COLWYN BAY	4 v 2	MOOR GREEN (152)
CHELMSFORD CITY	1 v 3	HENDON (651)
HAYES	6 v 1	TAMWORTH (243)
STEVENAGE BOROUGH *(w/o)*		HARLOW TOWN *(w'drew)*
HEYBRIDGE SWIFTS	2 v 1	CAMBRIDGE C. (129)
CORBY TOWN	1 v 4	BILLERICAY T. (235)
HITCHIN TOWN	3 v 1	B. STORTFORD (371)
STAINES TOWN	1 v 2	LEYTON (237)
BALDOCK TOWN	4 v 3	BARKING (175)
BOREHAM WOOD	3 v 1	AVELEY (71)
TOOTING & MITCHAM	0 v 1	WALTON & H. (147)

UXBRIDGE	3 v 2	BOGNOR REGIS (130)
ASHFORD TOWN	0 v 0	YEADING (276)
YEADING	5 v 2	ASHFORD T. (151)
MOLESEY	1 v 3	BASINGSTOKE (130)
WHYTELEAFE	2 v 2	HASTINGS T. (195)
HASTINGS TOWN	1 v 1	WHYTELEAFE (306)
HASTINGS TOWN	3 v 0	WHYTELEAFE (340)
CROYDON	0 v 1	DULWICH H. (180)
FAREHAM TOWN	2 v 2	MARGATE (125)
MARGATE	1 v 0	FAREHAM TOWN (350)
ANDOVER	0 v 3	ABINGDON T. (149)
CARSHALTON ATH.	1 v 2	CRAWLEY TOWN (427)
MARLOW	3 v 2	LEWES (170)
WEYMOUTH	2 v 2	NEWPORT A.F.C. (922)
NEWPORT A.F.C.	2 v 1	WEYMOUTH (397)
BARRI	2 v 1	BIDEFORD (205)
(played at Bideford)		
SALTASH UNITED	2 v 5	TROWBRIDGE (178)
DORCHESTER TOWN	3 v 1	WATERLOOVILLE (325)

The campaign opened without too many shocks. Perhaps the biggest upset of the day was in Essex where **Heybridge Swifts** put paid to the chances of Steve Fallon's **Cambridge City** by winning 2-1 at Scraley Road. Another Essex side to do well were **Billericay Town** who came away from Northamptonshire with an excellent 4-1 victory over **Corby Town**. Adrain West and prolific scorer Steve Jones were among Billericay's marksen. **Leyton**, from Diadora Division One, upset the form book by beating Premier Division **Staines Town** 2-1 at Wheatsheaf Lane. Up north, **Peterlee Newtown** ended **Guiseley's** first Trophy campaign with a 2-1 win.

Amongst the biggest victors were H.F.S. Loans Premier Division **Mossley**, who put six past Beazer Midland outfit **Dudley Town's** goalkeeper Ian Scarr, **Hayes** who overcame **Tamworth** by the rather surprising margin of 6-1, and **Trowbridge** who put behind them the memory of a recent F.A. Cup thrashing at Salisbury to win 5-2 at **Saltash United**.

David Stevens and Matthew Pearson of Carshalton Athletic combine to dispossess Martin Chester of Crawley Town. The Sussex side recorded a 2-1 win. Photo - Dennis Nicholson.

Solihull's Ricky Carter challenges 'keeper Giles Newcombe in the 1-1 draw at Gainsborough. Photo - Colin Stevens.

Chelmsford's Colin Lewington gathers safely under pressure from Hendon's Barry Blackman. Photo - John Hutton.

Willie Lillington hurdles Croydon's Mark Hopper as Dulwich Hamlet win the derby at the Arena. Photo - Dave West.

SECOND QUAL. ROUND

(SAT. 17th OCT. 1992)

(Attendances in brackets)

ACCRINGTON S.	5 v 0	EASINGTON COLL. (473)
SEAHAM RED STAR	2 v 4	SPENNYMOOR UTD (225)
PETERLEE NEWTOWN	1 v 1	SHILDON (42)
SHILDON	2 v 0	PETERLEE N. (78)
WORKINGTON	0 v 2	NEWCASTLE B.S. (165)
WEST AUCKLAND	1 v 1	CONSETT (56)
CONSETT	2 v 2	WEST AUCKLAND (40)
CONSETT	1 v 1	WEST AUCKLAND
WEST AUCKLAND	0 v 3	CONSETT (40)
STOCKTON	10 v 2	FERRYHILL ATH. (33)
NUNEATON BOROUGH	3 v 1	CONGLETON T. (794)
HEDNESFORD TOWN	1 v 2	HALESOWEN T. (685)
CAERNARFON TOWN	1 v 4	GOOLE TOWN (33)
WINSFORD UNITED	0 v 0	BUXTON (419)
BUXTON	0 v 3	WINSFORD UNITED (468)
WARRINGTON TOWN	3 v 0	SHEPSHED A. (138)
COLWYN BAY	0 v 1	SOLIHULL B. (149)
LEICESTER UNITED	3 v 1	MATLOCK TOWN (207)
MOSSLEY	3 v 1	EASTWOOD TOWN (220)
SUTTON COLDFIELD	2 v 1	LEYTON (191)
ST ALBANS CITY	3 v 2	HAYES (566)
BILLERICAY TOWN	3 v 4	STOURBRIDGE (403)
STEVENAGE BORO.	2 v 1	CHALFONT ST P. (415)
WEMBLEY	3 v 1	HITCHIN TOWN (89)
PURFLEET	3 v 2	BOREHAM WOOD (103)
HENDON	0 v 0	GRAYS ATHLETIC (203)
GRAYS ATHLETIC	2 v 1	HENDON (178)
BALDOCK TOWN	0 v 1	HEYBRIDGE S. (215)
BASINGSTOKE T.	2 v 0	CRAWLEY TOWN (415)
ABINGDON TOWN	2 v 1	MARLOW (211)
MARGATE	1 v 3	HASTINGS T. (435)
YEADING	2 v 2	MAIDENHEAD U. (146)
MAIDENHEAD UTD	1 v 3	YEADING (124)
WALTHAM & HER.	2 v 0	GRAVESEND & N. (196)
FISHER ATHLETIC	2 v 2	CANTERBURY C. (101)
CANTERBURY CITY	3 v 1	FISHER ATH. (56)
UXBRIDGE	0 v 2	DULWICH HAMLET (202)
DORCHESTER TOWN	1 v 2	POOLE TOWN (371)
TROWBRIDGE TOWN	0 v 1	NEWPORT A.F.C. (565)
BARRI	0 v 2	WESTON-S-MARE (110)

Caernarfon Town, who, due to lack of local support owing to their enforced exile at Curzon Ashton's National Park ground, unfortunately had not even the consolation of a good result. Defender David England struck twice to put their Premier Division opponents two up, and though Tony Livens found the mark with a far post header in the first minute of the second half, Goole scored further goals in the last ten minutes through Mark Wood and Iain Dunn. It was a truly wretched day for North Wales exiles as **Colwyn Bay** also suffered disappointment both on the pitch and at the turnstiles in their tie with **Solihull Borough** who are, coincidently, yet another groundsharing club. Only 149 clicked into the Drill Field to see Alan Byrne score the game's only goal with twenty minutes remaining. Maybe the 'Bay' were preoccupied as the match was sandwiched between their two F.A. Cup replays with Altrincham.

Preoccupation with the F.A. Cup was not a problem for a third exiled Welsh side, however. **Newport's** Trophy trip to **Trowbridge Town** came within 72 hours of a bruising two hours of F.A. Cup football at Clevedon, and just two days before the replay of that tie, but they still managed to achieve a commendable single goal success courtesy of a Chris Lilygreen effort midway through the second half. **Barri**, however, failed to make it a South Wales double when they were

beaten at home by two second half goals from **Weston-super-Mare's** Julian Stearnes.

The most eye-catching result of the Second Qualifying Round was in the North East where **Stockton** pulverised Northern League rivals **Ferryhill Athletic** to the tune of 10-2. Half the scoreline was achieved by the interval with the home side already 5-1 to the good. In all, Mark Jones scored five, George Woodhouse four and Jason Wright one as their side became the first to notch a double-figure tally in the Trophy since Slough Town ran riot at Stroud three years ago. John Parnaby, brother of former Gateshead manager Dave, and Kenny Littlejean scored to save some face for Ferryhill. Another Northern League side to make a good impression were 1989 quarter-finalists **Newcastle Blue Star** who won 2-0 at **Workington**. Veteran former professional Alan Shoulder volleyed the first from a half-cleared corner and ex-Gretna hot-shot Chris Pickford put the result beyond doubt five minutes before the interval.

Staying in the far North, **Spennymoor United** put their traumas of the previous week (a seven goal home F.A. Cup drubbing by Gateshead) behind them when they won 4-2 at **Seaham Red Star**, another side who had experienced a Cup exit seven days earlier. Incredibly, Red Star had taken an early two goal lead through Gary McDonald and Trevor Snowdon, but by half time Jason Ainsley and Steve Cuthbert had squared the contest. Spennymoor player-manager Mattie Pearson brought himself on and put the Moors ahead midway through the second period and, after the home side had suffered the further disappointment of a penalty miss by McDonald, Craig Veart put the issue beyond doubt with ten minutes left. Two all-Northern League ties pitted **Peterlee Newtown** against **Shildon**, with the latter winning after a replay, and **Consett** against near neighbours **West Auckland Town**, a side who are returning to the Vauxhall F.A. Trophy having competed in the Vase last season. This second tie was eventually decided at the fourth attempt, Consett winning 3-0 away to earn the right to travel to **Billingham Synthonia**.

There were no four-figure gates to report in the Second Qualifying Round, the largest attendance (794) being at Manor Park where the bubbling **Nuneaton Borough** side disposed of **Congleton Town**. Paul Culpin did the damage with two first half goals either side of an equaliser from Mark Jones, and Darren Bullock rounded off another good afternoon for the Boro' in the second half. Second highest scorers at the turnstiles were **Hednesford Town** who welcomed 685 to Cross Keys for the big derby against **Halesowen Town**. The Yeltz were finally able to to break their barren run in the Trophy (their last win in the competition dated back to a 2-1 Preliminary Round success at Darlaston in 1974, though it must be remembered that the club enjoyed a seven season successful spell in the F.A. Vase). With just ten minutes remaining, Halesowen appeared destined for more Trophy heartache as they trailed to a Joe O'Connor goal. Ian Bettles then equalised, and it was Malcolm Hazlewood with just two minutes left who scored the goal that sent the travelling fans home happy.

The big derby in the far South East was **Hastings Town's** visit to **Margate**. Hastings were competing in the Trophy for the first time, and scored a convincing away win. Over four hundred turned up at Hartsdown Park to see Steve Willard give the visitors a first half lead. Shaun Pilbeam put Margate back on level terms midway through the second half, but an own goal by David Lee and a late effort from Danny Ashworth settled the issue.

The Stockton goal avalanche aside, the highest aggregate score in one tie was registered at **Billericay Town**, and fortunately a very healthy crowd of over 400 was present to enjoy it. Visiting **Stourbridge** emerged triumphant by the odd goal in seven. They went ahead through Gary Bruce after just six minutes, conceded an equaliser to Steve Jones shortly after, but then moved comfortably ahead with a brace from Paul Joinson either side of the interval and a fourth, from Evron Wright, four minutes from time. Jones restored respectability to the scoreline by completing his hat-trick with two goals in the dying minutes, and his club will rufully reflect on the irony that in the previous season they went their exit from the F.A. Vase (in which they then competed) was also at the hands of a Beazer Midland side, Yate Town, and also by a score of 3-4 at home.

Stockton's Mark Jones hits his first (of five) in the 10-2 rout of unfortunate Ferryhill Athletic.

Paul Joinson of Stourbridge (left) tangles with Mark Entwistle in the thriller at Billericay. Photo - Paul Dennis.

Andy Cox (out of picture) scores Hayes' second at St Albans, but was not enough to save them. Photo - Eric Marsh.

THIRD QUAL. ROUND

(SAT. 28th NOV. 1992)

(Attendances in brackets)

FLEETWOOD TOWN	1 v 3	BLYTH SPAR.	(240)
GOOLE TOWN	0 v 1	BISHOP AUCK.	(238)
EMLEY	2 v 6	SPENNYMOOR U.	(379)
WARRINGTON TOWN	5 v 2	STOCKTON	(193)
MORECAMBE	2 v 2	SOUTHPORT	(948)
SOUTHPORT	1 v 3	MORECAMBE	(878)
HORWICH R.M.I.	1 v 2	WINSFORD UTD	(176)
MOSSLEY	2 v 4	FRICKLEY ATH.	(196)
GUISBOROUGH T.	2 v 0	SHILDON	(168)
WHITBY TOWN	2 v 1	SOUTH BANK	(281)
ACCRINGTON S.	6 v 0	TOW LAW TOWN	(511)
BILLINGHAM SYN.	1 v 0	CONSETT	(106)
CONSETT	2 v 6	BILLINGHAM S.	(82)
NORTHALLERTON T.	2 v 1	NEWCASTLE B.S.	(81)
NUNEATON BOR.	0 v 0	BURTON ALBION	(1019)
BURTON ALBION	0 v 3	NUNEATON	(633)
GRAYS ATHLETIC	2 v 1	ATHERSTONE UTD	(248)
HEYBRIDGE SWIFTS	1 v 0	HALESOWEN T.	(321)
WEALDSTONE	5 v 2	SOLIHULL B.	(295)
ST ALBANS CITY	2 v 0	PURFLEET	(471)
STOURBRIDGE	1 v 4	LEEK TOWN	(245)
STAFFORD RANGERS	1 v 1	WEMBLEY	(612)
WEMBLEY	0 v 1	STAFFORD RGRS	(111)
HARROW BOROUGH	2 v 2	STEVENAGE B.	(445)
STEVENAGE B.	4 v 0	HARROW BORO.	(361)
SUTTON COLDFIELD	1 v 1	V.S. RUGBY	(263)
V.S. RUGBY	5 v 4	SUTTON COLD.	(204)
CHESHAM UNITED	7 v 3	LEICESTER UTD	(391)
SLOUGH TOWN	3 v 1	BROMLEY	(860)
POOLE TOWN	1 v 1	BASHLEY	(402)
BASHLEY	2 v 2	POOLE TOWN	(219)
POOLE TOWN	2 v 4	BASHLEY	(279)
NEWPORT A.F.C.	1 v 2	SUTTON UTD	(400)
WESTON-S-MARE	1 v 0	WINDSOR & E.	(454)
BASINGSTOKE T.	3 v 0	DULWICH H.	(301)
ABINGDON TOWN	2 v 1	DORKING	(188)
KINGSTONIAN	5 v 0	CANTERBURY C.	(375)
YEADING	3 v 1	WALTON & HER.	(231)
WORCESTER CITY	2 v 1	SALISBURY	(650)
HASTINGS TOWN	2 v 1	WOKINGHAM	(403)

The most eye-catching scoreline of the Third Qualifying Round was **Spennymoor United's** 6-2 success at **Emley**. The Moors were the only Northern Counties East League team entered in the Vauxhall F.A. Trophy, and their victory was all the more noteworthy as Emley hail from two divisions higher up the Pyramid and had taken a second minute lead through Bob Clarke. The visitors raced into a strong half-time position with goals from Brian Healy and Steve Cuthbert and a couple of penalties from Keith Gorman. In the second half Craig Veart added two further efforts, either side of a lone reply by Tony Passmore.

It was quite a good day for the North East as Northern League **Blyth Spartans** put behind them the disappointment of their F.A. Cup defeat at the hands of Southport, and recorded an excellent 3-1 win at H.F.S. Loans Premier Division club **Fleetwood Town**. Steve Plaskett put them on their way after half an hour, and further goals just after the hour mark from Don Peattie and Neil Howie had the outcome settled before Stuart Diggle's late consolation strike for the Fishermen. The other Northern Leaguers were less fortunate. **Tow Law Town** became the latest side to come under the cosh at **Accrington Stanley**. Ace marksman Paul Beck

opened and closed the scoring, with John Burns, Steve Lampkin, Stewart Owen, and Charlie Cooper also finding the target in between. **Stockton** were never going to repeat their ten goal feat of the previous round, but were disappointed with a 2-5 reverse at **Warrington Town**. They were already five down before they got on the score-sheet with two late goals. Warrington's scorers were Joey Dunn with two, Gavin McDonald, Liam Watson and Paul McNally, and thus they reached the First Round Proper of the Trophy for the first time.

Staying in the North, the most notable tie was the derby between **Morecambe** and **Southport**, the top two clubs in the H.F.S. Loans League Premier Division. A crowd of nearly a thousand packed into the 'Crusty Pie' to see Chris Walmesley give the visitors an early lead, only for Paul Tomlinson to equalise and John Coleman to put Morecambe ahead. Peter Withers, however, rescued Southport with just five minutes remaining. At Haig Avenue two days later Morecambe got off to a flyer with Ian Cain scoring within a minute. Mark Schofield replied with twenty minutes remaining, but two goals from John McNally in the final ten minutes sent the Shrimps through to a home tie against **Frickley Athletic**. For their part, Frickley enjoyed a fine 4-2 success at **Mossley**. They were dealt a real blow in the first minute when David Blow scored for the home team, but stormed into an unassailable lead with Mark Hancock, Simon Fuller (twice) and ex-Leeds player Jack Ashurst scoring before Mark Henshaw offered a late reply.

Two other all-H.F.S. ties saw **Winsford United** win 2-1 at **Horwich R.M.I.** with a goal in each half from Harvey Cunningham and Darren Sheridan, and **Bishop Auckland** triumph 1-0 at **Goole Town** with a goal from Dale Anderson who thus celebrated his selection for the F.A. XI. Bishop Auckland's victory was made all the more creditable by the fact that during the first half they had seen Gary Hyde, their hat-trick hero from the previous week, stretchered off. **Leek Town**, Wembley Finalists in 1990, easily disposed of fellow Midlanders **Stourbridge** at Ambiecote. Darren Twigg headed the only goal of the first half, but in the second period two goals from Iain Sankey and one from Martin Smith made the match safe before Cadman got in a last minute strike for the Glassboys.

The high scores at Accrington and Emley (and later **Consett**, who were beaten 2-6 by **Billingham Synthonia** in a re-arranged tie) were bettered by an incredible ten goal tally at **Chesham United** where visitors **Leicester United** were hit by a 7-3 result. This match was played on Tuesday 1st December after the initial rendez-vous had been postponed, and Chris Tonge gifted the home side an early lead with an own goal. Tonge did atone with a proper goal late in the match, but the Diadora League leaders, for whom Chris Townsend hit a hat-trick, were quite unstoppable.

Wealdstone put behind them some of their behind-the-scenes traumas by recording a superb win over **Solihull Borough** at Vicarage Road. They got off to a dream start with a Kenny Gayle lob, and doubled the margin through Colin Tate before Rick Carter pulled one back on the half hour mark. The match was sealed in the second half as Tate scored his second, substitute Mark Rees put through his own goal, and Sean Pearson profited from good work by the long-serving Neil Cordice to make it five. A close range header from Alan Attwood near the end offered little consolation to Solihull whose first Trophy campaign ends in disappointment.

Another minor surprise was registered at Woodspring Park where **Weston-super-Mare** beat visiting **Windsor & Eton**. Hero for the Westerners was Paul Elson who delighted the 454 crowd by scoring the only goal after 72 minutes. Jousting with Weston and Spennymoor for 'result of the round' were **Heybridge Swifts** who continued their fine run by beating **Halesowen Town** with a fine late goal from Chris Moore.

Top scorers in Southern England were **Kingstonian** who hammered **Canterbury City** 5-0. It was quite an achievement for Chis Kelly's side as it came just three days after the humiliating 1-9 reverse at Peterborough in the eventually nullified F.A. Cup replay. K's remained frustrated until the 56th minute when Andy Parr set them on their way. David Harlow then doubled the lead, Parr got his second, and, finally, Kevin Sheldrick scored twice in the last five minutes.

Basingtoke's Paul Odey and Rudi Hedman of Dulwich context a high ball at the Camrose. Photo - Francis Short.

Spennymoor celebrate a goal Keith Gorman scored directly from a corner at Emley. Photo - Barry Lockwood.

A midfield tussle between Russell Priest of Weston-super-Mare and Windsor's Ian Richards. Photo - Paul Dennis.

FIRST ROUND PROPER

(SAT. 9th JAN. 1993)

(Attendances in brackets)

Spennymoor Utd 1 v 2 **Boston United**
Cuthbert 16 (431) Jones 15(p),
Chambers 27

Telford United 2 v 1 **Northwich V.**
Lee 4, Myers 58 (1,211) O'Connor 25

Marine 2 v 0 **Blyth Spartans**
Ward 63, Camden 90 (406)

Hyde United 1 v 2 **Runcorn**
Henshaw 24 (425) Anderson 29,
Parker 44

Warrington Town 2 v 1 **Guisborough T.**
McDonald 27, (248) Osborne 60
Warder 85

Gateshead 3 v 0 **Gretna**
Guthrie 10, Cook 14, (336)
Tupling 29

Barrow 0 v 1 **Billingham S.**
(1,203) Fletcher 60

Winsford Utd 1 v 0 **Altrincham**
Sheridan 71 (727)

Murton 1 v 2 **Nuneaton Bor.**
Burlinson 84 (253) Tarry 51,
Rosegreen 80

Stalybridge C. 2 v 0 **Accrington S.**
Power 7 72 (963)

Bishop Auckland 1 v 0 **Leek Town**
Lobb 13 (259)

Northallerton 3 v 0 **Whitby Town**
Stirland 13, (255)
McDonald 63, Lake 88

Morecambe 5 v 1 **Frickley Ath.**
Coleman 29 53, (588) Bennett 85
Cain 45 75 89

Macclesfield 0 v 0 **Witton Albion**
(890)

Witton Albion 2 v 1 **Macclesfield**
Played 18-1-93
Burke 77 89 (907) Doherty 14

Sutton United 3 v 0 **Woking**
Feltham 10, Evans 83, (1,884)
Byrne 88(p)

Basingstoke T. 1 v 4 **Kingstonian**
Odey 64 (521) Harlow 6,
Broderick 35 70,
Kempton 55

Yeading 1 v 1 **Slough Town**
Walton 19 (611) Friel 23

Slough Town 2 v 1 **Yeading**
Played 12-1-93
Sayer 16, Fiore 79 (755) Dicker 65

Welling United 2 v 1 **Aylesbury Utd**
Robbins 58 87 (743) Heath 68

Grays Athletic 1 v 0 **Stafford Rgrs**
Walker 44 (421)

Merthyr Tydfil 3 v 0 **Wivenhoe Town**
D'Auria 11, (653)
Abraham 66, Tucker 69

Heybridge Swifts 4 v 0 **Worcester C.**
Russell 12, Butler 27, (328)
Matthews 75 85

Yeovil Town 0 v 0 **Dagenham & R.**
(2,973)

Dagenham & R. 2 v 1 **Yeovil Town**
Played 12-1-93
Nuttell 81, (1,171) Spencer 43
Pamphlett 86

St Albans City 1 v 0 **Weston-s-Mare**
Adams 88 (730)

Dover Athletic 1 v 1 **Hastings Town**
Warner 70 (1,129) Willard 89

Hastings Town 0 v 2 **Dover Ath.**
Played 12-1-93
(611) Cuggy 37,
Blewden 71

Kidderminster 1 v 3 **Enfield**
Hadley 12 (1,280) Keen 65, Turner 75,
Collins 82

Wycombe Wdrs 3 v 1 **Cheltenham T.**
Carroll 2, Scott 8, (3,964) Eaton 15
Kerr 30

Stevenage Bor. 2 v 0 **Bath City**
Trebble 44, (907)
Gittings 63

Kettering Town 0 v 0 **Bromsgrove R.**
(1,723)

Bromsgrove R. 4 v 1 **Kettering T.**
Played 12-1-93
Gray 11, 82, (1,269) Riley 54
Stott 51, Webb 62(p)

Wealdstone 1 v 2 **Bashley**
Played 18-1-93
Baird 66(og) (274) Paskins 40,
Patmore 86

Farnborough T. 4 v 0 **Abingdon Town**
Broome 26, (690)
Leworthy 33,
Horton 68,
Newberry 86

V.S. Rugby 1 v 6 **Chesham United**
Olner 74 (564) Attrell 45 52,
Rake 47,
Adebowale 57,
Dawber 60,
Townsend 86

Four giant-killing acts were accomplished by **Winsford United**, who repeated last season's F.A. Cup win over **Altrincham**; **Stevenage Borough**, who accounted for **Bath City**; **Grays Athletic**, who almost predictably beat struggling **Stafford Rangers**; and **Enfield**, who scored an excellent 3-1 success over **Kidderminster Harriers** at Aggborough. Further results of note were Northern League **Billingham Synthonia**'s fine victory away to 1990 winners **Barrow**, now of the H.F.S. Loans League, and little **Heybridge Swifts'** staggering 4-0 annihilation of the once great **Worcester City**.

Interestingly, the only two sides from outside the Conference who made it to the Third Round in 1991-92, **Marine** and **Morecambe**, kept themselves in contention. The Crosby side would have been forgiven an aberration in their home tie against **Blyth Spartans** as it was played just three days before their re-arranged F.A. Cup Third Round visit to Crewe Alexandra, but to their utmost credit they kept their minds on the job in hand and safely won through. For their part, Morecambe scored a resounding 5-1 success against H.F.S. title rivals **Frickley Athletic**, and were justly rewarded with the biggest prize the Trophy can offer - a Second Round pairing with **Wycombe Wanderers**.

Gretna's Marc Irwin gets in a shot, but the Scottish side were well-beaten at Gateshead. Photo - Alan Watson.

Mark Smith and Neil Trebble (10) celebrate the goal that put Stevenage on course to beat Bath. Photo - Paul Dennis.

Paul Cavell of Dagenham holds of Yeovil's Mark Shail (left) but justs misses the target. Photo - John Collinge.

SECOND ROUND PROPER

(SAT. 30th JAN. 1993)

Farnborough Town	**4 v 0**	**Enfield**
Newbury 3 34,	(1,130)	
Leworthy 13 30		
Bishop Auckland	**0 v 1**	**Warrington Town**
	(323)	Dunn 6
St Albans City	**0 v 2**	**Witton Albion**
	(1,470)	Burke 22, Senior 36
Nuneaton Borough	**0 v 1**	**Marine**
	(1,165)	Ross 54
Northallerton Town	**1 v 0**	**Bashley**
Wasden 51	(319)	
Stevenage Borough	**0 v 1**	**Grays Athletic**
	(893)	Walks
Billingham Syn.	**1 v 2**	**Winsford United**
Fletcher 48	(338)	Cunningham 32, Collins 87
Welling United	**1 v 2**	**Boston United**
Abbott 27	(1,012)	Knight 6, Munton 88
Gateshead	**3 v 0**	**Heybridge Swifts**
Corner 28(p),	(367)	
Elliott 44, Halliday 46		
Kingstonian	**1 v 2**	**Telford United**
Braithwaite 89	(809)	Niblett 4, Green 79

Morecambe	**1 v 1**	**Wycombe Wdrs**
Green 86	(2,196)	Scott 58
Wycombe Wdrs	**2 v 0**	**Morecambe**
	Played 2-2-93	
Kerr 44, Scott 54	(4,490)	
Sutton United	**3 v 1**	**Slough Town**
Feltham 1 52 80	(1,374)	Hazel 40(p)
Chesham United	**1 v 0**	**Dover Athletic**
Coleman 36	(2,055)	
Bromsgrove Rovers	**3 v 1**	**Dagenham & R.**
Whitehouse 20 32,	(1,711)	Cavell 15
Crisp 43		
Gloucester City	**3 v 3**	**Runcorn**
Bayliss 54,	(577)	Anderson 17,
Hughes 86,		Connor 56 78
Buckland 88		
Runcorn	**2 v 2**	**Gloucester City**
	Played 2-2-93	
Brady 22,	(618)	Bayliss 50,
Anderson 27		Buckland 88
Gloucester City	**0 v 0**	**Runcorn**
	Played 8-2-93	
	(771)	
Runcorn	**4 v 1**	**Gloucester City**
	Played 11-2-93	
Brown 43,	(701)	Crouch 27
McKenna 48,		
Bywater 56(og),		
Shaughnessy 78		
Stalybridge Celtic	**1 v 1**	**Merthyr Tydfil**
Brown 84	(818)	C Williams 57(p)
Merthyr Tydfil	**1 v 0**	**Stalybridge C.**
	Played 2-2-93	
Coates 68	(704)	

Peter Risley of St Albans City prepares to clear the ball out of defence as Witton Albion's Steve Adams gets ready to challenge. Witton Albion, bottom of the Conference at the time, continued their recent excellent Trophy record with a 2-0 win a Clarence Park. Photo - Paul Dennis.

Billingham 'keeper Gary Popple shows a clean pair of hands, but Synners lose to Winsford. Photo - Colin Stevens.

Gary Butterworth and Paul Cavell sandwich a Bromsgrove player during Dagenham's defeat. Photo - John Collinge.

Kingstonian's Richard Cherry takes on the Telford United defence. Photo - Dennis Nicholson.

THIRD ROUND PROPER

(SAT. 20th FEB. 1993)

Northallerton Town 1 (Wasden 16)
Farnborough 3 (Collins 28, Coney 53, Leworthy 88)
Att: 671
Northallerton: Michael Devine, Graham Curry, Richard Dowson, Mark Forster, Mark Warrior, Michael Howell (David Keavney 74), Gary McDonald, Robert Lake, Archie Stephens (Steven Bell 59), Gary Stirland, Lee Wasden.
Farnborough: John Power, Steve Baker, Paul Manning, Danny Williamson, Andy Bye, Jim Wigmore, David Leworthy, Eamonn Collins, Dean Coney, Danny Holmes, Jamie Horton. Unused subs: David Coleman, Richard Newberry.

Runcorn 1 (Anderson 31)
Winsford United 0   Att: 1,276
Runcorn: Arthur Williams, Justin Wall, Paul Robertson, Graham Hill, Jimmy Brown, Garry Anderson, Ian Brady, Steve Shaughnessy, Neil Parker (Ian McInerny 88), Ken McKenna, Andy Taylor. Unused sub: Jamie Bates.
Winsford: Lee Williams, Michael Halliday, John Whitney, Cecil Edey, Terence Megram, Harvey Cunningham (Neil Hall 70), Wayne Collins, Darren Sheridan, David Maynard (Jimmy Cameron 70), Bevan Blackwood, Gerard Byrne.

Witton Albion 1 (Thomas 38)
Marine 0   Att: 1,171
Witton: Keith Mason, Stephen Senior, Lee Coathup, Stephen McNeilis, Jim Connor, Mark Lillis, Karl Thomas, Jason Gallagher, Darrell McCarty, Aidan Murphy, Steve Adams. Unused subs: Carl Alford, Paul Bancroft.
Marine: Kevin O'Brien, Tony Ward (Brendan Grant 65), David Roberts, John Roche (Neil Hanson), Andrew Draper, Keith Johnson, Eddie Murray, Graham Rowlands, Brian Ross, Chris Camden, Paul Dowson.

Wycombe Wanderers 2 (Stapleton 25, Scott 72)
Bromsgrove Rovers 0   Att: 4,907
Wycombe: Paul Hyde, Jason Cousins (Keith Ryan 43), Les Thompson, Andy Kerr, Matt Crossley, Simon Hutchinson, Dennis Greene, Steve Thompson, Simon Stapleton, Keith Scott, Steve Guppy. Unused sub: Mark West.
Bromsgrove: Ron Green, James Skelding, Shaun O'Meara, Lee Williams (Tom Daly 72), Paul Wardle, Paul Webb, Robert Shilvock, Steve Stott, Mark Whitehouse (Tony Grealish 85), Brian Gray, Mark Crisp.

Merthyr Tydfil 1 (C Williams 23)
Warrington Town 1 (Watson 85)   Att: 556
Merthyr: Gary Wager, Mark Williams, Ryan James, Terry Boyle, Mark Davies, Kevin Rogers, Mark Tucker, Marc Coates, Adrian Needs, Cerri Williams (David Cole 79), Tommy Hutchison. Unused sub: Chris Thomas.
Warrington: Steve Parsonage, Neil Cook (Paul Lambert 82), Paul McNally, Gary Finley, Chris Coulson, Michael Tandy, Gavin McDonald, Joey Dunn (Ken Saunders 80), Neil Whalley, Aidan Warder, Liam Watson.

Warrington 3 (McDonald 57, Watson 54, Dunn 95)
Merthyr Tydfil 2 (Needs 33, M Williams 77)
Played 24-2-93. Att: 1,447
Warrington: Steve Parsonage, Neil Cook, Paul McNally, Gary Finley, Chris Coulson, Michael Tandy, Gavin McDonald, Joey Dunn, Neil Whalley (Ken Saunders 92), Aidan Warder, Liam Watson. Unused sub: Paul Lambert.
Merthyr: Gary Wager, Mark Williams, Ryan James, Terry Boyle, Mark Davies, Adrian Needs, Mark Tucker, Marc Coates (Tommy Hutchison 68), David D'Auria, Cerri Williams, David Cole. Unused sub: Des Trick.

Chesham United 1 (Banton 46)
Sutton United 3 (Smart 37, Evans 51, Feltham 57)
Att: 1,516
Chesham: Andy Lomas, Andrew York, Naseem Bashir, Steve Bateman, Micky Barnes, Lee Costa, Mark Dawber (John Richardson 67), Andrew Adebowale, Michael Banton, Chris Townsend, Garry Attrell (Darren Coleman 73).
Sutton: Ron Fearon, Paul Gates, Steve Smart, Nigel Golley, Mark Costello, Mark Underdown, Peter Byrne, Dominic Feltham, Richard Evans (Mark Ford 85), Gary Thomas, Simon Quail (Robert Scott 76).

Grays Athletic 1 (Walker 70)
Gateshead 1 (Dobson 15)   Att: 1,013
Grays: Craig Tucker, Barry Fox, Steven Ward, Ian Brown, Andy Pask, Jason Walker (Nicky Crown 82), John Deadmam, Jimmy Sheringham, Ricky Walkes (Winston Whittingham 75), Ian Durant, Phil Sammons.
Gateshead: Simon Smith, Steve Higgins, Michael Farrey, Jeff Wrightson (John Cooke 62), David Corner, Bruce Halliday, Derek Bell, Simon Guthrie (Wayne Davison 84), Paul Dobson, Billy Askew, Alan Lamb.

Gateshead 3 (Dobson 66 88, Lamb 71)
Grays Athletic 0   Played 24-2-93. Att: 402
Gateshead: Simon Smith, Steve Higgins, Michael Farrey, Steve Tuplins, Jeff Wrightson, Bruce Halliday (John Cooke 42), Derek Bell, Simon Guthrie (Wayne Davison 45), Paul Dobson, Billy Askew, Alan Lamb.
Grays: Craig Tucker, Barry Fox, Steven Ward, Ian Brown, Andy Pask, Jason Walker, John Deadmam (Ricky Walkes 75), Jimmy Sheringham, Winston Whittingham, Ian Durant, Phil Sammons (Paul Timson 60).

Telford United 1 (Niblett 40)
Boston United 1 (Jones 82)   Att: 1,408
Telford: Darren Acton, David Pritchard (Andrew Cooke 25), Marcus Bignot, Andrew Lee, Nigel Niblett, Stuart Clarke, Martin Myers, Stephen Ferguson, Sean Francis, Stewart Bowen, Roy Green. Unused sub: Ian Benbow.
Boston: Paul Bastock, Paul Casey, Steve Stoutt, Martin Hardy, Ian Knight, Lee Howarth, Neil Grayson, Steve Chambers (Jon Graham 52), Gary Jones, Chris White, Dean Trott (Darren Munton 68).

Boston United 4 (Jones 15 45 79, Stoutt 88)
Telford United 0   Played 24-2-93. Att: 1,626
Boston: Paul Bastock, Paul Casey, Steve Stoutt, Martin Hardy, Chris White, Lee Howarth, Neil Grayson, Steve Chambers, Gary Jones, Jon Graham, Dean Trott. Unused subs: Ian Knight, Darren Munton.
Telford: Darren Acton, Stewart Bowen, Marcus Bignot, Andrew Lee, Nigel Niblett (Roy Green 30), Stuart Clarke, Martin Myers (Andrew Cooke 60), Stephen Ferguson, Sean Francis, Tim Langford, Ian Benbow.

Over the Second and Third Rounds, **Warrington Town** and **Sutton United** emerged as the giant-killers of this year's Vauxhall F.A. Trophy and became the only two 'non-Conference' sides left in the competition. Fortunately these clubs were paired in the Quarter-Finals guaranteeing one Semi-Finalist from below the top flight.

Both Sutton and Warrington enjoyed notable victories to reach this stage. The Surrey side followed up their First Round drubbing of Woking by scoring another three against high-flying **Slough Town**. Then they went to Diadora table-toppers **Chesham United** and knocked in another treble to secure a Quarter-Final berth. For their part, Warrington, of the First Division of the H.F.S. Loans League, won away to their Premier Division counterparts **Bishop Auckland** in the Second Round, and then saw off **Merthyr Tydfil** in Round Three.

Northern League **Northallerton Town** enjoyed a very creditable Trophy run for the second consecutive season. In the Second Round they defeated **Bashley** of the Beazer Homes League, but despite taking an early lead through Lee Wasden in the Third Round they met their match in **Farnborough Town**. The Conference side powered back with goals from Eammon Collins, Dean Coney and David Leworthy to reach the last eight for the first time.

Wycombe Wanderers became red hot favourites benefitting from three home draws out of four. It wasn't easy, though, for the Conference champions-elect. In their only Trophy journey they had to negotiate a difficult tie at **Morecambe**, emerging victorious after a replay, and in the Third Round they beat the strong **Bromsgrove Rovers** side with a first-half goal from Simon Stapleton and a Keith Scott penalty.

Runcorn clear despite the energetic efforts of Winsford's Bevan Blackwood (dark shirt). Photo - Colin Stevens.

Bromsgrove's Ron Green guesses wrong and is beaten by Keith Scott's penalty at Wycombe. Photo - Paul Dennis.

Gateshead's Alan Lamb runs at the Grays defence as the Tynesiders get a draw in Essex. Photo - Dennis Nicholson.

QUARTER FINALS
(SAT. 13th MARCH 1993)

WYCOMBE WANDERERS 1 (Guppy 90)
GATESHEAD 0
Att: 4,795
Wycombe: Paul Hyde, Jason Cousins, Les Thompson, Andy Kerr, Keith Ryan, Steve Thompson, Dennis Greene (Simon Hutchinson 59), Kim Casey, Simon Stapleton, Keith Scott, Steve Guppy. Unused subs: Ty Gooden.
Gateshead: Simon Smith, Michael Farrey, Jeff Wrightson, Tony Lowrey, David Corner, Bruce Halliday, Derek Bell, John Cooke, Paul Dobson, Simon Guthrie, Alan Lamb. Unused subs: Billy Askew, Shaun Elliott.

BOSTON UNITED 0
RUNCORN 2 (Parker 51, Anderson 66(p))
Att: 2,639
Boston: Paul Bastock, Steve Stoutt, Chris White, Martin Hardy, Ian Knight (Darren Munton 63), Robbie Curtis, Neil Grayson, Steve Chambers, Gary Jones, Drew Coverdale (Jon Graham 54), Dean Trott. Subs: Darren Munton, Jon Graham.
Runcorn: Arthur Williams, Justin Wall, Paul Robertson, Graham Hill, Jimmy Brown, Garry Anderson, Ian Brady, Joe Connor, Steve Shaughnessy, Neil Parker, Gary Brabin. Unused subs: Ian McInerny, Andy Taylor.

SUTTON UNITED 2 (Gates 47, Bryne 57(p))
WARRINGTON TOWN 1 (Dunn 44)
Att: 1,547
Sutton: Andy Harris, Paul Gates, Phil Barton, Nigel Golley, Mark Costello, Mark Ford, Peter Byrne, Dominic Feltham, Peter Evans, Gary Thomas, Simon Quail. Unused subs: Steve Browne, Billy Edwards.
Warrington: Steve Parsonage, Neil Williams, Colin Beck, Gary Finley, Paul McNally, Neil Cook, Gavin McDonald, Joey Dunn, Paul Lambert (Kenny Saunders 60), Aidan Warder, Liam Watson. Unused sub: Kenny Saunders, Alan Blair.

WITTON ALBION 3 (Thomas 24 25, Burke 68)
FARNBOROUGH 2 (Leworthy 17, Baker 85(p))
Att: 1,262
Witton: Joe Paladino, Steve Senior, Lee Coathup, Steve McNeilis, Jim Connor, Carl Alford (Mark Lillis 81), Karl Thomas, Colin Rose, Jason Gallagher, Brendan Burke, David Bancroft (Steve Adams 68).
Farnborough: John Power, Steve Baker, David Manning, Danny Williamson, Andy Bye, Bradley Pratt, David Leworthy, Eammon Collins (Phil Bell 68), Dean Coney, Danny Holmes, Matthew Holland. Unused sub: Jim Wigmore.

Red-hot Vauxhall F.A. Trophy favourites **Wycombe Wanderers** moved into the Semi-Finals with the ease that most pundits expected. The game against northern visitors **Gateshead**, through to the last eight for the first time in their sixteen year history, was in its final minute before Steve Guppy notched the all-important winning goal.

In the battle of the minnows, **Sutton United** overcame **Warrington Town**, the season's principal giant-killers, but only after having recovered from the shock of falling behind to a Joey Dunn goal two minutes before the interval. Paul Gates took only two minutes to equalise after the break and Peter Bryne scored the winner from the spot, but Sutton had to withstand some late pressure before they could be sure of their last four ticket.

Runcorn booked their passage with a 2-0 success at struggling **Boston United**. The first-half was very even, but Neil Parker fired Runcorn ahead six minutes after the break, and Garry Anderson added a second with a penalty after Ian Brady had been felled. In an exciting tie at Wincham Park, **Farnborough** absorbed a lot of early **Witton Albion** pressure before breaking to take the lead with an angled shot from David Leworthy. Karl Thomas, however, turned the tie on its head with two goals in a minute. The first arrived when John Power failed to claim a cross allowing Thomas to score from close-range, and the second was a rasping drive off the underside of the bar after another defensive lapse. With 'Boro committed to attack, Brendan Burke made it 3-1 after the break, but Steve Baker pulled one back from the spot.

Gateshead fans enjoyed a great day out at Adams Park, that is until the final minute of the match when a fine performance by their team was wrecked by Steve Guppy's winner for Wycombe Wanderers. Photo - Graham Cotterill.

Paul Bancroft crosses for Karl Thomas to score for Witton Albion against Farnborough. Photo - Keith Clayton.

John Cooke of Gateshead gets past Wycombe's Andy Kerr but can't convert the chance. Photo - Graham Cotterill.

Warrington's Neil Williams (left) and Dominic Feltham of Sutton in a sprint for the ball. Photo - Dennis Nicholson.

SEMI FINALS
(SAT. 3rd & 10th APRIL 1993)

First Leg
WYCOMBE WANDERERS   2
SUTTON UNITED   3
Att: 5,600

Wycombe Wanderers were firm favourites to make the semi-final second leg a mere formality by scoring enough goals in this home first leg at Adams Park, but Diadora League premier division side, Sutton United, had very different ideas.

Sutton, well renowned cup fighters, especially in the FA Cup, upset the form-book by winning the game 3-2. Having already ousted Conference clubs Slough Town and Woking from the competition, they took the lead after just 12 minutes when **Peter Byrne**, who ironically had a brief spell at Adams Park after moving down south to work, headed firmly past goalkeeper Paul Hyde.

Stunned by that goal, Wycombe came at the Sutton defence in a determined effort to equalise, and the 5,600 crowd didn't have to wait long for the goal to arrive. In fact, it was just six minutes later when the outstanding **Steve Guppy** scored direct from a corner, beating the despairing efforts of Sutton's young goalkeeper Andy Harris to keep the ball out.

Wycombe manager Martin O'Neill must have then looked forward to a comfortable ride for the rest of the game, but reckoned without **Simon Quail**, who restored Sutton's lead after 32 minutes with a tremendous 20-yard drive past Hyde.

The shocked crowd had to wait until the 52nd minute to see the Conference championship favourites force another equaliser, **Dave Carroll** beating Harris from close range, but Sutton again came back magnificently, and after 77 minutes the much-travelled **Steve Browne**, who numbers Wealdstone, Charlton, Barking, Grays Athletic and Maidstone United amongst his former clubs, capitalised on some slack defending to secure his team's surprise first leg lead.

Wycombe: Paul Hyde, Jason Cousins, Hakan Hayrettin, Andy Kerr, Anton Vircavs, Steve Thompson, Dave Carroll, Keith Ryan, Trevor Aylott (Dennis Greene 66), Mark West (Simon Hutchinson 78), Steve Guppy. *Sutton:* Andy Harris; Steve Smart, Phil Barton, Nigel Golley, Mark Costello, Paul Gates, Peter Byrne, Dominic Feltham, Steve Browne, Gary Thomas, Simon Quail. Unused subs: Billy Edwards, Mark Ford.

Second Leg
SUTTON UNITED   0
WYCOMBE WANDERERS   4
Att: 5,002

A big, all-ticket, crowd of over 5,000 turned up for the second leg at Gander Green Lane, many of whom were hoping to see the favourites beaten.

However, Wycombe, who had disappointed in the first game, came determined not to disappoint their vast army of travelling supporters this time. The whole Wycombe side was lifted by the surprise return of striker Keith Scott who had only trained briefly on the previous Thursday, but was declared fit to play. Martin O'Neill left out recent signing Anton Vircavs and Mark West and brought in prolific marksman Kim Casey to play alongside Scott. Sutton boss Alan Gane kept faith with the side that had done so well at Wycombe, altering only one of the substitutes.

The Conference leaders levelled the aggregate scores after 34 minutes when centre-half **Matt Crossley**, in for Vircavs after a spell on out with illness, headed home a Steve Guppy corner.

The home side's chances of a Wembley visit were effectively killed off within a few minutes of the second-half when two more corners caught them out. **Keith Scott** headed home the first, and seconds later **Crossley** became the unlikely Wanderers' goalscoring hero when he half-volleyed past Andy Harris for number three.

A Sutton United fightback was never allowed to happen by a strong Wycombe side, and the visitors sent their fans wild when **Dave Carroll** side-footed the fourth goal after 76 minutes. The return to the side of both Matt Crossley and Keith Scott undoubtedly had a major bearing on the outcome and, ironically, Crossley's brace were his first goals of the season!

Wycombe: Paul Hyde, Jason Cousins, Geoff Cooper, Keith Ryan, Matt Crossley, Steve Thompson, Dave Carroll, Kim Casey (Simon Hutchinson 77), Hakan Hayrettin, Keith Scott (Mark West 75), Steve Guppy. *Sutton:* As 1st leg. Subs: Robert Scott for Byrne (70), Billy Edwards for Berton (80).

First Leg
RUNCORN   2
WITTON ALBION   0
Att: 1,610

Commercial Manager Ken McKenna came up with a double bonus which gave Runcorn a valuable two-goal first leg lead at Canal Street. Witton had dominated a scrappy ill-tempered game until **McKenna** broke the deadlock after 70 minutes when he bundled the ball home after Ian Brady's header had been blocked on the line.

Twelve minutes later, McKenna's cross saw midfielder **Garry Anderson** score the second, and possibly crucial, goal. Anderson's strike kept up his remarkable record of having scored in every round of this season's Trophy run - quite an achievement for a midfield player.

Witton, last season's beaten finalists, must have disappointed their supporters in the 2,000+ crowd. They never really posed a serious threat to Arthur Williams in the Runcorn goal, despite dominating much of the midfield action.

Runcorn: Arthur Williams, Justin Wall, Paul Robertson, Graham Hill (Neil Parker 71), Garry Anderson, Ian Brady, Joe Connor, Steve Shaughnessy, Ken McKenna, Gary Brabin. Unused sub: Andy Taylor. *Witton:* Keith Mason, Steve Senior, Lee Coathup, Steve McNeilis, Matthew Lambert (Steve Gardner 82), Mark Lillis, Karl Thomas, Colin Rose, Jason Gallagher (Carl Alford 48), Brendan Burke, Steve Bullock.

Second Leg
WITTON ALBION   1
RUNCORN   0
Att: 2,033

Witton Albion, looking to overturn the two-goal deficit from the first game and a second successive Wembley visit, came up against a determined and powerful Runcorn side, who themselves were looking for a return to the Twin Towers, having been beaten finalists in 1986.

Like the first match, Witton dominated most of the game. In fact, they had enough chances to have won on aggregate. However, Witton in the end only had **Brendan Burke's** 20-yard strike, which flew past Runcorn 'keeper Arthur Williams in the 32nd minute, to show for their dominance.

Witton: Keith Mason, Steve Senior, Lee Coathup (Gallagher 79), Steve McNeilis, Jim Connor, Mark Lillis, Karl Thomas, Colin Rose, Carl Alford, Brendan Burke, Steve Adams (Paul Bancroft 79). *Runcorn:* Arthur Williams, Justin Wall, Paul Robertson, Graham Hill, Neil Parker, Garry Anderson, Ian Brady, Joe Connor, Steve Shaughnessy (Jimmy Brown 46 (Andy Taylor 71)), Ken McKenna, Gary Brabin.

Dave Carroll leads an attack, but Wycombe were beaten by Sutton at Adams Park. Photo - Roger Turner.

Keith Ryan leads the Wycombe celebrations after the dramatic turn around at Sutton. Photo - Paul Dennis.

Steve Senior of Witton chases after Paul Robertson in the decisive first leg at Runcorn. Photo - Paul Dennis.

VAUXHALL
F.A. TROPHY FINAL

Wycombe Wanderers 4 v 1 Runcorn

Cousins (2), Kerr (20), Shaughnessy (41)
Thompson (58), Carroll (90)

Attendance: 32,968

Wycombe Wanderers: Paul Hyde, Jason Cousins, Geoff Cooper, Andy Kerr, Matt Crossley, Steve Thompson (Hakan Hayrettin 65), Dave Carroll, Keith Ryan, Simon Hutvhinson, Keith Scott, Steve Guppy. Unused sub: Kim Casey.
Runcorn: Arthur Williams, Jamie Bates, Paul Robertson, Graham Hill, Ian Harold (Joe Connor 62), Garry Anderson, Ian Brady (Neil Parker 72), Jimmy Brown, Steve Shaughnessy, Ken McKenna, Gary Brabin.

Referee: Mr I J Borritt

Linesmen: Mr N S Barry, Mr G M Lee.

Poor Runcorn. Even arriving at Wembley two hours prior to kick-off it was apparent that they were just gatecrashing the Wycombe Wanderers party. The streets around the ground were already a bobbing navy and sky blue sea. The atmosphere inside the arena was no more encouraging for Runcorn with Wycombe fans spreading in a massive arc from the royal box right round behind the eastern goal and along the full length of the northern side. And it was not as if the supporters were manifesting the normal, acutely nervous, traits of a partisan Wembley crowd - they were there to sing, dance, celebrate a famous title win, and to bid a noisy farewell to Pyramid football.

On the weekend of the Vauxhall F.A. Trophy final, as much media attention was being paid to Wycombe's much sought after manager as to his side's quest to complete the non-League double. Just how much the fans' show of adoration had to do with Martin O'Neill's decision to turn down the chance to manage Nottingham Forest, we will perhaps never know. What is certain is that it is a wonderful tribute to Wycombe that their manager preferred to continue the job he has started at Adams Park to chancing his arm in the Football League First Division.

As the match got under way, O'Neill's Wycombe team stuck rigidly to the script and raced into an early lead, Jason Cousin's firmly struck low free-kick creeping round the Runcorn wall and inside the goalkeeper's left-hand post. Runcor did enjoy a fair slice of pressure during the first-half. They won a succession of corners, but their efforts were blunt in comparison to Wycombe's rapier-like raids. The second goal arrived after twenty minutes when Andy Kerr connected with a Dave Carroll free-kick from the right and sent an exquisite header whistling past Arthur Williams for what was probably the best goal of the game.

At this point, Runcorn were in danger of being swept away. They desperately needed to get back into the game before half-time, and when Steve Shaughnessy was given a good chance by a fine through ball in the 41st minute he knew he couldn't afford to miss. He didn't, flashing a fierce shot past the advancing Paul Hyde.

After the interval, the Wanderers were in even more authoritative form than during the first-half. The second, and decisive goal arrived just before the hour mark when Steve Thompson rose to head home a left-wing corner from Steve Guppy. From that moment on the game was safe, though Runcorn did have their moments, notably when Ken McKenna forced Hyde into an excellent full-stretch save and his side had a strong claim for a goal turned down by the referee who deemed it not to have crossed the line.

The final goal, in the very last minute, was somewhat indicative of the afternoon as a whole, i.e. everything was going Wycombe's way. There seemed to be little immediate danger as Dave Carroll took the ball into the Runcorn box on the right and hit a cross too close to the 'keeper. However, Williams made a wild flap rather than a clean catch and his defenders could only watch in agony as the ball dropped into the net.

So Wycombe bade the Pyramid farwell with a stylish display. They became the third team to achieve the non-League double of the G.M.V. Conference title and the F.A. Trophy in the same season, and are developing a taste for Wembley success having now won the Trophy in two of the past three season - who would bet against a return to the Twin Towers next spring in either the Third Division promotion play-offs or the Autoglass Trophy final.

J.W.

Scorer of Wycombe's third, Steve Thompson (left) battles for possession with Ian Brady. Photo - Dave West.

Paul Hyde claims a cross despite a challenge from Runcorn's Ken McKenna. Photo - Gavin Ellis-Neville.

Wycombe Wanderers, Vauxhall F.A. Trophy winners 1992-93. Photo - Paul Dennis.

Steve Shaughnessy rifles home Runcorn's only goal, just before half-time. Photo - Gavin Ellis-Neville.

Despair for Arthur Williams after his late fumble cost Runcorn the final goal. Photo - Gavin Ellis-Neville.

Martin O'Neill the Wycombe boss with the Vauxhall F.A. Trophy. Photo - Gavin Ellis-Neville.

F.A. TROPHY CELEBRATIONS

A post-match interview for Keith Ryan, Jason Cousins and Dave Carroll. Photo - Paul Dennis.

'Goal-scorers'! From left to right: Dave Carroll, Jason Cousins, Steve Thompson and Andy Kerr. Photo - Gavin Ellis-Neville.

PAST F.A. CHALLENGE TROPHY FINALS

1970 MACCLESFIELD TOWN 2 (Lyond, B Fidler) **TELFORD UNITED** 0   Ref: K Walker
Macc: Cooke, Sievwright, Bennett, Beaumont, Collins, Roberts, Lyons, B Fidler, Young, Corfield, D Fidler. *Telford:* Irvine, Harris, Croft, Flowers, Coton, Ray, Fudge, Hart, Bentley, Murray, Jagger. *Att:* 28,000.

1971 TELFORD UTD 3 (Owen, Bentley, Fudge) **HILLINGDON BORO.** 2 (Reeve, Bishop)   Ref: D Smith
Telford: Irvine, Harris, Croft, Ray, Coton, Carr, Fudge, Owen, Bentley, Jagger, Murray. *H'don:* Lowe, Batt, Langley, Higginson, Newcombe, Moore, Fairchild, Bishop, Reeve, Carter, Knox. *Att:* 29,500.

1972 STAFFORD RANGERS 3 (Williams 2, Cullerton) **BARNET** 0   Ref: P Partridge
Staff: Aleksic, Chadwick, Clayton, Sargeant, Aston, Machin, Cullerton, Chapman, Williams, Bayley, Jones. *Barnet:* McClelland, Lye, Jenkins, Ward, Embrey, King, Powell, Rerry, Flatt, Easton, Plume. *Att:* 24,000.

1973 SCARBOROUGH 2 (Leask, Thompson) **WIGAN ATHLETIC** 1 (Rogers) *aet*   Ref: H Hackney
Scarboro: Garrow, Appleton, Shoulder, Dunn, Siddle, Fagan, Donoghue, Franks, Leask (Barmby), Thompson, Hewitt. *Wigan:* Reeves, Morris, Sutherland, Taylor, Jackson, Gillibrand, Clements, Oats (McCunnell), Rogers, King, Worswick. *Att:* 23,000.

1974 MORECAMBE 2 (Richmond, Sutton) **DARTFORD** 1 (Cunningham)   Ref: B Homewood
M'cambe: Coates, Pearson, Bennett, Sutton, Street, Baldwin, Done, Webber, Roberts (Galley), Kershaw, Richmond. *D'ford:* Morton, Read, Payne, Carr, Burns, Binks, Light, Glozier, Robinson (Hearne), Cunningham, Halleday. *Att:* 19,000.

1975 MATLOCK TOWN 4 (Oxley, Dawson, T Fenoughty, N Fenoughty) **SCARBOROUGH** 0 Ref: K Styles
M'lock: Fell, McKay, Smith, Stuart, Dawson, Swan, Oxley, N Fenoughty, Scott, T Fenoughty, M Fenoughty. *S'boro:* Williams, Hewitt, Rettitt, Dunn, Marshall, Todd, Houghton, Woodall, Davidson, Barnby, Aveyard. *Att:* 21,000.

1976 SCARBOROUGH 3 (Woodall, Abbey, Marshall(p)) **STAFFORD R.** 2 (Jones 2) *aet*   Ref: R Challis
S'boro: Barnard, Jackson, Marshall, H Dunn, Ayre (Donoghue), HA Dunn, Dale, Barmby, Woodall, Abbey, Hilley. *S'ford:* Arnold, Ritchie, Richards, Sargeant, Seddon, Morris, Chapman, Lowe, Jones, Hutchinson, Chadwick. *Att:* 21,000.

1977 SCARBOROUGH 2 (Dunn(p), Abbey) **DAGENHAM** 1 (Harris)   Ref: G Courtney
S'boro: Chapman, Smith, Marshall (Barmby), Dunn, Ayre, Deere, Aveyard, Donoghue, Woodall, Abbey, Dunn. *D'ham:* Hutley, Wellman, P Currie, Dunwell, Moore, W Currie, Harkins, Saul, Fox, Harris, Holder. *Att:* 21,500.

1978 ALTRINCHAM 3 (King, Johnson, Rogers) **LEATHERHEAD** 1 (Cook)   Ref: A Grey
A'cham: Eales, Allan, Crossley, Bailey, Owens, King, Morris, Heathcote, Johnson, Rogers, Davidson (Flaherty). *L'head:* Swannell, Cooper, Eaton, Davies, Reid, Malley, Cook, Salkeld, Baker, Boyle (Bailey). *Att:* 20,000.

1979 STAFFORD RANGERS 2 (A Wood 2) **KETTERING TOWN** 0   Ref: D Richardson
S'ford: Arnold, F Wood, Willis, Sargeant, Seddon, Ritchie, Secker, Chapman, A Wood, Cullerton, Chadwick (Jones). *K'ring:* Lane, Ashby, Lee, Eastell, Dixey, Suddards, Flannagan, Kellock, Phipps, Clayton, Evans (Hughes). *Att:* 32,000.

1980 DAGENHAM 2 (Duck, Maycock) **MOSSLEY** 1 (Smith)   Ref: K Baker
D'ham: Huttley, Wellman, Scales, Dunwell, Mooore, Durrell, Maycock, Horan, Duck, Kidd, Jones (Holder). *M'ley:* Fitton, Brown, Vaughan, Gorman, Salter, Polliot, Smith, Moore, Skeete, O'Connor, Keelan (Wilson). *Att:* 26,000.

1981 BISHOP'S STORTFORD 1 (Sullivan) **SUTTON UNITED** 0   Ref: J Worrall
S'ford: Moore, Blackman, Brame, Smith (Worrell), Bradford, Abery, Sullivan, Knapman, Radford, Simmonds, Mitchell. *Sutton:* Collyer, Rogers, Green, J Rains, T Rains, Stephens (Sunnucks), Waldon, Pritchard, Cornwell, Parsons. *Att:* 22,578.

1982 ENFIELD 1 (Taylor) **ALTRINCHAM** 0   Ref: B Stevens
Enfield: Jacobs, Barrett, Tone, Jennings, Waite, Ironton, Ashford, Taylor, Holmes, Oliver (Flint), King. *A'cham:* Connaughton, Crossley, Davison, Bailey, Cuddy, King (Whitbread), Allan, Heathcote, Johnson, Rogers, Howard. *Att:* 18.678..

1983 TELFORD UTD 2 (Mather 2) **NORTHWICH VICTORIA** 1 (Bennett)   Ref: B Hill
Telford: Charlton, Lewis, Turner, Mayman (Joseph), Walker, Easton, Barnett, Williams, Mather, Hogan, Alcock. *N'wich:* Ryan, Fretwell, Murphy, Jones, Forshaw, Ward, Anderson, Abel (Bennett), Reid, Chesters, Wilson. *Att:* 22,071.

1984 NORTHWICH VICTORIA 1 (Chesters) **BANGOR CITY** 1 (Whelan)   *Att:* 14,200. Ref: J Martin
replay at Stoke: NORTHWICH 2 (Chesters(p), Anderson) **BANGOR** 1 (Lunn)   *Att:* 5,805
N'wich: Ryan, Fretwell, Dean, Jones, Forshaw (Power 65), Bennett, Anderson, Abel, Reid, Chesters, Wilson. *Bangor:* Letheren, Cavanagh, Gray, Whelan, Banks, Lunn, Urqhart, Morris, Carter, Howat, Sutcliffe (Westwood 105). Same teams in replay.

1985 WEALDSTONE 2 (Graham, Holmes) **BOSTON UNITED** 1 (Cook)   Ref: J Bray
W'stone: Iles, Perkins, Bowgett, Byatt, Davies, Greenaway, Holmes, Wainwright, Donnellan, Graham (N Cordice 89), A Cordice. *Boston:* Blackwell, Casey, Ladd, Creane, O'Brien, Thommson, Laverick (Mallender 78), Simpsom, Gilbert, Lee, Cook. *Att:* 20,775.

1986 ALTRINCHAM 1 (Farrelly) **RUNCORN** 0   Ref: A Ward
A'cham: Wealands, Gardner, Densmore, Johnson, Farrelly, Conning, Cuddy, Davison, Reid, Ellis, Anderson. Sub: Newton. *Runcorn:* McBride, Lee, Roberts, Jones, Fraser, Smith, S Crompton (A Crompton), Imrie, Carter, Mather, Carrodus. *Att:* 15,700.

1987 KIDDERMINSTER HARRIERS 0 **BURTON ALBION** 0   *Att:* 23,617. Ref: D Shaw
replay at West Brom: KIDDERMINSTER 2 (Davies 2) **BURTON** 1 (Groves)   *Att:* 15,685
K'minster: Arnold, Barton, Boxall, Brazier (sub Hazlewood in rep), Collins (sub Pearson 90 at Wembley), Woodall, McKenzie, O'Dowd, Tuohy, Casey, Davies. sub: Jones. *Burton:* New, Essex, Kamara, Vaughan, Simms, Groves, Bancroft, Land, Dorsett, Redfern, (sub Wood in replay), Gauden. Sub: Patterson.

1988 ENFIELD 0 **TELFORD UNITED** 0   *Att:* 20,161. Ref: L Dilkes
replay at West Brom: ENFIELD 3 (Furlong 2, Howell) **TELFORD** 2 (Biggins, Norris(p))   *Att:* 6,912
Enfield: Pape, Cottington, Howell, Keen (sub Edmonds in rep), Sparrow (sub Hayzleden at Wembley), Lewis (sub Edmonds at Wembley), Harding, Cooper, King, Furlong, Francis. *Enfield:* Charlton, McGinty, Storton, Nelson, Wiggins, Mayman, (sub Cunningham in rep (sub Hancock)), Sankey, Joseph, Stringer (sub Griffiths at Wembley, Griffiths in rep), Biggins, Norris.

1989 TELFORD UNITED 1 (Crawley) **MACCLESFIELD TOWN 0**   Ref: T Holbrook
Telford: Charlton, Lee, Brindley, Hancock, Wiggins, Mayman, Grainger, Joseph, Nelson, Lloyd, Stringer. Subs: Crawley, Griffiths. *Macclesfield:* Zelem, Roberts, Tobin, Edwards, Hardman, Askey, Lake, Hanton, Imrie, Burr, Timmons. Subs: Devomshire, Kendall. *Att: 18,102.*

1990 BARROW 3 (Gordon 2, Cowperthwaitee) **LEEK TOWN 0**   Ref: T Simpson.
Barrow: McDonnell, Higgins, Chilton, Skivington, Gordon, Proctor, Doherty (Burgess), Farrell (Gilmore), Cowperthwaite, Lowe, Ferris. *Leek:* Simpson, Elsby (Smith), Pearce, McMullen, Clowes, Coleman (Russell), Mellor, Somerville, Sutton, Millington. *Att: 19,011.*

1991 WYCOMBE WANDERERS 2 (Scott, West) **KIDDERMINSTER HARRIERS 1** (Hadley) Ref: J Watson
Wycombe: Granville, Crossley, Cash, Kerr, Creaser, Carroll, Ryan, Stapleton, West, Scott, Guppy (Hutchinson). *Kidderminster:* Jones, Kurila, McGrath, Weir, Barnett, Forsyth, Joseph (Wilcox), Howell (Whitehouse), Hadley, Lilwall, Humphries. *Att: 34,842.*

1992 COLCHESTER UTD 3 (Masters, Smith, McGavin) **WITTON ALBION 1** (Lutkevitch) Ref: K P Barratt
Colchester: Barrett, Donald, Roberts, Knsella, English, Martin, Cook, Masters, McDonough (Bennett 65), McGavin, Smith. *Witton:* Mason, Halliday, Coathup, McNeilis, Jim Connor, Anderson, Thomas, Rose, Alford, Grimshaw (Joe Connor), Lutkevitch (McCluskie). *Att: 27,806.*

Tony English of Colchester United with the Vauxhall F.A. Trophy in 1992. Photo - John Robinson.

F.A. TROPHY
Round by Round Chart

1st Rnd Proper	2nd Rnd Proper	3rd Rnd Proper	4th Rnd Proper	Semi-final	Final
Morecambe 5					
Frickley Ath. 1	Morecambe 1;0				
Wycombe Wdrs 3	Wycombe Wdrs 1;2				
Cheltenham T. 1		Wycombe Wdrs 2			
Kettering T. 0;1		Bromsgrove Rvrs 0			
Bromsgrove 0;4	Bromsgrove 3				
Yeovil Town 0;1	Dagenham & R. 1				
Dagenham 0;2			Wycombe Wdrs 1		
Stevenage B. 2			Gateshead 0		
Bath City 0	Stevenage B. 0				
Grays Athletic 1	Grays Athletic 1				
Stafford Rgrs 0		Grays Athletic 1;0			
Gateshead 3		Gateshead 1;3			
Gretna 0	Gateshead 3				
Heybridge S. 4	Heybridge S. 0				
Worcester City 0				Wycombe Wdrs 2;4	
V.S. Rugby 1				1st leg at Wycombe	
Chesham United 6	Chesham United 1			Sutton United 3;0	
Dover Ath. 1;2	Dover Athletic 0				
Hastings T. 1;0		Chesham Utd 1			
Sutton United 3		Sutton United 3			
Woking 0	Sutton United 3				
Yeading 1;1	Slough Town 1				
Slough T. 1;2			Sutton United 2		
Stalybridge C. 2			Warrington T. 1		
Accrington S. 0	Stalybridge 1;0				
Merthyr Tydfil 3	Merthyr Tydfil 1;1				
Wivenhoe Town 0		Merthyr Tydfil 1;2			
Bishop Auckland 1		Warrington T. 1;3			
Leek Town 0	Bishop Auckland 0				
Warrington 2	Warrington T. 1				
Guisborough 1					Wycombe Wdrs 4
St Albans City 1					Runcorn 1
Weston-s-Mare 0	St Albans City 0				
Macclesfield 0;1	Witton Albion 2				
Witton Albion 0;2		Witton Albion 1			
Murton 1		Marine 0			
Nuneaton B. 2	Nuneaton B. 0				
Marine 2	Marine 1				
Blyth Spartans 0			Witton Albion 3		
Northallerton 3			Farnborough T. 2		
Whitby Town 0	Northallerton 1				
Wealdstone 1	Bashley 0				
Bashley 2		Northallerton T. 1			
Farnborough 4		Farnborough T. 3			
Abingdon Town 0	Farnborough 4				
Kidderminster 1	Enfield 0				
Enfield 3				Witton Albion 0;1	
Basingstoke 1				1st leg at Runcorn	
Kingstonian 4	Kingstonian 1			Runcorn 2;0	
Telford United 2	Telford United 2				
Northwich Vics 0		Telford Utd 1;0			
Welling United 2		Boston United 1;4			
Aylesbury Utd 1	Welling United 1				
Spennymoor Utd 1	Boston United 2				
Boston United 2			Boston United 0		
Gloucester C.			Runcorn 2		
Bye	Gloucester 3;2;0;1				
Hyde United 1	Runcorn 3;2;0;4				
Runcorn 2		Runcorn 1			
Barrow 0		Winsford Utd 0			
Billingham S. 1	Billingham S. 1				
Winsford Utd 1	Winsford Utd 2				
Altrincham 0					

F.A CHALLENGE VASE

REVIEW 1992-93

EXTRA-PRELIM. ROUND

(SAT. 5th SEPT. 1992)

(Attendances in brackets)

SUND. IFG ROKER	1 v 0	HEATON STANN. (19)
PONTELAND UNITED	1 v 0	SEATON DELAVAL (65)
NEWTON AYCLIFFE	1 v 2	WALKER (27)
MARSKE UNITED	2 v 4	SOUTH SHIELDS (47)
GENERAL CHEMICALS	1 v 2	WYTHENSHAWE A. (25)
POULTON VICTORIA	4 v 3	HESWALL (78)
CASTLETON GABRIELS	2 v 3	ASHVILLE (39)
GROVE UNITED	2 v 1	ST DOMINICS (38)
ATHERTON COLL.	4 v 1	AYONE (30)
NEWTON	2 v 1	WESTHOUGHTON (19)
MAGHULL	3 v 1	BLACKPOOL MEC. (64)
KNYPERSLEY VICTORIA	1 v 5	WATERLOO DK (75)

(Played at Waterloo Dock)

CHEADE TOWN	0 v 1	MERSEY POLICE (46)
SUTTON TOWN	1 v 3	SHIREBROOK COL. (130)
ROSSINGTON MAIN	3 v 5	PRIORY EASTWOOD (40)
KIMBERLEY TOWN	2 v 3	STOCKSBRIDGE (52)
LIVERSEDGE	1 v 2	HALLAM (56)
BLIDWORTH M.W.	3 v 1	MICKLEOVER (30)
TADCASTER ALBION	2 v 6	PONTEFRACT COL. (58)
SELBY TOWN	3 v 2	YORKS AMATEUR (75)
WORSBORO. B.M.W.	2 v 0	WINTERTON RGRS (120)
CLIPSTONE WELFARE	3 v 2	HALL ROAD RGRS (81)
FRIAR LANE O.B.	4 v 2	IMMINGHAMM T. (57)
DUNKIRK	5 v 3	NETTLEHAM (47)
GLASSHOUGHTON	2 v 1	MALTBY M.W. (60)
HATFIELD MAIN	1 v 1	R.E.S. PARKGATE (50)
R.E.S. PARKGATE	1 v 3	HATFIELD MAIN (70)
COLESHILL TOWN	3 v 3	ANSTEY NOMADS (37)
ANSTEY NOMADS	5 v 2	COLESHILL TOWN (86)
ARMITAGE	2 v 0	STOURPORT S. (64)
ST ANDREWS	4 v 1	HIGHFIELD RGRS (61)
PELSALL VILLA	5 v 1	BIRSTALL UTD (144)
PEGASUS JUNIORS	1 v 0	DAVENTRY TOWN (28)
BRACKLEY TOWN	1 v 4	STAPENHILL (61)
ECCLESHALL	1 v 2	STEWART & L. (31)
WEST BROM. TOWN	1 v 2	BARWELL (28)
WESTFIELDS	3 v 2	OADBY TOWN (61)
LUTTERWORTH TOWN	0 v 2	KING'S HEATH (47)
MILE OAK ROVERS	5 v 2	KNOWLE (55)
CRADLEY TOWN	1 v 2	NORTHFIELD T. (61)
BOLEHALL SWIFTS	3 v 2	HOLWELL SPTS (85)
PERSHORE TOWN	1 v 0	HARROWBY UTD (170)
BLOXWICH TOWN	1 v 3	MEIR K.A. (10)
FAKENHAM TOWN	2 v 1	WOODBRIDGE T. (112)

SOMERSHAM TOWN	4 v 0	IPSWICH WDRS (49)
DOWNHAM TOWN	1 v 1	BRIGHTLINGSEA (120)
BRIGHTLINGSEA U.	1 v 1	DOWNHAM TOWN (125)
DOWNHAM TOWN	3 v 0	BRIGHTLINGSEA (145)
HADLEIGH UTD	7 v 0	STANSTED (93)
BRANTHAM ATH.	0 v 1	CHATTERIS T. (50)
SAWBRIDGEWORTH T.	2 v 1	WARBOYS TOWN (63)
NORWICH UNITED	2 v 1	CORNARD UNITED (62)
LONG SUTTON ATH.	2 v 4	SUDBURY WDRS (41)
ELY CITY	2 v 1	ST IVES TOWN (62)
TOTTERNHOE	2 v 1	STOTFOLD (53)
RAYNERS LANE	3 v 4	LONG BUCKBY (62)
HARPENDEN TOWN	6 v 0	THE 61 F.C. (50)
HILLINGDON BORO.	0 v 5	BROOK HOUSE (50)
AMERSHAM TOWN	1 v 5	LANGFORD (29)
VIKING SPORTS	1 v 2	LONDON COLNEY (40)
SHILLINGTON (W/O)		WOODFORD (SCR.)
WINGATE & FINCHLEY	5 v 2	WALTHAM ABBEY (85)
BEACONSFIELD UTD	1 v 2	COCKFOSTERS (45)

(Played at Cockfosters)

BOWERS UNITED	1 v 2	HANWELL TOWN (90)
BIGGLESWADE T.	0 v 2	LEVERSTOCK G. (39)
BRIMSDOWN ROVERS	4 v 0	KEMPSTON ROVERS (58)
CONCORD RANGERS	1 v 4	POTTERS BAR T. (90)
CROWBOROUGH ATH.	0 v 1	WEST WICKHAM (85)
HARTLEY WINTNEY	2 v 0	DEAL TOWN (97)
CRANLEIGH	4 v 0	BEDFONT
DARENTH HEATHSIDE	3 v 2	PETERSFIELD U. (41)
ASH UNITED	4 v 3	BROADBRIDGE H. (34)
GODALMING & GUIL.	0 v 3	SLADE GREEN (82)
FARLEIGH ROVERS	1 v 4	COBHAM (37)

(Played at Cobham)

DITTON	1 v 2	RAMSGATE (25)
CRAY WDRS (W/O)		FARNHAM TOWN (SCR.)
BICESTER TOWN	1 v 1	BROCKENHURST (61)
BROCKENHURST	1 v 0	BICESTER TOWN (148)
B.A.T.	3 v 3	SHERBORNE T. (55)
SHERBORNE TOWN	3 v 2	B.A.T. (90)
RYDE SPORTS	1 v 2	WANTAGE TOWN (87)
KINTBURY RANGERS	0 v 2	WOLLEN SPTS (49)
HAMWORTHY UTD	0 v 5	FLEET TOWN (100)
MILTON UNITED	0 v 2	A.F.C. LYMINGTON (43)
WOTTON ROVERS	0 v 2	BRIDGWATER T. (59)
BACKWELL UNITED	3 v 0	BISHOPS SUTTON (83)
NORTH LEIGH	6 v 2	FLIGHT REF. (75)
CIRENCESTER TOWN	2 v 0	OLD GEORGIANS (100)
LARKHALL ATHLETIC	1 v 4	CINDERFORD T. (51)
D.R.G. (F.P.)	2 v 4	BRISLINGTON (61)
PATCHWAY TOWN	1 v 1	FAIRFORD TOWN (37)
FAIRFORD TOWN	2 v 1	PATCHWAY (50)
CALNE TOWN	1 v 4	TUFFLEY ROVERS (83)
MORETON TOWN	1 v 2	BEMERTON H.H. (60)
ALMONDSBURY PICK.	3 v 2	SWINDON SUPER. (32)
TRURO CITY	0 v 1	CREDITON UNITED (136)
PORTHLEVEN	4 v 2	ELMORE (77)

Glasshoughton 'keeper Illidge bravely saves at the feet of Maltby's Hadrell. Photo - Colin Stevens.

A diving header from Barry Heard of Waterloo Dock just misses the Knypersley Victoria goal. Photo - Rob Ruddock.

Heron Wildman of Viking Sports takes a tumble over Steven Murphy of London Colney. Photo - Dave West.

Mark Watson hits a cross for Hamworthy who lost 0-5 to Fleet in their first ever Vase tie. Photo - Jon Holloway.

PRELIMINARY ROUND

(SAT. 3rd OCT. 1992)

(Attendances in brackets)

PRUDHOE E.E.	1 v 3	DURHAM CITY (102)
CLEATOR MOOR C.	3 v 2	ANNFIELD PLAIN (69)
ESH WINNING	5 v 1	WILLINGTON (25)
SHOTTON COMRADES	3 v 0	NORTON & S.A. (10)
HORDEN C.W.	0 v 3	BEDLINGTON T. (22)
BILLINGHAM TOWN	3 v 0	RYHOPE C.A. (48)
WALKER	1 v 1	PICKERING T. (85)
PICKERING TOWN	3 v 0	WALKER (137)
LANGLEY PARK	0 v 1	SUNDERLAND I. (63)
WASHINGTON	0 v 5	PONTELAND U. (30)

(Played at Hebburn F.C.)

DARLINGTON C.B.	2 v 1	HEBBURN (57)
SOUTH SHIELDS	2 v 0	PENRITH (150)
EVENWOOD TOWN	5 v 0	CROOK TOWN (25)
LANCASTER CITY	1 v 3	FLIXTON (75)
WATERLOO DOCK	3 v 2	ASHVILLE (42)
NEWTON	0 v 6	CLITHEROE (22)
GLOSSOP N.E.	2 v 3	ROCESTER (210)
ST HELENS T.	2 v 4	MAINE ROAD (41)
CHADDERTON	1 v 2	PRESCOT (134)
ATHERTON COLL.	1 v 0	MERSEY POLICE (60)
NETHERFIELD	5 v 0	OLDHAM TOWN (83)
BOOTLE	2 v 3	ROSSENDALE U. (47)
DARWEN	2 v 3	CURZON ASHTON (72)
MAGHULL	2 v 0	IRLAM TOWN (32)
FORMBY	0 v 2	ATHERTON L.R. (50)
WYTHENSHAWE A.	1 v 3	BURSCOUGH (60)
BLACKPOOL ROVERS	5 v 2	POULTON VICT. (64)
ASHTON UNITED	3 v 3	SKELMERSDALE U. (210)
SKELMERSDALE UTD	1 v 3	ASHTON UNITED (230)
GROVE UNITED	1 v 1	NANTWICH TOWN (194)
NANTWICH TOWN	1 v 4	GROVE UNITED (194)
SALFORD CITY	5 v 0	DOUGLAS HSOB (100)
LOUTH UNITED	5 v 4	HARWORTH C.I. (72)
GLASSHOUGHTON	3 v 2	SELBY TOWN (75)
FRIAR LANE O.B.	3 v 3	DENABY UNITED (179)
DENABY UNITED	2 v 2	FRIAR LANE (136)
DENABY UNITED	0 v 3	FRIAR LANE (152)
HINCKLEY TOWN	2 v 2	THACKLEY (70)
THACKLEY	3 v 1	HINCKLEY TOWN (104)
PRIORY EASTWOOD	3 v 1	OAKHAM UNITED (56)
BRIGG TOWN	3 v 0	SHEFFIELD (54)
CLIPSTONE WELFARE	4 v 2	HATFIELD MAIN (104)
OSSETT TOWN	2 v 3	RAINWORTH M.W. (120)
BORROWASH VIC.	2 v 3	SHIREBROOK C. (52)
GARFORTH TOWN	4 v 3	ECCLESHILL UTD (102)
DUNKIRK	1 v 3	ILKESTON T. (181)
HEANOR TOWN	0 v 2	ARNOLD TOWN (163)
BLIDWORTH M.W.	1 v 3	BRADFORD P.A. (110)
BELPER TOWN	4 v 3	PONTEFRACT C. (129)
ARMTHORPE WELF.	4 v 0	HALLAM (41)
WORSBORO. B.M.W.	1 v 1	OSSETT ALBION (140)
OSSETT ALBION	1 v 1	WORSBORO. B. (111)
WORSBORO. B.M.W.	3 v 3	OSSETT ALBION (182)
OSSETT ALBION	2 v 3	WORSBORO. B. (171)
STOCKSBRIDGE P.S.	4 v 1	HARROGATE T. (81)
HALESOWEN HAR.	3 v 0	WALSALL WOOD (50)
STRATFORD TOWN	2 v 0	NORTHFIELD T. (82)
BOLEHALL SWIFTS	2 v 1	BARWELL (52)
MILE OAK ROVERS	0 v 2	BOLDMERE S.M. (55)
WELLINGBOROUGH	0 v 4	ST ANDREWS (44)
PEGASUS JUNIORS	4 v 2	CHASETOWN (41)
HIGHGATE UTD	0 v 2	PELSALL VILLA (25)

ARMITAGE	1 v 2	ROTHWELL TOWN (62)
KINGS HEATH	1 v 4	STAPENHILL (30)
MEIR K.A.	1 v 1	LYE TOWN (56)
LYE TOWN	3 v 2	MEIR K.A. (72)
BILSTON TOWN	6 v 0	RUSHALL OLYM. (78)
RUSHDEN & D.	3 v 2	ANSTEY NOMADS (242)
R.C. WARWICK	1 v 2	OLDBURY UTD (76)
PAGET RANGERS	4 v 5	RAUNDS TOWN (53)
PERSHORE TOWN	0 v 1	STEWART & L. (150)
MALVERN TOWN	1 v 4	SANDWELL BORO. (22)
BLAKENALL	3 v 4	BRIDGNORTH (65)
WESTFIELDS	1 v 3	WEDNESFIELD (58)
CANVEY ISLAND	1 v 0	PETERBORO. C. (105)
NEWMARKET TOWN	1 v 2	SAWBRIDGEWORTH (99)
NORWICH UNITED	5 v 0	SOMERSHAM T. (29)
CHATTERIS TOWN	2 v 3	BOSTON (68)
SOHAM TOWN R.	6 v 2	THETFORD T. (82)
WATTON UNITED	2 v 0	BURY TOWN (110)
DESBOROUGH T.	1 v 4	TIPTREE UTD (60)
STOWMARKET TOWN	1 v 2	KING'S LYNN (156)
HADLEIGH UTD	6 v 2	WITHAM TOWN (124)
ELY CITY	1 v 2	EYNESBURY R. (69)
BASILDON UNITED	1 v 2	LOWESTOFT T. (67)
MARCH TOWN U.	0 v 1	STAMFORD (150)
HISTON	1 v 0	GORLESTON (56)
HALSTEAD TOWN	4 v 1	HOLBEACH UTD (106)
SUDBURY WDRS	4 v 1	FAKENHAM T. (103)
FELIXSTOWE T.	1 v 2	MIRRLEES BLACK. (70)
BERKHAMSTED T.	1 v 2	BOURNE TOWN (82)
DOWNHAM TOWN	0 v 3	ROYSTON TOWN (103)
KINGSBURY TOWN	2 v 1	LANGFORD (42)
CLAPTON	3 v 1	HORNCHURCH (38)
COCKFOSTERS	2 v 0	HARINGEY B. (65)
LEVERSTOCK GREEN	0 v 1	BROOK HOUSE (75)
ETON MANOR	1 v 2	HODDESON T. (27)
TOTTERNHOE	1 v 1	RAINHAM T. (42)
RAINHAM TOWN	3 v 1	TOTTERNHOE (68)
TRING TOWN	7 v 0	BRACKNELL T. (41)
COLLIER ROW	1 v 2	POTTERS BAR T. (86)
TILBURY	2 v 1	CHESHUNT (43)
SHILLINGTON	0 v 2	FELTHAM & H. (62)
BARTON ROVERS	4 v 1	ARLESEY TOWN (118)
HERTFORD TOWN	5 v 0	WELWYN GDN C. (80)
WOOTTON BLUE C.	1 v 1	BARKINGSIDE (55)
BARKINGSIDE	1 v 1	WOOTTON B.C. (59)
WOOTTON BLUE C.	2 v 1	BARKINGSIDE (139)
RUISLIP MANOR	9 v 0	LONDON COLNEY (120)
MILTON KEYNES B.	1 v 1	HARPENDEN (Aban.)
MILTON KEYNES B.	5 v 2	HARPENDEN T. (111)
HEMEL HEMPSTEAD	4 v 2	HANWELL TOWN (104)
WINGATE & FINCHLEY	0 v 2	WARE (95)
FLACKWELL HEATH	2 v 1	LETCHWORTH G.C. (30)
DUNSTABLE	5 v 1	LONG BUCKBY (48)
BRIMSDOWN ROVERS	2 v 0	BRAINTREE T. (60)
SOUTHALL	0 v 8	HAMPTON (196)
CRANLEIGH	2 v 1	FAVERSHAM T. (65)
EASTBOURNE P.S.	2 v 3	RINGMER (93)
RAMSGATE	3 v 1	EGHAM TOWN (82)
LANGNEY SPORTS	0 v 4	SITTINGBOURNE (216)
EASTBOURNE UTD	0 v 8	HAILSHAM T. (178)
CORINTHIAN	2 v 1	SLADE GREEN (42)
LEATHERHEAD	2 v 0	ALMA SWANLEY (79)
STEYNING TOWN	1 v 7	CORINTHIAN-CAS. (45)
TUNBRIDGE WELLS	1 v 1	THREE BRIDGES (128)
THREE BRIDGES	1 v 2	TUNBRIDGE W. (110)
CHICHESTER CITY	0 v 3	CRAY WDRS (95)
LANCING	0 v 4	CHIPSTEAD (117)
BECKENHAM TOWN	3 v 2	REDHILL (75)
CROYDON ATHLETIC	1 v 3	GREENWICH B. (43)
HORSHAM	2 v 1	PAGHAM (211)
WEST WICKHAM	3 v 4	SHOREHAM (60)
MERSTHAM	3 v 1	HORSHAM Y.M. (44)
WORTHING UNITED	1 v 2	OAKWOOD (25)
CAMBERLEY T.	3 v 0	HAYWARDS HTH (71)

A diving header from Steven Perkins (11) puts Burscough level at Wythenshawe Amateurs. Photo - Rob Ruddock.

Nantwich equalise at Grove, but were humbled 1-4 by the Mid-Cheshire side in the replay. Photo - Colin Stevens.

Barkingside come under intense pressure in the first-half at Wootton Blue Cross. Photo - Dave West.

WORTHING	2 v 0	COVE (267)	
TONBRIDGE	4 v 1	SOUTHWICK (438)	
BANSTEAD ATH.	2 v 2	WHITSTABLE T. (69)	
WHITSTABLE T.	1 v 1	BANSTEAD A. (137)	
BANSTEAD ATH.	2 v 1	WHITSTABLE (40)	
DARENTH HEATHSIDE	2 v 2	ARUNDEL (40)	
ARUNDEL	3 v 1	DARENTH H. (70)	
ASH UNITED	1 v 0	SHEPPEY UTD (48)	
EPSOM & EWELL	3 v 1	CHATHAM TOWN (70)	
WHITEHAWK	1 v 2	BURGESS HILL (66)	
WICK	6 v 0	SELSEY (74)	
ASHFORD (MIDDX)	0 v 3	HAVANT TOWN (47)	
BURNHAM	4 v 1	COBHAM (90)	
HARTLEY WINTNEY	3 v 0	PORTFIELD (65)	
SHOLING SPORTS	1 v 1	FLEET TOWN (68)	
FLEET TOWN	2 v 1	SHOLING SPTS (62)	
SHERBORNE TOWN	0 v 4	WITNEY TOWN (90)	
THATCHAM TOWN	2 v 0	BROCKENHURST (79)	
WESTBURY UTD	3 v 1	WANTAGE T. (102)	
ABINGDON UTD	1 v 3	FIRST TOWER (50)	
WOLLEN SPORTS	2 v 3	BOURNEMOUTH (25)	

DIDCOT TOWN	1 v 2	EASTLEIGH (80)
A.F.C. TOTTON	1 v 3	BANBURY UTD (75)
A.F.C. LYMINGTON	3 v 1	SWANAGE T.H. (134)
NEWBURY TOWN	6 v 2	ROMSEY TOWN (144)
OXFORD CITY	3 v 2	THAME UNITED (119)
MINEHEAD	1 v 2	BEMERTON H.H. (103)
BRISLINGTON	2 v 0	CIRENCESTER T. (65)
BRIDGWATER T.	0 v 4	CINDERFORD T. (135)
NORTH LEIGH	3 v 1	FAIRFORD T. (74)
BRISTOL MANOR F.	2 v 1	FROME TOWN (60)
TUFFLEY ROVERS	1 v 0	CHIPPENHAM T. (134)
CLEVEDON TOWN	6 v 1	DEVIZES TOWN (267)
BACKWELL UNITED	2 v 1	CHARD TOWN (56)
ALMONDSBURY P.	4 v 2	ODD DOWN (42)
GLASTONBURY	5 v 3	MELKSHAM TOWN (55)
MANGOTSFIELD UTD	4 v 1	WELLINGTON (107)
EXMOUTH TOWN	1 v 3	ILFRACOMBE T. (110)
BARNSTAPLE TOWN	3 v 1	PORTHLEVEN (97)
CREDITON UNITED	7 v 0	OTTERY ST MARY (100)
ST BLAZEY	3 v 1	TORPOINT ATH. (79)
NEWQUAY	3 v 2	LISKEARD ATH. (180)
TORRINGTON	0 v 2	TIVERTON TOWN (145)

Langney Sports' Chris Marshall (right) blocks a shot from Sittingbourne's Paul Burke. Photo - Roger Turner.

Paul Dunger of Fakenham makes a brilliant save to deny Chris King of Sudbury Wanderers. Photo - Richard Brock.

Tim Chapman of Biggleswade Town outpaces Gary Broadridge of Leverstock Green. Photo - Paul Dennis.

Ash United on their way to victory over visiting Sheppey United (striped shirts). Photo - Eric Marsh.

Chipstead's Bobby Horn in control at Lancing, as indeed his team were with a 4-0 win. Photo - Dennis Nicholson.

(Attendances in brackets)

DURHAM CITY	3 v 0	EVENWOOD T. (110)
SUND. IFG ROKER	0 v 1	ESH WINNING (43)
WEST ALLOTMENT C.	3 v 3	CHESTER-LE-S. (170)
CHESTER-LE-STREET	6 v 3	W. ALLOTMENT (97)
CLEATOR MOOR C.	2 v 2	PONTELAND UTD (70)
PONTELAND UNITED	6 v 3	CLEATOR MOOR (70)
ALNWICK TOWN	1 v 1	DUNSTON F.B. (74)
DUNSTON F.B.	3 v 2	ALNWICK T. (148)
PICKERING TOWN	3 v 3	SOUTH SHIELDS (151)
SOUTH SHIELDS	1 v 1	PICKERING T. (285)
SOUTH SHIELDS	3 v 4	PICKERING T. (130)

(Played at Ryhope C.A.)

BEDLINGTON TER.	0 v 2	EPPLETON C.W. (70)
SHOTTON COMRADES	1 v 0	DARLINGTON C.B. (18)
WHICKHAM	0 v 2	BILLINGHAM T. (65)
PRESCOT A.F.C.	0 v 1	SALFORD CITY (104)
BURSCOUGH	2 v 1	NETHERFIELD (128)
ROCESTER	0 v 2	FLIXTON (217)
ATHERTON COL.	4 v 1	BLACKPOOL RVRS (40)
RADCLIFFE BORO.	1 v 3	WATERLOO DOCK (123)
ATHERTON L.R.	2 v 0	GROVE UNITED (200)
CURZON ASHTON	3 v 3	CLITHEROE (72)
CLITHEROE	0 v 1	CURZON ASHTON (135)
ROSSENDALE UTD	2 v 5	ASHTON UNITED (205)
MAINE ROAD	3 v 1	MAGHULL (61)
STOCKSBRIDGE	2 v 0	FRIAR LANE (101)
HUCKNALL TOWN	2 v 1	LOUTH UNITED (174)
ARNOLD TOWN	3 v 0	SHIREBROOK C. (121)
BRIGG TOWN	2 v 1	BRADFORD P.A. (156)
GARFORTH TOWN	3 v 0	PRIORY EASTW. (110)
CLIPSTONE WELF.	6 v 2	GLASSHOUGHTON (116)
BELPER TOWN	4 v 3	RAINWORTH M.W. (130)
THACKLEY	1 v 2	WORSBOROUGH (149)
ILKESTON TOWN	2 v 2	LINCOLN UTD (729)
LINCOLN UNITED	2 v 1	ILKESTON TOWN (241)
HARROGATE R.A.	2 v 1	ARMTHORPE W. (66)
WEDNESFIELD	3 v 0	BOLDMERE S.M. (32)
WILLENHALL TOWN	0 v 0	STRATFORD T. (75)
STRATFORD TOWN	3 v 0	WILLENHALL T. (75)
OLDBURY UNITED	3 v 2	LYE TOWN (131)
PELSALL VILLA	4 v 0	RAUNDS TOWN (232)
BILSTON TOWN	2 v 1	PEGASUS JNRS (61)
ROTHWELL TOWN	4 v 0	BOLEHALL S. (109)
STEWART & LLOYDS	1 v 2	STAPENHILL (37)
ST ANDREWS	2 v 2	BRIDGNORTH (87)
BRIDGNORTH TOWN	3 v 1	ST ANDREWS (85)
RUSHDEN & D.	3 v 3	HALESOWEN H. (247)
HALESOWEN H.	0 v 2	RUSHDEN & D. (123)
NORTHAMPTON S.	0 v 3	SANDWELL BORO. (55)
WATTON UNITED	1 v 3	BOURNE TOWN (85)
HALSTEAD TOWN	1 v 3	STAMFORD (149)
HADLEIGH UNITED	1 v 2	HISTON (131)
LOWESTOFT T.	2 v 1	SUDBURY WDRS (190)

HAVERHILL ROVERS	0 v 1	SAWBRIDGEWORTH (85)
MIRR. BLACKSTONE	2 v 3	SPALDING UTD (110)
WROXHAM	0 v 3	CANVEY ISLAND (102)
EYNESBURY ROVERS	0 v 2	POTTON UNITED (285)
ROYSTON TOWN	2 v 2	TIPTREE UTD (74)
TIPTREE UNITED	1 v 0	ROYSTON TOWN (59)
NORWICH UNITED	4 v 0	SOHAM TOWN R. (40)
BOSTON	1 v 2	KING'S LYNN (155)
WARE	2 v 3	MILTON K. BORO. (97)
WOOTTON B.C.	1 v 4	BARTON ROVERS (112)
HODDESDON T.	1 v 0	HEMEL HEMPSTEAD (90)
RAINHAM TOWN	0 v 2	KINGSBURY T. (102)

(Played 30-10-92)

BURNHAM RAMBLERS	3 v 1	POTTERS BAR T. (107)
FLACKWELL HEATH	2 v 3	FELTHAM & H. (40)
RUISLIP MANOR	1 v 1	HAMPTON (178)
HAMPTON	1 v 2	RUISLIP MANOR (216)
BRIMSDOWN ROVERS	0 v 1	DUNSTABLE (58)
E. THURROCK UTD	2 v 4	CLAPTON (170)
HAREFIELD UTD	3 v 1	BROOK HOUSE (40)
FORD UNITED	1 v 0	TILBURY (55)

(Ford expelled due to two ineligible players)

LEIGHTON TOWN	1 v 3	TRING TOWN (417)
COCKFOSTERS	0 v 4	HERTFORD TOWN (106)
PEACEHAVEN & T.	5 v 1	HERNE BAY (211)
SHOREHAM	1 v 2	MERSTHAM (80)
HARTLEY WINTNEY	2 v 0	ARUNDEL (105)
CORINTHIAN-CAS.	6 v 0	WORTHING (90)
GREENWICH B.	1 v 3	CRANLEIGH (108)

(Played 1-11-92)

BURGESS HILL T.	2 v 3	TUNBRIDGE WELLS (116)
ERITH & BELVEDERE	2 v 1	RAMSGATE (189)
BECKENHAM TOWN	2 v 3	ASH UNITED (35)
LEATHERHEAD	1 v 0	RINGMER (76)
TONBRIDGE	4 v 0	CHIPSTEAD (485)
SITTINGBOURNE	7 v 0	CAMBERLEY T. (444)
BURNHAM	5 v 1	CORINTHIAN (82)
CRAY WANDERERS	2 v 1	OAKWOOD (55)
HAVANT TOWN	1 v 0	EPSOM & EWELL (128)
BANSTEAD ATHLETIC	4 v 3	HORSHAM (125)
HAILSHAM T.	3 v 2	WICK (330)
BANBURY UTD	2 v 2	FOREST GREEN (144)
FOREST GREEN R.	5 v 2	BANBURY UTD (84)
FLEET TOWN	0 v 2	WITNEY TOWN (85)
GOSPORT BOROUGH	2 v 4	BOURNEMOUTH (145)
THATCHAM TOWN	4 v 2	NEWBURY TOWN (379)
EASTLEIGH	1 v 3	OXFORD CITY (106)
WESTBURY UNITED	1 v 2	FIRST TOWER U. (125)
BRIDPORT	0 v 3	A.F.C. LYMINGTON (240)
BACKWELL UNITED	2 v 4	TAUNTON TOWN (94)
BEMERTTON HTH H.	2 v 1	BRISLINGTON (91)
WELTON ROVERS	2 v 0	TUFFLEY ROVERS (153)
CINDERFORD TOWN	6 v 2	GLASTONBURY (110)
CLEVEDON TOWN	7 v 1	MANGOTSFIELD U. (434)
NORTH LEIGH	2 v 1	BRISTOL MNR F. (67)
SHORTWOOD UTD	3 v 3	ALMONDSBURY P. (88)
ALMONDSBURY PICK.	3 v 0	SHORTWOOD UTD (83)
NEWQUAY	4 v 1	DAWLISH TOWN (152)
BARNSTAPLE T.	2 v 1	CREDITON UTD (145)
FALMOUTH TOWN	0 v 3	TIVERTON TOWN (411)
ILFRACOMBE T.	5 v 4	ST BLAZEY (110)

Garforth Town celebrate their first goal in the 3-0 demolition of Priory (Eastwood). Photo - Colin Stevens.

Shoreham's Simon Pierce powers his way through the Merstham defence. Photo - Dennis Nicholson.

Steve Davis of Greenwich tries to stop C Lamboll in the Sunday morning tie against Cranleigh. Photo - Dave West.

(Attendances in brackets)

GT HARWOOD TOWN	2 v 3	BAMBER BRIDGE	(385)
PICKERING TOWN	2 v 2	BILLINGHAM T.	(144)
BILLINGHAM T.	5 v 1	PICKERING TOWN	(120)
BRIDLINGTON T.	1 v 0	EPPLETON C.W.	(204)
CHESTER-LE-STREET	5 v 1	ESH WINNING	(117)
PONTELAND UNITED	3 v 1	GARFORTH TOWN	(72)
SHOTTON COMRADES	2 v 5	DURHAM CITY	(62)
HARROGATE R.A.	0 v 6	DUNSTON F.B.	(90)
ATHERTON COLL.	2 v 2	WORSBORO.	(ab. 90m.)
WORSBORO. B.M.W.	3 v 3	ATHERTON C.	(160)
ATHERTON COLL.	2 v 1	WORSBOROUGH	(130)
WATERLOO DOCK	2 v 6	ASHTON UNITED	(88)
ATHERTON L.R.	2 v 2	STOCKSBRIDGE	(188)
STOCKSBRIDGE P.S.	1 v 2	ATHERTON L.R.	(140)
KNOWSLEY UTD	3 v 2	ARNOLD TOWN	(88)
CURZON ASHTON	3 v 1	BELPER TOWN	(84)
BURSCOUGH	3 v 1	LINCOLN UTD	(141)
MAINE ROAD	5 v 5	FLIXTON	(107)
FLIXTON	2 v 1	MAINE ROAD	(188)
CAMMELL LAIRD	6 v 3	SALFORD CITY	(102)
EASTWOOD HANLEY	1 v 0	NTH FERRIBY U.	(47)
NEWCASTLE TOWN	3 v 4	BRIGG TOWN	(86)
HUCKNALL TOWN	0 v 3	CLIPSTONE W.	(289)
NORWICH UNITED	3 v 0	STAMFORD	(61)
ROTHWELL TOWN	5 v 2	WISBECH TOWN	(378)
PELSALL VILLA	1 v 1	W. MIDS POLICE	(206)
WEST MIDS POLICE	1 v 2	PELSALL VILLA	(127)
BILSTON TOWN	6 v 1	WEDNESFIELD	(96)
HISTON	2 v 3	HINCKLEY ATH.	(76)
RUSHDEN & D.	2 v 2	GRESLEY RVRS	(423)
GRESLEY ROVERS	3 v 1	RUSHDEN & D.	(717)
OLDBURY UNITED	1 v 2	STRATFORD TOWN	(83)
SPALDING UTD	2 v 2	BOURNE TOWN	(273)
BOURNE TOWN	4 v 1	SPALDING UTD	(203)
STAPENHILL	2 v 2	BRIDGNORTH	(135)
BRIDGNORTH T.	7 v 0	STAPENHILL	(105)
KING'S LYNN	2 v 1	SANDWELL BORO.	(277)
HARWICH & PARK.	2 v 1	ERITH & BEL.	(198)
PEACEHAVEN & T.	2 v 1	NORTHWOOD	(201)
CRAY WANDERERS	1 v 0	MERSTHAM	(62)
HAREFIELD UTD	0 v 0	KINGSBURY	(56)

(abandoned after 90 minutes)

KINGSBURY TOWN	1 v 3	HAREFIELD UTD	
MET. POLICE	0 v 6	TILBURY	(73)
HODDESDON TOWN	2 v 0	POTTON UNITED	(130)
GT YARMOUTH T.	0 v 0	LOWESTOFT T.	(154)
LOWESTOFT TOWN	2 v 0	GT YARMOUTH	(325)
EDGWARE TOWN	1 v 4	BARTON RVRS	(184)
HAILSHAM TOWN	4 v 3	CLAPTON	(287)
WALTHAMSTOW P.	1 v 0	TIPTREE UTD	(30)

(Replay ordered)

WALTHAMSTOW P.	1 v 0	TIPTREE UTD	(30)
SAFFRON WALDEN	3 v 1	RUISLIP MANOR	(155)
DUNSTABLE	1 v 1	BUCKINGHAM T.	(116)
BUCKINGHAM T.	2 v 1	DUNSTABLE	(86)

SITTINGBOURNE	4 v 2	CHERTSEY TOWN	(499)
SUDBURY TOWN	2 v 3	CANVEY ISLAND	(536)
TUNBRIDGE WELLS	3 v 1	TONBRIDGE	(754)
MILTON KEYNES B.	0 v 1	TRING TOWN	(102)
MALDEN VALE	3 v 0	HERTFORD TOWN	(122)
BURNHAM RAMBLERS	2 v 3	BANSTEAD ATH.	(102)
CORINTHIAN-CAS.	1 v 2	DISS TOWN	(70)
BURNHAM	3 v 2	SAWBRIDGEWORTH	(90)
ASH UNITED	0 v 0	LITTLEHAMPTON	(105)

(abandoned after 90 minutes)

LITTLEHAMPTON	4 v 0	ASH UNITED	(220)
NEWPORT I.W.	2 v 1	THATCHAM TOWN	(286)
CRANLEIGH	3 v 0	NORTH LEIGH	(157)
HUNGERFORD TOWN	0 v 3	WITNEY TOWN	(80)
HARTLEY WINTNEY	3 v 1	BOURNEMOUTH	(95)
OXFORD CITY	1 v 2	EVESHAM UNITED	(150)
FOREST GREEN R.	2 v 1	LEATHERHEAD	(123)
FIRST TOWER UTD	3 v 2	HAVANT TOWN	(150)
YATE TOWN	1 v 2	PAULTON RVRS	(132)
CLEVEDON TOWN	5 v 4	BARNSTAPLE	(324)
WIMBORNE TOWN	1 v 4	ALMONDSBURY	(542)
BEMERTON HTH H.	1 v 0	TAUNTON TOWN	(152)
WELTON ROVERS	1 v 0	ILFRACOMBE T.	(131)
NEWQUAY	1 v 0	A.F.C. LYMINGTON	(225)
TIVERTON TOWN	5 v 1	CINDERFORD T.	(355)

BYE: FELTHAM & HOUNSLOW BOROUGH

No question about the big F.A. Vase story of the round - **Almondsbury Picksons'** incredible 4-1 victory away to the holders **Wimborne Town** certainly took the biscuit. It was the Magpie's first match in the defence of their crown, but they were behind after only two minutes to a Rob Higgins goal. Mark Cooper extended Almondsbury's lead in the second half before Jason Lovell pulled one back to set up a rousing finale. The 1979 finalists were not to be denied though, and further goals from Mark Duckers and Marcus Jefferies put them in an unassailable position.

Sittingbourne's Dave Arter claimed a new Vase scoring record by hammering a hat-trick in the space of five minutes after coming on just twelve minutes from time in the 4-2 home win over **Chertsey Town.** Bourne were trailing 1-2 when Arter replaced Matt Stock, but after goals in the 84th, 85th and 89th minutes they cruised into the Third Round.

Sittingbourne at this stage looked one of the strongest contenders for the Vase, as did two strong challengers from the Great Mills League; **Clevedon Town** hit seven to demolish **Mangotsfield United** in the First Round, but struggled somewhat before beating **Barnstaple Town** by the odd goal in nine in Round Two. The other likely Great Mills lads were **Tiverton Town** who had a splendid 5-1 win over **Cinderford Town.**

Bamber Bridge also had strong credentials. Semi-finalists at their first attempt in 1991-92, they enjoyed an excellent 3-2 win away to near-neighbours **Great Harwood Town,** quarter-finalists themselves in 1991. In atrocious weather, Fornell scored first for the Bridge only for Peter Smith to force extra-time and Eatough to put the home side ahead. Bamber Bridge stormed back to win, however, Dewhurst and Hayes scoring.

The top gate of the Second Round was registered in Kent where nearly 800 turned up for the derby between **Tunbridge Wells** and **Tonbridge,** and the major surprise, the Wimborne upset aside, was **Canvey Island's** 3-2 victory at **Sudbury Town.** Meanwhile, the highest aggregate score in one match was the 5-5 draw between **Flixton** and **Maine Road.** Coincidentally Flixton were also involved in a ten goal tie last in 1991-92 when they defeated Borrowash Victoria 8-3.

Peter McConville scores one of Ashton United six goals as they end Waterloo Dock's run. Photo - Colin Stevens.

Hailsham Town's Dave Rowe gets above the Clapton defence as his side win a thriller. Photo - Dennis Nicholson.

An awkward pass is controlled by a Walthamstow Pennant player in the replayed Tiptree tie. Photo - Paul Dennis.

THIRD ROUND
(SAT. 12th DEC. 1992)

(Attendances in brackets)

BRIDGNORTH TOWN	4 v 0	ATHERTON COL.	(130)
KNOWSLEY UTD	5 v 2	FLIXTON	(101)
HINCKLEY ATH.	1 v 0	CLIPSTONE WF.	(273)
BAMBER BRIDGE	1 v 2	CAMMELL LAIRD	(437)
CURZON ASHTON	7 v 1	CHESTER-LE-S.	(104)
BURSCOUGH	1 v 0	PONTELAND UTD	(157)
DUNSTON F.B.	5 v 1	BILLINGHAM T.	(144)
BRIGG TOWN	1 v 3	BRIDLINGTON T.	(254)
ATHERTON L.R.	1 v 2	ASHTON UTD	(300)
EASTWOOD HANLEY	2 v 5	DURHAM CITY	(130)
CRAY WANDERERS	2 v 3	TRING TOWN	(77)
STRATFORD TOWN	0 v 2	BILSTON TOWN	(161)
BUCKINGHAM TOWN	3 v 2	SAFFRON WALDEN	(209)
HARWICH & PARK.	0 v 3	BANSTEAD ATH.	(228)
FELTHAM & H.	1 v 2	TUNBRIDGE W.	(98)
TILBURY	2 v 3	HODDESDON T.	(86)
BARTON ROVERS	2 v 1	DISS TOWN	(192)
BOURNE TOWN	4 v 4	PEACEHAVEN	(213)
PEACEHAVEN	4 v 0	BOURNE TOWN	(304)
NORWICH UNITED	1 v 2	HAREFIELD UTD	(64)
BURNHAM	1 v 2	GRESLEY ROVERS	(208)
CRANLEIGH	1 v 3	HAILSHAM T.	(285)
SITTINGBOURNE	4 v 2	MALDEN VALE	(761)
WALTHAMSTOW P.	0 v 1	LOWESTOFT T.	(51)
LITTLEHAMPTON T.	0 v 1	PELSALL VILLA	(305)
CANVEY ISLAND	1 v 0	KING'S LYNN	(411)
HARTLEY WINTNEY	0 v 3	ROTHWELL TOWN	(195)
NEWPORT I.O.W.	2 v 0	WELTON ROVERS	(303)
TIVERTON TOWN	2 v 1	ALMONDSBURY	(520)
FIRST TOWER UTD	0 v 0	PAULTON ROVERS	(163)
PAULTON ROVERS	5 v 1	FIRST TOWER	(209)
CLEVEDON TOWN	2 v 1	BEMERTON HTH	(437)
WITNEY TOWN	1 v 2	FOREST GREEN	(153)
NEWQUAY	1 v 3	EVESHAM UTD	(325)

Almondsbury Picksons were quickly brought back down from the elation of defeating the holders, and were removed from the competition by Tiverton Town. The 'tie of the round' attracted a large crowd to Tivvy's Ladysmead ground, but with less than twenty minutes to go things did not look too good for the home team. That was because Nick Showering had fired home a 25 yard shot after 64 minutes to put Almondsbury a goal to the good. However, an inspired substitution in the 68th minute tipped the balance in Tivvy's favour. Steve Daly was sent on, and within a minute he received a pass from prolific scorer Kevin Smith to net the equaliser. Then, after 74 minutes, Daly laid the ball off to Mark Short, and the latter's shot from the edge of the box put his side into the Fourth Round for the first time since 1989.

Tiverton Town's challengers in the Great Mills Western League, Clevedon Town, also continued their Vase progress. They got off to a flying start in their home tie against Bemerton Heath Harlequins. Stuart Minall put Town ahead with a well-placed shot after 21 minutes, and eight minutes later Brendan Dowd laid on the 29th goal of the season for Andy Perrett to all but settle the tie. After the break both Perrett and John Durham squandered further chances, and Ian Pollard raised the visitors' hopes for a while when he headed home a cross from substitute Kevin Smith after 78 minutes.

Evesham United ended the challenge of Newquay, the last surviving Jewson South Western League club. In front of their committed supporters at Mount Wise, and buoyant from a surprise win over A.F.C. Lymington in the previous round, Newquay got into the lead when the persistent David Ball laid on a goal for veteran forward Graham Nicholls. That goal arrived just seven minutes before the interval, and had the Peppermints been able to hang on until the break they would perhaps been in a strong position. Evesham, though, got in the pyschological blow of an immediate equaliser when Steve Jukes hit a twenty yard shot that went in via the woodwork, and after both teams had missed chances to secure the tie in normal time, Nick Jordan and Neil Emms hit the goals in the additional half hour that put the Midlanders through.

The Third Round marked the end of the road for some of the smaller clubs who had enjoyed notable success in earlier rounds. Hartley Wintney found Jackie Murray's Rothwell Town too hot to handle. The high-flying Hereward Sports United Counties League side came away from the Memorial Ground as 3-0 winners to earn a plum tie at home to Knowsley United, whilst Hartley Wintney's Parasol League rivals Cranleigh also had their dreams dashed. They had enjoyed a very exciting run in their first ever Vase participation, but went down 1-3 at home to Unijet Sussex Leaguers Hailsham Town. Notts Alliance side Clipstone Welfare raised quite a few eyebrows with their results in the early rounds, but they found a trip to Hinckley Athletic a little too difficult. The Boddington's League side have proved to be one of the most consistent performers in the competition over recent years, and a single goal was enough to take them through to a home Fourth Round tie against league rivals Pelsall Villa.

Pelsall, in fact, recorded one of the most notable results of the Round in winning away to 1991 Semi-Finalists Littlehampton Town. Another recent Semi-Finalist to slip by the wayside were Bamber Bridge who grabbed all the headlines with their historic run in 1991-92. The Bridge were humbled at home by Tetley Walker West Cheshire League champions Cammell Laird, the Wirral side who had an incredible run to the Fifth Round in 1991, their first season in the competition.

Hoddesdon's Martin Smith shields the ball from Martin Dale as his side win 3-2 at Tilbury. Photo - Francis Short.

Cray's Sean Cooney holds off a challenge from Michael Thomas (right) of Tring Town. Photo - Alan Coomes.

Tunbridge Wells' John Wingate lobs an equiliser despite the proximity of two Feltham defenders. Photo - Dave West.

FOURTH ROUND
(SAT. 16th JAN. 1993)

(Attendances in brackets)

BRIDLINGTON T.	5	v	3	CURZON ASHTON (252)
BURSCOUGH	0	v	1	CAMMELL LAIRD (457)
GRESLEY ROVERS	3	v	0	BRIDGNORTH T. (787)
HINCKLEY ATHLETIC	2	v	2	PELSALL VILLA (369)
PELSALL VILLA	4	v	1	HINCKLEY ATH. (433)
DUNSTON F.B.	3	v	1	DURHAM CITY (329)
BILSTON TOWN	3	v	0	ASHTON UNITED (184)
ROTHWELL TOWN	1	v	0	KNOWSLEY UTD (355)
NEWPORT I.W.	4	v	1	LOWESTOFT T. (424)
EVESHAM UNITED	0	v	2	CLEVEDON TOWN (525)

Replayed - Clevedon fielded ineligible player

EVESHAM UNITED	1	v	3	CLEVEDON TOWN (502)
HAREFIELD UNITED	2	v	2	CANVEY ISLAND (244)
CANVEY ISLAND	1	v	0	HAREFIELD UTD (681)
PEACEHAVEN & TEL.	4	v	1	SITTINGBOURNE (882)
TRING TOWN	0	v	1	BANSTEAD ATH. (111)
BUCKINGHAM TOWN	4	v	0	PAULTON ROVERS (192)
FOREST GREEN RVRS	6	v	5	HAILSHAM TOWN (251)
BARTON ROVERS	0	v	4	TIVERTON TOWN (379)
HODDESDON TOWN	3	v	1	TUNBRIDGE W. (252)

Peacehaven & Telscombe were the toast of Sussex on Saturday 16th January after a remarkable Vase Fourth Round victory over **Sittingbourne**. Challenging strongly for the Beazer Homes League Southern Division title, 'Bourne' had to be considered one of the hot favourites, and their elimination heartened other major contenders such as Bridlington and Gresley. Of as much surprise as the result itself was the manner of Peacehaven's victory. They got off to a flying start with a goal from Mark Taylor after just six minutes, and doubled the lead through Rene Duchossey just after the hour mark. The powerful Unijet Sussex County League champions then made the game safe with further goals from Richard Cheal, a penalty, and Alan Ingledew before Dave Arter grabbed a last minute consolation for the Kent side.

Sittingbourne's demise left recent finalists **Gresley Rovers** and **Bridlington Town** as favourites. The former eased their way into the last sixteen, Gil Land, Richard Denby and Mark Devaney getting the goals against **Bridgnorth Town**, but 'Brid' needed extra-time in a thriller at home to H.F.S. League rivals **Curzon Ashton**. They had appeared in complete control after goals from Ged Parkinson, Justin Robson (a brother of Bryan) and Ian Noteman had given them a three goal lead by the hour mark. But back came Curzon Ashton in true cup-fighting tradition, and strikes from Stuart Stacey, Dave Liptrot and on-loan Ian Redman forced the extra half-hour. It was then that Bridlington found a second wind, and new siging John Woods put them back ahead before Noteman, a double scorer in the

1992 final for Guiseley, settled the issue with a fifth on the final whistle.

The other notable surprise was **Rothwell Town's** win over **Knowsley United**. In gale-force conditions in Northamptonshire, Knowsley just about enjoyed the best part of the game, but they were unnerved by a penalty miss by Dave Siddell and ultimately conceded a last gasp decider to Terry O'Keefe.

Never before had the Great Mills League been so handily placed in the Vase. **Paulton Rovers** were well beaten at **Buckingham Town** where Tom Pearson starred with a hat-trick, but **Tiverton Town** and **Clevedon Town**, indisputedly the 'Best in the West' in 1992-93, both achieved emphatic wins on the grounds of sides from higher up the Pyramid. 1978 finalists **Barton Rovers** were Tivy's victims. Martyn Rogers headed in a Kevin Smith corner to give the Ambers a great start, and then Phil Everett doubled the margin thus making up for an earlier disallowed effort, and further goals from Lee Annunziata and Kevin Smith followed after the interval. Clevedon also benefitted from an early strike in their tie at **Evesham United**, John Durham forcing the ball home from close range after ten minutes. Evesham were close to an equaliser when Mark Stevens did well to hold a Rob Candy shot after 84 minutes, and that miss proved vital as the prolific Andy Perrett wrapped up the tie four minutes later with a drive from the edge of the box. However, a bombshell was dropped when it was revealed that the registration of Clevedon's Gary Marshall not in order. The sides had to meet again at Common Road the following Saturday, but the outcome again saw Clevedon through by a two goal margin.

The most remarkable game of the round was an incredible eleven goal thriller at Nailsworth where 1982 winners **Forest Green Rovers** just pipped **Hailsham Town**. Gary Marshall put the home side ahead in the seventh minute, and Christian White made it two from the spot ten minutes later. Both goals were equalised by Dave Rowe, but Forest Green still went into the half-time break two up after Marshall and White had doubled their tallies. Phil Comber pulled one back with a fiftieth minute penalty, but then White completed his hat-trick, again from the spot. Back came Hailsham with Rowe getting his third before Clint Gobey made it 6-4 with seven minutes left. Steve March got a late consolation for the visitors.

By now a strong southern bias had emerged in the competition, especially as the Fifth Round round draw paired two of the three remaining northern clubs; **Dunston Feds** and **Cammell Laird**, the latter being surprise winners at **Burscough**. Beazer Homes League clubs were in the ascendency in Round Four - joining Forest Green, Gresley and Buckingham in Round Five were **Bilston Town** who trounced **Ashton United** with goals from John Snaith, Mark Stanton, and John Baker, and **Newport Isle of Wight** who cruised past **Lowestoft Town**, Neil Darnton and a Paul Cenci hat-trick doing the damage.

Pelsall Villa's success story continued following a resounding 4-1 replay win over Boddington's League rivals **Hinckley Athletic**, whilst Diadora League interest was maintained by **Banstead Athletic**, winners at **Tring Town** courtesy of an Andy Yetzes goal. The longest running saga of the round saw **Canvey Island**, leaders of the Essex Senior League (the competition that has provided more Vase winners than any other), eventually triumph at home to **Harefield United** after a postponement and a 2-2 draw away. Finally, completing the Fifth Round line-up were Campri South Midlands League outfit **Hoddesdon Town**, the very first winners of the F.A. Challenge Vase, who ended the Winstonlead Kent League challenge with a 3-1 home win over **Tunbridge Wells**.

Burscough's Kevin Smith heads at the Cammell Laird goal, but his side were beaten 0-1. Photo - Colin Stevens.

Sittingbourne 'keeper Andy Hough beats Micky Farmer but had a torrid match at Peacehaven. Photo - Roger Turner.

Banstead Athletic's match-winner Andy Yetzes beats Tring's Stuart Blaik to get in a cross. Photo - Francis Short.

FIFTH ROUND
(SAT. 6th FEB. 1993)

BUCKINGHAM TOWN 1 (own goal 95)
PELSALL VILLA 0 Att: 310
Buckingham: Keith Baker, Terry Muckelberg, Declan Cuddy (Ian Bowyer 53), Keith Knight, Jess Mansfield, Mark Sherlock, John Corbett, Jon Ward, Jon Blencowe (Mark Jameson 106), Tom Pearson, Dave Hume.
Pelsall: Neil Jones, Phil Wood, Neil Coles, Nikki Alsop, Adrian Horne, Jon Chapman, Simon Turpin (Craig Davison 75), Phil Haywood, Mark O'Sullivan (Darrell Haytree 99), Kevin Gough, Dean Walters.

ROTHWELL TOWN 1 (O'Keefe 23)
BRIDLINGTON TOWN 2 (Robinson 15, France 118)
Att: 651
Rothwell Town: Danny Liquorish, Dave McHutchison, Les Hornby (Shaun Wills 81), Dennis Robertson, Nigel Bates, Adrian Sheerin, Kevin McDonald, Terry O'Keefe, Neil Edwards, Glyn Davies, Paul Murphy (Steve McIlroy 85).
Bridlington Town: Ian Taylor, Steve Brentano, Ian McKenzie (John Woods 90 mins), Neil Howie, Chris Swailes (Paul Bottomley 103), Dave Woodcock, Darren Robinson, Allan Roberts, Darren France, Ian Noteman, Ged Parkinson.

GRESLEY ROVERS 1 (Devaney 84)
PEACEHAVEN & TELSCOMBE 0
Att: 1,138
Gresley: Bob Aston, Scott Elliott, Dave Swainston, Richard Denby, Stuart Evans, Gil Land, Richard Wardle, Graham Rigg (Robert Briscoe 70), Paul Acklam, Martin Devaney, Craig Weston. Unused sub: Martin Dick.
Peacehaven: Keith Cheal, Alan Ingledew, David Robinson (Tony Coade 80), Micky Farmer, Daren Newman, Lee Cox, Graham Farmer, Paul Thomsett, Rene Duchossoy, Richard Cheal, Mark Taylor. Unused sub: Simon Edwards.

BANSTEAD ATHLETIC 3 (Yetzes 12 81, Grabban 20)
NEWPORT ISLE OF WIGHT 0 Att: 410
Banstead: Bobby Knock, Errol Vassell, Barry Laker, Michael Stratford, Keith Ward, Gerald Dawson, Vivian Jeffrey, Geoff Taylor, Andy Yetzes, Gary Grabban (Ian Kilpatrick 81), Stephen Shaw (Paul Meredith 75).
Newport: Keith Granger, Lee Phillipi, Gary Sperry, Andy Darnton, Mark Smith, Kevin Thorne, Tony Frankland (Justin Urry 68), Stuart Ritchie, Paul Cenci, Andrew Sampson. Unused sub: Roy Maskell.

FOREST GREEN ROVERS 0
TIVERTON TOWN 6 (Smith 3 57, Everett 48 66 83, Saunders 63) Att: 671
Forest Green: Gary French, Lee Spalding, Steve Sivell, Chris Wells, Wayne Harris, Gary Marshall (Mickey Pearce 46), Chris White, Richard Ford (Craig Hampson 60), Liam Dixon, Clint Gobey, Russell Wilton.
Tiverton: Ian Nott, Peter Rogers, Neil Saunders, Mark Saunders, Mark Short, Hedley Steele, Lee Annunziata, Kevin Smith (Matthew Scott 70), Phil Everett, Steve Daly (Jamie Wheatcroft 80).

DUNSTON F.B. 2 (Kendal 4, Mulholland 34)
CAMMELL LAIRD 1 (Noble 58)
Att: 530
Dunston: Damian Boyd, Tony Dawson, David Wright, Graham Mole, Tommy Ditchburn, Tony Halliday, Steve Kendal, David Willis, Martin Hamilton (John Peacock 68), Ian Mulholland, Nigel Walker. Unused sub: Steven Cockburn.
Cammell Laird: Ian Banford, Steve Parnell (Alan Greatbanks 88), Neil Sherlock, Steve Craven, Mick Connor, Ian Cooke, Jimmy Kelly, Ian Doran, Nick Dillon, Dale Galloway, Lee Noble. Unused sub: Robbie Glanvill.

BILSTON TOWN 3 (Stanton 44, Bowater 65, Jones 86)
HODDESDON TOWN 2 Laffar 22, Cummins 38)
Att: 241
Bilston: Alan Pemberton, Nigel Conniff, Gary Jones, Jim Skidmore (Paul Wilde 43), Mark Bowater, John Rhodes, Danny Williams, Steve Snaith, Mark Stanton, John Baker, Dave Morbey. Unused sub: Andy Ratcliffe.

Hoddesdon: Tony Tillbrook, Tim Bridge, David Wilson, Glenn Swaby (Wayne Morris 67), Tony Smith, Paul Robbins, Kelvin Williams, Martin Smith (Lee Browne 87), Gary Laffar, Gary Cummins, Jeff Cross.

CANVEY ISLAND 1 (McDonald 103)
CLEVEDON TOWN 0
Att: 1,123
Canvey: Gary Harrold, Scott Rogers, Michael Bright, Stephen White, Stephen Wiseman, Allan Jacobs (Ian Templeman 105), Andy McDonald, Tony Pizzey, Kevin Lee, Andy Jones, Tony Mahoney. Unused sub: Steve Hibbert.
Clevedon: Mark Stevens, Wayne Morris, Nigel Gillard, Brenden Dowd, Dave Ewens, Damon Palfrey, Jamie Ward, Nicky Brooks, John Durham (Gary Marshall 110), Andy Perrett, Stuart Minall. Unused sub: Ian Wilmott.

In the Fifth Round, two gates broke the four-figure mark. **Gresley Rovers** were the biggest crowd pullers with 1,138 witnessing the competition favourites beating **Peacehaven & Telscombe** with a late goal from Martin Devaney, but by all accounts the most incredible atmosphere was created by the 1,123 at Park Lane, **Canvey Island**. The local team were up against **Clevedon Town**, a side who like themselves were undefeated in league football all season. It was a close affair with the visitors having a goal disallowed in the first-half, but well into injury-time a header from Andy McDonald broke the deadlock and put the Islanders into the Quarter-Finals for the first time in their history.

It was heartening that the Essex public threw their weight whole-heartedly behind Canvey's Vase challenge because elsewhere response to success was poor. The entertaining match I witnessed at **Buckingham Town** was watched by a meagre 310, the majority of whom had travelled from **Pelsall Villa**, and there were seventy people fewer at **Bilston Town** where in a thrilling tie the home side came from two goals down to oust **Hoddesdon Town**.

Banstead Athletic provided the surprise of the round beating **Newport Isle of Wight** in front of another disappointing gate (410). Newport's cause was not helped by the fact that 'keeper Keith Granger was dismissed for a professional foul after just fifteen minutes. As in the last round, Andy Yetzes was Banstead's goalscoring hero. He scored a brace either side of the penalty Gary Grabban netted after Granger's foul to book a daunting trip to **Bridlington Town**.

Rothwell Town bowed out to **Bridlington Town** at Cecil Street, the visitors taking the lead in the 18th minute when **Darren Robinson** turned and drilled a left-foot drive past Rothwell keeper Danny Liquorish. The goal seemed to stun the home side into action, and after some sustained pressure they equalised eight minutes later when **Terry O'Keefe** received a deft pass from Paul Murphy on the edge of the box and hit a low shot past Ian Taylor. Then came ae bizarre incident which led to the sending-off of Rothwell captain Adrian Sheerin. A goalmouth melee eventually saw the ball deflected wide for a Bridlington corner. However, although the ball had clearly been tipped round the post by goalkeeper Liquorish, referee Paul Rejer, a F.I.F.A. official, pointed to the spot and sent Sheerin off, apparently for handball. Ironically, this was the first time that the Rothwell skipper had even been booked, never mind sent-off, in 15 years as a player. Local T.V. pictures two days later clearly showed the incident, and confirmed what most people in the ground had thought at the time - that Sheerin was innocent. Dave Woodcock missed the resultant penalty, and Rothwell held out well until deep into extra-time when Darren France, on loan from Hull City, poked home the winner.

Elsewhere, **Dunston F.B.** ended **Cammell Laird's** excellent run, **Buckingham** deservedly beat **Pelsall Villa** albeit with an extra-time own goal, and the **Tiverton Town** band-wagon rolled on courtesy of a six-goal romp at **Forest Green Rovers**.

Dunston's Damian Boyd denies Jimmy Kelly, but Lee Noble follows up for Cammell Laird. Photo - Rob Ruddock.

A superb jump by Martin Devaney to head Gresley's winner against Peacehaven. Photo - Keith Clayton.

Banstead's two-goal hero Andy Yetzes beats Newport's Andy Darnton to get in a cross. Photo - Roger Turner.

QUARTER FINALS
(SAT. 27th FEB. 1993)

GRESLEY ROVERS 2 (Denby 81, Acklam 89)
DUNSTON F.B. 0
Att: 1,610
Gresley: Bob Aston, Scott Elliott, Dave Swainston, Richard Denby, Stuart Evans, Gil Land, Richard Wardle, Craig Weston, Paul Acklam, Martin Devaney, Craig Michael Taplin (Robert Briscoe 75). Unused sub: Graham Rigg.
Dunston: Damian Boyd, Tony Dawson, David Wright, Graham Mole, Tommy Ditchburn, Martin Hamilton, Steve Kendal, David Willis, John Peacock (Paul Robertsob 83), Ian Mulholland, Nigel Walker. Unused sub: Steven Cockburn.

BUCKINGHAM TOWN 1 (Draper 31)
TIVERTON TOWN 4 (Daly 10, K Smith 58 73, Saunders 86)
Att: 765
Buckingham: Keith Baker, Terry Muckelberg, Mark Sherlock, Keith Knight, Ian Bowyer, Jeremy Mansfield, Jon Ward, Jon Blencowe, David Draper, Tom Pearson (Mark Jameson), Dave Hume. Unused sub: Jon Corbett.
Tiverton: Ian Nott, Jason Smith, Neil Saunders, Mark Saunders, Mark Short, Hedley Steele, Lee Annunziata, Kevin Smith (Matthew Scott 80), Phil Everett, Steve Daly (Peter Rogers 87).

BRIDLINGTON TOWN 1 (Jones 59)
BANSTEAD ATHLETIC 0
Att: 433
Bridlington: Ian Taylor, Steve Brentano, Ian McKenzie, Neil Howie (Allan Roberts 58), Paul Bottomley, Dave Woodcock, Chris Grocock, Lee Harvey, Graeme Jones, Alan Radford (David Robinson 87), Ged Parkinson.
Banstead: Bobby Knock, Errol Vassell, Barry Laker, Michael Stratford, Keith Ward, Phil Barnes (David Hyner 78), Vivian Jeffrey, Geoff Taylor, Andy Yetzes, Gary Grabban, Stephen Shaw. Unused sub: Paul Meredith.

CANVEY ISLAND 2 (Mahoney 15, McDonald 16)
BILSTON TOWN 0
Att: 1,854
Canvey: Gary Harrold, Scott Rogers, Allen Jacobs, Stephen White, Stephen Wiseman, Kevin Lee, Andy McDonald, Tony Pizzey, Gary Marshall, Andy Jones, Tony Mahoney. Unused subs: Kevin Newbury, Mark Dziadulewicz.
Bilston: Alan Pemberton, Nigel Conniff, Gary Jones, Michael Hart (Dave Morbey 58), Mark Bowater, Jim Skidmore, Danny Williams, Steve Snaith, Mark Stanton (Andy Ratcliffe 70), John Baker, Robert Bradley.

The two main contenders moved into the Semi-Finals, but not without some difficulty. **Bridlington Town** managed only a single goal home win against visiting Diadora League side **Banstead Athletic**, whilst it was only in the final ten minutes of their tie against **Dunston Feds** that **Gresley Rovers** made their superiority count. In fact, in a wind-spoilt match, the Tynesiders caused Rovers quite a few problems particularly when John Peacock rattled the bar with a twenty yard drive. A deflected shot from Richard Denby after good approach work by Dave Swainston, and a close range effort from Paul Acklam put Gresley through.

The real drama was to be found at **Buckingham Town** and **Canvey Island**. The latter, and Buckingham's visitors, **Tiverton Town**, both succeeded in reaching their first Vase Semi-Finals by recording convincing wins over sides from higher in the Pyramid. Tivvy steam-rollered the Robins to the tune of 4-1 to become the first Western League side since Exmouth Town in 1985 to reach the last four. Coincidentally, it was a striker who enjoyed many fruitful seasons with Exmouth, Kevin Smith, who did the damage scoring twice. At a freezing snow-blown Park Lane, Canvey stung **Bilston Town** with two goals in a minute early in the first half. The much experienced Tony Mahoney soared to head the first from an Andy McDonald free-kick, and McDonald himself then raced through to kill off the Black Country side with a solo goal.

Relief and disbelief are etched on the faces of Gresley and Dunston players respectively as Damian Boyd, who had a brilliant game in goal for the Tynesiders, concedes a scrambled last minute decisive goal to Paul Acklam. Photo - Paul Dennis.

Andy McDonald bursts through to scores Canvey's decisive second goal against Bilston. Photo - Roger Turner.

Canvey Island celebrate their qualification for the Semi-Finals. Photo - Roger Turner.

Gresley's Mike Taplin gets past a determined challenge from Martin Hamilton of Dunston. Photo - Paul Dennis.

SEMI FINALS
(SAT. 20th & 27th MARCH 1993)

BRIDLINGTON TOWN   2
GRESLEY ROVERS   1
Att: 1,626

When the semi-final draw was made, it ensured that the two 'favourites' would not do battle at Wembley Stadium on May 8th, as they were drawn together. Both Brid and Gresley had had recent experiences of Vase finals, so that may have had a bearing on the rather disappointing attendance of 1,626.

The home side, packed with players used to winning things from their days with the manager, Colin Richardson, at North Shields, started brightly and caused the Rovers defence plenty of early problems. In fact, it took only four minutes for the breakthrough to happen when a back-header from Dave Woodcock split the Gresley defence for **Alan Radford** to power a shot past goalkeeper Bob Aston. There was no respite for the visitors, beaten finalists in 1991, and **Radford** made it 2-0 in the 18th minute when he fired home through a crowded penalty area.

It was fully 20 minutes into the game before Bridlington 'keeper, Ian Taylor, was called into action, saving a curling shot from midfielder Tony Marsden, but that seemed to stir Rovers into life, and it was now Brid's back four who looked shaky. And, after 29 minutes, Gresley made the most of their pressure when **Martin Devaney**, who played in the 1989 final for Tamworth, managed to skip through a number of Bridlington defenders and chip past Taylor from 20 yards for a beautifully-taken goal.

However, it all went terribly wrong for the visitors. In the 37th minute, Gresley's former Grantham Town defender, Dave Swainston, was booked by referee Brian Coddington for dissent. Stupidly, only a minute later, Swainston sent Allan Roberts flying to earn himself a red card. The half ended with the referee exercising his writing skills a few more times, and half-time perhaps came at the right time for the game.

Ten-man Gresley came out for the second-half determined to make a fight of it, but in the 62nd minute their hopes nearly took another battering when Vase 'veteran', Ian Noteman, had the ball in the net, only to have the effort disallowed for a foul on Aston.

Bridlington managed to hold the brave Rovers side at bay, and Mr Coddington was forced to book three more home players as the visitors piled on some late pressure.

Bridlington: Ian Taylor, Steve Brentano, Ian McKenzie, Lee Harvey, Paul Bottomley (Chris Swailes 28), Dave Woodcock, Chris Grocock, Allan Roberts (Ian Noteman 55), Graeme Jones, Alan Radford, Ged Parkinson.
Gresley: Bob Aston, Russ Elliott (Graham Rigg 39), Dave Swainston, Richard Denby, Stuart Evans, Gil Land, Richard Wardle, Tony Marsden (Mike Taplin 78), Paul Acklam, Martin Devaney, Craig Weston.

GRESLEY ROVERS   1
BRIDLINGTON TOWN   1
Att: 2,481

Gresley started better than they did in the first game, and put the visitors under pressure right from the off. Paul Acklam had a diving header which went just wide in the 14th minute, and the same player went close with a tremendous 20-yard shot which flew just wide. It came as no surprise when Gresley pulled the tie level when **Martin Devaney** picked up a Richard Denby free-kick and fired home.

The joy was short-lived, as Bridlington went in front on aggregate in the 36th minute when **Graeme Jones** found himself with space in the Rovers area, and slammed the ball past a helpless Bob Aston.

Gresley came out for the second half knowing that they had to perform heroics. The dangerous Alan Radford nearly ended their hopes completely before Aston foiled him with a brave save. Allan Roberts hit a shot over the bar, and Jones had a curler saved by Aston. The introduction of Mark Hurst pepped-up Rovers, and he forced Taylor into a good save almost

immediately after coming on. The final stages of the game saw Gresley constantly pressurise the visiting defence, but they were to be denied their second final.

Gresley: Bob Aston, Nathan Foster, Dave Swainston, Richard Denby, Stuart Evans, Graham Rigg, Richard Wardle, Craig Weston, Paul Acklam (Tony Mardsen 80), Martin Devaney, Mike Taplin (Mark Hurst 63).
Bridlington: Ian Taylor, Steve Brentano, Ian McKenzie, Lee Harvey, Paul Bottomley, Chris James (Dave Woodcock 46), Chris Grocock, Allan Roberts (John Woods 75), Graeme Jones, Alan Radford, Ged Parkinson.

TIVERTON TOWN   2
CANVEY ISLAND   0
Att: 2,602

A new record crowd crammed into Ladysmead for the first leg of the semi-final against Essex Senior League side Canvey Island. Like Bridlington, Tiverton got off to the perfect start when after just three minutes, leading scorer **Kevin Smith** netted his ninth Vase goal, connecting with a Neil Saunders free-kick to send home a twenty-yard shot. Most of the 2,602 crowd, including FA Chief Graham Kelly, thought Smith's shot was going wide, but it beat Gary Harrold's outstretched arms and snuggly found the corner of the net.

The second-half started in similar fashion, and this time it was **Steve Daly** who pounced. The midfielder robbed Allen Jacobs on the edge of the area and struck a shot with the outside of his foot. That goal signalled a purple patch for the home side who spent the next 20 minutes camped in the islanders' half. Phil Everett forced Harrold into a superb one-handed save, Mark Saunders drove a shot just wide and Daly sent a dipping drive just over. Canvey manager Jeff King then brought on sub Steve White, and he went close on three occasions, including one half-volley which was cleared off the line.

Tiverton: Ian Nott, Jason Smith, Neil Saunders, Mark Saunders, Mark Short, Hedley Steele, Lee Annunziata, Kevin Smith, Phil Everett, Steve Daly, Steve Hynds. Unused subs: Matthew Scott, Peter Rogers.
Canvey: Gary Harrold, Scott Rogers, Micky Bright, Allen Jacobs (Steve White 70), Steve Wiseman, Kevin Lee, Andy McDonald, Tony Pizzey, Lee Marshall (John Potter 80), Andy Jones, Kevin Newbury.

CANVEY ISLAND   1
TIVERTON TOWN   0
Att: 2,600

The game at Canvey Island's tiny ground was a daunting one for Tiverton. The ground has become a fortress for the Essex Leaguers, unbeaten at home for over a year. For an hour, the visitors defended stoutly, with veteran skipper Hedley Steele and England under-18 player Jason Smith outstanding at the heart of the defence. Steele cleared from the feet of Andy Jones, and Andy McDonald sent a 10-yard drive into the side netting.

With Lee Marshall proving a real handful for Tiverton, it seemed only a matter of time before Canvey Island scored, but the fanatical Essex supporters had to wait until the 64th minute to cheer the goal. McDonald's centre was headed away by Smith, but it fell nicely for Steve Hibbert who crossed into the packed penalty area. **Marshall** battled for the loose ball and turned and shot past Ian Nott to make the score 2-1 on aggregate.

Despite their territorial advantage, Canvey Island found little room to get a pop at Knott's goal, until the very last seconds when only the width of the post denied McDonald, and the same player shot inches wide with the very last kick of the game.

Canvey: Gary Harrold, Scott Rogers, Micky Bright, Steve Hibbert (Steve White 85), Steve Wiseman, Kevin Lee, Andy McDonald, Tony Pizzey, Lee Marshall (Edward Carrick 68), Andy Jones, Kevin Newbury.
Tiverton: Ian Nott, Jason Smith, Neil Saunders, Mark Saunders, Mark Short, Hedley Steele, Lee Annunziata, Steve Daly, Phil Everett, Kevin Smith, Steve Hynds. Unused subs: Matthew Scott, Peter Rogers.

Kevin Smith (seated) celebrates his second minute strike for Tiverton against Canvey Island. Photo - Paul Dennis.

Richard Denby shows plenty of determination to get past a Bridlington defender. Photo - Paul Dennis.

Brid's Paul Bottomley consoles Gresley scorer Martin Devaney as his team-mates celebrate. Photo - Paul Dennis.

F.A. CHALLENGE
VASE FINAL

Bridlington Town 1 v 0 Tiverton Town
Radford (63)

Attendance: 9,061

Bridlington: Ian Taylor, Steve Brentano, Ian McKenzie, Lee Harvey, Paul Bottomley, David Woodcock, Chris Grocock, Allan Roberts, Graeme Jones, Alan Radford (Alan Tyrell 85), Ged Parkinson. Unused sub: Chris Swailes.
Tiverton: Ian Nott, Jason Smith, Neil Saunders, Mark Saunders, Mark Short (Matthew Scott 83), Hedley Steele, Lee Annunziata, Kevin Smith, Phil Everett, Steve Daly, Steve Hynds (Peter Rogers 75).

Referee: Mr R A Hart (Darlington)
Linesmen: Mr E Lomas, Mr B D Priest.

It was certainly not a brilliant game, but that will detract little from Bridlington's joy in putting behind them the disappointment of losing a replayed final three years ago. They were by far the better team on the day, and can move up to the F.A. Trophy happy that they have at last achieved their declared ambition of Vase success.

Tiverton Town fans had a distinct numerical advantage in the stands, but their Northern counterparts scored a higher decibel count. Standing on their seats bellowing a heart-felt 'Yorkshire, Yorkshire', the self-styled 'Seaside Mafia', predominently young and male, presented a stark contrast to the families of Devonians sitting sedately on the other side of the halfway line.

The contrast on the field was just as marked. Bridlington should have won with more ease than the scoreline suggests. The first-half was a one-sided affair from which the Westerners were very fortunate to emerge on level terms. Their forward line of Kevin Smith and Phil Everett was hopelessly isolated from the midfield and were left to forage for long balls. Everett did look sharp and composed when given the opportunity, but his more experienced side-kick Smith got absolutely no change out of the well-marshalled and equally experienced Brid defence.

The inevitable goal appeared to have arrived shortly before the interval when Graeme Jones netted from close-range. However, a linesman had spotted Alan Radford offside. Radford was to have the last laugh though. In the 64th minute he picked up a long pass from Steve Brentano and hared past Jason Smith, Tivvy's otherwise impressive England Youth international. Radford looked set to centre the ball, but instead he defied a narrow angle to shoot past Ian Nott, and Mark Saunders on the line could not quite prevent the ball entering the net.

Tiverton strived gallantly for an equaliser. They did however come off to a rousing reception from the fans, and have done the Western League proud in its centenary year.

Congratulations to Bridlington. League position suggests that they, as H.F.S. Loans League division one champions, were the strongest team in this year's event along with Beazer Southern champions Sittingbourne. But, whatever your advantage over the opposition, winning a competition as vast as the Vase is still a magnificent achievement.

Three members of the Bridlington party had already experienced Vase triumph. Manager Colin Richardson was with Whickham in 1981 when the Wearside League side recovered a two goal deficit to defeat Willenhall, whilst a decade later Allan Roberts and Paul Bottomley were at Wembley with Guiseley, Roberts scoring the last minute equaliser against Gresley. Those were probably the two most dramatic Vase finals of all time. Sadly, this season's event was not in the same league.

J.W.

Ian McKenzie of Bridlington takes on Tiverton's Steve Daly during the second-half. Photo - Dave West.

Bridlington's Alan Radford is mobbed by team-mates after scoring the winner. Photo - Francis Short.

Bridlington Town - F.A. Challenge Vase winners 1992-93. Photo - Graham Cotterill.

PAST F.A. CHALLENGE VASE FINALS

1975 HODDESDON T. 2 (Sedgwick 2) **EPSOM & EWELL 1** (Wales)   *Att: 9,500.* Ref: R Toseland
Hoddesdon: Galvin, Green, Hickey, Maybury, Stevenson, Wilson, Bishop, Picking, Sedgwick, Nathan, Schofield.
Epsom: Page, Bennett, Webb, Wales, Worby, Jones, O'Connell, Walker, Tuite, Eales, Lee.

1976 BILLERICAY TOWN 1 (Aslett) **STAMFORD 0** *(aet)*   *Att: 11,848.* Ref: A Robinson
Billericay: Griffiths, Payne, Foreman, Pullin, Bone, Coughlan, Geddes, Aslett, Clayden, Scott, Smith. *Stamford:*
Johnson, Kwiatkowski, Marchant, Crawford, Downs, Hird, Barnes, Walpole, Smith, Russell, Broadbent.

1977 BILLERICAY TOWN 1 (Clayden) **SHEFFIELD 1** (Coughlan OG) *(aet)*   *Att: 14,000.* Ref: J Worrall
B'cay: Griffiths, Payne, Bone, Coughlan, Pullin, Scott, Wakefield, Aslett, Clayden, Woodhouse, McQueen. Sub:
Whettell *Shef.:* Wing, Gilbody, Lodge, Hardisty, Watts, Skelton, Kay, Travis, Pugh, Thornhill, Haynes. Sub: Strutt.

Replay at Nottm Forest. BILLERICAY 2 (Aslett, Woodhouse) **SHEFFIELD 1** (Thornhill)   Ref: J Worrall
Billericay: Griffiths, Payne, Pullin, Whettell, Bone, McQueen, Woodhouse, Aslett, Clayden, Scott, Wakefield.
Sheffield: Wing, Gilbody, Lodge, Strutt, Watts, Skelton, Kay, Travis, Pugh, Thornhill, Haynes. *Att: 3,482.*

1978 NEWCASTLE BLUE STAR 2 (Dunn, Crumplin) **BARTON ROVERS 1** (Smith)   Ref: T Morris
Blue Star: Halbert, Feenan, Thompson, Davidson, S Dixon, Beynon, Storey, P Dixon, Crumplin, Callaghan, Dunn.
Sub: Diamond. *Barton:* Blackwell, Stephens, Crossley, Evans, Harris, Dollimore, Dunn, Harnaman, Fossey,
Turner, Smith. Sub: Cox. *Att: 16,858.*

1979 BILLERICAY TOWN 4 (Young 3, Clayden) **ALMONDSBURY GREENWAY 1** (Price)   Ref: C Seel
Billericay: Norris, Blackaller, Bingham, Whettell, Bone, Reeves, Pullin, Scott, Clayden, Young, Groom. Sub:
Carrigan. *Almondsbury:* Hamilton, Bowers, Scarrett, Sullivan, Tudor, Wookey, Bowers, Shehean, Kerr, Butt, Price.
Sub: Kilbaine. *Att: 17,500.*

1980 STAMFORD 2 (Alexander, McGowan) **GUISBOROUGH TOWN 0**   Ref: Neil Midgley
Stamford: Johnson, Kwiatkowski, Ladd, McGowan, Bliszczak I, Mackin, Broadhurst, Hall, Czarnecki, Potter,
Alexander. Sub: Bliszczak S. *Guisborough:* Cutter, Scott, Thornton, Angus, Maltby, Percy, Skelton, Coleman,
McElvaney, Sills, Dilworth. Sub: Harrison. *Att: 11,500.*

1981 WHICKHAM 3 (Scott, Williamson, Peck OG) **WILLENHALL 2** (Smith, Stringer) *(aet)*   Ref: R Lewis
Whickham: Thompson, Scott, Knox, Williamson, Cook, Ward, Carroll, Diamond, Cawthra, Robertson, Turnbull.
Sub: Allon. *Willenhall:* Newton, White, Dams, Woodall, Heath, Fox, Peck, Price, Matthews, Smith, Stringer. Sub:
Trevor. *Att: 12,000.*

1982 FOREST GREEN ROVERS 3 (Leitch 2, Norman) **RAINWORTH M.W. 0**   Ref: K Walmsey
Forest Green: Moss, Norman, Day, Turner, Higgins, Jenkins, Guest, Burns, Millard, Leitch, Doughty. Sub:
Dangerfield. *Rainworth:* Watson, Hallam, Hodgson, Slater, Sterland, Oliver, Knowles, Raine, Radzi, Reah,
Comerfield. Sub: Robinson. *Att: 12,500.*

1983 V.S. RUGBY 1 (Crawley) **HALESOWEN TOWN 0**   Ref: B Daniels
Rugby: Burton, McGinty, Harrison, Preston, Knox, Evans, Ingram, Setchell, Owen, Beecham, Crawley. Sub:
Haskins. *Halesowen:* Coldicott, Penn, Edmonds, Lacey, Randall, Shilvock, Hazelwood, Moss, Woodhouse, P
Joinson, L Joinson. Sub: Smith. *Att: 13,700.*

1984 STANSTED 3 (Holt, Gillard, Reading) **STAMFORD 2** (Waddicore, Allen)   Ref: T Bune
Stansted: Coe, Williams, Hilton, Simpson, Cooper, Reading, Callanan, Holt, Reeves, Doyle, Gillard. Sub: Williams.
Stamford: Parslow, Smitheringale, Blades, McIlwain, Lyon, Mackin, Genovese, Waddicore, Allen, Robson, Beech.
Sub: Chapman. *Att: 8,125.*

1985 HALESOWEN TOWN 3 (Moss, L Joinson 2) **FLEETWOOD TOWN 1** (Moran)   Ref: C Downey
Halesowen: Caldicott, Penn, Sherwood, Warner, Randle, Heath, Hazelwood, Moss (Smith), Woodhouse, P
Joinson, L Joinson. *Fleetwood:* Dobson, Moran, Hadgraft, Strachan, Robinson, Milligan, Hall, Trainor, Taylor
(Whitehouse), Cain, Kenneley. *Att: 16,715.*

1986 HALESOWEN TOWN 3 (Moss, L Joinson) **SOUTHALL 0**   Ref: D Scott
Halesowen: Pemberton, Moore, Lacey, Randle (Rhodes), Sherwood, Heath, Penn, Woodhouse, P Joinson, L
Joinson, Moss. *Southall:* MacKenzie, James, McGovern, Croad, Holland, Powell (Richmond), Pierre, Richardson,
Sweales, Ferdinand, Rowe. *Att: 18,340.*

1987 ST HELENS 3 (Layhe 2, Rigby) **WARRINGTON TOWN 2** (Reid, Cook)   Ref: T Mills
St Helens: Johnson, Benson, Lowe, Bendon, Wilson, McComb, Collins, (Gledhill), O'Neill, Cummins, Lay, Rigby.
Sub: Deakin. *Warrington:* O'Brien, Copeland, Hunter, Gratton, Whalley, Reid, Brownville (Woodyer), Cook,
Kinsey, Looker (Hill), Hughes. *Att: 4,254.*

1988 COLNE DYNAMOES 1 (Anderson) **EMLEY 0**   Ref: A Seville
Colne: Mason, McFafyen, Westwell, Bentley, Dunn, Roscoe, Rodaway, Whitehead (Burke), Diamond, Anderson,
Wood (Coates). *Emley:* Dennis, Fielding, Mellor, Codd, Hirst (Burrows), Gartland (Cook), Carmody, Green,
Bramald, Devine, Francis. *Att: 15,000.*

1989 TAMWORTH 1 (Devaney) **SUDBURY TOWN 1** (Hubbick) *aet*   Ref: C Downey
Tamworth: Belford, Lockett, Atkins, Cartwright, McCormack, Myers, Finn, Devaney, Moores, Gordon, Stanton.
Subs: Rathbone, Heaton. *Sudbury:* Garnham, Henry, G Barker, Boyland, Thorpe, Klug, D Barker, Barton,
Oldfield, Smith, Hubbick. Subs: Money, Hunt. *Att: 26,487.*

Replay at Peterborough. TAMWORTH 3 (Stanton 2, Moores) **SUDBURY TOWN 0**
Tamworth: Belford, Lockett, Atkins, Cartwright, Finn, Myers, George, Devaney, Moores, Gordon, Stanton. Sub:
Heaton. *Sudbury:* Garnham, Henry, G Barker, Boyland, Thorpe, Klug, D Barker, Barton, Oldfield, Smith, Hubbick.
Subs: Money, Hunt. *Att: 11,201.*

1990 YEADING 0 BRIDLINGTON TOWN 0   *Att: 7,932.* Ref: R Groves
Replay at Leeds.   YEADING 1 (Sweales) **BRIDLINGTON TOWN 0**   *Att: 5,000.* Ref: R Groves
Yeading: MacKenzie, Wickens, Turner, Whiskey (sub McCarthy at Wembley), Croad (sub McCarthy in rep), Denton
(Schwartz in rep), Matthews, James (sub Charles at Wembley), Sweales, Impey, Cordery.
Bridlington: Taylor, Pugh, Freeman, McNeil, Warburton, Brentano, Wilkes (sub Hall at Wembley, Brown in rep),
Noteman, Gauden (sub Downing in rep), Whiteman, Brattan (sub Brown at Wembley).

1991 GRESLEY ROVERS 4 (Rathbone, Smith 2, Stokes)
GUISELEY 4 (Tennison 2, Walling, A Roberts)   Ref: C Trussell
Replay at Bramall Lane. GUISELEY 3 (Tennison, Walling, Atkinson) **GRESLEY 1** (Astley)   Ref: C Trussell
Guiseley: Maxted, Bottomley (Annan in rep), Hogarth, Tetley, Morgan, McKenzie (sub Bottomley in rep), Atkinson
(sub Annan at Wembley), Tennison (sub Noteman in rep), Walling, A Roberts, B Roberts (sub Annan at Wembley).
Gresley: Aston, Barry, Elliott (sub Adcock at Wembley), Denby, Land, Astley, Stokes (sub Weston in rep), K Smith,
Acklam, Rathbone, Lovell (sub Weston at Wembley, Adcock in rep). *Att: 11,314 at Wembley, 7,585 at Sheffield.*

1992 WIMBORNE TOWN 5 (Richardson, Sturgess 2, Killick 2)
GUISELEY 3 (Noteman 2, Colville)   Ref: M J Bodenham
Wimborne: Leonard, Langdown, Wilkins, Beacham, Allan, Taplin, Ames, Richardson, Bridle, Killick, Sturgess (Lovell), Lynn. *Guiseley:* Maxted, Atkinson, Hogarth, Tetley (Wilson 68), Morgan, Brockie, A Roberts, Tennison, Noteman (Colville 80), Annan, W Roberts. *Att: 10,772*

Round by Round Chart 1992-93

3rd Rnd Proper	4th Rnd Proper	5th Rnd Proper	6th Rnd Proper	Semi-final	Final
Hartley Wint. 0					
Rothwell T. 3	Rothwell T. 1				
Knowsley Utd 5	Knowsley Utd 0				
Flixton 2					
Brigg Town 1		Rothwell Town 1			
Bridlington 3	Bridlington 5				
Curzon Ashton 7	Curzon Ashton 3	Bridlington 2			
Chester-le-Str. 1			Bridlington 1		
Cray Wdrs 2			Banstead Ath. 0		
Tring Town 3	Tring Town 0				
Harwich & Park. 0	Banstead Ath. 1	Banstead Ath. 3			
Banstead Ath. 3		Newport I.O.W. 0			
Newport I.O.W. 2	Newport I.O.W. 4				
Welton Rvrs 0	Lowestoft 1				
Walthamstow P. 0				Bridlington 2;1	
Lowestoft T. 1				1st leg at Bridlington	
Burnham 1				Gresley Rvrs 1;1	
Gresley Rvrs 2	Gresley Rvrs 3				
Bridgnorth 4	Bridgnorth 0	Gresley Rvrs 1			
Atherton Col. 0		Peacehaven 0			
Bourne T. 4;0					
Peacehaven 4;4	Peacehaven 4		Gresley Rvrs 2		
Sittingbourne 4	Sittingbourne 1		Dunston Feds 0		
Malden Vale 2					
Dunston Feds 5					
Billingham T. 1					
Eastwood Han. 2	Dunston Feds 3	Dunston Feds 2			
Durham City 5	Durham City 1	Cammell Laird 1			
Burscough 1					
Ponteland Utd 0					
Bamber Bridge 1	Burscough 0				Bridlington 1
Cammell Laird 2	Cammell Laird 1				
Buckingham 3	Buckingham T. 4				Tiverton 0
Saffron Walden 2	Paulton Rvrs 0				
First Tower 0;1		Buckingham 1			
Paulton 0;5		Pelsall Villa 0			
Hinckley Ath. 1	Hinckley A. 2;1				
Clipstone W. 0	Pelsall V. 2;4				
Littlehampton 0			Buckingham 1		
Pelsall Villa 1			Tiverton 4		
Witney Town 1					
Forest Green 2	Forest Green 6	Forest Green 0			
Cranleigh 1	Hailsham Town 5	Tiverton 6			
Hailsham Town 3					
Barton Rovers 2	Barton Rovers 0				
Diss Town 1	Tiverton 4				
Tiverton 2				Tiverton 2;0	
Almondsbury 1				1st leg at Tiverton	
Norwich Utd 1				Canvey Island 0;1	
Harefield Utd 2	Harefield 2;0				
Canvey Island 1	Canvey Is. 2;1	Canvey Island 1			
King's Lynn 0		Clevedon 0			
Newquay 1					
Evesham United 3	Evesham United 1		Canvey Island 2		
Clevedon Town 2	Clevedon Town 3		Bilston T. 0		
Bemerton Heath 1					
Stratford T. 0					
Bilston Town 2	Bilston Town 3	Bilston Town 3			
Atherton L.R. 1	Ashton Utd 0	Hoddesdon 2			
Ashton United 2					
Tilbury 2					
Hoddesdon T. 3	Hoddesdon T. 3				
Feltham & H. 1	Tunbridge W. 1				
Tunbridge Wells 2					

INTERNATIONAL &
F.A. REPRESENTATIVE
FOOTBALL

The England Semi-Professional International side that lost 1-3 to the Finland under-21 International side at Woking. Back Row (L/R): John Coleman, Brian Ross, Darren Collins, Paul Nicol, Ryan Price, Paul Richardson, Laurence Batty, Steve Conner, Mark Hone, Jim Conway (Physio). Front: Ron Reid (Asst Manager), Tony Hemmings, Paul Watts, Terry Robbins, Paul Shirtliff, Paul Cavell, Brian Butler, Paul Webb, Tony Jennings (Manager).

England played two full semi-pro internationals during the season. Wales were played, and beaten, in the now annual contest. An added bonus was a game against the Finland under-21 side played at Woking on 14th April.

ENGLAND 2, WALES 1

(at Cheltenham Town F.C., Tuesday 2nd March 1993)

The annual Semi-Professional international between England and Wales was contested at Whaddon Road, Cheltenham, on Tuesday 2nd March as part of Cheltenham Town's centenary celebrations. The game resulted in a 2-1 win for England who now extend their lead to five victories to three in the series of matches that started in 1984.

England's domination of the first half was almost total. David Leworthy, on his international debut, was particularly impressive, as was Wycombe's Steve Guppy who enjoyed many profitable forays down the left flank. However, the chances went begging and in the 42nd minute Wales stunned the crowd with a goal in almost their first serious attack. A high ball over the top found Carl Glover, and Ryan Price was unable to hold the Afan Lido striker's fierce shot, and **Bob Colville** slotted home the rebound from a tight angle.

This bombshell stung England into life, and they managed an equaliser in the few minutes that remained before half-time. A mix-up in the heart of the Welsh defence gave Steve Thompson a run on goal. He pushed the ball past David Morgan, and was clipped by the latter making a penalty award indisputable. **Terry Robbins**, who had hiitherto experienced a quiet half, made no mistake.

As an attacking force, the Welsh, controversially selected solely from the Konica League of Wales, were more prominent after the break. However, England, for whom Steve Thompson enjoyed a superb 45 minutes, always had the edge and the inevitable winner arrived in the 54th minute when **Leworthy** sneaked in to nod home a corner from the right. **J.W.**

England: Ryan Price (Stafford), **Paul Shirtliff, Paul Watts** (both Dagenham), **Mark Shail** (Yeovil), **Andy Kerr, Simon Stapleton, Steve Thompson** (all Wycombe), **Paul Richardson** (Dagenham), **Terry Robbins** (Welling), **David Leworthy** (Farnboro., (sub: **Brian Ross** (Marine) 81), **Steve Guppy** (Wycombe). Unused subs: **Paul Nicol** (Kettering), **John McKenna** (Dagenham), **David Moss** (Boston U.), **Paul Cavell** (Dagenham). Manager: Tony Jennings.

Wales: David Morgan (Aberystwyth), **Huw Knight** (Haverfordwest), **Kevin Lloyd** (Caersws), **Neil O'Brien** (Aberystwyth), **Jimmy Blackie** (Cwmbran), **Norman Parselle** (Cwmbran), **Jason Gummer** (Inter Cardiff, (sub: **Anthony Thomas** (Aberysthwyth) 75), **Carl Glover** (Afan Lido, (sub: **John Morgan** (Inter Cardiff) 67), **Nigel French** (Aberystwyth), **Bob Colville** (Bangor), (sub: **Steve Woods** (Ebbw Vale) 82), **Philip Davidson** (Llanelli). Unused sub: **Neil Griffiths** (Conwy). Manager: Tommy Morgan.

Referee: S W Dunn (Bristol)   **Linesmen:** W Bond & D K Curtis (Gloucestershire F.A.)

ENGLAND 1, FINLAND UNDER-21 3

(at Woking F.C., Wednesday 2nd March 1993)

One of England's brightest displays for years sadly brought no reward as a very efficient young Finland side were presented with a late goal against the run of play, and a victory scoreline that was hardly fair to Tony Jennings' squad. Without the Wycombe Wanderers players, who had fought-out a local derby with Slough Town the previous day, the England selection saw the introduction of three more debutants with two more newboys on the substitutes bench. Not surprisingly the team took a little time to settle down, and by then **Antti Sumiala** had converted a left-wing cross from Jokke Jangaskorpi, who had intercepted a poor clearance after seven minutes.

Finland had strength down the centre of their side as goalkeeper Antti Niemi, giant defender Sami Hyypia and ace striker Sumiala were all full internationals. Their experience and quality made all the difference as England's brand-new midfield struggled to adjust to the pace of the game and to each other's style. Once again, Paul Richardson showed his best form in an England shirt, and Brian Butler had a busy first-half. Bromsgroves' Paul Webb was a success as was the reliable Steve Conner, but by half-time England had only one goal to show for their efforts, and this came when **Paul Cavell**, who led the attack intelligently, sprang the offside trap and beat the on-rushing Niemi to equalise after thirteen minutes.

England also created half chances for Terry Robbins and Tony Hemmings, who were both causing the strong-tackling Finnish defenders some problems, but it was from a far post corner that Finland regained the lead after 34 minutes. Tommi Kautonen's long ball to **Sumiala** was headed home with confidence, but the cross really should have been intercepted, and a disappointed England side went in for half-time without really getting to grips with the game.

Enfield's Darren Collins came on for Butler, with local hero Laurence Batty taking over from Ryan Price at half-time, and Collins certainly gave England more width, enjoying an excellent half. Collins himself had three chances, Cavell also should have scored, and the team could be seen to be growing in confidence as they stretched the Finnish defence to the limit. It was at this stage that the visitors' goalkeeper Niemi showed his class, and with Brian Ross on for Hemmings, and late in the game, Morecambe's John Coleman replacing a slightly concussed Robbins, England deserved an equaliser.

Sadly, as so often happens, the attacking side were caught on the break, and substitute **Sami Vaisanen** hammered home a loose ball when Batty failed to collect a cross in the last minute. The fixture was a welcome addition to the calander, but what a pity that the Wycombe players were not available, and that Aldershot Town were playing on the same evening thus reducing the attence to 845. **T.W.**

England: Ryan Price (Stafford) (sub: **Laurence Batty** (Woking) 46), **Paul Shirtliff, Paul Watts** (both Dagenham), **Mark Hone** (Welling), **Steve Conner** (Dagenham & Redbridge), **Brian Butler** (Northwich Victoria) (sub: **Darren Collins** (Enfield) 46), **Paul Webb** (Bromsgrove Rovers), **Paul Richardson** (Dagenham & Redbridge), **Terry Robbins** (Welling United) (sub: **John Coleman** (Morecambe) 85), **Paul Cavell** (Dagenham & Redbridge), **Tony Hemmings** (Northwich Victoria) (sub: **Brian Ross** (Marine) 71), Unused sub: **Paul Nicol** (Kettering Town) **Finland: Antti Niemi** (HJK), **Jussi Nuorela** (FC Hake) (sub: **Sami Mahlio** (FC Hake) 75), **Jani Keula** (TPS), **Tommi Kautonen** (FC Hake), **Mike Wallden** (HJK), **Sami Hyypia** (Mypa), **Mike Nurmela** (Malmo), **Marko Helin** (HJK), **Antti Sumiala** (FC Jazz), **Jari Sulander** (FC Kuuysysl) (sub: **Kai Nyyssonen** (HJK) 71), **Jokke Jangaskorpi** (MP) (sub: **Sami Vaisanen** (FC Haka) 71). Unused Subs: **Tommi Kainulainen** (PK-37), **Kim Lehtonen** (TPS)

Referee: Roger Wiseman (Boreham Wood)   **Linesmen:** L Cabel & P Randall

FOUR NATIONS TOURNAMENTS 1979-87
and other Internationals

1979 (England)
Knock - out basis, England won final.

S/Final	England	5 v 1	Scotland
S/Final	Holland	3 v 0	Italy
3rd Place	Scotland	1 v 2	Italy
Final	England	1 v 0	Holland

1980 (Holland)

	P	W	D	L	F	A	PTS
Scotland	3	2	1	0	7	2	5
England	3	2	0	1	6	5	4
Italy	3	0	2	1	2	4	2
Holland	3	0	1	2	3	7	1

1981 (Italy)

	P	W	D	L	F	A	PTS
England	3	1	2	0	3	1	4
Italy	3	1	2	0	2	1	4
Scotland	3	0	3	0	2	2	3
Holland	3	0	1	2	2	5	1

1982 (Scotland)

	P	W	D	L	F	A	PTS
Scotland	3	1	2	0	5	4	4
England	3	1	2	0	2	1	4
Italy	3	0	2	1	4	6	2
Holland	3	1	0	2	5	5	2

1983 (England)

	P	W	D	L	F	A	PTS
England	3	3	0	0	10	1	6
Scotland	3	1	1	1	7	6	3
Holland	3	1	1	1	6	11	3
Italy	3	0	0	3	3	8	0

1984 (Italy)

	P	W	D	L	F	A	PTS
Italy	3	2	1	0	4	1	5
England	3	1	1	1	5	4	3
Holland	3	1	1	1	8	8	3
Scotland	3	0	1	2	2	6	1

1985 (Holland)

	P	W	D	L	F	A	PTS
Scotland	3	2	0	1	4	4	4
England	3	1	1	1	6	5	3
Italy	3	1	1	1	4	4	3
Holland	3	1	0	2	4	5	2

1986 (Scotland)
Competition cancelled - Italy withdrew.

1987 (Scotland)

	P	W	D	L	F	A	PTS
Italy	3	2	1	0	6	3	5
England	3	2	0	1	7	3	4
Scotland	3	1	0	2	4	6	2
Holland	3	0	1	2	0	5	1

OVERALL FOUR NATIONS TROPHY RECORD

	P	W	D	L	F	A	PTS
England	23	13	6	4	45	21	32
Italy	23	7	9	7	27	31	23
Scotland	23	7	8	8	33	37	22
Holland	23	5	5	13	31	47	15

OTHER RESULTS

v. WALES

		Eng.	Wales
1984	Newtown	1	2
1985	Telford	1	0
1986	Merthyr	1	3
1987	Gloucester	2	2
1988	Rhyl	2	0
1989	Kidderminster	2	0
1990	Merthyr	0	0
1991	Stafford	1	2
1992	Aberystwyth	1	0
1993	Cheltenham	2	1

v. REPUBLIC OF IRELAND

		Eng.	Ire.
1986	Kidderminster	2	1
1986	Nuneaton	2	1
1990	Dublin	2	1
1990	Cork	3	0

v. GIBRALTAR

		Eng.	Gib.
1982	Gibraltar	3	2

v. FINLAND (under-21)

		Eng.	Fin.
1993	Woking	1	3

v. ITALY

		Eng.	Italy
1989	La Spezia	1	1
1990	Solerno	0	2
1991	Kettering	0	0

ENGLAND'S Overall International Record

P	W	D	L	F	A
42	23	10	9	72	42

England Semi-Pro Caps 79-93 (Max 42)

(I - Italy, S - Scotland, W - Wales, H - Holland, E - Eire, F - Finland, G - Gibralter)

Gary Abbott (Welling) 87 I(s), S(s), 92 W(s) (3)
David Adamson (Boston Utd) 79 SH, 80 ISH (5)
Tony Agana (Weymouth) 86 E (1)
Jim Arnold (Stafford Rangers) 79 SH (2)
Noel Ashford (Enfield & Redbridge For.) 82 GHS, 83 IHS, 84 WHSI, 85 WI(s), 86 EE, 87 W(s), IHS, 90 WE, 91 I(s) (21)
John Askey (Macclesfield) 90 W, (1)
Paul Bancroft (Kidderminster) 89 IW, 90 IWE, 91 W (6)
Keith Barrett (Enfield) 81 HSI, 82 GIHS, 83 IHS, 84 W(s)HS, 85 IHS (16)
Laurence Batty (Woking) 93 F(s) (1)
Mark Beeney (Maidstone) 89 I(s) (1)
Colin Brazier (Kidderminster) 87 W (1)
Steve Brooks (Cheltenham) 88 W(s), 90 WE (3)
David Buchanan (Blyth) 86 E(s)E (2)
Brian Butler (Northwich) 93 F (1)
Steve Butler (Maidstone) 88 W, 89 IW (3)
Mark Carter (Runcorn & Barnet) 87 WIHS, 88 W, 89 IW, 90 IE, 91 IW(s) (11)
Kim Casey (Kidderminster) 86 WEE(s), 87 WI (5)
Paul Cavell (Kidderminster) 92 W, 93 F (2)
Kevin Charlton (Telford) 85 WI (2)
Andrew Clarke (Barnet) 90 EE (2)
David Clarke (Blyth Spartans) 80 IS(s)H, 81 HSI, 82 IHS, 83 HS, 84 HSI (14)
Gary Clayton (Burton) 86 E (1)
Robert Codner (Barnet) 88 W (1)
John Coleman (Morecambe) 93 F(s) (1)
Darren Collins (Enfield) 93 F(s) (1)
Steve Conner (Dartford, Redbridge & Dagenham & R) 90 I, 91 IW, 92 W, 93 F (5)
David Constantine (Altrincham) 85 IHS, 86 W (4)
Robbie Cooke (Kettering) 89 W(s), 90 I (2)
Alan Cordice (Wealdstone) 83 IHS, 84 WS(s), I(s), 85 IHS (9)
Paul Cuddy (Altrincham) 87 IHS (3)
Paul Culpin (Nuneaton B) 84 W, 85 W(s) IHS (5)
Paul Davies (Kidderminster) 86 W, 87 WIS, 88 W, 89 W (6)
John Davison (Altrincham) 79 SH, 80 IS, 81 HSI, 82 GIHS, 83 IHS, 84 WHIS, 85 IHS, 86 WEE (24)
John Denham (Northwich Victoria) 80 H (1)
Peter Densmore (Runcorn) 88 W, 89 I (2)
Phil Derbyshire (Mossley) 83 H(s)S(s) (2)
Mick Doherty (Weymouth) 86 W(s) (1)
Mick Farrelly (Altrincham) 87 IHS (3)
Trevor Finnegan (Weymouth) 81 HS (2)
Paul Furlong (Enfield) 90 IEE, 91 IW (5)
John Glover (Maidstone Utd) 85 WIHS (4)
Mark Golley (Sutton) 87 H(s)S, 88 W, 89 IW, 92 W (6)
Phil Gridelet (Hendon + Barnet) 89 IW, 90 WEE (5)
Steve Guppy (Wycombe) 93 W (1)
Steve Hancock (Macclesfield) 90 W (1)
Tony Hemmings (Northwich) 93 F (1)
Andy Hessenthaler (Dartford) 90 I (1)
Kenny Hill (Maidstone Utd) 80 ISH (3)
Mark Hone (Welling) 90 I, 93 F (3)
Gary Hooley (Frickley) 85 W (1)
Keith Houghton (Blyth Spartans) 79 S (1)
Barry Howard (Altrincham) 81 HSI, 82 GIHS (7)
David Howell (Enfield) 85 H(s)S(s), 86 WE, 87 WIHS, 88 W, 89 IW, 90 IEE (14)
Delwyn Humphreys (Kidderminster) 91 W(s), 92 W (2)
Steve Humphries (Barnet) 87 H(s) (1)
Nicky Ironton (Enfield) 83 H(s), 84 W(2)
Tony Jennings (Enfield) 79 SH, 80 ISH, 81 HSI, 82 GIHS (12)
Jeff Johnson (Altrincham) 81 SI, 82 GIHS, 83 IHS, 84 HSI, 84 IHS, 86 W(s)EE (18)
Tom Jones (Weymouth) 87 W (1)
Anton Joseph (Telford Utd + Kidderminster) 84 S(s), 85 WIHS, 86 W(s), 87 WI(s)H, 88 W, 89 IW, 90 IEE (14)
Andy Kerr (Wycombe) 93 W (1)

Mike Lake (Macclesfield) 89 I (1)
Andy Lee (Telford/Witton) 89 I(s), 91 IW (3)
David Leworthy (Farnborough) 93 W (1)
Kenny Lowe (Barnet) 91 IW (2)
John McKenna (Boston Utd) 88 W(s), 90 IEE, 91 IW, 92 W (7)
Bobby Mayes (Redbridge) 92 W (1)
Paul Mayman (Northwich Vic) 80 IS (2)
Stewart Mell (Burton) 85 W (1)
Neil Merrick (Weymouth) 80 I(s)S (2)
Trevor Morley (Nuneaton) 84 WHSI, 85 WS(s) (6)
Les Mutrie (Blyth Spartans) 79 SH, 80 ISH (5)
Mark Newson (Maidstone U) 84 WHSI, 85 W (5)
Doug Newton (Burton) 85 WHS (3)
Paul Nicol (Kettering T) 91 IW, 92 W (3)
Steve Norris (Telford) 88 W(s) (1)
Eamon O'Keefe (Mossley) 79 SH (2)
Frank Ovard (Maidstone) 81 H(s)S(s)I(s) (3)
Andy Pape (Harrow + Enfield) 85 W(s)HS, 86 W(s)E 87 WIHS, 88 W, 89 IW, 90 IWE (15)
Brian Parker (Yeovil Town) 80 S (1)
Trevor Peake (Nuneaton Bor) 79 SH (2)
David Pearce (Harrow Bor) 84 I(s) (1)
Brendan Phillips (Nuneaton B, Kettering) 79 SH, 80 S(s)H (2)
Gary Philips (Barnet) 82 G (1)
Ryan Price (Stafford) 92 W(s) 93 WF (3)
Simon Read (Farnborough) 92 W(s) (1)
Carl Richards (Enfield) 86 E (1)
Derek Richardson (Maidstone U) 83 I, 84 W, 86 E (4)
Paul Richardson (Redbridge) 92 W, 93 WF (3)
Terry Robbins (Welling) 92 W, 93 WF (3)
Peter Robinson (Blyth S) 83 IHS, 84 WI, 85 W (6)
John Rogers (Altrincham) 81 HSI, 82 I(s)S (5)
Paul Rogers (Sutton) 89 W, 90 IE(2), 91 IW (6)
Brian Ross (Marine) 93 W(s)F(s) (2)
Neil Sellars (Scarborough) 81 HSI, 82 GH(s)S, 83 IHS (9)
Mark Shail (Yeovil) 93 W (1)
Peter Shearer (Cheltenham) 89 I(s) (1)
Paul Shirtliff (Frickley & Boston) 86 EE, 87 WIH, 88 W, 89 IW, 90 IWEE, 92 W, 93 WF (15)
Paul Showler (Altrincham) 91 I(s)W (2)
Gordon Simmonite (Boston Utd) 79 S(s)H(s), 80 ISH (5)
Gary Simpson (Stafford) 86 EE, 87 IHS, 90 IWEE (9)
Glenn Skivington (Barrow) 90 IWE, 91 IW (5)
Alan Smith (Alvechurch) 82 GIS (3)
Ian Smith (Mossley) 80 ISH(s) (3)
Ossie Smith (Runcorn) 84 W(1)
Tim Smithers (Nuneaton), 85 W(s)I, 86 W (3)
Simon Stapleton (Wycombe) 93 W (1)
Mickey Stephens (Sutton Utd), 82 GS(s), 86 WEE(s) (5)
Bob Stockley (Nuneaton Bor) 80 H (1)
Peter Taylor (Maidstone) 84 HSI (3)
Shaun Teale (Weymouth) 88 W (1)
Brian Thompson (Yeovil & Maidstone) 79 SH, 81 HSI, 82 IHS, 83 IHS, 84 WHSI (15)
Steve Thompson (Wycombe) 93 W (1)
Kevin Todd (Berwick Rangers) 91 W (1)
Tony Turner (Telford) 85 W (1)
David Waite (Enfield) 82 G (1)
Paul Walker (Blyth) 86 WEE(s), 87 S(s) (4)
Mark Ward (Northwich Victoria) 83 S(s) (1)
John Watson (Wealdstone, Scarborough & Maidstone) 79 S(s)H, 80 ISH, 81 HSI, 82 IHS, 83 IHS, 84 W(s)HSI (18)
Paul Watts (Redbridge Forest) 89 W, 90 IEE, 91 I, 92 W, 93 WF (8)
Paul Webb (Bromsgrove) 93 F (1)
Mark West (Wycombe W) 91 W (1)
Barry Whitbread (Runcorn & Altrincham) 79 SH, 80 ISH, 81 I (6)
Russ Wilcox (Frickley) 86 WE (2)
Colin Williams (Scarborough & Telford) 81 HS, 82 IHS (5)
Roger Willis (Barnet) 91 I(s) (1)
Paul Wilson (Frickley) 86 W (1)

94

COUNTY
ASSOCIATION
COMPETITIONS
1992-93

This year we have included the results of all county finals (where notified) as well as the round-by-round results of senior cups. Our thanks go as usual to Mike Ford of 'The Bureau of non-League Football' (see advert at the end of this section) for senior cup scores, and to the counties who submitted information.

BEDFORDSHIRE

Senior Cup

Preliminary Round

Ampthill Town v Ashcroft	0-2	Luton Old Boys v Cranfield United	0-2
Langford v Toddington Rovers	4-0	Brache Sparta v Delco Products	4-1
The 61 F.C. v Bedford United	0-4	Wootton Blue Cross v Bedford Town	3-3(aet),2-0

First Round

Stotfold v Totternhoe	0-1	Shillington v Brache Sparta	0-1(aet)
Arlesey Town v Potton United	0-1	Wootton Blue Cross v Biggleswade Town	3-0
Cranfield United v Dunstable	1-3	Bedford United v Kempston Rovers	0-1(aet)
Barton Rovers v Ashcroft	1-2(aet)	Langford v Leighton Town	0-3

Quarter Finals

Ashcroft v Totternhoe	0-2	Dunstable v Kempston Rovers	*3-1
Brache Sparta v Wootton Blue Cross	0-1	Potton United v Leighton Town	1-2

* - Dunstable expelled - ineligible players

Semi-Finals

Totternhoe v Kempston (at Leighton T.)	0-1	Leighton T. v Wootton B.C. (at Kempston & Dunstable)	2-2(aet),1-0

Final *(at Barton Rovers FC, Tues 4th May)*: Leighton Town 2, Kempston Rovers 1

Premier Cup

First Round

Potton United v Dunstable	3-2	Barton Rovers v Cranfield United	8-2
Langford v Kempston Rovers	0-2	Stotfold v Luton Town	0-4
Shillington v Arlesey Town	0-2		

Quarter-Finals

Leighton Town v Luton Town	1-3	Potton United v Arlesey Town	2-2(13-12 on pens)
Kempston Rovers v Barton Rovers	1-4	Biggleswade Town v Wootton Blue Cross	4-2

Semi-Finals

Arlesey Town v Luton Town	1-3	Barton Rovers v Biggleswade Town	1-2

Final *(Two Legs)*: Biggleswade Town 0, Luton Town 2. Luton Town 2, Biggleswade Town 0

Other County Finals:

Intermediate Cup: Caddington 2, Shefford Town 1
Junior Cup: Elstow Abbey 5, Crawley Green 3 *(aet)*
Junior Charity Cup: Great Barford 4, Thresher 1
Sunday Cup: Celtic S.C. 1, Sacred Heart 0
Sunday Junior Cup: Elm Park 0, St Josephs (Luton) Reserves 1
Sunday Lower Junior Cup: Magnum A.B.C. 2, Renhold United 1

BERKS & BUCKS

Senior Cup

First Qualifying Round

Didcot Town v Abingdon United	1-3	Kintbury Rangers v Abingdon Town	0-3
Amersham Town *(scr.)* Thatcham Town *(w/o)*		Hungerford Town v Maidenhead United	1-1,2-3

Second Qualifying Round

Abingdon United v Abingdon Town	0-3	Beaconsfield United v Thatcham Town	0-2
New Bradwell St Peter v Bracknell Town	1-3	Milton Keynes Borough v Chalfont St Peter	3-2
Wantage Town v Newbury Town	0-4	Flackwell Heath v Buckingham Town	4-2
Milton United v Burnham	1-3	Winslow United v Maidenhead United	1-5

First Round

Bracknell Town v Reading	0-3	Milton Keynes Borough v Marlow	0-6
Maidenhead United v Wokingham Town	0-5	Windsor & Eton v Thatcham Town	4-2
Aylesbury United v Slough Town	1-0	Burnham v Abingdon Town	3-5
Flackwell Heath v Wycombe Wanderers	1-0	Chesham United v Newbury Town	2-1

Quarter-Finals

Windsor & Eton v Chesham United	1-4	Flackwell Heath v Aylesbury United	4-2
Reading Reserves v Abingdon Town	1-1,0-2	Marlow v Wokingham Town	2-0

Semi-Finals

Marlow v Abingdon Town	0-1	Flackwell Heath v Chesham United	0-4

Final *(at Aylesbury United FC, Sat 17th April)*: Chesham United 1, Abingdon Town 0

Other County Finals:

Senior Trophy: Eton Wick 2, Sandhurst Town 1
Sunday Cup: Winners: Reading Borough

BIRMINGHAM

Senior Cup
First Round

Boldmere St Michaels v Sandwell Borough	1-0	Northfield Town v Oldswinsford	1-1,3-4
Willenhall Town v Bolehall Swifts	1-0	Tividale v Halesowen Town	1-4
Evesham United v Atherstone United	0-2	Tamworth v Mile Oak Rovers & Youth	2-0
Oldbury United v West Bromwich Town	4-2	Halesowen Harriers v Banbury United	0-5
Hednesford Town v Worcester City	1-0	Lye Town v King's Heath	1-2
Coleshill Town v Moor Green	1-2	Racing Club Warwick v Redditch United	1-2
Nuneaton Borough v Wednesfield	6-1		

Second Round

Solihull Borough v Highgate United	5-1	Nuneaton Borough v West Midlands Police	3-2
Stratford Town v Banbury United	3-2	Oldswinford v Redditch United	3-3,1-0
Knowle v Wolverhampton Wanderers	2-2,1-4	V.S. Rugby v Moor Green	2-2,3-0
Coventry City v Dudley Town	1-1,2-2(8-9 pens)	Birmingham City v King's Heath	4-0
Atherstone Utd v Halesowen Town	0-0,2-1	Boldmere St Michaels v Aston Villa	0-7
Paget Rangers v Willenhall Town	2-1	Bedworth United v Burton Albion	2-2,2-2(6-5 pens)
Hednesford Town v Sutton Coldfield Town	2-1	Cradley Town v Tamworth	1-2
Walsall v Stourbridge	0-2	West Bromwich Albion v Oldbury United	1-0

Third Round

Stratford Town v Oldswinford	2-2,0-1	Dudley Town v Tamworth	1-1,2-2(5-6 pens)
V.S. Rugby v Paget Rangers	3-2	Birmingham City v Atherstone United	2-3
Wolverhampton Wanderers v Aston Villa	2-3	Hednesford Town v Bedworth United	2-5
West Bromwich Albion v Stourbridge	2-4	Nuneaton Borough v Solihull Borough	2-1

Quarter-Finals

Stourbridge v Tamworth	2-1	Nuneaton Borough v Aston Villa	3-2
Oldswinford v Bedworth United	0-1	Atherstone United v V.S. Rugby	1-2

Semi-Finals

Bedworth United v Nuneaton Borough	0-1	Stourbridge v V.S. Rugby	2-4

Final *(at West Bromwich Albion FC, Mon 19th April)*: Nuneaton Borough 2, V.S. Rugby 0

Other County Finals:
Challenge Vase *(at Boldmere St Michaels)*: Kenilworth Town 1, Hill Top Rangers 0
Lord Mayor's Charity Cup: Solihull Borough 2, Northfield Town 1
Junior Cup: Massey Ferguson 1, Continental Stars 0 *(after 1-1 draw)*
Sunday Cup: Birmingham Celtic 1, Slade Celtic 0
Sunday Challenge Vase: Wednesbury Manor 3, Manor 1
Sunday Junior Cup: Delta 3, British Lions 0
Minor Challenge Cup: Mount Nod Highway J.F.C. 3, Yenton 1
Youth Cup: Burton Albion 4, Jaguar Colts 0
Keegan Cup: Coventry & Dist. Sunday Minor Lge XI 2, 'Mitchells & Butlers' Nuneaton Sunday Lge XI 0
W.H.L. Harrison Shield: Tamworth Sunday Lge XI 1, Dudley & Cradley Heath Sunday Lge XI 0
Campbell Orr Shield: 'Mitchells & Butlers' Coventry Alliance XI 1, Birmingham A.F.A. XI 0

Kenilworth Town - Birmingham Challenge Vase Winners 1992-93. Photo - Gavin Ellis-Neville.

CAMBRIDGESHIRE

Invitation Cup
First Round

Chatteris Town v Cambridge City	2-5	Ely City v Philips U.K.	2-3
Wisbech Town v Soham Town Rangers	4-0	Histon v March Town United	5-3

Semi-Finals

Histon v Cambridge City	1-2	Philips U.K. v Wisbech Town *(at Wisbech)*	0-1

Final *(at Cambridge City FC, Wed 21st April)*: Cambridge City 3, Wisbech Town 1
(Senior Cup overleaf)

'Hereward Sports' Cambridgeshire Senior Cup

Preliminary Round

Whittlesey United v Foxton	0-1	Haddenham Rovers v Bluntisham Rangers	0-2
Levrington Sports v Orwell	4-0		

First Round

Longstanton v Foxton	0-3	Soham Town Rgrs Reserves v Cherry Hinton	2-2,1-2
West Wratting v St Ives Town Reserves	1-0	Gamlingay v Steeple Bumpstead	1-1,0-5
Philips U.K. v Newmarket Town Reserves	3-2	Histon Reserves v Godmanchester Rovers	3-1
Great Shelford v Wisbech Town Reserves	0-5	T.S.B. Rangers v Waterbeach	2-4
Bassingbourn v Linton Granta	1-4	Chatteris Town Reserves v Fulbourn Institute	0-2
Levrington Sports v Haslingfield	4-0	Purbeck v Somersham Town Reserves	2-2,1-2
Manea United v Willingham	4-2	Bluntisham Rangers v Cottenham United	2-1
Sawston Rovers v Over Sports	1-2	March Town United Reserves v Whittlesesy United	6-1

Second Round

Linton Granta v Somersham Town Reserves	3-0	Wisbech Town Reserves v Over Sports	5-0
Bluntisham Rangers v Fulbourn Institute	3-1	Foxton v Histon Reserves	3-2
Philips U.K. v West Wratting	3-0	Manea United v Cherry Hinton	1-2
Waterbeach v Steeple Bumpstead	2-4	March Town Utd Reserves v Levrington Sports	2-1

Quarter-Finals

Linton Granta v Wisbech Town Reserves	1-2	Steeple Bumpstead v Cherry Hinton	6-2
Foxton v Philips U.K.	2-4	March Town United Reserves v Bluntisham Rgrs	2-1

Semi-Finals

Wisbech T. Reserves v Steeple Bumpstead	2-1	March Town United Reserves v Philips U.K.	0-1

Final *(at Ely City FC, Sat 1st May)*: Philips U.K. 2, Wisbech Town Reserves 0

Other County Finals:
Sunday Challenge Cup *(14/3/93)*: Swaffham United 3, Haddenham Rovers 2
William Cockell Cup *(23/3/93)*: Foxton 3, Longstanton 2
Lower Junior Cup *(6/4/93)*: Foxton Reserves 1, Bell Walsoken 0
Munns Youth Cup *13/4/93)*: Abington 6, Cambridge Musketeers 1
Junior Cup *(12/4/93)*: Mildenhall United Reserves 4, Outwell 2 *(aet)*
Reg Haigh Cup *(21/4/93)*: Somersham Town 'A' 1, Milton 'A' 0 *(aet)*
Sunday Centenary Cup *(4/3/93)*: Freshfields United 1, Schering Rovers 0
John Ablett K.O. Cup *(28/4/93)*: Napp Sports 2, Somersham Town 'A' 0
North Cambs Cup *(14/4/93)*: Levrington Sports Reserves 3, Parson Drove 1
Pye Youth Cup *(5/5/93)*: Sawston Enterprises 1, Cherry Hinton 0

CHESHIRE

Senior Cup

Preliminary Round

Ellesmere Port Town '92 v Winsford Utd	2-4

First Round

Hyde United v Warrington Town	1-2	Vauxhall Motors v Winsford United	1-4
General Chemicals v Runcorn	0-1	Nantwich Town v Altrincham	0-1
Northwich Victoria v Congleton Town	3-1	Stalybridge Celtic v Colwyn Bay	1-0

Second Round

Macclesfield Town v Warrington Town	0-2	Witton Albion v Altrincham	3-3,3-1
Winsford United v Northwich Victoria	1-0	Stalybridge Celtic v Runcorn	0-0,1-0

Semi-Finals

Warrington Town v Witton Albion	2-4,1-2	Stalybridge Celtic v Winsford United	2-2,0-1

Final *(at Witton Albion FC, Mon 3rd May)*: Winsford United 3, Witton Albion 0

(Amateur Cup overleaf)

Cec Edey of Winsford receives the Senior Cup from Cheshire County F.A. President Alan Burbridge after leading his side to a sensational 3-0 win away to Witton Albion of the G.M. Vauxhall Conference. Photo - Keith Clayton.

'Cheshire Building Society' Cheshire Amateur Cup

First Round
Gatley v Old Stoconians	3-1	Poynton v Moreton	2-1 *(aet)*
Lymm v Dukinfield Town	0-4	Winnington Park v Malpas	2-3 *(aet)*
Styal v General Chemicals	2-8	Christleton v Crewe Rolls Royce	7-0

Second Round
Upton A.A. v Frodsham United	4-2 *(aet)*	Gatley v Wilmslow Albion	4-1
General Chemicals v Bollington Athletic	5-1	Littlemoor v Atlantic	8-1
Linotype v Broadheath Central	3-2	Partington Village v Barnton	2-3
I.C.I Pharmaceuticals v Newton (Wirral)	2-0	Middlewich Athletic v St Werburghs	2-10
Chester Nomads v Blacon Athletic	4-1	Bromborough Pool v Ashville	2-1
Mellor v Mond Rangers	0-1	Poynton v Christleton	1-3
Shell v Capenhurst	1-1,0-7	Cheadle Hulme v Woodley Sports Centre	1-4
Metro v B.I.C.C. Helsby	7-2 *(aet)*	Kelloggs B.A. v Mersey Royal	0-3
Cheadle Heath Nomads v Blacon Youth Club	1-4	Old Altrinchamians v Malpas	1-2
M.A.N.W.E.B. v Poulton Victoria	1-6	Newton Athletic v Alsager	4-2
Dukinfield Amateurs v Dukinfield Town	2-2,4-1	Willaston White Star v Hazel Grove	1-2 *(aet)*
Vauxhall Motors v Manor Athletic	9-0	West Kirby v Stockport Georgians	2-0 *(aet)*

Third Round
Mersey Royal v Mond Rangers	0-3	Linotype v Heswall	2-3 *(aet)*
Hazel Grove v Grove United	2-3	West Kirby v Malpas	3-4 *(aet)*
I.C.I. Pharmaceuticals v Bramhall	1-2	Knutsford v Newton Athletic	3-0
Poulton Victoria v Christleton	1-0	Gatley v Capenhurst	0-1
Disley Amateurs v Old Stopfordians	2-1	St Werburghs v Bromborough Pool	2-4
Blacon Youth Club v Metro	7-0	Chester Nomads v Vauxhall Motors	1-4
Upton A.A. v Dukinfield Amateurs	0-1	General Chemicals v Woodley Sports Centre	2-1 *(aet)*
Littlemoor v Barnton	2-2,1-2	Cammell Laird v Stork	3-1

Fourth Round
Heswall v General Chemicals	4-0	Vauxhall Motors v Grove United	2-2,3-2
Malpas v Blacon Youth Club	3-2	Cammell Laird v Barnton	4-0
Knutsford v Disley Amateurs	0-1 *(aet)*	Poulton Victoria v Bromborough Pool	1-0
Capenhurst v Mond Rangers	2-1	Dukinfield Amateurs v Bramhall	3-1

Quarter-Finals
Capenhurst v Dukinfield Amateurs	1-0	Malpas v Heswall	1-2
Disley Amateurs v Cammell Laird	1-2	Vauxhall Motors v Poulton Victoria	0-2

Semi-Finals
Capenhurst v Poulton Victoria	1-0	Cammell Laird v Heswall	0-0 *(aet)*,3-2 *(aet)*

Final: Cammell Laird 2, Capenhurst 0

Other County Finals:
Sunday Challenge Cup: Lache B.A. 3, Offerton United 2 *(aet)*
Youth Challenge Cup: Altrincham D.F.A. 4, Wirral D.F.A. 2
Youth Cup (under-17): Priory County 2, Mond Rangers 1
Junior Cup (under-15): Park Royal '88 1, Mountfield Rovers 0
Minor Cup (under-13): Ashville Youth 4, Heygarth United 0

CORNWALL

Senior Cup

First Round
St Agnes v St Dennis	1-2	Camelford v R.N.A.S. Culdrose	3-2

Second Round
Bugle v Mousehole	1-0	Roche v Illogan R.B.L.	2-0
Penryn Athletic v Helston Athletic	1-0	St Breward v R.A.F. St Mawgan	3-1
St Just v Camelford	1-3	Perranwell v Nanpean Rovers	3-3,6-3
Sticker v Tintagel	7-0		

Third Round
Bodmin Town v Camelford	9-1	Pendeen Rovers v Sticker	1-2
Bude v Launceston	1-9	Perranwell v Callington	4-2
Foxhole Stars v St Breward	1-3	Porthleven v Falmouth Town	0-4
Roche v Bugle	3-1	Liskeard Athletic v Saltash United	0-3
Ludgvan v St Dennis	2-2,2-5	St Austell v Penzance	6-3
St Blazey v Padstow United	5-0	Marazion Blues v Wadebridge Town	2-2,0-6
Mullion v Millbrook	2-1	Torpoint Athletic v Penryn Athletic	2-0
Truro City v St Ives Town	6-1	Newquay v Riviera Coasters	6-0

Fourth Round
Mullion v Sticker	2-1	St Blazey v Wadebridge Town	2-0
Newquay v St Austell	3-2	St Breward v Launceston	2-5
Perranwell v Saltash United	0-2	St Dennis v Falmouth Town	1-2
Roche v Truro City	3-5	Torpoint Athletic v Bodmin Town	2-2,1-4

Quarter-Finals
Launceston v Newquay	5-0	Bodmin Town v Mullion	1-1,1-0
Saltash United v St Blazey	2-1	Truro City v Falmouth Town	0-2

Semi-Finals
Saltash v Bodmin *(at Liskeard)*	3-1	Launceston v Falmouth Town *(at St Blazey)*	3-1

Final *(at Newquay FC, Mon 3rd May)*: Saltash United 3, Launceston 2

Other County Finals:
Junior Cup *(at Newquay FC, Mon 3rd May)*: Falmouth Athletic 2, Saltash Town 0

CUMBERLAND

Senior Cup

First Round

Silloth v Hearts of Liddesdale	2-0	Whitehaven Rangers v Whitehaven Miners Welfare	1-4
Museum v Penrith	0-5	Braithwaite v Egremont St Mary's	0-0,2-3
Sporting Club v Wigton	2-3	St Bees v Alston Town	0-2
Carlisle City v Northbank	3-1	Albert v Eden Athletic	5-0
Marchon Reserves v Cleator Moor Celtic	4-1	Windscales Barrow *(scr.)* v Gillford Park Res. *(w/o)*	

Second Round

Alston Town *(w/o)* Wigton Harriers *(scr.)*		Carlisle United v Langwathby	20-0
Greystoke v Longtown	2-3	Workington v Gretna	1-1,1-3
Kirkoswald v Mirehouse	4-3	Egremont St Mary's v Abbeytown	1-6
Penrith United v Windscales Barrow	3-1	Wigton v Whitehaven Miners Welfare	2-0
Penrith v Marchon	9-1	Carlisle City v Gillford Park	0-1
Keswick v Cumbria Teachers	7-1	Wetheriggs v Cleator Moor Celtic Reserves	1-2
British Steel v Silloth	5-0	Whitehaven v Windscales United Wearside	1-5
Marchon Reserves v Albert	6-2	Parton United v Cumbria Constabulary	3-2

Third Round

Parton United v Carlisle United	2-4	British Steel v Penrith	1-4
Longtown v Gretna	0-5	Keswick v Cleator Moor Celtic Reserves	2-1
Gillford Park v Alston Town	3-0	Windscales United Wearsides v Marchon Reserves	3-2
Wigton v Penrith United	4-5	Kirkoswald v Abbeytown	4-5

Quarter-Finals

Abbeytown v Keswick	1-2	Windscales United Wearside v Penrith United	10-2
Gretna v Carlisle Gillford Park	5-3	Penrith v Carlisle United	1-2

Semi-Finals

Keswick v Gretna	4-6	Carlisle United v Windscales United Wearside	3-1

Final *(at Carlisle United FC, Tues 20th April)*: Carlisle Utd 0, Gretna 0,
Replay *(at Gretna FC, Tues 27th April)*: Gretna 1, Carlisle United 3.

DERBYSHIRE

Senior Cup

First Round

Biwater v Blackwell Miners Welfare	2-0	Derby Rolls Royce v Derby Carriage & Reckitts	3-2
Kilburn Miners Welfare v Heanor Town	1-1,0-1	Borrowash Victoria v Shirebrook Colliery	1-3
Sandiacre Town v Newhall United	4-1	South Normanton Ath. v Long Eaton United	1-1,1-2
Glossop North End v Glapwell	4-2	Mickleover Ryl British L. v Shardlow St James	1-0

Second Round

Sandiacre Town v Glossop North End	2-4	Shirebrook Colliery v Heanor Town	2-5
Derby Rolls Royce v Stanton Ilkeston	1-1,1-2	Long Eaton United v Mickleover Royal British L.	0-1

Third Round

Glossop North End v Stanton Ilkeston	4-0	Matlock Town v Heanor Town	0-1
Gresley Rovers v Biwater	8-1	Mickleover Royal British L. v Stapenhill	2-2,0-3

Quarter-Finals

Ilkeston Town v Belper Town	2-0	Alfreton Town v Glossop North End	3-1
Stapenhill v Buxton	0-1	Heanor Town v Gresley Rovers	2-4

Semi-Finals

Alfreton Town v Buxton	2-1	Ilkeston Town v Gresley Rovers	2-1

Final. 1st leg *(Wed 5th May)*: Alfreton Town 0, Ilkeston Town 0
2nd leg *(Tues 11th May)*: Ilkeston Town 1, Alfreton Town 1 *(Ilkeston Town won 7-6 on penalties)*.

Other County Finals:
Centenary Cup: Derby County 4, Chesterfield 1
Divisional Cup (North): Gamesley 3, Matlock United 1
Divisional Cup (South): Normanton Athletic 4, Mackworth 1
Senior Sunday Cup: Chaddesden Jubilee 4, Mickleover Whitecross 1
Junior Sunday Cup: Eagle Markeaton 4, Gaslight 1
Junior Cup (North): Youlgrave Youth 3, Clown 0
Junior Cup (South): Grenville Athletic 2, Alvaston & Boulton O.B. 1

Ilkeston Town F.C. - Derbyshire Senior Cup winners 1992-93.

DEVON

Premier Cup
First Round

Buckfastleigh Rgrs v Plymouth Civil Service	4-0
Honiton Town v Parkhead	0-0,0-4
Newton Abbot v Brixham Villa	1-0
Newton Abbot Spurs v Teignmouth	1-0
Plymstock United v Holsworthy	1-3
Topsham Town v Dartmouth United	0-4
Upton Vale v Cullompton Rangers	3-2
Yealm United v Putford	4-1

Buckland Milton & Crapstone *(scr.)* Woodland Fort *(w/o)*	
Lapford v Buckland Athletic	3-3,1-3
Newton Abbot 66 v Dartington United	2-4
Newton St Cyres v Sidmouth Town	4-0
Shamwickshire Rovers v Weston Mill Oak Villa	2-1
Upton Athletic v Waldon	2-4
Willand Rovers v Fremington	5-3
Hooe St John v Satellite Sports	0-2

Second Round

Alphington v Chagford	2-3
Bradworthy United v Galmpton	5-1
Chelston v Barnstaple A.A.C.	5-1
Coxside United v Newton Abbot Spurs	1-3
Chivenor v Northern Telecom Paignton	1-4
Dolton Rangers v Appledore & B.	0-0,0-2
E.A.F. Plymouth v Newton Town	3-1
Hele Rovers v Parkhead	3-1
Horrabridge v Offwell & Widworthy	4-0
Lynton & Lynmouth v Elburton Villa	2-10
Mount Gould Athletic v Falstaff Wanderers	2-5
Newton Rangers v Holsworthy	1-2
Old Suttonians v Buckfastleigh Rangers	0-9
Plymouth Command v Chittlehampton	11-1
Stoke Gabriel v Plympton United	6-0
Upton Vale v Shamwickshire Rovers	2-1

Beer Albion v Tavistock	1-5
Braunton v Kingsteignton Athletic	3-2
Clyst Valley v St Martins	4-3
Watts Blake Bearne v Okehampton Argyle	2-1
Dartmouth Y.M.R.C. v Woodland Fort	6-1
Dynamo Villa v Ivybridge Towm	4-4,1-7
Exmouth Amateurs v Exeter Civil Service	2-3
Satellite Sports v A.A. Taxis	5-4
Buckland Athletic v Marjons	0-2
Mainstone C.A. v Devon & Cornwall Police	0-6
Newton Abbot v Budleigh Salterton	5-3
Newton St Cyres v Putford	4-2
Plume Princetown v Combe Martin	0-3
South Molton v Prince Rock	1-7
Waldon v Dartmouth United	1-2
Willand Rovers v Dartington United	5-1

Third Round

Bradworthy United v Exeter Civil Service	1-2
Combe Martin *(w/o)* Satellite Sports *(scr.)*	
Devon & Cornwall Police v Upton Vale	4-0
Falstaff Wanderers v Elburton Villa	6-1
Horrabridge v Newton Abbot	0-8
Plymouth Command v Braunton	8-0
Prince Rock v Watts Blake Bearne	6-2
Tavistock v Newton St Cyres	3-2

Clyst Valley v Marjons	2-1
Dartmouth Y.M.R.C. v Chagford	1-3
E.A.F. Plymouth v Dartmouth United	0-2
Holsworthy v Ivybridge Town	4-1
Newton Abbot Spurs v Hele Rovers	4-0
Northern Telecom Paignton v Buckfastleigh Rgrs	2-4
Stoke Gabriel v Appledore & Bideford A.A.C.	3-3,1-0
Willand Rovers v Chelston	3-1

Fourth Round

Buckfastleigh Rangers v Clyst Valley	12-1
Combe Martin v Tavistock	2-7
Newton Abbot v Devon & Cornwall Police	1-3
Stoke Gabriel v Plymouth Command	1-3

Chagford v Exeter Civil Service	1-4
E.A.F. Plymouth v Falstaff Wanderers	0-3
Prince Rock v Newton Abbot Spurs	1-3
Willand Rovers v Holsworthy	1-4

Quarter-Finals

Exeter Civil Service v Tavistock	4-1
Newton Abbot Spurs v Plymouth Command	2-3

Buckfastleight Rangers v Falstaff Wanderers	3-3,3-0
Holsworthy v Devon & Cornwall Police	1-2

Semi-Finals

Exeter Civil Service v Plymouth Command	2-0

Buckfastleigh Rangers v Devon & Cornwall Police	2-4

Final *(at Dawlish Town FC)*: Devon & Cornwall Police 2, Exeter Civil Service 0 *(aet)*

Devon & Cornwall Police - Devon Premier Cup Winners 1992-93. Back Row (L/R): Geoff Turner, Adrian Street, Simon Tremaine, Steve Gill, Wayne Arthur, Kevin Walsh, Chris Hayfield. Front: Steve Brownlow, Steve Spear, Terry Locock, Dave Street, Peter Small. Photo - Richard Brock.

Devon St Lukes College Cup
First Round

Ilfracombe Town v Tiverton Town	0-1
Elmore v Torrington	0-3
(continued overleaf)	

Bideford v Exmouth Town 4-4*(Exmouth won on pens)*	
Ottery St Mary v Clyst Rovers	0-2

Quarter-Finals

Heavitree United v Barnstaple Town	3-2	Clyst Rovers v Dawlish Town	1-0
Crediton United v Exmouth Town	1-0	Tiverton Town v Torrington	5-0

Semi-Finals

Heavitree United v Tiverton Town	1-5	Clyst Rovers v Crediton United	1-0

Final *(Mon 3rd May)*: Clyst Rovers 0, Tiverton Town 3

Other County Finals:
Senior Cup *(at Clyst Rovers FC)*: Barnstaple Town 2, Vospers (Plymouth) 0
Intermediate Cup *(at Stoke Gabriel FC)*: Combined '89 (Torquay) 4, Torquay Christians in Sport 1
Sunday Senior Cup *(at Devon & Cornwall Police FC)*: Mount Gould CC 2, Towers Civil Service 0 *(aet)*
Sunday Supplementary Cup *(at Exeter Civil Service FC)*: AFC St Thomas 2, Barley Mow 0 *(aet)*
Youth Cup *(at Newton Abbot FC)*: Stoke Gabriel 2, Buckland Athletic 1
Under-16 Cup *(at Buckfastleigh Rgrs FC)*: Broadmeadow ST (Teignmouth) 2, SB Frankfort (Plymouth) 1

DORSET

Senior Cup
First Round

Blandford United v Cranborne	9-0	Flight Refuelling v Hamworthy Engineering	1-3
Holt United v Bournemouth Sports	1-2	Gillingham Town v Portland United	1-2
Hamworthy United v Sherborne Town	3-1		

Second Round

Poole Town v Blandford United	4-1	Wimborne Town v Sturminster Newton United	6-0
Swanage Town & Herston v Wareham Rgrs	3-0	Bournemouth Sports v St Pauls (Jersey)	2-1
Weymouth v Portland United	2-1	Hamworthy United v Parley Sports	4-2
Bridport v Hamworthy Engineering	3-0	Northerners (Guernsey) v Shaftesbury	4-1

Quarter-Finals

Bridport v Weymouth	0-3	Swanage Town & Herston v Hamworthy United	2-0
Wimborne Town v Northerners (Guernsey)	4-1	Bournemouth Sports v Poole Town	1-4

Semi-Finals

Swanage Town & Herston v Weymouth	1-1,1-6	Wimborne Town v Poole Town	1-1,1-2

Final *(at Weymouth FC, Tues 20th April)*: Weymouth 4, Poole Town 0

DURHAM

'Commercial Union' Durham County Challenge Cup
First Qualifying Round

Swalwell v Peterlee Newtown	1-2	West Auckland Town v Silksworth	0-2

Second Qualifying Round

Shotton Comrades v Eppleton Colliery Welf.	0-2	Horden C. W. v Sunderland Vaux Ryhope C.W.	7-1
Tow Law Town v Peterlee Newtown	4-2	Silksworth v Newton Aycliffe	5-0
Esh Winning Albion v Wolviston	5-3	Crook Town v Hartlepool Town	1-4
Dunston Federation Brewery v Willington	2-1	Sunderland I.F.G. Roker v Hartlepool B.W.O.B.	1-5
Stanley United v Consett	1-4	Jarrow Roofing B.C.A. v Darlington Cleveland B.	0-2
Whickham v Easington Colliery	1-3	Hebburn Colliery v Spennymoor United	0-5
Wingate Mall v Boldon Com. Association	2-2,0-2	Langley Park v South Shields Cleadon Social C.	3-3
Shildon v Esh Winning	0-1	Herrington Colliery Welfare v Washington	5-1

Michael Hudson (right) of Hebburn Colliery gets in a shot, but visiting Spennymoor United were too good for the Vaux Wearside League side and won this tie 5-0 on Saturday 7th November. Photo - John Diamond.

First Round

Cockfield v Annfield Plain	3-0	Herrington Colliery Welfare v Durham City	0-4
Easington Colliery v Evenwood Town	0-2	Chester-le-Street T. v Boldon Community Assoc.	3-1
Silksworth v Consett	2-5	South Shields Cleadon S.C. v Esh Winning Alb.	7-2
Bishop Auckland v Seaham Red Star	1-0	Horden C.W. v Ryhope Community Association	1-0
Esh Winning v Billingham Town	1-2	Billingham Synthonia v Norton & Stockton Anc.	5-1
Spennymoor United v South Shields	4-1	Murton v Darlington Cleveland Bridge	4-2
Hartlepool Town v Ferryhill Athletic	4-1	Tow Law Town v Dunston Federation Brewery	2-1
Hebburn v Brandon United	3-2	Eppleton Colliery Welfare v Hartlepool B.W.O.B.	4-0

(continued opposite)

Second Round

Durham City v Tow Law Town	3-1	Bishop Auckland v Consett	3-1
Horden Colliery Welfare v Murton	1-4	Billingham Town v Hartlepool Town	3-0
Billingham Synthonia v Evenwood Town	4-1	Spennymoor United v Chester-le-Street Town	0-3
Hebburn v Cockfield	3-2	Eppleton C.W. v South Shields Cleadon S.C.	2-0

Quarter-Finals

Murton v Hebburn	5-2	Billingham Town v Chester-le-Street Town	3-0
Durham City v Bishop Auckland	1-2	Billingham Syn. v Eppleton Colliery Welfare	0-0,3-0

Semi-Finals

Billingham Synthonia v Murton	2-3	Bishop Auckland v Billingham Town	3-1

Final *(at Spennymoor United FC, Mon 3rd May)*: Murton 2, Bishop Auckland 1

Other County Finals:
County Trophy: Cockfield 4, South Shields County Kitchens Brinkburn 3
Minor Cup: Darlington Simpson Rolling Mills 3, West Auckland Eden Arms 2
Sunday Cup: Sunderland Redhouse W.M.C. 5, Sunderland Castletown W.M.C. 0 *(after 0-0 draw)*
Youth Cup U-18: Herrington Colliery Welfare 5, Bishop Auckland 0
Youth Minor Cup U-16: Billingham Synthonia 3, Washington Oxclose 0
Cameron Hall Yth Cup (joint U-18 competition with Northumberland): Prudhoe East End (Northumberland) 1, Gateshead Cleveland Hall Boys Club (Durham) 0

EAST ANGLIA

East Anglian Cup
First Round

Thetford Town v Gorleston	0-5	Norwich United v Holbeach United	1-2
Cornard United v Diss Town	1-0	Downham Town v Fakenham Town	3-4
Watton United v Stowmarket Town	3-1	Swaffham Town v King's Lynn	0-5
Sudbury Town *(bye)*		Wroxham v Long Sutton Athletic	9-0
Stamford v Huntingdon United	2-0	Somersham Town v Eynesbury Rovers	0-5
Bourne Town v Chatteris Town	4-3	Baldock Town v Biggleswade Town	2-1
St Ives Town v March Town United	1-4	Royston Town v Hertford Town	2-4
Wisbech Town v Mirrlees Blackstone	3-0	Ware v Letchworth Garden City	6-1
Sawbridgeworth Town v Hadleigh United	3-1	Bishop's Stortford v Braintree Town	3-2
Aveley v Barkingside	5-1	Stansted v Halstead Town	2-1
St Albans City v Romford	1-0	Witham Town v Heybridge Swifts	0-1
Woodford Town v Hoddesdon Town	2-3	Saffron Walden Town v Ely City	5-2
Harwich & Parkeston v Clacton Town	4-0	Bury Town v Cambridge City	1-8
Brantham Athletic v Burnham Ramblers	0-1	Soham Town Rangers v Haverhill Rovers	2-6
Tiptree United v Colchester United	3-1	Histon *(bye)*	
Woodbridge Town v Felixstowe Town	2-0	Rainham Town v Eton Manor	3-1

Group Semi-Finals

Sudbury Town v Cornard United	2-1	Wroxham v Fakenham Town	2-0
Gorleston v Watton United	3-0	Holbeach United v King's Lynn	2-0
Wisbech Town v Bourne Town	1-2	Ware v Baldock Town	1-2
Stamford v March Town United	3-2	Eynesbury Rovers v Hertford Town	2-0
Heybridge Swifts v Bishop's Stortford	1-3	Hoddesdon Town v Aveley	1-1,0-1
Sawbridgeworth Town v Stansted	5-0	Rainham Town v St Albans City	1-3
Histon v Cambridge City	1-3	Woodbridge Town v Burnham Rambers	2-1
Saffron Walden Town v Haverhill Rvrs	1-1,0-2	Harwich & Parkeston v Tiptree United	60-1

Group Finals

Sudbury Town v Gorleston	1-1,3-1	Wroxham v Holbeach United	2-1
Bourne Town v Stamfordn	0-1	Baldock Town v Eynesbury Rovers	3-0
Bishop's Stortford v Sawbridgeworth	2-2*(aet)*,3-1	Hoddesdon Town v St Albans City	0-1
Cambridge City v Saffron Walden Town	3-1	Woodbridge Town v Harwich & Parkeston	0-3

Quarter-Finals

Stamford v Sudbury Town	0-0,0-3	Harwich & Parkeston v Wroxham	3-1
Baldock Town v St Albans City	0-4	Bishop's Stortford v Cambridge	1-1*(Stortford w'drew)*

Semi-Finals

Sudbury Town v St Albans City	2-3	Cambridge City v Harwich & Parkeston	3-1

Final: *(at St Albans City FC, Mon 3rd May)*: St Albans City 4, Cambridge City 1

EAST RIDING

Senior Cup
First Round

Sculcoates Amateurs v Ideal Standard	5-4	Westella Shopacheck v Schultz Y.C.	3-1
Hilltop v Leconfield	2-0	Cavalier v Kelvin Hall	2-1
Dairycoates v Hotel Paragon	2-1	Hull City v Hull Old Grammarians	4-2

Second Round

Haltemprice v Hilltop	1-3	North Newbald v North Ferriby United	0-8
Reckitts v Sculcoates Amateurs	0-1	Kelvin Hall v Malet Lambert Y.C.	3-5
Arthur Fish v Dairycoates	1-1,2-3	Hull City v Hull Road Rangers	3-2
Hedon United *(bye)*		Westella Shopacheck v Bridlington Town	1-4*(ab.)*,0-6

Quarter-Finals

Malet Lambert Y.C. v Hedon United	8-3	Bridlington Town v Dairycoates	6-0
North Ferriby United v Hull City	1-0	Sculcoates Amateurs v Hilltop	4-2

Semi-Finals *(all three games played at Hall Road Rangers F.C.)*

Malet Lambert Y.C. v North Ferriby United	0-1	Bridlington Town v Sculcoates Amateurs	1-1,3-0

Final *(At Hull City FC, Thurs 13th May)*: Bridlington Town 3, North Ferriby United 1

Other County Finals
Senior Country Cup *(at Bridlington Town FC, Mon 3rd May)*: Filey Town 3, Beverley Old Grammarians 1
Intermediate Cup *(at Northern Foods FC, Wed 28th April)*: Hodgson Grovehill 4, Nth Ferriby Utd Reserves 2
Junior Cup *(at Hall Road Rangers FC, Thurs 6th May)*: Linley Haulage 'A' 2, Crown Sovereign 1
(continued overleaf)

(continued from page 103)
Qualifying Cup *(at Hall Road Rangers FC, Thurs 29th April)*: Dolphin 2, Kirkways 0
Intermediate Country Cup *(at Pocklington, Tues 4th May)*: Stamford Bridge 1, Hutton Cranswick 0
Junior Country Cup *(at Rudston Utd FC, Tues 11th May)*: Malton Bacon Factory 3, Sherburn 1
Qualifying Country Cup *(at Dunnington, Tues 27th April)*: Barlby 4, Ward Reserves 1
Midweek Cup *(at Hall Road Rangers FC, Wed 5th May)*: Hull College of FE 3, Wyke College 1
Frank Varey & Dr Lilley Cup *(at Hull City FC, Fri 7th May)*: Sculcoates Amateurs 2, Van Leer HPB 0
Youth Cup *(at Hall Road Rangers, Fri 23rd April)*: Fish Trades Eagles 4, Bridlington Rangers 2

ESSEX

Senior Cup
First Round

East Thurrock United v Wivenhoe Town	0-6	Grays Athletic v Witham Town	2-0
Tilbury v Rainham Town	2-4*(aet)*	Hornchurch v Purfleet	0-6
Aveley v Leyton Orient	4-6	Saffron Walden Town v Colchester United	5-1

Second Round

Harlow Town *(scr.)* Chelmsford City *(w/o)*		Southend United v Leyton	2-3
Heybridge Swifts v Dagenham & Redbridge	1-4	Purfleet v Leyton Orient	1-3
Wivenhoe Town v Braintree Town	2-0*(aet)*	Saffron Walden Town v Barking	6-2
Rainham Town v Grays Athletic	1-3	Billericay Town v Collier Row	3-2

Quarter-Finals

Chelmsford City v Billericay Town	10-3	Saffron Walden Town v Leyton Orient	1-4
Grays Athletic v Dagenham & Redbridge	0-1	Leyton v Wivenhoe Town	0-2

Semi-Finals

Dageham & Redbridge v Wivenhoe Town	1-2*(aet)*	Leyton Orient v Chelmsford City	2-4*(aet)*

Final *(at Braintree Town FC, Tues 6th April)*: Chelmsford City 1, Wivenhoe Town 0

Chelmsford City after a Tony Rogers goal was enough to win the Essex Senior Cup against Wivenhoe.

Senior Trophy
First Round

Burnham Ramblers v Canvey Island	1-4	Waltham Abbey v East Ham United	6-0
Stanway Rovers v Brentwood	1-0*(aet)*	Walthamstow Pennant v Clacton Town	2-1*(aet)*
Maldon Town v Halstead Town	0-1	Barkingside v Southend Manor	0-1
Hullbridge Sports v Romford	5-2	Bowers United v Basildon United	1-3

Second Round

Halstead Town v Waltham Abbey	1-4	Southend Manor v Brightlingsea United	2-0
Stansted v Eton Manor	5-2*(ab.)*,0-5	Canvey Island v Harwich & Parkeston	1-2
Tiptree United v Walthamstow Pennant	1-2*(aet)*	Ford United v Great Wakering Rovers	2-1*(aat)*
Hullbridge Sports v Basildon United	1-3	Concord Rangers v Stanway Rovers	1-1*(aet)*,2-1

Quarter-Finals

Harwich & Parkeston v Basildon United	2-1	Concord Rangers v Southend Manor	1-1*(aet)*,1-4
Walthamstow Pennant v Eton Manor	2-0	Waltham Abbey v Ford United *(at Ford United)*	1-2

Semi-Finals

Southend Manor v Ford United	2-0	Harwich & Parkeston v Walthamstow Pennant	3-1

Final *(At Chelmsford City FC, Sat 10th April)*: Southend Manor 1, Harwich & Parkeston 0

Other County Finals:
Sunday Intermediate Cup: *(at Dagenham & Redbridge FC)*: Fryerns Community 2, Attreed Sports 1
Sunday Junior Cup: *(at Tiptree United FC)*: Dorstel 1, Ford Basildon Reserves 0
Sunday Junior Trophy: *(at Burnham Ramblers FC)*: Cardinals 4, Burnham Spts Res. 1 *(Cardinals won 4-1 on pens)*

GLOUCESTERSHIRE

Northern Senior Cup
Preliminary Round
Cheltenham Town v Gloucester City   1-2

Semi-Finals
Gloucester City v Newport A.F.C.	2-1	Yate Town v Forest Green Rovers	2-1

Final *(at Yate Town FC, Wed 7th April)*: Yate Town 2, Gloucester City 3 *(aet)*

Challenge Trophy
First Round
Winterbourne United v Shortwood United	0-3	Harrow Hill v Patchway Town	2-3
Mangotsfield United v Stapleton	4-1	Campden Town v St Marks C.A.	0-2
Pucklechurch Sports v Wotton Rovers	0-2	Moreton Town v St Philips Marsh Adult Sch.	5-5,1-0
Ellwood v Fairford Town	1-0	Cheltenham Saracens v Old Georgians	1-1,2-1
Cirencester Town v Dowty Dynamoes	3-1	Smiths Athletic v Bristol Manor Farm	2-1
Hallen v Henbury Old Boys	3-2	D.R.G. (F.P.) v Cirencester United	0-2
Shirehampton v Tuffley Rovers	0-1	Cinderford Town v Longwell Green Abbotonians	6-1
Bishops Cleeve v Almondsbury Picksons	0-8	Cadbury Heath v Hambrook	2-1

Second Round
Cirencester United v Cadbury Heath	0-2	Shortwood United v Patchway Town	2-3
Ellwood v Cinderford Town	2-4	Hallen v Smiths Athletic	6-1
St Marks C.A. v Cheltenham Saracens	3-1	Mangotsfield United v Tuffley Rovers	4-0
Wotton Rovers v Cirencester Town	0-2	Almondsbury Picksons v Moreton Town	3-2

Quarter-Finals
St Marks C.A. v Cinderford Town	0-5	Cirencester Town v Patchway Town	4-0
Hallen v Cadbury Heath	2-1	Almondsbury Picksons v Mangotsfield United	2-1

Semi-Finals
Hallen v Cirencester T. *(at Mangotsfield)*	2-1	Almondsbury Picksons v Cinderford Town	
			1-1*(aet - at Forest G.)*,1-1*(aet, 2-4 pens - at Shortwood)*

Final *(at Yate Town FC, Mon 3rd May)*: Hallen 4, Cinderford Town 1

Other County Finals:
Sunday Intermediate Cup *(at Almondsbury Picksons FC)*: Bell Rhabits 4, Lebeq Tavern Reserves 0
Minor Cup *(at Sun Life FC)*: Blue Bowl Hanham 3, Longwell Green Sports Reserves 0
Primary Cup *(at Patchway Town FC)*: Archway St Philips Reserves 3, Avon Fire Brigade Reserves 2

HAMPSHIRE

Senior Cup
Preliminary Round
Fleet Town v Colden Common	1-0	Ryde Sports v Awbridge	4-0
Cowes Sports v Cove	2-1	Winchester City v A.C. Delco	4-3
Basingstoke Town v Bass Alton Town	3-1	Portsmouth Royal Navy v Horndean	0-2
Jersey Wanderers v Hartley Wintney	1-2	Sholing Sports v Locksheath	2-1
Whitchurch United v Alresford Town	7-0	Brockenhurst v New Milton	3-2
Newport I.O.W. *(w/o)* I.S.L. Midanbury *(scr.)*		East Cowes Victoria Ath. v Blackfield & Langley	1-0
Overton United v Malshanger	3-3,1-0	Fleetlands v D.C.A. Basingstoke	1-2
B.A.T. v Bournemouth	0-2	Aerostructures Sports & Social v Chirstchurch	0-7
A.F.C. Totton v Bemerton Heath Harlequins	0-3	Fareham Town v A.F.C. Lymington	1-0

First Round
Bournemouth v Bashley	0-1	Horndean v Overton United	1-0
Brockenhurst v Basingstoke Town	2-0	Andover v Christchurch	3-1
Waterlooville v Whitchurch United	4-1	Havant Town v Farnborough Town	1-4
Gosport Borough v Fleet Town	2-1	Petersfield United v D.C.A. Basingstoke	1-0
Downton v Romsey Town	4-1	Pirelli General v Hartley Wintney	0-2
Fareham Town v Sholing Sports	3-2	Vale Recreation v Winchester City	4-1
Eastleigh v Cowes Sports	0-2	Aldershot Town v Newport Isle of Wight	2-1
Ryde Sports v Bishops Waltham	3-2	Bemerton Heath Harlequins *(scr.)* East Cowes Vics *(w/o)*	

Second Round
Farnborough Town v Brockenhurst	5-1	Petersfield United v Ryde Sports	2-1
Bashley v Vale Recreation	4-3	East Cowes Victoria Athletic v Andover	1-3
Aldershot Town v Gosport Borough	2-0	Waterlooville v Hartley Wintney	4-0
Horndean v Cowes Sports	1-1,0-2	Downton v Fareham Town	0-2

Quarter-Finals
Andover v Fareham Town	1-2	Waterlooville v Aldershot Town	2-2,1-2
Bashley v Farnborough Town	3-4	Petersfield United v Cowes Sports	0-2

Semi-Finals
Aldershot Town v Farnborough Town	2-3	Fareham Town v Cowes Sports	2-0

Final *(at Southampton FC, Tues 27th April 1992)*: Fareham Town 4, Farnborough Town 1

Other County Finals:
Russell Cotes Cup *(at Bashley FC, Fri 7th May)*: Bashley 3, A.F.C. Lymington 1
Intermediate Cup *(at Waterlooville FC, Sat 24th April)*: Portsmouth Civil Service 4, Jubilee Utd 1
Saturday Junior 'A' Cup *(at Alton Town Bass FC, Sat 24th April)*: Lyndhurst 6, Long Sutton 5
Saturday Junior 'B' Cup *(at Aerostructures FC, Wed 28th April)*: S.D.E.S. 1, Phoenix '89 0
Sunday Senior Cup *(at Gosport Borough FC, Sun 4th April)*: Portsbridge 2, Riga 0
Sunday Intermediate Cup *(at Havant Town FC, Sun 18th April)*: Stockheath Rovers 1, Wheatsheaf (Gosport) 0
Sunday Junior 'A' Cup *(at Fleetlands FC, Sun 18th April)*: Ark 3, Dresden 1
Sunday Junior 'B' Cup *(at B.A.T. FC, Sun 18th April)*: Pope & Regan 5, Queen Anne 4

HEREFORDSHIRE

County Challenge Cup
First Round

Ross United v Woofferton	1-3	Weston v Ledbury Town '84	2-3

Second Round

Woofferton *(w/o)* Leominster Town *(scr.)*		Hereford Lads Club v Pegasus Juniors	2-5
Ledbury Town v Hinton	2-5	Wellington v Woodville	4-0
Fownhope v Kington Town	1-2	Thorn Ltg v Ewyas H. 8-6*(inc pens - Thorn expelled)*	
Bromyard Town v Golden Valley	3-1	Westfields v Colwall Rangers	2-0

Quarter-Finals

Woofferton v Pegasus Juniors	0-6	Hinton v Wellington	4-0
Kington Town v Ewyas Harold	1-2	Bromyard Town v Westfields	0-1

Semi-Finals

Pegasus Juniors v Hinton	0-1	Ewyas Harold v Westfields	1-2

Final *(at Hereford United FC)*: Hinton 3, Westfields 1

Other County Finals:
Charity Bowl: Hinton 3, Bromyard Town 1
Junior Cup: Hereford Tiles 5, Pembridge 1
Burghill Cup: Fownhope Reserves 2, Hereford Sports 1
Sunday Cup: Greyhound 3, Bromyard Town 1
Youth Cup: Westfields 3, Hereford Lads Club Colts 1

HERTFORDSHIRE

Senior Cup
First Round

Hertford Town v Watford	1-2	Berkhamsted Town v Royston Town	0-1
Ware v Stevenage Borough	1-3	St Albans City v Tring Town	6-0
Hitchin Town v Bishop's Stortford	0-2	Boreham Wood v Baldock Town	1-0

Quarter-Finals

Watford v Royston Town	6-0	Hemel Hempstead v Bishop's Stortford	0-1
Boreham Wood v St Albans City	0-1*(aet)*	Stevenage Borough v Barnet	1-3

Semi-Finals

St Albans City v Barnet	1-2	Bishop's Stortford v Watford	2-3*(aet)*

Final *(at Bishop's Stortford FC, Wed 12th May)*: Barnet 4, Watford 2 *(aet)*

Barnet captain Derek Payne proudly lifts the Senior Cup after his side's win over Watford. Photo - Richard Brock.

Hertfordshire Centenary Trophy
First Round
B.A.C. Stevenage v Hatfield Town   0-3   Bovingdon v Sandridge Rvrs1-1*(aet)*,1-1*(aet, 7-8 pens)*

Hatfield Town's Mark Watts tussles with B.A.C. Stevenage's Keith Seals during the latter's 3-0 home defeat in the First Round. Photo - Richard Brock.

Second Round

Sun Sports v Cuffley	3-1*(aet)*	Chipperfield Corinthians v Bedmond Spts & Soc.	2-1
Lucas Sports v Oxhey Jets	1-4	Hatfield Town v Wellcome	5-1
Tring Athletic v Sandridge Rovers	2-1*(aet)*	Park Street v Potters Bar Town	2-1
Welwyn Garden City v Cheshunt	1-5	St Margaretsbury v Walkern	6-2
Potters Bar Crusaders v Knebworth	3-2	Bushey Rangers v London Colney	0-5
Kings Langley v Kodak (Hemel Hemp.)3-3*(aet)*,1-6		Croxley Guild of Sport v Letchworth Garden City	1-4
Leverstock Green v Wormley Rovers	2-3	Sawbridgeworth Town v Colney Heath	6-1
Hoddesdon Town v Elliott Star	6-1	Pirton v Harpenden Town	1-2

Third Round

Wormley Rovers v Sawbridgeworth Town	1-2*(aet)*	Harpenden Town v Hoddesdon Town	0-1
Oxhey Jets v Kodak (Hemel Hempstead)	2-4	Cheshunt v Tring Athletic	2-1
Letchworth Garden City v Sun Sports	0-1	Chipperfield Cor. v Hatfield Town	0-2*(void)*,1-4*(aet)*
Potters Bar Crusaders v St Margaretsbury	2-3	Park Street v London Colney	1-2

Quarter-Finals

Kodak v Sawbridgeworth Town	0-3	Hoddesdon Town v St Margaretsbury	0-1
Sun Sports v London Colney	1-1*(aet)*,3-2	Hatfield Town v Cheshunt	0-1

Semi-Finals

Cheshunt v Sawbridgeworth Town	0-2	St Margaretsbury v Sun Sports	1-1,2-1

Final *(at Ware FC, Sat 24th April)*: St Margaretsbury 2, Sawbridgeworth Town 1

Hertfordshire Charity Cup
First Round

Stevenage Borough v Bishop's Stortford	5-1	Boreham Wood v Baldock Town	3-0
Ware v Hemel Hempstead Town	1-2*(aet)*	St Albans City v Hitchin Town	2-0

Semi-Finals

Hemel Hempstead v Boreham Wood	0-5	St Albans City v Stevenage Borough	1-0

Final *(at St Albans City FC, Tues 23rd March)*: St Albans City 1, Boreham Wood 0

Hertfordshire Charity Shield
First Round

Tring Town v Welwyn Garden City	0-1	Sun Sports v St Margaretsbury	3-3*(4-5 on pens)*
Potters Bar Town v London Colney	1-2	Sawbridgeworth Town v Elliott Star	5-1
Berkhamsted Town v Leverstock Green	0-1*(aet)*	Harpenden Town v Hoddesdon Town	5-4*(aet)*
Cheshunt v Hertford Town	3-2*(aet)*	Letchworth Garden City v Royston	2-2*(aet, 5-3 pens)*

Quarter-Finals

Cheshunt v Harpenden Town	1-2*(aet)*	London Colney v St Margaretsbury	1-0
Sawbridgeworth T. v Letchworth Gdn City	1-0	Welwyn Garden City v Leverstock Green	1-4

Semi-Finals

Sawbridgeworth Town v Leverstock Green	3-0	London Colney v Harpenden T. *(at Harpenden)*	3-1

Final *(at Ware FC, Tues 16th March)*: Sawbridgeworth Town 1, Leverstock Green 1 *(Sawbridgeworth Town won 6-5 on penalties).*

Other County Finals
Intermediate Cup: Metropolitan Police (Bushey) 5, Sun Sports Reserves 3 *(aet)*
Junior Cup: Shephall Athletic 5, Ware Lions St Marys 0
Saturday Inter-League Cup: Astral West Herts League XI 3, SCS Forklifts (Bishop's Stortford) Stansted & District League XI 1
Sunday Cup: St Josephs (South Oxhey) 1, Welwyn Arsenal 0
Sunday Intermediate Cup: The Badger 3, Lilley S.R. 0
Sunday Junior Cup: R.S.C. 7, St Josephs 0
Sunday Inter-League Cup: Welwyn, Hatfield Sunday League XI 2, Watford Sunday League XI 1

HUNTINGDONSHIRE

Premier Cup
First Round

Ely City v Peterborough City	5-0	St Ives Town v Ortonians	0-2
Biggleswade Town v Ramsey Town	2-1	Somersham Town *(scr.)* Eynesbury Rovers *(w/o)*	

Quarter-Finals

Eynesbury Rovers v Chatteris Town	1-2	Potton United v Biggleswade Town	0-2
Langford v Ortonians	3-0	Ely City v Warboys Town	4-1

Semi-Finals

Chatteris Town v Langford	1-2*(aet)*	Biggleswade Town v Ely City	6-1

Final: Biggleswade Town 3, Langford 2 *(aet)*

Ely City under pressure at home to Warboys Town in the first-half of their Premier Cup tie on 26th January, but they pulled through to win 4-1. Photo - Martin Wray.

Premier Cup
First Round

Warboys Town v Alconbury	3-0	Ramsey Town v St Ives Town	4-3
Peterborough City v Somersham Town	3-1	Ortonians v Stilton United	3-1
Hotpoint v Bluntisham Rangers	5-0		

Quarter-Finals

Ortonians v Eynesbury Rovers	0-2	Godmanchester Rovers v Peterborough City	1-3
Ramsey Town v Warboys Town	1-5	Stanground United *(withdrew)* Hotpoint *(w/o)*	

Semi-Finals

Eynesbury Rovers v Peterborough City	2-0	Warboys Town v Hotpoint	6-0

Final *(at Somersham Town FC, Mon 3rd May)*: Eynesbury Rovers 4, Warboys Town 2

Other County Finals:
Junior Cup: St Neots Town 2, Warboys Town Reserves 1
Scott Gatty Cup: Yaxley 4, St Neots Town 0
Lower Junior Cup: St Neots Town Reserves 2, Brampton Reserves 0
Benevolent Cup: St Neots Town 2, Yaxley Reserves 1
Sunday Cup: Godmanchester Town 3, Little Poxton 1
Youth (under-18) Cup: Eynesbury Rovers 3, St Neots Town Boys 2
Under-16: Yaxley United 3, St Ives Rangers 0

KENT

'Facit' Senior Cup
First Round

Welling United v Erith & Belvedere	2-0	Slade Green v Gravesend & Northfleet	0-4
Margate v Ashford Town	0-1	Dover Athletic v Canterbury City	4-0

Quarter-Finals

Gillingham v Gravesend & Northfleet	1-2	Ashford Town *(bye)*	
Dover Athletic v Welling United	0-1	Bromley *(bye)*	

Semi-Finals

Bromley v Welling Utd *(at Welling)*	4-2	Ashford Town v Gravesend & Northfleet	2-1

Final *(at Gillingham FC, Mon 3rd May)*: Ashford Town 3, Bromley 2

Senior Trophy
First Round

Alma Swanley v Deal Town	1-2	Eltham Town v Sittingbourne	2-1
Faversham Town v Thamesmead Town	0-1	Corinthian v Greenwich Borough	5-0
Folkestone Invicta v Tonbridge	1-0	Beckenham Town v Catford Wanderers	5-2
Sheppey United v Thames Polytechnic	6-1	Danson Furness United v Kent Police	0-1
Midland Bank v Cray Wanderers	0-2	Ramsgate v Chatham Town	3-0

Second Round

West Wickham v Eltham Town	1-1,2-0	Whitstable Town v Ramsgate	2-0
Herne Bay v Beckenham Town	1-2	Deal Town v Sheppey United	3-2
Folkestone Invicta v Cray Wanderers	3-4	Corinthian v Thamesmead Town	1-1,1-3
Tunbridge Wells v Kent Police	2-3	Catford Wanderers v Crockenhill	0-1

(continued on page 110)

John Raffington heads Bromley into a 2-1 lead in the second-half of the Kent Senior Cup final. Photo - Dave West.

Peter McRobert lifts the Facit Kent Senior Cup for Ashford Town. Photo - Dave West.

Quarter-Finals

Crockenhill v Deal Town	2-4	Cray Wanderers v Thamesmead Town	3-3(aet),3-2
Kent Police v Whitstable Town	0-2	West Wickham v Beckenham Town	3-0

Semi-Finals

Cray Wanderers v Deal Town	3-2(aet)	Whitstable Town v West Wickham	1-0

Final *(at Gillingham FC, Sat 17th April)*: Cray Wanderers 1, Whitstable Town 0

Other County Finals:
Intermediate Cup: Bromley Reserves 3, Dover Athletic Reserves 1
Intermediate Shield *(at Tonbridge AFC)*: Headcorn 3, Sevenoaks Town 2
Junior Cup 'A' *(at Corinthian FC)*: Strood County 3, Segas Bromley 1
Junior Cup 'B' *(at Darenth Heathside FC)*: Bridon Ropes 2, Lullingstone 1
Junior Cup 'C' *(at Chatham Town FC)*: Institute Sports 2, Hunton 1
Sunday Premier Cup *(at Deal Town FC)*: London Thistle 4, Active Signs 1
Sunday Junior Cup *(at Sittongbourne FC)*: Milton & Denton 3, Rainham Sports 0
Sunday Junior Trophy *(at Charlton Athletic FC)*: Elm Tree 2, Cromptons 0
Youth Cup (under-18): Gillingham 3, Tonbridge AFC 0
Youth Cup (under-16): Gillingham 3, Millstrood Rovers 1

LANCASHIRE

A.T.S. Challenge Trophy
First Round

Bamber Bridge v Atherton Collieries	3-1	Darwen v Clitheroe	0-3(abandoned),0-1
Barrow v Lancaster City	2-3	Marine v Skelmersdale United	3-2
Burscough v Bacup Borough	2-0	Radcliffe Borough v Westhoughton Town	4-3
Chorley v Blackpool Mechanics	6-1	Rossendale United v Nelson	3-1

Second Round

Accrington Stanley v Horwich R.M.I.	4-0	Lancaster City v Marine	0-3
Bamber Bridge v Chorley	2-3	Morecambe v Blackpool Rovers	1-0
Burscough v Radcliffe Borough	1-2	Rossendale United v Fleetwood Town	1-4
Great Harwood Town v Atherton L.R.	5-2	Southport v Clitheroe	4-1

Quarter-Finals

Accrington Stanley v Great Harwood Town	1-0	Fleetwood Town v Morecambe	1-1(aet),1-0
Chorley v Radcliffe Borough	2-1	Southport v Marine	1-0(aet)

Semi-Finals

Accrington Stanley v Chorley	3-5	Fleetwood Town v Southport	1-4

Final *(at Bolton Wanderers FC, Mon 19th April)*: Southport 5, Chorley 2 *(aet)*

LEICESTERSHIRE

Leicestershire 'Westerby' Challenge Cup
First Round

Holwell Sports v Hinckley Athletic	4-1	Lutterworth Town v Shepshed Albion	3-3,0-1

Quarter-Finals

Shepshed Albion v Friar Lane Old Boys	8-1	Leicester City v Leicester United	3-1
Hinckley Town v St Andrews S.C.	0-1	Holwell Sports v Barwell	1-1,4-1(aet)

Semi-Finals

Leicester City v St Andrews S.C.	3-0	Shepshed Albion v Holwell Sports	1-0

Final *(at Leicester City FC, Wed 28th April)*: Leicester City 0, Shepshed Albion 20

Leicestershire 'Jelson Homes' Senior Cup
First Round

Anstey Nomads v North Kilworth	5-4	Kirby Muxloe v Hillcroft	5-2
Barrow Town v Narborough & Littlethorpe	3-0	Newfoundpool W.M.C. v Sileby Town	1-2
Birstall United v Wigston Fields	2-0	Quorn v Aylestone Park Old Boys	2-0
St Andrews S.C. v Whetstone Athletic	1-0	Ibstock Welfare v Loughborough Dynamoes	5-6(aet)

Second Round

Anstey Nomads v Cottesmore Amateurs	4-2	Harborough Town Imperial v Huncote S. & S.C.	1-2
Anstey Town v Syston St Peters	0-5	Highfield Rangers v Burbage Old Boys	3-0(void),4-3
Asfordby Am. v Leicestershire Constabulary	0-3	Holwell Sports v Fosse Imps	6-1
Barlestone St Giles v Downes Sports	0-2	Leicester Y.M.C.A. v Houghton Rangers	4-1
Barwell v Barrow Town	5-2(aet)	Loughborough Dynamo v Quorn	5-1
Pedigree Petfoods v Birstall United	1-7	Castle Donnington Town v Thringstone M.W.	4-2
Sileby Town v Oadby Town	1-4	Earl Shilton Albion v Lutterworth Town	0-5
Friar Lane Old Boys v Ravenstone	5-1(aet)	St Andrews S.C. v Kirby Muxloe S.C.	1-2

Third Round

Leics Constabulary v Kirby Muxloe S.C.	1-2	Friar Lane Old Boys v Castle Donnington Town	5-2
Lutterworth Town v Highfield Rangers	3-2	Holwell Sports v Loughborough Dynamo	6-3(aet)
Barwell v Leicester Y.M.C.A.	6-4	Oadby Town v Downes Sports	3-5(aet)
Huncote S. & S.C. v Birstall United	2-5	Syston St Peters v Anstey Nomads	1-3

Quarter-Finals

Anstey Nomads v Holwell Sports	0-1	Barwell v Downes Sports	1-1(aet),1-4
Lutterworth Town v Birstall United	0-3	Kirby Muxloe S.C. v Friar Lane Old Boys	2-3

Semi-Finals

Birstall v Downes *(at Hinckley Ath.)*	1-0	Friar Lane v Holwell Spts *(at Shepshed)*	2-1

Final *(at Holmes Park, Whetstone, Mon 29th March)*: Friar Lane Old Boys 2, Birstall United 1 *(aet)*

Strood County of the Kent County League, Kent Junior 'A' Cup winners 1992-93. Photo - Richard Ralph.

Segas Bromley of the South London Alliance, Kent Junior 'A' Cup runners-up 1992-93. Photo - Richard Ralph.

The Cottesmore 'keeper makes a fine save in the 2-4 Leicestershire Senior Cup defeat at Anstey Nomads on Saturday 7th November. Photo - Rob Ruddock.

LINCOLNSHIRE

Lincolnshire Senior Cup
First Round
Lincoln City v Grimsby Town	4-1	Boston United v Scunthorpe United	2-0

Semi-Finals
Grimsby Town v Gainsborough Trinity	3-0	Lincoln City v Boston United	0-3

Final (at Grimsby Town FC, held over to start of 1993-94 season): Grimsby Town v Boston United

Lincolnshire Senior Cup 'A'
First Round
Nettleham v Bourne Town	0-3	Holbeach United v Spalding United	1-4
Louth United v Lincoln United	4-3	Stamford v Immingham Town	2-4

Quarter-Finals
Winterton Rangers v Lincoln United	1-1,1-5	Holbeach United v Nettleham	0-4
Boston FC v Stamford	1-1,3-4	Immingham Town v Mirrlees Blackstone	1-2

Semi-Finals
Mirrlees Blackstone v Immingham Town	4-1	Bourne Town v Brigg Town	3-1

Final (at Stamford FC, Tues 27th April): Mirrlees Blackstone 2, Bourne Town 1 (aet)

Lincolnshire Senior Cup 'B'
Preliminary Round
Mablethorpe Athletic v Louth Old Boys	3-0

First Round
Long Sutton Athletic v Bottesford Town	2-0	Mablethorpe Athletic v Immingham Blossom Way	3-6
Grimsby Ross Amateurs v Hykeham Town	2-3	Sleaford Town v Skegness Town	2-0
Humberside United v Spilsby Town	3-2	Lincoln Athletic v Deeping Rangers	1-4
Harrowby United v Wyberton	3-0	Appleby Frodingham Athletic v Ruston Sports	3-2

Quarter-Finals
Deeping Rangers v Sleaford Town	4-0	Humberside Utd v Hykeham Town (at Hykeham)	1-0
Immingham Blossom Way v Harrowby United	3-1	Appleby Frodingham Ath. v Long Sutton Athletic	2-0

Semi-Finals
Deeping Rangers v Humberside United	0-3	Appleby Frodingham v Immingham Blossom Way	0-3

Final (at Winterton Rangers FC, Wed 10th March): Appleby Frodingham Athletic 1, Humberside United 1 (Appleby Frodingham Athletic won 11-10 on penalties)

LIVERPOOL

Senior Cup
First Round
Burscough v Formby	5-1	St Helens Town v Prescot A.F.C.	1-0(aet)
Skelmersdale United v Knowsley United	0-3	Southport v Bootle	3-1

Quarter-Finals
Burscough v St Helens Town	1-0	Marine v Everton Reserves	0-3
Southport v Liverpool Reserves	2-1(aet)	Tranmere Rovers Reserves v Knowsley United	3-2

Semi-Finals
Everton Reserves v Burscough	0-2	Tranmere Rovers Reserves v Southport	0-3

Final (at Everton FC, Tues 11th May): Southport 2, Burscough 1

Other County Finals:
Challenge Cup (at Merseyside Police FC, Mon 26th April): Lucas Sports 3, St Dominics 2
Junior Cup (at Merseyside Police FC, Mon 19th April): Eagle Sports 2, Aigburth Peoples Hall Reserves 1
Intermediate Cup (at Bootle FC, Wed 21st April): St Aloysius 1, Blacklow Brow 1 (St Aloysius won 4-3 on penalties)
Youth Cup (at Maghull FC, Thurs 22nd April): Southport Youth 1, St Aidens Youth 1 (Southport won on penalties)
Sunday Premier Cup (at Bootle FC, Sun 25th April): Nicosia 3, Etnaward 1
Sunday Junior Cup (at B.R.N.E.S.C. FC, Sun 2nd May): Power 1, Pools 1 (Power won 3-1 on penalties)
Sunday Intermediate Cup (at Littlewoods FC, Sun 18th April): Redington 5, Black Bull 4
Inter-Lge under-18 (at Bellefield (Everton FCTraining Ground), Fri 23rd April): Wavertree Youth Alliance 3, Bootle & Netherton Junior League 1
Inter-Lge under-16 (at Knowsley United FC, Wed 14th April): Wavertree Youth Alliance 3, Maghull & Lydiate 0
Inter-Lge under-14 (at Melwood (Liverpool FC Training Ground), Wed 21st April): West Derby Junior League 1, Walton & Kirkdale Junior League 0
Inter-Lge under-12 (at Melwood (Liverpool FC Training Ground), Wed 21st April): Walton & Kirkdale Junior League 2, South Merseyside Junior League 1

LONDON

Challenge Cup
First Round
Bromley v Barking	7-1	Leyton Orient v Epsom & Ewell	2-1
Barnet v Hampton	5-2	Welling United v Collier Row	5-2
Hendon v Kingsbury Town	1-4	Clapton v Leyton	2-1
Uxbridge v Dulwich Hamlet	4-2	Fisher Athletic v Erith & Belvedere	2-2,2-1

Quarter-Finals
Leyton Orient v Clapton	7-1	Uxbridge v Welling United	1-2
Kingsbury Town v Barnet	1-4	Bromley v Fisher Athletic	5-0

Semi-Finals
Leyton Orient v Bromley	4-0	Welling United v Barnet	1-2

Final *(at Leyton Orient FC, Mon 26th April)*: Leyton Orient 3, Barnet 2

Senior Cup
First Round
Ford United *(bye)*		Southgate Athletic v Eltham Town	0-4
Croydon Athletic v Hoddesdon Town	2-4	Tower Hamlets v Haringey Borough	0-0,2-4
Danson Furness United v Corinthian-Casuals	0-1	Barkingside v Thamesmead Town	0-0,5-0
Bedfont v Civil Service	3-0		

Second Round
Ford United v Cockfosters	1-0	Hoddesdon Town v Barkingside	2-0
Eton Manor v Cray Wanderers	0-2	Brimsdown Rovers v Bedfont	2-2,3-0
Corinthian-Casuals v Hanwell Town	1-2	Wingate & Finchley v Woodford Town	4-1
St Andrews v East Ham United	0-4	Eltham Town v Haringey Borough	3-2

Quarter-Finals
Cray Wanderers v Eltham Town	3-0	Hoddesdon Town v Wingate & Finchley	2-1
East Ham United v Hanwell Town	2-5	Brimsdown Rovers v Ford United	2-1

Semi-Finals
Hanwell Town v Cray Wanderers	2-0	Hoddesdon Town v Brimsdown Rovers	2-2,1-1,0-2

Final *(at Wingate & Finchley FC, Sat 20th March)*: Hanwell Town 4, Brimsdown Rovers 3

Other County Finals
Intermediate Cup *(at Welling United FC)*: Craven 3, Bromley Reserves 2
Midweek Cup *(Thurs 15th April)*: Buckingham S.W.D.O. 4, Tottenham L.T. 1
Junior Cup *(Sat 17th April & 8th May)*: Faweh 4, Cambridge Univ. Mission 2 *(after 1-1 draw)*
Sunday Challenge Cup *(Sun 9th May)*: Ranelagh Sports 2, Defiance 1
Sunday Intermediate Cup *(Sun 4th April)*: Ordell (Iceland) 5, Coach & Horses (Plastow) 2
Sunday Junior Cup *(Sun 25th April)*: Enfield Lock 2, Ford P.T.A. 0

Hanwell Town rejoice after beating Brimsdown Rovers 4-3 to retain the London Senior Cup. Photo - Francis Short.

MANCHESTER

Premier Cup
First Round
Radcliffe Borough v Curzon Ashton	0-0,0-6	Droylsden v Irlam Town	3-0
Hyde United v Caernarfon Town	2-1	North Trafford v Mossley	5-2
Maine Road v Oldham Town	1-3	Salford City v Chadderton	0-1
Ashton United *(bye)*		Flixton v Glossop North End	1-4

Quarter-Finals
Ashton United v Oldham Town	6-0	Chadderton v Droylsden	1-2
Hyde United v Glossop North End	4-0	North Trafford v Curzon Ashton	2-4

Semi-Finals
Curzon Ashton v Hyde United	1-0	Droylsden v Ashton United *(aet)*	3-1

Final *(at Bolton Wanderers FC, Mon 26th April)*: Droylsden 2, Curzon Ashton 0 *(aet)*

Manchester Challenge Cup winners: Wythenshawe Town. **runners-up:** East Manchester.
Manchester Amateur Cup winners: Gorton Town. **runners-up:** Maine Road Reserves.

MIDDLESEX

Middlesex Senior Cup
Preliminary Round One
Hillingdon B. v Wingate & Finchley *(att: 15)*	0-1	
Brimsdown v Viking S. *(att: 36)* 1-1,2-0*(att: 35)*	
Rayners Lane v Hampton *(att: 80)*	2-5	
Brook House v Harefield United *(att: 82)*	6-2	

Potters Bar Town v Southgate Athletic *(att: 45)*	5-1
Feltham & H. v N. Greenford *(att: 39)* 0-0,4-0*(att: 50)*	
Kingsbury T. v Willesden Hawkeye *(att: 52)* 1-2*(aet)*	
Ashford Town (Middx) v Cockfosters *(att: 19)*	2-0

Preliminary Round Two
Brook House v Hanwell *(att: 39)* 0-0,2-0*(att: 43)*	
Ruislip Manor v Bedfont *(att: 107)*	4-0
Edgware T. v Welwyn Gdn City *(att: 65)*	7-1
Ashford Town (Middx) v Southall *(att: 93)*	3-0

Wealdstone v Harrow Borough *(att: 338)*	0-3
Feltham & Hounslow v Potters Bar T. *(att: 43)*	7-3
Wingate & Finchley v Brimsdown Rovers *(att: 40)* 1-2	
Willesden H'eye v Hampton *(att: 62)* 1-1,2-0*(att: 127)*	

First Round Proper
Hendon v Enfield *(att: 233)*	2-3
Edgware T. v Feltham & Hounslow *(att: 49)*	0-1
Willesden Hawkeye v Staines Town *(att: 40)*	0-1
Ashford Town (Middx) v Yeading *(att: 72)*	0-2

Brimsdown R. v Hayes *(att: 66)* 1-1,1-2*(aet, att: 107)*	
Uxbridge v Wembley *(att: 99)* 0-0,1-3*(att: 42)*	
Northwood v Brook House *(att: 72)*	5-0
Ruislip Manor v Harrow Borough *(att: 269)*	1-2

Quarter-Finals
Staines Town v Yeading *(att: 122)*	0-3
Northwood v Feltham & Hounslow *(att: 128)*	3-2

Harrow Borough v Hayes *(att: 257)* 2-2,3-1*(att: 224)*	
Wembley v Enfield *(att: 132)*	2-0

Semi-Finals
Harrow Borough v Northwood *(att: 361)*	5-0

Wembley v Yeading *(att: 92)*	
	2-2,0-0*(aet, att: 111)*,2-1*(att: 95)*

Final *(at Enfield FC, Mon 12th April)*: Harrow Borough 1, Wembley 0 *(att: 618)*

Senior Charity Cup
First Round
Harefield U. *(scr.)* Wingate & Finchley *(w/o)*	
Northwood v Potters Bar Town *(att: 87)*	3-1
Bedfont v Hillingdon Borough *(att: 24)* 4-3*(aet)*	
Ashford T. (Middx) v Welwyn G.C. *(att: 36)*	2-0

Willesden Hawkeye v Kingsbury Town *(att: 40)*	2-1
Rayners Lane v Viking Sports *(att: 86)*	2-4
Cockfosters v Feltham & Hounslow Boro. *(att: 41)* 2-0	
Hanwell Town v Southall *(att: 74)*	3-2*(aet)*

Second Round
Northwood v Harrow Borough *(att: 182)*	0-3
Brook House v Cockfosters *(att: 54)*	4-2
Hanwell Town v Southgate Athletic *(att: 24)*	6-0
Uxbridge v Ashford (Mx) *(att: 103)*	4-2*(aet)*
Staines Town v Viking Sports	3-0

Brimsdown Rovers v Wingate & Finchley *(att: 62)* 2-0	
Bedfont v Hendon *(att: 90)*	1-2
Viking Spts v North Greenford United *(att: 30)*	2-0
Willesden Hawkeye v Hampton *(att: 27)*	2-1

Third Round
Brimsdown Rovers v Hanwell Town *(att: 52)*	0-1
Uxbridge v Brook House *(att: 144)*	4-1
Hendon v Yeading *(att: 77)*	0-2
Harrow Borough v Hayes *(att: 244)*	4-2

Staines Town v Ruislip Manor *(att: 126)*	3-1*(aet)*
Edgware Town v Brentford *(att: 98)*	'0-3
Wembley v Willesden H. *(att: 109)*	2-2*(aet & pens)*
Viking Sports v Chelsea *(att: 348)*	2-2*(aet & pens)*

Quarter-Finals
Uxbridge v Brentford *(att: 248)*	2-1
Yeading v Chelsea *(att: 266)*	0-2

Staines Town v Hanwell Town	0-1*(aet)*
Harrow Borough v Willesden Hawkeye *(att: 115)* 3-0	

Semi-Finals
Hanwell Town v Uxbridge *(att: 185)*	2-0

Harrow Borough v Chelsea *(att: 628)*	4-1

Final *(at Uxbridge FC, Wed 5th May)*: Harrow Borough 3, Hanwell Town 1 *(aet, att: 304)*

Other County Finals:
Premier Cup *(at Yeading FC)*: Hampton Reserves 1, Edgware Town Reserves 0
Intermediate Cup *(at Northwood FC)*: Brimsdown R. 'A' 0, L.T. Metropolitan Railway 0 *(Brimsdown won on pens)*
Junior Cup *(at Brook House FC)*: Teddington Rangers 3, Exxon Associates 2
Junior Trophy *(at Staines Town FC)*: Viaduct 2, Westminster Widadia 1
Midweek Cup *(at Hanwell Town FC)*: Willesden Hawkeye 5, HASSRA (South) 2
Veteran's Cup *(at Northwood FC)*: Norseman 3, Priory 0
Junior Inter-Lge Cup *(at Hillingdon Borough FC)*: Charrington Chiltonian Lge 2, Middx County Lge 1
Sunday Premier Cup *(at Brentford FC)*: West Hendon E.S.C. 3, Hammersmith 1
Sunday Intermediate Cup *(at Edgware Town FC)*: Drayton Nomads 1, A.C. Milan 0
Sunday Junior Cup *(at Hendon FC)*: Hillingdon Rebels 6, St Peter's 1
Sunday Junior Trophy *(at Bedfont)*: Belstone Reserves 3, Field End Old Boys 0
Sunday Inter-Lge Cup *(at Northwood FC)*: Watford Sunday Lge 2, Marathon Sunday Lge 0

MIDLAND FLOODLIT CUP

Previous Winners: 1959-60: Peterborough U., 60-61: Worcester C., 61-62 & 62-63: Peterborough U. Res., 63-64: Cambridge U., 64-65: Worcester C., 65-66: Worcester C., 66-67: Wellington T., 67-68: Banbury U., 68-69: Nuneaton B., 69-70: Stafford R., 70-71 & 71-72: Telford U., 72-73: Atherstone T., 73-74: Nuneaton B., 74-75: Corby T., 75-76: Burton A., 76-77 & 77-78 & 78-79: Atherstone T., 79-80: Nuneaton B. 80-81 & 81-82: Kettering T., 82-83: Bedworth U., 83-84: Bedworth U./ Nuneaton B., 84-85: V.S. Rugby; 85-86 & 86-87 & 87-88: Cheltenham T., 88-89: Hinckley T., 89-90: V.S. Rugby, 90-91 & 91-92: Moor Green.

First Round (4 groups of 3)
Corby Town v Redditch United	3-3	
Hinckley Athletic v Corby Town	2-2	
Redditch United v Hinckley Athletic	1-0	
Hinckley Town v Leicester United	0-3	
Leicester United v Willenhall Town	2-1	
Willenhall Town v Hinckley Town	1-1	

Nuneaton Borough v Atherstone United	2-1
Atherstone United v Dudley Town	1-3
Dudley Town v Nuneaton Borough	1-1
Bedworth United v Moor Green	4-2
Moor Green v Tamworth	3-2
Tamworth v Bedworth United	2-2

Quarter-Finals
Redditch United v Nuneaton Borough	0-1	
Leicester United v Moor Green	1-2	

Dudley Town v Corby Town	1-0
Bedworth United v Willenhall Town	2-0

Semi-Finals
Moor Green v Dudley Town	3-0	

Bedworth United v Nuneaton Borough	2-1

Final *(at Moor Green FC)*: Moor Green 1, Bedworth United 3 *(aet)*

NORFOLK

Senior Cup

Preliminary Round

Mattishall v Wymondham Old Boys	1-4	Wortwell v Norwich Union	1-3
Hempnall v Mulbarton United	2-5	Newton Flotman v Dereham Town	1-2
Loddon United v Bradenham Wanderers	4-0	Harleston Town v Horsford United	1-2
Hellesdon v Coltishall H.V. '85	1-5	Wymondham Town v Carrow	3-2

First Round

Swaffham Town v Horsford United	2-3	Dereham Town v Thetford Town	3-2
Lakeford Rangers v Loddon United	4-3	Coltishall H.V. '85 v Blofield United	3-0
Mulbarton United v Overstrand	2-1	Wymondham Town v Wymondham Old Boys	3-3,3-0
Reepham Town v Norwich Union	4-0	St Andrews v Downham Town	3-0

Second Round

Mulbarton United v Dereham Town	0-4	Wroxham v Coltishall H.V. '85	5-3
Wymondham Town v St Andrews	4-0	Lakeford Rangers v Great Yarmouth Town	3-1
Horsford United v Watton United	0-1	Fakenham Town v King's Lynn	4-2
Gorleston v Norwich Utd	0-0,2-2,1-5	Reepham Town v Diss Town	2-1

Quarter-Finals

Wroxham v Lakeford Rangers	2-1	Norwich United v Wymondham Town	2-0
Reepham Town v Watton United	1-3	Fakenham Town v Dereham Town	2-0

Semi-Finals

Fakenham Town v Watton United	1-2	Norwich United v Wroxham	0-2

Final *(at Norwich City FC, Sat 17th April)*: Wroxham 3, Watton United 0

Other County Finals:

Junior (Saturday) Cup: North Walsham Town 3, Thorpe Village 1
Thursday Cup: Great Yarmouth Postels 3, British Rail 2 *(after 2-2 draw)*
Sunday Senior Cup: Poringland Wanderers 2, Schooners 0
Sunday Intermediate Cup: Coltishall H.V. '85 2, Black Swan 0
Sunday Junior Cup: Caister Athletic 2, Cranworth 1
Primary Cup: Fakenham Town 'A' 5, Ditchingham 1
Sunday Youth Cup: Gorleston Rangers 2, Great Yarmouth Town 1 *(aet)*
John Savage Cup: Downham Youth Club 8, Acle Boys 1
Minor Cup: Sprowston Youth 4, Hellesdon 0
S.R.B. Cowles Cup: Hewett High School 5, Sprowston High School 2

NORTHAMPTONSHIRE

Northamptonshire 'Hillier' Senior Cup

First Round

Daventry Town v Rothwell Town	0-1	Northampton Spencer v Cogenhoe United	6-1
Wellingborough Town v Long Buckby	1-3	Stewarts & Lloyds v Raunds Town	2-1
Rushden & Diamonds v Brackley Town	5-0	Corby Town v Desborough Town	4-0

Quarter-Finals

Kettering Town *(exempt)*		Long Buckby v Rothwell Town	1-0
Northampton Spencer v Corby Town	1-3	Rushden & Diamonds v Stewarts & Lloyds	4-0

Semi-Finals

Corby Town v Kettering Town	1-1,1-3	Long Buckby v Rushen & Diamonds	0-3

Final *(at Kettering Town FC, Tues 27th April)*: Kettering Town 2, Rushden & Diamonds 1

Other County Finals:

Junior Cup: *(at Kettering Town FC, 24th March)*: Raunds Town Reserves 4, Peterborough Perkins Sports 3
Lower Junior Cup: *(at Hayden Rd, Rushden, 30th March)*: Wilby 2, Corby Strip Mills Reserves 0
Area Cup: *(at Wellingborough Town FC, 6th April)*: Peterborough Molins Reserves 2, Weedon Reserves 1
Sunday Cup: *(at Rushden & Diamonds FC, 10th March)*: Corby Pheonix 3, Northampton Vanaid 2
Sunday Trophy: *(at Bugbrooke St Michael FC, 1st April)*: Northampton Bonner Athletic 1, Daventry Dun Cow 0
Sunday Vase: *(at Northampton Spencer FC, 14th April)*: Rushden King Edward 2, Towcester Pury Rangers 0
Sunday Shield: *(at Cogenhoe United FC, 20th April)*: Northampton Barratt Snooker 3, Higham Ferrers Reserves 1
Youth Invitation U-14: *(at Rothwell Town FC, 25th April)*: Wellingborough Colts 3, Billing United 0
Youth Invitation U-16: *(at Desborough Town FC, 18th April)*: Northampton Gregory Celtic 1, Corby Castle Rise 0

NORTH RIDING

Senior Cup Preliminary Round

Fishburn Park v Tees Components	1-2

Preliminary Round

Dormans Athletic v Tees Components	2-3	New Marske v Nunthorpe Ath.	1-1 *(aban.)*,1-0
Redcar Works B.S.C. v Marske United	0-1	Rowntrees v Richmond Town	3-1

Second Round

New Marske v Northallerton Town	1-0	Marske United v Rowntrees	0-1
Stockton v Pickering Town	3-3,2-4		
Whitby Town v Tees Components	5-1	Guisborough Town v South Bank	4-2

Quarter-Finals

Middlesbrough v Whitby Town	2-3	Rowntrees v Pickering Town	1-1,3-0
York City v Scarborough	2-5	New Marske v Guisborough Town	2-8

Semi-Finals

Scarborough v Rowntrees	1-2	Whitby Town v Guisborough Town	0-1

Final *(at Whitby Town FC, Wed 5th May)*: Guisborough Town 2, Rowntrees 0

Other County Finals:

County Cup *(at Pickering Town FC)*: Rowntrees 4, Grangetown 0
Saturday Challenge Cup *(at Guisborough Town FC)*: Loftus Athletic 2, Red Rose 1
Sunday County Cup *(at Guisborough Town FC)*: Shabs Morgage 2, Seven Stars 1
Sunday Challenge Cup *(at Northallerton Town)*: Normanby Hall 3, Robert Thompson 1
Junior Cup *(at Middlesbrough FC)*: Longlands Athletic 3, Nunthorpe Athletic 1

NORTHUMBERLAND

Senior Cup
First Round

Alnwick Town v Westerhope Hillheads	2-1	Seaton Delaval Amateurs v Prudhoe East End	2-1
Ashington v Ponteland United	2-4	Seaton Delaval Seaton Terrace v Benfield Park	3-1

Quarter-Finals

Newcastle United Reserves v Alnwick Town	10-0	Seaton Delaval Amateurs v Blyth Spartans	0-0,3-4
Ponteland United v Whitley Bay	1-1,0-3	Seaton Delaval Seaton Terrace v Newcastle B.S.	0-3

Semi-Finals

Newcastle Blue Star v Whitley Bay	1-0	Blyth Spartans v Newcastle United Reserves	1-3

Final *(at Newcastle United FC, Sat 1st May)*: Newcastle Blue Star 2, Newcastle United Reserves 1

Benevolent Bowl
First Round

Dudley v West Allotment Celtic	0-4	Walker v Blyth Kitty Brewster	2-1
Bedlington Terriers v Forest Hall	10-2	Newbiggin Central Welfare v North Shields	4-0
Haltwhistle Crown Paints v Spittal Rovers	4-2	Hirst Progressive v Morpeth Town	0-3
Wark v Longbenton	1-3	Percy Main v Heaton Stannington	3-3(aet),3-0

Quarter Finals

Haltwhistle Crown Paints v Longbenton	1-3	West Allotment Celtic v Bedlington Terriers	3-1
Percy Main v Newbiggin Central Welfare	1-3	Hirst Progressive v Walker	8-8(aet),2-7

Semi-Finalists

West Allotment Celtic v Longbenton	4-1	Walker v Newbiggin Central Welfare	3-1

Final *(at Blyth Spartans FC, Wed 14th April)*: West Allotment Celtic 4, Walker 3

Other County Finals:
Sunday Cup: Wallsend Labour 1, Balloon 0

West Allotment Celtic F.C. - Northumberland Benevolent Bowl winners 1992-93. Photo - Gavin Ellis-Neville.

NOTTINGHAMSHIRE

Senior Cup
First Round

Radford v Priory (Eastwood)	3-2	Bulwell Forest Villa v Nuthall	4-1
Dunkirk v Sneinton	0-2	John Player v Kimberley Town	0-1
Worthington Simpson v Arnold Town	0-1	Clipstone Welfare v Blidworth Welfare	3-2
Attenborough v Eastwood Town	1-2	City & Sherwood Hospital v Boots Athletic	3-6
Thoresby Colliery Welfare v Oakham United	3-0	Rainworth Miners Welfare v Cotgrave Colliery	6-2
Pelican v Bulwell United	4-3(aet)	Basford United v Ashfield United	0-3
Greenwood Meadows v Gedling Town	1-0	G.P.T. Plessey v Hucknall Rolls Royce Welfare	2-1
Hucknall Town v Notts Police	0-1	Ruddington (bye)	

Second Round

Arnold Town v Eastwood Town	5-3	Ashfield United v Clipstone Welfare	3-1
Ruddington v Sneinton	7-6 on pens	Boots Athletic v Rainworth Miners Welfare	0-1
Kimberley Town v Greenwood Meadows	3-0	G.P.T. Plessey v Bulwell Forest Villa	2-0
Radford v Hucknall Town	0-5	Pelican v Thoresby Colliery Welfare	2-1

Quarter-Finals

Ashfield United v Kimberley Town	5-1	Hucknall Town v Arnold Town	0-1
G.P.T. Plessey v Ruddington	1-3	Pelican v Rainworth Miners Welfare	1-2

Semi-Finals

Ruddington v Arnold Town	1-6	Rainworth M.W. v Ashfield Utd	1-1(aet, 4-3 on pens)

Final *(at Eastwood Town FC, Tues 27th April)*: Arnold Town 3, Rainworth Miners Welfare 1

(other finals opposite)

Other County Finals
County Cup: Nottingham Forest 3, Notts County 0
Intermediate Cup: Hucknall Town Reserves 4, Radcliffe Olympic 3
Junior Cup: Boots Athletic Reserves 2, Matrixgrade 1
Minor Cup: Gondola 5, Woodhouse '90 1
Thursday Cup: Selective T. 8, Lenton United 7
Sunday Morning Senior Trophy: Rolls Royce Celtic 1, Spot On 0
Sunday Morning Intermediate Cup: Wellington Inn 5, Bentinck Miners Welfare 0
Sunday Morning Junior Cup: Sandy Lane 7, Plough Inn 1
Sunday Afternoon Cup: Jacksdale S.C. 3, Radford Athletic 2

Arnold Town with the Notts Senior Cup (trophy on the right) won by the club for the first time in 22 years.

OXFORDSHIRE

Senior Cup
First Round

Blackbird Leys S.C. v Old Woodstock	3-1	Yarnton v A.P. Sports		5-1
Quarry Nomads v Chinnor	3-1			

Second Round

Garsington v Quarry Nomads	2-1	Woodstock Town v Kidlington		1-2
Banbury United v Oxford City	2-1	Peppard v Bletchingdon		8-0
Bicester Town v Eynsham Town	7-0	Chipping Norton Town v Henley Town	3-3*(aet)*,	6-1
Blackbird Leys S.C. v Yarnton	2-1	Thame United v Ardley United		4-0
Headington Amateurs v Clanfield	1-0	North Leigh v Wallington		5-1
Carterton Town v Easington Sports	6-0	Worcester College O.B. v Oxford University Press		0-3

Third Round

Kidlington v Chipping Norton Town	2-0	Oxford University Press v Garsington	2-1
North Leigh v Banbury United	0-1*(aet)*	Bicester Town v Thame United	2-4
Peppard v Carterton Town	10-0	Headington Amateurs v Blackbird Leys S.C.	3-0

Quarter-Finals

Oxford University Press v Peppard	1-0	Thame United v Kidlington	5-0
Banbury United v Oxford United	1-0	Witney Town v Headington Amateurs	2-0

Semi-Finals

Banbury Utd v Witney T. *(at Thame Utd)*	2-0	Thame United v Oxford Univ. Press *(at Witney Town)*	2-0

Final *(at Oxford United FC, Wed 21st April)*: Thame United 2, Banbury United 1 *(aet)*

Other County Finals:
Intermediate Cup: Peppard 4, Launton Sports 0

SHEFFIELD & HALLAMSHIRE

Senior Cup
First Qualifying Round

High Green Villa v Rossington Main	2-3	Treeton Welfare v Yorkshire Main	0-1
Sheffield Post Office v Clifton Rovers	1-2	Ash House v Woodsetts Welfare Sports	4-0
Wombwell Town v Sheffield Centralians	4-1	Swinton Athletic v Goldthorpe Colliery	1-3

Second Qualifying Round

A.B.M. v Kiveton Park	1-4	Rossington Main v Wombwell Town *(at Wombwell)*	1-2
Old Edwardians v Yorkshire Main	1-3	Abbeydale v Thurcroft Ivanhoe Hoults	1-2
Mexborough Main Street v Clifton Rovers	1-0	Sheffield University v Ash House	1-5
Goldthorpe Colliery v Ecclesfield Red Rose	3-0	British Gas Sports Club *(w/o)* Wombwell *(scr.)*	
Saint James v Sheffield Bankers	2-1	Sheffield Aurora v Denaby & Cadeby Miners W.	1-2
Penistone Church v Throstles Ridgeway	3-6*(aet)*	Rossington v Wath Saracens Athletic	3-1
Parramore Sports v White Rose Thistle	4-0	Frecheville Comm. A. v Brunsmeer Athletic	4-2
Industry v Staveley Miners Welfare	0-4	British Steel Stainless v Sheffield Oakhouse	3-5
Mexborough Town v Harworth Colliery Inst.	1-2	Rawmarsh & Ryecroft W.M.C. v Caribbean S.	3-3,0-3
Norton Woodseats v Sheffield Gas	3-1	Oughtibridge W.M.C. v Phoenix	3-2*(aet)*

First Round Proper

Mexborough Main Street v Sheffield	1-2	Oughtibridge W.M.C. v Norton Woodseats	2-2,0-2
Staveley Miners Welfare v Yorkshire Main	5-1	Maltby Miners Welfare v R.E.S. Parkgate	4-3
Emley v Denaby & Cadeby Miners Welfare	1-0	Kiveton Park v Throstles Ridgeway	2-1
Brodsworth Welf. v Rawmarsh & Ryecroft	2-0	Worksop Town v Wombwell Town	4-0
Hallam v Frickley Athletic	4-3	Thurcroft Ivanhoe Hoults v Sheffield Oakhouse	3-2
Denabu United v Parramore Sports	7-1	Harworth Colliery Inst. v Frecheville C.A.	1-2*(aet)*
Rossington v British Gas Spts Club	2-1	Stocksbridge Park Steels v Worsbrough Bridge	2-1
Ash House v Goldthorpe Colliery	2-0	Saint James v Rossington Main	0-3

Second Round Proper

Norton Woodseats v Hallam	2-4	Sheffield v Stocksbridge Park Steels	1-2
Rossington v Emley	1-3	Brodsworth Welfare v Frecheville C.A.	2-2,1-2*(aet)*
Maltby Miners Welfare v Denaby United	1-0	Worksop Town v Ash House	2-1
Kiveton Park v Thurcroft Ivanhoe Hoults	4-2	Staveley M.W. v Rossington M.	0-0,1-1*(aet, 3-4 pens)*

Quarter-Finals

Emley v Hallam	4-3*(aet)*	Worksop Town v Frecheville Community Assoc.	4-3
Rossington Main v Kiveton Park	2-3	Maltby Miners Welfare v Stocksbridge Park Steels	1-2

Semi-Finals

Worksop Town v Emley	1-0,3-1	Kiveton Park v Stocksbridge Park Steels	0-1,0-5

Final. First Leg *(Wed 14th April)*: Worksop Town 2, Stocksbridge Park Steels 3
Second Leg *(Tues 27th April)*: Stocksbridge Park Steels 2, Worksop Town 1

Other County Finals:
Junior Cup *(at Grimethorpe Miners Welfare FC, Mon 19th April)*: Darfield Road W.M.C. 3, Athersley Recreation 0
Sunday Cup *(at Frecheville Community Association FC, Sun 18th April)*: Mill '92 2, Hoyland Town Jaguars 1

SHROPSHIRE

Senior Cup
Semi-Final

Bridgnorth Town v Shrewsbury Town	1-6

Final: Telford United 2, Shrewsbury Town 0

County Cup
First Round

Snailbeach White Star v Donnington Wood	4-6	Admaston v Wem Town	1-2
Clun Valley v St Georges Town	2-0	Ellesmere Rangers v Madeley Town	7-4
Broseley Athletic v Ludlow Colts	0-3	Shifnal Town v Ludlow Town	2-1*(aet)*

Second Round

Tibberton v Oakengates Town	2-9	Wellington Amateurs v Shifnal Town	0-3
Ellesmere Rangers v Donnington Wood	0-1	Morda United v Ludlow Colts	1-3
Wem Town v Newport Town	3-1	Clun Valley v Whitchurch Alport	0-2
Albrighton S. & S. v Little Drayton Rgrs	0-0,2-1	Bridgnorth T. Res. v Meole Brace	4-4*(7-6 on pens)*

Quarter-Finals

Whitchurch Alport v Ludlow Colts	1-3	Oakengates Town v Bridgnorth Town Reserves	3-1
Shifnal Town v Donnington Wood	1-0	Albrighton S. & S. v Wem Town	2-2,3-1

Semi-Finals

Ludlow Town v Oakengates Town	2-3	Albrighton S. & S. v Shifnal Town	2-1

Final *(at Telford United FC, Tues 23rd March)*: Oakengates Town 0, Albrighton S. & S. 0.
Replay: Oakengates Town 1, Albrighton S. & S. 0

Other County Finals:
Junior Cup: Weston Rhyn United v Belvidere 0
Sunday Premier Cup: Newport R.B.L. 2, Shifnal Juniors 0
Sunday Cup: NALGO (Sunday) 4, Bulls Head (Whitchurch) 3

SOMERSET

Somerset & Avon (South) Premier Cup First Round

Larkhall Athletic v Paulton Rovers	0-3	Minehead v Glastonbury	5-4
Wellington v Bath City	0-5		

Second Round

Welton Rovers v Chard Town	4-0	Bath City v Keynsham Town	3-1
Clandown *(scr.)* Weston-super-Mare *(w/o)*		Bristol City Reserves v Paulton Rovers	0-4
Mangotsfield United v Frome Town	3-0	Bristol Rovers Reserves v Minehead	8-0
Radstock Town v Taunton Town	0-7	Clevedon Town v Yeovil Town	1-0
(continued opposite)			

Quarter-Finals

Bath City v Clevedon Town	3-1	Paulton Rovers v Weston-super-Mare	3-1
Taunton Town v Welton Rovers	2-1	Mangotsfield United v Bristol Rovers Reserves	0-6

Semi-Finals

Taunton Town v Paulton Rovers	3-0	Bristol Rovers Reserves 4, Bath City 1	4-1

Final. First Leg *(Mon 19th April)*: Taunton Town 1, Bristol Rovers Reserves 4
Second Leg *(Mon 26th April)*: Bristol Rovers Reserves 1, Taunton Town 0

Somerset & Avon (South) Senior Cup

First Round

Clevedon Town Reserves v Wells City	2-1	Bridgwater Town '84 v Welton Rovers Reserves	2-0
Burnham United v Mendip Wells	0-2	Timsbury Athletic v Imperial United	0-5
Glastonbury Reserves v P. & W. United	0-4	Cheddar v Frome Town Reserves	1-3
Clandown v Blackbrook	0-4	Clevedon United v Portishead	4-0
T.D.R. Dynamo v Banwell	3-4	Broad Plain House v Weston-super-Mare Reserves	3-4
Brislington v Peasedown Athletic	6-2	Stockwood Green v Watchet Town	3-4
Odd Down Res. v Blackwell Utd Reserves	1-0	Farleigh Sports v Hartcliffe Community Centre	1-0
Yatton Athletic v Castle Cary	1-3	Teyfant Athletic v Congresbury	0-6
Wrington-Redhill v Imperial Bristol	1-3	Hartcliffe Old Boys v Keynsham Town Reserves	2-3
Nailsea Town v Hartcliffe	2-4	Winscombe v Larkhall Athletic Reserves	0-1
Weston St John's v Fry Club	0-2	Westland Sports v Paulton Rovers Reserves	6-1
Long Sutton v Highridge United	2-1	Avon & Somerset Police v Ilminster Town	0-3
Dundry Athletic v Saltford	0-5	Nailsea United v Clutton	2-3
Keynsham Cricketers v St G. Easton-in-G.	0-1	Tunley Athletic v Westland United	3-2
Street v Bristol Spartak	0-1	Bishop Sutton v Shepton Mallet Town	1-3
Hengrove Ath., Temple Cloud *(byes)*			

Second Round

Congresbury v Clevedon United	2-7	Hengrove Athletic v Frome Town Reserves	1-2
Tunley Athletic v Clutton	2-4	Mendip Wells v Imperial Bristol	0-1
Ilminster Town v Weston-s-Mare Reserves	1-2	Larkhall Athletic Reserves v Odd Down Reserves	0-2
Castle Cary v Fry Club	2-2,5-0	Westland Sports v Clevedon Town Reserves	3-0
Farleigh Sports v Long Sutton	2-7	Hartcliffe v Imperial United	3-1
Bristol Spartak v P. & W. United	1-7	Brislington v Temple Cloud	7-0
Bridgwater Town v Shepton Mallet Town	7-0	St George Easton-in-Gordano v Banwell	6-0
Blackbrook v Saltford	2-3	Keynsham Town Reserves v Watchet Town	4-2

Third Round

Long Sutton v Frome Town Reserves	4-1	Imperial Bristol v Saltford	2-5
Westland Sports v Castle Cary	1-3	Hartcliffe v P. & W. United	0-4
Keynsham Town Reserves v Clutton	2-1	Bridgwater Town '84 v Clevedon United	3-3,3-1
Weston-super-Mare Reserves v Brislington	2-3	St G. Easton-in-Gordano v Odd Down Reserves	0-5

Quarter-Finals

Castle Cary v Odd Down Reserves	2-4	Keynsham Town Reserves v Long Sutton	0-3
P. & W. United v Brislington	0-0,0-3	Saltford v Bridgwater Town '84	2-1

Semi-Finals

Saltford v Long Sutton	1-0	Odd Down Reserves v Brislington	1-2

Final *(at Paulton Rovers FC, Mon 3rd May)*: Brislington 1, Saltford 0

Other County Finals:
Intermediate Cup *(at Frome Town FC, Tues 11th May)*: Odd Down 'A' 3, Bruton Town 1
Junior Cup *(at Glastonbury FC, Wed 21st April)*: Corinthian Sports 1, British Cellophane 0
Mavis Tate Inter-Lge Cup *(at Paulton Rovers FC, Wed 28th April)*: Mid-Somerset Lge 2, Yeovil & Dist. Lge 1
Sunday Challenge Cup *(at Backwell Utd FC, Sun 16th May)*: Anglo Glass Spts 6, Sartan United 2
Sunday Junior Cup *(at Bath City FC, Sun 9th May)*: Weston Ex-Services 2, Rosewarm Utd 0
Durnford Inter-Lge Cup *(at Long Sutton FC, Thurs 29th April)* Bridgwater Sunday Lge 1, Perry Street Lge 1.
Replay *(at Glastonbury FC, Wed 19th May)*: Bridgwater Sunday Lge 1, Perry Street Lge 0
Lewin Cup *(at Glastonbury FC, Sun 2nd May)*: Weston St John's Jnr 4, Galmington Yth 0
Youth Shields *(at Bridgwater Town FC, Sun 2nd May)*: Westland Sports 4, Street 0

STAFFORDSHIRE

Senior Cup Final 1991-92 (held over to 92-93)
First leg *(Sat 8th August 1992)*: Chasetown 0, Stafford Rangers 2
Second leg *(Tues 18th August)*: Stafford Rangers 2, Chasetown 2

Senior Cup 92-93
First Round

Armitage '90 v Dudley Town	1-1,1-4	Halesowen T. v Hednesford	1-1,2-2,1-2(void),3-5
Tamworth v Rushall Olympic	1-0	Sutton Coldfield Town v Stourbridge	4-1
Rocester v Kidsgrove Athletic	5-0	Boldmere St Michaels v Congleton Town	1-0
Chasetown v Wednesfield	5-0	Leek Town v Bilston Town	2-1
Newcastle Town v Blakenall	3-1	Oldswinford F. & S.C. v Eastwood Hanley	2-3
Stourport Swifts v Walsall Wood	1-2		

Second Round

Dudley Town v Boldmere St Michaels	1-1,2-0	Chasetown v Sutton Coldfield Town	2-0
Hednesford Town v Tamworth	3-1	Stafford Rgrs v Birmingham C. Reserves	1-2
Newcastle Town v Halesowen Harriers	1-0	Eastwood Hanley v Stoke City Reserves	0-4
Leek Town v Walsall Wood	6-1	Rocester v Port Vale Reserves	1-1,4-1

Quarter-Finals

Chasetown v Birmingham City Reserves	0-1	Hednesford Town v Newcastle Town	3-3,4-1
Dudley Town v Leek Town	0-1	Rocester v Stoke City Reserves	1-3

Semi-Finals

Hednesford Town v Birmingham City Res.	2-1	Leek Town v Stoke City Reserves	0-2

Final 1st leg: Stoke City Reserves 2, Hednesford Town 0
2nd leg: Hednesford Town 1, Stoke City Reserves 4

SUFFOLK

Premier Round Preliminary Round
Newmarket Town v Cornard United 1-1*(aban.)*,1-2

Quarter-Finals

Bury Town v Sudbury Town	0-1	Felixstowe Town v Brantham Athletic	2-2,1-2*(aet)*
Stowmarket Town v Lowestoft Town	2-3	Haverhill Rovers v Cornard United	1-1,2-8

Semi-Finals

Cornard Utd v Sudbury Town	1-1,2-4	Lowestoft Town v Brantham Athletic	2-3

Final *(at Sudbury Town FC, Mon 3rd May)*: Sudbury Town 2, Brantham Athletic 1

Senior Cup Preliminary Round
Halesworth Town v Woodbridge Town   0-1

First Round

Stowmarket Town v Bury Town Reserves	3-1	British Sugar Fonnereau Ath. v Brandon T.	4-4,3-2
Grundisburgh v Hadleigh United	1-0	Beccles Town v Old Newton United	1-1,2-0
Sudbury T. Reserves v Mildenhall Town	2-2,2-4	Sudbury Lucas Athletic v Oulton Broad	1-2
Walsham-le-Willows v Stutton	1-2	Felixstowe Town Reserves v Willis Corroon	3-1
Long Melford v Ipswich Wanderers	0-4	Lowestoft Town Reserves v R.S.S.C. Ransomes	2-0
Ashlea v Westerfield United	0-1	Kirkley v Sudbury Wanderers	0-2
Melton St Audrys v B.T. Research	3-2	Needham Market v Whitton United	2-1
Woodbridge Town v Haughley United	6-3	Stonham Aspal v Framlington Town	0-0,4-1

Second Round

British Sugar Fonnereau v Mildenhall Town	4-2	Felixstowe Reserves v Oulton Broad	2-2*(aet)*,4-3*(aet)*
Melton St Audrys v Ipswich Wanderers	1-2	Stonham Aspal v Lowestoft Town Reserves	6-2
Stutton v Beccles Town	5-0	Sudbury Wanderers v Stowmarket Town Reserves	3-0
Grundisburgh v Woodbridge Town	1-2	Westerfield United v Needham Market	1-3

Quarter-Finals

Sudbury Wanderers v Woodbridge Town	0-3	British Sugar Fonnereau Athletic v Stutton	2-1
Needham Market v Ipswich Wanderers	1-0	Felixstowe Town Reserves v Stonham Aspal	0-2

Semi-Finals

Stonham Aspal v British Sugar Fonnereau Ath.		Woodbridge Town v Needham Market	
(at Stowmarket Town FC)	3-1	*(at R.S.S.C. Ransomes FC)*	4-1

Final *(at Ipswich Town FC, Tues 27th April)*: Woodbridge Town 5, Stonham Aspal 2 *(aet)*

Other County Finals
Junior Cup *(at Needham Market FC, Sat 24th April)*: Newbury United 2, Ipswich Athletic 0
Primary Cup *(at Walsham-le-Willows FC, Sat 1st May)*: Lakenheath Reserves 2, Wanderers Social 0
Sunday Cup *(at Whitton Utd FC, Sun 2nd May)*: Heathfield 3, St Clements Hospital 2
Sunday Shield *(at Crane FC, Sun 25th April)*: Jewson 2, Duke of York 1
Sunday Trophy *(at Leiston FC, Sun 11th April)*: Gunton Old Boys 1, Hare & Hounds 0
Minor Cup *(at Hadleigh Utd FC, Sun 4th April)*: Sudbury Wanderers 5, Needham Phoenix 1

SURREY

'Ribero' Senior Cup First Qualifying Round

Ditton v Carshalton	3-0	Corinthian-Casuals v Farleigh Rovers	1-0
Ash United v Frimley Green	3-2	Malden Town *(w/o)* Farnham Town *(scr.)*	
Redhill v Merton	2-0	Ashford Town (Middx) v Kew Association	2-0
Cobham v Sheen Old Grammarians	4-1	Camberley Town v St Andrews	2-0

Second Qualifying Round

Banstead Athletic v Westfield	4-1	Merstham v Old Suttonians	4-1
Ditton v Chipstead	0-2	Corinthian-Casuals v Cranleigh	1-0
Godalming & Guildford v Horley Town	0-4	Ash United v Malden Town	6-2
Redhill v Ashford Town (Middx)	2-3	Cobham v Camberley Town	0-3

Third Qualifying Round

Banstead Athletic v Merstham	3-5	Chipstead v Corinthian-Casuals	1-3
Horley Town v Ash United	1-2	Ashford Town (Middx) v Camberley Town	3-1

Fourth Qualifying Round

Merstham v Leatherhead	0-5	Molesey v Malden Vale	0-1
Tooting & Mitcham Utd v Corinthian-Casuals	4-2	Ash United v Ashford Town (Middx)	3-2

First Round Proper

Sutton United v Epsom & Ewell	2-0	Leatherhead v Chertsey Town	2-1
Metropolitan Police v Kingstonian	2-1	Whyteleafe v Walton & Hersham	2-1
Dorking v Woking	2-2,2-0	Malden Vale v Croydon	4-0
Carshalton Athletic v Ash United	4-0	Tooting & Mitcham Utd v Egham Town	1-1,2-1

Quarter-Finals

Leatherhead v Sutton United	0-6	Metropolitan Police v Whyteleafe	5-2
Dorking v Malden Vale	0-1	Tooting & Mitcham Utd v Carshalton Athletic	1-2

Semi-Finals

Carshalton Athletic v Malden Vale	2-0	Sutton United v Metropolitan Police	1-1,3-2

Final *(at Sutton United, Wed 12th April)*: Sutton United 2, Carshalton Athletic 1 *(att: 1,452)*

Other County Finals
Premier Cup: Sutton United Reserves 3, Chobham 1
Intermediate Cup: Bradbank Sports 3, Shottermill 0
Junior Cup: Hale 5, University of Surrey 0 *(aet)*
Lower Junior Cup: Phoenix Sun 3, Lower Green 2
Sunday Senior Cup: Ranelagh Sports 1, West Ewell 0
Sunday Intermediate Cup: Bridge Boys 3, Morden Royals 1
Sunday Junior Cup: Ashtead Park 3, Everest 2
Lower Junior Cup: Auriol 2, Tornadoes 1
Midweek Cup: Kingston Police 2, Wimbledon Postal 1
Veterans Cup: Horley Town Casuals 2, Strollers 0
Saturday Inter-Lge Cup: Surrey County Premier Lge 6, Kingston & Dist. Lge 2
Sunday Inter-Lge Cup: Mitcham & Dist. Sunday Lge 2, South Thameside Sunday Lge 0

Sutton United (light shirts) start their Surrey Senior Cup run with a 6-0 romp at Leatherhead. Photo - Eric Marsh.

Lee Holman (right) battles as hard as his Ashford Town side beat Camberley Town 3-2. Photo - Eric Marsh.

Hale F.C. of Farnham, Surrey Junior Cup winners 1992-93. Photo - Eric Marsh.

SUSSEX

Senior Cup
First Round

Steyning Town v Worthing United	2-1	Southwick v Hassocks	1-2
Portfield v Selsey	0-1	Bexhill Town v Horsham Y.M.C.A.	0-2
Lancing v Shoreham	5-1	Little Common Albion v Horsham	0-5
Stamco v Sidley United	3-1	Eastbourne United v Mile Oak	0-2
Haywards Heath Town v Broadbridge Heath	0-3	Midhurst & Easebourne v Chichester City	1-0
Saltdean United v Seaford Town	1-2	East Grinstead v Crowborough Athletic	0-1

Second Round

Littlehampton Town v Three Bridges	2-1	Steyning Town v Langney Sports	0-3
Hassocks v Bognor Regis Town	2-4	Selsey v Ringmer	3-2
Eastbourne Town v Burgess Hill T.	3-3.1-5	Oakwood v Hailsham Town	4-1
Worthing v Crawley Town	3-1	Horsham Y.M.C.A. v Lancing	0-3
Horsham v Peacehaven & Telscombe	2-1	Stamco v Hastings Town	0-3
Mile Oak v Arundel	2-3	Broadbridge Heath v Midhurst & Easebourne	0-2
Newhaven v Pagham	1-2	Brighton & Hove Albion Reserves v Lewes	1-1,2-0
Seaford Town v Whitehawk	2-1	Wick v Crowborough Athletic	5-1

Third Round

Littlehampton Town v Langney Sports	2-5	Bignor Regis Town v Selsey	1-0
Burgess Hill Town v Oakwood	0-2	Worthing v Lancing	4-0
Horsham v Hastings Town	0-3	Arundel v Midhurst & Easebourne	1-2
Pagham v Brighton & Hove Albion Reserves	2-1	Seaford Town v Wick	0-1

Quarter-Finals

Langney Sports v Bognor Regis Town	1-2	Oakwood v Worthing	2-0
Hastings Town v Midhurst & Easebourne	2-0	Pagham v Wick	1-1,1-2

Semi-Finals

Bognor Regis v Oakwood *(at Horsham FC)*	1-2	Wick v Hastings Town *(at Lewes FC)*	2-0

Final *(at Brighton & Hove Albion, Mon 3rd May)*: Wick 3, Oakwood 1

Royal Ulster Rifles Charity Cup
Preliminary Round

Oakwood v Seaford Town	3-0*(aet)*	Crowborough Athletic v Little Common Albion	2-0
Pagham v Southwick	5-0	Broadbridge Heath v Midhurst & Easebourne	3-0

First Round

Whitehawk v Eastbourne United	8-1	Peacehaven & Telscombe v Stamco	2-1
Haywards Heath Town v Langney Sports	0-3	Ringmer v Bexhill Town	2-3*(aet)*
Oakwood v East Grinstead	1-3	Crowborough Athletic v Eastbourne Town	3-1
Sidley United v Saltdean United	1-3	Newhaven v Hailsham Town	0-1
Worthing United v Hassocks	1-2	Portfield v Wick	2-2*(aet)*,1-3
Lancing v Littlehampton Town	5-4*(aet)*	Selsey v Arundel	1-1*(aet)*,0-1
Pagham v Burgess Hill Town	7-2*(aet)*	Broadbridge Heath v Chichester City	1-3
Three Bridges v Shoreham	2-3	Mile Oak v Horsham Y.M.C.A.	0-4

Second Round

Saltdean United v Hailsham Town	0-3	Peacehaven & Telscombe v East Grinstead	2-1
Langney Sports v Crowborough Athletic	4-0	Bexhill Town v Whitehawk	4-3
Shoreham v Horsham Y.M.C.A.	2-1	Wick v Pagham	1-3
Lancing v Chichester City	1-0	Arundel v Hassocks	0-1

Quarter-Finals

Hailsham Town v Peacehaven & Telscombe	0-5	Bexhill Town v Langney Sports	1-0
Pagham v Hassocks	2-1	Lancing v Shoreham	2-2*(aet)*,2-2*(aet)*,3-2*(at Lancing)*

Semi-Finals

Bexhill Town v Lancing	0-1*(aet)*	Peacehaven & Telscombe v Pagham	1-0

Final *(at Lancing FC, Tues 2nd March)*: Lancing 1, Peacehaven & Telscombe 2

Sussex Floodlit Cup
Preliminary Round (all ties 2-legged)

Lewes v Selsey	3-1,0-1	Whitehawk v Wick	1-1,3-1*(aet)*
Newhaven v Burgess Hill Town	4-0,5-2	Haywards Heath Town v Hailsham Town	0-0,0-7
Portfield v Shoreham	2-1,4-2	Pagham v Oakwood	5-4,8-1
Eastbourne United v Worthing	2-2,0-11	Langney Sports v Horsham	2-2,2-3
Three Bridges v Lancing	3-1,0-0		

Second Round

Worthing v Lewes	1-1,1-5	Crawley v Shoreham	3-0,0-1*(ab. - fog - 40mins)*,3-1
Hailsham Town v Three Bridges	3-2,4-1	Horsham v Pagham	1-2,1-0*(P'ham win - away gls)*
Newhaven v Southwick	2-2,4-2*(aet)*	East Grinstead v Peacehaven & Telscombe	2-4,0-5
Ringmer v Horsham Y.M.C.A.	4-1,2-1	Wick v Littlehampton Town	3-2,1-1

Quarter-Finals

Hailsham Town v Newhaven	5-1,0-2	Peacehaven & Telscombe v Ringmer	4-2,2-1
Lewes v Crawley Town	3-4,2-4	Wick v Pagham	2-2,2-1

Semi-Finals

Hailsham Town v Wick	1-2,4-2	Peacehaven & Telscombe v Crawley Town	0-2,0-1

Final *(at Lancing FC, Tues 20th April)*: Crawley Town 5, Hailsham Town 1

Other County Finals:
Intermediate Cup: Crawley Town Reserves 3, St Francis Hospital 0
Junior Cup: Barclays Bank (Brighton) 5, Nutley 1
Sunday Senior Cup: Kings Head (Ore) 6, Newman 2
Sunday Junior Cup: Pagham Social Club 3, White Horse Rottingdean 2
Midweek Cup: Brighton Post Office 2, Gatwick Handling 1 *(aet)*
Inter-Lge Intermediate Cup: East Sussex Lge 2, Mid-Sussex Lge 1 *(aet)*
Inter-Lge Junior Cup: West Sussex Lge 6, East Sussex Lge 2

Wick celebrate at the Goldstone Ground after their Senior Cup success. Photo - Roger Turner.

Paul Smith whips in a cross for Pagham in the 7-2 win over Burgess Hill in the R.U.R. Cup. Photo - Graham Cotterill.

Phil Comber hits Hailsham's second, from the spot, at Saltdean in the R.U.R. Cup. Photo - Dennis Nicholson.

WEST RIDING

Senior Cup
First Round
Guiseley v Farsley Celtic	3-0	Hatfield Main v Eccleshill United	1-4
Thackley v Yorkshire Amateur	0-1	Ossett Town v Armthorpe Welfare ·	0-1

Second Round
Goole Town v Garforth Town	2-2,1-0	Glasshoughton Welfare v Bradford Park Avenue	4-0
Selby Town v Bradley Rangers	2-1	Eccleshill United v Pontefract Collieries	2-0
Yorkshire Amateur v Tadcaster Albiom	0-2	Liversedge v Harrogate Railway Athletic	2-0
Armthorpe Welfare v Ossett Albion	3-1	Guiseley v Harrogate Town	3-0

Quarter-Finals
Selby Town v Eccleshill United	3-1	Glasshoughton Welfare v Tadcaster Albion	1-0
Goole Town v Guiseley	1-0	Liversedge v Armthorpe Welfare	3-1

Semi-Finals
Selby Town v Liversedge	2-1	Glasshoughton Welfare v Goole Town	2-1

Final *(at Huddersfield Town FC, Thurs 29th April)*: Glasshoughton Welfare 4, Selby Town 2

Other County Finals:
Challenge Cup: Thorne Colliery 1, Ferrybridge Amateurs 0
Sunday Cup: Ventus United 4, Albion Sports 0
Minor Cup (Rep. sides): Leeds F.A. 2, Bradford F.A. 1
Junior Cup (under-16): Fryston Jnrs 1, Brayton Jnrs 0 *(after 1-1 draw)*

WESTMORLAND

Senior Cup First Round
Burneside v Wetheriggs	4-2	Corinthians v Kendal United	1-3
Greystoke v Burton Thistle	3-7	Ibis v Esthwaite Vale	3-1
Shap v Braithwaite	3-2	Netherfield v Appleby	2-2(aet),3-2(aet)
Sedburgh v Staveley	0-1	Kirkoswald v Victoria Sports	3-2
Kendal County v Kirkby Lonsdale	7-0		

Second Round
Burneside v Keswick	2-1	Staveley v Ambleside	0-3
Kendal County v Windermere	6-1	Netherfield v Kirby Stephen	5-2(aet)
Grasmere v Shap	1-2	Kirkoswald v Burton Thistle	1-4
Kendal United v Ibis	8-1	Endmoor K.G.R. v Coniston	0-4

Quarter-Finals
Shap v Kendal County	0-3	Coniston v Burneside	3-1
Burton Thistle v Ambleside	1-4	Burneside v Kendal United	4-1

Semi-Finals
Coniston v Kendal County	2-1	Kendal United v Ambleside	0-1

Final *(at Netherfield FC, Sat 17th April)*: Coniston 4, Ambleside 2 *(aet)*

WILTSHIRE

Premier Shield Preliminary Round
Salisbury v Calne Town	1-3

First Round
Trowbridge Town v Melksham Town	9-0	Warminster Town v Westbury United	1-1,0-1
Swindon Town v Chippenham Town	8-1	Devizes Town v Calne Town	1-2

Semi-Finals
Westbury United v Calne Town	2-0	Trowbridge Town v Swindon Town	1-0

Final: Trowbridge Town 1, Westbury United 0

Senior Cup First Round
Wroughton v Swindon Supermarine	0-6	Tisbury v Bemerton Heath Harlequins	0-6
Stratton Red Eagles v Amesbury Town	0-3	Bradford Town v Wollen Sports	0-4
Avebury Park v Malmesbury Victoria	5-2	Wootton Bassett Town v Highworth Town	2-1
Ferndale Athletic v Burmah Castrol	2-2,3-1	Bromham v Walcot Athletic	2-5
Corsham Town v Pinehurst	3-4	Shrewton United v Dunbar Wills	8-2
Purton v Biddestone	2-3	Chiseldon v Sanford	2-2,0-7
Marlborough Town v Aldbourne Park	1-3	Downton v Pewsey Vale	4-0
West Swindon *(scr.)* Plessey Semics *(w/o)*		Dorcan *(bye)*	

Second Round
Downton v Wootton Bassett Town	4-0	Wollen Sports v Shrewton United	2-1
Biddestone v Amesbury Town	5-1	Plessey Semics v Walcot Athletic	1-4
Ferndale Athletic v Swindon Supermarine	1-5	Sanford v Dorcan	4-1
Aldbourne Park v Bemerton Hth Harlequins	0-3	Pinehurst v Avebury Park	0-4

Quarter-Finals
Wollen Sports v Biddestone	2-0	Swindon Supermarine v Bemerton Hth Harlequins	0-2
Downton v Walcot Athletic	2-1	Avebury Park v Sanford	2-3

Semi-Finals
Sanford v Wollen Sports	0-3	Bemerton Heath v Downton	1-1(aet, 5-4 pens)

Final *(at Swindon Town FC, Wed 21st April)*: Bemerton Heath Harlequins 3, Wollen Sports 1

Wiltshire Premier Shield *(at Salisbury FC, 8th March)*: Salisbury 1, Trowbridge Town 2

Other County Finals:
Junior Cup: South Newton & Wishford 3, Airsprung '88 0
Sunday Cup: Juventus 1, New Century W.M.C. 0
Youth Cup: Devizes Town 4, Chippenham Town 2
Minor Cup (under-15): Corsham Boys 6, Oaksey 4
Minor Cup (under-13): Highworth Jnr 2, Ferndale Y.C. 0

WORCESTERSHIRE

Senior Cup

First Round

Solihull Borough v Moor Green	3-0	Evesham United v Stourbridge	0-3
Dudley Town v Redditch United	2-1		

Quarter-Finals

Solihull Borough v Worcester City	6-2	Kidderminster Harriers v Sutton Coldfield Town	3-2
Dudley Town v Bromsgrove Rovers	0-1	Barri v Stourbridge	2-2,4-1

Semi-Finals

Kidderminster Harriers v Bromsgrove R.	2-0	Barri v Solihull Borough	1-3

Final First Leg *(Wed 24th March)*: Solihull Borough 0, Kidderminster Harriers 1
Final Second Leg *(Mon 26th April)*: Kidderminster Harriers 2, Solihull Borough 1

Senior Urn

First Round

Alcester Town v Pershore Town	0-2	Pegasus Juniors v Kidderminster Harriers Res.	5-2
Stourport Swifts v Highgate Utd	0-0,1-0		

Semi-Finals

Pershore Town v Pegasus Juniors	2-1	West Midlands Police v Stourport Swifts	0-4

Final First Leg *(Wed 7th April)*: Stourport Swifts 1, Pershore Town 0
Final Second Leg *(Tues 20th April)*: Pershore Town 1, Stourport Swifts 3

Stourport Swifts, of the Boddingtons Bitter West Midlands League, take delight in the 3-1 win at Pershore Town that gave them the Worcestershire Senior Urn on a aggregate score of 4-1. Photo - Mark Wood.

Other County Finals

Junior Cup *(at Bromsgrove Rovers FC, Tues 27th April)*: Sutton Coldfield Town Reserves 4, Colletts Green 1
Minor Cup *(at Wolverley Athletic FC, Thurs 15th April)*: Worths 2, Areley Kings 0
Youth Cup *(at Kidderminster Harriers FC, Mon 3rd May)*: Kidderminster Harriers Youth 2, Boldmere St Michaels Youth 1
Sunday Premier Cup *(at Stourport Swifts FC, Sun 2nd May)*: Kingswinford 1, Garringtons Sunday 0
Sunday Junior Cup *(at Archdales FC, Sun 4th April)*: Brintons 2, Mayfly 0
Sunday Minor Cup *(at Pershore Town FC, Sun 25th April)*: Bredon 2, Briars 1
Sunday under-16s Cup *(at Archdales FC, Sun 25th April)*: Kidderminsters Harr. Boys 3, Bromsgrove Town Boys 2

Vol. 13 No. 1 *August 1993*

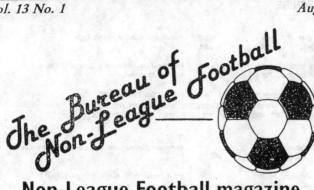

The Bureau of Non-League Football

Non-League Football magazine.

SENIOR CUP NEWS

TO MAKE SURE OF YOUR COPY; POSTED
1ST CLASS EACH MONTH SEND
£15-50
TO BNLF
173, LEYTONSTONE ROAD, LONDON E15 1LH.

F.A. COMPETITION RESULTS

FIXTURES

RESULTS

LEAGUE TABLES

+ News Snippets from around the country

G.M. VAUXHALL CONFERENCE

President: J C Thompson
Chairman: W J King
Vice-Chairman: G E Smith

Secretary: P D Hunter,
24 Barnehurst Road, Bexleyheath, Kent DA7 6EZ

Season 1992/93 proved to be another successful season for the Conference. Playing standards and attendance levels were maintained and media interest and coverage continued to increase.

Congratulations are extended to Wycombe Wanderersm who emulated Colchester United in winning the Conference Championship and the Vauxhall FA Challenge Trophy. We wish them continued success in the Football League. Let us hope that next season the critics of the automatic promotion system will be silenced by the promotion of Wycombe Wanderers. Of all our candidates for promotion they appear to have the qualification to make a success of the evelvation and hopefully set an example for others to follow.

Bromsgrove Rovers in their first season in the Conference must be congratulated on their last minute run-in to become creditable runners-up to Wycombe.

The Vauxhall FA Challenge Trophy Final at Wembley once again featured two Conference clubs. Played in front of a near record crowd, Wycombe defeated a very gallant Runcorn 4-1.

The FA Cup reflected the playing strength of Conference sides. Yeovil Town played their first major cup tie at their new stadium. They reached the Third Round and had the daunting task of playing the mighty Arsenal at The Huish. Seven clubs won places to the Second Round; Altrincham, Bath City, Macclesfield Town, Stafford Rangers, Woking, Wycombe Wanderers and Yeovil. Bath City, Woking and Wycombe went out after replays against Northampton Town, Brighton and West Bromwich Albion respectively.

The Bob Lord Challenge Trophy, re-named the Drinkwise Cup following the sponsorship of the competition by the Health Education Authority, was won by Northwich Victoria who defeated Wycombe Wanderers over the two legged final. The second leg played at Wycombe which Northwich won 3-2 after extra time in front of 4,264 spectators was an outstanding game. Both teams were congratulated on their performances which was a credit to all those involved. Our sponsors were impressed for they have agreed to extend their sponsorship for a further season.

Three new clubs will be playing in the Conference next season. A welcome is extended to Halifax Town, who like Lincoln City, Darlington and Colchester before them, will, we are sure, enjoy playing in the Conference. The two promoted clubs are Dover Athletic, Champions of the Beazer Homes League and Southport, Champions of the Northen Premier League. Dover have been knocking on the door for three seasons. Their promotion is well deserved. Southport, who worked miracles on their ground in order to meet the criteria in the time scale, are certain to be a credit to the Conference. What Southport have achieved should serve as an example to all clubs who have ambitions of promotion to the Conference.

It is very sad to record that one of our remaining Founder Member Clubs was relegated. Boston United were great members. We will miss all those connected with the club and the friendly atmosphere that always prevailed at Boston. It is interesting to note that only four clubs of the original composition of the Alliance Premier League remain in continuous membership. They are Altrincham, Kettering Town, Northwich Victoria and Telford United.

Farnborough Town, who we are losing for the second time, are wished every success next season. They have the prospect of playing next season without Ted Pearce, their long serving Club Manager.

Our sponsors continue to support us. Vauxhall Motors, The Mail on Sunday and Minerva Footballs remain with us in addition to the Drinkwise campaign. We are very grateful to them all for their continued interest and active support.

What does season 1993/94 have in store?

For Conference clubs it means facing far more stringent criteria for promotion of its Champions to the Football League. Therefore, the Conference has to consider whether or not in the future they can afford to promote clubs from the Feeder Leagues who do not have the potential for promotion to the Football League.

Will the new temporary transfer system for contract players between the FA Premier League, The Football League, The Conference, the Beazer Homes, Diadora and Northern Premier Leagues curb the unacceptable practices of Club managers in the past seasons?

There is always something new in football. No doubt season 1993/94 will be no exception!

P D Hunter (Secretary)

G.M. Vauxhall Conference

Final League Table 1992-93

	P	HOME W	D	L	AWAY W	D	L	F	A	Pts
WYCOMBE WANDERERS	42	13	5	3	11	6	4	84	37	83
BROMSGROVE ROVERS	42	9	7	5	9	7	5	67	49	68
DAGENHAM & REDBRIDGE	42	10	5	6	9	6	6	75	47	67
YEOVIL TOWN	42	13	5	3	5	7	9	59	49	66
SLOUGH TOWN	42	12	3	6	6	8	7	60	55	65
STAFFORD RANGERS	42	7	6	8	11	4	6	55	47	64
BATH CITY	42	9	8	4	6	6	9	53	46	59
WOKING	42	9	2	10	8	6	7	58	62	59
KIDDERMINSTER HARRIERS	42	9	5	7	5	11	5	60	60	58
ALTRINCHAM	42	7	7	7	8	6	7	49	52	58
NORTHWICH VICTORIA	42	5	6	10	11	2	5	68	55	56
STALYBRIDGE CELTIC	42	7	10	4	6	7	8	48	55	56
KETTERING TOWN	42	10	5	6	4	8	9	61	63	55
GATESHEAD	42	9	6	6	5	4	12	53	56	52
TELFORD UNITED	42	9	5	7	5	5	11	55	60	52
MERTHYR TYDFIL	42	4	9	8	10	1	10	51	79	52
WITTON ALBION	42	5	9	7	6	8	7	62	65	50
MACCLESFIELD TOWN	42	7	9	5	5	4	12	40	50	49
RUNCORN	42	8	3	10	5	7	9	58	76	49
WELLING UNITED	42	8	6	7	4	6	11	57	72	48
FARNBOROUGH TOWN	42	8	5	8	4	6	11	68	87	47
BOSTON UNITED	42	5	6	10	4	7	10	50	69	40

Dagenham & Redbridge -1 point for fielding an ineligible player.

RESULTS CHART 1992-93

HOME TEAM	1	2	3	4	5	6	7	8	9	10	11	12	13	14	15	16	17	18	19	20	21	22
1. Altrincham	*	1-0	1-1	2-2	1-0	2-2	0-1	3-0	2-2	1-0	0-1	0-0	0-2	1-1	1-5	0-0	0-3	2-0	2-1	1-0	0-2	1-2
2. Bath	3-0	*	2-1	0-3	2-1	5-2	1-1	0-0	2-1	0-0	1-3	0-5	1-1	0-1	1-1	4-1	1-1	0-0	2-0	2-0	0-0	
3. Boston	1-2	1-2	*	1-2	3-1	0-0	0-2	0-1	0-3	3-1	2-0	3-5	0-0	0-0	0-1	1-1	2-2	2-1	2-2	1-2	0-3	1-0
4. Bromsgrove	4-1	1-1	2-1	*	1-2	2-2	3-0	1-1	2-2	3-0	1-2	1-2	0-0	0-1	2-3	4-0	0-0	2-2	3-2	1-0	1-0	1-0
5. Dagenham	2-2	2-1	1-0	1-1	*	5-1	3-1	1-2	3-2	1-2	6-1	4-1	5-1	4-4	0-1	1-2	0-2	1-0	1-1	5-1	1-2	1-1
6. Farnborough	2-5	2-1	4-0	1-1	1-4	*	6-1	3-2	2-2	0-0	2-1	0-3	2-3	1-0	1-1	1-2	0-1	3-2	1-1	0-3	0-2	2-1
7. Gateshead	2-0	0-4	2-2	0-0	1-1	1-0	*	1-1	1-0	1-0	4-0	0-2	4-1	1-0	0-1	0-0	0-1	1-2	3-1	1-1	0-1	4-1
8. Kettering	1-1	0-1	3-3	3-2	0-0	2-1	2-0	*	1-2	1-0	1-3	2-1	3-3	5-0	2-0	2-0	1-1	2-4	2-1	0-1	4-0	3-0
9. Kidderminster	0-1	1-0	0-2	1-0	0-1	1-5	3-3	0-0	*	2-1	1-0	5-3	2-0	1-1	0-2	2-1	2-1	2-1	0-0	1-3	1-4	1-1
10. Macclesfield	1-1	1-0	2-1	0-2	1-1	1-2	1-0	1-0	1-1	*	0-1	1-2	1-1	1-2	4-1	1-0	1-1	1-1	1-0	1-1	1-1	1-1
11. Merthyr	2-2	1-1	0-3	1-1	0-2	1-3	1-1	2-1	4-3	1-2	*	3-0	0-3	1-1	0-0	1-1	4-0	1-1	0-2	1-5	1-4	1-1
12. Northwich	1-2	3-1	3-3	0-1	1-1	3-0	0-0	2-2	0-1	1-3	1-2	*	3-2	0-1	1-2	1-3	1-0	1-1	1-3	1-0	0-0	0-1
13. Runcorn	0-1	1-3	1-2	2-1	1-0	1-4	4-2	2-2	0-0	1-2	2-3	0-1	*	0-3	0-2	2-1	3-1	3-0	4-4	2-3	2-1	1-0
14. Slough	1-4	1-1	3-0	1-3	2-0	3-1	1-0	3-0	3-1	2-1	2-1	0-4	1-1	*	2-1	2-3	2-0	4-2	2-3	0-1	1-1	3-0
15. Stafford	0-0	3-2	0-0	3-4	0-1	2-2	2-1	2-4	0-1	1-0	0-1	1-0	1-0	1-0	*	0-0	2-1	4-3	1-1	0-0	0-1	0-1
16. Stalybridge	1-0	1-1	2-1	0-1	0-3	2-0	2-1	0-0	2-2	2-1	2-2	0-6	0-0	0-0	1-0	*	3-3	0-0	1-2	3-0	2-2	1-1
17. Telford	2-1	0-0	0-1	0-1	0-1	6-3	1-0	3-1	1-1	3-1	5-0	1-0	2-1	1-1	0-0	0-2	*	0-1	0-3	3-3	2-3	1-0
18. Welling	2-0	0-3	2-2	4-2	0-2	3-1	2-1	1-1	0-0	1-0	5-0	1-5	3-2	2-1	1-2	1-4	1-3	*	2-2	1-1	2-2	0-3
19. Witton	1-1	0-0	2-0	1-1	2-2	1-1	1-3	4-2	2-2	1-1	3-1	1-3	0-3	1-1	2-5	2-0	2-1	0-1	*	1-2	2-2	1-2
20. Woking	0-2	0-1	3-0	0-2	1-1	4-1	1-4	3-2	1-5	4-0	0-2	1-0	4-0	1-2	0-3	2-1	3-2	1-0	1-2	*	0-3	0-0
21. Wycombe	0-2	2-0	3-3	4-0	1-0	1-1	2-1	1-2	1-1	0-1	4-0	1-0	5-1	1-0	2-2	4-0	4-0	3-0	2-1	0-0	*	5-1
22. Yeovil	1-0	2-1	2-1	2-2	0-3	5-2	1-3	2-1	2-2	1-1	0-1	1-1	4-0	5-1	2-0	1-1	1-0	1-0	2-0	4-1	3-0	*

G.M. Vauxhall Conference

LEADING GOALSCORERS 1992-93

	CONFERENCE	FAC	FAT	DC	Total
DAVID LEWORTHY (*Farnborough Town*)	32	(1	5	1	39)
MARK WHITEHOUSE (*Bromsgrove Rovers*)	23	(-	2	1	26)
MALCOLM O'CONNOR (*Northwich Victoria*)	21	(2	1	3	27)
KEITH SCOTT (*Wycombe Wanderers*)	20	(1	5	2	28)
PAUL CAVELL (*Dagenham & Redbridge*)	19	(8	1	1	29)
TERRY ROBBINS (*Welling United*)	19	(1	2	1	23)
ANDY SAYER (*Slough Town*)	19	(1	1	-	21)
KARL THOMAS (*Witton Albion*)	19	(-	3	-	22)
GARY ABBOTT (*Welling United*)	17	(-	1	1	19)
PHIL BROWN (*Kettering Town*)	16	(2	-	-	18)
GARY JONES (*Boston United*)	16	(2	5	1	23)
MICKEY SPENCER (*Yeovil Town*)	16	(2	1	2	21)
TONY HEMMINGS (*Northwich Victoria*)	15	(1	-	4	20)
ALAN LAMB (*Gateshead*)	15	(7	1	-	23)

David Leworthy hits a right foot shot towards goal as Dagenham's Garry Butterworth tries to intercept.
Photo - Paul Dennis.

DRINKWISE (LEAGUE) CUP

First Round (2 Legs)

ALTRINCHAM	1	v	3	MACCLESFIELD TOWN	Att: 616
MACCLESFIELD TOWN	0	v	0	ALTRINCHAM	Att: 449
NORTHWICH VICTORIA	2	v	1	GATESHEAD	Att: 378
GATESHEAD	0	v	2	NORTHWICH VICTORIA	Att: 132
STAFFORD RANGERS	4	v	2	BROMSGROVE ROVERS	Att: 667
BROMSGROVE ROVERS	2	v	1	STAFFORD RANGERS	Att: 757
STALYBRIDGE CELTIC	1	v	1	KIDDERMINSTER HARRIERS	Att: 554
KIDDERMINSTER	4	v	2	STALYBRIDGE CELTIC	Att: 602
WOKING	1	v	2	WELLING UNITED	Att: 1,363
WELLING UNITED	2	v	2	WOKING	Att: 670
YEOVIL TOWN	2	v	0	SLOUGH TOWN	Att: 1,319
SLOUGH TOWN	2	v	2	YEOVIL TOWN	Att: 528

BYES TO SECOND ROUND:

Bath City, Boston United, Dagenham & Redbridge, Farnborough Town, Kettering Town, Merthyr Tydfil, Runcorn,Telford United, Witton Albion, Wycombe Wanderers.

Second Round

BATH CITY	0	v	0	YEOVIL TOWN	Att: 520
YEOVIL TOWN	1	v	0	BATH CITY	Att: 2,090
BOSTON UNITED	1	v	2	DAGENHAM & REDBRIDGE	Att: 537
KIDDERMINSTER	3	v	0	KETTERING TOWN	Att: 624
MERTHYR TYDFIL	4	v	2	FARNBOROUGH TOWN	Att: 404
RUNCORN	2	v	3	NORTHWICH VICTORIA	Att: 600
STAFFORD RANGERS	0	v	0	TELFORD UNITED	Att: 631
TELFORD UNITED	5	v	2	STAFFORD RANGERS	Att: 625
WELLING UNITED	2	v	3	WYCOMBE WANDERERS	Att: 452
WITTON ALBION	0	v	1	MACCLESFIELD TOWN	Att: 763

Third Round

DAGENHAM & REDBRIDGE	4	v	2	MERTHYR TYDFIL	Att: 525
MACCLESFIELD TOWN	3	v	1	KIDDERMINSTER HARRIERS	Att: 203
NORTHWICH VICTORIA	3	v	1	TELFORD UNITED	Att: 374
YEOVIL TOWN	0	v	1	WYCOMBE WANDERERS	Att: 2,330

Semi Finals (First & Second Legs)

NORTHWICH VICTORIA	2	v	0	MACCLESFIELD TOWN	Att: 821
MACCLESFIELD TOWN	1	v	1	NORTHWICH VICTORIA	Att: 422
WYCOMBE WANDERERS	3	v	1	DAGENHAM & REDBRIDGE	Att: 1,901
DAGENHAM & REDBRIDGE	0	v	0	WYCOMBE WANDERERS	Att: 1,247

Final (First & Second Legs)

NORTHWICH VICTORIA	0	v	0	WYCOMBE WANDERERS	Att: 1,005
WYCOMBE WANDERERS	2	v	3	NORTHWICH VICTORIA	Att: 3,784

GM VAUXHALL CONFERENCE LEAGUE ATTENDANCES

CLUB	Total	Games	Ave.	Highest	Lowest	Nos. of Gates over 1,000	2,000	3,000	4,000
Wycombe Wanderers	96,638	21	4,601	7,230 v Slough	3,290 v Gateshead	-	-	5	16
Yeovil Town	54,915	21	2,615	6,488 v Bath City	1,684 v Runcorn	5	13	1	2
Woking	41,722	21	1,986	4,911 v Wycombe	1,290 v Bath City	14	6	-	1
Kettering Town	30,534	21	1,454	3,021 v Wycombe	911 v Runcorn	17	2	1	-
Kidderminster	30,221	21	1,439	4,324 v Bromsgrove	716 v Gateshead	17	-	1	1
Bromsgrove	30,001	21	1,428	3,675 v Wycombe	923 v Gateshead	15	-	2	-
Slough Town	26,079	21	1,241	4,500 v Wycombe	771 v Yeovil T.	8	1	-	1
Dagenham & Red.	25,227	21	1,201	2,542 v Wycombe	805 v Merthyr T.	16	1	-	-
Boston United	21,940	21	1,044	1,481 v Kettering T.	814 v Telford U.	11	-	-	-
Telford United	21,476	21	1,022	1,741 v Wycombe	574 v Welling U.	10	-	-	-
Welling United	19,894	21	947	2,616 v Wycombe	633 v Northwich	3	1	-	-
Stafford Rangers	19,849	21	912	1,631 v Wycombe	538 v Gateshead	7	-	-	-
Witton Albion	19,095	21	909	2,442 v Northwich	541 v Welling U.	3	1	-	-
Farnborough	17,323	21	824	2,678 v Wycombe	504 v Bath City	1	2	-	-
Northwich Victoria	17,120	21	815	1,971 v Witton A.	508 v Bromsgrove	2	-	-	-
Stalybridge C.	16,984	21	808	1,694 v Wycombe	378 v Farnborough	3	-	-	-
Altrincham	16,982	21	808	1,512 v Wycombe	504 v Telford U.	3	-	-	-
Macclesfield T.	13,819	21	658	1,397 v Wycombe	429 v Boston U.	2	-	-	-
Bath City	13,281	21	632	1,283 v Wycombe	338 v Telford U.	2	-	-	-
Runcorn	12,913	21	614	953 v Woking	421 v Yeovil T.	-	-	-	-
Merthyr Tydfil	12,647	21	602	1,408 v Wycombe	380 v Woking/Telfd	1	-	-	-
Gateshead	8,822	21	420	815 v Wycombe	233 v Witton A.	-	-	-	-

First half action from Wycombe Wanderers versus Gateshead in front of an impressive crowd. Photo - V.J.Robertson.

G.M. Vauxhall Conference
TEN YEAR CLUB RECORD

	83/84	84/85	85/86	86/87	87/88	88/89	89/90	90/91	91/92	92/93
ALTRINCHAM	3	5	4	5	14	14	16	3	18	10
AYLESBURY UNITED	-	-	-	-	-	20	-	-	-	-
BANGOR CITY	21	-	-	-	-	-	-	-	-	-
BARNET	9	15	14	2	2	8	2	1	-	-
BARROW	-	18	22	-	-	-	14	10	22	-
BATH CITY	6	4	12	10	20	-	-	20	9	7
BOSTON UNITED	17	17	13	6	16	3	18	18	8	22
BROMSGROVE ROVERS	-	-	-	-	-	-	-	-	-	2
CHELTENHAM TOWN	-	-	11	11	13	15	11	16	21	-
CHORLEY	-	-	-	-	-	17	20	-	-	-
COLCHESTER UNITED	-	-	-	-	-	-	-	2	1	-
DAGENHAM	18	19	19	15	22	-	-	-	-	-
DAGENHAM & REDBRIDGE	-	-	-	-	-	-	-	-	-	3
DARLINGTON	-	-	-	-	-	-	1	-	-	-
DARTFORD	-	3	21	-	-	-	-	-	-	-
ENFIELD	14	7	1	4	12	13	22	-	-	-
FARNBOROUGH TOWN	-	-	-	-	-	-	21	-	5	21
FISHER ATHLETIC	-	-	-	-	15	18	19	22	-	-
FRICKLEY ATHLETIC	12	11	2	21	-	-	-	-	-	-
GATESHEAD	16	21	-	22	-	-	-	17	14	14
KETTERING TOWN	19	12	9	16	3	2	5	4	3	13
KIDDERMINSTER HARRIERS	10	8	3	12	7	5	13	13	19	9
LINCOLN CITY	-	-	-	-	1	-	-	-	-	-
MACCLESFIELD TOWN	-	-	-	-	11	7	4	7	13	18
MAIDSTONE UNITED	1	13	17	3	9	1	-	-	-	-
MERTHYR TYDFIL	-	-	-	-	-	-	9	9	4	16
NORTHWICH VICTORIA	7	9	16	17	17	10	15	12	11	11
NUNEATON BOROUGH	2	2	18	18	-	-	-	-	-	-
REDBRIDGE FOREST	-	-	-	-	-	-	-	-	7	-
RUNCORN	5	14	6	8	4	6	3	8	16	19
SCARBOROUGH	13	6	15	1	-	-	-	-	-	-
SLOUGH TOWN	-	-	-	-	-	-	-	19	20	5
STAFFORD RANGERS	-	-	7	13	6	19	17	15	17	6
STALYBRIDGE CELTIC	-	-	-	-	-	-	-	-	-	12
SUTTON UNITED	-	-	-	7	8	12	8	21	-	-
TELFORD UNITED	11	10	8	9	5	16	12	6	6	15
TROWBRIDGE TOWN	22	-	-	-	-	-	-	-	-	-
WEALDSTONE	4	1	10	19	21	-	-	-	-	-
WELLING UNITED	-	-	-	20	19	11	6	11	12	20
WEYMOUTH	15	16	5	14	10	21	-	-	-	-
WITTON ALBION	-	-	-	-	-	-	-	-	10	17
WOKING	-	-	-	-	-	-	-	-	-	8
WORCESTER CITY	8	20	-	-	-	-	-	-	-	-
WYCOMBE WANDERERS	-	-	20	-	18	4	10	5	2	1
YEOVIL TOWN	20	22	-	-	-	9	7	14	15	4

G.M. Vauxhall Conference

PREVIOUS SEASONS' TOP FOUR

Season	Max Pts	Champions	Pts	Runners-up	Pts	3rd Place	Pts	4th Place	Pts
1979/80	76	56 Altrincham		54 Weymouth		49 Worcester C.		45 Boston Utd.	
1980/81	76	54 Altrincham		51 Kettering T.		47 Scarborough		45 Northwich V.	
1981/82	126	93 Runcorn		86 Enfield		77 Telford Utd.		71 Worcester C.	
1982/83	126	84 Enfield		83 Maidstone U.		79 Wealdstone		72* Runcorn	
1983/84	105	70 Maidstone U.		69 Nuneaton Bor.		65 Altrincham		62* Wealdstone	
1984/85	105	62 Wealdstone		58 Nuneaton Bor.		57* Dartford		57* Bath City	
1985/86	105	76 Enfield		69 Frickley Ath.		67 Kidderminster		63 Altrincham	
1986/87	126	91 Scarborough		85 Barnet		73 Maidstone Utd.		70 Enfield	
1987/88	126	82 Lincoln City		80 Barnet		75 Kettering Town		74 Runcorn	
1988/89	126	84 Maidstone Utd.		76 Kettering Town		74 Boston Utd.		71 Wycombe W.	
1989/90	126	87 Darlington		85 Barnet		70 Runcorn		66 Macclesfield T.	
1990/91	126	87 Barnet		85 Colchester U.		82 Altrincham		80 Kettering T.	
1991/92	126	94 Colchester Utd		94 Wycombe Wdrs		73 Kettering Town		68 Merthyr Tydfil	
1992/93	126	83 Wycombe Wdrs		68 Bromsgrove R.		67 Dagenham & R.		66 Yeovil Town	

* Indicates position achieved through goal difference.

FOOTBALL LEAGUE MOVEMENTS

1987	Promoted to 4th Div.: **Scarborough**	Relegated to Conference: **Lincoln City**	
1988	Promoted to 4th Div.: **Lincoln City**	Relegated to Conference: **Newport County**	
1989	Promoted to 4th Div.: **Maidstone United**	Relegated to Conference: **Darlington**	
1990	Promoted to 4th Div.: **Darlington**	Relegated to Conference: **Colchester United**	
1991	Promoted to 4th Div.: **Barnet**	No relegation from 4th Div.	
1992	Promoted to 4th Div.: **Colchester United**	No relegation from 4th Div.	
1993	Promoted to 3rd Div.: **Wycombe Wanderers**	No relegation from 3rd Div.	

BOB LORD TROPHY
(NOW DRINKWISE CUP)

	Winner	Runner-up
1979/80	Northwich Victoria	Altrincham
1980/81	Altrincham	Kettering Town
1981/82	Weymouth	Enfield
1982/83	Runcorn	Scarborough
1983/84	Scarborough	Barnet
1984/85	Runcorn	Maidstone United
1985/86	Stafford Rangers	Barnet
1986/87	Kettering Town	Hendon (Isthmian)
1987/88	Horwich RMI (NPL)	Weymouth
1988/89	Barnet	Hyde United (HFS)
1989/90	Yeovil Town	Kidderminster H.
1990/91	Sutton United	Barrow
1991/92	Wycombe Wdrs	Runcorn
1992/93	Northwich V.	Wycombe Wdrs

CHAMPIONSHIP SHIELD
Conference Champions v Trophy Winners

	Winner	Runner-up
1980	Northwich V	Altrincham
1981	Altrincham	Kettering T.
1982	runcorn	Weymouth
1983	Enfield	Runcorn
1984	Maidstone U.	Scarborough
1985	Runcorn	Wealdstone
1986	Stafford R.	Enfield
1987	Kidderminster H.	Scarborough
1988	Lincoln City	Enfield
1989	Maidstone Utd.	Telford Utd.
1990	Darlington	Barrow
1991	Wycombe W.	Barnet
1992	Wycombe W.	Colchester Utd

PREMIER INTER-LEAGUE CUP

(also CLUBCALL CUP/ G.M.A.C. CUP - no longer contested)

	Winner	Runner-up
1987	**Kettering Town**	Hendon (Isthmian)
1988	**Horwich RMI (NPL)**	Weymouth
1989	**Barnet**	Hyde Utd. (HFS)

G.M. Vauxhall Conference

COMPLETE CLUB RECORD 1979-1993

	No. of Seasons	P	W	D	L	F	A	Pts
ALTRINCHAM #	14	578	248	151	179	898	724	808
A P LEAMINGTON #	3	118	21	32	65	119	234	78
AYLESBURY UNITED	1	40	9	9	22	43	71	36
BANGOR CITY #	4	160	44	45	71	201	273	150
BARNET #	12	494	209	114	174	759	658	688
BARROW #	9	370	108	103	159	452	575	387
BATH CITY #	12	496	176	133	187	640	660	605
BOSTON UNITED #	14	578	222	136	220	881	911	740
BROMSGROVE ROVERS	1	42	18	14	10	67	49	68
CHELTENHAM TOWN	7	292	93	92	107	420	458	358
CHORLEY	2	82	26	12	44	99	138	90
COLCHESTER UNITED	2	84	53	20	11	166	75	179
DAGENHAM	7	294	87	70	137	374	494	307
DAGENHAM & REDRIDGE	1	42	19	11	12	75	47	67
DARLINGTON	1	42	26	9	7	76	25	87
DARTFORD	3	126	35	31	60	155	199	122
ENFIELD	9	376	169	80	127	672	541	553
FARNBOROUGH TOWN	3	126	40	35	51	196	213	155
FISHER ATHLETIC	4	166	41	46	79	206	283	169
FRICKLEY ATHLETIC	7	290	108	69	113	432	458	337
GATESHEAD	6	252	67	66	129	312	455	254
GRAVESEND & NORTHFLEET #	3	118	40	28	50	148	168	118
KETTERING TOWN #	14	578	230	754	194	874	805	780
KIDDERMINSTER HARRIERS	9	10	418	166	96	698	775	569
LINCOLN CITY	1	42	24	10	8	86	48	82
MACCLESFIELD TOWN	6	250	94	72	84	336	312	354
MAIDSTONE UNITED #	10	410	179	113	118	684	492	589
MERTHYR TYDFIL	4	168	64	47	57	239	259	239
NORTHWICH VICTORIA #	14	578	207	151	220	783	780	714
NUNEATON BOROUGH #	7	286	104	79	103	425	408	333
REDBRIDGE FOREST	1	42	18	9	15	69	56	63
REDDITCH UNITED #	1	38	5	8	25	26	69	18
RUNCORN	12	502	219	137	146	799	652	766
SCARBOROUGH #	8	328	136	101	91	471	393	450
SLOUGH TOWN	3	126	44	23	59	167	217	155
STAFFORD RANGERS #	11	494	150	147	197	626	700	570
STALYBRIDGE CELTIC	1	42	13	17	12	48	55	56
SUTTON UNITED	5	208	76	59	73	352	305	287
TELFORD UNITED #	14	578	236	137	203	821	789	789
TROWBRIDGE TOWN	3	126	29	25	72	127	229	109
WEALDSTONE #	8	328	113	99	116	44	443	387
WELLING UNITED	7	292	92	79	121	399	460	355
WEYMOUTH #	10	410	164	102	144	603	553	524
WITTON ALBION	2	84	27	27	30	125	125	108
WOKING	1	42	17	8	17	58	62	59
WORCESTER CITY #	6	244	93	58	93	347	376	288
WYCOMBE WANDERERS	7	292	133	73	86	480	386	465
YEOVIL TOWN #	11	452	144	113	195	607	721	505

\# - Founder Member of Alliance Premier League in 1979.

(NEWPORT COUNTY - deleted record   29   4   7   18   31   62   19)

Last season we ommitted to print the 1991-92 G.M.V. Conference table, repeating the 1990-91 table instead. So collectors of this book can keep a complete record, the 1991-92 table is shown below.

G.M.V. CONFERENCE 1991-92

	P	W	D	L	F	A	PTS
Colchester Utd	42	28	10	4	98	40	94
Wycombe Wdrs	42	30	4	8	84	35	94
Kettering Town	42	20	13	9	72	50	73
Merthyr Tydfil	42	18	14	10	59	56	68
Farnborough T.	42	18	12	12	68	53	66
Telford United	42	19	7	16	62	66	64
Redbridge Forest	42	18	9	15	69	56	63
Boston United	42	18	9	15	71	66	63
Bath City	42	16	12	14	54	51	60
Witton Albion	42	16	10	16	63	60	58
Northwich Victoria	42	16	6	20	63	58	54
Welling United	42	14	12	16	69	79	54
Macclesfield Town	42	13	13	16	50	50	52
Gateshead	42	12	12	18	49	57	48
Yeovil Town	42	11	14	17	40	49	47
Runcorn	42	11	13	18	50	63	46
Stafford Rangers	42	10	16	16	41	59	46
Altrincham	42	11	12	19	61	82	45
Kidderminster Harr.	42	12	9	21	56	77	45
Slough Town	42	13	6	23	56	82	45
Cheltenham Town	42	10	13	19	56	82	43
Barrow	42	8	14	20	52	72	38

CONFERENCE DIARY 1992-93

(compiled by Steve Whitney)

1 - 24 AUGUST

Wycombe Wanderers are clear 7/4 favourites to win the championship with **Dagenham & Redbridge** (5/1) and **Kettering Town** (6/1) just behind in the betting. Adams Park boss Martin O'Neill accepts a new one year contract. **Northwich Victoria** sign the former Welsh international forward Gordon Davies while also new to Conference football is the experienced ex-Millwall and Brighton midfielder, Les Briley, who joins new **Slough Town** manager David Kemp as his player-coach. New **Boston United** manager, Peter Morris, clears the decks at York Street and brings in no fewer than 15 new players. Morris' former number two at **Kettering Town**, Ernie Moss, joins him in a similar capacity at his new club. The new man in charge at **Altrincham** is former Emley boss Gerry Quinn, who brings three of his players from the Northern Premier League club to Moss Lane. New boys **Stalybridge Celtic** sign the ex-Luton and Oldham striker, Frank Bunn. The Conference re-elect Bill King as Chairman for a further three-year term. **Kidderminster Harriers** set a new club record by paying **Telford United** £20,000 for defender Chris Brindley. **Farnborough Town** are the opening days biggest victors, beating **Gateshead** 6-1 at Cherrywood Road. Diadora League champions **Woking's** party is spoilt by **Stafford Rangers** who return home with an emphatic 3-0 win.

25 AUG - 7 SEP

Northwich Victoria boss Sammy McIlroy signs a new one year contract. The Conference sign a new deal with leading manufacturer Minerva Sports who will supply member clubs with match balls and training balls. Former Vietnamese Boat Boy, Hung Dang, signs for **Yeovil Town**. **Wycombe Wanderers** attract gates of over 3,000 for their first two home matches. **Welling United** are negotiating with neighbours Dartford for a groundshare agreement at Park View Road. The league sign a second new sponsorship deal, this time with the Health Education Authority who will sponsor the League Cup competition which will be known as The Drinkwise Cup. The only 100% record disappears when **Slough Town** are beaten 4-1 at home by **Altrincham**. Businessman Mark English departs **Kettering Town**. David Leworthy, the **Farnborough Town** striker, continues his good start to the season with a brace against **Kidderminster Harriers** in a 2-2 draw. **Welling United** remain point-less at the foot of the table after five games.

8 - 21 SEPTEMBER

Tottenham Hotspur make a six figure bid for **Altrincham** striker Charlie Bradshaw. The FA grant permission for **Yeovil Town** to launch a School of Excellence at Huish Park. With some clubs involved in FA Cup action, **Wycombe Wanderers** take advantage by opening a seven point gap at the top of the table. In the cup there are wins for **Altrincham**, **Boston United**, **Gateshead**, **Bath City**, **Macclesfield Town**, **Northwich Victoria** and **Stalybridge Celtic** but **Dagenham & Redbridge** are surprisingly held at home by Billericay Town and **Stafford Rangers** (at Alfreton Town) and **Slough Town** (at Corinthian Casuals) also face replays. Former Northampton, Maidstone, Nuneaton Borough and Blackpool boss, Graham Carr, takes over as manager at troubled **Kettering Town**, who also call in the Administrators. **Farnborough Town** boss Ted Pearce celebrates his 1,200th game in charge of the Hampshire club. **Wycombe Wanderers** sign the ex-Cambridge United skipper Colin Baillie. **Welling United** win their first game of the season, beating **Runcorn** 3-2 at Park View Road, leaving **Boston United** as the only side yet to register a victory. All Conference clubs come through their FA Cup replays safely, although little Corinthian-Casuals make life difficult for **Slough Town** who could only manage a 4-3 win. **Wycombe Wanderers'** gate of 4,282 for the visit of newboys **Bromsgrove Rovers** was the best atendance of the season so far.

22 SEP - 5 OCT

Leaders **Wycombe Wanderers** equal the Conference record for consecutive victories extending their winning sequence to nine matches with a 4-0 success at **Kettering Town**. **Dagenham & Redbridge** midfielder Jason Broom becomes the latest player to attract interest with West Ham United taking the 22-year-old on trial. Tommy Hutchison is apppointed as full-time Football in the Community Officer at **Merthyr Tydfil**. **Gateshead** striker Alan Lamb became the first Vauxhall Conference player this season to register four goals in a game netting the quartet in a 5-2 FA Cup success over Whitby Town. There are one or two shocks though. **Boston United** are beaten 1-2 at home by Aveley and **Northwich Victoria** lose 0-2 at the Drill Field to United Counties League side Raunds Town. **Dagenham & Redbridge** are the days biggest victors, beating Stowmarket Town 6-1 at Victoria Road. **Wycombe Wanderers** hopes of breaking the record for consecutive victories disappeared when **Bath City** inflicted a 2-0 defeat on the leaders. That defeat didn't stop Wanderers' boss Martin O'Neill winning the first Mail on Sunday Manager of the Month award though - **Gateshead's** Alan Lamb won the Goalscorer of the Month award. **Witton Albion** give manager Peter O'Brien a two-year extension to his existing contract at Wincham Park. His side now occupy second place in the table and along with **Stafford Rangers** are the only remaining unbeaten teams in the league.

6 - 19 OCTOBER

Two more Vauxhall Conference players are in demand with Manchester United offering trials to **Boston United's** Gary Jones and AFC Bournemouth bidding for **Gateshead's** Alan Lamb. The last remaining unbeaten starts to the campaign end when both **Witton Albion** and **Stafford Rangers** lose to Yeovil Town and Kettering Town respectively. **Bromsgrove Rovers** set a new post-war attendance record for the Victoria Ground when a crowd of 3,675 watched the 1-0 victory over leaders **Wycombe Wanderers**. The favourites took some consolation by defeating last season's champions Colchester United to retain the JC Thompson Championship Shield. **Gateshead** striker John Cooke registers the fastest hat-trick of the season, scoring three in seven minutes in the 7-0 FA Cup demolition of Spennymoor United. Fellow striker Simon Guthrie also notched a trio in that game. Accrington Stanley inflicted the only defeat on a Vauxhall Conference club, beating **Stalybridge Celtic** 1-2 at Bower Fold. The High Court grant an Administration Order for an initial three month period for **Kettering Town**. Bottom club **Boston United** extend their opening run without success to ten matches. The sequence equals the Conference record set two seasons ago by **Bath City**. David Leworthy continues to blaze a trail at the top of the scoring charts, netting another brace in **Farnborough Town's** 2-2 draw at **Altrincham**. Those two were the former Spurs striker's 14th and 15th goals of the season.

20 OCT - 2 NOV

Northwich Victoria part company with manager Sammy McIlroy after a 16-month term at the Drill Field. Former Altrincham and Runcorn boss John Williams takes over in a caretaker capacity. **Welling United** also part company with their manager, dimissing Nicky Brigden after a 12-year association with the Kent club the last five of which he held the post of manager. Veteran midfielder Ray Burgess takes over as caretaker. **Boston United** set a new Conference record as they extend their run without a victory to 11 games. The FA Cup 4th qualifying round saw defeats for Runcorn, beaten 1-4 at home by HFS Loans League neighbours Marine, **Welling United**, whose sad early season form continues with a 1-2 defeat at Kingstonian and **Telford United**, who are beaten 1-2 at Buck's Head by Diadora League highflyers St Albans City. **Altrincham**, who took three games to get by Colwyn Bay, overcame Gainsborough Trinity 2-0. **Wycombe Wanderers** announce a trading profit of £20,484 for the year ending May 1992. **Merthyr Tydfil** beat Second Division Swansea City 2-0 in the third round of the Welsh Cup. **Kidderminster Harriers** registered their largest league gate for 40 years when a crowd of 3,064 watched their 1-4 home defeat by **Wycombe Wanderers**.

3 - 16 NOVEMBER

Welling United appoint the youngest manager in senior football, naming striker Terry Robbins as player-manager at Park View Road. The 27-year-old becomes only the fourth manager at the Kent club. Meanwhile, troubled **Kettering Town** put the former Northampton, Nuneaton Borough and Maidstone boss, Graham Carr in charge following the departure of Dave Cusack. Carr had held the post temporarily since September. **Boston United** break their duck, beating **Merthyr Tydfil** 3-0 at Pennydarren Park. It was the Pilgrims' 12th league game of the season. **Wycombe Wanderers** remain 15 points clear at the top of the table, but they are held at home by **Stafford Rangers** after being two-nil ahead in front of a crowd of 4,569. **Stalybridge Celtic** lose the services of experienced striker Frankie Bunn for the "foreseeable future" due to his work commitments as Football Development Officer at Wigan Athletic. The First Round Proper of the FA Cup sees **Yeovil Town** set a new record by registering their 15th victory against Football League opponents with a 5-2 success at Torquay United. **Bath City** come from behind to beat Cardiff City 3-2 at Ninian Park, but the Conference lose most of their other contenders, although **Dagenham & Redbridge** were unfortunate to go out to neighbours Leyton Orient in a nine-goal thriller at Victoria Road. **Altrincham**, **Macclesfield Town** and **Stafford Rangers** live to fight another day after draws against Chester, Chesterfield and Lincoln respectively.

17 - 30 NOVEMBER

Slough Town boss David Kemp attends an interview for the vacant post at First Division Cambridge United. Meanwhile, his charges move up to second in the table with a 2-1 win at **Macclesfield Town**. **Welling United's** new player-manager, Terry Robbins, nets a hat-trick in his first game in charge. **Bath City** striker, Deion Vernon, becomes the latest Conference player to attract attention, the 19-year-old goes to Leeds United on trial. **Altrincham** equal **Yeovil Town's** record FA Cup victories over League opposition with a 2-0 win over Second Division Chester City at Moss Lane. Defender Clive Freeman's magnificent 89th minute strike was eventually to be named as BBC TV's 'Goal of the Month'. **Stafford Rangers** overcome Lincoln City 2-1 in their replay, but **Macclesfield Town** and Chesterfield have to go to penalties after drawing 2-2 after extra-time. However, the Conference side come out on top in the shoot-out 3-2. **Witton Albion** part company with striker Jim McCluskie following his poor disciplinary record. He becomes the second player to leave Wincham Park in those circumstances, Andy Grimshaw was released earlier in the season. Non-League football was saddened by the death of the former Barrow manager, Ray Wilkie, who died aged just 56. **Yeovil Town** manager, Steve Rutter, lifts the Mail on Sunday Manager of the Month award for November - the first time a Yeovil boss has won a managerial award since its

Kidderminster keeper Ron Green jumps with Altrincham's Charlie Bradshaw on the first. Photo - Paul Dennis.

John Smith of Northwich holds off Macclesfield's Neil Sorvel on August Bank Holiday Monday. Photo - Paul Dennis.

Clive Freeman hits Altrincham's fourth as they end Slough's unbeaten record. Photo - E Joy Griffiths/Kick.

introduction in 1987. **Farnborough Town** striker David Leworthy scores a hat-trick for the FA XI in their 6-1 demolition of the Diadora League to strengthen his claims for an England call-up.

1 - 14 DECEMBER

Merthyr Tydfil offer recently sacked Barnet boss Barry Fry the newly-created post of General Manager at Pennydarren Park. Terry Robbins accepts the post of full-time manager at **Welling United** and gives up his job in the City. **Northwich Victoria** end their seven and a half month wait for a Conference home win with a 3-2 success over **Runcorn**. The victory ends a 10-match run which accrued just 3 home points in the league. **Yeovil Town** set a new ground attendance record when a crowd of 8,085 watch the goalless draw with Hereford United in the Second Round of the FA Cup. **Altrincham** bow out after losing 1-4 at home to Port Vale, **Macclesfield Town** are beaten 0-2 by Stockport County, Marine beat another Conference side, **Stafford Rangers**, and both Sunday games end in draws with **Wycombe Wanderers** holding Second Division pacesetters West Brom 2-2 in front of 6,904 and Sky TV cameras at Adams Park, and **Bath City** are held to the same scoreline by Northampton Town. **Northwich Victoria** decide to appoint John Williams as manager after a successful spell as caretaker. The former Altrincham and Runcorn boss has an excellent record having previously lifted both the Conference championship and League Cup competitions with his ex-clubs. Barry Fry turns down the chance to move to **Merthyr Tydfil** after being re-instated as manager again at Barnet. **Bath City** striker Deion Vernon attends trials at a second FA Premier League club. The 19-year-old, who has already been to Leeds, goes to Southampton for a week. **Wycombe Wanderers** become the first club in the country's main three competitions to pass the 50-goal mark. **Boston United** have a mixed few days at York Street, beating **Macclesfield Town** 3-1 and then, three days later, losing 3-5 to **Northwich Victoria** for whom Malcolm O'Connor nets a hat-trick.

14 DEC - 4 JAN 93

Yeovil Town regain the record for FA Cup victories over League opponents by beating Hereford United 2-1 at Edgar Street. The win is their 16th against Football League opposition. Three days later, the club set a seasonal best attendance record when a crowd of 5,495 watch the game against **Bromsgrove Rovers**. **Northwich Victoria** register the largest away victory in the league when they beat **Stalybridge Celtic** 6-0 at Bower Fold with Tony Hemmings grabbing a hat-trick. **Boston United** come off the bottom of the table for the first time since beginning of September with a Boxing Day win over **Welling United**. **Kettering Town's** goalkeeping crisis continues with Mark Smith, on loan from Nottingham Forest becoming the sixth to wear the green jersey this season. **Yeovil Town** bow out of the FA Cup to giants Arsenal 1-3 in front of the highest ever attendance at Huish Park - 8,612. On Bank Holiday Monday the Glovers set another seasonal best when 6,488 watched the local derby win over **Bath City**. **Merthyr Tydfil** record their first home victory in the league by beating **Kidderminster Harriers** 4-3 at Pennydarren Park. The last remaining record came to an end when **Runcorn** broke their away duck, beating the new bottom markers, **Stafford Rangers** 1-0.

4 - 18 JANUARY

Witton Albion set a new seasonal record by extending their run of matches without a win to 13 following a 1-3 reversal at **Bromsgrove Rovers**. Tony Hemmings attends a trial period at First Division West Ham. The **Northwich Victoria** midfielder becomes the third Conference player to attend trials at Upton Park, following **Bromsgrove's** goalkeeper Scott Cooksey and **Dagenham & Redbridge** midfielder Jason Broom. David Leworthy nets his 20th goal of the season in **Farnborough Town's** 2-1 win over **Bath City**. Administrators, Pannell, Kerr & Forster are appointed in charge of affairs at **Kettering Town** for the remainder of the season following a meeting of creditors. Conference leaders **Wycombe Wanderers** received a set-back when skipper and centre half, Glyn Creaser, is ruled out for the rest of the season with a broken foot, an injury sustained at work. **Slough Town**, still second in the table, obtain the services of Wimbledon striker Carlton Fairweather on loan. Meanwhile, **Stafford Rangers** part company with experienced winger Nigel Callaghan. **Kidderminster Harriers** appoint former Leicester, Swindon and Wimbledon striker, Colin Gordon, as player-coach. **Witton Albion** end their 13-match run without a win when they beat **Merthyr Tydfil** 2-0 at Pennydarren Park.

19 JAN - 1 FEB

Macclesfield Town appoint their highly-rated striker Richard Mitchell to their commercial staff. However, the 19-year-old may not be in the job long as, following a recent trial period with Scottish club Dundee, Preston come in and also offer the former Port Vale player a trial. Quite a change in fortunes for **Boston United** manager Peter Morris as he leads the Mail on Sunday Manager of the Month table after three wins on the trot through January. That run is held up when **Farnborough Town** hold them to a goalless draw at York Street. **Altrincham** open a supporters club in - Kuwait! Only **Slough Town**, beaten 3-1 at Diadora League Sutton United, lose to teams from outside the Conference in the second round of the FA Trophy. **Bromsgrove Rovers** and **Boston United** go through at the expense of fellow Conference teams, **Dagenham & Redbridge** and **Welling United** respectively while **Stalybridge Celtic** and **Merthyr Tydfil** must try again after a 1-1 draw at Bower Fold. **Runcorn** and **Wycombe Wanderers** also face replays after being held away at Gloucester City and Morecambe.

2 - 15 FEBRUARY

Macclesfield Town became the fourth club to occupy the bottom spot in the Conference when they took over from **Stafford Rangers** following a 1-0 defeat at Marston Road. **Merthyr Tydfil** and **Wycombe Wanderers** win their Trophy replays, but **Runcorn** are held again by Gloucester City. **Kettering Town** use their seventh goalkeeper of the campaign when Luton's Jurgen Sommer dons the green jersey at Rockingham Road. A former Kettering player, winger Dave Tomlinson, joins **Stalybridge Celtic** - his seventh Conference club and his fifth different

Terry Robbins heads Welling's second as they record their first win - 3-2 against Runcorn. Photo - Keith Gillard.

Paul Cavell of Dagenham gets a hand from Yeovil's Jeff Sherwood in the F.A. Trophy. Photo - John Collinge.

Keith Scott (partly hidden by keeper) hits a shot for Wycombe at West Brom in the F.A. Cup. Photo - Paul Dennis.

club this season. **Yeovil Town** continue to set new crowd records as a new Drinkwise Cup record gate of 2,330 see them lose at home to **Wycombe Wanderers**. **Stafford Rangers'** excellent recent form continues with their fifth consecutive league win, 1-0 over **Dagenham & Redbridge**. **Altrincham** boss Gerry Quinn takes an unusual route to sign Harrogate Town's Steve Learoyd, finally signing him at the Premier League game between Leeds United and Manchester United at Elland Road. **Runcorn** finally overcome Beazer Homes League Gloucester City in the FA Trophy with a third replay 4-1 win. **Woking** defeat a strong Kispest-Honved side 2-1 in a friendly at Kingfield. The Hungarians included ten full internationals in their line-up. **Slough Town** go to the FA Tribunal for them to set a fee for midfielder Mark Fiore who has been the subject of interest from **Woking**. They set a fee of £15,000 for the former Wimbledon and Plymouth player.

16 FEB - 1 MARCH

Wycombe Wanderers became the first ever Pyramid club to break the 4,000 average attendane barrier. **Altrincham** are another Conference club with goalkeeping problems. Manager Gerry Quinn is forced to sign his third 'keeper in a less than a week. Paul Collings from Accrington Stanley follows Farsley Celtic's Wayne Baker and Leek's Andy Newell into Moss Lane. **Farnborough Town** reached the quarter-finals of the FA Trophy for the first time in their history when they beat Northern League side Northallerton Town 3-1 away. **Runcorn** overcome HFS Loans Leaguers Winsford United 1-0 at Canal Street, **Witton Albion** beat Marine, and **Wycombe Wanderers** win the all-Conference clash against Bromsgrove Rovers at Adams Park in front of a crowd of 4,907. **Boston United** overcome **Telford United** in a replay at York Street and **Gateshead** beat Diadora League Grays Atheltic at the International Stadium, but **Merthyr Tydfil** are surprisingly beaten by HFS Loans League division one side Warrington Town. **Farnborough Town** striker David Leworthy nets the fastest hat-trick of the season when he nets three in nine minutes against **Kidderminster Harriers**. **Witton Albion** drop to bottom of the table after a 2-1 defeat at Kettering Town. England Semi-Professional team manager, Tony Jennings, is forced to leave **Wycombe Wanderers** midfielder Dave Carroll out of his squad when it was discovered that he was Scottish!

2 - 15 MARCH

The Vauxhall Conference's last remaining unbeaten home record ends when leaders **Wycombe Wanderers** are beaten 2-1 by **Kettering Town**. It was the club's first league defeat at Adams Park since 28th September 1991. **Northwich Victoria** reach the final of the Drinkwise Cup by securing a 3-1 aggregate win over **Macclesfield Town**. **Witton Albion** end their five-month spell without a home win by beating **Merthyr Tydfil** 3-1 with ten men after Steve McNeilis had been sent-off. **Gateshead** sign Darlington striker Paul Dobson for a new club record fee. Dobson, who scored 7 goals whilst on loan at the International Stadium, becomes only the fourth money signing since the club were re-formed in 1977. **Wycombe Wanderers** join **Northwich Victoria** in the Drinkwise Cup final when they beat **Dagenham & Redbridge** 3-1 on aggregate. **Boston United** lose the services of striker David Moss, who signs for Third Division Doncaster Rovers. He had scored 10 goals in 16 games for the Pilgrims since signing from Worksop Town during the summer. He also made it into the England Semi-Pro squad during his time at York Street. HFS Loans League club, Morecambe, withdraw their candidacy for promotion to the Conference next season after discovering that the amount of work needed to bring their Christie Park ground up to standard was too expensive for them at the moment. **Witton Albion**, **Runcorn** and **Wycombe Wanderers** go through to the semi-finals of the FA Trophy. Witton beat **Farnborough Town** 3-2 at Wincham Park, courtesy of two goals from leading scorer Karl Thomas, Runcorn won 2-0 at **Boston United** and Wycombe needed a 90th minute Steve Guppy goal to beat **Gateshead** at Adams Park.

16 - 29 MARCH

Dagenham & Redbridge have one point deducted from their total for playing an ineligible player in their 1-1 draw with **Witton Albion** in December. Conference leaders **Wycombe Wanderers** boost their squad by signing **Telford United** striker Tim Langford for an undisclosed five-figure fee. Diadora League leaders, Chesham United, become the second from the feeder leagues to withdraw their candicacy for promotion to the Conference. Substantial work is needed on their Meadow Park ground to bring it up to standard and their would be no chance of that work being carried out in time to meet Conference deadlines. **Woking** lose their former FA Cup hero, Tim Buzaglo, who joins Marlow for £4,000. Moving in the opposite direction is Marlow's highly-rated winger, Ansil Bushay. Transfer deadline day sees the second highest number of transactions recorded in the competition's history with 41 players being registered. **Yeovil Town** were involved in the day's biggest deal when they sold England defender Mark Shail to Bristol City for an initial £45,000 fee. Leaders **Wycombe Wanderers** add five new players to their squad with Barnet duo Hakan Heyrettin and Geoff Cooper, experienced Gillingham striker Trevor Aylott, Luton 'keeper Jurgen Sommer and former Wycombe defender, Anton Vircavs from Cheltenham Town all arriving at Adams Park. The title favourites set a new seasonal attendance record when a crowd of 7,230 watched the 1-0 victory over second placed neighbours **Slough Town**. There were, in fact, an further 2,000 locked out. **Yeovil Town** equal the seasonal record for Conference home wins with their 12th victory on the trot, a 1-0 success over **Welling United**.

29 MAR - 13 APRIL

The longest managerial term in senior football will end in May when Ted Pearce finishes 23 years in charge at **Farnborough Town**. Dennis Booth steps down as manager of **Stafford Rangers** to take up the post of assistant-manager at First Division Bristol Rovers. **Northwich Victoria** striker Malcolm O'Connor becomes the first Conference player to net a hat-trick of hat-tricks this season. His third treble completed a 3-1 win over **Bath City** at the Drill Field, a result which took the Cheshire side to fifth in the table. **Woking's** deadline signing from Fulham, midfielder Paul Kelly, is involved in a fatal car accident shortly after making his debut for the Cards in the 1-1 draw at **Macclesfield Town**. Kelly, who was detained in hospital with neck injuries,

Karl Thomas of Witton Albion prepares to cross as Kidderminster's John McGrath looks on. Photo - Keith Clayton.

Gateshead's Billy Askew (white shirt) challenges Phil Sammons in the F.A. Trophy tie at Grays. Photo - Roger Turner.

Keith Scott of Wycombe shoots for goal as the Wanderers beat Bromsgrove in the F.A. Trophy. Photo - Paul Dennis.

lost control of the car he was driving resulting in the tragic death of one of his closest friends. **Wycombe Wanderers** are stunned as Sutton United win 2-3 at Adams Park in the first leg of the FA Trophy semi-final in front of 5,600 fans. **Runcorn** hold a 2-0 advantage over **Witton Albion** after their first game at Canal Street. Runcorn midfielder Garry Anderson set Trophy history in that game by becoming the first player in over a decade to score in every round up to and including the semi-final. **Gateshead** goalkeeper, Simon Smith, made his 400th consecutive appearance for the club in the 1-2 defeat at **Stalybridge Celtic**. **Yeovil Town's** unbeaten home record goes as **Dagenham & Redbridge** win emphatically at Huish Park 3-0. The 1993 FA Trophy Final at Wembley will be contested by **Wycombe Wanderers** and **Runcorn** following their second leg successes. Wycombe overcame a 2-3 deficit to beat Sutton United 4-0 at Gander Green Lane with two goals from defender Matt Crossley - his first goals of the season. Runcorn lost their second leg 1-0 at Wincham Park against **Witton Albion**, but went through 2-1 on aggregate. Runcorn manager John Carroll, who is in his testimonial season with the club, becomes the youngest ever manager to guide his side to a Wembley final.

14 - 26 APRIL

Wycombe Wanderers are confirmed as Conference champions, despite going down 0-2 at home to **Altrincham**. Martin O'Neill's side, who missed out last season only on goal difference, then played their fourth game in a week the following day against **Gateshead** and celebrated their title with a 1-0 victory over their Tyneside hosts. **Farnborough Town's** David Leworthy becomes the first Vauxhall Conference player since 1990/91 to score 30 goals in a season, passing the landmark with a brace in the 3-1 win at **Merthyr Tydfil**. **Kidderminster Harriers'** boss Graham Allner is appointed manager of the Middlesex Wanderers tour of northern Europe in late May. **Boston United** become the first club to be relegated following their 1-2 defeat at Yeovil Town. Boston were one of the original founder members of the competition in 1979, leaving only **Kettering Town, Altrincham, Telford United** and **Northwich Victoria** as the only founder members not to suffer relegation during the 14 years of the Alliance/Conference. **Stafford Rangers** announce their successor to manager Dennis Booth. Former England Semi-Professional midfielder, Brendan Phillips, previously in charge at Beazer Homes League club Bedworth United, was chosen from over 50 candidates. **Farnborough Town** also announced the successor to Ted Pearce. In the end, the directors went for an internal appointment in Alan Taylor, formerly coach under Pearce at Cherrywood Road. **Dagenham & Redbridge** announce that England internationals Paul Richardson and Paul Shirtliff are available for transfer. Manager John Still wants to introduce a more "localised" squad and both Richardson and England skipper Shirtliff hail from the northern end of the country.

27 APR - 9 MAY

Farnborough Town join **Boston United** in being relegated from the Conference. The Hampshire club weren't really in the frame until the final week of the season, but a run of just five wins in 24 games and a final day home hammering (2-5) by **Altrincham** sent them down. It was a sad way for Ted Pearce to bow out. However, striker David Leworthy did bring a little cheer to the club by lifting the Mail on Sunday Goalscorer of the Year award. **Bromsgrove Rovers** ended a brilliant first campaign as a Conference club by securing runners-up spot after a final day 1-0 win over fellow newcomers **Woking**. Rovers completed their inaugural season with only one defeat in 12 Conference matches and they occupied a top five position for almost the entire season. **Dagenham & Redbridge** lost out on second spot after losing 1-2 at home to **Kettering Town** on the last Saturday of the season. **Northwich Victoria** spoil **Wycombe Wanderers'** party by surprisingly winning 3-2 at Adams Park in the second leg of the Drinkwise Cup following a goalless first leg at the Drill Field. Veteran striker Gordon Davies was the hero, netting a hat-trick in front of a crowd of 3,748 - a record for the competition. It was Northwich's first national honour since 1984, but for manager John Williams it was his third League Cup success. Vauxhall Conference gates passed the 1,200 average-mark for the sixth season in succession The 1992/93 aggregate totalled 567,609 to reach its fourth highest level in the 14-year history of the competition. Champions **Wycombe Wanderers** recorded an aggregate of 96,638 with an average gate of 4,602 - the largest of any Pyramid club since the game was re-structured in 1979. The second biggest attendance in FA Trophy final history, 32,968, saw Wycombe clinch the non-League 'double' with a comfortable 4-1 win over **Runcorn** at Wembley Stadium. Jason Cousins, Andy Kerr, Steve Thompson and Dave Carroll scored Wanderers' goals with a lone Steve Shaughnessy reply coming from the Linnets. It is the second year in succession that the double has been won.

Wycombe players salute Matt Crossley's opener at Sutton in the F.A. Trophy Semi-Final. Photo - Paul Dennis.

Brendan Burke of Witton heads home in the derby against Northwich at Wincham Park. Photo - Keith Clayton.

Wycombe with the Championship Shield, won against 1992 champions Colchester. Photo - Ian Morseman.

Conference top-scorer David Leworthy (right) celebrates a goal with Farnborough team-mates. Photo - Mick Cheney.

Phil Brown somehow misses as Kettering lose at home to Merthyr Tydfil in October. Photo - Mick Cheney.

Kidderminster keeper Darren Steadman spectacularly tips a Woking effort over the bar. Photo - Kevin Harris.

ALTRINCHAM

Formed: 1891

President:
Noel White

Chairman:
Bill King

Vice Chairman
Gary Corbett

Football Secretary:
Jean Baldwin

Manager:
Gerry Quinn

Physiotherapist:
Gerry Brook

Commercial Manager:
Chris King

Press Officer:
Mark Harris

With the appointment of a new management team and the wholesale reconstruction of a side which had flirted dangerously with relegation, the 1992/93 season represented a journey into the unknown for all at Moss Lane.

New boss Gerry Quinn scoured the Northern Premier League and ex-Football League ranks to mould an excellent team spirit which saw the club notch its fifteenth League sclap by beating Chester City in the FA Cup. The Chester game also marked the club's first ever BBC 'Goal of the Month' award for skipper Clive Freeman's 35 yard thunderbolt.

League fortunes were mixed; a poor striking record balanced by a splendid defensive record achieved despite having to field six keepers throughout the campaign. A long run of injuries further hampered the manager's plans, with inspirational ex-Emley men Mike Farrar and Russell Green ruled out for long periods, whilst ex-Runcorn man Simon Rudge was forced to retire after two seasons of struggling against a damaged knee. A late comeback at Dagenham in February proved the turning point as Quinn's men grew in confidence; midfielders Harris and Carmody blossomed, whilst ex-Burnley defender France rightly took the Player of the Year vote. Robins must build on 10th spot without the luxury of limitless budgets, and with the addition of a class keeper and consistent scorer could well be a force to reckon with next season.

Mark Harris.

Altrincham 1992-93. Photo: Eric Marsh.

ALTRINCHAM MATCHFACTS 92-93

Key: Home fixtures are denoted by bold capitals. Numbers in brackets after players names indicate goals scored (an asterisk by the results denotes own goals). Only used substitutes are listed - substituted players are *italicised*.

Key to Competitions: GMVC: G.M. Vauxhall Conference. **CSC:** Cheshire Senior Cup. **DC:** Drinkwise (G.M. Vauxhall Conference) Cup. **FAC:** F.A. Cup. **FAT:** Vauxhall F.A. Trophy.

LEAGUE POSITION: 10th   **FA CUP:** Second Round   **FA TROPHY:** First Round

Date	Opponents	Comp.	Res	Gate	1.	2.	3.	4.	5.	6.	7.	8.	9.	10.	11.	Sub.	Sub.
22/08	Kidderminster H.	GMVC	1-0	1,223	Paladino	Freeman	Hayde	Green	Hodgett	Farrar	*Bradshaw*	Thompson	Harris(1)	Carmody	Dyson	Woodhead	
25/08	**GATESHEAD**	GMVC	0-1	814	Pollitt	Freeman	Hayde	Green	Hodgett	Farrar	Woodhead	Thompson	Harris	Carmody	Dyson	Woodhead	
29/08	**MERTHYR TYD.**	GMVC	0-1	729	Pollitt	Freeman	Hayde	Green	*Hodgett*	Farrar	Woodhead	Thompson	Harris	Carmody	Dyson	Rudge	
31/08	Witton Albion	GMVC	1-1	1,084	Pollitt	France	Sidderley	Freeman(1)	Green	Farrar	Bradshaw	Thompson	Harris	Carmody	*Woodhead*	Dyson	
05/09	Slough Town	GMVC	4-1	1,101	Pollitt	France	Sidderley	Freeman(1)	Green	Farrar	B'shaw(2)	Tho'son(1)	Harris	Carmody	Woodhead	Dyson	
08/09	**MACCLESFIELD T.**	DC	1-3	821	Pollitt	France	Sidderley	Freeman(1)	Green	Farrar	Bradshaw	Thompson	Harris	Carmody	Woodhead	Rudge	
12/09	**CURZON ASHTON**	FAC	3-0	594	Paladino	France	*Sidderley*	Freeman(1)	Green	Farrar	Bradshaw	Hayde(1)	Harris(1)	Carmody	Dyson	Woodhead	
16/09	Gateshead	GMVC	0-2	302	Paladino	France	*Sidderley*	Freeman	Green	Farrar	Bradshaw	Hayde	Harris	Carmody	Dyson	Woodhead	
19/09	**BOSTON UNITED**	GMVC	1-1	678	Paladino	France	Freeman(1)	*Harris*	Sidderley	Farrar	Bradshaw	*Lloyd*	Green	Carmody	Hayde	Woodhead	Dyson
22/09	Macclesfield T.	DC	0-0	449	Paladino	Freeman	Alcide	France	Sidderley	Farrar	*Bradshaw*	Rudge	Green	Carmody	*Dyson*	Hayde	W'head
29/09	**SHEFFIELD F.C.**	FAC	3-1	578	Paladino	France	Freeman(1)	France	Sid'ley(1)	Farrar	*Bradshaw*	Hayde	Harris(1)	Carmody	*Dyson*	Woodhead	Gresty
03/10	Woking	GMVC	2-0	2,060	Paladino	Woodhead	Freeman	*France*	Sidderley	Farrar	Harris(1)	Saunders	Green(1)	Carmody	*Alcide*	Hayde	
06/10	Northwich Vict.	GMVC	2-1	774	Paladino	Woodhead	*Freeman*	*France*	Sidderley	Farrar	Harris	Saunders	Green(2)	Carmody	*Alcide*	Hayde	Gresty
10/10	Colwyn Bay	FAC	3-3	601	Paladino	Woodhead	*Freeman(1)*	France	Sidderley	Farrar	*B'shaw(1)*	Saunders	Green(1)	Carmody	Harris	Hayde	Ogley
13/10	**COLWYN BAY**	FAC	1-1	784	Paladino	Woodhead	Freeman	France	*Sidderley*	Farrar	*Sa'ders(1)*	Ogley	Green	*Carmody*	Harris	Hayde	B'shaw
17/10	**FARNBOROUGH**	GMVC	2-2	746	Paladino	Woodhead	Freeman(1)	France	*Sidderley*	Farrar	Saunders	Ogley	Green	Carmody	Harris(1)	Bradshaw	
19/10	**COLWYN BAY**	FAC	3-1	805	Paladino	Woodhead	Freeman	France	*Sidderley*	Farrar	*Sa'ders(1)*	Ogley	Harris(1)	Carmody(1)	*Harris(1)* Rudge	Bradshaw	
24/10	Gainsborough	FAC	2-0	805	Paladino	Woodhead	Freeman	France	Sidderley	Farrar	*Saunders*	Ogley	Harris	Carmody	*Rudge(1)*	Hayde	B'shaw
30/10	Telford United	GMVC	1-2	1,063	Paladino	Woodhead	Freeman	France	Sidderley	Farrar	Saunders	*Ogley(1)*	Harris	Carmody	Rudge	Bradshaw	
07/11	**NORTHWICH VICT.**	GMVC	0-0	1,091	Paladino	Woodhead	Freeman	France	Sidderley	Farrar	Saunders	*Rudge*	Green	Carmody	Harris	Ogley	
10/11	Stafford Rgrs	GMVC	0-0	831	Paladino	Woodhead	Freeman	France	Sidderley	*Farrar*	*Saunders*	Ogley	Harris	Carmody	Rudge	Green	
14/11	Chester City	FAC	*1-1	4,030	Paladino	Woodhead	Freeman	France	Sidderley	Green	*Saunders*	Ogley	Harris	Carmody	Rudge	Bradshaw	
21/11	**KIDDERMINSTER**	GMVC	2-2	735	Paladino	Woodhead	Freeman(1)	*france*	Sidderley	Green	*Saunders*	Ogley	*Green*	Carmody(1)	Rudge	Green	
21/11	Bath City	GMVC	0-3	615	Paladino	Woodhead	Freeman	France	Sidderley	Green	Saunders	*Ogley*	Harris	Carmody	Rudge	Bradshaw	
25/11	**CHESTER CITY**	FAC	2-0	3,000	Paladino	Woodhead	Freeman(1)	France	Sidderley	Ogley	Saunders	Harris(1)	Green	Carmody	Rudge	Bradshaw	
28/11	**WYCOMBE WDRS**	GMVC	0-2	1,462	Paladino	Woodhead	Freeman	France	Sidderley	Ogley	Saunders	Harris	*Bradshaw*	Carmody	Rudge	Bradshaw	

Date	Opponent	Comp	Score	Att													
01/12	Nantwich Town	CSC	1-0	504	Paladino	Woodhead	Freeman(1)	France	Sidderley	Ogley	Dyson	Harris	Bradshaw	Carmody	*Rudge*	Hayde	Dyson(1)
05/12	PORT VALE	FAC	1-4	3,859	Paladino	Woodhead	Freeman	France	Sidderley	Ogley	*Saunders*	Harris	Bradshaw	Carmody	*Rudge*	Hayde	
12/12	Bromsgrove Rovers	GMVC	1-4	1,117	Paladino	Woodhead	Freeman	France(1)	Sidderley	Ogley	Saunders	Harris	*Tunnacliffe*	Carmody	Smith	Bradshaw	
19/12	WELLING UNITED	GMVC	2-0	631	Pollitt	Hayde	Freeman	France	Sidderley	*Farrar*	Wilson	Ogley	Tunnacliffe	Smith	Smith	Harris	
02/01	Runcorn	GMVC	1-0	780	Dennis	Woodhead	Hayde	France	Sidderley	Ogley	Wilson	B'shaw(1)	*Tunnacliffe*	Carmody	Smith	Hayde	Saunders
09/01	Winsford United	FAT	0-1	727	Dennis	Freeman	Hayde	France	Sidderley	Ogley	*Wilson*	Bradshaw	Tunnacliffe	Carmody	Smith	Hayde	Harris
16/01	SLOUGH TOWN	GMVC	1-1	832	Dennis	Freeman	Hayde	France	Sidderley	Ogley	Saunders	Harris	Tunnacliffe	Carmody(1)	Smith	Harris	W'head
23/01	Welling United	GMVC	0-2	857	Dennis	Freeman	Hayde	France	Sidderley	*Farrar*	Saunders	Harris	Tunnacliffe	Carmody	Smith	Harris	B'shaw
26/01	Witton Albion	CSC	3-3	466	Dennis	Freeman	Hayde	France	Sidderley	Farrar(1)	Sa'ders(1)	*Bradshaw*	Tunnacliffe	Carmody	*Smith*	Green(1)	W'head
30/01	STAFFORD RGRS	GMVC	1-5	858	Dennis	Woodhead	Hayde	France	Sidderley	Ogley	Sa'ders(1)	Harris	Tunnacliffe	Carmody	Freeman	Wilson	
02/02	WITTIN ALBION	CSC	1-2	503	Dennis	Woodhead	Freeman(1)	*France*	Hayde	Ogley	Saunders	Wilson	Harris(1)	Carmody	Dyson	Lloyd	
06/02	BATH CITY	GMVC	1-0	627	Dennis	Freeman(1)	Freeman(1)	France	*Sidderley*	Hayde	Saunders	Wilson	Harris	Ogley	Dyson	Smith	Smith
09/02	KETTERING	GMVC	3-0	528	Dennis	W'head(1)	Smith	france	Learoyde	Ogley	Saunders	Wilson	Harris(1)	Ogley	Dyson	Alcide	Smith
13/02	Yeovil Town	GMVC	0-1	2,198	Dennis	Woodhead	Freeman	France	Learoyde	Hayde	Saunders	Wilson	Harris	Ogley	*Sharpe*	Dyson	Sharpe
16/02	TELFORD UTD	GMVC	0-3	504	Baker	Woodhead	Smith	France	Sidderley	Learoyd	*Saunders*	*Wilson*	Harris	Ogley	*Dyson*	Sharpe	Smith
20/02	DAGENHAM & R.	GMVC	1-0	517	Newell	Woodhead	Smith(1)	France	Sidderley	Ogley	Saunders	Harris	T'cliffe(1)	*Carmody*	Dyson	Wilson	Sharpe
27/02	Dagenham & R.	GMVC	2-2	823	Newell	Woodhead	Smith(1)	France(1)	Sidderley	Ogley	Saunders	Harris	Tunnacliffe	Carmody	*Dyson*	Freeman	Hayde
06/03	WOKING	GMVC	1-0	839	Newell	Woodhead	Smith	France	Sidderley	Ogley	Saunders	Harris	Tunnacliffe	Carmody	*Dyson*	Hayde	Hayde
09/03	STALYBRIDGE C.	GMVC	0-0	844	Newell	Woodhead	Smith(1)	France	*Sidderley*	Ogley	Saunders	Harris	Tunnacliffe	*Carmody*	*Dyson*	Freeman	Hayde
13/03	Macclesfield T.	GMVC	1-1	875	Newell	Woodhead	Smith(1)	France	Sidderley	Ogley	Saunders	*Harris*	Tunnacliffe	Harris	Dyson	Freeman	*Richards*
20/03	YEOVIL TOWN	GMVC	1-2	722	Newell	Woodhead	Smith	*France*	Sidderley	Ogley	Saunders	Hayde	Tunnacliffe	Harris	Emmett(1)	Sharpe	
23/03	RUNCORN	GMVC	0-2	814	Baker	Woodhead	Smith	France	Sidderley	Ogley	Saunders	Hayde	Tunnacliffe	Carmody	Emmett	Dyson	
27/03	Stalybridge C.	GMVC	0-1	1,011	Gorton	Woodhead	Freeman	France(1)	Sidderley	Ogley	Saunders	*Saunders*	Tunnacliffe	Hayde	*Emmett*	Dyson	
30/03	Merthyr Tyd.	GMVC	2-2	458	Gorton	Woodhead	Smith(1)	France	Sidderley	Ogley	Smith	*Saunders*	Tunnacliffe	Carmody	*Emmett*	Richards	Dyson
10/04	Kettering	GMVC	1-1	1,299	Gorton	Woodhead	Smith	France	Sidderley	Ogley	Saunders	T'cliffe(1)	Harris	Hayde	Emmett	Carmody	Freeman
17/04	Wycombe W.	GMVC	2-0	6,284	Gorton	Woodhead	Smith	France(1)	Sidderley	Ogley	Saunders	Harris	T'cliffe(1)	*Hayde*	Dyson	Hayde	
22/04	WITTON ALB.	GMVC	2-1	925	Gorton	Woodhead	Smith	France	Sidderley	Ogley	Saunders	Harris	T'cliffe(1)	Carmody	Dyson	Hayde	
24/04	BROMSGROVE	GMVC	2-2	823	Gorton	W'head(1)	Smith(1)	France	Sidderley	*Ogley*	Saunders	Hayde	Harris	Comody	Raymond(1)	Freeman	Hayde
28/04	Boston United	GMVC	1-2	502	Gorton	W'head(1)	Smith	France(1)	Sidderley	Ogley	Saunders	Hayde	Harris	Carmody	Dyson	Raymond	
01/05	Farnborough	GMVC	5-2	738	Gorton	Woodhead	Hyde(1)	France(1)	Sidderley	Ogley	S'ders(1)	Harris	T'cliffe(1)	Carmody	Dyson(1)	Freeman	Raymond

League Appearances: Alcide 2(1): Baker 2: Bradshaw 9(5): Carmody 32(2): Dennis 6: Dyson 16(5): Emmett 4: Farrar 16: France 39: Freeman 26(6): Gorton 9: Green 13(1): Gresty 0(1): Harris 34(3): Hayde 20(9): Hodgert 3: Learoyd 3: Lloyd 1: Newell 6: Ogley 32(1): Paladino 13: Pollitt 5: Raymond 2(2): Richards 0(2): Rudge 6(1): Saunders 33(1): Sidderley 36: Sharpe 2(3): Smith 22(3): Tunnacliffe 21: Thompson 5: Wilson 6(2): Woodhead 36(3).

League Goalscorers: Freeman 8: France 7: Bradshaw, Tunnacliffe 5: Harris 4: Green, Smith, Woodhead 3: Carmody, Raymond, Saunders 2: Dyson, Emmett, Hayde, Ogley, Thompson 1.

Altrincham

GERRY QUINN

Gerry was appointed as manager of Altrincham in June 1992. He had previously been in charge at Northern Premier League Premier Division club Emley where he enjoyed a huge amount of success. A former player with the Yorkshire side, he took over as manager in 1984 and immediately set about winning honours for the club. They were Northern Counties East League runners-up in 1985/86, and won that league in 1987/88 when they also reached the FA Vase Final at Wembley. However, they came up against the fast-rising Colne Dynamoes side and lost the final 1-0. The previous season saw Emley reach the semi-final of the same competition but they lost on aggregate to St Helens Town despite winning the first leg in Lancashire.

After gaining promotion to the Northern Premier League, Gerry, who had been player-manager, hung up his boots for good and, following a season's consolidating, they won promotion to the Premier Division in 1991. That 1990/91 season also saw the club reach the quarter-finals of the FA Trophy. To reach that stage, Gerry's team had beaten Southport, Ferryhill Athletic, Morecambe, Hyde United and two Conference clubs, Telford United and Kettering Town.

Gerry brought number of former Emley players with him to Moss Lane.

Kidderminster goalkeeper, Ron Green, just manages to tip the ball over the bar during their game against Altrincham, in which The Robins won 1-0. Photo: Paul Dennis.

Programme details:
    32 pages for £1
    Editor - Mark Harris and
        Terry Surridge

Local Newspapers:
    Sale And Altrincham Messenger
    Sale and Altrincham Express
    Manchester Evening News
    Manchester Metro News

Local Radio Stations:
    GMR (BBC)
    Piccadilly Radio
    Signal Radio

ALTRINCHAM - PLAYING SQUAD 1992-93

Player	Honours	Birthplace and date	Transfer Fees	Previous Clubs
GOALKEEPERS				
Paul Collings		Liverpool 30/9/68		Ellesmere Port, Tranmere Rovers, Accrington Stanley
DEFENDERS				
Paul France		Holmfirth 10/9/68		Huddersfield Town, Bristol City, Burnley
Russell Green		Barnsley 6/10/70		Barnsley, Emley
Mick Farrar	FA XI	Rochdale 31/7/60		Rochdale, Bradley Rangers, Emley
Ray Sidderley		Manchester 29/8/60		Droylsden, Stockport Georgians, Droylsden, Accrington Stanley
Mark Ogley		Barnsley 10/3/67		Barnsley, Carlisle Utd, Aldershot, York City, Telford Utd
MIDFIELD				
Simon Woodhead		Dewsbury 26/12/63		Mansfield T, Crewe Alexandra, Burnley, Shepshed Charterhouse, Frickley Ath
Mick Hayde		St Helens 20/6/71		Liverpool, Chester City, St Helens Town
Mick Carmody		Huddersfield 9/2/66		Huddersfield Town, Emley, Tranmere Rovers, Emley
Robert Wilson	Eire U-21	Kensington 5/6/61		Fulham, Millwall, Luton, Fulham, Huddersfield, Rotherham U, Farnborough
John Smith		Liverpool 23/7/70		Tranmere Rovers, Stalybridge Celtic, Bangor City, Northwich Victoria
Colin Alcide		Huddersfield 14/4/72		Emley
FORWARDS				
Ian Tunnacliffe		Huddersfield 21/2/64		Storthes Hall, Emley
Ricky Harris		Manchester 12/7/67		Ashton Utd, Altrincham, Hyde Utd, Runcorn, Hyde Utd
Carl Dyson		Manchester 3/4/65		Altrincham, Stalybridge C, Ashton U, Flixton, Irlam, Runcorn, Witton A
David Lowe		Manchester 29/8/75		Youth team
Steve Raymond		Manchester 8/4/75		Youth team
Steve Saunders		Warrington 21/9/64		Bolton W, Crewe Alexandra, Preston NE, Grimsby, Scarborough, Runcorn

Departures during season:
Tony Edwards (Barrow), Tony Chilton (Gateshead), Ian Thompson (Frickley), Mark Henshaw (Chorley), Simon Gresty (Mold Alex), Charlie Bradshaw (Emley), Brian Kilshaw (Skelmersdale), Chris Molloy (Mossley), Steve Worrall (Chorley), Ray Dennis (Barrow), Simon Rudge, Clive Freeman & Carl Hodgert (Released), David Lloyd (Buxton).

Players on loan during season:
Mike Pollitt, Darren Emmett & Andy Gorton (Bury), Andy Maynard (Halifax), Peter Cole (Doncaster), Andy Newell (Leek), Wayne Baker (Farsley Celtic).

Moss Lane, Altrincham

Address and telephone number: Moss Lane, Altrincham, Cheshire WA15 8AP.
Tel: 061 928 1045. Fax: 061 926 9934.

Simple directions: M6 junction 19; A556/M56 (Manchester Airport) to junction 7; signs Hale and Altrincham; through 1st traffic lights and 3rd right into Westminster Road and continue into Moss Lane. Ground on right.

Capacity: 3,500   **Seated:** 1,000   **Covered terracing:** Yes

Record Attendance: 10,275 - Altrincham Boys v Sunderland Boys - English Schools Shield 3rd Round 28.02.25.

Club Shop: Open on matchdays only; programmes, badges, shirts, books & souvenirs.

Social Facilities: Four snack bars on ground for pies, crisps, soft drinks and chocolate etc; bar open on match days only.

Previous Grounds: Pollitts Field - 1903-1910

Altrincham Fact File

Nickname: The Robins

Club Co-Sponsors: N.E.S., Maunders

Previous Leagues: Manchester League 1903-1911, Lancashire Combination 1911-1919, Cheshire County League 1919-1968, Northern Premier League 1968-1979.

Club colours: Red & white striped shirts, black shorts and white socks.

Change colours: Sky blue shirts, dark blue shorts and sky blue socks.

Reserve team league: North West Combination.

Youth team league: Altrincham Independent Insurance League.

Midweek home matchday: Tuesday.

Record win:

Record defeat:

Record transfer fee: To Telford United for Ken McKenna - 1990.

Record transfer fee received: From Crewe Alexandra for Paul Edwards - 1988.

1992/93 Captain: Clive Freeman.

1992/93 Top scorer: Clive Freeman.

1992/93 Player of the Year: Paul France.

Club record goalscorer: Jack Swindells 252 - 1965-71.

Record appearances: John Davison 677 - 1971-86.

Past players who progressed to the Football League: Graham Barrow (Wigan Athletic, 1981), Eddie Bishop (Tranmere Rovers, 1988), Frank Carrodus (Manchester City, 1969), Peter Conning (Rochdale, 1986), Robert Dale (Bury, 1951), Nicky Daws (Bury, 1992), Paul Edwards (Crewe, 1988), Brian Green (Exeter City, 1962), John Hughes (Stockport County, 1976), Steve Johnson (Bury, 1977), Joe Kennedy (West Brom, 1948), Andy Kilner (Stockport County, 1990), Stan March (Port Vale, 1959), Charlie Mitten (Halifax Town, 1965), Brian Phillips (Middlesbrough, 1954), Andy Reid (Bury, 1992), Eric Robinson (West Brom, 1957), John Rogers (Wigan Athletic, 1982), Paul Showler (Barnet, 1991), Nelson Stiffle (Chesterfield, 1954), Jeff Street (Barrow, 1969).

Club Honours: Alliance Premier League Champions 1980,1981; FA Trophy Winners 1978,1986; Bob Lord Trophy Winners 1981; N.P.L. Cup Winners 1970; N.P.L. Shield Winners 1980; Cheshire County League Winners 1966,1967; Cheshire County League Cup Winners 1951,1953,1964; Cheshire Senior Cup Winners 1905,1934,1967,1982; Manchester League Champions 1905; Cheshire Amateur Cup Winners 1904.

BATH CITY

CITY MAINTAIN PROGRESS

Formed: 1889

President:
Mr F.A.Entwistle

Chairman:
Mr R.C.Stock

Vice Chairman
Mr C.Jefferis

Football Secretary:
Paul Britton

Manager:
A.Ricketts

Physiotherapist:
Rachel Jackson

Commercial Manager:
Paul Cater

Press Officer:
Paul Britton

Even though City failed to win any of their first six Conference fixtures, their early season form indicated that one right result could make all the difference. That first win came in an FA Cup Qualifying tie at Glastonbury, which was the start of a run of 24 games until the end of the year, of which only five resulted in defeat.

There were excellent home victories over Wycombe Wanderers, Woking and Farnborough Town and the team consistently picked up vital points on their travels. Steady progress was made in the Qualifying Rounds of the FA Cup, before the highlight of the season came with a marvellous 3-2 win at Cardiff City in the First Round Proper of the competition. Northampton Town provided the opposition in the Second Round, at Twerton Park, where a controversial first goal saw them gain a 2-2 draw. City were well beaten in the replay and their confidence and form slumped quite dramatically after that defeat, and a 5-0 home drubbing by Northwich Victoria at the end of January had City fans wondering if the club might be facing a battle to stay out of a relegation fight.

The club also lost to Stevenage in the First Round of the FA Trophy. Gradually, though, City regained some of their early season form and some excellent results were gained against teams in the top half of the table. The return of form saw the club climb slowly back up the table, to finish in a very creditable 7th position.

Once again, success was built on a solid defence, with the reliable David Mogg in goal and Grantley Dicks and Chris Banks performing consistently well in front of him. Player of the season, though, was Richard Crowley, who had an outstanding campaign. In addition to his excellent defensive qualities, Crowley finished as leading goalscorer, finding the back of the net on 13 occasions.

There is a feeling that if ambitious young manager Tony Ricketts can add one or two more quality players to his squad City can be a force to be reckoned with in the Conference next season.

Paul Britton.

Bath City striker Paul Randall in action during their GM Vauxhall Conference victory over Boston United. Photo: Paul Dennis.

BATH *MATCHFACTS* 92-93   BATH *MATCHFACTS* 92-93   BATH *MATCHFACTS* 92-93

Key: Home fixtures are denoted by bold capitals. Numbers in brackets after players names indicate goals scored (an asterisk by the results denotes own goals). Only used substitutes are listed - substituted players are *italicised*.

Key to Competitions: GMVC: G.M. Vauxhall Conference. **SPC:** Somerset Premier Cup. **DC:** Drinkwise (G.M. Vauxhall Conference) Cup. **FAC:** F.A. Cup. **FAT:** Vauxhall F.A. Trophy.

LEAGUE POSITION: 7th   **FA CUP:** Second Round   **FA TROPHY:** First Round

Date	Opponents	Comp.	Res	Gate	1.	2.	3.	4.	5.	6.	7.	8.	9.	10.	11.	Sub.	Sub.
22/08	Stalybridge C	GMVC	1-1	633	Mogg	Baverstock	*Palmer*	Smart(1)	*Crowley*	*Cousins*	Banks	Weston	Withey	Randall	Gill	Singleton	Dicks
25/08	**SLOUGH TOWN**	GMVC	0-1	592	Mogg	Baverstock	Dicks	Smart	Crowley	Cousins	Banks	*Weston*	Withey	Randall	Gill	Boyle	Boyle
29/08	**WITTON ALB.**	GMVC	0-0	521	Mogg	Palmer	Dicks	Smart	Crowley	Cousins	Banks	Weston	Withey	*Boyle*	*Gill*	Singleton	Elliott
31/08	Merthyr Tyd.	GMVC	1-1	808	Mogg	Palmer	Dicks	Smart	Crowley	Cousins	Banks	Weston	Withey	*Boyle(1)*	*Gill*	Singleton	Elliott
05/09	Macclesfield T.	GMVC	0-1	651	Mogg	*Palmer*	Dicks	Smart	*Crowley*	Cousins	Banks	*Weston*	Withey	Boyle	Gill	Singleton	Mings
08/09	**MERTHYR TYD.**	GMVC	1-3	616	Mogg	Randall	Dicks	Smart	Crowley	Cousins	Banks	Weston	Withey(1)	Boyle	Gill	Singleton	Mings
12/09	Glastonbury	FAC	4-0	402	Mogg	Palmer	Dicks	Gill	Crowley	Boyle	Banks	Singleton	*Withey(1)*	Randall(2)	*Mings*	Elliott	Smart(1)
15/09	**WOKING**	GMVC	2-0	801	Mogg	Palmer	Dicks	S'leton(1)	Crowley	Boyle	Banks	Cousins(1)	Withey	Randall	Gill	Elliott	
19/09	Stafford R.	GMVC	2-3	921	Mogg	Palmer	Dicks	Singleton	Crowley(1)	Cousins	Banks	Boyle	Withey(1)	*Randall*	Gill	Weston	Elliott
26/09	Falmouth	FAC	3-0	703	Mogg	Palmer	Dicks(1)	Gill	Crowley	Cousins	Banks	Boyle(1)	Withey(1)	*Randall*	Singleton	Weston	Smart
29/09	**WYCOMBE W.**	GMVC	2-0	1,283	Mogg	Palmer	Dicks	Singleton	Crowley	*Boyle*	Banks	Cousins(1)	Withey(1)	Randall	Gill	Smart	
03/10	Boston United	GMVC	2-1	841	Mogg	Palmer	Dicks	*Boyle*	Crowley(2)	Cousins	Banks	Singleton	*Withey*	Randall	Gill	Weston	Elliott
10/10	WEYMOUTH	FAC	2-0	890	Mogg	Palmer	Dicks	Singleton	Crowley	Cousins	Banks	*Weston*	*Withey*	Randall(1)	*Gill(1)*	Boyle	Elliott
13/10	**WELLING UTD**	GMVC	1-1	506	Mogg	Palmer	Dicks	*Boyle(1)*	Crowley	Cousins	Banks	Weston	Withey	Randall	Gill	Brown	Elliott
17/10	Wycombe W.	GMVC	0-2	4,085	Mogg	Elliott	Dicks	Weston	Crowley	Cousins	Banks	Singleton	Withey	*Randall*	Gill	Smart	
20/10	**YEOVIL TOWN**	DC	0-0	520	Mogg	Singleton	Dicks	Singleton	Crowley	Cousins	Banks	*Weston*	Withey	Randall	Gill	Brown	Randall
24/10	Tiverton	FAC	0-0	976	Mogg	Singleton	Dicks	Gill	Crowley	Cousins	Banks	Weston	Withey	*Boyle*	Smart	Smart(1)	V'non(1)
27/10	Tiverton	FAC	2-1	869	Mogg	Singleton	Dicks	Gill	Crowley	Cousins(1)	Banks	Weston	Withey	Boyle	Smart(1)	Boyle	V'non(2)
31/10	Gateshead	GMVC	4-0	373	Mogg	*Weston*	Dicks	Smart	Crowley	Cousins	Banks	Singleton	Withey	*Boyle(3)*	Gill	Brown	
07/11	**FARNBOROUGH**	GMVC	5-2	617	Mogg	Singleton	Dicks	Smart	Crowley(1)	Cousins(1)	Banks	Weston	*Withey(1)*	*Boyle*	Gill(1)	Randall	Vernon(1)
14/11	Cardiff City	FAC	3-2	4,506	Mogg	Palmer	Dicks	*Smart*	Crowley	Cousins	Banks	Weston	Withey(1)	*Boyle*	Gill(1)	Vernon(1)	Ricketts
17/11	Yeovil Town	DC	0-1	2,090	Mogg	Palmer	Dicks	Singleton	Crowley(1)	*Cousins*	Banks	Vernon	Boyle	*Boyle*	Gill	Weston	Singleton
21/11	**ALTRINCHAM**	GMVC	3-0	615	Mogg	Palmer	Dicks	Gill	Crowley	Cousins	Banks	Weston	*Withey*	*Smart*	Vernon(1)	Smart(1)	Singleton
28/11	**RUNCORN**	GMVC	1-1	673	Mogg	Palmer	Dicks	Gill(1)	Crowley	Cousins	Banks	Weston	*Withey*	Smart	Vernon	Randall	Singleton
06/12	**NORTHAMPTON**	FAC	2-2	3,626	Mogg	*Palmer*	Dicks,	Gill	Crowley	Cousins	Banks	Weston	Withey	Smart	Vernon	Singleton	Randall
12/12	Welling Utd	GMVC	3-0	862	Mogg	Palmer	Dicks	Singleton	Crowley	Cousins(1)	Banks	*Smart(1)*	Withey	*Randall(1)*	Gill	Ricketts	Vernon

Date	Opponent	Comp	Res	Att													
15/12	Northampton	FAC	0-3	2,420	Mogg	Palmer	Dicks	Ricketts	Crowley	Cousins	Banks	Gill	Withey	Smart	Randall	Randall	Vernon
19/12	**STALYBRIDGE**	GMVC	1-1	560	Mogg	Palmer	Dicks	Gill	Crowley	Cousins	Banks	Gill(1)	Withey	Vernon	Vernon	Vernon	Mings
26/12	**KIDDERMINSTER**	GMVC	2-1	870	Mogg	Palmer	Dicks	Singleton	Crowley(1)	Cousins	Banks	Singleton	Withey(1)	Smart	Gill(1)	Randall	Mings
28/12	Yeovil Town	GMVC	1-2	6,488	Mogg	Palmer	Singleton	Ricketts	Crowley	Cousins	Banks	Weston	Withey	Smart	Hedges	Vernon	Singleton
09/01	Stevenage B.	FAT	0-2	907	Mogg	Palmer	Maddison	Ricketts	Bailey	Cousins	Gill	Weston	Withey	Randall	Vernon(1)	Smart	
16/01	Farnborough	GMVC	1-2	504	Mogg	Bailey	Dicks	Ricketts	Mings	Cousins	Frankland	Gill	Withey	Vernon(1)	Vernon	Randall	
19/01	Wellington	SPC	5-0		Mogg	Palmer	Dicks	Singleton	Crowley	Cousins	Smart	Frankland	Withey	Boyle	Vernon		
30/01	**NORTHWICH V.**	GMVC	0-5	565	Mogg	Hedges	Dicks	Singleton	Crawley	Maddison	Maddison	Banks	Withey	Boyle	Smart	Randall	
02/02	Slough Town	GMVC	*1-1	1,021	Mogg	Hedges	Dicks	Maddison	Maddison	Cousins	Banks	Mings	Withey	Boyle	Mings	Vernon	Mings
06/02	Altrincham	GMVC	0-1	678	Mogg	Hedges	Dicks	Ricketts	Crowley	Weston	Banks	Smart	Smart	Randall	Randall	Mings	Boyle
09/02	**CLEVEDON T.**	SPC	3-1	216	Mogg	Hedges	Dicks	Smart	Crowley	Boyle	Banks	Boyle	Withey	Cousins	Gill	Cousins	Cousins
19/02	**BOSTON UTD**	GMVC	2-1	508	Mogg	Hedges	Dicks	Gill	Crowley(1)	Mings(1)	Banks	Singleton	Mings	Boyle	Gill	Vernon	
20/02	Kettering T.	GMVC	1-0	1,185	Mogg	Hedges	Palmer	Gill	Crowley(1)	Singleton	Banks	Randall	Randalls	Boyle	Smart	Vernon	
27/02	Telford Utd	SPC	0-0	618	Mogg	Hedges	Palmer	Smart	Crowley	Cousins	Banks	Singleton	Singleton	Boyle	Smart	Vernon	
02/03	Bristol Rovers	SPC	1-4	471	Mogg	Hedges	Dicks	Smart	Crowley	Gill	Banks	Boyle	Withey	Cousins	Vernon	Mings	Boyle
06/03	**MACCLESFIELD**	GMVC	0-0	478	Mogg	Hedges	Gill	Crowley	Cousins	Banks	Singleton	Singleton	Smart	Dicks	Cousins	Weston	Withey
13/03	Bromsgrove	GMVC	1-1	1,030	Mogg	Hedges	Dicks	Smart	Singleton	Boyle	Banks	Dicks	Mings	Boyle	Weston	Vernon	Withey
20/03	**BROMSGROVE**	GMVC	0-3	516	Mogg	Hedges	Dicks	Smart	Crowley	Mings	Banks	Boyle	Weston	Mings	Vernon	Vernon	
23/03	Woking	GMVC	1-0	1,290	Mogg	Hedges	Dicks	Smart	Crowley(1)	Boyle	Banks	Mings	Boyle	Smart	Cousins	Jones	
27/03	**DAGENHAM & R**	GMVC	2-1	570	Mogg	Palmer	Dicks	Cousins	Crowley	Gill	Banks	Weston	Smart	Mings	Vernon	Randall	Randall
03/04	Northwich Vic.	GMVC	1-3	641	Mogg	Hedges	Dicks	Cousins(1)	Crowley	Gill	Banks	Weston	Smart	Mings(1)	Vernon(1)	Randall	Randall
06/04	**TELFORD UTD**	GMVC	4-1	338	Mogg	Hedges	Jones	Cousins	Crowley(1)	Gill(1)	Banks	Weston	Vernon	Mings(1)	Vernon(1)	Singleton	Vernon
10/04	Kidderminster	GMVC	0-1	1,134	Mogg	Hedges	Jones	Cousins	Crowley	Gill	Banks	Weston	Withey	Smart	Singleton	Boyle	Randall
12/04	**YEOVIL TOWN**	GMVC	0-0	1,331	Mogg	Hedges	Jones	Singleton	Crowley	Gill	Banks	Vernon	Withey	Mings	Boyle	Vernon	Vernon
14/04	Witton Alb.	GMVC	0-0	622	Mogg	Hedges	Jones	Singleton	Crowley	Gill	Banks	Weston	Withey	Smart	Weston	Vernon	Boyle
17/04	Dagenham & R.	GMVC	1-2	924	Mogg	Hedges	Jones	Cousins	Crowley(1)	Gill	Banks	Weston	Withey	Mings	Boyle	Vernon	Randall
20/04	**KETTERING T.**	GMVC	0-0	386	Mogg	Hedges	Jones	Cousins	Crowley	Gill(1)	Banks	Boyle	Withey	Smart	Smart	Randall	
24/04	**STAFFORD R.**	GMVC	2-1	573	Mogg	Hedges	Dicks	Cousins	Crowley	Gill	Banks	Randall	Boyle	Smart	Randall	Vernon	
25/04	**GATESHEAD**	GMVC	1-1	491	Mogg	Hedges	Dicks	Cousins	Crowley	Gill	Banks	Smart(1)	Mings(1)	Boyle	Weston	Weston	
01/05	Runcorn	GMVC	*3-1	504	Mogg	Hedges	Dicks	Cousins	Crowley(1)	Gill	Banks	Weston	Boyle	Mings	Vernon(1)	Vernon(1)	

League Appearances: Bailey 1: Banks 41: Baverstock 2: Boyle 26(5): Brown 0(2): Cousins 37(1): Dicks 33(1): Elliott 0(5): Frankland 1: Gill 39: Hedges 21: Jones 6(1): Maddison 4: Mings 19(4): Mogg 42: Palmer 18: Randall 16(1): Ricketts 1(2): Singleton 21(7): Smart 31(4): Vernon 12(13): Weston 33(4): Withey 30(2).

League Goalscorers: Crowley 11: Boyle, Vernon 7: Gill 6: Mings, Smart, Withey 5: Cousins 4: Randall, Singleton 1.

Bath City

TONY RICKETTS

Tony took over as player-manager of the club midway through the 1990/91 season at a time when relegation to the Beazer Homes League looked inevitable. His determination and commitment saw City avoid the drop by 3 points and the following season he led the side to 9th position in the Conference. That he was able to improve on that in 1992/93, by achieving 7th place with very few changes in personal and working within an extremely tight budget, shows what an asset he has been to the club.

His playing career began with local side Clandown, before he joined Bath for the first time. He then had a successful spell as a player with local rivals Yeovil Town, before rejoining the club for whom he has an obvious affinity.

His success as a manager and his ambitions for the club have prompted City's directors to extend his contract until the end of the 1994/95 season.

Bath keeper David Mogg cuts out a low cross, with Martin Gittings of Stevenage (No.9) waiting to pounce. Photo: Francis Short.

Programme details:
    36 pages for £1
    Editor - Keith & Neil Brookman.

Any other club publications:
    Revenge of the Killer Penguin (Fanzine)

Local Newspapers:
    Evening Chronicle
    Evening Post
    Western Daily Press

Local Radio Stations:
    Radio Bristol
    GWR

BATH CITY - PLAYING SQUAD 1992-93

Player	Honours	Birthplace and date	Transfer Fees	Previous Clubs
GOALKEEPERS				
David Mogg	ES, EY	Bristol 11/2/62		Bristol C, Atvidaberg (Swe), Abbotonians, Bath C, Cheltenham, Gloucester C
DEFENDERS				
Richard Crowley	GSC, SSC, WLC	Bristol 28/12/59		Frome T, Bath C, Forest Green Rov, Cheltenham
Ian Hedges		Bristol 5/2/69	£7,500	Bristol Manor Farm, Gloucester C, AFC Bournemouth
David Palmer		Bristol 10/4/61		Bristol Rovers
Tony Ricketts	IL, AC Delco	Bath 21/6/59	£10,000	Clandown, Bath C, Yeovil
Grantley Dicks		Bristol 17/10/66		Clandown, Paulton Rovers
Chris Banks		Stone, Staffs 12/11/65		Port Vale, Exeter City
MIDFIELD				
Ian Weston		Bristol 6/5/68		Bristol Rovers, Torquay Utd
Wayne Noble	IL, SLM, AC Delco	Bristol 11/6/67		Bristol Rovers, Yeovil T, Gloucester C
Gary Smart		Kingston, Jam. 1/4/62		Glenside Hospital, Bristol Rovers, Cheltenham
David Singleton		Bournemouth 20/11/56		Taunton Town, Weymouth
Paul Chenoweth		Bristol 5/2/73		Bristol Rovers
Robert Cousins		Bristol 9/1/71		Bristol City
Jeremy Gill	SSC	Clevedon 8/9/70		Backwell Utd, Trowbridge T, Leyton Orient, Weston-Super-Mare
FORWARDS				
Deion Vernon		Bristol		Bristol City
Adie Mings		Chippenham 17/10/68		Chippenham Town
Martin Boyle		Bristol		Bristol Rovers, Trowbridge T, Mangotsfield Utd

Departures during season:
Keith Brown (Retired), Dean Radford (Weymouth), Ray Baverstock (Moreton T), Paul Randall (Weymouth), Graham Withey (Yate).

Players on loan during season:
Tony Frankland & Lee Maddison (Bristol City), Vaughan Jones (Britol Rovers).

Twerton Park, Bath

Address and telephone number: Twerton Park, Twerton, Bath Avon BA2 1DB.
Tel: 0225 423087
Simple directions: Twerton Park is situated on the A4/A36 Lower Bristol Road - on the Bristol side of Bath City Centre (Approx 2.5 miles). The area is serviced by J18 on the M4. From the centre of Bath the bus route is No.5 - Twerton High Street.
Capacity: 9,899   **Seated:** 1,017   **Covered terracing:** 4,800
Record Attendance: 18,020 v Brighton & Hove Albion, FA Cup.
Club Shop: Contact Mr P.Cater or Mr K.Sellick.
Social Facilities: Several bars open all week and full service with menu on match-days catering for up to 250 people.
Previous Grounds: Lambridge - 1889-1952

Bath Fact File

Nickname: Romans

Club Sponsors: Bath Advertiser.

Previous Leagues: Beazer Homes (Southern League)

Club colours: Black/white striped shirts, black shorts & black/white socks.

Change colours: Red/white

Midweek home matchday: Tuesday

Record win:

Record defeat:

Record transfer fee: £15,000 for Micky Tanner from Bristol City.

Record transfer fee received:

1992/93 Captain: Richard Crowley

1992/93 Top scorer: Richard Crowley

1992/93 Player of the Year: Richard Crowley

Club record goalscorer: Paul Randall

Record appearances:

Past players who progressed to the Football League: A.Skirton (Arsenal), T.Book (Plymouth Argyle, Manchester City), K.Allen (Bournemouth, Swindon Town), P.Rogers (Exeter City), R.Bourne (Torquay), D.Wilfil (Manchester City), S.Mortensen (Blackpool), B.Wade (Swindon Town), J.Meacham (Bristol Rovers), M.Hirst (Bristol City), P.Bodin (Swindon), G.Withey (Coventry), J.Dodd (Southampton).

Club Honours: Southern League (2); League Cup, Somerset Premier Cup (12); Anglo-Italian Cup finalists.

BROMSGROVE ROVERS

Formed:
1885

President:
Charles W.Poole

Chairman:
Keith MacMaster

Football Secretary:
Brian Hewings

Manager:
Booby Hope

Assistant Manager:
Doug Griffiths

Physiotherapist:
Paul Sunners

Commercial Manager:
Rebecca O'Neill

Press Officer:

Bromsgrove Rovers, record breakers in season 1992-92 did it again, turning the tables on the "Bookmakers" who had predicted relegation for us in season 1991-93, therefore an early return to the Beazer Homes League. The season was our first in the General Motors Vauxhall Conference, it was indeed an exciting event. Before hand we looked forward to matching ourselves against the top teams in the land. We were indeed to prove very good prospects, so much so that chants of "We're so good it's unbelievable" rang out amongst our supporters towards the end of a great season. Our supporters, came along in ever increasing numbers, which meant that the club had an increase percentage on last season of 71%.

Lets look at the season's achievements, a number of records were set this year, which included; the first promoted team not to have any "double" recorded against them. Rovers then achieved the highest place finish of any team promoted into the Vauxhall Conference. We recorded four "doubles" in our favour, most away wins, 9, again the highest number for a team on promotion to the GMVC. Bromsgrove did not have a Cup Final to look forward to at the end of our season, however as the crowd waited patiently for news to arrive after our final fixture, the two results announced, confirmed Bromsgrove as Runners-up, that then started the party!

As August came to a close, Rovers had two pieces of silverware displayed in the trophy cabinet, the Southern League Beazer Homes Championship Cup, after beating Dover, and the Bob Mann Trophy, against Worcester City. Who could have possibly known, or even have guessed that at the outset of our first season in the Vauxhall Conference, that we would finish second to Wycombe Wanderers. Wycombe deserved to win the GMVC, my congratulations to them, but I believe Rovers, earned their runners-up spot, which in our first season is surely an achievement in itself. When on Easter Monday, we failed to get maximum points, it then became mathmatically impossible for us to catch Wycombe. For 38 matches, we were still within reach of the top team in the GMVC, not bad for the team the "bookies" wanted to relegate.

On the playing side, the season was very enjoyable. Our players adjusted to the higher demands associated with this level of soccer. Loyalty has been this club's motto. Manager Bobby Hope has kept faith with many players, we have been rewarded by those who have been with the club since our days long ago in the Southern League Midland Division. The players now receiving various honours are, Paul Webb, who was voted player of the season by both his own players, and by the supporters. Paul became the club's first representative when he became a non-League English International, "Webby" was the only ever present during our 52 match season. Jimmy Skelding, who received the local press award as player of the season. Our sponsor's "All Saints" player of the season award went to Brian Gray, in his debut season at Bromsgrove, a good start. Kevin Richardson, who has joined Paul Webb, as the club's other capped non-League International, both Internationals along with Stewart Brighton, who received a special award, for scoring Bromsgrove's first ever Vauxhall Conference goal. They have all been chosen to represent the Middlesex Wanderers, for the forthcoming tour in the close season.

Bromsgrove featured in some very exciting finishes to matches. It is our habit of scoring some late goals, in fact, 20 goals were scored in the last ten minutes of our games, and this earned us 10 points. Our never sat die attitude, is a stong feature of our play. We did have one month which was to prove costly in our search for honours, February. Six matches were lost, one was drawn, (away to Merthyr), and only one victory, (away at Telford), so only four out of a possible 18 points. The worst part of all this was our three successive home defeats firstly against Dagenham & Redbridge 1-2, then Slough 0-1, and against Stafford 2-3, nine points lost!.....if only! We lost out in two knockout competitions away to our rivals Kidderminster, in the Worcestershire Senior Cup, and away to Wycombe in the F.A. Trophy.

Away from the playing side, we have continued to make real progress, on the commercial side, at the club's souvenir shop and with our match programme, one of the best in the Conference. As mentioned, loyalty does play a very big part at Bromsgrove Rovers, so I will take this opportunity to say a big thank you to the four players loaned to us during the season, Steve Brain, who was to score, then break his leg on his debut, Lee Williams, of Aston Villa, Michael Oakes also of Villa, and Ron Green. Michael and Ron both did well standing in for our goalkeeper Scott Cooksey, who missed a large part of the season injured. The youth team's first ever season was a sucess as they finished as Runners-up, and our reserves finished third in their league.

As I reflect on the season overall, it is difficult not to day-dream of what might have been. For eight seasons, one player has always scored 20+ goals a season. Chris Hanks added only one goal to his club record of 231 goals. Chris was unjured for 90% of the season, so my day-dreaming of what could have happened, with 20+ goals from Chris, playing in partnership with Mark Whitehouse, perhaps a second successive championship, and another promotion, may have been celebrated at the Victoria Ground.

Well there's always next season! **Brian Perry**

Key: Home fixtures are denoted by bold capitals. Numbers in brackets after players names indicate goals scored (an asterisk by the results denotes own goals). Only used substitutes are listed - substituted players are *italicised*.

Key to Competitions: **GMVC**: G.M. Vauxhall Conference. **WSC**: Worcestershire Senior Cup. **DC**: Drinkwise (G.M. Vauxhall Conference) Cup. **FAC**: F.A. Cup. **FAT**: Vauxhall F.A. Trophy. **BHL**: Beazer Homes League Championship Shield.

Date	Opponents	Comp.	Res	Gate	1.	2.	3.	4.	5.	6.	7.	8.	9.	10.	11.	Sub.	Sub.
22/08	Witton Albion	GMVC	1-1	912	Cooksey	Skelding	Brighton(1)	Richardson	O'Meara	Shilvock	Grealish	Webb	*Whitehouse*	Crisp	Daly	Crisp	Hanks
25/08	**BOSTON UNITED**	GMVC	2-1	1,235	Cooksey	Skelding	Brighton	Richardson	O'Meara	Shilvock	Grealish	Webb(1)	Whiteh.(1)	Crisp	*Burgher*		Hanks
29/08	Dagenham & Red.	GMVC	1-1	1,078	Cooksey	Skelding	Brighton	Richardson	O'Meara	Shilvock(1)	Grealish	Webb	Whitehouse	Crisp	*Daly*		Hanks
31/08	**DOVER ATH.**	BHL	2-0	730	Cooksey	Skelding	Brighton	Wardle	O'Meara	Shilvock(1)	Stott	Webb(1)	Hanks	Crisp	Burgher	Whitehouse	Gray
5/09	**NORTHWICH V.**	GMVC	1-2	1,125	Cooksey	Skelding	Brighton	Richardson	O'Meara	Shilvock	*Grealish*	Webb	Hanks	*Crisp*	Stott	Whitehouse	Daly
8/09	Stafford Rgrs	DC	2-4	677	Cooksey	Skelding	Brighton	Richardson(1)	O'Meara	Shilvock	Grealish	Webb	Whiteh.(1)	Shilvock	Burgher	Crisp	Hanks
12/09	**WELLING UTD**	GMVC	2-2	957	Cooksey	Skelding	Brighton	Richardson	*O'Meara*	Shilvock	Grealish	Stott	Hanks(1)	Shilvock	Whitehouse	Daly(1)	
15/09	**MACCLESFIELD**	GMVC	3-0	1,065	Cooksey	Skelding	Brighton	Richardson	O'Meara	Shilvock(1)	*Grealish*	Stott	Webb(2)	Burgher	Daly	Whitehouse	
19/09	Wycombe Wdrs	GMVC	0-4	4,282	Cooksey	Skelding	*Davis*	Richardson	O'Meara	*Shilvock*	Daly	Stott	Hanks	Crisp	Webb	Wardle	Cooper
22/09	**STAFFORD R.**	DC	*2-1	757	Cooksey	Skelding	Burgher	Rich'son(1)	Wardle	Shilvock	*Daly*	Webb	Hanks	Crisp	Cooper	Davis	Gray
26/09	**YEOVIL TOWN**	GMVC	1-0	1,196	Cooksey	Skelding	O'Meara	Richardson	Wardle	Shilvock	*Daly*	Stott	Gray	Webb(1)	Cooper	Crisp	
3/10	Slough Town	GMVC	3-1	866	Cooksey	Skelding	Brighton	Richardson	Wardle	Shilvock	Cooper(1)	Stott	Whiteh.(1)	Webb	Gray(1)	Crisp	
10/10	**WYCOMBE WDRS**	GMVC	1-0	3,675	Cooksey	Skelding	Brighton	Richardson	Wardle	Shilvock	Cooper	Stott	Whiteh.(1)	Webb	Gray	Crisp	
17/10	Stalybridge C.	GMVC	1-0	771	Cooksey	Skelding	Brighton	Richardson	Wardle	Shilvock	Cooper	Grealish	Whitehouse	Webb	Gray(1)		
24/10	Stafford Rgrs	FAC	0-3	1,274	Cooksey	Skelding	Brighton	Richardson	Wardle	Shilvock	Cooper	Stott	Whitehouse	Webb	Gray(1)	O'Meara	Crisp
31/10	Woking	GMVC	2-0	1,832	Cooksey	Skelding	Brighton	Richardson	Wardle	Crisp	Daly	Grealish	Whitehouse	Webb	Gray(1)	Cooper(1)	
3/11	**TELFORD UTD**	GMVC	0-0	1,543	Cooksey	Skelding	Brighton	Richardson	Wardle	Crisp	Grealish	Burgher	Whitehouse	Webb	*Gray*	Cooper	
7/11	Gateshead	GMVC	0-0	405	Cooksey	Skelding	Brighton	Richardson	Wardle	Crisp	Daly	*Grealish*	*Whitehouse*	Webb	*Gray*	Cooper	Stott
14/11	Farnborough	GMVC	1-1	533	Cooksey	Skelding	Brighton	Cooper	Wardle(1)	Crisp	Daly	Stott	*Whitehouse*	Webb	Gray	Grealish	
18/11	Dudley Town	WSC	*1-0	346	Cooksey	Skelding	Brighton	Cooper	Wardle	Crisp	Daly	Stott	Shilvock	Webb	Gray	Honeyfield	Grealish
21/11	Kettering T.	GMVC	2-3	1,328	Cooksey	Skelding	Brighton	Cooper	O'Meara	Crisp	*Daly*	Stott(1)	Whiteh.(1)	Webb	Gray	Shilvock	
28/11	**MERTHYR TYD.**	GMVC	1-2	1,306	Cooksey	Skelding	Brighton	Richardson	Wardle	Crisp	*Cooper*	Stott	Whiteh.(1)	Webb	Gray	Shilvock	
1/12	Northwich V.	GMVC	1-0	508	Cooksey	Skelding	Brighton	Richardson	Wardle	Shilvock	Cooper	Stott	Whitehouse	Webb	Crisp(1)	Hanks	
12/12	**ALTRINCHAM**	GMVC	4-1	1,117	*Cooksey*	Skelding	Brighton	Richardson	Wardle	Shilvock	Daly(1)	Stott	Whiteh.(2)	Webb(1)	Crisp	O'Meara	
19/12	Yeovil Town	GMVC	2-2	5,495	Oakes	Skelding	Brighton	*Richardson*	Wardle	Shilvock(1)	Daly	Ross	Whitehouse	Webb(1)	Crisp	O'Meara	
26/12	**FARNBOROUGH**	GMVC	2-2	1,780	Oakes	Skelding	Brighton	Whiteh.(1)	Wardle	Stott	Daly	Ross	*Hanks*	Webb	Crisp(1)	Gray	
28/12	Kidderminster	GMVC	0-1	912	Oakes	Skelding	Brighton	Whitehouse	Wardle	Crisp	Daly	Stott	Burgher	Webb	Gray	Gray	

Date	Opponent	Comp	Score	Att												
9/01	Kettering T.	FAT	0-0	1,723	Oakes	Skelding	Brighton	Richardson	Wardle	Shilvock	Daly	Stott	Gray	Webb	Crisp	
12/01	KETTERING T.	FAT	4-1	1,269	Oakes	Skelding	Brighton	Richardson	Wardle	Crisp	Burgher	Stott(1)	Whitehouse	Webb(1)	Gray(2)	Daly
16/01	WITTON ALBION	GMVC	3-2	1,145	Oakes	Skelding	Brighton	Rich'son(1)	Wardle	Crisp(1)	Daly	Stott	Whiteh.(2)	Webb	Gray	O'Meara
23/01	KETTERING T.	GMVC	1-1	1,297	Green	Skelding	Brighton	Richardson	Wardle	Webb	Daly	Stott	Whitehouse Crisp	Crisp(1)	Shilvock	O'Meara
30/01	DAGENHAM & R.	FAT	3-1	1,711	Green	Skelding	Brighton	Richardson	Wardle	Webb	Daly	Webb	Whiteh.(2)	Crisp(1)	Shilvock	Grealish
1/02	Kidderminster	WSC	0-2	1,331	Green	Skelding	Davis	Richardson	O'Meara	Webb	Burgher	Stott	Whitehouse Crisp	Shilvock	Daly	
6/02	DAGENHAM & R.	GMVC	1-2	1,120	Green	Skelding	Davis	Richardson	O'Meara	Webb	Daly	Stott	Whiteh.(1)	Crisp	Daly	Gray
9/02	Telford United	GMVC	1-0	935	Green	Skelding	Webb	Richardson	Wardle	Burgher	Daly	Stott	Whitehouse Crisp	Daly(1)	Gray	Grealish
13/02	SLOUGH TOWN	GMVC	0-1	1,456	Green	Skelding	Brighton	Richardson	Wardle	Webb	Daly	Stott	Whitehouse Crisp	Gray	Shilvock	O'Meara
16/02	Merthyr Tydfil	GMVC	1-1	546	Green	Skelding	Brighton	Richardson	O'Meara	Williams	Burgher	Stott	Whitehouse Webb	Gray(1)	Shilvock	Williams
20/02	Wycombe Wdrs	FAT	0-2	4,907	Green	Skelding	O'Meara	Williams	Wardle	Webb	Shilvock	Stott	Whitehouse Gray	Crisp	Grealish	Daly
23/02	STAFFORD RGRS	GMVC	2-3	1,130	Green	Skelding	O'Meara	Williams	Wardle	Webb(1)	Daly	Stott	Whiteh.(1)	Gray	Burgher	Daly
27/02	Runcorn	GMVC	1-2	459	Green	Skelding	Brighton	Richardson	Wardle	Webb	Shilvock	Stott	Whiteh.(1)	Gray	Williams	Daly
6/03	STALYBRIDGE	GMVC	4-0	945	Green	Skelding	Brighton	Richardson	Wardle	Webb	Shilvock	Brain(1)	Whiteh.(2)	Williams	Gray(1)	Grealish
13/03	BATH CITY	GMVC	1-1	1,030	Green	Grealish	Wardle	Webb	Shilvock	Whiteh.(1)	Williams	Grealish	Crisp	Cooper	Daly	
20/03	Bath City	GMVC	3-0	516	Green	Greallish	Davis	Crisp	Wardle	Webb	Shilvock	Stott	Whiteh.(2)	Carty	Gray(1)	O'Meara
27/03	Welling Utd	GMVC	2-4	750	Green	Greallish	Brighton	Crisp	Wardle	Webb(1)	Shilvock	Stott	Whitehouse Carty(1)	Carty	Gray(1)	O'Meara
29/03	RUNCORN	GMVC	0-0	963	Green	Skelding	Skelding	Richardson	Wardle	Webb(1)	Burgher	Stott	Whitehouse Gray	Gray	Carty	
06/04	GATESHEAD	GMVC	3-0	923	Green	Skelding	Brighton	Rochardson	Wardle	Webb	Carty	Stott	Whiteh.(1)	Burgher(1)	Gray(1)	
10/04	Boston Utd	GMVC	2-1	1,037	Cooksey	Skelding	Skelding	Richardson	Wardle	Webb	Shilvock	Stott(1)	Whiteh.(1)	Gray	Daly	
12/04	KIDDERMINSTER	GMVC	2-2	3,185	Cooksey	Webb	Brighton	Richardson	O'Meara	Webb	Daly	Stott	Whiteh.(1)	Burgher	Gray(1)	Shilvock
17/04	Macclesfield	GMVC	2-0	604	Cooksey	Webb	Brighton	Richardson	O'Meara	Shilvock	Carty	Stott	Whiteh.(2)	Crisp	Gray	
20/04	Stafford Rgrs	GMVC	4-3	1,126	Cooksey	Webb	Brighton	Richardson	Scandrett	Shilvock(1)	Daly	Stott	Crisp(2)	Gray	Burgher(1)	
24/04	Altrincham	GMVC	2-2	1,010	Cooksey	Webb	Brighton	Richardson	O'Meara	Shilvock	Carty	Stott	Whitehouse Crisp(2)	Gray	Gray	
01/05	WOKING	GMVC	1-0	1,808	Cooksey	Webb	Brighton	Richardson	O'Meara	Shilvock(1)	Carty	Stott	Whitehouse Crisp(2)	Gray	Scandrett	

LEAGUE APPEARANCES: Webb 52, Skelding 46, Whirehouse 43(4), Brighton 42, Richardson 41, Stott 41, Crisp 36(8), Wardle 34(4), Shilvock 34(4), Cooksey 30, Daly 27(11), Gray 31 (6), O'Meara 20(17), Grealish 13(9), Green 16, Cooper 12(4), Burgher 16, Hanks 7(5), Williams 6(1), Oakes 6, Davis 4(2), Carty 5, Ross 2(1), Scandrett 1(1), Brain 1, Honeyfield 0(1).

LEAGUE GOALSCORERS: Whitehouse 26; Webb 10; Gray 9; Crisp 8; Shilvock 6; Stott, Daly 4; Richardson, Cooper, Burgher 2; Brighton, Wardle, O'Meara, Hanks, Carty, Brain 1.

Bromsgrove Rovers

BOBBY HOPE

Bobby Hope was born in Bridge of Allan, Scotland. He began his playing career with West Bromwich Albion whom he joined in 1959 as a junior. He went on to make over 330 appearances at The Hawthorns before moving on to Birmingham City and Sheffield Wednesday. Bobby represented Scotland at Schoolboy, Under-23 and twice at Full International level.

He is now in his second spell in charge of Bromsgrove Rovers after leaving for a brief period with Burton Albion. His excellent leadership qualities have shown through to lead the club into the GM Vauxhall Conference for the first time.

Bromsgrove defender Shaun O'Meara clears the ball out of the danger area closely watched by Keith Scott of Wycombe. Photo: Paul Dennis.

Programme details:
    36 pages for £1
    Editor - Terry Brumpton

Any other club publications:

Local Newspapers:
    Bromsgrove Advertiser
    Bromsgrove Messenger

Local Radio Stations:
    BBC Hereford & Worcester.

BROMSGROVE ROVERS - PLAYING SQUAD 1992-93

Player	Honours	Birthplace and date	Transfer Fees	Previous Clubs
GOALKEEPERS				
Scott Cooksey	BHP	Birmingham 24/6/72		Derby County, Shrewsbury
DEFENDERS				
Jimmy Skelding	BHP	Bilston 30/5/64		Bilston, Wolves, Bromsgrove Rov, Burton Alb., Worcester C
Lee Evans		Birmingham		Halesowen T
Stewart Brighton	BHP, FA XI	Bromsgrove 3/10/66		Crewe Alexandra
Shaun O'Meara	BHP, WSC	Bromsgrove 24/4/56		Bromsgrove Rov, Stourbridge, Alvechurch, Bromsgrove Rov, Worcester C
Chris Hodges				Walsall, Rushall Olympic
Kevin Richardson	BHP, FA XI	Walsall 22/11/62		Pelsall V, Sutton C, Stafford R, Worcester C, Sutton C, Alvechurch, Hednesford
Paul Wardle	BHP	Burton-on-Trent 1/2/70		Belper Town, Denaby Utd
MIDFIELD				
Paul Webb	BHP, FA XI	Wolverhampton 30/11/67		Bilston, Shrewsbury
Rob Shilvock	SLM, SLC, WML, BSC, FA X	Stourbridge 26/10/61		Halesowen T, Bromsgrove Rov, Kidderminster H, Halesowen T
Steve Stott	BHP	Leeds 3/2/65		Bromsgrove Rov, Alvechurch
Symon Burgher	BHP	Birmingham 29/10/66		Exeter
Steve Cooper	BHP	Worcester 29/5/70		Malvern T, Alvechurch
Tony Grealish	Rep of Ireland	Paddington 27/9/56		Leyton Orient, Luton, Brighton, WBA, Man City, Rotherham, Walsall
FORWARDS				
Mark Whitehouse	FA XI	Birmingham 27/9/61		Moor Green, Oldbury, Tamworth, Redditch, Worcester, Burton Alb, Kidderminster H
Tommy Daly	BHP	Birmingham 24/10/63		Coleshill T
Mark Crisp	BHP	Birmingham		Smethwick, Redditch Utd, Bromsgrove Rov, Bromsgrove Rov, Alvechurch
Chris Hanks	BHP	Alvechurch 29/4/63		Studley Sporting
Brian Gray		Birmingham		Birmingham City

Departures during season:
Jason Ross (Hednesford), Nigel Larkins (Worcester C).

Players on loan during season:
Lee Williams (Aston Villa), Simon Brain (Hereford), Paul Byrne (Port Vale).

Victoria Ground, Bromsgrove

Address and telephone number: Victoria Ground, Birmingham Road, Bromsgrove, Worcs, B61 0DR Tel: 0527 76949 (Office), 0527 78260 (Social Club).

Simple directions: The Victoria Ground is situated on the north side of Bromsgrove on the Birmingham Road, which is off the A38 Bromsgrove by pass. The M5 and M42 join the A38 to the north of the town making it easy to get to the ground without having to go into town. The 144 Midland Road bus runs from New Street Station Birmingham and passes the ground.

Capacity: 4,893   **Seated:** 390   **Covered terracing:** 1,738

Record Attendance: 7,389 v Worcester City - 1957.

Club Shop: Sells all kinds of replica clothing & souvenirs. Contact Doug Bratt (0527 74997).

Social Facilities: Clubhouse - Serves hot & cold food. Big screen satellite TV, pool table & darts. Open matchdays, Sunday 12.00-2.00 and week-day evenings.

Previous Grounds: Old Station Road 1885-1887, Recreation Ground 1887-1889, Churchfields 1889-1891, Well Lane 1891-1910.

Bromsgrove Fact File

Nickname: Rovers or Greens

Club Sponsors: All Saints of Bromsgrove.

Previous Leagues: Birmingham Combination 1910-1953, Birmingham/W.Midlands League 1953-1973, Southern League (N.Division) 1973-1986, Southern League (Premier) 1986-1992.

Club colours: Green & white shirts, black shorts & green socks.

Change colours: All white.

Reserve team league: Ansells Combination Reserve Division.

Midweek home matchday: Tuesday

Record win:

Record defeat:

Record transfer fee:

Record transfer fee received: £30,000 from Crystal Palace for Martin O'Connor - 1992.

1992/93 Captain: Kevin Richardson

1992/93 Top scorer: Mark Whitehouse

1992/93 Player of the Year: Paul Webb

Club record goalscorer: Chris Hanks

Record appearances: Shaun O'Meara

Past players who progressed to the Football League: Mike McKenna (Northampton 1946), Ray Hartle (Bolton 1952), Angus McLean (Bury 1953), Alan Smith (A.Villa 1954), Mike Deakin (C.Palace 1954), Brain Puster (Leicester 1958), Tom Smith (Sheff.Utd 1978), Malcolm Goodman (Halifax 1979), Steve Smith (Walsall 1980), Gary Hackett (Shrewsbury 1983), Bill McGarry, Martyn O'Connor (C.Palace 1992).

Club Honours: Vauxhall Conference R-up 1992-93; Southern League Premier Champions 1991-92; Southern League Prem. R-up 1986-87; Southern League Mid. Champions 1985-86; Bill Dellow Cup Winners 1985-86; Southern League Champions v Cup Winners Cup Winners 1992-93; Worcester Senior Cup Winners 1946-47, 1947-48, 1959-60, 1986-87; Birmingham Senior Cup Winners 1946-47; West Midlands League Champions 1960-61; Birmingham Combination Champions 1946-47.

DAGENHAM & REDBRIDGE

Formed:
1992

President:
Barry East BSC

Joint Chairmen:
Dave Andrews
Norman Sparrow

Football Secretary:
Derek Almond

Manager:
John Still

Physiotherapist:
Jim Stannard

Press Officer:
Steve Warren

At the start of the 1992-93 campaign, newly amalgamated Dagenham & Redbridge F.C. were quoted by some some bookmakers as second favourites to lift the GM Vauxhall Conference championship trophy. This forecast was based largely on the strength of manager John Still's knowledge of Conference football and the close season enhancement of an already very experienced squad of players.

No less than six England non-League internationals lined up for the Reds' in the opening day 2-0 victory at Merthyr and after despatching Farnborough 5-1 at Victoria Road the following Tuesday evening, the East London club began to harbour ambitions of a serious challenge for the title.

At the turn of the year the club held a top three position and along with Slough Town were keeping the pressure up on leaders Wycombe. But the Reds championship challenge was to all but disappear following a disastrous spell of poor form which began on the 23rd of January.

In the next six weeks the club picked up just five points from a possible twenty-four and consequently was forced to mount a new challenge for the runners-up place, which was eventually lost to newcomers Bromsgrove Rovers on the last day of the season.

Semi-finals were reached in both the Drinkwise and Essex Senior Cups and the Reds bowed out of the FA Trophy following a disappointing 2nd round defeat at Bromsgrove.

However, the FA Cup provided a memorable occasion when near neighbours from the 2nd Division of the Football League, Leyton Orient, were the visitors to Victoria Road for a 1st round tie. In a pulsating match the Reds held leads of 2-0 and 3-1 but the O's called upon reserves of superior stamina to run-out eventual winners by 4-5.

With all the individual aspects of the season added up, all those connected with the newly formed club can look back on a very enjoyable first year and look forward to an exciting future with even greater progress anticipated during the coming year.

Steve Warren (Press Officer).

Dagenham & Redbridge 1992-93 - Back Row (L-R): Physio, T.Pamphlett, P.Richardson, J.McKenna, M.Nuttell, S.Conner, M.Walsh, B.Mayes, G.Owers, J.Broom, P.Cavell, J.Still. Front Row: G.Butterworth, G.Blackford, P.Watts, P.Shirtliff, G.Stebbing. Photo: V.J.Robertson.

DAGENHAM & REDBRIDGE MATCHFACTS 92-93

Key: Home fixtures are denoted by bold capitals. Numbers in brackets after players names indicate goals scored (an asterisk by the results denotes own goals). Only used substitutes are listed - substituted players are *italicised*.

Key to Competitions: GMVC: G.M. Vauxhall Conference. **DC:** Drinkwise (G.M. Vauxhall Conference) Cup. **FAC:** F.A. Cup. **FAT:** Vauxhall F.A. Trophy.

FA CUP: First Round
FA TROPHY: Second Round
LEAGUE POSITION: 3rd

Date	Opponents	Comp.	Res	Gate	1.	2.	3.	4.	5.	6.	7.	8.	9.	10.	11.	Sub.
22/08	Merthyr Tyd.	GMVC	2-0	1,397	McKenna	Shirtliff	Watts	Pamphlett	Conner	Brown(1)	Owers	Rich'son(1)	Cavell	Walsh	Blackford	
25/08	**FANBOROUGH**	GMVC	*5-1	1,318	McKenna	Shirtliff	Watts	Pamphlett	Conner	Broom	Owers	Rich'son(1)	Cavell(2)	Walsh	Bl'ford(1)	Warner
29/08	**BROMSGROVE**	GMVC	1-1	1,078	McKenna	Shirtliff	Watts	Pamphlett	Conner	Broom	Owers	Richardson	Cavell	Walsh(1)	Blackford	Butterworth
31/08	Slough Town	GMVC	0-2	1,813	Pape	Shirtliff	Watts	Porter	Conner	Butterworth	Conners	Richardson	Cavell	Walsh	Blackford	Kimble Warner
05/09	Gateshead	GMVC	1-1	387	McKenna	Shirtliff	Watts	Pamphlett	Conner	Butterworth	Kimble	Richardson	Cavell(1)	Warner	Blackford	Warner
12/09	**BILLERICAY**	FAC	1-1	963	McKenna	Shirtliff	Watts	Pamphlett	Conner	Broom	Kimble	Richardson	Cavell(1)	Walsh	Blackford	Butterworth Warner
16/09	Billericay	FAC	4-1	1,018	McKenna	Smart	Watts	Pamphlett	Conner	Broom	Kimble	Bu'worth(1)	Cavell	Walsh(2)	Blackford(1)	Warner
19/09	Kidderminster	GMVC	1-0	1,089	McKenna	Shirtliff	Watts	Pamphlett	Conner	Broom	Kimble	Richardson	Cavell(1)	Nutell	Butterworth	Warner
26/09	**STOWMARKET**	FAC	6-1	868	McKenna	Shirtliff	Watts(1)	Pamphlett	Conner(1)	Broom(2)	Kimble	Butterworth	Cavell(1)	Nutell(1)	Owers	Smart
29/09	Kettering T.	GMVC	0-0	1,341	McKenna	Shirtliff	Watts	Pamphlett	Conner	Broom	Owers	Butterworth	Cavell	Nutell	Blackford	
03/10	**NORTHWICH V.**	GMVC	4-1	923	McKenna	Shirtliff	Watts	Pamphlett	Conner	Broom(1)	Owers	Butterworth	Cavell(1)	Nutell(1)	Bl'ford(1)	
06/10	**WOKING**	GMVC	5-1	1,648	McKenna	Shirtliff	Watts	Pamphlett	Conner	Bu'worth(2)	Broom(1)	Owers	Cavell(1)	Nutell	Blackford	Kimble(1) Georgiou
11/10	Wealdstone	FAC	6-1	823	McKenna	Shirtliff	Watts	Pamphlett	Conner	Broom(1)	Owers	Butterworth	Cavell(3)	Nutell(1)	Blackford(1)	Georgiou Kimble
17/10	**MACCLESFIELD**	GMVC	1-2	1,303	McKenna	Shirtliff	Watts	Pamphlett	Conner	Broom(1)	Owers	Butterworth	Cavell	Nutell	Blackford	Kimble
24/10	Hednesford	FAC	3-1	1,311	McKenna	Shirtliff	Watts	Pamphlett	Conner	Broom(1)	Owers	Butterworth	Cavell(2)	Nutell	Blackford	Georgiou
31/10	**RUNCORN**	GMVC	5-1	1,404	McKenna	Shirtliff	Watts	Pam'lett(1)	Conner(1)	Broom(1)	Owers	Bu'worth(1)	Blackford	Cavell(1)	Georgious	Kimble Walsh
07/11	Witton Albion	GMVC	2-2	812	McKenna	Shirtliff	Watts	Pamphlett	Conner	Broom	Owers	Bu'worth(1)	Cavell	Nutell	Blackford(1)	Kimble
14/11	Leyton Orient	FAC	4-5	5,300	McKenna	Shirtliff	Watts	Pam'lett(1)	Conner(1)	Broom(1)	Owers	Bu'worth	Cavell(1)	Nutell	Blackford	Georgiou Kimble
17/11	**BOSTON UTD**	GMVC	1-1	1,048	McKenna	Shirtliff	Watts	Pamphlett	Conner(1)	Broom	Owers	Butterworth	Cavell	Nutell	Blackford	Walsh Kimble
21/11	Stafford Rgrs	GMVC	1-0	786	McKenna	Blackford	Watts	Pamphlett	Conner	Broom	Owers	Butterworth	Georgiou	Nutell	Kimble	Walsh(1)
28/11	**TELFORD UTD**	GMVC	0-2	1,302	McKenna	Shirtliff	Watts	Pamphlett	Conner	Broom	Kimble	Butterworth	Georgiou	Nutell	Blackford	Walsh Allen
01/12	Woking	GMVC	1-1	1,734	McKenna	Shirtliff	Watts	Pam'lett(1)	Conner	Broom	Owers	Butterworth	Georgiou	Allen	Nutell	Walsh
05/12	**STALYBRIDGE**	GMVC	1-2	1,052	McKenna	Shirtliff	Watts	Pamphlett	Conner(1)	Broom	Stebbing	Butterworth	Cavell	Nutell(1)	Tomlinson	Allen Walsh
12/12	Stalybridge	GMVC	3-0	752	McKenna	Shirtliff	Watts	Pamphlett	Conner(1)	Broom	Owers	Butterworth	Cavell	Nutell(1)	Blackford(1)	Walsh(1) Kimble
19/12	**WITTON ALB.**	GMVC	1-1	1,076	McKenna	Shirtliff	Watts	Pamphlett	Conner	Broom(1)	Owers	Butterworth	Cavell	Nutell	Blackford	Hayes Stebbing

Date	Opponent	Comp	Score	Att													
26/12	**YEOVIL TOWN**	GMVC	1-1	1,072	McKenna	Shirtliff	Watts	Pamphlett	Conner	Broom	Owers	Butterworth	Cavell	Nuttell	B'ford(1)	Stebbing	
28/12	Welling Utd	GMVC	*2-0	1,357	McKenna	Shirtliff	Watts	Pamphlett	Conner	Stebbing	Owers	Butterworth	Cavell(1)	Nuttell	Blackford	Hayes	
09/01	Yeovil Town	FAT	0-0	2,973	McKenna	Shirtliff	Watts	Pamphlett	Conner	Stebbing	Owers	Butterworth	Cavell	Nuttell(1)	Blackford	Broom	Kimble
12/01	**YEOVIL TOWN**	FAT	2-1	1,171	McKenna	Shirtliff	Watts	Pam'lett(1)	Conner	Stebbing	Owers	Butterworth	Cavell	Nuttell(1)	B'ford(1)	Broom	Kimble
16/11	**GATESHEAD**	GMVC	3-1	1,022	McKenna	Shirtliff	Watts	Pam'lett(2)	Conner	Stebbing	Owers	Butterworth	Cavell(1)	Nuttell	Blackford	Broom	Kimble
23/01	Runcorn	GMVC	0-1	475	McKenna	Shirtliff	Watts	Pamphlett	Marquis	Stebbing	Owers	Butterworth	Mayes	Nuttell	Blackford	Broom	Nuttell
30/01	Bromsgrove	FAT	1-3	1,711	McKenna	Shirtliff	Broom	Marquis	Conner	Stebbing	Owers	Butterworth	Cavell(1)	Mayes	Blackford	Owers	Nuttell
03/02	Boston Utd	GMVC	1-3	1,137	McKenna	Walsh	Watts	Marquis	Conner(1)	Broom	Owers	Butterworth	Cavell(1)	Mayes	Blackford	Owers	
06/02	Bromsgrove	GMVC	2-2	1,120	McKenna	Shirtliff	Broom	Marquis	Conner(1)	Broom(1)	Owers	Butterworth	Mayes	Mayes	Kimble	McKenna	
06/12	Bromsgrove	GMVC	4-4	1,335	McKenna	Broom	Watts	Marquis	Conner	Stebbing(1)	Owers	Butterworth	Mayes	Pamphlet	Kimble(1)	Blackford	
08/02	**SLOUGH TOWN**	GMVC	0-1	1,015	McKenna	Shirtliff	Watts	Marquis	Conner	Broom(1)	Owers	Bu'worth(1)	Cavell(1)	Mayes	Kimble(1)	Blackford	Nuttell
13/02	**STAFFORD RGRS**	GMVC	0-1	5,106	McKenna	Marquis	Watts	Pamphlett	Conner	Stebbing	Owers	Butterworth	Cavell	Mayes	Blackford	Mayes	
16/02	Wycombe W.	GMVC	0-1	517	McKenna	Shirtliff	Watts	Pamphlett	Conner	Stebbing	Owers	Butterworth	Nuttell	Mayes	Mayes	Kimble	Rich'son
20/02	Altrincham	GMVC	2-2	823	McKenna	Shirtliff	Watts	Pamphlett	Conner	Stebbing	Owers	*Blackford*	Nuttell	Blackford	Nuttell	Butterworth	Owers
27/02	**ALTRINCHAM**	GMVC	4-1	655	McKenna	Shirtliff	Watts	Rich'son(P)	Conner	Bu'worth(1)	Owers	Owers	*Mayes*	Nuttell(1)	Blackford	Stebbing	Rich'son
06/03	Farnborough	GMVC	3-2	1,004	McKenna	Shirtliff	Watts	Rich'son(P)	Conner	Stebbing(1)	Owers(1)	Butterworth	Owers	Nuttell(2)	Blackford	Blackford	Kimble
13/03	**KIDDERMINSTER**	GMVC	1-1	387	McKenna	Richardson *Smart*	Watts	Owers	Conner	Butterworth Stebbing	Owers	Cavell(1)	De Souza	B'ford(2)	Broom	Kimble	
16/03	Macclesfield	GMVC	1-0	757	McKenna	Shirtliff	Watts	Owers	Conner	Stebbing	Owers	Butterworth Cavell(1)	Broom	Nuttell	Blackford	Blackford	
20/03	Telford Utd	GMVC	1-2	2,542	McKenna	Stebbing	Watts	Owers	Conner	*Kimble*	Broom	Butterworth Cavell(1)	Broom	Nuttell	Blackford	Richardson (P)	
25/03	**WYCOMBE W.**	GMVC	1-2	570	McKenna	Stebbing	Watts	Owers	Conner	Rich'son(P)	Broom	Butterworth Cavell(1)	Rich'son(P) *Kimble*	Nuttell	Blackford	Kimble	
27/03	Bath City	GMVC	6-1	805	McKenna	Stebbing	Watts	Owers	Conner	Rich'son(l)	Broom	Butterworth Cavell(1)	Rich'son(I)	Nuttell	Blackford	Rich'son(l)	
06/04	**MERTHYR TYD.**	GMVC	3-0	2,847	McKenna	Stebbing	Watts	Owers(1)	Conner	Broom	Rich(l)(1)	Butterworth Cavell(3)	Broom	Nuttell(/2)	Blackford	Rich'son(P)	Kimble
10/04	Yeovil Town	GMVC	1-0	1,288	McKenna	Stebbing	Watts	Owers	Conner	Broom	Richardson	Butterworth Cavell	Souza(1)	Nuttell(1)	B'ford(1)		
12/04	**WELLING UTD**	GMVC	2-1	924	McKenna	Stebbing	Watts	Owers	Conner	Rich'son(1)	Broom	Butterworth Cavell	Brown	Nuttell(1)	Blackford	Kimble	
17/04	**BATH CITY**	GMVC	1-1	735	McKenna	Stebbing	Watts	Owers	Conner	Brown	Richardson	Butterworth Cavell(1)	Brown	Nuttell	*Blackford*	Kimble	
24/04	Northwich V.	GMVC	1-1	1,225	McKenna	Stebbing	Watts	Owers	Conner	De Souza	Richardson	Butterworth Cavell(1)	De Souza	Nuttell	Blackford	Kimble	
01/05	**KETTERING T.**	GMVC	2-1	1,225	McKenna	Stebbing	Watts	Owers	Conner	De Souza	Richardson	Butterworth Cavell(1)	De Souza	Nuttell	Broom	Shirtliff	

League Appearances: Allen 1(1): Blackford 34(2): Broom 36(1): Butterworth 38(3): Cavell 38: Conner 38: De Souza 3: Georgiou 3(2): Kimble 10(15): Marquis 6: Mayes 7(2): McKenna 40(1): Nuttell 29(2): Owers 32(1): Pamphlett 29: Pape 1: Porter 1: Ian Richardson 9(2): Paul Richardson 9(4): Shirtliff 32(1): Smart 2(1): Stebbing 22(3): Tomlinson 2: Walsh 6(6): Warner 1(1): Watts 41.

League Goalscorers: Cavell 19: Nuttell 8: Butterworth 7: Broom, Pamphlett 6: Walsh 5: Conner 4: Ian Richardson 3: Blackford, Kimble, Paul Richardson 2: De Souza, Owers, Stebbing 1.

Dagenham & Redbridge

JOHN STILL

John Still's playing career ended through injury prematurely but he had played for the winning Bishop's Stortford side in the last FA Amateur Cup Final and was a well respected centre half with Leyton Orient (as an apprentice), Ilford, Dagenham and Bishop's Stortford.

His amazing success as a manager is based on his excellent knowledge of players and he has guided his clubs to triumphs in the Southern, Isthmian and Conference (Maidstone United) competitions. His clubs, all of whom won honours, are Leytonstone-Ilford, Maidstone United and Redbridge Forest.

John now has the task of guiding the newly merged Dagenham and Redbridge club. Third place in their first season represents a good start.

Micky Nuttell flicks the ball over his head into the opponents penalty area. Dave Newman and Andy Salako are Welling players nearest the ball. Photo: Paul Dennis.

Programme details:
    30 pages for £1
    Editor - John Hillier

Any other club publications:
    'Raise Your Game' (Fanzine)

Local Newspapers:
    Dagenham Post
    Waltham Forest Guardian
    Ilford Recorder

Local Radio Stations:
    Breeze AM
    BBC Radio Essex
    Capital Radio

Dagenham & Redbridge
FOOTBALL CLUB
SEASON 1992 - 1993

DAGENHAM & REDBRIDGE FOOTBALL CLUB
are sponsored by THE DAGENHAM POST
and today welcome our visitors

v. YEOVIL TOWN

DAGENHAM & REDBRIDGE - PLAYING SQUAD 1992-93

Player	Honours	Birthplace and date	Transfer Fees	Previous Clubs
GOALKEEPERS				
Kevin Foster	IL	Essex 22/12/60		Chelmsford C, Wealdstone, Dag & Red, Erith & Belvedere, Chelmsford C
John McKenna	ESP, FA XI, LSC	Liverpool 21/3/62	Undiscld	Everton, Formby, Morecambe, Durban(SA), Mamelodi(SA), Nuneaton B, Boston Utd
DEFENDERS				
Tony Pamphlett	GMVC, SLP, ILP	London 13/4/60		Cray Wanderers, Dartford, Maidstone Utd, Redbridge Forest
Steve Conner	ESP, ILP	Essex 14/7/64	£3,500	Grays Athletic, East Thurrock Utd, Tilbury, Dartford, Redbridge Forest
Paul Watts	ESP, ILP, IL Div 1	London 20/9/62		Barking, Redbridge Forest
MIDFIELD				
Gary Butterworth		Peterborough 8/9/69		Peterborough Utd
Gary Stebbing	EY	Croydon 11/8/65		Crystal Palace, KV Ostend(Bel), Maidstone Utd, Kettering T
Garry Kimble		Poole 6/8/66		Charlton Athletic, Cambridge Utd, Gillingham, Peterborough Utd
Paul Richardson	ESP, GMVC, Middx W	Nottingham 7/11/62	Undiscld	N Forest, Eastwood T, Nuneaton B, Derby, Kettering T, Barnet, Boston Utd
Gary Blackford		Redhill 25/9/68	£12,000	Whyteleafe, Croydon, Fisher Ath, Barnet, Redbridge Forest
Adrian Owers		Danbury 26/2/65		Southend Utd, Chelmsford City, Brighton, Maidstone Utd
FORWARDS				
Paul Cavell	ESP, Middx W	Worksop 13/5/63	Undiscld	Worksop Town, Goole Town, Stafford R, Boston Utd, Redbridge Forest
Jason Broom	ILP, Middx W	Essex 15/10/69	£3,000	Eton Manor, Billericay Town, Redbridge Forest
David Crown		Enfield 16/2/58		Walthamstow Ave, Brentford, Portsmouth, Reading, Camb Utd, Southend, Gillingham
John Warner		Paddington 20/11/61		Burnham R, Colchester Utd, Heybridge S, Colchester Utd, Billericay T, Dagenham

Departures during season:
Pat Jackman (St Albans), Steve Porter, Rob Sinclair (Released), Greg Allen (Billericay), Dave Tomlinson (Witton Alb), George Giorgiou (Purfleet), Spencer Barham (Billericay), Mario Walsh (Enfield), Paul Shirtliff (Gateshead), Micky Nuttell (Rushden & Diamonds).

Players on loan during season:
Paul Marquis (West Ham), Glen Knight (Millwall).

Victoria Road, Dagenham

Address and telephone number: Victoria Road, Dagenham RM10 7XL.
Tel: 081 592 7194
Simple directions: On A112 between A12 & A13. Buses 103 & 174 or, exit Dagenham East tube station, turn left and after approximately 500 yards take 5th turning left into Victoria Road.
Capacity: 5,500   **Seated:** 700   **Covered terracing:** 3,000
Record Attendance: 5,300 v Leyton Orient - FA Cup 1st Rnd - 14.11.92.
Club Shop: Sells programmes, badges, replica shirts, scarves, hats etc. Contact John Hillier for more details.
Social Facilities: Clubhouse open 11.00am -11.00pm on match days. Hot & cold food available.
Previous Grounds: None

Dagenham & Red. Fact File

Nickname: Reds or Daggers

Club Sponsors: Barking & Dagenham Post
Previous Leagues: None
Club colours: Red shirts, blue shorts and red socks.
Change colours: All yellow.
Reserve team league: Essex & Herts Border Combination.
Midweek home matchday: Monday
Record win: 6-1 (3 times)
Record defeat: 3-1 (3 times)
Record transfer fee: £30,000 to Boston United for Paul Cavell & Paul Richardson - 1991.
Record transfer fee received: £65,000 from Watford for Andy Hessenthaler - 1991.
1992/93 Captain: Tony Pamphlett
1992/93 Top scorer: Paul Cavell - 31 goals.
1992/93 Player of the Year: Steve Conner
Club record goalscorer: Paul Cavell - 31
Record appearances: John McKenna - 56
Past players who progressed to the Football League: None

Club Honours: None since amalgamation.

DOVER ATHLETIC

Formed:
1983

Chairman:
Mr J.T.Husk

Football Secretary:
Mr J.F.Durrant

Manager:
Chris Kinnear

Physiotherapist:
Bob Jennings

Commercial Manager:
Mr B.Greenfield

Press Officer:
Mr J.F.Durrant

After the disappointment of finishing runners up to Bromsgrove Rovers the previous season, Manager Chris Kinnear re-vamped his squad for the new season. Leaving the club were Tony Rogers (to Chelmsford City for a Club record fee of £11,500), Terry Cordice (Chelmsford City), Kenny Dyer (Cyprus), Leroy Ambrose (Sittingbourne), Lenny Lee (Margate), Paul Malcolm (Erith & Belvedere). Players signed during the Summer were Russell Milton (Hong Kong), Steve Cuggy (Maidstone United), Steve Warner (Dagenham), Corey Browne (Fulham), Nicky Dent (Poole Town) and Richmond Donkor (Maidstone United).

Dover Athletic got off to a flying start yet again, winning 9 out of the first 10 league games and only suffering their first defeat when going down 2-1 at Crawley on January 19th. By that time however they had amassed 52 points from the first 22 games.

During the League campaign they lost only four matches, the only game lost at Crabble was when Cheltenham won 1-0 on the 17th April, which incidentally was the first home league defeat for two seasons.

Dover Athletic's outstanding season meant that 'keeper Maurice Munden conceded only 33 goals in the 40 league matches with only seven of those conceded at Crabble.

The league title was clinched as early as Easter Monday and the final total of 86 points was 13 more than second place Cheltenham Town. One interesting statistic shows that over the five years Dover Athletic competed in the Beazer Homes Premier League they amassed 415 points (an average of 83 points per season).

On the cup front disappointing defeats at Dorking and Chesham United both by 1-0, meant early exits from the F.A. Competitions. However, Athletic again progressed to the final of the Southern League Cup albeit losing 3-2 to Midland Division side Stourbridge. The chance of a cup and league double was therefore lost.

The goal scoring was shared by the four front runners used by Chris Kinnear, namely Steve Cuggy, Nicky Dent, Colin Blewden and Steve Warner. The consistency of the defence shows that Maurice Munden, Tony Dixon, Ian O'Connell, David Walker and Jason Bartlett missed only nine games between them all season.

So after the disappointment of 1990, promotion to the G M Vauxhall Conference has finally been achieved. The season 1993-1994 promises to be most exciting yet in the brief 10 year history of Dover Athletic.

J.T.Husk (Chairman)

Dover Athletic - Beazer League Premier Division Champions 1992-93. Back Row (L-R): Tom Terry (Asst. Pysio), Bob Jennings (Physio), David Scott, Tony Dixon, Jason Bartlett, Joe Jackson, Maurice Munden, Nicky Dent, Dave Walker, Steve Cuggy, Corey Browne, Kevin raine 9Scout), Chris Kinnear (Manager). Front Row: Richmond Donkor, Colin Blewden, Tim Dixon, Steve Warner, Barry Little, Nigel Donn, Iain O'Connell, Tony MacDonald, Russell Milton, Paul O'Brien.

DOVER MATCHFACTS 92-93 DOVER MATCHFACTS 92-93 DOVER MATCHFACTS 92-93 DOVER MATCHFACTS 92-93

Key: Home fixtures are denoted by bold capitals. Numbers in brackets after players names indicate goals scored (an asterisk by the results denotes own goals). Only used substitutes are listed - substituted players are *italicised*.

Key to Competitions: **BHL**: Beazer Homes League. **BHLCM**: Championship Match (Beazer Homes). **BCSC**: Barclays Commercial Services Cup. **KSC**: Kent Senior Cup. **EFC**: Eastern Floodlit Cup. **FAC**: F.A. Cup. **FAT**: Vauxhall F.A. Trophy.

Date	Opponents	Comp.	Res	Gate	1.	2.	3.	4.	5.	6.	7.	8.	9.	10.	11.	Sub.	Sub.
22/08	BURTON ALBION	BHL	3-0	1,022	Munden	Donn(1)	Bartlett	Dixon	O'Connell	MacDon'l(1)	Jackson	Blewden	Warner	Little	Milton(1)	Donkor	
26/08	Cambridge City	BHL	2-1	379	Munden	Donn	Bartlett	Dixon	O'Connell	MacDonald	Jackson	Blewden(1)	Warner	Little	Milton	Cuggy(1)	
29/08	Waterlooville	BHL	4-0	265	Munden	Donn	Bartlett	Dixon	O'Con.(1)	MacDonald	Jackson(1)	Blewden	Warner(1)	Little	Milton	Cuggy(1)	Dent
31/08	Bromsgrove	BHLCM	0-2	730	Munden	Down	Bartlett	Dixon	O'Connell	MacDonald	Jackson	Blewden	Warner	Browne	Milton	Cuggy	Browne
05/09	ATHERSTONE	BHL	2-0	1,160	Munden	Donn	Bartlett	Dixon	O'Connell	MacDonald	Jackson	Blewden	Warner	Little	Milton	Cuggy(2)	Cuggy
08/09	CRAWLEY	BHL	0-0	1,429	Munden	Donn	Bartlett	Dixon	O'Connell	MacDonald	Browne	Cuggy	Blewden	Little	Milton	Dent	
12/09	Tonbridge	FAC	0-0	1,012	Munden	Donn	Bartlett	Dixon	O'Connell	MacDonald	Browne	Cuggy	Blewden	Little	Milton	Warner	Dent(1)
15/09	TONBRIDGE	FAC	2-1	1,127	Munden	Harrop	Bartlett	Dixon	O'Connell	MacDonald	Browne	Warner(1)	Blewden	Warner	Milton(1)	Donkor	
19/09	Worcester City	BHL	2-1	656	Munden	Harrop	Bartlett	Dixon	O'Connell	MacDonald	Browne	Warner	Brewden	Warner	Milton(1)	Donkor(1)	
26/09	BANSTEAD	FAC	0-0	978	Munden	Donkor	Bartlett	Dixon	O'Connell	MacDonald	Browne	Warner	Blewden	Little	Milton	Cuggy	Harrop
29/09	Banstead	FAC	1-0	300	Munden	Dent(1)	Bartlett	Dixon	O'Connell	MacDonal'd	Browne	Cuggy	Blewden	Little	Milton	Donkor	
03/10	V.S.RUGBY	BHL	1-0	1,303	Munden	Harrop	Bartlett	Dixon	Walker	Husk	Browne	Cuggy	Blewden(1)	Little	Milton	Donkor	Harrop
06/10	Margate	BCSC	1-2	565	Munden	Harrop	Bartlett	Dixon	O'Connell	Walker	Browne	Warner	Donkor	Little	Milton(1)	Donkor	Harrison
10/10	Dorking	FAC	0-1	623	Munden	Harrop	Bartlett	Dixon	O'Connell	Walker	Browne	Warner	Blewden	Dent	Milton(1)	Donkor	Dent
17/10	BASHLEY	BHL	*3-2	1,265	Munden	Donn	Bartlett	Dixon	O'Connell	Walker	Browne	Warner	Blewden(1)	Dent(3)	Jackson	Donkor	
20/10	MARGATE	BCSC	3-1	497	Munden	Donn	Bartlett(1)	Dixon	O'Connell	Walker	Browne	Warner	Blewden	Dent(1)	Milton	Donkor	Browne
31/10	Hednesford	BHL	1-0	667	Munden	MacDonald	Bartlett	Dixon	O'Connell	Walker	Donkor	Dent	Blewden	Dent	Milton(1)	Donkor	Cuggy
03/11	CANTERBURY	KSC	*4-0	505	Munden	MacDonald	Bartlett	Dixon	O'Connell	Walker	Browne	Dent	Blewden	Dent(3)	Milton	Cuggy(1)	Cuggy
07/11	SOLIHULL BORO*	BHL	1-0	1,276	Munden	Little	Bartlett	Dixon	O'Connell	Walker	Browne	Donn	Blewden	Dent(1)	Milton	Little	
11/11	Canterbury C.	BCSC	3-1	253	Munden	Donn	Bartlett	Dixon	O'Connell	Walker	Browne	Little	Blewden(2)	Dent	Milton(1)	Warner	
14/11	Gloucester C.	BHL	1-1	568	Munden	Donn	Bartlett	Dixon	O'Connell	Walker(1)	Browne	Dent	Blewden	Little	Milton(1)	Warner	
21/11	HALESOWEN T.	BHL	1-1	1,127	Munden	Donn	Bartlett	Dixon	Husk	Walker	Browne	Dent	Blewden	Little	Milton(1)	Warner	
24/11	ASHFORD	EFC	3-1	371	Munden	Donn	Bartlett	Dixon	O'Connell	Walker	Harrison	Warner	Dent(1)	Browne	Milton(1)	Warner	
28/11	TROWBRIDGE	BHL	4-0	1,475	Munden	Donn	Bartlett	Dixon	Husk	Walker	Jackson	Dent	Dent(3)	Browne	Milton(1)	Warner	
01/12	FOLKESTONE I.	EFC	7-1	390	Munden	Whibley	Harrop	Castle	O'Connell	Childs	Warner(1)	Dent(2)	Blewden(2)	Little	Cuggy(5)	Dixon T.	L'rence
05/12	MOOR GREEN	BHL	2-0	1,245	Munden	Donn	Bartlett	Dixon	O'Connell	Walker	O'Brien	O'Brien	Harrison(1)	Little	Milton	Cuggy	
07/12	Chelmsford	BHL	1-1	1,048	Munden	Donn	Bartlett	Dixon	O'Connell	Walker	Smith	Little(1)	Blewden(1)	Little	Milton	Cuggy	
12/12	WEYMOUTH	BHL	2-0	1,197	Munden	Donn	Bartlett	Dixon	O'Connell	Walker	Smith	Dent(1)	Blewden	Dent	Milton	Cuggy	
15/12	GRAVESEND	BCSC	3-0	423	Munden	Donn	Bartlett(1)	Dixon	O'Connell	Walker	Browne(1)	Dent	Blewden(1)	Little(1)	Milton	Browne	Warner
22/12	Ashford	EFC	4-1	187	Munden	Donn	Bartlett	Dixon	O'Connell	Walker	Browne	Dent(1)	Blewden(1)	Little	Milton	Cuggy(2)	Warner
28/12	HASTINGS	BHL	2-1	2,014	Munden	Donn	Bartlett	Dixon	O'Connell	Walker	Browne	Dent	Blewden(1)	Little(1)	Milton	Warner	
02/01	Dorchester	BHL	1-0	716	Munden	Donn	Bartlett	Dixon T.	O'Connell	Smith	Browne	Cuggy(1)	Blewden	Little	Milton	Warner	Cuggy(1)

Date	Opposition	Comp	Res	Att	1	2	3	4	5	6	7	8	9	10	11	Subs
05/01	**CAMBRIDGE C.**	BHL	*5-0	1,169	Munden	Donn	Bartlett(2)	Dixon	O'Connell	Smith(1)	Browne	Cuggy(1)	Blewden	Little	Milton	Warner
09/01	**HASTINGS T.**	FAT	1-1	1,129	Munden	Donn	Bartlett	Dixon	O'Connell	Smith	Browne	Cuggy	Blewden	Little	Milton	Warner(1)
12/01	Hastings T.	FAT	2-0	611	Munden	Donn	Bartlett	Dixon	O'Connell	Smith	Browne	Cuggy(1)	Blewden(1)	Walker	Milton	Little, Dent
16/01	Moor Green	BHL	1-0	439	Munden	Donn	Bartlett	Dixon	O'Connell	Walker	Browne	Smith(1)	Blewden	Cuggy	Milton	Little, Dent(1)
19/01	Crawley	BHL	1-2	1,273	Munden	Donn	Bartlett	Dixon	O'Connell	Walker	Browne	Smith	Blewden	Warner	Milton	
21/01	Folkestone I.	EFC	2-0	200	Chivers	Whibley	Childs	Castle(1)	Husk	Burroughs	Harrison	Dixon T(1)	Scott	Warner	Dent	Fox, Friend
23/01	**WATERLOOVILLE**	BHL	2-0	1,476	Munden	Donn	Bartlett	Dixon	O'Connell	Walker	Browne	Smith	Blewden	Dent(1)	Milton	Little, Cuggy
30/01	Chesham Utd	FAT	0-1	2,055	Munden	Donn	Bartlett	Dixon	O'Connell	Smith	Browne	Walker	Blewden	Dent	Milton	Cuggy, Warner
02/02	**WELLING UTD**	KSC	0-1	1,006	Munden	Little	Bartlett	Dixon	O'Connell	Smith	Browne	Walker	Blewden	Dent(2)	Milton	Donn, Warner
06/02	**DORCHESTER**	BCSC	3-0	1,276	Munden	Little	Bartlett	Dixon	O'Connell	Walker	Browne(1)	Smith	Blewden(1)	Dent(1)	Milton	Scott
09/02	Crawley	BCSC	2-1	837	Munden	Donn	Bartlett	Dixon	O'Connell	Walker	Browne	Little	Blewden	Dent(1)	Milton	Tim Dixon, Scott
13/02	Burton Albion	BHL	0-0	725	Munden	Donn	Bartlett	Dixon	O'Connell	Walker	Browne	Smith	Blewden	Dent	Little	Tim Dixon, Warner
16/02	**SUDBURY**	BCSC	1-0	750	Munden	Donn	Bartlett	Dixon	O'Connell	Walker	Browne	Smith	Blewden	Dent	Milton	Tim Dixon, Warner
20/02	**CORBY**	BHL	2-0	1,914	Munden	Little	Bartlett	Dixon	O'Connell	Walker	Browne	Smith	Blewden	Dent	Milton	Tim Dixon, Warner
23/02	**CHELMSFORD**	BHL	1-0	1,344	Munden	Donn	Bartlett	Dixon	O'Connell	Walker	Browne	Smith	Blewden	Dent	Milton	Cuggy(1)
27/02	**GLOUCESTER**	BHL	2-0	1,540	Munden	Little	Bartlett	Dixon	O'Connell	Walker	Browne	Smith	Blewden	Dent	Milton	Cuggy
01/03	Corby	BHL	0-1	452	Munden	Little	Bartlett	Dixon	O'Connell	Walker	Browne	Smith	Blewden	Warner	Milton(1)	Cuggy, Jackson
06/03	Trowbridge	BHL	2-0	626	Munden	Donn	Scott	Dixon	O'Connell	Walker	Browne	Jackson	Blewden	Warner	Milton	Cuggy
09/03	Sudbury	BCSC	1-2	534	Munden	Donn	Bartlett	Dixon	O'Connell	Walker	Browne	Jackson	Blewden	Warner	Milton	Scott
13/03	Bashley	BHL	1-1	457	Munden	Donn	Bartlett	Dixon	O'Connell	Walker	Browne	Jackson(1)	Blewden	Warner	Milton	Cuggy(1)
16/03	Cheltenham	BHL	1-1	1,159	Munden	Scott	Bartlett	Dixon	O'Connell	Walker	Browne	Jackson	Blewden	Warner	Milton	Dent, Cuggy(1)
23/03	V.S.Rugby	BHL	3-2	383	Munden	Scott	Bartlett	Dixon	O'Con.(1)	Walker	Browne	Jackson	Blewden	Cuggy	Milton	Little
27/03	Weymouth	BHL	1-1	831	Munden	Scott(1)	Bartlett	Dixon	O'Connell	Walker	Browne(1)	Jackson	Blewden	Cuggy(1)	Milton	Warner, Cuggy(1)
30/03	Halesowen	BHL	1-1	988	Munden	Scott	Bartlett	Dixon	O'Con.(1)	Walker	Browne	Jackson	Blewden	Cuggy(1)	Milton	Warner
03/04	**WORCESTER**	BHL	1-1	1,947	Munden	Scott	Bartlett	Dixon	O'Connell	Walker	Browne	Jackson	Blewden	Cuggy	Milton	Warner
06/04	Stourbridge	BCSC	0-2	684	Munden	Scott	Bartlett	Dixon	O'Connell	Walker	Browne	Jackson	Blewden	Cuggy	Milton	Warner, Little
07/04	Saffron Walden	EFC	1-3	200	Chivers	Donn	Childs	Castle	Husk	Burroughs	Harrison	Lawrence	Warner	Dent(1)	O'Brien	Fox
12/04	Hastings	BHL	1-1	1,774	Munden	Scott	Bartlett	Dixon	O'Connell	Walker	Browne	Jackson	Blewden	Cuggy(1)	Milton	Little
17/04	**CHELTENHAM**	BHL	0-1	2,093	Munden	Little	Bartlett	Dixon	Scott	Walker	Browne	Jackson	Blewden	Warner	Milton	Donn, Warner
20/04	**STOURBRIDGE**	BCSC	2-1	1,093	Munden	Dent	Bartlett	Dixon	O'Connell	Walker	Browne	Jackson	Blewden	Warner	Milton	Donn, Scott
24/04	Atherstone	BHL	0-0	326	Munden	Donn	Bartlett	Dixon	O'Connell	Walker	Browne(2)	Jackson	Blewden	Cuggy	Milton	Scott, Cuggy(2)
29/04	Solihull	BHL	2-1	257	Munden	Donn	Bartlett	Dixon	O'Connell	Walker	Browne	Jackson	Blewden	Cuggy	Milton	Dent, Warner
01/05	**HEDNESFORD**	BHL	2-1	1,234	Munden	Donn	Bartlett	Dixon T.	O'Connell	Walker	Browne	Jackson	Blewden	Cuggy(1)	Milton(1)	Scott, Warner

League Appearances: Munden 40: Tony Dixon 40: Bartlett 40: Blewden 39: O'Connell 39: Milton 39: Browne 32(1): Walker 32(1): Donn 26(2): Little 24(6): Warner 17(19): Dent 14(13): Smith 14: Jackson 16(3): Cuggy 11(22): MacDonald 7: Scott 7(3): Harrop 2: O'Brien 1: Donkor 0(6): Tin Dixon 0(3).

League Goalscorers: Cuggy 14: Blewden 11: Dent 9: Milton 7: Browne, Warner 4: Bartlett, O'Connell, Walker, Smith, Jackson 2: Donn, Little, MacDonald, Scott 1.

Dover Athletic

CHRIS KINNEAR

Chris Kinnear joined the club seven years ago as a player but unfortunately broke his leg. He was appointed manager in November 1985 and has won trophies in every season since. Chris is now recognised as one of the best non-League managers around.

Chris began his playing career with West Ham United as an apprentice professional. He moved on to Leyton Orient before he joined the non-League game with Wealdstone. Successful spells with Maidstone United, Barnet and Dagenham followed before joining Dover Athletic. Whilst with Maidstone and playing in the Alliance Premier League (GMVC), Chris twice won the club's player of the year trophy.

A Dover corner is superly held by Wycombe goalkeeper Paul Hyde. Photo: Paul Dennis.

Programme details:
    32 pages for £80p
    Editor - Chris Collings - 0304 822074

Any other club publications:
    'Tales from the River End'
    'Dover Sole' (both fanzines)

Local Newspapers:
    Dover Express.
    East Kent Mercury.

Local Radio Stations:
    Radio Kent
    Invicta FM

DOVER ATHLETIC - PLAYING SQUAD 1992-93

Player	Honours	Birthplace and date	Transfer Fees	Previous Clubs
GOALKEEPERS				
Maurice Munden	BHP (2)	Stepney 8/11/63		Charlton Ath.,Folkestone, Welling Utd
DEFENDERS				
Jason Bartlett	BHP	Folkestone 25/11/65		Folkestone
Barry Little	EY, BHP, PILC, KSC	Greenwich 25/8/64		Charlton Ath., Dagenham, Barnet, Fisher Ath
David Scott	BHP, BHS, EU	Carlisle 15/4/67		Penrith, Hastings T, Canterbury, Hastings T
Tony Dixon	BHP	Stockwell 17/3/61		Gravesend, Erith & Belvedere, Tonbridge
Tony MacDonald	BHP	Tenterden 19/10/63		Ashford T, Welling Utd,
MIDFIELD				
Tim Dixon	BHP	Dover 31/11/65		Southampton, Waterford
Nigel Donn	BHP (2)	Maidstone 2/3/62		Gillingham, Fulham, Maidstone Utd
Iain O'Connell	BHP	Rochford 9/10/70		Southend Utd
Russell Milton	BHP, KS	Folkestone 12/1/69		Arsenal, Double Flower(HK) Instant Dict(HK)
Dave Walker	BHP	London 29/11/67		West Ham Utd
Joe Jackson	BHP	Wolverhampton 22/4/66		Wolves, Bilston, Hednesford, Willenhall, Gresley R, Worcester, Yeovil
FORWARDS				
Nicky Dent	BHP	Bristol 30/12/67	£8,000	Bristol Manor Farm, Bristol City, Yeovil, Poole
Colin Blewden	BHP, SLC	Pembury 12/8/65	£6,000	Gillingham, Tonbridge, Gravesend
Steve Cuggy	BHP	Wallsend 18/3/71		Sunderland, Blyth Spartans, Maidstone Utd
Corey Browne	BHP	Enfield 2/7/70		Tottenham Hotspur, Watford, Exeter, Fisher Ath., Wealdstone, Fulham

Departures during season:
Tony Rogers (Chelmsford)

Players on loan during season:
Paul Smith (Southend Utd).

Crabble Athletic Ground, Dover Athletic

Address and telephone number: Crabble Athletic Ground, Lewisham Road, River, Dover. Tel: 0304 822373

Simple directions: Main A2 from Canterbury to Hammonds roundabout, follow directions to Town Centre, left at mini-roundabout right at traffic lights where ground is sign-posted.
Nearest station - Dover Priory. Regular bus service from Town Centre to the ground.

Capacity: 6,500   **Seated:** 700   **Covered terracing:** 4,900

Record Attendance: 4,035 v Bromsgrove Rovers, Beazer Homes League April 1992.

Club Shop: Open match days only. Sells home/away programmes, replica shirts home/away, general souvenirs - mugs, bagdes etc. Contact Jean Haves 0304 240041.

Social Facilities: Social Club open 7 days a week. Meals available.
Steward - Gavin Hughes 0304 822306.

Previous Grounds: None

Dover Fact File

Nickname: Lilywhites

Club Sponsors: Countrywide Derv Ltd.

Previous Leagues: Kent League

Club colours: White shirts, black shorts and socks.

Change colours: Yellow shirts, green shirts and yellow socks.

Reserve team league: Winstonlead Kent League Div.2.

Midweek home matchday: Tuesday

Record win: 7-0 v Weymouth 3rd April 1990.

Record defeat: 1-7 v Poole Town.

Record transfer fee: £10,000 for Joe Jackson from Yeovil Town - 1991.

Record transfer fee received: £11,500 for Tony Rogers from Chelmsford City 1992.

1992/93 Captain: Barry Little

1992/93 Top scorer: Steve Cuggy - 25 goals.

1992/93 Player of the Year: Iain O'Connell.

Club record goalscorer: Lennie Lee - 160.

Record appearances: Jason Bartlett - 460.

Past players who progressed to the Football League:

Club Honours: Beazer Homes League Premier Division Champions 1989/90, 1992/93; Beazer Homes League Southern Division Champions 1987/88; Beazer Homes League Championship Cup Winners 1990/91; Premier Inter League Cup Winners 1990/91; Southern League Cup Winners 1990/91; Kent Senior Cup Winners 1990/91; Knight Floodlit Cup Winners 1987/88, 1988/89.

GATESHEAD

Formed:
1977

President:
J.C.Thomas

Chairman:
J.Gibson

Vice Chairman
C.Thirkell

Football Secretary:
Clare Tierney

Manager:
Tommy Cassidy

Coach:
Malcolm Crosby

Physiotherapist:
Terry Ainsley

Press Officer:
Jeff Bowron

For Gateshead, the Conference's most northerly outpost, the 1992-93 campaign was very much a season of two halves. In 5th place at Christmas the Tynesiders fell away badly in the New Year and still needed a point from their final game of the season to confirm Conference survival. A superb 4-1 victory over high-flying Yeovil Town duly banished any lingering relegation worries and enabled the club to finish in 14th place - the same position as in the previous season.

If League form ultimately proved disapointing there were creditable performances in both the FA Cup and the Trophy. A resounding 7-0 win at Spennymoor United in the 3rd Qualifying Round of the Cup was the icing on the cake with Gateshead scoring 18 goals en route to the 1st Round Proper for the first time since 1980. A 2-3 defeat at former Football League colleagues Accrington Stanley ended hopes of a money spinning Cup run and left the Tynesiders to concentrate their attentions on the FA Trophy. Comfortable victories over Gretna and Heybridge Swifts paved the way for a replay triumph over another Diadora League outfit Grays Athletic. Gateshead had reached the Quarter-Final of the Trophy for the first time but their elation was to turn to heartache when Conference champions-elect, Wycombe Wanderers, grabbed the only goal of the game three minutes into injury time at Adams Park.

It was a blow, accepted by most of the 4,500 crowd as cruel and unjust, that Tommy Cassidy's men never fully recovered from. League form dipped with only four wins registered from 22 games in 1993 and a season that had promised so much ended only in disappointment and frustration. The club has strengthened its squad during the summer with the arrival of seasoned campaigners John Borthwick from York City, Paul Proudlock and Ian Dalziel from Carlisle United, ex-Newcastle winger Lee Payne and England non-League International defender Paul Shirtliff from Dagenham and Redbridge.

Former Sunderland FA Cup final manager Malcolm Crosby has also joined the club as coach as Gateshead make a determined bid to push for promotion and reclaim the Football League place taken from them in 1960.

Jeff Bowron.

Gateshead F.C. 1992-93.

GATESHEAD MATCHFACTS 92-93

GATESHEAD MATCHFACTS 92-93 GATESHEAD MATCHFACTS 92-93

Key: Home fixtures are denoted by bold capitals. Numbers in brackets after players names indicate goals scored (an asterisk by the results denotes own goals). Only used substitutes are listed - substituted players are *italicised*.

Key to Competitions: **GMVC**: G.M. Vauxhall Conference. **DC**: Drinkwise (G.M. Vauxhall Conference) Cup. **FAC**: F.A. Cup. **FAT**: Vauxhall F.A. Trophy.

LEAGUE POSITION: 14th   FA CUP: First Round   FA TROPHY: Quarter-Final

Date	Opponents	Comp.	Res	Gate	1.	2.	3.	4.	5.	6.	7.	8.	9.	10.	11.	Sub.	Sub.
22/08	Farnborough	GMVC	1-6	637	Smith	Higgins	Chilton	Roche	Wrightson	S.Elliott	Mason	Cooke	Guthrie	Askew	Lamb	Pyle	Farrey
25/08	Altrincham	GMVC	1-0	814	Smith	Higgins	Chilton	Wrightson	Corner	S.Elliott	Roche	Cooke	Guthrie	Askew	Lamb(1)	Pyle	Farnaby
29/08	Wycombe W.	GMVC	1-2	3,290	Smith	Higgins(1)	Chilton	Wrightson	Bell	S.Elliott	Roche	Cooke	Guthrie	Askew	Lamb	Farrey	
31/08	**RUNCORN**	GMVC	4-1	547	Smith	Higgins	Chilton	Wrightson	Bell	S.Elliott	Farnaby	Cooke(1)	Guthrie(1)	Askew(1)	Lamb(1)	Farnaby	A.Elliott
05/09	**DAGENHAM & R.**	GMVC	1-1	387	Smith	Farrey	Chilton	Higgins	Bell	Higgins	Farnaby	Cooke(1)	Guthrie	Askew(1)	Lamb	Johnson	Johnson
08/09	Northwich V.	DC	1-2	173	Smith	Farrey	Farrey	Wrightson	Bell	Farnaby	Cooke	A.Elliott	Cooke	Dixon	Johnson		
12/09	**BILLINGHAM**	FAC	3-1	302	Smith	Higgins	Chilton	Wrightson	Bell	S.Elliott	Farnaby	Cooke(2)	Guthrie	Askew	Lamb(1)	Johnson	
16/09	**ALTRINCHAM**	GMVC	2-0	1,808	Smith	Higgins	Chilton	Wrightson	Bell	S.Elliott	Johnson	Cooke	Farrey	Askew	Lamb(2)	Lowery	
19/09	Yeovil Town	GMVC	3-1		Smith	Higgins	Chilton	Wrightson	Bell	S.Elliott	Johnson	Cooke	Farrey(1)	Askew	Lamb(2)	Lowery	
23/09	**NORTHWICH V.**	DC	0-2		Smith	Higgins	Chilton	Wrightson	Bell	S.Elliott	Lowery	Cooke	Farrey	Askew	Lamb	Lowery	
26/09	**WHITBY**	FAC	5-2	237	Smith	Higgins	Chilton	Wrightson	Bell	Halliday	Johnson	Cooke	Guthrie(1)	Farrey(1)	Lamb(4)		Farnaby
03/10	**TELFORD UNITED**	GMVC	0-1	371	Smith	Higgins	Chilton	Wrightson	Bell	S.Elliott	Farnaby	Cooke	Guthrie	Askew	Lamb	Askew	A.Elliott
06/10	Runcorn	FAC	2-4	471	Smith	Higgins	Chilton	Wrightson	Halliday	Farnaby	A.Elliott	Farnaby(1)	Guthrie	Askew(1)	Lamb	Johnson	
10/10	Spennymoor	FAC	7-0	647	Smith	Higgins	Farrey	Wrightson	Halliday	Farnaby	Johnson	Cooke(3)	Guthrie	Askew	Lamb(1)	Cooke(6)	A.Elliott
17/10	**WELLING UTD**	GMVC	1-2	517	Smith	Higgins	Farrey	Wrightson	Halliday	Bell	Johnson	Cooke(1)	Guthrie	Askew	Lamb(1)	A.Elliott	A.Elliott
24/10	Whitley Bay	FAC	3-0	652	Smith	Higgins	Farrey	Wrightson	Halliday	Bell	Johnson	Cooke(1)	Guthrie(2)	Askew	Lamb	Chilton	A.Elliott
27/10	Witton Albion	GMVC	3-1	771	Smith	Higgins	Farrey(2)	Wrightson	Halliday	Bell	Johnson	Cooke	Guthrie	Askew	Lamb(1)	Farnaby	A.Elliott
31/10	**BATH CITY**	GMVC	0-4	373	Smith	Higgins	Farrey	Wrightson	Bell	S.Elliott	Johnson	Cooke	Guthrie	Askew	Lamb	Farnaby	A.Elliott
07/11	**BROMSGROVE**	GMVC	0-0	405	Smith	Higgins	Nicholson	Wrightson	Bell(1)	S.Elliott	Farrey	Cooke	Halliday	Askew	Lamb	Farnaby	A.Elliott
14/11	Accrington S.	FAC	2-3	2,420	Smith	Higgins	Halliday	Wrightson	Bell	S.Elliott	Farrey	Cooke	Guthrie	Askew	Lamb(1)		Corner
18/11	**WITTON ALBION**	GMVC	3-1	233	Smith	Higgins	Nicholson	Bell	Corner	S.Elliott	Farrey	Cooke(1)	Farrey(1)	Wrightson	Lamb	Corner	
21/11	Woking	GMVC	4-1	1,722	Smith	Farrey(1)	Higgins	Wrightson	Halliday	S.Elliott	Halliday	Cooke	Corner	Farnaby(2)	Lamb	Farnaby	Guthrie(1)
28/11	Kettering T.	GMVC	0-2	1,455	Smith	Higgins	S.Elliott	Wrightson	Corner	Halliday	Farnaby	Bell	Guthrie	Farrey	Lamb	Guthrie(1)	A.Elliott
05/12	**FARNBOROUGH**	GMVC	1-0	346	Smith	Higgins(1)	S.Elliott	Wrightson	Corner	Halliday	Farnaby	Cooke	Bell	Farrey	Lamb	Askew	Guthrie
12/12	**KIDDERMINSTER**	GMVC	1-0	321	Smith	Farrey	S.Elliott	Wrightson	Corner	Halliday	Farrey	Cooke	Bell	Bond	Lamb	Askew	Guthrie
19/12	**MACCLESFIELD**	GMVC	1-0	375	Smith	Farrey	S.Elliott	Wrightson	Corner(1)	Halliday	Bell	Cooke	Bond	Tupling	Lamb	Askew	Guthrie

Date	Opponent	Comp	Score	Att	1	2	3	4	5	6	7	8	9	10	11	Sub	Sub
28/12	**STALYBRIDGE C.**	GMVC	0-0	631	Smith	Higgins	Farrey	Wrightson	Corner	Halliday	Bell	Cooke	Guthrie	Lamb	Askew	Tupling	
09/01	**GRETNA**	FAT	3-0	336	Smith	Higgins	Farrey	Wrightson	Corner	Halliday	Bell	Cooke(1)	Guthrie(1)	Lamb	Askew	Tupling(1)	A.Elliott
16/01	Dagenham & R.	GMVC	1-3	1,022	Smith	Higgins	Farrey	Wrightson	Corner	Halliday	Bell	Cooke	Guthrie	Lamb	Askew	Tupling	
23/01	**WOKING**	GMVC	1-1	626	Smith	Farnaby	Farrey	S.Elliott(1)	Corner	Halliday	Bell	Cooke	Askew	Lamb(1)	Wrightson	Askew	A.Elliott
26/01	Stafford R.	GMVC	1-2	367	Smith	Farnaby	Farrey	S.Elliott	Corner(1)	Halliday(1)	Bell	Cooke	Askew	Lamb	Tupling	Askew	A.Elliott
30/01	**HEYBRIDGE S.**	FAT	3-1	672	Smith	Higgins	S.Elliott(1)	Wrightson	Corner(1)	Halliday	Tupling	Cooke	Askew	Lamb	Farnaby	Askew	A.Elliott
02/02	Northwich V.	GMVC	0-0	362	Smith	Higgins	Farrey	Wrightson	Corner	Johnson	Tupling	Davison	Askew	Lamb	Johnson	Askew	
06/02	**BOSTON UNITED**	GMVC	2-2	297	Smith	Higgins	Farrey	Wrightson	Corner(1)	Halliday	Tupling	Davison	Askew	Lamb	Cooke	Askew	A.Elliott
10/02	**STAFFORD R.**	GMVC	0-1	537	Smith	Higgins	Farrey	Wrightson	Corner	Halliday	Tupling	Davison	Dobson	Lamb	A.Elliott	Askew	A.Elliott
13/02	Merthyr Tyd.	GMVC	1-1	1,013	Smith	Higgins	Farrey	Wrightson	Farnaby	Halliday	Bell	Davison	Dobson(1)	Lamb	Johnson	Askew	
20/02	Grays Ath.	FAT	1-1	402	Smith	Higgins	Farrey	Wrightson	Corner	Halliday	Bell	Guthrie	Dobson(2)	Lamb(1)	Davison	Askew	
24/02	**GRAYS ATH**	FAT	3-0	347	Smith	Higgins	Farrey	Wrightson	Corner	Halliday	Bell	Cooke	Askew	Lamb(1)	Davison	Askew	Cooke
27/02	**SLOUGH TOWN**	GMVC	1-0	716	Smith	Higgins	Farrey	Tupling	Wrightson	Halliday	Davison	Cooke	Dobson(1)	Lamb	Lowery	Askew	Cooke
01/03	Kiddersminster	GMVC	3-3	633	Smith	S.Elliott	Farrey	Bell	Wrightson	Halliday	Davison	Cooke(1)	Dobson	Lamb(1)	S.Elliott	Askew	
06/03	Telford Utd	FAT	0-1	4,795	Smith	Farrey	Stephenson	Bell	Wrightson	Halliday	Tupling	Cooke	Dobson	Lamb	S.Elliott	Askew	Farnaby
13/03	Wycombe W.	FAT	0-1	862	Smith	Farrey	Wrightson	Lowery	Corner	Halliday	Bell	Cooke	Guthrie	Lamb	S.Elliott	Guthrie	Davison
20/03	Slough Town	GMVC	0-1	473	Smith	Farrey	Wrightson	Lowery	Corner	Halliday	Bell	Cooke	Guthrie	Lamb	S.Elliott	Guthrie	Askew
23/03	Macclesfield	GMVC	1-1	478	Smith	Farrey	Wrightson	Tupling	Corner	Halliday	Bell	Cooke	Askew	Lamb	S.Elliott	Guthrie	Guthrie
27/03	**KETTERING**	GMVC	2-0	1,137	Smith	Farrey	Wrightson	Lowery	Corner	Halliday	Bell	Cooke	Guthrie	Lamb(1)	Askew	Askew	Farnaby
03/04	Boston Utd	GMVC	0-3	923	Smith	Tupling	S.Elliott	Wrightson	Corner	Halliday	Bell	Cooke	Dobson(1)	Lamb	A.Elliott	Guthrie	
06/04	Bromsgrove	GMVC	0-2	349	Smith	Farrey	S.Elliott	Tupling	Wrightson	Halliday	Bell	Cooke	Dobson	Lamb(1)	A.Elliott	Farnaby	Askew
10/04	**NORTHWICH VIC.**	GMVC	1-2	558	Smith	Farrey	S.Elliott	Wrightson	Corner	Halliday	Bell	Askew	Guthrie	Lamb	A.Elliott	Guthrie	Askew
12/04	Stalybridge	GMVC	1-2		Smith	Farrey	S.Elliott	Tupling	Corner	Halliday	Bell	Cooke	Guthrie	Lamb	A.Elliott	Guthrie	
17/04	**MERTHYR TYD.**	GMVC	4-0	343	Smith	Wrightson	S.Elliott	Tupling	Farrey	Halliday	Farnaby	Dobson(1)	Guthrie	Lamb(1)	A.Elliott	Guthrie	Tupling
18/04	**WYCOMBE W.**	GMVC	0-1	815	Smith	Wrightson	S.Elliott	Tupling	Farrey	Halliday	Bell	Farnaby	Guthrie	Lamb	A.Elliott	Guthrie	Askew
24/04	Welling Utd	GMVC	1-2	1,049	Smith	Wrightson	Farrey	Farrey(1)	Corner	Halliday	Bell	Farnaby	Dobson	Lamb	Askew	Askew	Tupling
25/04	Bath City	GMVC	1-1	491	Smith	Wrightson	Farrey	A.Elliott	S.Elliott	Halliday	Bell	Farnaby	Dobson(1)	Lamb	Guthrie	Askew	Higgins
01/05	**YEOVIL TOWN**	GMVC	4-1	397	Smith	Wrightson	Farrey(1)	Farrey(1)	S.Elliott	Halliday	Bell	Farnaby	Dobson(3)	Lamb	Higgins	Askew	

League Appearances: Askew 26(12): Bell 32: Chilton 8(1): Bond 2: Cooke 31(2): Corner 26: Davison 5(1): Dobson 18: A.Elliott 2(14): S.Elliott 28(5): Farnaby 20(2): Farrey 35(2): Guthrie 21(6): Halliday 33: Higgins 25(1): Jonhson 6(4): Lamb 40: Lowery 3(3): Mason 1: Nicholson 2: Pyle 0(2): Roache 4: Smith 42: Stephenson 1: Tupling 13(3): Wrightson 38(1).

League Goalscorers: Lamb 11: Dobson 8: Farrey 6: Farnaby 5: Cooke, Corner 3: Askew, Guthrie, Higgins 2: S.Elliott 1.

Gateshead

TOMMY CASSIDY

Replaced Tony Lee as Gateshead manager in November 1991 after previously spending 8 months at the International Stadium as Commercial Manager. A former Northern Ireland International who represented his country on 24 occasions, including the 1982 World Cup Finals. During a 10 year association with Newcastle United he made 212 appearances. He played in the 1974 FA Cup Final and 1976 League Cup Final before transferring to Burnley in 1980.

His first experience of management came with Cypriot club Apoel Nicosia where he spent 4 successful seasons.

After taking over at Gateshead he guided tham to their highest league placing and made further progress in the 1992/93 season.

Gretna's John Halpin evades the challenge from Gateshead's Bruce Halliday, during Gateshead's 3-0 FA Trophy 1st round victory. Photo: Alan Watson.

Programme details:
    24 pages for 70p
    Editor - Jeff Bowron (091 4823242)

Any other club publications:
    Supporters Club Broadsheet

Local Newspapers:
    Gateshead Post
    Newcastle Chronicle & Journal

Local Radio Stations:
    BBC Radio Newcastle
    Metro Radio

GATESHEAD - PLAYING SQUAD 1992-93

Player	Honours	Birthplace and date	Transfer Fees	Previous Clubs
GOALKEEPERS				
Simon Smith	NPL, NL, FA XI	Newton Aycliffe 16/9/62		Newcastle Utd, Whitley Bay, Gateshead, Blyth Spartans
DEFENDERS				
Steve Higgins	FAT, NPL(3), FA XI	Gateshead 6/10/60		Gateshead, Barrow, Newcastle Blue Star
Paul Shirtliff	ESP, LSC FA XI	Hoyland 03/11/62	£5,000	Sheffield Wed, Northampton T, Frickley A, Boston Utd, Dagenham & Redbridge
Michael Farrey	Wearside Lge	Gateshead 17/8/65		Chester-Le-Street, Whickham
Bruce Halliday		Sunderland 3/1/61		Newcastle Utd, Bury, Bristol C, Hereford Utd, Bath C, Apia(Aust)
Shaun Elliott	EY, E"B", GMVC, FAT	Hebden Bridge 26/1/58		Sunderland, Norwich City, Blackpool, Colchester Utd
Jeff Wrightson	FAYC	Newcastle 18/5/68		Newcastle Utd, Preston NE
David Corner	EY, Div 4, GMVC	Sunderland 15/5/66		Sunderland, Leyton Orient, Darlington
Ian Dalziel		Sunderland 24/10/62		Derby Co, Hereford Utd, Carlisle Utd
MIDFIELD				
Craig Farnaby		Hartlepool 8/8/67		Hartlepool Utd, Middlesbrough, Halifax, Stockport Co, Finland, Whitby T
Billy Askew		Lumley 2/10/59		Middlesbrough, Hull City, Newcastle Utd
Andy Elliott		Newcastle 2/5/74		Luton Town
Tony Lowery	FRT	Wallsend 6/7/61		WBA, Mansfield T, Carlisle Utd
Billy Johnson	NPL Div 1,	North Shields 9/2/65		Newcastle Utd, Brandon Utd, North Shields, Whitley Bay
FORWARDS				
John Cooke	EY	Salford 25/4/62		Sunderland, Sheffield Wed, Carlisle Utd, Stockport Co, Chesterfield
Lee Payne		Luton 12/12/66		Barnet, Newcastle United, Reading, Veendam (Holland)
Paul Proudlock		Hartlepool 25/10/65		Hartlepool Utd, Middlesbrough, Carlisle Utd
John Borthwick	GMVC	Hartlepool 24/3/64		Hartlepool Utd, Darlington, York City
Alan Lamb	E U-16	Gateshead 30/10/70		Notts Forest, Hartlepool Utd, Brandon Utd
Paul Dobson		Hartlepool 17/12/62	Undisclo	Newcastle U, Hartlepool, Horden CW, Torquay, Doncaster, Lincoln, Darlington

Departures during season:
Neil Howie & Steve Pyle (Blyth Spartans), Tony Chilton (Gretna), Wayne Davison (Released), Simon Guthrie (Kettering T), Derek Bell (Bridlington T).

Players on loan during season:
Richard Bond (Blackpool).

International Stadium, Gateshead

Address and telephone number: International Stadium, Neilson Road, Gateshead, NE10 0EF
Tel: 091 478 3883

Simple directions: from the South follow A1(M) to Granada services (Birtley), take right hand fork off motorway marked A194 (Tyne Tunnel, South Shields) follow A194 to first roundabout. Turn right at traffic lights into Neilson Road. By Rail to Newcastle Central Station transfer to Metro System to Gateshead Stadium.

Capacity: 11,750   **Seated:** 11,750   **Covered terracing:** 3,300

Record Attendance: 5,012 v Newcastle United 20/08/84 (Testimonial).

Club Shop: Run by the Supporters club. On sale - badges, scarves, programmes etc. Contact: Ian Hearns Tel: 091 4900541.

Social Facilities: The Stadium Public House adjacent to ground.

Previous Grounds: Redheugh Park - 1930-1971

Gateshead Fact File

Nickname: The Tynesiders

Club Sponsors: Cameron Hall Developments Ltd

Previous Leagues: Football League Division 3 North 1930-1958, Football Lge Div.4 1958-1960, Northern Counties League 1960-1962, North Regional League 1962-1968, Northern Premier League 1968-1970, Wearside League 1970-1971, Midland League 1971-1972, Northern Premier League 1973-1983, Alliance Premier League 1983-1985, Northern Premier League 1985-1986, Vauxhall Conference 1986-1987, Northern Premier League 1987-1990.

Club colours: Black/white halved shirts, black shorts and socks.

Change colours: All yellow.

Midweek home matchday: Wednesday

Record win: 8-0 v Netherfield.

Record defeat: 0-9 v Sutton United - 22/09/90 - GMVC.

Record transfer fee: £5,000 for Paul Shirtliff from Dagenham & Redbridge.

Record transfer fee received: £3,000 from Sunderland for John McGinley - 1981.

1992/93 Captain: David Corner

1992/93 Top scorer: Alan Lamb - 23

1992/93 Player of the Year: Michael Farrey

Club record goalscorer: Bob Topping

Record appearances: Simon Smith - 405 - 1985-1993

Past players who progressed to the Football League: Osher Williams (Southampton, Stockport, Port Vale, Preston), John McGinley (Sunderland, Lincoln), Billy Askew (Hull City, Newcastle United), Lawrie Pearson (Hull City, Port Vale), Ian Johnson (Northampton Town), Ken Davies (Stockport).

Club Honours: Football League Division 3 North R-up 1931-32, 1949-50; FA Cup Quarter-Finalists 1952-53; Northern Premier League Champions 1982-83, 1985-86; Northern Premier League R-up 1989-90; Northern Premier League Cup Finalists 1989-90.

HALIFAX TOWN

Formed:
1911

President:
J.S.Crowther

Chairman:
S.J.Brown

Vice Chairman
D.C.Greenwood

Football Secretary:
Mr. Bev Fielding

Manager:
P.Wragg

Coach:
M.Rathbone

Physiotherapist:
M.Rathbone

Commercial Manager:
N.Beaumont

In one of football's cruel twists, the last League goal to be scored at the Shay was by former Halifax player Derek Hall. His 62nd minute strike in the last game of the season, combined with Northampton's win at Shrewsbury, condemned Town to non-League life. Away wins at Bury and Doncaster towards the end gave the club real hope of clawing their way to safety, but failure to score in the final three matches shattered that illusion.

The season will be remembered as the most tragic in Halifax Town's troubled life. October saw the club's directors reveal huge financial difficulties amid speculation that they might not reach the season's end. Poor home results and perhaps more importantly, poor performances, only drew small crowds. Spiralling costs and debts, offset by low income from the turnstiles meant that quality players could not be signed in an effort to improve results.

Following these revelations, John McGrath decided that he could not function effectively as manager, and he duly resigned. Mick 'Basil' Rathbone, the club physiotherapist, was appointed as Halifax Town's 27th, and possibly final League manager. Rathbone, an honest and likeable chap, did his absolute best with the meagre resources available, but luck had deserted the team and results failed to improve.

The season had started optimistically. Ex-Liverpool and Southampton star Jimmy Case joined the club. At last a big name signing and much-needed publicity, and hope for the fans. However, only one win in the first seven games brought everyone down to earth with a heavy bump.

A good run during October saw the best League position of 10th obtained. this was highlighted by a superb 5-2 away win at Northampton, in which defender-turned-striker, Ian Thompstone, hit a glorious hat-trick.

With the club out of the Coca-Cola cup at the first stage, the Directors were hoping for an FA Cup run to boost the ailing finances. Non-League Marine were the first round opponents, but the part-timers humiliated and out-played the Shaymen, and deservedly won by four goals to one. Defeats by Bradford City and Huddersfield Town in the Autoglass Trophy, a competition in which Halifax failed to score a single goal, closed another avenue to possible financial salvation.

So, a paltry return of only three home league wins and just 20 goals at the Shay condemned Halifax Town to life outside the Football League. How they will cope remains to be seen, but credit goes to the board for deciding to retain a full-time playing staff in an effort to win back League football at the first attempt.

G.R.Dimmock (Club Statistician).

Halifax Town 1992/93.

HALIFAX MATCHFACTS 92-93   HALIFAX MATCHFACTS 92-93   HALIFAX MATCHFACTS 92-93

Key: Home fixtures are denoted by bold capitals. Numbers in brackets after players names indicate goals scored (an asterisk by the results denotes own goals). Only used substitutes are listed - substituted players are listed in *italicised*.

Key to Competitions: **BL**: Barclays League. **CC**: Coca Cola Cup. **FAC**: F.A. Cup. **AT**: Autoglass Trophy.

FA CUP: 1st Round   COCA COLA CUP: 1st Round   AUTOGLASS TROPHY: Preliminary Round

LEAGUE POSITION: 24th

Date	Opponents	Comp.	Res	Gate	1.	2.	3.	4.	5.	6.	7.	8.	9.	10.	11.	Sub.	Sub.
15/08	Rochdale	BL	3-2	2,497	Bracey	Megson	Wilson(1)	Lucketti	Th'stone	Bradley	Matthews	Case	Thomas	*Juryeff*	H'sley(2)	Gayle	
18/08	**HARTLEPOOL**	CC	1-2	1,370	Bracey	Megson(1)	Wilson	Lucketti	Th'stone	Bradley	Matthews	Cases	Thomas	*Juryeff*	Hildersley	Greenwood	
22/08	**SCUNTHORPE U.**	BL	0-0	1,793	Bracey	Megson	Wilson	Lucketti	Th'stone	Bradley	Matthews	Case	Thomas	Gayle	Hildersley	Greenwood	German
26/08	Hartlepool	CC	2-3	2,191	Bracey	Megson	Wilson	Lucketti(1)	Lewis	Bradley	Matthews	German	Thomas(1)	*Greenwood*	*Hildersley*	Thomstone	German
29/08	Cardiff City	BL	1-2	7,692	Bracey	Megson	Wilson	Lucketti(1)	Lewis	Bradley	Matthews	Case	Thomas	Gayle	Peake	Lewis	German
01/09	Crewe Alex.	BL	0-2	3,228	Bracey	Megson	Wilson	Lucketti	Lewis	Bradley	Matthews	Case	Thomas	Greenwood	Peake	Gale	
12/09	Lincoln City	BL	1-2	2,689	Bracey	Megson	Wilson	Lucketti(1)	Th'stone	Bradley	Matthews	Case	Thomas	Greenwood	Peake		
15/09	**DARLINGTON**	BL	1-0	1,287	Bracey	Megson	Wilson	Lucketti	Th'stone	Bradley	Matthews	Case	*Thomas*	Greenwood	Peake	Hildersley	
19/09	**SCARBOROUGH**	BL	3-4	1,230	Bracey	Megson	Wilson(1)	Lucketti	Th'stone	Bradley	Matthews	Case	*Thomas*	G'wood(1)	Peake	Kamara	German
26/09	Northampton T.	BL	5-2	2,021	Bracey	Megson	Wilson	Lucketti(1)	T'stone(3)	Bradley	*Matthews*	Case	*Thomas*	G'wood(1)	Peake	German	H'sley
03/10	Carlisle Utd	BL	1-1	3,824	Bracey	Barr	Wilson	Lucketti	*Th'stone*	Bradley(1)	Matthews	Case	Lewis	Greenwood	Peake	German	H'sley
10/10	**COLCHESTER U.**	BL	2-4	2,445	Bracey	Barr	Wilson	Lucketti	Th'stone	Griffiths	Mat'hews(1)	Case	Lewis	Greenwood	Peake	German	
17/10	Walsall	BL	2-1	3,867	Bracey	Barr	Wilson	Lucketti	Th'stone	Bradley	Matthews	German	Hildersley	*Greenwood*	Peake(1)	Case	Lewis
24/10	**GILLINGHAM**	BL	2-0	1,216	Bracey	Barr	Wilson	Lucketti	Th'stone	Bradley	Mat'hews(1)	German	Lewis	Wright	Peake	Case	
31/10	Hereford Utd	BL	0-3	1,936	Bracey	Barr	Wilson	Lucketti	Th'stone	Bradley	Matthews	German	*Hindersley*	Lewis	Peake	Case	Patterson
03/11	Shrewsbury T.	BL	0-1	2,704	Bracey	Lewis	Wilson	Lucketti	Th'stone	Bradley	Matthews	Case	Greenwood	*Thomas*	Peake	Patterson	
07/11	**TORQUAY UTD**	BL	0-2	1,661	Bracey	Lewis	Wilson	Lucketti	Th'stone	Bradley	Matthews	Case	Thomas	*Greenwood*	Peake	Hildersley	
14/11	Marine	FAC	1-4	1,892	Bracey	Lewis	Wilson	Lucketti	Th'stone	*Bradley*	Matthews	Case	Thomas	*Patterson*	Peake	German(1)	
21/11	Wrexham	BL	1-1	1,873	Bracey	Megson	Wilson	Lucketti	Lewis	Barr	German	Case	Patterson	*Lancashire*	*Hildersley*	Hardy(1)	Edmonds
28/11	**CHESTERFIELD**	BL	1-1	1,432	Bracey	Th'stone	Wilson	Lucketti	Lewis	Bradley	Matthews	German	Patterson	Lancashire	Hardy(1)	Megson	
01/12	**BRADFORD**	AT	0-4	1,434	Bracey	Megson	wilson	Lucketti	Th'stone	Bradley	Matthews	Case	Patterson	*Lancashire*	Hardy	Barr	
05/12	**BARNET**	BL	1-2	1,253	Bracey	Megson	Wilson	Lucketti	Th'stone	Bradley	Matthews	Barr	Hildersley	G'wood(1)	Hardy	German	
15/12	Huddersfield	AT	0-5	1,236	Bracey	Barr	Wilson	German	Lucketti	*Bradley*	Paterson	Peake	Th'stone	Greenwood	Hildersley	Hildersley	Edmonds
19/12	**BURY**	BL	0-1	1,760	Bracey	Megson	Wilson	German	Lucketti	Barr	*Williams*	Peake	Th'stone	Brown	Hildersley	Hildersley	

Date	Opponent		Result	Att	1	2	3	4	5	6	7	8	9	10	11	Subs
26/12	DONCASTER R.	BL	2-2	1,854	Bracey	Megson(1)	Wilson	German	Lucketti	Barr	Williams	Peake	Ridings	T'stone(1)	Brown	Hardy
29/12	York City	BL	1-1	4,068	Bracey	Megson	Wilson	German	Lucketti	Barr	Williams(1)	Peake	Ridings	T'stone	Brown	Hardy
09/01	Darlington	BL	3-0	1,984	Bracey	Megson	Wilson	Hardy	Lucketti	Barr	Williams	Ridings(2)	T'stone	Patterson	Christie	
16/01	NORTHAMPTON	BL	2-2	1,323	Bracey	Megson	Hardy	German	Lucketti	Barr	Williams	Ridings(2)	T'stone	Patterson	Christie	Hildersley
23/01	Scarborough	BL	0-2	1,552	Bracey	Megson	Hardy	German	Lucketti	Barr	Williams	Ridings	T'stone	Patterson	Christie	Peake
26/01	CARDIFF CITY	BL	0-1	1,339	Bracey	German	Hardy	Peake	Lucketti	Bradley	Williams	Ridings	T'stone	Patterson	Christie	
30/01	Scunthorpe Utd	BL	1-4	2,460	Bracey	German	Hardy	Peake	Lucketti	Bradley	Williams	Ridings	T'stone	Pterson(1)	Christie	
06/02	ROCHDALE	BL	2-3	1,906	Bracey	German	Hardy	Case	Lucketti	Bradley	Williams	Ridings	T'stone	Greenwood	Peel	Bradley
16/02	LINCOLN CITY	BL	2-1	1,260	Bracey	German	Hardy	Case(1)	Lucketti	Bradley	Peake	Ridings	T'stone	Greenwood(1)	Peel	
20/02	CREWE ALEX.	BL	1-2	1,604	Bracey	German	Hardy	Case(1)	Lucketti	Bradley	Peake	Ridings	T'stone	Greenwood	Peel	Christie
26/02	Colchester Utd	BL	1-2	3,007	Bracey	German	Hardy	Matthews	Lucketti	Bradley	Megson	Ridings	T'stone(1)	Greenwood	Peake	Christie
06/03	CARLISLE UTD	BL	0-2	1,309	Bracey	German	Ever'ham	Matthews	Lucketti	Bradley	Barr	Ridings	T'stone	Greenwood	Hardy	Christie
13/03	Torquay Utd	BL	0-2	3,345	Brown	German	Hardy	Matthews	Lucketti	Bradley	Barr	Ridings	T'stone	Patterson	Peake	Megson, G'wood
20/03	SHREWSBURY T.	BL	1-1	3,872	Brown	German	Hardy	Matthews	Lucketti	Bradley	Peake	Ridings	G'wood(1)	Patterson	Christie	
23/03	Chesterfield	BL	1-2	2,382	Bracey	German	Barr	Matthews	Lucketti	Bradley	Peake	Ridings	Greenwood	Patterson	T'stone(1)	
26/03	WREXHAM	BL	0-1	3,970	Bracey	German	Barr	Matthews	Lucketti	Bradley	Peake	Ridings	Greenwood	Patterson	Craven	Thomas, Circuit
03/04	Barnet	BL	0-0	3,042	Bracey	German	Barr	Hardy	Lucketti	Megson	Peake	Ridings	Greenwood	Patterson	Craven	Thomas
10/04	Doncaster	BL	1-0	2,160	Bracey	German	Barr(1)	Hardy	Lucketti	Megson	Peake	Ridings	Thomas	Patterson	Craven	Obebo
12/04	YORK CITY	BL	0-1	3,983	Bracey	Megson	Barr	Hardy	Lucketti	Bradley	Peake	Ridings	Greenwood	Patterson	Craven	German, Obebo
17/04	Bury	BL	2-1	3,039	Bracey	German(1)	Barr	Hardy	Lucketti	Bradley	Peake	Ridings	Megson	Pterson(1)	Craven	
24/04	WALSALL	BL	0-4	2,829	Bracey	German	Barr	Hardy	Lucketti	Bradley	Peake	Ridings	Megson	Patterson	Craven	Obebo, Christie
01/05	Gillingham	BL	0-2	7,157	Bracey	German	Barr	Hardy	Lucketti	Bradley	Peake	Ridings	Megson	Patterson	Craven	Greenwood
08/05	HEREFORD UTD	BL	0-1	7,451	Bracey	German	Barr	Hardy	Lucketti	Bradley	Peake	Ridings	Megson	Patterson	Craven	Greenwood

League Appearances: Bracey 41: Megson 24(2): Wilson 22: Lucketti 42: Thompstone 31: Bradley 29(1): Matthews 23: Case 17(4): Thomas 10(2): Juryeff 1: Hildersley 7(6): Gayle 2(3): German 28(7): Greenwood 21(4): Lewis 10(3): Peake 32(1): Hardy 20(2): Christie 6(3): Barr 28: Craven 7: Patterson 18(5): Ridings 21: Peel 3: Edmonds 0(2): Williams 9: L.Brown 3: Wright 1: Kamara 0(1): Lancashire 2: Circuit 0(1): N.Brown 1: Everingham 2: Griffiths 1: Obebo 0(3).

League Goalscorers: Thompstone 9: Greenwood 5: Ridings 4: Barr 3: Case, German, Hardy, Lucketti, Matthews, Patterson, Hildersley, Wilson 2: Bradley, Peake, Megson, Williams 1.

Halifax Town

PETER WRAGG

Peter played for Leek Town, winning the Cheshire League. He became manager when injury ended his career and the club came 4th and 2nd during his two years in charge. He then had spells with Stalybridge Celtic, Chorley and Hyde United, taking the latter to the First Round of the FA Cup for the first time in 20 years.

In early 1986 he joined Macclesfield Town and took them to an unprecedented treble of Northern Premier League, League Cup and Presidents Cup and promotion to the Conference. After consolidating saw The Silkmen go from strength to strength, including reaching Wembley in the 1989 FA Trophy Final - his proudest moment to date.

Peter parted company with Macclesfield at the end of last season and signed up for Halifax during the summer.

Midfield action from Priestfield Stadium where Gillingham won this relegation battle 2-0 against a very spirited Halifax Town. Photo: Dave West.

Programme details:
  32 pages for £1
  Editor - Nick Beaumont (0422 36336)

Any other club publications:

Local Newspapers:
  Halifax Courier
  Yorkshire Post
  Telegraph Argus

Local Radio Stations:
  Pennine Radio
  Radio Leeds

HALIFAX TOWN - PLAYING SQUAD 1992-93

Player	Honours	Birthplace and date	Transfer Fees	Previous Clubs
GOALKEEPERS				
Nick Brown		Northampton 25/1/73		Norwich City
Lee Bracey		Ashford 11/9/68	£47,500	West Ham Utd, Swansea City
DEFENDERS				
Elfyn Edwards	WSP, WY, NPL, APL, NPLC, CCS4/5/60	Aberystwyth		Wrexham, Tranmere, Runcorn, Altrincham, Macclesfield
Martin Filson	NPL	St Helens 25/6/68	£3,000	Tranmere R, Wrexham, Blackpool, Rhyl, Stalybridge Celtic
Chris Lucketti		Littleborough 28/9/71		Rochdale, Stockport County
Mick Rathbone	EY	Birmingham 6/11/58		Birmingham, Blackburn R, Preston NE
Jason Hardy		Burnley 14/12/69		Burnley
MIDFIELD				
David German		Sheffield 16/10/73		None
Jason Peake		Leicester 29/9/71		Leicester City
David Ridings		Manchester		Curzon Ashton, Macclesfield Town, Curzon Ashton
Scott Longley		Wakefield 16/7/73		YTS
Colin Lambert			£5,000	Winsford Utd, Macclesfield T
Billy Barr		Halifax 21/6/69		None
FORWARDS				
Nigel Greenwood		Preston 27/11/66		Preston NE, Bury, Preston NE
Jamie Paterson		Dumfries 26/4/73		None
Kevin Megson		Bradford 1/2/71	£5,000	Bradford City

Scott Booth, Grant Dunning, Ben Fellows, Tony Gaffney, Adam Hamer, Robert Junk, Ashley Maynard, Linton Williams (Apprentices)

Departures during season:
Russell Bradley, David Evans, Neil Griffiths, Paul Wilson, Greg Abbott, Nick Richardson, Ian Thompstone, Ian Juryeff.

Players on loan during season:

The Shay, Halifax Town

Halifax's lively young striker Jamie Patterson infront of a packed terrace. Photo: Dave West.

Address and telephone number: The Shay, Halifax, West Yorkshire HX1 2YS.
Tel: 0422 361582 Fax: 0422 349487
Simple directions: From North: Take A629 to Halifax Town Centre. Take 2nd exit at roundabout into Broad Street and follow signs for Huddersfield (A629) into Skircoat Road. From South, East & West: Exit M62 junction 24 and follow Halifax (A629) signs to Town centre into Skircoat Road for ground.
Capacity: 8,041   **Seated:** 1,878   **Covered terracing:** 6,000 (Approx)
Record Attendance: 36,885 v Tottenham - 5th Round FA Cup - 14.02.53
Club Shop: Contact Nick Beaumont on 0422 363336 for details.
Social Facilities: No facilities on the ground.
Previous Grounds: Sandhall Lane 1911-15, Exley 1919-21.

Halifax Fact File

Nickname: The Shaymen

Club Sponsors: Paraglas

Previous Leagues: Yorkshire Combination 1911-12, Midland League 1912-21, Division 3 North 1921-58, Division 3 1958-63, 1969-76, 1992, Division 4 1963-69.

Club colours: Blue & white

Change colours: White/green & purple

Reserve team league: Neville Midland Senior League

Midweek home matchday: Tuesday

Record win: 12-0 v West Vale Ramblers - 1st Qualifying Round FA Cup - 1913-14

Record defeat: 0-13 v Stockport County - Division 3 North - 1933-34

Record transfer fee:

Record transfer fee received:

1992/93 Captain: Russell Bradley

1992/93 Top scorer: Ian Thompstone

1992/93 Player of the Year: Billy Barr

Club record goalscorer: Albert Valentine

Record appearances: John Pickering

Past players who progressed to the Football League: N/A

Club Honours: Promoted to Division 3 1968-69

KETTERING TOWN

Formed:
1880

President:
T.F.Bradley

Chairman:
P.Mallinger

Vice Chairman
P.Oliver

Football Secretary:
G.P.Knowles

Manager:
Graham Carr

Coach
Clive Walker

Physiotherapist:
Richie Norman

Commercial Manager:

Press Officer:
G.P.Knowle

The start of the 1992/93 campaign was eagerly awaited by Poppies fans. The team had finished in third place the previous season, new boss Dave Cusack had introduced some impressive newcomers to the squad and owner Mark English was promising much.

However, by September, things were very much different. English had departed in mysterious circumstances, the club were deep in financial trouble (again!) and Cusack was 'suspended' by the newly appointed firm of administrators. Players left by the truck load and supporters' morale was once again at a low ebb.

Graham Carr, who had led county rivals Northampton Town to the Fourth Division title in 1987 and had plenty of non-League experience as a manager and player, was brought in as temporary, unpaid manager. He used his vast contacts to sign players and, although he was unable to pay much in wages, managed to bring in sufficient quality to improve results - very much against the odds.

The Administrators confirmed Carr as permanent boss and, despite a wage budget that would have struggled to pay for a team two rungs lower in the Pyramid, Carr's motivating abilities brought some surprising results, including Wycombe Wanderers' first home league defeat of the season.

After a hiccup, new owner Peter Mallinger, a former Newcastle United Vice-Chairman whose business career began in Kettering, has set about 'cleaning-up' the mess that English had left and Carr was able to go about strengthening his squad.

With the manager's ability, an enthusiastic new chairman and a fantastic set of supporters, don't be surprised if the Poppies are challenging for promotion once again.

Steve Whitney.

David Riley scores for Kettering in their Conference match against Merthyr Tydfil. Photo: Mick Cheney.

KETTERING MATCHFACTS 92-93 KETTERING MATCHFACTS 92-93 KETTERING MATCHFACTS 92-93

Key: Home fixtures are denoted by bold capitals. Numbers in brackets after players names indicate goals scored (an asterisk by the results denotes own goals). Only used substitutes are listed - substituted players are italicised.

Key to Competitions: **GMVC**: G.M. Vauxhall Conference. **NSC**: Northamptonshire Senior Cup. **DC**: Drinkwise (G.M. Vauxhall Conference) Cup. **FAC**: F.A. Cup. **FAT**: Vauxhall F.A. Trophy.

LEAGUE POSITION: 13th   FA CUP: First Round   FA TROPHY: First Round

Date	Opponents	Comp.	Res	Gate	1.	2.	3.	4.	5.	6.	7.	8.	9.	10.	11.	Sub.	Sub.	Sub.
22/08	Slough Town	GMVC	0-3	1,095	Reece	Reddich	Gernon	Nicol	Swales	Docker	T'linson	Adams	Riley	Brown	Sowden	Curtis		Russell
25/08	**WOKING**	GMVC	0-1	2,120	Reece	Reddish	Gernon	Nicol	Bancroft	Docker	T'linson	Adams	Gavin	Brown	Sowden	Curtis		
29/08	**MACCLESFIELD**	GMVC	1-0	1,209	Reece	Reddish	Gernon	Nicol	Swailes	Bancroft	T'linson	Bancroft	Gavin	Brown	Hill(1)	Curtis		
31/08	Kidderminster	GMVC	0-0	1,608	Reece	Reddish	Gernon	Nicol	Bancroft	Bancroft	Bancroft	Adams	Curtis	Brown	Hill			Brown
05/09	Yeovil Town	GMVC	1-2	2,006	Reece	Reddish	Gernon	Nicol	Swailes	Docker	T'linson	Bancroft	Gavin(1)	Riley	Sowden	Curtis		Brown
08/09	**FARNBOROUGH**	GMVC	2-1	1,395	Reece	Reddish	Gernon	Nicol	Curtis	Docker	T'linson(1)	Bancroft	Nuttell(1)	Riley	Hill	Adams		Underw'd
15/09	Telford United	GMVC	1-3	1,328	H'phries	Grnw'd	Gernon	Nicol	Sowden	Docker	T'linson	Bancroft(1)	Riley	Brown	Curtis	Adams		
19/09	Northwich Vic.	GMVC	2-2	721	H'phries	Sowden	Gernon	Nicol	Sowden	Docker	T'linson	Bancroft(1)	Riley	Whitehst	Adams	Adams		
26/09	**WYCOMBE W.**	GMVC	0-4	3,051	H'phries	Sowden	Gernon	Nicol	Hill	Docker(1)	Brown	Bancroft	Adams	Whitehst	Adams	Smalley		
29/09	**DAGENHAM & R**	GMVC	0-0	1,341	H'phries	Brown	Gernon	Nicol	Smalley	Docker	North	Bancroft	Riley	Whitehst	Hill	Riley		
03/10	Witton Albion	GMVC	2-4	986	H'phries	Brown	Swailes	Nicol	Smalley	Docker	Radford	Bancroft	Riley	Adams	Hill			
06/10	**STAFFORD RGRS**	GMVC	2-0	1,260	H'phries	Brown	Gernon	Nicol	Smalley	Docker	North	Murphy(2)	Riley	Adams	Hill	Riley		Ellis
10/10	Farnborough T.	GMVC	2-3	1,007	H'phries	Brown(1)	Gernon	Nicol	Smalley	Docker	Adams	Murphy(2)	Riley	Bancroft(1)	Hill	Riley	Price	
17/10	**MERTHYR TYD.**	GMVC	1-3	1,356	H'phries	Reed	Gernon	Nicol	Smalley	Docker	North	Murphy	North	Bancroft	Donald	Adams	W'hurst	Price
19/10	Kidderminster	DC	0-3	624	H'phries	Reed	Gernon	Nicol	Wood	Docker	Adams	Brown	Riley	Brown	Hill	Price		Radford
24/10	**CORBY**	FAC	2-1	3,273	H'phries	Reed	Gernon	Nicol	Smalley	Smalley	Brown(1)	Donald	Riley	Ellis	Hill	Price		
31/10	Macclesfield	GMVC	0-1	731	H'phries	Reed	Gernon	Nicol	Smalley	Stebbing	Brown	Donald	Riley	Murphy(1)	Wood			
03/11	**SLOUGH TOWN**	GMVC	5-0	1,205	Beasley	Reed	Gernon	Nicol	Smalley	Stebbing	Brown	Donald	Riley(2)	Murphy	Hill(2)			
07/11	Runcorn	GMVC	2-2	492	Beasley	Reed	Gernon	Nicol	Smalley	Stebbing	Brown	Donald	Riley(1)	Wood	Wood			
14/11	Gillingham	FAC	2-3	3,962	Beasley	Reed	Gernon	Nicol	Smalley	Stebbing	Docker	Donald	Riley	Murphy(1)	Hill(1)	Wood	Docker	
21/11	**BROMSGROVE**	GMVC	3-2	1,328	Barber	Reed	Gernon	Nicol	Smalley	Stebbing	Brown	Brown(2)	Riley	Murphy	Hill(1)	Wood		
28/11	**GATESHEAD**	GMVC	2-0	1,455	Barber	Reed	Gernon	Nicol	Smalley	Stebbing	Brown	S'tellow	Riley(1)	Murphy(1)	Wood(1)			
05/12	**WELLING UNITED**	GMVC	2-4	1,488	Barber	Reed	Gernon	Nicol	Smalley	Clarke	Brown(1)	Wood	Riley(1)	Martin	Martin	Price		C'ham
12/12	**YEOVIL TOWN**	GMVC	3-0	1,337	Barber	Reed	Gernon	Nicol	Hope(1)	Clarke	Brown(2)	Wood	Riley	Martin	Martin	Wood		
19/12	Stafford Rgrs	GMVC	4-2	815	Howells	Reed	Gernon	Smalley	Hope(1)	Clarke	Brown(1)	Wood	Riley(1)	Martin(1)	Price	Wright		
28/12	**BOSTON UTD**	GMVC	3-3	2,592	Smith	Reed	Gernon	Nicol	Hope	Clarke	Brown(2)	Wood	Riley	Martin(1)	Hill	Price		Price

Date	Opponent	Comp	Score	Att	1	2	3	4	5	6	7	8	9	10	11	Subs
09/01	**BROMSGROVE**	FAT	0-0	1,723	Barber	Reed	Gernon	Smalley	Hope	Clarke	Brown	*Wood*	Riley	Donald	Hill	*Wood*
12/01	Bromsgrove	FAT	1-4	1,269	Barber	Reed	Gernon	Smalley	Hope	Clarke	Brown	Murphy	Riley(1)	Donald	Hill	
23/01	Bromsgrove	GMVC	1-1	1,297	Barber	Price	McKernon	Smalley	Hope	Taylor	Brown(1)	Wood	Riley	Donald	Roderick	
02/02	**TELFORD**	GMVC	1-1	1,221	Sommer	McKernon	Wood	Smalley	Price	Taylor	Brown(1)	Murphy	Riley	Donald	Roderick	Wright(1)
06/02	Welling Utd	GMVC	1-1	838	Sommer	Reed	Wood	Retallick	Hope	Price	Brown	McKernon	Riley	Clarke	Roderick	Murphy
09/02	Altrincham	GMVC	0-3	810	Sommer	McKernon	Gernon	Price	Hope	Price	Brown	Murphy	Riley(2)	Retallick	Roderick	Murphy
13/02	**NORTHWICH VIC.**	GMVC	2-1	1,221	Sommer	Reed	*Wood*	Price	Hope	Taylor	Brown	Wright	Riley	Retallick	Roderick	Murphy
15/02	Corby	NSC	1-1	956	Sommer	McKernon	Gernon	Nicol	Hope	Price(1)	Brown	Wright	Riley	Smalley	Wood	Roderick
20/02	**BATH CITY**	GMVC	0-1	1,185	Sommer	Reed	Gernon	Price	Hope	Donald	Brown	Wright	Riley	Shearer	Roderick	
27/02	**WITTON ALBION**	GMVC	2-1	1,090	Sommer	Price	*Gernon*	Nicol	Hope	*Shearer*	Brown	Wright	Riley	Donald(1)	Roderick	Hodges(1), McK'non
02/03	**RUNCORN**	GMVC	3-3	911	Sommer	McKernon	Wood	Price	Hope(1)	Hodges(1)	Brown(1)	Wright	North	Donald	Roderick	
06/03	Wycombe W.	GMVC	2-1	4,430	Sommer	McKernon	Wood	Nicol	Hope	Price	Brown(1)	Wright	Hodges(1)	Donald	Roderick	Harris
09/03	Methyr Tyd.	GMVC	1-2	486	Sommer	McKernon	Wood	*North*	Price	Price(1)	Brown	*Wright*	Hodges	Donald	Roderick	Harris
16/03	**CORBY**	NSC	3-1	1,560	Sommer	McKernon	Nicol	North	Price	*Harris*	Brown(1)	Wright(1)	Hodges(1)	Donald	Roderick	Shearer, Reed
20/03	Woking	GMVC	2-3	1,560	Sommer	*McKernon*	Wood	Reed	Price	Wood	Brown	Wright	Hodges	Donald	Roderick	Harris(1)
27/03	Gateshead	GMVC	1-1	478	Lim	*Reed*	Wood	Price	Hope	Harris(1)	Brown	Wright	Hodges	Donald(1)	Roderick	Shearer, Reed
03/04	**STALYBRIDGE**	GMVC	2-0	1,137	Lim	Price	Gernon	Oxbrow	Hope	*Harris(1)*	Brown	Wright	Hodges	Donald(1)	Wood	Shearer
10/04	**ALTRINCHAM**	GMVC	1-1	1,299	Lim	Price	Gernon	Oxbrow	Hope	*Harris*	Brown(1)	Wright	Hodges	Donald	Wood	Roderick
14/04	Boston United	GMVC	1-0	1,481	Lim	Price	Gernon	Oxbrow	*Smalley*	Roderick	Brown(1)	Wright	Hodges	Donald	Wood	Reed
17/04	Stalybridge	GMVC	0-0	805	Lim	Price	Gernon	Oxbrow	Hope	*Roderick*	Brown	Wright	Hodges	Donald	Wood	Donovan
20/04	Bath City	GMVC	0-0	386	Lim	Price	*Gernon*	Oxbrow	Hope	Roderick	Brown	Wright	Hodges	Donald	Wood	
24/04	**KIDDERMINSTER**	GMVC	1-2	1,365	Lim	Price	Gernon	*Smalley*	Hope	Roderick	Brown(1)	Wright	Hodges(1)	Donald	Hill	Harris
27/04	**RUSHDEN/DIAM**	NSC	2-1	873	Lim	Reed	Gernon	Wood	Hope	Price	Roderick	Wright	Hodges(1)	Brown(1)	Hill	Donovan
01/05	Dagenham & R	GMVC	2-1	1,225	Lim	Price	Wood	Smalley	Hope	Roderick	Brown	Wright	Shearer	Donald	Harris	*Donovan(2)*, Harris

League Appearances: Adams 9(1): Bancroft 11: Barber 5: Beasley 2: Brown 41(1): Clarke 5: Cunningham 3(1): Docker 18: Donald 21: Donovan 1(2): Ellis 2(1): Gavin 3: Gernon 31(1): Greenwood 4: Harris 6(3): Hill 13: Hodges 11(1): Hope 19: Howells 1: Humphries 10: Lim 6: Martin 1: Martin 5: McKernon 9: Murphy 11(1): Nicol 26: North 5: Nuttall 1: Oxbrow 5: Price 26(2): Radford 4: Reddish 6: Reece 6: Reed 20(1): Retallick 2: Riley 26(1): Roderick 17(1): Russell 1(1): Shearer 9(1): Smalley 22(1): Smith 1: Sommer 10: Sowden 9(1): Stebbing 5: Stringfellow 1: Swailes 5: Taylor 3: Tomlinson 8: UNderwood 3: Whitehurst 3(1): Wood 25(1): Wright 18(1).

League Goalscorers: Brown 16: Riley 9: Murphy 6: Bancroft, Harris, Hill, Hodges, Hope 3: Donald, Donovan, Martin 2: Docker, Gavin, Nuttall, Price, Roderick, Tomlinson, Wood, Wright 1.

Kettering Town

GRAHAM CARR

One of the most respected managers in the league, Graham was appointed as manager by the administrators in September last year and, with an extremely low budget to work within, managed to attract enough quality players to Rockingham Road to keep them safely in the Vauxhall Conference. After the club came out of administration and was taken over in the summer, Graham was rewarded with a well-deserved three-year contract.

A hard, uncompromising defender, Graham made 160 Football League appearances with Northampton Town, York City and Bradford Park Avenue, winning England Youth caps as well, before going non-League with the likes of Dartford, Telford United, Altrincham, Tonbridge and Weymouth. His managerial career began as player-boss at Weymouth and Dartford before taking over at Nuneaton Borough where he led the club to runners-up spot in the Alliance Premier League (Conference). Whilst at Nuneaton, Graham brought on the likes of Trevor Morley, Eddie McGoldrick, Paul Culpin and Richard Hill who all went on to enjoy League careers. Since then he has managed in the Football League at Northampton Town (winning the Fourth Division title in 1987), Blackpool and Maidstone United.

Dave Tomlinson evades a tackle from a Northwich player. Photo: Mick Cheney.

Programme details:
    32 pages for £1.00
    Editor: Paul Harrison

Any other club publications:
    Poppies at the Gates of Dawn (Fanzine)

Local Newspapers:
    Evening Telegraph
    Chronicle & Echo
    Herald & Post
    Citizen
Local Radio Stations:
    Radio Northampton
    Northants 96
    KCBC

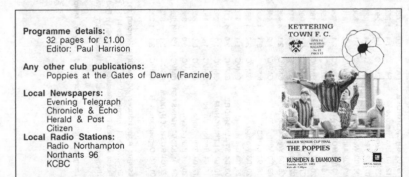

KETTERING TOWN - PLAYING SQUAD 1992-93

Player	Honours	Birthplace and date	Transfer Fees	Previous Clubs
GOALKEEPERS				
Russell Hoult		Leicester 22/11/72		Leicester City (Loan)
DEFENDERS				
Phil Mason		Consett 3/12/71		Newcastle Utd
Darren Oxbrow		Ipswich 1/9/69		Ipswich T, Maidstone U, Barnet
Gareth Price		Swindon 21/2/70		Mansfield Town, Bury
Terry Muckelberg	OxfSC	Banbury 29/9/66		Oxford Utd, Banbury Utd, Oxford City, Brackley T, Buckingham T
Graham Reed	Div 4	Doncaster 24/6/61		Barnsley, Frickley Ath, Northampton, Aylesbury Utd, VS Rugby
Shaun Wood		Leicester 21/4/67		St.Andrews
MIDFIELD				
Warren Donald	ES, Div 4	Uxbridge 7/10/64		West Ham Utd, Northampton T, Colchester Utd
Robin Taylor				Camb City, Shepshed Alb, Hinckley T, Kettering T, Peterboro'
Simon Clarke		Chelmsford 23/9/71		West Ham United
Martin Roderick	British Univ. British Students	Portsmouth 28/10/67		Portsmouth, Farnborough, Wycombe W, Harrogate Town, Shepshed Albion
Tony Loughlan		Croydon 19/1/70		Leicester United, Nottingham Forest
FORWARDS				
Owen Wright		Leicester 8/3/67		Worcester C, Bedworth U, Leicester U, Shepshed Chart, Aylesbury U, Shepshed A
Simon Guthrie		Newcastle 24/6/72		Sunderland, Portsmouth, Gateshead
Phil Brown	GMVC, Div 4 FA XI	Sheffield 16/1/66		Chesterfield, Stockport Co, Lincoln City
Adrian Thorpe		Chesterfield 25/11/63		Mansfield, Heanor T, Bradford C, Notts Co, Walsall, Northampton, Instant Dict(HK)
Dean Martin		Islington 31/8/72		Fisher Athletic, West Ham Utd
Neil Donovan		Limerick 4/12/68		Daventry Town

Departures during season:
Kevin Shoemake (Rushden & Diamonds), Mick Nuttell, Dave Tomlinson & Gary Stebbing (Dag & Red), Richard Huxford (Barnet), Shaun Sowden (Sudbury), Simon Underwood & Roger Greenwood (Released), Andy Curtis & Robin Taylor (Peterborough), Chris Swailes & Mick Shearer (Bridlington), Neil Ellis (Corby), Paul Bancroft (Kidderminster), Steve Adams (Witton Alb), Billy Whitehurst (Goole), David Riley (FC Ponsonby NZ), Mark Smalley (Erith), Craig McKernon (Hinckley T), Jamie Cunningham (Cogenhoe), Ian Docker (Bromley), Frank Murphy (Cray W), Richard Hill (Retired), Paul Nicol (Boston Utd), Irvin Gernon (Telford Utd), Terry Harris (Grantham), David Hodges (Released),

Players on loan during season:
Paul Reece (Grimsby), Shane Reddish (Doncaster), Pat Gavin, Fred Barber & Graham Retallick (Peterborough), Andy Beasley & Ian Stringfellow (Mansfield), Simon Clarke & Dean Martin (West Ham), Mark Smith (Notts Forest), Jurgen Sommer (Luton), Harvey Lim (Gillingham), Darren Oxbrow (Barnet).

Rockingham Road, Kettering

Address and telephone number: Rockingham Road, Kettering, Northants, NN16 9AW.
Tel: 0536 83028/410815 (Office). 0536 410962 (Social Club).
Simple directions: M1 junction 15, A43 to Kettering use A14 and Kettering Northern by pass, turn right A6003, ground half a mile. A1 use A14 at Huntingdon then as above. British Rail - Inter-City Midland - 50mins from London (St.Pancras), 20mins from Leicester.
Capacity: 6,100   **Seated:** 1,800   **Covered terracing:** 4,000
Record Attendance: 11,536 Kettering v Peterborough (pre-Taylor report).
Club Shop: Opening before season - contact club for details.
Social Facilities: Social Club (Poppies), Vice-Presidents Bar.
Previous Grounds: None

Kettering Fact File

Nickname: Poppies

Club Sponsors:

Previous Leagues: Southern League, Northants League, Midland League, Birmingham League, Central Alliance, United Counties League.

Club colours: Red shirts, white shorts and red socks.

Change colours: All blue.

Midweek home matchday: Tuesday

Record win:

Record defeat:

Record transfer fee: £17,500 to Grantham for Gary Jones.

Record transfer fee received: £150,000 from Newcastle United for Andy Hunt.

1992/93 Captain: Paul Nicol.

1992/93 Top scorer: Phil Brown.

1992/93 Player of the Year: Phil Brown.

Club record goalscorer: A Woolhead.

Record appearances: R Ashby.

Past players who progressed to the Football League: B.Kellock (Peterborough), G.Wood (Notts Co.), D.Longhurst (Nott'm Forest), S.Endersby (ipswich), S.Fallon (Cambridge Utd), J.Sellers (Manchester Utd), A.Rogers (Plymouth), M.Foster (Northampton), J.Brown (Chesterfield), Cohen Griffith (Cardiff City), Andy Hunt (Newcastle).

Club Honours: Premier Inter League Cup winners; FA Trophy finalists; Alliance Premier League r-up (x2); Southern League Winners, County Cup Winners, Daventry Charity Cup Winners (x2); Northants Senior Cup (x2); Maunsell Cup Winners.

KIDDERMINSTER HARRIERS

Formed:
1886

Chairman:
David L Reynolds

Vice Chairman
J. Richard Painter

Football Secretary:
Ray Mercer

Manager:
Graham Allner

Assistant Manager:
Jimmy Conway

Coach:
Colin Gordon

Physiotherapist:
Jimmy Conway

Commercial Manager:
Philip Wright

Press Officer:
Ray Mercer

The 1992/93 season ended on a bright note with the Harriers enjoying a 10 match unbeaten run which included winning the Worcestershire Senior Cup for the 20th time and their 4th success in just five seasons.

Chris Brindley arrived from Telford United just prior to the commencement of the 1992/93 season for a record fee of £20,000. He played in all 57 matches and was voted Player of the Year.

Harriers eventually finished 9th in the League (their highest position since 1988/89), and during the season notched some notable victories including a 1-0 victory against local rivals Bromsgrove Rovers at Christmas, before a record 'Conference' gate, at Aggborough, of 4,324. There was also an amazing 5-1 success at Woking courtesy of a superb hat-trick by Jon Purdie. Veteran striker Paul Davies scored another 19 goals during the season, and has now made 486 first team appearances scoring 232 goals.

In the FA Cup 1st Round Proper Harriers lost 1-0 at Exeter City whilst in the Vauxhall FA Trophy, Harriers were dismissed at the first hurdle by Diadora League Enfield. Bangor City inflicted a Round Three replay defeat in the Allbright Bitter Welsh Cup.

During the latter part of the season several experienced players arrived including Simeon Hodson (ex-Mansfield), Wayne Williams (ex-Walsall), Neil Cartwright (ex-WBA) plus the much-travelled Colin Gordon who arrived from Leicester City to take up a new role as player/coach at Aggborough.

Philip Wright (Commercial Manager).

Kidderminster Harriers 1992/93 - Back Row (L-R): Gary Walsh, Paul Grainger, David Benton, Jon Hanson, Craig Gillett, Mark Wolsey. Middle Row: Paul Davies, Matthew Davis, Ron Green, Darren Steadman, John McGrath, Brett Wilcox. Front Row: Graham Allner (Manager), Antone Joseph, David Hadley, Les Palmer, Richard Forsyth, Jimmy Conway (Asst.Manager).

Key: Home fixtures are denoted by bold capitals. Numbers in brackets after players names indicate goals scored (an asterisk by the results denotes own goals). Only used substitutes are listed - substituted players are *italicised*.

Key to Competitions: **GMVC**: G.M. Vauxhall Conference. **WSC**: Worcestershire Senior Cup. **DC**: Drinkwise (G.M. Vauxhall Conference) Cup. **FAC**: F.A. Cup. **FAT**: Vauxhall F.A. Trophy. **WC**: Welsh Cup.

LEAGUE POSITION: 9th

FA CUP: First Round.   FA TROPHY: First Round.

Date	Opponents	Comp.	Res	Gate	1.	2.	3.	4.	5.	6.	7.	8.	9.	10.	11.	Sub.	Sub.
22/08	**ALTRINCHAM**	GMVC	0-1	1,225	*Green*	Benton	McGrath	Weir	Brindley	Forsyth	Deakin	Grainger	Davies	Hanson	*Humphreys*	Wilcox	Palmer
25/08	Northwich Vic.	GMVC	1-0	629	Steadman	Benton	McGrath	Weir	Brindley	Forsyth	Deakin	Grainger	Davies	Palmer(1)	Hadley		
29/08	Boston United	GMVC	3-0	1,228	Steadman	Benton	McGrath	Weir	Brindley	Forsyth(1)	Deakin	Grainger(1)	Davies(1)	Palmer	Hadley		
31/08	**KETTERING**	GMVC	0-0	1,608	Steadman	Benton	McGrath	Weir	Brindley	Forsyth	Deakin	Wilcox	Davies	Palmer	Hadley		Joseph
5/09	Farnborough	GMVC	2-2	565	Steadman	Benton	McGrath	Weir	Brindley	Forsyth	Deakin	Grainger	Davies(1)	*Palmer*	Hadley(1)	Joseph	Hanson
8/09	Stalybridge C.	DC	1-1	554	Steadman	Benton	Gillett	Weir	Brindley	Forsyth	Deakin	Grainger	Davies(1)	Palmer	Hadley		Hanson
12/09	**WOKING**	GMVC	1-3	1,759	Steadman	Benton	McGrath	Weir	Brindley	Forsyth	Deakin	Grainger	Davies	*Palmer(1)*	*Hadley*	Humphreys	Joseph
19/09	**DAGENHAM & R.**	GMVC	0-1	1,089	Steadman	Benton	McGrath	Weir	Brindley	Forsyth	Joseph	Grainger	Davies	Palmer	Hadley	Humphreys	Hanson
21/09	**STALYBRIDGE**	GMVC	4-2	602	Steadman	Benton	McGrath	Weir	Brindley	Forsyth	Wilcox	Grainger	Davies(1)	*Palmer(2)*	*Humphreys(1)*	Hanson	
26/09	Runcorn	GMVC	0-0	512	Steadman	Benton	McGrath	Weir	Brindley	Forsyth	Wilcox	Grainger	Davies	*Palmer*	*Humphreys*	Hanson	
3/10	**WELLING UTD**	GMVC	2-1	1,018	Steadman	Wilcox	McGrath	Weir	Brindley	Forsyth(1)	Deakin	Grainger(1)	Davies	Palmer	*Humphreys*	Hanson	Hadley
10/10	Caersws	WC	2-2	382	Steadman	Benton	McGrath	Weir	Brindley	Forsyth	Deakin	Grainger	Davies(1)	Palmer	Hanson(1)		Gillett
13/10	Telford United	GMVC	1-1	1,692	Steadman	Benton	McGrath	Weir	Brindley	Forsyth	Deakin	Grainger	Davies(1)	Palmer	Hanson		
15/10	**CAERSWS**	WC	4-3	474	Green	Benton(1)	Gillett	Weir	Brindley(1)	Forsyth	Deakin(1)	Wolsey	Davies	*Palmer*	Hanson	Wilcox(1)	Hadley
17/10	**WITTON ALBION**	GMVC	0-0	1,268	Steadman	Benton	McGrath	Weir	Brindley	Forsyth	Deakin	Grainger	Davies	Palmer	Hanson	Hadley	Hadley
19/10	**KETTERING**	DC	3-0	624	Steadman	Benton	Gillett	Weir	Brindley	Forsyth(1)	Deakin(1)	Grainger	Davies	Hadley(1)	*Hanson*	Wilcox	Gillett
24/10	**ATHERSTONE U.**	FAC	2-0	1,139	Steadman	Benton	Gillett	Weir	Brindley	Forsyth(1)	Deakin	Grainger	Davies	*Hadley*	Hanson(1)	Wilcox	
31/10	**WYCOMBE WDRS**	GMVC	1-4	3,064	Steadman	Benton	McGrath	Gillett	Brindley	Forsyth	Deakin	Grainger	Davies(1)	Hadley	Wilcox		Palmer
2/11	**SUTTON C'FIELD**	WSC	3-2	385	Steadman	Benton	McGrath	Weir	Brindley	*Forsyth*	Deakin	Grainger	Davies(2)	Palmer	*Wilcox(1)*	Wolsey	Hanson
7/11	**BANGOR CITY**	WC	2-2	644	Steadman	Wilcox	McGrath	Weir	Brindley	Forsyth(1)	Deakin	Grainger	Davies(1)	Palmer	Hanson		
10/11	Bangor City	WC	1-2	363	Steadman	Benton	McGrath	Weir	Brindley	Forsyth(1)	Deakin	Grainger	Davies	Palmer	Hanson		
14/11	Exeter City	FAC	0-1	3,082	Steadman	Benton	McGrath	Weir	Brindley	Forsyth	Deakin	Grainger	Davies	Palmer	*Hanson*	Wilcox	Hadley
17/11	Altrincham	GMVC	2-2	678	Steadman	Benton	McGrath	Weir	Brindley	Forsyth(1)	Deakin	Grainger(1)	Davies(1)	Palmer	Yates	Wilcox	Hadley
21/11	**STALYBRIDGE**	GMVC	2-1	1,047	Steadman	Benton	McGrath(1)	Weir	Brindley	Forsyth(1)	Deakin	Grainger	Davies(1)	Hadley	Yates		Hadley
5/12	**SLOUGH TOWN**	GMVC	1-1	1,175	Steadman	Benton	McGrath	Weir	Brindley	Forsyth	Deakin	Wilcox	Hadley(1)	Howell	Humphreys		
12/12	Gateshead	GMVC	0-1	321	Steadman	Benton	McGrath	Weir	Brindley	Forsyth	Deakin	*Wilcox*	*Davies*	Howell	Hadley	Wolsey	
15/12	Macclesfield T.	DC	1-3	203	Steadman	Benton	*McGrath*	Weir	Brindley	Forsyth	Deakin	*Wolsey*	Palmer	Howell	Hadley(1)	Wilcox	Palmer
19/12	**RUNCORN**	GMVC	2-0	1,065	Steadman	Benton	Gillett	Weir	Brindley	Forsyth(1)	Deakin	Grainger(1)	Piggott	Howell	Hadley	Wilcox	Davies
26/12	Bath City	GMVC	1-2	870	Steadman	Benton	Gillett	Weir	Brindley	Forsyth	Deakin	Grainger	*Piggott*	Howell	*Hadley(1)*	Davies	

Date	Opponent	Comp	Res	Att	1	2	3	4	5	6	7	8	9	10	11	Subs
28/12	**BROMSGROVE**	GMVC	1-0	4,324	Steadman	Benton	McGrath	Weir	Brindley	Forsyth	Humphreys	Grainger	Davies	Howell	Hadley	Deakin(1)
2/01	Merthyr Tydfil	GMVC	3-4	657	Steadman	Benton	McGrath	Weir	Brindley	Forsyth	Deakin(1)	Grainger(1)	Davies	Howell	Piggott	Wilcox
9/02	**ENFIELD**	FAT	1-3	1,280	Steadman	Benton	McGrath	Benton	Brindley	Forsyth	Deakin	Grainger	Davies	Hadley	Hadley(1)	Hadley(1)
16/01	**BOSTON UNITED**	GMVC	0-2	954	Steadman	Sullivan	McGrath	Benton	Brindley	Richardson	Deakin	Grainger	Davies	Hadley	Purdie	Purdie
23/01	Slough Town	GMVC	0-1	1,069	Steadman	Hodson	McGrath	Weir	Brindley	Richardson	Deakin	Gordon	Davies	Hadley	Purdie	Davies
30/01	**MACCLESFIELD**	GMVC	1-1	1,032	Steadman	Hodson	McGrath	Weir	Brindley	Forsyth	Deakin	Richardson	Gordon	Hadley(1)	Purdie(1)	Palmer
1/02	**BROMSGROVE**	WSC	2-0	1,331	Steadman	Hodson	McGrath	Weir	Brindley	Forsyth(1)	Deakin	Gordon	Gordon	Hadley(1)	Palmer(1)	Palmer
6/02	Wycombe Wdrs	GMVC	1-1	4,379	Steadman	Hodson	McGrath	Weir	Brindley	Forsyth	Deakin	Richardson	Gordon	Hadley	Purdie(1)	Grainger
9/02	Welling United	GMVC	0-0	663	Steadman	Hodson	McGrath	Weir	Brindley	Forsyth	Deakin	Gordon	Gordon	Hadley	Purdie	Stokes
13/02	Stalybridge C.	GMVC	2-2	702	Steadman	Hodson	McGrath	Weir	Brindley	Forsyth	Deakin	Gordon	Gordon	Hadley(1)	Purdie(1)	Stokes
16/02	Stafford Rgrs	GMVC	1-0	1,294	Steadman	Hodson	McGrath	Weir	Brindley	Forsyth	Deakin	Gordon	Gordon	Hadley(1)	Purdie(1)	Palmer
20/02	**YEOVIL TOWN**	GMVC	1-1	1,257	Steadman	Benton	McGrath	Weir	Brindley	Forsyth	Deakin	Gordon	Stokes	Hadley	Purdie	Hanson
27/02	**FARNBOROUGH**	GMVC	1-5	1,120	Steadman	Benton	McGrath	Weir	Brindley(1)	Forsyth	Deakin(1)	Stokes	Grainger	Hadley	Purdie(1)	Stokes
1/03	**GATESHEAD**	GMVC	3-3	716	Steadman	Benton	McGrath	Weir	Brindley	Forsyth	Deakin	Davies(1)	Grainger	Hadley	Purdie	Stokes
6/03	Yeovil Town	GMVC	2-2	2,159	Steadman	Benton	McGrath	Weir	Brindley	Forsyth	Deakin	Gordon(2)	Grainger	Hadley	Purdie	Davies
9/03	Witton Albion	GMVC	2-2	638	Steadman	Benton	McGrath	Weir	Brindley	Forsyth	Deakin	Gordon	Grainger	Davies	Purdie	Davies
13/03	Dagenham & Red.	GMVC	2-3	1,004	Steadman	Benton	Gillett	Weir	Brindley	Forsyth	Cartwright(1)	Gordon	Grainger	Davies	Purdie	Stokes
20/03	**STAFFORD RGRS**	GMVC	0-2	1,234	Steadman	Benton	Rogers	Gillett	Brindley	Wolsey	Deakin	Gordon	Grainger	Davies	Purdie	Hudson
24/03	Solihull Boro.	WSC	1-0	353	Steadman	Williams	Gillett	Weir	Brindley	Forsyth(1)	Humphreys	Gordon	Grainger	Gillett	Purdie	
27/03	**MERTHYR TYD.**	GMVC	*1-0	1,158	Steadman	Williams	Gillett	Weir	Brindley	Benton	Humphreys	Gordon	Grainger	Davies	Purdie(3)	Benton
30/03	Macclesfield T.	GMVC	1-1	593	Steadman	Williams	Gillett	Weir(1)	Brindley	Forsyth	Cartwright	Gordon	Grainger	Davies(1)	Purdie	
3/04	Woking	GMVC	5-1	1,537	Steadman	Williams	Gillett	Weir(1)	Brindley	Forsyth(1)	Cartwright	Gordon	Grainger	Davies(1)	Purdie	
10/04	**BATH CITY**	GMVC	1-0	1,134	Steadman	Williams	McGrath	Weir	Brindley	Forsyth(1)	Cartwright	Gordon	Grainger	Hadley	Purdie	Gillett
12/04	Bromsgrove	GMVC	2-2	3,185	Steadman	Benton	McGrath	Weir	Brindley	Forsyth(1)	Cartwright	Gordon(1)	Grainger	Davies	Purdie	Humphreys
17/04	**TELFORD UTD**	GMVC	2-1	1,532	Steadman	Williams	McGrath	Weir	Brindley	Forsyth	C'twright	Gordon	Grainger	Davies	Purdie(1)	Gillett
24/04	Kettering T.	GMVC	2-1	1,365	Steadman	Williams	McGrath	Weir	Brindley	Forsyth	Cartwright	Gordon	Grainger	Davies(1)	Purdie	Humphreys
26/04	**SOLIHULL B.**	WSC	2-1	783	Steadman	Benton	McGrath	Weir	Brindley	Forsyth	Cartwright	Gordon	Grainger	Davies(2)	Purdie	Humphreys
01/05	**NORTHWICH V**	GMVC	5-3	1,417	Steadman	Williams	McGrath	Weir	Brindley	Forsyth(1)	C'wright(1)	H'phrey(1)	Grainger	Davies	Purdie(2)	Palmer

LEAGUE APPEARANCES: Bancroft 0(1), Benton 30(3), Brindley 42, Cartwright 8, Davis 30(3), Deakin 30(2), Forsyth 38, Gillett 6(1), Gordon 16, Grainger 32(1), Green 1, Hadley 26(3), Hodson 6, Howell 6, Humphreys 8(5), Joseph 1(3), McGrath 36, Palmer 19(7), Piggott 3, Purdie 18(1), Richardson 4, Rogers 1, Steadman 41, Stokes 1(5), Sullivan 1, Weir 40, Wilcox 4(2), Williams 8(2), Wolsey 2(1), Yates 2.

LEAGUE GOALSCORERS: Davis 11; Purdie 9; Forsyth, Hadley 7; Grainger, Palmer 6; Cartwright, Deakin, Gordon 3; Benton, Brindley, Humphreys, McGrath, Weir 1.

Kidderminster Harriers

GRAHAM ALLNER

Graham Allner joined Kidderminster Harriers as manager in October 1983. Formerly assistant manager at Cheltenham Town, he had won the Southern League championship when manager of the now defunct AP Leamington.

Graham's playing days began at Walsall where he gained England Youth honours. He then moved into non-league football where he played at Worcester City, Stafford Rangers and Alvechurch.

During his time at Aggborough, Graham has encouraged youth through their YT programme and many of his young players have come through to the first team.

Delwyn Humphreys sets off another attack for Kidderminster in their local derby against Bromsgrove Rovers at Aggborough last December.

Programme details:
> 40 pages for £1
> Editor - Roger Barlow

Any other club publications:
> The Soup (Fanzine)

Local Newspapers:
> Kidderminster Shuttle/Times
> Kidderminster Chronicle
> Evening Mail
> Express & Star
> Worcester Evening News

Local Radio Stations:
> BBC Hereford & Worcester
> Radio Wyvern

KIDDERMINSTER HARRIERS - PLAYING SQUAD 1992-93

Player	Honours	Birthplace and date	Transfer Fees	Previous Clubs
GOALKEEPERS				
Kevin Rose		Evesham 23/11/60		Ledbury T, Lincoln C, Ledbury T, Hereford, Bolton W, Rochdale
Darren Steadman	ES	Kidderminster 26/1/70		None
DEFENDERS				
John McGrath	FA XI, Middx W	Dumbarton 20/12/63		Shrewsbury T, Worcester City
Chris Brindley	FAT, FA XI	Stoke 5/7/69	£20,000	Hedneford Town, Wolves, Telford Utd
David Benton		West Bromwich 8/1/71		None
Martin Weir	FA XI, Middx W	Birmingham 4/7/68		Birmingham City
Simeon Hodson		Lincoln 5/3/66		Notts Co, Charlton A, Lincoln C,, Newport Co, WBA, Doncaster, Kidderminster, Mansfield
Wayne Williams	WC	Delford 17/11/63		Shrewsbury, Northampton T, Walsall
Craig Gillett		Dudley 17/10/72		None
MIDFIELD				
Richard Forsyth	FA XI	Dudley 3/10/70		Stourbridge
Paul Grainger	FAT, FA XI	Walsall 28/1/68	£10,000	Aston Villa, Mile Oak Rovers, Wolves, Telford Utd
John Deakin		Sheffield 29/9/66		Barnsley, Doncaster, Grimsby, Frickley, Ards, Shepshed, Birmingham, Carlisle, Wycombe
Paul Bancroft	ESP	Derby 10/9/64		Derby, Northampton, Nuneaton B, Burton A, Kidderminster H, Kettering T
Delwyn Humphreys	ESP, SSC	Shrewsbury 13/2/65	£10,000	Newtown, Bridgnorth Town
Neil Cartwright		Stourbridge 20/2/71		West Bromwich Albion
Mark Wolsey		Birmingham 27/12/73		None
FORWARDS				
Paul Davies	ESP, FAT, FA XI, Middx W	Kidderminster 9/10/60		Cardiff City, Trowbridge T, SC Hercules(Holl)
Martin Goldsmith		Walsall 4/11/6		Walsall, Atherstone Utd
Les Palmer		Birmingham 5/9/71		West Bromwich Albion
Colin Gordon		Sturbridge 17/1/63		Swindon, Wimbledon, Reading, Fulham, Birmingham C, Leicester C
Jon Purdie	ES	Corby 22/2/67		Arsenal, Wolves, Oxford Utd, Brentford, Shrewsbury, Worcester C, Cheltenham T
David Hadley		Birmingham 7/12/64	£10,000	Moor Green, Mile Oak Rovers, Tamworth

Departures during season:
Peter Howell (Burton Albion), Antone Joseph (Hednesford), Ron Green (Colchester), Brett Wilcox (Bridgnorth), Simeon Hodson (Mansfield), Keiron Sullivan (Released), Jon Hanson (Tamworth).

Players on loan during season:
Mark Yates (Burnley), Paul Richardson (Dag & Red), Neil Cartwright (WBA), Darren Rogers (Birmingham), Wayne Williams (Walsall).

Aggborough, Kidderminster Harriers

Address and telephone number: Aggborough Staduim, Hoo Road, Kidderminster, DY10 1NB. Tel: 0562 740 198 (Social Club). Fax: 0562 823 931 (Vice Presidents Club).

Simple directions: From North - exit M5 at junction 3, follow A456 to Kidderminster and on reaching the town at first traffic lights turn left into Chester Road. At next traffic lights turn right into Comberton Road, continue past station and Hoo Road is on the left halfway down the hill. From the South & West - exit M5 at junction 6. Follow A449 to Kidderminster. At first roundabout (Adjacent to railway viaduct) turn right into Chester Road and first left into Hoo Road. From London direction via M42 then follow M5 north to junction 4 (Lydiate Ash). Exit motorway turn left and follow A491 towards Stourbridge. At Hagley roundabout turn left and follow A456 to Kidderminster as above.

Capacity: 5,965   **Seated:** 338   **Covered terracing:** 5,000

Record Attendance: 9,155 - Hereford United - FA Cup 1st Round Proper 27.11.48.

Club Shop: Open Monday to Friday 9am-5pm plus 1st Xi match days. Phone Philip Wright on 0562 823931 for details.

Social Facilities: Vice Presidents lounge bar for members, officials & players. Social & supporters club (3 bars) open to visiting supporters before & after the match, temporary admission fee 50p. Hot & cold food available.

Kidderminster Fact File

Nickname: Harriers

Club Sponsors: Ansells

Previous Leagues: Birmingham League 1889-1890, 1891-1939, 1947-1948, 1960-1962, Midland League 1890-1891, Southern League 1939-1945 (Abandoned - World War II), 1948-1960, 1972-1983, Birmingham Combination 1945-1947, West Midlands League 1962-1972.

Club colours: Red & white

Change colours: Yellow & blue

Reserve team league: Ansells Combination Reserve League

Midweek home matchday: Mondays 7.45pm.

Record win: 25-0 v Hereford (H) - 12.10.1889 - Birmingham Senior Cup 1st Rnd.

Record defeat: 0-13 v Darwen (A) - 24.01.1891 - FA Cup 1st Rnd Proper.

Record transfer fee: £20,000 for Chris Brindley from Telford - 1992

Record transfer fee received: £60,000 each for Paul Jones from Wolves - 1991 & Steve Lilwall from W.B.A - 1992.

1992/93 Captain: John McGrath

1992/93 Top scorer: Paul Davies

1992/93 Player of the Year: Chris Brindley

Club record goalscorer: Peter Wassall 432 - 1963-1974

Record appearances: Brendan Wassall 686 - 1962-1974

Past players who progressed to the Football League: To numerous to list.

Club Honours: FA Trophy Winners 1987, Runners-up 1991; Welsh FA Cup finalists 1986, 1989; Southern League Cup 1980; Worcester Senior Cup (19); Birmingham Senior Cup (7); Staffordshire Senior Cup (4); West Midland League Champions (6), Runners-up (3); Southern Premier Runners-up (1); West Midland League Cup winners (7); Keys Cup winners (7); Border Counties Floodlit League Champions (3), Camkin Floodlit Cup Winners (3); Bass County Vase Winners (1).

MACCLESFIELD TOWN

Formed:
1874

Chairman:
A.Brocklehurst
Vice Chairman
A.Jones
Football Secretary:
C.Garlick

Directors:
R.Isherwood
R.Higginbotham
J.Brooks
N.Bardsley
A.Masheder
B.Lingard
R.Curran
A.Cash

Manager:
Sammy McIlroy
Assistant Manager:
Gil Prescot

Physiotherapist:
Eric Campbell

Commercial Manager:
D.Johnson

Press Officer:
A.Jones

Macclesfield's season started off well when they entertained Wycombe Wanderes in the first game of the season. Wycombe, who were to later justify their pre-season favourites label, were very lucky to leave the Moss Rose with a point. Macclesfield progressed to the semi-finals of the Drinkwise Cup with victories over Altrincham, Witton Albion and Kidderminster Harriers. In the semi-final they bowed out to Northwich Victoria, who went on to beat Wycombe Wanderers in the final. Witton Albion gained revenge for their Drinkwise defeat knocking Macclesfield out of the F.A. Trophy after three attempts.

Warrington Town put pay to any hopes Macclesfield had of retaining the Cheshire Senior Cup. Some Cup sucess was achieved last season in the FA Cup. In total they played nine games before falling to Stockport County in the second round. In the previous round Macclesfield had knocked out league opposition in the shape of Chesterfield.

From early February Macclesfield could not be sure that they would not be one of the two sides that would be relegated from the GM Vauxhall Conference. Wins were what was needed to lift them from the relegation zone. Unfortunately they could only manage 12 draws from their last 16 games prior to their two final games of the season. Despite beating Witton Albion 1-0 in their last home fixture they still had to travel to champions Wycombe needing a win or a draw whilst hoping results elsewhere went in their favour. Roy Green provided Macclesfield with the only goal of the game and the much needed victory. Macclesfield's Conference future now depended on other results and it was neighbours and arch rivals Altrincham that helped the Silkmen, their 5-2 win at Farnborough meaning it was Farnborough Town who joined Boston United at the bottom.

Macclesfield's Mike Doherty heads the ball towards goal despite the challenge of Northwich Victoria's defender Chris Blundell. Photo: Paul Dennis.

MACCLESFIELD *MATCHFACTS* 92-93 **MACCLESFIELD** *MATCHFACTS* 92-93 **MACCLESFIELD** *MATCHFACTS* 92-93

Key: Home fixtures are denoted by bold capitals. Numbers in brackets after players names indicate goals scored (an asterisk by the results denotes own goals). Only used substitutes are listed - substituted players are *italicised*.

Key to Competitions: GMVC: G.M. Vauxhall Conference. **DC:** Drinkwise (G.M. Vauxhall Conference) Cup. **FAC:** F.A. Cup. **FAT:** Vauxhall F.A. Trophy.

FA CUP: Second Round
FA TROPHY: First Round

LEAGUE POSITION: 18th

Date	Opponents	Comp.	Res	Gate	1.	2.	3.	4.	5.	6.	7.	8.	9.	10.	11.	Sub.	Sub.
22/08	WYCOMBE W.	GMVC	1-1	1,397	S.Farrelly	Shepherd	Johnson	Edwards	O'Neil	Savel	Timmons	Lambert(1)	Doherty	Carberry	Leicester		Green	Kendall
25/08	Runcorn	GMVC	2-1	757	S.Farrelly	Shepherd	Carberry	Edwards	O'Neil	Savel	Askey	M.Fa'elly(1)	Lambert(1)	Mitchell	Leicester	Green	Mitchell	Farrelly
29/08	Kettering T.	GMVC	0-1	1,029	S.Farrelly	Shepherd	Johnson	Edwards	O'Neil	Dempsey	Leicester	Savel	Lambert	Timmons	Carberry	Sorvel	Sorvel	
31/08	NORTHWICH VIC.	GMVC	1-2	1,068	S.Farrelly	Shepherd	Johnson	Farrelly	O'Neil	Dempsey	Timmons	Green(1)	Lambert	Doherty	Carberry	Johnson	Carberry	Mitchell
05/09	BATH CITY	GMVC	1-0	651	S.Farrelly	Shepherd	Johnson	Farrelly	Farrelly	Dempsey	Askey	Sorvel(1)	Lambert	Timmons	Leicester	Carberry	Carberry	Mitchell
12/09	Glossop	FAC	*1-0	805	S.Farrelly	Shepherd	Johnson	Kendall	O'Neill	Dempsey	Askey	Carberry	Lambert	Doherty	Leicester	Doherty	Doherty	Mitchell
15/09	Bromsgrove R.	GMVC	0-3	1,067	S.Farrelly	Shepherd	Carberry	Edwards	Farrelly	Dempsey	Askey	Sorvel	Lambert(1)	Doherty	Leicester	Kendall	Kendall	Mitchell
19/09	FARNBOROUGH	GMVC	1-2	574	S.Farrelly	Bimson	Johnson	Edwards	Farrelly	M.Farrelly	Askey	Timmons	Lambert(1)	Doherty	Leicester	Dempsey	Dempsey	Mitchell
26/09	Hucknall Town	FAC	1-1	1,305	S.Farrelly	M.Farrelly	Bimson	Edwards	Carberry	Dempsey	Askey(1)	Timmons	Lambert	Doherty	Leicester	Johnson	Dempsey	Mit'el(1)
29/09	HUCKNALL TOWN	FAC	3-1	635	S.Farrelly	M.Farrelly	Bimson	Edwards	Kendall	Bimson	Askey(1)	Timmons(1)	Lambert	Doherty	Leicester	Sorvel	Johnson	Mitchell
03/10	Merthyr Tyd.	GMVC	2-1	554	S.Farrelly	Farrley	Johnson	Edwards	Kendall	M.Farrelly	Askey	Timmons	Lambert(1)	Doherty	Leics'(1)	Johnson	Dempsey	Mitchell
10/10	HORWICH RMI	FAC	1-0	789	S.Farrelly	Shepherd	Bimson	Edwards	Kendall	M.Farrelly	Askey	Dempsey	Lambert(1)	Doherty	Leicester	Johnson	Johnson	Kendall
13/10	Northwich Vic.	GMVC	3-1	785	S.Farrelly	Shepherd	Bimson	Edwards	Farrelly	Sorvel	Askey	Timmons	Lambert(1)	Mitchell(1)	Leics'(1)	Dempsey	Dempsey	Kendall
17/10	Dagenham & R	GMVC	2-1	1,303	S.Farrelly	Farrelly	Bimson	Edwards	Kendall	Sorvel(1)	Askey	Timmons(1)	Lambert	Mitchell(1)	Leicester	Johnson	Johnson	
24/10	Netherfield	FAC	1-1	918	S.Farrelly	Shepherd	Bimson	Edwards	Kendall	McMahon	Doherty	Timmons	Lambert	Mitchell	Leicester	Dempsey	Dempsey	
31/10	KETTERING T	GMVC	1-0	731	S.Farrelly	Shepherd	Bimson	Edwards	Kendall	Sorvel	Askey(1)	Timmons	Mitchell	McMahon	Leics'(1)	Doherty	Doherty	
02/11	NETHERFIELD	FAC	5-0	903	S.Farrelly	Sheph'd(1)	Bimson	Edwards	Kendall(1)	Sorvel	Askey	Timmons	Mitchell(1)	McMan'(1)	Leics(1)			
07/11	Telford United	GMVC	1-3	1,175	S.Farrelly	Shepherd	Bimson	Edwards	Kendall	Sorvel	Askey	Timmons	Lambert	Mitchell(1)	Leicester	McMahon	McMahon	
14/11	CHESTERFIELD	FAC	0-0	3,063	S.Farrelly	Shepherd	Bimson	Edwards	Kendall	Sorvel	Askey	Timmons	Lambert	Mitchell	Leicester			
17/11	STAFFORD RGRS	GMVC	4-1	473	S.Farrelly	Shepherd	Bimson	Edwards	Kendall	Sorvel	Askey	Timmons(1)	Lambert	Leicester	Mitchell(2)	McMahon	Blain(1)	McMan'
21/11	SLOUGH TOWN	GMVC	1-2	651	S.Farrelly	Shepherd	Bimson	Edwards	Kendall	McMahon	Blain	Timmons	Lambert	Mitchell(1)	Leicester	Sorvel	Farrelley	Sorvel
25/11	Chesterfield	FAC	2-2	4,143	S.Farrelly	Shepherd	Bimson	Edwards	Kendall	McMahon	Askey	Timmons	Lambert	Mitchell(2)	Leicester	Farrelly	Farrelly	Doherty
28/11	Welling Utd	GMVC	0-0	959	S.Farrelly	Shepherd	Bimson	Edwards	Kendall	McMahon	Askey	Timmons	Lambert	Mitchell	Leicester	Farrelly	Farrelly	
09/12	Boston United	GMVC	1-3	818	Sutton	Shepherd	Johnson	Farelly	Kendall	McMahon	Askey	Timmons	Lambert(1)	Leicester	Mitchell	Sorvel	Sorvel	Sorvel
12/12	Slough Town	GMVC	*1-2	930	S.Farrelly	Shepperd	Bimson	Edwards	Kendall	Farrelly	Askey	Sorvel	Lambert	Timmons	Mitchell	Doherty	Blain	Doherty
19/12	Gateshead	GMVC	0-1	375	S.Farrelly	Shepherd	Kendall	Kendall	McMahon	Johnson	Askey	Mitchell	Timmons	Blain	Leicester	Doherty	Sorvel	Doherty

League 1992–93 match-by-match appearances

Date	Opponent	Comp	Res	Att	1	2	3	4	5	6	7	8	9	10	11	Subs
02/01	Witton Alb.	GMVC	1-1	1,110	S.Farrelly	Shepherd	Bimson	Edwards	Kendall	McMahon	Askey	Timmons	Mitchell(1)	Blain	Leicester	Doherty, Dempsey
09/01	WITTON ALB.	FAT	0-0	890	S.Farrelly	Shepherd	Bimson	Edwards	Kendall	McMahon	Askey	Dempsey	Timmons	Mitchell	Leicester	Lambert, Pickering
12/01	Witton Albion	FAT	0-0	901	S.Farrelly	Shepherd	Bimson	Edwards	Sorvel	Timmons	Askey	McMahon	Doherty	Blain	Demsey	Mitchell, Dempsey
16/01	MERTHYR TYD.	GMVC	0-1	459	S.Farrelly	Shepherd	Bimson	Edwards	Kendall	McMahon	Blain	Sorvel	Mitchell	Timmons	Leicester	McMahon, Leicester
18/01	Witton Alb.	FAT	1-2	907	S.Farrelly	McMahon	Bimson	Edwards	Kendall	Sorvel	Doherty	Timmons(1)	Lambert	Mitchell	Leicester	Mitchell, McMah'
23/01	YEOVIL TOWN	GMVC	1-1	431	S.Farrelly	Shepherd	Bimson	Edwards	Sorvel	Sorvel	Askey	Timmons	Mitchell	Doherty	Dempsey	Doherty, Blain
30/01	Kidderminster	GMVC	1-2	1,032	S.Farrelly	Shepherd	Bimson	Edwards	Kendall	McMahon	Leicester	Timmons	Doherty	Doherty	Dempsey	McMahon
06/02	Stafford Rgrs	GMVC	0-1	1,025	S.Farrelly	Shepherd	Bimson	Edwards	Kendall	Sorvel	Blain	Timmons	Lambert	Doherty	Dempsey	Blain
09/02	BOSTON UTD	GMVC	2-1	421	S.Farrelly	Shepherd	Bimson	Edwards	Kendall	Sorvel	Blain(1)	Mitchell	Lambert(1)	Doherty	Dempsey	Mitchell
13/02	TELFORD UTD	GMVC	1-1	476	S.Farrelly	Shepherd	Bimson	Edwards	Kendall	Sorvel	Leicester	Sorvel	Lambert	Doherty	Dempsey	Hardman, Hardman
20/02	Woking	GMVC	0-4	1,868	S.Farrelly	Halliday	Johnson	Edwards	Kendall	Sorvel	Leicester	Mulligan	Lambert	Timmons	Hardman	Leicester, Mitchell
27/02	WELLING UTD	GMVC	1-1	437	S.Farrelly	Shepherd	Johnson	Edwards	Kendall	Hardman	Leicester	Bunter	Lambert(1)	Timmons	McMahon	Leicester, Leicester
06/03	Bath City	GMVC	0-0	478	S.Farrelly	Shepherd	Bimson	Edwards	Kendall	Sorvel	Sorvel	Timmons	Lambert	Green	Blain	Halliday
13/03	ALTRINCHAM	GMVC	1-1	875	S.Farrelly	McMahon	Bimson	Edwards	Kendall	Hardman	Askey(1)	Timmons	Lambert	Green	McMahon	Blain
16/03	DAGENHAM & R.	GMVC	1-1	387	S.Farrelly	Shepherd	Bimson	Edwards	Kendall	Hardman	Askey(1)	Sorvel	Lambert	Green	McMahon	Doherty
20/03	Stalybridge	GMVC	1-2	822	S.Farrelly	Shepherd	Bimson	Edwards	Kendall	Leicester	Askey(1)	Sorvel	Timmons	Green	Blain	Mitchell
23/03	GATESHEAD	GMVC	0-1	473	S.Farrelly	Shepherd	Bimson	Edwards	Kendall	Leicester	Askey	Sorvel	Timmons	Green	McMahon	Blain(1)
27/03	WOKING	GMVC	1-1	879	S.Farrelly	Shepherd	Bimson	Edwards	Kendall	Leicester	Askey(1)	Sorvel(1)	Timmons	Blain	McMahon	Mitchell
30/03	KIDDERMINSTER	GMVC	1-1	593	S.Farrelly	Shepherd	Bimson	Edwards	Kendall	Johnson	Askey	Sorvel	Timmons	Doherty	Leicester	Hardman
03/04	Yeovil Town	GMVC	1-1	2,515	S.Farrelly	Shepherd	Bimson	Edwards	Kendall	Sorvel	Johnson	Sorvel	Timmons	McMahon	Leicester	Green
10/04	STALYBRIDGE	GMVC	1-0	844	S.Farrelly	Shepherd	Bimson	Edwards	Kendall	Sorvel	Blain(1)	Timmons	Askey	Doherty	Leicester	Hardman
12/04	Altrincham	GMVC	0-1	1,143	S.Farrelly	Shepherd	Bimson	Edwards	Kendall	Hardman	Blain	Timmons	Askey	Doherty	McMahon	Mitchell
17/04	BROMSGROVE	GMVC	0-2	604	S.Farrelly	Shepherd	Bimson	Edwards	Kendall	Sorvel	Blain	Sorvel	Timmons	Timmons	Leicester	Leicester
20/04	RUNCORN	GMVC	1-1	631	S.Farrelly	Shepherd	Bimson	Edwards	Kendall	McMahon	Askey	McMahon	Green	Timmons(1)	Green	Mitchell
24/04	Farnborough	GMVC	0-0	676	S.Farrelly	Shepherd	Bimson	Edwards	Kendall	Sorvel	Askey(1)	Timmons	Timmons(1)	Green	Green	
27/04	WITTON ALBION	GMVC	1-0	762	S.Farrelly	Shepherd	Bimson	Edwards	Kendall	Sorvel	Askey	Timmons	McMahon	Leicester	Leicester	
01/05	Wycombe W.	GMVC	1-0	5,748	S.Farrelly	Shepherd	Bimson	Edwards	Kendall	Sorvel	Askey	Timmons	McMahon	Leicester	Green(1)	

League Appearances: Askey 31: Bimson 32: Blain 12(9): Bunter 1: Carberry 4(1): Dempsey 4(1): Doherty 10(9): Edwards 39: Farrelly 9(3): S.Farrelly 41: Green 5(2): Roy Green 5: Halliday 1(1): Hardman 5(7): Johnson 12(3): Kendall 33(4): Lambert 24(1): Leicester 32(4): McMahon 21(5): Mitchell 16(13): Mulligan 1: O'Neill 4: Pickering 0(1): Roberts 0(1): Shepherd 39: Sorvel 35(5): Sutton 1: Timmons 40.

League Goals: Lambert, Mitchell, Askey 7: Blain, Sorvel, Timmons 3: Green, Leicester 2: Dempsey, Farelly 1.

Macclesfield Town

SAMMY McILROY

The last of the 'Busby Babes', Sammy followed in the footsteps of the legendary George Best when he moved from his native Belfast to join Manchester United as a raw teenager in the late sixties. He became an established member of the highly successful and exciting United side built by Tommy Docherty. In all he made 418 appearances for United, the highlight being the 1978 FA Cup Final success over Liverpool.

In 1982 he moved to Stoke City where he played 144 times before heading back to Manchester to join United's deadly rivals, City. His time at Maine Road was curtailed when he accepted an offer to join Bury, then managed by Martin Dobson, whom he was to succeed at Northwich Victoria. He then took up a post as player-coach with Preston, but a severe knee injury virtually ended his playing days.

In July 1991, he was appointed as manager at Northwich Victoria. Coming into the job cold with virtually no experience of the non-league scene, everyone at the club was delighted with his own, and his team's performance. Happily his own injuries recovered sufficiently for him to make a welcome, and most effective comeback as a player with the Vics towards the end of the season. The experience of playing in a green shirt again no doubt brought back memories of his 78 appearance in an emerald shirt for his country, Northern Ireland.

Sammy left Northwich Victoria in 1992 and became manager of Ashton United for short spell before joining Macclesfield Town for the start of the 1993/94 season.

A fine save from Northwich Victoria's Tony Bullock is enough to keep Macclesfield out this time. Photo: Paul Dennis.

Programme details:
    36 pages for £1
    Editor - Dennis Johnson. (Asst.Editor: Joanne Foy)

Any other club publications:
    Silk Yarns (Fanzine)

Local Newspapers:
    Macclesfield Express
    Manchester Evening News
    Manchester Evening News Pink
    Local Radio Stations:
    GMR (BBC)
    BBC Radio Stoke
    Piccadilly Radio
    Signal Radio

MACCLESFIELD TOWN - PLAYING SQUAD 1992-93

Player	Honours	Birthplace and date	Transfer Fees	Previous Clubs
GOALKEEPERS				
Steve Farrelly	CSC	Manchester		Chester City, Knowsley Utd
DEFENDERS				
George Shepherd	CSC, LYC	Manchester	£6,000	Man City, Bolton W, Preston NE, Hyde Utd
Graham Roberts				British Steel FC, Mold Alexandra, Flint Town, Colwyn Bay
Mike Farrelly	ESP, ES, FAT	Manchester 1/11/62		Preston NE, Altrincham
Stuart Bimson	NPLC, LSC CSC	Liverpool 29/9/69	£5,000	Prescot, Ellesmere Port, Southport
Paul Kendal	GMVC	Halifax 19/10/64		Halifax, Scarborough
MIDFIELD				
Colin Blain	SSC, MSC	Davyhulme 7/3/70		Curzon Ashton, Halifax, Northwich Victoria, Hyde Utd
John Timmons	NPLC, CSC, FA XI	Manchester 11/7/60	£6,000	Hyde Utd, Altrincham
Mark Dempsey		Manchester 14/1/64		Man Utd, Sheffield Utd, Rotherham Utd
John McMahon		Liverpool 19/5/64		Everton, Southport, Sth Liverpool, Altrincham, Witton Alb, Runcorn, Altrincham, Morecambe
John Askey	ESP, FA XI, Middx W	Stoke 4/11/64		Port Vale, Milton Utd
FORWARDS				
Chris Sharratt		West Kirby 13/8/70		Caernarfon T, Stalybridge Celtic, Wigan Athletic
Stuart Leicester	NPL	Altrincham 11/8/66		Irlam Town, Stalybridge Celtic
Roy Green		Birmingham		Aston V, Lye T, Oldbury U, Dudley, Tamworth, Atherstone U, Telford U
Richard Mitchell		Stoke 14/9/73		Port Vale

Departures during season:
Paul Clayton (Stafford), Andy Green (Morecambe), Jim Carberry (Released), John O'Neil (Hyde), Paul Johnson (Leek), Mick Doherty (Marine), Colin Lambert & Elfyn Edwards (Halifax).

Players on loan during season:
Stewart Sutton (Stoke), Neil Sorvel (Crewe), Damian Horsefield (Blackpool).

Moss Rose, Macclesfield

Address and telephone number: Moss Rose, London Road, Macclesfield, Cheshire SK11 7SP. Tel: 0625 511545 (Commercial Office). 0625 424324 (Social Club). 0891 12 15 46 (Club Call).
Simple directions: Approximately 1 mile south of the Town Centre on the A523 (Leek Road). British Rail Macclesfield approximately 1.5 miles, regular bus service on Match day. Ample unrestricted parking around the ground.
Capacity: 6,000   **Seated:** 600   **Covered terracing:** 2,500
Record Attendance: 9,003 v Winsford United - Cheshire Senior Cup 2nd Round 04.02.48.
Club Shop: Open Monday - Friday 10.00 to 4.00 and on match days. Contact Andy Ridgway on 0625 423099 for more details.
Social Facilities: The Blues Club - open match days and functions.
Previous Grounds: None

Macclesfield Fact File

Nickname: Silkmen

Club Sponsors: Zeneca Pharmaceutical

Previous Leagues: Manchester League, Cheshire League, Northern Premier League.

Club colours: Blue & white

Change colours: All yellow

Reserve team league: North West Alliance League

Midweek home matchday: Tuesday

Record win: 15-0 v Chester St.Marys - Cheshire Senior Cup 2nd Round 16.02.1886.

Record defeat: 13-1 v Tranmere Rovers Reserves 03.05.1929.

Record transfer fee: £7,000 to Binche for Andy Green - 1991.

Record transfer fee received: £40,000 for Mike Lake from Sheffield United - 1988.

1992/93 Captain: Elfyn Edwards.

1992/93 Top scorer: Richie Mitchell.

1992/93 Player of the Year: John Timmons.

Club record goalscorer: Albert Valentine 84 - 1933-34.

Record appearances: Keith Goalen - 1957-1970.

Past players who progressed to the Football League: Numerous.

Club Honours: FA Trophy Winners 1970, Runners-up 1989, 1986; NPL Challenge Cup 1986; Presidents Cup 1986; Cheshire Senior Cup 1890, 1891, 1894, 1896, 1911, 1930, 1935, 1951, 1952, 1954, 1960, 1964, 1969, 1971, 1973, 1983; Cheshire County League 1932, 1933, 1953, 1961, 1964, 1968.

MERTHYR TYDFIL

Formed:
1945

Joint President:
The Archbishop of
Cardiff
His Grace John
Aloysious Ward
The Lord Bishop of
Llandaff
The Right Rev. Roy
Davies

Chairman:
John Reddy

Football Secretary:
Peter Hunt

Manager:
Wynford Hopkins

Assistant Manager:
Tommy Hutchison

Physiotherapist:
Ken Davey

Commercial Manager:
Ken Massey

Press Officer:
Anthony Hughes

Home Advantage - Who Needs it!

A 4-1 win over a full strength Brentford side at Penydarren Park in late July suggested that at home at least, the Martyrs would be a tough nut to crack!

We couldn't have been more wrong!

It took until January 2nd 1993 for Merthyr to record their first Conference victory at Penydarren Park and that after Kidderminster led by three goals to nil at half-time! In stark contrast by that time, out of nine away Conference encounters, the Martyrs had won six, drawn two and lost only once.

That in itself was quite fortunate really because had it not been for the quite outstanding away record, relegation would have been a certainty - not a possibility.

However, once that first home win had been achieved surely the bogy would be laid to rest? Not for one minute as Merthyr, at the end of the campaign, managed home wins over only Kidderminster, Kettering, Northwich Victoria and Telford United. As it turned out ten away victories just about secured Conference survival.

In the cup campaigns things took on something more like normality with Merthyr unbeaten at home in all competitions. The annual encounter against Swansea City in the Allbright Bitter Welsh Cup lived up to expectations (the two clubs have been drawn together for the last six seasons!) with the Martyrs running out 2-0 winners at a time when the Swans sat on top of Division Two! In the end it was the Wrexham team, who would later earn promotion to Division Two, who knocked out Merthyr in the quarter-finals - but by the only goal and after an excellent performance from the Martyrs. There were good performances in the Drinkwise Cup, FA Cup and FA Trophy also, although the manner in which they made their exit varied. Wycombe in the FA Cup brought no reward and a defeat by Northern Premier League side Warrington brought their FA Trophy campaign to a disappointing end.

Although Merthyr start 1993/94 full of hope and as a GM Vauxhall Conference member, the threat of the Konica League still hangs over the club and one feels that the team will never really perform consistently to their full capabilities whilst the uncertainty remains.

Anthony Hughes

Merthyr's David D'Auria fires a shot at goal, with Woking's Shane Wye (6) and Tim Alexander (4), trying to close-in at Kingfield. Photo: Dave West.

MERTHYR MATCHFACTS 92-93

Key: Home fixtures are denoted by bold capitals. Numbers in brackets after players names indicate goals scored (an asterisk by the results denotes own goals). Only used substitutes are listed - substituted players are *italicised*.

Key to Competitions: **GMVC:** G.M. Vauxhall Conference. **WC:** Allbright Bitter Welsh Cup. **SWSC:** South Wales Senior Cup. **DC:** Drinkwise (G.M. Vauxhall Conference) Cup. **FAC:** F.A. Cup. **FAT:** Vauxhall F.A. Trophy. **Fr.:** Friendly.

Date	Opponents	Comp.	Res	Gate	1.	2.	3.	4.	5.	6.	7.	8.	9.	10.	11.	Sub.	Sub.
22/08	**DAGENHAM & R.**	GMVC	0-2	746	Wager	M Williams	James	Boyle	Trick	Rogers	C Williams	Webley	D'Auria	Tucker	Coates	Gill	
25/08	Yeovil Town	GMVC	*1-0	1,834	Wager	M Williams	James	Boyle	Trick	Rogers	Beattie	Coates	D'Auria	C Williams	Tucker	Gill	
29/08	Altrincham	GMVC	1-0	729	Wager	M Williams	James	Boyle	Trick	Rogers	Beattie(1)	Coates	D'Auria	C Williams	Tucker	Gill	
31/08	**BATH CITY**	GMVC	1-1	808	Wager	M Williams	James	Boyle	Trick	Rogers	Beattie	Coates	D'Auria	C Williams	Tucker(1)	Gill	
5/09	**STAFFORD RGRS**	GMVC	0-0	694	Wager	M Williams	James	Boyle	Trick	Rogers	Coates	Beattie	D'Auria	Tucker	C Williams		
8/09	Bath City	GMVC	3-1	615	Wager	M Williams	James	Boyle	Trick	Rogers	Coates(1)	Beattie	D'Auria	Tucker(1)	C Will.(1)		Chiverton
12/09	**WYCOMBE WDRS**	GMVC	1-4	1,403	Wager	M Williams	James	Boyle	Trick	Rogers	Coates	Beattie	D'Auria	Gill	C Will.(1)	Webley	Davies
19/09	Stalybridge Celtic	GMVC	2-2	817	Wager	M Williams	James	Boyle	Trick	Rogers	Beattie	Coates(1)	D'Auria	Tucker	C Will.(1)	Webley	Webley
26/09	**WELLING UTD**	GMVC	1-1	655	Wager	M Williams	James	Boyle	Trick	Rogers	Beattie	Coates	D'Auria	Tucker	C Will.(1)	Webley	Davies
3/10	**MACCLESFIELD**	GMVC	1-2	554	Wager	M Williams	James	Boyle	Trick	Rogers	Beattie	Coates	D'Auria	Webley(1)	C Williams		Tucker
6/10	Farnborough Town	GMVC	1-2	602	Wager	M Williams	James	Boyle	Trick	Rogers	Beattie	Coates	D'Auria	Webley(1)	C Williams		
10/10	Cwmbran Town	WC	1-0		Morris	Davies	James	Boyle	Trick	Rogers	Beattie	Coates	D'Auria	Webley	C Will.(1)		Tucker
17/10	Kettering Town	GMVC	3-1	1,354	Morris	M Will.(1)	James	Boyle	Trick	Rogers	Beattie	Tucker	D'Auria	Webley(2)	C Williams		Davies
18/10	A.F.C. Porth	SWSC	0-1		Morris	Twooze	Hopkins	Needs	Hegarty	Coates	Roger L.	Gill	Puckett	Hutchison	Brooker	Thomas	
20/10	**FARNBOROUGH**	DC	4-2	404	Morris	M Williams	James	Boyle	Davies	Rogers	Beattie	Tucker	D'Auria(1)	Webley(1)	C Will.(2)	Coates	
24/10	Abingdon Town	FAC	0-0	800	Morris	M Williams	James	Boyle	Davies	Rogers	Beattie	Tucker	D'Auria	Webley	C Williams		Coates
27/10	**SWANSEA CITY**	WC	2-0	2,516	Morris	M Williams	James	Boyle	Davies	Rogers	Beattie	Tucker	D'Auria	Webley(1)	C Will.(1)		
29/10	**ABINGDON TOWN**	FAC	2-1	868	Morris	M Williams	James	Boyle	Davies	Rogers(1)	Beattie	Tucker	D'Auria	Webley(1)	C Williams		
31/10	Northwich Vict.	GMVC	2-1	583	Morris	M Williams	James	Boyle	Davies	Rogers	Beattie	Tucker(1)	D'Auria	Webley	C Williams	Coates(1)	
7/11	**BOSTON UNITED**	GMVC	0-3	606	Morris	M Williams	James	Boyle	Davies	Rogers	Beattie	Tucker	D'Auria	Webley	C Williams		
13/11	Wycombe Wdrs	FAC	1-3	4,322	Morris	M Williams	James	Boyle	Davies	Rogers(1)	Beattie	Davies	D'Auria	Coates	C Williams	Coates	
15/11	**CELTIC**	Fr.	1-1		Morris	M Will.(1)	James	Trick	Abrahams	Rogers(1)	Beattie	Davies	D'Auria	Coates	C Williams	Boyle	
21/11	Welling United	GMVC	0-5	760	Morris	M Williams	James	Boyle	Abrahams	Rogers	Tucker	Davies	D'Auria	Coates	C Williams	Boyle	
24/11	**WOKING**	GMVC	1-5	380	Morris	M Will.(1)	James	Trick	Abrahams	Rogers	Beattie	Davies	D'Auria	Coates(1)	Tucker	C Williams	Hutchison
28/11	Bromsgrove Rovers	GMVC	2-1	1,306	Wager	M Williams	James	Boyle	Abrahams	Rogers	Tucker	Tucker	D'Auria	Hutchison	C Will.(1)	Trick	Beattie
12/12	**BANGOR CITY**	WC	3-2	825	Wager	Trick	James	Boyle	Abrahams	Rogers	Tucker	Coates(3)	D'Auria	Hutchison	C Williams	Webley	Beattie
15/12	Dagenham & R.	DC	2-4	525	Wager	Trick	James	Boyle	Abrahams	Rogers(1)	Tucker	Coates(1)	D'Auria	Hutchison	C Williams	Webley	Beattie

Date	Opponent	Comp	Score	Att													
19/12	Wycombe Wdrs	GMVC	0-4	3,716	Wager	Trick	James	Boyle	Abrahams	Rogers	Tucker	Coates	D'Auria	Hutchison	C Williams	Webley	Beattie
26/12	Slough Town	GMVC	1-2	1,325	Wager	Trick	James	M Williams	Abrahams	Rogers	Tucker	Coates	D'Auria	Hutchison	C Will.(1)	Webley	Beattie
2/01	**KIDDERMINSTER**	GMVC	4-3	657	Wager	Wager	M Williams	James	Abrahams	Rogers	Tucker(2)	Coates	D'Auria(1)	Webley	C Will.(1)		
9/01	**WIVENHOE TOWN**	FAT	3-0	633	Wager	Wager	M Williams	James	Abrahams	Rogers	Tucker(1)	Coates	D'Auria(1)	Webley	C Williams	Hutchison	
16/01	Macclesfield T.	FAT	1-0	419	Wager	Wager	M Williams	James	Abrahams	Rogers	Tucker	Coates	D'Auria	Webley(1)	C Williams	Hutchison	Beattie
23/01	**WITTON ALBION**	GMVC	0-2	592	Wager	Wager	M Williams	Davies	Abrahams	Rogers	Tucker	Coates	D'Auria	Hutchison	C Williams	Beattie	Needs
30/01	Stalybridge C.	FAT	1-1	818	Wager	Wager	M Williams	James	*Trick*	Davies	Tucker	Coates	D'Auria	C Will.(1)	Needs		
2/02	**STALYBRIDGE**	FAT	1-0	704	Wager	Wager	M Williams	James	Davies	Rogers	Tucker	Coates(1)	D'Auria	C Williams	*Needs*		
6/02	Wrexham	WC	0-1	3,174	Wager	Wager	M Williams	James	Davies	Rogers	Tucker	Coates	D'Auria	C Williams	*Trick*	Gill	
13/02	Gateshead	GMVC	1-1	537	Wager	Wager	M Williams	James	Davies	Needs	Tucker	Coates	D'Auria	C Williams	*Gill*	Hutchison	
16/02	**BROMSGROVE R.**	GMVC	1-1	546	Wager	Wager	M.Williams	James	Boyle(1)	Needs(1)	Tucker	Coates	Hotham	*C.Williams*	Hutchison	Gill	
20/02	**WARRINGTON T.**	FAT	1-1	556	Wager	Wager	M Williams	James	Boyle	Needs	Tucker	Coates	Needs	*Will.(1)*	Hutchison		
24/02	Warrington Town	FAT	2-3	1,447	Wager	Wager	M.Will.(1)	James	Boyle	Needs(1)	Tucker	*Coates*	*D'Aur*	*C.Williams*	Cole	Hutchison	
27/02	Woking	GMVC	2-0	2,049	Wager	Wager	M Williams	James	Boyle	Davies	Tucker	Coates(1)	D'Auria	C Will.(1)	Hotham	Rogers	
03/03	Stafford Rangers	GMVC	1-0	618	Wagers	Wager	M Williams	James	Boyle	Davies	Tucker	*Hutchison*	D'Auria	C Will.(1)	Hotham	Rogers	Needs
06/03	Witton Alb.	GMVC	1-3	614	Harris	Wager	M Williams	James	Boyle	Davies	Tucker	Benbow(1)	D'Auria	*Williams*	Hotham	Rogers	
09/03	**KETTERING**	GMVC	2-1	486	Harris	Wager	M Williams	James	Boyle	Davies	*Tucker*	Benbow(1)	D'Auria	C Will.(1)	Hotham	Coates	
13/03	**NORTHWICH**	GMVC	3-0	609	Harris	Wager	M Williams	James	Boyle	Davies	Tucker(1)	Benbow	D'Auria(1)	C Will.(1)	*Hotham*	Coates	
16/03	**STALYBRIDGE**	GMVC	1-1	628	Harris	Wager	M Williams	James	Boyle	Davies	Tucker	Benbow	D'Auria	C Will.(1)	*Hotham*	Coates	
20/03	Runcorn	GMVC	3-2	483	Harris	Hotham	M Williams	James	Boyle	Davies	Tucker(1)	*Benbow(1)*	D'Auria	C Williams	Coates(1)	Rogers	
27/03	Kidderminster	GMVC	0-1	1,158	Harris	*Hotham*	M Williams	James	Boyle	Davies	Tucker	Coates	D'Auria	C Williams	Coates	Rogers	
30/03	**ALTRINCHAM**	GMVC	2-2	458	Harris	*Hotham*	M Williams	James	Boyle	Davies	Tucker(1)	Coates	Rogers	C Will.(1)	Benbow		
06/04	Dagenham & R.	GMVC	1-6	805	Wager	M Williams	James	Boyle	*Cole*	Rogers	*Tucker*	Coates	Benbow(1)	C Williams	Davies	Holtham	
10/04	**SLOUGH TOWN**	GMVC	1-1	589	Wager	M Williams	James	Boyle	Trick	Davies	*Tucker*	Benbow	D'Auria	C Williams	Rogers(1)	Coates	
12/04	Telfrod Utd	GMVC	0-5	703	Wager	M Williams	James	Boyle	Cole	Davies	Rogers	Benbow	D'Auria	C Williams	Coates		
14/04	**FARNBOROUGH**	GMVC	1-3	402	Wager	M Williams	James	Boyle	*Cole*	Davies	Tucker	Rogers	D'Auria	C Williams	Benbow	Coates(1)	
17/04	Gateshead	GMVC	0-4	343	Wager	M Williams	James	Boyle	Trick	Davies	Tucker	Coates	D'Auria	C.Will.(1)	Rogers		
20/04	**YEOVIL TOWN**	GMVC	1-1	461	Wager	M Williams	*James*	Boyle	Trick	Davies	Tucker	Benbow	D'Auria	Cole	Rogers	C.Williams	
24/04	**RUNCORN**	GMVC	0-3	451	Wager	M Williams	James	Boyle	Trick	Davies	Tucker	Benbow	D'Auria	Coates	Rogers		
27/04	**TELFORD UTD**	GMVC	4-0	380	Wager	M Will.(1)	Davies	Boyle	Trick	Rogers(1)	Holtham	Hutchison	D'Auria	C Will.(1)	Coates(1)		
01/05	Boston Utd	GMVC	0-2	734	Wager	M Williams	Davies	Boyle	Trick	Rogers	Holtham	*Benbow*	D'Auria	C Williams	*Hutchison*	Cole	James

LEAGUE APPEARANCS: Abrahams 7, Beattie 15(4), Benbow 14, Boyle 41, Chiverton 1, Coates 31(6), Cole 11(1), D'Auria 39, Davies 34(4), Gill 2(2), Hotham 12(2), Hutchinson 6(3), James 39(1), Morris 12, Needs 4(2), Rogers 33(4), Trick 24(2), Tucker 33(3), Wager 30, Webley 14(3), C.Williams 39(1), M.Williams 35.

LEAGUE GOALSCORERS: C.Williams 15; Coates 7; Tucker, Webley 5; Benbow 4; M.Williams 3; Rogers 2; Beattie, Boyle, D'Auria 1.

Merthyr Tydfil

WYNFORD HOPKINS

Wynford Hopkins was born in Mountain Ash, Mid Glamorgan on the 18th July 1953. His first contact with Merthyr Tydfil came in the mid-seventies as a player in their Southern League days, and his playing career took him to Newport County, Gloucester City, Ton Pentre and Pontllanfraith in the Welsh League. It was at Pontllanfraith where Wynford first experienced management, enjoying a highly successful spell with the Gwent Valley club. From there he answered an S.O.S. from Merthyr manager Lyn Jones to bolster the midfield once again, shortly afterwards taking over as Jones' number two. As a partnership they enjoyed unparalleled success and therefore it seemed the natural progression for the club to make Wynford caretaker manager when Lyn Jones resigned in March 1991. After only 4 games. a 100% record and Conference survival almost assured, the offer of a permanent post came and, shortly after the end of the 1990/91 campaign, a new management team was formed with the appointment of Tommy Hutchison, the former Scottish International, as assistant manager.

Merthyr's Terry Boyle (left) and Liam Herbert of Abingdon follow the path of the ball. Photo: Francis Short.

Programme details:
        32 pages for £1.00
        Editor - Anthony Hughes (0685 359921 H)
-        (0685 874221 B)
Any other club publications:
        Dial 'M' for Merthyr (Fanzine)
        The Junior Martyr - For Junior Members
Local Newspapers:
        Merthyr Express
        Merthyr Herald and Post
        South Wales Echo
        Western Mail
Wales on Sunday
Local Radio Stations:
        Radio Wales
        Red Dragon Radio

MERTHYR TYDFIL - PLAYING SQUAD 1992-93

Player	Honours	Birthplace and date	Transfer Fees	Previous Clubs
GOALKEEPERS				
Gary Wager	WSP, BHL, WC	Bridgend 21/5/62		Bridgend Town, Folkestone,
Steve Morris				Merthyr Tydfil, Plymouth Argyle
DEFENDERS				
Mark Williams	WSP, WS, WY	Merthyr 11/8/70		Aston Villa
Terry Boyle	Wales Int., WSP, W U-21	Ammanford 29/10/58		Tootenham Hotspur, Newport Co, Crystal Palace, Cardiff C, Swansea C
Ryan James		Blackwood 3/12/71		Blackpool
David Cole		Barnsley 28/9/62		Sunderland, Swansea C, Swindon, Torquay Utd, Rochdale, Exeter C
Mark Davies		Swansea 9/8/72		Swansea City
Des Trick		Swansea 7/11/69		Swansea City
MIDFIELD				
Kevin Rogers	WSP, BHL, SWSC	Merthyr 23/9/63		Aston Villa, Birmingham C, Wrexham, Rhyl
Mark Tucker	WSP, WY, WS, SWSC	Pontypool 10/2/63		Abergavenny Thursdays
David D'Auria	WS, WY	Swansea 26/3/70		Swansea City
Matthew Holtan	WY	Swansea		Luton Town
Andrew Needs		Swansea		Swansea City, Honk Kong
Tommy Hutchison	Scottish Int, Scot U-23	Cardenden 22/9/47		Alloa Ath, Blackpool, Coventry, Man City, Burnley, Swansea C
FORWARDS				
Ian Benbow		Hereford 9/1/69	£8,000	Hereford Utd, Telford Utd
Cerri Williams	WSP, BHL, WY, SWSC	Tonyfail 16/10/65		Blaenrhondda, Newport Co
Marc Coates		Swansea		Swansea City

Departures during season:
Dave Webley (Inter Cardiff), Andy Beattie (Newport AFC).

Players on loan during season:
Gareth Abraham (Cardiff).

Penydarren Park, Merthyr Tydfil

Address and telephone number: Pennydarren Park, Merthyr Tydfil, Mid Glamorgan.
Tel: 0685 371395. Fax: 0685 382882.
Simple directions: South A470 Express Way to Merthyr Tydfil, through Town Centre to Pontmorlais (traffic lights) turn left then first right, first right at Catholic Church and right again into Park Terrace to ground. North Heads of the Valley road to Town Centre, to Pontmorlais (traffic lights) turn right, then first right again first right at Catholic Church and right again into Park Terrace to ground.
Capacity: 10,000   **Seated:** 1,500   **Covered terracing:** 5,000
Record Attendance: 21,000 v Reading - FA Cup 2nd Rnd - 1949/50
Club Shop: Sells replica kits, clubs souvenirs & programmes. Contact Mr Mel Jenkins 0443 692336.
Social Facilities: Open Monday to Sunday 6-30 to 11-00pm. Two club cafes open on match days for hot food.
Previous Grounds: None

Merthyr Fact File

Nickname: Martyrs

Club Sponsors: Hoover PLC

Previous Leagues: Southern League, Beazer Homes (Midland Division), Beazer Homes (Premier Division).

Club colours: Grey Black & white

Change colours: All red

Midweek home matchday: Tuesday

Record win: 11-0

Record defeat: 9-2

Record transfer fee:

Record transfer fee received: £12,000 for Ray Pratt from Exeter City - 1981

1992/93 Captain: Kevin Rogers

1992/93 Top scorer: Ceri Williams

1992/93 Player of the Year: Mark Williams

Club record goalscorer:

Record appearances:

Past players who progressed to the Football League: Syd Howarth (Aston Villa), Cyril Beech, Gilbert Beech, Bill Hullet, Ken Tucker (Cardiff City), Nick Deacy (Hereford United), Gordon Davies (Fulham), Ray Pratt (Exeter City), Peter Jones, Paul Giles (Newport County).

Club Honours: Welsh FA Cup Winners 1948/49, 1950/51, 1986/87; Southern League 1947/48, 1949/50, 1950/51, 1951/52, 1953/54; Southern League (Midland) Winners 1987/88; Southern League (Premier) Winners 1988/89; Southern League Cup Winners 1947/48, 1950/51.

NORTHWICH VICTORIA

ONE HUNDRED & NINETEEN - AND STILL NOT OUT!

Requested to compile a summary of Vics' season I could not help but think "where on earth do I start?", for if the truth be known I could easily write a book on the events at the Drill Field last season, as each and every week brought another new twist to the story of one of football's oldest clubs.

Undoubtedly the most important event came twenty-four days after the Vics' most successful campaign for nearly a decade when they faced the most vital away fixture in the club's 119 year history. The venue was the High Court in Liverpool. The opponents were a property company who were looking to gain possession of the famous old Drill Field, in order to recoup a sum of £170,000 that the club owed to them. The equation was simple, if Vics lost then the club would go out of existence in a matter of weeks if not days.

Thankfully a white knight in the shape of 'The Drill Field Trust Fund' arrived on the scene to save the day. Formed by ordinary fans a year earlier to save the world's oldest football stadium. They had raised the magnificent sum of £60,000 through donations and fund raising events but, with time running out, even these superb efforts seemed to have been in vain. But the feeling for the club in the area should never be underestimated, and a last minute appeal saw the fund's coffers swell virtually overnight. Young and old, new fans and loyal long standing supporters, gave whatever they could afford, from coppers to hundreds and thousands. And so, in her hour of need, the club's many friends came to her and the day was saved. The Trust Fund now aim to repay every penny and ensure that the famous old stadium will be in existence for the future generations of Northwichers as it has been for thousands in the past.

If there was one sad aspect of the battle it was that one of its Generals, President Ken Edwards, did not witness the final victory as, sadly, he passed away just days before the future of the Drill Field was assured. He did, however, leave a marvellous legacy in his superb history of the Vics 'A Team For All Seasons' which, despite ill health, he managed to publish just before Christmas. It is a book that will bring huge enjoyment to Vics fans for many years to come and a fitting tribute to Ken.

All the events off the field could have easily overshadowed those on it, but this suprisingly never proved to be the case. The season started off well enough, but following a shocking 2-0 home defeat in the FA Cup by United Counties League unknowns Raunds Town, the team's discipline and form took a sharp nose-dive. Even so it came as some shock when he Board decided to despense with the services of popular manager Sammy McIlroy in mid-October. With the club in turmoil both on and off the field it needed a cool and experienced head, and who better to do the job than former Runcorn, Altrincham, Stafford and Fleetwood boss, John Williams.

With the addition of one or two new faces the team discovered a new spirit and self confidence and quickly began to play some sparkling football. This was especially true away from home where they acheived some amazing wins - such as 6-0 at Stalybridge, Bath (5-0), Slough (4-0) and Welling (5-1). Not surprisingly they equalled the club's record for number of away league wins in a season which had been set up in the Green's last championship winning season in 1957. At the Drill Field though it was a far different story as just five league wins were recorded all season long. Strangely enough, this also equalled a club record for a 42 match season, albeit in this case a more recent one set up in 1986!

As mentioned earlier the FA Cup again proved to be a sore point for Vics and in general the other cups also proved to be a huge disappointment - with one major exception! Having been the inaugural winners of the GMVC's own cup competition, 'The Bob Lord Trophy', in 1980, Vics' recent record in the competition had been poor. However following wins over Gateshead, Runcorn, Telford and Macclesfield, they again reached the final where they met Champions-elect Wycombe. After a goal-less first leg at the Drill Field, Vics produced one of the best performances in living memory to win the second leg 3-2 at Adams Park. To those loyal fans in amongst the 3-400 who made the trip, the success was all the more sweet given the agonies that they have seen their club go through in the last few years. It also proved to be a personal triumph for that wily old fox Gordon Davies who netted a hat-trick and his delight was matched by his team-mates and those on the terraces.

Staying on the personnel side, two players, Tony Hemmings and the dynamic Brian Butler - earned the club's first England caps since 1983. Vics' record signing notched his 100th goal for the club in the Christmas derby match at Witton and he is now well on the way to breaking the club's goalscoring record. Central defenders Mark Hancock and Jeff Parker were also models of consistency whilst new boys Mark Simms and Charlie Boyd proved to be excellent acquisitions.

With virtually all of last season's squad retained for the coming campaign, there is a quiet air of optimism at the Drill Field after so many years of pessimism. Many fans feel that last season's Bob Lord Trophy triumph - Vics' first major piece of silverware since 1984 - could be the first of many.

Key: Home fixtures are denoted by bold capitals. Numbers in brackets after players names indicate goals scored (an asterisk by the results denotes own goals). Only used substitutes are listed - substituted players are *italicised*.

Key to Competitions: **GMVC**: G.M. Vauxhall Conference. **CBSSC**: Cheshire Senior Cup. **MCSC**: Mid Cheshire Senior Cup. **DC**: Drinkwise (G.M. Vauxhall Conference) Cup. **FAC**: F.A. Cup. **FAT**: Vauxhall F.A. Trophy.

LEAGUE POSITION: 11th

FA CUP: Second Qualifying Round   FA TROPHY: First Round

Date	Opponents	Comp.	Res	Gate	1.	2.	3.	4.	5.	6.	7.	8.	9.	10.	11.	Sub.	Sub.
22.08	Yeovil Town	GMVC	1-1	2,110	Berryman	Locke	Butler	Jones	Hancock	Parker	Smith	Donnelly	Davies(1)	O'Connor	Blain	Blundell	Stinger
25/08	**KIDDERMINSTER**	GMVC	0-1	629	Berryman	Locke	Butler	*Jones*	Hancock	Parker	Smith	*Dorrelly*	Davies	*O'Connor*	Blain	Blundell	Parker
29/08	**SLOUGH TOWN**	GMVC	0-1	565	Berryman	Locke	Blundell	Jones	Hancock	Stringer	Smith	Butler	Davies	O'Connor	Blain	Parker	
31/08	Macclesfield	GMVC	2-1	1,058	Bullock	Locke	Blundell	Jones	Hancock	*Stringer*	Smith	Butler	Davies	O'Con*(1)	Blain(1)	Donnelly	
05/09	Bromsgrove R.	GMVC	2-1	1,125	Bullock	Locke	Blundell	Jones	Hancock	*Simms*	Smith	Butler	Davies(1)	O'Con*(1)	Ainsworth	Blain	
08/09	**GATESHEAD**	DC	2-1	368	Bullock	Locke	Blundell	Jones	Hancock	Simms	Smith	Butler(1)	Parker	O'Con*(1)	Blain		Bennett
12/09	**WINSFORD UTD**	FAC	4-1	1,154	Bullock	Locke	Blundell	Jones	Hancock	Simms	Smith	Butler(1)	Hemmin'(1)	O'Con*(1)	Blain(1)	Parker	
15/09	Runcorn	GMVC	1-0	787	Bullock	Locke	Blundell	Jones	Hancock	Simms(1)	Smith	Butler	Hemmings	O'Connor	Blain	Parker	
19/09	**KETTERING**	GMVC	2-2	721	Bullock	Locke	Blundell	Jones	Parker	Ainsworth	Smith(1)	Butler	Davies	O'Connor	Blain	Parker	Bennett
23/09	Gateshead	DC	2-0	132	Bullock	Blain	Simms	Locke	Parker	Ainsworth	Smith	Butler	Davies(2)	O'Connor	Himmin'	Blain	
26/09	**RAUNDS**	FAC	0-2	585	Bullock	*Blain*	Simms	Parker	Locke	Simms	Smith	Butler	Hemmings	O'Connor	*Hemmings*	Bennett	
29/09	**STALYBRIDGE**	GMVC	1-3	691	Bullock	Bennett	Simms	Parker	Locke	Ainsworth	Smith	Butler	Davies	O'Connor	Hemmin'(1)	Bennett	Blundell
03/10	Dagenham & R.	GMVC	1-4	963	Siddall	Bennett	Blundell	*Simms*	Hancock(1)	Ainsworth	Smith	McIlroy	Davies	O'Connor	Hemmings	Parker	
06/10	**ALTRINCHAM**	GMVC	1-2	779	Siddall	Bennett	*Blundell*	Parker	Hancock(1)	Ainsworth	Smith	Butler	Davies	O'Connor	Hemmings	Williams	
13/10	**MACCLESFIELD**	GMVC	1-3	783	Bullock	Bennett	Thelwell	Jones	Parker	Ainsworth	Smith	Butler(1)	Davies	O'Connor	Hemmings	Donnelly	Blundell
17/10	Woking	GMVC	0-1	1,992	Siddall	Bennett	Simms	Jones	Parker	*Thelwell*	*Smith*	Butler	Davies	O'Connor	Hemmings	Donnelly	
20/10	Runcorn	DC	3-2	600	Bullock	Blundell	Simms	Jones	Parker	Bennett	Easter	*D'elly(1)*	Davies	O'Connor	Hemmin(2)	Smith	Blundell
31/10	**MERTHYR TYD.**	GMVC	1-2	583	Bullock	Butler	Bennett	Parker	Simms	*Bishop*	Westray	Donnelly	Davies	Paxton(1)	Easter	Kidd	
07/11	Altrincham	GMVC	0-0	924	Bullock	Butler	*Blundell*	Parker	Hancock	Simms	Westray	Donnelly	Davies	O'Connor	Hemmings	Bishop	
14/11	**WELLING UNITED**	GMVC	1-1	529	Bullock	Butler	Simms	Hancock	Parker	Boyd	Westray	Donnelly(1)	Davies	O'Connor	Hemmings		
24/11	**CONGLETON T.**	CBSSC	3-1	211	Bullock	Locke	Simms	*Rutter*	Parker	Boyd	Westray	Butler(1)	Hemmin(1)	O'Con*(1)	*Paxton*	Davies	Donnelly
28/11	Farnborough	GMVC	3-0	702	Bullock	Butler	Simms	Hancock	Parker	Boyd	Westray	Donnelly	Davies(2)	O'Con*(1)	Hemmings	Paxton	Davies
01/12	**BROMSGROVE**	GMVC	0-1	508	Bullock	Butler	Simms	Locke	Parker	Boyd	Westray	Donnelly	*Davies*	O'Connor	*Hemmings*	Parker	
05/12	**RUNCORN**	GMVC	3-2	772	Bullock	Bullock	Simms	Bullock	Parker	Boyd	*Westray*	Butler(1)	*Davies*	O'Con*(1)	Hemmin(1)	Donnelly	Paxton
12/12	Boston United	GMVC	5-3	924	Bullock	Locke	Simms	Hancock	Parker	*Boyd*	Westray	Butler(1)	Davies	O'Con*(3)	Hemmin(1)	Donnelly	Paxton

Date	Opponent	Comp	Score	Att													
15/12	TELFORD UNITED	DC	3-1	374	Bullock	Locke(1)	Simms	Hancock	Parker	Boyd	Westray	Donnelly	Davies	O'Connor	Hemmin(2)	Blundell	
19/12	FARNBOROUGH	GMVC	3-2	610	Bullock	Locke	Simms	Hancock	Parker	Boyd	Westray	Donnelly	Davies(1)	O'Con'(2)	Hemmin(1)	Blundell	
28/12	Witton Albion	GMVC	3-1	2,442	Bullock	Locke	Simms	Hancock	Parker	Boyd(1)	Westray	Butler	Davies	O'Con'(2)	Hemmin'(3)	Donnelly	Paxton
02/01	Stalybridge C.	GMVC	6-0	1,111	Bullock	Locke	Simms	Hancock	Parker	Boyd	Westray	Butler	Davies	O'Con'(1)	Hemmings	Paxton	
09/01	Telford United	FAT	1-2	1,211	Bullock	Locke	Simms	Hancock	Parker	Boyd	Westray	Butler	Davies	O'Con'(1)	Hemmings	Jones	Paxton
16/01	Wycombe W.	GMVC	0-1	4,060	Bullock	Locke	Simms	Hancock	Parker	Boyd	Westray	Butler	Davies	Paxton	Hemmings	Simms	Butler
20/01	Winsford Utd	CBSSC	0-1	477	Bullock	Butler	Blundell	Jones	Parker	Boyd	Westray	Donnelly	Davies	O'Con'(1)	Hemmin(1)	Paxton	
30/01	Bath City	GMVC	5-0	535	Bullock	Blundell	Blundell	Hancock	Parker(1)	Boyd	Westray	Butler	Davies(2)	O'Connor	Hemmings	Davies(2)	
02/02	GATESHEAD	GMVC	0-0	672	Bullock	Locke	Simms	Hancock	Parker	Boyd	Westray	Butler	Davies	O'Con'(1)	Hemmin(1)	Paxton	Jones
06/02	WOKING	GMVC	1-0	989	Bullock	Locke	Simms	Hancock	Parker	Boyd	Westray	Butler	Davies	O'Con'(1)	Hemmin(1)	Paxton	
13/02	Kettering	GMVC	1-2	1,221	Bullock	Locke	Simms	Hancock	Parker	Boyd	Westray	Butler	Davies	O'Con'(1)	Hemmings	Jones	
20/02	Slough Town	GMVC	4-0	946	Bullock	Locke	Simms	Hancock(2)	Parker	Boyd	Westray	Butler	Davies	O'Con'(1)	Hemmin(1)	Paxton	Jones
24/02	MACCLESFIELD	DC	2-0	812	Bullock	Locke	Simms	Hancock	Parker	Boyd	Westray	Butler	Paxton(1)	O'Con'(1)	Hemmings	Jones	Blundell
27/02	WYCOMBE W.	GMVC	0-0	1,860	Bullock	Locke	Simms	Jones	Parker	Boyd	Paxton	Butler	Davies	O'Connor	Hemmings	Westray	Blundell
02/03	Macclesfield	DC	1-1	422	Bullock	Locke	Simms	Jones	Parker	Boyd	Westray	Butler	Davies	O'Con'(1)	Hemmings	Blundell	McGhee
06/03	BOSTON UNITED	GMVC	3-3	809	Bullock	Locke	Simms	Hancock	Parker(1)	Boyd	Westray	Butler(1)	Davies	O'Con'(1)	Hemmings	Hemmings	
13/03	Merthyr Tyd.	GMVC	0-3	609	Bullock	Jones	Simms	Jones	Parker	Boyd	Westray	Butler	Davies	O'Connor	Hemmings	Locke	
20/03	Telford United	GMVC	0-1	703	Bullock	Locke	Simms	Jones	Parker	Boyd	Westray	Butler	Davies	O'Connor	Hemmin(1)	Paxton	Blundell
20/03	Welling Utd	GMVC	5-1	633	Bullock	Locke	Simms	Jones	Parker	Boyd	Westray	Butler	Davies	O'Con'(3)	Hemmings	Blundell	
23/03	TELFORD UTD	GMVC	1-0	612	Bullock	Locke	Simms	Hancock	Boyd	Jones	Blundell	Butler	Hardy(1)	O'Connor	Hemmings	McGee	
27/03	YEOVIL TOWN	GMVC	0-1	873	Nixon	Locke	Simms	Hancock	Parker	Boyd	Hardy	Butler	Davies	O'Con'(3)	Hemmings	McGee	Blundell
03/04	BATH CITY	GMVC	3-1	641	Nixon	Locke	Simms	Hancock	Parker	Boyd	Jones	Butler	Hardy	Paxton	Hemmin(1)	Davies	Nassari
06/04	STAFFORD RGRS	GMVC	1-2	802	Bullock	Locke	Blundell	Hancock	Parker	Boyd	Hardy	McGee	McGee	O'Connor	Hemmin(1)	Jones	
08/04	WINSFORD UTD	MCSC	1-3	668	Bullock	Jones	Simms	Hancock	Parker	Boyd	Blundell	Hardy	Hardy	O'Connor	Hemmin(1)	McGee	
10/04	Gateshead	GMVC	2-0	349	Bullock	Locke	Simms	Hancock	Parker	Boyd(1)	Westray	Blundell	Davies(1)	O'Connor	Hemmings	Jones	Blundell
12/04	WITTON ALBION	GMVC	1-3	1,971	Bullock	Locke	Simms	Hancock	Parker	Boyd	Westray	Blundell	Hardy	O'Connor	Butler(1)	Jones	
17/04	Stafford Rgrs	GMVC	0-1	953	Bullock	Locke	McGee	Hancock	Parker	Boyd	Westray	Butler(1)	Hardy	O'Connor	Hemmings	Blundell	
20/04	WYCOMBE W.	DC	0-0	1,005	Bullock	Locke	McGee	Jones	Parker	Boyd	Westray	Butler	Davies	O'Connor	Hemmings	Hardy	
24/04	DAGENHAM & R.	GMVC	1-1	735	Bullock	Locke	McGee	Jones	Blundell	Boyd	Westray	Paxton	Nassari	O'Connor	Hemmings	Hardy	
27/04	Wycombe W.	DC	3-2	3,714	Bullock	Locke	Simms	Jones	Parker	Boyd	Hardy	Butler	Davies(3)	O'Connor	Hemmings	Hardy	
01/05	Kidderminster	GMVC	3-5	1,417	Bullock	Locke	Simms	Hancock	Jones	Boyd	Hardy	Butler	Davies(2)	O'Connor	Hemmings	McGee	Paxton

LEAGUE APPEARANCES: Ainsworth 5, Bennett 5(2), Berryman 3, Bishop 1(1), Blain 6(2), Blundell 12(8), Boyd 28, Bullock 35, Butler 38, Davies 35(1), Donnelly 8(6), Easter 1, Hancock 30, Hardy 7(1), Hemmings 35, Jones 20(5), Kidd 0(1), Locke 32(1), McGee 2(4), McIlroy 1, Nassari 1(1), Nixon 2, O'Connor 41, Parker 34(4), Paxton 4(11), Siddall 2, Simms 34, Smith 12, Stringer 2(1), Thelwell 1(1), Westray 24(1), Williams 0(1).

LEAGUE GOALSCORERS: O'Connor 21; Hemmings 15; Davies 12; Butler 4; Hancock 3; Boyd, Parker 2; Blain, Donnelly, Hardy, Paxton, Smith, Westray 1.

Northwich Victoria

JOHN WILLIAMS

Undoubtedly the most experienced manager in the Conference, John Williams' pedigree in the non-League game is virtually second to none. After finishing his playing career - which encompassed spells with Everton, Crewe and Ellesmere Port - John took charge of Welsh side Portmadoc with no little success. His next move was to Vics near neighbours Winsford United where he produced an outstanding team which included the likes of Neville Southall. Trophy after trophy duly arrived at the Barton Stadium, but in 1980 Runcorn made him an offer he could not refuse. In just over six seasons at Canal Street he guided the Linnets to the Conference & NPL titles, two Bob Lord Trophy wins, the FA Trophy final and last, but not least, two Cheshire Senior Cup successes, not to mention unearthing such players as Ossie Smith and Mark Carter.

In the summer of 1986 he moved to Altrincham but this proved to be an unhappy time and after just over a year at Moss Lane John was sacked. Subsequent moves took him to Stafford, Chorley and Fleetwood but he found success at these clubs elusive.

He arrived at the Drill Field in late October as care-taker manager when the club was in turmoil both on and off the field, but his quiet but firm style quickly changed the club's fortunes and after being appointed to the job on a permanent basis in early December, he promptly won The 'Manager of the Month' award.

This early success proved to be no fluke and John's side went on to produce some of the best football that many Vics' fans could remember. To cap it all he guided the Vics to their first major Trophy since 1984 when they beat double winners Wycombe in the final at the Bob Lord Trophy.

It maybe too much to expect that John will be able to guide Vics to bigger and better things on what is still a tight budget, but at least the Drill Field faithful know that, on the playing side at least, the club is in safe hands.

Vics second-half substitute, Paul Donnelly, takes advantage of a few gaps in the Macclesfield defence as he thunders a shot towards goal. Photo: Paul Dennis.

Programme details:
    32 pages (16 editorial) for £1
    Editor - Terry Mortram (0744 57726)
Any other club publications:
    'A Team for All Seasons' - Club History
    Hardback £14.95 plus p&p.
    Available from the club shop.
    'Resign Roberts Re-Sign'
    Fanzine, £1 plus p&p.
Local Newspapers:
    Northwich Guardian (Wednesday) 0606 43333
    Northwich Chronicle (Wednesday) 0606 42272
    Daily Post
    Manchester Evening News Pink (Saturday evenings)
Local Radio Stations:
    GMR (BBC Manchester)
    Piccadilly Radio, Signal Radio

NORTHWICH VICTORIA - PLAYING SQUAD 1992-93

Player	Honours	Birthplace and date	Transfer Fees	Previous Clubs
GOALKEEPERS				
Tony Bullock	BLT, MSC, SSC, FA XI	Northwich 18/2/72		Barnton
DEFENDERS				
Mark Jones	MCSC, SSC, BLT, FA XI	Liverpool 16/9/60		Runcorn, Preston NE, Southport
Mark Hancock	FAT, BLT, MSC, SSC	Ellesmere Port 30/9/60	£3,000	Van Leer, Telford Utd
Mark Simms	BLT	Southport 17/10/70		Blackburn Rovers, Preston NE, Bury, Fleetwood Town
Jeff Parker	BLT	Liverpool 23/1/69		Everton, Crewe Alexandra
Darren Tinson	NPL 1 NPL 1C			Connah's Quay Nomads, Colwyn Bay
Tony McGhee	BLT	Liverpool		
MIDFIELD				
Charlie Boyd	BLT	Liverpool 20/9/69		Liverpool, Chesterfield, Bristol Rovers, Chorley, Runcorn, Droylsden
Brian Butler	ESP, BLT, MSC, FA XI	Salford 4/7/66		Blackpool, Stockport County, Halifax Town
Tony Hemmings	ESP, MSC BLT, FA XI		£8,000	Burton Albion, Rocester
Neil Hardy	BLT			Tranmere Rovers, Crewe Alexandra
Kane Westray	BLT			Middlewich Ath
FORWARDS				
Malcolm O'Connor	NPLC, MCSC, SSC, FA XI	Ashton-U-Lyne 25/4/65	£10,000	Curzon Ashton, Notts Forest, Rochdale, Curzon Ashton, Hyde Utd
Peter Donnelly	NPL1 NPL 1C	Chester 11/5/65		Chester C, Oswestry T, Rhyl, Colwyn Bay
Dave Paxton	BLT	Liverpool		Maghull

Departures during season:
Colin Blain (Hyde), Barry Siddall (Preston), Graham Easter (Dulwich H), Darren Lenton (Mossley), John Stringer (Retired), John Smith (Altrincham), Steve Berryman & Paul Donnelly (Bamber Bridge), Mark Rutter (Bangor C), Andy Feeley (Atherton LR), Mike Bennett (Curzon Ashton), Dave O'Gorman (Connah's Quay N), John Bishop (Local football), Stuart Locke (Stalybridge), Chris Blundell, Gordon Davies & Jamie Williams (Released).

Players on loan during season:
Gareth Ainsworth (Camb Utd), Kevin Thelwell (Shrewsbury), Craig Nixon (Bury), Derek Nassari (Chester), Neil Hardy (Crewe).

Drill Field, Northwich Victoria

Address and telephone number: The Drill Field, Drill Field Road, Northwich, Cheshire. Tel: 0606 41450. Fax: 0606 330577.

Simple directions: Leave M6 at Junc.19 and follow A556 towards Chester. At second roundabout (approx. 6 miles), turn right onto A533. Ground on right 1.5 miles behind Volunteer Public House.

Capacity: 14,000 (currently limited to 3,500)   **Seated:** 660   **Covered terracing:** 2,000

Record Attendance: 11,290 v Witton Albion, Cheshire League, Good Friday 1949.

Club Shop: Located inside ground. Open match days. Manager: Andy Dakin.

Social Facilities: Large social club with members lounge and seperate function room - both available for hire Tel: 0606 43120. Food available on matchdays with prior notice. Bass beers, Pool, Darts, TV.

Previous Grounds: None

Northwich Fact File

Nickname: The Vics

Club Sponsors: Morgan Contractors.

Previous Leagues: The Combination 1890-1892, Football League Div.2 1892-94, The Combination 1894-1898, The Cheshire League 1898-1900, Manchester League 1900-12, Lancashire 1912-19, Cheshire County League 1919-68, Northern Premier League 1968-79.

Club colours: Green & white halved shirts, green shorts and white socks.

Change colours: Claret shirts, sky blue shorts and claret socks.

Midweek home matchday: Tuesday

Record transfer fee: £10,000 to Hyde United for Malcolm O'Connor - August 1988.

Record transfer fee received: £50,000 from Chester City for Neil Morton - October 1990.

Club record goalscorer: Peter Burns 160 - 1955-65.

Record appearances: 970 by Ken Jones 1969-85.

Past players who progressed to the Football League: To numerous to list.

Club Honours: Welsh Cup Runners-up 1881/82,1888-89; FA Trophy Winners 1983/84, Runners-up 1982/83; Bob Lord Trophy Winners 1979/80, 1992/93; Northern Premier League Runners-up 1976/77; Northern Premier League Cup Winners 1972/73, Runners-up 1978/79; Cheshire County League Champions 1956/57, Runners-up 1924/25,1947/48; Cheshire County League Cup Winners 1925/35; Manchester League Champions 1902/03, Runners-up 1900/01,1903/04,1907/08,1908/09,1911/12; The Combination Runners-up 1890/91;
Cheshire Senior Cup Winners 1880-81,1881/82,1882/83,1883/84,1884/85,1885/86,1928/29,193-6/37,1949/50,1954/55,1971/72,1976/77,1978/79,1983/84
Runners-up 1891/92,1896/97,1905/06,1908/09,1947/48,1950/51,1963/64,
1965/66,1969,1970/71,1977/78,1985/86;
Staffordshire Senior Cup Winners 1978/79, 1979/80, 1989/90, Runners-up 1986/87, 1990/91;
Cheshire Amateur Cup Winners 1901/02, Runners-up 1898/99,1902/93;
Northwich Senior Cup Winners 1948/49,1958/59,1959/60,1963/64,1964/65,1965/66,1967/68,-1968/69,1969/70,1971/72,1974/75,
Runners-up 1953/54,1954/55,1955/56,1957/58,1960/61,1961/62,1972/73; Mid Cheshire Senior Cup Winners 1984/85,1985/86,1987/88,1989/90, Runners-up 1982/83,1983/84,1990/91,-1992/93; North-West Floodlit League Winners 1966/67,1975/76; Cheshire League Lancashire Combination Inter-League Cup Winners 1961/62; Guardian Charity Shield Winners 1985/86,1986/87,1987/88.

RUNCORN

Formed:
1918

Chairman:
Mr D.Robinson

Vice Chairman
Mr P.Saunders Lee

Football Secretary:
Mr G.Worrall

Manager:
Mr J.F.Carroll

Assistant Manager:
Mr B.Rodaway

Physiotherapist:
Mr J.Graham

Commercial Manager:
Mr J.Graham

Press Officer:
Mr P.Saunders Lee

As always happens hope springs eternal, the pre-season campaign gave every reason for optimism. Unfortunately hopes were jolted by injuries to key players before a ball was kicked in the league programme. Even more tragic was the enforced retirement of Nigel Shaw a major blow to John Carroll's plans.

The league position constantly gave reason for concern and worries concerning relegation were manifest throughout the club and a huge sense of relief was evident at the end.

Evidence of the unpredictability of football came with a brilliant campaign in the FA Trophy with a superb away victory at Boston, at home against Winsford and over two legs against old rivals Witton Albion in the semi-final.

To play at Wembley is a milestone in any player's career and indeed with club officials and supporters alike and indeed it was a brilliant day. So we lost 1-4, by common consent the score did not reflect the game, so we returned to our hotel, heads high and enjoyed ourselves. Next year we will hopefully try again, it's not often you meet a team like Wycombe in the final. They will be in pastures new and our best wishes go with them.

G.H.Worrall (Secretary)

Runcorn 1992-93 - Back Row (L-R): Andy Taylor, Alan Richards, John Routledge, John Carroll, Darrell McCarty, Graham Hill, Arthur Williams, Terry Bratt (Kit Manager), Ian Brady, Barry Wellings. Front Row: Billy Rodaway (Assistant Manager), Gary Brabin, Gary Anderson, Justin Wall, Ian Harold, Steve Byrne, Nigel Shaw, Paul Mullen, Steve Shaughnessey, Sean Lundon, Jamie Bates, Jimmy Graham (Physio).

RUNCORN MATCHFACTS 92-93

Key: Home fixtures are denoted by bold capitals. Numbers in brackets after players names indicate goals scored (an asterisk by the results denotes own goals). Only used substitutes are listed - substituted players are *italicised*.

Key to Competitions: **GMVC**: G.M. Vauxhall Conference. **CSC**: Cheshire Senior Cup. **DC**: Drinkwise (G.M. Vauxhall Conference) Cup. **FAC**: F.A. Cup. **FAT**: Vauxhall F.A. Trophy.

LEAGUE POSITION: 19th

FA CUP: Fourth Qualifying Round

FA TROPHY: Runners-up

Date	Opponents	Comp.	Res	Gate	1.	2.	3.	4.	5.	6.	7.	8.	9.	10.	11.	Sub.	Sub.
22/08	Boston United	GMVC	0-0	1,418	Routledge	Wall	Byrne	Bates	Carroll	Harold	Brady	Anderson	Sh'nessy	Shaw	McCarty	Mullen	
25/08	**MACCLESFIELD**	GMVC	1-2	757	Routledge	Wall	Byrne	Bates	Carroll	Harold	*Brady*	Anderson	Sh'nessy(1)	*Shaw*	McCarty	Mullen	Brabin
29/08	**FARNBOROUGH**	GMVC	1-4	448	Routledge	Wall	Mullen	Bates	Carroll	Harold	Richards	Anderson	Sh'nessy	Brabin	McCarty(1)		Donnery
31/08	Gateshead	GMVC	1-4	547	Routledge	Wall	Mullen	Bates	Carroll	Harold	Ludon	Anderson	Sh'nessy(1)	Brabin	McCarty	*Wellings*	Donnery
05/09	Woking	GMVC	0-4	1,829	Routledge	Wall	Mullen	Bates	Carroll	Harold	Sang	Anderson	Sh'nessy	Brabin	McCarty	Richards	
12/09	**YEOVIL TOWN**	GMVC	1-0	421	Routledge	Wall	Wilson(1)	Bates	Carroll	Harold	Sang	Anderson	Sh'nessy	Brabin	Lundon		
15/09	**NORTHWICH V.**	GMVC	0-1	787	Routledge	Wall	*Wilson*	Bates	Carroll	Harold	Lundon	Anderson	Sh'nessy(1)	Brabin	McCarty	Cotton	
19/09	Welling United	GMVC	2-3	842	Routledge	Cotton(1)	Lundon	Bates	Carroll	Harold	Sang	Anderson	Sh'nessy(1)	Brabin	McCarty		
26/09	**KIDDERMINSTER**	GMVC	0-0	512	Routledge	Bates	Lundon	Cotton	Carroll	Harold	Mullen	Anderson	Sh'nessy	Brabin	McCarty	Sang	Boyd
29/09	**TELFORD UNITED**	GMVC	3-1	532	Routledge	Bates	Lundon	Mullen	Carroll(1)	Harold	Sang(1)	Anderson	Sh'nessy(1)	Brabin	McCarty	Cotton	
03/10	Yeovil Town	GMVC	0-4	1,684	Routledge	Bates	Lundon	Mullen	Carroll	Harold	Sang	Anderson	Sh'nessy	Brabin	McCarty		
06/10	**GATESHEAD**	GMVC	4-2	471	Routledge	Bates	Lundon(1)	Mullen(1)	Carroll	Harold	McInery(1)	Anderson	Sh'nessy	Brabin	Parker(1)	Sang	
13/10	**STALYBRIDGE C.**	GMVC	2-1	700	Routledge	Bates	Lundon	Brown(1)	Carroll	Harold	McInerney	Anderson	Sh'nessy	Brabin(1)	Parker		
17/10	**SLOUGH TOWN**	GMVC	0-3	526	Routledge	Bates	Lundon	Brown	Carroll	Harold	McInerney	Anderson	Sh'nessy	Brabin	Parker		
20/10	**NORTHWICH V.**	DC	2-3	600	Routledge	Bates	Lundon	Byrne	Gallagher	Harold	McInerney	Anderson	Sh'nessy(1)	Brabin(1)	McCarty(1)	Parker	Brown
24/10	**MARINE**	FAC4	1-4	749	Routledge	Bates	Lundon	Byrne	Gallagher	Harold	McInerney	Anderson	Sh'nessy	Brabin	McCarty(1)	Parker	Brown
31/10	Dagenham & R.	GMVC	1-5	1,404	Williams	Bates	Wall	Byrne	Gallagher	Harold(1)	McInerney	McCarty	Sh'nessy	Brown	Anderson	Parker	Parker
07/11	**KETTERING T.**	GMVC	2-2	492	Williams	Bates	Wall	Byrne	Gallagher	Brady	McInerney	McCarty	Sh'nessy	Brown(1)	Anderson	Parker	Taylor
17/11	Stalybridge C.	GMVC	0-0	509	Williams	Bates	Wall	*Byrne*	Gallagher	Brady	Jackson	McCarty	Sh'nessy	Brown	Anderson	Parker	Parker
21/11	**WYCOMBE W.**	GMVC	2-1	850	Williams	Bates	Wall	Taylor	Gallagher	Brady	McInerney	McCarty	Sh'nessy	Brown(2)	Anderson	McInerny	Parker
24/11	Gen. Chemicals	CSC	1-0	300	Williams	Bates	Wall	Taylor	Gallagher	Brady	Harold	McCarty	Mcl'ny(1)	Brown	Anderson	McInerny	
28/11	Bath City	GMVC	1-1	673	Williams	Bates	Wall	Taylor	Gallagher	Brady	Harold	McCarty	Sh'nessy	Brown	Anderson	McInerny	Parker
05/12	Northwich V.	GMVC	2-3	772	Routledge	Williams	Wall(1)	Taylor	Gal'gher(1)	Harold	Brabin(1)	McCarty	Parker	Brown	Anderson	McInerny	Lundon
12/12	**WOKING**	GMVC	2-3	598	Williams	Wall	Robertson	Taylor	Gal'gher(1)	Mcl'ny(1)	Brady	McCarty	Sh'nessy	Brown	Anderson	Brabin	Parker
19/12	Kidderminster	GMVC	0-2	1,065	Williams	Wall	Robertson	Hill	Gallagher	Harold	Brady	McInerny	Sh'nessy	Brown	Anderson	Brabin	
28/12	Stafford R.	GMVC	1-0	876	Williams	Wall	Robertson	Hill	Gallagher	Harold	Brady	McInerny	Sh'nessy(1)	Brown	Anderson	Brabin	

Date	Opponent	Comp	Res	Att	1	2	3	4	5	6	7	8	9	10	11	Subs
02/01	ALTRINCHAM	GMVC	0-1	780	Williams	Wall	Robertson	Hill	Gallagher	Harold	Brabin	McInerny	Sh'nessy	Brown	Brady	Bates, Brown
09/02	HYDE	FAT	2-1	425	Williams	Wall	Robertson	Hill	Brabin	Harold	Brady	McInerny	Sh'nessy	Parker(1)	And'son(1)	Brown
16/01	Telford United	GMVC	1-2	947	Williams	Wall	Robertson	Hill	Gallagher	Brabin	Brady	Connor(1)	McKenna	Parker	Anderson	Brown
19/01	Stalybridge C.	CSC	0-0	3-3	Williams	Wall	Robertson	Hill	Gallagher	Brabin	Brady	Conner	Parker	McKenna	Anderson	McInerny
23/01	Dagenham & R.	GMVC	1-0	475	Williams	Wall	Robertson	Carroll	Gallagher	Anderson	Brady	Conner	Parker	McKenna	Brabin(1)	Brown
30/01	Gloucester	(FAT)	3-3	577	Williams	Wall	Robertson	Hill	Gallagher	And'son(1)	Brady	Connor(2)	Sh'nessy	McKenna	Brabin	Parker, Brown
02/02	GLOUCESTER	(FATR)	2-2	618	Williams	Wall	Robertson	Hill	Gallagher	And'son(1)	Brady(1)	Connor	Sh'nessy	McKenna	Brabin	Parker, Brown
06/02	Farnborough	GMVC	3-2	581	Williams	Wall	Robertson	Hill	Gallagher	Anderson	Brady	Connor	Sh'nessy(1)	McKenna	Brabin	Parker
08/02	Gloucester	(FATR)	0-0	771	Williams	Wall	Robertson	Hill	Gallagher	Anderson	Brady	Connor	Sh'nessy	McKenna	Brabin	Parker
11/02	GLOUCESTER	FATR	4-1	701	Williams	Wall	Robertson	Hill	Brown(1)	Anderson	Brady	Connor	Sh'nessy	McKenna	Brabin	McInerny, Bates
13/02	WELLING UTD	GMVC	3-0	778	Williams	Wall	Robertson	Hill	Brown(1)	Anderson	Brady	Connor	Sh'nessy	McKen'(1)	Brabin	Parker, Bates
16/02	STALYBRIDGE C.	GMVC	0-1	474	Williams	Wall	Bates	Taylor	Carroll	Anderson	Brown	Connor	Parker	McKenna	Brabin	Bates
20/02	WINSFORD UTD	FAT	1-0	1,276	Williams	Wall	*Robertson*	Hill	Brown	And'son(1)	Brady	Sh'nessy	Parker	McKenna	Brabin	McInerny
27/02	BROMSGROVE	GMVC	2-1	459	Williams	Wall	Robertson	Hill	Brown	And'son(1)	Brady	Connor	Sh'nessy(1)	McKenna	Brabin	McInerny
02/03	Kettering	GMVC	3-3	911	Williams	Wall	Robertson	Hill	Brown	And'son(1)	Brady	Connor	Sh'nessy	McKen'(2)	Brabin	McInerny
06/03	Slough Town	GMVC	1-1	803	Williams	Wall	Robertson	Hill	Brown	Taylor	Brady	Connor	Sh'nessy(1)	McKenna	Brabin	Parker
13/03	Boston United	FAT	2-0	2,625	Williams	Wall	Robertson	Hill	Brown	And'son(1)	Brady	Connor	Sh'nessy	Parker(1)	Brabin	Taylor
20/03	MERTHYR TYD.	GMVC	2-3	483	Williams	Wall	Robertson	Hill	*Brown*	Taylor	Brady(1)	Connor	Sh'nessy	Parker	*Brabin*	McInerny, Bates
23/03	Altrincham	GMVC	2-0	814	Williams	Wall	Robertson	Hill	Brown	Taylor(1)	Brady	Connor	Sh'nessy	McKen'(1)	Brabin	Bates
27/03	BOSTON UNITED	GMVC	1-2	645	Williams	Wall	Robertson	Hill	*Brown*	Brabin	Brady	Connor	Sh'nessy	McKenna	*Parker*	McInerny
29/03	Bromsgrove	GMVC	0-0	963	Williams	Wall	Robertson	Hill	*Brown*	Anderson	Brady	Connor	Sh'nessy	McKenna	Brabin	Parker
03/04	WITTON ALB.	GMVC	2-0	1,610	Williams	Wall	Robertson	Hill	Brown	And'son(1)	Brady	Connor	Sh'nessy	McKen'(1)	Brabin	Parker
10/04	Witton Alb.	FAT	0-1	2,033	Williams	Wall	Robertson	Hill	Brown	Anderson	Brady	Connor	Sh'nessy	McKenna	Brabin	Parker
12/04	STAFFORD RGRS	GMVC	0-2	596	Williams	Bates	Robertson	Hill	McInerny	Anderson	Brady	Connor	Parker	McKenna	*Brabin*	Taylor
15/04	Wycombe	GMVC	1-5	6,220	Smith	Bates	Robertson	Hill	McInerny	Anderson	Brady	Connor	Sh'nessy	McKen'(1)	Brabin	McInerny
17/04	WITTON ALB.	GMVC	*4-4	753	Williams	*Williams*	Robertson	Hill	Taylor	Anderson	Brady	Connor	Parker(1)	McKen'(1)	Brabin(1)	McInerny, Sh'nessy
20/04	Macclesfield	GMVC	1-1	631	Williams	*Wall*	Robertson	Hill	Harold	Anderson	Brady	Connor	Sh'nessy(1)	McKenna	Brabin	Bates
24/04	Merthyr Tyd.	GMVC	3-0	451	Williams	Bates	Robertson	Brady	Harold	And'son(1)	Brown(1)	Connor	Sh'nessy	McKen'(1)	Brabin	McInerny
29/04	Witton Alb.	GMVC	*3-0	963	Williams	Bates	Robertson	Brady	Harold	Anderson	Brown(1)	Parker	Sh'nessy	McKen'(2)	Brabin	Connor, Wilson
01/05	BATH CITY	GMVC	1-3	504	Williams	Bates	Robertson	Brady	Harold	Anderson	Brown	Parker(1)	Sh'nessy(1)	McKenna	Brabin	Connor
09/05	Wycombe W.	FAT	1-4	32,968	Williams	Bates	Robertson	Hill	*Harold*	Anderson	*Brady*	Brown	Sh'nessy(1)	McKenna	Brabin	Connor, Parker

LEAGUE APPEARANCES: Anderson 37; Bates 26(12); Brabin 30(3); Brady 25(3); Brown 26(7); Byrne 5(3); Carroll 14; Connor 16(3); Cotton 2(5); Gallagher 13; Harold 25; Hill 18; Jackson 1; Lundon 10(4); McCarty 16; McInerny 11(18); McKenna 15; Mullen 6(4); Parker 16(20); Richards 1(1); Robertson 22; Routledge 16; Sang 5(1); Shaughnessy 38; Shaw 2; Taylor 9(9); Wall 29(9); Williams 26; Wilson 26; Wilson 1.

LEAGUE GOALSCORERS: McKenna 12: Brown 6: Brabin 5: Anderson 4: Parker 3: Connor, Gallagher, McCarty, McInerny 2: Brady, Carroll, Cotton, Harold, Lundon, Sang, Taylor, Wall, Wilson 1.

Runcorn

JOHN CARROLL

John Carroll became Runcorn's third manager in a year when he was appointed to take over permanently at Canal Street after a short period as caretaker-manager. Peter O'Brien had filled the vacancy left by Barry Whitbread but left to take over at Witton Albion.

Carroll, aged 33, played for South Liverpool and Weymouth and has now made over 200 appearances for the Linnets and is regarded as one of the best centre backs in the Vauxhall Conference. The highlight of his managerial career to date has undoubtedly been guiding Runcorn to the 1993 FA Trophy Final.

Wycombe's Paul Hyde punches clear from Runcorn's Ken McKenna, in last year's FA Trophy final. Photo: G.M.Ellis-Neville.

Programme details:
  32 pages for 80p
  Editor: P.Saunders-Lee c/o Halton Print 0928 560269

Any other club publications:
  The Jolly Green Giant (Fanzine)

Local Newspapers:
  Runcorn Weekly News
  Liverpool Echo
  Runcorn World

Local Radio Stations:
  Radio Merseyside
  Radio City

RUNCORN - PLAYING SQUAD 1992-93

Player	Honours	Birthplace and date	Transfer Fees	Previous Clubs
GOALKEEPERS				
Arthur Williams		Widnes 14/7/64		General Chemicals
DEFENDERS				
Jamie Bates		Manchester		Maine Road
Sean Lundon		Liverpool 7/3/69		Everton, Chester City, Bath City
Justin Wall				Crewe Alexandra
Paul Robertson		Stockport 5/2/72		York City, Stockport County, Bury
Andy Taylor		Manchester		Liverpool, Winsford United
Graham Hill		Manchester		Curzon Ashton
Michael Gallagher		Liverpool		Merseyside Police
Ian Harold		Liverpool 16/1/69		Newton
John Carroll	CSC	Liverpool 6/8/59		Sth Liverpool, Weymouth
MIDFIELD				
Gary Brabin		Liverpool 9/12/70		Kirkby Town, Stockport County, Gateshead
Garry Anderson	FAT, CSC	Liverpool 5/1/60		Altrincham, Sth Liverpool, Altrincham, Runcorn, Altrincham
Ian Brady		Liverpool		Bootle, Heswall
Jimmy Brown		Liverpool		Bootle, Vauxhall GM, Morecambe
FORWARDS				
Karl Thomas	NPL	Liverpool 1/9/63	Undiscl	South Liverpool, Colne Dynamoes, Witton Albion
Ken McKenna	CSC, ShSC, FA XI	Birkenhead 2/7/60		Poulton V, Tranmere R, Telford U, Tranmere Runcorn, Telford U, Altrincham, Barrow
Joe Connor	NPL	Stockport	P/Exch	Stockport County, Hyde Utd, Mossley, Hyde Utd, Witton Albion
Neil Parker		Liverpool		Waterloo Dock, Caernarfon Town, Waterloo Dock

Departures during season:
Barry Wellings (Droylsden), Steve Saunders & Mark Henshaw (Altrincham), Nigel Shaw (Retired), Darryl McCarty (Witton Alb), Steve Shaughnessy (Stalybridge), Steve Byrne (Ashton Utd).

Players on loan during season:
Mike Jackson (Crewe)

Canal Street, Runcorn

Address and telephone number: Canal Street, Runcorn, Cheshire.
Tel: 0928 560076. Fax: 0928 560076.
Simple directions: South: M6. Take M56 to junction 11. Follow signs for Warrington. Left at min-roundabout (signed Liverpool/Runcorn) for 3 miles. Sign at slip road Runcorn Old Town, right at junction, follow road to Egerton Arms, turn right and right again to ground. North: leave M62 at Widnes, through Widnes to Runcorn/Widnes bridge, turn left, through town to Egerton Arms.
Capacity: 6,000   **Seated:** 670   **Covered terracing:** 2,000
Record Attendance: 10,111 v Preston North End - FA Cup - 1938/39
Club Shop: Sells scarves, hats, shirts, flags etc. Contact Mrs Redican 0928 560076.
Social Facilities: Clubhouse open before and after matches. Pies & sandwiches available.
Previous Grounds: None

Runcorn Fact File

Nickname: The Linnets

Club Sponsors:

Previous Leagues: Lancashire Combination 1918-19, Cheshire County League, Northern Premier League, Alliance Premier League.

Club colours: Yellow/green

Change colours: Red/white

Midweek home matchday: Tuesday

Record win: 11-0 v Congleton

Record defeat: 8-0 v South Shields

Record transfer fee: £17,000 to Hyde for Simon Rudge

Record transfer fee received: £80,000 from Nottingham Forest for Ian Woan

1992/93 Captain: I.Harold/G.Anderson

1992/93 Top scorer: S.Shaughnessy/K.McKenna

1992/93 Player of the Year: A.Williams

Club record goalscorer: Alan Ryan

Record appearances:

Past players who progressed to the Football League: Mark McCarrik, Eddie Bishop, Jimmy Cumbes, Graham Abel, Barry Knowles, Mark Jones, Don Page, David Pugh, Ian Woan.

Club Honours: Lancaster Junior Cup 1918/19; Cheshire League Champions 1919/20, 1936/37, 1938/39, 1939/40, 1962/63; Cheshire Senior Cup Winners 1924/25, 1935/36, 1961/62, 1964/65, 1967/68, 1973/74, 1974/75, 1984/85, 1985/86, 1986/87, 1987/88, 1988/89; Cheshire County Bowl Winners 1937/38; Northern Premier League Champions 1975/76, 1980/81; N.P.L. Challenge Cup Winners 1974/75, 1979/80, 19080/81; N.P.L. Challenge Shield Winners 1980/81, 1981/82; Alliance Premier League Champions 1981/82; Gola League Championship Shield champions 1982/83, 1985/85; Bob Lord Trophy winners 1982/83, 1984/85, Runners-up 1991/92; FA Challenge Trophy runners-up 1985/86, 1992/93.

SLOUGH TOWN

Formed:
1890

Chairman:
A.A.Thorne

Vice Chairman
B.A.Thorne

Football Secretary:
Richard Hayward

Manager:
John Docherty

Physiotherapist:
Kevin McGoldrick

Commercial Manager:
John Linton

Press Officer:
As secretary

This was by far Slough's best season out of its three in the Conference. Many pundits had Slough as relegation favourites, but David Kemp and his team proved them all wrong.

Wycombe Wanderers were pushed by Slough Town throughout the season, with an aggregate of over 12,000 watching the two tremendous fixtures between the sides.

First place after four wins out of four games and troubling most sides they were difficult to beat. Only over the last five games did a lack of form and loss of key players see the Rebels end the season in a creditable though somewhat disappointing 5th place. FA Cup action was entertaining, having to start in the First Qualifying Round away at Corinthian Casuals. 0-1 down and with 26 minutes to go, a penalty was enough to draw the match. The replay had Slough win by the odd goal in a seven goal thriller. Progress was made via a 1-0 victory over Met Police, away, a 2-1 home win over Yeading and a trip into Kent saw the Rebels win 2-1 against Ashford Town. This led to the First Round Proper where they met Colchester United, an old adversary. The 4-0 defeat was disappointing as some indifferent refereeing and a player dismissal spoilt any hope of glory and success.

Trophy success came in the third qualifying round with a 3-1 home win over Bromley. This led to a further meeting with Yeading, the 5th in the two seasons, and went to two games, Slough winning 2-1 at home. Any chance of getting to Wembley disappeared at Sutton United as Slough went down 1-3.

In the county cup Slough lost 0-1 away at Aylesbury United. Despite there being no honours gained, Slough won a lot of supporters and praise, and season 93/94 promises to be rewarding with the leadership and professionalism of new manager John Docherty.

Slough Town 1992-93 - Back Row (L-R): Ian Pluckrose, Carlton Fairweather, Stephen Scott, Trevor Bunting, Paul McKinnon, Ian Hazel, Mark Fiore, Darren Anderson. Front Row: Brian Lee, George Friel, Les Briley, Steve Whitby, David Greene, Mark Quamina, Andy Sayer. Photo: Dave West.

SLOUGH MATCHFACTS 92-93

Key: Home fixtures are denoted by bold capitals. Numbers in brackets after players names indicate goals scored (an asterisk by the results denotes own goals). Only used substitutes are listed - substituted players are *italicised*.

Key to Competitions: **GMVC:** G.M. Vauxhall Conference. **BABSC:** Berks & Bucks Senior Cup. **DC:** Drinkwise (G.M. Vauxhall Conference) Cup. **FAC:** F.A. Cup. **FAT:** Vauxhall F.A. Trophy.

FA CUP: First Round   FA TROPHY: Second Round

LEAGUE POSITION: 5th

Date	Opponents	Comp.	Res	Gate	1.	2.	3.	4.	5.	6.	7.	8.	9.	10.	11.	Sub.	Sub.
22/08	**KETTERING T.**	GMVC	3-0	1,095	Bunting	Whitby	Hemsley	Briley	Foran	Anderson	Hazel	*Quamina*	Sayer(1)	*Mckin'(1)*	Pluckro'(1)	Scott	Fielder
25/08	Bath City	GMVC	1-0	592	Bunting	Whitby	Hemsley	Briley	Foran	Anderson	Hazel	*Quamina*	Sayer	McKinnon	Pluckro'(1)	Scott	
29/08	Northwich Vic.	GMVC	1-0	565	Bunting	Whitby	Hemsley	Briley	Foran	An'son(1)	Hazel	*Quamina*	Sayer	*McKinnon*	Pluckro'(1)	Friel	
31/08	**DAGENHAM & R**	GMVC	2-0	1,813	Bunting	Whitby	Hemsley	Briley	Foran	Anderson	*Hazel(1)*	Quamina	Sayer(1)	*McKinnon*	Pluckrose	Friel	
05/09	**ALTRINCHAM**	GMVC	1-4	1,101	Bunting	Whitby	Hemsley	Briley	Foran	Anderson	Hazel(1)	Quamina	Sayer	*Mckinnon*	Pluckrose	Scott	
08/09	Yeovil Town	DC	0-2	1,319	Bunting	Whitby	Hemsley	Briley	Foran	Maxwell	Hazel	*Quamina*	Sayer	*Friel*	Pluckrose	Scott	
12/09	Corinthian Cas.	FAC	1-1	264	Bunting	Hancock	Hemsley	Briley	Foran(1)	Powell	Hazel(1)	Quamina	Sayer	*Friel*	Pluckrose	Scott	
15/09	**CORINTHIAN CAS.**	FAC	4-3	518	Bunting	Hancock	Hemsley	Scott	Foran(1)	Powell	Hazel(1)	Friel(1)	Sayer(1)	McKin'(1)	Pluckrose	Friel	
19/09	**TELFORD UTD**	GMVC	2-0	914	Bunting	Whitby	Hemsley	Briley	Foran	Anderson	Hazel	Scott	Sayer(1)	McKinnon	Pluckrose	Whitby	Stanley
22-09	**YEOVIL TOWN**	DC	2-2	528	Bunting	Whitby	Hemsley	Briley	Foran	Anderson	Hazel(2)	Quamina	Friel	McKinnon	*Stanley*	Pluckrose	
26/09	Met Police	FAC	1-0	350	Bunting	Whitby	Hemsley	Briley	Foran	Anderson	*Hazel*	Scott	Sayer	McKinnon	Pluckrose	Friel(1)	
03/10	BROMSGROVE	GMVC	1-3	866	Bunting	Whitby	*Maxwell*	Briley	Foran	Anderson	Hazel	Scott	Sayer(1)	McKinnon	Pluckrose	Friel(1)	
06/10	Welling Utd	GMVC	1-2	721	Bunting	Whitby	*Hemsley*	Briley	Foran	Anderson	Hazel	Maxwell	Sayer(1)	McKinnon	Pluckrose	Friel	
10/10	YEADING	FAC	2-1	930	Bunting	Whitby	*Maxwell*	Briley	Foran	An'son(1)	Hazel	*Friel*	Sayer	McKinnon	Pluckrose	Scott	S'ley(1)
13/10	**YEOVIL TOWN**	GMVC	3-0	771	Bunting	Whitby	Stanley	Briley	Foran	Anderson	Hazel	Friel	Sayer(1)	McKin'(2)	Pluckrose	Scott	
17/10	Runcorn	GMVC	3-0	526	Bunting	Whitby	Stanley	Briley	Foran	Anderson	Hazel	Friel(1)	Sayer(2)	McKinnon	Pluckrose	Scott	
24/10	Ashford Town	FAC	2-1	1,051	Bunting	Whitby	Stanley(1)	Briley	Foran	Anderson	Hazel	Friel	Sayer	McKin'(1)	Pluckrose	Scott	
31/10	**BOSTON UNITED**	GMVC	3-0	906	Bunting	Whitby	Stanley	Briley	Foran(1)	Anderson	Hazel	Friel	Sayer	McKin'(2)	Pluckrose	Scott	
03/11	Kettering Town	GMVC	0-5	1,205	Bunting	Whitby	*Stanley*	Briley	Foran	Maxwell	Hazel	Friel	Sayer	McKinnon	Pluckrose	Fiore	
07/11	Staybridge C	GMVC	0-0	786	Bunting	Whitby	Pluckrose	Briley	Foran	Anderson	Hazel	Scott	Sayer	McKinnon	Fiore		
10/11	**WELLING UTD**	GMVC	4-2	905	Bunting	Whitby	Pluckrose	*Stanley*	Foran	Anderson	Hazel	Scott	Sayer(2)	McKin'(2)	Fiore	Friel	
14/11	Colchester U.	FAC	0-4	3,858	Bunting	Whitby	Pluckrose	Briley	Foran	Anderson	Hazel	Scott	Sayer	McKinnon	Fiore		
21/11	Macclesfield	GMVC	2-1	651	Bunting	Whitby	Pluckrose	Briley	Foran	Anderson	Quamina	Scott(1)	Sayer	McKinnon	Fiore(1)		
28/11	**BROMLEY**	FAT	3-1	860	Bunting	Whitby	Pluckrose	Briley	Foran(2)	*Hemsley*	Stanley	Scott(1)	Sayer	McKinnon	Fiore	Friel(1)	
05/12	Kidderminster	GMVC	1-1	1,175	Bunting	Whitby	Pluckrose	Quamina	Foran	*Hemsley*	Hazel	Scott(1)	Sayer	McKinnon	Fiore		
12/12	**MACCLESFIELD**	GMVC	2-1	930	Bunting	Whitby	Pluckrose	Stanley	Foran	*Frie(1)*	Hazel	Scott	Sayer	McKinnon	Fiore(1)	Hancock	

Date	Opponent	Comp	Score	Att													
19/12	Telford Utd	GMVC	1-1	968	Bunting	Whitby	Pluckrose	Briley	Foran	Stanley	Anderson	Scott	Sayer	McKin'(1)	Fiore	Friel	Hazel
26/12	MERTHYR TYD.	GMVC	2-1	1,175	Bunting	Whitby	Pluckrose	Briley	Foran	Friel	Anderson	Scott	Sayer(1)	McKin'(1)	Fiore	Friel	Greene
02/01	WOKING	GMVC	0-1	2,480	Bunting	Whitby	Pluckrose	Briley	Stanley	Friel	Stanley	Scott	Sayer	McKinnon	Fiore	Hazel	Stanley
09/01	Yeading	FAT	1-1	611	Bunting	Whitby	Pluckrose	Briley	Stanley	Anderson	Anderson	Hazel	Sayer(1)	McKinnon	Fiore	Friel	Quamina
12/01	YEADING	FAT	2-1	755	Bunting	Whitby	Pluckrose	Briley	Stanley	Friel(1)	Anderson	Hazel	Sayer(1)	McKinnon	Fiore(1)	Friel	Hancock
16/01	Altrincham	GMVC	2-1	832	Bunting	Whitby	Pluckrose	Briley	Stanley	Friel	Anderson	Hazel	Sayer	McKinnon	Fiore(1)	Friel	Hancock
19/01	Aylesbury Utd	B&BSC	0-1	437	Bunting	Hancock	Bedford	Powell	Greene	Hazel	Anderson	Quamina	Goodliff	Walker	Friel	Briley	Hodson
23/01	KIDDERMINSTER	GMVC	3-1	1,069	Bunting	Whitby	Pluckrose	Briley	Foran(1)	Fairweather	Anderson	Hazel(1)	Sayer(1)	McKin'(1)	Fiore	Friel	Briley
26/01	FARNBOROUGH	GMVC	3-1	1,180	Bunting	Whitby	Pluckrose	Briley	Foran	Fairweather	Anderson	Hazel	Sayer(2)	McKinnon	Fiore	Friel	Stanley
30/01	Sutton United	FAT	1-3	1,374	Bunting	Whitby	Pluckrose	Briley	Foran	Stanley	Anderson	Hazel(1)	Sayer	McKinnon	Fairweather	Friel	Friel
02/02	BATH CITY	GMVC	1-1	1,021	Bunting	Whitby	Pluckrose	Briley	Foran	Stanley	Anderson	Hazel	Sayer	McKinnon	Fairweather	Friel	Friel
06/02	STALYBRIDGE	GMVC	2-3	859	Bunting	Whitby	Pluckrose	Briley	Quamina	Stanley	Anderson	Hazel	Sayer(1)	McKinnon	Fiore	Fairweather	F'ther
08/02	Dagenham & R	GMVC	4-4	1,355	Bunting	Whitby	Pluckrose	Briley(1)	Quamina	Stanley	An'son(1)	Hazel	Sayer(1)	McKin'(1)	Fairweather	Fairweather	Friel
13/02	Bromsgrove R.	GMVC	1-0	1,456	Bunting	Whitby	Pluckrose	Friel	Quamina	Stanley	Anderson	Hazel	Sayer	McKin'(1)	Fairweather	Fairweather	Fairweather
20/02	NORTHWICH VIC	GMVC	0-4	946	Bunting	Whitby	Pluckrose	Friel	Quamina	Stanley	Anderson	Hazel	Sayer	McKinnon	Fiore	Fairweather	Greene
23/02	Farnborough	GMVC	0-1	842	Bunting	Whitby	Pluckrose	Briley	Quamina	Stanley	Anderson	Hazel	Sayer	McKinnon	Fiore	Greene	Quamina
27/02	Gateshead	GMVC	0-1	347	Bunting	Whitby	Pluckrose	Briley	Lee	Quamina	Anderson	Hazel	Sayer	McKinnon	Fiore	Friel	Friel
06/03	RUNCORN	GMVC	1-1	803	Bunting	Whitby	Pluckrose	Briley(1)	Lee	Stanley	Anderson	Hazel	Sayer	McKinnon	Fiore	Friel	Stanley
09/03	Woking	GMVC	2-1	1,948	Bunting	Whitby	Pluckrose	Briley	Lee	Quamina	Anderson	Hazel	Sayer	McKinnon	Fiore	Stanley	Stanley
20/03	GATESHEAD	GMVC	1-0	862	Emberton	Whitby	Pluckrose	Briley	Edwards	Stanley	Anderson	Hazel	Sayer	McKin'(1)	Fiore(1)	Friel	Friel
23/03	Wycombe W.	GMVC	0-1	7,230	Bunting	Whitby	Pluckrose	Briley	Edwards	Quamina	Anderson	Hazel	Sayer	McKinnon	Fiore	Stanley	Stanley
27/03	Witton Alb.	GMVC	1-1	742	Bunting	Whitby	Pluckrose	Briley	Edwards	Quamina	Anderson	Hazel	Sayer	McKin'(1)	Fiore	Friel	Friel
03/04	STAFFORD RGRS	GMVC	2-1	823	Bunting	Whitby	Pluckrose	Briley	Edwards	Stanley	Anderson	Hazel	Sayer	Friel	Fiore(1)	McKinnon	Q'mina
10/04	Merthyr Tyd.	GMVC	1-1	589	Bunting	Scott	Pluckrose	Briley	Edwards	Quamina	Lee	Hazel	Sayer	Friel(1)	Fiore	Stanley	Stanley
13/04	WYCOMBE W.	GMVC	1-1	4,500	Bunting	Lee	Pluckrose	Briley	Edwards	Stanley	Anderson	Hazel(1)	Sayer	Friel	Fiore	McKinnon	McKinnon
17/04	Yeovil Town	GMVC	1-5	2,451	Bunting	Lee	Pluckrose	Briley	Edwards	Anderson	Anderson	Hazel(1)	Sayer	Quamina	Fiore	McKinnon	McKinna
24/04	WITTON ALB.	GMVC	2-3	1,060	Bunting	Quamina	Pluckrose	Briley	Edwards	Stanley(1)	Anderson	Scott	Sayer	McKinnon	Fiore(1)	McKinnon	McKinnon
01/05	Stafford	GMVC	0-1	886	Bunting	Lee	Pluckrose	Briley	Edwards	Quamina	Anderson	Hazel	Sayer	McKinnon	Fiore	Friel	Scott

LEAGUE APPEARANCES: Anderson 37: Briley 37: Bunting 40: Edwards 10: Emberson 2: Fairweather 7(1): Fielder 1(1): Fiore 27(1): Foran 23: Friel 30(14): Greene 2(1): Hancock 1(1): Hazel 39(2): Hemsley 8: Lee 8: Maxwell 3: McKinnon 40(3): Pluckrose 42: Quamina 23(3): Sayer 42: Scott 17(6): Stanley 27(6): Whitby 37.

LEAGUE GOALSCORERS: Sayer 19: McKinnon 13: Fiore 7: Hazel 7: Friel 4: Pluckrose 3: Anderson, Briley, Foran, Scott 2: Fairweather, Stanley 1.

Slough Town

JOHN DOCHERTY

John joined in June 1993. He had made his name in professional football both as a player and manager.

Firstly, as a player with Brentford in 1959. From 1961 he was with Sheffield United for four years until he returned to Brentford for a further three seasons. A two year spell with Reading was followed by John's third and final playing term with Brentford.

Secondly, as a youth coach in 1974 with Queens Park Rangers then as manager of Brentford (1975/1976) before joining Cambridge United. Six years were spent with Cambridge as manager before John went back, yet again, to Brentford, this time as assistant manager. During his time as manager of Millwall (1986/90), he led his side to a Division Two championship and consequently place in the First Division.

John's last spell as a League club manager was spent at Bradford City and it is hoped that with his expertise and knowledge he can lead the Rebels through to a successful conclusion in what is his first season in non-League football.

Altrincham's Ray Sidderley (stripes) slides in to stop Slough's Andy Sayer. Photo: Chris Roberts/Kick Photography.

Programme details:
   28 pages for £1
   Editor - John Linton/Eddie Marr

Any other club publications:
   Rebels Without a Clue
   (Fanzine)
Local Newspapers:
   Slough Observer
   Slough Express

Local Radio Stations:
   Berkshire Radio
   Radio 210

SLOUGH TOWN - PLAYING SQUAD 1992-93

Player	Honours	Birthplace and date	Transfer Fees	Previous Clubs
GOALKEEPERS				
Trevor Bunting		Chalfont St.Giles 22/5/68		Burnham, Wycombe W, Marlow
DEFENDERS				
Darren Anderson	EY	Merton 6/9/66		Charlton Ath, Aldershot
Steve Whitby		Edgware 27/8/70	£8,000	Berkhamsted T, Wycombe W
Brian Lee		London		Millwall
Stuart Hemsley	SSC, FA XI	Carshalton 18/11/64		Croydon, Sutton Utd
Mark Foran		Aldershot 30/10/73		Millwall
Tony Powell		London		Milwall, Leyton-Wingate, Carshalton Athletic
MIDFIELD				
Les Briley		Lambeth 2/10/56		Chelsea, Hereford Utd, Wimbledon, Aldershot, Milwall, Brighton
Mark Quamina		Guyana 25/11/69		Wimbledon, Plymouth Argyle
Steve Scott		Chiswick 8/5/67		QPR, Friska Viljor (Swe), Farnborough, Harrow Borough, Hibs (Malta)
Ian Hazell		Merton 1/12/67		Wimbledon, Bristol Rovers, Maidstone Utd
Mark Fiore		Southwark 18/11/69		Wimbledon, Plymouth Argyle
FORWARDS				
Paul McKinnon	IL, SSC	Camberley 1/8/58		Trelleborg(Swe), Sutton U, Teg(Swe), Sutton U, B'burn, Orebro(Swe), Sutton U
Andy Sayer		Brent 6/6/66		Wimbledon, Fulham, Leyton Orient
Neal Stanley		Banbury 30/5/61		Wokingham Town, Wycombe W
George Friel	IL	Reading 11/10/70		Reading, Woking

Departures during season:
Colin Fielder (Woking), Paul Maxwell (Dorchester), Dave Greene (Woking), Phil Stacey (Aylesbury).

Players on loan during season:
Carlton Fairweather (Wimbledon), Brian Lee & Carl Emberson (Millwall), Russell Edwards (Crystal Palace).

Wexham Park Stadium, Slough

Address and telephone number: Wexham Park Stadium, Wexham Road, Slough, Berks SL2 5Q1
Tel: 0753 523358 Fax: 0753 516956
Simple directions: From North: M25 J16 East London M40 J1 - South A412 through Iver Heath to George Green. 2nd set lights turn right by George PH, George Green. Church Lane 1 mile to end, then small roundabout, turn left, ground 1/4 mile on right. From East: M25 J15/M4 J5 to A4 West to Co-Op Superstore on right, A412 North (Uxbridge), dual carriageway to 4th set lights. Church Lane, then as from North. From South: If M25 then as from East. From Windsor A355 under M4 J6 to A4, turn right, pass Brunel Bus station on left, Tesco Superstore, also on left, then first left, Wexham Road, signposted Wexham Park Hospital, ground just over 1 mile on left. From West: If M4 J6 then as from South.
Capacity: 5,000   **Seated:** 390   **Covered terracing:** 1,500
Record Attendance: 8,000 Schoolboys U15 Final Slough v Liverpool - 1976
Club Shop: Contact John Linlow 0753 571710
Social Facilities: Rebels bar & Lounge bar open weekdays 7pm-11pm, weekends lunchtime/evenings. Banqueting hall for all types of functions. 25 bay golf driving range due to be opened.
Previous Grounds: Dolphin Playing Fields, Chalvey Road Sports Ground, York Road Maidenhead 1920, Centre Sports Ground 1936-42.

Slough Fact File

Nickname: The Rebels

Club Sponsors:
Previous Leagues: Southern Alliance 1892/93, Berks & Bucks 1901/05, Great Western S.W.Suburban, Spartan 1920/39, Herts & Middx 1940/45, Corinthian 1946/63, Athenian 1963/73, Isthmian 1973/90.
Club colours: Amber/navy blue
Change colours: All white
Reserve team league: Suburban Football League
Midweek home matchday: Tuesdays
Record win: 17-0 v Railway Clearing House - 1921/22
Record defeat: 1-11 v Chesham Town 1922
Record transfer fee: £18,000 for Colin Fieldon from Farnborough - 1991
Record transfer fee received: £22,000 from Wycombe for Steve Thompson - 1992
1992/93 Captain: Les Bailey
1992/93 Top scorer: Andy Sayer - 21
1992/93 Player of the Year: Les Bailey
Club record goalscorer: Terry Norris 85 - 1925/26
Record appearances: Terry Reardon 487 - 1964/81
Past players who progressed to the Football League: Paul Barron, Dave Kemp, Roy Davies, Mickey Droy, Eric Young, Alan Paris, Tony Dennis.

Club Honours: FA Amatuer Cup Finalists 1972/73; Spartan Runners-up 1920/21, 22/22, 31/32, 32/33, 38/39; Corinthian Champions 1950/51, Runners-up 45/46, 46/47, 55/56, 56/57, 57/58; Athenian Division 1 Champions 1964/65, Premier Champions 1967/68, 71/72, 72/73, Runners-up 68/69, League Cup Winners 64/65, 71/72, 72/73; Isthmian Division 2 Runners-up 1973/74, Premier Champions 1980/81, 89/90, League Cup Winners 1980/81, 89/90; Berks & BUcks FA Senior Cup Winners (9) 1902/03, 19/20, 23/24, 35/36, 54/55, 70/71, 71/72, 76/77, 80/81.

SOUTHPORT

Formed:
1881

President:
Jack Carr

Chairman:
Charles Clapham

Football Secretary:
Roy Morris

Manager:
Brain Kettle

Assistant Manager
Steve Joel

Physiotherapist:
Dave Knight

Press Officer:
Roy Morris

A truly magnificent season, crowned with promotion to the GM Vauxhall Conference, that really sums-up Southport's 1992/93 campaign.

Brain Kettle's team have really done him and the club's supporters proud, and their style of football has won them many friends, especially away from home where they scored an amazing 60 goals, 103 in all in the league, with only 31 against.

Wherever you look in the Port squad one can find success, but surely one of Kettle's major captures was that of striker Steve Haw from Marine. He netted 44 goals and formed a much-feared partnership in attack with another shrewd signing, former Runcorn forward, Peter Withers, who notched 26 goals. Goalkeeper Paul Moore, defenders Mark Schofield, Dave Fuller and Ian Baines, midfielders Dave Gamble and Mark Brennan, plus late season capture, Leroy Dove, all made significant contributions to the Haig Avenue club's revival.

The league was more competitive this year than for some time, as the likes of Witton Albion, Colne Dynamoes and Stalybridge Celtic all won the title by quite big margins. But the 1992/93 campaign has seen a much closer battle, with Southport making a timely move back up the Pyramid.

Much work has been done to their Haig Avenue ground. In fact, many thought that the task was beyond their means, especially with the time limit imposed for improvements to be made. However, thanks to grants from the Football Trust and contributions of over £100,000 from their Ground Development Appeal, the ground, which of course hosted League football not so many years ago, is now a credit to the club.

Amongst the improvements carried out is new covered terracing for over 1,000 spectators behind the Scarisbrook Road goal, new terracing for over 800 behind the Blowick end and more new terracing on the popular side for a further 1,200 fans which, when added to the 1,650 seats in the newly renovated Main Stand, takes the capacity beyond the 5,000-mark.

The Sandgrounders will be a welcome addition to the Conference circuit, and their attacking style of play will go down well with fans from every club.

TEAM TALK MAGAZINE.

Southport 1992-93 - Back Row (L-R): Alex Harrison, Derek Goulding, Leroy Dove, David Gamble, Paul Moore. 2nd Back: Andy Matthews, Mark Brennan, Chris Walmsley, Peter Withers, Ian Baines, Steve Haw, Max Thompson. 2nd Front: Roy Morris (Sec.), Steve Joel (Asst.Man), Brian Kettle (Man.), Kevin Mooney, Charlie Clapham (Chairman), Dave Knight (Physio). Front: Jon Senior, Dave Fuller, Neil Rigby, Paul Morris (Mascot), Alan McDonald, Mark Schofield.

SOUTHPORT MATCHFACTS 92-93   SOUTHPORT MATCHFACTS 92-93   SOUTHPORT MATCHFACTS 92-93

Key: Home fixtures are denoted by bold capitals. Numbers in brackets after players names indicate goals scored (an asterisk by the results denotes own goals). Only used substitutes are listed - substituted players are *italicised*.

Key to Competitions: **NPL**: Northern Premier League. **PC**: Northern Premier League Presidents Cup. **HFSC**: Northern Premier League Cup. **LSC**: Liverpool Senior Cup. **ATS**: Lancashire ATS Challenge Trophy. **FAC**: F.A. Cup. **FAT**: Vauxhall F.A. Trophy.

FA CUP: 2nd Round Proper   FA TROPHY: 3rd Qualifying Round

LEAGUE POSITION: 1st

Date	Opponents	Comp.	Res	Gate	1.	2.	3.	4.	5.	6.	7.	8.	9.	10.	11.	Sub.	Sub.
22/08	EMLEY	NPL	1-2	419	Moore	McDonald	Fuller	Mooney	Schofield	Goulding	*Senior*	Brennan(1)	Jarvis	*Gamble*	Withers	Walmsley	Joel
26/08	Fleetwood T.	NPL	2-1	334	Moore	McDonald	Fuller	Mooney	Schofield	Goulding	Senior	Brennan	*Withers*	Gamble(1)	Jarvis(1)	Walmsley	
29/08	Buxton	NPL	2-0	327	Moore	McDonald	Fuller	Mooney	Schofield	Goulding	Senior(1)	Brennan(1)	Withers	Walmsley	Jarvis		
31/08	CHORLEY	NPL	7-1	526	Moore	McDon'd(1)	Fuller	Mooney	*Schofield*	Goulding	Senior(1)	Brennan(2)	Withers	*Walmsley*	Jarvis(2)	Gamble(1)	Joel
05/09	GOOLE TOWN	FAC	3-0	382	Moore	McDonald	Fuller	Mooney	Schofield	Goulding	Senior	*Brennan(1)*	Withers	*Walmsley*	Jarvis(1)	Baines	Joel
08/09	Morecambe	NPL	2-0	680	Moore	McDonald	Fuller	Mooney	Schofield	Goulding	Senior	*Brennan*	Withers	*Baines(1)*	Jarvis	Gamble	Joel
12/09	BUXTON	FAC	0-0	432	Moore	McDonald	Fuller	Mooney	*Schofield*	Goulding	Senior	Baines	Withers	Gamble	*Jarvis*	Walmsley	Howard
15/09	Buxton	FAC	2-1	316	Moore	McDon'd(1)	Fuller	Mooney	*Schofield*	Goulding	Senior	*Brennan*	Withers	Gamble(1)	Baines	Walmsley	Howard
19/09	Matlock Town	NPL	5-1	367	Moore	McDonald	Fuller	Mooney	Schof'd(1)	*Goulding*	Senior	*Brennan(1)*	Haw(2)	Baines	Gamble	Wal'ley(1)	Howard
22/09	HYDE UNITED	NPL	1-0	534	Moore	McDonald	Fuller	Mooney	Schofield	Baines	Senior	Brennan	Haw	Gamble(1)	Withers(1)	Walmsley	
26/09	CHADDERTON	FAC	2-0	542	Moore	McDonald	Fuller	Mooney	Schofield	Baines	Senior	Brennan(1)	Haw	Gamble	Withers(1)	Walmsley	
30/09	Knowsley Utd	PC	4-1	206	Moore	McDonald	Fuller	Mooney	Schof'd(1)	Schofield	Senior	Brennan(1)	Haw	Gamble(1)	Withers(1)	Walmsley	
03/10	MOSSLEY	NPL	3-0	544	Moore	McDonald	Fuller	Mooney	Schof'd(1)	Walmsley	Senior	Brennan	Haw	Gamble(1)	Withers(1)	Baines	
06/10	MORECAMBE	NPL	1-1	904	Moore	McDonald	Fuller	Mooney	Goulding	Walmsley	Jarvis	Brennan	*Haw(1)*	*Gamble*	Withers	Walmsley	Schofield
10/10	Brigg Town	FAC	2-0	324	Moore	McDonald	Fuller	Mooney	Goulding	Schofield	Senior	*Brennan*	Haw(1)	Gamble	Withers	Walmsley	
13/10	Barrow	NPL	2-0	1,510	Moore	McDonald	Fuller	Mooney	Goulding(1)	Schofield	Senior(1)	Baines	*Haw(1)*	Gamble	Withers	Walmsley	
17/10	BISHOP A.	NPL	1-0	678	Moore	McDonald	Fuller	Mooney	Goulding	Schofield	Senior(1)	Baines	Haw	Gamble	Withers	Walmsley	
20/10	Chorley	NPL	6-1	501	Moore	McDonald	Fuller	Mooney	*Goulding*	Schofield	Senior(1)	Baines(1)	Haw(3)	Gamble	Withers(1)	Walmsley	Brennan
24/10	BARROW	FAC	0-0	1,545	Moore	McDonald	Fuller	Mooney	Goulding	Schofield	Senior	Baines	Haw	*Gamble*	Withers	Walmsley	
27/10	BARROW	FAC	3-2	2,082	Moore	McDon'd(1)	Fuller	Mooney	Goulding(1)	Schofield	*Senior*	Baines	Haw	*Gamble*	Withers	Walmsley	Brennan
31/10	Accrington S.	PC	5-3	571	Moore	McDonald	Fuller	Mooney	*Goulding*	Schofield	Wal'ley(2)	Brennan	Haw(1)	Withers(1)	*Baines(1)*	Dove	Rigby
07/11	Leek Town	NPL	0-1	633	Moore	McDonald	Fuller	Mooney	Goulding	Schofield	Walmsley	Brennan	Haw	*Brennan*	Withers	Dove	Gamble
10/11	HORWICH RMI	NPL	3-2	883	Moore	McDonald	Fuller	Mooney	Goulding	*Schofield*	*Walmsley*	Senior	Haw(1)	Gamble	Withers(2)	Baines	Brennan
14/11	Blyth Spartans	FAC	2-1	2,206	Moore	McDonald	Fuller	Mooney	Goulding	Schofield	Senior	Brennan	Haw(1)	Baines	Withers(1)	Baines	
17/11	ACCRINGTON S.	NPL	2-2	1,328	Moore	McDonald	Fuller	Mooney	Goulding	Schofield	Brennan(1)	*Baines*	Haw	Brennan	Withers	Wal'ley(1)	Gamble
21/11	Whitley Bay	NPL	5-1	205	Moore	McDonald	Fuller	Mooney	Schof'd(1)	Dove	Walmsley	Baines	Haw(2)	*Brennan*	Withers(2)		
24/11	BOOTLE	LSC	3-1	392	Moore	Rigby	Fuller	Mooney	Dove	Walmsley	Senior(1)	Gamble(1)	Haw	Thompson	*Withers(1)*	Baines	
28/11	Morecambe	FAT	2-2	948	Moore	McDonald	Fuller	Mooney	*Baines*	Schofield	Wal'ley(1)	Baines	Haw	Gamble	Withers(1)	Thompson	
30/11	MORECAMBE	FAT	1-3	887	Moore	McDonald	Fuller	Mooney	Goulding	Schof'd(1)	Walmsley	Brennan	Haw	Gamble	Withers	Thompson	
06/12	Hartlepool Utd	FAC	0-4	4,171	Moore	McDonald	Fuller	Mooney	Goulding	Schofield	*Walmsley*	Brennan	Haw	*Gamble*	Withers	Senior	
09/12	COLWYN BAY	NPL	2-0	765	Moore	McDonald	Rigby	Mooney	Dove	Schofield	Walmsley	Brennan	Haw(2)	Baines	Withers	Baines	

Match-by-match line-ups (League and Cup):

Date	Opposition	Comp	Res	Att	1	2	3	4	5	6	7	8	9	10	11	Sub	Sub
12/12	BUXTON	HFSC	4-1	462	Moore	McDonald	Fuller	Mooney	Dove	Schofield(2)	Wal'ley(1)	Brennan	Haw(1)	Baines	Withers	Senior	Gamble
19/12	Winsford Utd	NPL	2-1	801	Moore	McDonald	Fuller	Mooney	Dove	Schofield	Walmsley	Brennan	Haw(2)	Gamble	Withers	Baines	Gamble
26/12	MARINE	NPL	0-0	2,078	Moore	McDonald	Fuller	Mooney	Dove	Schofield	Walmsley	Brennan	Haw	Senior	Withers	Baines	Gamble
06/12	Horwich RMI	NPL	1-1	339	Moore	McDonald	Fuller	Mooney	Dove	Schofield	Wal'ley	Brennan	Haw(1)	Gamble	Withers	Baines	
09/12	BUXTON	NPL	2-1	752	Moore	McDonald	Fuller	Mooney	Dove	Schofield	Walmsley	Brennan	Haw(1)	Gamble	Withers	Senior	Gamble
13/12	Accrington S.	NPL	2-2	641	Moore	McDonald	Fuller	Mooney	Dove(1)	Schofield	Walmsley	Brennan	Haw(1)	Gamble(1)	Withers(1)	Quinlan	Senior
16/01	Frickley Ath.	NPL	5-2	393	Moore	McDonald	Fuller	Mooney	Dove	Schofield	Walmsley	Baines(1)	Haw(1)	Gamble	Withers(3)	Quinlan	Mellish
19/01	CLITHROE	ATS	4-1	472	Routledge	McDonald	Fuller	Mooney	Dove(1)	Schofield	Wal'Ley(1)	Brennan	Haw(1)	Gamble(2)	Withers	Baines	
23/01	Gainsborough T.	NPL	1-1	520	Routledge	McDonald	Fuller	Mooney	Dove	Schofield	Walmsley	Brennan	Haw(1)	Gamble(1)	Withers(1)	Baines	Mellish
27/01	LIVERPOOL	LSC	2-1	1,285	Routledge	McDonald	Fuller	Mooney	Dove(1)	Schofield	Walmsley	Brennan	Haw(1)	Gamble(1)	Withers(1)	Baines(2)	Mellish
30/01	Goole Town	NPL	5-0	298	Moore	Baines(1)	Fuller	Mooney	Dove(1)	Baines	Walmsley	Brennan(1)	Haw(1)	Gamble	Withers	Schofield	Goulding
02/02	Workington	HFSC	1-2	310	Moore	Baines	Fuller	Mooney	Dove	Schofield	Walmsley	Brennan	Haw	Gamble	Withers	McDonald	
06/02	MATLOCK TOWN	NPL	3-0	913	Moore	Baines	Fuller	Mooney	Dove	Schofield	Baines	Brennan	Haw	Gamble(1)	Withers(1)	McDonald	Mellish
09/02	Droylsden	NPL	5-2	593	Moore	McDonald	Fuller	Mooney	Goulding	Schofield	Walmsley	Brennan	Haw(3)	Gamble	Withers(1)	Brennan	
13/02	WHITLEY BAY	NPL	1-0	1,128	Moore	McDonald	Fuller	Mooney	Dove(1)	Schofield	Walmsley	Brennan	Haw	Gamble(1)	Withers(1)	Baines	
16/02	MARINE	ATS	1-0	1,018	Moore	Schofield	Fuller	Mooney	Dove	McDonald	Walmsley	Brennan	Haw	Gamble	Withers	McDonald	Mellish
20/02	LEEK TOWN	NPL	0-0	1,157	Moore	McDonald	Fuller	Mooney	Dove	Schofield	Walmsley	Brennan	Haw	Gamble	Withers	Schofield	
23/02	FLEETWOOD	NPL	5-0	1,207	Moore	McDonald	Fuller	Mooney	Dove(1)	Goulding	Walmsley	Brennan	Haw(3)	Gamble(1)	Withers(1)	Baines	Baines
27/02	Mossley	NPL	2-0	567	Moore	McDonald	Fuller	Mooney	Dove	Goulding	Walmsley	Brennan	Haw	Gamble	Withers(1)	Walmsley	Baines
03/03	Fleetwood T.	ATS	4-1	456	Moore	McDonald	Fuller	Mooney	Dove(1)	Goulding	Walmsley	Brennan	Haw(2)	Gamble	Withers	Baines	Mellish
06/03	GAINSBOROUGH	NPL	0-0	1,007	Moore	Joel	Fuller	Mooney	Dove	Goulding	Baines	Senior	Haw	Gamble(1)	Withers	Mellish(1)	
09/03	MORECAMBE	PC	2-0	816	Moore	McDonald	Fuller	Mooney	Dove	Goulding	Baines	Brennan	Haw(1)	Gamble(1)	Withers	Walmsley	
13/03	Bishop Auckland	NPL	3-1	426	Moore	McDonald	Fuller	Mooney	Dove	Goulding	Baines(1)	Brennan	Haw	Gamble(1)	Withers(1)	Mellish	
16/03	Morecambe	PC	0-1	512	Moore	Baines	Fuller	Mooney	Dove(1)	Goulding	Walmsley	Senior	Haw	Gamble	Withers	Brennan	Senior
20/03	Hyde United	NPL	1-1	576	Moore	Baines	Fuller	Mooney	Dove	Goulding	Walmsley	Brennan	Haw	Gamble	Withers(2)	Baines	
24/03	Colwyn Bay	NPL	4-2	350	Moore	Baines	Fuller	Mooney	Dove	McDonald	Walmsley	Brennan	Haw(2)	Gamble	Withers	McDonald	
27/03	DROYLSDEN	NPL	1-1	1,185	Moore	McDonald	Fuller	Mooney	Goulding	Schofield	Senior(2)	Brennan	Haw	Gamble	Withers	Brennan	
30/03	Tranmere R.	LSC	3-0	1,110	Moore	McDonald	Fuller	Mooney	Goulding(1)	Dove	Senior	Brennan	Haw(1)	Gamble	Withers	McDonald	Brennan
10/04	BARROW	NPL	3-0	1,723	Moore	Baines	Fuller	Mooney	Goulding	Dove	Wal'ley(1)	Senior	Haw(1)	Gamble	Withers	McDonald	
12/04	Marine	NPL	1-2	1,611	Moore	Baines	Fuller	Mooney	Goulding(1)	McDonald	Walmsley	Senior	Haw(1)	Gamble	Withers	Baines(1)	Mellish
17/04	Emley	NPL	4-0	504	Moore	McDonald	Fuller	Mooney	Goulding	Schofield	Walmsley	Brennan	Haw	Gamble	Withers(3)	Schofield	Bren. (2)
19/04	Chorley	ATS	5-2	1,529	Moore	McDonald	Fuller	Mooney	Goulding	Schofield	Walmsley	Brennan	Haw	Gamble	Withers(2)	Baines	Senior
21/04	Winsford Utd	PC	0-2	587	Moore	McDonald	Fuller	Mooney	Goulding	Mellish	Walmsley	Brennan	Haw	Gamble	Withers	Schofield	Senior
24/04	FRICKLEY ATH	NPL	2-1	2,230	Moore	McDonald	Fuller	Mooney	Goulding	Schofield	Walmsley	Brennan	Haw(2)	Gamble	Withers	Dove	Walmsley
27/04	WINSFORD UTD	PC	4-3	1,137	Moore	McDonald	Fuller	Mooney	Goulding	Brennan	Walmsley	Dove	Haw(3)	Gamble	Withers	Schofield	Walmsley
01/05	WINSFORD UTD	NPL	0-1	1,177	Moore	Baines	Fuller	Mooney(1)	Goulding(1)	Schofield	Walmsley	Brennan	Haw(1)	Dove	Withers	Senior	Moore
11/05	Burscough	LSC	2-1	2,000	Moore	McDonald	Fuller	Mooney	Goulding(1)	Schofield	Walmsley	Brennan	Haw(1)	Dove	Withers	Baines	Mellish

LEAGUE APPEARANCES: Baines 23+12, Brennan 32+4, Dove 23+2, Fuller 41, Gamble 30+7, Goulding 26, Haw 36, Howard 0+1, Jarvis 7, Joel 0+2, McDonald 37+3, Mellish 0+6, Mooney 42, Moore 41, Quinlan 0+2, Rigby 1, Routledge 1, Schofield 31+2, Senior 23+4, Walmsley 28+11, Withers 40.

LEAGUE GOALSCORERS: Haw 32; Withers 18; Gamble 10; Brennan, Baines 8; Dove, Senior 6; Schofield 5; Walmsley, Jarvis 4; McDonald, Mooney 1.

Southport

BRIAN KETTLE

Brian, a former England Youth International, began his career as an apprentice with Liverpool. However, due to the tremendous strength in depth in the Anfield squad during the early 1970s, Brian's first-team appearances were restricted to three matches.

In August 1980, Brian transferred to Wigan Athletic where he made 14 League appearances before joining the North American Soccer League circus with Houston Hurricane.

Upon his return to England, Brian played semi-professionally for Runcorn and South Liverpool before taking over as player-manager at the latter. He then joined Southport three years ago with last season's Northern Premier League Championship being the culmination of three years of steady progress.

Brian likes to play attacking football, and his principles won't change now that the former Football League club are only one step away from re-claiming the place they lost in 1973.

The Southport defence clear under pressure at Hartlepool. Photo: Dennis Nicholson.

Programme details:
    44-52 pages for 70p
    Editor - Derek Hitchcock 0704 579458

Any other club publications:

    Local Newspapers:
    Southport Visitor
    Southport Star

Local Radio Stations:
    Radio Merseyside
    Red Rose
    Radio City

SOUTHPORT - PLAYING SQUAD 1992-93

Player	Honours	Birthplace and date	Transfer Fees	Previous Clubs
GOALKEEPERS				
Paul Moore	NPL, NPLC,	Liverpool 1/4/61		Rhyl, Worcester C, Alvechurch, Morecambe
DEFENDERS				
Kevin Mooney	NPL (2), NPLC, BLT, LSC	Liverpool 23/8/59		Bangor C, Bury, Karlskrona, Telford Utd, Tranmere Rov, Stafford R, Bangor C
Alan McDonald	NPL, NPLC, LSC	Liverpool 17/12/63		St Helens T, Gen Chemicals, Southport, Witton Alb, Accrington S, Altrincham
Paul Comstive	WC	Southport 12/11/61		Blackburn R, Wigan, Wrexham, Burnley, Bolton W, Chester City
Derek Goulding	NPL, APL, SSC	Liverpool 6/5/63		Altrincham, Bangor C, Stafford R, Oswestry, Bangor C, Chorley
MIDFIELD				
Chris Walmesley	NPL, GMAC	Wigan 21/7/66		Daisy Hill, Horwich RMI, Atherton LR, Horwich RMI, Fleetwood
David Gamble	NPL	23/3/71		Grimsby, Altrincham
Stuart Mellish	NPL	Hyde 19/11/69		Blackpool, Rochdale, Altrincham, Witton Alb, Morecambe, Nth Trafford, Barrow
Ian Baker	NPL	Liverpool		Sth Liverpool, Altrincham, Sth Liverpool, Bootle, Sth Liverpool
FORWARDS				
Darren Lyons		Manchester 9/11/66	£3,000	Oldham Ath, Rhyl, Droylsden, Macclesfield, Leek, Mossley, Ashton U, Acc Stan, Bury
Steve Haw	NPL, BLT, CSC, LSC	Liverpool 9/11/62		Wigan Ath, Runcorn, Kirkby T, Marine, Altrincham, Marine
Peter Withers	NPL, LSC	Huyton 2/5/66		Sth Liverpool, Runcorn
Phil Quinlan	EY	Southport 17/4/71		Everton, Doncaster Rovers
John Waring				Telford Utd, Runcorn, Mossley, Droylsden, Bangor C

Departures during season:
Tony Jarvis (Gt Harwood), Bob Howard (Burscough), Stuart Thompson (Clitheroe), Jon Senior (Accrington Stanley), Ian Baines (Marine), Mark Schofield (Chorley).

Players on loan during season:

Haig Avenue, Southport

Address and telephone number: Haig Avenue, Southport, Merseyside. Tel: 0704 533422

Simple directions: Signposted from all entrances to town.

Capacity: 5,500 **Seated:** 1,880 **Covered terracing:** 1,100

Record Attendance: 20,000 v Newcastle United - FA Cup - 1932

Club Shop: Scarves, replica kits, programmes and various other souvenirs for sale. Contact Southport FC.

Social Facilities: Open 7.30-11.00 every night and match days.

Previous Grounds: Ash Lane

Southport Fact File

Nickname: The Sandgrounders

Club Sponsors: Apollo Leisure

Previous Leagues: Northern Premier League, Football League, Lancashire Combination

Club colours: Old Gold & black

Change colours: White & black

Midweek home matchday: Tuesday

Record win: 8-1 v Nelson - 01.01.31.

Record defeat: 0-11 v Oldham - 26.12.62

Record transfer fee: £6,000 for Malcolm Russell

Record transfer fee received: £20,000 from Rochdale for Steve Whitehall - 1991

1992/93 Captain: K.Mooney

1992/93 Top scorer: Steve Haw 45

1992/93 Player of the Year: K.Mooney

Club record goalscorer: Alan Spence 98

Record appearances: Arthur Peat 401 - 1962-72

Club Honours: Football League Division Four Champions 1972/73, Runners-up 1966/67; HFS Loans League Champions 1992/93; Third Division North Section Cup Winners 1937/38; Liverpool Senior Cup Winners 1930/31, 1931/32, 1943/44, 1957/58 (shared), 1963/64 (shared), 1974/75, 1990/91, 1992/93; Lancashire Senior Cup Winners 1904/05; Lancashire Junior Cup Winners 1919/20, 1992/93; HFS Loans League Cup Winners 1990/91.

STAFFORD RANGERS

Formed:
1876

President:
R.N.Heath
Chairman:
R.J.Horton
Vice Chairman
L.H.Douglas
Football Secretary:
Mr M.T.Hughes
Manager:
Brendan Phillips
Coach:
Steve Burr
Physiotherapist:
Barrie Whittaker
Commercial Manager:
George Berry
Press Officer:
Chris Godwin

The 1992/93 season provided long suffering Stafford Rangers supporters plenty to cheer after four disappointing campaigns with success in the Conference, FA Cup and held over 1991/92 Staffordshire Senior Cup Final.

Perhaps the highlight of the season was the marathon nine match FA Cup run from the First Qualifying Round to the Second Round Proper which included victory over Lincoln City, Rangers' first against Football League opposition since 1975. Commencing with a 3-0 victory over Alfreton Town after a replay, the team travelled to Bedworth United, managed at that time by Brendon Phillips. The Beazer Homes League side looked set to cause an upset after taking a first-half lead and as the match progressed Rangers became more frustrated; however, Ian Rutherford managed to scramble home an 88th minute equaliser. No mistake was made in the replay and subsequent home victories over Frickley Athletic and Bromsgrove Rovers earned a First Round trip to Lincoln City. At Sincil Bank, the whole team produced one of the best tactical performances of the season to earn a goalless draw with rock solid defence. With a trip to Marine awaiting the winner, Rangers took an early 10 minute lead in the replay through Darren Boughey who latched onto a clearance by Nigel Callaghan, sprinted clear, sidestepped the advancing keeper and shot into an empty net. The Imps levelled on 49 minutes but on the hour left full-back Mark Bradshaw scored what proved to be the winner, converting a low Callaghan cross from close range. In the Second Round tie Rangers got stuck in the Rossett Park mud as Marine coped best with a near waterlooged pitch. The HFS Loans Leaguers took a decisive three goal lead and despite a late rally which saw Steve Essex and George Berry reduce the deficit Rangers FA Cup dream ended with a disappointing 3-2 defeat.

In the Conference, hopes were high that Rangers would emerge from four difficult seasons and challenge for position in the upper reaches of the table. Faced with a difficult opening fixture at Woking, Rangers played some attractive football and stunned the previously all conquering newboys by three clear goals. Excellent form continued as Rangers built up a seven match unbeaten run to establish a position in the top five. However, the prolonged FA Cup run plus replays in both the Drinkwise Cup and Vauxhall FA Trophy took its toll on the players as Rangers plummeted down the table to reach bottom position at the end of December but with plenty of games in hand. In the first five months of the campaign Dennis Booth's men played 34 matches of which 18 were cup games. As 1993 arrived, the question on everybody's lips was could the team turn those games in hand into vital points required to move out of the relegation battle. The answer was yes as Rangers became the Conference's form team during the climb from 22nd to a final position of 6th, which equalled the club's previous best set in 1987/88.

At the end of March, Dennis Booth resigned as Stafford Rangers Manager after fifteen months in charge to take up the position of Assistant Manager to John Ward at Bristol Rovers. Appointed as successor was Bedworth United's manager Brendon Phillips, a former England non-League International who is no stranger to the Conference having played for Kettering Town, Boston United and Aylesbury United.

Chris Bedford (Programme Editor).

Stafford Rangers · 1993-94.

STAFFORD MATCHFACTS 92-93 STAFFORD MATCHFACTS 92-93 STAFFORD MATCHFACTS 92-93

Key: Home fixtures are denoted by bold capitals. Numbers in brackets after players names indicate goals scored (an asterisk by the results denotes own goals). Only used substitutes are listed - substituted players are *italicised*.

Key to Competitions: GMVC: G.M. Vauxhall Conference. SSC: Staffordshire Senior Cup. DC: Drinkwise (G.M. Vauxhall Conference) Cup. FAC: F.A. Cup. FAT: Vauxhall F.A. Trophy.

FA TROPHY: First Round
FA CUP: Second Round
FA CUP: First Round

LEAGUE POSITION: 6th

Date	Opponents	Comp.	Res	Gate	1.	2.	3.	4.	5.	6.	7.	8.	9.	10.	11.	Sub.	Sub.
11/08	Chasetown	SSC F	2-0	536	Price	Pearson	Bradshaw	Skipper	Essex	Berry	Boughey(1)	Jones.P	Wood	Palgrave(1)	Circuit		
18/08	**CHASETOWN**	SSC F	2-2	434	Price	Pearson	Bradsh'(2)	*Skipper*	Essex	Simpson	Boughey	Jones.P	Wood	Palgrave	Circuit	Hemming	
22/08	Woking	GMVC	3-0	2,044	Price	Pearson	Bradshaw	Simpson	Essex	Berry	Boughey(1)	Jones.P	Clayton(2)	Palgrave	Circuit		
25/08	**STALYBRIDGE C.**	GMVC	0-0	1,133	Price	Pearson	Bradshaw	Simpson	Essex	Berry	Boughey	Jones.P	Clayton	Palgrave	Circuit	Hemming	
29/08	**WELLING UTD**	GMVC	*4-3	786	Price	Pearson	Bradshaw	Simpson(1)	Essex	Berry(1)	Boughey	*Jones.P*	Clayton(1)	Palgrave	Circuit		
02/09	Boston United	GMVC	1-0	985	Price	Pearson	Bradshaw	Simpson	Essex	Berry	Boughey	Jones.P(1)	Clayton	Palgrave	Curcuit	Hemming	
05/09	Merthyr Tyd.	GMVC	0-0	694	Price	Pearson	Bradshaw	Simpson	Essex	Berry	*Boughey*	*Jones.P*	Clayton	Palgrave	Circuit	Hemming	
08/09	**BROMSGROVE**	DC	4-2	667	Price	Pearson	Bradshaw	Simpson(1)	Essex	Berry(1)	Hemm'(1)	Rutherford	Clayton	Palgrave	Circuit	Boughey	Wood(1)
12/09	Alfreton Town	FAC	0-0	381	Price	Pearson	Bradshaw	Simpson(1)	Essex	Hemming	Boughey	Jones.P	Clayton	Palgrave	Rutherford	Skipper	Wood
15/09	**ALFRETON TOWN**	FAC	3-0	750	Price	Pearson	Bradshaw	*Simpson*(1)	*Essex*	Berry	Hemm'(1)	Jones.P	Wood	*Palgrave*	Ruth'ford(1)	Boughey	Lyons
19/09	**BATH CITY**	GMVC	3-2	921	Price	Pearson	Bradshaw	*Simpson*	Essex	Berry(1)	Hemming	Jones.P	Clayton(1)	Palgrave(1)	Skipper	Boughey	Wood
22/09	Bromsgrove	DC	1-2	757	Price	Pearson	Bradshaw	Skipper	Essex	Berry	Hemming	Jones.P	Clayton(1)	Boughey	Boughey	Circuit	Wood
26/09	Bedworth Utd	FAC	1-1	401	Price	Pearson	*Bradshaw*	Skipper	Essex	Berry	Hemming	Jones.P	Clayton	Ruth'ford(1)	Boughey	Simpson	Rford
29/09	**BEDWORTH UTD**	FAC	1-0	762	Price	Pearson	Bradshaw	Skipper	Essex	Berry	Hemming	Jones.P	Clayton	Palgrave(1)	Simpson	Boughey	
03/10	**FARNBOROUGH**	GMVC	2-2	947	Price	Pearson	Hemming	Bradshaw	Essex	Berry	Boughey(1)	Jones.P	Clayton	Palgrave	Simpson	Simpson	Bradshaw
06/10	Kettering T	GMVC	0-2	1,260	Price	Pearson	Bradshaw	Skipper	Essex	Berry	Boughey	Jones.P	Clayton	Palgrave	Simpson	Circuit	Lyons
10/10	**FRICKLEY ATH.**	FAC	3-0	840	Price	Pearson	Bradshaw	Skipper	Essex(1)	Berry(1)	Boughey	Jones.P(1)	*Clayton*	Palgrave	Simpson		
13/10	**BIRMINGHAM C.**	SSC	1-2	420	Price	Pearson	Bradshaw	Skipper	Essex	Berry	Callaghan	Circuit	Wood(1)	Palgrave	Simpson	Boughey	
17/10	Yeovil Town	GMVC	0-2	1,903	Price	Pearson	Bradshaw	*Skipper*	Essex	Berry	Circuit	*Callaghan*	Clayton	Palgrave	Simpson	Boughey	Wood
20/10	**TELFORD UNITED**	DC	0-0	631	Price	Pearson	Simpson	Skipper	Circuit	Berry	Boughey	Jones.P	Clayton	Palgrave	Callaghan	Simpson	Wood
24/10	**BROMSGROVE**	FAC	3-0	1,274	Price	Pearson	Simpson	Skipper	Essex(2)	Berry(1)	Circuit	Jones.P	Callaghan	Palgrave	Clayton	Boughey	
27/10	Telford United	DC	*2-5	651	Price	Pearson	Bradshaw	Simpson	Essex	Berry(1)	*Boughey*	Jones.P	*Circuit*	Palgrave	Clayton	Boughey	Wood
31/10	**YEOVIL TOWN**	GMVC	0-1	854	Price	Pearson	Bradsh'(1)	Skipper	Essex	Berry	Simpson	Jones.P	*Callaghan*	Palgrave	Clayton	Boughey	Wood
07/11	Wycombe W.	GMVC	2-2	4,569	Price	Pearson	Bradshaw	Skipper	Essex	Berry	Simpson	Jones.P	*Callaghan*	Palgrave	Clayton(1)	Boughey	Wood
10/11	**ALTRINCHAM**	GMVC	0-0	831	Price	Pearson	Bradshaw	Circuit	Essex	Berry	Simpson	Jones.P	Boughey	Palgrave	*Clayton*	Griffiths	
14/11	Lincoln City	FAC	0-0	3,380	Price	Pearson	Bradshaw	Simpson	Essex	Berry	Wood	Jones.P	Whitehurst	Palgrave	Clayton	Boughey	
17/11	Macclesfield	GMVC	1-4	473	Price	Pearson	Bradshaw	Simpson	Essex	Berry	Calla'han(1)	Jones.P	Whitehurst	Palgrave	*Wood*	Circuit	
21/11	**DAGENHAM & R.**	GMVC	0-1	786	Price	*Pearson*	Bradshaw	Simpson	Essex	Berry	Callaghan	*Jones.P*	Whitehurst	Palgrave	Circuit	Griffiths	
14/11	Lincoln City	FAC	0-0	3,380	Price	Pearson	Bradshaw	Simpson	Essex	Berry	Wood	Jones.P	Callaghan	Palgrave	Clayton	Griffiths	Wood

Date	Opponent	Comp	Score	Att	1	2	3	4	5	6	7	8	9	10	11	Subs
25/11	**LINCOLN CITY**	FAC	2-1	2,209	Price	Circuit	Bradsh'(1)	Wood	Essex	Berry	Boughey(1)	Griffiths	Clayton–Wood(1)	Palgrave	Callaghan	Oskar, H'ming
28/11	**WEMBLEY**	FAT	1-1	812	Price	Circuit	Bradshaw	Jones.P	Essex	Berry	Boughey	Griffiths	Wood(1)	Palgrave(1)	Hemming	Wood
05/12	Marine	FAC	2-3	1,965	Price	Circuit	Bradshaw	Simpson	Essex	Berry(1)	Boughey	Jones.P	Callaghan	Palgrave(1)	Hemmings	
10/12	Wembley	FAT	1-0	111	Price	Pearson	Bradshaw	Simpson	Essex	Berry	Boughey	Henry(1)	Callaghan	Wood	Clayton	
19/12	**KETTERING**	GMVC	2-4	815	Price	Pearson	Bradshaw	Wood	Essex(1)	Berry	Boughey	Henry	Edwards	Palgrave	Clayton	
28/12	**RUNCORN**	GMVC	0-1	876	Price	Pearson	Bradshaw	Simpson	Essex	Jones	Boughey	Hemmings	Edwards	Wood	Jones.P	
09/01	Grays Athletic	FAT	0-1	421	Price	Simpson	Bradshaw	Wood	Essex(1)	Berry	Boughey	Jones.P	Wood	Palgrave	Clayton	Jones.M
26/01	**GATESHEAD**	GMVC	2-1	538	Price	Simpson	Bradshaw	Hemm'(1)	Essex(1)	Berry	Boughey(1)	Jones.M	Wood(1)	Palgrave	Griffiths(1)	Clay'(1)
30/01	Altrincham	GMVC	5-1	858	Price	Simpson	Bradshaw	Hemming	Essex	Berry	Boughey	Jones	Burr	Palgrave(1)	Clayton	
06/02	**MACCLESFIELD**	GMVC	1-0	1,025	Price	Simpson	Bradshaw	Hemming	Essex	Wood	Boughey	Jones	Burr(1)	Palgrave	Clayton	
10/02	Gateshead	GMVC	1-0	297	Price	Simpson	Bradshaw	Hemming	Essex	Wood	Boughey	Jones.P	Burr	Palgrave	Clayton	
13/02	Dagenham & R.	GMVC	0-1	1,015	Price	Simpson	Bradshaw	Hemming	Essex	Wood	Boughey	Jones.P	Burr	Palgrave	Clayton	Dawson
16/02	**KIDDMINSTER**	GMVC	0-1	1,294	Price	Simpson	Bradshaw	Hemming	Essex	Wood	Boughey	Jones.P	Burr	Palgrave	Clayton	
23/02	Bromsgrove	GMVC	3-2	1,130	Price	Simpson	Bradshaw	Hemmings	Essex	Jones.M	Boughey(1)	Jones.P(1)	Burr	Palgrave	Clayton(1)	
27/02	Stalybridge	GMVC	0-1	752	Price	Jones	Bradshaw	Hemming	Essex	Berry	Boughey	Jones.P	Burr	Palgrave	Wood	
03/03	**MERTHYR TYD.**	GMVC	0-1	618	Price	Wood	Bradshaw	Hemming	Essex	Berry	Dawson	Jones.P	Burr	Clayton	Clayton	Clay(1)
06/03	Welling Utd	GMVC	2-1	712	Price	Simpson	Bradshaw	Hemming	Essex	Berry	Boughey	Jones.P	Burr(1)	Clayton	Clayton	
09/03	Telford Utd	GMVC	0-0	1,068	Price	Simpson	Bradshaw	Hemming	Essex	Berry	Boughey(2)	Jones.P(1)	Burr	Clayton	Palgrave	
13/03	**WOKING**	GMVC	0-0	1,062	Price	Simpson	Bradshaw	Hemming	Essex	Wood	Boughey	Jones.P	Burr	Clayton(1)	Clayton	Wood
16/03	Witton Alb.	GMVC	5-2	695	Price	Simpson	Bradsh'(1)	Hemming	Essex	Berry	Boughey	Jones.P	Burr(1)	Clayton	Palgrave	Wood
20/03	Kidderminster	GMVC	2-0	1,234	Price	Simpson	Bradshaw	Hemming	Essex	Wood	Boughey	Jones.P	Burr	Clayton	Fisher	
23/03	**BOSTON UTD**	GMVC	0-0	848	Price	Simpson	Bradshaw	Hemming	Essex	Berry	Boughey	Jones.P	Burr	Clayton	Dawson	Wood
27/03	Farnborough	GMVC	1-1	741	Price	Mettioui	Bradshaw	Hemming	Essex	Berry(1)	Boughey	Jones.P	Burr(1)	Clayton	Fisher	
30/03	**WITTON ALB.**	GMVC	1-1	912	Price	Jones	Bradshaw	Hemming	Essex	Berry	Boughey	Jones.P	Burr	Palgrave	Palgrave	
03/04	Slough Town	GMVC	1-2	823	Price	Griffiths	Bradshaw	Hemming	Essex	Berry	Dawson	Jones.P	Burr	Clayton	Fisher	
06/04	Northwich Vic.	GMVC	2-1	802	Price	Simpson	Bradshaw	Hemm'(1)	Essex	Wood	Boughey(1)	Griffiths	Burr	Mettioui	Fisher	
10/04	**TELFORD UTD**	GMVC	2-1	1,007	Price	Simpson	Bradshaw	Hemming	Essex	Wood	Boughey	Griffiths	Burr	Mettioui	Dawson	
12/04	Runcorn	GMVC	2-0	596	Price	Simpson(1)	Bradshaw	Hemming	Essex	Wood	Boughey	Griffiths	Burr(1)	Mettioui	Griffiths	
17/04	**NORTHWICH**	GMVC	1-0	953	Price	Simpson	Bradshaw	Hemming	Essex	Wood	Boughey(1)	Griffiths	Burr	Mettioui(1)	Wood	
20/04	**BROMSGROVE**	GMVC	3-4	1,126	Price	Simpson	Bradshaw	Hemming	Essex	Wood(1)	Boughey	Griffiths	Burr	Mettioui(1)	Berry	
24/04	Bath City	GMVC	1-2	573	Price	Simpson	Bradshaw	Hemming	Essex	Wood	Boughey	Griffiths	Burr	Jones	Berry	
29/04	**WYCOMBE W.**	GMVC	0-1	1,631	Price	Simpson	Bradshaw	Hemming	Essex	Wood	Boughey	Simpson	Burr	Jones	Berry	Clayton
01/05	**SLOUGH TOWN**	GMVC	1-0	886	Price	Wood	Bradshaw	Hemming	Essex	Berry(1)	Boughey	Simpson	Clayton	Jones	Clayton	

LEAGUE APPEARANCES: Berry 29(3); Boughey 33(5); Bradshaw 41; Burr 23; Callaghan 5; Circuit 9(1); Clayton 22(8); Dawson 12(2); Edwards 2; Essex 40; Fisher 7(2); Griffiths 12(4); Hemming 29(3); Henry 2; M.Jones 6(1); P.Jones 34(2); Lyons 0(1); Mettioui 6; Palgrave 29(3); Paul 0(1); Pearson 16; Price 42; Simpson 37; Skipper 5; Whitehurst 2: Wood 19(11).

LEAGUE GOALSCORERS: Clayton 9: Boughey 7: Burr 6: Berry, Palgrave 4: Bradshaw, Essex, Mettioui, Simpson 3: Dawson, Hemming, P.Jones, Wood 2: Callaghan, Fisher, Griffiths, Henry 1.

Stafford Rangers

BRENDAN PHILLIPS

Brendan was appointed as manager at Marston Road towards the end of last season after Dennis Booth departed for Bristol Rovers. Prior to his appointment, Brendan had been in charge at Beazer Homes League club Bedworth United for two successful years.

During his playing career, Brendan served 12 clubs, played in the Football League for Mansfield Town and represented the England semi-professional side on four occasions. A skilfull midfield player, Brendan took in spells with Peterborough United, Burton Albion, Nuneaton Borough (twice), Kettering Town, Boston United (twice), Mansfield, Scarborough (twice), Shepshed, Corby Town, Aylesbury United and Atherstone United before joining Bedworth.

Wayne Simpson and Mark Bradshaw (3) tangle with Wycombe's Simon Hutchinson. Photo: V.J.Robertson.

Programme details:
  40 pages for £1.00
  Editor - C & W Bedford

Any other club publications:

Local Newspapers:
  Staffordshire Newsletter
  Express & Star
  Evening Sentinel

Local Radio Stations:
  Radio Stoke
  Beacon Radio
  Signal Radio

STAFFORD RANGERS - PLAYING SQUAD 1992-93

Player	Honours	Birthplace and date	Transfer Fees	Previous Clubs
GOALKEEPERS				
Ryan Price	ESP, FA XI, SSC	Wolverhampton 13/3/70		Bolton Wanderers
DEFENDERS				
Wayne Simpson	FA XI	Newcastle, Staffs 19/9/68		Port Vale
Mark Bradshaw	SSC	Ashton-Under-Lyme 7/9/69		Blackpool
George Berry	Wales Int., League Cup	Rostrup, Ger 19/11/57		Wolves, Stoke City, Peterborough Utd, Preston NE, Aldershot
Steve Essex	FA XI	Walsall 2/10/60	£7,000	Darlaston, Blakenall, Rushall O, Wolves Utd, Gresley R, Burton Alb, Aylesbury Utd
Chris Hemming		Newcastle, Staffs 13/4/66		Stoke City, Hereford Utd, Merthyr Tydfil
MIDFIELD				
Fraser Wood	FAT, NPL	Wednesbury 18/12/58	£2,000	Tipton Town, Stafford Rangers, Kidderminster H
Darren Boughey	E U-19	Stoke 30/11/70		Stoke City
Tony Griffiths	FAT	Stoke 1/4/63		Port Vale, Stafford, Leek Town, Telford Utd, Leek Town
FORWARDS				
Brian Palgrave		Birmingham 12/7/66		Walsall, Nuneaton Borough, Port Vale, Bromsgrove Rovers
Paul Clayton	FAYC	Dunstable 4/1/65		Norwich City, Darlington, Crewe Alexandra, Macclesfield T
Steve Burr	NPL, NPLC	Birmingham 12/1/61	£4,000	Lichfield, Atherstone T, Stafford Rangers, Macclesfield T, Hednesford T
Danny Williams		Wolverhampton 29/10/68		Blakenall, Harrisons, North Park, Bloxwich, Wolves, Bilston T
Jason Dawson		Stoke 9/2/71		Port Vale, Rochdale, Macclesfield T

Departures during season:
Peter Skipper (Wigan), Tony Henry (Hyde), Steve Circuit & Ian Pountney (Released),, Nigel Callaghan (Boreham Wood), Jon Pearson (Solihull), Dean Edwards, Paul Jones & David Jones (Released).

Players on loan during season:
Ian Rutherford & Ahmed Mettioui (Crewe), Marcus Jones (Stoke).

Marston Road, Stafford Rangers

Address and telephone number: Marston Road, Stafford St16 3BX.
Tel: 0785 42750
Simple directions: From M6 junction 14, A34 (Stone) to roundabout, straight over into Beaconside, take third right into Common Road, ground one mile ahead. From Town Centre, follow signs for B5066 (Sandon) turn left by Lotus shoe factory. Two miles from railway station.
Capacity: 6,000　　　　　　　**Seated:** 426　　　　　　**Covered terracing:** 3,000
Record Attendance: 8,536 v Rotherham United FA Cup Third Round - 4.1.1975
Club Shop: Two shops, one containing a large stock of old programmes and one specialising in souvenirs run by Jim & Irene Dalglish.
Social Facilities:
Previous Grounds: Lammascotes, Stone Road, Newtown, Doxey (until 1896)

Stafford Fact File

Nickname: Boro

Club Sponsors: Sentinal Newspapers

Previous Leagues: Shropshire League 1891/93, Birmingham League 1893/96, 1921/40, North Staffordshire League 1896/1900, Cheshire League 1900/01, Birmingham Combination 1900/12, 1946/52, Cheshire County League 1952/69, Northern Premier League 1969/79, 1983/85, Alliance Premier League 1979/83.

Club colours: Black & white striped shirts, black shorts & socks

Change colours: All yellow

Midweek home matchday: Tuesday

Record win: 11-0 v Dudley Town, FA Cup - 6.9.58

Record defeat: 0-12 v Burton Town, Birmingham Lge - 13.12.30

Record transfer fee: £13,000 for Stephen Butterworth from VS Rugby - 1990

Record transfer fee received: £100,000 from Crystal Palace for Stan Collymore - 1990

1992/93 Captain: Steve Essex

1992/93 Top scorer: Paul Clayton

1992/93 Player of the Year: Chris Hemming

Club record goalscorer: M.Cullerton 176

Record appearances: Jim Sargent

Past players who progressed to the Football League: M.Alckisie (Plymouth, Luton, Spurs), J.Arnold (Blackburn, Everton, Port Vale), R.Williams, M.Cullerton, T.Bailey (all Port Vale), K.Barnes (Man. City), A.Lee (Tranmere Rovers), E.Cameron, (Exeter), W.Blunt (Wolves), G.Bullock (Barnsley), K.Mottershead (Doncaster), McIlvenny (WBA), S.Collymore.

Club Honours: Birmingham Combination Champions 1912-13; Birmingham League Champions 1925-26; Northern Premier League Champions 1971-72, 1984-85; FA Trophy Winners 1971-72, 1978-79, Runners-up 1975-76; Bob Lord Trophy 1985-86; Wednesday Charity Cup Winners 1920-21; Midland Floodlight Cup Winners 1970-71; NPL Championship Shield Winners 1984-85; Jim Thompson Shield Winners 1986-87; Staffs Senior Cup Winners 1954-55, 1956-57, 1962-63, 1971-72, 1977-78, 1986-87, 1991-92.

STALYBRIDGE CELTIC

Formed:
1908

President:
J.Knott
Chairman:
Peter Barnes
Vice Chairman
Derek Wolsterholme
Football Secretary:
Martyn Torr
Manager:
Phil Wilson
Assistant Manager:
Dave Stewart
Physiotherapist:
Dave Stevens
Commercial Manager:
Martyn Torr
Press Officer:
Martyn Torr

Stalybridge Celtic's inaugural season in the Vauxhall Conference was disappointing.

Regarded by many as the weakest of the three promoted clubs, they surprised most pundits by their solid, if unspectacular performances from the word go.

They carried an unbeaten run for nine games, losing in somewhat unsatisfactory fashion at Witton, to disputed penalty in first-half unjury time and an own goal in injury time. That match extended Witton's own unbeaten run. It was to prove a watershed. Celtic took stock, a deep breath and pressed on with their determined style while Witton plummetted and only just avoided relegation. The lesson is that early season traumas or sucesses need to be kept in context. Defeat was not the end of the world for Stalybridge, in fact it helped the club keep its feet firmly on the ground.

They didn't exactly set the league alight after that defeat, losing badly at eventual champions Wycombe before hitting a purple patch of away form with victories at Dagenham and, with what was probably their best performance of the season, at Telford. The Telford win saw what was easily the outstanding individual performance of the season by a Celtic player, with Mark Edwards in devasting form. He went on to finish the side's top scorer and it will be interesting to see how they cope without his blockbusting shooting and ferocious rading down the left flank. He has chosen to play in the less arduous and less time-consuming Northern Premier League next season to fit in with the commitments of his business.

Those six points put Celtic on line for their mid-season target and it was just as well, for the home form was worrying. Too many draws were causing the alarm bells to tinkle, if not ring, although the fans were enjoying some thrilling games. The 3-3 Bower Fold match with Telford was a gem, equalled only by the 2-2 home draw with Wycombe when Celtic were agonisingly close to a memorable triumph.

Late goals were also becoming a feature and two, in particular, spring to mind that could have seriously derailed Celtic's season. An equaliser for Yeovil left the players and fans smarting at an offside decision which never arrived and at Kidderminster a goal nine minutes into injury time left Celtic beaten, this goal being awarded after a shot came back off the 'keeper and play being waved on before officials gave the goal and immediately blew for time.

It was to the team's credit that these incidents were forgotten as the quest for points continued to bear fruit away from home. The pattern, set with a superb 4-1 win at Welling, continued with another fine triumph at Farnborough where 'keeper Russ Hughes, eventually to be voted player of the season, saved a penalty.

Arguably the most impressive win was still to come. The side travelled to Slough anticipating a tough game against a side second in the table and for whom victory would have put them only six points adrift of Wycombe, with two games in hand and two games to play against the top dogs. Slough went in front before Celtic produced three memorable goals and eventually won 3-2 with much praise going to manager Phil Wilson for his tactics. The selection of five centre-backs raised a few eyebrows, but he had obviously done his homework for the tactics nullified Slough's traditional power game.

The arrival of Stuart Anderson, from Morecambe for £2,500 stiffened the midfield, and Celtic, once safe from relegation, began to think of grander targets.

A defeat at home to their nemesis side Witton and home draws with Kettering and Welling, proved costly and as Celtic slipped out of the top ten to finsih a creditable 12th, Altrincham sneaked above them to head the Cheshire clubs.

Celtic's 'goals for' column was often a problem, though not as acute as some might imagine if the figures of rivals are studied. The loss of former Oldham striker Frank Bunn, after only 14 games due to work commitments, was a major blow and the broken bone suffered by record signing Paul Kirkham virtually ended his goal-scoring run. He had nine goals in 16 games up to the injury, but only four more up to the end of the season.

The defence, though, remained reliable and this department was the team's strength in a satisfactory, if ultimately mildly disappointing season.

Martyn Torr (Secretary)

Stalybridge Celtic 1992-93.

STALYBRIDGE MATCHFACTS 92-93

Key: Home fixtures are denoted by bold capitals. Numbers in brackets after players names indicate goals scored (an asterisk by the results denotes own goals). Only used substitutes are listed - substituted players are *italicised*.

Key to Competitions: GMVC: G.M. Vauxhall Conference. **CSC:** HFS Loans League Challenge Shield. **DC:** Drinkwise (G.M. Vauxhall Conference) Cup. **FAC:** F.A. Cup. **FAT:** Vauxhall F.A. Trophy. **CS:** Cheshire Building Society Senior Cup.

LEAGUE POSITION: 12th   **FA CUP:** Third Qualifying Round   **FA TROPHY:** Second Round

Date	Opponents	Comp.	Res	Gate	1.	2.	3.	4.	5.	6.	7.	8.	9.	10.	11.	Sub.	Sub.
15/08	**MARINE**	CS	1-1#	522	Hughes	*Bennett*	Edmonds	Dixon	Aspinall	Filson	Brown(1)	*Edwards*	Kirkham	Morgan	*King*	H'botham	Booth
22/08	**BATH CITY**	GMVC	1-1	633	Hughes	Bennett	Edmonds	Dixon	Aspinall	Filson	Brown	Edwards	Kirkham(1)	Morgan	King	Bunn	Booth
25/08	Stafford Rgrs	GMVC	0-0	1,133	Hughes	Bennett	Edmonds	Dixon	*Aspinall*	*Filson*	Brown	Edwards	Kirkham	*Morgan*	King	Bunn	Booth
29/08	**WOKING**	GMVC	3-0	968	Hughes	Bennett	Edmonds	Dixon	Booth	*Filson*	Brown	Edwards(2)	Kirkham	Bunn(1)	King	Hill	Bauress
31/08	**TELFORD UTD**	GMVC	3-3	1,339	Hughes	Bennett	Edmonds	Dixon	Booth	Filson(1)	Brown	Edwards	Kirkham	Bunn(1)	Bauress	Bauress	Power(1)
05/09	Welling Utd	GMVC	4-1	791	Hughes	Bennett	Edmonds	Dixon	Booth	Filson	Brown	Power	Kirkham(2)	*Bunn(1)*	Bauress	Edwards(1)	King
08/09	**KIDDERMINSTER**	DC	1-1	554	Hughes	Bennett	Edmonds	Dixon	Booth	Filson	Brown	Edwards	Kirkham	H'botham	Bauress	Priest(1)	Priest
12/09	Stocksbridge	FAC	4-0	501	Hughes	Bennett	Edmonds	Dixon	Booth	*Filson*	Brown	Edwards(3)	Kirkham(1)	Bunn	Bauress	Wood	Priest
15/09	Witton Albion	GMVC	0-2	961	Hughes	Bennett	Edmonds	Dixon	Booth	Filson	Brown	Edwards	*Kirkham*	Bunn	*Bauress*	Wood	Priest
19/09	**MERTHYR TYD**	GMVC	2-2	817	Hughes	Bennett	Edmonds	Dixon	Booth	Filson	Brown	*Edwards*	Kirkham(2)	Bunn	Bauress	Wood	Priest
21/09	Kidderminster	GMVC	2-4	602	Hughes	Bennett	Edmonds	Dixon	Booth	Blackman	Brown	Edwards	*Kirkham(2)*	Power	Bauress	Wood	Priest
26/09	Warrington	FAC	3-0	638	Hughes	Bennett	Edmonds(1)	Dixon	Booth	Filson(1)	Brown	Edwards(1)	Power	Bunn	Bauress	Wood	Wood
29/09	Northwich Vic.	GMVC	3-1	691	Hughes	Bennett	Edmonds	Dixon	Booth	Filson	Wood(1)	Edwards	Power(2)	Priest	Bauress	Hill	H'both.
03/10	Wycombe W.	GMVC	0-4	4,120	Hughes	Hill	Edmonds	Dixon	Booth	Filson	*Wood*	*Edwards*	Power	Bunn	Bauress	Brown	H'both.
10/10	**ACCRINGTON S.**	FAC	1-2	1,323	Hughes	Bennett	Edmonds	Dixon	Aspinall	*Filson*	Booth	Priest	Bunn	Power(1)	*Buaress*	Priest	Hill
13/10	Runcorn	GMVC	1-2	700	Hughes	Bennett	Edmonds	*Dixon*	Aspinall	*Filson*	Brown	Edwards	Priest(1)	Power	Booth	H'Botham	Hill
17/10	**BROMSGROVE**	GMVC	0-1	770	Hughes	Bennett	Edmonds	Dixon	Aspinall	*Booth*	*Brown*	Edwards	Bunn	Power	Hill	Wood	Hill
24/10	**BOSTON UTD**	GMVC	2-1	480	Hughes	Bennett	Edmonds	Dixon	Aspinall	Filson	Brown	Edwards(1)	Bunn	*Power(1)*	Hill	Priest	Priest
31/10	Farnborough	GMVC	2-1	606	Hughes	Bennett	Edmonds	Dixon	Aspinall	Filson(1)	Brown	Edwards	Bunn	H'both(1)	Hill		
07/11	**SLOUGH TOWN**	GMVC	0-0	786	Hughes	Bennett	Edmonds	Dixon	Aspinall	Filson	Brown	Edwards	Bunn	H'botham	Hill		
14/11	Boston Utd	GMVC	1-1	943	Hughes	Bennett	Edmonds	Dixon	Aspinall	Filson	Brown	Edwards(1)	Boyle	H'botham	Hill	Kirkham	
17/11	**RUNCORN**	GMVC	0-0	509	Hughes	Bennett	Edmonds	Dixon	Aspinall	Filson	Brown	Edwards	Kirkham	H'botham	Hill		
21/11	Kidderminster	GMVC	1-2	1,047	Hughes	Bennett	Edmonds	Dixon	Aspinall	*Filson*	Brown	Edwards(1)	Kirkham(1)	H'botham	*Hill*	Bauress	
24/11	**COLWYN BAY**	CSC	1-0	254	Hughes	Bennett	Edmonds	Dixon	Boyle	Bauress	Brown	Edwards(1)	Kirkham	Morgan	Hill	Mayo	Boyle
28/11	**YEOVIL TOWN**	GMVC	1-1	753	Hughes	Bennett	Edmonds	Blackman	Aspinall	Filson	Brown	Edwards(1)	Kirkham	*Morgan*	Bauress	Bunn	Filson

Date	Opponent	Comp	Score	Att	1	2	3	4	5	6	7	8	9	10	11	12	13
01/12	Telford Utd	GMVC	2-0	960	Hughes	Bennett	Edmonds	Dixon	Aspinall	Filson	Brown	Edwards(2)	Kirkham	Morgan	Bauress	Booth	
05/12	Dagenham & R	GMVC	2-1	1,052	Hughes	Hill	Edmonds	Boyle	Aspinall	Filson	Brown	Edwards(1)	Kirkham(1)	Morgan	Bauress	Bennett	
12/12	DAGENHAM & R	GMVC	0-3	752	Hughes	Hill	Edmonds	Boyle	Aspinall	Filson	Brown	Edwards	Kirkham	Morgan	Bauress	Morgan	
19/12	Bath City	GMVC	1-1	560	Hughes	Bennett	Booth	Boyle	Aspinall	Filson	Brown	Edwards	Kirkham	Hill	Bauress	Power	Morgan(1)
28/12	Gateshead	GMVC	0-0	631	Hughes	Bennett	Booth	Boyle	Aspinall	Filson	Brown	Edwards	Kirkham	Morgan	Bauress	Hill	Edmonds
02/01	NORTHWICH VIC.	GMVC	0-6	1,111	Hughes	Bennett	Booth	Boyle	Aspinall	Filson	Brown	Morgan	Morgan	Power(2)	Bauress	Morgan	Edmonds
09/01	ACCRINGTON S.	FAT	2-0	963	Hughes	Bennett	Booth	Boyle	Aspinall	Filson	Brown	Edwards	Kirkham	Edwards	Bauress	Hill	Morgan
19/01	RUNCORN	CSC	0-0	303	Hughes	Bennett	Booth	Boyle	Aspinall	Filson	Brown	Edwards	Kirkham	Edwards	Bauress	Morgan	
23/01	WYCOMBE W.	GMVC	2-2	1,694	Hughes	Hill	Booth	Boyle	Aspinall	Morgan	Brown(1)	Edwards	Kirkham	Edmonds	Bauress	Filson	Morgan
30/01	MERTHYR TYD	FAT	1-1	814	Hughes	Hill	Booth	Boyle	Aspinall	Morgan	Brown	Edwards	Power	Edmonds	Bauress	Kirkham	Kirkham
02/02	Merthyr Tyd	FAT	0-1	707	Hughes	Hill	Booth	Boyle	Aspinall	Morgan	Brown	Edwards	Power	Edmonds	Bauress	Filson	Filson
06/02	Slough Town	GMVC	3-2	857	Hughes	Burrell	Booth	Boyle	Aspinall	Filson	Brown	Tomlinson	Kirkham(1)	Power	Bauress	Kirkham	Kirkham
13/02	KIDDERMINSTER	GMVC	2-2	702	Hughes	Burrell	Booth	Edmonds	Aspinall	Filson	Brown	Tomlinson	Kirkham	Power(2)	Bauress	Edwards(1)	
16/02	Runcorn	CSC	1-0	474	Hughes	Edmonds	Booth	Dixon(1)	Aspinall	Filson	Brown	Edwards	Kirkham	Edmonds	Bauress	Edwards	
27/02	STAFFORD RGRS	GMVC	1-0	752	Hughes	Burrell	Booth	Dixon	Aspinall	Filson	Brown	Tomlinson	Kirkham	Power	Bauress(1)	Morgan	Kirkham
02/03	WINSFORD	CSC	2-2	401	Hughes	Burrell	Booth	Dixon	Aspinall	Boyle	Brown	Tomlinson	Edwards(1)	Power	Bauress	Morgan	Morgan
06/03	Bromsgrove	GMVC	0-4	945	Hughes	Burnell	Boyle	Dixon	Aspinall	Bennett	Brown	Tomlinson	Edwards	Power	Bauress	Kirkham	Morgan
09/03	Altrincham	GMVC	0-0	844	Hughes	Bennett	Boyle	Dixon	Aspinall	Filson	Brown	Morgan	Kirkham	Power	Bauress	Edwards	Kirkham
13/03	Yeovil Town	GMVC	1-1	1,844	Hughes	Bennett	Boyle	Dixon	Aspinall	Filson	Anderson	Morgan(1)	Kirkham	Power	Bauress	Edwards	
16/03	Merthyr Tyd.	GMVC	1-1	628	Hughes	Bennett	Boyle	Dixon	Aspinall	Burnell	Anderson	Morgan(1)	Kirkham	Power	Bauress	Kirkham(1)	Burnell
20/03	Macclesfield	GMVC	2-1	822	Hughes	Bennett	Boyle	Dixon(1)	Aspinall	Filsa	Anderson	Edwards	Edwards	Power	Bauress	Morgan	
24/03	Winsford	CSC	0-1	407	Hughes	Bennett	Boyle	Dixon	Aspin'l(1)	Filson	Anderson	Edwards	Kirkham	Power	Bauress	Brown	Kirkham
27/03	ALTRINCHAM	GMVC	1-0	1,011	Hughes	Bennett	Boyle	Dixon	Aspinall	Filsa	Anderson	Edwards	Kirkham	Power	Bauress	Boyle	
03/04	Kettering	GMVC	0-2	1,137	Hughes	Bennett	Boyle	Dixon	Aspinall	Filson	And'son(1)	Edwards	Kirkham	Brown	Bauress	Boyle	Brown
06/04	FARNBOROUGH	GMVC	2-0	378	Hughes	Bennett	Booth	Dixon	Aspinall	Filsa	Anderson	Edwards	Edwards	Brown	Bauress	Edwards	
10/04	Macclesfield	GMVC	0-1	844	Hughes	Bennett	Booth	Dixon	Aspinall	Filsa	And'son(1)	Edwards	Kirkham	Brown(1)	Bauress	Higginbotham	Tom'son
12/04	GATESHEAD	GMVC	2-1	558	Hughes	Bennett	Booth	Dixon	Aspinall	Filsa	Brown	Brown	Kirkham	Brown	Bauress	Edwards	Power
17/04	KETTERING	GMVC	0-0	805	Hughes	Bennett	Booth	Dixon	Aspinall	Filson	Anderson	Brown	Kirkham	Power(1)	Bauress	Higginbotham	
24/04	Woking	GMVC	1-2	1,713	Hughes	Bennett	Booth	Dixon	Edmonds	Boyle	Anderson	Brown	Kirkham	Power	Bauress	H'both	Edwards
01/05	WELLING UTD	GMVC	0-0	705	Hughes	Bennett	Booth	Dixon	Aspinall	Boyle	Anderson	Edwards	Edwards	Power	Bauress	Edmonds	Kirkham

LEAGUE APPEARANCES: Anderson 12; Aspinall 34(1); Bauress 30(3); Bennett 35(1); Blackman 1; Booth 22(2); Boyle 19(3); Brown 36(2); Bunn 10(2); Burrell 5(1); Dixon 33; Edmonds 25(3); Edwards 33(8); Filson 34(1); Higginbotham 5(5); Hill 12(4); Hughes 42; King 4(1); Kirkham 27(5); Morgan 13(4); Power 21(4); Priest 3(3); Tomlinson 4(1); Wood 2(2).

LEAGUE GOALSCORERS: Edwards 12; Kirkham 9; Power 8; Anderson, Bunn 3; Brown, Filson, Morgan 2; Bauress, Dixon, Higginbotham, Priest, Wood 1.

\# - Won 5-3 on penalties.

Stalybridge Celtic

PHIL WILSON

Phil Wilson joined Stalybridge Celtic in November 1989 on the dismissal of Kevan Keelan. Celtic survived being relegated by the skin of their teeth, and in his first full season finished runners up, before taking the title in 1991-92.

Wilson, 40, played as a 17-year-old for New Brighton and had an illustrious non-league career with Runcorn, Mossley, Altrincham and Northwich Victoria, winning NPL championships with Runcorn and Mossley and a Conference medal with Altrincham. He appeared in seven FA Trophy semi-finals and reached three finals at Wembley, finally getting a winners' medal with Northwich, who beat Bangor City in a replay at the Victoria Ground, Stoke. He captained Caernarfon Town to the third round proper of the FA Cup and managed the Welsh side for a season.

A fully qualified FA Coach, he is director of the Tranmere Rovers' Centre of Excellence on the Wirral.

Paul Kirkham of Stalybridge Celtic and Nigel Beaumont of Telford United in action. Photo: Colin Stevens.

Programme details:
40 pages for £1
Editor - Mick Shaw (061 633 1117)

Any other club publications:

Local Newspapers:
Manchester Evening News
Manchester Evening News Pink (Saturday evenings)

Local Radio Stations:
GMR (BBC Manchester)
Piccadilly Radio, Signal Radio

STALYBRIDGE CELTIC - PLAYING SQUAD 1992-93

Player	Honours	Birthplace and date	Transfer Fees	Previous Clubs
GOALKEEPERS				
Russ Hughes	NPL, NPLC	30/1/61		Tranmere Rovers, Sth Liverpool, Caernarfon Town
DEFENDERS				
John Aspinall	NPL	Birkenhead 15/3/59		Cammell L, Tranmere, Altrincham, Bangor C, Tranmere, Bangor C, Northwich, Chorley
Lee Coathup		Singapore 2/5/67		Everton, Newtown, Vauxhall GM, Stalybridge Celtic, Witton Albion
Stuart Locke	MCSC	Manchester		Manchester City, Crewe Alexandra
Kevin Booth	NPL, NWCL	Manchester 3/11/62		Stalybridge Celtic, Bacup Borough, Stalybridge Celtic, Curzon Ashton
Paul Dixon	NPL, GB Fire Serv	Chadderton 26/10/64		Chadderton, Curzon Ashton
Gary Boyle	NPL	Southend 27/6/63		Walton & Hersham, Macclesfield Town, Witton Albion
Phil Lockett		Stockport 6/9/72		Rochdale
MIDFIELD				
Jonathon Hill		Wigan 26/8/70		Crewe Alexandra, Rochdale,
Peter King		Liverpool 5/7/64		Liverpool, Crewe A, Southport, Marine, Stafford R, Chorley, Barrow, Marine
Paul Bennett	NPL	Liverpool 30/1/61		Everton, Port Vale, Northwich V, Telford Utd, Northwich V, Buxton
John Brown	NPL, FA XI	Winsford 6/12/67		Liverpool, Winsford Utd, Witton Albion
Neil Edmonds	NPL	Accrington 18/10/68		Oldham A, Rochdale, Karlskrona(Swe), Mylakoski(Fin), East Bengal(India)
Stewart Anderson	NPL, FAV, NWCL	Manchester 20/11/59	£2,250	Chadderton, Colne Dynamoes, Witton Albionn, Morecambe
FORWARDS				
Phil Power	FAT, GMAC CSC	Salford 25/7/66		Northwich V, Witton Albion, Crewe A, Horwich RMI, Sliema W(Malta), Barrow,
Steve Shaughnessy		Manchester		Maine Road Runcorn
Paul Kirkham	NPLC, CSC	Manchester 5/7/69	Undiscld	East Manchester, Manchester Utd, Huddersfield T, Hyde Utd
Dave Kershaw		Manchester		Whitworth Valley, Oldham Town, Droylsden, Chadderton
Paul Higginbotham	NPL		£1,250	Altrincham, Witton Albion, Flixton, Witton Albion, Glossop
Frank Bunn		Birmingham 6/11/62		Luton Town, Hull City, Oldham Athletic
Steve Morgan	WY	Wrexham 28/12/70		Oldham Athletic, Rochdale

Departures during season:
Steve Wood (Chadderton), Ricky Blackman, Mark Edwards, Mark Burrell, Gary Bauress & Eric Priest (Ashton Utd), Martin Filson (Halifax).

Players on loan during season:
Jon Mayo (Bolton).

Bower Fold, Stalybridge Celtic

Address and telephone number: Bower Fold, Mottram Road, Stalybridge, Cheshire SK15 2RT. Tel: 061 338 2828

Simple directions: M6 to A556 to M63 to M67; end of Motorway through roundabout to traffic lights, left; left at end into Molttram Road, up hill, down hill into Stalybridge, ground on left next to Hare & Hounds pub.

Capacity: 6,000   **Seated:** 600   **Covered terracing:** 1,300

Record Attendance: 9,753 v WBA - FA Cup replay - 1922-23

Club Shop: Contact Martyn Torr for details (061 338 2828)

Social Facilities: Clubhouse open matchdays and evenings during the week. Food available on matchdays.

Previous Grounds: None

Stalybridge Fact File

Nickname: Celtic

Club Sponsors: Hickson Manro Ltd

Previous Leagues: Lancashire Combination 1911-12, Central League 1912-21, Football League 1921-23, Cheshire League 1923-1982, Bass NWCL 1982-87, Northern Premier League 1987-92.

Club colours: Blue & white

Change colours: All green

Midweek home matchday: Tuesday

Record win: 10-0 twice. v Netherfield and Ashton Town

Record defeat: 0-6 v Northwich Victoria

Record transfer fee: Paul Kirkham from Hyde

Record transfer fee received: £3,000 for Martin Tilson from Halifax Town

1992/93 Captain: Paul Bennett

1992/93 Top scorer: Mark Edwards

1992/93 Player of the Year: Russ Hughes

Club record goalscorer: Not known

Record appearances: Kevin Booth

Past players who progressed to the Football League: To numerous to list.

Club Honours: HFS Loans League Premier Division Champions 91-92, NPL Runners-up 90-91 (Div.1 runners-up 87-88); Cheshire County League 79-80 (Runners-up 77-78), League Cup 21-22 (Runners-up 46-47,81-82); Challenge Shield 77-78 (runners-up 79-80), Reserves Division runners-up 81-82), NW Counties League 83-84, 86-87 (Lge Cup Runners-up 83-84), Champions v Cup Winners Trophy 83-84, (reserves Division Runners-up 82-83; Lancashire Combination Division 2 11-12; Cheshire Senior Cup 52-53 (runners-up 54-55, 80-81; Manchester Cup 22-23 (Intermediate Cup 57-58, 68-69 (runners-up 56-57, 67-68, 69-70)); Challenge Shield 54-55, (Junior Cup 62-63), Lancashire Floodlit Cup 88-89 (runners-up 89-90); Reporter Cup Runners-up 74-75; Edward Case Cup 77-78.

TELFORD UNITED

Formed:
1876

President:
G.E.Smith

Chairman:
A.H.Esp

Football Secretary:
M.J.Ferridan

Manager:
G.Daly

Assistant Manager:
K.Burns

Physiotherapist:
C.McBride

Commercial Manager:
Bev Cooper

Press Officer:
Robert Cave

As the 1992-93 season drew to a close it was the all too familiar story of 'what might have been' at the Buck's Head, a sentiment echoed by most clubs at this time of the year. Telford United had been as unpredictable as ever, fluctuating between would be contenders for at least the runners-up spot and the look of relegation strugglers in the Vauxhall Conference.

The final league position was a great disappointment and the club is not without its problems, the main one, typically finances. However the new Board are tackling the problem systematically and meanwhile there have been pluses on the playing side. A number of younger players have emerged who do not look out of place in Conference football and Manager Gerry Daly will be looking for their continued development next season. The lack of fire-power up front, particularly after the departures of Ian Benbow to Merthyr Tydfil and Tim Langford to Wycombe Wanderers, caused serious problems in the latter stages of the season allied to the loss of key figures, central defender Nigel Niblett and skipper Steve Fergusson who required surgery on his damaged cartilage.

With such a small squad and no reserve side, injuries can be catastrophic and the club certainly had more than their fair share throughout the season. In addition, Gerry Daly was forced to make changes simply to try new players in match situation as he draws up his plans for next season. As he says "I don't like it any more than the fans, but it is the only method available - far from ideal but another of the hard facts of football life at this level".

Apart from the disappointing finish to the league programme there were big disappointments in Cup Competitions going out of the FA Cup at the 4th Qualifying Round stage with a 2-1 defeat at home by Diadora League side St.Albans City, defeat by Northwich Victoria in the Drinkwise Cup and after disposing of the same opponents, then Kingstonian, suffering an ignominious defeat in a replay at Boston United in the FA Challenge Trophy. That 4-0 defeat more or less signalled the end of Telford United's season.

Looking towards the future, Gerry Daly remains optimistic and the fact that he has turned down offers to move into the football league is a measure of his commitment to Telford's cause. He believes that he is in for a busy summer looking to unearth similar talent to the likes of Nigel Niblett in the lower leagues of the pyramid and also scouring the list of free transfers from football league clubs, whence came players like Dave Pritchard (ex-WBA) and Marcus Bignot (ex-Birmingham City). Daly is also acutely aware that to achieve success, a blend of youth and experience is required; he already has Fergusson and Andy Lee now in his second spell at The Buck's Head as the 'oldest heads', but with the rest of the squad having an average age of around 18-19 years,   the ratio of experienced players to youngsters will need to be increased if they are to overcome the inconsistency that generally goes hand-in-hand with very young sides. Daly too, is under no illusions about the task before him. He knows the frustration of having to part with players of the calibre of Chris Brindley, Paul Grainger and Tim Langford but he intends staying put - "I want to stay at Telford. I don't know why - I can't explain it. In some macabre fashion I enjoy it here".

Maybe 1993-94 will see Daly's faith in Telford United rewarded. As ever only time will tell.

TELFORD MATCHFACTS 92-93   TELFORD MATCHFACTS 92-93   TELFORD MATCHFACTS 92-93

Key: Home fixtures are denoted by bold capitals. Numbers in brackets after players names indicate goals scored (an asterisk by the results denotes own goals). Only used substitutes are listed - substituted players are *italicised*.

Key to Competitions: **GMVC:** G.M. Vauxhall Conference. **DC:** Drinkwise (G.M. Vauxhall Conference) Cup. **FAC:** F.A. Cup. **FAT:** Vauxhall F.A. Trophy. **SSC:** Shropshire Senior Cup.

LEAGUE POSITION: 15th   FA CUP: Fourth Qualifying Round   FA TROPHY: Third Round

Date	Opponents	Comp.	Res	Gate	1.	2.	3.	4.	5.	6.	7.	8.	9.	10.	11.	Sub.	Sub.
7/08	SHREWSBURY T.	SSC	2-0	747	Acton	Pritchard	Bignot	Parrish	Brindley	Beaumont	Myers	Fergusson	Benbow(2)	Langford	Francis		Garrett
22/08	Welling United	GMVC	3-1	875	Acton	Pritchard(1)	Bignot	Beaumont	Nelson	*Parrish*	Myers	Fergusson	Benbow(1)	Langford(1)	Francis	May	Ogley
25/08	WITTON ALBION	GMVC	0-3	1,160	Acton	Pritchard	*Bignot*	Nelson	*Nelson*	Parrish	Myers	Fergusson	Benbow	Langford	Francis		Ogley
29/08	YEOVIL TOWN	GMVC	1-0	1,015	Acton	Pritchard	Bignot	Nelson	Beaumont	Parrish(1)	Myers	Fergusson	Benbow	Langford(1)	*Francis*	Ogley	May
31/08	Stalybridge C.	GMVC	3-3	1,334	Acton	*Pritchard*	Bignot	Nelson	Beaumont	Parrish(1)	Myers	Ferg'son(1)	Benbow(1)	Langford	*Francis*	Ogley	Garrett
5/09	Wycombe Wdrs	GMVC	0-4	3,414	Acton	Pritchard	Bignot	Nelson	Beaumont	Parrish	Myers	Fergusson	Benbow	Langford	*Francis*	Francis(1)	
12/09	FARNBOROUGH	GMVC	6-3	1,031	Acton	Pritchard	Bignot	Lee	Beaumont	Parrish(1)	Myers(2)	Fergusson	Benbow	*Langford*	Green(2)		Ogley
15/09	KETTERING T.	GMVC	3-1	1,327	Acton	Pritchard	Bignot	Lee	Beaumont	Parrish	Myers(1)	Ferg'son(1)	Benbow	Langford(1)	Green	Francis	
19/09	Slough Town	GMVC	0-2	914	Acton	Pritchard	*Bignot*	Lee	Beaumont	*Parrish*	Myers	Nelson	Benbow	Langford	Green	Ogley	Francis
26/09	WOKING	GMVC	3-3	1,463	Acton	Pritchard	Bignot	Lee	Beaumont	Parrish	Myers	Ferg'son(2)	Benbow	Langford(1)	Green	Francis	
29/09	Runcorn	GMVC	1-3	532	Acton	Pritchard	*Bignot*	Lee	Beaumont	Parrish	Myers	Fergusson	Benbow(1)	Langford	*Green*	Ogley	Francis
3/10	Gateshead	GMVC	1-0	371	Grange	Pritchard	Bignot	Lee	Beaumont	Parrish	Myers	Fergusson	Benbow(1)	Langford	Nelson	Ogley	Green
13/10	KIDDERMINSTER	GMVC	1-1	1,692	Grange	Pritchard	Bignot	Lee	Beaumont	Parrish	Myers	Niblett	Benbow(1)	Langford	*Nelson*	Green	
17/10	Boston United	GMVC	2-2	841	Grange	Pritchard	Bignot	Lee	Niblett	Parrish	Myers	Ferg'son(1)	Benbow	*Langford*	Green	Francis(1)	
20/10	Stafford Rgrs	DC	0-0	631	Grange	Pritchard	Nelson	Lee	Niblett	Parrish	Myers	Fergusson	Benbow	Francis	Green		
24/10	ST ALBANS C.	FAC	1-2	1,132	Grange	Pritchard	Bignot	Lee	Nelson	Clarke(3)	*Myers*	Ferg'son(1)	Cooke(1)	Francis	Green(1)	Beaumont	Garrett
27/10	STAFFORD R.	DC	5-2	625	Acton	Pritchard	Bignot	Lee	Niblett	Clarke	Bowen	Ferg'son(1)	Cooke	Francis	Green	Beaumont	Benbow
31/10	ALTRINCHAM	GMVC	2-1	1,063	Acton	Pritchard	Bignot(1)	Lee	Niblett	Clarke	Bowen	Fergusson	Cooke	Francis	Green	Benbow	
3/11	Bromsgrove R.	GMVC	0-0	1,543	Acton	Pritchard	Bignot	Lee	Niblett	Clarke	Bowen	Fergusson	Cooke	Francis	Green	Green	Benbow
7/11	MACCLESFIELD	GMVC	3-1	1,175	Acton	Pritchard	Bignot(1)	Lee	Niblett	Clarke	Bowen(1)	Fergusson	Benbow(1)	Francis	Green	Green	
28/11	Dagenham & Red.	GMVC	2-0	1,302	Acton	Beaumont	Bignot	Lee	Niblett	Parrish	Bowen	Fergusson	Benbow(1)	Langford	Francis(1)		Green
1/12	STALYBRIDGE	GMVC	0-2	985	Acton	Pritchard	Bignot	Lee	Niblett	Parrish	Bowen	Fergusson	Benbow	Langford	*Francis*	Francis	
5/12	BOSTON UNITED	GMVC	0-1	924	Acton	Pritchard	Bignot	*Lee*	Niblett	Parrish	Bowen	Fergusson	*Benbow*	Langford	Green	Beaumont	Francis
12/12	Farnborough T.	GMVC	1-0	617	Acton	Pritchard	Bignot	Beaumont	Niblett	Parrish	Bowen(1)	Fergusson	Benbow	Langford(1)	Green	Beaumont	Francis
15/12	Northwich Vict.	DC	1-3	374	Acton	Pritchard	*Bignot*	Beaumont	Niblett	Parrish	Bowen	Fergusson	Benbow	Langford	*Green*	Francis	Clarke
19/12	SLOUGH TOWN	GMVC	1-1	960	Acton	Pritchard	Bignot	Beaumont	Niblett	Parrish	Bowen	Fergusson	Benbow	Langford(1)	*Francis*	Myers	Francis

Date	Opponent	Comp	Res	Att	1	2	3	4	5	6	7	8	9	10	11	Sub	Sub
9/1	NORTHWICH V.	FAT	2-1	1,211	Acton	Pritchard	Bignot	Lee(1)	Niblett	Parrish	Bowen	Fergusson	Benbow	Langford	Green	Myers(1)	
30/1	Kingstonian	FAT	2-1	809	Acton	Pritchard	Bignot	Lee	Niblett(1)	Parrish	Clarke	Fergusson	Benbow	Myers	Green(1)	Clarke	Garratt
2/02	Kettering Town	GMVC	1-1	1,221	Acton	Pritchard	Bignot	Lee	Niblett	Francis	Clarke	Fergusson	Benbow	Myers	Green	Cooke(1)	Cooke
6/02	Yeovil Town	GMVC	0-1	2,207	Acton	Pritchard	Bignot	Lee	Beaumont	Clarke	Bowen	Fergusson	Benbow	Myers	Hunter	Wolverson	Wolverson
9/02	BROMSGROVE R.	GMVC	0-1	935	Acton	Pritchard	Bignot	Lee	Niblett	Clarke	Bowen	Fergusson	Benbow	Myers	Hunter	Wolverson	Cooke
13/02	Macclesfield T.	GMVC	1-1	470	Acton	Pritchard	Bignot	Lee	Niblett	Beaumont	Myers	Green(1)	Francis(1)	Bowen	Cooke	Cooke	
16/02	Altrincham	FAT	3-0	510	Acton	Pritchard	Bignot	Lee	Niblett(1)	Clarke(1)	Myers	Cooke(1)	Francis	Bowen	Green	Green	Cooke
20/02	BOSTON UNITED	FAT	1-1	1,408	Acton	Bowen	Bignot	Lee	Niblett	Clarke	Myers	Fergusson	Benbow	Langford	Green	Cooke	Cooke
24/02	Boston United	FAT	0-4	1,626	Acton	Pritchard	Bignot	Lee	Niblett	Clarke	Myers	Fergusson	Benbow	Langford	Green	Green	Bowen
27/02	BATH CITY	GMVC	0-0	618	Acton	Pritchard	Bignot	Lee	Beaumont	Clarke	Myers	Fergusson	Francis	Langford	Green	Cooke	Cooke
06/03	GATESHEAD	GMVC	1-0	633	Acton	Pritchard	Bignot	Lee	Bowen	Parrish	Myers	Fergusson	Francis	Langford	Rollason	Beaumont	Benbow
09/03	STAFFORD	GMVC	0-0	1,068	Acton	Pritchard	Bignot	Lee	Bowen	Parrish	Myers	Fergusson	Rollason	Langford	Hodgin	Clarke	H'gin(1)
16/03	NORTHWICH V.	GMVC	1-0	703	Acton	Pritchard	Bignot	Lee	fergusson	Parrish(1)	Myers	Francis	Rollason	Moore	Bowen	Moore	
20/03	DAGENHAM & R.	GMVC	0-1	757	Acton	Pritchard	Bignot	Beaumont	Fergusson	Parrish	Myers	Mulligan	Rollason	Moore	Bowen	Clarke	B'mont
23/03	Northwich	GMVC	0-1	612	Acton	Pritchard	Bignot	Beaumont	Fergusson	Fergusson	Myers	Mulligan	Rollason	Clarke	Bowen	Francis	Hodgin
30/03	Woking	GMVC	2-3	1,317	Acton	Pritchard	Bignot	Lee	Beaumont	Parrish(1)	Myers	Clarke	McBean	Moore(1)	Clarke	Beaumont	Francis
03/04	WELLING UTD	GMVC	0-1	574	Acton	Pritchard	Bignot	Lee	Beaumont	Parrish	Myers	Clarke	Francis	McBean	Moore	Hodgin	Rollason
06/04	Bath City	GMVC	1-4	338	Acton	Beaumont	Bignot	Lee	Beaumont	Parrish	Myers	Rollason	McBean	Bowen	Mulligan(1)	Moore	
10/04	Stafford Rgrs	GMVC	1-2	1,007	Acton	Beaumont	Bignot	Lee	Niblett	Parrish	Myers	Clarke	Francis(2)	Moore	Mulligan(1)	Moore	Francis
12/04	MERTHYR TYD.	GMVC	5-0	703	Acton	B'mont(1)	Bignot(1)	Lee	Niblett(1)	Parrish	Myers	Hodgin	Francis	Moore	Mulligan	Moore	
17/04	Kidderminster	GMVC	1-2	1,532	Acton	Pritchard	Bignot(1)	Beaumont	Beaumont	Parrish	Myers	Hodgin	Francis	Moore	Mulligan(1)	McBean	Francis
24/04	WYCOMBE W.	GMVC	2-3	1,741	Acton	Pritchard	Bignot(1)	Lee	Niblett	Parrish	Myers	McBean	Francis	Moore(1)	Bowen	Hodgin	
01/05	Witton Alb.	GMVC	1-2	756	Acton	Pritchard	Bignot	Beaumont	Niblett	Clarke	Myers	McBean	Francis(1)	Moore	Hodgin	Rollason	Garnett

LEAGUE APPEARANCES: Acton 39, Beaumont 25(4), Benbow 24(2), Bignot 40, Bowen 19, Clarke 14(2), Cooke 4(4), Fergusson 29, Francis 22(8), Garrett 1(4), Grange 3, Green 16(12), Hodgin 7(4), Hunter 2, Langford 22, Lee 32, May 0(4), McBean 7(1), Moore 9(1), Mulligan 7, Myers 33(2), Nelson 11, Niblett 21, Ogley 0(4), Parrish 33, Pritchard 39, Rollason 6(2), Wolverson 0(2).

LEAGUE GOALSCORERS: Fergusson 8; Benbow, Francis 7; Langford 6; Bignot, Parrish 4; Mulligan, Myers 3; Cooke, Green, Moore 2; Beaumont, Bowen, Clarke, Hodgin, Niblett, Pritchard 1.

Telford United

GERRY DALY

Gerry was born in Dublin and joined Manchester United from Irish side Bohemians in April 1973. During a distinguished playing career, Gerry made over 400 League appearances with United, Derby County, Coventry City, Birmingham City, Shrewsbury and Stoke City as well as gaining international honours for the Republic of Ireland, including 46 full caps.

He arrived at the Bucks Head from Doncaster Rovers in December 1989 as assistant player-coach to Derek Mann, who had just replaced the long-serving Stan Storton. Gerry then took over as player-manager in the summer of 1990 and in his two seasons in charge has guided the club to sixth position on both occasions.

Telford United's defence manage to get the ball away from the danger area in their FA Trophy tie against Kingstonian. Photo: Dave West.

Programme details:
28 pages for 80p
Editor - Bernard G Bagnall

Any other club publications:

Local Newspapers:
Shropshire Star
Telford Journal

Local Radio Stations:
BBC Radio Shropshire
Beacon Radio

TELFORD UNITED - PLAYING SQUAD 1992-93

Player	Honours	Birthplace and date	Transfer Fees	Previous Clubs
GOALKEEPERS				
Darren Acton				Ex-YTS
Damian Grange				Aston Villa
DEFENDERS				
Marcus Bignot				Birmingham City
Derek Statham	England (3),	Wolverhampton 24/3/59		West Brom, Southampton, Stoke, Walsall
Irvin Gernon	EY, EU-21	Birmingham 30/12/62		Ipswich T, Gillingham, Reading, Northampton T, Kettering T
Dave Pritchard		Wolverhampton 27/5/72		West Bromwich Albion
Nigel Beaumont		Hemsworth 11/2/67		Bradford City, Wrexham
Andy Lee	ESP, ES, FAT, NPL	Liverpool 14/9/62		Tranmere, Camb U, Runcorn, Altrincham, Telford U, Colne D, Witton A, Altrincham
Nigel Niblett	SLC, BSC, MFC FA XI	Stratford 12/8/67	Undiscld	Snitterfield Sports, Stratford T, VS Rugby
Stewart Bowen		Birmingham		Coventry City
MIDFIELD				
Martin Myers		Birmingham 10/1/66		Shrewsbury Town, Tamworth
Ian Mitchell		Birmingham		Solihull, M Green, Highgate, Nuneaton, Willenhall, Banbury, Solihull, Barri
Steve Fergusson	WSC	Birmingham 21/4/61	£6,000	Bromsgrove R, Redditch Utd, Alvechurch, Redditch Utd, Worcester C, Gloucester C
Sean Parrish		Wrexham 14/3/72		Shrewsbury Town
FORWARDS				
Sean Francis		Birmingham 1/8/72		Birmingham City
Colin Taylor	EY	Liverpool 25/12/71		Wolverhampton W
Lee Rollason		Birmingham		Tipton Town

Departures during season:
Chris Brindley (Kidderminster), Stuart Leeding (Dudley), Leroy May (Tividale), Steve Nelson (Burton Alb), Paul Hunter (Barri), Roy Green (Macclesfield), Ian Benbow (Merthyr T), Tim Langford (Wycombe), Andy Cooke (Newtown), Peter McBean & Chris Hodgin (Released).

Players on loan during season:
Steve Perks (Shrewsbury), Jason Wolverson (Worcester), James Mulligan (Stoke), Michael Moore (Derby).

Bucks Head, Telford United

Address and telephone number: Bucks Head Ground, Watling Street, Wellington, Telford, Shropshire TF1 2NJ.
Tel: 0952 223838
Simple directions: M54 Junction 6, A518 to B5061 (Watling Street). Ground is on several bus routes.
Capacity: 6,400   **Seated:** 1,200   **Covered terracing:** 2,500
Record Attendance: 13,000 v Shrewsbury Town - Birmingham League - 1936.
Club Shop: Contact Shirley Finnigan on 0952 223838 for details.
Social Facilities: Social club adjacent to ground - open matchdays and selected other hours.
Previous Grounds: None

Telford Fact File

Nickname: Lilywhites

Club Sponsors: National Power

Previous Leagues: Southern League, Cheshire League, Birmingham League.

Club colours: White shirts, blue shorts and white socks.

Change colours: Yellow shirts, red shorts and yellow socks.

Midweek home matchday: Tuesday

Record win:

Record defeat:

Record transfer fee: £10,000 to Northwich Victoria for Paul Mayman.

Record transfer fee received: £50,000 from Scarborough for Stephen Norris.

1992/93 Captain: Steve Ferguson

1992/93 Top scorer: Steve Ferguson

1992/93 Player of the Year:

Club record goalscorer:

Record appearances:

Past Players who progressed to the Football League: A.Walker (Lincoln City), G.French (Luton Town), K.McKenna (Tranmere Rovers), S.Norris (Scarborough).

Club Honours: Birmingham League 1920-21, 1934-35, 1935-36; Cheshire League 1945-46, 1946-47, 1951-52; Edward Case Cup 1952-53, 1954-55; Welsh Cup 1901-02, 1905-06, 1939-40; Birmingham Senior Cup 1946-47; Walsall Senior Cup 1946-47; Birmingham League Challenge Cup 1946-47; Shropshire Senior Cup (30); Southern League Cup 1970-71; Midland Floodlit Cup 1970-71; Midland Floodlit Cup 1970-71, 1982-83, 1988-89, Runnser-up 1969-70, 1987-88.

WELLING UNITED

Late run of form ensures Conference status

Formed:
1963

President:
E.Brackstone
Chairman:
P.Websdale
Vice Chairman
S.Pain
Football Secretary:
Barrie Hobbins
Manager:
Terry Robbins
Assistant Manager
Ray Burgess
Coach:
Paul Haverson
Physiotherapist:
Peter Green
Commercial Manager:
G.Hobbins
Press Officer:
Paul Carter

A goalless draw at Stalybridge on the final day of the season, combined with Farnborough's 5-2 home defeat by Altrincham on the same day, ensured Conference football at Park View Road in 1993-94, albeit only because neither Chesham United or St. Albans City could meet grading standards for the Conference.

Having said that, Terry Robbins' side deserve credit for a run of form that saw them take thirteen points from their last six matches, after looking certainties for relegation as April approached.

The season had begun with an abundance of optimism at the Kent club, with six new additions to the Wings' first team squad, and nine full time Youth Training players commencing duties with the club for its first season in the scheme. Sadly, all that optimism evaporated in the opening fifteen days of the season as Welling lost all of their first five matches, conceding 17 goals in the process. The first point of the season came in a 2-2 draw at newly promoted Bromsgrove Rovers, and a week later the Wings secured their first win of the season, twice coming from behind to beat Runcorn 3-2 at Park View Road.

The tide appeared to be turning after that victory, with only one defeat in the next six Conference outings, and eventual champions Wycombe Wanderers were forced to surrender a two goal lead before eventually winning their Drinkwise Cup tie in extra time.

Just four days later, however, form hit rock bottom as Kingstonian dumped Welling out of the F.A. Cup in the 4th Qualifying Round - the first time since 1985 that Welling had failed to reach the competition proper.

That defeat led to a parting of the ways with Manager Nicky Brigden, a difficult and sad decision after the loyal, and largely successful, service given by Bridgen since joining the club as Youth Team Coach in 1980.

When the club announced the new manager 12 days later it took everyone by surprise, with striker Terry Robbins given a Player-Manager role, ahead of over 20 applicants, and becoming, at 27-years-old, the youngest manager in senior football.

His first two matches were both away, yielding one point from trips to Slough Town and Northwich Victoria, but it was his home debut as boss that captured the headlines. Following a goalless first-half, Robbins hit a second-half hat-trick as the Wings trounced Merthyr Tydfil 5-0, a game that sadly saw the last appearance of the season by Tony Reynolds, who played through the match after colliding with a goal post in the first-half, only to find out the following Monday, after a weekend of great discomfort, that he had broken his neck. Fortunately the damage was not permanent, and Reynolds remains optimistic of playing in 1993-94.

Seven points in three matches following the Merthyr victory suggested that the new appointment had led to an upturn in fortunes, only for four successive defeats in December to put the club back among the strugglers.

Two Conference victories between New Year and March, a spell that saw yet another early F.A. Trophy exit, this time at home to Boston United, made relegation look a formality, especially as their rivals all had several games in hand. The victory that the club desperately needed to get them back on the winning trail came on the last Saturday of March when Bromsgrove Rovers were beaten 4-2 at Park View Road. One week later Mark Hone's first goal for 18 months gave Welling their first ever away victory at Telford, and suddenly life looked a lot brighter at Park View Road.

After an unlucky defeat at Dagenham & Redbridge on Easter Monday the Wings won their last two home matches, against Farnborough Town and Gateshead to give themselves real hope of survial as they travelled to Stalybridge on May 1st.

Despite retaining Conference status nobody at Park View Road is in any doubt as to how much work is required. On the bright side however the first year of the YT scheme ended with the Welling side, consisting largely of 16 and 17-year-olds, coming runners-up in the Southern Youth League, and with six further full time youngsters joining the present nine in the summer there could be a good crop of youngsters coming to the fore in a couple of years. For the present the club's playing fortunes lie with their elder colleagues, and if they can repeat that late season form in August and beyond, 1993-94 will hopefully be memorable for all the right reasons.

Welling United 1992/93 - Back Row (L-R): R.Burgess, N.Ransom, S.White, M.Hone, G.Abbott, D.McGinley, N.Sullivan, A.Salako, P.Grees. Front Row: L.Dennis, P.Collins, J.Francis, T.Robbins, T.Reynolds, S.Robinson, K.Hoddy.

WELLING MATCHFACTS 92-93

Key: Home fixtures are denoted by bold capitals. Numbers in brackets after players names indicate goals scored (an asterisk by the results denotes own goals). Only used substitutes are listed - substituted players are *italicised*.

Key to Competitions: GMVC: G.M. Vauxhall Conference. **DC:** Drinkwise (G.M. Vauxhall Conference) Cup. **FAC:** F.A. Cup. **FAT:** Vauxhall F.A. Trophy. **KSC:** Kent Senior Cup. **LCC:** London Challenge Cup.

LEAGUE POSITION: 20th **FA CUP:** Fourth Qualifying Round **FA TROPHY:** Second Round

Date	Opponents	Comp.	Res	Gate	1.	2.	3.	4.	5.	6.	7.	8.	9.	10.	11.	Sub.	Sub.
22/08	**TELFORD UNITED**	GMVC	1-3	875	Sullivan	Hone	Collins	Newman	Ransom	Smith	*White*	Hoddy	Abbott	Robbins(1)	Dennis	Salako	
25/08	Wycombe W.	GMVC	0-3	3,530	Sullivan	Hone	Collins	Hoddy	Ransom	Newman	White	Smith	Abbott	Robbins	Dennis		
29/08	Stafford R.	GMVC	3-4	786	Sullivan	Hone	Collins	Hoddy	Ransom	Newman	White(1)	Smith	Abbott(2)	Robbins	Dennis	Salako	Francis
31/08	**YEOVIL TOWN**	GMVC	0-3	963	Sullivan	*Hone*	Robinson	Glover	Ransom	*Smith*	White	Smith	Abbott	Robbins	Dennis	Dennis	Hoddy
05/09	**STALYBRIDGE C.**	GMVC	1-4	719	Sullivan	Hone	Robinson	Glover	Ransom	Smith	White(1)	Hoddy(1)	Abbott	Robbins(1)	*Salako*	Dennis	Hoddy
08/09	Woking	DC	2-1	1,363	Harrison	Hone	Clem'nce	Glover	Ransom	Smith	White	Hoddy	*Abbott(2)*	Robbins	Dennis		Robinson
12/09	Bromsgrove	GMVC	2-2	957	Harrison	Hone	*Clem'nce*	Glover	Ransom	Smith	White	Reynolds	Abbott(1)	Robbins(2)	Dennis	Newman	
19/09	**RUNCORN**	DC	3-2	842	Harrison	Hone	Clem'nce	Glover	Ransom	Smith	White	Hoddy	Abbott	Robbins	Dennis		
22/09	**WOKING**	GMVC	2-2	670	Harrison	Hone	Clem'nce	Glover	Collins	Smith	White	Reynolds	Abbott(1)	Robbins	Dennis(2)		
26/09	Merthyr Tyd.	GMVC	1-1	655	Harrison	Hone	*Clem'nce*	Glover	Ransom	Smith	Salako	Hoddy	Abbott	Robbins	Dennis(1)	Hoddy	
03/10	Kidderminster	GMVC	1-2	1,018	Turner	Hone	Clem'nce	Glover	Ransom	Smith	White	Reynolds	Abbott(1)	Robbins(1)	Dennis		
06/10	**SLOUGH TOWN**	GMVC	2-1	721	Harrison	Hone	Clem'nce	Glover	Ransom	Smith	White	Reynolds	Abbott	Robbins(1)	*Dennis(1)*	Collins	Hoddy
10/10	**BOSTON UNITED**	GMVC	2-2	912	Harrison	Hone	*Clem'nce*	Glover	*Ransom*	Smith	White	Reynolds	Abbott	Robbins(2)	Dennis	Collins	
13/10	Bath City	GMVC	1-1	506	Harrison	Hone	Robinson	Glover	Collins	Smith	White	Reynolds	Abbott	Robbins	*Dennis(1)*	Clem'nce	
17/10	Gateshead	GMVC	2-1	517	Harrison	Hone	Robinson	Glover	Collins	Smith	White	*Reynolds*	*Abbott(1)*	Robbins	Dennis(1)	Clem'nce	Hoddy
20/10	**WYCOMBE W.**	DC	2-3	452	Harrison	Hone	Robinson	Glover	Ransom	*Smith(1)*	White	*Hoddy*	Abbott	Robbins	Dennis(1)	Ransom	Salako
24/10	Kingstonian	FAC	1-2	861	Williams	Hone	Robinson	Glover	Collins	Salako	White(1)	Hoddy	Abbott	Robbins(1)	Dennis		
31/10	**WITTON ALBION**	GMVC	2-2	927	Harrison	Hone	Robinson	Glover	Collins	Salako	White	Reynolds	Abbott	Robbins(1)	Dennis		
03/11	Farnborough	GMVC	2-3	513	Harrison	Hone	Robinson	Glover	Collins	*Salako*	White	Reynolds	*Abbott(2)*	Robbins(1)	Dennis	Hoddy	Cl'ence
10/11	Slough Town	GMVC	2-4	905	Harrison	Hone	Robinson	Glover	Collins	Collins	White	Reynolds	Abbott	Robbins	Dennis(1)	Hoddy	Dennis
14/11	Northwich V.	GMVC	1-1	529	Williams	Salako	Robinson	Collins	*Ransom*	Clem'nce	White	Reynolds	Abbott	Robbins	Hone	Dennis	
21/11	**MERTHYR TYD.**	GMVC	5-0	720	Williams	Hone	Robinson	Collins	Ransom	Clem'nce	White(1)	Salako	Abbott(1)	Robbins(3)	Reynolds		
24/11	**ERITH & BEL.**	KSC	2-0	404	Williams	Hone	Robinson	Collins	Ransom	Clem'nce	Newman	Salako	Abbott(1)	Robbins(1)	Dennis		
28/11	**MACCLESFIELD**	GMVC	1-0	959	Williams	Hone	Robinson	Collins	Ransom	Clem'nce	White	Salako	Abbott(1)	Robbins	Tivey		
05/12	Kettering T.	GMVC	4-2	1,488	Williams	Hone	Robinson	Collins	Ransom(1)	Clem'nce	White	Salako(1)	Abbott	Robbins(2)	Tivey		

Date	Opponent	Comp	Score	Att	1	2	3	4	5	6	7	8	9	10	11	Subs
08/12	**WOKING**	GMVC	1-1	1,077	Williams	Hone	Robinson	Collins	Ransom	Clem'nce	White	Salako	Abbott	Robbins(1)	Tivey	Dennis, Newman
12/12	**BATH CITY**	GMVC	0-3	862	Williams	Hone	Robinson	Collins	Ransom	Clem'nce	White	Salako	Abbott	Robbins	Tivey	Dennis
19/12	Altrincham	GMVC	0-2	631	Williams	Hone	Robinson	Collins	Ransom	Clem'nce	White	Salako	Abbott	Robbins	Newman	Tivey
26/12	Boston United	GMVC	1-2	1,309	Williams	Hone	Robinson	Collins	Ransom	Clem'nce	White	Salako	Abbott	Robbins	Newman	Dennis(1)
28/12	**DAGENHAM & R.**	GMVC	0-2	1,357	Williams	Hone	Robinson	Collins	Ransom	Hoddy	Dennis	Salako	Abbott(1)	Robbins(1)	Newman	Tivey, Ransom
02/01	**WYCOMBE W.**	GMVC	2-2	2,616	Williams	Hone	Robinson	Collins	Ransom	Hoddy	Dennis	Salako	Abbott	Robbins(2)	Newman	Newman
09/01	**AYLESBURY**	FAT	2-1	743	Williams	Hone	Newman	Collins	Ransom	Smith	Hoddy	Salako(1)	Abbott(1)	Dennis(1)	Tivey	Smith
12/01	**COLLIER ROW**	LCC	5-2	202	Williams	Hone	Hoddy	Collins	Ransom	Smith	Smith	Salako	Abbott(1)	Robbins	Tivey(2)	Burgess, Smith
16/01	Woking	GMVC	0-1	1,647	Williams	Hone	Newman	Collins	Ransom	Smith	Dennis	Salako	Abbott	Robbins	Tivey	Dennis
23/01	**ALTRINCHAM**	GMVC	2-0	857	Williams	Hone	Robinson	Collins	Ransom	Burgess	Hoddy	Salako	Abbott	Robbins	Tivey	Dennis(2), Cl'ence
30/01	**BOSTON UNITED**	FAT	1-2	1,012	Williams	Hone	Robinson	Collins	Ransom	Newman	White	Salako	Abbott(1)	Dennis	Tivey	Robbins
02/02	Dover Athletic	KSC	1-0	1,006	Williams	Hone	Robinson	Collins	Ransom	Newman	White(1)	Smith	Abbott	Dennis	Cooper	Clem'nce
06/02	**KETTERING T.**	GMVC	1-1	838	Williams	Hone	Robinson	Collins	Ransom	Newman	White	Smith	Abbott	Robbins(1)	Cooper	Dennis
09/02	**KIDDERMINSTER**	GMVC	0-0	663	Williams	Hone	Robinson	Collins	Ransom	Newman	White	Smith	Abbott	Robbins	Cooper	Dennis
13/02	Runcorn	GMVC	0-3	778	Williams	Hone	Robinson	Collins	Ransom	Hoddy	White	Smith	Abbott	Robbins	Cooper	Dennis
16/02	Uxbridge	(LCC)	2-1	162	Williams	Salako	Robinson	Collins	Ransom(1)	Newman(1)	Hoddy	Smith	Abbott	Dennis(1)	Clem'nce	Robbins, Barnes
23/02	Witton Albion	GMVC	1-0	541	Williams	Hone	Robinson	Collins	Ransom	Clem'nce(1)	Hoddy	Smith	Abbott	Robbins	Cooper	White, Dennis
27/02	Macclesfield	GMVC	1-1	437	Williams	Salako	Robinson	Collins	Ransom	Clem'nce	Hoddy	Smith	Abbott	Robbins(1)	Cooper	White, Dennis
06/03	**STAFFORD R.**	GMVC	1-2	712	Williams	Newman(1)	Robinson	Collins	Ransom	Clem'nce	White	Smith	Abbott	Robbins	Dennis	Hoddy, Burgess
09/03	**BARNET**	LCC	1-2	377	Williams	Salako	Robinson	Collins	Ransom	Clem'nce	White(1)	Newman	Abbott	Robbins(1)	Hoddy	Dennis, Burgess
16/03	**BROMLEY**	KSC	2-4	503	Wild	Hone	Robinson	Collins	Ransom	Clem'nce	White	Newman	Abbott	Robbins	Hoddy	Dennis, Cl'ence
20/03	**NORTHWICH V.**	GMVC	1-5	633	Williams	Hone	Robinson	Collins	Ransom	Smith	White	Salako	Abbott	Robbins(1)	Hoddy	Smith, Cl'ence
23/03	Yeovil Town	GMVC	0-1	2,019	Williams	Hone	Robinson	Collins	Ransom	Clem'nce	White	Dennis	Abbott(2)	Robbins	Hoddy	Dennis
27/03	**BROMSGROVE**	GMVC	4-2	750	Williams	Hone(1)	Robinson	Collins	Ransom	Clem'nce	White	Brown	Abbott	Robbins(1)	Holman	Dennis
03/04	Telford United	GMVC	1-0	574	Williams	Hone	Robinson	Collins	Ransom	Clem'nce	White	Brown	Abbott	Robbins	Holman	Dennis
12/04	Dagenham & R.	GMVC	0-1	1,288	Williams	Hone	Robinson	Collins	Ransom	Clem'nce	White	Brown	Abbott	Robbins	Holman	Dennis
17/04	**FARNBOROUGH**	GMVC	3-1	842	Williams	Hone(1)	Robinson	Collins	Ransom	Clem'nce	White	Brown	Abbott(1)	Robbins(1)	Holman	Dennis, Hoddy
24/04	**GATESHEAD**	GMVC	2-1	1,049	Williams	Hone	Robinson	Collins	Ransom	Clem'nce	White	Brown	Abbott(1)	Robbins(1)	Holman	Dennis, Hoddy
01/05	Stalybridge	GMVC	0-0	705	Williams	Hone	Robinson	Collins	Ransom	Clem'nce	White	Brown	Abbott	Robbins	Hoddy	Dennis

LEAGUE APPEARANCES: Abbott 42; Brown 6; Clemmence 27(5); Collins 34(2); Cooper 5; Dennis 19(16); Francis 0(1); Glover 13; Harrison 10; Hoddy 18(7); Hone 39(2); Holman 4; Newman 12(2); Ransom 36(1); Reynolds 12; Robbins 42; Robinson 30(1); Salako 18(2); Smith 22(1); Sullivan 5; Tivey 7(2); Turner 1; White 34(3); Wild 1; Williams 25.

LEAGUE GOALSCORERS: Robbins 19; Abbott 17; Dennis 9; White 4; Hone 2; Clemmence , Newman, Ransom, Salako 1.

Welling United

TERRY ROBBINS

Has been with the club for seven years as a player, and more recently as player-manager.

Terry joined 'The Wings' from Crawley Town for £8,000 and has been top goal scorer for the club in every season since then. It was this goalscoring record that gained him International recognition with his first cap for the England semi-pro team last season.

Poor Conference form and a shock FA Cup defeat culminated in Nicky Brigden parting company with the club and Terry Robbins taking over as player-manager. At 27-years-old Terry became the youngest manager in senior football.

Terry's first term as manager was successful in that relegation was avoided and, if the form that saw them through the end of last season can be maintained, 1993/94 could be a good year for 'The Wings' and Terry.

Gary Abbott scores Welling's first goal in a 2-2 draw with Bromsgrove. Photo: K.Gillard.

Programme details:
>   32 pages for £1
>   Editor - Paul Carter

Any other club publications:
>   Wings Review
>   'Winning isn't Everything' (Fanzine)

Local Newspapers:
>   Kentish Times
>   Bexleyheath & Welling Mercury
>   **Local Radio Stations:**
>   Radio Kent
>   Radio Invicta

WELLING UNITED - PLAYING SQUAD 1992-93

Player	Honours	Birthplace and date	Transfer Fees	Previous Clubs
GOALKEEPERS				
Darren Williams		Plaistow 11/5/66		Dagenham, Barnet Wealdstone, Sorrento (Aust)
DEFENDERS				
Mark Hone	ESP, LSC	Croydon 21/8/69	£10,000	Crystal Palace
Nigel Ransom	LSC, KSC, SLP, MW	London 12/3/59		None
Paul Collins	SLP	Southwark 1963		Millwall, Fisher Ath
Steve Robinson	SLP, SLS, KSC	London 7/9/63	£3,500	Arsenal, Dartford, Leyt & Ilf, Dartford
David Newman		London		Crystal Palace, Whyteleafe, Bromley, Dulwich Hamlet
MIDFIELD				
Neil Clemmence	LSC, SLP, KSC	Gravesend 29/7/64		Dartford
Kevin Hales		Dartford 13/1/61		Chelsea, Leyton Orient
Stuart White	SLP, LSC, KSC	Ashford 30/11/63		Charlton Ath, Gillingham, Brighton
Kevin Hoddy		Romford 6/1/68		Fulham, Charlton Ath.,
Tony Reynolds	LSC	Ashford 24/4/63		Folkestone, Ashford, Maidstone Utd
Ray Burgess	SLP, LSC, KSC	London 14/10/56		None
Gary Smith	BBCS	London 3/12/68		Fulham, Colchester U, Enfield, Wycombe W
FORWARDS				
Terry Robbins	ESP, GMVC LSC, MW	London 18/7/65	£8,000	Spurs, Gilligham, Maidstone Utd, Crawley
Gary Abbott	ESP, KSC,	Catford 7/11/64	£30,000	Welling Utd, Barnet, Enfield
Paul Copley				Crockenhill
Mark Tivey				Thamesmead Town

Departures during season:
John Glover, Wayne Brown, Andy Salako & Lenny Dennis (Released)

Players on loan during season:
Lee Harrison (Charlton), Geoff Cooper (Barnet), Rob Wild (Barnet), Mark Holman (Crystal Pal).

Park View Road, Welling

Address and telephone number: Park View Road Ground, Welling, Kent DA16 1SY.
Tel: 081 3011196 Fax: 081 3015676
Simple directions: M25, then A2 towards London. Take Welling turn-off, ground 1 mile. By rail to
Welling station (B.R.) - ground 3/4 mile.

Capacity: 5,500   **Seated:** 500   **Covered terracing:** 1,500

Record Attendance: 4,100 v Gillingham, FA Cup
Club Shop: On sale programmes (League & non-League), scarves, mugs, caps, hats, badges,
replica kits - matchday manager Peter Mason.
Social Facilities: Clubhouse open on match days
Previous Grounds: Butterfly Lane, Eltham - 1963/78

Welling Fact File

Nickname: The Wings

Club Sponsors: Welling Building Services Ltd

Previous Leagues: Eltham & District League 1963/71, London Spartan League 1971/77, Athenian
League 1977/79, Southern League 1979/86.

Club colours: Red shirts & shorts

Change colours: All white

Midweek home matchday: Tuesday

Record win: 7-1

Record defeat: 0-7

Record transfer fee: £30,000 for Gary Abbott from Enfield

Record transfer fee received: £22,000 from Barnet for Duncan Horton

1992/93 Captain: Nigel Ransom

1992/93 Top scorer: Terry Robbins

1992/93 Player of the Year: Paul Collins

Club record goalscorer: John Bartley 533

Record appearances: Ray Burges 1,022

Past players who progressed to the Football League: Paul Barron (Plymouth, Arsenal, Stoke,
WBA, C.Palace, Q.P.R.), Andy Townsend (Southampton, Norwich, Chelsea), Ian Thompson
(Bournemouth), John Bartley (Millwall), Dave Smith (Gillingham, Bristol City), Murray Jones
(C.Palace, Bristol City, Exeter City), Kevin Shoemaker (Peterborough), Tony Agana (Watford,
Sheffield Utd), Duncan Horton (Barnet)

Club Honours: London Spartan League 1978; Southern League Premier Division 1985/86; Kent
Senior Cup 1985/86; London Senior Cup 1989/90; London Challange Cup 1991/92.

WITTON ALBION

Formed:
1887

President:
T.Stelfox

Chairman:
G.D.Shirley

Vice Chairman
D.Lloyd

Football Secretary:
David Leather

Manager:
Michael Mackenzie

Coach:
Oshor Williams

Commercial Manager:
Rod Price

Press Officer:
Rod Price

Attempting to consolidate on what had been a fairly successful first season in the Conference, the team was reinforced with a couple of experienced ex-Football League players, namely Mark Lillis and Steve Senior. These together with exciting youngster Brendan Burke certainly got the season off to a good start. After the first nine matches Witton were the only unbeaten team, lying in second position. However it was to be an unwanted record that then followed as thirteen league games went by before they secured another win by which time they were languishing close to the bottom of the league. From then on right up to the final match of the season, Witton were in great danger of finding themselves back in the N.P.L. Forced to cram in sixteen league games alone in the last eight weeks took its obvious toll on the staff and only a tremendous effort, in winning three of the five games played in the final week, pulled them clear of the relegation duo.

The FA Trophy saw Witton, for the third season running, making it to the semi-finals just missing out on a consecutive Wembley appearance on a 1-2 scoreline. This after outplaying the opposition throughout most of the 180 minutes.

The same can be said for the FA Cup tie at Bury, where a 2-0 result flattered the Football League side. A corner count of 20-6 in Witton's favour, together with the awarding of three penalties to the Gigg Lane outfit, tells the story!

Over the season 35 players were utilised and Karl Thomas again finished top scorer. His last three seasons have produced 105 goals.

By the end of the season only seven of the previous season's squad remained and with growing unrest among supporters and board members alike, the inevitable result saw all three managerial staff severing their connection with the club. Replacing them were the highly successful team of Mike Mackenzie and Oshor Williams who'd brought a brand of football to Winsford United that used to be the hallmark of past Witton teams.

Phil Chadwick

Witton Albion 1992/93 - Back Row (L-R): Kevan Keelan (Asst.Manager), Joe Connor, Mark Hughes, Jim Connor, Carl Alford, Keith Mason, Ian Redman, Mark Lillis, Peter O'Brien, Billy Dodds (Trainer). Front Row: Keith Higgins (Physio), Stewart Anderson, Karl Thomas, Lee Coathup, Steve Senior, Brendan Burke, Jason Gallagher. Richard Maloney (Mascot). Photo: Keith Clayton.

WITTON MATCHFACTS 92-93 WITTON MATCHFACTS 92-93 WITTON MATCHFACTS 92-93

Key: Home fixtures are denoted by bold capitals. Numbers in brackets after players names indicate goals scored (an asterisk by the results denotes own goals). Only used substitutes are listed - substituted players are *italicised*.

Key to Competitions: GMVC: G.M. Vauxhall Conference. **MCSC:** Mid-Cheshire Senior Cup. **DC:** Drinkwise (G.M. Vauxhall Conference) Cup. **FAC:** F.A. Cup. **FAT:** Vauxhall F.A. Trophy. **CSC:** Cheshire Senior Cup.

FA CUP: First Round   **FA TROPHY:** Semi-Final

LEAGUE POSITION: 17th

Date	Opponents	Comp.	Res	Gate	1.	2.	3.	4.	5.	6.	7.	8.	9.	10.	11.	Sub.	Sub.
22/08	BROMSGROVE	GMVC	1-1	912	Mason	Senior	Coathup	Kelly	J.Connor	Redman	Thomas(1)	Lillis	Lutkevitch	Burke	Rose	Alford	
25/08	Telford United	GMVC	3-0	1,160	Mason	Senior	Coathup	McNeilis	J.Connor	Redman	Thomas(2)	Lillis	Kelly	Burke	Rose	Alford(1)	Lutkev'ch
29/08	Bath City	GMVC	0-0	521	Mason	Senior	Coathup	McNeilis	J.Connor	Anderson	Thomas	Lillis	Kelly	Burke	Rose	Alford	McClusk.
31/08	ALTRINCHAM	GMVC	1-1	1,084	Mason	Senior	Coathup	McNeilis	J.Connor	Anderson	Thomas	Alford	Bondll(1)	Burke	Rose	Lutkevitch	Smart
05/09	BOSTON UNITED	GMVC	2-0	746	Mason	Senior	Coathup	McNeilis	J.Connor	Lillis(1)	Thomas	Alford	Bondwell	Burke(1)	Hughes	McCluskie	Anderson
15/09	STALYBRIDGE C.	GMVC	2-0	961	Mason	Senior	Coathup	McNeilis	J.Connor	Lillis	Thomas(1)	Bondswell	Hughes	Burke	Jo.Connor	Alford	Stewart
19/09	Woking	GMVC	2-1	2,041	Mason	Senior	Coathup	McNeilis	J.Connor	Lillis	Thomas	Alford(1)	Hughes(1)	Burke	Jo.Connor	Redman	G'gher
26/09	Farnborough	GMVC	1-1	704	Mason	Senior	Coathup	Redman	J.Connor	Lillis	Thomas	Alford(1)	Hughes	Burke	Jo.Connor	Anderson	G'gher
03/10	KETTERING T.	GMVC	4-2	986	Mason	Senior	Coathup	Redman	J.Connor	Lillis	Kilner	Alford	Hughes(2)	Stewart(2)	Jo.Connor	Burke	G'gher
10/10	YEOVIL TOWN	GMVC	1-2	952	Mason	Senior	Coathup	Redman	J.Connor	Lillis	Kilner(1)	Alford	Hughes	Stewart	Jo.Connor	Thomas	G'gher
17/10	Kidderminster	GMVC	0-0	1,268	Mason	Senior	Coathup	McNeilis	J.Connor	Lillis	Thomas	Redman	Hughes	Stewart	Kilner	Alford	G'gher
20/10	MACCLESFIELD	DC	0-1	763	Mason	Senior	Coathup	McNeilis	J.Connor	Lillis	Thomas	Stewart	Hughes	Burke	Kilner	Alford	G'gher
24/10	Wycombe W.	GMVC	1-2	4,731	Mason	Senior	Coathup	McNeilis	J.Connor	Redman	Thomas	Lillis	Alford	Burke(1)	Stewart	Kilner	G'gher
27/10	GATESHEAD	GMVC	1-3	771	Mason	Senior	Coathup	McNeilis	J.Connor	Lillis	Thomas(1)	Stewart	Alford	Burke	Kilner	Gallagher	Jo.Con.
31/10	Welling Utd	GMVC	2-2	927	Mason	Senior	Coathup	McNeilis	J.Connor	Lillis	Rose	Smart	Burke(2)	Gallagher	Adams	Stewart	Jo.Con.
07/11	DAGENHAM & R.	GMVC	2-2	812	Mason	Senior	Coathup	McNeilis	J.Connor	Lillis	Thomas	Rose	Gallagher	Burke(1)	Adams	Jo.Connor	Alford
14/11	Bury	FAC	0-2	2,682	Mason	Senior	Coathup	McNeilis	J.Connor	Lillis	Thomas	Rose	Gallagher	Burke	Adams	Alford	
18/11	Gateshead	GMVC	1-3	233	Mason	Senior	Coathup	McNeilis	J.Connor	Lillis(1)	Thomas	Rose	Gallagher	Burke	Adams	Jo.Connor	Alford
21/11	Yeovil Town	GMVC	0-2	2,316	Mason	Senior	Coathup	McNeilis	J.Connor	Lillis	Alford	Rose	Gallagher	Burke	Adams	Jo.Connor	Holt
05/12	WINSFORD UTD	MCSC	2-2	697	Mason	Senior	Coathup	McNeilis	J.Con.(1)	Holt	Thomas	Gallagher	Jo.Connor	Burke	Adams	Alford	Rose
12/12	WYCOMBE W.	GMVC	2-2	1,272	Mason	Senior	Coathup	McNeilis	J.Connor	Lillis	Thomas(2)	Holt	Gallagher	Burke	Jo.Connor	Alford	
19/12	Dagenham & R.	GMVC	1-1	1,076	Mason	Senior	Coathup	McNeilis	J.Connor	Adams	Thomas(1)	Holt	Gallagher	Burke	Jo.Connor	Alford	T'linson
28/12	NORTHWICH V.	GMVC	1-3	2,442	Mason	Senior	Coathup	McNeilis	J.Connor	Adams	Thomas	Holt	Gallagher	Burke(1)	Jo.Connor	Alford	Lillis
02/01	MACCLESFIELD	GMVC	1-1	1,110	Mason	Senior	Coathup	Alford(1)	J.Connor	Lillis	Thomas	Holt	Gallagher	Burke	Jo.Connor	Lillis	Tomlinson
09/01	Macclesfield	FAT	0-0	890	Mason	Senior	Coathup	McNeilis	J.Connor	Lillis	Thomas	Tomlinson	Alford	Burke	Adams	Adams	

Date	Opponent	Comp	Score	Att	Mason	Senior	Coathup	McNeilis	J.Connor	Lillis	Thomas	Rose	Alford	Burke	Adams	Tomlinson	G'gher
12/01	MACCLESFIELD	FAT	0-0	901	Mason	Senior	Coathup	McNeilis	J.Connor	Lillis	Thomas	Rose	Alford	Burke	Adams	Thomas	Alford
16/01	Bromsgrove	GMVC	2-3	1,145	Mason	Senior	Coathup	McNeilis	J.Con.(2)	Gallagher	Holt	Rose	McCarty	Burke	Adams	Rose	Alford
18/01	MACCLESFIELD	FAT	2-1	907	Paladino	Senior	Coathup	McNeilis	J.Connor	Gallagher	Thomas	Alford	Rose	Burke(2)	Adams	Rose(1)	Bancroft
23/01	Merthyr Tyd.	GMVC	2-0	592	Mason	Senior	Coathup	McNeilis	J.Connor	Gallagher	Thomas	Alford(1)	McCarty	Burke(2)	Adams	Alford(1)	
26/01	ALTRINCHAM	CSC	3-3	466	Mason	Senior	Coathup	McNeilis	J.Connor	Gallagher	Thomas	Alford(1)	Holt	Burke	Adams	Alford(2)	
30/01	St.Albans C.	FAT	2-0	1,470	Paladino	Senior	Coathup	McNeilis	J.Connor	Redman	Thomas	Gallagher	McCarty	Burke(1)	Adams	Bancroft	Murphy
02/02	Altrincham	CSC	3-1	503	Mason	Senior	Coathup(1)	McNeilis	J.Connor	Lillis	Thomas	Alford	McCarty	Burke	Adams	Bancroft	Adams
13/02	WOKING	GMVC	1-2	930	Mason	Senior	Coathup	McNeilis	J.Connor	Lillis	Thomas	Gallagher	McCarty	Burke(1)	Adams	Bancroft	Murphy
20/02	MARINE	FAT	1-0	1,171	Mason	Senior	Coathup	McNeilis	J.Connor	Adams	Thomas(1)	Gallagher	McCarty	Murphy	Adams	Bancroft	Alford
23/02	WELLING UNITED	GMVC	0-1	541	Mason	Senior	Coathup	Adams	J.Connor	Lillis	Thomas	Gallagher	McCarty	Burke	Murphy	Holt	Alford
27/02	Kettering T.	GMVC	1-2	1,090	Mason	Senior	Coathup	Gallagher	J.Connor	Lillis	Thomas	Gallagher	McCarty	Burke	Adams	Grant	Bancroft
03/03	Warrington T.	CSC	4-2	617	Mason	Senior	Coathup	Gallagher	J.Connor	Lillis	Thomas(2)	Rose	Gallagher	Burke(1)	Bancroft	Alford	Alford(1)
06/03	MERTHYR TYDFIL	GMVC	3-1	641	Mason	Senior	Coathup	McNeilis	J.Connor	Lillis	Thomas(1)	Rose	Gallagher	Burke(1)	Bancroft	Alford(2)	
09/03	KIDDERMINSTER	GMVC	2-2	638	Mason	Senior	Coathup	McNeilis	J.Connor	Lillis	Thomas(2)	Rose(1)	Gallagher	Burke	Alford	Bancroft	
13/03	FARNBOROUGH	FAT	3-2	1,262	Paladino	Senior	Coathup	McNeilis	J.Connor	Alford	Thomas(1)	Rose(1)	Gallagher	Burke(1)	Bancroft	Alford(1)	
16/03	STAFFORD R.	GMVC	2-5	680	Paladino	Senior	Coathup	McNeilis	J.Connor	Alford	Thomas(2)	Rose	Gallagher	Burke	Bancroft	Alford(2)	Gardner
20/03	Boston United	GMVC	2-2	939	Paladino	Senior	Coathup	Lambert	J.Connor	Lillis	Thomas(1)	Rose	Gallagher	Burke	Gardner	Bancroft	
23/03	WARRINGTON T.	CSC	2-1	501	Mason	Senior	Coathup	McNeilis	J.Connor	Lillis	Thomas(2)	Rose	Murphy	Burke	Adams	Holt	Alford
27/03	SLOUGH TOWN	GMVC	1-1	742	Mason	Senior	Coathup	McNeilis	J.Connor	Lillis	Thomas(2)	Rose(1)	Murphy	Burke	Adams	Grant	
30/03	Stafford R.	GMVC	1-1	912	Mason	Senior	Gallagher	McNeilis	Bullock	Lillis	Thomas	Rose	Lambert	Burke	Grant	Alford	
03/04	Runcorn	FAT	0-2	1,610	Mason	Senior	Gallagher	McNeilis	Lambert	Lillis	Thomas	Rose	Gallagher	Burke	Bullock	Alford	Gardner
10/04	RUNCORN	FAT	1-0	2,033	Mason	Senior	Coathup	McNeilis	J.Connor	Lillis	Thomas	Rose	Alford	Burke	Adams	Alford	
14/04	BATH CITY	GMVC	0-0	622	Mason	Senior	Coathup	McNeilis	J.Connor	Lillis	Thomas	Rose	Alford(1)	Burke	Adams	Grant	Bancroft
17/04	Runcorn	GMVC	4-4	753	Paladino	Gallagher	Senior(1)	McNeilis	J.Con.(1)	Gallagher	Thomas(1)	Rose	Alford	Burke	Adams	Grant	Grant
20/04	FARNBOROUGH	GMVC	1-1	546	Paladino	Senior	Coathup	McNeilis	Lambert	Lillis	Thomas(1)	Gallagher	Alford	Grant	Adams	Grant	Rose
24/04	Slough Town	GMVC	3-2	1,060	Paladino	Senior	Gardner	McNeilis	J.Connor	Lillis	Thomas(1)	Rose	Alford(2)	Grant	Adams	Holt	
26/04	Stalybridge	GMVC	2-1	634	Paladino	Senior	Gardner	McNeilis	J.Connor	Lillis	Thomas(2)	Rose	Alford	Bancroft	Adams	Healey	
29/04	RUNCORN	GMVC	0-3	963	Paladino	Senior	Coathup	Gallagher	Gardner	Lillis	Thomas	Rose	Bancroft	Grant	Adams	Holt	Bancroft
01/05	TELFORD UTD	GMVC	2-1	756	Paladino	Senior	Coathup	McNeilis	Gardner	Gallagher	Thomas(1)	Rose	Alford(1)	Holt	Grant	Lillis	Bancroft

LEAGUE APPEARANCES: Adams 23(1); Alford 24(12); Bancroft 5(10); Bondswell 3; Bullock 1; Burke 32(1); Coathup 38; Jim Connor 38; Joe Connor 8(5); Gallagher 25(6); Gardner 5(1); Grant 4(5); Healey 1(1); Holt 6(3); Hughes 7; Kelly 3; Kilner 4(1); Lambert 4; Lillis 33(3); Lutkevich 1(2); Mason 29; McCarty 5; McCluskie 0(2); McNeilis 33; Murphy 2(2); Paladino 13; Redman 9(1); Rose 23(3); Senior 39; Smart 1; Stewart 5(2); Thomas 37(2); Tomlinson 0(3).

LEAGUE GOALSCORERS: Thomas 20, Alford 14; Burke 12, Jim Connor, Hughes 3; Lillis, McCarty, Murphy, Rose, Stewart 2; Bondswell, Joe Connor, Kilner 1.

Witton Albion

MIKE MACKENZIE

Mike Mackenzie's playing career started with a short spell at Manchester City. He then moved into non-Legaue football with Stalybridge Celtic for a period of four and a half years before moving onto Hyde United and then playing in the GM Vauxhall Conference for Northwich Victoria.

Mike's managerial career started when he took over as manager of a very successful Sunday league side called Astro. From there he moved on to become the manager of Winsford United before moving to witton Albion in the summer of 1993.

Mark Hughes is tackled by Kidderminster's Chris Brindley. Photo: Keith Clayton.

Programme details:
 32 pages for £1
 Editor - Rod Price

Any other club publications:
 'Not The Albion Review' (Fanzine)

Local Newspapers:
 Northwich Chronicle
 Northwich Guardian
 Manchester Evening News

Local Radio Stations:
 BBC Radio Manchester
 Piccadilly Radio
 Signal Radio

WITTON ALBION - PLAYING SQUAD 1992-93

Player	Honours	Birthplace and date	Transfer Fees	Previous Clubs
GOALKEEPERS				
Keith Mason	NPL, FAV, NPL Div 1	Leicester 19/7/58		Wigston Fields, Leicester City, Huddersfield, Colne Dynamoes
DEFENDERS				
Cec Edey		Manchester		Lancaster C, Chorley, Lancaster C, Morecambe, Winsford Utd
Steve Senior	Div 4	Sheffield 15/5/63		York City, Northampton T, Wigan Ath, Preston NE
Jim Connor	CSC	Stockport 31/1/59		Stockport Co, Northwich Victoria, Napier C(NZ), Mossley, Macclesfield T
Steve McNeilis	NPL, MCSC	Liverpool		Formby, Burscough, Northwich Victoria, Colne Dynamoes
Jason Smart		Rochdale 15/2/69		Rochdale, Crewe Alexandra
MIDFIELD				
Colin Rose		Winsford 22/1/72		Crewe Alexandra
Paul Kelly		Urmston 6/3/71		Manchester City, Crewe Alexandra
Jason Gallagher		Liverpool 25/3/72		Marine, Ternia(Belgium)
Andy Bondswell		Bradford 28/12/64		Halifax, Accrington Stanley, Altrincham
Matthew Holt		Lancashire 9/9/72		Blackburn Rovers, Mossley
Neil Hall				Winsford Utd
Steve Adams	GMVC	Sheffield 7/5/59		Rotherham Utd, Worksop T, Scarborough, Doncaster, Boston Utd, Kettering T
FORWARDS				
Brendan Burke	MPC	Manchester 13/10/70		Oldham Town, Mossley
Carl Alford		Manchester 11/2/72		Rochdale, Stockport Co, Burnley
Aidan Murphy	EY, ES	Manchester 17/9/67		Manchester Utd, Crewe Alexandra, Woking, Mossley
Bevon Blackwood				Salford, Hyde Utd, Lancaster C, Winsford Utd
Darryl McCarty	LYC	Lancaster 28/7/64	P/Exch	Chorley, Leyland M, Bolton, Marine, Leyland M, Morecambe, Horwich, Runcorn
Brendan Grant	NPLC, LSC	Liverpool 28/8/65		Marine, Bootle, Burscough, Southport, Caernarfon, Colne D, Warrington, Marine

Departures during season:
Mike Lutkevitch (Accrington Stanley), Andy Grimshaw & Stewart Anderson (Morecambe), Andy Kilner (Chorley), Gary Stewart (Curzon Ashton), Mark Hughes (Congleton), Dave Tomlinson (Stalybridge), Joe Connor (Runcorn), Lee Coathup (Stalybridge), Karl Thomas (Runcorn).

Players on loan during season:
Matthew Lambert & Steve Gardner (Bury), Steve Bullock (Stockport).

Wincham Park, Witton Albion

Address and telephone number: Wincham Park, Chapel Street, Wincham, Northwich, Cheshire. Tel: 0606 43008

Simple directions: M6 junction 19. Follow A556 towards Northwich, after 3 miles turn onto A559 at beginning of dual carriageway, after three-quarters of a mile turn left opposite Black Greyhoud Inn and ground is half a mile on left immediately after crossing Canal Bridge.

Capacity: 4,500   **Seated:** 650   **Covered terracing:** 1,650

Record Attendance: 3,940 v Kidderminster Harriers - FA Trophy Semi-Final   1991

Club Shop: Contact Rob Flavell for more details (0606 75469 evenings only).

Social Facilities: Concert room and Vice-Presidents room open matchdays, Tuesday, Thursday, Friday and Sunday evenings. Food available for private functions.

Previous Grounds: Central Ground, Witton Street, Northwich.

Witton Fact File

Nickname: Albion

Club Sponsors:

Previous Leagues: Lancashire Combination, Cheshire County League, Northern Premier League

Club colours: Red & white stripes

Change colours: Mauve

Midweek home matchday: Tuesday

Record win: 6-0 v Stafford Rangers - 1992/93

Record defeat: 0-4 v Wycombe Wanderers - 1991-92

Record transfer fee: £10,000 (twice) for Karl Thomas from Colne Dynamoes and for Jim McCluskie from Hyde United both 1990.

Record transfer fee received: £11,500 for Peter Henderson from Chester City.

1992/93 Captain: Mark Lillis

1992/93 Top scorer: Karl Thomas

1992/93 Player of the Year: Steve McNeils

Club record goalscorer: Frank Fidler - 122

Record appearances: John Gorle - 652

Past players who progressed to the Football League: P.Henderson (Chester City), Chris Nicholl (ex-Southampton manager), Phil Powell (Crewe), Neil Parsley & Mike Whitlow (Leeds).

Club Honours: Northern Premier League champions 1990-91; Cheshire County League champions 1948-49, 1949/50, 1953/54, Runners-up 1950/51; Cheshire County League Cup winners 1953/54, 1975/76; Cheshire County Senior Cup winners five times; FA Trophy finalists 1992.

WOKING

Formed:
1889

President:
L.A.Gosden MBE

Chairman:
A.E.Hills

Vice Chairman
P.J.Ledger

Football Secretary:
P.J.Ledger J.P.

Manager:
G.Chapple

Coach:
C.Lippiatt

Physiotherapist:
Barry Kimber

Press Officer:
P.J.Ledger

CLUB HISTORY

The first recorded existence of Woking Football Club is the year 1887. On the 5th November of that year a Woking XI beat Chertsey by six goals to two. The 1889/90 season is generally regarded as the first organised season.

A fixture list of 22 friendlies was issued which included two second XI games. Seven games were cancelled due to bad weather but fifteen were played. Of those, three were victories, five were draws and there were seven defeats.

Woking have played on six different grounds during their history, the first was Wheatsheaf Common and the next move was a little further along the Chobham Road to its junction with Woodham Road, however both these stays were brief. The next move was to Church Hill Estate, Horsell. This ground was let to the club by the then vicar of Horsell, the Rev.John Black. When required for building land the club was on the move again this time to the R.A.F. Sports Ground at Pembroke Road, Woking and then on to Hobbs Field, Kingfield. The move to The Sports Field, Kingfield in 1923 provided the club with a new home and when in 1947 the club obtained the freehold of the ground the permanence of the move was confirmed.

To many the greatest moment in the Club's history was the Final of the FA Amateur Cup on the 12th April 1958 at Wembley Stadium when after a three goals to nil victory over Ilford, Charlie Mortimore lifted the Amateur Cup from the Lord Mayor of London and provided the town with a weekend of celebrations. The team itself was arguably the first ever to pull on the cardinal and white halves. With four of the forward line England amateur internationals, Woking possessed the most potent and prolific forward line in amateur football.

When the Amateur Cup was succeeded by the FA Trophy success has been rare with the exception of the 1979/80 season when the semi-final was reached. The FA Cup runs over the past years have been few with the notable exception of 1907/08, when for the first time the club reached the 1st Round Proper. The 1st Round has been reached on a further eight occasions. The most memorable Cup run was in the 1990/91 season when the fourth round was reached. On the way to the fourth round, victories over teams from higher leagues in every round was a tremendous feat. The win at West Bromwich Albion, a Division Two side, was the pinnacle. Turning round at half-time a goal down, Woking outplayed the opposition and went on to win by four goals to two. The Fourth Round saw another superb performance at Goodison Park, the home of Everton, where to lose by only a goal to their 1st Division opponents was confirmation that Woking, under manager Geoff Chapple had assembled the best ever team to wear the colours of Woking.

Woking 1992/93 - Back Row (L-R): T.Buzaglo, K.Brown, T.Baron, B.Pratt, L.Batty, R.Nugent, M.Ogley, T.Senior. Front Row: W.Stemp, M.Fleming, R.Carroll, G.Friel, S.Steele, M.Biggins, D.Brown. Photo: V.J.Robertson.

WOKING MATCHFACTS 92-93   WOKING MATCHFACTS 92-93   WOKING MATCHFACTS 92-93

Key: Home fixtures are denoted by bold capitals. Numbers in brackets after players names indicate goals scored (an asterisk by the results denotes own goals). Only used substitutes are listed - substituted players are *italicised.*

Key to Competitions: **GMVC:** G.M. Vauxhall Conference. **SSC:** Surrey Senior Cup. **DC:** Drinkwise (G.M. Vauxhall Conference) Cup. **FAC:** F.A. Cup. **FAT:** Vauxhall F.A. Trophy. **CS:** Charity Shield.

FA CUP: Second Round   FA TROPHY: First Round

LEAGUE POSITION: 8th

Date	Opponents	Comp.	Res	Gate	1.	2.	3.	4.	5.	6.	7.	8.	9.	10.	11.	Sub.	Sub.	Sub.
22/08	**STAFFORD RGRS**	GMVC	0-3	2,044	Batty	K.Brown	Finch	Nugent	Baron	*Clement*	D.Brown	Biggins	Senior	Puckett	Fleming	Steele		
25/08	Kettering T.	GMVC	1-0	2,200	Batty	K.Brown	Joyce	Nugent	Baron	Clement	D.Brown	Biggins	Senior	Puckett	Flemming(1)	Steele		Buzaglo
29/08	Stalybridge C	GMVC	0-3	968	Batty	K.Brown	Joyce	Nugent	Baron	Fielder	D.Brown	*Biggins*	*Senior*	Buzaglo(2)	*Flemming*	Steele		
31/08	Grays Ath.	CS	5-1	478	Batty	K.Brown	*Joyce*	Nugent(1)	Baron	Fielder	D.Brown	Biggins	Puckett(2)	Buzaglo(2)	Steele			
05/09	**RUNCORN**	GMVC	4-0	1,890	Batty	K.Brown	Joyce	Nugent	Baron	Fielder	D.Brown	Biggins(1)	Puckett(1)	Buzaglo	Steele			
08/09	**WELLING UTD**	DC	1-2	1,363	Batty	K.Brown	Joyce	Nugent	Baron	*Fielder*	D.Brown	Biggins(1)	Puckett(1)	Buzaglo	Steele	Fleming		
12/09	Kidderminster	GMVC	3-1	1,759	Batty	K.Brown	Joyce	Nugent	Baron(1)	Fielder	D.Brown	Biggins	Puckett	*Buzaglo*	Steele(1)	Fleming		
15/09	Bath City	GMVC	0-2	801	Batty	K.Brown	Joyce	Nugent	Baron	Fielder	D.Brown	Biggins	Puckett	Buzaglo	Steele	Senior		
19/09	**WITTON ALB.**	GMVC	1-2	2,041	Batty	K.Brown	Joyce	Nugent	Baron	Fielder	D.Brown	Biggins	Puckett(1)	*Roffe*	Steele	Senior		
22/09	Welling Utd	DC	2-2	670	Batty	K.Brown	Joyce	*Nugent*	Baron(1)	Fielder	D.Brown	Biggins	Puckett	Senior(1)	Carroll	Broderick		
26/09	**BROMSGROVE R.**	GMVC	3-3	1,463	Batty	K.Brown	Fleming	Nugent(1)	Broderick	Fielder	D.Brown	Biggins(1)	Puckett(1)	Senior	Carroll	Fleming		
03/10	**ALTRINCHAM**	GMVC	0-2	2,060	Batty	K.Brown	Joyce	Nugent	Broderick	Fielder	D.Brown	Biggins	Puckett	Senior	Carroll	Fleming		
06/10	Dagenham & R	GMVC	1-5	1,648	Batty	K.Brown	Fleming(1)	Nugent	Broderick	Fielder	*D.Brown*	Biggins	Puckett	Buzaglo	Murphy	Senior		
17/10	**NORTHWICH V.**	GMVC	1-0	1,992	Batty	K.Brown	Fleming	Nugent	Baron	Fielder	Murphy	Biggins	Senior	Puckett(1)	Steele			
31/10	**BROMSGROVE R.**	GMVC	0-2	1,832	Pape	K.Brown	L.Wye	Nugent	Baron	Fielder	S.Wye	Biggins	Fleming	Puckett	*Steele*	Milton		
07/11	Yeovil Town	GMVC	*1-4	2,911	Horne	K.Brown	Fielder	Nugent	Baron	S.Wye	D.Brown	Biggins	*Roffe*	Puckett	L.Wye	Carroll		
14/11	**NUNEATON**	FAC	3-2	3,280	Batty	Clement(1)	L.Wye	Nugent	Baron	S.Wye	Fielder	Biggins(1)	Puckett	Senior	*Steele*	Carroll(1)		
21/11	**GATESHEAD**	GMVC	1-4	1,722	Batty	Clement	L.Wye	Nugent	Baron	S.Wye	Fielder	Biggins	Puckett	Senior(1)	*Steele*	Carroll		
24/11	Merthyr Tyd.	GMVC	5-1	380	Batty	Clement	L.Wye	Nugent	Alexander	S.Wye	Fielder(1)	Biggins	Milton(2)	Senior(2)	Fleming			
28/11	Boston Utd	GMVC	2-1	1,135	Batty	Clement	L.Wye	Nugent	Alexander	S.Wye	Fleming	Biggins(1)	Senior(1)	*Milton*	Fielder	D.Brown		
01/12	**DAGENHAM & R.**	GMVC	1-1	1,734	Batty	Clement	L.Wye	Nugent	Alexander	S.Wye	Fleming	*Biggins(1)*	Senior	Milton	Fielder	Carroll(1)		
05/12	Brighton & HA	FAC	1-1	9,208	Batty	Clement	L.Wye	Nugent	Alexander	S.Wye(1)	Fleming	Biggins	Senior	*Puckett*	Fielder	Carroll		
08/12	Welling Utd	GMVC	*1-1	1,077	Batty	Clement(1)	*L.Wye*	K.Brown	Alexander	S.Wye	Fleming	Biggins	Milton	*Carroll*	Fielder	Buzaglo		D.Brown
12/12	Runcorn	GMVC	3-2	953	Batty	Clement(1)	Fleming(1)	K.Brown	Alexander	S.Wye	D.Brown	Biggins	Rowe	Buzaglo	Fielder	Puckett(1)		
16/12	**BRIGHTON & HA**	FAC	1-2	5,870	Batty	Fleming	L.Wye	Alexander	K.Brown	S.Wye	D.Brown	Biggins	Senior(1)	Puckett	Fielder	Puckett(1)		
19/12	**BOSTON UTD**	GMVC	3-0	1,652	Honey	Clement	L.Wye	Alexander	Nugent	S.Wye	Fleming	Biggins	Senior(2)	Puckett(1)	K.Brown	Buzaglo		

Date	Opponent	Comp	Res	Att													
26/12	WYCOMBE W.	GMVC	0-3	4,911	Batty	Clement	L.Wye	Alexander	Nugent	S.Wye	Fleming	*Biggins*	Senior	Puckett	K.Brown	Buzaglo	
28/12	Farnborough	GMVC	3-0	2,287	Batty	Clement	L.Wye	Alexander	Nugent	S.Wye	D.Brown	Biggins	Senior	Puckett(2)	K.Brown	Buzaglo	
02/01	Slough Town	GMVC	1-0	2,480	Batty	Clement	L.Wye	Alexander	Nugent	S.Wye	Fleming	Biggins(1)	Senior	Puckett	K.Brown	Biggins	Buz(1)
05/01	Dorking	SSC	2-2	656	Batty	Fleming	L.Wye	Alexander	Nugent	S.Wye	D.Brown	Carroll('(1)	Senior	Puckett	K.Brown	Buzaglo	
09/01	Sutton Utd	FAT	0-3	1,884	Batty	Fleming	Fleming	Alexander	*Nugent*	Steele	D.Brown	Biggins	Senior	*Puckett*	K.Brown	Buzaglo	D.Brown
12/01	DORKING	SSC	0-2	932	Batty	Carroll	L.Wye	Alexander	K.Brown	S.Wye	Fleming(1)	Biggins	Senior	*Puckett*	Steele	Buzaglo	
16/01	WELLING UTD	GMVC	1-0	1,647	Batty	Clement	L.Wye	Alexander	K.Brown	S.Wye	Fleming	Biggins	Senior(1)	*Puckett*	Steele	Buzaglo	D.Brown
23/01	Gateshead	GMVC	1-1	627	Batty	Clement	L.Wye	Alexander	K.Brown	S.Wye	Fielder	Biggins	Senior	Puckett	Steele	Buzaglo	D.Brown
30/01	YEOVIL TOWN	GMVC	0-0	2,370	Batty	*Clement*	L.Wye	Alexander	K.Brown	S.Wye	D.Brown	Fielder	Senior	Puckett	Steele(1)	Buzaglo	D.Brown
06/02	Northwich V.	GMVC	0-1	984	Batty	Fleming	L.Wye	Alexander	Nugent	S.Wye(1)	D.Brown(1)	D.Brown	Senior	Buzaglo	Steele(1)	Puckett	
13/02	Witton Alb.	GMVC	2-1	930	Batty	Caroll	L.Wye	Alexander	Nugent	S.Wye	D.Brown	K.Brown	Senior(1)	Buzaglo	Steele	Puckett	
20/02	MACCLESFIELD	GMVC	4-0	1,868	Batty	Caroll(1)	L.Wye	Alexander	Nugent	S.Wye	D.Brown	K.Brown	Senior	*Buzaglo*	Steele(1)	Milton	
27/02	MERTHYR TYD.	GMVC	0-2	2,049	Batty	Caroll	L.Wye	Alexander	Coleman	S.Wye	*D.Brown*	K.Brown	Senior	Puckett	Steele	Puckett	
06/03	Altrincham	GMVC	0-1	839	Batty	Caroll	Coleman	Alexander	Nugent	Fleming	D.Brown	K.Brown	*Senior*	Bushay	Puckett	Puckett	Fielder
09/03	SLOUGH TOWN	GMVC	1-2	1,948	Batty	*Fielder*	Coleman(1)	Alexander	Nugent	Fleming	D.Brown	Alexander	Senior	Bushay	Carroll	Steele	
13/03	Stafford Rgrs	GMVC	0-0	1,062	Batty	Fielder	Coleman	Alexander	Nugent	Fleming	D.Brown	Alexander	Carroll	Bushay	K.Brown	Puckett	
20/03	KETTERING T.	GMVC	3-2	1,586	Batty	*Fielder*	Coleman	K.Brown	Nugent	Fleming	D.Brown	Carroll	Puckett(1)	Bushay(1)	R.Buz.(1)	Steele	Clement
23/03	BATH CITY	GMVC	0-1	1,290	Batty	Clement	Fleming	Alexander	*Nugent*	Fielder	D.Brown	Coleman	Puckett	Bushay	K.Brown	Steele	R.Buz.
27/03	Macclesfield	GMVC	1-1	879	Batty	Clement	Peters	Alexander	K.Brown	Kelly	D.Brown	*Carroll*	Senior	Bushay(1)	Steele(1)	Puckett	
30/03	TELFORD UTD	GMVC	3-2	1,317	Batty	Fielder	Peters	Alexander	K.Brown	Clement	D.Brown	*R.Buzaglo*	Senior(1)	Bushay	Steele(1)	Puckett	Greene
03/04	KIDDERMINSTER	GMVC	1-5	1,537	Batty	Fielder	Peters	Alexander	K.Brown	Clement	D.Brown(1)	*R.Buzaglo*	Senior	Bushay	Steele	Greene	
06/04	Wycombe W.	GMVC	0-0	5,000	Batty	Alexander	Fielder	K.Brown	Nugent	Clement	D.Brown	Peters	Bushay	Greene	Steele	Greene	
12/04	FARNBOROUGH	GMVC	*4-1	2,433	Batty	Fleming(1)	Fielder	Nugent(1)	K.Brown	Clement(1)	D.Brown	Peters	Bushay	Greene	Steele	Puckett	
24/04	STALYBRIDGE	GMVC	2-1	1,713	Batty	Fleming	Fielder	K.Brown	Nugent	Clement	Peters	Greene(1)	Greene	Puckett	Steele	Puckett	Senior(1)
01/05	Bromsgrove	GMVC	0-1	1,808	Batty	Fielder	Peters	K.Brown	Clements	B.Brown	Bushay	*Steele*	Greene	Nugent	Senior	Puckett	Puckett

LEAGUE APPEARANCES: Alexander 24, Baron 11, BAtty 39, Biggins 26, Broderick 3, Brown 29(3), Brown 38, Bushay 12, Buzaglo 7(7), R.Buzaglo 3(1), Carroll 11(5), Clement 23(10, Coleman 6, Fielder 27(1), Finch 1, Fleming 28(1), Greene 4(2), Honey 1, Horne 1, Joyce 7, Kelly 1, Milton 4(3), Murphy 2, Nugent 32, Peters 7, Pape 1, Puckett 25(9), Roffe 2, Rowe 1, Senior 26(5), Steele 22(7), S.Wye 17, S.Wye 18

LEAGUE GOALSCORERS: Senior 11; Puckett 9; Biggins, Fleming, Steele 5; D.Brown, Bushay, Buzaglo, Carroll, Clement, Milton, Nugent 2; Baron, R.Buzaglo, Coleman, Fielder, Greene, S.Wye 1.

Woking

GEOFF CHAPPLE

The 87 supporters who witnessed Woking's 1-0 victory over Clapton on 29th September 1984 probably had little idea that the game would become a landmark in the history of the club. Not because it was the first game of the season that didn't end in defeat, but because it was the first match for the new manager Geoff Chapple.

Chapple joined Aldershot from school but did not play first team football. He played for Woking in the 1970's and also had a spell with Guildford City. He broke a leg whilst playing for Windsor & Eton in 1980 and then became manager of that club before moving to Kingfield in 1984. The game referred to above was in Division One of the Isthmian League and ended a run of seven consecutive defeats since the first game of the season. Even Chapple was unable to prevent relegation that season and for the first time in their history Woking played Division Two football.

Chapple, however, used the time to build a firm foundation which was to produce arguably one of the best ever Isthmian League sides. Promotion to Division One did not come until the 86/87 season when the club won the title scoring 110 goals in the process. The Cards eventually re-claimed their place in the Premier Division in 1990 and just two seasons later the club claimed it's place in the top level of non-league football.

Geoff Chapple's nine year reign as manager has now been rewarded with a full time contract. That September day in 1984 saw the start of the Chapple revolution, who is to say where it will end?

Woking's Steve Milton (12) moves away from two Brentford players. Photo: V.J.Robertson.

Programme details:
    36 pages for £1
    Editors - Mike Deavin

Any other club publications:
    'Wubble Yoo' (Fanzine)

Local Newspapers:
    Woking News/Mail
    Surrey Advertiser
    Woking Herald

Local Radio Stations:
    County Sound

WOKING - PLAYING SQUAD 1992-93

Player	Honours	Birthplace and date	Transfer Fees	Previous Clubs
GOALKEEPERS				
Laurence Batty	ESP, ILP, FA XI	Westminster 15/2/64		Maidenhead Utd, Fulham, Brentford, Farense(Belg)
DEFENDERS				
Kevan Brown	Div 3	Andover 2/1/66		Southampton, Brighton, Aldershot
Mark Fleming	EY	Hammersmith 11/8/69		QPR, Brentford, Farnborough T
Andy Clement	WY	Cardiff 12/11/67		Wimbledon, Woking, Plymouth Argyle
Trevor Baron	ILP	London		Marlow, Burnham, Chertsey, Windsor & Eton, Slough T, Windsor & Eton
MIDFIELD				
Colin Fielder	BHP, HSC	Winchester 5/1/64	P/Exch	Aldershot, Farnborough T, Slough T
Dereck Brown	FA XI	London 8/8/63		Wembley, Hendon, Wembley, Hendon
Mark Biggins	ILP, FA XI	Middlesbrough 18/4/63	£2,500	Hampton, Hanwell, Feltham, Maidenhead U, St Albans C, Windsor
Greg Roffe		Horsham 1/1/68		Horsham, Southwater, Molesey, Broadbridge Heath
Scott Steele	S U-14	Motherwell 19/9/71		Airdrie
FORWARDS				
Trevor Senior	Div 3	Dorchester 28/11/61		Dorchester T, Portsmouth, Reading, Watford, Middlesbrough. Reading
David Puckett	Div 3	Southampton 29/10/60		Southampton, Bournemouth, Aldershot, Bournemouth
Ansil Bushay				Marlow, Flackwell Heath, Beaconsfield Utd, Chalfont St Peter, Marlow
Robbie Carroll	BLT, HSC, FA XI	Perivale 15/2/68		Southampton, Gosport Borough, Brentford, Fareham Town, Yeovil Town
Dave Greene	SLC, ESC	Stoke Newington 14/4/65		Basildon U, Woodford, Sawbridgeworth, Saffron W, Stevenage B, Chelmsford, Slough

Departures during season:
Mark Ogley (Telford), Wayne Stemp (Staines), George Friel (Slough), Shane & Lloyd Wye (Mt Manganui NZ), Tim Buzaglo (Marlow), Steve Milton (Released), Aidan Murphy (Mossley), Tony Joyce (Leighton), Richard Nugent (Stevenage).

Players on loan during season:
John Finch (Fulham), Brian Horne (Millwall), Tim Alexander & Andy Pape (Barnet), Dave Coleman (Farnborough), Paul Kelly (Fulham), Rob Peters (Brentford).

Kingfield Sports Ground, Woking

Address and telephone number: Kingfield Sports Ground, Kingfield, Woking, Surrey. Tel: 0483 772470

Simple directions: M25 J10 or 11, signposted from outskirts of Town. Ground 1 mile. Woking B.R.Station & buses from Woking.

Capacity: 6,000　　　　　**Seated:** 500　　　　　**Covered terracing:** 2,000

Record Attendance: 6,000 v Swansea, FA Cup - 1978/79

Club Shop: Phone 0483 772470 for details.

Social Facilities: Clubhouse open on matchdays. Food available.

Previous Grounds: Wheatsheaf, Ivy Lane (pre 1923)

Woking Fact File

Nickname: The Cards

Club Sponsors: O.L.C.

Previous Leagues: Isthmian 1991/92

Club colours: Red/white halves & black shorts

Change colours: All yellow

Reserve team league: Capital/Suburban League

Midweek home matchday: Tuesday

Record win:

Record defeat:

Record transfer fee: £15,000 for Steve Milton (Fulham) - 1991/92

Record transfer fee received: £4,000 from Marlow for Tim Buzaglo - 1993

1992/93 Captain: A.Clement

1992/93 Top scorer: D.Puckett 12

1992/93 Player of the Year: K.Brown

Club record goalscorer:

Record appearances:

Past players who progressed to the Football League: Ray Elliott (M'wall 1946), Charlie Mortimore (A'shot 1949), Robert Edwards (Chelsea 1951), Ron Newman (Portsmouth 1955), Mervyn Gill (Southampton 1956), John Mortimore (Chelsea 1951), Reg Stratton (Fulham 1959), George Harris (Newport 1961), Norman Cashmore (A'shot 1963), Alan Morton (C.Palce 1967), William Holmes (Millwall 1970), Richard Forbes (Exeter 1979).

Club Honours: FA Amateur Cup 57-58; Isthmian League R-up 56-57, Lge AC Delco Cup 90-91, Div.1 R-up 89-90, Div.2 South 86-87, Reserve Section (2); West Surrey Lge (4), London Senior Cup R-up 82-83; Surrey Lge 12-13, 26-27, 55-56, 56-57, 71-72, 90-91; Surrey Senior Shield (9); Surrey Premier Cup (2); Surrey Invitation Cup 66-67; Surry Intermediate Cup (2); Channel Islands Victory Cup (2); Suburban Lge (2), Lge Cup (2); Diadora Premier Division 91-92; Isthmian Charity Shield 91-92.

YEOVIL TOWN

Formed:
1895

President:
Norman Burfield

Chairman:
Bryan Moore

Vice Chairman
Allan Houghton

Football Secretary:
Roger Brinsford

Manager:
Steve Rutter

Coach:
Paul Rogers

Physiotherapist:
Tony Farmer

Commercial Manager:
Alan Skirton

Press Officer:
Secretary

Having survived the previous year's traumas the first few fixtures of the 1992/93 campaign were perhaps not faced in quite the right competitive spirit, and it took a bad defeat at Bromsgrove and a place back at the foot of the table to force the club to look at itself realistically.

A magnificent run until Christmas then saw a race up the table, and superb FA Cup victories at Torquay United (5-2) and Hereford United (2-1) brought a home tie against Arsenal in the Third Round.

The FA Cup run raised £80,000, but three cup defeats in a week left the club with a distinct hang-over. Conference results also slumped until an end of season revival took The Glovers back into contention for prize money at the top of the table.

Great home results were recorded against Wycombe Wanders (3-0) and Slough Town (5-1) but defeats at home by Dagenham, and on the last day away to Gateshead, left Yeovil in a best ever fourth-place.

Club captain Mark Shail was sold to Bristol City for a record breaking £40,000 in March, he will be missed. Steve Rutter, Wayne Dobbins and Andy Wallace all suffered long term injuries but Mickey Spencer was again top scorer and very consistent seasons were enjoyed by David Coles, Jeff Sherwood, Phil Ferns, Richard Cooper, Paul Batty and Paul Wilson.

Perhaps the most significant statistic for the season however was when the club announced a profit for the year and considering recent financial problems this was a triumph for eveyone involved.

Tony Williams.

Yeovil Town 1993/94 - Back Row (L-R): Paul Sanderson, Andy Wallace, Malcolm McPherson, Richard Cooper, David Coles, Dave Leonard, Nick Flory, Paul Nevin, Andy Bye. Front Row: Steve Sivell, Steve Harrower, Terry Connor, Neil Coates, Tony Farmer (Physio), Steve Rutter (Manager), Paul Rodgers (Coach), Jeff Sherwood, Mickey Spencer, Wayne Dobbins, Andy Gorman. Insets: Phil Ferns, Nathan Bush, Paul Wilson. Photo: Tilzey Studios, Yeovil.

Key: Home fixtures are denoted by bold capitals. Numbers in brackets after players names indicate goals scored (an asterisk by the results denotes own goals). Only used substitutes are listed - substituted players are *italicised*.

Key to Competitions: GMVC: G.M. Vauxhall Conference. **SPC:** Somerset Premier Cup. **DC:** Drinkwise (G.M. Vauxhall Conference) Cup. **FAC:** F.A. Cup. **FAT:** Vauxhall F.A. Trophy. **Fr.:** Friendly.

LEAGUE POSITION: 4th

FA TROPHY: First Round

FA CUP: Third Round

Date	Opponents	Comp.	Res	Gate	1.	2.	3.	4.	5.	6.	7.	8.	9.	10.	11.	Sub.	Sub.
22/08	**NORTHWICH V.**	GMVC	1-1	2,110	Coles	Sherwood	Harrower	Shail(1)	Rutter	*Dobbins*	Coates	Wallace	*Wilson*	Spencer	*Sanderson*	Cooper	Ferns
25/08	**MERTHYR TYD.**	GMVC	0-1	1,834	Coles	Sherwood	Harrower	Shail	Rutter	*Dobbins*	*Coates*	Wallace	*Wilson*	Spencer	Sanderson	Cooper	Nevin
29/08	Telford United	GMVC	0-1	1,015	Coles	Sherwood	Harrower	Shail	Rutter	*Dobbins*	Sanderson	Wallace	Wilson	Spencer	Ferns	Ferns	Nevin
31/08	Welling United	GMVC	3-0	963	Coles	Sherwood	Harrower	Shail(1)	Rutter	Cooper	Sanderson	Wallace	*Wilson(1)*	Spencer	Ferns	Ferns	Nevin(1)
5/09	**KETTERING T.**	GMVC	2-1	2,006	Coles	Sherwood	Harrower	Shail	Rutter	Cooper	*Sanderson*	Wallace(2)	Wilson	Spencer(1)	Ferns	Batty	Nevin
8/09	**SLOUGH TOWN**	DC	2-0	1,319	Coles	Sherwood	*Harrower*	Shail	Rutter	Cooper	San'son(1)	Wallace	*Wilson*	*Spencer(1)*	Ferns	Batty	Dang
12/09	Runcorn	GMVC	0-1	421	Coles	Sherwood	Harrower	Shail	Rutter	Cooper	*Sanderson*	Wallace	Nevin	*Spencer*	*Ferns*	Coates	Dang
15/09	Wycombe Wdrs	GMVC	*1-5	3,769	Coles	Sherwood	Harrower	Shail	*Rutter*	Cooper	Sanderson	Wallace	*Nevin*	Spencer	*Ferns*	Dang	Coates
19/09	**GATESHEAD**	GMVC	1-3	1,808	Coles	Sherwood	Harrower	Shail	Rutter	*Cooper*	Sanderson	Wallace	Nevin(1)	Spencer	*Ferns*	Coates	Dang
22/09	Slough Town	DC	2-2	528	Coles	Coates	Harrower	Sherwood	Shail	Cooper	*Sanderson*	Wallace	*Nevin*	*Spencer(1)*	Ferns	Batty	Dang(1)
26/09	Bromsgrove R.	GMVC	0-1	1,196	Coles	Coates	Harrower	Shail	*Sherwood*	Cooper	Sanderson	*Wallace*	Wilson	Spencer	Ferns	Batty	Dang
3/10	**RUNCORN**	GMVC	4-0	1,684	Coles	Dobbins	Sherwood	Shail	Rutter	Cooper	Sanderson	Batty	Wilson(3)	*Dang*	Harrower(1)	Wallace	Spencer
10/10	Witton Albion	GMVC	2-1	952	Coles	*Dobbins*	Sherwood	Shail	Rutter	Cooper	Sanderson	Batty	Wilson	*Spencer(1)*	Harrower	Wallace	Dang(1)
13/10	Slough Town	GMVC	0-3	771	Coles	Dobbins	Sherwood	Shail	Rutter	*Cooper*	Sanderson	Batty	*Wilson*	Spencer	Harrower	Wallace	Dang
17/10	**STAFFORD R.**	GMVC	2-0	1,903	Coles	*Dobbins*	Sherwood	Shail	*Rutter*	Cooper	*Sanderson*	Batty	Wilson	Spencer(1)	Harrower(1)	Wallace	Nevin
20/10	Bath City	DC	0-0	520	Coles	*Dobbins*	Sherwood	Shail	Ferns	Cooper	Sanderson	Batty	Nevin	Spencer(1)	Harrower(1)	Wallace	Coates
24/10	Crawley Town	FAC	2-1	1,898	Coles	Sherwood	Harrower	Shail	Ferns	Cooper	Sanderson	*Batty(1)*	Wilson	*Spencer(1)*	*Dobbins*	Wallace	Coates
31/10	Stafford Rgrs	GMVC	1-0	854	Coles	Dobbins	Sherwood	Shail	Ferns	*Cooper*	Sanderson	Batty	Wilson	*Spencer(1)*	Harrower	Wallace	Coates
7/11	**WOKING**	GMVC	4-1	2,911	Coles	*Coates*	Sherw'd(1)	Shail	Ferns	Cooper(1)	San'son(1)	Batty	*Wilson*	*Spencer(1)*	Harrower	Wallace	Nevin
14/11	Torquay United	FAC	5-2	3,453	Coles	*Coates*	Sherwood	Shail	Ferns	Cooper	Sanderson	Batty(3)	Wilson(1)	Spencer	Harrower	Wallace	Nevin
17/11	**BATH CITY**	DC	1-0	2,090	Coles	Coates	Sherwood	Wallace	Ferns	Cooper	San'son(1)	Batty	*Wilson*	Spencer	Harrower	Nevin	
21/11	**WITTON ALBION**	GMVC	2-0	2,316	Coles	Coates	Sherwood	Shail	Ferns	Cooper(1)	Sanderson	Batty	*Wilson*	Spencer	Harrower	Wallace	Nevin(1)
28/11	Stalybridge C.	GMVC	1-1	753	Coles	Coates	Sherwood	Shail	Ferns	Dobbins	Sanderson	Batty	Wilson(1)	Spencer	*Nevin*	Hughes	Hughes
5/12	**HEREFORD UTD**	FAC	2-2	8,085	Coles	Coates	Sherwood	Shail	Ferns	Batty	*Sanderson*	Wallace	Wilson	Spencer	*Dobbins*	Hughes	Hughes
12/12	Kettering Town	GMVC	0-3	1,337	Coles	Coates	Sherwood	Shail	Ferns	Batty	Dobbins	*Wallace*	Wilson	Spencer	*Hughes*	Sanderson	Nevin
16/12	Hereford United	FAC	2-1	6,051	Coles	Dobbins	Sherwood	Shail	Ferns	*Cooper*	San'son(1)	Batty	Wilson	Spencer	Harrower	Coates(1)	

Date	Opposition	Comp	Score	Att												Subs	
19/12	**BROMSGROVE**	GMVC	2-2	5,495	Coles	Dobbins	Sherwood	Shall(1)	Ferns	Cooper	Sanderson	Batty(1)	Wilson	Spencer	Harrower	Hughes	Wilson
26/12	Dagenham & Red.	GMVC	1-1	1,072	Coles	Dobbins	Sherwood	Shall	Ferns	Cooper	San'son(1)	Batty	*Nevin*	Spencer	Harrower	Coates	Wilson
28/12	**BATH CITY**	GMVC	2-1	6,488	Coles	Dobbins	Sherwood	Shall	Ferns	Coates	*Sanderson*	Batty(1)	*Wilson*	Spencer(2)	Harrower	Nevin	Nevin
2/01	**ARSENAL**	FAC	1-3	1,834	Coles	Dobbins	Sherwood	Wallace	*Rutter*	*Cooper*	Sanderson	Batty(1)	Taylor	Spencer	Harrower	Coates	McPherson
6/01	Clevedon Town	SPC	0-1	613	Coles	Sherwood	Harrower	Coates	Ferns	Batty	Sanderson	Wallace	*Taylor*	Spencer	Dobbins	McPherson	Wilson
9/01	**DAGENHAM & R.**	FAT	0-0	2,973	Coles	Coates	Sherwood	Shall	Ferns	Dobbins	Sanderson	Batty	Wilson	Spencer	Harrower	McPherson	McPherson
12/01	Dagenham & Red.	FAT	1-2	1,171	Coles	Coates	Sherwood	Shall	Ferns	*Nevin*	Nevin	Batty	Wilson	Spencer(1)	Harrower	McPherson	McPherson
23/01	Macclesfield T.	GMVC	1-1	431	Coles	Dobbins	Sherwood	Shall	Ferns	Coates	*Sanderson*	Batty	Wilson(1)	Nevin	Harrower		
30/01	Woking	GMVC	0-0	2,427	Coles	Coates	Sherwood	Shall	Ferns	Dobbins	San'son	Batty	Wilson	Nevin	Harrower		
6/02	**TELFORD UTD**	GMVC	1-0	2,207	Coles	Coates	Sherwood	Shall	Ferns	Dobbins	Sanderson	Batty	Wilson	Spencer	Harrower		
9/02	**WYCOMBE WDRS**	DC	0-1	2,330	Coles	Coates	*Sherwood*	Shall	*Ferns*	*Dobbins*	Sanderson	Batty	Wilson	Spencer	Harrower	Nevin	Rutter
13/02	**ALTRINCHAM**	GMVC	1-0	2,198	Coles	Coates	Sherwood	Shall	Ferns	Cooper	Sanderson	Batty	Wilson	Spencer(1)	Harrower	Rutter	Nevin
20/02	Kidderminster	GMVC	1-1	1,257	Coles	*Coates*	Sherwood	Shall	Ferns	McPherson	Sanderson	Batty	Wilson	Spencer(1)	Harrower	Rutter	Coates
27/02	Boston United	GMVC	0-1	1,118	Coles	Rutter	Sherwood	Shall	Ferns	Cooper	Sanderson	Batty	Nevin	Spencer	Harrower	Coates	Ferns
3/03	**TOTTENHAM H.**	Fr.	1-1	3,800	Coles	Coates	Sherwood	Shall(1)	Rutter	Cooper	Sanderson	Batty	Wilson(1)	Spencer	Harrower	Leonard	Ferns
6/03	**KIDDERMINSTER**	GMVC	2-2	2,159	Coles	Coates	Sherwood	Shall	Ferns	Cooper	Nevin	Batty	Wilson(1)	Spencer	Harrower	Sanderson	Sanderson
9/03	Farnborough	GMVC	1-2	582	Coles	Coates	Sherwood	Shall	Ferns	*Cooper*	Nevin	Batty(1)	Rutter	Spencer	Harrower	Sanderson	Sanderson
13/03	**STALYBRIDGE**	GMVC	1-1	1,844	Coles	Coates	Sherwood	Shall	Rutter	Cooper	Sanderson	Batty(1)	Wilson(1)	Spencer	Harrower		
16/03	**WYCOMBE W.**	GMVC	*3-0	2,667	Coles	Coates	Sherwood	Shall	Ferns	*Cooper*	Sanderson	Batty	Wilson(1)	Spencer	Harrower	Harrower(1)	Nevin
20/03	Altrincham	GMVC	2-1	722	Coles	Coates	Sherwood	Shall	Ferns	Taylor	Sanderson	Batty	Wilson(1)	Taylor	Harrower		
23/03	**WELLING UTD**	GMVC	1-0	2,019	Coles	Coates	Sherwood	Williams	Ferns	Taylor	Sanderson	Batty(1)	Wilson	Spencer	Harrower		
27/03	Northwich Vic.	GMVC	1-0	873	Coles	Coates	Sherwood	Williams	Ferns	Leonard	*Sanderson*	Batty(1)	Wilson	Spencer	Harrower	Nevin	Flory
30/03	**FARNBOROUGH**	GMVC	5-2	2,404	Coles	Coates	Sherwood	Sherw'd(1)	Ferns	Leonard	Sanderson	Batty	Wilson(2)	Spencer(2)	Harrower	Nevin	
03/04	**MACCLESFIELD**	GMVC	1-1	2,515	Coles	Coates	Rutter	Rutter	Ferns	Cooper	Sanderson	Batty	Wilson	Spencer	Harrower		
10/04	**DAGENHAM & R.**	GMVC	0-3	2,847	Coles	Coates	Sherwood	*Rutter*	Ferns	Cooper	*Nevin*	Batty	Wilson	Spencer	Harrower	Sanderson	McPh'n
12/04	Bath City	GMVC	0-0	1,331	Coles	Coates	Sherwood	Williams	Ferns	Cooper	Sanderson	Batty	Wilson	Spencer	Harrower		
17/04	**SLOUGH TOWN**	GMVC	5-1	2,451	Coles	Coates	Sherwood	*Williams*	Flory	Cooper(1)	Sanderson	Batty(2)	*Wilson*	Spencer(2)	Harrower	Sivell	Nevin
24/04	**BOSTON UNITED**	GMVC	2-1	3,049	Coles	Coates	Sherwood	Shall	Ferns	Cooper	Sanderson	Batty	Wilson	Spencer(2)	Harrower	Harrower	
01/05	Gateshead	GMVC	1-4	397	Coles	Coates	Sherwood	Shall	Ferns	Cooper	*Sanderson*	Batty	Wilson(1)	Spencer	*Harrower*	Nevin	McPhers'

LEAGUE APPEARANCES: Batty 33(22); Coates 27(5); Coles 42; Cooper 29(3); Dance 1(6); Dobbins 17; Ferns 34(1); Flory 2(1); Harrower 39; Hughes 1(2); Leonard 2; McPherson 1(3); Nevin 12(14); Rutter 17(2); Sanderson 37(4); Shall 33; Sherwood 41; Sivell 0(1); Spencer 38(1); Taylor 2; Wallace 10(6); Williams 7; Wilson 35(1).

LEAGUE GOALSCORERS: Spencer 15; Wilson 13; Batty 6; Sanderson, Shall 4; Cooper, Harrower, Nevin 3; Sherwood, Wallace 2; Coates 1.

Yeovil Town

STEVE RUTTER

Steve took over as player-manager during the 1990/91 campaign, following the departure of Clive Whitehead. He led the club to safety then and did the same again in his first full season in charge, despite crippling financial constraints which earned him the respect of officials, players and supporters of Yeovil Town.

An uncompromising defender with strong leadership qualities, he joined the club from the Police Force, having played for Rushden Town, Northampton Town, Kettering Town, Wellingborough Town and Wealdstone.

Although the financial state of the club will still not allow him to go out and spend a fortune in the transfer market, the character of the man will lift the players at his disposal and continue the excellent team spirit he has fostered.

Yeovil's Mickey Spencer heads just wide of the Welling goal. Photo: Alan Coomes.

Programme details:
    52 pages for £1.00
    Editor - Roger Brinsford

Any other club publications:

Local Newspapers:
    Western Gazette
    Western Daily Press, Somerset Star,
    Sunday Independant, Yeovil Express

Local Radio Stations:
    Radio Bristol
    Radio Camelot (Hospital)
    Orchard FM, Somerset Sound

YEOVIL TOWN - PLAYING SQUAD 1992-93

Player	Honours	Birthplace and date	Transfer Fees	Previous Clubs
GOALKEEPERS				
David Coles	Finland Lge	Wandsworth 15/9/64		Aldershot, HJK Helsinki (Fin), Crystal Pal, Brighton, Aldershot, Fulham
DEFENDERS				
Phil Ferns	IL, AC Delco	Liverpool 12/9/61		AFC Bournemouth, Charlton Ath, Blackpool, Aldershot, Yeovil, Poole
Andy Gorman		Cardiff 13/9/74		Cardiff City
Steve Harrower	Div 4	Exeter 9/10/61		Dawlish, Exeter
Andy Bye	SL, HSC, FA XI	Winchester 5/6/63	£5,000	Gosport Boro, Fareham T, Hampton, Farnborough T
Jeff Sherwood	IL, BLT, AC Delco, FA XI	Bristol 5/10/59		Minehead, Taunton, Bath, Bristol R, Bath, Yeovil, Gloucester
Steve Rutter	IL, BLT, AC Delco	Northampton 14/10/62		Rushden, Kettering, Wellingborough, Wealdstone
MIDFIELD				
Richard Cooper		London 7/5/65		Sheff Utd, Lincoln, Exeter, Weymouth
Terry Connor	E-U21, EY, UEFAYC	Leeds 9/11/62		Leeds Utd, Brighton, Portsmouth, Swansea, Bristol City
Andy Wallace	IL, BLT, AC Delco	London 30/6/62		Met Police, Kingstonian, Wealdstone
Wayne Dobbins		Bromsgrove 30/8/68		WBA, Torquay
Dave Leonard				Saltash Utd
Neil Coates	BLT	Templecombe 15/1/68		Watford, AFC Bournemouth, Yeovil, Dorchester
FORWARDS				
Mickey Spencer	Comb Serv, Army, BLT	Manchester 27/11/62		Bury, Wokingham
Paul Wilson	ESP	Doncaster 16/11/60	£13,000	Frickley, Boston Utd
Paul Sanderson		Blackpool 28/7/64		Fleetwood, Man City, Chester, Halifax, Cardiff, Walsall, Newport Co, Merthyr
David Bright				Paulton Rovers
Paul Nevin		Lewisham 23/6/69		Shrewsbury, Evansville Aces (USA), Carlisle Utd

Departures during season:
Mike McEvoy (Waikato NZ), Mark Shail Bristol C £45,000), Hung Dang (Salisbury)

Players on loan during season:
Mark Hughes (Witton Alb), John Williams (Cardiff).

Huish Park, Yeovil Town

Address and telephone number: Huish Park, Lufton Way, Yeovil, Somerset BA22 8YF
Tel: 0935 23662. Fax: 0935 73956

Simple directions: Leave A303 at Cartgate roundabout and take A3088 signposted Yeovil. Take first exit at next roundabout and first exit again at next roundabout into Lufton Way. Railway Station - Yeovil Pen Mill (Bristol/Westbury to Weymouth) 2.5 miles from ground. Yeovil Junction (Waterloo - Exeter - 4 miles). Bus service - from both stations on Saturday - matchdays.

Capacity: 8,718   **Seated:** 5,050   **Covered terracing:** 5,050

Record Attendance: 8,612 v Arsenal - 3rd Round FA Cup - 02/01/93

Club Shop: Sells replica kits, badges, stickers, pennants, books, Team Talk magazines, subbuteo teams, hats etc.

Social Facilities: Matchdays - hot and cold food available. Weekdays - meals can be ordered provided advance notice is given.

Previous Grounds: Pen Mill 1895-1920, Huish 1920-1990.

Yeovil Fact File

Nickname: Glovers

Club Sponsors: Martock Watermans

Previous Leagues: Western League, London Combination, Southern League, Alliance Premier, Isthmian League.

Club colours: Green & white striped shirts, white shorts and white socks.

Change colours: Old gold and black.

Reserve team league: Neville Ovenden Football Combination.

Midweek home matchday: Tuesday

Record win:

Record defeat:

Record transfer fee: £15,000 to Worcester City for Joe Jackson - 1990.

Record transfer fee received: £40,000 from Bristol City for Mark Shail - 1993.

1992/93 Captain: Mark Shail (Jeff Sherwood - 1993/94)

1992/93 Top scorer: Mickey Spencer.

1992/93 Player of the Year: Paul Batty.

Club record goalscorer: Dave Taylor 285 - 1960-69

Record appearances: L.Harris

Past players who progressed to the Football League: Over 40 players + 18 mangers including, since 1985: Nigel Jarvis (Torquay); Ian Davies (Bristol Rovers); Alan Pardew (Crystal Palace); Paul Miller (Wimbledon); John McGinlay (Shrewsbury); Guy Whittingham (Portsmouth); Mark Shail (Bristol City).

Club Honours: Southern League 1954/55, 1963/64, 1970/71, Runners-up 1923/24, 1931/32, 1934/35, 1969/70, 1972/73; Southern League Cup: 1948/49, 1954/55, 1960/61, 1965/66. Vauxhall-Opel League 1987/88, Runners-up 1985/86, 1986/87; A.C. Delco Cup 1987/88; FA Cup 5th Round 1948/49; Bob Lord Trophy 1989/90.

DIADORA LEAGUE

Chairman: Alan C.F. Turvey.

Hon. Secretary: Nicholas Robinson.
226 Rye Lane, Peckham, London SE15 4NL.

"CHESHAM UNITED - IMPRESSIVE CHAMPIONS"

Marlow FC were the team who made the headlines during this season taking the place of Woking FC as FA Cup success team. They were good enough to reach the third round of the FA Cup where they were rewarded with a home tie against Tottenham Hotspur which was switched to White Hart Lane. This provided a magnificent day out for manager Dave Russell and his team and the score-line was perhaps a little harsh on Marlow. They never seemed quite able to reproduce their Cup form in league matches in the latter part of the season but they did have one piece of silverware in that they won the League cup for the first time in an exciting final played at Aldershot Town on the first Bank Holiday Monday.

That brings us on to the exploits of Aldershot Town, who arose, like the phoenix in their badge, from the ashes of Aldershot FC from the Football League, and with a very sound financial background competed extremely well in Division Three, in fact winning the championship with just over two weeks of the season still to play. The attendances both at Aldershot and at grounds where Aldershot played were quite remarkable for this division but we must not lose sight of the fact that another club who joined the ranks this season, Leighton Town, also produced a healthy increase in attendances and they will no doubt be disappointed not to be joining Aldershot Town in division two next season. The other two promotion places are taken by Collier Row and Thame United both of whom competed extremely well throughout the season. Mention must also be made of Cove Football Club who had a quite remarkable success story from Christmas onwards, and if they had been able to produce the post Christmas form in the early part of the season would undoubtedly have been promoted.

In division two we saw Southall and Harefield United both playing at Harefield's ground and coincidentally both suffering the same fate of relegation. At the top end of the table Worthing justified the early season confidence shown in the team by the club who placed a bet with William Hill who offered rather good odds against the club winning the championship. It is good to see Worthing coming back up the table after a couple of years in the doldrums. Joining them will be Ruislip Manor who will be making their first venture into division one and Berkhamsted who also have not played at division one level before and who narrowly beat off the challenge of Hemel Hempstead and Metropolitan Police to gain the last promotion place on the final day of the season.

Chesham United, Premier Division Champions 1992-93. Back Row (L-R): Power (Coach), Gary Cobb, Andy Lomas, Mickey Barnes, Adie Adebowale, Steve Bateman, Chris Townsend, Garry Attrell, Mick Gilchrist (Coach). Front Row: Andy Yorke, Mickey Banton, Tony Hopkins, Naseem Bashir, Lee Costa, Dave Webley, Ross Eames (Mascot). Photo - Keith Clayton.

Commiserations, particularly to Hemel Hempstead who sufferd a fire at their ground during the season and had to overcome all the problems which that entailed as well as 42 hard-fought games.

Clubs in division one say it is the hardest division to get out of and this season the division was one team short because Harlow Town were unable to complete their fixtures and accepted a one year suspension from the League to give them time to try and put their house in order. Accordingly only two clubs were to be relegated but three would still be promoted. The three clubs actually promoted, Hitchin Town, Molesey and Dorking were perhaps easily identifiable during the season but it was not until the very last day that that the champions were known. Purfleet and Bishop's Stortford both played a tremendous support role and Abingdon Town, who lost a lot of fixtures when their home ground was flooded, finished a very creditable sixth having to face a large number of games in the last few weeks of the season. At the other end of the table Lewes make an immediate return to division two and are joined by bottom club Aveley who at one stage suffered a run of eleven successive defeats. Nevertheless it was Hitchin Town who were the eventual champions compiling at one stage a run of thirteen games undefeated. Hitchin Town have new made certain of promotion to the premier division where there will undoubtedly be a number of clubs looking round to see how the Canaries fare.

Moving on then to the premier division, this was a virtual two-horse race through the season between Chesham United and St.Albans City. Chesham enjoyed a twenty-three match undefeated run during the season and clinched the championship in the last match of the season. Both Chesham United and St.Albans City scored over 100 goals and played attractive football throughout. The great pity is that neither of these clubs will be making the move to the Conference, each for different reasons having to withdraw their applications. It is to be hoped that they can maintain the momentum they have begun this season and try again for the Conference next year. We will not be losing a club from the top end of the table but at the other end we will be saying goodbye to Bognor Regis, Windsor & Eton and Staines, and so the teams who were reprieved from relegation at the end of 1991/92 season were relgated after all. One thing, for certain though, is that all these clubs will be endeavouring to regain their premier division status at the earliest possible opportunity.

I have made mention of the League cup when referring to the eventual winners Marlow FC, but one must also give credit to their opponents, Molesey FC, who competed extremely well and who will undoubtedly be a threat to premier division sides next season.

In the Full Members Cup a tremendous final was witnessed at Kingstonian between Dorking and Tooting & Mitcham United who were the eventual winners by a single goal and most present agreed that it was one of the best finals witnessed in the League.

In the Associate Members Trophy, Northwood FC, from division three, beat Barton Rovers FC from division two in an absorbing final, played at Chesham United FC, which gave Northwood a success in their first season in the League.

Overall we saw a 10% increase in attendances and more than three goals per game in three out of four divisions. All in all a success which gives us much to look forward to in season 1993/94.

Nick Robinson (League Secretary).

St.Albans City - Premier Division Runners-up 1992. Back Row (L-R): Steve Ketteridge (Asst. Manager), Martin Gurney, Gary Westwood, Shaun Brett, Martin Duffield, Steve Clark, Roy Race (main Sponsor), Allan Cockram, Kevin Mudd, Paul Price, Peter Hayward (Physio), John Mitchell (Manager & vice chairman). Front Row: John Colfer (Player/commercial manager), Dean Williams, Jimmy King, Bradley Anderson, Roy Edwards, Peter Risley, Steve Scott. Photo - John Sherwood.

Allan Cockram and Roy Edwards of St Albans City against Chesham United's Barry Rake during the 1-1 draw between the top two clubs at Clarence Park on 13th January. The match attracted a gate of 3,120. Photo - John Sherwood.

Leighton defender Steve Drewe (nearest camera) takes on Hornchurch defender Tony Fleming during the 1-1 Third Division draw on 3rd April. Photo - Robert Monger.

DIADORA LEAGUE CUP 1992-93

Preliminary Round	Res	Att
Billericay Town v East Thurrock Utd	2-0	258
Bracknell Town v Banstead Ath.	0-3	38
Camberley Town v Edgware Town	1-0	88
Cove v Berkhamsted Town	3-2	88
Feltham & H.B. v Barton Rovers	2-1	91
Flackwell Heath v Chertsey Town	1-3	100
Hemel Hempstead v Lewes	3-1	84
Hertford Town v Southall	3-1	69
Hungerford Town v Met. Police	1-5	89
Kingsbury Town v Harefield United	2-0	64
Leatherhead v Aldershot T. (aet)	1-1	780
Aldershot Town v Leatherhead	3-2	1510
Leighton Town (w/o) Farnham T. (scr)		
Northwood v Collier Row	4-1	134
Petersfield United v Horsham	2-3	120
Purfleet v Royston Town	3-1	120
Rainham Town v Hampton	1-5	
Saffron Walden v Newbury Town	2-0	119
Thame United v Epsom & Ewell	3-0	105
Tilbury v Ruislip Manor (aet)	2-4	74
Tring Town v Egham Town	1-2	75
Ware v Malden Vale	1-2	92
Witham Town v Clapton	1-0	50
Worthing v Hornchurch	2-0	139

First Round	Res	Att
Abingdon Town v Camberley Town	3-1	106
Aylesbury United v Aveley	4-2	343
Barking v Wivenhoe Town	1-6	58
Basingstoke Town v Walton & Hers.	3-0	241
Bognor Regis Town v Met. Police	1-3	175
Boreham Wood v Feltham & H. (aet)	4-1	51
Chalfont St Peter v Saffron Walden T.	2-1	92
Chertsey Town v Egham Town (aet)	2-3	225
Cove v Hayes	0-5	118
Croydon v Carshalton Ath. (aet)	3-3	178
Carshalton Athletic v Croydon	0-1	274
Dulwich v St Albans (aet, at Tooting)	1-0	164
Enfield v Whyteleafe	7-0	196
Grays Athletic v Windsor & Eton	2-3	137
Hampton v Dorking (aet)	1-0	186
Harrow Borough v Bromley	3-0	208
Hemel Hempstead v Marlow	1-4	108
Hendon v Hertford Town	7-0	164
Horsham v Staines Town	2-4	189
Kingstonian v Malden Vale	3-2	320
Kingsbury Town v Aldershot Town	0-1	310
Leighton Town v Tooting & Mitcham	2-3	425
Leyton v Chesham United	2-1	138
Maidenhead United v Yeading (aet)	1-1	147
Yeading v Maidenhead United	4-1	190

	Res	Att
Molesey v Bishop's Stortford	2-1	98
Purfleet (w/o) Harlow Town (scr)		
Ruislip Manor v Heybridge Swifts	3-0	174
Stevenage Borough v Billericay Town	1-2	473
Sutton United v Hitchin Town	2-0	381
Thame United v Wembley	3-1	117
Uxbridge v Northwood	0-1	164
Wokingham Town v Witham Town	2-0	156
Worthing v Banstead Ath. (aet)	3-1	142

Second Round	Res	Att
Abingdon Town v Molesey (aet)	3-3	103
Molesey v Abingdon Town (aet)	1-0	45
Aldershot Town v Hampton (aet)	5-2	1950
Aylesbury Utd v Thame Utd (aet)	3-3	480
Thame Utd v Aylesbury Utd (aet)	2-3	280
Basingstoke Town v Met. Police	0-1	167
Boreham Wood v Purfleet	2-0	92
Dulwich Hamlet v Worthing	1-3	222
Hayes v Croydon	2-1	82
Hendon v Ruislip Manor	2-1	157
Kingstonian v Billericay (aet)	1-0	307
Leyton v Tooting & Mitcham Utd	2-3	81
Marlow v Egham Town	5-1	155
Northwood v Windsor & Eton	2-3	184
Staines Town v Yeading	0-1	277
Sutton United v Chalfont St Peter	4-1	325
Wivenhoe Town v Harrow Borough	2-1	109
Wokingham Town v Enfield	0-1	258

Third Round	Res	Att
Aylesbury United v Enfield	1-2	199
Hendon v Aldershot Town	2-1	679
Marlow v Yeading	3-1	201
Metropolitan Police v Wivenhoe T.	1-2	69
Molesey v Tooting & Mitcham Utd	3-0	101
Sutton United v Boreham Wood	3-0	336
Windsor & Eton v Hayes	0-1	174
Worthing v Kingstonian	1-2	402

Quarter Finals	Res	Att
Hendon v Enfield (aet)	1-1	229
Enfield v Hendon	2-0	226
Kingstonian v Marlow	0-4	301
Molesey v Hayes	2-0	228
Wivenhoe Town v Sutton United	1-2	209

Semi Finals	Res	Att
Enfield v Molesey	1-0	334
Molesey v Enfield	5-0	350
(Molesey win 5-1 on aggregate)		
Marlow v Sutton United	2-1	385
Sutton United v Marlow	0-2	445
(Marlow win 4-1 on aggregate)		

FINAL: AT ALDERSHOT TOWN FC, 3rd MAY 1993

MARLOW (1)2 (Blackman 7, Watkins 90), **MOLESEY** (1)1 (Rose 16(p))
Att: 944.
Marlow: S Ellis, J Regan, S Holmes, C Ferguson, A J Hannigan, R Mikurenda, D Lay, K Glasgow, T Buzaglo (M WAtkins 69), G Blackman, J Caesar. Unused sub: P Byrne. *Molesey:* D Brace, R Winterhalter, T Boorman, R Worrall, T McCoy, D Patullo, S Rice, D Rattue, M Rose, N Pearson, P Adams. Unused sub: B Penfold, N Hopkinsy.

DIADORA LEAGUE CUP ATTENDANCES 1992-93

Round	Matches (1991-92 figures in brackets)	Total	Average	% Change compared with 1991-92
Preliminary	23 (26)	4352 (3193)	189 (123)	+ 53.6
First	33 (34)	6448 (6905)	195 (203)	- 3.9
Second	18 (17)	5274 (3693)	293 (217)	+ 35.0
Third	8 (10)	2161 (2459)	270 (246)	+ 9.7
Fourth	4 (4)	1425 (1836)	356 (459)	- 22.4
Semi Final	4 (4)	1425 (1836)	356 (459)	- 22.4
Final	1 (1)	944 (1264)		
Total	**92 (97)**	**21797 (21897)**	**237 (226)**	**+ 4.6**

Marlow captain David Lay lifts the League Cup, presented by Sebastian Coe, after the 2-1 win over gallant Division One battlers Molesey at Aldershot Town. Photo - Eric Marsh.

The victorious Marlow team. Photo - Eric Marsh.

ISTHMIAN LEAGUE CHARITY SHIELD 1992-93

(Annual Challenge between League Champions and League Cup Winners)
(Played at Sutton United FC, Monday 31st August 1992)

WOKING (4)5 *(Buzaglo 3 19,Puckett 5 20,Nugent 49)*, **GRAYS ATHLETIC** (0)1 *(Durrant 59)*
Woking: L Batty, K Brown, T Joyce (T Senior 50), R Nugent, T Baron, C Fielder, D Brown, M Biggins, (M Fleming 59), D Puckett, T Buzaglo, S Steele.   *Grays:* A Williams, B Fox, D Crumpton, A Alexander, I Durant, I Brown, T Williams, P Sammons, J Campbell (N Poulson 65), W Whittingham, N Crown (J Walker 45).

281

FULL MEMBERS CUP 1992-93

First Round	Res	Att
Abingdon Town v Basingstoke Town	1-2	90
Aveley v Bromley	2-5	120
Aylesbury United v Marlow	2-5	168
Bishop's Stortford v Billericay Town	5-0	310
Chesham United v Stevenage Borough	1-3	345
Hayes v Wembley	1-0	83
Heybridge Swifts v Wivenhoe Town	0-1	96
Molesey v Dulwich Hamlet	2-0	102
Sutton United v Lewes	3-1	271
Uxbridge v Harrow Borough	0-1	161
Wokingham Town v Chalfont St Peter	2-0	132

Second Round	Res	Att
Barking v Leyton	0-2	98
Bishop's Stortford v Hayes	1-2	268
Bromley v Maidenhead United	3-0	78
Carshalton Athletic v Bognor Regis	1-0	253
Croydon v Wokingham Town	1-2	46
Dorking v Walton & Hersham	1-0	180
Grays Athletic v Wivenhoe Town	2-0	122
Hendon v B'ham Wd (aet 2-4 pens)	0-0	87
Marlow v St Albans City	3-2	295
Molesey v Staines Town	2-0	100
Purfleet v Harrow Borough	2-1	132

	Res	Att
Stevenage Borough v Enfield	0-2	637
Sutton United v Kingstonian	2-1	618
Tooting & Mitcham v Basingstoke	3-1	120
Windsor & Eton v Whyteleafe	3-0	126
Yeading v Hitchin Town	1-2	119

Third Round	Res	Att
Boreham Wood v Hayes	2-4	146
Bromley v Dorking (at Dorking)	2-4	176
Enfield v Grays Athletic	1-2	160
Hitchin v Leyton (aet, 1-4 pens)	1-1	247
Marlow v Purfleet	2-3	155
Sutton Utd v Tooting & Mitcham Utd	2-3	356
Windsor & Eton v Molesey	2-1	126
Wokingham v Carshalton (aet 3-4 pns)	2-2	167

Quarter Finals	Res	Att
Carshalton Athletic v Windsor & Eton	6-1	316
Dorking v Hitchin Town (aet)	2-1	193
Hayes v Grays Athletic	2-1	108
Tooting v Purfleet (aet 4-2 pens)	1-1	64

Semi Finals	Res	Att
Carshalton Athletic v Dorking	1-2	355
Hayes v Tooting & Mitcham United	0-2	176

FINAL: AT KINGSTONIAN FC, WED 5th MAY 1993

TOOTING & MITCHAM UNITED (0)1 *(Stephens 69)*, **DORKING** (0)0
Tooting: L Orkney, P Shaw, B Dennington, D Taylor, R Cowan, J Myatt, M Stephens, P Loughlin, M Tompkins, J Collins, T Hope. Unused subs: N Frankum, D Gabriel. *Dorking:* P Mills, D Bird, G Marriner (C Anderson 75), M Mahoney, G Berry, J Dack, N Robson, P Grainger, S Lunn, M Hanlan, T Worsfold. Unused sub: L Thornton.

FULL MEMBERS CUP ATTENDANCES 1992-93

Round	Matches (1991-92 figures in brackets)	Total	Average	% Change compared with 1991-92
First	11 (11)	1878 (1648)	171 (150)	- 14.0
Second	16 (16)	3274 (3599)	205 (225)	- 8.8
Third	8 (8)	1533 (2054)	192 (257)	- 25.2
Fourth	4 (4)	681 (1686)	170 (422)	- 59.7
Semi Final	2 (2)	531 (1178)	266 (589)	- 54.8
Total	**42 (42)**	**8570 (13230)**	**204 (315)**	**- 35.2**

Tooting's Micky Stephens lifts the Full Members Cup after victory over Dorking. Photo - Andrew Relton.

RESULTS SERVICES 1992-93

Division	Played	Home Wins	Away Wins	Draws	Goals Total
Premier	462 (100%)	184 (39.8%)	156 (33.8%)	122 (26.4%)	1428 (3.09/game)
First	420 (100%)	179 (42.6%)	123 (29.3%)	118 (28.1%)	1181 (2.81/game)
Second	462 (100%)	197 (42.6%)	153 (33.1%)	112 (24.2%)	1432 (3.10/game)
Third	380 (100%)	154 (40.5%)	134 (35.3%)	92 (24.2%)	1262 (3.32/game)

ASSOCIATE MEMBERS TROPHY 1992-93

First Round	Res	Att
Aldershot Town v Chertsey Town	4-1	1136
Banstead v Egham *(aet, 5-4 pens)*	1-1	41
Barton Rovers v Clapton	3-0	50
Bracknell Town v Newbury Town	0-2	41
East Thurrock Utd v Collier Row	1-0	112
Hemel Hempstead v Tring T. *(aet)*	2-4	108
Hungerford Town v Hampton	0-1	70
Leighton Town v Flackwell Heath	2-1	178
Royston Town v Hornchurch	3-0	44
Saffron Walden Town v Ware	1-0	143

Second Round	Res	Att
Berkhamsted Town v Tring Town	2-1	99
Cove v Banstead *(ab.(fog) in e.t.)*	2-3	73
Banstead Athletic v Cove	0-2	32
Edgware Town v Hertford Town	4-1	63
Horsham v Aldershot Town	0-1	792
Leatherhead v Camberley *(aet 4-1 pens)*	1-1	52
Leighton Town v Barton Rovers	1-2	180
Met. Police v Feltham & H. Boro.	4-0	99
Newbury T. v Hampton *(aet 6-5 pens)*	1-1	121
Northwood v East Thurrock United	3-1	138
Petersfield United v Malden Vale	1-3	50
Royston Town v Saffron Walden Town	1-2	123

	Res	Att
Ruislip Manor v Rainham Town	3-1	75
Southall v Epsom & Ewell	3-2	22
Tilbury v Kingsbury Town	1-4	67
Thame United v Witham Town	2-1	140
Worthing v Harefield United	4-0	142

Third Round	Res	Att
Barton Rovers v Ruislip Manor	3-0	70
Berkhamsted T. v Edgware Town *(aet)*	0-2	129
Cove v Thame United	0-2	142
Kingsbury Town v Saffron Walden	4-3	88
Met. Police v Leatherhead *(aet)*	3-2	140
Newbury Town v Malden Vale	3-1	131
Southall v Northwood	1-2	80
Worthing v Aldershot *(aet 5-3 pens)*	4-4	625

Quarter Finals	Res	Att
Kingsbury T. v Barton Rvrs *(aet)*	0-1	52
Newbury Town v Met. Police	3-7	154
Northwood v Edgware Town	3-2	151
Thame United v Worthing	0-1	164

Semi Finals	Res	Att
Barton Rovers v Met. Police *(aet)*	2-2	128
Met. Police v Barton Rovers	1-2	73
Northwood v Worthing *(aet)*	3-1	235

FINAL: AT CHESHAM UNITED FC, 28th APRIL 1993

NORTHWOOD (0)(1)3 *(Schwartz 62,Holland 92,Omere 107)*, **BARTON ROVERS** (0)(1)1 *(Golds 90)*
Attendance: 332
Northwood: K Lavender, T McAuliffe, J Parsons, R John, R Holland, S Sailsman, P Rogan, T Vincent, T Ventnor (D Nolan 57), V Schwartz, F Omere. Unused sub: H Pacquette. *Barton:* L Bozier, C McGill, D Foster, D Turner, B Goodyear, G Golds, S Endacott (R King 68), B Lalor, F Geddes, P Olney, S Merrick (G Bambrick 83).

ASSOCIATE MEMBERS TROPHY ATTENDANCES 1992-93

Round	Matches (1991-92 figures in brackets)	Total	Average	% Change compared with 1991-92
First	10 (11)	1923 (670)	192 (61)	+ 214.7
Second	17 (16)	2268 (1268)	133 (79)	+ 68.3
Third	8 (8)	1405 (596)	176 (75)	+ 134.6
Fourth	4 (4)	521 (420)	130 (105)	+ 23.8
Semi Final	3 (3)	436 (489)	145 (163)	- 11.0
Final	1 (1)	332 (241)		+ 37.7
Totals	**43 (43)**	**6885 (3684)**	**160 (86)**	**+ 86.0**

REPRESENTATIVE MATCHES 1992-93

At St Albans City FC, Tuesday 24th November 1992

DIADORA LGE X1 (0)1 *(Clark 66)*
F.A. X1 (0)6 *(Leworthy 46 67 83,Scott 52,Thompson 62,Robbins 78)*
Attendance: 245.
Diadora League: D Root (Hendon - sub A Lomas (Chesham)), S Mitchell (Basingstoke), P Risley (St Albans), P Price (St Albans - sub B Dowie (St Albans)), P Chambers (Basingstoke), S Bateman (Chesham - sub A Cockram (St Albans)), A Adebowale (Chesham - sub M Cox (Carshalton)), P Hobson (Enfield), J Warden (Carshalton - sub B Blackman (Hendon)), R Garvey (Hendon).

At Aldershot Town FC, Tuesday 9th February 1993

COMBINED SERVICES (1)2 *(Bates 8 59)*
DIADORA LEAGUE X1 (0)0
Attendance: 200.
Diadora League: A Blake (Kingstonian - sub R Wilmot (Stevenage)), S Mitchell (Basingstoke), M Hill (Hendon - sub J Daly (Hendon)), J Warden (Carshalton - sub A Cockram (St Albans)), M Barnes (Chesham - sub P Chambers (Basingstoke)), S Clark (Hendon), B Blackman (Hendon), D Harlow (Kingstonian), R Evans (Sutton Utd), J Bolton (Carshalton), I Cox (Carshalton - sub R Braithwaaite (Kingstonian).

ATTENDANCE ANALYSIS 1992-93

PREMIER DIVISION

Top Gates (each club)

3120	St Albans v Chesham (13/2/93)
1512	Chesham v Harrow (28/12/92)
1288	Carshalton v Sutton (26/12/92)
1220	Enfield v Chesham (17/10/92)
1173	Sutton v Kingstonian (28/12/92)
1134	Aylesbury v Chesham (24/4/93)
1107	Stevenage v St Albans (23/1/93)
897	Kingstonian v Sutton (26/12/92)
829	Marlow v Chesham (26/12/92)
759	Hendon v Enfield (28/12/92)
752	Dulwich v Hendon (3/10/92)
662	Staines v Chesham (27/10/92)
605	Basingstoke v Sutton (7/11/92)
596	Hayes v Yeading (26/12/92)
588	Bromley v Dulwich (26/12/92 at Dulwich)
561	Wokingham v Chesham (23/1/93)
544	Yeading v Hayes (12/4/93)
502	Wivenhoe v Enfield (23/1/93)
485	Grays v Enfield (20/3/93)
440	Windsor & Eton v Sutton (10/10/92)
434	Harrow v Chesham (5/9/92)
425	Bognor v Sutton (29/8/92)

Total Attendances (91-92 figures in brackets)

	Total	Games	Ave.	% change
Aug	14650 (26395)	34 (49)	431 (539)	-20.0
Sep	20724 (19978)	44 (35)	471 (571)	-17.5
Oct	22699 (23503)	52 (47)	437 (500)	-12.6
Nov	17776 (29449)	39 (56)	456 (525)	-13.1
Dec	29308 (15548)	55 (32)	533 (486)	+9.6
Jan	16891 (26446)	38 (48)	445 (551)	-19.7
Feb	24322 (30984)	53 (64)	459 (484)	-5.1
Mar	29292 (28702)	67 (61)	437 (471)	-7.2
Apr	29510 (20316)	69 (59)	428 (497)	-13.8
May	5361 (4493)	11 (11)	487 (408)	+19.3
Tot	210533 (234814)	462 (462)	456 (508)	-10.2

Best gate achieved in August: 1 club
Best gate achieved in September: 4 clubs
Best gate achieved in October: 2 clubs
Best gate achieved in November: 1 club
Best gate achieved in December: 7 clubs
Best gate achieved in January: 3 clubs
Best gate achieved in February: 1 club
Best gate achieved in March: 2 clubs
Best gate achieved in April: 1 club
Best gate achieved in May: 0 clubs

DIVISION ONE

Top Gates (each club)

804	Hitchin v Uxbridge (1/5/93)
465	Billericay v Heybridgee (26/12/92)
414	Dorking v Molesey (14/4/93)
364	Bishop's Stortford v Lewes (30/1/93)
312	Purfleet v Aveley (19/4/93)
286	Heybridge v Billericay (12/4/93)
260	Chalfont v Hitchin (24/4/93)
256	Abingdon v Hitchin (10/4/93)
252	Walton & H. v Molesey (12/4/93)
245	Tooting v Billericay (30/1/93)
237	Molesey v Dorking (20/2/93)
225	Aveley v Billericay (23/12/92)
209	Maidenhead v Tooting (28/12/92)
207	Whyteleafe v Molesey (17/4/93)
196	Barking v Hitchin (20/2/93)
185	Boreham Wood v Hitchin (26/12/92)
185	Lewes v Billericay (3/10/92)
177	Leyton v Billericay (12/12/92)
170	Uxbridge v Hitchin (9/1/93)
150	Croydon v Whyteleafe (31/8/92)
130	Wembley v Maidenhead (8/9/92)
130	Wembley v Hitchin (5/12/92)

Total Attendances (91-92 figures in brackets)

	Total	Games	Ave.	% change
Aug	3374 (7201)	22 (38)	153 (190)	-19.4
Sep	5909 (6730)	40 (33)	148 (153)	-3.2
Oct	7622 (9766)	52 (49)	147 (199)	-26.1
Nov	5862 (7108)	37 (47)	158 (151)	+4.6
Dec	7998 (5132)	48 (33)	167 (156)	+7.0
Jan	7483 (8999)	45 (44)	166 (205)	-19.0
Feb	7684 (9630)	48 (62)	160 (155)	+3.2
Mar	8895 (9486)	55 (58)	162 (164)	-1.2
Apr	11067 (8127)	63 (47)	176 (173)	+1.7
May	2253 (1286)	10 (9)	225 (143)	+57.3
Tot	68147 (71775)	420 (420)	162 (171)	-5.2

Best gate achieved in August: 0 clubs
Best gate achieved in September: 1 club
Best gate achieved in October: 1 club
Best gate achieved in November: 0 clubs
Best gate achieved in December: 5 clubs
Best gate achieved in January: 3 clubs
Best gate achieved in February: 3 clubs
Best gate achieved in March: 2 clubs
Best gate achieved in April: 7 clubs
Best gate achieved in May: 1 club

DIVISION TWO

Top Gates (each club)

1130	Hemel H. v Berkhamsted (12/4/93)
940	Worthing v Tilbury (27/4/93)
426	Berkhamsted v Barton (1/5/93)
374	Ruislip M. v Chertsey (1/3/93)
300	Newbury v Hungerford (12/4/93)
279	Chertsey v Egham (12/4/93)
276	Egham v Chertsey (26/12/92)
265	Met Police v Chertsey (6/2/93)
264	Tilbury v Banstead (28/12/92)
255	Leatherhead v Worthing (12/4/93)
251	Hungerford v Newbury (26/12/92)
243	Ware v Saffron W.T. (28/12/92)
235	Edgware v Worthing (27/3/93)
226	Saffron Walden v Witham (26/12/92)
205	Hampton v Egham (13/10/92)
183	Malden Vale v Egham (26/10/92)
169	Barton v Ware (26/12/92)
146	Witham Town v Worthing (17/4/93)
143	Harefield v Southall (12/4/93)
135	Rainham v Tilbury (26/12/92)
108	Banstead v Worthing (20/4/93)
97	Southall v Chertsey (7/11/92)

Total Attendances (91-92 figures in brackets)

	Total	Games	Ave.	% change
Aug	2757 (4258)	22 (35)	125 (122)	+2.4)
Sep	5019 (4926)	50 (45)	100 (109)	-8.2
Oct	6128 (6212)	58 (60)	106 (104)	+1.9
Nov	4903 (5780)	41 (54)	120 (107)	+12.1
Dec	5568 (3548)	38 (32)	147 (111)	+32.4
Jan	4788 (6468)	42 (49)	114 (132)	-13.6
Feb	7187 (6696)	56 (62)	128 (108)	+18/5
Mar	8315 (6229)	71 (56)	117 (111)	+5.4
Apr	8315 (6944)	71 (58)	161 (120)	+34.1
May	1359 (1487)	10 (11)	136 (135)	+0.7
Tot	57943 (52492)	462 (462)	125 (114)	+9.6

Best gate achieved in August: 0 clubs
Best gate achieved in September: 0 clubs
Best gate achieved in October: 2 clubs
Best gate achieved in November: 1 club
Best gate achieved in December: 7 clubs
Best gate achieved in January: 1 club
Best gate achieved in February: 1 club
Best gate achieved in March: 2 clubs
Best gate achieved in April: 8 clubs
Best gate achieved in May: 1 club

DIVISION THREE

Top Gates (each club)

2923	Aldershot v Collier R. (23/1/93)
2046	Camberley v Aldershot (10/11/92)
1798	Cove v Aldershot (1/5/93)
1750	Petersfield v Aldershot (28/12/92)
1525	Leighton v Aldershot (30/1/93)
1352	Bracknell v Aldershot (17/3/93)
1087	Epsom & E. v Aldershot (17/4/93)
1021	Horsham v Aldershot (27/2/93)
914	Northwood v Aldershot (16/1/93)
826	Feltham v Aldershot (19/9/92)
785	Tring v Aldershot (27/3/93)
750	Thame v Aldershot (14/11/92)
680	Hertford v Aldershot (10/10/92)
656	Royston v Aldershot (13/2/93)
585	Hornchurch v Aldershot (5/12/92)
558	Flackwell Heath v Aldershot (27/10/92)
545	Clapton v Aldershot (2/1/93)
543	East Thurrock v Aldershot (3/10/92)
444	Collier Row v Aldershot (2/9/92)
349	Kingsbury v Aldershot (2/3/93)

Total Attendances (91-92 figures in brackets)

	Total		Games		Ave.		% change
Aug	5173	(3097)	19	(31)	272	(100)	+172.0
Sep	11480	3382	48	(40)	239	(85)	+181.1
Oct	13165	(4007)	55	(46)	239	(87)	+174.7
Nov	9430	(3264)	34	(42)	277	(78)	+243.5
Dec	11514	(2590)	42	(31)	274	(84)	+226.1
Jan	9267	(4853)	33	(46)	281	(106)	+165.09
Feb	7046	(5418)	40	(60)	176	(90)	+95.5
Mar	12860	(6037)	51	(64)	252	(94)	+168.0
Apr	11446	(4497)	51	(50)	224	(90)	+148.8
May	2514	(1327)	7	(10)	359	(133)	+169.9
Tot	93895	38472	380	(420)	247	(92)	+168.4

Best gate achieved in August: 0 clubs
Best gate achieved in September: 2 clubs
Best gate achieved in October: 3 clubs
Best gate achieved in November: 2 clubs
Best gate achieved in December: 2 clubs
Best gate achieved in January: 4 clubs
Best gate achieved in February: 2 clubs
Best gate achieved in March: 3 clubs
Best gate achieved in April: 1 club
Best gate achieved in May: 1 club

DIVISION THREE (excluding Aldershot Town)

Top Gates (each club)

631	Leighton v Tring (26/12/92)
398	Tring v Leighton (12/4/93)
332	Thame v Leighton (28/12/92)
265	Royston v Leighton (22/8/92)
242	Horsham v Epsom & E. (26/12/92)
233	Cove v Collier Row (13/2/93)
214	East Thurrock v Collier R. (28/12/92)
208	Northwood v Leighton (3/10/92)
156	Collier Row v Leighton (27/2/93)
152	Camberley v Collier R. (12/12/92)
144	Hertford v Royston (12/4/93)
127	Kingsbury v Northwood (13/4/93)
126	Feltham & H. v Leighton (20/3/93)
120	Flackwell Heath v Leighton (9/1/93)
111	Epsom & E. v Horsham (12/4/93)
102	Horbchurch v Collier Row (31/10/92)
95	Clapton v Collier Row (13/3/93)
86	Bracknell Town v Horsham (20/10/92)
75	Petersfield v Bracknell (13/10/92)
75	Petersfield v Horsham (10/11/92)
75	Petersfield v Northwood (28/11/92)
75	Petersfield v Camberley (27/2/92)

Total Attendances (91-92 figures in brackets)

	Total		Games		Ave.		% change
Aug	1828	(3097)	17	(31)	108	(100)	+8.0
Sep	4359	3382	43	(40)	101	(85)	+18.8
Oct	4869	(4007)	49	(46)	99	(87)	+13.7
Nov	2606	(3264)	30	(42)	87	(78)	+11.5
Dec	5143	(2590)	38	(31)	135	(84)	+60.7
Jan	3356	(4853)	29	(46)	116	(106)	+9.43
Feb	3374	(5418)	37	(60)	91	(90)	+1.1
Mar	4135	(6037)	45	(64)	92	(94)	-2.1
Apr	5521	(4497)	48	(50)	115	(90)	+27.7
May	716	(1327)	6	(10)	119	(133)	-10.5
Tot	35907	38472	342	(420)	105	(92)	+14.1

Best gate achieved in August: 1 club
Best gate achieved in September: 0 clubs
Best gate achieved in October: 4 clubs
Best gate achieved in November: 2 clubs
Best gate achieved in December: 2 clubs
Best gate achieved in January: 1 club
Best gate achieved in February: 3 clubs
Best gate achieved in March: 2 clubs
Best gate achieved in April: 4 club
Best gate achieved in May: 0 clubs

Aldershot Town took huge crowds with them to each Division Three ground. Here Kevin Baker clears under pressure from Nigel Webb in the last ever league game at Epsom & Ewell's West Street ground. Photo - Dave West.

Premier Division

	P	W	D	L	W	D	L	F	A	Pts
			HOME			AWAY				
CHESHAM UNITED	42	17	3	1	13	5	3	104	34	98
ST. ALBANS	42	15	5	1	13	4	4	103	50	93
ENFIELD	42	13	1	7	12	5	4	94	48	81
CARSHALTON ATH.	42	10	7	4	12	3	6	96	56	76
SUTTON UNITED	42	12	5	4	6	9	6	74	57	68
GRAYS ATHLETIC	42	13	6	2	5	5	11	61	64	65
STEVENAGE BORO'	42	10	2	9	8	6	7	62	60	62
HARROW BOROUGH	42	7	8	6	9	6	6	59	60	62
AYLESBURY UNITED	42	9	4	8	10	1	10	70	76	62
HAYES	42	7	8	6	9	5	7	64	59	61
BASINGSTOKE	42	7	10	4	5	7	9	49	45	53
HENDON	42	6	11	4	6	6	9	51	54	53
KINGSTONIAN	42	8	5	8	6	5	10	59	58	52
DULWICH HAMLET	42	6	5	10	6	9	6	52	66	50
MARLOW	42	4	7	10	8	4	9	72	73	47
WOKINGHAM	42	7	9	5	4	4	13	62	81	46
BROMLEY	42	6	4	11	5	9	7	51	72	46
WIVENHOE TOWN	42	10	2	9	3	5	13	41	75	46
YEADING	42	5	5	11	6	1	14	58	66	45
STAINES TOWN	42	7	5	9	3	8	10	59	77	43
WINDSOR & ETON	42	3	4	14	5	3	13	40	90	31
BOGNOR REGIS	42	3	5	13	2	5	14	46	106	25

Top League Goalscorers

Jimmy Bolton (Carshalton Athletic)	37
Steve Clark (St.Albans City)	36
Dave Pearce (Kingstonian) (Includes 15 for Hayes)	27
Chris Townsend (Chesham United)	24
Graham Westley (Aylesbury United) (Includes 5 for Enfield)	23
Darren Collins (Enfield) (Includes 8 for Aylesbury United)	23

THE PREMIER DIVISION RESULT CHART 1992-93

HOME TEAM	1	2	3	4	5	6	7	8	9	10	11	12	13	14	15	16	17	18	19	20	21	22
1. Aylesbury	*	1-1	2-0	6-1	3-2	1-4	0-2	1-1	1-2	0-1	1-1	1-1	2-0	0-3	3-2	5-3	1-2	0-4	3-0	1-2	1-0	1-1
2. Basingstoke	1-2	*	0-0	1-1	0-1	0-0	2-1	4-0	4-0	0-0	1-0	1-1	0-0	2-1	1-2	1-1	0-0	1-1	3-0	1-1	5-0	0-6
3. Bognor	4-5	1-3	*	3-2	0-6	0-4	2-2	0-6	4-1	1-2	1-2	3-4	1-5	2-6	0-0	1-1	1-1	0-1	2-0	2-2	1-1	1-4
4. Bromley	1-2	1-0	3-0	*	0-4	2-2	0-5	2-3	1-3	1-1	1-0	0-2	0-1	1-3	4-1	1-2	1-1	3-2	1-2	3-0	0-2	1-0
5. Carshalton	1-0	0-0	2-0	0-2	*	1-1	2-2	1-2	2-1	1-1	1-1	3-1	3-0	3-2	3-5	2-1	3-1	2-1	1-3	3-1	1-1	1-1
6. Chesham	2-1	2-1	6-1	0-0	5-1	*	4-0	0-1	3-2	2-2	1-0	4-0	2-1	4-3	2-2	1-0	7-1	7-0	1-0	2-1	3-1	3-0
7. Dulwich	0-1	0-0	2-2	1-1	1-7	1-4	*	1-2	2-0	1-2	1-1	1-1	0-5	2-0	0-2	0-2	0-0	5-0	2-1	0-1	0-1	
8. Enfield	3-1	4-1	6-2	2-0	2-1	0-1	1-2	*	2-1	0-1	2-3	0-2	2-2	1-4	0-2	4-1	1-0	1-0	6-0	4-0	3-0	4-1
9. Grays Ath.	2-1	3-2	2-1	4-1	2-2	0-0	3-2	*	2-1	1-0	0-0	1-1	1-2	3-0	1-1	2-1	1-3	0-0	2-1	2-0	3-0	
10. Harrow	2-3	0-0	2-0	0-2	2-4	0-3	1-1	1-0	0-0	*	2-2	1-1	2-0	2-5	3-6	2-2	3-1	4-3	0-0	0-0	4-1	3-0
11. Hayes	4-0	1-3	2-0	3-3	0-4	1-3	0-0	1-1	1-1	2-2	*	1-1	2-3	2-0	0-0	4-0	0-1	2-2	7-1	2-1	4-2	0-0
12. Hendon	1-1	0-0	1-0	1-1	1-2	2-1	0-0	0-1	1-2	2-0	*	1-0	0-0	2-2	1-1	1-1	2-0	1-1	1-0	1-1	1-1	3-3
13. Kingstonian	7-1	1-1	0-0	2-2	0-2	0-1	2-2	2-3	1-0	2-1	1-1	2-4	*	2-0	1-3	3-1	0-2	0-1	3-0	0-1	3-1	2-0
14. Marlow	3-4	0-0	1-2	2-2	0-5	1-4	0-1	1-1	1-1	1-2	1-2	3-0	1-1	*	1-1	5-2	2-3	1-1	0-2	5-1	3-2	1-2
15. St. Albans	1-0	4-1	2-1	4-0	3-2	1-1	3-1	0-0	2-1	1-2	2-1	2-0	5-1	*	2-2	2-1	2-2	2-1	3-0	7-2	1-1	
16. Staines	1-4	0-1	3-0	2-3	0-3	0-2	1-1	2-2	6-0	1-0	0-1	3-3	1-0	1-4	2-1	*	2-2	1-1	3-0	1-2	0-1	2-0
17. Stevenage	1-3	0-2	4-1	0-1	3-2	1-0	2-4	0-3	6-1	0-0	1-2	4-1	2-0	2-0	1-2	1-2	*	1-0	0-1	1-0	1-1	2-0
18. Sutton	4-0	1-0	0-0	3-1	3-1	0-1	2-0	3-2	1-1	2-1	1-2	0-2	1-1	2-1	1-3	2-4	1-1	*	5-2	3-0	2-0	2-2
19. Windsor	2-3	1-0	2-2	0-1	1-4	2-5	2-2	1-3	3-3	0-1	2-3	1-2	1-0	1-2	0-3	3-1	2-4	0-3	*	1-1	1-2	0-2
20. Wivenhoe	2-1	3-2	4-1	1-0	0-4	0-0	0-1	0-4	0-2	3-0	3-1	2-0	2-3	2-1	0-2	1-1	0-2	1-1	2-0	*	1-0	1-3
21. Wokingham	0-2	3-1	1-3	1-1	2-2	0-0	3-1	0-3	2-0	1-1	5-0	2-2	0-4	2-2	1-3	2-2	3-0	3-3	3-1	2-0	*	2-2
22. Yeading	2-1	1-2	2-1	0-0	1-1	1-2	0-2	3-5	2-3	4-0	1-2	1-3	1-2	0-0	1-2	0-1	2-2	4-0	1-0	0-0	2-4	*

THE DIADORA LEAGUE PREMIER DIVISION ATTENDANCE CHART 1992-93

HOME TEAM	1	2	3	4	5	6	7	8	9	10	11	12	13	14	15	16	17	18	19	20	21	22
1. Aylesbury	*	467	500	506	673	1134	303	903	503	549	403	346	410	768	748	542	977	602	555	409	477	753
2. Basingstoke	337	*	299	229	424	544	361	492	195	371	331	334	402	333	555	363	449	605	297	314	302	345
3. Bognor R.T.	230	220	*	320	240	417	290	250	140	360	268	330	300	210	240	210	285	425	210	160	230	170
4. Bromley	210	246	369	*	510	342	588	412	439	205	192	380	456	228	403	452	270	339	400	391	283	322
5. Carshalton	508	393	336	406	*	601	447	502	465	381	328	365	551	328	566	345	463	1288	402	271	409	331
6. Chesham	1266	694	789	905	805	*	1108	1064	809	1512	1044	910	910	1107	1456	871	710	806	675	785	643	844
7. Dulwich	272	227	124	431	390	416	*	724	152	366	301	752	374	263	263	314	292	401	502	230	507	330
8. Enfield	1070	671	574	727	742	1220	555	*	385	476	732	851	715	843	1116	465	952	809	624	690	665	408
9. Grays Ath.	373	301	231	238	265	468	346	485	*	347	302	417	367	289	382	351	320	402	277	348	245	310
10. Harrow	300	257	230	307	304	434	302	412	236	*	292	420	345	276	386	294	356	263	249	289	325	281
11. Hayes	333	305	206	369	284	513	249	465	204	351	*	380	419	295	469	301	311	448	313	278	270	596
12. Hendon	204	253	201	257	237	476	238	759	174	263	357	*	357	303	403	216	374	504	247	227	211	186
13. Kingstonian	693	560	483	638	503	703	398	773	403	735	505	625	*	458	695	574	503	897	540	443	742	405
14. Marlow	410	229	232	258	301	829	270	619	278	357	255	287	361	*	580	260	266	308	290	242	386	210
15. St Albans	1302	837	619	597	814	3120	955	1643	617	903	610	865	742	722	*	809	910	867	526	472	647	727
16. Staines	554	255	328	237	330	682	328	490	275	384	326	416	506	287	356	*	564	447	274	383	264	
17. Stevenage	605	501	463	456	704	871	862	785	665	525	563	619	459	531	1107	454	*	583	637	481	414	683
18. Sutton Utd	678	709	821	682	807	672	630	714	583	408	574	674	1173	479	728	625	597	*	382	580	501	584
19. Windsor	248	196	168	263	163	415	1687	386	148	200	255	153	286	265	369	221	269	440	*	185	265	190
20. Wivenhoe	282	166	282	291	172	284	206	502	347	258	303	273	258	216	242	196	323	393	241	*	462	166
21. Wokingham	299	345	305	285	219	561	271	396	299	289	440	245	530	317	446	258	348	435	457	233	*	266
22. Yeading	258	189	110	262	221	383	251	370	208	262	544	297	306	206	386	191	286	282	320	307	233	*

NB. Bromley v Windsor, Hendon, Yeading, Dulwich Carshalton, Aylesbury, Basingstoke, Hayes, Wokingham, Sutton and St Albans played at Dulwich Hamlet. Bromley v Chesham, Stevenage, Marlow and Enfield played at Croydon FC. Bromley v Harrow played at Walton & Hersham. Dulwich v St Albans played at Bromley FC, Dulwich v Bognor played at Tooting & Mitcham, Dulwich v Grays played at Bognor Regis Town.

Diadora League Premier Division Ten Year Record

	83/4	84/5	85/6	86/7	87/8	88/9	89/90	90/1	91/2	92/3
Aylesbury United	-	-	-	-	-	-	3	3	7	9
Barking	16	19	18	8	19	10	20	21	-	-
Basingstoke Town	-	-	-	-	22	-	8	18	14	11
Billericay Town	15	18	21	-	-	-	-	-	-	-
Bishop's Stortford	11	16	7	10	13	7	9	13	22	-
Bognor Regis Town	13	6	15	5	16	9	19	17	21	22
Bromley	22	-	-	11	2	14	21	-	12	17
Carshalton Athletic	20	15	20	15	9	4	10	9	8	4
Chesham United	-	-	-	-	-	-	-	-	4	1
Croydon	17	12	4	7	18	22	-	-	-	-
Dagenham	-	-	-	-	-	18	6	14	9	-
Dulwich Hamlet	10	7	9	18	20	16	22	-	-	14
Enfield	-	-	-	-	-	-	-	2	2	3
Epsom & Ewell	-	13	22	-	-	-	-	-	-	-
Farnborough Town	-	-	3	9	8	2	-	-	-	-
Grays Athletic	-	-	-	-	-	5	5	6	15	6
Harlow Town	12	22	-	-	-	-	-	-	-	-
Harrow Borough	1	8	5	6	12	19	18	18	8	8
Hayes	5	9	16	16	6	8	14	8	19	10
Hendon	9	17	19	4	10	12	12	15	17	12
Hitchin Town	6	20	17	20	21	-	-	-	-	-
Kingstonian	-	-	8	12	14	6	4	5	10	13
Leytonstone-Ilford	19	21	-	-	4	1	(see Redbridge)			
Leyton-Wingate	-	-	-	-	17	15	7	22	-	-
Marlow	-	-	-	-	-	20	17	7	6	15
Redbridge Forest	-	-	-	-	-	-	11	1	-	-
St Albans City	-	-	-	14	15	17	15	16	13	2
Slough Town	3	14	6	3	3	3	1	-	-	-
Staines Town	14	-	-	-	-	-	16	19	20	20
Stevenage Borough	-	-	-	-	-	-	-	-	-	7
Sutton United	4	1	1	-	-	-	-	-	3	5
Tooting & Mitcham United	21	10	12	19	11	21	-	-	-	-
Walthamstow Avenue	18	11	13	22	-	-	(see Redbridge)			
Windsor & Eton	-	5	11	13	7	13	13	12	11	21
Wivenhoe Town	-	-	-	-	-	-	-	10	16	18
Woking	-	-	-	-	-	-	-	4	1	-
Wokingham Town	8	4	10	17	5	11	2	11	5	16
Worthing	2	2	14	21	-	-	-	-	-	-
Wycombe Wanderers	7	3	-	1	-	-	-	-	-	-
Yeading	-	-	-	-	-	-	-	-	-	19
Yeovil Town	-	-	2	2	1	-	-	-	-	-
No. of clubs competing	22	22	22	22	22	22	22	22	22	22

AYLESBURY UNITED

Aylesbury United F.C. 1992-93. Photo - Bucks Herald.

Chairman: D W Pigott   **President:** J Durban   **Vice Chairman:** K T Arnold.
Secretary/Press Officer: Tony Graham c/o the club. (0296 88178 H / 436350 or 436525 B)
Manager: Alan Davies   **Coach:** Mick Walsh   **Physio:** Nick Grove
Commercial Manager: Eric Norman.
Ground: The Stadium, Buckingham Road, Aylesbury HP20 2AQ (0296 436350/436525).
Directions: On A413 to Buckingham, just off ring road opposite Horse & Jockey PH. Arriving from Buckingham ground is on left - from all other directions follow Buckingham signs and ground on right. Half hour walk from Buckingham (BR).
Capacity: 4,035   **Cover:** 891   **Seats:** 400   **Floodlights:** Yes   **Metal Badges:** Yes
Club Shop: Yes, selling programmes, magazines, souvenirs, leisurewear. Contact secretary.
Colours: Green shaded quarters   **Change colours:** Red & black stripes.
Newsline: 0891 446 824   **Midweek home matchday:** Tuesday
Previous Leagues: Bucks Contiguous 1897-1903/ South Eastern 03-07/ Spartan 07-51/ Delphian 51-63/ Athenian 63-76/ Southern 76-88/ GMV Conference 88-89.
Previous Grounds: Printing Works Ground 1897-1935/ Sports Stadium, Wendover Rd (ground name later changed to The Stadium, Turnfurlong Lane) 35-85/ shared grounds 85-86.
Previous Name: Night School, Printing Works (merged in 1897).
Record Attendance: 6,000 v England 1988 *(at old ground: 7,500 v Watford, FA Cup 1st Rd 1951)*.
Best F.A. Cup season: 2nd Rd 88-89 89-90 91-92 (1st Rd 51-52 85-86 86-87 87-88 90-91).
League clubs defeated in F.A. Cup: Southend Utd 89-90.
Record Fees - Paid: £15,000 for Glenville Donegal (Northampton, 1990)
Received: £35,000 for Glenville Donegal (Maidstone Utd, 1991).
Players progressing to Football League: Ray Mabbutt (Bristol Rovers), Phil Barber (Crystal Palace 1986)
Clubhouse: Pub hours, but shut during matches. Function room available for hire(0296 436891). Bar snacks available.
Club Record Scorer: Cliff Hercules   **Record Appearances:** Cliff Hercules.
92-93 Captain: Andy Robinson
92-93 P.o.Y.: Cliff Hercules
92-93 Top scorer: Cliff Hercules 17 (Graham Westley 27 inc 9 for Enfield).
Local Newspapers: Bucks Herald, Bucks Advertiser, Herald & Post.
Local Radio Stations: BBC Radio Beds, Chiltern Radio, Fox FM.
Honours: Southern Lg 87-88 (Mids Div R-up 84-85, Sth Div R-up 79-80), Athenian Lg Div 2 R-up 67-68, Delphian Lg 53-54 (R-up 52-53, Lg Cup 59-60), Spartan Lg 08-09 (R-up 52-53, West Div 28-29 (R-up 45-46), Div 1 38-39 (R-up 34-35)), Berks & Bucks Snr Cup 13-14 85-86), FA Trophy 4th Rd replay 80-81.

PROGRAMME DETAILS:
Pages: 32 **Price:** £1
Editor: Dave Gamage

BASINGSTOKE TOWN

Basingstoke Town 1992-93. Back Row (L/R): Gary Joseph, Barry Cranmere (Captain), Vernon Pratt, Deane Beale, Paul Odey, Peter Terry, Paul Chambers, Dean Callaghan. Front: Stewart Mitchell, Paul Holohan, David Hawtin, Paul Coombs, Barry Blankley. Photo - V J Robertson.

Chairman: Gordon A Hill   **President:** Charles Foyle, Esq
Secretary/Press Officer: David Knight, 1 The Vale, Oakley, Basingstoke RG23 7LB (0256 781422)
Manager: Alan Humphries   **Asst Manager/Coach:** Ernie Howe.
Physio: Trevor Croft.
Ground: Camrose Road, Western Way, Basingstoke RG24 6HW (0256 781422).
Directions: Exit 6 off M3 and follow A30 west, ground off Winchester Road. Two miles from bus and rail stations.
Capacity: 6,000   **Cover:** 1,500   **Seats:** 840   **Club Shop:** Yes   **Metal Badges:** Yes
Colours: All blue (gold trim)   **Change colours:** All gold
Sponsors: Basingstoke Press.
Previous Leagues: Hants 1900-40 45-71/ Southern 71-87.
Previous Ground: Castle Field 1896-1947.
Midweek home matchday: Tuesday   **Reserve Team's League:** None.
Record Attendance: 4,091 v Northampton, FA Cup 1st Rd 1971.
Best F.A. Cup season: 2nd Rd 89-90 (lost 2-3 at home to Torquay). Also 1st Rd 71-72.
League clubs defeated in F.A. Cup: None.
Record Fees - Paid: £4,750 for Steve Ingham (Gosport Borough)
Received: £6,750 for Steve Ingham (Bashley)
Players progressing to Football League: Tony Godfrey (Southampton 1958), John Neale (Exeter 1972), Mike Doherty (Reading 1982), Micky Cheetham (Ipswich 1988), Matt Carmichael (Lincoln), Tony Franklin (Exeter), Steve Welsh (Peterborough 1990).
Clubhouse: Open every day (including lunchtime)(0256 464353)   **Steward:** Colin Wood
Club Record Goalscorer: Unkown   **Club Record Appearances:** Billy Coombs
92-93 Captain: Paul Chambers
92-93 P.o.Y.: Paul Chambers
92-93 Top scorer: Paul Combs.
Local Newspapers (+Tel.Nos.): Basingstoke Gazette (461131).
Local Radio Stations: Radio 210 (0734 413131)
Honours: Southern Lg Southern Div 85-86, Isthmian Lg Div 1 R-up 88-89, Hants Lg 67-68 69-70 70-71 (R-up 65-66 66-67 68-69, North Div 11-12 19-20), Hants Senior Cup 70-71 89-90

PROGRAMME DETAILS:
Pages: 40 Price: 70p
Editor: Secretary

BROMLEY

Bromley F.C. 1992-93. Back Row (L/R): R Kiersterson (Assistant Manager), G Wakeling (Manager), P McMenemy, I Rawlings, C Hayes, S Hamberger, J Raffington, K Sharman, M Morgan, P Taylor. Front: J De Palma (Physio), J Francis, G Campbell, S Devine, F Coles, P Gordon, I Docker.

Chairman: M Perry **President:** G T Ransom, AM Inst BE, MHTTA
Secretary: Brian Traer, 43 Fairway, Pettswood, Kent BR5 1EE (0689 820457).
Team Manager: George Wakeling **Asst Mgr:** R Kiersterson. **Coach:** P Taylor.
Press Officer: Ian Pettyfer **Physio:** J De Palma
Ground: Hayes Lane, Bromley, Kent BR2 9EF (081 460 5291).
Directions: 1 mile from Bromley South (BR). Buses 146 and 119 pass ground. Junction 4 off M25, then A21.
Capacity: 8,500 **Cover:** 4,000 **Seats:** 2,000 **Floodlights:** Yes **Metal Badges:** Yes.
Club Shop: Yes.
Colours: White/black/white **Change colours:** All red
Previous Leagues: South London - 1894/ Southern 94-96/ London 96-98 99-1901/ Kent 1898-99/ Spartan 07-08/ Isthmian 08-11/ Athenian 19-52.
Prev. Grounds: White Hart Field Cricket Ground, Widmore Rd (pre-1904)/ Plaistow Cricket Field 1904-37.
Midweek home matchday: Tuesday **Reserve Team's League:** Suburban
Record Attendance: 12,000 v Nigeria, 1950. **Newsline:** 0898 122 904.
Best F.A. Cup season: 2nd Rd replay v Scarborough 37-38, Lincoln 38-39, Watford 45-46.
Record Fees - Paid: Undisclosed **Received:** £50,000 for Jon Goodman (from Millwall, 1990).
Players progressing to Football League: Roy Merryfield (Chelsea), Stan Charlton (Arsenal 1952), Roy Heckman (Orient 1955), John Gregory (West Ham 1951), Bill Lloyd (Millwall 1956), Brian Kinsey (Charlton 1956), Harold Hobbs (Charlton & England), Matt Carmichael (Lincoln 1990), Leslie Locke (QPR 1956), Jon Goodman (Millwall).
Clubhouse: Open matchdays. Food available.
Club Record Goalscorer: George Brown 570 (1938-61)
Club Record Apps: George Brown
92-93 Captain: Frank Coles
92-93 P.o.Y.: Joe Francis
92-93 Top scorer: Sean Devine.
Local Newspapers: Bromley Times (081 309 1234), Bromley Advertiser (081 668 4811).
Local Radio Stations: Radio Kent, Bromley Hospital Radio, Bromley Local Radio.
Honours: FA Amtr Cup 10-11 37-38 48-49, Isthmian Lg(4) 08-11 53-54 60-61
(R-up 52-53 55-56 87-88), Div 1 R-up 79-80 85-86 90-91, Prince Phillip 5-a-side
Cup 1979), Athenian Lg 22-23 48-49 50-51 (R-up 35-36), London Lg Div 2
1896-97, Spartan Lg 07-08, London Snr Cup 09-10 45-46 50-51, Kent Senior
Cup 49-50 76-77 91-92, Kent Amtr Cup(12) 07-08 31-32 35-37 38-39 46-47 48-
49 50-51 52-53 53-55 59-60, FA Tphy 2nd Rd 91-92.

CARSHALTON ATHLETIC Robins

Carshalton Athletic 1992-93, with the London Challenge Cup won last Spring.

Chairman: Trevor Cripps   **Vice Chairman:** John Carpentiere   **President:** Bill Cooper
Secretary: Ron McLean, 27 White Lodge, Upper Norwood, London SE19 3HR (081 764 6233).
Manager: Billy Smith   **Asst Manager:** Bobby Green   **Coach:** Colin Turner
Press Officer: Secretary   **Physio:** Ken Jones
Ground: War Memorial Sports Ground, Colston Av, Carshalton SM5 2PW (081 642 8425).
Directions: Turn right out of Carshalton BR Station, and Colston Avenue is first left. Entrance 150 yards on right.
London Transport bus 151 from Morden to Wrythe Green Lane.
Capacity: 8,000   **Cover:** 4,500   **Seats:** 240   **Floodlights:** Yes   **Metal Badges:** Yes.
Club Shop: Yes, selling hats, scarves, T-shirts, programmes and various football souvenirs.
Colours: White (maroon trim)/maroon   **Change colours:** Maroon/white.
Prev. Lges: Southern Suburban (pre-1911)/ Surrey Snr 22-23/ London 23-46/ Corinthian 46-56/ Athenian 56-73.
Previous Grounds: Wrythe Recreation Ground 1907-14/ Culvers Park 19-20.
Midweek home matchday: Monday   **Reserve Team's League:** Suburban.   **Sponsors:** T C Cleaning.
Record Attendance: 7,800 v Wimbledon, London Senior Cup.
Best F.A. Cup season: 2nd Rd 82-83, lost 1-4 at Torquay. (1st Rd 69-70 87-88).
Record win: 13-0 v Worthing, Loctite Cup Third Round 28/2/91.
League clubs defeated in F.A. Cup: None.
Record Fees - Paid: £2,000 for Jimmy Bolton, 1990.
        Received: £15,000 for Curtis Warmington (Enfield).
Players progressing to Football League: Ernie Taylor (Newcastle, Blackpool, Manchester United), Billy Barragon
(QPR), John McDonald (Notts County 1948), Frank George (Orient 1954), Thomas Williams (Colchester 1956),
Alan Eagles (Orient 1957), Derek Razzell (QPR), Terry Stacey (Plymouth 1959), Roy Lunnes (Crystal Palace 1960),
Les Burns (Charlton 1967), Ron Walker (Watford), Nobby Warren (Exeter), Gus Caesar (Arsenal).
Clubhouse: Open every evening and weekend lunches. Licenced bar, pool, darts, machines, discos on Saturday.
Separate function hall (bookings taken). Food: sandwiches, rolls, burgers, hot dogs, teas, coffees and soft drinks.
(081 642 8658).
Club Record Goalscorer: Jimmy Bolton
Club Record Appearances: Jon Raffington and Jon Warden.
92-93 Captain: Andy Riley.
92-93 P.o.Y.: Shaun Priddle.
92-93 Top scorer: Jimmy Bolton.
Club Newsline: 0891 446849.
Local Newspapers: Wallington & Carshalton Advertiser (668411), Carshalton
Herald (6612221).
Local Radio Stations: Capital.
Hons: Isthmian Lg Div 2 R-up 76-77, Corinthian Lg 52-53 53-54, Surrey Snr
Lg R-up 22-23, Surrey Snr Cup(3) 88-90 91-92, Surrey Snr Shield (R-up(2)),
London Challenge Cup 91-92, F.A. Trophy 3rd Rd 80-81 (lost 0-3 at home to
Mossley (eventual R-up)).

PROGRAMME DETAILS:
Pages: 14 **Price:** 60p
Editor: Roger Fear

CHESHAM UNITED

Chesham United's leading goalscorer Chris Townsend sprints clear of the Staines Town defence. Photo - Keith Clayton.

Chairman: Tony Aplin **Directors:** A Aplin, R Old, J Conrad, P Gibbins.
Secretary: David Stanley, 17 Old Vicarage Gdns, Markyate, St Albans, Herts AL3 9PW (0582 840707).
Manager: Gerald Aplin **Asst Manager:** Alan Randall **Coach:** Micky Gilchrist
Fitness Coach: Keith Power **Physio:** Ann Wheeler
Commercial Manager: Paul Barnes.
Ground: Meadow Park, Amy Lane, Amersham Road, Chesham HP5 1NE (0494 783964 - ground clubhouse. 0494 791608 - fax. 0898 884580 - match information service).
Directions: M25 junction 18, A404 to Amersham, A416 to Chesham - go down to r-about at foot of Amersham Hill, then sharp left. 10 mins walk from Chesham station (Metropolitan Line).
Capacity: 5,000 **Cover:** 2 sides **Seats:** 224 **Floodlights:** Yes **Metal Badges:** Yes
Club Shop: Yes. Open matchdays - Manager: Bob Day (0494 786661).
Colours: Claret & blue **Change colours:** Yellow & black. **Sponsors:** M.F.I.
Previous Leagues: Spartan 17-47/ Corinthian 47-63/ Athenian 63-73.
Midweek home matchday: Wednesday **Reserve Team's League:** N/A.
Record Attendance: 5,000 v Cambridge Utd, FA 3rd Rd 5/12/79.
Best F.A. Cup season: 3rd Rd as above (lost 0-2). Also 1st Rd 66-67 68-69 76-77 82-83.
Best F.A. Trophy season: 3rd Rd 92-93 (lost 1-3 at home to Sutton United).
Record Fees - Paid: Undisclosed (club policy).
Received: Undisclosed (club policy).
Players progressing to Football League: William Shipwright & Jimmy Strain (Watford 1953 & 55), Stewart Scullion (Charlton 1965), John Pyatt (L'pool 1967), Brian Carter (Brentford 1968), Kerry Dixon (Spurs 1978), Tony Currie (Torquay 1984).
Clubhouse: Open every evening. Bar snacks. Available for hire (business training meetings, weddings etc).
Club Record Goalscorer: Arthur Howlett, John Willis (50 in 1963)
Club Record Appearances: Martin Baguley (600+).
92-93 Captain:
92-93 P.o.Y.:
92-93 Top scorer: Chris Townsend, 24.
Local Newspapers: Bucks Examiner (0494 792616), Bucks Advertiser (0895 632000), Bucks Free Press (0494 21212).
Local Radio Stations: Radio Chiltern (0582 666001).
Honours: FA Amtr Cup R-up 67-68, Isthmian Lg 92-93 (Div 1 90-91, Div 2 Nth 86-87, Associate Members Cup R-up 90-91), Athenian Lg Div 1 Cup 63-64 68-69, Corinthian Lg R-up(2) 60-62 (Lg Cup 60-61), Spartan Lg(4) 21-23 24-25 32-33 (R-up 26-27 29-30 33-34), Berks & Bucks Snr Cup 21-22 25-26 28-29 33-34 47-48 50-51 64-65 66-67 75-76.

v WINDSOR & ETON

Saturday 3rd October 1992

PROGRAMME DETAILS:
Pages: 28 **Price:** £1
Editor: John Ashworth

DORKING

Dorking F.C. 1992-93. Back Row (L/R): John Rains (Manager, now left), Michael Stewart (committee), Dennie Rose (Physio), Tony Rains (Asst Manager, now left), Steve Tutt, Phil Grainger, Peter Mills, Carey Anderson, Tony Welch, Lee Orkney, Kevin Wedderburn, Chris Collis (Press Officer), Derek Plumridge (Secretary). Front: Caroline Bruwer (Physio), Steve Rogers (Coach), Neil Robson, Matthew Hanlan, Chris Lewington, Steve Lunn, Lee Thornton, Daren Bird, Graham Marriner. Photo - Eric Marsh.

Chairman: Alan Iveson   **President:** Martin Collins
Vice Chairmen: Martin Collins/ Tom Dixon.
Secretary: Mr Derek Plumridge, 20 Alexander Rd, South Park, Reigate, Surrey RH2 8EA (0737 241536).
Manager: Steve Tutt   **Asst Manager:** Robin Lewis   **Coach:** Robin Lewis
Press Officer: Chris Collis (0293 821380)   **Physio:** Dennie Rose.
Ground: Meadowbank, Mill Lane, Dorking, Surrey RH4 1DX (0306 884112).
Directions: Mill Lane is off Dorking high street next to Woolworths and Marks & Spencers opposite the White Horse pub. Fork right in Mill Lane past the Malthouse pub. Half mile from both Dorking and Deepdene (BR) stations.
Capacity: 3,600   **Cover:** 800   **Seats:** 200   **Floodlights:** Yes   **Metal Badges:** Yes
Club Shop: Yes, selling badges, scarves, programmes, books, anything! Contact Brain Savory (081 668 1810).
Colours: Green & white hoops/white/white   **Change colours:** All blue
Previous Ground: Prixham Lane (until 1953).
Previous Leagues: Surrey Senior 22-56 77-78/ Corinthian 56-63/ Athenian 63-74 78-80/ Southern 74-77.
Previous Names: Guildford & Dorking United (when club merged with Guildford in 1974)/Dorking Town 77-82.
Midweek home matchday: Tuesday   **Reserve Team's League:** Suburban
Best F.A. Cup season: 1st Round Proper 92-93 (lost 2-3 at home to Plymouth Argyle).
Record Attendance: 4,500 v Folkestone Town, F.A. Cup 1st Qualifying Round 1955.
Record win: 7-0 v Barking, Isthmian League Division One, 31/10/92.
Players progressing to Football League: Steve Scrivens & John Finch (Fulham), Andy Ansah (Brentford 1989).
Clubhouse: Open matchdays, weekends and training nights. Hot & cold food on matchdays. Pool, bar billiards, widescreen TV, Fruit Machines.
Club Record Goalscorer: Andy Bushnell.
Club Record Appearances: Steve Lunn.
92-93 Captain: Tony Welch
92-93 P.o.Y.: Neil Robson.
92-93 Top scorer: Steve Lunn 28.
Local Newspapers: Dorking Advertiser, Surrey Mirror.
Local Radio Stations: County Sound, Radio Surrey, Radio Mercury.
Honours: Isthmian Lg Div 2 Sth 88-89 (Full Members Cup R-up 92-93), Surrey Snr Cup R-up 1885-86 1989-90, Surrey Snr Shield(2) 58-60 (R-up 07-08 10-11 60-61), Surrey Snr Lg(4) 28-30 54-56 (R-up 51-52 53-54, Lg Cup 48-49 50-51 53-54, Lg Charity Cup(4) 48-49 53-54(jt), 54-56 (R-up(5) 28-30 46-47 50-51 77-78)), Gilbert Rice F'lit Cup 87-88 (R-up 89-90), Surrey I'mediate Cup 56-57 (R-up 54-55), Southern Comb. Challenge Cup 92-93, FA Tphy 2nd Rd 91-92, FA Vase 3rd Rd(3) 83-84 86-88.

WELCOME TO MEADOWBANK
THE HOME OF
DORKING FOOTBALL CLUB

THE DIADORA FOOTBALL LEAGUE
DIVISION ONE

PROGRAMME DETAILS:
Pages: 48+ Price: 80p
Editor: Chris Collis
(0293 821380)

DULWICH HAMLET

Dulwich Hamlet F.C. 1992-93. Back Row (L/R): J Cannon (Manager), M Dodman, M Norris, R Cowan, J Donegan, B Davis, D Morgan, N Ferguson, R Hedman, D Coppin, D Elliott (Kit Man). Centre: S Rollison, W Kerrins, M Gillam, A Fisher, J Daly, J Egan, J Harris (Physio). Front: K Fowler, L Best, G Wilgoss, G Hewitt, P Rogers, N Missen, D Gill (Asst Manager). Photo - Andy Hobdell.

Chairman: Steve Dye   **Vice Chairman:** Glyn Beverley   **President:** Tommy Jover
Secretary: Terry Stephens, 27 Christchurch Close, Colliers Wood SW19 2NZ (081 542 8905).
Manager: Jim Cannon   **Coach:** Dixon Gill   **Physio:** John Harris
Press Officer: John Lawrence (071 733 6385)
Ground: Champion Hill Stadium, Dog Kennel Hill, East Dulwich, London SE22 8BD (071 274 8707).
Directions: East Dulwich station, 200yds. Denmark Hill station, 10 mins walk. Herne Hill station then bus 37 stops near ground. Also buses 184 from Elephant & Castle, 185 from Victoria.
Capacity: 3,000   **Cover:** 1,000   **Seats:** 500   **Floodlights:** Yes   **Metal Badges:** Yes
Club Shop: New shop to open in season 1993-94.
Previous Grounds: Woodwarde Road 1893-95/ College Farm 95-96/ Sunray Avenue 96-1902/ Freeman's Ground, Champion Hill 02-12/ Champion Hill (old ground) 1912-92/ Sandy Lane (groundshare with Tooting & Mitcham F.C.) 91-92.
Colours: Pink & blue stripes/blue/blue   **Change colours:** All yellow
Club Sponsors: B.C.A. Music Clubs.
Previous Leagues: Camberwell 1894-97/ Southern Suburban 1897-1900 01-07/ Dulwich 00-01/ Spartan 07-08.
Midweek home matchday: Tuesday   **Former Name:** Camberwell
Reserve Team's League: Suburban.
Record Attendance: 20,744, Kingstonian v Stockton, F.A. Amateur Cup Final 1933.
Best F.A. Cup season: 1st Rd replay 30-31 33-34. 1st Rd on 13 occasions; 25-31 32-38 48-49.
Record Fees - Paid: T Eames, G Allen   **Received:** Emeka Nwajiobi (Luton).
Record win: 13-0 v Walton-on-Thames, 37-38.
Record defeat: 1-10 v Hendon, 63-64.
Players progressing to Football League: W Bellamy (Spurs), A Solly (Arsenal), J Moseley & E Tozer (Millwall), G Pearce (Plymouth), Gordon Jago (Charlton 1951), Ron Crisp (Watford 1961), James Ryan (Charlton 1963), Emeka Nwajiobi (Luton 1983), Andy Gray (Crystal Palace 1984), C Richards (Bournemouth), Phil Coleman (Millwall 1986), Andy Perry (Portsmouth 1986).
Clubhouse: Open 7 days a week, 3 bars. Function rooms and meeting room available for hire. Gymnasium, squash courts (071 274 8707).
Club Record Goalscorer: Edgar Kail 427 (1919-33).
Club Record Appearances: Reg Merritt 571 (50-66).
92-93 Captain: John Egan
92-93 P.O.Y.: John Egan
92-93 Top scorer: Willie Lillington 15
Local Newspapers: South London Press (081 769 4444), S.E. London & Kentish Mercury (081 692 1122).
Honours: F.A. Amateur Cup 19-20 31-32 33-34 36-37, Isthmian Lg 19-20 25-26 32-33 48-49 (R-up(7) 21-22 23-24 29-31 33-34 46-47 58-59, Div 1 77-78), London Snr Cup 24-25 38-39 49-50 83-84 (R-up 05-06 07-08 20-21 27-28), Surrey Snr Cup(16) 04-06 08-10 19-20 22-23 24-25 27-28 33-34 36-37 46-47 49-50 57-59 73-75 (R-up(6) 11-12 31-33 37-38 50-51 67-68), London Chal. Cup R-up 91-92, London Charity Cup(12) 10-11(jt) 19-21 22-23 23-24(jt) 25-26 27-29 30-31(jt) 47-48 56-58, Surrey Snr Shield 72-73, Surrey Centen. Shld 77-78, Sth of the Thames Cup(4) 56-60, Southern Comb Cup 73-74, FA Tphy QF 79-80.

PROGRAMME DETAILS:
Pages: 36   Price: 70p
Editor: R Stanley

ENFIELD

Hendon 0, Enfield 0 - 28/12/92. Hendon's Simon Clark slips over in the penalty area and loses possession to an Enfield player. Photo - Paul Dennis.

Chairman: A Lazarou   **President:** T F Unwin.
Secretary: Alan Diment, 30 Apple Grove, Enfield, Middx EN1 3DD (081 363 6317).
Manager: Graham Roberts   **Asst Manager:** N/A   **Coach:** Paul Brush.
Press Officer: Lee Harding   **Physio:** M Banks
Marketing Mgr: Jonathon Moreland.
General Manager: Eddie McCluskey.   **Newsline:** 0891 122920.
Ground: The Stadium, Southbury Road, Enfield EN1 1YQ (081 292 0665).
Directions: At junction of A10 & A110. 800 yards from Southbury Road station. Buses from town centre.
Capacity: 8,500   **Cover:** 3,500   **Seats:** 820   **Shop:** Yes
Metal Badges: £2 - special club centenary badge.
Colours: White/blue   **Change colours:** Blue (white & red trim)
Sponsors: Cable London Plc.
Previous Leagues: Tottenham & Dist 1894-95/Nth Middx 96-1903/ London 03-13 20-21/Middx 08-12 19-20/ Athenian 12-14 21-39 45-63/Herts & Middx Comb 39-42/ Isthmian 63-81/ GMV Conference 81-90.
Previous Name: Enfield Spartans   **Prev. Ground:** Cherry Orchard Lane 1894-1914 1919-36.
Midweek matchday: Tuesday   **Reserve Team's League:** Capital.
Record Attendance: 10,000 (10/10/62) v Spurs, floodlight opener.
Best F.A. Cup season: 4th Rd replay 80-81 (lost 0-3 to Barnsley at Spurs (Att 35,244) after 1-1 draw).
League clubs beaten in F.A. Cup: Wimbledon, Northampton 77-78, Hereford, Port Vale 80-81, Wimbledon 81-82, Exeter 84-85, Orient 88-89, Aldershot 91-92.
Record Fees - Paid: For Gary Abbott (Barnet)
          Received: For Paul Furlong (Coventry City)
Players progressing to Football League: John Hollowbread & Peter Baker (Spurs 1952), Terry McQuade (Millwall 1961), Roger Day (Watford 1961), Jeff Harris (Orient 1964), Peter Feely (Chelsea 1970), Carl Richards (B'mouth 1980), Paul Furlong (Coventry 1991), Andy Pape (Barnet 1991).
Clubhouse: Starlight Suite. Bar open every lunch & evening, snacks available. Starlight nightclub, cabaret, dinner & dance.
Club Record Goalscorer: Tommy Lawrence
Club Record Appearances: Steve King 617
92-93 P.o.Y.: John Bailey.
92-93 Top scorer: John Bailey, 17.
Local Press: Enfield Gazette (081 367 2345), Enfield Advertiser, Enfield Independent, Enfield Town Express.
Hons: FA Tphy 81-82 87-88, FA Amtr Cup R-up 66-67 69-70 (R-up 63-64 71-72), GMV Conference 82-83 85-86 (R-up 81-82, Lg Cup R-up 81-82), Isthmian Lg(7) 67-70 75-78 79-80 (R-up(6) 64-65 71-72 74-75 80-81 90-92, Lg Cup(2) 78-80 (R-up 91-92)), Athenian Lg(2) 61-63 (R-up 34-35), London Lg Div 1 11-12 (R-up 04-05 06-07, Middx Snr Cup(13) 13-14 46-47 61-62 65-66 68-71 77-81 88-89 90-91 (R-up(12) 10-11 20-21 47-48 51-52 57-60 62-63 66-67 72-73 75-76 84-85), London Snr Cup(6) 34-35 60-61 66-67 71-73 75-76 (R-up 63-64 67-68 70-71), Middx Lg (West) 09-10 (R-up 10-11), European Amtr Cup Winners Cup 69-70.

HARROW BOROUGH
Diadora League Premier Division

£1

PROGRAMME DETAILS:
Pages: 24 **Price:** £1
Editor: Lee Harding

GRAYS ATHLETIC

The Blues

Grays Athletic 1992-93. Back Row (L/R): Peter Nicholls (Scout), Jason Walker, John Deadman, Winston Whittingham, Jeff Saxton (Twin Manager), Craig Tucker, Fred Saxton (Twin Manager), Jim Sheringham, Phil Sammons, Peter Carey (Coach), Vince Craven (Asst Manager). Front: Nicky Crown, Steve Ward, Ricky Walker, Barry Fox (Captain), Ian Brown, Andy Pask, Ian Durant, Ted Cribb (Physio).

Chairman: Frank Harris   **Twin Managers:** Fred & Jeff Saxton
Secretary: Jeff Saxton, 216 Thundersley Park Road, South Benfleet, Essex SS7 1HP (0268 756964).
Asst Manager: Vince Craven   **Physio:** Ted Cribb/Paul Smith   **Coach:** P Carey
Commercial Mgr: Leigh Windsor.   **Press Officer:** Gordon Norman (04024 51733)
Ground: Recreation Ground, Bridge Road, Grays RM17 6BZ (0375 391649).
Directions: Seven minutes walk from Grays station - turn right round one way system, right into Clarence Road, and at end into Bridge Road. Bus No. 370. By road - A13 towards Southend from London, take Grays exit and follow signs to town centre, keep left on one-way system, continue up hill for about half a mile, turn right into Bridge Road, ground half mile on right.
Capacity: 4,500   **Cover:** 1,200   **Seats:** 300   **Floodlights:** Yes   **Metal Badges:** Yes
Club Shop: Yes, selling official club history 'The First Hundred Years' (priced £6.95), club sweaters, T-shirts, replica shirts, mugs, scarves, ties, pennants, pens, key fobs, lapel badges, bookmarks, stickers, diaries. Contact Bill Grove (0875 391649).
Colours: Royal & white   **Change colours:** All yellow.
Sponsors: Cory Environmental, London Advertising Centre Ltd, Harris Commercials.
Previous Leagues: Athenian 12-14 58-83/ London 14-24 26-39/ Kent 24-26/ Corinthian 45-58.
Midweek home matchday: Tuesday   **Reserve Team's League:** Essex & Herts Border Comb.
Record Attendance: 9,500 v Chelmsford City, F.A. Cup Fourth Qualifying Round 1959.
Best F.A. Cup season: 1st Rd 51-52 88-89.
Record Fees - Paid: For Ian Durant (Canvey Island)
       Rec'd: Undisclosed for Tony Witter (C. Palace) and Dwight Marshall (Plymouth 1991).
Players progressing to Football League: John Jordan (Spurs 1947), Ray Kemp (Reading 1949), Barry Silkman & Tony Banfield (Orient), Gary O'Reilly (Spurs), Wayne Entwhistle (Bury 1983), Michael Welch (Wimbledon 1984), Tony Witter (C Palace 1990), Dwight Marshall (Plymouth 1991).
Clubhouse: Bar, pool, darts, bar snacks available. Indoor sports hall, en-tout-cas surface 70' x 120' (0375 377753). Bar open every day.
Steward: Pam & Peter Levett.
Club Record Goalscorer: Harry Brand 269 (1944-52)
Club Record Appearances: Phil Sammons, 515.
92-93 Captain: Barry Fox
92-93 P.o.Y.: Barry Fox.
92-93 Top scorer: Winston Whittingham, 28.
Local Newspapers: Thurrock Gazette (0375 372293)
Local Radio: BBC Essex, Radio Essex.
Hons: Isthmian Div 1 R-up 87-88 (Div 2 Sth 84-85, Lg Cup 91-92), Athenian Lg R-up 82-83 (Reserve Section R-up 58-59 (Cup R-up 59-60)), Corinthian Lg 45-46 (R-up 51-52 54-55 56-57, Lg Cup(2) 45-47, Mem. Shield(4) 45-47 77-78 79-80), L'don Lg 21-22 26-27 29-30 (R-up(4) 20-21 27-29 30-31, Lg Cup 36-37), Essex Snr Cup 14-15 20-21 22-23 44-45 56-57 87-88 (R-up(9) 19-20 23-24 25-26 52-55 57-58 65-66 88-89), East Anglian Cup 44-45 (R-up 43-44 54-55), Essex Thameside Tphy(6) 47-48 78-79 80-81 87-89 90-91 (R-up(6) 45-46 58-59 61-62 68-69 84-86), Essex Elizabeth Trophy 76-77 (R-up 65-66), Claridge Tphy 87-88 88-89, Mithras Cup 79-80, Essex Int Cup(3) 56-57 58-60 (Junior Cup 19-20 (R-up 58-59)), Essex & Herts Border Comb. East 87-88 (Ancillary Cup 78-79, Comb Cup 82-83), Fred Budden Tphy 86-87, Hornchurch Charity Cup 78-79 86-87, Neale Tphy 50-51, Ford Rate Tphy 83-84 85-86 87-88 (R-up 84-85 86-87).

PROGRAMME DETAILS:
Pages: 48 **Price:** 60p
Editor: Jeremy Mason
(0375 376428)

HARROW BOROUGH

Harrow Borough F.C. 1992-93. Back Row (L/R): Andy Prutton, Warren May, John Ridout, Phil Sheddon (Physio), George Borg (Manager), Dave Anderson (Asst Manager), Micky Engwell, Martin St Hilaire, Keith Cooper, Jason Shaw (Captain). Middle: Pat Ryan, Kenton Campbell, Dave Bensted, Andy Pape, Steve Conroy, Gerry Solomon, Mark Pye. Front: Paul Ripley, David Gipp.

Chairman: Martin Murphy   **Vice Chairman:** Jim Ripley   **President:** Jim Rogers
Secretary/Press Off.: Peter Rogers, 21 Ludlow Close, South Harrow, Middx HA2 8SR (081 422 8606).
Manager: George Borg   **Asst Manager:** Dave Anderson   **Physio:** Phil Sheddon
Ground: Earlsmead, Carlyon Avenue, South Harrow, Middx HA2 8SS (081 422 5989/5221).
Directions: Underground to Northolt (Central Line) then 140 or 282 bus, or to South Harrow (Piccadilly Line) then 114 or H10. By road leave A40 at Target PH towards Northolt station (A312 north), left at lights, right at next island, ground 5th turning on right.
Capacity: 3,070   **Cover:** 1,000   **Seats:** 200   **Floodlights:** Yes   **Metal Badges:** Yes.
Club Shop: Yes. Various items including programmes, scarves, badges, mugs, T-shirts, replica kits. Contact Bill Porter C/O The Club.
Colours: Red & white   **Change colours:** Yellow & blue   **Sponsors:** Rowan Erection.
Previous Leagues: Harrow & Dist 33-34/ Spartan 34-58/ Delphian 58-63/ Athenian 63-75.
Previous Names: Roxonian 1933-38/ Harrow Town 38-66.   **Previous Ground:** Northolt Road 33-34.
Midweek home matchday: Tuesday   **Reserve Team's League:** N/A
Record Attendance: 3,000 v Wealdstone, F.A. Cup 1st Qualifying Round 1946.
Best F.A. Cup season: 2nd Rd 83-84, lost 1-3 at home to Newport County.
League clubs defeated in F.A. Cup: None.
Record Fees - Paid: To Dagenham for George Duck & Steve Jones
       Received: £15,000 for Chris Hutchings (Chelsea)
Record win: 13-0 v Handley Page (A), Middlesex Snr Lg 18/10/41.
Record defeat: 0-8 on five occasions: Wood Green Town (A) Middx Lge 14/9/40, Met. Police (A) Spartan Lge 2/2/52, Briggs Spts (A) Spartan Lge 31/10/53, Hertford Town (A) Spartan Lge 24/4/56, Hendon (A) Middx Snr Cup 15/3/65.
Players progressing to Football League: Denis Russell (Arsenal 1946), Malcolm Lucas (Leyton Orient & Wales), Ron Shaw (Torquay 1947), Terry Eden (Raith Rovers 1948), Tom Carpenter (Watford 1950), Mike Bottoms (QPR 1960), Chris Hutchings (Chelsea 1980), Robert Holland (Crewe 1985), John Kerr (Portsmouth 1987), David Howell, Andy Pape & Eddie Stein (Barnet), David Byrne (Gillingham), Robert Rosario (Norwich), David Kemp (Crystal Palace), Mick Doherty (Reading), Dave Bassett (Wimbledon), Gary Borthwick (Bournemouth), Benny Laryea (Torquay).
Clubhouse: Open every day with normal licensing hours. Four bars, games room, varied entertainment venue for major sporting and social events. Hot and cold food available, buffets by prior request.
Club Record Scorer: Dave Pearce, 153
Club Record Appearances: Steve Emmanuel 478 (1st team only), Les Cunell 582, Colin Payne 557.
92-93 Captain: Jason Shaw
92-93 P.O.Y.: Micky Engwell
92-93 Top scorer: Steve Conroy, 26.
Local Papers: Harrow Observer (081 427 4404).
Local Radio: None.
Honours: Isthmian Lg 83-84 (Div 1 R-up 78-79), Athenian Lg Div 2 R-up 63-64, Spartan Lg R-up 57-58, Spartan Lg R-up 57-58 (Div 2 West 38-39 (R-up 37-38)), Middx Senior Cup 82-83 92-93, Harrow & Dist. Lg Div 1 R-up 33-34, Middx Charity Cup 79-80 92-93 (R-up 78-79), F.A. Trophy SF 82-83, F.A. Amateur Cup 2nd Rd 63-64.

HENDON
SATURDAY 2nd DAY of JANUARY 1986

**Official Programme
Season 1992/3**
70p

PROGRAMME DETAILS:
   Pages: 28 Price: £1
   Editor: Jim Rogers
     (081 422 8606)

HAYES

Hayes F.C. 1992-93. Back Row (L/R): Reg Leather (Asst Manager), Andy Cox, Steve Baker, Roy Marshall, Phil Wingfield, John Lawford, Ian Chatfield, Neil Henry, Clive Griffiths (Manager), Rod Haider (Coach). Front: Tony Kelly, Warren Kelly, John Stephen, Chris Walton, Andy Dear (Captain), Mick Cuffie. Photo - V J Robertson.

Chairman: Derek Goodall **Vice Chairman:** Alan Golby **President:** Les Lovering
Secretary: John Price, 18 Ickenham Court, West Ruislip, Middx HA4 7DJ (0895 631933).
Manager: Clive Griffiths **Asst Manager:** Carl Ballard **Coach:** T.B.A.
Press Officer: Alan Golby **Physio:** Carl Ballard.
Commercial Manager: T.B.A. **Sponsors:** McEwans Lager.
Ground: Townfield House, Church Road, Hayes, Middx UB3 2LE (081 573 4598).
Directions: M4 jct 3 onto Hayes bypass (The Parkway), A4020 to Hayes, 2nd major left turn (Church Rd), ground half mile on right. 1 mile from Hayes & Harlington (BR) - take bus H98 to Royal Oak pub. From Uxbridge tube station (Metropolitan line) take bus 207 to Adam & Eve pub opposite Church Rd.
Capacity: 9,500 **Cover:** 1,350 **Seats:** 450 **Floodlights:** Yes **Metal Badges:** Yes
Club Shop: Yes. Wide range of programmes (League and non-League). Replica kits, souvenirs, books and videos. Contact Lee Hermitage c/o Hayes F.C.
Cols: Red & white stripes/black/black **Change colours:** All blue
Prev. Lges: Local Lges 09-14/ Gt Western Suburban 19-22/ London 22-24/ Spartan 24-30/ Athenian 30-71.
Previous Ground: Botwell Common. **Previous Names:** Botwell Mission 1909-24.
Midweek home matchday: Tuesday **Reserve Team's League:** Suburban (North).
Record Attendance: 15,370 v Bromley, F.A. Amateur Cup, 10/2/51.
Best F.A. Cup season: 2nd Rd replay 72-73. 1st Rd 13 times 27-28 31-32 33-34 38-39 46-47 64-65 72-74 87-92.
League clubs defeated in F.A. Cup: Bristol Rovers 72-73, Cardiff 90-91, Fulham 91-92.
Record Fees - Paid: £6,000 for Gary Keen (Hendon, 1990).
Received: £30,000 for Les Ferdinand (Queens Park Rangers, 1987).
Players progressing to Football League: Cyril Bacon (Orient 1946), Phil Nolan (Watford 1947), Dave Groombridge (Orient 1951), Jimmy Bloomfield (Brentford 1952), Derek Neale & Les Champelover (Brighton 1956 & 57), Gordon Phillips (Brentford 1963, Robin Friday (Reading 1974), Les Smith (A Villa & England), Cyrille Regis (WBA 1977), Les Ferdinand (QPR 1987).
Clubhouse: (081 573 0933). Sat 12-3 & 4.45-11pm. Midweek matchnights 6.30-11pm. Some cold snacks available. Dancehall. Steward: Fred Heritage
Club Record Scorer: Unknown.
Club Record Appearances: Reg Leather, 701
92-93 Captain: Andy Dear
92-93 P.o.Y.: Roy Marshall
92-93 Top scorer: Phil Wingfield, Dave Pearce (20 each).
Local Newspaper: Hayes Gazette (0895 37161).
Local Radio Stations: Capital.
Honours: FA Amtr R-up 30-31 (SF 56-57), Isthmian Lg Cup R-up 78-79 80-81 87-88, Athenian Lg 56-57 (R-up 31-32 49-50), Spartan Lg 27-28 (R-up 25-26), Gt Western Suburban Lg(4) 20-24 (R-up 19-20), London Snr Cup 31-32 80-81 (R-up 36-37), Middx Snr Cup(8) 19-21 25-26 30-31 35-36 39-40 49-50 81-82, Middx Charity Cup (16 times), London Charity Cup 60-61, London Challenge Cup R-up 73-74, Middx Mnr Cup 11-12, FA Tphy QF 78-79, Premier Midweek f'lit Lge 75-76, Middx Premier Cup 86-87 87-88 88-89, Suburban Lg (Nth) 88-89 91-92 (Champions Cup 92-93).

HAYES FOOTBALL CLUB

THE DIADORA FOOTBALL LEAGUE

PREMIER DIVISION

HAYES F.C.

STEVENAGE BOROUGH F.C.

PROGRAMME DETAILS:
Pages: 24 Price: 80p
Editor: Committee

HENDON

Hendon F.C. 1992-93n Campbell, Victor Green (Chairman), Ronnie Duke (Coach), Paul Shirt, Andy Beattie, Kurt Davidson, Robbie Garvey, Dave Root, Adam King, Nigel Keen, Jude Monteath (Physio), Malcolm Stewart, Michael Cox (Secretary), Gwyn Walters (Manager). Front: Uche Egbe, Gary Keen, Roy Parkyn, Colin Sowerby, Marc Das, Tony Hopkins, Mark Xavier, Simon Clark.

Chairman: Victor Green   **Presidents:** Monty Hyams and Bobbie Butlin
Secretary: Graham Etchell, 63 Alexandra Rd, London NW4 2RX (081 203 4654).
Manager: Peter Taylor   **Asst Manager:** Allan Gemmell   **Coach:** Malcolm Stewart
Press Officer: Secretary   **Physio:** Jude Monteath, MCSP, SRP.
Commercial Manager: Dennis Pobjoy.
Ground: Claremont Road, Cricklewood, London NW2 1AE (081 201 9494 (Fax: 081 9055966)).
Directions: From Brent Cross tube station (Northern Line) to the east take first left after flyover on North Circular - Claremont Rd is then left at 3rd mini-r'bout. From Golders Green station (Northern Line) take bus 226 or 102. From Cricklewood main line station, turn left out of station and Claremont Rd is first left - ground half mile down on right. Buses 102, 210, 226 and C11 pass ground.
Capacity: 8,000   **Cover:** 5,500   **Seats:** 500   **Floodlights:** Yes   **Metal Badges:** Yes.
Club Shop: (081 455 2219 matchdays) Sells kit, bags, badges, pens, mugs, scarves, ties, programmes and other football souvenirs.
Colours: Green/white/green   **Change colours:** All yellow   **Sponsors:** TBA.
Previous Leagues: Finchley & Dist. 08-11/ Middx 10-11/ London 11-14/ Athenian 14-63.
Previous Names: Hampstead Town 08-33/ Golders Green 33-46.
Previous Grounds: Kensal Rise 08-12/ Avenue Ground, Cricklewood Lane 12-26.
Midweek matchday: Tuesday
Reserve Team's League: None.   **Record Gate:** 9,000 v Northampton, FA Cup 1st Rd 1952.
Record win: 13-1 v Wingate (H), Middx Senior Cup 2/2/57.
Record defeat: 2-11 v Walthamstow Avenue (A), Athenian League 9/11/35.
Best F.A. Cup season: 3rd Rd replay 73-74 (lost 1-4 to Newcastle at Watford after 1-1 draw away). 1st Rd (15) 34-35 52-53 55-56 60-61 64-67 69-71 72-74 75-76 77-78 81-82 88-89.
League clubs defeated in F.A. Cup: Reading 75-76.
Record Fees - Paid: £4,500 for Martin Duffield (Enfield).   **Received:** £30,000 for Iain Dowie (Luton).
Players progressing to Football League: Arnold Siegel (Orient 1946), William Dare (Brentford 1948), Roy Stroud (West Ham 1952), Miles Spector (Chelsea 1950), Jeff Darey (Brighton), Doug Orr (QPR 1957), Peter Shearing (West Ham 1960), Iain Dowie (Luton 1988), Peter Anderson (Luton), Jeff Harris (Orient), Phil Gridelet (Barnsley 1990), Gerry Soloman (Leyton Orient 1991).
Clubhouse: (081 455 9185 - contact Sally Brewster). Two bars and function hall open normal licensing hours 7 days a week. Hot & cold food, pool, darts, bingo, members club, satelite TV, entertainments. Available for private hire.
Club Record Goalscorer: Freddie Evans 176 (1929-35)
Club Record Apps: Bill Fisher 787 (1940-62).
92-93 Captain: Malcolm Stewart.
92-93 P.O.Y.: Simon Clark.
92-93 Top scorer: Barry Blackman.
Local Newspaper: Hendon Times (081 203 0411).
Local Radio Stations: Capital.
Hons: FA Amtr Cup 59-60 64-65 71-72 (R-up 54-55 65-66), European Amtr Champions 72-73, Isthmian Lg 64-65 72-73 (R-up 63-64 65-66 73-74, Lg Cup 76-77 (R-up 86-87)), Premier Inter-League Cup R-up 86-87, Middx Lge 12-13 13-14, Athenian Lg 52-53 55-56 60-61 (R-up 28-29 32-33 47-48 48-49 51-52), London Lg Div 1 R-up 12-13 (Amtr Div 13-14), Finchley & Dist. Lg 10-11, London Snr Cup 63-64 68-69 (R-up 35-36 50-51 54-55 58-59 71-72), Middx Snr Cup(11) 33-34 38-39 55-56 57-58 59-60 64-65 66-67 71-74 85-86 (R-up 83-84), Middx Charity Cup(14) 21-22 26-27 35-36 44-48 53-54 56-57 75-77 78-79 84-85 87-88, FA Tphy 3rd Rd replay 76-77 77-78, London Intermediate Cup 64-65 72-73 75-76 79-80 (R-up 63-64 68-69), Middx Intermediate 64-65 66-67 72-73, Suburban Lg 92-93 (R-up 84-85).

PROGRAMME DETAILS:
Pages: 54 **Price:** £1
Editor: Secretary

HITCHIN TOWN

Hitchin Town F.C. - Diadora League Division One champions 1992-93. Photo - Alan J Millard.

Chairman: Terry Barratt
Secretary: Alan Sexton, 66 Ninespring Way, Hitchin, Herts SG4 9NU (0462 456003).
Manager: Andy Melvin   **Coach:** Robin Wainwright
Press Officer: Neil Jensen (0462 454678(H) 071 4394545(B)   **Physio:** Peter Prince.
Newsline: 0898 122 934   **Commercial Manager:** Jack Russell
Ground: Top Field, Fishponds Road, Hitchin SG5 1NU (0462 459028).
Directions: On A505 near town centre opposite large green. 1 mile from Hitchin (BR).
Capacity: 4,000   **Cover:** 1,000   **Seats:** 400   **Floodlights:** Yes   **Metal Badges:** Yes.
Club Shop: Yes. Programmes etc. Contact Irvin Morgan.
Colours: Yellow/green/yellow   **Change:** Black & white stripes/black/black.
Sponsors: T.B.A.
Previous Leagues: South Eastern 01-08/ Spartan 09-11 28-39/ Athenian 45-63.
Midweek home matchday: Tuesday   **Reserve Team:** No.
Record win (in Isthmian League): 9-1 v Worthing (H), Division One, January 1991.
Record defeat (in Isthmian League): 0-10 v Kingstonian and v Slough Town.
Record Attendance: 7,878 v Wycombe Wanderers, F.A. Amateur Cup 3rd Rd 18/2/56.
Best F.A. Cup season: QF 1871-72. Also 2nd Rd replay (v Swindon) 1976-77, 2nd Rd (v Boston Utd) 73-74.
Record Fees - Paid: £2,000 for Ray Seeking (Potton United, 1989)
                Received: £6,000 for Steve Conroy (Kingstonian, 1990).
Players progressing to Football League: Reg Smith (Millwall & England skipper), Len Garwood (Spurs 1946), C J Walker, W Odell, S Foss, R Stevens, T Clarke, G Goodyear, L Harwood, P Burridge, Ray Kitchener (Chelsea 1954), D Bumstead, M Dixon, David Pacey (Luton 1956), Mike Dixon & Brian Whitby (Luton 1957), Keith Abiss (Brighton 1957), D Hille, G Ley, R Morton, L Payne (Newcastle & Reading), Micky Small (Brighton), Richard Nugent (Barnet).
Clubhouse: (0462 434483). Members' bar, kitchen and function hall (hireable). Open every day. Ample parking, new Ashe Boardroom (1985). Charrington's beer.
Club Record Goalscorer (in one season): Eddie Armitage 84, 1931-32.
Club Record Appearances: Paul Giggle 950+ 67-88.
92-93 Captain: Mark Burke
92-93 P.o.Y.: Steve Miller
92-93 Top scorer: Gary Williams.
Local Papers: Hitchin Gazette & Express (59651), Hitchin Comet (31666), Hitchin Herald & Post.
Local Radio Stations: Radio Chilton (0582 666766), BBC Radio Beds (0582 455555).
Hons: F.A. Amateur Cup SF 60-61 62-63, Isthmian Lg R-up 68-69 (Div 1 92-93), Spartan Lg 34-35, AFA Snr Cup 30-31, Herts Snr Cup(18-record) 1894-96 97-98 89-1900 02-03 04-05 09-10 30-32 33-34 37-39 40-41 42-43 61-62 69-70 74-77, London Snr Cup 69-70 (R-up 72-73), East Anglian Cup 72-73, Herts Charity Cup(16) 01-03 04-05 39-40 43-44 54-55 60-61 67-68 75-80, Herts I'mediate Cup(8) 39-40 46-47 48-49 56-57 60-62 67-69, Woolwich Tphy 82-83, Televised Sport International Cup 88-89 90-91, Southern Comb. Snr Floodlit Cup 90-91, F.A. Tphy 3rd Rd replay 76-77. Only Surviving FA founder member (1867).

PROGRAMME DETAILS:
Pages: 48 Price: 50p
Editor: Barry Swain

KINGSTONIAN

Liam Barham (far left) gets a header on target, but Peterborough United goalkeeper Ian Bennett saves during the F.A. Cup First Round replay at London Road. Kingstonian lost 9-1, but the match was declared void because their goalkeeper, Adrian Blake, was injured by a coin thrown from the Peterborough supporters' end. In the replayed game, behind closed doors, the First Division side could only manage a single goal win. Photo - Francis Short.

Chairman: Barry Chauveau   **Vice Chairman:** David Gardener.
Secretary: W R McNully, 71 Largewood Ave., Tolworth, Surbiton KT6 7NX (081 391 4552).
Manager: Chris Kelly   **Asst Manager:** N/A   **Coach:** Richard Parkin.
Press Officer: B P Frawley (081 541 5250)   **Physio:** Gary Scott
Ground: Kingsmeadow Stadium, Kingston Road, Kingston-on-Thames KT1 3PB (081 547 3335).
Directions: From town centre - Cambridge Rd on to Kingston Rd (A2043) to Malden Rd. Half mile from Norbiton (BR), one mile from Kingston (BR). Bus 131 passes the ground.
Capacity: 5,000   **Cover:** 1,000   **Seats:** 680   **Floodlights:** Yes   **Metal Badges:** Yes.
Club Shop: Yes, selling programmes and other souvenirs. Contact Mrs Jill Trevor (0932 561 790).
Cols: Red & white hoops/black/black   **Change colours:** All white   **Fanzine:** Yes.
Club Sponsors: General Portfolio.
Previous Lges: Kingston & Dist./ West Surrey/ Southern Suburban/ Athenian 1919-29.
Previous Names: Kingston & Surbiton YMCA 1885-87/ Saxons 87-90/ Kingston Wanderers 1893-1904/ Old Kingstonians 08-19.
Newsline: 0891 884 441.   **Prev. Ground:** Various to 1921/ Richmond Rd 21-89.
Midweek home matchday: Tuesday   **Reserve Team's League:** Suburban (South).
Record win: 15-1 v Delft, friendly 5/9/51 (competitive: 10-0 v Hitchin (H), Isthmian Lge 19/3/66).
Record defeat: 0-11 v Ilford (A), Isthmian Lge 13/2/37.
Record Attendance: 3,826 v Peterborough Utd, F.A. Cup 1st Rd 14/11/92. At Richmond Rd - 11,000 v Bishop Auckland, F.A. Amateur Cup 5/2/55.
Best F.A. Cup season: 1st Rd replay 31-32 (after 2-2 draw at Luton lost 2-3 at home), 92-93 (after 1-1 draw v Peterborough lost 0-1 away). 1st Rd on three other occasions; 1926 (0-1 at Nunhead), 1930 (0-3 at Tunbridge Wells), 1933 (1-7 at home to Bristol City).
League clubs defeated in F.A. Cup: None.
Record Fees - Paid: £12,000 for Richard Cherry (Grays Athletic, 1991)
            Received: £3,000 for Graham Drake (Hayes, 1980-81)
Players progressing to Football League: Carlo Nastri (Crystal Palace), Hugh Lindsay (Southampton 1965), Giles Still (Brighton 1979), David Byrne (Gillingham 1985), John Power (Brentford 1987).
Clubhouse: (081 547 3336). Open every lunchtime and evening. Three separate functions rooms with conference and banqueting facilities for all social and business events.
Club Record Goalscorer: Johnny Wing 295
Club Record Appearances: Micky Preston 555.
92-93 Captain: Adie Cowler/ David Harlow/ David Kempton.
92-93 P.o.Y.: David Harlow & John Finch (shared).
92-93 Top scorer: Francis Vines, 16.
Local Newspaper: Surrey Comet (081 546 2261).
Local Radio Stations: County Sound.
Hons: FA Amtr Cup 32-33 (R-up 59-60), Isthmian Lg 33-34 36-37 (R-up 47-48 62-63, Div 1 R-up 84-85), Athenian Lg 23-24 25-26 (R-up 26-27), London Snr Cup 62-63 64-65 86-87 (R-up 23-24 25-26 30-31 46-47 83-84), Surrey Snr Cup(9) 25-26 30-32 34-35 38-39 51-52 62-64 66-67 (R-up 90-91).

PROGRAMME DETAILS:
Pages: 32 **Price:** 80p
Editor: Ann Marie Dickinson
(081 547 3335)

MARLOW

Marlow in jubilant mood after they had capped a fine season by winning the League Cup, beat First Division Molesey in the final at Aldershot. Photo - Eric Marsh.

Chairman: Michael Eagleton   **Vice Chairman:** Terry Staines   **President:** Len Goodway.
Secretary: Paul Burdell, 69 Wycombe Road, Marlow, Bucks SL7 3HZ (0628 483722).
Manager: Dave Russell   **Coach:** Laurie Craker   **Physio:** Steve Jarrett
Press Officer: Terry Staines   **Commercial Manager:** Michael Eagleton.
Ground: Alfred Davis Memorial Ground, Oak Tree Road, Marlow SL7 3ED (0628 483970).
Directions: A404 to Marlow (from M4 or M40), then A4135 towards town centre. Turn right into Maple Rise (by ESSO garage), ground in road opposite (Oak Tree Rd). 1 mile from Marlow (BR). Beeline bus to Chapel Street.
Capacity: 3,500   **Cover:** 600   **Seats:** 250   **Floodlights:** Yes   **Metal Badges:** Yes
Club Shop: Yes, selling programmes, badges, ties, pens, videos, souvenirs.
Colours: Royal blue (white trim)   **Change colours:** Gold/black
Sponsors: Platts of Marlow.
Previous Leagues: Reading & Dist./ Spartan 1908-10 28-65/ Great Western Suburban/ Athenian 65-84.
Previous Name: Great Marlow.
Previous Grounds: Crown Ground (prior to 1919)/ Star Meadow 19-24.
Midweek home matchday: Tuesday   **Reserve Team's League:** Suburban.
Record Attendance: 8,000 Slough Town v Wycombe Wanderers, Berks & Bucks` Snr Cup Final 1973.
Best F.A. Cup season: Semi-Finals 1882. Also 3rd Rd 92-93 (lost 1-5 at Tottenham) and 1st Rd on 18 other occasions: 1871-85 86-88 92-93 1991-92.
Record Fees - Paid: £4,000 for Tim Buzaglo (Woking, 1993).
            Received: £5,000 for Al-James Hannigan (Enfield, 1993).
Players progressing to Football League: Leo Markham (Watford 1972), Naseem Bashir (Reading).
Clubhouse: Weekdays 7-11pm, matchdays 1-11pm. Snack bar open matchdays: rolls, sandwiches, pies, pasties, chips, drinks.
Club Record Goalscorer: Kevin Stone 31 (in one season)
Club Record Appearances: Mick McKeown 500+.
92-93 Captain: David Lay
92-93 P.o.Y.: John Caesar
92-93 Top scorer: David Lay
Local Newspapers: Marlow Free Press (0494 21212), Maidenhead Advertiser (0628 771155), Evening Post (0734 575833).
Local Radio Stations: Radio 210
Honours: Isthmian Lg Div 1 87-88 (Div 2 South R-up 86-87, Lg Cup 92-93), Spartan Lg Div 1 37-38 (Div 2 West 29-30), Berks & Bucks Senior Cup 1880-81 82-83 84-85 85-86 87-88 88-89 89-90 93-94 96-97 98-99 99-1900 90-91, FA Trophy 1st Rd 1987-88 91-92, FA Vase 5th Rd replay 74-75.

PROGRAMME DETAILS:
Pages: 36 Price: T.B.A.
Editor: Paul Birdell
(0628 483722)

MOLESEY

Molesey F.C. 1992-93. Back Row (L/R): R Winterhalter, D Rattue, B Penfold, S Donnelly, N Pearson, D Brace, M Rose, N Hopkins, D Pattulo, C Vidal, D Shepherd. Front: R Best (Coach), T McCoy, R Harmsworth, A Dunne (Manager), M Eede (Chairman), R Worrall, A Brilliant (Physio), R Higgs (Asst Manager). Photo - Dave West.

Chairman: Martin Eede **President:** Fred Maynard
Secretary: John Chambers, 293 Walton Rd, West Molesey, Surrey KT8 0JN (081 979 4454).
Manager: Tony Dunne **Physio:** Alan Brilliant **Coach:** Richard Higgs.
Press Officer: Peter Bowers (0420 89085). **Commercial Manager:** Ray Best.
Ground: 412 Walton Road, West Molesey, Surrey KT8 0JG (081 979 4823).
Directions: A3 from London to Hook, then A309 to Marquis of Granby pub, right to Hampton Court station, turn right for West Molesey, ground one mile on left.
Capacity: 4,000 **Cover:** 600 **Seats:** 400 **Floodlights:** Yes **Metal Badges:** Yes
Colours: White/black/black **Change colours:** Yellow/blue/yellow **Club Shop:** Yes.
Previous Leagues: Surrey Intermediate 53-56/ Surrey Snr 56-59/ Spartan 59-72/ Athenian 72-77.
Sponsors: Ivy Express Transport **Previous Name:** Molesey St Pauls 1950-53.
Midweek home matchday: Wednesday **Reserve Team's League:** Suburban.
Record Attendance: 1,255 v Sutton United, Surrey Senior Cup Semi-Final 1966.
Best F.A. Cup season: 3rd Qualifying Rd 76-77.
League clubs defeated in F.A. Cup: None.
Record Fees - Paid: £500 for Chris Vidal (Leatherhead, 1988)
  Received: £5,000 for Chris Vidal (Hythe Town, 1989).
Players progressing to Football League: John Finch (Fulham), Cyrille Regis (WBA, Coventry & England).
Clubhouse: Open every evening and weekend lunchtimes. 2 bars, discos, live artists, darts, bingo, pool.
Steward: John Chambers
Club Record Goalscorer: Michael Rose, 130
Club Record Appearances: Frank Hanley, 453
92-93 Captain: Roger Worrall.
92-93 P.o.Y.: Roger Worrall.
92-93 Top Scorer: Neil Pearson.
Local Newspapers: Surrey Comet, Surrey Herald, Molesey News.
Local Radio Stations: County Sound, Capital.
Honours: Isthmian Lg Div 1 R-up 92-93 (Div 2 South R-up 89-90, Lg Cup R-up 92-93), Surrey Senior Lg 57-58, (Lg Charity Cup 56-57), Spartan Lg R-up 59-60 (Lg Cup 61-62 (R-up 63-64)), Surrey Senior Shield R-up 74-75, Southern Combination Cup 90-91, FA Vase 6th Rd 81-82, FA Tphy 1st Rd replay 90-91.

PROGRAMME DETAILS:
Pages: 26 Price: 60p
Editor: Roger Bowers
(0420 89085)

ST ALBANS CITY

St Albans City celebrate their third cup in six weeks with a 4-1 win over Cambridge City in the final of the East Anglian Cup on 3rd May. Back Row (L/R): Peter Hayward (Physio), Derek Mardle (Coach), Steve Scott, Dean Williams, Steve Ketteridge, Kevin Mudd, Gary Westwood, Erskine Smart, Ian Rutherford, Bob Dowie, Shaun Brett, Mark Harvey, John Mitchell (Manager). Front: Jimmy King, Martin Duffield, Peter Risley, Allan Cockram, Martin Gurney, Steve Clark, John Harvey.

Chairman: Bernard Tominey   **Vice Chairman:** John Mitchell   **President:** Cllr Malcolm McMillan
Secretary: Steve Trulock, 42 Heath Road, St Albans AL1 4DP (0727 834920).
Manager: Steve Ketteridge   **Physio:** Andy Page   **Newsline:** 0891 664354
Press Officer: Dave Taverner (0582 401487)   **Commercial Manager:** John Colfer (0727 844555).
Ground: Clarence Park, York Rd, St Albans, Herts AL1 4PL (0727 866819).
Directions: Turn left out of St Albans station - Clarence Park 200yds ahead across Hatfield Rd. By road from M25 (clockwise) - jct 21 to Noke Hotel island, straight on thru Chiswell Green towards St Albans, straight over 2 mini-r'bouts and one larger island, thru two sets of lights and right at island at far end of city centre (St Peters Str.) into Hatfield Rd, over 1 mini-r'bout, left at 2nd lights into Clarence Rd, ground on left. From M25 (anticlockwise), jct 22 onto A1081 towards city centre, 3rd exit at 2nd island, thru two lights, right at island just before Odeon into Alma Rd, right at lights, straight thru next 2 sets (road bends considerably) into Clarence Rd, ground on left.
Capacity: 6,000   **Cover:** 1,900   **Seats:** 904   **Floodlights:** Yes   **Metal Badges:** Yes
Club Shop: Managed by Terry Edwards (0727 833685) and Ray Stanton. Large selection of club merchandise and League and non-League programmes. Magazines, videos etc.
Cols: Blue (old gold arms)/blue/blue (thick old gold band).   **Change cols:** Gold (green trim)/blue/gold.
Previous Leagues: Herts County 08-10/ Spartan 08-20/ Athenian 20-23.
Midweek home matchday: Tuesday   **Reserve Team's League:** Capital.
Record Attendance: 9,757 v Ferryhill Athletic, F.A. Amateur Cup QF 27/2/26 (won 4-1)
Record win: 14-0 v Aylesbury United (H), Spartan League 19/10/12 (3 Aylesbury players turned up just before half-time - St Albans led 9-0 at the interval).   **Record loss:** 0-11 v Wimbledon (H), Isthmian Lg 9/11/46.
Best F.A. Cup season: 2nd Rd replay 68-69 (lost 1-3 at Walsall after 1-1 draw), 80-81 (lost 1-4 at Torquay after 1-1 draw). Also 1st Rd 25-26 26-27 92-93.   **League clubs defeated in F.A. Cup:** Brentford 24-25.
Record Fees - Paid: £5,000 for Martin Duffield (Sutton United, March 1992)
Received: £45,000 for Tony Kelly (Stoke City, January 1990).
Players progressing to Football League: Ronnie Burke (Man Utd), John Meadows (W'ford 1951), Mike Rose (Charlton 1963), Lee Kinear (Spurs 1965), John Mitchell (Fulham 1972), Allan Cockram (Brentford 1988), Dean Austin (Southend 1990), Tony Kelly (Stoke 1990), Robert Peters (Brentford), Michael Danzey (Cambridge 1992).
Clubhouse: Tea bar within ground serves hot food. Clubhouse open matchdays and available for daytime and evening functions. Clubhouse manager, Ray McCord (0727 866819 or 837956).
Club Record Goalscorer: W H (Billy) Minter 365 (top scorer for 12 consecutive seasons 1920-32).
Club Record Appearances: Phil Wood 1,017 (63-84)
92-93 Captains: Peter Risley, Allan Cockram, Kevin Mudd, Martin Duffield.
92-93 P.o.Y.: Steve Clark   **92-93 Top scorer:** Steve Clark 45 (35 lge)
Local Newspapers: Herts Advertiser, St Albans Review, St Albans Herald, St Albans Observer. **Local Radio Stations:** BBC Radio Beds, Chiltern Radio.

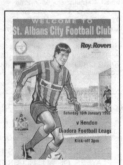

PROGRAMME DETAILS:
Pages: 48 Price: £1.20
Editor: Ray Stanton
(0727 864182)

Hons: Isthmian Lg 23-24 26-27 27-28 (R-up 54-55 92-93, Div 1 85-86, Div 2 R-up 83-84, Lg Cup R-up 89-90, Res. Sect. R-up 48-49 60-61 61-62), Athenian Lg 20-21 21-22 (R-up 22-23), Spartan Lg 11-12 (R-up 12-13, East Div 09-10), Herts Co. Lg 09-10 (West Div 08-09, Aubrey Cup(res) 61-62), London Snr Cup 70-71 (R-up 69-70), AFA Snr Cup 33-34 (R-up 30-31 32-33 34-35), E Anglian Cup 92-93, Herts Snr Cup(12) 24-25 28-29 34-35 43-44 46-47 50-51 54-57 65-66 67-69 (R-up 10-11 41-42 42-43 47-48 52-53 57-58 64-65 70-71 78-79 89-90), Herts Snr Tphy 86-87, Herts Charity Cup(25) 09-10 12-13 20-26 28-29 38-39 40-42 50-51 52-54 55-58 66-67 68-72 86-87 92-93 (R-up(18) 11-12 13-14 26-28 31-33 34-35 37-38 45-46 48-50 51-52 54-55 62-63 76-77 81-82 87-89), Mithras Cup 64-65 71-72 (R-up 76-77), Wycombe F'llt Cup(2) 68-70, St Albans Hosp Cup 45-46, Hitchin Centenary Cup 70-71 (R-up 71-72), Victory Cup 25-26 27-28, Liege Cup 26-27, Billy Minter Invit. Cup 90-91 91-92 92-93, FA Amtr Cup SF(4) 22-23 24-26 69-70, FA Tphy 2nd Rd 81-82 92-93 (1st Rd 86-87). *Res.:* Wallspan Southern Comb. 82-83 (R-up 83-84, Lg Cup 87-88 (R-up 83-84)), Herts I'mediate Cup(8) 47-48 49-50 50-51 53-54 57-58 62-64 66-67, Herts Jnr Cup 13-14, Bingham Cox Cup 12-13, Herts Charity Shld 24-25 31-32 37-38 (R-up 23-24 30-31). *Youth:* South Co's Yth Lg 91-92, MBS Lg 88-89, Kermat Lg Cup 87-88, Southern Co's Yth Cup R-up 91-92, FA Yth Cup 2nd Rd 91-92.

STEVENAGE BOROUGH

Stevenage Borough, pictured before their 3-1 win at Ruislip Manor in the F.A. Cup. Back Row (L/R): P Fairclough (Manager), R Lainchbury (Physio), N Blackwell, P Bowgett (Captain), R Wilmot, S Graham, I Furguson, N Trebble, M Gittings, P Peterson (Coach), R Brandon (Asst Coach). Front: E Richards (Man. Liaison Officer), M Smith, D Wood, D Brown, S Cook, S Cox, S Marshall. Photo - Eric Marsh.

Chairman: Ken Vale   **Vice Chairmen:** Keith Berners, John Jackson   **President:** Rod Resker
Secretary: John Jackson, 36 Kessingland Avenue, Stevenage, Herts SG1 2JR (0438 362045).
Manager: Paul Fariclough   **Asst Mgr:** Paul Peterson   **Coach:** Paul Peterson.
Press Officer: Martin Rosenberg (0438 743482)   **Physio:** Ray Lainchbury.
Commercial Manager: Mike Kitchener   **Treasurer:** Ken Solly.
Promotions Manager: Peter Taylor
Ground: Stevenage Stadium, Broadhall Way, Stevenage SG2 8RH (0438 367059).
Directions: Stevenage South exit off A1(M). Ground on right at second roundabout. One mile from Stevenage (BR). Buses SB4 and SB5.
Capacity: 6,000   **Cover:** 700   **Seats:** 500   **Floodlights:** Yes   **Metal Badges:** Yes.
Club Shop: Yes, selling programmes, scarves and other club merchandise. Contact Mrs Lynn Gamby.
Cols: Red & white stripes/red/red   **Change colours:** Blue   **Sponsors:** T.B.A.
Previous Leagues: Cliltern Youth 76-79/ Wallspan Southern Combination 79-80/ United Counties 80-84.
Midweek home matchday: Monday   **Reserves' League:** Essex & Herts Border Comb.
Record Gate: 3,000 v All Stars XI, May 1980. *(For league match: 1,551 v Hitchin, October 1991).*
Record win: 11-1 v British Timken Athletic (H), United Counties League 80-81.
Record defeat: 0-7 v Southwick (H), Vauxhall-Opel Isthmian League 87-88.
Best F.A. Cup season: Third Qualifying Rd replay 92-93 (lost at St Albans City).
League clubs defeated in F.A. Cup: None.
Players progressing to Football League: Richard Wilmot and Neil Trebble (both Scunthorpe, 1993).
Clubhouse: Open daily (lunch & evening). Dancehall, darts, pool. New clubhouse due to be constructed. Tea bar selling hot snacks within ground. Steward: Dave Wraight.
Club Record Scorer: Martin Gittings **Record Appearances:** Denny Tyler
92-93 Captain: Paul Bowgett
92-93 P.O.Y.: Mark Smith   **92-93 Top Scorer:** Martin Gittings
Local Newspapers: Stevenage Gazette, Comet, Herald & Post.
Local Radio Stations: Chiltern Radio, BBC Radio Bedfordshire.
Honours: Isthmian Lg Div 1 91-92 (Div 2 (North) 85-86 90-91), Utd Counties Lg Div 1 80-81 (Div 1 Cup 80-81), Herts Snr Cup R-up 85-86, Herts Charity Shield R-up 83-84, Televised Sports Snr Floodlit Cup 89-90, Eastern Professional F'llt Cup Group winners 81-82 85-86 86-87 88-89 90-91 91-92, South Co's Comb. Cup 91-92.

PROGRAMME DETAILS:
Pages: 40+ Price: T.B.A.
Editor: Simon Mortimer
(0438 725263)

SUTTON UNITED

Sutton United before the 4-1 win over Chalfont St Peter in the Second Round of the Diadora League Cup. Back Row (L/R): Nigel Golley, Steve Browne, Simon Quail, Gary Thomas, Andy Scott (now Sheffield United), Mark Costello, Paul Gates, Peter Byrne, Robert Scott. Front: Ron Fearon, Mark Jenkins, Robin Seagroatt, Phil Barton.

Chairman: David G Hermitage   **Vice Chairman:** Bruce Elliott   **President:** Andrew W Letts.
Secretary: Brian Williams, 49 Panmure Rd, Sydenham, London SE26 6NB (081 699 2721).
Manager: Alan Gane   **Asst Manager/Physio:** Frank Dotson.
Press Officer: Tony Dolbear   **Coach:** Richard Parkin.
Commercial Manager: Mike Baker.
Ground: Borough Sports Ground, Gander Green Lane, Sutton, Surrey SM1 2EY (081 644 5120/4440 Fax: 081 6445120).
Directions: Gander Green Lane runs between A232 (Cheam Road - turn by Sutton Cricket Club) and A217 (Oldfields Road - turn at 'Gander' PH lights). Ground opposite 'The Plough' 50 yards from West Sutton BR station. Bus 413 passes ground.
Capacity: 6,200   **Cover:** 1,800   **Seats:** 765   **Floodlights:** Yes   **Metal Badges:** Yes.
Club Shop: Open on matchdays selling full range of souvenirs, match programmes, scarves, hats, replica kits. Mail orders accepted - contact Paul Hedburn via club.
Colours: Amber (chocolate trim)   **Change colours:** White (chocolate trim).   **Sponsors:** Securicor.
Previous Leagues: Sutton Junior/ Southern Suburban 10-21/ Athenian 21-63/ Isthmian 63-86/ GMVC 86-91.
Previous Names: Sutton Association, Sutton Guild Rovers (merged in 1898).
Midweek home matchday: Tuesday   **Reserve Team's Lge:** Suburban. (Midweek: Capital).
Record Attendance: 14,000 v Leeds United, FA Cup 4th Rd 24/1/70.
Best F.A. Cup season: 4th Rd 69-70 88-89. Also 3rd Rd 87-88, 2nd Rd 81-82.
League clubs defeated in F.A. Cup: Aldershot, Peterborough 87-88/ Coventry City 88-89.
Record Fees - Paid: To Malmo FF for Paul McKinnon
Received: For Efan Ekoku (Bournemouth)/ Andy Barnes (Crystal Palace).
Players progressing to Football League: M Robinson (Crystal Palace), Charles Vaughan (Charlton 1947), Roy Hancox & Len Coules & Ray Colfar & Steven Galloway (Crystal Palace 1950 & 51 & 58 & 84), T Barton (Fulham), Phil Woosnam (Orient 1955), Derek Gamblin (Portsmouth 1965), Mike Pentecost (Fulham 1966), John Faulkner (Leeds 1970), Mike Mellows (Reading 1970), Mick Fillery (Chelsea & QPR), Frank Cowley (Derby 1977), Paul McKinnon (Blackburn 1986), Ron Fearon (I'wich 1987), Paul Harding (Notts Co via Barnet), Efan Ekoku (Bournemouth 1991), Mark Golley (Maidstone), Andy Barnes (Crystal Paleace 1991), Paul Rogers (Sheffield Utd 1992), Stuart Massey (Crystal Palace 1992), Andy Scott (Sheffield United 1993).
Clubhouse: Open every day, normal pub hours, when sandwiches and hot meals are available. Halls and meeting rooms for hire.
Club Record Scorer: Paul McKinnon
Club Record Appearances: Larry Pritchard 781 (1965-84)
92-93 Captain: Nigel Golley
92-93 P.O.Y.: Paul Gates.
92-93 Top scorer: Dominic Feltham
Local Newspapers: Sutton Herald, Croydon Advertiser, Sutton Guardian.
Hons: Alliance Prem. Lg Bob Lord Trophy 90-91, FA Trophy R-up 80-81 (SF 92-93), FA Amtr Cup R-up 62-63 68-69 (SF 28-29 36-37 67-68), Isthmian Lg(3) 66-67 84-86 (R-up 67-68 70-71 81-82, Lg Cup(3) 82-84 85-86 (R-up 79-80), Loctite Cup 91-92), Athenian Lg 27-28 45-46 57-58 (R-up 46-47, Lg Cup 45-46 55-56 61-62 62-63, Reserve Section 61-62 (R-up 32-33)), Anglo Italian Semi-Pro Cup 1979 *1st British winners* (R-up 1980 1982), London Snr Cup 57-58 82-83, London Charity Cup 69-70 (R-up(3) 67-69 72-73), Surrey Snr Cup(12) 45-46 64-65 67-68 69-70 79-80 82-88 92-93 (R-up(8) 44-45 54-55 61-64 65-66 75-76 81-82), Surrey Prem. Cup 82-83 92-93 (R-up 85-86 88-89), Surrey Intermediate Cup 66-67 71-72 78-79 81-82 (R-up 49-50 51-52 59-60 61-62 64-65 74-75), Surrey Jnr Cup R-up 09-10, Surrey Snr Charity Shield(3) 33-34 36-38 (R-up 21-22 23-24 30-31 34-35 38-39 59-60, Surrey Intermediate Charity Cup 31-32 (R-up 34-35 38-39), Dylon Charity Shield 1984 (R-up 1980 1982 1983 1985), Suburban Lg 74-75 77-78 78-79 81-82 83-84 84-85 85-86 91-92 (R-up 71-72 72-73 80-81 92-93, Lg Cup 80-81 (R-up 86-87)), Southern Youth Lg 86-87 87-88 88-89 (R-up 84-85 91-92, Lg Cup 86-87 (R-up 84-85 85-86 88-89)), Groningen Yth tournament 1983 1985 (R-up 1979 1981 1989 1991), John Ullman Invitation Cup 88-89.

PROGRAMME DETAILS:
Pages: 48 Price: £1
Editor: Tony Dolbear

Formed: 1925   # WIVENHOE TOWN   The Dragons

Wivenhoe Town's Broad Lane ground. Photo - Nigel Upson.

Chairman: David Watts   **Vice Chairman:** Lewis Parnell.
Secretary: Ron Bennett, 20 Belle Vue Rd, Wivenhoe, Essex (0206 822596).
Manager: Chris Symes   **Asst Manager:** Keith Smith
Ground: Broad Lane Ground, Elmstead Road, Wivenhoe CO7 7HA (0206 823416).
Directions: Coming out of Colchester towards Clacton take first turning (right) towards Wivenhoe, first left and ground clearly visible on right at cross-roads. 1 mile from Wivenhoe (BR).
Capacity: 3,000   **Cover:** 1,300   **Seats:** 250   **Floodlights:** Yes   **Metal Badges:** Yes
Club Shop: Yes, selling club scarves, key rings, pens, bobble hats, car stickers, metal badges, handbooks plus non-League and Football League programmes and magazines.
Colours: Royal/white/royal   **Change colours:** All white
Previous Leagues: Brighlingsea & District 1927-50/ Colchester & East Essex 50-71/ Essex & Suffolk Border 71-79/ Essex Senior 79-86.
Previous Grounds: Spion Kop/ Broomfield/ Claude Watcham's Meadow/ Vine Farm/ Spion Kop/ Broomfield/ King George V Playing Fields/ Essex University.
Midweek matchday: Monday   **Reserve Team's League:** Essex & Herts Border Comb.
Record Attendance: 1,912 v Runcorn, FA Trophy 1st Rd, Feb 1990.
Best F.A. Cup season: 4th Qual Rd 89-90 (lost 2-3 at Halesowen Town).
Record Fees - Paid: N/A   **Received:** £5,875 for Bobby Mayes (Redbridge Forest).
Record win: 18-0 v Nayland.   **Record defeat:** 0-7 v Brantham Athletic.
Players progressing to Football League: None.
Clubhouse: (0206 825380). Open normal pub hours.
Club Record Goalscorer: Paul Harrison, 258 goals in 350 games.
Club Record Appearances: Keith Bain, 536.
92-93 Captain: Steve Wright
92-93 P.o.Y.: Steve Dowman
92-93 Top scorer: M Springett.
Local Newspapers: East Anglian Daily Times, Colchester Evening Gazette.
Local Radio Stations: BBC Radio Essex, Radio Orwell, BBC TV (Norwich).
Hons: FA Tphy 2nd Rd replay 89-90, FA Vase 5th Rd 82-83, Isthmian Lg Div 1 89-90 (Div 2 Nth 87-88), Essex Snr Lg R-up 79-80 81-82 85-86 (Harry Fisher Tphy 83-84 85-86), Essex & Suffolk Border Lg 78-79 (Div 1 72-73, Div 2 71-72, Lg Cup R-up(2) 75-77), Colchester & East Essex Lg 52-53 55-56 (R-up 70-71, Div 1 59-60 69-70, Div 2 R-up 68-69, Lg KO Cup 51-52 52-53 54-55 55-56 (R-up 59-60), Challenge Cup 52-53), Brighlingsea & Dist Lg Div 1 35-36 36-37 47-48 (R-up 37-38, Lg KO Cup 36-37 37-38 47-48, Challenge Cup 36-37), Essex Snr Tphy 87-88, Essex Jnr Cup R-up 55-56 78-79 (Group Finalists(3) 52-53 70-72), Amos Charity Cup(7) 36-38 51-56 (R-up 72-73), Stokes Cup(3) 48-49 52-54, Wivenhoe Charity Cup 52-53 68-69 73-74 78-79 (R-up 55-56 65-66 69-70 72-73), Cristal Monopole Cup 68-69 78-79 79-80 80-81 81-82 (R-up 65-66 67-68), Sidney James Mem. Tphy 69-70 (R-up 72-73), Tolleshunt D'Arcy Mem. Cup(3) 71-74 (R-up 70-71 77-78), Walton & District Charity Cup 73-74 78-79, Coggeshall Brotherhood Cup 80-81, Brantham Charity Cup R-up 82-83, Worthington Evans Cup 81-82 (R-up 80-81 85-86), Harwich Snr Cup R-up 84-85, Woodbridge Chal. Cup 91-92, Mat Fowler Shield 92-93.

WIVENHOE TOWN F.C.

Season 1991/92
Price 50p

PROGRAMME DETAILS:
Pages: 20+ **Price:** £1
Editor:

WOKINGHAM TOWN

Wokingham Town goalkeeper Peter Scrivens is at full stretch to stop a Dulwich attack. Wokingham lost 1-2 in this the first night game at Dulwich's refurbished ground. Photo - Dave West.

Chairman: P Walsh   **Vice Chairman:** R Croyden   **President:** G Gale.
Secretary: John Aulsberry, 8 Paice Green, Wokingham RG11 1YN (0734 790441).
Manager: Roy Merryweather   **Asst Manager:** Terry Brown   **Coach:** Terry Brown
Press Officer: John Ansell (0734 787699)   **Physio:** Dave Lane
Commercial Manager: Roy Merryweather (0734 780253).
Ground: Town Ground, Finchampstead Road, Wokingham, Berks RG11 2NR (0734 780253).
Directions: Half mile from town centre on A321 (signed Camberley & Sandhurst) Finchampstead Rd - walk down Denmark Street to swimming pool and straight on onto Finchampstead Rd. Half mile from Wokingham (BR) - turn right out of station, walk along Wellington Rd to swimming pool, right into Finchampstead Rd - ground entrance on right immediately after railway bridge.
Capacity: 4,500   **Cover:** 1,500   **Seats:** 250   **Floodlights:** Yes   **Metal Badges:** Yes.
Club Shop: Progs, scarves, magazines & club souvenirs. Contact Brian & Sue McKeown at club on matchdays.
Colours: Amber/black/black   **Change colours:** Red/white/red.
Sponsors: Wokingham Pet Shop.
Previous Leagues: Reading & Dist./ Great Western Comb 07-54/ Metropolitan 54-57/ Delphian 57-59/ Corinthian 59-63/ Athenian 63-73.
Previous Grounds: Oxford Road 1875-1883/ Wellington Road 83-96/ Langborough Rd 96-1906.
Midweek home matchday: Tuesday   **Reserve Team's Leagues:** Suburban, Capital.
Record Attendance: 3,473 v Norton Woodseats, FA Amateur Cup 57-58.
Best F.A. Cup season: 1st Rd replay 82-83 (lost 0-3 at Cardiff after 1-1 draw).
League clubs defeated in F.A. Cup: None.
Record Fees - Paid: £5,000 for Fred Hyatt (Burnham, 1990)
             Received: £25,000 for Mark Harris (Crystal Palace, 1988).
Players progressing to Football League: Ian Kirkwood (Reading 1953), John Harley (Hartlepool 1976), Kirk Corbin (Cambridge 1978), Phil Alexander (Norwich 1981), Doug Hatcher (Aldershot 1983), Steven Butler & George Torrance (Brentford 1984), Mark Harris (Crystal Palace 1988), Gary Smart (Oxford 1988), Darren Barnard (Chelsea 1990), Paul Holsgrove (Luton Town 1991).
Clubhouse: Mon-Sat 12-3 & 7-11pm (12-3 & 4.30-11pm Sat matchdays), Sun 12-2.30pm. Hot & cold food & snacks.
Club Record Goalscorer: Dave Pearce, 79.
Club Record Appearances: Dave Cox, 533.
92-93 Captain: Andy McKenzie.
92-93 P.O.Y.: Tommy Langley
92-93 Top scorer: Tommy Langley, 21
Local Newspapers: Wokingham Times (782000), Wokingham News (Bracknell 20363), Reading Evening Post (55875).
Local Radio Stations: Radio 210.
Honours: Isthmian Lg R-up 89-90 (Div 1 81-82), Berks & Bucks Snr Cup 68-69 82-83 84-85, Berks & Bucks Intermediate Cup 52-53, FA Tphy SF 87-88, FA Amtr Cup 4th Rd 57-58.

PROGRAMME DETAILS:
Pages: 32 **Price:** 80p
Editor: Mrs Anne Gale
(c/o the club)

YEADING

A flash-back to Yeading's triumphant F.A. Vase year of 1990; action from their decisive 2-0 home leg victory against Hythe Town in the Semi-Finals. Photo - Francis Short.

Chairman: Phillip Spurden **Vice Chairman:** Steve Perryman **President:** Mr R Carter
Secretary: Peter Bickers, 140 Hercies Rd, Hillingdon, Middx (0895 811061).
Manager: Gordon Bartlett **Asst Manager:** Leo Morris **Coach:** W Wordsworth.
Press Officer/Commercial Manager: Neil Roberts **Physio:** Edward Cole
Ground: The Warren, Beaconsfield Road, Hayes, Middx (081 848 7362).
Directions: Two miles from Hayes (BR) - take Uxbridge Road and turn right towards Southall, right into Springfield Road and then left into Beaconsfield Road. Bus 207 stops half mile from ground.
Capacity: 3,000 **Cover:** 300 **Seats:** 100 **Shop:** Planned **Metal Badges:** Yes
Colours: Red & black stripes/black/black **Change colours:** All white.
Sponsors: Heineken.
Previous Leagues: Hayes & District Yth/ Uxbridge/ S W Middx 1967-74/ Middx 74-84/ Spartan 1984-87.
Midweek home matchday: Tuesday **Reserve Team's League:** None.
Record Attendance: 3,000 v Hythe Town, F.A. Vase SF 1990.
Best F.A. Cup season: 4th Qualifying Rd.
League clubs defeated in F.A. Cup: None.
Record Fees - Paid: **Received:**
Players progressing to Football League: None.
Clubhouse: Open normal pub hours.
Club Record Goalscorer: D Burt 327
Club Record Appearances: Norman Frape.
92-93 Captain: Steve Croad.
92-93 P.o.Y.: Phil Dicker.
92-93 Top scorer: Lee Charles 15.
Local Newspapers: Hayes Gazette.
Honours: F.A. Vase 89-90, F.A. Tphy 3rd Qual. Rd 90-91, Isthmian Lg Div 2 Sth 89-90 (Div 1 R-up 91-92), Spartan Lg 86-87 (R-up 85-86, Senior Div R-up 84-85, Lg Cup 85-86 86-87), Middx Snr Lg(6) 71-73 74-76 81-82 83-84 (R-up 73-74 74-75 78-79, Lg Cup(6) 72-73 75-76 79-83), South West Middx Lg(2) 69-71, Middx Snr Cup 89-90 91-92, Middx Prem. Cup 80-81, Middx I'mediate Cup(5) 70-72 74-76 77-78, Middx Jnr Cup(4) 68-69 70-72 74-75, Uxbridge Lg 66-67, Middx Border Lg Cup 86-87 (AJA Cup 86-87), Suburban Lg Nth 87-88, Allied Counties Yth Lg 89-90 (Lg Cup 89-90).

1992/1993 PROGRAMME

Yeading FC
POWERED BY
WINGS LUXURY TRAVEL LTD.

70p

PROGRAMME DETAILS:
Pages: 36 Price: £1
Editor: Les Pratt

First Division

	P	HOME			AWAY			F	A	Pts
		W	D	L	W	D	L			
HITCHIN TOWN	40	14	3	3	11	4	5	67	29	82
MOLESEY	40	12	5	3	11	6	3	81	38	80
DORKING	40	14	0	6	9	9	2	73	40	78
PURFLEET	40	11	7	2	8	5	7	67	42	69
BISHOPS STORTFORD	40	12	3	5	7	7	6	63	42	67
ABINGDON TOWN	40	8	7	5	9	6	5	65	47	64
TOOTING & MITCHAM	40	12	5	3	5	7	8	68	46	63
BILLERICAY TOWN	40	12	4	4	6	2	12	67	61	60
WEMBLEY	40	7	8	5	7	7	6	44	34	57
WALTON & HERSHAM	40	9	5	6	5	7	8	58	54	54
BOREHAM WOOD	40	5	8	7	7	6	7	44	43	50
MAIDENHEAD UTD	40	8	8	4	2	10	8	45	50	48
LEYTON	40	7	7	6	4	7	9	56	61	47
WHYTELEAFE	40	8	6	6	4	4	12	63	71	46
UXBRIDGE	40	7	7	6	4	6	10	50	59	46
HEYBRIDGE SWIFTS	40	6	2	12	5	7	8	47	65	42
CROYDON	40	7	6	7	4	3	13	54	82	42
CHALFONT ST.PETER	40	5	11	4	2	6	12	48	70	38
BARKING	40	6	5	9	4	3	13	42	80	38
LEWES	40	5	5	10	4	5	11	34	80	37
AVELEY	40	4	6	10	5	1	14	45	87	34

Top League Goalscorers

Mark Hynes (Whyteleafe)	30
Steve Lunn (Dorking)	22
Neil Pearson (Molesey)	22
John Collins (Tooting & Mitcham United)	21
Steve Jones (Billericay Town)	18
Michael Rose (Molesey)	18

THE FIRST DIVISION RESULT CHART 1992-93

HOME TEAM	1	2	3	4	5	6	7	8	9	10	11	12	13	14	15	16	17	18	19	20	21
1. Abingdon	*	4-1	1-2	4-1	1-1	2-1	5-1	1-1	1-1	2-5	0-1	4-0	2-2	0-0	0-2	3-3	1-1	0-1	2-1	2-0	4-2
2. Aveley	1-5	*	2-2	0-2	1-0	0-2	2-1	1-3	1-3	2-2	1-1	4-0	1-3	3-3	2-3	0-2	2-2	0-0	1-4	0-1	2-1
3. Barking	1-0	2-1	*	1-1	1-2	1-0	2-1	1-2	0-2	1-2	0-0	1-2	3-1	1-0	0-5	0-2	0-1	1-1	1-1	1-1	0-1
4. Billericay	0-1	2-0	3-2	*	4-0	2-2	4-0	3-2	1-3	2-1	0-2	1-1	1-3	3-2	2-0	3-0	2-1	4-2	1-1	3-1	
5. Bishops S.	0-1	3-0	5-1	4-1	*	1-0	1-1	2-0	1-2	2-1	0-1	6-0	3-3	0-0	1-2	1-0	2-1	1-1	2-0	0-1	3-2
6. Boreham W.	2-1	3-0	5-1	2-1	0-1	*	2-2	0-1	0-0	1-1	0-1	2-0	1-1	2-2	0-0	0-0	0-4	0-1	0-2	0-2	1-1
7. Chalfont	2-2	2-2	3-0	2-0	2-2	1-1	*	1-1	2-2	0-1	0-1	4-1	1-1	1-1	1-1	2-2	2-1	0-1	0-2	2-1	1-1
8. Croydon	0-0	1-2	1-0	0-4	3-2	4-3	2-4	*	1-1	5-0	0-3	2-2	2-2	3-3	0-3	0-5	2-1	1-1	1-2	1-0	4-2
9. Dorking	0-1	4-2	7-0	2-1	1-0	0-2	4-1	2-1	*	2-1	1-0	5-0	2-1	1-0	1-2	0-1	3-1	1-0	4-0	1-3	2-3
10. Heybridge	0-1	1-2	2-1	1-2	0-1	1-1	0-2	3-0	0-2	*	0-7	1-2	2-3	0-1	2-1	0-1	1-2	1-0	3-3	1-0	2-1
11. Hitchin	1-1	3-0	3-2	2-1	2-3	1-0	6-0	2-0	1-2	1-0	*	1-0	2-0	1-1	2-0	3-1	2-1	1-2	0-0	3-0	
12. Lewes	0-3	0-1	1-2	2-0	2-1	0-0	1-1	3-0	1-1	1-3	0-2	*	1-0	0-0	3-5	0-1	0-2	2-0	2-2	0-3	0-2
13. Leyton	0-1	2-1	0-1	2-2	0-1	1-0	2-1	0-2	0-0	2-0	0-0	*	1-1	2-4	4-1	2-0	4-4	1-1	0-3	5-0	
14. Maidenhead	0-0	1-0	3-4	3-1	0-2	1-1	2-2	1-0	0-1	0-0	2-3	4-0	1-0	*	0-0	2-2	1-1	1-0	3-1	0-0	3-0
15. Molesey	2-1	1-2	2-0	4-1	0-0	1-2	4-0	4-2	1-1	3-1	0-0	0-1	2-0	2-0	*	2-1	2-2	4-0	2-0	1-1	5-1
16. Purfleet	0-1	2-1	2-0	2-2	2-0	1-0	0-0	3-1	2-0	1-2	3-1	3-0	2-3	2-2	*	1-1	3-3	0-0	2-1	1-1	
17. Tooting & M	5-0	1-0	6-1	2-0	0-1	0-0	1-0	6-0	1-0	1-1	2-0	6-1	1-1	3-0	1-1	0-4	*	3-2	2-1	1-1	2-6
18. Uxbridge	0-1	4-1	2-0	3-2	1-1	1-4	3-2	3-2	1-2	2-1	1-2	1-1	1-1	1-1	1-1	1-1	0-2	*	0-0	2-3	2-0
19. Walton & H.	2-2	6-0	1-2	0-2	0-0	3-0	1-1	0-1	3-0	2-2	2-1	1-2	4-1	2-1	0-2	1-3	0-0	1-0	*	1-0	3-2
20. Wembley	3-2	3-1	1-1	3-0	1-1	0-1	2-0	1-0	1-1	0-2	1-1	1-1	0-2	1-2	0-1	1-1	1-0	0-0	1-1	*	0-0
21. Whyteleafe	0-2	3-1	2-2	0-1	1-2	1-2	3-0	3-3	2-2	1-1	1-0	4-0	4-2	5-1	1-2	1-0	1-1	1-3	2-0	0-0	*

THE DIADORA LEAGUE FIRST DIVISION ATTENDANCE CHART 1992-93

HOME TEAM	1	2	3	4	5	6	7	8	9	10	11	12	13	14	15	16	17	18	19	20	21
1. Abingdon T	*	209	197	202	165	232	126	127	171	204	256	130	136	220	157	102	186	218	226	145	203
2. Aveley	105	*	148	225	125	155	72	95	115	103	125	85	85	85	105	210	105	85	95	90	80
3. Barking	93	57	*	137	108	137	90	56	98	103	196	67	75	79	71	102	55	64	61	79	83
4. Billericay	246	329	305	*	341	252	304	249	307	465	312	274	256	257	286	327	302	261	326	330	277
5. B Stortford	318	319	305	320	*	317	298	308	295	322	301	364	328	323	261	302	362	325	252	240	308
6. Boreham Wd	148	71	126	139	167	*	108	92	162	55	180	81	129	107	72	171	62	71	69	102	
7. Chalfont SP	108	72	135	198	135	105	*	84	165	95	280	101	75	173	101	82	113	200	85	119	121
8. Croydon	45	36	49	50	80	75	28	*	85	46	43	63	70	70	52	48	78	44	121	60	150
9. Dorking	312	256	254	252	249	187	89	192	*	230	193	193	285	257	414	271	312	153	183	283	231
10. Heybridge	168	123	149	286	184	138	151	129	145	*	156	146	104	104	128	128	148	162	144	152	146
11. Hitchin T.	292	415	297	584	561	543	580	253	746	417	*	268	289	378	393	280	265	804	427	279	446
12. Lewes	154	169	127	185	159	101	147	117	132	112	122	*	80	122	122	71	97	90	122	94	110
13. Leyton	102	97	140	177	167	111	124	124	114	127	147	113	*	114	122	85	152	77	98	118	106
14. Maidenhead	202	144	169	207	154	177	173	166	162	151	167	156	182	*	159	127	209	166	156	201	165
15. Molesey	105	65	75	105	129	65	180	137	237	189	204	99	105	128	*	86	79	70	236	84	80
16. Purfleet	79	312	157	286	262	79	86	103	123	135	197	97	88	178	183	*	142	105	135	93	123
17. Tooting	64	155	139	245	121	92	125	134	203	125	165	128	148	141	225	78	*	148	145	86	155
18. Uxbridge	140	128	100	151	108	97	168	97	130	92	170	128	96	160	111	134	103	*	103	105	92
19. Walton & H.	119	149	129	176	151	124	105	132	143	123	122	126	81	144	252	141	156	145	*	96	131
20. Wembley	76	104	102	115	107	72	101	61	120	82	130	78	82	110	78	87	*	82			
21. Whyteleafe	93	131	100	173	187	87	74	175	118	70	98	91	102	134	207	130	125	102	118	100	*

Div. One 10-year record	83/4	84/5	85/6	86/7	87/8	88/9	89/90	90/1	91/2	92/3
Abingdon Town	-	-	-	-	-	-	-	-	6	6
Aveley	12	13	22	-	-	-	-	4	21	21
Barking	-	-	-	-	-	-	-	-	12	19
Basildon United	-	16	18	12	7	21	-	-	-	-
Basingstoke Town	-	-	-	-	-	2	-	-	-	-
Billericay Town	-	-	-	-	13	20	-	-	-	8
Bishop's Stortford	-	-	-	-	-	-	-	-	-	5
Boreham Wood	5	17	9	8	4	11	7	14	4	11
Bracknell Town	-	-	-	3	19	20	-	-	-	-
Bromley	-	8	2	-	-	-	-	2	-	-
Chalfont St Peter	-	-	-	-	-	16	11	11	13	18
Chesham United	9	4	20	-	18	14	10	1	-	-
Cheshunt	21	-	-	-	-	-	-	-	-	-
Clapton	20	21	-	-	-	-	-	-	-	-
Collier Row	-	-	-	-	-	19	-	-	-	-
Croydon	-	-	-	-	-	-	17	17	18	17
Dorking	-	-	-	-	-	-	6	10	11	3
Dulwich Hamlet	-	-	-	-	-	-	-	12	3	-
Epsom & Ewell	2	-	-	20	-	-	-	-	-	-
Farnborough Town	6	1	-	-	-	-	-	-	-	-
Feltham	22	-	-	-	-	-	-	-	-	-
Finchley	-	-	13	22	-	-	-	-	-	-
Grays Athletic	-	-	14	6	2	-	-	-	-	-
Hampton	7	9	5	11	9	17	19	-	-	-
Harlow Town	-	-	21	-	-	-	8	13	17	-
Hertford Town	14	22	-	-	-	-	-	-	-	-
Heybridge Swifts	-	-	-	-	-	-	-	18	19	16
Hitchin Town	-	-	-	-	-	4	4	5	8	1
Hornchurch	18	18	19	-	-	-	-	-	-	-
Kingsbury Town	-	-	-	7	14	8	22	-	-	-
Kingstonian	19	2	-	-	-	-	-	-	-	-
Leatherhead	11	3	15	10	10	12	20	-	-	-
Lewes	16	15	11	15	16	6	15	20	-	20
Leytonstone-Ilford	-	-	12	1	-	-	-	-	-	-
Leyton (-Wingate)	-	-	6	2	-	-	-	-	14	13
Maidenhead United	4	11	17	21	-	-	-	-	16	12
Marlow	-	-	-	-	1	-	-	-	-	-
Metropolitan Police	8	20	-	-	-	13	9	21	-	-
Molesey	-	-	-	-	-	-	-	8	10	2
Oxford City	15	14	4	17	12	-	-	-	-	-
Purfleet	-	-	-	-	-	-	21	-	-	4
St Albans City	-	6	1	-	-	-	-	-	-	-
Southwick	-	-	-	4	11	15	3	19	-	-
Staines Town	-	10	8	14	5	1	-	-	-	-
Stevenage Borough	-	-	-	16	21	-	-	-	1	-
Tilbury	10	7	16	19	-	-	-	-	-	-
Tooting & Mitcham United	-	-	-	-	-	-	12	6	7	7
Uxbridge	-	-	7	9	17	9	18	16	15	15
Walthamstow Avenue	-	-	-	-	15	-	-	-	-	-
Walton & Hersham	17	12	10	18	8	7	5	7	9	10
Wembley	3	5	3	5	6	10	16	15	5	9
Whyteleafe	-	-	-	-	-	-	14	9	20	14
Windsor & Eton	1	-	-	-	-	-	-	-	-	-
Wivenhoe Town	-	-	-	-	-	5	1	-	-	-
Woking	13	19	-	-	3	3	2	-	-	-
Wolverton Town	-	-	-	-	22	-	-	-	-	-
Worthing	-	-	-	-	13	18	13	22	-	-
Yeading	-	-	-	-	-	-	3	2	-	-
No. of clubs competing	22	22	22	22	22	21	22	22	21	21

ABINGDON TOWN

Abingdon Town F.C. 1992-93. Photo - Eric Marsh.

Chairman: Keith Measor **Vice Chairman:** Craig Norcliffe **President:** Dr Tim Reynolds
Secretary: Ted Quail, 107 Park Lane, Thatcham, Berks RG13 4BH (0635 86896).
Manager: Paul Lee **Asst Manager:** Roger Nichols **Physio:** Ian Cummings.
Coach: Keith Appleton **Commercial Manager:** Peter Edwards
Press Officer: Nick Quail (0235 832499)
Ground: Culham Road, Abingdon OX14 3BT (0235 555566-boardroom & press box).
Directions: On A415 half a mile south of town centre. Radley (BR) 3 miles - frequent buses to Abingdon. Didcot Parkway and Oxford (BR), 6 and 8 miles respectively with two hourly bus services.
Capacity: 3,000 **Cover:** 900 **Seats:** 200 **Floodlights:** Yes **Metal Badges:** £2
Club Shop: Yes, selling programmes, magazines, scarves etc. Contact John Lawson on club number.
Colours: Yellow/green/yellow **Change colours:** Blue & white.
Sponsors: Courage
Previous Name: Abingdon FC (amalgamated with St Michaels in 1899).
Previous Leagues: Oxford & District/ West Berks/ Reading Temperance/ North Berks/ Reading & District 1927-50/ Spartan 50-53/ Hellenic 53-88/ London Spartan 88-89.
Midweek home matchday: Tuesday **Reserve Team's League:** Suburban (West).
Record Attendance: 1,400 v Oxford City, FA Cup September 1960. (Crowds of over 5,000 in 20s and 30s).
Best F.A. Cup season: 4th Qualifying Rd 60-61 (lost 0-2 v Hitchin), 89-90 (0-3 at home to Slough), 92-93 (lost 1-2 at Merthyr Tydfil after 0-0 draw).
Players progressing to Football League: Maurice Owen (Swindon), George Buck (Stockport & Reading), Sammy Chung (Reading, Norwich, Watford & Wolves).
Clubhouse: (0235 521684). 7.30-11pm. 6pm matchdays. 12.30-2.30, 4-11 on Saturdays. Hot food on matchdays. Pool, darts, jukebox, canteen. **Steward:** John Hamlet.
92-93 Captain: John Harvey-Lynch.
92-93 P.o.Y.:
92-93 Top scorer: Liam Herbert.
Local Newspapers: Oxford Mail, Oxford Times, Abingdon Herald, South Oxon Guardian.
Hons: F.A. Vase 5th Rd rep 89-90, Berks & Bucks Snr Cup 58-59 (R-up 88-89), Isthmian Lg Div 2 (Sth) 90-91 (Associate Members Tphy R-up 90-91), London Spartan Lg 88-89 (Lg Cup SF 88-89), Hellenic Lg(4) 56-57 58-60 86-87 (R-up(3) 70-72 87-88, Lg Cup 57-58 70-71 81-82 (R-up 83-84 86-87), Div 1 75-76, Div 1 Cup 75-76, Res. Div(3) 69-71 86-87, Res. Div Cup 70-71 85-86, Res. Div Suppl. Cup 74-75), Oxford & Dist Lg(3) 1898-1901, Reading & Dist Lg 47-48, Berks & Bucks Jnr Cup 06-07, Abingdon Centen. Cup 58-59, Joan Lee Mem. Cup 69-70 70-71 86-87, Oxford I'mediate Lg (Reserves) 47-48.

Abingdon Town Football Club

PROGRAMME DETAILS:
Pages: 40 Price: 50p
Editor: Simon Ellerman
(0235 555566)

BARKING

Barking F.C. 1992-93, pictured before the 1-0 victory over Boreham Wood that secured the Blues' Division One status. Back Row (L/R): Andy Meredith, Sylvia Rutherford (Physio), Lee Parish, Craig Coney, Robbie Gammons, Steve Wallduck, Paul Evans (Captain), Brett Patience, Jeff Wood, John Spencer (Coach), Stuart Harvey. Front: Perry Coney (Player-Manager), Charlie Wright, Jay Coney (Mascot), Steve Munday, Mick Tarling, Chris Harvey, Peter Shea.

Chairman: Alan R Wetherall　　**President:** Mr John Knight.
Secretary: Terry Horgan, 138b Church Rd, Harold Wood, Essex RM3 0SB (0708 347 5564).
Manager: Perry Coney　　**Asst Manager:** N/A　　**Coach:** John Spencer
Press Officer: Secretary　　**Physio:** Sylvia Rutherford　　**Comm Manager:** John Knight
Ground: Mayesbrook Park, Lodge Avenue, Dagenham RM8 2JR (081 595 6511).
Directions: Come off A13 on A1153 (Lodge Avenue), and ground 1 mile on left. Bus 162 from Barking station. Nearest tube station is Becontree.
Capacity: 4,200　　**Cover:** 600　　**Seats:** 200　　**Floodlights:** Yes
Club Shop: Yes, selling programmes & magazines. Run by secretary and Norman Dean.
Colours: Blue & white　　**Change colours:** All yellow　　**Sponsors:** T.B.A.
Previous Leagues: London 1896-98 1909-26/ South Essex/ Athenian 23-52.
Previous Names: Barking Rovers, Barking Institute, Barking Woodville, Barking Town.
Previous Grounds: Eastbury Field, Vicage Field (until 1973).
Midweek home matchday: Tuesday
Record Attendance: (At Mayesbrook) 1,972 v Aldershot FA Cup 2nd Rd 1978.
Record win: 10-2 v Chelmsford City (A), F.A. Trophy, 11/11/78.
Record defeat: 0-8 v Marlow.
Best F.A. Cup season: 2nd Rd replay 81-82 (lost 1-3 at Gillingham after 1-1 draw). Also 2nd Rd 78-79 79-80 83-84, and 1st Rd 26-27 28-29 78-80.
League clubs defeated in F.A. Cup: Oxford Utd 79-80.
Record Fees - Paid: None over £1,000　　**Received:** £6,000 for Alan Hull (Orient).
Players progressing to Football League: Don Colombo (Portsmouth 1953), Wally Bellet (Chelsea 1954), John Smith (Millwall 1956), Peter Carey (Orient 1957), Lawrie Abrahams (Charlton 1977), Kevin Hitchcock (Nottm Forest 1983), Dennis Bailey (Fulham 1986), Alan Hull (Orient 1987).
Clubhouse: 2 large bars, open daily 11am-11pm (Sundays Noon-11pm). Hot & cold food and drinks.
Club Record Goalscorer: Micky Guyton 135 (1924-30)
Club Record Appearances: Bob Makin 566
92-93 Captain: Paul Evans
92-93 P.o.Y.: Jeff Wood
92-93 Top scorer: Jeff Wood, 14.
Local Newspapers: Dagenham & Barking, Barking & Dagenham Post.
Local Radio Stations: BBC Radio Essex.
Honours: FA Amateur Cup R-up 26-27, Isthmian Lg 78-79 (Lg Cup R-up 76-77), Athenian Lg 34-35 (R-up 24-25), London Lg 20-21 (Div 1 (A) 09-10), South Essex Lg Div 1 1898-99 (R-up 08-09, Div 2 1900-01 01-02 04-05 05-06), London Senior Cup 11-12 20-21 26-27 78-79 (R-up 19-20 75-76 79-80), Essex Senior Cup 1893-94 95-96 1919-20 45-46 62-63 69-70 89-90, Dylon Shield 79-80, Eastern Floodlit R-up 85-86, London Intermediate Cup 85-86.

PROGRAMME DETAILS:
Pages: 28 **Price:** 60p
Editor: Brad Robinson
(081 590 0934)

BERKHAMSTED TOWN

Berkhamsted Town F.C. 1992-93, promoted from Division Three. Photo - Eric Marsh.

Chairman: Bob Sear   **Vice Chairman:** Brian McCarthy   **President:** George Kite
Secretary: Alan Dumpleton, 44 Woodlands Av., Berkhamsted, Herts HP4 2JQ (0442 863929).
Manager: Roy Butler
Press Officer: Graham Hastie   **Physiq:** Kevin Burke.
Commercial Manager: Jim Cleaver/ Bob Turnham.
Ground: Broadwater, Lower Kings Road, Berkhamsted, Herts HP4 2AA (0442 862815).
Directions: Adjacent to Berkhamsted station (Euston-Birmingham line). A41 to Berkhamsted town centre traffic lights, left into Lower Kings Road.
Capacity: 2,000   **Seats:** 120   **Cover:** 200   **Floodlights:** Yes   **Founded:** 1895
Colours: White/black/black   **Change:** Green & white halves.   **Metal Badges:** Yes.
Club Shop: Old programmes and club scarves, ties, boot bags, and baseball hats available. See Graham Hastie.
Previous Ground: Sunnyside Enclosure 1895-1919/ Sports Ground 1919-83.
Previous Leagues: W Herts & Herts Co. 95-22/ Spartan 22-51 66-75/ Delphian 51-63/ Athenian 63-66 83-84/ London Spartan 75-83.
Midweek Matchday: Tuesday   **Sponsors:** Phillips Construction.
Reserve Team's League: Essex & Herts Border Combination.
Record Gate: 1,163 v Barnet, FA Cup 3rd Qual. Rd 1987.
Best FA Cup year: 3rd Qual Rd 87-88
Players progressing to Football League: Frank Broome, Maurice Cook.
Clubhouse: Open 7 days a week. Pool & darts.
Club Record Goalscorer:
Club Record Apps:
92-93 Captain: Paul Hobbs.
92-93 P.o.Y.: Paul Hobbs.
92-93 Top scorer: Gary Harthill 17.
Local Press: Berkhamsted Herald, Berkhamsted Gazette.
Local Radio Stations: Chiltern Radio, Radio Beds.
Hons: Herts Snr Cup 52-53, London Spartan Lg 79-80 (Div 2 26-27), Herts Char. Shld 73-74 79-80 84-85 90-91 50-51(Jt), Aubrey Cup 52-53, St Marys Cup(12), Apsley Snr Char. Cup(9), Wallspan Sthn Com. 84-85 (F'lit Cup 84-85).

PROGRAMME DETAILS:
Pages: 28 Price: 40p
Editor: Bob Sear
(0442 864547)

BILLERICAY TOWN

Billericay Town 1992-93. Back Row (L/R): John Kendall (Manager), Steve Jones, Mark Jenkins, Paul Taylor, Neville Ovenden (Ovenden Papers - Main Sponsor), Dave Cass, Shaun Gore, Dave Roser (Captain), Adrian West, Peter Brabrook (Coach). Front: Nobby Brown (Asst Coach), Mark Entwistle, Darren Southgate, Mike Cole (now Barking), Burgess Pocock, Steve Munday (now Purfleet), Peter Williams (Physio). Photo - Southend Evening Echo.

Chairman: Brian Cornes   **Vice Chairman:** Roy Hassell   **President:** Vacant.
Secretary: Len Dewson, 14 Graham Close, Billericay, Essex CM12 0QW (0277 622375).
Manager: John Kendall   **Coach:** Ken Varney   **Asst Manager:** Vacant.
Press Officer: Phil Heady (0277 652226)   **Physio:** Peter Williams.
Ground: New Lodge, Blunts Wall Road, Billericay CM12 0QW (0277 655177).
Directions: From Shenfield (A129) turn right at 1st lights then 2nd right. From Basildon (A129) proceed over 1st lights in town, then left at next lights and 2nd right. Half mile from Billericay (BR) station (London Liverpool Str.-Southend line). Ground 5 mins walk from buses 222, 251, 357, 255, 551.
Capacity: 3,600   **Seats:** 236   **Cover:** 1,140   **Founded:** 1880   **Metal Badges:** Yes
Colours: Royal/white/royal   **Change colours:** Yellow/black/black
Club Shop: Yes, open matchdays for souvenirs, metal badges, old progs etc. Contact Steve Lewis (0277 625679).
Previous Ground: Archer Hall, Laindon (pre-1971)   **Midweek Matches:** Tuesday.
Previous Leagues: Romford & Dist. 1890-1914/ Mid Essex 18-47/ South Essex Comb. 47-66/ Essex Olympian 66-71/ Essex Snr 71-77/ Athenian 77-79.
Sponsors: To be drawn.   **Reserves' Lge:** Essex & Herts Border Comb.
Best F.A. Cup year: 4th Qual Rd 77-78   **Best F.A. Vase year:** Winners
Record Gate: 3,841 v West Ham Utd, Floodlight opener 28/9/77. Competitive: 3,193 v Farnborough Town, F.A. Vase SF 1st leg 13/3/76.
Record win: 11-0 v Stansted (A), Essex Senior League 5/5/76.
Record defeat: 3-10 v Chelmsford City (A), Essex Senior Cup 4/1/93.
Record Fees - Paid: Undisclosed.
         Received: £22,500 (plus increments) for Steve Jones (West Ham Utd, 1992).
Players progressing to Football League: Danny Westwood (Queens Park Rangers & Gillingham), Alan Hull, Danny Carter & Dave Cass (Orient), Steve Jones (West Ham Utd).
Clubhouse: (0277 652188) Tues-Thurs 8-10.30pm, Fri 8-11pm, Sat noon-2 & 4-11pm, Sun noon-2 & 7-10.30pm. Discos, live entertainment, alcoves on ground floor and glass fronted viewing gallery on second.
Club Record Goalscorer: Fred Clayden 273
Club Record Appearances: John Pullen 418.
92-93 Captain: Mark Entwistle
92-93 P.o.Y.: Micky Hall
92-93 Top scorer: Steve Jones 26 (in 21 games).
Local Press: Evening Echo (0268 522792), Billericay Gazette 0245 262421).
Local Radio Stations: BBC Radio Essex (0268 522792), Essex Radio (0702 33311).
Hons: FA Vase (3 - a record) 75-77 78-79, Essex Snr Lg(3) 72-73 74-75 75-76 (R-up 71-72 73-74, Lg Cup(4) 71-74 76-77 (R-up 74-75)), Isthmian Lg Div 1 R-up 80-81, Athenian Lg(2) 77-79 (Lg Cup 77-78), East Anglian Cup R-up 79-80 84-85, Essex Snr Cup 75-76 (R-up 85-86), Essex Snr Tphy 77-78 79-80, Essex Thameside Tphy 86-87 91-92 (R-up 90-91), Essex F'lit Tphy 77-78, Phillips F'lit Tphy 76-77.

PROGRAMME DETAILS:
Pages: 40 **Price:** 50p
Editor: Geoff Gardner
(0277 656838)

BISHOP'S STORTFORD

Lee Burns of Bishop's Stortford takes on Maidenhead United defender during the league fixture at the George Wilson Stadium on 10th October. Photo - Robbie Pragnell.

Chairman: Gordon Lawrence **President:** B W A Bayford
Secretary: Jim Reynolds, 182 Fold Croft, Harlow CM20 1SN (0279 652531).
Manager: John Radford **Assistant Manager/Coach:** Ray Wickenden.
Physio: Micky Stevens **Press Officer:** Gareth Stephens (0279 813944).
Newsline: 0891 300109 **Commercial Manager:** John Radford.
Ground: George Wilson Stadium, Rhodes Ave., Bishop's Stortford CM23 3JN (0279 654140(club) 656538(office).
Directions: M11 jct 11, A120 towards town centre, right at crossroads into London Rd (A1184), right at mini-r'bout and cross railway bridge, right at next island (by garage), Rhodes Avenue is 2nd left (5-10 mins from M11). By rail: BR West Anglia Line (London Liverpool Str.-Cambridge) cross BR car park from main station entrance, over footbridge, thru 'maltings' area and 2nd left into South Rd, pass Rhodes Centre, Rhodes Avenue 1st right (5-10 mins walk from station).
Capacity: 6,000 **Cover:** 1,770 **Seats:** 270 **Floodlights:** Yes **Metal Badges:** Yes
Club Shop: Full stock inc. scarves, badges and other souvenirs. Massive stock of programmes and books etc. Catalogue available from shop manager Andy Stalley (0279 658536).
Cols: White & blue stripes/blue/blue **Change colours:** All red **Sponsors:** T.B.A.
Previous Leagues: Stansted & District 1890-1921 approx/ East Herts 1896-1921 approx/ Herts County 08-29/ Spartan 29-51/ Delphian 51-63 Athenian 63-71
Prev. Grounds: Silver Leys 1874-1900 approx/ Plaw Hatch 1900-1905 approx/ The Laundry Field 05-25.
Midweek home matchday: Tuesday **Reserve Team's League:** Essex & Herts Border Comb.
Record Attendance: 6,000 v Peterborough United, F.A. Cup 2nd Rd 1972 & v Middlesbrough F.A. Cup 3rd Rd replay, 1983 (lost 1-2 after 2-2 draw).
Best F.A. Cup season: 3rd Rd replay (see above). 1st Rd 70-71 72-73 74-76 81-83 84-87.
League clubs betean in FA Cup: Reading 82-83.
Record win: 13-1 v Army XI (H), friendly 20/4/40.
Record defeat: 1-11 v Leavesden Mental Hospital (A), Herts Senior Cup 20/1/34.
Record Fees - Paid: £1,000 for Carl Zacchau (Walthamstow Avenue, 1987)
 Received: £10,000 for Carl Hoddle (Leyton Orient, 1989)
Players progressing to Football League: Bryan Atkinson (Watford 1954), Mick Hallow (Orient 1962), Peter Phillips (Luton 1969), Tom English (Colchester), Carl Hoddle (Orient).
Clubhouse: Open matchdays and Mondays (bingo). Available for hire (weddings/functions). Rolls, crisps available - hot food on matchdays from tea-bar within ground. Clubroom also houses seven executive boxes available for hire per match or per season - further details from Commercial Manager.
Club Record Scorer: (Since 1929) Jimmy Badcock 123
Club Record Appearances: Gordon Atkinson 596 (56-69)
92-93 Captain: Phil Hopkins
92-93 P.O.Y.: Marc Das (club), Kevin Jordan (supporters')
92-93 Top scorer: Marc Das.
Local Newspapers: Bishop's Stortford Gazette, Herts & Essex Observer, Herald & Post.
Local Radio Stations: BBC Essex, Essex Radio, Breeze AM.
Honours: FA Trophy 80-81, FA Amateur Cup 73-74, Isthmian Lg Div 1 80-81 (Lg Cup 88-89, Associate Members Cup 90-91), Premier Inter Lg Cup 89-90, Athenian Lg 69-70 (R-up 66-67, Div 1 65-66, Div 2 R-up 64-65), Delphian Lg 54-55, Spartan Lg Div 2 (East) 31-32, London Senior Cup 73-74, Herts Senior Cup 32-33 58-59 59-60 63-64 70-71 72-73 73-74 75-76 86-87, East Anglian Cup 81-82, Herts Charity Cup 62-63 65-66 73-74 81-82 82-83 84-85 87-88, Herts Charity Shield 54-55, Courage Eastern Floodlit Cup 84-85, Essex Floodlit Cup 67-68, East Herts Lg 19-20, Stansted & District Lg 19-20.

PROGRAMME DETAILS:
Pages: 32 Price: 60p
 Editor: Dave Ryan
 (0279 812725)

BOGNOR REGIS TOWN The Rocks

Despite a brave dive, Bognor goalkeeper Tyronne Hall cannot prevent Jon Daly pouncing to put Dulwich Hamlet 1-0 ahead in an early season game while Dulwich were still using Tooting & Mitcham's Sandy Lane ground. Bognor fought back to draw 2-2. Photo - Dave West.

Chairman: Mr J Pearce   **Vice Chairman:** Mr M Rowland   **President:** Mr S Rowlands
Secretary: Ted Brice, c/o The Club. (0243 864228(H)).
Manager: Mick Pullen   **Asst Manager:** Neil Hider   **Physio:** Steve Robinson
Press Officer: Mr B Maxfield   **Comm. Manager:** Maurice Warner **Gen. Manager:** Jack Pearce
Ground: Nyewood Lane, Bognor Regis PO21 2TY (0243 822325).
Directions: West along seafront from pier, past Aldwick shopping centre, and right into Nyewood Lane.
Capacity: 6,000   **Cover:** 3,800   **Seats:** 243   **Floodlights:** Yes   **Metal Badges:** Yes
Club Shop: Yes, selling programmes and normal club items.
Colours: White (green trim)/green/white   **Change colours:** All yellow
Previous Leagues: West Sussex 1896-1926/ Brighton, Hove & District 26-27/ Sussex County 27-72/ Southern 72-81
Midweek home matchday: Wednesday   **Reserve's League:** None.
Record Attendance: 3,642 v Swansea FA Cup 1st Rd replay, 1984.
Sponsors: Spindlers Lamps & Lights, Bognor Regis.
Best F.A. Cup season: 2nd Rd 84-85 (lost 2-6 at Reading), 85-86 (1-6 at Gillingham), 88-89 (lost 0-1 at home to Cambridge). 1st Rd 72-73 86-87 87-88.
League clubs beaten in FA Cup: Swansea 84-85, Exeter 88-89.
Record Fees - Paid: None
        Received: £10,500 for John Crumplin & Geoff Cooper (Brighton & Hove Albion, 1987) & Simon Rodger (Crystal Palace, 1989).
Players progressing to Football League: Ernie Randall (Chelsea 1950), John Standing (Brighton 1961), Andy Woon (Brentford 1972), John Crumplin & Geoff Cooper (Brighton 1987), Simon Rodger (Crystal Palace 1989).
Clubhouse: Open every night, matchdays and Sunday lunchtimes. Hot food available.
Club Record Goalscorer: Kevin Clements
Club Record Appearances: Mick Pullen, 871.
92-93 Captain: E Rustell
92-93 P.o.Y.: C Matthews
92-93 Top scorer: G Biddle
Local Newspapers (+Tel.Nos.): Bognor Regis Joural & Guardian (865421), Bognor Observer (864267), Brighton Argus (606799), Portsmouth News (64488).
Local Radio Stations: Radio Sussex, Ocean Sound, Radio Solent, Southern Sound.
Hons: Isthmian Lg Div 1 R-up 81-82, (Lg Cup 86-87), Southern Lg R-up 80-81 (Lg Cup R-up 80-81, Merit Cup 80-81), Sussex Lg 48-49 71-72 (R-up 38-39 51-52, Div 2 70-71, Invitation Cup 40-41 49-50 62-63 71-72), Brighton Lg R-up 26-27, W Sussex Lg(5) 20-25 (R-up 1896-97, 25-26), W Sussex Jnr Lg 10-11 13-14, Southern Co's Comb 78-79, Sussex Snr Cup(8) 54-56 79-84 86-87 (R-up 51-52 58-59 84-85), Sussex Prof. Cup 73-74, Sussex RUR Cup 71-72, Sussex I'mediate Cup 52-53, Littlehampton Hosp. Cup 29-30 33-34, Bognor Charity Cup(8) 28-29 30-31 32-33 37-38 47-48 58-59 71-73, Gosport War Mem. Cup(2) 81-83 (R-up 86-87), Snr Midweek F'lit Cup R-up 74-75, FA Amtr Cup 1st Rd 71-72, FA Tphy 1st Rd 80-81 90-91.

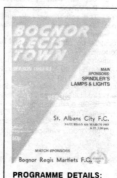

PROGRAMME DETAILS:
Pages: 36 Price: 60p
Editor: Secretary

BOREHAM WOOD

Boreham Wood F.C. 1992-93. Back Row (L/R): Andrew Gunn, Marc Dalli, Phil Lovell, Dave Hatchett, John Marggerison, Alistair Ryan, Robert Bourne, Martin Gardener, Lee Faulkner, Dave Dicken (Physio). Front Row: Jimmy Hughes, Joe Simmonds, Colin Cardines, Gary Seymour, Tony Flanagan, Matt Howard. Photo - Dave West.

Chairman: Phil Wallace   **Vice Chairman:** A Perkins   **President:** W F O'Neill.
Secretary: A Perkins, 48 Saltash Road, Hainault IG6 2NL (081 500 3902).
Manager: Bobby Makin   **Asst Manager:**   **Coach:** Alan Carrington
Press Officer: John D Gill (081 998 6446)   **Physio:** Dave Dickens
Ground: Meadow Park, Broughinge Road, Boreham Wood, Herts WD6 5AL (081 953 5097).
Directions: A1 towards London from M25, 1st turn off for Boreham Wood, head for town centre, into into Brook Rd at r'bout before town centre, Broughinge Rd is 1st left. 1 mile from Elstree & Boreham Wood station (Thameslink), then bus 292 or 107 to Red Lion (5 minutes walk).
Capacity: 3,500   **Cover:** 850   **Seats:** 250   **Floodlights:** Yes   **Metal Badges:** Yes
Club Shop: Yes, selling old and new programmes, replica shirts, scarves, hats, magazines, club badges etc.
Colours: White/black/red   **Change colours:** Red/red/black
Previous Leagues: Mid Herts 48-52/ Parthenon 52-57/ Spartan 56-66/ Athenian 66-74.
Previous Ground: Eldon Avenue 1948-63
Previous Names: Boreham Wood Rovers and Royal Retournez, amalgamated in 1948 to form the current club.
Midweek home matchday: Tuesday   **Reserve Team's League:** Essex & Herts Border Comb.
Sponsors: L. & M. Foods/ Wansons/ Daly Markets.
Record Attendance: 2,500 v St Albans, F.A. Amateur Cup 70-71.
Best F.A. Cup season: 1st Rd replay (v Swindon) 77-78. Also 1st Rd (v Southend) 73-74.
Players progressing to Football League: Colin Franks (Watford & Sheff Utd), Charles Ntamark (Walsall).
Clubhouse: (081 953 5097). Holds 250, open normal pub hours. Hall available for hire. Sandwiches, filled rolls, hot pasties etc available.
Club Record Goalscorer: Micky Jackson 208
Club Record Appearances: Steve Waller 575
92-93 Captain: Tony Flanagan
92-93 P.o.Y.: Dave Hatchett
92-93 Top scorer: Andy Weddell
Local Newspapers: Boreham Wood Times, Watford Observer, Herts Advertiser.
Local Radio Stations: Chiltern Radio.
Honours: FA Amateur Cup 3rd Rd replay 70-71, FA Tphy 1st Rd replay 86-87, Isthmian Lg Div 2 76-77 (Yth Cup R-up 80-81), Athenian Lg 73-74 (Div 2 68-69, Div 1 R-up 69-70), Spartan Lg R-up 65-66, Herts Senior Cup 71-72 (R-up 66-67 74-75 79-80 87-88), Herts Junior Cup 51-52, Parthenon Lg 55-56 (R-up(2) 53-55 56-57, Herts Charity Shield 64-65, Herts Intermediate Cup 69-70, Herts Charity Cup(5) 80-81 83-84 85-86 88-90 (R-up 71-72 84-85 86-87 90-91 91-92 92-93), London Senior Cup R-up 89-90, London Intermediate Cup 70-71, Neale Trophy 69-70, Essex & Herts Border Comb 72-73 (Lg Cup 72-73, Western Div R-up 82-83 89-90), Mithras Cup 76-77, Middx Border Lg 81-82 (Lg Cup 79-80), Wallspan Floodlit 86-87.

PROGRAMME DETAILS:
Pages: 32 **Price:** 60p
Editor: J D Gill
(081 998 6446)

CHALFONT ST PETER <small>The Saints</small>

Two Chalfont St Peter players combine to shut out Darren Colwill of Uxbridge during an away Division One fixture. Photo - Roy Green.

Chairman: David Pembroke **President:** Vacant. **Secretary:** Mr Peter Court, 8 Lovel End, Chalfont St Peter, Bucks SL9 9NZ (0753 888583).
Manager: Dave Alexander **Asst Manager:** T.B.A. **Coach:** T.B.A.
Press Officer: Malcolm Upton **Physio:**
Commercial Manager: Ken Power.
Ground: The Playing Fields, Amersham Road, Chalfont St Peter SL9 7BQ (0753 885797).
Directions: A413 from Uxbridge (London) to Chalfont. Turn left 100 yds after 2nd major roundabout (between Ambulance station and Community Centre. Two miles from Gerrards Cross (BR), regular buses from Slough.
Capacity: 4,500 **Cover:** 220 **Seats:** 220 **Floodlights:** Yes **Metal Badges:** Yes.
Club Shop: Yes.
Colours: Red & green quarters/green/green **Change colours:** Yellow/blue/blue
Previous Leagues: Great Western Combination 1948-58/ Parthenon 58-59/ London 60-62/ Spartan 62-75/ London Spartan 75-76/ Athenian 76-84.
Midweek home matchday: Tuesday **Reserve Team's League:** Suburban
Record Attendance: 2,500 v Watford, benefit match 1985.
Best F.A. Cup season: 3rd Qualifying Rd 85-86 (wins over Banbury, King's Lynn and Barking).
League clubs defeated in F.A. Cup: None.
Record Fees - Paid: £750 to Chertsey (Steve Church, March 1989)
Players progressing to Football League: None.
Clubhouse: Open every evening, Saturday afternoons and Sunday lunchtimes.
Club Record Goalscorer: Unknown.
Club Record Appearances: Colin Davies.
92-93 Captain: Tony Knight
92-93 P.o.Y.: Leroy Lacroix
92-93 Top scorer: Lance Cadogan 12.
Local Newspapers: Bucks Advertiser (0753 888333), Bucks Examiner, Bucks Free Press, Wycombe Midweek.
Local Radio Stations: Chilton Radio.
Honours: Isthmian Lg Div 2 87-88, Athenian Lg R-up 83-84 (Lg Cup 76-77 82-83), London Spartan Lg Div 2 75-76, Berks & Bucks Intermediate Cup 52-53, FA Tphy 3rd Qualifying Rd 89-90 91-92, FA Vase 4th Rd 87-88, Berks & Bucks Benevolent Cup 64-65.

PROGRAMME DETAILS:
Pages: 16 **Price:** 60p
Editor: Malcolm Upton

CROYDON

Croydon 4, Boreham Wood 3 - Diadora League Division One 12/10/93. Croydon goalkeeper Engin Salih watches the ball sail into the net for Boreham Wood's equaliser at 1-1. Photo - Dave West.

Chairman: T W Fogarty   **Vice Chairman:** J Langford.
Secretary: Geoff Beeson, 13 Impact Court, Stembridge Road, Anerley SE20 7UP (081 778 7163).
Manager: Bobby Langford   **Asst Manager:** N/A   **Coach:** J Johnson.
Press Officer: John Sanford (081 654 9835).   **Physio:** Ron Chance.
Ground: Croydon Sports Arena, Albert Road, South Norwood SE25 4QL (081 654 3462).
Directions: Train to East Croydon or Norwood Junction, then bus 12 to either Belmont or Dundee Road. Walk down either - ground at bottom. 5 mins walk from Woodside (BR).
Capacity: 8,000   **Cover:** 450   **Seats:** 450   **Club Shop:** Yes   **Metal Badges:** £2.50
Colours: Sky blue/blue   **Change colours:** All red   **Sponsors:** T.B.A.
Previous Leagues: Surrey Senior 53-63/ Spartan 63-64/ Athenian 64-74.
Midweek home matchday: Monday   **Previous Name:** Croydon Amateurs 1953-74.
Record Attendance: 1,450 v Wycombe, FA Cup 4th Qualifying Rd 1975.
Best F.A. Cup season: 2nd Rd replay 79-80 (lost 2-3 to Millwall after 1-1 draw).
Record Fees - Paid: Steve Brown
          Received: Peter Evans (to Sutton Utd).
Players progressing to Football League: Alan Barnett (Plymouth 1955), Peter Bonetti (Chelsea), Leroy Ambrose (Charlton 1979), Steve Milton (Fulham - via Whyteleafe), Murray Jones (Crystal & Exeter - via Carshalton).
Clubhouse: (081 654 8555). Open every evening and lunchtime, holds 250, snacks available. Dancing, discos, bingo. Lounge bar available for private hire.
Club Record Appearances: Alec Jackson (400+)
92-93 Captain: Several
92-93 P.o.Y.: Engin Salih
92-93 Top scorer: Richard Wilson.
Local Newspapers: Croydon Advertiser (081 668 4111), Croydon Midweek Post, Croydon Times, Croydon Guardian.
Hons: F.A. Amateur Cup 3rd Rd 71-72, F.A. Tphy 2nd Rd(2) 81-83, Isthmian Lg Div 2 R-up 75-76, Surrey Snr Cup 81-82 (R-up 76-77), Surrey Prem Cup 86-87, Spartan Lg 63-64, Athenian Lg R-up 71-72 (Div 2 65-66 (R-up 70-71)), Surrey Snr Lg R-up 56-57 60-61 62-63 (Lg Cup 60-61, Charity Cup 53-54 62-63, Res Section 57-58), London Snr Cup R-up 78-79, Suburban Lg South 86-87 (Lg Cup(2)), Southern Yth Lg 85-86 (Lg Cup 85-86 87-88), Berger Yth Cup 78-79.

CROYDON FOOTBALL CLUB

CANTERBURY CITY
Saturday 12th September 1992

PROGRAMME DETAILS:
Pages: 24 **Price:** 50p
Editor: John Sanford
(081 654 9835)

HEYBRIDGE SWIFTS

Heybridge Swifts goalkeeper Mark McCutcheon makes an excellent catch under pressure from Laurie Ryan during the F.A. Cup defeat against Cambridge City at Scarley Road. Photo - D Pettengell.

Chairman: Michael Gibson   **Vice Chairman:** Paul Wilkinson   **President:** John Knight
Secretary: Dennis Fenn, 31 Saxon Way, Maldon, Essex CM9 7JN (0621 854798).
Manager: Gary Hill   **Asst Manager:** Mick Loughton   **Coach:** Micky Stead
Press Officer: Tim Huxtable.   **Physio:** Barry Anthony
Commercial Manager: Neil Foster.
Ground: Scraley Road, Heybridge, Maldon, Essex (0621 852978).
Directions: Leave Maldon on main road to Colchester, pass through Heybridge then turn right at sign to Tolleshunt Major (Scraley Road). Ground on right. Six miles from nearest station (Witham). By bus via Chelmsford and Maldon.
Capacity: 5,000   **Cover:** 200   **Seats:** 200   **Floodlights:** Yes   **Metal Badges:** Yes
Club Shop: No, but club sweaters, enamel badges, old programmes sold on request.
Colours: Black & white stripes/black/black & white   **Change colours:** All yellow.
Sponsors: Knight Contractors Ltd
Previous Leagues: North Essex/ South Essex/ Essex & Suffolk Border/ Essex Senior 1971-84.
Midweek home matchday: Tuesday   **Reserve Team's League:** Essex & Herts Border Comb.
Record Attendance: 572 v Dartford, FA Cup 3rd Qualifying Rd 89-90.
Best F.A. Cup season: 4th Qualifying Rd 90-91 (lost 1-3 at Barnet).
League clubs defeated in F.A. Cup: None.
Best F.A. Trophy season: 2nd Rd Proper 92-93 (lost at Gateshead).
Record Fees - Paid: None   **Received:** £12,000.
Players progressing to Football League: Simon Royce (Southend United).
Clubhouse: Two bars open every night. Games room, boardroom, kitchen (on matchdays).
Club Record Goalscorer: J Lamb 115
Club Record Appearances: H Askew 500+.
92-93 Captain: Micky Stead
92-93 P.o.Y.: Dave Matthews
92-93 Top scorer: Dave Matthews.
Local Newspapers: Maldon & Burnham Standard (0621 8522233).
Local Radio Stations: BBC Essex, Essex Radio.
Honours: Isthmian Lg Div 2 North 89-90, Essex Senior Trophy 81-82, Essex Senior Lg 81-82 82-83 83-84 (Lg Cup 82-83), JT Clarke Cup 82-83, Thorn EMI National Floodlit Competition R-up 82-83, Essex & Herts Border Combination R-up 88-89 90-91.

'THE NON-LEAGUE PLAYERS'
1993-94 EDITION

AVAILABLE DURING THE SEASON, WILL FEATURE DETAILS OF HEYBRIDGE'S PLAYERS, AND INDEED THE PLAYERS OF ALL CLUBS IN THE TOP FOUR PYRAMID LEAGUES. FOR MORE DETAILS ON THIS PUBLICATION SEE THE ADVERT NEAR THE FRONT OF THIS DIRECTORY.

PROGRAMME DETAILS:
Pages: TBA **Price:** TBA
Editor: Peter Fenn
(0621 740878)

LEYTON

The Wingate-Leytpn Stadium, Lea Bridge Road. Photo - Dave West.

Chairman: George Gross   **President:** Laurie Aldridge
Joint Vice-Chairmen: Harry Stone/ David Ward.
Secretary: Mike Roberts, 168 Dawlish Drive, Ilford, Essex IG3 9EG (081 599 2384).
Manager: Peter McGillicuddy   **Asst Manager:** Kevin Moran   **Coach:** Alex Welsh
Press Officer: George Gross (081 850 9082).   **Physio:** Michael Hearn.
Commercial Manager: Chas E Gross (081 850 9082).
Ground: Wingate-Leyton Stadium, 282 Lea Bridge Road, Leyton E10 7LD (081 539 6861).
Directions: Lea Bridge Rd is A104 - ground next to Hare & Hounds PH. Leyton (Central Line) thence bus 58 or 158 to Lea Bridge Rd. Clapton (BR) walk 100yds to Lea Bridge Rd r'bout buses 48 or 56 to ground. Blackhorse Road (Victoria Line), thence bus 158 to Lea Bridge Rd. Bus 48 runs direct to ground from London Bridge (BR) station.
Capacity: 1,500   **Cover:** 600   **Seats:** 200   **Floodlights:** Yes   **Metal Badges:** Yes.
Club Shop: Sells programmes, pennants, scarves, badges etc. Contact Ian Wells c/o the club.
Colours: White/navy/white   **Change colours:** All navy
Sponsors: Under negociation.
Previous Names: Wingate FC (founded 1946) and Leyton FC (previously Matlock Swifts, founded 1895) merged in 1975. Leyton-Wingate 1975-92.
Previous Leagues: Athenian 1975-82. *(Predecessors, Leyton(1): Leyton & District Alliance/ South Essex/ Southern 05-11, London 20-26, Athenian 27-75).*
Midweek home matchday: Tuesday   **Reserve Team League:** Essex & Herts Border Comb.
Record Attendance: 500 v Whickham, FA Vase 6th Rd 83-84 *(100,000 saw Leyton v Walthamstow Avenue F.A. Amateur Cup final at Wembley, April 26th 1952).*
Record win: 10-2 v Horsham, 1982   **Record defeat:** 1-11 v Barnet, 1946.
Best F.A. Cup season: 1st Rd 85-86. *(Leyton(1) reached 3rd Rd in 09-10, and 1st Rd on 14 other occasions).*
League clubs defeated in F.A. Cup: None. *(Leyton(1) beat Stockport (09-10) and Merthyr Town (29-30).*
Record Fees - Paid: £200 for Dwight Marshall (Hampton)
            Received: £6,000 for T Williams (Redbridge Forest).
Players progressing to Football League: None. *(From predecessors - Ken Facey (Orient 1952), Mortimer Costello (Aldershot 1956), David Clark (Orient 1961)).*
Clubhouse: (081 539 5405). Open 11am-11pm Mon-Sat, 12-3 & 7-10.30pm Sun. Pool, darts, music, cribbage. No hot food - hot snacks are sold at tea bar on matchdays.
Club Record Goalscorer: Steve Lane 118
Club Record Appearances: Steve Hamberger 387.
92-93 Captain: Stuart McLean.
92-93 P.o.Y.: Tony Samuels.
92-93 Top scorer: Tony Samuels, 29.
Local Press: Waltham Forest Guardian, Hackney Gazette
Local Radio Stations: LBC.
Honours: Isthmian Lg Div 1 R-up 86-87 (Div 2 North 84-85), Athenian Lg 76-77 81-82 (R-up 77-78, Div 1 76-77), Essex Snr Tphy 84-85 (R-up 81-82), Essex Thameside Trophy 81-82, Thorn EMI National Floodlight Cup, FA Trophy 3rd Rd 87-88, FA Vase 6th Rd 83-84. As Leyton(1); FA Amateur Cup 26-27 27-28 (R-up 28-29 33-34 36-37 51-52), London Charity Cup 34-35 36-37 (R-up 32-33 46-47 66-67 70-71), London Senior Cup 03-04 (R-up 33-34 37-38 45-46), London Lg 23-24 24-25 25-26 (R-up 26-27, Lg Cup 56-57), Athenian Lg 28-29 65-66 66-67 (R-up 45-46 64-65, Div 2 Cup R-up 69-70), London Challenge Cup R-up 09-10 27-28, Essex Senior Cup 1896-97 97-98 99-1900 00-01 02-03 29-30 30-31 34-35, East Anglian Cup R-up 45-46 72-73, Essex Thameside Trophy 64-65 66-67 (63-64), Parthenon Lg 51-52, Leyton & Dist. Alliance 1892-93 93-94, Sth Essex Lg 1895-96 96-97 99-1900.

PROGRAMME DETAILS:
Pages: 32 **Price:** 70p
Editor: George Gross
(081 850 9082 (tel + fax))

MAIDENHEAD UNITED

Magpies

Maidenhead United F.C. 1992-93. Back Row (L/R): Jim Barrs (Physio), Cliff Alleyne, Ben Laryea, Richard Elliott, Micky Poole, Peter McNamee, Kevin Brown, Stuart Muir. Front: Mike Floyd, Steve Dale, Christian Bartlett, Paul Mulvaney, Francis Araguez, Tyrone Houston. Photo - V J Robertson.

Chairman: Jim Parsons   **Vice Chairman:** Jon Swan   **Presidents:** C West.
Secretary: Stan Payne, 14 Brookside, Honeycroft Hill, Uxbridge UB10 9NH (0895 236709).
Manager: John Watt   **Asst Manager:** Derek Sweetman   **Coach:** Various.
Press Officer: John Swan (0628 473411)   **Physio:** T.B.A.
Commercial Manager: Roger Coombs.
Ground: York Road, Maidenhead, Berks SL6 1SQ (0628 24739).
Directions: In town centre, 400 yds from station and two minutes from town centre car parks.
Capacity: 2,500   **Cover:** 800   **Seats:** 400   **Floodlights:** Yes   **Metal Badges:** Yes
Club Shop: Yes, selling programmes, souvenirs etc. Contact Mark Smith (0753 854674).
Colours: White/black/red   **Change colours:** All blue, or red/red/white
Sponsors: Maidenhead Advertiser.
Previous Name: Maidenhead/ Maidenhead Norfolkians.
Previous Leagues: Great Western Combination/ Spartan/ Corinthian/ Athenian/ Southern.
Midweek home matchday: Tuesday   **Reserve Team's League:** Suburban.
Record Attendance: 7,920 v Southall, FA Amateur Cup 1936.
Best F.A. Cup season: Quarter Finals 1873-74 74-75 75-76.
Players progressing to Football League: Alan Cordice, Paul Priddy, David Kemp, Laurie Sanchez, Eddie Kelsey, Jackie Palethorpe, Benny Laryea, Roy Davies.
Clubhouse: Open every evening. Hot and cold food, dancehall, darts, pool.
Club Record Goalscorer: George Copas
Club Record Appearances: B Randall.
92-93 Capt: Steve Emmanuel
92-93 P.o.Y.: Paul Dadson
92-93 Top scorer: Paul Mulvaney 11.
Local Newspapers: Maidenhead Advertiser, Reading Evening Post.
Local Radio Stations: Radio 210, Capital.
Hons: FA Amtr Cup SF 35-36, Isthmian Lg Div 2 Sth R-up 90-91 (Yth Cup R-up 77-78), Spartan Lg(3) 26-27 32-34, Corinthian Lg 57-58 60-61 (R-up 59-60, Shield 56-57 (R-up(3) 50-51 59-61), Neale Cup 48-49 57-58 60-61, Res. Div 50-51 62-63), Gt Western Lg 19-20, Gt Western Comb. 48-49, Berks & Bucks Snr Cup(16) 1894-96 1906-07 11-12 27-28 29-32 38-39 45-46 55-57 60-61 62-63 65-66 69-70 (R-up(14) 1881-82 92-94 97-98 1913-14 19-20 22-23 26-27 28-29 35-38 57-58 59-61), Mithras Cup 62-63 66-67 (R-up 79-80), Reading Snr Cup 55-56 58-59, Berks & Bucks Benev. Cup(6) 30-31 36-37 39-40 58-61 (R-up 48-49 50-51), Berks & Bucks I'mediate Cup 57-58 65-66, Southern Comb. Cup R-up 82-83, Berks & Bucks Yth Cup 83-84 90-91.

PROGRAMME DETAILS:
Pages: 28 **Price:** 60p
Editor: Andy Ross
(c/o The Club)

PURFLEET

The 300-seater stand at Purfleet's Ship Lane ground. Photo - J.W.

Chairman: Harry South   **Vice Chairman:** Ken Worrall   **President:** Keith Parker.
Secretary/Press Officer: Norman Posner, 1 Chase House Gdns, Hornchurch, Essex RM11 2PJ (0708 458301).
Manager: Gary Calder   **Asst Manager:** Chris King   **Coach:** Dennis Moore
Commercial Manager: Bob Andrews (0376 376602)   **Physio:** Bob Johnson.
Ground: Thurrock Hotel, Ship Lane, Grays, Essex (0708 868901).
Directions: M25 or A13 to Dartford tunnel r'bout. Ground is fifty yards on right down Ship Lane. Nearest station is Purfleet, two miles from ground.
Capacity: 4,500   **Cover:** 1,000   **Seats:** 300   **Floodlights:** Yes
Club Shop: Yes, selling programmes and magazines. Contact Tommy South (0708 868901).
Colours: Yellow/green/yellow   **Change colours:** Blue & white.
Sponsors: John Joy Welding Ltd   **Previous Names:** None.
Previous Grounds: None.   **Previous League:** Essex Senior 85-89.
Midweek home matchday: Monday   **Reserve Team's League:** Essex Business Houses.
Record Attendance: 950 v West Ham United, friendly 1989.
Best F.A. Cup season: Second Qualifying Rd replay 92-93 (lost 0-1 at Corby after 2-2 draw).
Record win: 10-0 v Stansted (H) 86-87, v East Ham Utd (A) 87-88 (both Essex Senior League).
Record defeat: 0-5 v Kingsbury Town (H), Isthmian Lge Division One 89-90.
Players progressing to Football League: Paul Cobb (Leyton Orient).
Clubhouse: 10am-11pm every day. Snooker, squash, weights room, aerobics, a-la carte restaurant, steam room. Two bars, 56 bedroom hotel.
Steward: Tom South.
Club Record Goalscorer: Terry Bellamy, 59.
Club Record Appearances: Colin McBride, 234.
92-93 Captain: Jimmy McFarlane
92-93 P.o.Y.: Chris Blakeborough.
92-93 Top scorer: George Georgiou, 12.
Local Newspapers: Thurrock Recorder, Thurrock Gazette.
Local Radio Stations: Essex Radio, BBC Radio Essexx.
Hons: Isthmian Lg Div 2 91-92 (Div 2 Nth R-up 88-89, Loctite Tphy 91-92), Essex Snr Lg 87-88 (Lg Cup(2) 86-88), Stanford Charity Cup 87-88 (R-up 85-86).

PROGRAMME DETAILS:
Pages: 24 Price: 60p
Editor: Secretary

RUISLIP MANOR

Ruislip Manor F.C. 1992-93. Back Row (L/R): Alan Witham (Asst Manager), Martin Rowen, Fred Cummings, Tony Waugh, Martin Howard, Mick Simmons, Jon Wood, Chris Balls, Tom Lacey, Dave Henstock, Brian Pettifer (Coaching Staff). Front: Andy Skyers, Gary Collinson, Robert Haynes, Kevin Quinn, Mick Schools (Manager), Roger Goodhind (Coach), Peter Wilkins (Captain), Paul Fitzgerald, Spud Murphy, Gary Farrant.

Chairman: Jim Klarfield   **Vice Chairman:** Maurice Cuell   **President:** J Barnett
Secretary: Miss Rhonda Ferry, 50 Martindale, Iver, Bucks SL0 0HY (0753 650944).
Manager: Michael Schools   **Asst Manager:** Alan Witham
Coach: Roger Goodhind/ Brian Pettifer.
Press Officer: Chris Pacey (081 459 9337)   **Comm. Mgr:** James Klarfield
Ground: Grosvenor Vale, off West End Road, Ruislip, Middx (0895 637487-office, 676168-boardroom).
Directions: From London: A40 to Ruislip, turn off on A4180, right at r'bout into West End Rd, right into Grosvenor Vale after a mile and a half - ground at end. From Ruislip Manor station (Metropolitan Line) turn left out of station, then first right into Shenley Avenue, third left into Cranley Drive - ground 150 yds on left. E2 bus (Ealing Broadway-Ruislip Station) is only bus that passes top of Grosvenor Vale.
Capacity: 3,000   **Seats:** 175   **Cover:** 300   **Floodlights:** Yes   **Metal Badges:** Yes
Colours: White/black/black   **Change cols:** Yellow/red/yellow.
Club Shop: Operated by Supporters Club. Sells metal badges, programmes, sweatshirts, coffee mugs, key-rings, pens, leisure tops, pennants, baseball caps, ties. Mr J Brennan, 119 Shenley Ave., Ruislip, Middx.
Midweek Matchday: Monday   **Sponsors:** Light Years.
Previous Leagues: Uxbridge 38-39/ Middx Snr 39-46/ Spartan 58-65/ Athenian 65-84.
Previous Names: None.   **Previous Ground:** Sidmouth Drive.
Record Gate: 2,000 v Tooting & Mitcham United, F.A. Amateur Cup 1962.
Best F.A. Cup year: Fourth Qualifying Round 90-91 (lost 2-5 at Halesowen Town).
Record transfer fee received: £6,000 for Dave Carroll (Wycombe Wanderers, July 1988).
Clubhouse: Mon-Fri noon-3.30 & 5.30-11pm, noon-3 & 7.30-10.30. Apart from normal range of beer, during football season there is real ale on hand pump. A catering mangeress does hot & cold meals before and after any match - menu ranges from steak, chips, peas to a ham sandwich.
Players progressing to Football League: Dave Carroll (via Wycombe Wanderers).
92-93 Captain: Peter Wilkins
92-93 P.o.Y.: Mick Simmons
92-93 Top scorer: Dave Henstock.
Local Press: Ruislip Northwood Gazette, All Sport Weekly
Hons: London Lg R-up 51-52 (Div 1 R-up 47-48), Isthmian Lg Div 2 R-up 92-93 (Associate Members Tphy 90-91), Athenian Lg Div 2 72-73, Middx Snr Cup SF(6), Middx Charity Cup R-up 90-91.

PROGRAMME DETAILS:
Pages: 32 **Price:** 60p
Editor: T.B.A.

STAINES TOWN

The Swans

The Staines defence comes under pressure away to champions-elect Chesham United. Photo - Keith Clayton.

Chairman: Alan Boon   **Vice Chairman:** Andy Jones   **President:** Nigel Iggulsden
(Acting) Secretary: Steven Parsons, 3 Birch Green, Staines, Middx TW18 4HA (0784 450420).
Manager: Chris Wainwright   **Asst Manager:** Keith Bristow   **Physio:** Peter Judd
Commercial Mgr: Ken Williams   **Press Officer:** Steven Parsons (0784 450420)
Ground: Wheatsheaf Park, Wheatsheaf Lane, Staines TW18 2PD (0784 455988).
Directions: M25 jct 13 onto A30 Staines by-pass as far as Crooked Billett r'bout, town centre exit (A308) passing bus garage and under iron bridge where you turn left into South Street (1-way), pass central bus station then bear left into Laleham Rd, Wheatsheaf Lane 1km on right and ground 50m on left (large car park). From Staines Central (BR) station (linked to Waterloo, Reading, Windsor, Aldershot, Weybridge, Clapham Junction) turn right into Gresham Rd (crossing footbridge if coming from Egham or Windsor) and follow until turning left into Laleham Rd - Wheatsheaf Lane 1km on right. Buses 218, 518 and 767 pass Wheatsheaf Lane.
Capacity: 2,500   **Cover:** 2,050   **Seats:** 250   **Shop:** No   **Metal Badges:** £2.50
Colours: Old gold (blue trim)/blue/blue (old gold trim).
Change colours: Sky blue & white halves (black trim)/black or white/white or yellow.
Previous Leagues: West London Alliance (pre-1900)/ West London/ West Middx (pre-1905)/ Gt Western Suburban 05-13 20-24/ Gt Western Comb/ Munitions Lg (World War 1)/ London Works (World War 1)/ Hounslow & District 19-20/ Spartan 24-35 58-71/ Middx Senior 43-52/ Parthenon 52-53/ Hellenic 53-58/ Athenian 71-73.
Previous Names: Staines Albany and St Peters Institute (merged) in 1905/Staines 05-18/Staines Lagonda 18-25/Staines Vale (pre-2nd World War).
Previous Grounds: Hammonds Farm, Linoleum Sports Grounds, Staines Moor, The Anglers Rest, Gorings Meadow, Shepperton Road (Laleham), Mill Mead (pre-1951).
Record Gate: 2,750 v Banco de Roma (Barassi Cup) 1975 *(70,000 saw 1st leg in Rome).*
Best F.A. Cup year: 1st Rd 84-85 (0-2 at Burton Alb) & 1879-80 (as St Peters Institute).
Midweek home matchday: Tuesday
Club Sponsors: McVities.   **Reserve team's league:** Suburban (since 1972).
Record win: 14-2 v Old Lyonians (Middx Senior Cup, 19/10/68).   **Record defeat:** v Wycombe Wdrs
Record Fees - Paid: Undisclosed for Richard Teale (Slough, August 1981)
Received: Undisclosed for Mark Dawber (Chesham, December 1989).
Players progressing to Football League: Robert Bennett (Southend 1972), John Love (C Palace 1975), Peter Shaw (Charlton 1977), Eric Young (Brighton, W'don), Gordon Hill (M'wall), Man Utd, Derby, Wayne Stemp (Brighton), Martin Ferney (Fulham).
Clubhouse: Fully furnished clubhouse & function hall, open 7-11 matchdays and every evening. Rolls and other snacks available.
Club Record Goalscorer: Alan Gregory 122
Club Record Appearances: Dickie Watmore 840
92-93 Captain: John Crouch/ Paul Rumble/ Tony Knight.
'Dick Watmore' P.O.Y. 92-93: Gary Crawshaw.
92-93 Top scorer: Gary Crawshaw, 29
Local Newspapers: Staines & Ashford News, Middx Chronicle.
Local Radio Stations: County Sound, LBC, GLR, Capital.
Hons: Isthmian Lg Div 1 74-75 88-89 (Div 2 74-75), Athian Lg Div 2 71-72 (Div 1 R-up 72-73), Spartan Lg 59-60 (R-up 71-72, Lg Cup 68-69 (R-up 70-71)), Hellenic Lg R-up 55-56 (Lg Cup R-up 53-54 55-56), Gt Western Suburban Lg Div 1 R-up 11-12 22-24 (Div 2 (Middx) 20-21), West London Alliance Div 1 1899-1900, West London Lg Div 1 00-01, West Middx Lg 04-05 (R-up 03-04), London Snr Cup 76-77 80-81, Middx Snr Cup(5) 74-77 87-88 89-90 (R-up 09-10 32-33 79-80), Middx Jnr Cup 01-02 03-04, Barassi Cup 1976, Southern Amtr Comb Cup 64-65 66-67 68-69 (R-up 67-68), W Middx Cup 23-24, Staines Cottage Hosp Cup 24-25, Merthyr Middx Charity Shield 90-91, F.A. Amtr Cup 3rd Rd 23-24, F.A. Tphy 2nd Rd 2nd rep 76-77.

PROGRAMME DETAILS:
Pages: 40 Price: 70p
Editor: R Stanley

TOOTING & MITCHAM UTD

Tooting & Mitcham United 1992-93. Back Row (L/R): Trevor Ford (Manager), Sean Fay, Mickey Stephens, John Collins, Tony Williams, David Gabriel, Brian Frampton, Peter Shaw (Coach), Danny Keenan (Physio). Front Row: Dave Taylor, Noel Frankum, John Myatt, Mark Tompkins, Paul Loughlin, Bobby Dennington, Danny Wood.

Chairman: Jack Payne   **Vice Chairman:** Dave McCann   **President:** Les Walters.
Secretary: Chris Jackson, 1 Abercorn Close, Selsdon, South Croydon CR2 8TG (081 651 2568).
Manager: Trevor Ford   **Asst Manager:** N/A   **Coach:** Peter Shaw
Press Officer/Commercial Mgr: John Pollard.   **Physio:** Danny Keenan
Ground: Sandy Lane, Mitcham, Surrey CR4 2HD (081 648 3248).
Directions: Tooting (BR) quarter mile. Sandy Lane is off Streatham Road near Swan Hotel.
Capacity: 8,000   **Cover:** 1,990   **Seats:** 1,990   **Floodlights:** Yes   **Metal Badges:** Yes
Club Shop: Yes, selling souvenirs and confectionary, etc.
Colours: White & black   **Change colours:** All red.
Sponsors: Claremont Coaches.
Previous Leagues: London 32-37/ Athenian 37-56.
Midweek home matchday: Tuesday   **Reserve Team's League:** Suburban.
Record Attendance: 17,500 v QPR, FA Cup 2nd Rd 56-57.
Best F.A. Cup season: 4th Rd 75-76 (lost 1-3 at Bradford City). Also 3rd Rd 58-59, 2nd Rd 56-57 76-77, 1st Rd 48-49 50-51 63-64 74-75 77-78.
Record win: 11-0 v Welton Rovers, F.A. Amateur Cup 62-63.
Record defeat: 1-8 v Kingstonian, Surrey Snr Cup 66-67 & v Redbridge F. (H), Loctite Cup 3rd Rd 19/2/91.
League clubs defeated in F.A. Cup: Bournemouth & Boscombe Ath, Northampton 58-59, Swindon 75-76.
Record Fees - Paid: £9,000 for Dave Flint (Enfield)
               Received: £10,000 for Herbie Smith (Luton).
Players progressing to Football League: Trevor Owen (Orient 1958), Dave Bumpstead (Millwall 1958), Paddy Hasty (Aldersot 1958), Walter Pearson (Aldershot 1961), Richie Ward & Alex Stepney (Millwall 1962 & 63), Vic Akers (Watford 1975), Paul Priddy (Wimbledon 1978), Carlton Fairweather & Brian Gayle (Wimbledon 1984).
Clubhouse: Open every evening and weekend lunchtimes. Wide variety of food.
Club Record Goalscorer: Alan Ives 92 (1972-78)
Club Record Appearances: Danny Godwin 470.
92-93 Captain: Micky Stephens
92-93 P.o.Y.: Dave Taylor
92-93 Top scorer: John Collins
Local Newspapers: Mitcham News (081 672 1077), South London Press (081 769 4444), South London Guardian (081 644 4300).
Local Radio Stations: Capital.
Honours: Isthmian Lg 57-58 59-60 (Full Members Cup 92-93), Athenian Lg 49-50 54-55, London Challenge Cup R-up 59-60, Surrey Senior Cup 37-38 43-44 44-45 52-53 59-60 75-76 76-77 77-78, London Senior Cup 42-43 48-49 58-59 59-60 (R-up 43-44 44-45), South Thames Cup 69-70, Surrey Senior Shield 51-52 60-61 61-62 65-66, FA Tphy 2nd Qual Rd Replay 71-72 81-82, FA Amateur Cup 1st Rd replay 22-23.

PROGRAMME DETAILS:
Pages: 24 Price: 50p
Editor: Ian Bullock

UXBRIDGE

Uxbridge F.C. 1992-93. Back Row (L/R): Ernie Kempster (Physio), Mark Gill, Darren Colwill, Paul McCluskey, Gavin Hughes, Gary Downes (Captain), Sean Dawson, Troy Birch, Fergus Moore, Andy Clarke, Gary Williams, Henry Turnbridge (Asst Manager). Front: Alan Holloway (Chairman), Bobby Roper, Barry Roberts, Gerry Crawford, Nicky Ryder, Jeff Hamlet, George Talbot (Manager). Photo - Roy Green.

Chairman: Alan Holloway   **V. C'man/Jt Pres.:** Tom Barnard   **Joint President:** Alan Odell.
Secretary: Graham Hiseman, 96 New Peachey Lane, Cowley, Uxbridge, Middx UB8 3SY (0895 237195).
Manager: George Talbot   **Asst Mgr:** Henry Tumbridge   **Coach:** Micky Nicks.
Press Officer: Andy Peart (0895 444946)   **Physio:** Ernie Kempster
Ground: Honeycroft, Horton Road, West Drayton, Middx UB7 8HX (0895 445830).
Directions: From West Drayton (BR) turn right then 1st left (Horton Road). Ground 1 mile on left. From Uxbridge (LT) take 222, U3 or U5 bus to West Drayton station, then follow as above. By road, ground 1 mile north of M4 jct 4 taking road to Uxbridge and leaving by first junction and turning left into Horton Rd - ground 600yds on right.
Capacity: 5,000   **Cover:** 480   **Seats:** 201   **Floodlights:** Yes   **Metal Badges:** Yes.
Club Shop: Yes, selling club badges, ties, pennants, mugs, T-shirts, jumpers, programmes (League & non-League), pens, key-rings etc. Contact secretary.
Colours: Red/white/red   **Change colours:** All sky
Previous Leagues: Southern 1894-99/ Gt Western Suburban 1906-19 20-23/ Athenian 1919-20 24-37 63-82/ Spartan 37-38/ London 38-46/ Gt Western Comb. 39-45/ Corinthian 46-63.
Prev. Name: Uxbridge Town (23-45)   **Prev. Grnds:** RAF Stadium 23-48/ Cleveland Rd 48-76.
Midweek home matchday: Tuesday   **Reserve Team's League:** Suburban (North Division).
Record Attendance: 1,000 v Arsenal, floodlight opening 1981.
Best F.A. Cup season: 2nd Rd 1873-74. 1st Rd on three other occasions 1883-84 84-85 85-86.
Players progressing to Football League: William Hill (QPR 1951), Lee Stapleton (Fulham 1952), Gary Churchouse.
Clubhouse: (0895 443557). Large clubhouse with bar and dance hall. Open every evening and every lunchtime except Monday. Hot & cold snacks available on matchdays & at lunchtime. Opens at midday and 7pm (earlier for midweek evening games).
Club Record Scorer: Danny Needham, 125
Club Record Appearances: Roger Nicholls, 1054.
92-93 Captain: Gary Downes
92-93 Top Scorer: Nicky Ryder, 19.
92-93 P.o.Y.: Paul McCluskey.
92-93 Players' P.o.Y.: Gary Downes.
Only everpresent 92-93: Sean Dawson, 55 games
Local Newspapers (+Tel.Nos.): Middx Gazette (0895 58290).
Local Radio Stations: Capital, Greater London Radio.
Honours: FA Amateur Cup R-up 1897-98, FA Tphy 1st Rd replay 88-89, FA Vase 4th Rd 83-84, Isthmian Lg Div 2 South R-up 84-85 (Lg Cup R-up 85-86), Athenian Lg Cup R-up 81-82 (Div 2 Cup R-up 70-71, Reserve Section 69-70, Reserve Cup 68-69), Corinthian Lg 59-60 (R-up 49-50, Lg Memorial Shield 50-51 52-53), London Lg Western Div R-up 45-46, Middx Senior Cup 1893-94 95-96 1950-51, Middx Senior Charity Cup 07-08 12-13 35-36 81-82 (R-up 69-70 82-83 85-86), Allied Counties Yth Lg 92-93 (Lg Cup 86-87, Lg Shield 88-89 92-93).

PROGRAMME DETAILS:
Pages: 32-48 Price: 50p
Editor: A Peart/M Bodman
(0895 444946/813445)

WALTON & HERSHAM

F.A. Trophy action at Stompond Lane. Photo - Francis Short.

Chairman: N F Swindley   **President:** W Bigmore.
Secretary: Gerry Place, 24 Stratton Road, Sunbury, Middx TW16 6PQ (0932 782414).
Manager: Neil Price   **Asst Manager/Coach:** Chris McLaren
Press Officer: Brian Freeman (0932 560738)   **Physio:** T.B.A.
Commercial Manager: T.B.A.
Ground: Sports Ground, Stompond Lane, Walton-on-Thames (0932 245263).
Directions: Ten minutes walk fron Walton-on-Thames (BR). Bus 218 passes ground.
Capacity: 6,500   **Cover:** 2,500   **Seats:** 500   **Floodlights:** Yes   **Metal Badges:** Yes.
Club Shop: Yes.
Colours: Red & white/white/red   **Change colours:** Blue & black stripes/black/back.
Previous Leagues: Surrey Senior/ Corinthian 45-50/ Athenian 50-71.
Midweek home matchday: Tuesday   **Reserve Team's League:** Suburban.
Sponsors: General Data.
Record Gate: 6,500 v Brighton, F.A. Cup First Round 73-74.
Best F.A. Cup season: 2nd Rd 72-73 (v Margate), 73-74 (v Hereford).
League clubs defeated in F.A. Cup: Exeter 72-73, Brighton 73-74.
Players progressing to Football League: Denis Pacey (Orient 1951), John Whitear (Aston Villa 1953), Andy McCulloch (QPR 1970), Mick Heath (Brentford 1971), Paul Priddy (Brentford 1972), Richard Teale (Queens Park Rangers 1973), Steve Parsons (Wimbledon 1977).
Clubhouse: (0932 245263). Open most nights. Bar, TV, darts, pool, refreshments on matchdays.
92-93 Captain: Mark Wilson
92-93 P.o.Y. Ross Davidson
92-93 Top Scorer: Alan Gregory 12.
Local Newspapers: Surrey Herald.
Local Radio Stations: County Sound.
Honours: F.A. Amateur Cup R-up 72-73 (SF 51-52 52-53), Isthmian Lg R-up 72-73, Barassi Cup 73-74, Athenian Lg 68-69 (R-up 50-51 69-70 70-71, Lg Cup 69-70), Corinthian Lg(3) 46-49 (R-up 49-50), Premier Midweek F'lit Lg(3) 67-69 70-71 (R-up 71-72), Surrey Snr Cup 47-48 50-51 60-61 61-62 70-71 72-73 (R-up 46-47 51-52 59-60 69-70 71-72 73-74), London Snr Cup R-up 73-74, Southern Combination Cup 82-83 88-89 91-92, Surrey Combination Cup 49-50 91-92, John Livey Memorial Trophy 91-92.

PROGRAMME DETAILS:
Pages: 40 **Price:** 50p
Editor: Brian Freeman
(0932 560738)

WEMBLEY

Bobby Hutchinson (left) is strongly challenged by Barry Hope of Welwyn Garden City as Wembley record a 5-0 home win in this F.A. Cup Preliminary Round tie on Saturday 29th August. Photo - Paul Dennis.

Chairman: Brian Gumm   **Vice Chairman:** Eric Stringer   **President:** Jim Bryan, BEM
Secretary: Mrs A Lewin, 12 Perkin Close, Sudbury, Wembley, Middx HA0 2LY (081 904 4673).
Manager: Alan Dafforn   **Commercial Manager:** Glen Charles
Press Officer: R Markiewicz (081 902 0541)
Ground: Vale Farm, Watford Road, Sudbury, Wembley HA0 4UR (081 908 8169).
Directions: Sudbury (BR) 400 yds, or 10 mins walk from Nth Wembley tube. Buses 18, 92, 245 & 182.
Capacity: 2,000   **Cover:** 350   **Seats:** 350   **Club Shop:** No   **Metal Badges:** £2
Colours: Red & white   **Change colours:** All white.
Sponsors: G & B Builders.
Previous Leagues: Middx 46-49/ Spartan 49-51/ Delphian 51-56/ Corinthian 56-63/ Athenian 63-75.
Midweek home matchday: Tuesday   **Reserve Team's League:** Suburban (North).
Record Attendance: 2,654 v Wealdstone, F.A. Amateur Cup 52-53.
Best season in F.A. Cup: 1st Round Proper 1980-81 (lost 0-3 at Enfield).
Record win: 11-1 v Hermes, London Senior Cup 1963.
Record defeat: 0-16 v Chelsea, London Challenge Cup 59-60.
Record Fees - Paid: Nil   **Received:** £10,000 for Gary Roberts (Brentford, 1981).
Players progressing to Football League: Ken Coote (Brentford 1949), Keith Cassells (Watford 1977), Mike O'Donague (Southampton 1979), A McGonigle (Olympiakos), Gary Roberts (Brentford 1980), Richard Cadette (Orient 1984).
Clubhouse: (081 904 8169). Open every night & weekend lunchtimes. Hot food on matchdays.
Club Record Goalscorer: Bill Handrahan 105 (1946-52)
Club Record Apps: Spud Murphy 505 (78-88).
92-93 Captain & P.o.Y.: Paul Shields   **92-93 Top Scorer:** Bobby Hutchinson.
Local Newspapers: Wembley & Harrow Observer.
Honours: FA Amateur Cup 2nd Rd 66-67 68-69, FA Tphy 1st Rd Proper 91-92, Middx Senior Cup 83-84 86-87 (R-up 55-56 68-69 78-79 87-88 91-92), Middx Lg 47-48 (Lg Cup 46-47), Middx Charity Cup 67-68(joint) 80-81(joint) 82-83 86-87 (R-up 83-84 87-88), Middx Invitation Cup 56-57, Athenian Lg R-up 74-75 (Div 1 R-up 67-68), Corinthian Lg Memorial Shield R-up 58-59, Delphian Lg R-up 55-56, Spartan Lg Div 1 West 50-51 (Dunkel Trophy 50-51(joint)), London Senior Cup R-up 55-56, Hitachi Cup SF 83-84, Suburban Lg North 85-86 (Lg Cup 84-85 (R-up 83-84)).

PROGRAMME DETAILS:
Pages: 28 **Price:** 50p
Editor: Roy Calmels
(0767 51539)

WHYTELEAFE

A bad start to the season for Whyteleafe; they lose 2-4 at local rivals Croydon on the opening day. Here Richard Wilson slots home the first goal for the home side. Photo - Dave West.

Chairman: A F Lidbury   **Vice Chairman:** Alan Howland   **President:** F E Ovenden
Secretary: Ian Robertson (0883 622096).
Manager: Paul Hinshelwood   **Asst Manager/Coach:** Keith Wilkinson
Press Officer: Tony Lidbury (0883 622720)
Commercial Manager: Paul Owens.
Ground: 15 Church Road, Whyteleafe, Surrey CR3 0AR (081 660 5491).
Directions: Five minutes walk from Whyteleafe (BR) - turn right from station, and left into Church Road.
Capacity: 5,000   **Cover:** 200   **Seats:** 200   **Floodlights:** Yes   **Metal Badges:** Yes
Colours: Green & white/green/white   **Change colours:** Yellow/black/black
Sponsors: Sunday Sport.
Previous Leagues: Caterham & Edenbridge/ Croydon/ Thornton Heath & Dist./ Surrey Intermediate (East) 54-58/ Surrey Senior 58-72/ Spartan 75-81/ Athenian 81-84.
Midweek matchday: Tuesday   **Reserve Team's League:** Suburban.
Record Attendance: 533.
Best F.A. Cup season:
League clubs defeated in F.A. Cup: None.
Record Fees - Paid: £1,000 for Gary Bowyer (Carshalton)
        Received: £25,000 for Steve Milton.
Players progressing to Football League: Steve Milton (Fulham).
Clubhouse: Open every lunchtime and evening. Hot and cold food, pool, darts, gaming machines.
92-93 Captain:
92-93 P.O.Y.:
92-93 Top scorer: Mark Hynes 30.
Local Press: Croydon Advertiser.
Local Radio Stations:
Honours: FA Vase 5th Rd 80-81 85-86, FA Tphy 3rd Qualifying Rd 89-90, Isthmian Lg Div 2 South R-up 88-89, Surrey Senior Lg 68-69 (Lg Cup R-up 68-69, Lg Charity Cup 71-72, Reserve Section 62-63 (Challenge Cup 62-63 (R-up 59-60), Surrey Senior Cup 68-69 (R-up 87-88), Surrey Premier Cup R-up 84-85, East Surrey Charity Cup 79-80 (R-up 76-77 77-78), Thornton Heath & Dist Lg 51-52 (Lg Cup 51-52, Div 4 R-up 51-52), Edenbridge Charity Cup 51-52, Caterham & Purley Hospital Cup 51-52, Surrey County Intermediate Lg East Section 1 55-56 Surrey Junior Cup R-up 51-52, Caterham & Edenbridge Lg Div 3 51-52, Borough of Croydon Charity Cup 56-57, Southern Yth Lg 89-90 (R-up 88-89, Lg Cup 88-89 89-90).

Whyteleafe Football Club

50p

PROGRAMME DETAILS:
Pages: 36 Price: 70p
Editor: Tony Lidbury

Formed: 1892

WINDSOR & ETON

The Royalists

Windsor & Eton goalkeeper Kevin Mitchell bravely spreads himself at the feet of Dulwich Hamlet's Gary Hewitt. Photo - Alan Coomes.

Chairman: Michael Broadley　　**President:** Sir David Hill-Wood, Bt
Secretary: Peter Jackson, 19 Friary Court, Goldsworth Park, Woking, Surrey (0483 797202).
Manager: T.B.A.　　**Asst Manager:** T.B.A.　　**Coach:** T.B.A.
Press Officer: Ian Lucas (0753 863918)　　**Physio:** Janet Howarth.
Ground: Stag Meadow, St Leonards Road, Windsor SL4 3DR (0753 860656).
Directions: A332 from M4 junct 6. Left at lights (B3173), ground 500 yards on right on B3022 opposite Stag & Hounds PH. 1 mile from town centre.
Capacity: 4,500　　**Cover:** 650　　**Seats:** 320　　**Floodlights:** Yes　　**Metal Badges:** Yes
Club Shop: Yes, selling replica kits, scarves, ties, badges, pennants and a selection of programmes.
Colours: Red (green piping)/red/white　　**Change colours:** White/red/black
Sponsors: Rational Kitchens
Previous Leagues: Southern 1895-96/ West Berks/ Great Western Suburban 1907-22/ Athenian 22-29 63-81/ Spartan 29-32/ Great Western Comb/ Corinthian 45-50/ Metropolitan 50-60/ Delphian 60-63.
Previous Ground: Ballon Meadow 1892-1912.
Midweek home matchday: Tuesday　　**Reserve Team's League:** Suburban
Record Gate: 8,500 (Charity match).　　**League clubs defeated in F.A. Cup:** None.
Best F.A. Cup season: 2nd Rd replay 83-84. 1st Rd on seven occasions; 25-26 80-81 82-86 91-92.
Record Fees - Paid: £9,000　　**Received:** £10,000
Players progressing to Football League: Reg Dare (Southampton 1949), Steve Adams (Charlton 1979), Dave Barnett (Colchester 1988), Vic Woodley (Chelsea & England), Billy Coward (QPR, Walsall), Ken Groves (Preston), Dave Regis (Notts County).
Clubhouse: (0753 860656). Open six days a week 7.30-11 pm and Sunday lunchtimes. Darts & Pool. Club and pitch available for hire - contact Alan Baker on aforementioned number.
92-93 Captain:
92-93 P.o.Y.:　　**92-93 Top scorer:** Michael Creighton 11.
Local Newspapers: Windsor & Eton Express, Windsor & East Berks Observer, Evening Post.
Local Radio Stations: Radio 210　　**Club Newsline:** 0836 40 39 30.
Hons: Isthmian Lg Div 1 83-84 (Div 2 R-up 82-83), Athenian Lg 79-80 80-81 (Lg Cup 79-80 (R-up 78-79 80-81), Div 2 Cup 63-64 (R-up 68-69)), Spartan Lg R-up 36-37 37-38 (Div 1 30-31), Metropolitan Lg R-up 53-54 (Lg Amtr Cup 51-52 52-53, Lg Cup 52-53 (R-up 53-54 54-55)), Gt Western Suburban Lg R-up 21-22, Berks & Bucks Snr Cup(11) 10-11 36-38 40-45 61-62 87-89 (R-up 07-08 24-25 26-27 38-39 46-47 62-63), Berks & Bucks Benev. Cup 35-36 37-38 46-47 62-63 (R-up 38-39 47-48 49-50), FA Amtr Cup 4th Rd 21-22, FA Vase SF 80-81 (QF 79-80), FA Tphy 3rd Rd 88-89.

PROGRAMME DETAILS:
Pages: 50 Price: 80p
Editor: Steve Rowland

'THE NON-LEAGUE PLAYERS'
1993-94 EDITION

AVAILABLE DURING THE SEASON, WILL FEATURE DETAILS OF WINDSOR & ETON'S PLAYERS, AND INDEED THE PLAYERS OF ALL CLUBS IN THE TOP FOUR PYRAMID LEAGUES. FOR MORE DETAILS ON THIS PUBLICATION SEE THE ADVERT NEAR THE FRONT OF THIS DIRECTORY.

WORTHING

Worthing F.C., Diadora League Division Two champions 1992-93. Back Row (L/R): Beau Reynolds (Chairman), Alan Robinson, Garry Penhaligan, Dave Stevens, Richard Tiltman, Matthew Ball, Graham Waller, Richard Knight, Mark Nye, Ivan Cocker (Asst Manager), Gerry Armstrong (Manager). Front: John Robson (Coach), Cameron Johnson, Sandy Brown, Jan Kanczler, Darren Freeman, Darren Robson, Michael Montague, Simon Beckford (Mascot). Photo - Roger Turner.

Chairman: Beau Reynolds **Vice Chairman:** Ray Smith **President:** Monty Hollis.
Secretary: Alan Evans, 105 St Andrews Rd, Worthing, West Sussex BN13 1HR (0903 268253).
Manager: Gerry Armstrong **Asst Mgr:** Ivan Cocker **Coach:** John Robson
Physio: Jack Anderson **Press Officer:** Secretary.
Ground: Woodside Road, Worthing, West Sussex BN14 7HQ (0903 239575).
Directions: Follow A24 to town, at end of Broadwater Rd having gone over railway bridge, take 1st right into Teville Rd, take right into South Farm RD, 2nd left into Pavilion Rd, Woodside Rd is first right. Half a mile from Worthing (BR).
Capacity: 4,500 **Seats:** 450 **Cover:** 1,000 **Midweek matches:** Tuesday.
Colours: All red **Change colours:** All blue
Reserves' League: Unijet Sussex Res. Section.
Shop: Yes, selling T-shirts, sweatshirts, scarves, mugs, pens, progs (League & non-League), small pennants.
Previous Leagues: West Sussex/ Sussex County 20-48/ Corinthian 48-63/ Athenian 63-77.
Record Gate: 4,500 v Depot Battalion Royal Engineers, FA Amtr Cup 07-08.
Best FA Cup year: 2nd Rd 82-83, lost 0-4 to Oxford Utd. Also 1st Rd 36-37.
Record Fees - Paid: £1,000 for Steve Guille (Bognor Regis Town, 1989).
  Received: £7,500 for Tim Read (Woking, 1990).
Record win: 0-13 v Carshalton Athletic (A), Loctite Cup Third Round 28/2/91.
Clubhouse: Open two hours before kick-off and closes 11pm. Hot & cold food available.
Players progressing to Football League: Ken Suttle (Chelsea 1948), Alan Arnell & Fred Perry (Liverpool 1954).
Club Record Scorer: Mick Edmunds 482
Club Record Appearances: Paul Lelliot 542.
92-93 Captain: Graham Waller
92-93 Top scorer: Darren Freeman
92-93 P.o.Y.: Richard Knight
Local Press: Evening Argus, Worthing Gazette & Herald.
Local Radio: Radio Sussex.
Hons: FA Vase 5th Rd 78-79, FA Amtr Cup QF Rep. 07-08, FA Tphy 3rd Rd Rep. 84-85, Isthmian Lg R-up(2) 83-85 (Div 1 82-83, Div 2 81-82 92-93), Athenian Lg Div 1 R-up 63-64 (Div 2 R-up 71-72, Lg Cup R-up 72-73, Mem. Shield 63-64), Sussex Snr Cup(19) 1892-93 1903-04 07-08 13-14 19-20 22-23 26-27 28-29 34-35 39-40 44-45 46-47 51-52 56-57 58-59 60-61 74-75 76-78, Sussex RUR Char. Cup(14) 03-04 06-08 09-10 13-14 19-20 22-23 26-27 33-34(jt) 41-42 44-45 48-49(jt) 52-54, Sussex Co. Lg(8) 20-22 26-27 28-29 30-31 33-34 38-40, W Sussex Lg(7) 1898-99 1903-04 06-08 09-10 12-14, Brighton Char. Cup(9) 29-31 34-35 62-63 69-71 73-74(jt) 80-82, Worthing Char. Cup(10) 11-12 25-27 30-31 32-35 37-39 64-65, AFA Invit. Cup 63-64 68-69 73-74 75-76 (Snr Cup R-up 36-37 46-47 48-49), Corinth. Lg Mem. Shield R-up 49-50 (Neale Tphy 58-59), Roy Hayden Mem. Tphy 1975(jt), 1977 1978, Don Morecraft Tphy 1972 1973 1976 1981 1982, Sussex F'llt Cup(2) 88-90, Sussex I'mediate Cup 34-35 64-65, Brighton Chal. Shield 29-30 31-32.

PROGRAMME DETAILS:
Pages: 24 **Price:** 50p
Editor: Secretary

Second Division

	P	W	D	L	W	D	L	F	A	Pts
			HOME			AWAY				
WORTHING	42	15	4	2	13	3	5	105	50	91
RUISLIP MANOR	42	14	6	1	11	6	4	78	33	87
BERKHAMSTED T.	42	13	3	5	11	5	5	77	55	80
HEMEL HEMPSTEAD	42	15	4	2	7	8	6	84	52	78
MET. POLICE	42	14	2	5	8	4	9	84	51	72
MALDEN VALE	42	11	3	7	9	6	6	78	54	69
CHERTSEY TOWN	42	10	2	9	10	5	6	84	60	67
SAFFRON WALDEN	42	11	5	5	8	5	8	63	49	67
NEWBURY TOWN	42	7	11	3	7	7	7	53	51	60
HAMPTON	42	10	5	6	6	6	9	59	59	59
EDGWARE TOWN	42	9	6	6	7	4	10	84	75	58
EGHAM TOWN	42	7	5	9	9	4	8	60	71	57
BANSTEAD ATHLETIC	42	9	5	7	5	8	8	67	52	55
LEATHERHEAD	42	9	5	7	5	6	10	66	61	53
WARE	42	5	9	7	7	2	12	68	76	47
WITHAM TOWN	42	6	6	9	4	10	7	54	65	46
TILBURY	42	6	7	8	6	1	14	55	101	44
BARTON ROVERS	42	6	9	6	3	5	13	40	66	41
HUNGERFORD TOWN	42	7	4	10	4	4	13	37	93	41
RAINHAM TOWN	42	4	5	12	5	5	11	56	80	37
HAREFIELD UNITED	42	4	4	13	6	3	12	37	72	37
SOUTHALL	42	5	2	14	2	5	14	43	106	28

Top League Goalscorers

Steve Newing (Hemel Hempstead)	27
(Includes 23 for Edgware Town)	
Peter Skerritt (Egham Town)	23
(Includes 7 for Chertsey Town)	
Andy Linsell (Hemel Hempstead)	20
Daniel Freeman (Worthing)	19
Richard Tiltman (Worthing)	18
Stan Blair (Malden Vale)	17

THE SECOND DIVISION RESULT CHART 1992-93

HOME TEAM	1	2	3	4	5	6	7	8	9	10	11	12	13	14	15	16	17	18	19	20	21	22
1. Banstead	*	2-2	0-1	0-1	1-2	1-2	1-1	5-2	1-1	8-0	4-2	2-0	1-0	0-1	4-1	1-2	1-0	1-0	4-1	2-2	0-0	0-3
2. Barton R.	1-0	*	1-1	2-2	3-0	0-0	1-0	0-0	0-3	0-0	0-3	0-1	0-1	1-1	2-1	2-2	1-1	0-2	3-2	1-1	0-2	
3. Berkhamsted	1-1	2-0	*	4-0	3-3	1-2	6-1	1-0	1-3	2-2	2-1	1-0	1-2	2-1	2-1	1-0	3-1	6-3	3-0	2-0	0-3	1-2
4. Chertsey	1-2	0-1	5-1	*	5-1	0-3	2-1	3-0	1-0	7-2	2-1	1-3	1-3	1-1	2-4	2-1	2-3	5-0	6-1	2-3	1-1	1-2
5. Edgware	1-1	2-1	0-3	4-0	*	1-0	4-1	6-1	2-2	4-1	1-1	1-1	3-1	1-2	2-2	0-1	1-2	4-4	2-3	5-2	4-2	1-2
6. Egham	0-2	0-0	1-1	1-2	2-5	*	1-2	1-3	6-4	1-1	3-2	0-2	2-0	1-1	2-0	1-3	2-0	3-2	2-1	1-3	3-3	2-5
7. Hampton	0-0	2-0	0-	1-3	3-3	2-3	*	2-2	1-0	1-3	3-2	0-1	1-3	0-0	2-0	1-1	1-0	0-2	7-0	3-1	3-0	3-0
8. Harefield	3-2	0-2	0-0	0-2	1-2	1-0	0-1	*	1-1	0-1	0-1	0-3	0-2	2-2	2-0	0-1	0-1	0-0	3-0	1-4	1-2	0-4
9. H.Hempstead	1-1	3-0	0-1	2-1	2-0	2-0	1-0	1-0	*	3-0	1-1	2-1	1-0	3-2	4-2	1-4	3-0	4-3	2-1	1-0	0-0	0-0
10. Hungerford	0-5	2-0	0-1	1-0	1-1	0-2	0-3	1-3	1-6	*	2-1	0-0	1-0	1-4	0-0	0-1	1-0	1-4	2-1	1-3	1-1	
11. Leatherhead	0-0	3-1	5-0	0-1	5-3	4-0	3-3	2-0	1-1	3-0	*	2-2	1-1	1-2	0-1	0-2	1-2	3-0	3-0	0-2	2-1	0-2
12. Malden V.	3-0	2-2	3-4	0-0	2-1	1-0	1-1	0-1	3-2	5-1	1-2	*	3-1	1-2	1-2	1-2	2-0	2-3	3-1	4-3	3-0	2-1
13. Met.Police	4-1	4-2	3-0	0-1	0-2	5-0	4-0	2-1	3-1	4-1	1-1	3-1	*	4-1	4-0	1-1	1-3	3-2	5-1	5-1	0-1	0-1
14. Newbury	1-1	2-2	0-2	2-2	1-0	0-0	3-1	0-1	2-2	0-0	2-2	2-1	3-0	*	3-2	0-0	1-1	1-0	0-1	1-1	0-0	3-1
15. Rainham	2-0	3-0	2-4	2-2	0-2	1-3	1-2	3-0	2-3	3-0	0-1	0-0	2-4	1-2	*	0-2	0-4	2-2	1-3	0-4	1-1	1-1
16. Ruislip	1-1	4-0	4-0	1-0	3-1	0-0	1-1	2-1	1-0	1-0	5-0	2-0	0-0	1-1	2-1	*	3-2	4-0	8-0	0-3	2-2	3-2
17. Saffron W.	0-2	2-0	2-1	2-2	2-0	2-0	1-0	1-0	1-1	1-2	1-2	2-2	1-0	2-3	0-0	1-1	*	3-0	0-1	4-0	3-0	3-2
18. Southall	0-3	0-3	0-2	0-5	1-0	0-2	1-1	3-0	0-1	1-0	0-2	0-3	3-6	3-0	0-4	1-2	1-1	*	1-0	2-4	2-1	1-2
19. Tilbury	3-2	2-1	0-3	1-3	0-4	1-1	1-1	0-3	4-4	3-4	3-2	3-3	0-1	4-2	2-1	1-2	2-2	0-0	*	1-0	2-2	1-3
20. Ware	2-1	2-0	0-2	0-3	4-1	2-3	2-2	2-2	2-3	2-3	1-1	0-3	1-1	1-1	1-1	1-1	1-1	2-1	2-0	*	1-1	3-4
21. Witham	2-2	2-2	1-1	1-3	1-2	1-4	0-1	0-2	0-0	2-0	2-1	2-3	2-0	1-0	0-0	1-3	0-2	7-0	1-1	1-0	*	1-5
22. Worthing	2-1	4-0	2-2	2-1	2-2	4-0	3-0	6-0	2-3	3-1	3-1	2-3	2-2	1-1	5-2	2-0	3-1	5-1	3-0	1-0	3-2	*

HOME TEAM	1	2	3	4	5	6	7	8	9	10	11	12	13	14	15	16	17	18	19	20	21	22
1. Banstead	*	44	39	78	31	29	78	43	63	36	82	58	67	57	39	43	47	42	51	48	29	108
2. Barton Rvrs	127	*	154	134	136	119	104	92	158	92	64	107	94	137	112	128	103	94	90	169	88	97
3. Berkhamsted	107	426	*	156	93	71	232	65	247	60	261	65	82	142	111	254	144	92	94	108	116	91
4. Chertsey	151	141	133	*	204	279	237	189	221	188	192	143	213	193	173	141	142	208	168	122	183	201
5. Edgware	74	65	164	172	*	167	125	116	136	128	126	53	152	157	145	216	146	57	108	104	143	235
6. Egham	74	54	78	276	109	*	151	77	111	76	125	47	75	168	83	143	57	120	97	51	111	132
7. Hampton	119	160	148	202	157	205	*	167	166	201	187	155	165	118	142	164	140	146	115	154	131	193
8. Harefield	93	94	97	140	132	72	108	*	141	103	95	48	53	83	96	140	25	143	72	71	40	101
9. Hemel H.	110	138	1130	107	120	148	102	92	*	72	90	72	146	113	44	152	102	90	120	98	78	145
10. Hungerford	66	84	74	96	76	71	81	82	63	*	76	80	59	251	93	90	62	100	71	84	74	84
11. Leatherhead	85	87	94	130	80	86	90	82	109	82	*	105	116	110	80	117	85	92	86	85	90	255
12. Malden V.	104	102	91	168	122	183	136	107	114	90	98	*	93	92	97	102	164	73	88	88	81	158
13. Met Police	150	154	86	265	106	100	170	102	95	72	140	151	*	110	105	154	70	105	121	75	97	172
14. Newbury	152	131	165	249	136	230	151	110	132	300	142	102	137	*	104	189	121	122	61	115	126	182
15. Rainham	67	57	52	65	46	38	65	64	51	51	53	37	22	43	*	81	52	50	135	45	56	65
16. Ruislip M.	117	168	105	374	258	127	175	215	317	135	174	115	248	135	137	*	271	179	153	228	178	234
17. Saffron W.	149	138	148	136	162	131	157	139	139	198	136	156	168	148	141	186	*	146	149	126	226	206
18. Southall	18	44	25	67	30	26	45	30	57	42	35	16	20	18	40	44	29	*	21	25	15	50
19. Tilbury	264	64	53	147	42	68	44	51	59	56	66	71	61	87	98	68	41	42	*	46	96	74
20. Ware	92	167	133	122	115	89	117	85	139	102	85	119	97	98	112	136	243	132	89	*	98	124
21. Witham	65	65	73	103	87	95	98	90	103	84	90	87	80	60	91	130	123	84	96	50	*	146
22. Worthing	124	302	192	230	214	325	243	416	203	278	214	241	203	674	197	495	189	159	940	614	224	*

NB. Hemel Hempstead v Rainham played at Tring Town FC. Newbury v Tilbury played at Wokingham Town FC. Southall v Ruislip Manor played at Hemel Hempstead FC. All other Southall home games at Harefield Utd FC. All Rainham home games at Purfleet FC.

Diadora League Division Two Ten Year Record

(See page 351 for clubs who only played in Div. 3 or Regionalised Div. 2)
(N - Denoted Division Two (North), S - Denotes Division Two (South))

	83/4	84/5	85/6	86/7	87/8	88/9	89/90	90/1	91/2	92/3
Banstead Athletic	-	9S	11S	17S	21S	16S	11S	11S	14	13
Barton Rovers	14	15N	17N	7N	15N	8N	5N	10N	11	18
Basildon United	1	-	-	-	-	-	7N	18N	-	-
Berkhamsted Town	-	9N	10N	16N	4N	15N	17N	5N	18	3
Billericay Town	-	-	-	-	-	6N	15N	3N	3	-
Chertsey Town	-	19S	-	6S	6S	12S	13S	14S	-	7
Corinthian-Casuals	5	-	-	-	-	-	-	-	-	-
Dorking (Town)	9	12S	9S	3S	3S	1S	-	-	-	-
Eastbourne United	20	16S	15S	11S	12S	11S	16S	20S	-	-
Edgware Town	-	-	-	-	-	-	-	14N	-	11
Egham Town	11	6S	17S	14S	14S	10S	10S	3S	6	12
Epping Town	12	-	-	-	-	-	-	-	-	-
Finchley	19	2N	-	-	12N	3S	18N	21N	-	-
Grays Athletic	8	1S	-	-	-	-	-	-	-	-
Hampton	-	-	-	-	-	-	-	12S	-	10
Harefield United	-	18N	18N	10S	13S	5S	12S	7S	19	21
Hemel Hempstead	17	14N	14N	20N	19N	12N	14N	9N	9	4
Horsham	22	10S	18S	13S	15S	20S	21S	15S	-	-
Hungerford Town	6	4S	13S	9S	8S	6S	9S	9S	10	19
Leatherhead	-	-	-	-	-	-	-	10S	4	14
Letchworth Garden City	15	10N	12N	6N	11N	21N	22N	-	-	-
Lewes	-	-	-	-	-	-	-	-	2	-
Leyton-Wingate	3	1N	-	-	-	-	-	-	-	-
Malden Vale	-	-	-	-	-	-	15S	4S	15	6
Metropolitan Police	-	-	7S	7S	2S	-	-	-	7	5
Molesey	13	3S	6S	19S	17S	4S	2S	-	-	-
Newbury Town	16	18S	4S	20S	18S	19S	7S	8S	22	9
Purfleet	-	-	-	-	-	2N	-	7N	1	-
Rainham Town	18	13S	13N	18N	16N	19N	21N	8N	16	20
Ruislip Manor	-	11S	19S	5S	9S	7S	4S	5S	5	2
Saffron Walden Town	-	5N	9N	11N	18N	20N	10N	11N	8	8
St Albans City	2	-	-	-	-	-	-	-	-	-
Southall	10	7S	8S	21S	16S	18S	6S	6S	20	22
Southwick	-	-	1S	-	-	-	-	-	21	-
Tilbury	-	-	-	-	3N	17N	6N	17N	-	17
Tring Town	4	6N	7N	8N	10N	3N	19N	22N	-	-
Uxbridge	7	2S	-	-	-	-	-	-	-	-
Ware	21	20N	15N	10N	6N	11N	13N	4N	17	15
Witham Town	-	-	-	-	7N	13N	20N	6N	13	16
Worthing	-	-	-	-	-	-	-	-	12	1
No. of clubs competing	22	20N	20N	22N	22N	22N	22N	22N	22	22
		19S	20S	21S	22S	21S	21S	22S		

ALDERSHOT TOWN (1992)

Chairman: Terry Owens   **President:** Arthur English
Secretary: Peter Bridgeman, 4 Shortheath Rd, Farnham, Surrey GU9 8SR (0252 725437. Fax: 0252 733659).
Manager: Steve Wignall   **Coach:** Paul Shrubb/ Keith Baker   **Physio:** Edward McAlister
Commercial Manager: Kevin Donegan   **Press Officer:** Nick Fryer.
Ground: Recreation Ground, High Street, Aldershot, Hants GU11 1TW.
Directions: Ground situated on eastern end of High Street next to large multi-storey B.T. building. From M3 (jct 4) take A325 to Aldershot. After five miles at r'bout take 1st exit marked town centre (A323) into Wellington Ave. At Burger King r'bout take 2nd exit into High Street - ground on left, large car park adjacent. 5 mins walk from Aldershot (BR).
Capacity: 5,000   **Cover:** 4,500   **Seats:** 1,800   **Founded:** 1992.   **Metal Badges:** Y
Cols: Red & blue stripes/red/blue   **Change colours:** White & blue stripes/blue/blue.
Club Shop: Yes. Range of souvenirs, programmes, replica kits. Open matchdays or contact Bob Newell (0252 26620) for mail order.
Sponsors: Datrontec.   **Players progressing to Football League:** N/A.
Previous Leagues: None.   **Previous Name:** None.   **Nickname:** Shots
Midweek home matchday: Tuesday   **Reserve Team's League:** Suburban.
Programme: 40 pages, £1   **Programme Editor:** Karl Prentice (0256 471630).
Record win: 6-1 v Camberley, 20/3/93   **Record defeat:** 1-2 v Clapton, 2/1/93.
Record Attendance: 5,961 v Farnborough Town, Hants Senior Cup SF 16/3/93. *Ground record: 19,138 Aldershot FC v Carlisle United, FA Cup 4th Rd replay 28/1/70.*
Clubhouse: 7-11pm every evening and matchdays. Pool, darts, juke box, satellite T.V. Steward: Ian Andrews c/o the club.
92-93 Captain: Dave Osgood   **92-93 P.o.Y.:** Mark Butler   **92-93 Top scorer:** Steve Stairs 32.
Local Newspapers: Aldershot News (0252 28221), Farnham Herald (0252 725224).
Local Radio: County Sound (203m m/w, 1476 khz), BBC Radio Surrey (104.6 fm), Radio 210 (210m m/w).
Hons: Isthmian Lge Div 3 92-93, Simpsonair Tphy 92-93, Skol Invitation Tphy 92-93, Hant Snr Cup SF 92-93.

Aldershot Town - Diadora League Division Three Champions 1992-93. Photo - Ian Morseman.

AVELEY

Chairman: Tony Wallace   **Vice C'man:** Bill Maddicks   **President:** Ken Clay
Secretary: Ken Sutliff, 9 Westlyn Close, Rainham, Essex RM13 9JP (0708 555271).
Team Manager: Colin McBride   **Asst Mgr/Coach:** Fran Cowley
Press Officer: Alan Suttling   **Physio:** Phil Hunter
Ground Address & Tel: 'Mill Field', Mill Road, Aveley, Essex RM15 4TR (0708 865940).
Directions: London - Southend A13, turn into Sandy Lane at Aveley. Rainham or Purfleet BR stations then bus No. 723 to the ground.
Capacity: 8,000 (400 Covered)   **Seats:** 400   **Floodlights:** Yes **Shop:** No **Metal Badges:** Yes
Colours: Royal blue/white/royal blue   **Change colours:** All yellow.
Founded: 1927   **Nickname:** Millers.
Previous Leagues: Thurrock Combination 46-49/ London 49-57/ Delphian 57-63/ Athenian 63-73.
Midweek home matchday: Tuesday   **Reserve Team's League:** Essex & Herts Border Comb.
Record Attendance: 3,741 v Slough Town, FA Amateur Cup 27/2/71.
Best F.A. Cup season: 1st Rd 70-71 (lost 0-1 to Yeovil).
League clubs defeated in F.A. Cup: None.   **Record win:** 11-1 v Histon, 24/8/63
Record defeat: against Orient, Essex Thameside Trophy, 11/4/85.
Players progressing to Football League: David Case & Alan Hull (Orient), Alan Parkinson (Orient 1967), Yilmaz Orhan (W Ham 1972), Keith Day (Colchester 1984), Paul Williams (Charlton & Sheff Wed).
Clubhouse: Normal pub hours. All kinds of bar snacks and hot food.
Club Record Goalscorer: Jotty Wilks, 214   **Club Record Appearances:** Ken Riley, 422
92-93 Captain: Mark Kuene   **92-93 Player of the Year:** Mark Kuene
92-93 Top scorer: John Gilliland, 10
Local Press: Thurrock Gazette (0375 372293).   **Local Radio:** Radio Essex, Essex Radio.
Honours: Isthmian Lg Div 2 (North) R-up 89-90 (Lg (AC Delco) Cup 89-90), London Lg 51-52 54-55 (R-up 55-56, Lg Cup 53-54), Delphian Lg R-up 57-58 (Lg Cup 61-62), Athenian Lg 70-71 (Div 2 R-up 68-69), Essex Junior Cup 47-48 48-49, Essex Thameside Trophy 79-80, Hornchurch Charity Cup 81-82 (R-up 83-84), East Anglian Cup 88-89, FA Amateur Cup QF 70-71, FA Tphy 3rd Qualifying Rd replay 74-75, FA Vase 3rd Rd 89-90.

Aveley F.C. 1992-93.

BANSTEAD ATHLETIC

Chairman: Terry Molloy   **President:**
Secretary: Gordon Taylor, 116 Kingston Avenue, North Cheam, Surrey SM3 9UF (081 641 2957).
Manager: Bobby Mapleson   **Asst Mgr:** Michael Sorenson   **Physio:** Kevin Taylor
Press Officer: Colin Darby   **Commercial Manager:** Alan McIlvenna
Ground: Merland Rise, Tadworth, Surrey KT20 5JG (0737 350982).
Directions: Follow signs to Tattenham Corner (Epsom racecourse), then to Banstead Sports Centre. Ground adjacent to swimming pool. Half a mile from Tattenham Corner (BR). Bus 420 from Sutton stops outside ground. Also buses 406 & 727 from Epsom.
Capacity: 3,500   **Seats:** 250   **Cover:** 500   **Floodlights:** Yes   **Founded:** 1944
Colours: Amber/black/black   **Change colours:** Red & white   **Nickname:** A's.
Programme: 28 pages, 50p   **Editor:** Secretary   **Club Shop:** No
Midweek Matchday: Tuesday   **Previous Ground:** Tattenham Way Rec. 1944-50.
Previous Leagues: Surrey Int./Surrey Snr 49-65/ Spartan 65-75/ London Spartan 75-79/ Athenian 79-84.
Reserve Team's League: Suburban
Sponsors: PDM Marketing   **Record Gate:** 1,400 v Leytonstone, FA Amateur 1953.
Best FA Cup year: 3rd Qual.Rd. 86-87
Record win: 12-0 v Reigate Priory   **Record defeat:** 0-10 v St Albans City.
Players progressing to Football League: W Chesney & B Robinson (Crystal Palace).
Clubhouse: Mon-Sat noon-11pm, noon-2 & 7.30-11pm Sun. 2 bars, real ale, bar snacks.
Club Record Scorer: Harry Clark   **Club Record Appearances:** Dennis Wall.
92-93 Captain: Steve Shaw   **92-93 P.o.Y.:** Vivian Jeffrey   **92-93 Top scorer:** Andy Yetzes 29
Local Press: Banstead Herald.   **Local Radio Stations:**.
Hons: F.A. Vase QF 92-93, Surrey Snr Lg(6) 50-54 56-57 64-65 (R-up(5) 49-50 54-56 57-59, Lg Cup 57-58, Charity Cup 52-53 58-59), London Spartan Lg R-up 77-78 (Lg Cup(2) 65-67), Surrey Prem. Cup R-up 91-92, Surrey Snr Shield 55-56, Gilbert Rice F'lit Cup 81-82 86-87 (R-up(4) 82-86), Athenian Lg Cup(2) 80-82 (R-up 82-83 (SF 79-80)), Surrey Int. Lg(2) 47-49, Surrey Int. Cup 46-47 54-55, E. Surrey Charity Cup(4) 59-60 66-67 76-78 (R-up 79-80, I'mediate Sect. 75-76 (R-up 76-77), Jnr Sect. 81-82), Southern Comb. Cup R-up 69-70, Suburban Lg R-up 86-87.

Banstead Athletic pictured before their F.A. Vase Fifth Round victory at home to Newport Isle of Wight. Photo - Eric Marsh.

BARTON ROVERS

Chairman: R E Roberts **Vice Chairman:** A F Monks **President:** P Howarth.
Secretary: Owen Clark, 108 Manor Road, Barton-le-Clay, Bedford MK45 4NS (0582 882398).
Manager: Gordon Taylor **Gen. Manager:** Mick Huckle **Coach:** Bob Peck.
Press Officer: N Rhodes (0462 834980) **Physio:** Roy Cullis.
Ground: Sharpenhoe Road, Barton-le-Clay, Bedford MK45 4SD (0582 882607).
Directions: M1 Jct 12, from London exit turn right, take 2nd right through Harlington and Sharpenhoe. Ground on right entering village. Four and a half miles from Harlington (BR), 6 miles from Luton (BR), good bus service from Luton.

Capacity: 4,000	**Seats:** 120	**Cover:** 1,120 **Floodlights:** Yes	**Founded:** 1898
Colours: Blue/white/blue		**Change colours:** All red.	**Shop:** Not at pres.
Programme: 36 pages, 50p		**Editor:** Nick Rhodes (0462 733670)	**Metal Badges:** Yes
Previous Ground: Barton Rec.		**Midweek Matchday:** Tuesday	

Previous Leagues: Luton & Dist. 47-54/ South Midlands 54-79.
Reserve Team's League: Campri Sth Mids.
Record Gate: 1,900 v Nuneaton, FA Cup 4th Qual. Rd 1976. **Nickname:** Rovers
Best F.A. Cup year: 1st Rd. 80-81 (lost 0-2 at Torquay United). **Sponsors:** N/A.
Record win: 17-1 v Flitwick Athletic (H), South Midlands Lge Division One 55-56.
Record defeat: 1-11 v Leighton United (H), South Midlands Lge Premier Division 62-63.
Record Fees - Paid: £1,000 for B Baldrey (Hitchin Town, 1980).
  Received: £1,000 for B Baldrey (Bishop's Stortford, 1981).
Players progressing to Football League: Kevin Blackwell (Notts County, Scarborough).
Clubhouse: Noon-3pm weekends (no football), noon-11pm (matchdays), 7-11pm weekdays. Real ale, hot & cold snacks, pool, darts, gaming machines.
Club Record Appearances: W Goodyear, 16.
92-93 Top scorer: Gordon Guile 16 **92-93 Captain & P.o.Y.:** Danny Turner.
Local Press: Luton News, Herald. **Local Radio:** Radio Chiltern, Radio Beds.
Hons: F.A. Vase R-up 77-78 (SF 76-77 81-82, QF 75-76 78-79), Sth Mids Lg(8) 70-73 74-79 (R-up 67-68, Div 1 64-65 (R-up 55-56), Div 2 54-55, Lg Shield 57-58 60-61 68-69, Chal. Tphy 71-72 74-75 77-78 78-79), Beds Snr Cup (5) 71-73 80-82 89-90 (R-up(3) 74-76 82-83 90-91), Beds Premier Cup R-up 81-82 83-84 88-89, Beds Intermediate Cup 53-54, Luton & Dist. Lg Div 3 47-48, North Beds Charity Cup 72-73 74-75 76-77 77-78 79-80 80-81 (R-up 70-71), Isthmian Lg Associate Members Tphy R-up 92-93.

CHERTSEY TOWN

Chairman: David Rayner **Vice Chairman:** Chris Mason **President:** Cllr Chris Norman
Press Officer/Secretary: Chris Gay, 23 Richmond Close, Frimley, Camberley, Surrey GU16 5NR (0276 20745).
Manager: Jim Kelman **Asst Manager:** Steve Nicholls **Coach:** John Granville.

Physio: Jean Lewis **Comm. Manager:** Brain Walker
Ground: Alwyns Lane, Chertsey, Surrey KT16 9DW (0932 561774).
Directions: Alwyns Lane is off Windsor Street at north end of shopping centre. 10 mins walk from Chertsey (BR). London Country bus.

Capacity: 3,000	**Seats:** 200	**Cover:** 400	**Floodlights:** Yes **Founded:** 1890
Colours: Blue & white stripes/white/blue			**Change colours:** All gold.
Club Shop: Yes (manager - Martin Gay 0276 20745)			**Sponsors:** Data Express.
Programme: 32 pages, 60p		**Programme Editor:** Secretary	**Metal Badges:** £2
Previous Ground: The Grange (pre-World War 1)/ The Hollows (pre-1929).			

Midweek Matchday: Tuesday
Previous Leagues: West Surrey (pre-1899)/ Surrey Jnr 1899-1920/ Surrey Intermediate 20-46/ Surrey Snr 46-63/ Metropolitan 63-66/ Gtr London 66-67/ Spartan 67-75/ London Spartan 75-76/ Athenian 76-84/ Isthmian 84-85/ Combined Counties 85-86.
Nickname: Curfews **Youth Team's League:** Allied Counties.
Record Gate: 1,480 v Walton & Hersham, FA Amtr Cup 1962.
Best F.A. Cup year: 3rd Qualifying Rd 92-93 (lost 1-3 at home to Kingstonian).
Record win: 10-1 v Clapton (H), Isthmian Lge Division Three, 91-92.
Record defeat: 1-12 v Bromley (H), F.A. Cup Preliminary Rd, 82-83.
Players progressing to Football League: Rachid Harkouk (Notts County).
Clubhouse: Open weekday evenings and weekend lunchtimes. Dancehall, pool, darts.
Club Record Goalscorer: Alan Brown.
92-93 Captain: Darren Britnell **92-93 P.o.Y.:** Paddy McCarthy
92-93 Top scorer: Marco Ellerker. **Local Press:** Surrey Herald.
Hons: FA Vase QF 87-88 91-92, Isthmian Lg Div 3 R-up 91-92, Surrey Snr Lg 59-60 61-62 62-63 (Lg Cup 59-60 61-62), Combined Co's Lg R-up 85-86 (Concours Tphy 85-86), Surrey Snr Cup R-up 85-86, Spartan Lg & Lg Cup R-up 74-75.

PHOTOS OPPOSITE

Top: Barton Rovers F.C. 1992-93. Back Row (L/R): D Kerridge (Trainer), G Brown (Coach), G Bambrick, P Palma, L Bozier, P Olney, S Merrick, M Huckle (General Manager). Front: S Flain, G Golds, F Geddes, D Turner (Captain), B Lalor, S Endacott, D Foster, C McGill.

Centre: Chertsey's Bradley Pratt is sandwiched by two Hungerford Town players. Photo - Vanessa Hardwick.

Foot: Chertsey Town F.C. 1992-93. Back Row (L/R): Marco Ellerker, Sean West, Adam Walker, Jason Tucker, Simon Line, Trevor Algrave, John Granville, Michael Putnam, Jon Turner, Darren Britnell (Captain). Front: Patrick McCarthy, Sean Norman, Andy Driscoll, Dean Callaghan. Photo - Richard Brock.

COLLIER ROW

Chairman: Alan Punter **Vice Chairman:** Ron Walker **President:** George Rose.
Secretary: Phil Sammons, 41 Riversdale Rd, Collier Row, Romford, Essex RM5 2NP (0708 768845).
Manager: Reg Wells **Coach:** Micky Cleaver
Press Officer: George Rose (0708 722675) **Comm. Mgr:** John Barrington
Ground: 'Sungate', Collier Row Rd, Collier Row, Romford, Essex (0708 722766).
Directions: A12 from London, left at Moby Dick (PH) traffic lights, right at next r'bout, ground entrance signposted 200 yards on right.
Capacity: 2,000 **Seats:** 110 **Cover:** 200 **Floodlights:** Yes **Founded:** 1929
Colours: Red/black/black **Change colours:** White/red/red **Nickname:** The Row
Club Shop: Yes, selling programmes, scarves, T-shirts, sweatshirts, badges, pennants, pens, key-rings. Contact Ian Ansell (081 500 9778).
Reserve's Lge: Essex Business Houses **Club Sponsors:** K-Sports. **Metal Badges:** Yes
Programme: 20 pages, 50p **Editor:** Phil Sammons (0708 768845)
Midweek Matchday: Wednesday **Previous Leagues:** London Spartan 81-86.
Previous Names: None **Previous Grounds:** None.
Record Gate: 1,095 v Garforth Town, FA Vase 6th Rd 1987.
Best F.A. Cup year: 1st Qualifying Rd replay 91-92, lost 0-1 v Purfleet (H) after 2-2 draw.
Clubhouse: Two function rooms, one members' bar. Normal pub hours, bar food available.
Club Record Scorer: Steve Thompson 158
Club Record Appearances: Graham Cole 278.
92-93 Captain: Gary Nisbet **92-93 P.o.Y & Top scorer:** Billy Read.
Local Press: Havering Recorder **Local Radio:** Essex Radio, BBC Essex.
Hons: F.A. Vase SF 86-87 (QF 84-85), London Spartan Lg 83-84 85-86 (R-up 84-85), Senior Div 82-83, Lg Cup R-up 84-85), Isthmian Lg Div 2 North R-up 87-88, Knight Floodlit Cup R-up 89-90.

Collier Row F.C. 1992-93. Back Row (L/R): Leroy Houston, Robert Mansfield, Tony Scawthorn, Billy Read, Steve Goodman, Kevin Tredgold, Gary Nisbet, Andy Brennan. Front: Dave Bushell, Ian Jenkins, Ian Little, Pat Kelly, Terry O'Neill, Brian Balkwell. Photo - Richard Brock.

EDGWARE TOWN

Chairman: Vince Deritis **President:** M Flynn **Patron:** Russell Grant.
Secretary: Thomas Higgins, 34 Francis Rd, Harrow, Middx HA1 2QX (081 863 4022).
Manager: Brian Rider **Coach:** J McGleish
Treasurer: T Donohue **Physio:** J Tyler MCSP
Press Officer: Brian Rider (081 907 6158)
Ground: White Lion Ground, High Street, Edgware HA8 5AQ (081 952 6799).
Directions: Edgware station, turn left, left again, ground on right. Buses 186 and 142.
Capacity: 6,000 **Seats:** 220 **Cover:** 1,200 **Floodlights:** Yes **Founded:** 1939
Colours: All green **Change colours:** All blue
Programme: 6 pages with admission **Editor:** Barry Boreham (081 952 1685).
Club Shop: No **Metal Badges:** Planned.
Midweek Matchday: Wednesday
Previous Leagues: Corinthian 46-63/ Athenian 64-84/ London Spartan 84-90.
Previous Names: Edgware F.C. **Previous Grounds:** None.
Reserve Team's League: Suburban **Nickname:** Wares.
Record Gate: 8,500 v Wealdstone, FA Cup 1948.
Clubhouse: Open nightly and weekend lunchtimes. Dancehall, three bars, pool, darts, juke box.
Steward: J Connell.
92-93 Captain: Seamus Finnerty **92-93 P.o.Y:** John Manhan **92-93 Top scorer:** Steve Newing 25
Hons: FA Vase 5th Rd 91-92, Isthmian Lg Div 3 91-92, London Spartan Lg 87-88 89-90 (Lg Cup 87-88), Corinthian Lg R-up 53-54 (Memorial Shield 52-53 61-62), Athenian Lg R-up 81-82, Middx Snr Lg 40-41 41-42 42-43 43-44 44-45, Middx Snr Cup 47-48 (R-up 73-74), London Snr Cup R-up 47-48, Middx Border Lg Cup 79-80, Suburban Lg Div R-up 89-90.

EGHAM TOWN

Chairman: Pat Bennett   **Vice Chairman:** Peter Barnes   **President:** Archie Doye
Secretary: Keith Thompson, 15a Clarence Str., Egham, Surrey (0784 433277).
Manager: Eric Howard   **Physio:** Des Hunt.
Press Officer: Mark Ferguson (0932 783333)   **Comm. Mgr:** Chris Thompson
Ground: Tempest Road, Pooley Green, Egham, Surrey TW20 9DW (0784 436466).
Directions: M25 jct 13, follow signs to Egham, under M25 at r'bout, left to end, left at mini-r'bout, over railway crossing, left to end (Pooley Green Rd), right, ground on right after 'Compasses' and 'Robin Hood' pubs. Bus 441 from Staines to Poolley Green. Forty mins walk from Egham (BR) station.
Capacity: 3,000   **Seats:** 230   **Cover:** 1,120   **Floodlights:** Yes   **Founded:** 1896
Colours: Royal & gold   **Change colours:** All white   **Club Shop:** No
Programme: 12 pages, 60p   **Editor:** Mark Ferguson (0932 783333)   **Metal Badges:** £1.70
Club Sponsors: Paton of Walton   **Midweek Matches:** Tuesday.   **Nickname:** Sarnies
Previous Leagues: Parthenon 64-65/ Surrey Snr 65-67/ Spartan 67-74/ Athenian 74-77.
Prev. Name: Egham F.C. 1896-1963   **Reserve Team's League:** Suburban
Best FA Cup year: 4th Qual Rd 90-91 (lost 0-2 at Telford United.
Record Gate: 1,400 v Wycombe Wanderers, F.A. Cup 2nd Qualifying Rd 1972.
Record Fees - Paid: £3,000 for Mark Butler, 1990.
     Received: £4,000 for Mark Butler (Wycombe Wanderers, 1988).
Record win: 10-1 v Camberley Town, 81-82
Record defeat: 1-7 v Worthing (A), F.A. Cup 1st Qualifying Rd replay, 92-93.
Clubhouse: (0784 435226) 7-11pm and weekend lunchtimes. Members bar, function hall and pool room.
Club Record Scorer: Mark Butler 50 (91-92)   **Club Record Appearances:** Dave Jones 850+.
92-93 Captain: John Exer   **92-93 P.o.Y.:** Jason Day   **92-93 Top scorer:** David Trayler, 20.
Local Press: Herald & News (0932 561111).   **Local Radio:** County Sound.
Hons: Isthmian Lg Loctite Tphy R-up 91-92, Spartan Lg 71-72 (Lg Cup R-up 67-68), Athenian Lg R-up 75-76 (Div 2 74-75), Surrey Snr Cup R-up 91-92.

HAMPTON

Chairman: Robert Hayes   **Vice C'men:** John Roberts/Ken Gazzard   **President:** Alan Simpson
Secretary: Adrian Mann, 30 Burniston Court, Manor Rd, Wallington, Surrey SM6 0AD (081 773 0858).
Manager: Mark Fewings   **Assistant Manager:** Tim Hollands   **Physio:** Glen Hayler.
Press Officer: Ray Franks (0932 227303)
Ground: Beveree Stadium, Beaver Close, off Station Rd, Hampton TW12 2BX (081 941 4936-boardroom).
Directions: 5 mins walk along Station Rd from Hampton (BR) - half hourly service from London Waterloo via Clapham Junction, Wimbledon & Kingston. Buses 111 (Hampton-Heathrow) & 216 (Kingston-Staines) stop in Station Rd. 726 (Dartford-Kingston-Windsor) & 267 (Hammersmith-Hampton Court) stop in nearby Church Street. By road; A3 out of London, fork left (signed Staines/Esher/Sandown Pk) onto A243, A309 Staines exit to Hampton Ct at 'Scilly Isles' r'bout, left at r'bout after Hampton Court Bridge onto A308, after 1 mile right into Church Street (A311), left after White Hart after 200yds into High Street, Station Rd on right just before junction with A308. From M25; jct 12, M3 towards London, jct 1 for the A308 (Sunbury) and turn right under M'way onto A308 for Kingston & Hampton, continue past racecourse, left into Hampton High Street just after waterworks (on right), Station Rd is 1st left.
Capacity: 2,000   **Seats:** 200   **Cover:** 1,000   **Floodlights:** Yes   **Founded:** 1920
Colours: Red & blue/white/blue   **Change:** White/tangerine/tangerine.   **Nickname:** Beavers
Club Shop: Yes, selling various club souvenirs and programmes. Contact Les Rance (081 898 1085).
Programme: 28 pages, 50p   **Programme Editor:** Secretary   **Metal Badges:** Yes
Midweek Matchday: Tuesday   **Sponsors:** Saft-Nife Ltd.
Previous Leagues: Kingston & District 21-33/ South West Middx 33-59/ Surrey Snr 59-64/ Spartan 64-71/ Athenian 71-73.
Previous Names: None   **Previous Grounds:** None
Record win: 11-1 v Eastbourne United, Isthmian League Division Two (South), 91-92
Record defeat: 0-13 v Hounslow Town, 62-63.
Reserve Team's League: Suburban   **Record gate:** Unknown.
Best F.A. Cup year: 4th Qualifying Round 77-78 (lost 1-2 v Barnet).
Record Fees - Paid: £400 for Peter Shodiende (Hendon, 1981)
     Received: £2,500 from APOP (Cyprus) for Ricky Walkes (June 1989).
Clubhouse: (081 979 2456). Lounge bar and Hall, open on matchdays and training nights. Hall available for hire.
Steward: Steve Penny.
Players progressing to Football League: Andy Rogers (Southampton, Plymouth, Reading), Dwight Marshall (Plymouth), Paul Rogers (Sheffield Utd).
Club Record Goalscorer: Peter Allen   **Club Record Appearances:** Joe Andrews.
92-93 Captain: Malcolm Dickenson   **92-93 P.o.Y.:** Steve Cheshire   **92-93 Top scorer:** Steve Kuhne 19
Local Newspapers: Middx Chronicle, Surrey Comet, Richmond & Twickenham Times, The Informer.
Hons: London Snr Cup(2) 86-88, Spartan Lg(4) 64-67 69-70 (R-up 67-68, Lg Cup(4) 64-68 (R-up(2) 68-70), Reserve Section 66-67 67-68, Reserve Cup 64-65 65-66 70-71), Surrey Snr Lg 63-64 (Lg Cup R-up 60-61, Reserve Cup 61-62), Middx Charity Cup 69-70 (R-up 68-69 71-72 89-90), Middx Snr Cup R-up 71-72 76-77, Athenian Lg Div 2 R-up 72-73, Southern Comb. Cup 68-69 71-72 76-77 81-82 83-84 85-86 (R-up 77-78 79-80), Middx Premier Cup(res) 92-93 (R-up 85-86 86-87), London I'mediate Cup(res) SF 64-65, Suburban Lg(Sth) R-up 85-86 (Lg Cup 85-86).

Hampton players acknowledge goalkeeper David Hook - ever-present for two seasons. Photo - Les Rance.

HEMEL HEMPSTEAD

Chairman: Roy Howells **President:** R Doyle **Vice President:** T Abbott
Secretary: T.B.A.
Manager: Gordon Taylor **Assistant Manager:** Bob Peck **Coach:** Bob Peck
Press Off.: Roy Howells (0442 258554) **Physio:** Ken McParland **Comm. Mgr:** D Evans
Ground: Vauxhall Ground, Adeyfield Rd, Hemel Hempstead HP2 4HW (0442 242081-club, 259777-boardroom).
Directions: Euston to Hemel Hempstead Station. H2 or H3 bus to Windmill Rd, Longlands.
Capacity: 3,000 **Seats:** 100 **Cover:** Yes **Floodlights:** Yes **Founded:** 1885
Colours: All red **Change colours:** All blue
Club Shop: Yes **Metal Badges:** No **Sponsors:** County Cable.
Programme: 36 pages, 50p **Editor:** D Evans (0442 259777).
Midweek Matchday: Tuesday **Previous Leagues:** Spartan 22-52/ Delphian 52-63/ Athenian 63-77.
Previous Names: Apsley 1885-1947)/ Hemel H'stead Town (merged with Hemel H'stead Utd in 1947).
Previous Grounds: Crabtree Lane (til '71).
Reserve Team's League: Essex & Herts Border Combination **Nickname:** Hemel
Record Gate: 2,000 v Watford 1985 (at Crabtree Lane: 3,500 v Tooling, FA Amtr Cup 1st Rd 1962).
Best FA Cup year: Never past Qualifying Rounds.
Clubhouse: (0442 259777). 7-11pm weekends, noon-11pm weekends and Bank Holidays. Pool, darts. Bingo Tuesday. Race nights. Dancing Fri, Sat & Sun nights. Tea bar open matchdays; teas, soup, burgers, hot dogs.
Players progressing to Football League: Colin and Ernie Bateman (Watford).
Club Record Goalscorer: Dai Price **Club Record Apps:** John Wallace, 1012.
92-93 Captain: **92-93 P.o.Y.:** **92-93 Top scorer:** Steve Newing 29 (25 for Edgware)
Local Press: Hemel Gazette, Herald. **Local Radio:** Beds Radio.
Hons: Herts Snr Cup 05-06 07-08 08-09 25-26 61-62 65-66 91-92, Herts Charity Cup/Shield 25-26 34-35 51-52 63-64 76-77 83-84 (R-up 90-91), Spartan Lg 33-34, Herts Intermediate Cup 54-55 65-66 83-84, West Herts St Mary Cup 70-71 75-76 82-83 85-86 90-91 91-92, Athenian Lg Div 1 R-up 64-65 (Reserves Cup 65-66), Delphian Lg(reserves) 54-55 (Reserves Cup 54-55 61-62).

HUNGERFORD TOWN

Chairman: Ron Tarry **Vice Chairman:** Alan Richards **President:** Sir Seton Wills.
Secretary: Eric Richardson, 3 Windermere Way, Thatcham, Berks RG13 4UL (0536 68674).
Manager: Gerry Smith **Asst Manager:** Norman Matthews **Coach:** Darren Angell
Press Officer: Michael Hall (0488 685241) **Physio:** Steve Puffet.
Ground: Town Ground, Bulpit Lane, Hungerford RG17 0AY (0488 682939-club, 684597-boardroom).
Directions: M4 jct 14 to A4, right and left at Bear Hotel, through town centre on A338, left into Priory Rd, second left into Bulpit Rd, over crossroads, ground on left. Three quarters of a mile from Hungerford BR station.
Capacity: 4,500 **Seats:** 130 **Cover:** 700 **Floodlights:** Yes **Founded:** 1886
Colours: White/blue/white **Change colours:** All red.
Metal Badges: Yes
Club Shop: Yes. Programmes, books, ties and scarves from Martin Wiltshire (0488 682218).
Programme: 24 pages, 30p **Editor:** Martin Wiltshire (0488 682218).
Midweek Matchday: Tuesday **Prev. Lges:** Newbury & D./ Swindon & D./ Hellenic 58-78.
Previous Names: None **Previous Grounds:** None.
Nickname: Crusaders. **Reserve Team's League:** Suburban (West)
Record Gate: 1,684 v Sudbury Town, FA Vase SF 1st leg 88-89 (20,000 v Modena in Italy 1981).
Record transfer fee paid: £4,000 for Joe Scott (Yeovil Town)
   received: £3,800 for Joe Scott (Barnstaple Town).
Best FA Cup year: 1st Rd 79-80 (lost 1-3 at Slough Town).
Clubhouse: (0488 682939). Open every evening and lunchtimes under Sunday. 2 bars, dancehall, boardroom/committee room, darts, pool, fruit machines. Hot & cold snacks. Stewards: Bob & Sandra Ponsford.
Players progressing to Football League: Steve Hetzke (Reading, Blackpool, Sunderland), Bruce Walker (Swindon, Blackpool), Des McMahon (Reading), Brian Mundee (Bournemouth, Northampton), Darren Anderson.
Club Record Scorer: Ian Farr (200+) **Club Record Appearances:** Dean Bailey (approx 400)
92-93 Capt.: Warren Angell **92-93 P.o.Y.:** Micky Cummins **92-93 Top scorer:** Steven Tucker 12
Local Press: Newbury Weekly News, Newbury Evening Post **Local Radio:** Brunel Radio, Radio 210.
Hons: FA Vase SF 77-78 79-80 88-89, Berks & Bucks Snr Cup 81-82 (R-up 75-76 76-77), Hellenic Lg Div 1 70-71 (Prem Div Cup 77-78, Div 1 Cup 70-71, Benevolent Cup 60-61).

LEATHERHEAD

Chairman: Tony Bates   **Vice Chairman:** Lance Dooley   **President:** G Darby
Secretary: Martyn Cole, 1 Elm Tree Ave., Esher, Surrey KT10 8JG (081 398 1751).
Manager: Mickey Byrne   **Assistant Manager:** Paul Andrews   **Coach:** Tony Combe.
Press Officer: G Darby   **Physio:** Ted Richards.
Ground: Fetcham Grove, Guildford Rd, Leatherhead, Surrey KT22 9AS (0372 377636-boardroom).
Directions: M25 jct 9 to Leatherhead; follow signs to Leisure Centre, ground adjacent. Half mile from Leatherhead (BR). London Country Buses 479 and 408 - ground opposite bus garage.
Capacity: 3,400   **Seats:** 200   **Cover:** 445   **Floodlights:** Yes   **Founded:** 1946
Colours: Green/black/black   **Change colours:** White/green/green   **Nickname:** Tanners
Programme: 20 pages, 40p   **Editor:** Neil Grant (0372 386628)   **Club Shop:** No
Midweek Matchday: Tuesday   **Sponsors:** Champs Fun Pubs   **Metal Badges:** No
Previous Leagues: Surrey Snr 46-50/ Metropolitan 50-51/ Delphian 51-58/ Corinthian 58-63/ Athenian 63-72.
Previous Name: None   **Previous Grounds:** None.
Reserve's League: Suburban (South)   **Record Gate:** 5,500 v Wimbledon, 1976.
Record win: Unknown   **Record defeat:** 1-11 v Sutton United.
Best F.A. Cup year: Fourth Round 74-75 (lost 2-3 at Leicester City). Also 2nd Rd Proper 75-76 76-77 78-79, 1st Rd 77-78 80-81.
League Clubs defeated in FA Cup: Colchester, Brighton 74-75/ Cambridge Utd 75-76/ Northampton 76-77.
Players progressing to Football League: Chris Kelly (Millwall), B Friend (Fulham), L Harwood (Port Vale), John Humphrey (Millwall).
Record Fees - Paid: £1,500 to Croydon (B Salkeld)   **Rec'd:** £1,500 from Croydon (B Salkeld)
Clubhouse: (0372 372634) Licensed bar open noon-11pm matchdays. Burgers, hot dogs, tea & coffee etc on matchdays.
92-93 Captain: Bryan Stannard   **92-93 P.O.Y. & Top Scorer:** Ray Arnett.
Local Radio: County Sound.   **Local Press:** Leatherhead Advertiser, Surrey Advertiser
Hons: Isthmian Lg Cup 77-78, Corinthian Lg 62-63, Athenian Ld Div 1 63-64, Surrey Snr Cup 68-69 (R-up 64-65 66-67 74-75 78-79), Surrey Snr Lg 46-47 47-48 48-49 49-50 (Lg Cup 49-50, Charity Cup 46-47 49-50), East Surrey Charity Cup 68-69 (R-up 67-68), Surrey Snr Shield 68-69, FA Amtr Cup SF 70-71 73-74 (QF 65-66 66-67 71-72), FA Tphy R-up 77-78, London Snr Cup R-up 74-75 77-78, Surrey Intermediate Cup, Southern Combination Cup 89-90.

LEWES

Chairman: P Brook   **President:** W D Carr, Esq
Secretary: Mr John Lewis (0273 472822).
Manager: Gary Allen   **Asst Manager:**   **Coach:**
Press Officer: **Commercial Manager:**   **Physio:**
Ground: The Dripping Pan, Mountfield Road, Lewes BN7 1XN (0273 472574).
Directions: Two minute walk from Lewes (BR) - turn left out of station and left into Mountfield Road. Ground 100 yards on right.
Capacity: 5,000   **Cover:** 400   **Seats:** 400   **Nickname:** Rooks   **Founded:** 1885
Metal Badges: Yes   **Club Shop:** Yes.
Colours: Black & red hoops/black/red   **Change colours:** Yellow/blue
Sponsors: Nico Construction Ltd
Programme: 32 pages, 50p
Programme Editor: M J Webster.
Previous Leagues: Mid Sussex 1886-1920/ Sussex County 20-65/ Athenian 65-77.
Midweek home matchday: Tuesday   **Reserve Team's League:** Sussex Co. reserve section.
Record Attendance: 2,500 v Newhaven, Sussex County Lg 26/12/47.
Best F.A. Cup season: 4th Qualifying Rd (lost to Harwich & Parkeston)
League clubs defeated in F.A. Cup: None.
Record Fees - Paid: **Received:** £2,500 for Grant Horscroft (Brighton)
Players progressing to Football League: (to Brighton unless stated) Don Bates (1950), Peter Knight (1964), Terry Stanley (1969), Colin Woffuden (1970), G Elphick & Steve Ford (Stoke 1981), Glen Geard, Grant Hrscroft (1987), J Hammond (Fulham), S Funnell, L Allen (Wimbledon), M Rice (Watford).
Clubhouse: (0273 472100). Bar, tea bar, pool, table tennis.   **Steward:** P Brook.
Club Record Goalscorer: Pip Parris 332   **Club Record Apps:** Terry Parris 641
92-93 Captain: **92-93 P.O.Y.:**   **92-93 Top scorer:** Mark Rice 9.
Local Newspapers (+Tel.Nos.): Evening Argus, Sussex Express.
Local Radio Stations: BBC Radio Sussex, Southern Sound.
Honours: Isth. Lg Div 2 R-up 79-80 91-92, Alh'n Lg Div 1 69-70 (Div 2 67-68), Sussex Co. Lg 64-65 (R-up 24-25 33-34 58-59 63-64, Lg Cup 39-40), Mid Sussex Lg 10-11 13-14, Sussex Snr Cup 64-65 70-71 84-85 (R-up 79-80 82-83 87-88), Sussex Royal Ulster Rifles Charity Cup(3) 61-63 64-65, Gilbert Rice F'lit Cup 82-83 88-89, Neale Tphy 68-69, Sussex F'lit Cup 76-77 (SF 83-84), Southern Counties Comb Div 1 80-81, FA Tphy 1st Rd 82-83, FA Amtr Cup 2nd Rd 67-68, FA Vase 1st Rd 79-80.

METROPOLITAN POLICE

Chairman: Desmond Flanders **Vice Chairman:** Terry Siggs OBE **President:** Paul Condon GPM
Secretary: Derek Alldridge MBE, 'Woodbeck', 3 Elmshorn, Epsom Downs, Surrey KT17 3PE (0737 50525).
Manager: Colin Rose **Coach:** John Cottam
Physio: Dick Pierce **Press Officer:** Cliff Travis (0932 782215).
Ground: Metropolitan Police Sports Ground, Imber Court, East Molesey (081 398 7358).
Directions: From London: A3 then A309 to Scilly Isles r'bout, right into Hampton Court Way, left at 1st r'bout into Imber Court Rd - ground faces in 300yds. From M25 jct 10: A3 towards London for 1 mile, A307 through Cobham, left immediately after Sandown Park into Station Rd - ground 1 mile on left. Half mile from either Thames Ditton or Esher BR stations.
Capacity: 3,000 **Seats:** 427 **Cover:** 1,800 **Floodlights:** Yes **Founded:** 1919
Colours: All blue **Change colours:** All yellow **Nickname:** Blues.
Programme: 10 pages, 50p **Editor:** Chris Travis (0932 782215) **Club Shop:** No
Midweek Matchday: Tuesday **Club Sponsors:** McDonalds. **Metal Badges:** No
Previous Leagues: Spartan 28-60/ Metropolitan 60-71/ Southern 71-78.
Previous Name: None **Previous Grounds:** None.
Reserve Team's League: Suburban **Record Gate:** 4,500 v Kingstonian, FA Cup 1934.
Record win: 7-0 v Camberley, 1981 **Record defeat:** 1-11 v Wimbledon, 1956.
Best F.A. Cup year: 1st Rd 32-33 (0-9 at Northampton Town), 84-85 (0-3 at home to Dartford).
Clubhouse: (081 398 1267). Four bars, dancehall, cafeteria open 9am-11pm. Hot & cold food.
Club Record Scorer: Mario Russo **Club Record Appearances:** Pat Robert.
92-93 Captain: Mark Read **92-93 P.o.Y.:** Paul Carruth **92-93 Top scorer:** Mario Russo.
Local Radio: County Sounds. **Local Press:** Surrey Comet, Surrey Herald.
Hons: Isthmian Lg Div 2 R-up 77-78 87-88, Spartan Lg 28-29 29-30 36-37 38-39 45-46 53-54 54-55 (R-up 47-48, Lg Cup 59-60 (R-up 57-58)), Middx Snr Cup 27-28, Surrey Snr Cup 32-33, Surrey Charity Shield 38-39, Metropolitan Lg Cup 68-69 (Amtr Cup 68-69 69-70), London Snr Cup R-up 34-35 40-41, Herts & Middx Comb. 39-40.

Metropolitan Police F.C. 1992-93. Back Row (L/R): Simon Young, Billy Mochan, Paul Carruth, Ian Pendry, Marco Russo, Leslie Bateman, Chris Holding. Front: Carl Naylor, Paul Richardson, Ken McKenzie, Eamonn Clarke, Mark Read, Mark Adams.

MALDEN VALE

Chairman: Steve Pearce **President:** John Sladden.
Secretary: Andrew Pearce, 31 Ancaster Cres., New Malden, Surrey KT3 6BD (081 949 1475).
Manager/Coach: Michael Browne **Asst Mgr/Coach:** Ged Murphy
Press Officer: Jim Wallbridge **Commercial Manager:** Trevor Pearce.
Ground: Grand Drive, Raynes Park, London SW20 9NB (081 542 2193).
Directions: M25, jct 10, A3 towards London, turn off onto A298, right at 1st lights into Grand Drive, ground 200yds on left. Half mile from Raynes Park (BR). Buses 77a and 77c.
Capacity: 3,000 **Seats:** 120 **Cover:** 170 **Floodlights:** Yes **Founded:** 1967
Colours: Royal/royal/red **Change colours:** Green & white/green/green.
Club Shop: Yes. Programmes, badges, scarves, ties, jumpers. Contact Trevor Pearce (081 542 2193).
Programme: 10 pages, 50p **Editor:** Len Langham (081 337 5064)
Midweek Matchday: Monday **Nickname:** The Vale.
Previous Leagues: Surrey Snr 77-78/ London Spartan 78-84/ Combined Counties 84-89.
Previous Name: None **Previous Grounds:** None.
Sponsors: Fullers of Malden (Ford Main Dealers) 081 949 3331.
Reserve Team's League: Suburban **Rec. Gate:** 2,000 v Eastenders, Charity Match, 1991.
Best FA Cup year: Second Qualifying Rd 89-90 (lost 0-2 at Whyteleafe).
Clubhouse: Mon-Fri 6.30-11pm, Sat 12-11pm, Sun 12-3pm. Two bars, hot food.
Club Record Scorer: Martin Caller **Club Record Appearances:** David Stroud 1040, Trevor Pearce 940.
92-93 Captain: Rory Gleeson **92-93 P.o.Y.:** Rob Jones **92-93 Top scorer:** Stan Blair.
Local Press: Surrey Comet, Morden Guardian, Wimbledon News. **Local Radio:** County Sounds.
Hons: London Spartan Lg 80-81 (R-up 83-84, Div 3 78-79 79-80, Lg Cup 80-81 83-84 (R-up 81-82 82-83)), Combined Co's Lg 84-85 (R-up 88-89, Concours Tphy 84-85 (R-up 85-86), Div 2 81-82), Surrey Snr Lg 77-78, Southern Combination Cup 78-79, Loctite Tphy QF 90-91.

NEWBURY TOWN

Chairman: J Holt   **Vice Chairman:** R Meagrow
Secretary: W Dent, 66 Volunteer Rd, Theale, Reading, Berks RG7 5DN (0734 323570).
Manager: M Deaner   **Asst Manager:** R Mellor   **Coach:** M Hicks
Press Officer: W Dent   **Physio:** P Turner
Commercial Manager: H Wylie
Ground: Faraday Road, Newbury RG13 2AD (0635 40048-club, 36601-office).
Directions: A34 Robin Hood r'bout then A4 towards Reading, right at lights after 100 yards into Faraday Road. Ground at end.
Capacity: 2,500   **Seats:** 450   **Cover:** 450   **Floodlights:** Yes   **Founded:** 1887
Colours: Orange/white   **Change colours:** Green & white
Club Shop: Yes   **Metal Badges:** Yes
Programme: 12 pages, 40p   **Editor:** Secretary.
Midweek Matchday: Tuesday   **Sponsors:** T.B.A.
Previous Leagues: Gt Western Suburban 04-27/ Hants 27-28/ Reading & Dist. 28-52/ Metropolitan 52-59/ Hellenic 59-82/ Athenian 82-83.
Previous Names: None   **Previous Grounds:** None
Reserves' League: Suburban   **Record Gate:** 2,300 Reading v Southampton, Hants Lg.
Best FA Cup year: Third Qualifying Round 80-81 (lost 1-4 to Farnborough).
Record Fees - Paid: £300   **Received:** £2,500   **Nickname:** Town.
Clubhouse: (0635 36601). Every night, Thurs-Sun lunchtimes. Two bars, function room, kitchen.
Players progressing to Football League: D McCartney (WBA), Darren Angell (P'smouth), Brett Angell (Southend), M Berry (Southampton), Ian Maidment (Reading).
92-93 Captain: Peter Rhodes-Brown   **92-93 P.O.Y.:** S Kean   **92-93 Top scorer:** Matthew McDonald
Local Press: Newbury Weekly News, Newbury Evening Post.   **Local Radio:** Radio 210, Reading.
Hons: FA Vase 5th Rd 79-80, Athenian Lg 82-83, Berks & Bucks Snr Cup 1897-98 (Jnr Cup 1898-99 1900-01), Hellenic Lg 78-79 80-81 (Lg Cup 59-60 68-69), Metropolitan Lg Amtr Cup(6) 54-60, Newbury (Graystone Cup), Reading & District Lg(5), Hungerford Cup 88-89 89-90 90-91, Reading Town Snr Cup 31-32.

RAINHAM TOWN

Chairman: Tony Brooking   **Vice Chairman/President:** G W Burrell
Secretary/Press Officer: Terry M King, 5 Syracuse Ave., Rainham, Essex RM13 9SR (0708 557596).
Manager: Mick Acland   **Assistant Manager/Coach:** Dennis Pollock.
Physio: Roy Davison   **Commercial Manager:** Mrs M Haynes.
Ground & Directions: As for Purfleet F.C. (see Division One).   **Nickname:** Reds.
Colours: Red & white   **Change colours:** Yellow & blue.   **Founded:** 1945
Programme: 20 pages, 50p   **Editor:** T King, S Acland.   **Club Shop:** No
Midweek Matchday: Wednesday   **Sponsors:** Byrne Brothers.   **Metal Badges:** Yes
Previous Leagues: South Essex 45-48/ London 48-51/ Delphian 51-61/ Metropolitan 61-64/ Athenian 64-77.
Previous Grounds: Rainham Working Mens Ground 1945-48/ Deri Park, Wennington Rd 1948-91.
Record Gate: 1,760 v Finchley, F.A. Amateur Cup 1952 (at Deri Park).
Best F.A. Cup year: 3rd Qualifying Round 57-58 (0-6 at Chelmsford), 58-59 (0-2 at Woodford).
Record win: 6-0 v Hertford Town   **Record defeat:** 0-11 v Romford.
Record transfer fee paid: £3,000 for Brian Smart (Brechin City).
Clubhouse: Thurrock Hotel (see Purfleet F.C.). Hot & cold food & drinks in ground on matchdays.
Players progressing to Football League: Liburd Henry (Watford), Richard Iles (Bristol Rovers).
Club Record Scorer: Steve Kirby   **Club Record Appearances:** Steve Kirby, 348.
92-93 Captain: Micky Heselden   **92-93 P.o.Y & Top scorer:** Micky Waite
Local Radio: BBC Essex, Essex Radio.   **Local Press:** Romford Recorder (0708 766044)
Hons: Essex Snr Tphy R-up 87-88, Athenian Lg Div 2 R-up 73-74, Delphian Lg R-up 56-57, Essex Thames-side Tphy R-up 92-93 (SF 82-83), Essex Snr Cup SF 81-82, Sth Essex Lg 47-48 (Lg Cup 47-48 (R-up 45-46 46-47)), Grays County Cup 46-47, Essex Elizabethan Tphy 58-59 (R-up 75-76 77-78 78-79), Hornchurch Charity Cup 47-48 83-84, Romford Charity Cup 46-47 84-85.

Rainham Town 1992-93. Back Row (L/R): Dave Gordon, Tony Fleming, Micky Waite, Micky Heselden, Brian Smart, Steve Kirby, Andy Sawyer, Kevin Alexander. Front: Peter McKey, Barry Movyia, Dave Allen, Micky Lane, Jimmy Asplin, Mickey Linnell. Photo - Richard Brock.

SAFFRON WALDEN TOWN

Chairman: S Lander   **Vice Chairman:** P Diggons.
Secretary: H J Harvey, 1 New Willow Cottage, Langley, Essex CB11 4RC (0799 550615).
Manager: Tony Mercer   **Assistant Manager:** Bob Dodd   **Coach:** Don Wiltshire.
Press Officer: Gary Phillips   **Physio:** Peter White.
Ground: Catons Lane, Saffron Walden, Essex CB10 2DU (0799 22789).
Directions: In Saffron Walden High Street turn into Castle Street, left at T-junction, 1st left by Victory pub.
Capacity: 5,000   **Seats:** 500   **Cover:** 2,000   **Floodlights:** Yes   **Founded:** 1872
Colours: Red/black/white   **Change colours:** All yellow.   **Nickname:** Bloods.
Programme: 24 pages, 50p   **Editor:** Glyn Thomas (0799 521103)   **Club Shop:** No
Midweek Matchday: Tuesday   **Club Sponsors:** Tolly Cobbold.   **Metal Badges:** No
Previous Leagues: Haverhill & Dist./ Stansted & Dist./ Cambridgeshire/ Nth Essex/ Herts Co./ Spartan 33-49 50-54/ Parthenon 49-50/ Essex Snr 71-74/ Eastern Co's 74-84.
Previous Grounds: None   **Previous Names:** None.   **Clubhouse:** No.
Record Gate: 6,000 v Rainham Ath., Essex Junior Cup Final 1926 (played at Crittals, Braintree).
Reserve Team's League: Essex & Herts Comb.
Best F.A. Cup year: Second Qualifying Round replay 84-85 (lost 1-2 at King's Lynn).
Club Record Scorer: John Tipputt   **Club Record Appearances:** Les Page, 700+.
92-93 Captain: David Cooper   **92-93 P.o.Y.:** Kevin Austin/ Gary Dean.
92-93 Top scorer: Wayne Mitchell, 23.
Local Radio: Essex Radio, Radio Essex.   **Local Press:** Saffron Walden Weekly News, Herald & Post.
Hons: Essex Snr Lg 73-74, Eastern Co's Lg 82-83, Spartan Lg Eastern Div 2 36-37, Essex Snr Tphy 82-83 83-84 84-85, Eastern F'lit Competition 91-92 (R-up 88-89, Nth Thames Group B 82-83), Essex Jnr Cup 1896-97 (R-up 25-26), Cambs Lg R-up 22-23, Essex & Herts Border Lg R-up 25-26(joint), Stansted & Dist. Lg 07-08 08-09 09-10 11-12 20-21 22-23 23-24, Haverhill & Dist. Lg 08-09 22-23 23-24 29-30 33-34.

THAME UNITED

Chairman: Mr O J Tite   **Vice Chairman:** Mr P K Smith
Secretary: Mr D W Blake, 4 Sun Crescent, Oakley, Aylesbury, Bucks HP18 9RF (0844 237573).
Manager: Bob Pratley   **Asst Manager:** Malcolm McIntosh   **Physio:** Chris Perkins
Press Officer: Mr N Crocker
Ground: Windmill Road, Thame, Oxon OX9 2DR (0844 213017).
Directions: Into Nelson Street from Market Square. 3 miles from Haddenham & Thame Parkway (BR). Nearest bus stop at Town Hall (half mile away).
Capacity: 2,500   **Seats:** 230   **Cover:** 400   **Floodlights:** Yes   **Founded:** 1883
Colours: Red & black   **Change colours:** Black & white   **Club Shop:** No
Programme: 24 pages, 50p   **Programme Editor:** Paul Smith (0844 213482).
Midweek Matchday: Tuesday   **Sponsors:** Dayla Soft Drinks (Aylesbury).
Previous Leagues: Oxon Snr/ Hellenic 59-87/ Sth Midlands 87-91.
Previous Name: Thame F.C.   **Previous Grounds:** Various pre-1950s
Record Gate: 2,000.   **Nickname:** United
Reserve Team's League: Suburban.
Record win: 9-0 v Bracknell, 31/10/92   **Record defeat:** 4-11 v Hungerford, F.A. Cup 1984.
Best FA Cup year: Third Qualifying Round 91-92 (lost 0-4 to Salisbury).
Clubhouse: Open every evening and weekend lunchtimes. Banquetting facilities for 200 (weddings, dinners, dances etc).
92-93 Captain: Julian Dark   **92-93 P.o.Y.:** Michael Faulkner **92-93 Top scorer:** Nigel Mott 34
Local Press: Oxford Mail, Thame Gazette, Bucks Free Press.   **Local Radio:** BBC Radio Oxford, Fox FM.
Hons: Isthmian Lg Div 3 R-up 92-93, Hellenic Lg 61-62 69-70 (Premier Div Cup(4)), Sth Mids Lg 90-91, Oxon Snr Cup 1894-95 05-06 08-09 09-10 75-76 80-81 92-93, Oxon Intermediate Cup 76-77 78-79 91-92, Oxon Charity Cup.

Thame United, Diadora League Division Three runners-up 1992-93. Back Row (L/R): Phil Rodney, Steve Mayhew, Martin Shepherd, Matt Hayward, Ade Blake, Michael Faulkner, Mark O'Haer. Front: John Thorne, David Watson, Ronnie Russell, Julian Dark, Kelly Lonergan, Gary Sealey, David Winwood.

TILBURY

Chairman: R Nash   **Vice Chairman:** H McGill   **President:** J B Wilson.
Secretary: L P Brown, 52 Lionel Oxley House, New Rd, Grays, Essex RM17 6PP (0375 377427).
Manager: Nicky Phillips   **Asst Mgr:** Ian Bodley   **Coach:** Paul Joynes.
Comm. Manager: Paul Joynes.   **Physio:** Ian Bodley   **Press Officer:** Secretary
Ground: Chadfields, St Chad's Rd, Tilbury, Essex RM18 8NL (0375 23093).
Directions: BR from Fenchurch Street to Tilbury Town then bus 377 or 20 mins walk - right out of station, walk along Left Hand Road fork to town centre traffic lights, left into St Chads Rd, Chadfields 1 mile on left. By road; M25 (jct 30 or 31) - A13 Southend bound, Tilbury Docks turn off after 4 miles, Chadwell St Mary turn off (left) after another one and a half miles, left again after 400 metres, right at r'bout (signed Tilbury), right into St Chad's Rd after half mile, 1st right into Chadfields for ground.
Capacity: 3,500   **Seats:** 250   **Cover:** 1,000   **Floodlights:** Yes   **Founded:** 1900
Colours: Black & white stripes/black/black   **Change:** Red/red or white/red or white.
Programme: Min 32 pages, 50p   **Editor:** Lloyd Brown.   **Club Shop:** No.
Midweek Matchday: Tuesday   **Club Sponsors:** None.   **Nickname:** Dockers
Previous Leagues: Grays & Dist. + Sth Essex (simultaneously)/ Kent 27-31/ London 31-39 46-50 57-62/ Sth Essex Comb. (war-time)/ Corinthian 50-57/ Delphian 62-63/ Athenian 63-73.
Previous Names: None
Previous Grounds: Green & Silley Weir Ground 1900-11/ Orient Field 19-38.
Reserve Team's League: Essex & Herts Border Comb.
Record Gate: 5,500 v Gorleston, F.A. Cup 4th Qual. Rd 19/11/49 (won 2-0).
Best FA Cup year: 3rd Rd Proper 77-78 (lost 0-4 at Stoke City). Also 1st Rd 49-50 (0-4 at Notts Co.)
Record Fees - Paid: £2,000 for Tony Macklin (Grays Athletic, 1990)
            Received: £2,000 for Steve Conner (Dartford, 1985)
Record win: 17-0 v No.9 Company Royal Artillery (H), South Essex League 4/10/02. In Senior Football: 13-2 v Chalfont National (A), London League 28/4/92.
Record defeat: 1-10 v Maidstone United (A), Corinthian League 4/9/62.
Clubhouse: Open every evening, all day Friday & Saturday, and Sunday lunchtimes. Pool, darts, TV, Function Hall. Hot and cold food available at most times.
Players progressing to Football League: I Le May, T Scannell, T Oakley, J Evans.
Club Record Scorer: Ross Livermore 305 (in 282 games, 1958-66).
Club Record Appearances: Nicky Smith 424 (1975-85).
92-93 Captain: Andy Swann   **92-93 P.O.V.:** Peter Gray   **92-93 Top scorer:** Mark Phillips 15.
Local Radio: Essex Radio, BBC Essex.   **Local Press:** Thurrock Gazette, Thurrock Recorder.
Hons: FA Amtr Cup QF, Isthmian Lg Div 1 75-76 (Div 1 Cup 74-75), Athenian Lg 68-69 (Div 2,62-63), London Lg 58-59 59-60 60-61 61-62 (Lg Cup 58-59 60-61 61-62 (R-up(3))), Delphian Lg 67-68 (Div 2 62-63), Essex Snr Cup 60-61 63-64 72-73 74-75 (R-up 46-47 47-48 69-70 71-72 78-79), Essex Professional Cup 75-76, Mithras Cup 72-73 75-76 76-77 78-79 (R-up 71-72 74-75), Essex Elizabethan Tphy 63-64 68-69 (R-up 55-56 59-60 64-65 67-68 70-71), Essex Floodlit Competition 68-69, Anglo-Italian Barassi Cup R-up 75-76, Essex Jnr Cup 08-09 24-25 (R-up 03-04), Stanford Charity Cup 62-63 92-93, Grays & Dist. Lg(numerous), Neale Trophy 65-66, Memorial Shield R-up 87-88.

WARE

Chairman: C T Hudson
Secretary: M L Rose, 12 The Green, Ware, Herts SG12 0QN (0920 464448).
Manager: Stuart Todd   **Asst Mgr:** N/A
Physio: Frank Roberts   **Coach:** John Godleman
Commercial Manager: N/A   **Press Officer:** Cecil Hudson (0992 581862)
Ground: Buryfield, Park Road, Ware, Herts SG12 0AJ (0920 463247).
Directions: A10 off at junction A602 & B1001 signposted Ware, in Ware Park Road is on right behind 'Rank' factory. 1 mile from Ware (BR) station (Liverpool Street-Hertford East line).
Capacity: 3,000   **Seats:** 170   **Cover:** 600   **Floodlights:** Yes   **Founded:** 1892
Colours: Blue & white stripes/blue/red   **Change colours:** Amber/black
Club Shop: No   **Metal Badges:** No
Programme: 12-20 pages, 30p   **Editor:** C T Hudson (0992 581862).
Midweek Matchday: Tuesday   **Sponsors:** Charvill Bros Ltd.
Prev. Lges: East Herts/ North Middx & District 07-08/ Herts County 08-25/ Spartan 25-55/ Delphian 55-63/ Athenian 63-75.
Previous Names: None
Previous Grounds: Highfields/ Canons Park/ London Rd, Presdales Lower Park 1921-26.
Reserve Team's League: Essex & Herts Border Comb.
Record Gate: 2,500 v Arsenal XI 1974.
Record win: 10-1 v Wood Green Town   **Record defeat:** 0-11 v Barnet.
Best FA Cup year: First Round Proper 68-69 (lost 1-6 to Luton Town).   **Nickname:** Blues.
Clubhouse: Licensed bar open matchdays. Light snacks at refreshment bar.
Players progressing to Football League: Derek Saunders (Chelsea), Ken Humphrey (QPR).
Club Record Scorer: M Hibbert 229   **Club Record Appearances:** Gary Riddle 496.
Record Scorer in one season: George Dearman 98 (1926-27).
92-93 Captain: Jon Bridge   **92-93 P.O.V.:** Spencer Pugh   **92-93 Top scorer:** Damon Miles 26.
Local Press: Herts Mercury, Herts Star (0920 554611), Herald & Post (0279 655225).
Hons: Herts Snr Cup 1898-99 03-04 06-07 21-22 53-54, Herts Charity Shield 26-27 56-57 58-59 62-63 85-86, Herts Charity Cup R-up 64-65 65-66 78-79 89-90, Spartan Lg 52-53 (Div 1 Sect.B 51-52, Div 2 Sect.A 26-27), Athenian Lg Div 2 Cup 65-66 72-73 (Div 2 Reserve Sect. 66-67 70-71), East Anglian Cup 73-74, Herts Co. Lg 08-09 21-22, East Herts Lg 04-05 06-07 (Lg Cup 06-07), Perry Cup 26-27 28-29 37-38 51-52 52-53 53-54 55-56, Dunkels Cup 52-53, Rolleston Cup 39-40 51-52.

WITHAM TOWN

Chairman: Mr A Marshall   **Vice Chairman:** Reg Wright   **President:** Mr B Olley.
Secretary: Reg Wright, 28 Mersey Rd, Witham, Essex CM8 1LJ (0376 512990).
Manager: Craig Johnson   **Asst Mgr:** Dennis Pollock   **Coach:** Gary Smith-Herzberg
Physio: Tony McCulloch   **Press Officer:** Matthew Wright (0376 512990)
Ground: Spa Road, Witham, Essex CM8 1UN (0376 511198-lounge, 500146-reception).
Directions: From Witham BR (network S.E.) station; through pub car park and follow road to Faulkbourne, at main r'bout turn left and ground is on the right. By road; Off A12 at Witham sign, left at 1st lights (Spinks Lane), right at end of road, follow road under railway bridge - ground 100yds on left.
Capacity: 2,000   **Seats:** 150   **Cover:** 150   **Floodlights:** Yes   **Founded:** 1947
Colours: Red & black stripes/black/black   **Change colours:** Green & yellow
Nickname: Town   **Metal Badges:** No
Programme: 24 pages, 40p   **Editor:** Matthew Wright (0376 512990)   **Club Shop:** No.
Midweek Matchday: Tuesday   **Reserve Team's League:** Essex & Herts Border Comb.
Previous Leagues: Mid Essex/ Essex & Suffolk Border/ Essex Senior 71-87.
Previous Names: None   **Previous Ground:** None.
Record Gate: 800 v Billericay Town, Essex Senior League, May 1976.
Best F.A. Cup year: 2nd Qual. Rd 87-88 (v Gravesend), 88-89 (v B. Stortford), 89-90 (v Dartford).
Record transfer fee received: for Steve Tilson (Southend).
Record win: 7-0 v Southall 14/11/92   **Record defeat:** 1-6 v Saffron Walden 22/10/91.
Clubhouse: Three bars and large function room. Open every night and weekend lunctimes. Hot bar snacks and occasional a la carte dinners (max. seating 24). Darts, pool, table tennis teams.
Steward: Richard Green.
Players progressing to Football League: Steve Tilson (Southend).
Club Record Scorer: Colin Mitchell
Club Record Appearances: Keith Dent (16 years)
92-93 Captain: Alan Vincent   **92-93 P.O.Y.:** Kingsley Banks   **92-93 Top scorer:** Jason Thompson 16
Local Press: Witham & Braintree Times, Essex Chronicle, East Anglian Daily Times.
Local Radio: BBC Essex, Essex Radio.
Hons: Essex Snr Lg 70-71 85-86 (R-up 84-85 86-87), Essex Snr Tphy 85-86 (R-up 88-89), FA Vase 5th Rd 85-86, Loctite Tphy SF 90-91.

Julian Dark, of promoted Thame United, battles for possession with Mick Lowe (right) during the league fixture at Hornchurch on 20th September. Photo - Rob Monger.

DIADORA LEAGUE AVERAGE ATTENDANCES 1992-93

Club	Total 92-93	Ave. 92-93	Ave. 91-92	% Change	Club	Total 92-93	Ave. 92-93	Ave. 91-92	% Change
PREMIER DIVISION					**DIVISION TWO**				
Aylesbury United	12,528	597	720	-17.0	Banstead Athletic	1,112	53	45	+17.7
Basingstoke Town	7,882	375	512	-26.7	Barton Rovers	2,399	114	115	-0.9
Bognor Regis Town	5,495	262	267	-1.8	Berkhamsted	3,017	144	90	+60.0
Bromley	7,437	354	516	-31.3	Chertsey Town	3,822	182	139	+30.9
Carshalton Athletic	9,686	461	427	+7.9	Edgware Town	2,789	133	155	-16.5
Chesham United	19,733	940	566	+66.0	Egham Town	2,215	105	97	+8.2
Dulwich Hamlet	7,631	363	149	+143.6	Hampton	3,353	160	161	-0.6
Enfield	15,235	725	581	+24.7	Harefield United	1,947	93	109	-17.2
Grays Athletic	7,012	334	372	-10.2	Hemel Hempstead	3,269	156	115	+35.7
Harrow Borough	6,558	312	346	-9.8	Hungerford Town	1,817	87	107	-23.0
Hayes	7,358	350	303	+15.5	Leatherhead	2,116	101	128	-26.7
Hendon	6,447	307	295	+4.0	Malden Vale	2,351	112	105	+6.7
Kingstonian	12,276	585	688	-14.9	Metropolitan Police	2,600	124	95	+30.5
Marlow	7,228	344	356	-3.3	Newbury Town	3,157	150	85	+76.5
St Albans City	19,304	919	497	+84.9	Rainham Town	1,195	57	62	-8.8
Staines Town	8,199	390	403	-3.2	Ruislip Manor	4,043	193	163	+18.4
Stevenage Borough	13,318	633	643	-1.3	Saffron Walden	3,276	156	120	+30.0
Sutton United	15,601	648	728	-10.9	Southall	697	33	52	-57.6
Windsor & Eton	5,232	249	316	-21.2	Tilbury	1,598	76	72	-5.5
Wivenhoe Town	5,843	278	243	+14.4	Ware	2,494	119	132	-10.9
Wokingham Town	7,258	346	383	-9.6	Witham Town	2,177	104	106	-1.9
Yeading	5,272	251	144	+74.3	Worthing	6,677	318	176	+80.7
DIVISION ONE					**DIVISION THREE**				
Abingdon Town	3,165	181	248	-27.0	Aldershot Town	39,718	2,090		
Aveley	2,293	115	99	+16.1	Bracknell Town	2,361	124	65	+90.7
Barking	1,849	92	107	-14.0	Camberley Town	3,536	186	83	+124.0
Billericay Town	5,995	300	253	+18.5	Clapton	1,415	74	44	+68.1
Bishop's Stortford	6,164	308	338	-8.8	Collier Row	2,285	120	83	+44.5
Boreham Wood	2,213	111	142	-21.8	Cove	3,747	197	87	+126.4
Chalfont St Peter	2,490	125	125		East Thurrock	2,791	64	147	
Croydon	1,293	65	106	-38.6	Epsom & Ewell	2,594	137	71	+92.9
Dorking	4,796	240	172	+39.5	Feltham & Houns.	2,208	116	46	+152.1
Heybridge Swifts	2,991	150	157	-4.4	Flackwell Heath	13,571	41	41	
Hitchin Town	8,497	425	330	+28.7	Hertford Town	2,182	115	83	+38.5
Lewes	2,433	122	180	-32.2	Hornchurch	1,824	96	67	+43.2
Leyton	2,415	121	116	+4.3	Horsham	3,862	203	176	+15.3
Maidenhead United	3,373	169	217	-22.1	Kingsbury Town	1,407	74	74	
Molesey	2,458	123	98	+25.5	Leighton Town	7,522	396		
Purfleet	2,945	147	92	+59.7	Northwood	3,377	178		
Tooting & Mitcham	2,820	141	149	-5.3	Petersfield United	2,785	147	66	+122.7
Uxbridge	2,463	123	117	+5.1	Royston Town	3,088	163	121	+34.7
Walton & Hersham	2,745	137	149	-8.0	Thame United	3,219	169	101	+67.3
Wembley	1,884	94	119	-21.0	Tring Town	2,617	138	61	+126.2
Whyteleafe	2,415	121	108	+12.0					

Witham Town enjoy the luxury of the main stand at Watford before their F.A. Cup tie against Wealdstone on Sunday 13th September. Photo - Eric Marsh.

Third Division

		HOME			AWAY					
	P	W	D	L	W	D	L	F	A	Pts
ALDERSHOT TOWN	38	14	5	0	14	3	2	90	35	92
THAME UNITED	38	10	7	2	11	4	4	84	38	74
COLLIER ROW	38	9	7	3	12	4	3	68	30	74
LEIGHTON TOWN	38	11	5	3	10	5	4	89	47	73
COVE	38	13	2	4	8	6	5	69	42	71
NORTHWOOD	38	12	4	3	7	7	5	84	68	68
ROYSTON TOWN	38	11	3	5	6	5	8	59	42	59
EAST THURROCK U.	38	9	4	6	8	3	8	69	58	58
KINGSBURY TOWN	38	10	4	5	5	5	9	62	59	54
HERTFORD TOWN	38	6	4	9	8	6	5	61	64	52
FLACKWELL HEATH	38	8	5	6	7	1	11	82	76	51
TRING TOWN	38	6	6	7	6	5	8	59	63	47
HORNCHURCH	38	7	6	6	4	7	8	53	52	46
HORSHAM	38	8	3	8	4	4	11	63	72	43
EPSOM & EWELL	38	3	7	9	7	4	8	52	67	41
BRACKNELL TOWN	38	3	8	8	4	5	10	52	94	34
CLAPTON	38	6	1	12	2	6	11	46	74	31
CAMBERLEY TOWN	38	2	4	13	6	3	10	37	72	31
PETERSFIELD UTD	38	2	6	11	4	6	9	36	90	30
FELT. & HOUNSLOW	38	4	1	14	1	3	15	47	119	19

Top League Goalscorers

Steve Drewe (Leighton Town)	30
David Whitehead (Hertford Town)	29
Tony Read (Collier Row)	28
Stephen Stairs (Aldershot)	27
Nigel Mott (Thame United)	26
Daniel Wallace (East Thurrock United)	25

THE THIRD DIVISION RESULT CHART 1992-93

HOME TEAM		1	2	3	4	5	6	7	8	9	10	11	12	13	14	15	16	17	18	19	20
1.	Aldershot	*	2-2	6-1	4-2	1-1	1-1	1-0	1-1	2-0	3-1	0-0	5-2	3-2	4-0	2-1	4-0	3-0	1-0	2-1	4-0
2.	Bracknell	3-3	*	3-3	1-3	1-1	0-1	2-3	2-0	2-1	0-4	5-2	0-0	1-1	0-2	0-4	0-0	0-0	0-1	2-4	2-2
3.	Camberley	1-3	0-0	*	1-0	0-1	1-2	0-3	0-1	2-1	0-2	0-2	1-2	2-2	0-1	0-3	1-4	1-1	1-1	0-2	0-4
4.	Clapton	2-1	1-2	1-4	*	0-3	2-1	1-2	1-3	1-2	0-6	2-3	2-1	1-3	1-1	1-2	0-1	4-0	3-4	5-1	1-0
5.	Collier Row	1-2	5-1	1-0	0-0	*	1-1	3-1	5-1	2-0	3-1	0-0	0-0	1-0	2-2	2-4	5-0	3-0	0-1	0-0	0-0
6.	Cove	1-3	3-2	2-0	1-0	3-1	*	3-1	4-3	6-0	1-0	3-1	1-5	3-0	2-1	0-1	0-0	1-1	3-0	2-3	3-0
7.	E.Thurrock	0-1	2-2	4-2	2-0	0-2	1-1	*	3-0	4-2	1-4	3-0	1-3	3-2	2-2	2-3	4-1	1-1	2-1	1-4	3-1
8.	Epsom & E.	1-2	0-2	0-3	1-1	1-0	2-2	1-1	*	1-1	1-1	2-3	2-2	3-0	5-3	1-4	2-5	2-4	1-1	0-1	0-1
9.	F.&Hounslow	1-3	3-5	1-3	4-1	0-4	0-1	0-1	1-3	*	1-4	2-3	2-2	0-5	1-5	2-7	3-5	3-2	3-2	0-5	3-1
10.	Flackwell	3-6	0-4	4-0	4-2	3-4	0-3	3-1	0-0	4-1	*	3-3	1-2	2-1	1-0	2-1	2-2	2-2	1-0	1-1	2-3
11.	Hertford	2-3	3-2	3-1	0-2	0-0	1-2	1-2	1-2	4-0	4-6	*	3-1	2-2	1-0	0-2	3-3	1-0	0-1	0-3	1-1
12.	Hornchurch	1-3	2-0	0-1	1-1	1-2	0-0	1-0	0-1	3-0	5-2	0-0	*	2-1	3-1	0-0	1-1	0-0	1-2	0-1	2-0
13.	Horsham	0-1	2-2	2-3	3-0	0-2	1-0	1-0	2-1	6-0	2-1	0-2	3-1	*	5-3	1-1	2-3	0-1	1-1	1-2	2-4
14.	Kingsbury	0-1	4-0	0-0	3-1	0-0	1-3	0-4	0-3	3-2	2-1	4-1	2-1	3-0	*	1-0	1-1	3-1	1-0	1-1	1-3
15.	Leighton	1-0	6-0	4-2	2-0	1-3	4-2	3-2	3-3	4-1	3-1	1-2	1-1	2-3	0-0	*	4-1	4-1	2-0	1-1	2-2
16.	Northwood	1-1	4-3	3-1	2-0	1-2	0-1	2-3	1-0	2-2	5-4	2-1	4-3	5-1	3-2	1-1	*	5-0	1-1	2-1	3-2
17.	Petersfield	0-3	0-0	1-0	1-1	0-2	0-0	0-4	1-1	3-0	0-6	2-5	3-3	2-3	2-5	1-2	1-3	*	0-4	0-5	1-1
18.	Royston	0-1	9-0	1-0	2-1	0-3	1-0	0-0	2-1	2-0	6-0	1-2	3-0	1-1	1-0	2-2	3-2	1-2	*	2-3	1-0
19.	Thame	2-2	9-0	1-1	1-1	2-0	3-0	2-0	2-0	3-3	1-0	1-1	1-0	4-1	1-1	3-2	0-2	8-0	0-0	*	0-1
20.	Tring	0-2	4-1	0-1	1-1	2-3	1-6	2-2	1-2	3-1	2-0	0-0	1-1	4-1	2-3	1-1	3-3	0-2	3-1	3-1	*

DIADORA LEAGUE THIRD DIVISION ATTENDANCE CHART 1992-93

HOME TEAM	1	2	3	4	5	6	7	8	9	10	11	12	13	14	15	16	17	18	19	20
1. Aldershot T	*	2241	1921	1620	2923	2432	1758	1976	2278	1836	1995	1854	1725	2372	2106	2110	1891	2164	2466	2052
2. Bracknell	1302	*	70	28	62	83	65	62	80	32	48	56	86	48	51	46	62	52	70	58
3. Camberley	2046	146	*	48	152	132	84	68	51	84	58	58	76	55	115	72	54	92	67	78
4. Clapton	545	36	30	*	95	42	76	45	34	42	55	35	46	52	52	36	46	42	75	31
5. Collier Row	444	107	107	75	*	97	92	76	110	110	97	127	98	89	156	107	87	102	97	107
6. Cove	1798	83	157	89	233	*	104	109	104	82	128	68	103	86	95	127	92	78	114	97
7. E Thurrock U.	543	113	90	148	214	118	*	125	121	120	103	161	123	90	176	136	86	102	130	92
8. Epsom & E.	1087	79	91	88	78	70	107	*	99	82	67	84	111	87	69	93	72	65	99	66
9. Feltham & H.	826	82	79	79	35	92	48	74	*	84	93	77	87	77	126	87	21	87	68	86
10. Flackwell H.	558	35	35	40	60	40	40	35	40	*	35	30	35	30	120	55	34	35	70	30
11. Hertford	680	60	98	90	67	78	85	72	66	80	*	88	70	95	103	120	46	144	70	70
12. Hornchurch	585	70	20	70	102	76	107	35	62	68	90	*	74	70	89	70	60	60	40	76
13. Horsham	1021	87	162	184	232	94	88	242	195	146	183	180	*	98	183	186	110	156	151	164
14. Kingsbury	349	39	41	57	51	39	67	61	43	42	30	54	60	*	87	127	39	48	72	71
15. Leighton	1525	246	278	258	407	372	308	327	318	250	346	224	403	309	*	323	299	423	225	631
16. Northwood	914	126	84	82	146	158	144	97	129	180	117	138	146	150	208	*	129	126	117	124
17. Petersfield	1750	75	75	50	50	70	65	30	50	50	70	60	75	50	75	*	45	45	50	
18. Royston	656	148	110	68	124	106	186	240	60	126	186	112	79	86	265	216	68	*	106	146
19. Thame Utd	750	105	129	151	159	106	143	112	112	192	109	134	120	97	332	156	95	108	*	109
20. Tring T.	785	96	46	58	85	85	86	102	49	62	58	105	127	66	398	106	126	72	105	*

NB. Hornchurch v Epsom & Ewell, Camberley Town and Thame United played at Tilbury F.C.

Diadora League Division Two/Three Ten Year Record
(N - Denoted Division Two (North), S - Denotes Division Two (South))

	83/4	84/5	85/6	86/7	87/8	88/9	89/90	90/1	91/2	92/3
Abingdon Town	N/A	-	-	-	-	-	-	3S	1S	-	-
Aldershot Town 1992	N/A	-	-	-	-	-	-	-	-	1
Aveley	N/A	-	-	5N	21N	9N	2N	-	-	-
Bracknell Town	N/A	8S	2S	-	-	-	19S	17S	17	16
Camberley Town	N/A	15S	16S	15S	19S	14S	17S	22S	15	18
Chalfont St Peter	N/A	7N	6N	8S	1S	-	-	-	-	-
Chertsey Town	N/A	19S	-	6S	6S	12S	13S	14S	2	-
Chesham United	N/A	-	-	1N	-	-	-	-	-	-
Cheshunt	N/A	12N	4N	22N	-	-	-	-	-	-
Clapton	N/A	-	19N	19N	13N	7N	12N	20N	20	17
Collier Row	N/A	-	-	9N	2N	-	8N	12N	10	3
Cove	N/A	-	-	-	-	-	-	19S	6	5
Eastbourne United	N/A	(see page 335 for Div.2 record)							21	-
East Thurrock United	N/A	-	-	-	-	-	-	-	-	8
Edgware Town	N/A	(see page 335 for Div.2 record)							1	-
Epsom & Ewell	N/A	-	-	-	5S	9S	14S	13S	9	15
Feltham	N/A	14S	10S	4S	4S	8S	18S	18S		
Feltham & Hounslow Boro.	N/A								16	20
Flackwell Heath	N/A	8N	14S	16S	20S	13S	8S	16S	7	11
Hampton	N/A	(see page 335 for Div.2 record)							4	-
Haringey Borough	N/A	19N	11N	3N	20N	-	-	-	-	-
Harlow Town	N/A	-	-	17N	5N	1N	-	-	-	-
Hertford Town	N/A	-	5N	15N	22N	10N	3N	15N	13	10
Heybridge Swifts	N/A	3N	3N	4N	9N	5N	1N	-	-	-
Hornchurch	N/A	-	-	14N	14N	16N	16N	19N	18	13
Horsham	N/A	(see page 335 for Div.2 record)							5	14
Kingsbury Town	N/A	17N	2N	-	-	-	-	13N	12	9
Leighton Town	N/A	-	-	-	-	-	-	-	-	4
Maidenhead United	N/A	-	-	-	11S	17S	5S	2S	-	-
Marlow	N/A	13N	20S	2S	-	-	-	-	-	-
Northwood	N/A	-	-	-	-	-	-	-	-	6
Petersfield United	N/A	17S	12S	18S	22S	21S	20S	21S	14	19
Royston Town	N/A	11N	8N	21N	17N	18N	9N	16N	11	7
Stevenage Borough	N/A	4N	1N	-	-	4N	4N	1N	-	-
Thame United	N/A	-	-	-	-	-	-	-	8	2
Tilbury	N/A	(see page 335 for Div.2 record)							3	-
Tring Town	N/A	(see page 335 for Div.2 record)							19	12
Vauxhall Motors	N/A	-	16N	13N	8N	14N	11N	2N	-	-
Whyteleafe	N/A	5S	5S	12S	7S	2S	-	-	-	-
Wivenhoe Town	N/A	-	12N	1N	-	-	-	-	-	-
Woking	N/A	-	3S	1S	-	-	-	-	-	-
Wolverton Town	N/A	16N	20N	2N	-	22N	-	-	-	-
Yeading	N/A	-	-	-	10S	15S	1S	-	-	-
No. of clubs competing	N/A	20N	20N	22N	22N	22N	22N	22N	21	20
		19S	20S	21S	22S	21S	21S	22S		

BRACKNELL TOWN

Chairman: Dave Mihell **Vice Chairman:** Paul Broome **President:** Ian McGregor.
Secretary: Cliff McFadden, 15 Goodways Drive, Bracknell, Berks RG12 3AU (0344 52803).
Manager: Phil Alexander **Asst Manager:** Nick Collier **Coach:** Andy Ritchie
Press Officer: Robert Scully **Commercial Mgr:** Phil Alexander **Physio:** T.B.A.
Ground: Larges Lane, Bracknell RG12 3AN (0344 412305).
Directions: Off A329 just before Met Office r'bout by Bracknell College, ground 200 yards. From Bracknell (BR)/bus station - right out of station, follow path over bridge, left down steps and follow cycle path ahead, after 300yds follow curve over footbridge, right and follow lane to end, left and ground on left after bend.
Capacity: 2,500 **Seats:** 150 **Cover:** 200 **Floodlights:** Yes **Founded:** 1896
Colours: All red **Change colours:** All blue **Nickname:** Robins
Programme: 32 pages, 50p **Editor:** Robert Scully (0344 423749) **Metal Badges:** Yes
Club Shop: To open 1993-94, selling club badges, programmes, 'Team Talk' magazine etc. Contact Keith Smith c/o Bracknell Town F.C.
Previous Grounds: None **Midweek Matchday:** Tuesday
Previous Leagues: Great Western Comb./ Surrey Snr 63-70/ London Spartan 70-75.
Reserve's League: Suburban (west) **Record Gate:** 2,500 v Newquay, F.A. Amateur Cup 1971.
Best F.A. Cup season: 4th Qualifying Rd 1988 (lost 1-2 v Cheltenham Town).
Record win: 7-0 v Royston Town **Record defeat:** 0-9 v Royston & v Thame Utd.
Players progressing to Football League: Willie Graham (Brentford).
Clubhouse: Members' bar open 11am-11pm Mon-Sat, 12-3 & 7-10.30pm Sun. Function hall bookable.
Club Record Scorer: Richard Whithy **Club Record Appearances:** James Woodcock.
92-93 Captain & P.o.Y: Tony Carter **92-93 Top scorer:** Justin Day
Hons: Isthmian Lg Div 2 Sth R-up, Berks & Bucks Snr Cup R-up, Spartan Lg 82-83 (R-up(2)), Surrey Snr Lg 69-70 (Lg Cup 68-69 69-70).

CAMBERLEY TOWN

Chairman: Ian Waldren **Vice Chairman:** Gordon Foss **President:** Paul Prentice
Secretary: Ron Trindles, 26 Mathon Court, Cross Lane, Guildford GU1 1TD (0483 60829).
Manager: Paul Holden **Asst Manager:** Nigel Wiscombe **Coach:** Paul Holden
Press Officer: Barrie Funnell **Comm. Manager:** Andy Jennings **Physio:** Doug Peters.
Ground: Krooner Park, Krooner Road, off Frimley Rd, Camberley, Surrey GU15 2QP (0276 65392).
Directions: M3 Jct 4, follow signs to Frimley, follow B3411 towards Camberley, ground on left opposite 'The Standard' pub.
Capacity: 3,000 **Seats:** 195 **Cover:** 195 **Floodlights:** Yes **Founded:** 1896
Colours: Red (white trim)/red/red **Change colours:** All yellow **Metal Badges:** Yes.
Club Shop: Yes, selling programmes, scarves, shirts, bags, pullovers, ties, badges. Contact Barry Funnell c/o the club.
Programme: 24 pages, 50p **Midweek Matchday:** Tuesday **Sponsors:** Zip Print
Previous Grounds: London Rd Rec 1898-1905 12-18/ Southwell Park Rd 05-09/ Martins Meadow 09-12.
Previous Leagues: Ascot & District/ West Surrey/ Aldershot Snr/ Surrey Snr 22-73/ Spartan 73-75/ Athenian 75-77 82-84/ Isthmian 77-82.
Previous Names: Camberley F.C., Yorktown F.C. (clubs merged in 1969)
Reserve's League: Suburban **Nickname:** 'Krooners', 'Reds' or 'Town'.
Record Gate: 3,500 v Crystal Palace, floodlight opening, 14/10/74. *Competitive: 2,066 v Aldershot Town, Isthmian League Division 3, 1/11/92.*
Best F.A. Cup year: 3rd Qual. Rd 78-79 **Record win:** 15-0 v Royal Engineers, friendly, 20/9/19.
Record defeat: 0-11 v Abingdon Town (A), Isthmian League Division Two (South) 25/8/90.
Clubhouse: Open matchdays and most evenings. Large bar and function hall, pool, darts. Local band on Fridays. Food available from burger bar on matchdays.
92-93 Captain: Paul Xiberras **92-93 P.o.Y.:** Rory Todd. **92-93 Top scorer:** Stephen Russell 10
Local Press: Camberley News (0276 64444). **Local Radio:**
Hons: FA Vase QF 85-86, Isthmian Lg Div 2 R-up 78-79, Surrey Snr Lg 30-31 31-32 32-33 (R-up 46-47 61-62, Lg Charity Cup 37-38 51-52 (R-up 31-32 36-37 54-55 72-73)), Surrey Snr Cup 78-79 (R-up 35-36), W. Surrey Lg 13-14 (R-up 12-13), Ascot & Dist Lg 03-04, Surrey Jnr Charity Cup R-up 08-09, Surrey Jnr Cup 1897-98 1909-10 (R-up 07-08), Aldershot Snr Lg 12-13 (Lg Charity Cup R-up 21-22), Southern Comb. Cup 80-81 (R-up 78-79 85-86 87-88).

Camberley Town F.C. 1992-93.

CHESHUNT

Chairman: Mr Tony Wilson   **Vice Chairman:** Mr Bill Moye   **President:** Mr Alan Burt.
Secretary/Press Officer: Mr Fred Beer, 10 Hyde Court, Parkside, Waltham Cross (0992 761138).
Manager: Mr Dave Bidwell   **Physio:** Mr Lou Dedman.
Ground: The Stadium, Theobalds Lane, Cheshunt, Herts (0992 26752).
Directions: M25 to junction 25, A10 nort towards Hertford past ground on right, turn back towards London at first traffic lights to enter. 400yds from Theobalds Grove BR station - turn left and left again for ground. Buses 279, 242, 715 and 310 to Theobalds Grove station.

Seats: 200 **Cover:** 1,200	**Capacity:** 2,000 **Floodlights:** Yes	**Founded:** 1946.
Colours: Yellow/blue	**Change colours:** All blue	**Nickname:** Ambers
Programme: 20 pages, 50p	**Editor:** Alan Timpson (0707 874028)	**Club Shop:** No.
Midweek matchday: Tuesday	**Previous Ground:** Broomfield Lane 52-56.	
Club Sponsors: Trific Linde	**Reserve team's League:** Essex & Herts Border Comb.	

Previous Leagues: Athenian 19-20 21-31 64-77/ London 20-21 24-25 46-51 55-59/ Delphian 51-55/ Aetolian 59-62/ Spartan 62-64/ Isthmian 77-87.
Best FA Vase season: Qtr Final 81-82   **Best FA Cup season:** 4th Qual. Rd(4)
Record gate: 7,000 v Bromley, London Senior Cup 1947.
Record transfer fee paid: £250 for Tony Tillbrook (Boreham Wood, 1988).
Record transfer fee received: £1,500 for Andy Prutton (Dartford, 1989).
Top Scorer 92-93: Matt Barlow 30   **Capt. & P.O.Y. 92-93:** Danny Smith   **Clubhouse:** Yes.
Hons: Athenian Lg 75-76 (R-up 73-74, Div 1 67-68, Div 2 R-up 65-66, Lg Cup 74-75 75-76), Spartan Lg 62-63 (Lg Cup 63-64 92-93 (R-up 89-90)), London Lg 49-50 (R-up 56-57, Div 1 47-48 48-49 (R-up 46-47), Park Royal Cup 46-47), Isthmian Lg Div 2 R-up 81-82, Herts Snr Cup 23-24, Herts Charity Cup 00-01 05-06, Herts Charity Shield 46-47 65-66, Herts Snr Centenary Tphy 91-92.

Cheshunt F.C., promoted from the Spartan League. Back Row (L/R): Lou Dedman (Physio), Danny Brown, Manuel Luque, Richard Davies, Danny Andrews, Paul Read, Dave Robotham, Matt Barlow, Jamie Hoy, Nick Sparrow (Asst Manager). Front: Paul Mann, Andy King, Danny Bidwell, Paul Cotterell, Clyde Rudd, Ryan Harris, Danny Smith, Paul Holloway. Photo - Francis Short.

CLAPTON

Chairman: Mike Fogg   **Vice Chairman:** A Sawyer   **President:** M Gliksten
Secretary: Roger Chilvers, 50 Harrow Rd, Barking, Essex IG11 7RA (081 591 5313).
Manager: J Arnold   **Asst Manager:** N/A   **Coach:** B Balkwill
Press Officer: P Caulfield   **Physio:** P Kelly.
Ground: The Old Spotted Dog, Upton Lane, Forest Gate, London E7 9NP (081 472 0822).
Directions: BR to Forest Gate, tube to Plaistow (District Line), or bus 278 passes ground. Officials entrance in Upton Lane, spectator's in Disraeli Rd.

Capacity: 2,000 **Seats:** 150	**Cover:** 500	**Floodlights:** Yes	**Founded:** 1878
Colours: Red & white stripes/black/black		**Change colours:** All gold	
Club Shop: No		**Sponsors:** None	
Programme: 16 pages, 50p	**Editor:** Peter Pendle (081 519 1084).		**Metal Badges:** Yes
Previous Grounds: None	**Midweek Matchday:** Tuesday		**Nickname:** Tons

Previous Leagues: Southern 1894-96 (founder members)/ London 1896-97.
Record Gate: 12,000 v Tottenham Hotspur, F.A. Cup 1898-99.
Best F.A. Cup year: 3rd Rd Proper 25-26 (lost 2-3 to Swindon at Upton Park.
League clubs defeated in F.A. Cup: Norwich City 1925-26.
Clubhouse: Licensed bar. Also tea bar open during matches.
Club Record Goalscorer: Unknown   **Club Record Appearances:** Dave Fahy.
92-93 Captain: Alan Bowers   **92-93 P.O.Y.:** Peter Mason   **92-93 Top scorer:** Tony Marsh
Hons: FA Amtr Cup 06-07 08-09 14-15 23-24 24-25 (R-up 04-05), Isthmian Lg 10-11 22-23 (R-up 05-06 07-08 09-10 24-25, Div 2 82-83), Essex Thames-side Tphy(2), A.F.A. Invitation Cup(2), London Snr Cup(2), London Charity Cup, Essex Snr Cup(4), First English team to play on the continent.

Clapton F.C. 1992-93. Back Row (L/R): Jim McMillan (Physio), Lloyd Moncur, Paul Monk, Leon Pickering, Andrew Marsh, Bill Bailey, Mark Hunt, Dave Fahy, Brian Balkwell (Coach), John Arnold (Manager). Front: Tarquin Mustaqa, Paul French, Eddie Selwyn, George Dalarto, Tony Marsh, Alan Bowers, Peter Mason. Photo - Paul Dennis.

COVE

Chairman: Bob Clark **President:** Ron Brown
Secretary: Dave Grenham, 149 Aldershot Rd, Church Crookham, Hants GU13 0JS (0252 623021).
Manager: Chick Botley **Asst Manager:** Jerry Kerrigan
Press Officer: Chick Botley (0252 518587) **Physio:** Trevor Croft.
Ground: Oak Farm, off Romayne Close, Cove, Farnborough, Hants GU14 8LB (0252 543615).
Directions: Farnborough (BR) 2 miles; right into Union Street, right at lights into Prospect Rd, left into West Heath Rd, right into Romayne close and follow signs to Cove FC. Or, M3 jct 4, follow A325 signed Aldershot & Farnham, right into Prospect Avenue (signposted Cove FC and Farnborough Town FC), then as above.
Capacity: 3,500 **Seats:** 75 **Cover:** 475 **Floodlights:** Yes **Founded:** 1897
Colours: Amber/black **Change colours:** All red **Nickname:** None.
Club Shop: No, but club ties, badges and lighters are on sale in clubhouse.
Programme: 24 pages, 50p **Editor:** Graham Brown (0252 541152). **Metal Badges:** Yes
Previous Grounds: Cove Green 1897-1973/ Southwood Rd.
Previous Leagues: Aldershot Jnr/ Aldershot Intermediate 45-48/ Surrey Intermediate 48-71/ Surrey Snr 71-73/ Hants 74-81/ Combined Counties 81-90.
Midweek Matchday: Tuesday **Sponsors:** Murata Electronics/ Oasis soft drinks
Reserve Team's League: Suburban **Record Gate:** 1,798 v Aldershot, Isthmian Lg Div 3, 1/5/93.
Best F.A. Cup year: First Qualifying Round replay 91-92 (lost 0-4 at Burgess Hill Town).
Record transfer fee paid: £250 for Nick Horton (Egham Town, 92-93).
Record win: 10-2 v Sway (H), 17/2/74. In Senior Football: 8-1 v Cobham (H), Comb. Co's Lg, 16/9/89.
Record defeat: 2-8 v Merrow (A), 17/1/69. In Senior Football: 1-6 v Hungerford (A), Isthmian Lg, 16/3/91.
Players progressing to Football League: Frank Broome, Maurice Cook.
Clubhouse: Mon-Fri 7-11pm, Sat noon-11pm, Sunday noon-3pm & 7-11pm. Juke box, pool, darts. Matchday hot food includes burgers, hot-dogs, chips, soup plus variety of sandwiches and other snacks.
Club Record Scorer: Nigel Thompson 129 **Record Appearances:** Nigel Thompson, 188 in four seasons.
92-93 Captain: Martin Duffy **92-93 Top Scorer:** Nigel Thompson.
92-93 Manager's P.o.Y.: Paul Riley **92-93 Players' P.o.Y.:** Peter Browning.
Hons: Surrey I'mediate Lg, Surrey Prem. Lg 49-50 52-53 53-54 63-64 67-68 (R-up 48-49 61-62 64-65, Lg Cup 59-60 60-61 69-70, Sportmanship Award 64-65 65-66 69-70, Reserve Section 59-60 60-61 61-62 64-65 (R-up 63-64 66-67 67-68 68-69), Reserve Cup 60-61 61-62), Combined Co's Lg Cup 81-82, Hants Lg Div 3 76-77 (Div 4 73-74, Div 2 R-up 77-78), Aldershot Snr Cup 71-72 77-78 79-80 90-91 91-92 (R-up 72-73), Aldershot Snr Shield 37-38 38-39 46-47 71-72, Aldershot Snr Lg 53-54 (Div 2 32-33 37-38 38-39, Div 2 Cup 50-51, Div 4 Cup 30-31).

Cove F.C. 1992-93. Back Row (L/R): Tommy Hammond, John Cassidy (Player-Coach), Peter Hughes, Richard Sugg, Martin Duffy, Ricky Jones, Paul Riley, Steve Flanaghan, Micky Street, Craig Jeffery, Darren Broad, Andy Pagden, Jerry Gerrigan (Asst Manager), Ian Jopling. Front: Chick Botley (Manager), David Newbery, Nicky Horton, Shaun Dowling, Nigel Thompson, Peter Browning, Ken McMillan. Photo - Eric Marsh.

EAST THURROCK UNITED

Chairman: Brian Grover   **Vice Chairman:** Trevor Firman   **President:** Len Firman
Secretary/Press Officer: Malcolm Harris, 14 Colne Valley, Upminster, Essex RM14 1QA (07082 28812).
Manager: Glen Case   **Coach:** Kevin Desbrow   **Physio:** Roger Hutton.
Ground: Rookery Hill, Corringham, Essex (0375 644166-club, 641009-boardroom).
Directions: A13 London-Southend, take 1014 at Stanford-le-Hope for two and a half miles - ground on left. Two miles from Stanford-le-Hope and Basildon BR stations.
Seats: 160   **Cover:** 360   **Capacity:** 3,000   **Floodlights:** Yes   **Founded:** 1969.
Colours: Amber/black/black   **Change colours:** Blue/white/white   **Nickname:** Rocks
Programme: 20 pages   **Editor:** Ian Firmin (0702 470109)   **Metal Badges:** Yes
Sponsors: Partridge's Dairies.   **Club Shop:** Yes. Selling programmes and magazines.
Record Gate: 947 v Trevor Brooking XI, May 1987. Competitive: 845 v Bashley, F.A. Vase 1989.
Previous Name: Corringham Social (pre-1969 Sunday side).
Prev. Lges: Sth Essex Comb./ Gtr London/ Metropolitan 72-75/ London Spartan 75-79/ Essex Snr 79-92.
Previous Grounds: Billet, Stanford-le-Hope 70-73 74-76/ Grays Athletic F.C. 73-74/ Tilbury F.C. 77-82/ New Thames Club 82-84.
Record Transfer Fee Paid: £2,000 + 10% of future fee for Greg Berry (Orient, 1989).
Players progressing to Football League: Greg Berry (Leyton Orient).
Clubhouse: Open all day seven days a week. Hot and cold snacks. Darts, pool, indoor bowls.
Club Record Goalscorer: Graham Stewart 102
Club Record Appearances: Glen Case 600+.
92-93 Captain: Paul Driscoll   **92-93 P.O.Y.:** Danny Smith   **92-93 Top Scorer:** Danny Wallace.
Local Press: Thurrock Gazette/ Thurrock Recorder   **Local Radio:** BBC Essex.
Honours: Metropolitan Lg Div 2 72-73, Essex Snr Lg R-up 88-89 (Lg Cup 88-89 91-92, Harry Fisher Mem. Tphy 83-84 90-91, Sportsmanship Award 81-82 86-87 89-89), Essex Snr Tphy R-up 91-92, Fred Budden Tphy R-up 89-90, Essex & Herts Border Comb. 89-90 (Lg Cup 89-90).

EPSOM & EWELL

Chairman: Peter Atkins   **Vice Chairman:** Stella Lamont.
Secretary: David Wilson, 33 Delaporte Rd, Epsom, Surrey KT17 4AF (0372 729817).
Manager: Adrian Hill   **Coach:** John Wood   **Physio:** Charlie Millard.
Press Officer: Stella Lamont (0737 356245)   **Ground:** As Banstead Athletic F.C. (see page 337).
Club Shop: No   **Sponsors:** T.B.A.   **Nickname:** E's.   **Founded:** 1917
Colours: Royal & white   **Change colours:** All yellow.
Programme: 28/32 pages, 35p   **Editor:** Stella Lamont (0737 356245).
Midweek Matches: T.B.A.   **Reserve Team's League:** Suburban
Previous Leagues: Surrey Snr 24-27 73-75/ London 27-49/ Corinthian 49-63/ Athenian 63-73 75-77.
Previous Names: Epsom Town (previously Epsom FC) merged with Ewell & Stoneleigh in 1960.
Previous Grounds: Horton Lane, Epsom 1925-26/ West Street, Ewell 26-93.
Best F.A. Cup year: 1st Rd Proper 33-34, lost 2-4 at Clapton Orient.
Best FA Vase year: Finalists 74-75   **Best FA Trophy year:** 2nd Rd Proper 81-82.
Record Gate: 5,000 v Kingstonian, F.A. Cup Second Qualifying Rd, 15/10/49.
Players progressing to Football League: Matt Elliott (Torquay), Chris Powell (Southend), Paul Harding (Notts County), Murray Jones (Grimsby), Alan Pardew (Charlton), Mick Leonard (Chesterfield).
Clubhouse: Normal licensing hours, food available.
92-93 Captain: Ray Purvis   **92-93 Top Scorer:** Marcus Alcindor 14.
92-93 P.O.Y.: Ray Purvis (1st team), Dave Bruty (Reserves), Neil Wallis (Youth).
Club Record Scorer: Tommy Tuite   **Club Record Appearances:** Unknown.
Hons: F.A. Vase R-up 74-75, London Lg 27-28 (R-up 31-32 32-33 34-35 36-37 37-38), Corinthian Lg Memorial Shield 59-60 (R-up 51-52 56-57), Athenian Lg Div 2 R-up 75-76 (Lg Cup R-up 76-77, Div 2 Cup R-up 67-68), Isthmian Lg Div 2 77-78 (Div 1 R-up 83-84), Surrey Snr Lg 25-26 26-27 74-75 (R-up 73-74, Lg Cup 73-74 74-75, Charity Cup 26-27 (R-up 73-74), Res. Section 74-75, Res. Cup 75-76 (R-up 73-74)), Surrey Snr Cup 80-81 (R-up 28-29 53-54 83-84), Surrey Snr Shield 32-33 54-55, Surrey Intermediate Cup 29-30, Surrey Intermediate Charity Cup 57-58, Surrey Jnr Cup R-up 22-23, Surrey Yth Cup 33-34 (R-up 50-51), Southern Comb. Cup 79-80 (R-up 82-83 92-93), Southern Yth Lg (East) 91-92 (R-up 82-83 85-86, Lg Cup 91-92 (R-up 87-88)).

Epsom & Ewell before their last match at West Street, against Aldershot Town on 17th April. Back Row (L/R): Adrian Hill (Manager), Dean Meyer, Tim Tweedy, Ray Purvis, Paul Meredith, Tony Webb, Richard Strong, Graham Morris, Charlie Millard (Physio), John Wood (Asst Manager). Front: Andy Nimmo, Nigel Webb, Nigel Bennett, Martin Taylor, Marcus Alcindor, Simon Alldridge. Photo - Stan Caryer.

FELTHAM & HOUNSLOW BOROUGH

Chairman: W F P Seuke & S Das   **President:** E J Pauling MBE, JP.
Secretary: Mrs Ann Wilson, 2 Farrier Close, Sunbury-on-Thames, Middx TW16 6NJ (0932 789492).
Manager: Bruce Butler   **Physio:** Sarah Whitworth   **Coach:** Bruce Butler
Ground: Feltham Arena, Shakespeare Avenue, Feltham, Middx TW14 9HY (081 890 6241-club, 6905/6119-ground). *Nb- the club have an artificial pitch.*
Directions: BR to Feltham then 5 mins walk through Glebelands Park. Buses 90, 285, 117, 237, H24 or H25 to Feltham station, or 116 to top of Shakespeare Avenue. By car; M3, M4, A312 Staines road towards Bedfont, second left is Shakespeare Avenue.
Capacity: 10,000   **Seats:** 750   **Cover:** 1,500   **Floodlights:** Yes   **Founded:** 1991
Colours: Royal blue & red stripes/red/blue   **Change colours:** Blue & white/blue/white.
Club Shop: No (old progs from Robert Healy, C/O the club)   **Metal Badges:** No
Programme: 20 pages, 30p   **Editor:**   **Nickname:** Borough.
Midweek Matchday: Wednesday   **Reserve Team's League:** Suburban.   **Sponsors:**
Previous Names: 1991 merger of Feltham FC and Hounslow FC. Feltham previously Tudor Park, Hounslow previously Hounslow Town.
Previous Grounds: Feltham: Rectory Fields, Glebelands, *Hounslow:* Denbigh Road.
Previous Leagues: Feltham: West Middx Sunday/ Staines & Dist./ Hounslow & Dist./ Surrey Snr 63-68/ Spartan 68-73/ Athenian 74-77. *Hounslow: West London/ West Middx/ London 1898-99 1927-29/ Gt Western Suburban/ Spartan 29-46/ Corinthian 46-55/ Athenian 55-76/ Southern 76-83 86-90/ Hellenic 83-86 90-91.*
Record Gate: 826 v Aldershot Town, Isthmian Lg Div 3, 19/9/92. As Feltham FC: 1,938 v Hampton, Middx Snr Cup 1968 (*Hounslow; 8,546 v Wycombe, FA Amtr Cup 53-54*).
Best FA Cup year: Preliminary Replay 91-92 (lost 0-4 at home to Burnham). As *Feltham FC: 3rd Qual Rd 77-78 (lost 1-4 to Tilbury)* 82-83 (0-1 v Chesham). As *Hounslow: 1st Rd Proper 55-56 (lost to Hastings United).*
Record Fees - Paid: Martin Tyler (Kingstonian)   **Rec'd:** Rachid Harkouk (C Palace).
Clubhouse: Sun, Mon, Wed-Sat. 2 bars, dancehall available for hire. Pool, darts. **Steward:** P Bennett.
Players progressing to Football League: Rachid Harkouk (Crystal Palace, QPR, Notts Co), Andy Pape (QPR), Pat Gavin (Gillingham, Leicester), Bobby Wilson (Brentford), Tony Witter (Crystal Palace).
Club Record Scorer: Paul Clarke 130   **Club Record Appearances:** Paul Clarke 326.
92-93 Captain: **92-93 P.o.Y.:**   **92-93 Top scorer:** Mark Lester 18.
Local Press: Middx Chronicle, Hounslow Feltham & Hanworth Times, Hounslow Borough Recorder.
Local Radio: Capital, Capital Gold, County Sounds.
Hons: Surrey Snr Lg R-up 65-66 (Lg Cup 65-66, Charity Cup 63-64 65-66), Southern Comb. Cup(2)(R-up(2)), Middx Summer Cup, Ashford Cup R-up. *Hounslow: FA Amtr Cup R-up 61-62 (SF 53-54), Hellenic Lg R-up 85-86 (Lg Cup 85-86), Gt Western Suburban Lg 24-25, Spartan Lg 45-46, West London Lg 1895-96, FA Vase 5th Rd 87-88.*

Feltham & Hounslow Borough F.C. 1992-93. Photo - Alan Coomes.

FLACKWELL HEATH

Chairman: D Smith   **Vice Chairman:** W J Tapping   **President:** Ken Crook
Secretary: Cyril Robinson, 5 Chapman Lane, Flackwell Heath, High Wycombe, Bucks HP10 9AZ (0628 526204).
Ground: Wilks Park, Heath End Rd, Flackwell Heath, High Wycombe, Bucks HP10 9EA (0628 523892).
Directions: M40 jct 4, follow A404 towards High Wycombe, 1st turning into Daws Hill Lane, continue for 2 miles until you see signs for the club, left into Magpie Lane, ground at rear of Magpie (PH). Bus 301 either from bus station or High Street near bottom of Crendon Street which comes from BR station. Ask for Oakland Way.
Capacity: 2,000   **Seats:** 150   **Cover:** Yes   **Floodlights:** Yes   **Founded:** 1907
Club Shop: No   **Metal Badges:** No   **Programme:** Yes   **Editor:** TBA   **Sponsors:** TBA
Colours: Red/white/red   **Change colours:** Yellow/black/yellow
Midweek Matches: Tuesday.   **Reserve Team's League:** Middx County
Record. win: 6-0 v Clapton & v Petersfield (both away)   **Record defeat:** 0-6 v Royston (A).
Best F.A. Cup season: 2nd Qualifying Round replay 1990-91 (lost 0-3 at Grays after 2-2 draw).
Previous Leagues: Wycombe & District/ Gt Western Comb./ Hellenic 76-82/ Athenian 82-84.
Record Gate: 4,500 v Oxford U., charity game 1986 (competitive: 700 v Aldershot Town, 27/10/92).
Clubhouse: Open every night 6.30-11pm and before and after matches. Hot food in tea bar.
Club Record Scorer: Tony Woods   **Club Record Appearances:** Tony Woods.
92-93 Captain: Ben Richards   **92-93 P.o.Y.:** R Swallow   **92-93 Top Scorer:** Tony Woods, 33.
Hons: Gt Western Combination 57-58 62-63, Hellenic Lg Div 1 R-up 76-77, Berks & Bucks Snr Cup SF 85-86.

The Feltham & Hounslow Borough saves bravely from Aldershot Town's Mark Butler. Photo - Ian Morseman.

HAREFIELD UNITED

Chairman: Mr Dave West   **President:** Mr Ivor Mitchell
Secretary: Terry Devereux, 132 Organ Hall Rd, Boreham Wood WD6 4TL (081 207 0324).
Manager: Dave Finn   **Assistant Manager:** Bill Dowd
Press Officer: T.B.A.   **Physio:** Alan Carpenter, John Godfrey.
Ground: Preston Park, Breakespeare Rd, North Harefield, Middx UB9 6DG (0895 823474).
Directions: M25 jct 17, follow signs to Swakely corner then to Harefield A40. Denham (BR). Bus 347 from Watford.
Capacity: 2,000   **Seats:** 150   **Cover:** Yes   **Floodlights:** Yes   **Founded:** 1868
Colours: Red & white/black/red   **Change colours:** Sky & navy.
Club Shop: No   **Metal Badges:** Yes   **Sponsors:**
Programme: 12-40 pages, 30p   **Editor:** Secretary
Midweek Matchday: Tuesday   **Previous Leagues:** Uxbridge & Dist./ Gt Western Comb. 46-64/ Parthenon 64-68/ Middx 68-75/ Athenian 75-84.
Reserve Team's League: Suburban   **Nickname:** Hares.
Record Gate: 430 v Bashley, FA Vase.
Best FA Cup year: 2nd Qual. Rd replay 80-81 (lost 1-5 at Maidenhead), 86-87 (0-2 at Aylesbury).
Clubhouse: (0895 823474). Lunchtimes and evenings. Two bars, cold snacks (hot on matchdays).
92-93 Captain: Tom Murphy   **92-93 P.o.Y.:** Tom Murphy   **92-93 Top scorer:** Andy McShannon 9.
Local Newspapers: Watford Observer, Harefield Gazette, Sports Weekly.
Local Radio: Hillingdon Hospital, Chiltern.
Hons: Middx Premier Cup 85-86, Athenian Lg R-up 83-84, Parthenon Lg 64-65 (Div 1 Cup 65-66), Middx Lg 66-67 68-69 69-70 70-71 (Lg Cup 66-67 68-69).

HARLOW TOWN

Secretary: Mr S Ray, 13 Church End, Harlow, Essex CM19 5PQ (0279 419610).
(We have not been advised of any personnel, but understand that the Woodford Town F.C., who have resigned their place in the Essex Senior League, form the basis of the club).
Ground: Harlow Sports Centre, Hammarsjkold Rd, Harlow (0279 421927/635100).
Directions: Near town centre, 10 mins walk from Harlow (BR) station.
Capacity: 10,000   **Cover:** 450   **Seats:** 450   **Floodlights:** Yes
Colours: All red   **Change colours:** Blue
Previous Leagues: Spartan 32-39 46-54/ London 54-61/ Delphian 61-63/ Athenian 63-73/ Isthmian 73-92/ 92-93 did not compete in any league.
Previous Grounds: Marigolds 1879-1930/ Green Man Field 30-60.
Midweek home matchday: TBA   **Reserve's League:** Essex & Herts Border Comb.
Record Attendance: 9,723 v Leicester, FA Cup 3rd Rd replay 8/1/80.
Best F.A. Cup season: 4th Rd 79-80 (lost 3-4 at Watford). Also 1st Rd 80-81 81-82.
League clubs defeated in F.A. Cup: Southend, Leicester 79-80.   **Record Fees:** Undisclosed.
Players progressing to Football League: Jeff Wood (Charlton 1975), Neil Prosser (B'mouth 1980)
Club Record Goalscorer: Jeff Wood (44 in 88-89)
Club Record Apps: Norman Gladwin (646 1949-70)
Local Press: Harlow Citizen (451698), Harlow Star (420333), Harlow Herald & Post (0279 655225).
Local Radio Stations: Essex Radio, BBC Essex.
Honours: FA Amtr Cup 2nd Rd 72-73, FA Tphy 2nd Rd(2) 80-82, FA Vase 3rd Rd 88-89, Isthmian Lg Div 1 78-79 (R-up 82-83, Div 2 Nth 88-89, Yth Cup 77-78), Ath'n Lg Div 1 71-72, E Angl. Cup 89-90, Knight F'lit Cup R-up 87-88, Essex Snr Cup 78-79, Essex F'lit Competition R-up 71-72, London Lg Chal. Cup 59-60, Spartan Lg Cup 52-53, Epping Hosp. Cup(3) 46-49, Essex & Herts Border Comb Cup 75-76, Fred Budden Tphy 88-89 89-90, Chelmsford Yth Lg 86-87 (Lg Cup 86-87 87-88).

HERTFORD TOWN

Chairman: Bernard Molloy   **President:** Jock Gillam   **Vice Chairman:** Graham Wood.
Secretary: Stephen Hedley, 28 Cherry Tree Green, Hertford SG14 2HP (0992 587011).
Manager: John Walsh   **Asst Manager:** John Downey   **Coach:**
Press Officer: Graham Wood   **Treasurer:** Mrs Carol Slade   **Physio:** Ray Price
Ground: Hertingfordbury Park, West Street, Hertford (0992 5837011).
Directions: Rail to Hertford Nth (from Moorgate) or Hertford East (Liverpool Str.); both 15 mins walk. Green Line bus to town centre then 10 mins walk. By road; off bypass heading east, turn off at Trimoco garage.
Capacity: 6,500   **Seats:** 200   **Cover:** 1,500   **Floodlights:** Yes   **Founded:** 1908
Colours: All navy blue   **Change colours:** All red   **Club Shop:** No.
Metal Badges: Yes. Available from Graham Showell, 5 Beehive Lane, Welwyn Garden City AL7 4BB.
Midweek Matches: Tuesday.   **Nickname:** Blues
Previous Leagues: Herts Co./ Spartan 21-47 48-59/ Delphian 59-63/ Athenian 63-72/ Eastern Co's 72-73.
Previous Names: None   **Previous Grounds:** None.
Programme: 24 pages, 30p   **Reserve Team's League:** Essex & Herts Border Comb.
Programme Editor: Graham Wood (assisted by Stephen Hedley/ Graham Showell).
Best F.A. Cup year: Fourth Qualifying Rd 73-74 (lost 1-2 at Hillingdon Borough).
Record Gate: 5,000 v Kingstonian, F.A. Amateur Cup 2nd Rd 55-56.
Players progressing to Football League: G Mazzon (Aldershot)
Clubhouse: Old clubhouse burnt down in 1992. New clubhouse to be built on same site with new tea-bar and toilet facilities.
92-93 Captain: John Meakes   **92-93 Top Scorer:** David Whitehead 29.
Local Newspapers: Hertfordshire Mercury
Hons: Herts Charity Cup 72-73, Herts Snr Cup 66-67, Hertford Charity Shield 19-20 20-21 35-36 49-50 55-56 59-60, Eastern Co's Lg Cup 72-73, East Anglian Cup 62-63 69-70, Mithras Cup SF 85-86.

HORNCHURCH

Chairman: James Bradshaw   **Vice Chairman:** K Nicholls.
Secretary: Mr Edward Harris, 13 Claremont Gdns, Upminster, Essex RM14 1DW (0402 227891).
Manager: Keith Newman   **Asst Mgr & Coach:** John Kerslake
Press Officer: Robert Monger (0702 460539)   **Physio:** D Edkins.
Commercial Manager: P O'Connor
Ground: The Stadium, Bridge Avenue, Upminster, Essex RM14 2LX (0402 220080).
Directions: Fenchurch Street to Upminster (BR) then 10 mins walk. Or tube to Upminster Bridge (LT), right outside station, 2nd right into Bridge Ave., ground 150yds on right. Bus 248 Romford-Upminster. Also buses 246 & 370.
Capacity: 3,000   **Seats:** 300   **Cover:** 350   **Floodlights:** Yes   **Founded:** 1923
Colours: White (red trim)/white/white   **Change colours:** All sky.
Club Shop: Yes, selling programmes, handbooks, scarves, hats, souvenirs etc. Contact Ron Quantock, 120 The Avenue, Hornchurch, Essex RM12 4JC (0708 455529).
Programme: 16-20 pages with admission   **Programme Editor:** F Hawthorn (0708 225451).
Midweek Matchday: Tuesday   **Previous Ground:** Upminster Rec.
Previous Leagues: Romford 1925-38/ Spartan 38-52/ Delphian 52-59/ Athenian 59-75.
Previous Names: Hornchurch & Upminster (Upminster FC pre-1950s) merged with Upminster Wanderers in 1961.
Reserve Team's League: Essex & Herts Border Comb.   **Nickname:** Urchins.
Sponsors: Premier Snacks   **Record Gate:** 3,000 v Chelmsford, FA Cup 66-67.
Best FA Cup year: 4th Qualifying Rd 66-67, lost 0-4 at home to Chelmsford City.
Clubhouse: Mon-Fri 7.30-11pm, Sat noon-11pm, Sun noon-3pm. Bar snacks only (crisps, peanuts etc), but cafeteria open matchdays within ground.
Players progressing to Football League: D Armstrong (Millwall), R Lee (Charlton), Nicky Bissett (Brighton).
92-93 Captain: Ian North   **92-93 P.o.Y.:** Brian Weekes   **92-93 Top scorer:** Brian Weekes.
Local Press: Romford Recorder (0708 766044)   **Local Radio:** Beds Radio.
Hons: Athenian Lg 66-67, Romford Lg(2), Essex Snr Cup R-up 86-87, Essex Jnr Cup, Essex Thamesside Tphy 84-85, F.A. Vase 5th Rd 74-75, Isthmian Yth Cup.

Hornchurch. Back (L/R): Derek Edkins (Physio), Lenny Clarke, Gary Moulding, Brian Weekes (Supporters' P.o.Y.), Keith Newman (Mgr), Dave Curtis (Players' P.o.Y.), Tony Fleming, Steve Farrugia, John Kerslake (Asst Mgr). Front: Tony Moore, Andy Skinner, Dave Guthrie, Mick Lowe, Sean O'Dea, Neil Roe, Mark Embery. Photo - Rob Monger.

HORSHAM

Chairman: Maureen Smith   **President:** G G HoLtom
Secretary: Frank King, 51 Laughton Rd, Horsham, West Sussex RH21 4EJ (0403 64647).
Manager: John Yems   **Asst Manager:** Keith Oakley   **Coach:** John Yems.
Physio: Geoff Brittain   **Press Officer:** Ben Maher (0444 455334).
Ground: Queen Street, Horsham RH13 5AD (0403 65787).
Directions: From Brighton Rd proceed into Queen Street towards town centre - ground entrance opposite Queens Head. 10 mins walk from Horsham (BR) station; along North Street past Arts Centre, fork left, left at lights, ground opposite Queens Head. Buses 107, 137, 2, 283 to Horsham Carfax then thru East Street under Iron Bridge and turn left.
Capacity: 4,300   **Seats:** 300   **Cover:** 1,800   **Nickname:** Hornets   **Founded:** 1885
Colours: Amber/green/amber   **Change colours:** All white.
Club Shop: New venture to be started in old boardroom inside clubhouse. Metal badges, old progs etc.
Programme: 36 pages, 70p   **Editor:** Maurice Shevlin (0403 242863).
Midweek Matchday: Tuesday   **Previous Ground:** Horsham Park.
Previous Leagues: W Sussex/ Sussex County 26-51/ Metropolitan 51-57/ Corinthian 57-63/ Athenian 63-73.
Reserve's League: Suburban   **Record Gate:** 8,000 v Swindon, FA Cup, November 1966.
Best FA Cup year: 1st Rd 47-48 (lost 1-9 at Notts County), 66-67 (lost 0-3 v Swindon).
Clubhouse: Normal licensing hours. Hot and cold snacks, dancehall, darts.
92-93 Captain: Keith Oakley   **92-93 P.o.Y.:** Not given   **92-93 Top scorer:** Paul Harris 18.
Local Press: West Sussex County Times: Market Square, Horsham (0403 53371).
Hons: Sussex Snr Cup 33-34 38-39 49-50 53-54 71-72 73-74 75-76, Sussex RUR Charity Cup 1899-1900 30-31 31-32 33-34(jt with Worthing) 34-35 35-36 36-37 37-38(jt with Southwick) 45-46 48-49(jt with Worthing) 50-51 51-52 56-57, Sussex County Lg 31-32 32-33 34-35 35-36 36-37 37-38 46-47 (R-up 29-30 30-31 47-48 48-49, Lg Cup 45-46 46-47), Metropolitan Lg 51-52, Athenian Lg Div 2 72-73.

KINGSBURY TOWN

Chairman: Eurek Patel   **President:**
Secretary: Peter Green, 57 Wembley Park Drive, Wembley, Middx HA9 8HE (081 902 1561).
Manager: Frank O'Brien   **Assistant Manager:** Peter Blain   **Coach:** F O'Brien
Press Officer/Commercial Mgr: Alan Davies (0895 443761)   **Physio:**
Ground: Silver Jubilee Park, Townsend Lane, Kingsbury, London NW9 0DE (081 205 1645-club, 5204-boardroom).
Directions: Underground to Kingsbury, cross road and take bus 183 to Townsend Lane.
Capacity: 4,000   **Seats:** 200   **Cover:** 300   **Club Shop:** No   **Founded:** 1927
Colours: Blue/white/blue   **Change colours:** Yellow/navy/yellow.
Programme: 28 pages, 50p   **Editor:** Alan Davies (0895 443761)
Midweek Matchday: Tuesday   **Previous Leagues:** Willesden & District 30-43/ Middx Snr 44-47/ Parthenon 47-59/ / Spartan 59-76 78-81/ Athenian 76-78 81-84.
Previous Name: Davis Sports   **Previous Grounds:** None.   **Nickname:** Town
Reserve Team's League: Suburban   **Sponsors:** VPA Entertainment Technology.
Record Gate: 1,112 v Spurs, 1981.   **92-93 Top scorer:** Mark Ivers/ Ian Brown-Peterside both 12
Best FA Cup year: 3rd Qualifying Round 87-88 (lost 0-1 at home to Leytonstone-Ilford).
Record Fees - Paid: £500   **Received:** £600.
Clubhouse: (081 205 1645). Mon-Fri 7-11pm, Sat 12-2.30pm. Pool, darts, dancehall, food on matchdays.
Players progressing to Football League: Billy Dare, John Meadows, Dave Underwood, Dwight Marshall (Plymouth).
Local Press: Harrow Observer, Hendon Times, Willesden Chronicle, Allsport Weekly, Edgware & Finchley Times.
Hons: FA Vase 4th Rd 74-75, Isthmian Lg Div 2 Nth R-up 85-86, Spartan Lg Cup R-up 59-60 64-65, Parthenon Lg 51-52 (Prem Charity Cup 52-53 53-54, Snr Charity Cup 53-54), Middx Lg Charity Cup(3) 44-47, Willesden & Dist. Lg R-up 30-31 (Div 2 34-35).

Hornchurch's Tommy Stimson (right) sees the ball out under pressure from a Kingsbury Town midfielder during a pre-season friendly. Photo - Rob Monger.

LEIGHTON TOWN

Chairman: Bruce Warner **Vice Chairman:** Eric Butler **President:** Mike Hide.
Secretary/Press Off.: Robert McClelland, 193 Grasmere Way, Leighton Buzzard, Beds LU7 7QB (0462 670471).
Manager: William Harrison **Physio:** George Lathwell **Coach:** Peter Mead.
Ground: Bell Close, Lake Street, Leighton Buzzard, Beds (0525 373311).
Directions: Off A5 at Stanbridge for Leighton Buzzard then follow Billington Rd (A4146) towards town centre. Ground behind Camden Motors just before town centre. Half mile from Leighton Buzzard (BR). Buses from Luton, Aylesbury and Milton Keynes.
Capacity: 2,500 **Seats:** 155 **Cover:** 750 **Floodlights:** Yes **Founded:** 1885
Colours: Red & white **Change colours:** All blue **Nickname:** Reds.
Club Shop: Yes, selling badges, shirts, pennants, programmes, Leighton Town prime reserve wine. Contact Paul Smith (0525 852461).
Programme: 32 pages, 50p **Editor:** Paul Smith (0525 852461). **Metal badges:** Yes.
Midweek Matchday: Tuesday **Sponsors:** Camden Motors/ Chiltern Industrial doors.
Previous Leagues: Leighton & District/ South Midlands 22-24 26-29 46-54 55-56 76-92/ Spartan 22-53 67-74/ United Counties 74-76.
Previous Name: Leighton United **Previous Grounds:** None.
Reserve Team's League: Campri Sth Mids Reserve Division. **Record win:** 7-2.
Record Gate: 1,522 v Aldershot T., Isthmian Lg Div 3, 30/1/93 **Record defeat:** 1-6.
Best F.A. Cup year: Third Qualifying Rounds 70-71, lost 1-2 at St Albans City.
Clubhouse: Normal licensing hours. Snack/refreshment bar on matchdays - full rang of hot snacks & drinks.
92-93 Captain: Paul Firth **92-93 P.o.Y.:** Steve Norman **92-93 Top scorer:** Steve Drewe
Local Press: Leighton Buzzard Observer/ The Herald/ The Citizen.
Local Radio: Three Counties Radio/ Radio Chiltern.
Hons: Sth Midlands Lg 66-67 91-92 (Lg Cup 90-91, O'Brien Tphy 90-91, Reserve Div 1 87-88 91-92, Reserve Div 2 76-77), Beds Snr Cup 26-27 67-68 68-69 69-70 92-93, Spartan Lg Div 2 23-24 27-28, Leighton & District Lg, Beds Intermediate Cup 90-91, Beds Yth Cup 91-92 92-93.

NORTHWOOD

Chairman: Andy Johnson **Vice Chairman:** Geoff Foster **President:** T.B.A.
Secretary: Steve Williams, 35 Evelyn Drive, Hatch End, Pinner, Middx HA5 4RL (081 428 1533 - home + fax).
Manager: Alan Merison **Physio:** George Price **Coach:** John Toogood.
Press Officer: Mick Russell (0923 827690) **Commercial Mgr:** Simon Friend.
Ground: Northwood Park, Chestnut Avenue, Northwood (0923 827148).
Directions: A404 (Pinner-Rickmansworth) - Chestnut Ave. on left by large grey iron railway bridge and Shell petrol station. Third of a mile from Northwood Hills station (Metropolitan Line) - turn right out of station to r'bout, left into Pinner Rd, left into Chestnut Ave. by Shell petrol station after 300yds. Buses 282 and H11 to Northwood Hills.
Capacity: 2,000 **Seats:** 150 **Cover:** 200 **Floodlights:** Yes **Founded:** 1907.
Colours: All red **Change colours:** Yellow & green **Midweek Matches:** Tuesday
Programme: 30 pages, 50p **Editor:** Alan Evans (081 566 2880) **Club Shop:** No
Reserve Team's League: Suburban **Sponsors:** IFS Freight Forwarding **Nickname:** Woods.
Previous Leagues: Harrow & Wembley 32-49/ Middx 49-78/ Hellenic 79-84/ London Spartan 84-92.
Previous Grounds: None. **Previous Names:** Northwood Town.
Record Gate: 914 v Aldershot Town, Isthmian League Division Three, 16/1/93.
Best F.A. Vase year: 4th Rd 91-92. **Best F.A. Cup year:** Prel. Rd(4) 89-93.
Clubhouse: Hot weekends and most evenings from 6pm. Bar. Hot and cold food. Pool, darts, juke-box.
Players progressing to Football League: Gavin McGuire (Portsmouth).
Club Record Scorer: Garfield Blackman **Club Record Appearances:** Peter Lammin
92-93 Captain: Robert Holland **92-93 P.o.Y.:** Paul Rogan/ Ronnie John.
92-93 Top scorer: Vic Schwartz.
Local Newspapers: Ruislip & Northwood Gazette, Allsport Weekly
Hons: Isthmian Lg Associate Members Cup 92-93, London Spartan Lg 91-92 (R-up 89-90, Lg Cup 89-90 91-92), Hellenic Lg Div 1 78-79 (Prem Div Cup R-up 81-82, Div 1 78-79), Middx Lg 77-78 (R-up 72-73 76-77, Div 1 R-up 71-72, Challenge Cup 74-75 76-77 77-78), Middx Snr Cup SF 91-92 92-93, Middx Jnr Cup 46-47 47-48 48-49, Harrow & Wembley Lg 31-32 32-33 33-34 34-35 35-36 36-37 46-47 47-48 48-49.

Northwood F.C. before their victory over Barton Rovers in the Associate Members Trophy final at Chesham.

OXFORD CITY

Chairman: M Woodley   **Vice Chairman:** R Holt   **President:** M Harris.
Press Officer/Secretary: John Sheppard, 20 Howe Close, Wheatley, Oxford OX33 1SS (0865 872181).
Manager: Peter Foley   **Asst Manager:** S Hayward   **Physio:** G Bowerman.
Ground: Court Place Farm, Marsh Lane, Marston, Oxford.
Directions: From London M40/A40, ring-road to North, take 1st slip road, follow signs to John Radcliffe hospital, ground on left after leaving flyover. From the north same ring-road.
Capacity: 2,000   **Seats:** 150   **Cover:** 150   **Floodlights:** Yes   **Founded:** 1882
Colours: White & blue hoops   **Change colours:** Red & yellow   **Nickname:** City.
Programme: 60 pages, 50p   **Programme Editor:** Secretary   **Club Shop:** No.
Midweek Matchday: Wednesday   **Sponsors:** Unipart O.C.M.
Prev. Grnds: The White Horse 1882-1988/ Cutteslowe Pk 1990-91/ Pressed Steel, Romanway, Cowley 91-93.
Previous League: Isthmian 07-88/ South Midlands 90-93.
Record Gate: 9,500 v Leytonstone, F.A. Amateur Cup 1950.
Best FA Cup year: Second Round 69-70 (lost 1-5 at home to Swansea Town).
Record Fees - Paid: £3,000 for S Adams (Woking)   **Received:** £2,000 for P Dallaway (Witney Town).
Reserve Team's League: 'Minerva' South Midlands Reserve Section.
Clubhouse: Open matchdays, most refreshments available.
Club Record Scorer: John Woodley   **Club Record Appearances:** John Woodley.
92-93 Captain: Jon Hawkins   **92-93 P.O.Y.:** Andy Thomas   **92-93 Top scorer:** Mark Thomas.
Local Press: Oxford Mail   **Local Radio:** BBC Radio Oxford, Fox FM.
Hons: FA Amteur Cup 05-06 (R-up 02-03 12-13), Isthmian Lg R-up 34-35 45-46 (Div 1 R-up 77-78), South Midlands Lg 92-93, Oxon Snr Cup(26).

ROYSTON TOWN

Chairman: Bill Cosgrove   **Vice Chairman:** Bernard Brown   **President:** F Bradley
Secretary/Press Officer: Trevor Glasscock, 14 Goodwood Rd, Royston, Herts SG8 9TF (0763 244580).
Manager: John Hallewell   **Asst Mgr:** Kevin Roack   **Coach:** Doug Bailey/ Terry Graves
Physio: Brian O'Flanaghan   **Commercial Manager:** John Penny.
Ground: Garden Walk, Royston, Herts SG8 7HP (0763 241204).
Directions: From Baldock, A505 to Royston bypass, right at 2nd island onto A10 towards London, 2nd left is Garden Walk; ground 100 yds on left. From A11, exit 10 turning left onto A505, left at 1st island, 2nd left is Garden Walk. Ten mins walk from Royston (BR).
Capacity: 4,000   **Seats:** 300   **Cover:** 300   **Floodlights:** Yes   **Founded:** 1875
Colours: White/black/black   **Change colours:** Red/white/white   **Metal Badges:** Yes
Shop: Badges, old progs, clubs scarves available from club officials   **Nickname:** Crows.
Programme: 16 pages, 30p   **Editor:** Bernard Brown (0763 243969).
Midweek Matchday: Wednesday   **Sponsors:** A.B.A. Consultants.
Previous Leagues: Buntingford & Dist. 18-28/ Cambs 28-50/ Herts Co. 50-59 62-77/ Sth Mids 59-62 77-84.
Previous Names: None   **Previous Grounds:** Newmarket Rd, Baldock Rd, Mackeral Hall.
Record Gate: 876 v Aldershot, 13/2/93   **Reserve Team's League:** Essex & Herts Border Comb.
Record win: 13-2 v Addult, 78-79   **Record loss:** 0-9 v Bromley & v Stevenage Borough.
Best FA Cup year: Second Qualifying Round 59-60 (lost 0-9 at Barnet), 89-90 (lost 0-3 at Bromley).
Clubhouse: Mon-Thurs 7-11pm, Fri 11am-3 & 7-11pm, Sat 11am-3 & 4-11pm, Sun noon-3pm. Large hall. Darts, pool, discos and live bands. **Steward:** Mr & Mrs P Nesbitt.
Players progressing to Football League: John Smith (Spurs).
Club Record Scorer: Trevor Glasscock 289 (1968-82)   **Club Record Appearances:** Fred Bradley 713.
92-93 Capt.: Terry Graves   **92-93 P.O.Y.:** John Moulding   **92-93 Top scorer:** Paddy Butcher 28.
Local Radio: Radio Cambridgeshire, Radio Bedfordshire, Chiltern Radio.
Local Press: Royston Crow (0763 245142), Cambridge Evening News (0223 358877).
Hons: Herts Co. Lg 76-77 (Div 1 69-70 76-77), Sth Mids Lg R-up 79-80 (Div 1 78-79, Chall. Cup R-up 78-79, Res Div 1 79-80 (Div 2 78-79), Res Section Tphy R-up 82-83), Herts Charity Shield 81-82 89-90 (R-up 78-79 88-89), Creake Shield 20-21, Cambs Lg Div 2 29-30, Herts Intermediate Cup 88-89 (R-up 89-90), Nth Herts Lg 4 Cup 78-79 79-80 (Div R-up 82-83, Div 3 R-up 81-82, Div 4 R-up 79-80) Televised Spts Lg 88-89 (F'lit Cup 89-90), Chiltern Yth Lg 89-90 (Lg Cup R-up 86-87 88-89 90-91), Southern Comb. Res. F'lit Cup 91-92, Greg Cup R-up 90-91.

Royston Town F.C. 1992-93. Duncan Easley, Kevin Roeack, Danny Silver, Terry Graves, Anthony Hallewell, Steve Franklin, Stuart Brown, Jon Dobson, Peter Richardson, Doug Bailey, John Hallewell (Manager). Front: Julian Thrope, John Moulding, Ian Glasscock, Simon Dobson, Paddy Butcher, Paul Dockree, Brian O'Flanaghan (Physio).

SOUTHALL

Chairman: J J Loftus   **President:** R E Fowler
Secretary: Maria Smith, 22 Barchester Rd, Harrow Weald, Middx HA3 5HH (081 863 6888).
Manager: TBA   **Assistant Manager:** TBA   **Coach:**
Press Officer: Chairman   **Physio:** George Richardson
Ground: Western Road, Southall, Middx UB2 5HX (081 574 1084). *Important Note: Western Road is being redeveloped, and Southall are playing home matches at Harefield United F.C. This arrangement will last throughout the 1993-94 season.*
Directions: See Harefield United F.C. Ground details below apply to Western Rd.
Capacity: 10,000   **Seats:** 200   **Cover:** 400   **Floodlights:** Yes   **Founded:** 1871
Colours: Red & white   **Change colours:** Grey & white   **Nickname:** Fowlers
Club Shop: No   **Metal Badges:** No
Programme: 6 pages, 50p   **Programme Editor:** Secretary   **Record win:** 7-1
Midweek Matchday: Tuesday   **Sponsors:** Longwood Builders   **Record loss:** 0-8
Reserve Team's League: Middx County. **Record Gate:** 17,000 v Watford, F.A. Cup 3rd Rd 1935.
Previous Leagues: Southern 1896-1905/ Gt Western Suburban/ Herts & Middx/ Athenian 19-73.
Previous Grounds: None   **Prev. Name:** Southall & Ealing Borough 1975-80.
Best F.A. Cup year: 3rd Round 35-36 (lost 1-4 at home to Watford). Also 1st Rd 25-26 27-28 28-29 36-37 55-56.
League clubs defeated in F.A. Cup: Swindon Town 35-36.
Record Fees - Paid: **Received:** £5,000 for Alan Devonshire.
Players progressing to Football League: Alan Devonshire (West Ham), Gordon Hill (Millwall, Manchester Utd, Derby), Chris Hutchings (Chelsea, Brighton), Roger Joseph (Brentford), Les Ferdinand (Q.P.R. & England).
Clubhouse: Normal pub hours. Hot snacks available on matchdays.
Club Record Scorer: Steve Fraser   **Record Appearances:** Hammid Harrak (from Youth team on).
92-93 Captain: Rod Shearer   **92-93 P.o.Y.:** Hammid Harrak   **92-93 Top scorer:** Phil Scott.
Local Radio: Capital.   **Local Press:** Ealing Gazette, Allsports Weekly.
Hons: FA Amtr Cup R-up 24-25 (SF 25-26 52-53), FA Vase R-up 85-86, Isthmian Lg Div 2 R-up 74-75, Gt Western Suburban Lg 12-13, Athenian Lg 26-27 (R-up 54-55), Middx Snr Cup(12) 07-08 10-11 11-12 12-13 22-23 23-24 24-25 26-27 36-37 44-45 53-54 54-55, Middx Charity Cup 10-11 11-12 13-14 22-23(jt with Botwell Mission) 23-24(jt with Botwell Mission) 27-28 36-37 51-52 68-69 83-84, London Snr Cup SF 35-36 84-85.

TRING TOWN

Chairman: Mr Roger Payne   **President:** Mr G Smith.   **Secretary:** David G Bradding, 71 Faversham Close, Tring, Herts (0442 824118).
Manager: Tudor Lewis   **Asst Manager:** Mr J Selmes   **Coach:** John Wortley
Physio: Mr B Huff   **Press Officer:** Alan Lee   **Commercial Mgr:** John Wortley
Ground: Pendley Sports Centre, Cow Lane, Tring, Herts HP23 5NS (0442 23075).
Directions: One mile from Tring centre on A41. One and a half miles from Tring (BR). Numerous buses from station and Watford-Aylesbury routes serve ground.
Capacity: 2,500   **Seats:** 200   **Cover:** 230   **Floodlights:** Yes   **Founded:** 1904
Club Shop: No   **Metal Badges:** No   **Record win:** 12-0   **Record loss:** 1-9
Colours: Red/white/red   **Change colours:** All blue.   **Nickname:** Tee's.
Programme: 40p   **Programme Editor:** Alan Lee.   **Sponsors:** T.B.A.
Midweek Matchday: Monday   **Reserve Team's League:** Essex & Herts Border Comb.
Previous Leagues: Gt Western Combination/ Spartan 53-75/ Athenian 75-77.
Previous Names: None   **Prev. Ground:** Tring Cricket Ground (40 yrs).
Record Attendance: 2,500 v West Ham United, friendly. Competitive game: 2,000 for Aylesbury United v Slough Town, F.A. Cup First Round replay, 1986.
Best F.A. Cup year: 3rd Qualifying Rd replay 84-85, lost 0-5 at Fisher after 1-1 draw.
Clubhouse: All licensing hours. Dancehall, pool, darts, kitchen.
Players progressing to Football League: Peter Gibbs (Watford).
Club Record Scorer: Gary Harthill   **Club Record Appearances:** Gary Harthill.
92-93 Captain: Enzo Miceli   **92-93 P.o.Y.:** Michael Thomas   **92-93 Top scorer:** Chris Campbell
Local Radio: Chiltern, BBC Radio Bedford **Local Press:** Bucks Herald, Tring Gazette, Watford Observer.
Hons: Spartan Lg 66-67, Herts Charity Shield (many times), Athenian Lg Div 2 R-up 76-77, Herts Snr Cup R-up.

Tring Town F.C. 1992-93. Photo - Dave West.

SPARTAN LEAGUE

Presidents: K.G.Aston **Chairman:** B.Stallard
Hon. Secretary: D.Cordell, 44 Greenleas,
Waltham Abbey, Essex (0992 712428)

For the first time for many seasons the premier division had a compliment of 22 clubs. It might have been a bad omen because the weather was not very kind to the fixture list causing many postponements and in consequence during the year, the league table had an even balance to the number of fixtures played by clubs. It was not until towards the end of the season that the leaders began to emerge.

The new clubs in the premier division gave a good account of themselves with Willesden topping the division for many weeks but finally finishing in fourth place and with the record of being the highest goal-scorers. St. Margaretsbury also finished high up in the division in their first year after a very slow start. They remained unbeaten after Christmas to reach sixth place. The other two new clubs, St.Andrews and Tower Hamlets finished ninth and tenth respectively.

The main battle for league honours eventually revolved around Brimsdown Rovers and two previous members of the Isthmian League, Corinthian Casuals and Cheshunt. Brimsdown had their most successful league season, eventually finishing five points ahead of Corinthian Casuals who at one time must have thought the championship was theirs, but a few defeats by the odd goal each time dented their hopes. Cheshunt, who had to finish in the top three to be considered for promotion to the Isthmian League, can thank their defence for keeping Willesden in fourth place because it was only their goal difference that gave them the third place.

Fortunes were not so good for several of the high-flyers of the previous season. Haringey Borough (15th), Barkingside (16th) and Brook House (14th) all failed to perform as well as last season. On the other hand Eltham Town, who had been in the basement position for a few seasons, managed to score double the number of goals as the previous season and consequently scored 30 points more. They finished in 18th position. The bottom four clubs did not improve on their previous season's performances.

In the League Cup Cheshunt beat Brook House at Hillingdon Borough F.C. and therefore had some consolation in not taking the League championship.

Once again League clubs fared well in outside cup competitions. For the third year in succession two Spartan League clubs contested the London Senior Cup final. Hanwell Town followed up last season's success with a win over Brimsdown Rovers in a match which Brimsdown were well ahead on play and goals until late in the game. Hanwell fought back from being behind to win 4-3. As previously mentioned, St.Margaretsbury had a good second half to the season and they managed to put their name on the Herts F.A. Senior Trophy for the first time. In the Middlesex C.F.A. Charity Cup Hanwell Town lost to Harrow Borough.

Not to be out done by their senior brothers Craven won the London Intermediate Cup. This win meant the League had had one of their clubs as a winner in each of the last six seasons. The intermediate clubs in division one have always been strong and a number have progressed to the premier division and beyond, but suitable grounds have precluded many from moving foward. Divison one was won by an old club, Metrogas, beating Craven into second place. Bridon Ropes, who won division two, also won the Kent F.A. Junior Cup.

At the instigation of the club it was agreed that the premier division should, within 3 years, be only open to clubs with floodlights. At the same time certion ground improvements were made mandatory. The biggest drawback is in the main, money, but there is also the authorities who could help their local clubs by giving them permission to carry out the work without making the clubs fight every inch of the way.

There is little change in the constitution for next season, there are no clubs coming up from the leagues below the Spartan. With the loss of Chesthunt to the Isthmian League the premier division will once again fall short of 22. **Basil Stallard (Chairman)**

Champions Brimsdown Rovers attack in a league cup tie at Eltham Town. Photo - Francis Short.

SPARTAN LEAGUE TABLES 1991-92

Premier Div.	P	W	D	L	F	A	Pts
Brimsdown R.	42	31	4	7	99	27	97
Corinthian-C.	42	29	5	8	98	31	92
Cheshunt	42	27	8	7	92	29	89
Willesden Hawk.	42	27	8	7	102	50	89
Hanwell Town	42	27	7	8	100	50	88
St Margaretsbury	42	25	5	12	93	64	80
Walthamstow P.	42	21	10	11	72	44	73
Cockfosters	42	21	6	15	84	65	69
St Andrews	42	15	12	15	70	85	57
Tower Hamlets	42	17	4	21	83	83	55
Croydon Athletic	42	13	15	14	72	59	54
Waltham Abbey	42	13	13	16	65	71	52
Beaconsfield Utd	42	14	9	19	68	85	51
Brook House	42	14	6	22	72	99	48
Haringey B.	42	11	12	19	59	80	45
Barkingside	42	9	13	20	52	80	40
Hillingdon Boro.	42	10	10	22	59	99	40
Eltham Town	42	11	6	25	50	95	39
North Greenford	42	11	5	26	53	100	38
Amersham Town	42	8	11	23	49	93	35
Beckton United	42	9	5	28	68	117	32
Southgate Ath.	42	6	12	24	48	103	30

Division One	P	W	D	L	F	A	Pts
Metrogas	28	24	2	2	94	31	74
Craven	28	20	2	6	120	45	62
Clapton Villa	28	18	5	5	93	41	59
Old Roan	28	17	3	8	81	48	54
Leyton County	28	16	6	6	67	41	54
Lewisham Elms	28	16	4	8	89	46	52
W'stow Trojans	28	12	4	12	63	48	40
A.F.C. Eltham	28	12	4	12	70	59	40
Cray Valley	28	11	6	11	50	46	39
Metpol Chigwell	28	10	3	15	66	67	33
Woolwich Town	28	7	7	14	58	71	28
Chingford Town	28	8	2	18	38	79	26
Catford Wdrs	28	5	6	17	41	60	21
S.E. Olympic	28	5	3	20	60	99	18
Swanley Town	28	0	1	27	15	224	1

Division Two	P	W	D	L	F	A	Pts
Bridon Ropes	24	22	2	0	101	27	68
Lewisham Town	24	18	3	3	103	42	57
W'stow Troj. Rs	24	18	3	3	97	37	57
Leyton Co. Rs	24	12	4	8	45	33	40
Marshall	24	12	3	9	65	61	39
Ollerton	24	9	4	11	65	74	31
Woolwich T. Rs	24	8	3	13	39	59	27
Singh Sabha	24	7	5	12	45	63	26
Catford W. Rs	24	6	4	14	32	58	22
Metpol (Chig) Rs	24	5	6	13	38	68	21
Lewisham E. Rs	24	6	2	16	41	95	20
Garfield	24	5	4	15	42	67	19
Loughton	24	5	3	16	35	64	18

PREMIER DIVISION RESULT CHART 1992-93

HOME TEAM	1	2	3	4	5	6	7	8	9	10	11	12	13	14	15	16	17	18	19	20	21	22
1. Amersham	*	4-1	1-2	2-1	1-2	1-1	1-1	0-2	1-1	3-1	0-2	2-1	0-3	3-0	1-1	2-3	4-4	1-6	0-1	1-0	2-1	
2. Barkingside	3-0	*	3-2	2-1	1-1	1-1	2-2	0-2	0-1	0-0	1-1	2-3	3-1	0-0	1-2	0-2	2-3	4-3	2-4	0-0	0-1	1-2
3. Beaconsfield	4-0	4-0	*	1-2	0-1	3-3	0-3	1-2	1-4	2-2	5-0	2-1	0-1	3-0	1-2	4-2	1-1	2-1	0-3	2-2	0-3	0-1
4. Beckton Utd	3-3	2-3	6-0	*	2-1	4-2	2-1	1-2	1-4	2-2	1-3	1-3	2-0	3-4	3-4	0-1	2-2	1-2	1-2	0-4		
5. Brimsdown	2-0	4-0	8-0	10-0	*	0-1	0-0	3-0	2-0	0-1	1-0	5-0	3-0	1-0	3-0	7-1	2-0	3-1	3-1	1-1	1-0	3-2
6. Brook House	2-1	2-2	1-2	6-3	1-2	*	2-1	5-1	1-4	0-0	2-0	0-5	1-0	2-0	5-0	1-1	4-0	0-4	5-2	0-1	0-1	0-1
7. Cheshunt	7-1	4-0	2-2	4-0	1-0	2-0	*	1-0	3-4	2-0	2-1	2-0	1-1	8-0	1-0	2-1	0-1	3-0	5-1	3-0	3-0	0-2
8. Cockfosters	0-0	1-1	1-2	3-1	1-0	6-1	0-0	*	1-5	4-3	2-1	1-3	1-3	4-2	2-2	3-1	8-1	0-5	1-0	5-1	0-1	1-1
9. Corinth.-C.	1-1	1-2	0-0	4-1	1-1	4-0	0-2	0-1	*	1-0	0-0	2-1	9-0	2-0	4-0	5-1	2-0	1-1	2-0	3-1	2-0	5-1
10. Croydon Ath.	3-0	1-2	2-2	5-0	1-3	3-0	2-2	1-2	0-2	*	4-0	2-2	3-0	4-0	1-2	1-1	0-0	2-3	3-1	3-4	0-0	1-1
11. Eltham Town	3-1	2-1	4-1	3-2	0-3	2-5	0-2	2-1	1-0	1-2	*	4-2	1-1	4-1	2-1	0-0	0-4	1-3	1-0	1-1	1-2	1-1
12. Hanwell	2-0	3-0	3-0	4-1	4-3	10-0	2-0	2-1	0-2	1-1	5-1	*	4-2	1-1	4-0	1-3	1-1	2-1	3-2	2-0	2-0	2-2
13. Haringey	3-0	2-0	2-2	2-2	1-2	2-0	0-0	0-1	2-0	0-0	3-1	1-2	*	1-1	6-3	3-1	1-1	0-2	2-3	3-4	1-1	0-4
14. Hillingdon	3-3	3-4	3-3	2-1	0-2	5-3	1-3	2-1	0-2	1-3	2-2	3-2	*	1-1	2-0	2-4	0-1	2-1	3-2	1-6	0-2	
15. N Greenford	3-0	2-1	1-0	3-2	0-1	2-3	0-1	2-3	1-5	2-4	6-0	1-2	1-3	2-0	*	3-2	0-0	1-3	3-1	0-1	1-5	2-3
16. Southgate	4-0	1-1	2-6	1-2	0-2	1-5	0-3	0-5	0-2	0-1	2-3	0-6	0-0	1-1	5-1	*	1-3	1-0	0-5	1-1	1-1	0-5
17. St Andrews	1-3	1-1	1-2	1-1	2-4	8-1	1-4	3-2	1-5	0-4	2-0	0-0	2-1	3-3	0-0	2-0	*	2-2	4-1	2-1	0-4	1-1
18. St Margaret.	3-0	6-2	2-1	1-0	0-2	2-1	1-5	0-2	0-1	3-2	1-2	3-2	4-2	6-0	1-2	6-1	*		2-1	2-1	2-1	1-4
19. Tower Ham.	3-1	1-0	3-1	4-2	0-2	3-2	0-2	2-3	0-1	2-1	4-1	1-2	5-0	2-1	5-2	1-1	3-1	2-3	*	0-5	2-1	3-3
20. Waltham Ab.	2-2	2-2	1-2	0-1	0-2	2-0	0-2	2-1	1-5	1-1	4-1	1-3	1-4	4-0	2-2	5-2	1-4	2-2	*		0-0	0-2
21. W Pennant	3-1	0-0	4-1	4-2	0-3	2-0	0-2	2-4	2-0	5-1	3-1	0-1	2-2	1-1	1-1	3-0	2-0	0-0	2-1	2-1	*	2-0
22. Willesden	2-1	2-0	1-1	8-2	3-0	5-1	1-0	3-2	1-0	5-2	4-2	2-1	3-1	4-1	3-0	4-0	0-3	0-3	3-0	2-2	3-3	*

SPARTAN LEAGUE CUP 1992-93

First Round

Brook House v Haringey Borough	4-0
St Andrews v Eltham Town	1-1,0-1
Cockfosters v Tower Hamlets	8-0
St Margaretsbury v Hanwell Town	0-3

Walthamstow Pennant v Catford Wanderers	2-1
Cheshunt v Southgate Athletic	4-0
Corinthian-Casuals v North Greenford Utd	2-2(aet),0-5

Second Round

Beaconsfield United v Brook House	0-2
Cheshunt v Amersham Town	4-0
Beckton United v Hillingdon Borough	4-3
Waltham Abbey v Hanwell Town (at Hanwell)	0-3

Croydon Athletic v North Greenford United	2-3
Walthamstow Pennant v Willesden Hawkeye	1-1(aet),2-3
Eltham Town v Brimsdown Rovers	2-3
Cockfosters v Barkingside	3-5

Third Round

Beckton United v Hanwell Town	2-4
Brook House v Barkingside	1-1,1-0

Cheshunt v North Greenford United	2-0
Brimsdown Rovers v Willesden Hawkeye	3-0

Semi-Finals

Hanwell Town v Brook House	0-0,1-2

Cheshunt v Brimsdown Rovers	1-1,0-0(aet 5-4 pens)

Final (at Hillingdon Borough FC)

Brook House v Cheshunt	3-2

Spartan Football League Premier Division Ten Year Record

	83/4	84/5	85/6	86/7	87/8	88/9	89/0	90/1	91/2	92/3
Abingdon Town						1				
Ambrose Fleming	15									
Amersham Town	11	11	15	10	15	13	19	10	16	20
Barkingside				12	9	5	8	2	6	16
Beaconsfield Utd	6	9	6	16	11	18	17	13	14	13
Beckton United	7	15	13	13	13	19	10	14	18	21
Bracknell Town	4									
Brimsdown Rovers	3	3	5	3	5	7	14	7	2	1
B R O B Barnet	12	17								
Bromley Athletic (see Eltham Town)										
Brook House							11	12	4	14
Burnham		1								
Cheshunt					4	6	4	4	8	3
Chingford	14									
Cockfosters									12	8
Collier Row	1	2	1							
Corinthian-Casuals		16		14	17	16	5	5	9	2
Crown & Manor			11	9	16	20				
Croydon Athletic					10	2	13	15	10	11
Danson (Bexley Borough)		12	12	15						
Edgware Town		14	7	4	1	4	1			
Eltham Town						17	18	18	19	18
Greenwich Borough	8									
Hanwell Town		5	9	11	6	11	12	8	7	5
Haringey Borough							6	6	3	15
Highfield	13									
Hillingdon Borough								16	13	17
Malden Vale	2									
Merstham	10									
North Greenford United						14	15	17	17	19
Northwood		6	8	7	12	3	2	3	1	
Pennant (see Walthamstow Pennant)										
Redhill		7	3	2	7					
St Andrews										9
St Margaretsbury										6
Southgate Athletic				5	2	8	3	11	15	22
Southwark Borough					3	9				
Swanley Town	9	13	16							
Thamesmead Town						15	16	19		
Thatcham Town		4	4							
Tower Hamlets										10
Ulysses				17						
Waltham Abbey	5	8	10	6	14	12	9	9	11	12
Walthamstow Pennant		10	14	8	8	10	7	1	5	7
Wandsworth & Norwood (see Croydon Athletic)										
Willesden (Hawkeye)										4
Yeading			2	1						
No. of Clubs competing	15	17	16	17	17	20	19	19	19	22

Bridon Ropes FC, Division Two champions 1992-93. Back Row (L/R): R Clements (Manager), T Smith, L Wright, L Potter, A Lucas, M Smillon, L Adams, S Edwards, B White (Physio). Front: S Pettengell, M Merdsan, G Austin, S Donovan, M Laroche. Photo - Richard Brock.

PREMIER DIVISION CLUBS 1993-94

AMERSHAM TOWN

Chairman: Raymond Jones   **Vice Chairman:** Mike Gagahan   **President:** Graham Taylor
Secretary: Raymond Jones, Tudor Court, 73 Woodside Rd, Amersham, Bucks HP6 6AA (0494 431851).
Manager: Steve Simmons   **Coach:** Oscar Ringsell   **Commercial Mgr/Press Officer:** David Rake.
Ground: Spratley's Meadow, School Lane, Amersham (0494 727428).   **Directions:** A413 London to Aylesbury road, right into Mill Lane at end of Amersham old town, left into School Lane at top of Hill Lane, ground on left 200yds past school. 1 mile from Amersham Station - BR & underground Metropolitan Line.
Seats: None   **Cover:** No   **Capacity:** 1,500   **Floodlights:** No   **Founded:** 1890
Previous Leagues: Wycombe & Dist. Comb./ Aylesbury & Dist./ Chesham/ Gt Western Suburban 20-23/ Spartan 23-53 61-62/ Hellenic 53-61 62-72.   **Rec. Gate:** 2,000 v Aston V., centenary match 1990 (at Chesham).
Colours: Black & white   **Change:** Tangerine   **Prev. Grnd:** Barn Meadow (pre-1920).
Midweek home matches: Tuesday   **Reserve's League:** Middx Co.   **Nickname:** Magpies.
Programme: With admission   **Editor:** David Rake (0844 290176)   **Club Shop:** No.
Clubhouse: Open matchdays. Bar facilities. Teas, coffees and light snacks (+ Jess Pearce's rock cakes!).
Captain 92-93: Scott Bailies   **92-93 P.o.Y.:** Richard Coppinger   **Top Scorer 92-93:** Del Rodney.
Hons: Hellenic Lg 63-64 (R-up 64-65 65-66, Div 1 62-63, Lg Cup 53-54), London Spartan Lg R-up 79-80, St Marys Cup 89-90 (R-up 90-91), Berks & Bucks Jnr Cup 22-23 (Snr Cup SF 79-80 80-81), Wycombe Chal. Cup 23-24.

Amersham concede a goal to St Margaretsbury in the thrilling 4-4 opening day draw. Photo - Neil Whittington.

BARKINGSIDE

President: A Smith   **Chairman:** K Harris.
Secretary/Press Officer: N A Ingram, 45 Cheneys Rd, Leytonstone, London E11 3LL (081 555 1447).
Manager: W Reed   **Asst Manager:** R Reed   **Physio:** M Stevens
Ground: Oakside, Station Road, Barkingside, Ilford, Essex (081 550 3611).   **Club Shop:** No.
Directions: From London A12 Eastern Avenue to Green Gate, left into Hurns Rd to Barkingside, right into Craven Gardens, right again Carlton Drive leading to Station Road, under bridge and ground entrance on right. Adjacent to Barkingside station (Central Line), 3 miles from Ilford station (BR). Bus 169 to Craven Gardens.
Seats: 60   **Cover:** 60   **Capacity:** 1,000   **Floodlights:** Yes   **Founded:** 1898.
Previous Leagues: Ilford & Dist. 1898-1925 44-47/ Ilford Minor 25-44/ Sth Essex 47-48/ Walthamstow 48-50/ London 50-64/ Gtr London 64-71/ Metropolitan-London 71-75.
Previous Grounds: Fulwell Cross PF 1898-1921/ Clayhall Rec 21-29/ Hainault PF 29-33/ Barkingside Rec 33-57.
Cols: Blue & white hoops/white/blue   **Change colours:** All Red   **Sponsors:** Directa
Programme: £1.50 with admission   **Editor:** Mr M Gold.   **Midweek home matchday:** Tuesday
Reserve's lge: Ess. & Herts Border Comb   **Record Gate:** 957 v Arsenal Res., London Lg 1957.
Clubhouse: Saturdays 1pm-midnight, midweek matchnights 6.30-11pm. Rolls, hotdogs, hamburgers.
1992-93 Captain: R O'Brien   **1992-93 P.o.Y. & Top-scorer:** L Parnell.   **Hons:** S. Ess. Lg R-up 46-47, L'don Lg R-up 49-50 (Lg Cup 55-56 (R-up 52-53 62-63)), Ilford Fest. Cup 51-52, Romford Char. Cup 51-52, Gtr L'don Lg 64-65, L'don Spartan Lg R-up 90-91 (Harry Sunderland Shld 83-84 (R-up 84-85)).

Barkingside FC. Back (L/R): Jox Oxby, Russell Sparrey, Kevin Costello, Micky Farrall, Darren Knox, Paul Shaw, Lee Parnell. Front: Richard Jackson, Trevor Royce, Ricky Parnell, Mickey Moore, Simon Binet. Photo - Richard Brock.

BEACONSFIELD UNITED

President: T Keylock   **Chairman:** J McDaid.
Secretary: Dean Howkins, 28 Manor Gardens, High Wycombe, Bucks HP13 5HD (0494 437689).
Manager: **Programme Editor:**
Coach: Martyn Busby
Ground: Holloways Park, Slough Road, Beaconsfield, Bucks (0494 676868).
Directions: M40 (Jct 2), 1st exit to A355. Club 100yds on right. One and a miles from Beaconsfield (BR). Bus 441 Slough/ High Wycombe.
Seats: None   **Cover:** 60   **Capacity:** 1,000   **Floodlights:** Yes   **Founded:** 1921.
Previous Leagues: Wycombe & District/ Maidenhead
Best FA Vase season: 1st Rd 83-84 85-86 87-88.
Record Gate: 300 v Chesham United, Berks & Bucks Snr Cup 1985.
Cols: Blue & black stripes/black/black   **Change colours:** Red & black stripes/black/black
Local Newspapers: Bucks Advertiser, Bucks Free Press, Slough Observer.
Clubhouse: Open evenings and matchdays. Bar, Committee Room, Hall, Kitchen, Changing Room

BECKTON UNITED

Secretary: Paul Atteridge, 53 Burnham Road, Chingford, London E4 8DP (081 559 3364).
Ground: East Ham, Manor Way, London E6, near Industrial Park (071) 476 4857
Directions: A13 from City or Essex, Nth Circular Rd from Middlesex. By rail, East Ham (Underground). Buses from East Ham or North Woolwich.
Seats: None   **Cover:** 150   **Capacity:** 1,000   **Floodlights:** No   **Founded:** 1966.
Previous Name: Ceevor FC   **Previous Grounds:** None.
Colours: Green & white stripes/black/green   **Change colours:** Yellow/red/red
Clubhouse: None; adjacent pub used   **Best FA Vase season:** 3rd Rd 85-86.

BRIMSDOWN ROVERS

Secretary: Graham Dodd, 57 Roundmoor Drive, Cheshunt, Herts EN8 9HU (0992 26820).
Ground: Goldsdown Road, Enfield, Middlesex (081 804 5491).
Directions: BR from Liverpool Street to Brimsdown (half mile away), by road off Green Street (A1010), itself off Hertford Road (A10). Buses 191 or 307.
Seats: None   **Cover:** 50   **Capacity:** 1,000   **Floodlights:** Yes   **Founded:** 1948.
Previous Leagues: Northern Suburban
Previous Name: Durham Rovers/ Brimsdown FC
Colours: Black & white stripes/black/black   **Change colours:** All yellow
Best FA Vase season: 2nd Rd rep. 84-85
Best FA Cup season: 3rd Qual. replay 91-92
Record Gate: 412 v Chesham Utd, FA Cup 3rd Qual. Rd 12/10/91.
Clubhouse: Large lounge & clubroom, games room & stage. 3 bars (300 capacity)
Hons: Spartan Lg 92-93.

Brimsdown Rovers goalkeeper McCaulsky is helpless to prevent a header from Eltham Town's Haynes (11) taking the score to 2-2 in this League Cup Second Round tie. Photo - Francis Short.

BROOK HOUSE

Secretary: G Bundy, 43 Heatherwood Drive, Hayes, Middlesex UB4 8TN (081 845 7355).
Ground: Farm Park, Kingshill Avenue, Hayes, Middlesex (081 845 0110).
Directions: From London or North Circular Road: A40 Western Avenue to Target roundabout, turn left towards Hayes, turn right at traffic lights in to Kingshill Avenue.
Seats: None   **Cover:** Yes   **Capacity:**   **Floodlights:** Yes   **Founded:**
Colours: Blue & white stripes/blue/blue   **Change colours:** Green & white/green/green
Best FA Vase season: Preliminary Rd 90-91 91-92.

COCKFOSTERS

Chairman: Frank Brownlie   **Vice Chairman:** Ken Harris   **President:** Vic Bates
Secretary: Graham Bint, 15 Chigwell Park, Chigwell, Essex IG7 5BE (081 500 7369).
Manager: Dave Purser   **Asst Manager:** Bobby Long   **Coach:** Les Picking
Physio: Derek Carlisle   **Press Off.:** Frank Brownlie   **Comm. Mgr:** Alan Simmons
Ground: Cockfosters Sports Ground, Chalk Lane, Cockfosters, Barnet (081 449 5833).
Directions: Ground on A111. M25 Jct 24 (Potters Bar), take A111 signed   Cockfosters - ground 2 miles on right. Adjacent to Cockfosters underground station (Picadilly Line). Bus 298 to Cockfosters station.
Seats: None   **Cover:** 50   **Capacity:** 1,000   **Floodlights:** No   **Founded:** 1921.
Colours: All Red   **Change colours:** All White   **Nickname:** Fosters
Previous Grounds: None   **Previous Name:** Cockfosters Athletic
Previous Leagues: Wood Green & District 21-46/ Northern Suburban 46-66/ Herts Snr Co. 66-91.
Record Gate: 408 v Saffron Walden, Herts Senior County Lg 68-69.
Programme: 12 pages, £1 with entry   **Editor:** Alan Simmons (081 440 7998)   **Club Shop:** No.
Sponsors: Walvis Plastil Engineering Co. Ltd
Midweek home matchday: Tuesday   **Reserve team's League:** Middx County.
Record win: 10-1 v Rickmansworth T.   **Record defeat:** 2-7 v Leggatts Old Boys (both 1968)
Clubhouse: 7-11pm Tues & Thurs, 4-11pm Sat, noon-3pm Sunday. Hot and cold food on matchdays.
Captain 92-93: Graham Poulton   **P.o.Y. 92-93:** Steve Potter
Top Scorer 92-93: Paul Flatt/ Robbie Bunton/ Dave Martin (24 each).
Club record scorer: Peter Benham   **Club record appearances:** Bob Davis (500+).
Hons: London Intermediate Cup 70-71 89-90, Herts Snr Co. Lg 78-79 80-81 83-84 (R-up 82-83 84-85, Aubrey Cup 78-79 84-85 (R-up 70-71 77-78)), Herts Intermediate Cup 78-79 (R-up 71-72 73-74 74-75), Northern Suburban Lg 61-62 (R-up 50-51 65-66, Div 1 49-50 60-61 (R-up 46-47 48-49)), F.A. Vase 2nd Rd 91-92.

CORINTHIAN CASUALS

Manager: Steve Bangs   **Secretary:** K Nicholls, C/O the club.
Ground: King George's Field, Hook Rise, South Tolworth, Surrey KT6 7NA (081 397 3368).
Directions: A3 to Tolworth (The Toby Jug). Hook Rise is slip road behind the Toby Jug, 2nd left under railway bridge - ground immediately on right. Half mile from Tolworth (BR); turn left, continue to Toby Jug, then as above. K2 Hoppa bus from Kingston passes ground.
Seats: 30   **Cover:** 150   **Capacity:** 1,700   **Floodlights:** Yes   **Founded:** 1939.
Previous Leagues: Isthmian 39-84
Previous Names: Casuals (founded 1883), Corinthians (founded 1882) merged in 1939.
Previous Grounds: Many, including The Oval, Wimbledon Park Stadium, Tooting & Mitcham United FC.
Colours: White/navy/navy   **Change colours:** Chocolate & Pink/Navy/Navy
Programme: 24-48 pages, 50p
Best FA Cup season: 1st Rd replay 85-86.
Clubhouse: Evenings, matchdays, Sunday lunchtimes. Darts, pool, hot & cold snacks on matchdays.
Hons: FA Amtr Cup R-up 55-56 (SF 56-57), London Spartan Lg R-up 92-93 (Lg Cup R-up 91-92), London Snr Cup R-up 91-92.

Corinthian-Casuals F.C., London Spartan League runners-up 1992-93. Photo - Dave West.

CROYDON ATHLETIC

Chairman: Keith Tuckey   **Vice Chairman:** Ken Fisher.
Secretary: Tony Peck, 60 Cheviot Road, West Norwood, London SE27 0LG (081 670 2556).
Manager: Martin Caller   **Asst Manager:** Barry Barnes   **Physio:** Tony Peck.
Press Officer: Clive Thompson
Ground: N.F.C. Sports off Mayfield Road, Thornton Heath (081 684 4951).
Directions: From Norbury follow London Rd towards Croydon, turn right into Headcorn Rd, left into Silverleigh Rd, right into Mayfield Crescent, right into Mayfield Rd, left at end and follow road/path to ground. One mile from Norbury (BR). Buses 109, 154.
Seats: 110   **Cover:** 110   **Capacity:** 3,000   **Floodlights:** Yes   **Founded:** 1986.
Colours: Maroon & white   **Change colours:** All white   **Nickname:** Rams.
Prev. Names: Wandsworth FC (est 1948), Norwood FC (est 1947) merged 1986/ Wandsworth & Norwood 86-90.
Previous Grounds: Norwood FC - Lloyds Park 1961-81, Wisley R.H.S. 77-88/ Wandsworth FC - Morfax (Fisher Athletic's original ground) 82-86.
Best FA Vase season: 2nd Rd 89-90   **Best FA Cup season:** 1st Qual. Rd Rep. 89-90
Record Gate: 400   **Reserve Team's League:** Suburban (South)
Programme: 38 pages   **Programme Editor:** Secretary
Club Shop: Club badges, baseball hats, programmes available. Contact Mr B Byles at ground.
Club Sponsors: T.C.S. Media   **Midweek home matchday:** Tuesday
Record win: 7-1 v Walthamstow Pennant 88-89.
Record defeat: 1-9 v Yeading 86-87.
Clubhouse: Open matchdays (inc Reserve & Youth) and Sun noon-3pm, Tues & Thurs & Fri 7-11pm, Sat noon-11pm. Bar, pool, canteen, darts, dominoes. Hot & cold snacks, tea & coffee.
Captain & P.o.Y. 92-93: Leon Maxwell   **Top Scorer 92-93:** Paul Gall
Club record scorer: Graham Edginton   **Club record appearances:** Graham Edginton/ Paul Gall.
Hons: London Spartan Lg R-up 88-89 (Reserve Div R-up 88-89, Reserve Cup 88-89), London Snr Cup R-up 91-92, Southern Youth Lg 92-93.

Croydon Athletic 1992-93. Back Row (L/R): Ken Fisher (General Manager), Dean Fisher (Kit Manager), Andy Gayle, Paul Gall, Dave Bygraves, Robert Frankland, Simon Ford, John Gallagher, Nick Sargent, Nigel Skeet, Tony Peck (Secretary). Front: Dean Davenport, Gary Flemington, Noel Kidney, Martin Caller (Manager), Darren Tucknott, Hughie Mann, Leon Maxwell. Photo - Dave West.

HANWELL TOWN

Chairman/Press Officer: Bob Fisher   **President:** Sam Kelso
Secretary/Manager: Roy Nairn, 45 St Dunstans Rd, Hanwell W7 (081 579 3311).
Asst Manager: Arthur Rowlands   **Physio:** Roy Tyler   **Coach:** Tim Soutar
Ground: Reynolds Field, Perivale Lane, Perivale, Greenford, Middx (081 9981701).
Directions: A40 Oxford road from London, exit B456 for Ealing, ground on corner of junction approached immediately via left turn into Perivale Lane. 3rd of a mile from Perivale tube station.
Seats: None   **Cover:** 200   **Capacity:** 2,000   **Floodlights:** Yes   **Founded:** 1948
Previous Grounds: Local parks.   **Previous Leagues:** Middx/ Middx County   **Club Shop:** No.
Colours: Black & white stripes   **Change colours:** All red.
Nickname: The Town   **Record Gate:** 600 v Spurs, Floodlight opening October 1989.
Midweek home matchday: Wednesday   **Reserve team's League:** Suburban.
Record defeat: 0-6.   **Record win:** 10-0 v Brook House, Spartan Lge
Record transfer fee paid: Nil   **Received:** £2,000 for Pat Gavin (Gillingham, 1990).
Programme: 16 pages, 50p   **Editor:** Julie Soutar, C/O The club.
Clubhouse: Saturday matchdays 2-11pm, Wednesdays 6-11pm, Non-matchdays 7.30-11pm.
Captain 92-93: Ray Duffy   **Top Scorer 92-93:** Chris Boothe, 43.   **P.o.Y. 92-93:** Jason Dewcata
Club record scorer: Tony Pickering   **Club record appearances:** Phil Player, 19 seasons, 586 games.
Hons: London Spartan Lg 83-84, London Snr Cup 91-92 92-93, Middx Charity Cup R-up 92-93.

HARINGEY BOROUGH

Secretary: S O'Connell, 64a Station Road, Wood Green, London N22 4SY (081 881 7631).
Ground: Coles Park, White Hart Lane, Wood Green N22 (081 8819184).
Directions: Wood Green (Picadilly Line). BR (Eastern Region) to White Hart Lane, W3 bus passes ground A105 or A10 from Nth. Circular to Wood Green.
Seats: 280   **Cover:** Yes   **Capacity:** 2,500   **Floodlights:** Yes   **Founded:**
Previous Leagues: London 07-14/ Isthmian 19-52 84-88/ Spartan 52-54/ Delphian 54-63/ Athenian 63-84.
Previous Names: Edmonton/ Tufnell Park/ Tufnell Park Edmonton/ Edmonton & Haringey.
Colours: All green   **Change colours:** All white   **Clubhouse:** Open 7 days a week

HILLINGDON BOROUGH

Secretary: J C Whitehead, 43 Frays Waye, Uxbridge, Middlesex UB8 2QU (0895 231012).
Manager: Tony Choules   **Asst Manager:** John Morris   **Coach:** Dave Killick
Physio: Dave Pook   **Commercial Mgr:** Tony Choules   **Press Officer:** John Mason.
Ground: Middlesex Stadium, Breakspear Road, Ruislip, Middx HA4 7SB (0895 639544).
Directions: From A40 take B467 (signed Ickenham), left at 2nd r'bout into Breakspear Rd South, right after 1 mile by Breakspear pub - ground half mile on left. Nearest station is Ruislip. Bus U1 passes ground.
Seats: 150   **Cover:** 150   **Capacity:** 1,500   **Floodlights:** Yes   **Founded:** 1990
Midweek Matches: Wednesday   **Sponsors:** Airport Motor Radiator Co.   **Nickname:** Boro.
Colours: White/blue/blue   **Change colours:** Tangerine/white/tangerine
Programme: 20 pages   **Editor:** John Mason (081 868 7551)   **Club Shop:** No.
Clubhouse: Mon-Fri 7.30-11pm, Sat lunchtimes (functions in evening), Sun lunchtime & 7.30-10.30pm.
Reserve team's League: Suburban.   **Received:** £1,000 for Craig Johnson (Wealdstone).
Record win: 5-3 v Brook House   **Record defeat:** 0-8 v Newport A.F.C.
Captain 92-93: Malcolm Dunn   **Top Scorer 92-93:** Danny Thompson 17   **P.o.Y. 92-93:** Barry Fields

NORTH GREENFORD UNITED

Secretary: R Johnson, 63 Berkeley Avenue, Greenford, Middlesex UB6 0NY (081 864 2645).
Ground: Berkeley Fields, Berkeley Avenue, Greenford, Middlesex (081 422 8923).
Directions: A406 or A40 from London to Hanger Lane, A40 westwards approx 2 miles to junction with A4127. Right into Greenford Rd at r'bout, through lights, next right is Berkeley Avenue.
Colours: Blue & white/blue/blue   **Change colours:** Yellow/black/yellow.

ST ANDREWS

Secretary: Martin Feeley, 98 Endymion Rd, Brixton, London SW2 2BP (081 671 8690).
Colours: Navy/white/red   **Ground:** Herne Hill Stadium, Burbage Rd, London SE24.
Directions: A2214 (Half Moon Lane) from Herne Hill, Burbage Rd quarter mile on right, ground on right.
Prev. Lge: Surrey Premier (pre-1992)   **Hons:** Surrey Premier Lg 91-92.   **Clubhouse:** Yes

ST MARGARETSBURY

Chairman: D Bates   **President:** R L Growcott
Secretary: Alan B Green, 133 Caxton Rd, Hoddesdon, Herts EN11 9NX (0992 464682).
Manager: K Hart   **Asst Manager:** D Steedman   **Coach:** I Wolstenholme
Ground: Station Road, Stansead, St Margaretsbury, Nr Ware, Herts (0920 870473).
Directions: Harlow/Chelmsford exit from A10 to A414, take B181 at Amwell after 300yds towards Stanstead Abotts - ground quarter mile on right. 300yds from St Margaretsbury BR station (Liverpool Str.-Hertford East line).
Seats: 60   **Cover:** 60   **Capacity:** 1,000   **Floodlights:** No   **Founded:** 1894
Colours: Red & black   **Change colours:** All white   **Nickname:** The Bury.
Previous Grounds: Mill Field, Stansead Abbotts pre-1932/ Cappell Lane, Stanstead Abbotts 32-62.
Previous Leagues: East Herts/ Hertford & Dist./ Waltham & District 47-48/ Herts Co. 48-92.
Programme: 16 pages, £1.50 with entry   **Editor:** Jane Free (0920 870431)   **Club Shop:** No.
Record Gate: 327   **Sponsors:** Universal Office Automation, Ware.
Midweek home matchday: Tuesday   **Reserve team's League:** Hertford & District.
Clubhouse: Bar open 7-11pm (Sat noon-2.30 & 4-11pm). Teas and rolls available matchdays.
Captain 92-93: Paul Letts   **Top Scorer & P.o.Y. 92-93:** Barry White, 31
Hons: Herts Snr Centenary Tphy 92-93, Herts County Lg Div 2 48-49 (Aubrey Cup 48-49 71-72, Reserve Div 1 82-83 86-87, Reserve Cup 84-85 86-87 87-88), Waltham & Dist Lg 46-47.

St Margaretsbury F.C. 1992-93. Back Row (L/R): Ian Wolstenholme (Coach), Lee Johnson, Dave Fearey, Gary Smith, Ray Tomlins, Mark Foster, Paul Letts, Gary Watson, Kevin Gilzean, Kelvin Hart (Manager). Front: Derek Ridgewell (Physio), Gary Stanton, Darren Wilson, Darren White, Barry White, Che Roberts. Photo - Richard Brock.

SOUTHGATE ATHLETIC

Secretary: K P Cullen, 39 Hillrise, Potters Bar, Herts EN6 2RX (0707 56136).
Ground: Tottenhall Road Sports, Tottenhall Road, Palmers Green, London N13 (081 8881542).
Directions: From west; To Green Lanes on to North Circular Road, turn right and second left (Tottenhall Road), ground on right. From east; under underpass on A406, turn off left at Wolves Lane to r'bout, left in to Tottenhall Road. One mile from Wood Green (BR). Bus No. 34.
Seats: None   **Cover:** 50   **Capacity:** 500   **Floodlights:** No   **Founded:** 1939.
Colours: Amber/black/black   **Change colours:** All blue
Record Gate: 290 v Northampton Spencer, FA Vase November 1987.   **Previous Names:** None
Previous Grounds: None.   **Clubhouse:** Open normal hours. Hot & cold snacks.

TOWER HAMLETS

Chairman: Roy Manning   **Vice Chairman:** Ray Gipson.
Secretary/Commercial Manager: John Westwood, 69 Chadbourn Str., Poplar, London E14 (071 515 9830).
Manager: Henry Carter   **Asst Manager:** Kevin Gray
Press Officer: Ray Gipson   **Physio:** Howard Cooper
Ground: Mile End Stadium, Rhodeswell Road (081 980 1885).
Directions: From Blackwall tunnel left into East India Dock Road to Commercial Road, right into Burdett Road, ground on left. From Mile End tube (District Line) take 3rd left out of station (Canal Rd) keep right of fork and stadium on left.
Capacity: 5,000   **Cover:** 300   **Seats:** 300   **Floodlights:** Yes   **Club Shop:** No
Programme: 12 pages, £1 with entry (Editor: Darren Gallery 071515 9830)   **Founded:**
Colours: Blue/white/blue   **Change colours:** Yellow/blue/yellow
Club Nickname: Tipples   **Club Sponsors:** Alexio Roofing.
Midweek matchday: Wednesday   **Record win:** 22-0   **Record defeat:** 0-8
Previous Name: K.G.P. Tipples   **Record Gate:** Unknown.
Previous Leagues: Clapton Stoke Newington/ South West Essex/ Eastern Suburban
Previous Grounds: Burgess Rd 79-85/ Victoria Park 85-86.
Record Fees - Paid: None   **Received:** Tracksuits from Charlton for Danny Warden.
Clubhouse: Open 2 hours before kick-off and 3 hours after selling rolls and pies etc. New clubhouse being built, hopefully to open next season.
Club Record Scorer: Darren Gallery   **Club Record Appearances:** Darren Gallery.
92-93 Captain & P.O.Y.: David May   **92-93 Top scorer:** Darren Gallery.
Honours: Spartan Lg Div 1 89-90 (Div 2 88-89), London Intermediate Cup 88-89 90-91 (R-up 91-92).

Tower Hamlets F.C. 1992-93. Back Row (L/R): Terry Hobbrough, Henry Carter (Manager), Micky Myers, Lee Davis, Graham Poultney, Steve Ruddick, Timmy Hambley, Darren Gallery, Kevin Gray (Asst Manager). Front: Howard Cooper (Physio), Warren Wolfe, David Grinwood, Jason Maclaine, Wayne Silk, Nicky Potts, Joe Moran, David May. Photo - Francis Short.

WALTHAM ABBEY

Chairman: Tony Hodges   **President:** John King
Secretary: Mr David Brittain, The Gables, Avey Lane, Waltham Abbey, Essex (0992 716747).
Manager: Denis Tekel   **Asst Manager:** Joe Collins.
Ground: Capershotts, Sewardstone Road, Waltham Abbey, Essex (0992 711287).
Directions: Just off M25 jct 26. Waltham Cross (BR Eastern Region) station three miles distant. 242 Bus.
Seats: None   **Cover:** 100   **Capacity:** 2,000   **Floodlights:** Yes   **Founded:** 1948.
Colours: Green & white   **Change colours:** Red & black   **Nickname:** The Abbey
Previous Leagues: Northen Suburban   **Midweek matchday:** Wednesday
Rec. Gate: 1,800 v Spurs, charity game   **Reserve's Lge:** Essex & Herts Border Combination
Previous Names: W. Abbey Utd/ W. Abbey Beechfield
Programme: 8 pages, £1.50 with entry   **Editor:** David Hodges (0992 652594)   **Club Shop:** No.
Best FA Cup season: Prel. Rd 90-91   **Best FA Vase season:** Prel. Rd 87-88 88-89 89-90
Clubhouse: 7-11pm Mon-Fri, 11am-11pm Sat, noon-3pm Sun. Cold snacks, pool, darts.
Captain 92-93: Ray Simpson   **Top Scorer 92-93:** Mark Lilley   **P.O.Y. 92-93:** T.B.A.
Club record scorer: Paul Holloway   **Club record appearances:** Colin Winter.

WALTHAMSTOW PENNANT

Chairman: R Wren   **Vice Chairman:** C Dowsett   **President:** M Holmwood.
Secretary: Bert Hepburn, 57 Rowan Ave., Chingford E4 8QT (081 531 5238).
Manager: J Smith   **Asst Manager:** C Rufus   **Physio:** G Stiles
Press Officer: J Solkhon   **Commercial Manager:** J Clark.
Ground: Wadham Lodge, Brookscroft Road, Walthamstow, London E7 (081 527 2444).
Directions: North Cirular Road to Crooked Billet, turn into Chingford Road, Brookscroft Road first turning on left. Walthamstow Central tube (Victoria Line) one mile away, then buses W21 or 256.
Seats: 200   **Cover:** 200   **Capacity:** 1,000   **Floodlights:** Yes   **Founded:** 1966
Colours: White/blue/blue   **Change colours:** Yellow/green/yellow   **Club Shop:** No.
Previous Name: Pennant   **Previous Grounds:** None.
Previous Leagues: South West Essex 66-74/ Metropolitan London 74-83.
Record Gate: 860 v Leyton Orient, Floodlight opening 1989.
Midweek matchday: Wednesday   **Reserve's League:** Essex & Herts Border Comb.
Programme: £1.50 with admission   **Programme Editor:** J Clark (081 527 5034).
Record win: 9-1   **Record defeat:** 1-8.
Best FA Vase season: 5th Rd 90-91   **Best FA Cup season:** 1st Qual. Rd 89-90 90-91 91-92
Clubhouse: Bars open before and after all matches. Pool, darts. Teas & rolls on matchdays.
Hons: London Spartan Lg 90-91 (Lg Cup 88-89 90-91), S.W. Essex Lg 72-73 (Jnr Cup 68-69, Intermediate Cup 69-70, Snr Cup 70-71), London Jnr Cup 73-74.

WILLESDEN HAWKEYE

Chairman: Rodney Gooden   **Vice Chairman:** Hugh Harrison   **President:** Jerry Anderson
Secretary: Clifton Jackson, Flat 1 Vale Farm House, 76 Watford Rd, Sudbury, Middx HA0 3HG (081 908 2664).
Manager: **Physio:** Linval Sayles   **Coach:** Pat Watters.
Press Officer: Livon Houslin   **Commercial Manager:** Roy Forbes-Allen.
Ground: West London Stadium, Du Cane Rd, London W12 (081 749 5505).
Directions: A40 to White City, right at underpass into Scrubs Lane, 1st left into Du Cane Rd, stadium behind Hammersmith Hospital. Nearest tube White City or East Acton.
Seats: 300   **Cover:** 300   **Capacity:** 1,000   **Floodlights:** Yes   **Founded:** 1984
Colours: Red & white/red/red   **Change Colours:** Blue/black/black   **Club Shop:** No.
Previous Ground: Willesden Sports Centre, Donnington Rd (until 1992).
Previous Name: Hawkeye (Willesden)   **Previous Leagues:** London West End/ Middx Co.
Programme: Yes   **Sponsors:** Marlin House Trading Co. Ltd (Dragon Stout)
Nickname: Hawks.   **Record Gate:** 100 v Staines, Middx Snr Cup 20/1/93.
Midweek home matchday: Wednesday   **Clubhouse:** Matchday cafeteria on site. Bar due 93-94.
Captain 92-93: Clive Collins   **Top Scorer 92-93:** Conley Hall   **P.O.Y. 92-93:** Dave Kellman.
Hons: Spartan Lg Div 1 91-92.   **Club record appearances:** Ruben Kildare.

Catford Wanderers F.C. 1992-93. Back Row (L/R): J Hassett, M Tilbury, D Wilkinson, R Hadgiyiani, A Fanning, P Henderson, P Reeves, S P Wiseman (Manager). Front: S Hadgiyiani, L Millar, D Tickner, G McCullough, S Denyer. Photo - Richard Brock.

SPARTAN LEAGUE DIVISION ONE CLUBS 1993-94

A.F.C. ELTHAM
Secretary: Roy Williams, 90 Earlshore Rd, Eltham, London SE9 1PR (081 850 1894).
Ground & Directions: Whitehorse Sports Club, Footscray Road, New Eltham. A20 from London to Fiveways junction, left into Southwood Road, rights at lights, ground 200 yds on left. New Eltham (BR).
Colours: Red & black stripes/black   **Change Colours:** Blue & white

BRIDON ROPES
Secretary: R Clements, 3 Fenwick Close, Woolwich SE18 4DD (081 854 9844).
Ground & Directions: Meridian Sports Club, Charlton Park Lane, Charlton SE7 (081 856 1923). Central London exit from Blackwall Tunnel, left at island, 6th right, ground on left. Woolwich Arsenal (BR).
Colours: All red   **Change Colours:** Green/white

CATFORD WANDERERS
Secretary: John Hassett, 15 Broadheath Drive, Chislehurst, Kent BR7 6EU (081 467 9882).
Ground & Directions: Beckenham Hill Road, Catford SE6 (081 698 1259). From Bromley Road, left into Sainsbury Homebase and left into car park. Beckenham Hill (BR).
Colours: Black & white/black   **Change Colours:** Red/white

CHINGFORD TOWN
Secretary: Guy Brown, 82 Armstrong Ave., Woodford Green, Essex IG8 9PM (081 531 8341).
Ground & Directions: Chingdale Road, Friday Hill, Chingford (081 529 0485). North Circular to Woodford New Road, into Chingford Lane, into Chingdale Road at r'bout. Chingford bus to Friday Hill.
Colours: Red/white/red   **Change Colours:** Sky/white or black

CLAPTON VILLA
Secretary: G Kendrick, 51 Lakeside Crescent, East Barnet, Herts EN4 8QH (081 440 1938).
Ground & Directions: Douglas Eyre Sports Centre, Coppermill Lane, Walthamstow (081 520 4918). 5 mins walk from Blackhorse Road (Victoria Line). By road; Forest Road from Woodford, Lea Bridge Road and Blackhorse Road from south of Thames.
Colours: All sky   **Change Colours:** White (black trim)/black

CRAVEN
Secretary: T Day, 23 Chudleigh Crescent, Ilford, Essex IG3 9AT (081 590 4471).
Ground & Directions: Jenkins Lane, Barking (081 594 8442). 200 yds east from junction of A406 (North Circular) and A13 (Newham Way) on A13. Barking (BR).
Colours: Sky/royal/royal.   **Change Colours:** All green.

CRAY VALLEY
Secretary: Mick Bedworth, 1 Spencer Close, Orpington, Kent BR6 9QZ (0689 871078).
Ground & Directions: S.T.C. Ivor Grove, New Eltham (081 850 2057). A20 from London to Fiveways junction, left into Southwood Road, left at lights, Ivor Grove on left. New Eltham (BR).
Colours: Black & white/black/black   **Change:** Blue & sky blue stripes

ILFORD
Secretary: Michael Foley, 21 South Park Drive, Ilford, Essex IG3 9AA (081 599 8950).
Ground & Directions: Cricklefield Stadium, Ilford.

LEWISHAM (ELMS)
Secretary: C Rhule, 6 Waldon Close, Croydon CR0 4JP (081 680 6893).
Ground & Directions: Elm Lane, Catford Hill, London SE6 (081 311 3123). One minute from South Circular. Catford Bridge (BR).
Colours: Red & white stripes/navy   **Change:** Red & black/black/blue
Previous Name: Elms FC (pre-1992).

LEYTON COUNTY
Secretary: K Kirwan, 120 Malvern Road, Leytonstone E11 3DL (081 539 9210).
Ground & Directions: Crawley Road, Leyton E10 (081 539 1924). Approx one and a half miles from Leyton station, in direction of Walthamstow.
Colours: All white   **Change Colours:** Yellow/blue/yellow

METPOL CHIGWELL
Secretary: B Hunt, 134 Stanley Avenue, Gidea Park, Romford RM2 5DA (0708 743533).
Ground & Directions: Met Police Sports Ground, Chigwell (081 500 2735 or 500 1017). A113 Chigwell Road off North Circular, left at mini r-about for just over a mile. Club on left after junction with Chigwell Rise. Chigwell (tube - Central Line).
Colours: White (red & black trim)   **Change:** All blue or black & red

METROGAS
Secretary: Sandra Payne, 59 Blendon Rd, Bexley, Kent DA5 1BN (081 303 6959).
Ground & Directions: Forty Footway, Eltham (081 859 1579 or 081 859 4534). A20 from London to Fiveways junction, left into Southwood Road, on to Averyhill Road, ground on left in Forty Footway. New Eltham (BR).
Colours: Royal/white/blue   **Change Colours:** All green

OLD ROAN
Secretary: Ian Stuart Daniels, Garden Flat, 67 Shooters Hill Rd, Blackheath, London SE3 7HS (081 858 0278).
Ground & Directions: Roan School Playing Fields, Kidbrooke Park Road, London SE12 (081 856 1915). At start of A20. Kidbrooke (BR) or buses 21 and 22.
Colours: Blue/black/black   **Change Colours:** All red

SOUTH EAST OLYMPIC
Secretary: D Wilson, 74 Shrofford Road, Bromley BR1 5PF (081 698 1192).
Ground & Directions: Elliott Sports, Manor Way, Blackheath SE3 (081 852 3602). Lee Green into Lee Road - Manor Way 2nd right. Blackheath (BR).
Colours: All blue   **Change Colours:** White/silver/black

WALTHAMSTOW TROJANS

Secretary: Troy Townsend, 54 Grove Park Ave., Chingford E4 8SS (081 527 7911).
Ground & Directions: Ive Farm Arena, Villiers Close, Leyton E10 (081 539 6352). From Lea Bridge Road turn into Church Road, then after half a mile right into Villiers Close. Leyton (tube - Central Line).
Colours: All sky   **Change Colours:** All amber

WOOLWICH TOWN

Secretary: Micky Spires, 137 Harland Ave., Sidcup, Kent DA5 7HZ (021 309 1276).
Ground & Directions: Flamingo Park, Sidcup by-pass (A20)(081 300 6754). Blackwall Tunnel to A20, past Crossways to St Marys r'bout, past Beaver Wood Club, next left. New Eltham (BR).
Colours: Yellow & black/black/black   **Change Colours:** All red & black

DIVISION TWO CLUBS 1993-94

CLASSIC INTER

Secretary: Lloyd Joseph, 27 Benson Ave., East Ham, London E6 3EE (081 552 3132).
Ground: Ive Farm Sports Ground, Leyton, London E10.

LEWISHAM TOWN

Secretary: Mike Cheeseman, 142 Old Bromley Rd, Downham, Bromley, Kent (081 290 5558).
Ground & Directions: TBA.
Colours: TBA   **Change Colours:** TBA
Previos Leagues: Chigwell & District (pre'91)/ South East London 91-92.

LEYTON COUNTY RESERVES (details as per page 373)

LOUGHTON

Secretary: K Campen (081 508 4757).
Ground: London Polytechnic Sports Ground, Luxborough Lane, Chigwell.
Colours: Red/black/black   **Change Colours:** Green/black/green.
Previous Lge: Essex I'mediate (pre'92)   **Hons:** Essex I'mediate Lg Snr Div 3 91-92.
Previous Ground: Roding Valley Playing Fields, Roding Road, Loughton (pre'92).

Loughton F.C. 1992-93. Back Row (L/R): J Curff (Chairman), W Filby, M Purton, L Dobson, M Kenneally, R McDonald, I Taylor, R Wilson, M Newman, R Shatford, P Lovett (Manager), K Campen (Secretary). Front: C Muckley, R Moore, R Montano, I Potter, P Sear, M Fortag. Photo - Richard Brock.

MARSHALLS

Secretary: Ian Marshall, 21 Liphook Crescent, London (081 699 6080).
Ground: Cold Harbour Sports, Chapel Farm Road, Eltham.
Colours: All White   **Change:** All blue.

Marshalls F.C. 1992-93. Back Row (L/R): Gavin Travia, Sullivan Reid, Gary Blaize, Peter Houllett, Dave Jackson, Colin Blaize, Lenny Nadison. Front: Tony Mayers, Tim Jackson, Bobby Nawol, Eddie Blaize, Steve Griffith, Ray Leahy. Photo - Richard Brock.

MAYO
Secretary: Joe McNamara, 14 Dando Cres., Ferrier Est., Kidbrooke, London SE3 9PB (081 319 2590).
Ground & Directions: As South East Olympic (see page 373).

OLLERTON
Secretary: Mr B Marrion, 55 Ollerton Green, Jodwell Rd, London Bow (081 980 6685).
Ground: Drapers, Gorton Road, Leyton.
Colours: Green/green/black   **Change Colours:** Claret & blue/claret/white.

S.T.C. IVOR GROVE
Secretary: Terry Quick, 1 The Gardens, Chelsfield House, Bucks Cross Rd, Chelsfield, Orpington, Kent BR6 7RG (0689 874182).
Ground & Directions: As Cray Valley (see page 373).

TOTTENHAM WINE
Secretary:
Ground:

WALTHAMSTOW ST MARYS
Secretary: Eddy Webb, 34 Bidwell Gardens, Rounds Green, London, N11 2AU (081 881 0538).
Ground & Directions: As Ilford (see page 373).

Reserve Division 1993-94: Beckton United Res., Catford Wanderers Res., Cray Valley Res., Haringey Borough Res., Lewisham (Elms) Res., Metpol Chigwell Res., South East Olympic Res., Walthamstow Trojans Res., Willesden Hawkeye Res., Woolwich Town Res.

HOUNSLOW & DISTRICT LEAGUE

(Affiliated to the Middlesex F.A.   Established 1897)
President: S Spikins. **Chairman:** R D Goodsir.
Vice Chairman: N Palmer. **Secretary:** V E Leggatt.

PREM. DIV.	P	W	D	L	F	A	PTS
Abbey	18	13	2	3	53	31	28
Exxon Associates	18	10	5	3	50	39	25
Phoenix	18	7	6	5	58	42	*20
Teddington Rgrs	18	8	4	6	51	51	+20
Ashford United	18	7	5	6	47	38	19
Osterley 'A'	18	6	4	8	48	45	16
Inwood Rangers	18	6	3	9	48	51	15
Northfield Shamrocks	18	5	5	8	34	44	15
Park Celtic	18	3	7	8	23	50	=13
East Fulham	18	2	5	11	31	52	9

* - 2 pts deducted. + - 2 pts awarded. = - 2 pts awarded for unplayed match. *Stocks FC and Whitton FC withdrawn*

DIV. ONE	P	W	D	L	F	A	PTS
Westminster Widadia	21	18	3	0	81	31	=29
C.B. United	22	15	5	2	74	28	35
East Fulham Res.	22	12	5	5	49	36	29
Bedfont 'A'	22	10	6	6	49	29	26
Spelthorne Spts 'A'	22	10	4	8	46	32	24
Bison	22	8	4	10	56	51	=20
Bedham Old Boys	21	9	2	10	44	48	+20
Blondin	22	6	8	8	45	50	20
Marble Hill Rgrs	22	5	8	8	48	38	23
Abbey Res.	22	6	5	11	40	42	17
Whitton Tornadoes	22	3	2	17	24	59	*+8
Laleham United	22	0	1	21	10	122	1

Westminster Widadia v Bedham Old Boys declared null & void by Middx FA.
* - 2 pts deducted. + - 2 pts awarded. = - 2 pts awarded for unplayed match.

DIV. TWO	P	W	D	L	F	A	PTS
The Bells	22	19	2	1	89	25	40
Abbey Veterans	22	12	5	5	45	29	=29
Heston Fire Station	22	12	2	8	64	48	26
Inwood Rgrs Res.	22	11	2	9	54	44	24
Eutectic	22	10	2	10	64	51	22
Cedars United	22	9	4	9	56	54	22
Ashford Warriors	22	8	5	9	52	53	21
Hounslow '91 Res.	22	8	3	11	39	62	19
Hoechst	22	9	1	12	61	91	=19
Feltham Aces	22	8	1	13	67	81	17
Hounslow Postal	22	5	4	13	34	59	=14
Bedfont Green Jnrs	22	4	3	15	37	65	11

= - 2 pts awarded for unplayed match.

Unplayed games: *Cedars Utd v Abbey Vets 3/10/92, Hounslow Postal v Heston Fire Station (17/10/92), Osterley 'A' v Park Celtic (14/11/92), Laleham Utd v Whitton Tornadoes (21/11/92), Feltham Aces v Hoechst (2/1/93), Osterley 'A' v Phoenix (6/3/93), Whitton v Phoenix (13/3/93), Bison v Laleham Utd (27/3/93), Whitton Tornadoes v Westminster Widadia - Tornadoes withdrawn.*

FRED BARNARD CUP First Round
Inwood Rangers 1, Whitton Tornadoes 0
Bison 1, Phoenix 3
Bedfont 'A' 0, Spelthorne Spts 'A' 2
Bedham Old Boys 1, Abbey 4
C.B. United 2, Exxon Associates 3
East Fulham 14, Stocks 1

Second Round
Whitton 2, Northfield Shamrocks 5
East Fulham 4, Exxon Associates 1
Blondin 3, Park Celtic 0
Inwood Rgrs 3, Teddington Rgrs 2
Ashford Utd 8, Spelthorne Spts 'A' 0
Osterley 'A' 2, Abbey 1
Mable Hill *w/o* Westminster W. *withdrew*
Laleham United 0, Phoenix 14

Quarter-Finals
Phoenix and Osterley *(both expelled)*
Blondin 0, Inwood Rangers 1
East Fulham 5, Ashford United 3
Northfield S. 2, Marble Hill Rgrs 2
Marble Hill 1, Northfield Shamrocks 6

Semi-Finals
Northfield Shamrocks 0, Inwood Rgrs 7
East Fulham *(bye)*

Final
Inwood Rangers 4, East Fulham 2 *(aet)*

JUBILEE CUP First Round
Inwood Rangers Res. 3, The Bells 3
The Bells 3, Inwood Rgrs Res. 1
Hoechst 2, Bedfont Green Jnrs 3
Eutectic 1, Cedars United 7
Feltham Aces 1, Hounslow Postal 1
Hounslow Postal 2, Feltham Aces 2
Feltham Aces 2, Hounslow Postal 3
Heston Fire Station 5, Abbey Res. 0

Quarter-Finals
Hounslow '91 Res. 4, Hounslow Postal 1
Cedars United 4, East Fulham Res. 0
Ashford Warriors 0, The Bells 1
Heston Fire St. 2, Bedford Green 2
Bedfont Green 1, Heston Fire Station 3

Semi-Finals
The Bells 2, Heston Fire Station 2
Heston Fire Station 1, The Bells 5
Hounslow '91 Res. 1, Cedar United 2

Final
The Bells 4, Cedars United 3 *(aet)*

SOUTH LONDON FOOTBALL FEDERATION

(Affiliated to London F.A. and Kent F.A.   Established 1991)

PREM. DIV.	P	W	D	L	F	A	PTS
Keyworth	20	15	2	3	83	29	32
Camb. Univ. Mission	20	15	2	3	46	22	32
Cambridge	20	15	3	2	66	23	*31
Staveley	20	11	3	6	51	31	*23
Graham Athletic	20	10	3	7	55	38	23
Park Ryls Athletic	20	9	2	9	42	54	20
Cray Valley Res.	20	6	3	11	35	53	15
Eltham Town Res.	20	5	4	11	41	55	14
Seven Seals Utd	20	5	2	13	36	54	12
Bromley Baptist	20	5	2	13	41	69	12
Silenzio Postal	20	0	2	18	25	93	2

* - 2 points deducted

Constitution 93-94: Allbrighton (formerley Continental Star), Bromley Baptist, Cambridge, Cambridge University Mission, Eltham Town, Graham Athletic, Hitech Rangers, Keyworth, Park Royals Athletic, Seven Seals Utd, Staveley.

DIV. ONE	P	W	D	L	F	A	PTS
Hitech Rangers	22	13	3	6	55	33	29
Contintal Star	22	11	5	6	56	41	27
Odua United	22	12	3	7	52	38	27
Churchdown	22	11	5	6	50	44	27
Umojah	22	8	8	6	44	39	24
Red Star '87	22	10	3	9	44	45	23
Selworthy Park	22	8	6	8	44	46	22
Keyworth Res.	22	9	3	10	38	49	21
S.E. Olympic Res.	22	9	1	11	34	42	19
Phoenix Spts Res.	22	8	2	12	55	55	18
Eltham Palace Res.	22	6	4	12	32	44	16
Middle Park Res.	22	3	3	15	32	60	9

Constitution 93-94: Belvedere, Churchdown, Erith Albion, Green Eagles, Huntsman, Odua United, Red Star '87, Selworthy Park, Silenzio Postal, Silverdale (formerly Catford Wanderers 'A'), South East Olympic Reserves, Umojah.

DIV. TWO	P	W	D	L	F	A	PTS
Belvedere	20	14	3	3	65	33	31
Catford Wdrs 'A'	20	10	6	4	80	46	26
P.A.B.Y.A.	20	11	4	5	64	40	26
Hilly Fields	20	10	3	7	56	43	23
Locksley	20	10	3	7	56	31	23
Regal	20	8	4	8	43	54	20
Marseans	20	7	4	9	48	42	18
A.F.C. Sydenham	20	7	4	9	56	52	18
Eltham Invicta	20	8	2	10	37	49	18
Croydon Strikers	20	4	3	13	51	88	11
E.S.C.	20	2	2	16	24	82	6

NB. *Mayo resigned mid-season.*

Constitution 93-94: A.F.C. Sydenham, African Braves, Eltham Invicta, Eltham Palace Res., Hillyfields, Keyworth Res., Locksley, Marseans, Middle Park Res., Norwood Town Sports, P.A.B.Y.A., Regal, Wagoners.

DIV. THREE	P	W	D	L	F	A	PTS
Norwood T. Spts	22	20	1	1	88	37	41
Erith Albion	22	16	4	2	64	27	36
S.E. Olympic 'A'	22	16	3	3	102	41	35
Siemens Plessey	22	12	3	7	91	65	27
Star Athletic	22	10	5	7	60	63	25
Abbeymead	22	10	3	9	68	42	23
Delta Royals	22	8	7	7	57	54	23
Lower Sydenham	22	6	4	12	47	87	16
Eltham Villa	22	5	3	14	44	75	13
Thomas Guy	22	6	0	16	39	55	12
Eltham Palace 'A'	22	3	3	16	30	80	7
Lewisham T. Res.	22	1	2	19	24	88	4

Constitution 93-94: Bostall Park, Catford Wanderers 'B', Croydon Strikers, Delta Royals, Eltham Villa, E.S.C., Final Furlong, Havelock, Lower Sydenham C.I.U., Siemens Sports, Star Athletic, Swanley Town.

DIV. FOUR	P	W	D	L	F	A	PTS
Wagoners	16	16	0	0	98	14	32
Catford Wdrs 'B'	16	12	1	3	68	14	25
Bostall Park	16	10	2	4	63	20	22
Tressillian	16	10	1	5	47	39	21
Belvedere Res.	16	5	2	8	36	43	12
Brockley 'A'	16	3	4	9	31	55	10
Santos United	16	5	0	11	24	91	10
Kameroon	16	2	3	10	18	48	7
Bromley United	16	1	1	14	19	80	3

NB. *Latter Day Saints, Marseans Reserves and New Cross All Stars all resigned.*

Constitution 93-94: Belvedere Res., Bostall Park Res., Brockley 'A', Eltham Palace 'A', E.S.C. Res., Marseans Res., North Kent, Norwood Town Sports Res., Santos United, Siemens Sports Res., Tressillian, Wagoners Res.,

LEAGUE CUP FINALS

Federation Cup: Cambridge University Mission 1, Erith Albion 3

Senior Cup: Hitech Rangers 4, Keyworth 7

Junior Cup: Bostall Park 0, Norwood Town Sports 1

Below: *Keyworth F.C., South London Federation Premier Division champions 1992-93. Back Row (L/R): David Halford (Joint Manager), Ken Mansfield (Captain), Roger Williams, John Keane, Robert Soaft, Stephan Halford, Martyn Jones, Malcolm Weekes, John Norman (Joint Manager). Front: Paul Power Wayne O'Dwyer, Oliver Mallaghan, Micky Soaft, Mark McDermott, Terry Seales.*

HERTS SENIOR COUNTY LEAGUE

President: Mr W.J.R. Veneear
Chairman: Mr C.T. Hudson
Secretary: Mr E.H. Dear,
48 Wilshere Road, Welwyn, Herts

"SUN SPORTS SHINE BRIGHTLY"

Given a 39-club base for both Senior and Reserve Sections the League decided on a two division constitution for each section, the seniors dividing into a Premier of 20 teams and a division one of 19 whilst the reserves split to a top division of 19 and a lower division of 20. Although it was regarded as a brave decision, it was however considered better to give clubs large league programmes utilising the full season span rather than having smaller divisions with a league programme finishing very early. As usual the British weather intervened - and very early at that. By the start of the new year the League had a backlog of well over 100 fixtures through postponements and a previously un-used rule had to be invoked whereby clubs who had not met during the season to date played one game for double points to decide the home and away fixtures. In the premier division the early pacesetters were Park Street. By March however the battle was developing into a two horse race between Sun Sports and newly promoted Bovingdon. A midweek home win over Oxhey Jets in front of several hundred spectators clinched the title for Sun, who had a five point winning margin at the end.

At the other end of the table matters were slightly clouded by the prospect of fixed post and rail rather than playing ability earning teams premier status for the 1993-94 season. Croxley Guild, Kodak and BAC finished in the relegation spots but of those only Kodak will not be operating in the premier this season.

In order that the League retains senior status, the F.A. ruling that all premier division clubs have fixed post and rail enclosures to their pitches has been imposed. Only true casualties are Walkern who finished 16th but were relegated. Lucas Sports have left the league, a knock-on effect of the company's reduction in size at Hemel Hempstead, and Park Street have been forced to close owing to financial difficulties.

In division one Allenburys Sports led the league from August until April but were eventually forced into third place by Metropolitan Police (Bushey) who won the championship, and newcomers Valmar L.R.. Both of these clubs will play in the premier division in 1993-94, but Allenburys, due to ground difficulties, will remain in division one.

In the reserve section Sun Sports completed a double over Bovingdon, pipping them for the reserve division one title with a 1-0 home win when the clubs met in their last game of the season.

As in the senior section Wormley Rovers finished third.

In reserve division two Wellcome won the title with Kodak second and Metropolitan Police (Bushey) third.

The Aubrey Cup final saw Bovingdon pick up their third runners-up medals of the season with outsiders Chipperfield Corinthians taking the trophy 2-0 at Colney Heath F.C. on May Day.

The reserve cup produced a third winner's trophy for Sun Sports as they beat Colney Heath 5-0 in the final at London Colney F.C.

In the Herts Intermediate Cup Final Metropolitan Police's (Bushey) first team overcame Sun Sports reserves 5-2 in extra-time to bring the trophy to a County League club for the first time for several years.

There was disappointment for the League's representative side who drew 2-2 in the Herts Inter-League competition before going down on penalties to the Bishops Stortford, Stanstead & District League in the first round.

The 1993-94 constitution will persist with two division sections. Apart from the loss of Lucas and Park Street, Stevenage C.I.U. have withdrawn from the League and Little Goddesden won't be operating a reserve team. The only newcomers are Codicote who at present don't have a reserve side whilst Wellcome will now operate under the title of Roussell Sports.

Kevin Folds (Management Committee)

PREM. DIVISION	P	W	D	L	F	A	PTS
Sun Sports	38	25	8	5	76	35	83
Bovingdon	38	22	12	4	59	28	78
Wormley Rovers	38	20	11	7	83	56	71
Chipperfield Cor.	38	20	11	7	68	49	71
Wellcome	38	20	8	10	71	49	68
Knebworth	38	19	8	11	65	49	65
Sandridge Rovers	38	18	10	10	79	49	64
Park Street	38	16	12	10	55	45	60
Colney Heath	38	17	7	14	67	49	58
Bushey Rangers	38	17	7	14	60	52	58
Elliott Star	38	17	6	15	78	61	57
Bedmond Social	38	15	8	15	74	67	53
Cuffley	38	13	9	16	55	55	48
Kings Langley	38	13	7	18	58	64	46
Lucas Sports	38	9	6	23	46	86	33
Walkern	38	9	6	23	48	89	33
Oxhey Jets	38	8	8	22	44	79	32
B.A.C. Stevenage	38	9	2	27	48	109	29
Kodak (Hemel H.)	38	7	7	24	38	73	28
Croxley Guild	38	6	7	25	46	88	25

Top Scorers: M McGinty (Colney Hth) 30, G Ferguson (Wormley) 24, K Lowe (Knebworth) 23, P Rastrick (Chipperfield) 22, R Wilson (Bushey Rgrs) 22, J McQuire (20), D Day (Wellcome) 18, M Hymes (Sandridge) 16, D Pearce (Kodak) 16, I Poupart (Bovingdon) 16, M Johns (Wormley) 16, R Agomber (Sandridge) 16, A Walker (Wellcome) 15, I Holdam (Oxhey), G Pineda (Park Street), B Purby (Cuffley) 13, D Weller (Elliott Star) 13, J Field (Sun) 13, F Tyler (Knebworth) 13, S Mahoney (Walkern) 13.

DIVISION ONE	P	W	D	L	F	A	PTS
Met Pol. (Bushey)	36	18	4	4	118	45	88
Valmar L.R.	36	25	8	3	94	29	83
Allenburys Spts	36	24	5	7	71	37	77
Welwyn	36	25	1	10	101	42	76
St Peters	36	22	5	9	83	57	71
Hertford Youth	36	18	9	9	109	62	63
Dynamics	36	19	4	13	72	59	61
Evergreen	36	17	9	10	83	56	60
Whitwell Ath.	36	18	5	13	94	77	59
Stevenage C.I.U.	36	12	6	18	68	68	52
Sarratt	36	11	9	16	48	73	42
Somersett Ambury	36	10	9	17	51	61	39
I.C.L. Letchworth	36	9	10	17	51	82	37
Kimpton Rovers	36	9	8	19	43	67	35
Little Gaddesden	36	9	7	20	46	104	34
Standon & Puck.	36	10	3	23	54	86	33
Harpenden Rovers	36	7	5	24	45	100	26
North Mymms	36	4	12	20	39	81	24
St Ippolyts	36	3	5	28	31	116	14

Top Scorers: J Moss (Valmar) 31, P McCormack (Welwyn) 28, G McGregor (St Peters) 27, S Frazer (Met Police Bushey) 27, R Grant (Met Police Bushey) 26, G Matthews (Allensburys) 24, K Minnis (Whitwell) 24, T Legate (Whitwell (12 for I.C.L.)) 23, M Swayland (Evergreen) 21, S Sarwa (St Peters) 20, M Driver (Little Gaddesden) 19, J Hooker (Hertford Yth) 17, H Baldwin (Met Police Bushey) 16, D Boston (Whitwell) 15, M Castle (Hertford Yth) 14, S Clarke (Dynamics (9 for Stevenage C.I.U.)) 14, B Roberts (Standon & Puckeridge) 14, S Rayment (Hertford Yth) 14, M Mitchell (Stevenage C.I.U.) 14, A Smith (Dynamics) 14, B McComb (Hertford Yth) 13, S Manning (Kimpton) 13, S Gummer (Somersett) 13.

RESERVE DIV. 1	P	W	D	L	F	A	PTS
Sun Spts Res.	36	28	4	4	100	38	88
Bovingdon Res.	36	27	4	5	77	25	85
Wormley R. Res.	36	25	7	4	80	39	82
Colney Hth Res.	36	25	3	8	97	35	78
Sandridge R. Res.	36	17	5	14	63	54	56
Elliott Star Res.	36	13	12	11	69	58	51
Knebworth Res.	36	14	9	13	60	68	51
Oxhey Jets Res.	36	14	8	14	66	61	50
BAC Stev. Res.	36	16	2	18	50	81	50
Chipperfield Res.	36	13	5	18	67	66	44
King Langley Res.	36	13	5	18	59	70	44
Walkern Res.	36	13	5	18	62	79	44
Welwyn Res.	36	13	4	19	56	82	43
Dynamics Res.	36	13	3	20	73	85	42
Park Street Res.	36	13	8	17	73	89	41
Bedmond Res.	36	12	4	20	64	89	40
Bushey Rgrs Res.	36	10	4	22	62	85	34
Croxley Gld Res.	36	7	5	24	52	88	26
Lucas Spts Res.	36	6	7	23	40	71	25

Top Scorers: T Seabrook (Sun) 32, J Harrison (Sun) 32, S James (Colney Hth) 24, I Pepper (Sun) 24, P Jewell (Bovingdon) 23, D Marriott (Bedmond) 23, N Layton (Wormley) 19, L Tiernam (Dynamics) 18, M Lafayette (Wormley) 17, A Grew (Kings Langley) 13, P Richardson (Dynamics) 13, G Mooney (Park Street) 13, A Dance (Knebworth) 12, D Brown (Park Street) 12, M Olaseinde (Walkern) 12, D Purkis (Bovingdon) 12, M Bond (Colney Hth) 12, T Bond (Colney Hth) 12.

RESERVE DIV. 2	P	W	D	L	F	A	PTS
Wellcome Res.	38	27	6	5	103	39	87
Kodak H.H. Res.	38	26	7	5	118	47	85
Met P. (Bush.) Res.	38	26	4	8	113	50	82
Valmar L.R. Res.	38	24	7	7	92	28	79
Hertford Yth Res.	38	22	9	7	91	51	75
Cuffley Res.	38	23	4	11	104	63	73
Stev. C.I.U. Res.	38	18	10	10	69	42	64
St Peters Res.	38	20	3	15	86	69	63
Evergreen Res.	38	17	5	16	75	60	56
Sarratt Res.	38	15	14	13	57	53	55
Somersett A. Res.	38	14	8	16	67	70	50
Allenburys Res.	38	15	5	18	67	79	50
Nth Mymms Res.	38	13	10	15	62	62	49
Whitwell A. Res.	38	12	6	20	82	114	42
ICL Letchworth Res.	38	10	7	21	60	89	37
Kimpton R. Res.	38	9	6	23	39	94	33
Harpenden R. Res.	38	7	9	22	53	84	30
St Ippolyts Res.	38	4	9	25	44	118	21
Little Gadd. Res.	38	5	6	27	34	123	21
Standon & P. Res.	38	5	5	28	37	125	20

Top Scorers: G Donnison (Met Police Bushey) 31, K Spink (Kodak) 26, A Kemp (Sarratt) 24, G Bartlett (Somersett) 24, M Baker (Valmar) 22, A Moss (Valmar) 22, N Cave (Allenburys) 19, P Burgess (Met Police Bushey) 19, P Lewis (Hertford Yth) 19, M Owen (Cuffley) 18, D Campbell (Whitwell) 18, S Timbs (St Peters) 18, D Jones (North Mymms) 17, C Murphy (Wellcome) 16, P Coyle (Hertford Yth) 15, D Gallagher (St Peters) 15, M Lupton (Hertford Yth) 14, A Clark (Somersett) 14, T Morgan (Wellcome) 13, P Mitchell (Stevenage C.I.U.) 13, D Boom (Standon & Puckeridge) 13, D Crichton (Valmar) 13, S Cotterill (Cuffley) 13, S Hancock (Kodak) 13.

AUBREY (LEAGUE) CUP 1992-93

First Round

Evergreen v St Ippolyts	1-0
Kimpton Rovers v Whitwell Athletic	0-1 *(aet)*
North Mymms v Stevenage C.I.U.	0-2
Valmar L.R. v Metropolitan Police (Bushey)	0-2
Harpenden Rovers v Standon & Puckeridge	0-1
Little Gaddesden v Hertford Youth	4-3
St Peters v Somersett Ambury V. & E.	3-1

Second Round

B.A.C. Stevenage v Elliott Star	3-2
Bushey Rangers v Chipperfield Corinthians	2-4
Evergreen v Sun Sports	1-2
Kings Langley v Sarratt	4-0
Knebworth v Oxhey Jets	5-1
St Peters v Whitwell Athletic	7-0
Stevenage C.I.U. v Colney Heath	0-5
Wellcome v Metropolitan Police (Bushey)	1-0
Bedmond Social v Cuffley	3-1
Dynamics Stevenage v Welwyn	0-1
I.C.L. Letchworth v Croxley Guild	1-1,0-3(aet)
Kodak Hemel Hempstead v Bovingdon	2-4
Park Street v Little Gaddesden	8-0
Sandridge Rovers v Allensbury Sports	4-2
Standon & Puckeridge v Lucas Sports	1-2
Walkern v Wormley Rovers	0-3

Third Round

Wellcome v Bedmond Social	2-1
Lucas Sports v Chipperfield Corinthians	3-3,2-4

(continued opposite)

Third Round (continued)

Colney Heath v Sandridge Rovers	0-2	St Peters v Wormley Rovers	1-2
Kings Langley v Knebworth	0-3	Sun Sports v Park Street	0-1
B.A.C. Stevenage v Welwyn	6-2	Croxley Guild v Bovingdon	2-3

Quarter Finals

Wellcome v Chipperfield Corinthians	1-3	Sandridge Rovers v Wormley Rovers	4-2*(aet)*
Knebworth v Sun Sports	0-2	Bovingdon v B.A.C. Stevenage	3-1

Semi Finals

Chipperfield Corinthians v Sandridge Rovers	4-1	Bovingdon v Sun Sports	1-1,2-3*(aet)*

Final (Colney Heath FC): Chipperfield Corinthians 2, Bovingdon 0

RESERVE CUP 1992-93

First Round

Allensbury Sports Res. 3, St Peters Res. 2	3-2	Harpenden R. Res. v Standon & Puckeridge Res.	1-1,0-2
Kimpton Rovers Res. v Little Gaddesden Res.	2-3	North Mymm Res. v St Ippolyts Res	1-0
Sarratt Res. v Whitwell Athletic Res.	7-1	Stevenage C.I.U. Res. v Somersett Ambury V & E	1-4
Valmar L.R. Res. v Met Police (Bushey) Res.	0-1		

Second Round

Bedmond Social Res. v B.A.C. Stevenage Res.	2-3	Chipperfield Corinthians Res. v Bovingdon Res.	1-2
Colney Heath Res. v Elliott Star Res.	5-1	Evergreen Res. v Lucas Sport Res.	1-0
Hertford Yth Res. v Bushey Rangers Res.	2-5	I.C.L. Letchworth Res. v Croxley Guild Res.	1-4
North Mymms Res. v Kings Langley Res.	4-2*(aet)*	Kodak H.H. Res. v Met Police (Bushey) Res.	2-3*(aet)*
Oxhey Jets Res. v Walkern Res.	7-2	Sandridge Rovers Res. v Little Gaddesden Res.	7-0
Sarratt Res. v Knebworth Reserves	2-1	Somersett Ambury V. & E. Reserves v Welwyn Res.	2-5
Standon & Puckeridge Res. v Cuffley Res.	3-4	Sun Sports Res. v Allensbury Sports Res.	3-2
Wellcome Res. v Dynamics Stevenage Reserves	2-1	Wormley Rovers Reserves v Park Street Res.	3-2

Third Round

Met Police (Bushey) Res. v Sun Spts Res.	3-9	Standon & Puckeridge Res. v BAC Stevenage Res.	3-4
Sarratt Res. v Wormley Rovers Reserves	0-5	Sandridge Rovers Res. v Bovingdon Reserves	1-2
Colney Heath Res. v Bushey Rgrs Reserves	8-1	Welwyn Reserves v Evergreen Reserves	1-0
Wellcome Reserves v North Mymms Reserves	2-1	Croxley Guild Reserves v Oxhey Jets Reserves	1-2

Quarter Finals

Sun Sports Reserves v B.A.C. Stevenage Res.	7-0	Wormley Rovers Reserves v Bovingdon Reserves	0-3
Colney Heath Res. v Welwyn Reserves	3-2	Wellcome Reserves v Oxhey Jets Reserves	4-0

Semi-Finals

Colney Heath Reserves v Wellcome Reserves	4-0	Sun Sports Res. v Bovingdon Res.	2-2,1-1*(aet, 9-8 pens)*

Final (at London Colney FC): Sun Sports Reserves 5, Colney Heath Reserves 0

PREMIER DIVISION RESULT CHART 1992-93

HOME TEAM	1	2	3	4	5	6	7	8	9	10	11	12	13	14	15	16	17	18	19	20
1. BAC Stevenage		2-1	0-3	2-1	3-0	1-1	4-1	1-3	2-4	3-3	1-3	4-3	0-3	2-0	0-1	1-4	0-7	0-2	2-1	0-7
2. Bedmond	3-1	*	0-1	2-1	+	0-1	2-2	0-3	3-3	5-1	0-1	4-0	8-1	2-2	0-0	4-2	3-7	1-3	0-3	1-0
3. Bovingdon	3-1	2-0	*	1-1	0-3	1-1	3-2	+	1-1	3-0	1-0	2-0	+	1-1	0-0	1-0	2-2	1-1	1-2	1-0
4. Bushey Rgrs	6-1	1-2	0-2	*	1-1	2-0	1-1	6-1	1-0	+	0-4	5-1	6-0	2-3	0-1	1-4	1-3	3-0	1-0	3-1
5. Chip'field	4-1	1-1	2-1	3-1	*	2-0	4-3	0-4	3-1	2-0	1-2	1-0	1-1	2-0	1-1	2-0	1-1	0-6	0-0	4-2	1-1
6. Colney Hth	3-0	0-0	0-1	1-3	2-0	*	6-2	2-4	1-0	2-0	1-2	1-1	5-0	5-0	3-1	0-2	2-5	+	3-1	1-2
7. Croxley Gld	5-2	0-4	0-0	1-1	0-3	0-4	*	1-0	3-6	+	1-3	0-3	3-5	3-1	2-2	1-0	0-1	2-1	3-1	1-0
8. Cuffley	2-1	0-4	1-3	0-2	0-1	1-0	2-1	*	2-2	2-3	0-2	2-3	0-2	1-1	2-0	0-0	1-2	2-0	2-1	1-1
9. Elliott Star	4-0	4-1	2-1	7-0	1-3	0-6	0-0	1-0	*	3-0	3-1	2-0	3-1	1-5	+	3-1	0-1	5-1	3-0	1-3
10. K. Langley	4-1	1-0	0-3	0-1	3-0	0-2	3-0	2-1	2-3	*	1-1	2-3	2-0	4-4	1-1	0-2	1-3	6-0	1-3	1-1
11. Knebworth	0-1	1-3	0-2	1-1	2-1	4-0	1-0	2-2	5-2	1-2	*	3-1	1-0	1-0	0-1	1-1	0-0	3-1	0-3	0-2
12. Kodak	2-1	0-3	1-2	0-1	0-5	5-1	3-1	1-1	1-5	1-3	1-2	*	0-2	1-1	0-3	3-4	1-2	+	+	0-1
13. Lucas Spts	2-3	3-2	1-5	3-0	1-2	0-3	2-0	1-3	0-0	1-0	1-4	0-0	*	1-3	1-1	1-3	1-3	2-0	2-4	1-3
14. Oxhey Jets	4-3	2-5	2-3	0-2	0-0	0-0	2-1	0-0	1-3	2-1	1-3	1-2	+	*	1-3	0-1	3-1	0-1	1-3	0-1
15. Park Street	2-1	2-0	0-3	0-1	2-2	1-0	2-1	2-2	4-1	2-3	1-3	0-0	4-1	3-0	*	1-1	0-2	3-1	$	0-2
16. Sandridge	4-2	1-1	0-1	3-1	2-2	1-3	2-1	2-2	2-1	4-1	2-2	1-0	1-1	6-0	4-0	*	2-1	7-0	1-1	+
17. Sun Sports	4-0	2-0	1-1	2-0	1-2	0-0	2-1	1-4	1-0	2-1	2-0	+	1-1	3-2	0-0	3-0	*	1-1	1-0	3-1
18. Walkern	2-0	2-3	2-2	0-2	1-4	3-4	3-1	0-2	2-1	1-5	1-1	0-0	5-3	2-1	1-3	3-1	1-4	*	0-2	2-3
19. Wellcome	4-0	2-4	1-1	0-0	3-4	1-0	2-2	2-1	2-1	1-1	4-1	7-0	3-0	+	3-6	2-2	3-1	2-1	*	1-0
20. Wormley R.	3-1	9-2	0-0	1-1	1-2	3-3	3-0	2-1	1-1	+	4-4	x	4-1	6-0	2-2	4-0	0-1	5-2	2-2	*

+ - Due to fixture backlog rule 10a invoked whereby home & away fixtures played simultaneously; win 6pts, draw 2pts
x - Non-fulfilled fixture - pts awarded to home team
$ - Non-fulfilled fixture - pts awarded to away team

DIVISION ONE RESULT CHART 1992-93

HOME TEAM	1	2	3	4	5	6	7	8	9	10	11	12	13	14	15	16	17	18	19
1. Allenburys	*	1-0	1-0	2-3	2-0	2-0	6-0	2-2	2-2	2-2	5-0	+	2-1	2-1	5-0	4-1	0-2	2-0	2-1
2. Dynamics	0-2	*	0-1	3-2	2-4	4-0	2-1	3-1	2-4	5-0	1-0	4-1	3-0	2-1	2-1	+	0-0	2-5	6-0
3. Evergreen	0-0	3-1	*	2-1	2-2	6-2	4-1	0-1	2-0	5-1	5-0	1-3	2-0	1-0	6-1	6-2	1-1	+	0-0
4. Harp. Rvrs	0-4	3-1	2-2	*	4-2	1-0	1-0	2-0	2-7	1-3	2-2	2-3	2-5	1-2	1-2	4-2	0-3	1-4	+
5. Hertford Y.	1-4	1-1	3-6	9-1	*	+	4-0	7-1	1-2	2-2	8-1	4-2	2-1	1-2	2-1	6-1	1-2	2-1	1-0
6. ICL Letch.	+	1-1	1-1	5-0	1-1	*	1-0	4-2	1-4	0-0	3-0	2-5	2-2	0-2	4-0	0-6	1-7	0-2	1-5
7. Kimpton	2-2	2-2	0-2	2-1	2-2	1-3	*	4-0	1-6	1-1	2-1	2-3	0-1	3-1	1-0	1-1	0-2	1-3	1-1
8. Little Gad.	1-3	2-3	2-2	1-1	1-7	4-1	3-2	*	0-2	3-3	2-0	+	2-0	1-1	2-2	0-5	1-12	2-1	1-7
9. Met Police	0-1	3-1	4-1	6-3	6-2	4-1	+	4-0	*	6-1	3-1	4-0	2-1	4-1	2-0	3-1	3-1	2-1	7-3
10. Nth Mymms	0-2	1-3	2-1	3-0	+		0-1	1-1	+	*	3-0	0-1	1-1	2-3	2-3	1-1	1-4	0-3	1-6
11. St Ippolyts	1-2	1-2	2-8	1-1	1-13	1-2	3-2	2-3	2-4	2-2	*	1-5	+	0-3	2-3	3-0	1-1	0-4	1-5
12. St Peters	1-0	6-2	2-1	5-1	1-1	4-0	3-0	5-3	1-4	4-1	7-0	*	1-1	1-0	1-1	1-2	3-2	0-5	3-1
13. Sarratt	1-2	3-1	1-1	2-0	0-6	2-2	0-3	0-2	4-3	2-2	1-0	1-1	*	0-2	5-3	3-1	1-5	1-5	0-4
14. Somersett	0-3	0-2	3-5	1-1	3-3	1-1	0-0	0-1	0-2	2-1	0-0	1-4	2-2	*	5-2	2-3	3-3	1-1	5-1
15. Stan & Puck.	1-2	2-3	+	6-0	1-3	+	0-1	5-1	0-6	2-0	3-1	1-0	0-2	1-2	*	0-7	0-2	4-2	3-5
16. Stev. CIU	5-0	0-2	4-1	1-0	2-3	3-3	0-2	1-0	0-2	6-1	+	1-1	0-0	+	1-3	*	4-1	0-6	
17. Valmar LR	3-0	3-1	5-1	+	1-2	4-2	1-1	4-0	0-2	4-0	3-1	3-0	1-0	1-1	2-0	*		2-0	1-1
18. Welwyn	5-0	2-0	5-1	7-1	1-2	5-2	4-1	8-0	3-2	2-0	2-1	1-3	5-0	2-0	4-0	2-1	0-2	*	2-1
19. Whitwell	1-2	2-5	3-3	2-0	4-1	2-5	3-2	+	3-3	4-1	5-0	4-1	1-4	4-1	3-2	5-4	1-5	0-3	*

+ - Due to fixture backlog rule 10a invoked whereby home & away fixtures played simultaneously; win 6pts, draw 2pts

RESERVE DIVISION ONE RESULT CHART 1992-93

HOME TEAM	1	2	3	4	5	6	7	8	9	10	11	12	13	14	15	16	17	18	19
1. BAC Stevenage	+	0-4	2-1	1-3	$	2-1	3-1	3-0	+	0-2	x	1-6	4-1	+	2-6	2-1	+	0-3	
2. Bedmond	4-4	*	0-2	3-1	2-1	0-9	4-1	3-6	4-0	2-4	1-4	3-1	2-0	+	5-0	0-4	2-3	0-1	0-3
3. Bovingdon	0-1	5-1	*	2-0	4-1	1-0	+	2-1	2-2	2-1	0-2	2-1	+	1-1	3-1	3-0	4-2	4-1	2-1
4. Bushey Rgrs	+	4-0	1-2	*	2-4	0-3	2-2	1-2	0-4	4-1	1-1	$	1-4	3-3	2-1	+	5-1	2-1	2-6
5. Chip'field	5-3	3-6	0-2	2-6	*	2-4	3-0	5-3	0-1	2-2	0-3	x	2-3	3-3	1-2	2-0	4-1	3-4	1-1
6. Colney Hth	4-0	7-4	1-2	8-1	2-2	*	5-1	2-0	+	4-0	+	2-0	3-1	3-1	0-1	0-3	4-0	3-1	3-4
7. Croxley Gld	+	1-2	0-5	3-0	+	1-4	*	3-1	1-1	6-0	8-2	0-4	0-1	7-1	0-3	0-3	0-1	3-2	0-2
8. Dynamics	2-1	4-4	0-2	0-2	2-1	1-2	2-4	*	1-3	+	1-0	11-1	1-3	1-0	0-0	2-5	1-5	4-0	1-3
9. Elliott Star	4-1	+	1-1	5-1	3-3	1-3	1-1	5-3	*	3-1	3-3	x	1-1	3-5	0-0	0-2	4-1	3-2	1-4
10. K. Langley	4-0	6-3	1-1	4-1	0-1	1-3	2-0	0-2	2-2	*	3-1	2-0	2-0	2-3	0-1	0-6	x	3-0	2-5
11. Knebworth	1-1	0-2	0-1	1-4	3-1	2-1	3-3	5-2	1-1	0-3	*	1-1	2-1	2-2	2-0	2-2	1-5	4-0	+
12. Lucas Spts	6-2	4-1	0-4	0-2	2-4	0-2	1-1	1-2	5	2-0	0-4	*	1-5	2-3	1-1	2-2	0-1	0-1	$
13. Oxhey Jets	5-2	2-1	1-0	4-2	+	+	2-1	1-4	4-2	2-2	7-0	1-1	*	6-3	0-2	1-1	1-1	0-3	0-0
14. Park Street	4-2	3-3	1-2	0-5	1-2	2-2	5-0	1-1	1-4	4-3	5-0	3-1	5-1	*	3-2	$	0-3	0-1	$
15. Sandridge	0-1	+	1-0	5-0	2-1	2-5	2-1	1-3	2-2	2-1	1-1	0-1	5-1	4-1	*	2-6	2-1	2-3	4-1
16. Sun Spts	5-1	2-1	1-0	4-2	2-0	+	2-1	4-1	2-1	3-2	3-1	2-1	8-1	5-1	0-3	*	3-2	+	1-1
17. Walkern	1-3	+	0-7	2-1	4-2	0-6	7-2	3-1	2-1	1-1	2-4	1-1	+	2-3	2-4	1-4	*	3-1	1-3
18. Welwyn	2-0	4-1	1-4	2-2	+	1-2	3-0	3-1	2-6	3-2	1-2	2-2	x	5-3	2-3	0-8	2-2	*	2-3
19. Wormley	5-1	x	0-1	3-1	2-3	0-0	5-0	5-2	1-1	1-2	2-0	4-2	2-2	4-1	3-2	2-1	+	0-0	*

+ - Due to fixture backlog rule 10a invoked whereby home & away fixtures played simultaneously; win 6pts, draw 2pts
x - Non-fulfilled fixture - pts awarded to home team
$ - Non-fulfilled fixture - pts awarded to away team

RESERVE DIVISION TWO RESULT CHART 1992-93

HOME TEAM	1	2	3	4	5	6	7	8	9	10	11	12	13	14	15	16	17	18	19	20
1. Allenburys	*	1-6	3-1	3-0	0-4	2-0	4-0	0-2	x	2-1	1-2	+	5-2	3-1	3-1	4-3	0-1	0-3	2-5	2-1
2. Cuffley	2-3	*	0-3	3-2	4-1	3-2	3-2	4-1	1-4	1-3	1-0	5-1	5-1	1-2	6-1	+	3-3	1-5	2-4	7-0
3. Evergreen	1-0	2-4	*	2-1	0-2	4-0	2-1	1-2	2-2	0-4	1-1	5-0	0-2	3-0	5-3	3-1	1-3	+	1-1	3-5
4. Harp. Rvrs	4-1	0-2	0-3	*	1-5	1-1	2-3	0-3	4-3	2-4	4-0	2-0	0-3	1-1	1-4	0-1	1-1	0-5	2-0	4-4
5. Hertford Y.	0-2	0-5	0-0	2-1	*	5-2	x	1-1	2-0	2-1	+	4-1	2-1	1-1	2-3	6-0	1-0	2-0	1-0	4-1
6. ICL Letch.	2-1	3-6	3-2	0-2	1-5	*	3-0	5-7	1-1	2-4	0-1	4-0	2-3	1-2	+	1-6	2-4	3-2	3-3	3-0
7. Kimpton	3-1	1-2	0-4	1-1	2-3	0-2	*	0-1	0-2	0-8	2-0	1-1	2-1	0-4	1-1	7-0	x	0-0	2-6	2-2
8. Kodak	5-2	2-0	1-1	3-2	3-1	7-0	+	*	9-0	2-2	2-2	5-0	5-3	0-1	3-1	5-0	0-0	1-4	3-1	8-1
9. Little Gadd.	1-2	0-5	1-2	3-1	1-6	1-1	2-2	0-4	*	0-7	+	1-6	1-10	1-0	$	2-2	1-4	1-8	1-2	3-3
10. Met Police	3-1	3-2	2-3	3-1	2-2	+	8-2	2-6	4-1	*	1-1	3-1	4-1	2-1	5-3	5-1	0-1	2-0	1-2	4-0
11. Nth Mymms	5-0	3-3	2-1	0-0	1-1	+	8-1	1-4	5-1	1-5	*	2-1	0-1	4-4	1-1	3-1	2-1	1-2	+	+
12. St Ippolyts	2-2	0-4	5-9	2-2	2-1	1-2	2-0	1-3	4-3	+	2-3	*	1-5	0-5	+	1-1	+	0-3	0-7	2-2
13. St Peters	3-1	3-1	1-2	2-1	0-3	+	+	2-4	1-3	2-1	3-2	3-3	*	1-3	3-0	4-0	4-1	1-1	0-1	5-0
14. Sarratt	1-1	1-6	2-0	+	2-2	1-1	1-2	1-4	3-0	1-1	5-1	2-0	2-6	*	2-1	+	0-0	2-2	0-2	0-1
15. Somersett	2-2	0-0	4-3	0-0	4-5	2-2	6-0	3-1	4-1	0-4	4-3	6-0	0-1	3-1	*	3-2	0-2	0-1	1-2	+
16. Stand. & P.	1-1	1-2	1-3	3-1	0-3	0-5	+	0-7	3-2	0-5	1-5	4-1	+	0-3	1-1	*	0-4	0-4	0-4	2-2
17. Stev. CIU	2-1	0-1	1-2	2-4	3-2	4-1	3-0	+	4-1	1-4	0-0	1-1	3-1	$	3-0	7-0	*	2-0	1-1	2-4
18. Valmar LR	3-0	1-1	1-0	4-1	2-2	6-0	4-0	2-0	+	+	1-0	7-0	1-1	2-0	3-1	7-1	+	*	0-3	4-1
19. Wellcome	6-2	3-0	1-0	3-1	2-2	3-0	0-1	2-2	+	1-3	4-0	5-0	5-1	x	1-0	8-0	2-3	1-1	*	8-2
20. Whitwell	0-9	1-2	+	4-3	2-6	0-2	5-1	1-2	11-0	4-2	3-2	6-3	4-5	0-2	3-4	6-1	2-2	0-3	1-2	*

+ - Due to fixture backlog rule 10a invoked whereby home & away fixtures played simultaneously; win 6pts, draw 2pts
x - Non-fulfilled fixture - pts awarded to home team
$ - Non-fulfilled fixture - pts awarded to away team

PREMIER DIVISION CLUBS 1993-94

B.A.C. STEVENAGE

Secretary: Raymond C Poulter, 292 Jessop Rd, Stevenage, Herts SG1 5NA (0438 358078).
Ground & Directions: Bragbury End, Stevenage (0438 812985). A1(M) to Stevenage Sth (jct 7), A602 Hertford/Ware signs to Bragbury End, ground on left at just past golf course.
Seats: None **Cover:** Yes **Programme:** Yes **Nickname:** **Founded:** 1953
Colours: Blue/blue/red **Change colours:** Amber/black/amber.
Previous League: Nth Herts/Sth Mids **Hons:** Aubrey Cup 87-88.

BEDMOND SPORTS & SOCIAL

Secretary: W E (Bill) Smith, 95 Breakspeare Rd, Abbots Langley, Herts WD5 0ER (0923 267991).
Ground: The Pavillion, Toms Lane, Bedmond (0923 267991).
Directions: M1 jct 8, then A4147 to 2nd r'bout, bear right to Bedmond at church (Bedmond Rd), right in village into Toms Lane at mini r'bout, ground 300yds on left.
Seats: None **Cover:** Yes **Programme:** Yes **Nickname:** **Founded:** pre-1913
Colours: Green & red/green/green **Change colours:** White (red pin stripes)/red/red
Previous Leagues: West Herts/ Watford & District **Hons:** Herts Lg 84-85 85-86 (Aubrey Cup 80-81)

BOVINGDON

Sec: Ronald Carter, 21 Yew Tree Drive, Chipperfield Rd, Bovingdon, Hemel Hempstead HP3 0TA (0442 834414).
Ground & Directions: Green Lane, Bovingdon (0442 832628). From Hemel Hempstead to Bovingdon, left by Halfway House then right into Green Lane. Ground on left at top of hill.
Seats: Yes **Cover:** Yes **Programme:** No **Nickname:** None
Colours: Green & white stripes/green/green **Change colours:** Tangerine/black/tangerine.
Previous League: West Herts **Hons:** Herts Lg Div 1 55-56 80-81 83-84 (Div 2 69-70).

BUSHEY RANGERS

Secretary: Rowland Marshall, 45 Blackwell Drive, Watford, Herts WD1 4HP (0923 816856).
Ground: Moatfield, Bournehall Lane, Bushey (081 950 1875).
Directions: A41 to Hartspring Lane, into Aldenham Rd, left at r'bout into the Avenue, right at top into Herkomer Rd, take 4th left.
Seats: None **Cover:** Yes **Programme:** No **Nickname:** Rangers
Colours: Blue (white sleeves)/blue/white **Change colours:** All white.

CHIPPERFIELD CORINTHIANS

Secretary: Stephen J Hall, 3 Rowley Close, Oxhey, Watford, Herts WD1 4DT (0923 253803).
Ground: Queen Street, Chipperfield.
Directions: To Chipperfield via Kings Langley. Take 1st left, over crossroads, ground 400yds on right.
Seats: None **Cover:** Yes **Programme:** Yes **Nickname:** None **Founded:** 1987
Colours: Red & black stripes/red/red **Change colours:** All sky.
Previous Leagues: None **Prev. Names:** Chipperfield FC, Tudor Corinthians (merged 1987)
Hons: Herts Lg Div 1 87-88 (Aubrey Cup 92-93), Herts Interm. Cup 87-88.

COLNEY HEATH

Secretary: Martin Marlborough, 16 Meadway, Colney Heath, St Albans AL4 0PT (0727 824820).
Ground: The Pavillion Recreation Ground, High Street, Colney Heath (0727 826188).
Directions: Turn off A414 in Colney Heath village, ground behind school on left.
Seats: None **Cover:** Yes **Programme:** Yes **Nickname:** Magpies **Founded:** 1907
Colours: White & black stripes/black/black **Change colours:** Yellow (blue trim)/yellow/yellow.
Previous Leagues: Nth Mymms & District/Mid Herts.
Hons: Herts Lg 58-59 (Div 1 55-56 88-89, Div 2 53-54, Aubrey Cup 53-54 59-60), Herts I'mediate Cup 59-60).

Colney Heath F.C. 1992-93. Back Row (L/R): Steve Ringrose (Coach), Steve Stott, Mark McGinty, Nick Thompson, Tom Bond, Kenny Groom, Pat Morrissey (Player-Manager), Brian Sibley (Asst Manager). Front: Tony Trundley, Craig Penrice, Miles Milton, Paul Murphy, Steve King, Paul Dawson, Geoff Games. Photo - Richard Brock.

CROXLEY GUILD OF SPORT

Secretary: Dave Rickman, 18 Tudor Walk, Watford, Herts WD2 4PA (0923 231543).
Ground: Croxley Guild of Sport, The Green, Croxley Green (0923 770534).
Directions: M25 to Chorleywood (jct 18), left off slip road (A404) to r'bout (2 miles), 1st exit to next r'bout, follow Watford sign (A412) to next r'bout, 1st exit, ground 300 yds on right opposite Artichoke pub.
Seats: None **Cover:** No **Programme:** No **Nickname:** Dicko's **Founded:** 1920
Previous Leagues: West Herts/Middx County. **Reformed:** 1983
Cols: White & black stripes/black/black **Change colours:** All red.

Croxley Guild F.C. 1992-93. Back Row (L/R): I Phillips, I Jennings, N Burnham, S Gravestock, D Wilkinson, R Nelmes, T Hughes, D Rickman (Manager). Front: P Glide, G Scott, A Clark, L Kelly, G Wiggins, L Fitzgerald, T Collins. Photo - Martin Wray.

CUFFLEY

Secretary: David C Chapman, 51 Woodlands Rd, Hertford, Herts SG13 7JF (0992 582358).
Ground: King Georges Playing Fields, Northaw Rd East, Cuffley (0707 875395).
Directions: A121 from Potters Bar or Cheshunt, 5 miles from either Jct 25 or 26 on M25.
Seats: None **Cover:** None **Programme:** No **Nickname:** Zeplins **Founded:** 1958
Colours: Maroon/sky/maroon **Change colours:** White & blue stripes/white/blue.
Previous Leagues: Barnet/ Nth London Combination. **Hons:** Herts Lg Div 2 77-78.

Cuffley F.C. 1992-93. Back Row (L/R): Tony Chappell (Asst Manager), Graham Hicks, Martin Coomber, Bobby Purdy, Dave Willis, Danny Yates, Wes Attrell, Steve Sale (Manager). Front: Chris Carter, Kevin Gibbons, Jeff Richards, Mrs D Willis (Sponsor), Martin Neiland, Craig Hewitt, Adie Uwins.

ELLIOTT STAR

Secretary: Tracy Hudson, 2 Norton Close, Boreham Wood, Herts WD6 5DW (081 207 5912).
Ground: GEC Sports Centre, Rowley Lane, Boreham Wood (081 953 5087).
Directions: A1 to Elstree Moat House, turn left (flyover) into town and turn into Elstree Way. Ground on right behind Clarenden Garage. One mile from Elstree & Boreham Wood (BR).
Seats: None **Cover:** None **Programme:** No **Nickname:** None **Founded:** 1957
Colours: Black & red hoops/black/red **Change colours:** Sky/navy/navy.
Previous League: London Commercial **Hons:** FA Vase 2nd Rd 91-92.

KINGS LANGLEY

Secretary: Brian Aldersley, 12 Elm Grove, Watford, Herts WD2 6QE (0923 251130).
Ground: Leavesden Hospital Ground, Woodside Rd, Abbots Langley.
Directions: A405 to Garston traffic lights. From Watford turn left (from St Albans, right) into Horseshoe Lane. Woodside Rd is one mile on right, ground quarter mile on left.
Seats: Yes   **Cover:** Yes   **Programme:** No   **Nickname:** None   **Founded:** 1886
Colours: Blue/black/black   **Change colours:** Black & white stripes/black/black.
Previous League: West Herts.
Hons: Herts Lg 47-48 49-50 51-52 65-66 66-67 (Div 1 75-76, Aubrey Cup 67-68).

KNEBWORTH

Secretary: John Stevens, 12 Olden Mead, Letchworth, Herts SG6 2SP (0462 673735).
Ground: Old Knebworth Lane, Stevenage (0438 313320).
Directions: A1(M) to Stevenage South, A602 towards Hertford, 3rd exit at 2nd r'bout (B197). Follow to Roebuck Inn and turn right opposite pub into Old Knebworth Lane. Ground 200yds on left.
Seats: Yes   **Cover:** Yes   **Programme:** Yes   **Nickname:** None   **Founded:** 1901
Colours: Tangerine/black/black   **Change colours:** Sky/blue/white
Previous Leagues: Nth Herts/Sth Mids.   **Hons:** Herts Lg 73-74 (Div 1 76-77, Aubrey Cup 76-77).

Knebworth F.C. 1992-93. Back Row (L/R): K Lowe, S Armsley, F Tyler, J Colgan, M Westley, M Allinson. Back Row (L/R): R Lawson, S Cutts, P Gittas, D Tyler, A Gittens, S Stoughten. Photo - Martin Wray.

METROPOLITAN POLICE (BUSHEY)

Secretary: Brian Southern, c/o Met Police Spts Club, Aldenham Rd, Bushey, Herts WD2 3TR (0923 243947).
Ground: Aldenham Road, Bushey (0923 243947).
Directions: M1 jct 5, A41 for Harrow/South Watford, at 1st r'bout right into Hartspring Lane which runs into Aldenham (A4008). Ground quarter mile on left opposite Caledonian School.
Seats: None   **Cover:** No   **Programme:** No   **Nickname:** None
Colours: Yellow/red/red   **Change colours:** Green/black/green.
Hons: Herts County Lg Div 1 92-93.

OXHEY JETS

Secretary: John Elliott, 7 Brampton Rd, South Oxhey, Watford, Herts WD1 6PF (081 428 6382).
Ground: Chilwell Gardens, South Oxhey (081 421 4965).
Directions: Follow Bushey signs from Watford centre, at Bushey Arches turn right into Eastbury Rd, left into Brookdene Avenue, continue along Prestwick Rd past station, right into Northwick Rd and left into Chilwell Gdns.
Seats: None   **Cover:**   **Programme:** No   **Nickname:** Jets   **Founded:** 1972
Colours: All blue   **Change colours:** All yellow.
Previous Leagues: Watford & District/West Herts.

ROUSSEL SPORTS

Secretary: Stephen Sells, 1 Robin Hill, Berkhamsted, Herts HP4 2HX (0442 864649).
Ground: Kitcheners Field, Castle Hill, Berkhamsted (0442 74937).
Directions: A41 into Berkhamsted. At main lights turn into Lower Kings Rd, at railway station turn left under bridge, then 2nd right. Entrance on next corner.
Seats: None   **Cover:** None   **Programme:** No   **Nickname:** None   **Founded:** 1967
Colours: Blue/white/blue   **Change colours:** Green/white/green.
Previous Name: Wellcome (pre-1993)   **Previous League:** West Herts Sunday
Hons: Herts Lg Div 1 82-83 91-92 (Div 2 81-82).

SANDRIDGE ROVERS

Secretary: Graham C Hardwick, 21 Woodcock Hill, Sandridge, St Albans AL4 9EF (0727 855334).
Ground: Spencer Recreation Ground, Sandridge (0727 55159).
Directions: B651 from St Albans or Wheathampstead to High Street. Ground at rear of public car park.
Seats: None   **Cover:** Yes   **Programme:** Yes   **Nickname:** Rovers   **Founded:** 1896
Colours: Black & white stripes/black/red   **Change colours:** Green & white stripes/white/green.
Prev. Lge: Mid Herts   **Hons:** Herts Lg 81-82 82-83 87-88 (Div 1 68-69), Herts Intermediate Cup 81-82.

SUN SPORTS

Secretary: Dave Price, 62 The Ridgeway, Watford, Herts WD1 3TL (0923 231347).
Ground: Bellmont Wood Avenue, Watford (0703 254364).
Directions: From Kings Langley to Watford on Hempstead road, turn right at Langley lights, right at r'bout then 1st left. Entrance 50yds on right.
Seats: None   **Cover:** Yes   **Programme:** Yes   **Nickname:**   **Founded:**
Colours: Yellow/blue/white   **Change colours:** Yellow/blue/blue.
Previous Leagues: Watford & District/West Herts.
Hons: Aubrey Cup 88-89, Herts Intermediate Cup 75-76.

(G.D.S.) VALMAR

Secretary: John Walsh, 44 Western Avenue, St Albans, Herts AL3 5HP (0727 833511).
Ground: Lemsford Village Hall, Brocket Road, Lemsford (0707 335548).
Directions: Welwyn Garden City exit from A1(M), left to Stanborough 'Ball' r'bout, 2nd exit towards Wheathipstead, Lemsford three quarters of a mile on the right.
Seats: None   **Cover:** No   **Programme:** No   **Nickname:** None
Colours: Red & black hoops/black/black   **Change colours:** Sky/navy/navy
Previous League: Mid Herts   **Previous Name:** Valmar L.R. (pre-1993).
Hons: Herts County Lg Div 1 R-up 92-93.

WORMLEY ROVERS

Secretary: David M Smith, 19 Nursery Gardens, Enfield, Middx EN3 5NG (081 804 3608).
Ground: Sports Club, Church Lane, Wormley (0992 460650).
Directions: From A10 take A1170 turning for Broxbourne and Turnford. Left at New River Arms, left again into Church Lane. Ground quarter mile on right.
Seats: None   **Cover:** No   **Programme:** No   **Nickname:** Robins   **Founded:** Unknown
Colours: Red & black hoops/black/black   **Change colours:** All blue.
Previous Leagues: Ware & District/Hertford & District/Northern Suburban.
Hons: Herts Lg Div 1 86-87 (Div 3 76-77).

DIVISION ONE CLUBS 1993-94

ALLENSBURYS SPORTS

Secretary: Graham Stuart, Osprey House, Briardale, Ware, Herts SG12 0XF (0920 468120).
Ground: Harris Lane, Ware (0920 462742).
Directions: From A10, take B1001 to Ware. 3rd right into Fanshawe Crescent, over crossroads into Harris Lane, ground on right.
Seats: None   **Cover:** No   **Programme:** No   **Nickname:** None
Colours: Blue/blue/yellow   **Change colours:** Yellow/blue/blue
Previous League: Hertford & District   **Hons:** Herts Lg Div 2 90-91

CODICOTE

Secretary: Richard Hunt, 68a Vaughan Rd, Stotfold, Hitchin, Herts SG5 4EN (0462 835623).
Ground: Bury Lane, Codicote.
Directions: A1(M) jct 6, head for Welwyn and Codicote via B656, in village turn right into Bury Lane (after Bell pub), ground entrance opposite church.
Seats: None   **Cover:** No   **Programme:** Yes   **Nickname:** None   **Founded:** 1945
Cols: White & blue/white/blue & white   **Change colours:** Green & white hoops/white/green.
Previous Leagues: North Herts.

DYNAMICS

Secretary: Kevin Folds, 6 Lanthony Ct, High Street, Arlesey, Beds SG15 6TU (0462 834084).
Ground: Fairview Road, Stevenage, Herts (0438 736284).
Directions: A1(M) to Stevenage South (A602). Exit towards industrial area then turn left at next r'bout into Gunnelswood Rd. Take underpass and at following r'bout turn right into Fairlands Way. 1st left into Fairview Rd, ground 150yds on right.
Seats: None   **Cover:** Yes   **Programme:** No   **Nickname:** None   **Founded:** 1955
Colours: White/black/white   **Change colours:** Claret/sky/claret.
Previous League: North Herts

EVERGREEN

Secretary: Dennis McCrystal, 76 Woodmere Ave., Watford, Herts WD2 4LW (0923 465750).
Ground: Southway, Abbots Langley (0927 767812).
Directions: A41 or A405 to r'bout junction and head for Leavesden. Right at next r'bout towards Abbots Langley, pass Rolls Royce works, then first left into Southway. Clubhouse entrance in Essex Lane at end of Southway.
Seats: None   **Cover:** No   **Programme:** No   **Nickname:** None   **Founded:** 1957
Cols: Green & white hoops/white/red   **Change colours:** Black & blue stripes/black/black.
Previous Leagues: West Herts Youth.   **Hons:** Herts Lg 64-65 67-88 68-69 69-70 70-71 71-72 79-80 (Aubrey Cup 64-65 66-67 69-70 70-71), Herts Intermediate Cup 79-80.

HARPENDEN ROVERS

Secretary: Fred Day, 69 Tassell Hall, Redbourn, St Albans, Herts AL3 7JD (0582 792408).
Ground: Acres Corner, Harpenden Common, Cravells Rd, Harpenden.
Directions: Cravells Rd is on A1081 (formerly A6) between Harpenden and St Albans at end of golf course.
Seats: None   **Cover:** No   **Programme:** No   **Nickname:**   **Founded:** 1928
Colours: Red/white/red   **Change colours:** Blue/black/yellow.
Previous League: Mid Herts   **Hons:** Herts Lg Div 3 66-67.

HERTFORD YOUTH

Secretary: Malcolm Allington, Palmer Court, Chapmore End, Ware, Herts SG12 0PR (0920 460653).
Ground: Crouchfields, Wadesmill Rd, Chapmore End, Nr Ware.
Directions: Head for Bengeo from Hertford and take B158 through Bengeo forking right at small r'bout into Wadesmill Rd. Ground about one mile on right.
Seats: None   **Cover:** No   **Programme:** No   **Nickname:**   **Founded:** 1980
Colours: Gold & red stripes/black/yellow   **Change colours:** Blue/black/yellow.
Previous League: Hertford & District   **Hons:** Herts Lg Div 2 91-92.

I.C.L. LETCHWORTH

Secretary: Geoff Holbrook, 126 West View, Letchworth, Herts SG6 3QJ (0462 674493).
Ground: Whitehorn Lane, Letchworth (0462 673789).
Directions: A1 to Letchworth Gate, at elongated r'bout take 2nd left, then 2nd right into Whitehorn Lane. Ground 200yds on left.
Seats: None   **Cover:** No   **Programme:** No   **Nickname:** None   **Founded:** 1925
Colours: Gold/black/black   **Change colours:** Blue/black/black
Previous League: Mid Herts   **Hons:** Herts Lg Div 1 58-59 65-66 (Div 2 54-55).

KIMPTON ROVERS

Secretary: Neil Matthews, 30 Commons Lane, Kimpton, Herts SG4 8QG (0438 832625).
Ground: Recreation Ground, High Street, Kimpton.
Directions: Kimpton is between Stevenage, Luton & Welwyn on insection of B651 and B652. Ground is set back on hill off the High Street.
Seats: None   **Cover:** No   **Programme:** No   **Nickname:** Rovers   **Founded:** 1910
Colours: White/blue/white   **Change colours:** Dark yellow/blue/white.
Previous Leagues: Nth Herts/Mid Herts

KODAK HEMEL HEMPSTEAD

Secretary: Brian Pollard, The Laurels, Wood Rising Lodge, High Street Green, Hemel Hempstead HP2 7AA (0442 256720).
Ground: Kodak Sports Ground, Wood End Lane, off Maylands Avenue, Hemel Hempstead (0442 242597).
Directions: M1 jct 8, right at 2nd r'bout (A4147) to lights, then right into Wood End Lane. Ground quarter mile on right.
Seats: None   **Cover:** No   **Programme:** No   **Nickname:**   **Founded:** 1960
Colours: Green & black stripes/black/black   **Change colours:** Yellow (red pin stripes)/black/black.
Previous League: West Herts/Sth Mids   **Hons:** Herts Lg Div 2 87-88.

LITTLE GADDESDEN

Secretary: Paul Woods, 15 Little Gaddesden, Berkhamsted, Herts HP4 1PA (0442 842717).
Ground: Church Road, Little Gaddesden, Berkhamsted.
Directions: From Hemel Hempstead follow Leighton Buzzard road. Take 2nd left after Red Lion in Waterend and follow signs to Little Gaddesden. Church Rd is 2nd right in village.
Seats: None   **Cover:** None   **Programme:** No   **Nickname:** None   **Founded:** 1936
Colours: Gold/black/black   **Change colours:** Red & black stripes/black/black.
Previous Leagues: West Herts   **Hons:**

NORTH MYMMS

Secretary: Mick Fitt, 61 Holloways Lane, North Mymms, Hatfield, Herts AL9 7NU (0707 269790).
Ground: Recreation Ground, Dellsome Lane, Welham Green (07072 66972/60338).
Directions: Welham Green is 2 miles south of Hatfield. At village crossroads turn north into Dellsome Lane. Ground on left.
Seats: None   **Cover:** None   **Programme:** No   **Nickname:** None   **Founded:** 1968
Colours: Sky/navy/sky   **Change colours:** Red/red/red.

ST IPPOLYTS

Secretary: Elizabeth Maxwell, 12 Orchard Close, St Ippolyts, Herts SG4 7RH (0462 453482).
Ground: Recreation Ground, Orchard Close, off Mill Road, St Ippolyts (0462 456748).
Directions: B656 from Welwyn. Left at St Ippolyts crossroads, right into The Crescent, left into Mill Rd. Orchard Close is a turning off this road.
Seats: None   **Cover:** No   **Programme:** No   **Nickname:** Saints   **Founded:** 1908
Colours: Black & red stripes/black/black   **Change colours:** Blue/black/blue.
Previous League: North Herts.

ST PETERS (ST ALBANS)

Secretary: Peter Garden, 63 Ladies Grove, St Albans, Herts AL3 5TZ (0727 855286).
Ground: Toulmin Drive, St Albans, Herts.
Directions: St Albans ring-road towards Betchwood Golf Club. 20 yds from north entrance turn into Green Lane. At top of hill turn left into Toulmin Drive.
Seats: Yes   **Cover:** Yes   **Programme:** No   **Nickname:** Saints   **Founded:** pre-1904
Colours: Maroon & blue/white/maroon   **Change colours:** Red/black/red.
Previous League: Mid Herts

SARRATT

Secretary: Mick Warner, 'Colinwood', 45 Church Lane, Sarratt, Herts WD3 6HN (0923 264618).
Ground: King George V Playing Fields, King George Avenue, Sarratt.
Directions: To Kings Langley, and then via Chipperfield.
Seats: None   **Cover:** Yes   **Programme:** No   **Nickname:**   **Founded:** Unknown
Colours: Black & amber/black/black   **Change colours:** Red & black stripes/black/red.
Previous League: West Herts   **Hons:** Herts Lg Div 2 79-80.

SOMERSETT AMBURY V & E

Secretary: Ian Whittle, 21 Kilwardby Street, Ashby-de-la-Zouch, Leics LE65 2FR (0530 413471).
Ground: V & E Youth Club, Goffs Lane, Cheshunt (0992 24281).
Directions: M25 jct 25, A10 north, left at 1st r'bout onto Flamstead End relief road to r'bout with Goffs Lane. Right into Goffs Lane, clubhouse immediately on right.

Seats: None	**Cover:** No	**Programme:** No	**Nickname:**	**Founded:** 1960
Colours: White/blue/blue		**Change colours:** Red/black/black.		

Previous Leagues: Enfield Alliance, Hertford & District.

STANDON & PUCKERIDGE

Secretary: David North, 66 Batchelors, Puckeridge, Nr Ware, Herts SG11 1TJ (0920 821838).
Ground: Recreation Ground, Station Rd, Standon, Nr Ware (0920 822489.
Directions: A10 6 miles north of Ware or 4 miles south from Buntingford. Take A120 from A10 Bishop's Stortford r'bout. Over Standon Hill and into Station Rd (3rd left after r'bout), ground quarter mile on left.

Seats: None	**Cover:** No	**Programme:** No	**Nickname:** None	**Founded:** 1931
Colours: Blue & white/white/blue		**Change colours:** White/green/green.		

Previous League: Hertford & District/Norhern Suburban Intermediate.

WALKERN

Secretary: Brian Murphy, Tangle Reah, 25 Church Path, Little Wymondley, Herts SG4 7JE (0438 355426).
Ground: High Street, Walkern (0432 861615).
Directions: Leave A1(M) for Stevenage South, over 1st r'bout (A602), left at 2nd r'bout (Burger King), over next and right at swimming pool. Follow signs to Walkern (B1037) and in village turn right at junction. Ground 200yds on left.

Seats: None	**Cover:** No	**Programme:** No	**Nickname:** None	**Founded:** 1899
Colours: Yellow/sky/white		**Change colours:** Sky/navy/navy.		

Previous League: North Herts.

WELWYN

Secretary: Michael Pestle, 4 Marsden Close, Welwyn Garden City, Herts AL8 6YE (0707 335503).
Ground: Welwyn Playing Field, Ottway Walk, London Rd, Welwyn (0438 714183).
Directions: From A1(M) take A1000 turning 1st left off r'bout, then 1st right at Nodeway filling station into London Rd. Ground quarter mile on left opposite Steamer pub.

Seats: None	**Cover:** No	**Programme:** Yes	**Nickname:** None	**Founded:** 1893
Colours: All blue		**Change colours:** All red.		

Previous Leagues: North Herts/Mid Herts **Hons:** Herts Lg Div 1 79-80.

WHITWELL ATHLETIC

Secretary: Michael Atkinson, 17 Dalton Way, Whitwell, Nr Hitchin, Herts SG4 8BG (0438 871250).
Ground: King Georges Recreation Ground, Bradway, off Horn Hill, Whitwell.
Directions: B651 from St Albans. From A1 via Welwyn and Codicote.

Seats: None	**Cover:** Yes	**Programme:** No	**Nickname:** None	**Reformed:** 1991
Colours: White/white/blue		**Change colours:** Red & white/white/red.		

RESERVE SECTION CONSTITUTIONS 1993-94

Division One
1. BAC Stevenage Reserves
2. Bedmond Sports & Social Reserves
3. Bovingdon Reserves
4. Chipperfield Corinthians Res.
5. Colney Heath Reserves
6. Dynamics Reserves
7. Elliott Star Reserves
8. Kings Langley Reserves
9. Knebworth Reserves
10. Kodak Reserves
11. Met Police Bushey Reserves
12. Oxhey Jets Reserves
13. Roussel Sports Reserves
14. Sandridge Rvrs Reserves
15. Sun Sports Reserves
16. Walkern Reserves
17. Welwyn Reserves
18. Wormley Rovers Reserves

Division Two
1. Allensbury Sports Reserves *
2. Bushey Rangers Reserves
3. Croxley Guild Reserves
4. Cuffley Rangers
5. Evergreen Reserves
6. Harpenden Rovers Reserves
7. Hertford Youth Reserves
8. I.C.L. Letchworth Reserves
9. Kimpton Rovers Reserves
10. North Mymms Reserves
11. St Ippolyts Reserves
12. St Peters Reserves
13. Sarratt Reserves
14. Somersett Ambury Reserves
15. Standon & Puckeridge Reserves
16. (G.D.S.) Valmar Reserves
17. Whitwell Athletic Reserves

* - Subject to availability of ground.

MIDDLESEX COUNTY LEAGUE

Patron: Russell Grant,
President: Peter Rogers,
Chairman: Fred Griggs,
Hon. Secretary: Keith Chamberlin,
4 Shelley Ave., Greenford, Middx UB6 8RU.

CHAMPIONSHIP RACE GOES TO THE WIRE

There was a breathtaking finale to the season, as for the first time in the history of the County League, the champions of all three divisions had to wait until their final match to claim their respective crown.

There was also further glory afield for the Middlesex County League, as its senior representative side finished an undefeated fourth in the South Eastern Intermediate Inter-League Competition, while the junior representative side were narrowly defeated in the final of the Middlesex County F.A. Junior Inter-League Cup. At club level, Brimsdown Rovers 'A' claimed the Middlesex Intermediate Cup in a nail-biting penalty shoot-out.

Of the three divisional champions, Shamrock were set the hardest task, when Broadwater United finished their league programme in mid-April, nine points ahead of the chasing rivals, who had to win all of their remaining fixtures to claim the title. This Shamrock did, to shade their second championship in five years, on the narrowest of goal differences.

Division One champions Northolt Saints had a May Bank holiday to remember - on the Saturday they defeated Premier Division opponents Neasden on penalties, to win the Alec Smith Cup - the League's senior Knockout Cup - and just two days later they clinched a tremendous league and cup double with victory in their final match of the season, away to Cockfosters Reserves.

From quite early on, the Division Two championship became a two-horse race, as Scolar and Brimsdown Rovers 'A' sped away from the chasing pack, and the season ended fittingly with honours for both clubs. A draw for Scolar in their final fixture, against Brimsdown, secured the league title, while Brimsdown enjoyed a 'cup double' by defeating Scolar in the Division Two Cup final, so adding to their Middlesex Intermediate Cup success.

The powerful line-up of clubs in each division for 1993-94 reflects the depth of quality so evident throughout the League last season, and the requirement for Premier Division clubs to acquire Middlesex County F.A.-accredited Intermediate status by May 1994 leaves the league strongly placed to pursue a more elevated position within the Pyramid in the near future.

Nigel Hickes, League Registrar.

Premier Division	P	W	D	L	F	A	PTS
Shamrock	26	18	4	4	70	45	58
Broadwater United	26	18	4	4	77	44	58
Simba All Stars	26	17	5	4	59	44	*55
Osterley	26	15	2	9	56	32	47
Technicolor Spts	26	13	6	7	56	48	45
CAV Northolt	26	9	8	9	47	45	35
Spelthorne Spts	26	10	5	11	42	48	35
Northfield Rgrs	26	10	3	13	51	51	33
Neasden	26	9	5	12	57	52	32
Hanworth Villa	26	9	3	14	38	61	30
New Hanford	26	7	6	13	45	58	*26
Pitshanger	26	5	10	11	38	51	25
Maple Cross	26	5	3	18	33	78	18
Willesden Const.	26	3	4	19	35	68	13

* - Denotes one point deducted

Division One	P	W	D	L	F	A	PTS
Northolt Saints	24	19	3	2	97	28	60
St Clarets (Hayes)	24	18	3	3	73	23	*56
Flackwell Hth Res.	24	12	7	5	51	38	*42
Bridge Park	24	12	2	10	54	45	38
Southgate Ath. Res.	24	11	5	8	57	56	38
Hounslow T. '91	24	10	6	8	64	59	36
Brimsdown R. Res.	24	11	2	11	55	38	35
Cockfosters Res.	24	9	7	8	67	47	34
Rayners Lane Res.	24	9	6	9	56	53	33
Brook House Res.	24	7	3	14	37	51	*23
Harrow St Marys	24	6	3	15	30	87	21
Southall Res.	24	4	3	17	34	83	15
Beaconsfield U. Res.	24	2	2	20	23	90	6

* - denotes 1 point deducted

Division Two	P	W	D	L	F	A	PTS
Scolar	28	25	3	0	119	27	78
Brimsdown Rvrs 'A'	28	24	3	1	106	25	75
Osterley Res.	28	18	4	6	88	41	58
N Greenford U. Res.	28	14	4	10	58	51	46
Amersham T. Res.	28	14	2	12	64	70	44
Northfield Rgrs Res.	28	13	1	14	53	55	40
New Hanford Res.	28	12	4	12	58	64	39
Northolt Dynamo	28	11	6	11	65	72	39
Pitshanger Res.	28	11	4	13	50	68	37
Neasden Res.	28	9	6	13	57	74	32
St Clarets Res.	28	7	6	15	59	74	27
CAV Northolt Res.	28	7	4	17	45	70	25
Technicolor S. Res.	28	6	4	18	46	91	22
Spelthorne S. Res.	28	5	6	17	44	79	21
Hanwell Town 'A'	28	2	7	19	32	84	13

PREMIER DIVISION RESULTS 1992/93

HOME TEAM	1	2	3	4	5	6	7	8	9	10	11	12	13	14
1. Broadwater United	*	3-2	3-0	6-0	3-1	3-4	7-3	1-0	3-1	0-3	1-3	6-1	3-3	1-0
2. CAV Northolt	1-2	*	2-3	5-3	1-1	1-1	1-0	1-4	0-0	3-3	1-3	0-1	4-2	1-0
3. Hanworth Villa	0-2	3-3	*	1-3	1-4	1-3	1-4	3-1	0-2	3-0	1-3	2-1	2-1	2-1
4. Maple Cross	0-5	1-2	1-3	*	4-4	3-0	0-2	0-1	0-2	2-3	2-3	2-0	1-5	1-1
5. Neasden	2-4	2-1	2-3	5-0	*	W-L	5-1	1-2	3-1	1-2	4-3	2-3	2-3	3-3
6. New Hanford	3-5	1-3	3-1	7-1	3-3	*	1-1	0-5	2-1	1-2	0-2	4-2	1-3	1-1
7. Northfield Rangers	2-2	0-3	1-2	5-0	1-2	1-0	*	1-3	4-1	1-2	3-2	6-3	1-1	4-0
8. Osterley	1-2	1-3	5-1	3-2	2-1	1-1	4-2	*	4-0	0-2	1-3	3-0	3-0	3-1
9. Pitshanger	2-2	1-1	1-1	1-1	2-2	4-0	2-1	0-0	*	1-4	0-2	1-2	2-2	3-4
10. Shamrock	3-4	2-0	2-1	9-0	3-2	3-2	4-1	0-2	5-3	*	1-1	1-1	6-1	5-1
11. Simba All Stars	3-0	3-1	0-0	2-1	2-1	2-0	1-0	3-1	3-3	1-1	*	1-0	2-3	3-1
12. Spelthorne Sports	1-2	2-2	6-1	0-1	0-3	2-2	3-2	2-1	3-0	0-2	1-1	*	1-1	3-1
13. Technicolor Sports	3-3	1-1	2-1	0-4	1-0	5-3	0-2	2-0	3-2	2-0	2-1	1-3	*	7-0
14. Willesden (Constantine)	2-4	5-1	3-1	1-2	1-2	0-4	2-2	1-2	5-6	0-1	0-2			*

DIVISION ONE RESULTS 1992/93

HOME TEAM	1	2	3	4	5	6	7	8	9	10	11	12	13
1. Beaconsfield Utd Res.	*	0-1	0-1	2-0	0-2	3-3	1-2	2-5	3-4	1-5	2-2	2-3	0-7
2. Bridge Park	1-2	*	1-2	2-0	2-0	4-0	5-1	4-2	1-4	3-1	5-1	1-2	0-2
3. Brimsdown Rovers Res.	5-0	0-0	*	0-1	3-2	0-1	6-1	3-3	1-4	3-1	2-0	0-1	0-1
4. Brook House Res.	2-0	5-4	1-2	*	1-1	2-3	0-2	0-4	0-2	2-1	6-0	0-2	0-3
5. Cockfosters Res.	7-0	6-0	3-2	1-1	*	2-0	16-0	2-2	0-2	5-0	5-2	0-0	1-1
6. Flackwell Hth Res.	3-2	1-0	1-0	3-1	4-3	*	3-1	0-1	2-2	1-1	6-1	3-3	1-1
7. Harrow St Mary's	3-1	3-5	3-2	1-5	1-3	0-3	*	2-2	1-3	3-4	1-1	5-0	1-5
8. Hounslow Town '91	5-0	1-1	1-2	4-4	5-3	2-2	3-1	*	0-8	1-4	4-1	7-1	6-4
9. Northolt Saints	7-1	2-3	4-1	4-0	7-0	2-0	6-1	6-1	*	3-1	10-3	5-0	0-4
10. Rayners Lane Res.	6-0	1-7	3-1	5-1	0-0	2-2	2-1	3-5	2-2	*	5-1	2-3	0-2
11. Southall Res.	2-1	0-3	2-5	2-0	5-1	1-4	2-2	1-0	2-3	1-2	*	2-4	0-4
12. Southgate Ath. Res.	12-0	2-1	2-4	0-3	4-4	4-2	1-4	2-0	3-3	3-3	4-0	*	0-1
13. St Clarets (Hayes)	2-0	7-0	2-0	3-2	5-0	0-3	8-0	0-3	2-2	4-2	4-1	*	

DIVISION TWO RESULTS 1992/93

HOME TEAM	1	2	3	4	5	6	7	8	9	10	11	12	13	14	15
1. Amersham Town Res.	*	0-3	3-0	4-3	5-2	1-1	3-2	2-1	2-3	0-4	1-2	5-2	0-3	2-1	4-1
2. Brimsdown Rovers 'A'	6-1	*	2-1	6-0	5-1	W-L	6-0	7-2	7-2	6-2	2-0	1-1	2-2	5-2	5-0
3. CAV Northolt Res.	5-1	1-3	*	0-1	1-2	1-4	0-1	0-2	5-1	1-2	4-0	2-5	1-6	1-1	3-2
4. Hanwell Town 'A'	1-2	1-2	1-1	*	0-1	3-5	1-2	1-2	2-5	1-2	2-2	1-1	0-9	0-0	2-3
5. Neasden Res.	3-1	1-3	3-4	1-0	*	2-5	2-1	4-1	4-3	2-4	1-1	2-3	2-3	5-5	3-0
6. New Hanford Res.	1-2	0-8	0-3	2-0	1-1	*	1-2	1-2	3-4	1-2	3-1	4-2	4-10	1-0	0-3
7. North Greenford Res.	1-2	4-1	4-4	2-2	5-0	1-1	*	0-2	4-0	0-2	6-2	2-1	0-2	2-1	6-1
8. Northfield Rgrs Res.	1-4	0-4	1-0	4-2	1-1	0-1	5-0	*	1-3	2-5	6-0	1-3	0-2	4-0	3-4
9. Northolt Dynamo	3-2	0-4	1-3	2-2	5-2	2-3	4-1	0-3	*	2-2	2-3	3-3	0-2	2-2	3-3
10. Osterley Res.	5-1	2-3	5-1	11-0	4-1	2-0	1-3	4-0	0-0	*	1-3	1-0	6-6	6-0	5-0
11. Pitshanger Res.	3-6	0-2	3-0	3-2	4-2	2-1	2-2	1-1	2-3	2-1	*	3-2	1-5	2-3	2-1
12. St Clarets Res.	2-2	1-5	4-0	2-2	2-2	4-5	2-3	1-3	3-4	1-4	2-0	*	2-4	3-2	6-2
13. Scolar	6-2	0-0	6-0	8-0	3-0	3-1	2-0	2-1	3-2	1-0	2-1	6-0	*	6-0	3-2
14. Spelthorne Spts Res.	3-1	0-5	1-1	1-0	2-6	1-2	1-4	0-2	1-3	2-2	3-4	3-0	0-7	*	8-0
15. Technicolor Spts Res.	2-5	1-3	5-2	1-2	2-2	2-4	0-2	3-1	0-3	2-3	1-1	2-1	0-7	3-1	*

ALEC SMITH LEAGUE CUP 1992-93

First Round

Hounslow Town '91 v Maple Cross	3-3,3-2
Neasden v Technicolor Sports	3-2
St Clarets (Hayes) v Osterley	0-3
Southgate Athletic Reserves v Spelthorne Spts	3-2
Flackwell Hth Reserves v Northfield Rgrs	2-2,3-0
Southall Reserves v Simba All Stars	0-4
Willesden (Constantine) v Bridge Park	5-3
Pitshanger v New Hanford	1-2
Northolt Saints v Harrow St Mary's	6-0
Rayners Lane Res. v Beaconsfield Utd Reserves	5-2
Brimsdown Rovers Reserves v Broadwater United	1-3

Second Round

Hounslow Town '91 v Willesden (Constantine)	4-0
C.A.V. Northolt v Brook House Reserves	1-0
Northolt Saints v Southgate Ath. Reserves	3-1
Shamrock v Broadwater United	1-0
Neasden v New Hanford	6-2
Osterley v Cockfosters Reserves	4-1
Rayners Lane Reserves v Flackwell Hth Reserves	0-2
Hanworth Villa v Simba All Stars	1-2

Quarter-Finals

Northolt Saints v Flackwell Hth Reserves	3-2
C.A.V. Northolt v Osterley	1-2
Shamrock v Simba All Stars	3-0
Hounslow Town '91 v Neasden	1-2

Semi-Finals

Neasden v Osterley	1-0
Northolt Saints v Shamrock	2-0

Final *(at Staines Town FC, Sat 1st May)*: Northolt Saints 1, Neasden 1 *after extra-time, Northolt Saints won 4-2 on penalties.*

DIVISION TWO CUP

First Round

Hanwell Town 'A' v Osterley Reserves	1-2
Northolt Dynamo v Brimsdown Rovers 'A'	2-4
Scolar v United Biscuits (Harlesden)	3-1
Spelthorne Spts Res. v St Clarets Reserves	0-4
Technicolor Spts Reserves v New Hanford Res.	0-1
Nth Greenford Utd Res. v Northfield Rgrs Res.	3-2
Pitshanger Reserves v Amersham Town Reserves	1-0
Neasden Reserves v Northolt Saints Reserves	3-1

Quarter-Finals

Osterley Reserves v New Hanford Reserves	3-1
Scolar v Pitshanger Reserves	4-1
Brimsdown Rovers 'A' v Nth Greenford Utd Res.	4-0
St Clarets (Hayes) Reserves v Neasden Reserves	1-2

Semi-Finals

Osterley Reserves v Brimsdown Rovers 'A'	1-3
Scolar v Neasden Reserves	3-2

Final: Brimsdown Rovers 'A' 2, Scolar 0

PREMIER DIVISION CLUBS 1993-94

BROADWATER UNITED
Secretary: Godfrey Lowe, 53 Rochford Griffin Road, Tottenham N17 6HX (081 801 7616).
Ground: Lordship Lane Recreation Ground, Lordship Lane, Tottenham, London N17 (081 880 3944).
Colours: All blue　　　　　　　**Change colours:** Red/white/red.
Hons: Middx Lg R-up 92-93 (Div 1 91-92).

HANWORTH VILLA
Secretary: David Brown, 93 Tudor Drive, Kingston KT2 5NP (081 546 5979).
Ground: Twickenham Park Golf Club, Staines Road, Twickenham TW2 5JD (081 783 1748).
Colours: White (sky sleeves)/sky/sky　　　　　　**Change colours:** Red/sky/sky.

NEASDEN
Secretary: Everton King, 109 Village Way, Neasden NW10 0LN (081 450 9747).
Ground: Chalkhill Youth Community Centre, Poplar Grove, Wembley, Middx (081 904 1974).
Colours: Blue & red hoops/black/red　　　　　**Change colours:** Yellow/black/red.
Hons: Alec Smith Cup R-up 92-93.

NEW HANFORD
Secretary: Jerry Scanlon, 70 Bridge Avenue, Hanwell W7 3DJ (081 575 0113).
Ground: Drayton Manor Playing Fields, Greenford Ave., Hanwell, London W7 (081 578 5831).
Colours: Sky/navy/navy　　　　　**Change Colours:** Red & black/black/black.
Ground: Birkbeck College PF, Birkbeck Ave., Greenford (pre-1993).

NORTHFIELD C.A.V.
Secretary: Pauline Jones, 6 Siverst Close, Northolt, Middx UB5 4NJ (081 422 8012).
Ground: Yeading F.C. (see page 309).
Colours: Yellow/black/yellow　　　　　**Change Colours:** Blue/navy/navy.
Previous Names: C.A.V. Northolt/ Northfield Rangers (clubs merged in 1993).
Previous Ground: (C.A.V. Northolt): Armenian Community Centre, West End Rd, Northolt (pre-1993).
Hons: Middx Lg 91-92 (as Northfield Rgrs).

NORTHOLT SAINTS
Secretary: Robert Bevis, c/o Northolt Saints F.C. (address as below) (081 841 6558).
Ground: Lord Halsbury Playing Fields, Eastcote Lane, Northolt, Middx (081 841 1249).
Colours: Yellow/blue/yellow　　　　　**Change colours:** Blue/blue/yellow.
Hons: Middx Lg Div 1 92-93 (Alec Smith Cup 92-93).

OSTERLEY
Secretary: David Bull, 508 Great West Rd, Hounslow, Middx TW5 0TE (081 569 6889).
Ground: The White Lodge Club, Syon Lane, Osterley, Middx (081 758 1191).
Colours: Blue & white stripes/white/blue　　**Change Colours:** Red & white stripes/white/white.

PITSHANGER
Secretary: Chris Green, 14 Silver Birch Close, Ickenham, Middx UB10 8AP (0895 231796).
Ground: Pitshanger Park, Scotch Common, Ealing, London W13 (081 991 9826).
Colours: Tangerine/black/black　　　　　**Club Colours:** White/white/orange.
Hons: Middx Lg Div 1 R-up 91-92 (Alec Smith Cup 91-92).

ST CLARETS (HAYES)
Secretary: Paul Treanor, 310 Balmoral Drive, Hayes, Middx UB4 8DH (081 848 3500).
Ground: As Pitshanger F.C. (above)
Colours: Yellow/green/yellow　　　　　**Change colours:** Sky/navy/sky.
Previous Ground: Cranford Comm. Sch., High Str., Cranford, Hounslow (pre-1993).
Hons: Middx County Lg Div 1 R-up 92-93.

SHAMROCK
Secretary: Richard Gallagher, 32 Beamont Avenue, Wembley HA0 3BZ (081 902 3591).
Ground: Shamrock Club House, Horn Lane, Acton, London W3 (081 993 1270).
Colours: Green & white green/green.　　**Change colours:** White/green/green.
Hons: Middx County Lg 92-93 (R-up 91-92).

SIMBA ALL STARS
Secretary: Lewis John, 64b Southerton Road, Hammersmith, London W6 (081 748 0389).
Ground: West London Stadium, Artillery Lane, Du Cane Road, London W12 (081 749 5505).
Colours: All sky　　　　　**Change colours:** All white.

SPELTHORNE SPORTS
Secretary: Ron Ford, 35 Walton Gardens, Feltham, Middx TW13 4QY (081 890 8346).
Ground: Spelthorne Spts Ground, 296 Staines Rd West, Ashford Common, Middx (0932 783625).
Colours: Sky/navy/navy　　　　　**Club Colours:** Yellow/nany/navy.

STONEBRIDGE SCOLAR
Secretary: Brian Wilson, 19 Severn Way, Neasden NW10 2UU (081 459 4545).
Ground: C.R.S. Cardinals Club, 565 Great West Rd, Hounslow, Middx (081 572 8236). *Reserves: Bridge Park, Brentfield, Harrow Road, London NW10 0RG (081 961 5353).*
Colours: Red & grey/black/black　　　　**Change colours:** Sky & white/sky/sky
Previous Names: Bridge Park/ Scolar (clubs merged in 1993).
Hons: Middx County Lg Div 2 91-92(Bridge Pk) 92-93(Scolar).

TECHNICOLOR SPORTS
Secretary: Roy Shields, 26 Shorediche Road, Ickenham, Uxbridge UB10 8EB (0895 679031).
Ground: Technicolor Sports Ground, Springfield Road, Hayes, Middx (081 573 1203).
Cols: Claret & blue/white/claret & blue　　**Change Cols:** Black & white stripes/black/black.

DIVISION ONE CLUBS 1993-94

AMERSHAM TOWN RESERVES *(See page 366 for full details)*

BRIMSDOWN ROVERS RESERVES *(See page 367 for full details)*

BROOK HOUSE RESERVES *(see page 367 for full details)*

COCKFOSTERS RESERVES *(see page 368 for full details)*

FLACKWELL HEATH RESERVES *(see page 356 for full details)*

HARROW ST MARY'S
Secretary: David Campbell, 11 Walford Road, Uxbridge UB8 2NF (0895 272473).
Ground: Harrow Recreation Ground, Roxborough Road, Harrow (081 427 0661).
Colours: White/black/red **Change colours:** Yellow/black/green.

HOUNSLOW TOWN '91
Secretary: Irene Ambrose, 171 Heath Rd, Hounslow, Middx TW3 2NR (081 568 9635).
Ground: Ingwood Park, Ingwood Road, Hounslow, Middx.
Colours: White/orange/orange & black **Change colours:** Red & black/red/red.

NORTH GREENFORD UNITED RESERVES *(See page 370 for full details)*

NORTHFIELD C.A.V. *(See page 389 for full details)*

OSTERLEY RESERVES *(See page 389 for full details)*

RAYNERS LANE RESERVES *(See Hellenic League section for full details)*

SOUTHGATE ATHLETIC RESERVES *(see page 371 for full details)*

WILLESDEN (CONSTANTINE)
Secretary: Dwight John, 29 Tangmere Gardens, Northolt UB5 6LS (081 845 9887).
Ground: Alperton Spts Ground, Alperton Lane, Alperton, Middx.
Directions: A4005 Hanger Lane turn off Hanger Lane Gyratory System, left by petrol station on left into Alperton Lane (B456), ground entrance 350m on right. Tube to Alperton (Piccadilly Line) or Hanger Lane (Central Line).
Colours: All blue **Club Colours:** Red & white stripes/white/red.
Previous Ground: Roe Green Park, Bacon Lane, Kingsbury (pre-1993).

DIVISION TWO CLUBS 1993-94

BEACONSFIELD UNITED RESERVES *(see page 367)*

BRIMSDOWN ROVERS 'A' *(see page 367)*

BROADWATER UNITED RESERVES *(see page 389)*

CIRCLE
Secretary: Dorothy Davies, 109 Kenmore Rd, Harrow HA3 9EY (081 204 0462).
Ground: Whitchurch Playing Fields, Wemborough Rd, Stanmore, Middx.
Colours: Tangerine/black/black **Change Colours:** Blue & white stripes/black/black.

HANWELL TOWN 'A' *(See page 369)*

HOUNSLOW '91 RESERVES *(see page 389)*

NEW HANFORD RESERVES *(See page 389)*

NORTHOLT DYNAMO
Secretary: Martin Copeland, 19 Ribblesdale Avenue, Northolt, Middx UB5 4NF (081 423 1019).
Ground: As Osterley FC (page 389).
Colours: Red/white/red **Change colours:** Yellow/white/red.

NORTHOLT SAINTS RESERVES *(see page 389)*

PITSHANGER RESERVES *(see page 389)*

SOUTHALL RESERVES
Ground: Western Rd, Southall, Middx (081 574 1084) *(other details as page 362).*

SPELTHORNE SPORTS RESERVES *(see page 389)*

STONEBRIDGE SCOLAR RESERVES *(see page 389)*

TECHNICOLOR SPORTS RESERVES *(see page 389)*

PARASOL COMBINED COUNTIES LEAGUE

Hon. Secretary: J J Whitefoot,
8 Compton Rd, Church Crookham,
Fleet, Hants GU13 0JF (0252 617851)

PEPPARD TAKE LEAGUE BY STORM

As expected, Peppard took the Parasol League by storm and won the title by a clear eight points in their first season since promotion from the Charrington Chiltonian League. However, there was an unhappy ending for the Berkshire club. Despite negociating the use of the impressive Palmer Park stadium in Reading, their application for Diadora League status was rejected.

Chipstead made up for the disappointment of being pushed into second place by winning the Parasol Challenge Cup beating Ashford Town in the final at Woking. In the Challenge Vase final, also at Kingfield, Bedfont claimed their first senior honour in the league by beating Sandhurst Town, a club who had a much improved season in 1992-93.

The Parasol League welcomes three new clubs for 1993-94. The progressive Eton Wick join after two highly successful seasons in the Charrington Chiltonian League and will be looking to emulate Peppard's achievements. The other new entrants are both former members of the league; Farnham Town resume playing after a season of inactivity, whilst Virginia Water rejoin after a number of seasons in the Surrey County Premier League. Leaving the league are Steyning Town who rejoin the geographically more suitable Unijet Sussex County League, and Malden Town whose difficulties forced them to resign in mid-season.

Peppard F.C. - Parasol Combined Counties League champions 1992-93. Photo - Eric Marsh.

LEAGUE TABLES 1992-93

Premier Division	P	W	D	L	F	A	PTS
Peppard	36	27	3	6	111	39	85
Chipstead	36	19	10	7	78	47	67
Ashford T. (Middx)	36	18	13	5	67	36	67
Merstham	36	16	11	9	67	66	59
Viking Sports	36	15	10	11	67	56	55
Ash United	36	15	10	11	49	48	55
Sandhurst Town	36	14	11	11	48	52	53
Hartley Wintney	36	14	10	12	60	47	52
Godalming & G.	36	14	8	14	51	61	49
Cranleigh	36	12	11	13	66	59	47
Steyning Town	36	12	8	16	55	69	44
Bedfont	36	10	13	13	51	46	43
DCA Basingstoke	36	11	8	17	50	67	42
Horley Town	36	10	12	14	60	73	41
Frimley Green	36	11	7	18	43	55	40
Farleigh Rovers	36	11	5	20	46	65	38
Cobham	36	9	10	17	54	78	37
Ditton	36	9	9	18	48	71	36
Westfield	36	6	9	21	32	68	27

Reserve Section	P	W	D	L	F	A	PTS
Peppard Res	34	24	6	4	74	33	78
Ashford (Mx) Res	34	19	9	6	73	44	66
Hartley Win. Res	34	19	1	14	67	68	58
Cobham Res	34	16	9	9	56	37	57
Chipstead Res	34	15	9	10	63	40	54
Viking Sports Res	34	16	4	14	64	56	52
Bedfont Res	34	15	7	12	50	43	52
Ditton Res	34	14	8	12	76	75	50
Westfield Res	34	13	10	11	54	40	49
Farleigh R. Res	34	14	6	14	77	58	48
Godalming Res	34	13	8	13	58	48	47
Merstham Res	34	10	11	13	57	65	41
Horley Town Res	34	11	7	16	57	75	40
Sandhurst T. Res	34	10	8	16	50	88	38
Ash United Res	34	10	7	17	62	73	37
Grimley Green Res	34	8	9	17	56	80	33
Cranleigh Res	34	5	11	18	50	78	26
DCA Res	34	6	6	22	29	72	24

PREMIER DIVISION RESULT CHART 1992-93

HOME TEAM	1	2	3	4	5	6	7	8	9	10	11	12	13	14	15	16	17	18	19
1. Ash United	*	0-1	3-2	1-1	1-3	0-3	3-0	0-0	3-2	1-1	1-0	2-0	1-0	3-0	2-2	0-3	1-1	2-2	1-0
2. Ashford (Mx)	1-0	*	2-2	1-1	7-2	2-0	2-0	2-1	1-1	1-1	1-1	2-0	1-2	1-1	2-1	3-1	4-3	3-1	2-0
3. Bedfont	0-0	1-1	*	0-1	2-0	0-1	2-1	3-0	1-2	1-0	0-1	3-1	1-1	1-1	0-1	2-2	2-3	2-2	2-2
4. Chipstead	2-2	1-0	0-0	*	2-2	1-1	6-1	2-0	2-1	2-0	5-1	4-1	2-2	0-1	2-4	3-0	1-3	1-0	6-2
5. Cobham	0-2	0-5	0-4	2-0	*	1-1	1-2	1-4	4-2	0-1	1-1	1-1	1-2	1-4	1-7	4-1	4-0	1-1	1-1
6. Cranleigh	4-1	0-2	2-0	3-5	3-3	*	2-2	2-1	0-2	1-1	0-1	2-1	2-3	6-0	1-6	3-1	1-1	1-4	3-0
7. DCA	2-2	0-3	0-2	1-1	3-1	1-1	*	2-1	1-1	1-2	3-0	4-6	3-3	0-0	0-3	1-1	1-0	1-2	3-0
8. Ditton	2-0	0-0	3-2	0-2	4-1	2-0	2-0	*	0-2	1-4	1-2	1-7	1-1	1-3	0-2	0-2	1-2	1-5	3-2
9. Farleigh R.	0-3	1-2	1-0	1-3	4-2	1-2	0-1	0-2	*	2-1	1-5	0-3	4-1	0-2	2-4	5-1	0-1	0-0	2-0
10. Frimley G.	0-1	3-2	0-2	2-0	2-2	1-1	0-3	3-0	*	0-2	2-3	0-1	2-1	0-5	1-2	2-0	0-1	4-1	
11. Godalming	1-4	2-1	3-2	2-2	0-1	1-5	1-3	4-2	1-0	0-3	*	2-0	4-3	6-1	1-1	0-0	0-1	3-1	0-3
12. Hartley W.	0-0	1-1	1-1	0-2	0-1	3-1	4-0	1-1	3-1	1-0	3-0	*	2-1	0-0	0-0	0-3	0-1	1-1	2-2
13. Horley T.	1-3	2-2	1-1	2-4	1-4	0-0	2-0	3-0	4-1	0-0	0-3	3-2	*	2-6	0-1	1-2	2-6	2-1	2-2
14. Merstham	3-0	1-1	1-1	3-3	1-0	4-3	2-1	2-2	1-2	3-1	3-0	1-2	3-3	*	2-1	2-1	2-2	0-4	2-0
15. Peppard	5-0	2-3	6-2	4-2	0-0	3-2	4-1	4-3	1-2	2-0	3-0	1-3	4-2	7-1	*	2-0	2-0	4-0	4-1
16. Sandhurst	1-3	0-0	1-0	0-2	2-2	1-1	2-1	1-1	3-1	1-1	1-1	2-2	2-1	4-2	2-1	*	1-0	1-2	1-0
17. Steyning T.	3-1	1-3	0-4	0-3	5-2	0-0	2-4	2-2	2-2	3-2	1-1	2-1	1-3	2-4	1-3	3-0	*	2-2	1-0
18. Viking Spts	0-1	0-2	1-1	3-1	1-4	3-2	2-4	4-0	2-0	5-0	3-0	1-0	2-2	3-3	1-5	1-3	3-1	*	1-1
19. Westfield	2-1	2-0	1-2	1-3	1-0	0-5	0-2	1-1	0-0	2-1	1-1	0-2	1-1	0-1	0-4	0-2	2-0	1-2	*

RESERVE SECTION RESULTS 1992-93

HOME TEAM	1	2	3	4	5	6	7	8	9	10	11	12	13	14	15	16	17	18
1. Ash United Res	*	2-4	1-3	3-1	2-2	3-2	5-1	4-0	4-1	3-1	3-3	1-2	4-2	0-2	1-3	5-2	1-1	0-1
2. Ashford Town (Mx) Res	2-0	*	2-1	2-0	1-5	4-4	4-0	0-0	2-0	3-0	0-1	4-0	4-1	0-0	0-4	7-2	3-2	2-1
3. Bedfont Res	3-1	0-1	*	0-2	0-0	2-0	2-1	2-3	2-0	1-0	0-3	1-3	1-0	3-0	1-3	3-0	1-0	1-0
4. Chipstead Res	2-1	3-0	1-2	*	0-0	2-2	2-0	6-0	1-1	4-0	0-2	2-1	3-2	1-1	1-2	4-1	0-4	0-0
5. Cobham Res	6-1	2-0	1-2	0-2	*	1-0	2-0	1-1	2-0	3-2	2-1	1-0	1-1	3-0	1-3	0-0	3-1	1-0
6. Cranleigh Res	1-1	2-2	1-1	1-7	3-1	*	0-0	5-3	0-4	1-1	3-4	2-4	0-1	2-2	0-2	4-1	1-2	2-3
7. DCA Basingstoke Res	3-3	1-4	2-1	0-1	0-3	2-4	*	0-4	0-1	2-1	3-2	0-1	4-2	1-1	0-0	2-0	0-2	1-1
8. Ditton Res	0-2	1-1	1-4	0-0	4-0	0-0	4-0	*	2-4	2-4	3-2	7-0	1-5	5-4	0-3	2-3	2-2	1-0
9. Farleigh Res	1-1	1-1	2-2	0-4	4-2	3-2	4-2	6-0	*	4-1	2-1	6-1	1-3	2-2	0-0	8-1	1-2	0-0
10. Frimley Green Res	2-4	3-3	0-4	2-2	0-0	2-1	4-1	5-5	3-1	*	0-4	0-1	1-2	1-2	1-3	0-0	5-2	2-9
11. Godalming & G. Res	4-0	1-1	0-0	0-3	1-0	3-0	0-0	2-2	3-2	2-0	*	0-1	4-0	0-1	4-3	3-0	2-2	
12. Hartley Wintney Res	4-1	1-4	3-1	2-0	0-3	4-0	3-0	2-3	0-7	0-3	3-0	*	5-0	4-7	1-3	7-1	3-2	2-1
13. Horley Town Res	2-1	1-3	2-0	2-5	2-0	4-3	3-2	0-3	2-1	0-3	0-0	4-1	*	0-5	2-3	1-1	0-2	1-1
14. Merstham Res	2-2	4-3	2-2	2-0	0-0	2-3	2-0	0-3	3-1	1-1	3-2	0-2	2-2	*	3-2	2-3	0-1	0-0
15. Peppard Res	2-1	0-0	4-2	2-0	3-1	1-1	2-0	0-2	2-1	2-2	4-0	2-0	2-2	4-1	*	4-2	2-1	2-3
16. Sandhurst T. Res	3-1	0-0	2-2	4-3	0-2	2-1	0-1	2-6	1-5	1-1	1-0	1-3	5-3	3-1	1-0	*	1-4	1-1
17. Viking Spts Res	3-0	1-4	2-0	0-0	2-6	2-0	3-0	4-2	2-3	5-2	3-2	1-1	2-1	3-0	1-2	0-1	*	1-4
18. Westfield Res	2-0	1-2	0-0	1-1	1-1	4-0	1-0	2-4	4-1	2-3	1-0	1-2	3-2	2-1	1-2	4-1	1-0	*

TOP SCORERS 1992-93

Premier Division: A Shildrick (Peppard) 34, M Flemmington (Horley) 29, Y Lavetive (Merstham) 29, D Smith (Peppard) 24, C Lamboll 22, G Price (Sandhurst) 20, D Hooker (Ash United) 19, A Smith (Ashford) 19, A Smith (Viking) 19, M Spiers (Hartley Wintney) 19, D Fry (Chipstead) 18.

Reserve Division: A O'Neil (Ashford) 20, P Gibbons (Farleigh) 18, L Hawking (Viking) 16, J Rowland (Peppard) 16, N Morwood (Ashford) 15, P McMahon (Hartley Wintney) 14, L Braby (Godalming & Guildford) 13, A Cane (Ash United) 12, G Case (Cranleigh) 11, S Dale (Peppard) 11, D Wade (Ditton) 11.

LEAGUE CHALLENGE CUP 1992-93 First Round

| Bedfont v Merstham | 1-0 | Malden Town v Horley Town | 4-2 |
| Peppard v Ash United | 1-2 | Viking Sports v Chipstead | 1-2 |

Second Round

Ashford Town (Middx) v Sandhurst Town	2-1	Chipstead v Hartley Wintney	3-0
D.C.A. Basingstoke v Bedont	0-1	Ditton v Westfield	2-1
Farleigh Rovers v Ash United	1-1(aet),0-4	Godalming & Guildford v Cranleigh	1-1(aet)
Malden Town v Frimley Green	1-0	Steyning Town v Cobham	1-3

Quarter-Finals

| Ashford Town (Middx) v Ash United | 1-0 | Befont v Cranleigh | 2-1 |
| Chipstead v Ditton | 3-1 | Malden Town (withdrew) v Cobham (w/o) | |

Semi-Finals

| Bedfont v Ashford Town (Middx) | 1-2 | Chipstead v Cobham | 3-2 |

Final (at Woking FC, Fri 30th April): Chipstead 2, Ashford Town (Middx) 1

Celebration time for Chipstead at Woking after their Challenge Cup win. Photo - Eric Marsh.

CHALLENGE VASE (formerly Elite Class Cup) 1992-93 First Round

| Ash United v Cranleigh | 1-1(aet),0-4 | Ashford Town (Middx) v Westfield | 0-1 |
| Cobham v Viking Sports | 1-6 | Ditton F. & S.C. v Chipstead | 1-2 |

Second Round

Cranleigh v Godalming & Guildford	2-0	D.C.A. Basingstoke v Chipstead	1-2
Frimley Green v Farleigh Rovers	1-2	Hartley Wintney v Peppard	2-3
Horley Town v Westfield	3-1	Malden v Bedfont 1-1(aet),2-2(aet, Bedfont on pens)	
Merstham v Viking Sports	4-1	Sandhurst Town v Steyning Town	4-0

Quarter-Finals

| Bedfont v Horley Town | 5-4 | Farleigh Rovers v Merstham | 0-1 |
| Peppard v Chipstead | 2-1 | Sandhurst Town v Cranleigh | 4-2 |

Semi-Finals

| Merstham v Bedfont | 2-3 | Peppard v Sandhurst Town | 0-1 |

Final (at Woking FC, Fri 7th May): Bedfont 2, Sandhurst Town 1

Bedfont F.C. - Parasol Challenge Vase winners 1992-93. Back Row (L/R): Gordon McEnvoy, Brian MacHenny, Les Stevenson, Andy Stevenson, Steve Pope, Mark Silbury, Jason Santos, Cliff Williamson. Front: Steve Jones, James Williams, George Lloyd, Barry Osborne. Photo - Dave West.

RESERVE SECTION CHALLENGE CUP 1992-93

First Round

Sandhurst Res v Godalming & G. Res	0-1
Frimley Green Res v Chipstead Reserves	1-4
Ditton Reserves v Bedfont Reserves	4-1
Horley Town Reserves v Hartley Wintney Res	0-1

Second Round

Ditton Res v Farleigh Rovers Reserves	3-0
Chipstead Reserves v Merstham Reserves	6-1
Malden Town Res v Viking Spts Reserves	5-1
Godalming Res v D.C.A. Basingstoke Res	2-1
Peppard Reserves v Westfield Reserves	3-2
Cranleigh Reserves *(w/o)* Farham Town Res *(withdrew)*	
Cobham Reserves v Ash United Reserves	2-0
Horley Town Res v Ashford Town (Mx) Res	5-1

Quarter-Finals

Ditton Reserves v Chipstead Reserves	2-3
Ash United Reserves v Cranleigh Reserves	4-2
Peppard Reserves v Horley Town Reserves	5-1
Godalming & G. Res *(w/o)* Malden Town Res *(withdrew)*	

Semi-Finals

Godalming & Guildford Res v Peppard Res	1-0
Chipstead Reserves v Ash United Reserves	2-0

Final *(at Egham Town FC)*: Chipstead Reserves 3, Godalming & Guildford Reserves 2

Chipstead Reserves proudly parade the Reserve Cup after their victory over Godalming. Photo - Eric Marsh.

PARASOL (COMBINED COUNTIES) LEAGUE TEN YEAR RECORD

	83/4	84/5	85/6	86/7	87/8	88/9	89/0	90/1	91/2	92/3
Alton Town	16	-	-	-	-	-	-	-	-	-
Ashford Town (Middx)	-	-	-	-	-	-	-	5	6	3
Ash United	3	5	3	1	13	10	4	8	9	6
B.A.e. Weybridge					(See Weybridge Town)					
Bedfont	-	-	-	-	11	12	16	7	8	12
Chertsey Town	-	-	2	-	-	-	-	-	-	-
Chessington United	17	-	-	-	-	-	-	-	-	-
Chipstead	-	-	-	4	7	4	1	2	3	2
Chobham	4	13	12	12	15	18	18	-	-	-
Cobham	10	17	8	11	4	11	8	10	4	17
Cove	13	18	13	13	12	17	3	-	-	-
Cranleigh	15	12	17	16	16	15	17	15	7	10
D.C.A. Basingstoke	-	-	-	-	-	-	-	-	-	13
Ditton F. & S.C.	-	-	-	-	-	-	-	-	5	18
Farleigh Rovers	-	11	15	14	14	8	9	6	11	16
Farnham Town	8	10	5	2	3	5	6	1	1	-
Fleet Town	-	19	19	-	-	-	-	-	-	-
Frimley Green	12	14	18	15	17	16	13	9	13	15
Godalming (Town)(& Guildford)	1	9	10	7	5	13	10	13	17	9
Guildford & Worplesdon	7	-	-	-	-	-	-	-	-	-
Hartley Wintney	5	16	11	8	10	7	11	14	15	8
Horley Town	-	15	16	9	9	9	14	16	18	14
Malden Town	2	6	6	10	6	14	5	3	2	*
Malden Vale	-	1	4	3	8	2	-	-	-	-
Merstham	-	3	7	6	2	3	2	4	14	4
Peppard	-	-	-	-	-	-	-	-	-	1
Sandhurst Town	-	-	-	-	-	-	-	17	19	7
Southwick	-	2	-	-	-	-	-	-	-	-
Steyning Town	-	-	-	-	-	6	7	12	10	11
Viking Sports	-	-	-	-	-	-	-	-	12	5
Virginia Water	9	7	14	18	-	-	-	-	-	-
Westfield	6	8	9	17	18	19	15	11	16	19
Weybridge Town	11	4	1	5	1	1	12	-	-	-
Yateley Town	14	-	-	-	-	-	-	-	-	-
No. of Clubs	17	19	19	18	18	19	18	17	19	19

* - Withdrew in mid-season

ASHFORD TOWN (MIDDX)

President: E Britzman   **Chairman:** R Parker   **Vice Chairman:** S Clark
Secretary: A B J Constable, 30 Marlborough Rd, Ashford, Middx TW15 3QA (0784 244515).
Manager: M Snowden   **Asst Manager:** P Newey
Physio: D Hanks   **Press Secretary:** D Baker
Ground: Short Lane, Stanwell, Staines, Middx (0784 245908).
Directions: M25 jct 13, A30 towards London, 3rd left at footbridge after Ashford Hospital crossroads - ground signposted after quarter of a mile on right down Short Lane. Two miles from Ashford (BR) and Hatton Cross (tube) stations. Bus route 116.
Seats: None   **Cover:** 75   **Capacity:** 2,000   **Floodlights:** No   **Year Formed:** 1964
Colours: Tangerine & white   **Change colours:** All blue   **Nickname:** Ash Trees
Programme: 20 pages, 50p   **Programme Editor:** Secretary
Club Shop: No, but secretary always willing to swap any non-Lge progs for old Ashford progs.
Previous Leagues: Hounslow & Dist. 64-68/ Surrey Intermediate 68-82/ Surrey Premier 82-90.
Midweek matchday: Tuesday   **Previous Ground:** Clockhouse Lane Rec.
Sponsors: Gildas Morris & Co Builders   **Record Gate:** 750 v Brentford, friendly 29/7/86.
Record win: 11-2 v Pyrford, 12/2/83   **Record defeat:** 0-7 v Tolworth, 3/12/83.
Clubhouse: Open 7 days a week. Refreshments always available - hot food on matchdays. Fruit machine, patio and barbecue, boardroom.
Captain 92-93: Mark Harrison   **Top Scorer 92-93:** Andy Smith   **P.o.Y. 92-93:** Graham Hill
Club record scorer: Andy Smith   **Club record appearances:** Alan Contable 650.
Hons: Combined Co's Lg Chall. Cup R-up 92-93 (Dan-Air Elite Class Cup R-up 91-92), Surrey Intermediate Lg, Surrey Prem. Cup 89-90, Middx Prem. Cup R-up 89-90.

Ashford Town (Middx) 1992-93. Back Row (L/R): M Snowden (Manager), P Oram, S Baughn, B Collacott, P Burgess, D Hillier, J Mills (Captain), N Jones, C Morlese, D Baker (Asst Manager). Front: G Hawkett, I Miles, A Smith, A Desbonne, N Lyons. Photo - V J Robertson.

ASH UNITED

President: Mrs B Williams   **Chairman:** R T Atkins
Secretary: Mrs L Foster, 52a Edwins Close, Ash, Nr Aldershot, Hants GU12 6SA.
Ground: Youngs Drive, off Shawfield Rd, Ash, Nr Aldershot (0252 20385).
Directions: A323 towards Ash, left into Shawfield Rd, right into Ash Church Rd, right at crossroads into Shawfield Rd. 1 mile from both Ash and Ash Vale BR stations.
Seats: None   **Cover:** None   **Capacity:** 1,500   **Floodlights:** No   **Founded:** 1911
Colours: Green/red/red   **Change colours:** All blue   **Programme:** Sometimes.
Midweek Matchday: Tuesday   **Previous Ground:** Ash Common Rec. 70-71
Previous Leagues: Surrey Snr, Aldershot Snr

Ash United pictured before their F.A. Vase tie against Littlehampton Town. Photo - Eric Marsh.

BEDFONT

President: Jack Newman **Vice President:** Les Evans **Treasurer:** Alan Hale.
Secretary: Tom Fountain (081 890 4490).
Manager: Alan Humphries **Coach:** Cliff Williamson.
Ground: The Orchard, Hatton Rd, Middx (081 890 7264).
Directions: Turn down Faggs Rd opposite Hatton Cross (Picadilly Line) station on Great South Western Rd (A30), then
sharp right into Hatton Rd. Ground opposite Duke of Wellington pub.
Seats: None **Cover:** 50 **Capacity:** **Floodlights:** Yes **Founded:** 1968.
Colours: Gold/blue/blue **Change colours:** Blue/yellow/yellow.
Previous Names: Bedfont Institute, Bedfont Rangers, Fairholme Youth Club (clubs merged in 1968).
Previous Ground: Bedfont Rec.
Clubhouse: Yes. **Programme:** Yes.
Captain 92-93: Cairon Dixon.
Hons: Combined Counties Lg Chall. Vase 92-93 (Reserve Div R-up 88-89, Reserve Cup R-up 89-90, Grant McClennan
Yth Cup 91-92), Middx Lg 73-74 76-77 (Div 1(res) 71-72 78-79 79-80, Div 1 Cup 71-72 78-79 79-80), Surrey Premier Lg
84-85 86-87, Middx Intermediate Cup 69-70 76-77, International Contois Tournament 1992, Liege Euromann
Tournament 1989, Harold Clayton Cup 90-91, Hounslow & Dist. Lg Div 1(res) 86-87.

*Alan Stevenson (6) of Bedfont prepares to tackle Ditton's Andy Boxall. Bedfont recorded a 3-0 win in this August Bank
Holiday league fixture. Photo - Dave West.*

CHIPSTEAD

President: B Nicholls **Chairman:** Keith Rivers
Secretary: K Allsopp, 51 Lakers Rise, Woodsterne, Banstead, Surrey SM7 3JX (0737 359989).
Manager: John Sears **Coach:** Paul Duffield.
Ground: High Road, Chipstead, Surrey (0737 553250).
Directions: Brighton Road northbound, left into Church Lane, left into Hogcross Lane, right into High Road. One and a
half miles from Chipstead (BR).
Seats: 30 **Cover:** 30 **Capacity:** 2,000 **Floodlights:** Due **Founded:** 1906
Cols: Green & white stripes/green/black **Change cols:** Yellow & white **Programme:** 44 pages
Previous Leagues: Surrey Intermediate 62-82/ Surrey Premier 82-86 **Nickname:** Chips
Hons: Surrey Premier Lg R-up 82-83 83-84 85-86 (Lg Cup 82-83 84-85 85-86), Combined Co's Lg 89-90 (R-up 90-91
92-93, Lg Cup 86-87 90-91 92-93, Elite Class Cup R-up 89-90, Reserve Section Cup 92-93).

COBHAM

Chairman: E Strange **Sec:** A O'Dea, 53 Cotwood Gdns, Collier Wood, London SW19 2DS (081 542 8860).
Ground: Leg O'Mutton Field, Downside Bridge Rd, Cobham, Surrey (0932 65959).
Directions: A307 (Portsmouth Road) towards Leatherhead, right into Between Streets, right into Downside Rd then
right opposite car park. Two miles from Cobham & Stoke D'Abernon (BR).
Seats: None **Cover:** No **Capacity:** 2,000 **Floodlights:** No **Founded:** 1892
Colours: Red/white/red **Change colours:** All yellow.
Previous League: Surrey Senior. **Previous Grounds:** Cobham Rec.
Programme: FA Vase matches only **Record Gate:** 2,000 v Showbiz team, charity match 1975.

CRANLEIGH

Chairman: Peter Slater   **Vice Chairman:** Trevor Moor   **President:** Alan Pavia.
Secretary: Mark Edwards, 42 Finnart Close, Weybridge, Surrey (0932 856716).
Manager: Tom Kelsey   **Asst Manager:** Dave Smith.
Ground: Snoxall Playing Fields, Knowle Lane, Cranleigh (0483 275295).
Directions: A281 from Guildford towards Horsham, at Shalford take B2128 to Cranleigh High Street, right opposite Onslow Arms into Knowle Lane, ground half mile on left. Public transport: Guildford (BR) then bus 273 or 283.
Seats: None   **Cover:** No   **Capacity:** 450   **Floodlights:** No   **Founded:** 1893.
Colours: Royal blue   **Change colours:** Grey/black.   **Nickname:** Cranes.
Record Gate: 450 v C Palace, friendly 1989. Competitive: 285 v Hailsham, F.A. Vase 3rd Rd 12/12/92.
Sponsors: R W Coupe - Est. Agents   **Clubhouse:** Licensed bar. Hot food on matchdays.
Programme: £1 with admission   **Editor:** Peter Slater (0483 894248)   **Club Shop:** No.
Midweek home matchday: Tuesday   **Rec. win:** 9-1 v Merstham, Dan-Air Elite Class Cup QF 91-92
Captain 92-93: Gerry Robinson   **Top Scorer & P.o.Y. 92-93:** Chris Lamboll.
Hons: West Sussex County Times Cup 92-93, F.A. Vase 3rd Rd 92-93.

Cranleigh forward Micky Hunt gives a helping hand to Greenwich Borough goalkeeper Mick Orme during his side's excellent 3-1 away win in the First Round of the F.A. Vase. Photo - Dave West.

D.C.A. BASINGSTOKE

Chairman: M A Davis   **Vice Chairman:** K R W Haystaff   **President:** K J Dudley
Secretary: D J Brand, 128 Stratfield Rd, Oakridge, Basingstoke, Hants RG21 2SA (0256 57309).
Manager: Alec Walker   **Asst Manager:** Alan Tait/ Mark Gardener.
Ground: Whiteditch Playing Field, Sherbourne Rd, Basingstoke, Hants (0256 844866).
Directions: From Basingstoke BR station, turn right out of main entrance towards Chapel Hill, continue past Rising Sun pub, right into Sherbourne Rd, ground 800yds up on right.
Seats: None   **Cover:** None   **Capacity:** Unknown   **Floodlights:** No.   **Founded:** 1971
Colours: Navy & sky   **Previous Name:** Soldiers Return.   **Programmes:** No.
Previous Grounds: None   **Prev. Lges:** North Hants/ Hants (pre-'92)   **Club Shop:** No.
Midweek home matchday: Tuesday   **Clubhouse:** Approx. one mile from ground.
Clubhouse: Evenings 7-11pm, matchdays 12-11pm. Bar snacks.
Captain 92-93: John Hawke   **P.o.Y. 92-93:** Brian Cook
Hons: Hants Lg Div 2 88-89 (Div 1 R-up 90-91), Basingstoke Snr Cup 83-84 87-88 90-91, North Hants Lg 87-88, North Hants Snr Cup 87-88 88-89 (R-up 90-91).

D.C.A. Basingstoke F.C. 1992-93. Photo - Eric Marsh.

DITTON F. & S.C.

Chairman: Steve Rabbetts   **Vice Chairman:** Les Bond   **President:** Roy May.
Secretary: T.B.A.
Manager: Phil Nash   **Asst Mgr:** Barry Nicholas   **Coach:** Chris Hatchwell.
Ground: Ditton Recreation Ground, Windmill Lane, Long Ditton, Surbiton, Surrey (081 398 7428).
Directions: At A307/A309 'Scilly Isles' r'bout east of Esher, take A307 towards Surbiton. Windmill Lane is one and a half miles on right. One and a half miles from Surbiton (BR); turn left into Victoria Rd, right at crossroads, left into Balaclava, right into Effingham Rd and right into Windmill Lane.
Seats: None   **Cover:** No   **Capacity:**   **Floodlights:** No   **Founded:** 1912
Colours: Yellow/green/yellow   **Change colours:** White/black/white   **Programme:** T.B.A.
Previous Leagues: Kingston & Dist./ Middx Snr/ Surrey I'mediate/ Surrey Comb. 72-85/ Surrey Premier.
Club Sponsors: T.B.A.   **Record Gate:** 200 v Malden T., Comb. Co's Lg 1/1/92.
Midweek home matchday: Tuesday   **Clubhouse:** Adjacent to Long Ditton Recreation ground. Open near normal licensing hours throughout season. Burgers and rolls available before and after matches.
Captain & P.o.Y 92-93: Andy Boxall   **Top Scorer 92-93:** Andy Cortick.
Club record appearances: Andy Boxall.
Hons: Surrey Premier Lg 85-86 88-89 89-90 (Lg Cup 87-88 88-89 90-91), Surrey Co. Premier Cup R-up 85-86, Surrey I'mediate Cup R-up 53-54 81-82 83-84, Surrey Comb. 84-85, Surrey Jnr Charity Cup 22-23 (R-up 21-22 44-45), Surrey Lower Jnr Cup 81-82, War Emergency Cup 46-47.

Ditton F.C. 1992-93. Photo - Dave West.

ETON WICK

Chairman: J Bussey   **Manager:** J Hartridge.
Secretary: Pauline Marks, 28 Colemorton Cres., Eton Wick, Windsor, Berks (0753 841886).
Ground: Haywards Mead, Eton Wick, Windsor (0753 852749).   **Directions:** Windsor Rd Slough under M4 m'way to r'bout, 1st exit to lights at Eton College, turn right - club one and a half miles on left in Eton Wick.
Seats: Yes   **Cover:** Yes   **Programme:** Yes   **Founded:** 1881.
Colours: Amber/black   **Local Press:** Slough Windsor Observer/ Express
Previous Leagues: Windor Slough & Dist. (pre-'91)/ Chiltonian 91-93.
Clubhouse: Full facilities, open all sessions.
Hons: Chiltonian Lg 92-93 (Div 1 91-92, Lg Cup R-up 91-92), Slough Town Cup 91-92, Berks & Bucks Intermediate Cup 91-92.

FARLEIGH ROVERS

President: C D Scott   **Chairman:** TBA   **Secretary:** TBA.
Ground: Parsonage Field, Harrow Road, Warlingham, Surrey (0883 626483).
Directions: Limpsfield Road (B269) south eastwards, left into Farleigh Rd, left at T-junction, right into Harrow Rd, right into Green Lane. Three miles from Upper Warlingham (BR); left into Chelsham Rd 1 mile left into Harrow Rd. Bus 403 to Harrow Rd.
Seats: None   **Cover:** No   **Capacity:** 2,000   **Floodlights:** No   **Founded:** 1922
Colours: Red/black/black   **Change colours:** Blue & black/blue/blue   **Programme:** Yes
Previous Name: Farleigh & Chelsham Utd (pre-1929)   **Previous Ground:** Farleigh Common (pre-1925).
Previous League: Surrey Premier   **Record Gate:** 130 v Chipstead, League 28/12/87.
Hons: Combined Co's Cup R-up 91-92.

FARNHAM TOWN

Chairman: J Butters   **President:** D Russell
Secretary: Mr G Southgate, 42 Merrow Lane, Guildford, Surrey (0483 64192).
Manager: **Asst Manager:**   **Coach:**
Press Officer: **Commercial Mgr:**   **Physio:**
Ground: Memorial Ground, Babbs Mead, West Street, Farnham, Surrey (0252 715305).
Directions: Take A325 (West Street) at junction with A31 Farnham by-pass, then first right. From Farnham (BR), left into Station Hill, left into Union Rd, round Downing Street, left into West Street and Babbs Mead is 3rd left.
Capacity: 2,000   **Seats:** None   **Cover:** 150   **Floodlights:** Yes   **Founded:** 1921
Colours: Claret & sky stripes/sky/claret   **Change colours:** Yellow & black   **Club Shop:** No
Programme: Yes   **Editor:**   **Metal Badges:**
Previous Name: Farnham Star   **Previous Grounds:** Farnham Park.
Previous Leagues: Surrey Intermediate/ Surrey Snr 47-71/ Spartan 71-75/ London Spartan 75-80/ Combined Counties 80-92.
Midweek Matchday: **Sponsors:** Frazer Freight.
Record Gate: 500 v Kingstonian, Surrey Snr Cup 1960.   **Nickname:**
Reserve Team's League: **Best FA Cup year:** Never past Qualifying Rounds
Clubhouse: Yes
Hons: Combined Counties Lg 90-91 91-92 (Challenge Tphy 91-92 (R-up 89-90).

FRIMLEY GREEN

President: Vic Fennell   **Chairman:** Trevor Brown
Secretary: James McKane, 79 Gifford Drive, Farnborough (0252 541980).
Manager: Steve Hibbins   **Asst Manager:** Chris Vaughan
Coach: Steve Hallgalley   **Physio:** Bob Dunster.
Ground: Recreation Ground, Frimley Green Road, Frimley Green (0252 835089).
Directions: M3 jct 4, A321 towards Aldershot, follow Frimley signs (still A321) at 1st island, continue thru Frimley High Street & past Johnson Wax factory into Frimley Green - ground half mile on left. From A325 (Portsmouth road) south westwards into town centre, left into Grove Cross and straight over into Frimley Green Rd. 2 miles from Frimley (BR) - turn right into Frimley High Str., fork right into Church Rd and right into Frimley Green Rd.
Seats: None   **Cover:** 100   **Club Shop:** No   **Floodlights:** No   **Founded:** 1919
Colours: White/white/blue   **Change colours:** All red   **Nickname:** The Green
Club Sponsor: Chessington Tyres   **Previous Lges:** Surrey Snr/ (London) Spartan 74-81
Programme: 20 pages, 50p   **Editor:** Stuart Dwaikira (0483 571399 (306580fax))
Clubhouse: Open Tuesday & Thursday evenings 7-11pm, matchdays noon-11pm. Food available.
Captain 92-93: Paul Ashley   **Top Scorer 92-93:** Andy Leader   **P.O.Y. 92-93:** Bob Ryan
Club record scorer: Not known   **Club record appearances:** Steve Read.
Hons: Combined Co's Lg Dan-Air Elite Class Cup 90-91 (Res. Sect. R-up 90-91, Res. Sect. Cup 90-91).

Frimley Green F.C. 1992-93.

GODALMING & GUILDFORD

President: W Kyte   **Chairman:** M Palmer   **Manager:** Tim Daly
Secretary: Mrs J Phillips, 135 Manor Rd, Stoughton, Guildford, Surrey GU2 6NR (0483 571372).
Ground: Weycourt, Meadrow, Godalming, Surrey (0483 417520).
Directions: A3100 from Guildford to Godalming, road becomes Meadrow after Godalming High Street, turn left into Weycourt after bridge over River Wey. Three quarters of a mile from Farncombe (BR).
Seats: Yes   **Cover:** 200   **Capacity:** 1,500   **Floodlights:** No   **Programme:** Yes
Colours: Green & white/white   **Change colours:** All yellow.   **Founded:** 1971
Previous Lge: Surrey County Snr   **Previous Ground:** Broadwater Pk, Farncombe 71-73
Previous Names: Godalming & Farncombe 71-80/ Godalming Town 80-92.
Record Gate: 600+ - Ex-Guildford City XI v Ex-Football Lg XI, Tony Burge benefit, 1991.
Hons: Combined Co's Lg Reserve Challenge Cup 91-92 (R-up 92-93).

HARTLEY WINTNEY

President: D Gorsky   **Chairman:** W Mitchell
Secretary: S Pratt, 'Grafton', 29 Queens Rd, Fleet, Hants GU13 9LA (0252 623956).
Ground: Memorial Playing Fields, Green Lane, Hartley Wintney, Hants (0251 263586).
Directions: A30 west through Camberley, left at parade of shops at beginning of village then sharp right - ground on right. Two miles from Winchfield (BR).
Seats: 2 benches   **Cover:** No   **Capacity:** 2,000   **Floodlights:** No   **Founded:** 1897
Colours: Tangerine/black/tangerine   **Change colours:** White/blue/blue   **Programme:** Yes
Previous Leagues: Basingstoke/ Aldershot   **Nickname:** The Row

Hartley Wintney F.C. who enjoyed their best ever run in the F.A. Vase last season. Photo - Eric Marsh.

HORLEY TOWN

Chairman: Mr S Munday   **Vice Chairman:** Mr G McLaren   **President:** Mr K Pritchard
Secretary: Mr P C Freeman, Long Acre, 140 Balcombe Rd, Horley, Surrey RH6 9DS (0293 784368).
Joint Managers: Andy Wastell/ Laurence Gearey   **Physio:** Philip Sparkes.
Ground: The Defence, Smallfield Rd, Horley, Surrey (0293 786075).
Directions: From Horley (BR) station turn right down Station Approach, left into The Grove, over traffic lights into Smallfield Rd - ground 1 mile on left down Smallfield Rd.
Seats: None   **Cover:** 100   **Capacity:** 1,000   **Floodlights:** Yes   **Founded:** 1898
Colours: Claret & blue/white/white   **Change colours:** All sky   **Programme:** 50p
Midweek matchdays: Tuesday   **Prev. Ground:** Gasworks Grnd, Balcombe Rd (pre 1948)
Previous Leagues: Redhill & District 45-49/ Surrey Intermediate 49-72/ Surrey Senior 72-78/ London Spartan 78-81/ Athenian 81-84.
Sponsors: Carter Thorne Carpets   **Record Gate:** 1,000 v Spurs, pre-season friendly 1983
Record win: 10-0 v Lion Sports 1978   **Record defeat:** 0-10 v Southwick 1985   **Club Shop:** No.
Clubhouse: Evenings 7-11pm, weekend lunchtimes. Hot food on matchdays only.
Captain 92-93: Jimmy Mahoney   **Top Scorer & P.o.Y. 92-93:** Mark Fremington (26 goals)
Club record scorer: Ian Peters   **Club record appearances:** Dave Jupp.
Hons: Surrey Snr Lg 76-77 (Charity Cup 76-77 77-78), Surrey Intermediate (Eastern) Lg Cup 66-67.

MERSTHAM

President: Stan Baker   **Chairman:** Geoff Taylor   **Vice Chairman:** Steve D'Arcy.
Secretary: Mrs Sheila Williams, 33 Lymden Gdns, Reigate, Surrey (0737 245877).
Manager: Joe McElligott   **Asst Manager:** Martin Rosser   **Coach:** Allan Cook.
Physio: Carl Burke   **Press Officer:** Roger Peerless.
Ground: Merstham Rec., Weldon Way, Merstham, Redhill, Surrey (0737 43279).
Directions: Leave Merstham village (A23) by School Hill, take 5th right (Weldon Way), clubhouse and car park 100m on right. Ground also accessible from Albury Rd (2nd right off School). 10 mins walk from Merstham (BR); down School Hill, under railway bridge, fork left then right into Albury Road, ground entrance half way down on left.
Seats: 100   **Cover:** 100   **Capacity:** 2,000   **Floodlights:** Yes (177 lux)
Colours: Amber & black   **Change colours:** Silver grey   **Founded:** 1892.
Club Sponsors: Whitbread   **Midweek home matchday:** Tuesday
Record win: 11-0   **Record defeat:** 1-9
Previous Leagues: Redhill & Dist./ Surrey Co. S.E. I'mediate/ Surrey Snr 64-78/ London Spartan 78-85.
Previous Grounds: Merstham Weir/ Merstham Lime Works (pre-1920s).
Clubhouse: Across adjacent footpath. Open daily (am & pm). Snacks available.
Captain & P.o.Y. 92-93: Brian Jupp   **Top Scorer 92-93:** Yul Laretive.
Hons: Combined Co's Lg R-up 87-88 89-90 (Elite Class Cup 89-90 (R-up 90-91), Reserve Section 90-91), London Spartan Lg 79-89 (Lg Cup 79-80), Surrey Snr Lg 71-72, Surrey Snr Charity Cup 79-80, East Surrey Charity Cup 80-81, Surrey I'mediate Lg 52-53.

PEPPARD

Chairman: C F Clayton   **Vice Chairman:** R Pigden   **President:** V F Clayton
Secretary/Press Officer: D North, 35 Oregon Ave., Tilehurst, Reading, Berks RG4 6RZ (0734 423557).
Manager: Graham Haddrell   **Asst Manager:** A Grover   **Physio:** A Rogers.
Ground: Palmer Park Stadium, Reading, Berks.
Seats: 850   **Cover:** 950   **Capacity:** 4,500   **Floodlights:** Yes   **Founded:** 1903
Colours: Red/white   **Change colours:** Sky & navy   **Club Shop:** No.
Previous Lges: Reading & Dist. 70-87/ Chiltonian 87-92/ Combined Counties 92-93.
Previous Names: Sonning Common Peppard (Peppard FC merged with Sonning Common FC in 1984 - name reverted to Peppard FC in 1990).
Previous Ground: Bishopswood Spts Centre, Horsepond Lane, Sonning Common (pre-1993).
Programme: 44 pages, 50p   **Programme Editor:** Reece Pigden (0734 723445)
Midweek matchday: Monday   **Sponsors:** Greenwood Tighe Public Relations
Reserve Team's League: Suburban.   **Clubhouse:** Normal bar hours. Snacks available.
Captain 92-93: Kevin Watkins   **Top Scorer 92-93:** Andy Shildrick   **P.O.Y.** 92-93: Matthew Webb
Club record scorer: Jim Aberdein   **Club record appearances:** Ray Will.
Local Newspapers: Reading Evening Post, Henley Standard   **Local Radio:** Radio 210, Radio Oxford.
Hons: Combined Co's Lg 92-93, Chiltonian Lg(2) 90-92 (R-up 89-90, Lg Cup(4) 87-89 90-92), Reading & Dist. Lg(7) 74-75 77-78 79-82 84-85 86-87, Oxon Snr Cup 79-80 81-82 (R-up 89-90), Oxon I'mediate Cup(3) 74-76 92-93(res), Reading Snr Cup(6) 79-82 89-92, Wycombe Snr Cup 91-92, Reading Jnr Cup 60-61 81-82(res) 87-88(res).

SANDHURST TOWN

Chairman: M J Morgan   **Secretary:** J Parker (0276 32308).
Manager: Tony O'Connor   **Coach:** Steve Atkins.
Ground: Memorial Ground, Yorktown Rd, Sandhurst (0252 873767).
Directions: A30 westwards through Camberley, right at r-bout with traffic lights, past superstore turning right, left at next r'bout. Ground next to Town & Council offices and Community Sports Centre.
Seats: None   **Cover:** No   **Floodlights:** No   **Programme:** Yes   **Nickname:** Fizzers
Colours: Red/black/black   **Change colours:** All gold   **Metal Badges:** Yes
Previous Leagues: Reading & Dist./ East Berks/ Aldershot Snr 79-84/ Chiltonian 84-90.
Captain 92-93: Mel Coombs   **Top Scorer 92-93:** Glenn Price.
Hons: Combined Co's Lg Chal. Vase R-up 92-93 (Reserve Chal. Cup R-up 91-92), Chiltonian Lg R-up 86-87, Aldershot Snr Lg R-up 83-84.

VIKING SPORTS

President: Roy Bartlett   **Chairman:** Gary Yost
Secretary: John Bennett, 6 Bridge House, Boston Manor Rd, Brentford TW8 9LH (081 568 9047).
Ground: Avenue Park, Western Avenue, Greenford, Middx (081 578 2706).
Directions: On London-bound carriageway of A40, 300 yds before Greenford flyover and slip road to A4127. 12 mins walk from Greenford (Central Line) station - turn right out of station and to A40 and turn right - ground quarter mile on right.
Seats: 50   **Cover:** 100   **Capacity:** 400   **Floodlights:** Yes   **Founded:** 1945
Colours: Tangerine   **Change colours:** Sky/maroon   **Nickname:** Vikings.
Programme: 12 pages, 20p   **Editor:** Andy Evans (081 991 1930)   **Club Shop:** No.
Clubhouse: Open every evening except Sunday and matchdays. Hot & cold snacks on matchdays.
Midweek matchday: Tuesday   **Record Gate:** 180 v Lambourn, Hellenic Lg 1982
Prev. Lge: Middx 70-80/ Hellenic 80-91   **Prev. Grounds:** Churchfield (pre-1965)   **Metal Badges:** Yes.
Players progressing to Football League: Gordon Bartlett (Portsmouth), Alan Devonshire (West Ham).
Club Sponsors: Measham Self-Drive   **Club Record Scorer:** Frank Healy, 43.
Record win: 8-0 v Aldermaston, 1986   **Record defeat:** 1-7 v Bicester Town, 1988.
Captain 92-93: Cliff Jones   **Top Scorer & P.O.Y.** 92-93: Tony Smith.
Hons: Hellenic Lg Div 1 85-86 (Div 1 Cup R-up 90-91).

Viking Sports 1992-93. Back Row (L/R): Roy Datway, Steve Curry, Paul Stewart, Chris Sparks, Cliff Jones, Mick Kelly, Jim Conway. Front: Gus Marsh, Wayne Haley, Randy Richmond, John Richardson, Heron Wildman, Jez Markwick. Photo - Dave West.

VIRGINIA WATER

Chairman: R Fisher   **Vice Chairman:** G Underdown   **President:** H Zeisel
Secretary: John Brooks, 40 Robinsway, Hersham, Surrey KT12 5QN (0932 242968).
Manager: Seamus Dowling   **Asst Manager/Coach:** Keith Powelsland
Physio: Tim Jones   **Press Officer:** Ron Fisher.
Ground: 'The Timbers', Crown Rd, Virginia Water, Surrey (0344 843811).
Directions: M25 jct 11, follow signs to Chertsey, Thorpe, then Virginia Water.
Seats: None   **Cover:** No   **Capacity:**   **Floodlights:** No   **Founded:** 1921
Colours: Red & green   **Change colours:** All white   **Club Shop:** No.
Previous Leagues: Surrey Snr 68-75/ Combined Co's 79-87/ Surrey Comb. 87-91/ Surrey South Eastern Comb. 91-92/ Surrey Premier 92-93.
Programme: Due to start 93-94.   **Rec. Gate:** 250 v Raynes Park, 27/4/93.   **Nickname:** Waters
Record win: 9-1 (reserves: 11-0)   **Record defeat:** 1-4 (reserves: 0-6).
Clubhouse: Noon-7.30pm matchdays, 7-9.30pm training nights. Variety of sandwiches, burgers, sausage rolls, chips, pasties, jacket potatoes.
Captain 92-93: Paul Bullivant   **Top Scorer 92-93:** Nigel Kayes   **P.O.Y. 92-93:** Sammy Eason
Club record scorer: Nigel Kaye   **Club record appearances:** Sammy Eason.
Hons: Surrey Premier Lg 92-93, Surrey County Cup 90-91, Surrey S.E. Comb. R-up 91-92 (Lg Cup R-up 91-92).

Virginia Water - Surrey County Premier League champions 1992-93. Photo - Gavin Ellis-Neville.

WESTFIELD

Chairman: E Strange   **Manager:** John Martin.
Secretary: T Rolfe (0486 78177).
Ground: Woking Park, Kingfield, Woking, Surrey (no telephone).
Directions: Adjacent to Woking FC (see GMV Conference section).
Seats: None   **Cover:** No   **Capacity:**   **Floodlights:** No   **Programme:** No
Colours: All royal   **Change colours:** All yellow.   **Previous League:** Surrey Co. Snr.

Merstham F.C. 1992-93. Back Row (L/R): M Rosser (Asst Manager), K Rodger, A Renton, L Butler, M Retter, A Chapman, K Rathbom, S Mills, C Burke (Physio), M Retter (Mascot). Front: K D'Arcy, J McElligott (Player-Manager), B Jupp, N Vernon, P Turner, Y Laretive, J Drennan, A Gorman. Photo - Dennis Nicholson.

SC Johnson
SURREY COUNTY
PREMIER LEAGUE

President: L F J Smith.
Chairman: R A Mendham.
Hon. Secretary: D Havenhand, 2 Balmoral Cres.,
Farnham GU9 0DN (0252 722798)

Last season, the eleventh in our brief history, was the first to see a full complement of sixteen clubs. And what a season to choose, losing over a month of Saturdays in mid-season because of the 'monsoon'. Nevertheless, our Fixtures Secretary Alan Constable, ably supported by Referees' Secretary Peter Foster and the clubs, managed to get all games played - the last one being on Wednesday 26th May!

The Premier Division was eventually a triumph for newcomers Virginia Water, but only after much chopping and changing at the top, with Raynes Park, Chobham, Netherne and briefly Hersham R.B.L. in the frame. It was Virginia Water's consistency in the latter part of the season which eventually paid off. They now leave us for the Parasol Combined Counties League, where we are confident they will give a good account of themselves.

The Reserve Division, on the other hand, appeared for most of the season to be a one horse race - and that horse was not the eventual winner, Surbiton Town Reserves! Raynes Park Reserves went top in September, and apart from a short period when they didn't play for a month because of the 'monsoon' they stayed top until the very last day of the season - 26th May! Surbiton Town also fell well behind with their fixtures and eventually had nine games to play in a month, requiring 25 points to take the title. One of those games was against Raynes Park, whom they beat 3-0 which proved to be vital as they subsequently pipped Raynes Park by one point being way behind on goal difference.

The Cup competitions resulted in new names appearing on all four trophies. The Premier final was not so one-sided as the 5-1 score implies - but you can't concede three goals in five minutes and recover, as Burpham found to their cost. The other finals were all very close affairs - in the balance until the last kick and whistle.

Although they had a miserable season, Ashtead are congratulated on a remarkable disciplinary record (one caution only) and for thus winning the Sportsmanship Trophy (£150) by a 'mile'.

The Representative side covered themselves in glory, winning the South East Intermediate Inter-League competition for the second year in succession and also adding the Surrey County Inter-League Trophy for good measure. Managers Mick Taylor and Robin Denman have set themselves a difficult task for next season!

In the County Cups, three of our clubs (Chobham, Netherne and Virginia Water) reached the Semi-Finals of the Surrey Premier Cup, Chobham eventually progressing to the final where they lost 1-3 to a very good Sutton United Reserves team. In the Surrey Intermediate Cup, Raynes Park Reserves progressed furthest - to the Fourth Round.

Finally, we must thank our sponsors, S.C. Johnson (Johnson Wax) for their invaluable support and encouragement.

D Havenhand, Hon. Secretary.

The League Representative team. Back Row (L/R): D Havenhand (Secretary), T Hermitage (Netherne), P Ottoway (Croydon M.O.), A Hilton (Hersham), R Luffman (Frinton), D Loosley (Burpham), K Simpson (Netherne), D Laing (Ottershaw), R Denman (Asst Manager). Front: M Taylor (Manager), C Pittifield (Frinton), P Rochester (Ashtead), S Parker (Netherne), A Payne, A Bessom (both Frinton). Photo - Dave West.

PREM. DIV.	P	W	D	L	F	A	PTS
Virginia Water	30	20	7	3	66	27	67
Raynes Park	30	20	6	4	64	27	66
Chobham	30	17	8	5	65	42	59
Hersham R B L	30	18	4	8	73	54	58
Frinton Rovers	30	14	6	10	67	47	48
Netherne	30	14	6	10	73	59	48
Surbiton Town	30	13	9	8	55	43	48
Burpham	30	13	8	9	64	47	47
Croydon M O	30	12	4	14	52	64	40
Ottershaw	30	10	4	16	35	62	34
Vandyke	30	9	6	15	54	58	33
Walton Casuals	30	10	3	17	48	74	33
Springfield B I	30	6	13	11	51	53	31
B T	30	6	7	17	34	61	25
Sheerwater	30	3	7	20	36	74	16
Ashtead	30	4	4	22	43	88	16

RESERVE DIV.	P	W	D	L	F	A	PTS
Surbiton T. Res.	30	24	4	4	88	39	70
Raynes Park Res.	30	21	6	3	105	26	69
Virginia Wtr Res.	30	20	5	5	70	25	65
Croydon MO Res.	30	19	4	7	95	57	*60
Frinton R. Res.	30	15	6	9	67	47	51
Chobham Res.	30	14	7	9	61	44	49
Ottershaw Res.	30	13	5	12	54	54	44
Vandyke Res.	30	13	3	14	69	57	42
Burpham Res.	30	13	2	15	56	64	41
Springfield Res.	30	10	6	14	50	62	36
Netherne Res.	30	11	2	17	59	73	35
Ashtead Res.	30	11	2	17	53	112	35
B T Res.	30	7	5	18	34	60	26
Walton Casuals	30	5	7	18	39	90	22
Sheerwater Res.	30	5	5	20	46	93	20
Hersham RBL Res.	30	4	5	21	36	79	17

* - 1pt deducted

PREMIER DIVISION RESULTS

HOME TEAM		1	2	3	4	5	6	7	8	9	10	11	12	13	14	15	16
1.	Ashtead	*	3-2	2-3	1-6	4-0	0-2	1-3	3-4	3-3	2-4	6-3	0-4	1-2	1-2	0-1	2-1
2.	B.T.	0-0	*	2-2	0-1	2-3	1-2	3-2	3-6	1-2	0-5	3-1	3-3	0-2	2-1	1-2	3-3
3.	Burpham	2-1	1-2	*	2-3	1-0	3-3	2-3	2-2	7-0	0-1	1-0	2-1	1-2	7-1	1-1	7-1
4.	Chobham	2-1	1-1	0-0	*	2-0	3-1	4-1	3-1	0-1	4-2	3-0	1-0	2-2	0-2	2-2	3-1
5.	Croydon M.O.	2-1	1-2	1-3	1-5	*	2-1	2-3	2-4	4-2	1-5	2-1	1-1	2-1	2-2	2-0	4-0
6.	Frinton Rover	4-0	0-0	1-0	3-4	2-3	*	5-3	4-0	4-0	0-3	2-1	3-1	2-3	2-4	1-2	4-1
7.	Hersham R.B.L.	3-1	3-0	0-0	5-2	3-1	1-1	*	3-1	1-1	0-2	4-1	3-2	0-0	0-4	3-2	4-1
8.	Netherne	3-1	0-0	1-2	5-1	3-4	2-5	2-5	*	8-0	3-2	4-1	4-2	0-0	2-2	1-2	2-1
9.	Ottershaw	2-1	2-0	1-2	1-3	1-2	0-1	0-4	1-1	*	0-3	1-0	1-0	1-3	4-3	0-1	4-0
10.	Raynes Park	6-0	2-1	1-0	1-0	1-1	1-1	2-3	1-0	3-2	*	1-1	4-1	1-1	2-0	0-0	2-1
11.	Sheerwater	5-2	1-0	2-4	2-2	1-2	1-5	1-0	1-4	2-2	1-2	*	1-1	0-0	1-1	1-1	1-2
12.	Springfield Batt. I.	6-0	2-0	2-2	0-0	1-1	1-1	3-4	1-1	1-0	0-2	4-3	*	1-1	2-5	1-1	3-1
13.	Surbiton Town	1-1	4-0	2-3	2-2	2-1	4-2	4-3	2-4	1-2	1-3	4-0	2-2	*	5-1	0-3	1-3
14.	Vandyke	6-2	0-1	2-2	1-2	2-1	2-2	0-1	0-1	0-1	4-1	1-1	0-2	*	0-4	5-0	4-1
15.	Virginia Water	2-2	3-0	5-0	2-3	5-2	1-0	3-0	3-1	3-1	1-0	3-1	2-2	1-0	2-1	*	3-1
16.	Walton Casuals	4-1	3-1	4-2	1-1	3-1	0-3	3-5	2-3	2-0	0-0	2-1	3-2	0-1	4-2	0-3	*

PREMIER DIVISION TOP SCORERS: Nigel Kay (Virginia Water) 26, Sean Underdown (Virginia Water) 24, Neville Hatcher (Chobham) 22, Jamie Allen (Croydon M.O.) 22, Paulo Santana (Raynes Park) 22, Paul Mills (Hersham R.B.L.) 21, Kevin Hains (Netherne) 21.

PREMIER CHALLENGE CUP

First Round

Sheerwater v Virginia Water	1-3	Raynes Park v Ottershaw	4-0
Netherne v Surbiton Town	1-0	Springfield Battersea Ironsides v Vandyke	3-0
Walton Casuals v Frinton Rovers	2-0	Burpham v B.T.	1-0
Chobham v Hersham Royal British Legion	0-2	Ashtead v Croydon Municipal Officers	3-1(aet)

Quarter-Finals

Virginia Water v Burpham	1-4	Netherne v Hersham Royal British Legion	2-1(aet)
Raynes Park v Ashtead	0-0(aet),4-0	Springfield Battersea Ironsides v Walton Casuals	0-1

Semi-Finals

Burpham v Walton Casuals	2-1	Netherne v Raynes Park	4-2

Final *(at Dorking FC):* Netherne 5, Burpham 1

RICHARD PARTINGTON MEMORIAL CUP

First Round

Vandyke v Frinton Rovers — 1-5

Quarter-Finals

Netherne v Virginia Water	1-2	Springfield Battersea Ironsides v Surbiton Town	1-2
Sheerwater v Walton Casuals	2-1	Frinton Rovers v Ottershaw	1-0

Semi-Finals

Sheerwater v Surbiton Town	2-3(aet)	Virginia Water v Frinton Rovers	4-0

Final *(at Ashford Town (Middx) FC):* Surbiton Town 2, Virginia Water 1 *(aet)*

RESERVE CHALLENGE CUP

First Round

Sheerwater Res. v Burpham Reserves	2-0	Croydon M.O. Res. v Vandyke	3-3(aet),0-0(2-4 pens)
Netherne Res. v Walton Casuals Reserves	4-1	Hersham R.B.L. Res. v Surbiton Town Res.	0-5
Raynes Park Res. v Springfield B.I. Res.	4-2(aet)	Frinton Rovers Res. v B.T. Reserves	2-1
Ottershaw Res. v Virginia Water Res.	1-3	Chobham Reserves v Ashtead Reserves	0-5
		(Ashtead expelled for fielding ineligible players)	

Quarter-Finals

Frinton Rovers Res. v Vandyke Reserves	0-3	Sheerwater Reserves v Netherne Reserves	1-3
Raynes Park Reserves v Surbiton Town Res.	0-1	Chobham Res. v Virginia Water Reserves	1-2(aet)

Semi-Finals

Virginia Water Res. v Vandyke Reserves	1-3	Surbiton Res v Netherne Reserves	3-3(aet),3-1

Final *(at Dorking FC):* Vandyke Reserves 2, Surbiton Town Reserves 1 *(aet)*

RESERVE CHARITY CUP

First Round

Netherne Res. v Frinton Rvrs Reserves   0-4   Ottershaw Res. v Springfield B.I. Res.   2-0

Quarter-Finals

Surbiton T. v Vandyke Res.   2-2*(aet)*,3-0   Walton Casuals Reserves v Chobham Reserves   2-4

Sheerwater Reserves v Frinton Rvrs Res.   1-9   Ottershaw Res. v Virginia Water Reserves   2-3

     (Virginia Water expelled for fielding ineligible player)

Semi-Finals

Ottershaw Res. v Frinton Rovers Reserves   1-0   Chobham Reserves v Surbiton T. Reserves   2-1*(aet)*

Final *(at Ashford Town (Middx) FC)*: Ottershaw Reserves 2, Chobham Reserves 2 *(aet, Ottershaw won 5-4 on penalties)*

SURREY COUNTY PREMIER LEAGUE CLUBS 1993-94

BATTERSEA IRONSIDES

Secretary: Les Barker, 165 Washington Rd, Worcester Park KT4 8JQ (081 337 8665).

Ground: Battersea Ironsides Sports Club, Open View, Burntwood Lane SW18 (081 874 9913).

Directions: The ground is on corner of Openview and Burntwood Lane, opposite Springfield Hospital.

Colours: Red/blue/red   **Change colours:** All white, or blue & white stripes.

Previous Names: Springfield Hospital F.C. and Battersea Ironsides F.C. merged in 1992 to form Springfield Battersea Ironsides. Name now reverted to Battersea Ironsides.

Previous League: Surrey South Eastern Combination (pre-1992).

BISLEY SPORTS

Secretary: Mrs Julie Robertson, 17 Cobbetts Walk, Bisley, Woking GU24 9DT (0483 481345).

Ground: Recreation Ground, Guildford Rd, Bisley.

Colours: Blue & black stripes/black/black.

Previous League: Surrey Intermediate (West)(pre-1993).

B.T.

Secretary: Graham Moxham, 75 Shaxton Crescent, New Addington CR0 0NW (0689 843338).

Ground: LTR/ASA Spts Grnd, Plough Lane, Wallington (081 647 17117).

Colours: All royal blue   **Change colours:** All red.

BURPHAM

Secretary: Kevin Brookham, 104 Manor Rd, Guildford GU2 6NR (0483 36713).

Ground: Sutherland Playing Fields, Clay Lane, Burpham, Guildford.

Colours: Yellow/green/yellow   **Change colours:** Blue/black/black.

CHOBHAM

Secretary: Mrs Daisey Walley, 8 Brook Green, Chertsey Rd, Chobham GU24 8PN   (0276 858039).

Ground: Recreation Ground, Station Road, Chobham (0276 857876)

Colours: All sky   **Change colours:** Yellow/navy/yellow.

Previous League: Combined Counties (pre-1990).

CROYDON MUNICIPAL OFFICERS

Secretary: Tony Osborn, 15 Long Lane, Croydon CR0 7AR (081 6566120).

Ground: Russell Hill Reservoir, Pampisford Road, Purley.

Colours: Blue & white/blue/blue.

FRINTON ROVERS

Secretary: Allen Bassom, 107 Stanley Park Rd, Carshalton SM5 5JJ (071 280 4606).

Ground: Thornton Heath Sports Club, Mayfield Rd, Thornton Heath.

Directions: Adjacent to Croydon Athletic F.C. (see page 369)

Colours: Red/black/black   **Change colours:** All blue.

Frinton Rovers F.C. 1992-93. Photo - Gavin Ellis-Neville.

HERSHAM ROYAL BRITISH LEGION

Secretary: Rod Stevens, 13 Leybourne Ave., Byfleet, Surrey KT14 7HB (0932 351725).
Ground: Coronation PF, Molesey Rd, Hersham (0932 227014-club, 223037-ground).
Directions: On left hand of Molesey Rd coming from Hersham BR midway between station & Barley Row r'bout.
Colours: Sky/navy/navy *(Reserves: Sky/maroon/sky).*

HINCHLEY WOOD

Secretary: Bill Jasper, 6 Paddock Close, Silverdale Rd, London SE26 4SS (081 659 0736)
Ground: Strenue Association, Lynwood Rd, Hinchley Wood, Esher (off Claygate Lane)(081 398 5374)
Directions: A3 southbound, bear left on Esher Rd (A309) directly after Aces of Spades underpass, right at 1st r'bout into Claygate Lane - Lynwood Rd turning off Claygate Lane (signposted Strenue Association).
Colours: Green & white/green/white   **Change colours:** White/blue/blue.
Previous Name: Surbiton Town (pre-1993).

HOLMESDALE

Secretary: Mark Hayes, 45 Acacia Rd, Mitcham, Surrey CR4 1LS (081 715 7679)
Ground: John Ruskin PF, Combe Lodge, Oaks Rd, Shirley, Croydon (081 654 3804).
Colours: Yellow & green stripes/yellow/yellow.   **Change colours:** White/navy/navy.
Previous League: Surrey South Eastern Combination (pre-1993).
Previous Ground: Croydon College, Coopers Rd, Waddon (pre-1992).

NETHERNE

Secretary: Steve Clark, 28 Lackford Rd, Chipstead, Surrey CR5 3TA (0737 552200).
Ground: Netherne Hospital Sports Field, Woodplace Lane, Coulsdon (0737 552064).
Directions: Star Lane traffic lights, Brighton Rd, Hooley - follow signs to Netherne Hospital.
Colours: Blue & black stripes/white/white.
Previous Name: Reedham Park (pre-1991).

OTTERSHAW

Secretary: Steve Caswell, 16 The Maples, Ottershaw KT16 0NU (0932 872133).
Ground: Woodham Court Sports Club, Martyrs Lane, Woodham, Woking.
Colours: Yellow/blue/yellow.   **Previous Ground:** Abbeylands, School Lane, Addlestone.

RAYNES PARK

Secretary: Paul Armour, 6 Woodstock Rise, Sutton, Surrey SM3 3JE (081 644 2444).
Ground: Raynes Park Sports Ground, Taunton Avenue, Raynes Park SW20 (081 946 8385).
Colours: Red & black stripes/black/black.   **Change colours:** White/black.black.

VANDYKE

Secretary: Paul Smith, 76 Court Ave., Old Coulsdon CR3 1HE (0737 552617).
Ground: Bodnant Gardens, Raynes Park.
Colours: Blue/white/blue *(Reserves: Blue & yellow/blue/yellow)*
Previous Ground: West Park Hospital, Horton Lane, Epsom (pre-1993).

WALTON CASUALS

Secretary: Stuart Roberts, 47 Foxholes, Weybridge KT13 0BN (0932 845923).
Ground: Franklyn Road Sports Ground, off Waterside Drive, Walton-on-Thames (0932 247318).
Colours: Orange & white/white/white   **Change colours:** White/blue/white

B.T. 'keeper Geoff Goveia claims a cross in a 0-0 draw at Frinton Rovers on 1st September. Photo - Dave West.

	P	W	D	L	F	A	PTS
Surrey Premier Lge	4	3	1	0	11	3	10
Sussex Co. (Div 3)	4	2	1	1	10	9	7
Essex Int. Lge	4	1	1	2	5	5	4
Middx Co. Lge	3	0	3	0	5	5	3
Kent County Lge	3	0	0	3	3	12	0

NORTH BERKSHIRE LEAGUE

DIVISION ONE	P	W	D	L	F	A	PTS
Harwell	24	20	3	1	81	17	43
Faringdon Town	24	15	6	3	53	17	36
Drayton	24	15	2	7	56	37	32
Saxton Rovers	24	13	3	8	58	36	29
Berinsfield	24	9	7	8	68	60	25
Great Shefford	24	10	5	9	45	45	25
Botley United	24	7	9	8	48	50	23
Sutton Courtenay	24	8	6	10	40	49	22
Woodcote	24	9	3	12	41	61	21
Didcot Casuals	24	6	7	11	43	61	19
Marcham	24	6	6	12	41	56	18
A.E.A.	24	2	6	16	22	59	10
Long Wittenham	24	2	5	17	27	75	9

DIVISION TWO	P	W	D	L	F	A	PTS
Benson	25	19	4	2	75	25	42
Radley	25	15	6	4	93	33	36
Grove Rangers	26	15	6	5	70	45	36
Uffington Utd	26	14	6	6	65	42	34
Wootton Sandford	26	14	5	7	75	36	33
Steventon	26	11	9	6	51	39	31
RAF Benson	26	13	2	11	75	46	28
Shrivenham	26	12	3	11	65	47	27
Saxton Rovers R.	26	5	10	11	35	54	20
Hanney United	26	9	1	16	42	72	19
Hagbourne United	26	7	3	16	33	68	17
L.Wittenham R.	26	6	3	17	41	90	15
Warborough	26	5	2	19	24	73	12
Ardington Lock	26	5	2	19	29	103	12

Divsion Three	P	W	D	L	F	A	PTS
Blewbury	24	17	3	4	78	29	37
Challow	24	16	3	5	69	32	35
Appleton	24	14	4	6	58	32	32
Radley Res.	24	10	8	6	58	49	28
Grove Res	24	9	9	6	57	49	27
Shrivenham Res	24	9	9	6	60	53	27
Stanford in the VA	24	12	2	10	54	51	26
Lambourn Res	24	8	6	10	44	49	22
Botley Res	24	9	2	13	40	74	20
Aea Res	24	8	3	13	36	46	19
Dorchester	24	4	8	12	48	71	16
Buckland	24	5	4	15	38	71	14
Faringdon Res	24	3	3	18	38	72	9

Division Four	P	W	D	L	F	A	PTS
Drayton Res	26	22	2	2	87	28	46
G Shefford Res	26	21	2	3	67	18	44
Brimpton	26	20	2	4	111	40	42
Thatcham T. 'A'	26	12	4	10	78	46	28
Harwell Res*	26	11	7	8	53	51	28
Childrey United	26	12	3	11	52	49	27
Wootton Res	26	11	5	10	57	55	27
Didcot Cas Res	26	9	4	13	55	52	22
Challow Res	26	9	3	14	50	73	21
Steventon Res	26	8	4	14	52	71	20
Coleshill	26	8	2	16	56	84	18
Woodcote Res	26	6	4	16	36	86	16
Stanford Res	26	4	4	18	35	81	12
A.E.A. 'A'	26	6	0	20	25	81	12

* - 1pt deducted.

Division Five	P	W	D	L	F	A	PTS
Sutton C. Res	28	22	2	4	96	26	46
Berinsfield Res	28	19	3	6	108	43	41
Blewbury Res	28	16	5	7	80	43	37
Faringdon A	28	14	7	7	76	57	35
Southmoor	28	12	7	9	56	59	31
Uffington Res	28	12	6	10	61	54	30
Benson Res	28	12	5	11	71	84	29
Micro Focus	28	12	4	12	66	55	28
Marcham Res	28	11	4	13	60	59	26
Dorchester Res	28	11	1	16	57	74	23
Ardington Res	28	7	6	15	43	63	20
Warborough Res	28	7	6	15	50	89	20
Coleshill Res	28	7	6	15	57	97	20
Buckland Res	28	8	2	18	36	71	18
Hagbourne Res	28	6	4	18	32	75	16

LUTON DISTRICT & SOUTH BEDS LEAGUE

PREMIER DIV.	P	W	D	L	F	A	PTS
Four Horseshoes	26	21	2	3	86	28	44
Studham	26	20	2	4	86	31	42
Luton O.B. Res.	26	17	3	6	83	42	37
Christians in Spt	26	13	3	10	78	45	29
Lewsey Park	26	12	5	9	66	48	29
A.C. Cadoza	26	12	4	10	68	59	28
Rotheram Old Boys	26	12	4	10	57	58	28
Luton Singh Sabha	26	10	5	11	49	51	25
Ebony Phoenix	26	10	4	12	58	55	24
Stockwood Ath.	26	10	4	12	57	63	24
Kent Athletic	26	9	4	13	51	68	22
Cricketers F.C.	26	7	1	18	42	106	15
Eaton Bray	26	6	2	18	50	84	14
Thistle	26	1	1	24	22	115	3

DIVISION ONE	P	W	D	L	F	A	PTS
Dagnall	24	18	4	2	84	22	40
Manshead (O'Ds)	24	19	2	3	82	32	40
Crawley Green	24	16	6	2	81	35	38
Kent Ath. Res.	24	14	3	7	60	38	31
Flitwick Town	24	11	7	6	72	54	29
Monarch A'craft Eng	24	11	7	6	55	41	29
Luton O.B. 'A'	24	10	2	12	48	58	22
Celtic S.S. Club	24	7	6	11	60	58	20
Luton Eagles	24	7	6	11	57	63	20
Lewsey Park Res.	24	6	3	15	50	73	15
Markyate	24	5	5	14	29	54	15
High Town O.B.	24	5	2	17	33	86	12
Eaton Bray Res.	24	0	1	23	19	116	1

DIVISION TWO	P	W	D	L	F	A	PTS
Thresher	24	22	2	0	107	22	46
Studham Res.	24	14	4	6	61	49	32
Brickmakers	24	14	3	7	77	37	31
Bitter End	24	11	6	7	63	52	28
Christ. in S. Res.	24	9	8	7	52	32	26
First & Last	24	11	3	10	64	49	25
Flitwick T. Res.	24	8	8	8	42	49	24
Sportsman Dunstable	24	9	6	9	42	50	24
Sportsman Harlington	24	9	2	13	41	50	20
Manshead Res.	24	7	5	12	53	77	19
Whitbread S.S. Club	24	7	4	13	43	59	18
Thistle Res.	24	6	2	16	36	88	14
Markyate Res.	24	2	1	21	20	87	5

Stanville F.C. Thornton Heath League Division One champions and Junior Cup winners 1992-93. Photo - Dave West.

B.K.T. Wanderers - Thornton Heath League Junior Cup runners-up 1992-93. Photo - Dave West.

SURREY SOUTH EASTERN COMBINATION LEAGUE

Presidents: L.P.Leech & B.F.Scott
Chairman: G.E.Ellis
Hon. Secretary: G.W.Worsfold, 41 Ballards Way,
South Croydon, CR2 7JP (081 6510856)

Despite the bad weather either side of Christmas, and the loss of four clubs from the Intermediate section almost before the season was under way, this, the second season of the League proved to be another successful one.

In five of the seven divisions there were close finishes, with the Intermediate divisions 1 & 3, each being finally decided by the last games of the season, and Intermediate division 2 being sorted out in the penultimate game. In the Junior Section, divisions 1 & 3 were also decided on the last games of the season as was the runners-up place in division 4. Holmesdale won promotion to the Surrey Premier League in their first season in division 1, by taking the one point required in their last match, after some heart-stopping moments for supporters, congratulations to them, and commiserations to Chessington & Hook United for coming so close. Raynes Park "A", in junior division 4 had a marvellous season only dropping one point in 20 games, to run away with the title, also winning the "Golden Goals" award in the process.

All five finals were closely fought battles with four being decided by a single goal, and the fifth by two late goals when the game appeared to be heading for extra-time. Thanks to all the finalists for these excellent games, several of which deserved larger attendances than they achieved.

Several clubs had successful seasons in both the League and Cup competitions. The first of these was Chessington & Hook United, who finished runners-up in intermediate division 1 and junior division 1, won junior division 3 and finished third in junior division 4, and also won both the intermediate and junior shield competitions, with their secretary, Alan Warwick winning the Secretary's award. Coney Hall won the junior division 1 and were runners-up in junior division 4 and the junior shield, also winning the linesman's award. Cobham won junior division 2, the junior league cup and were runners-up in the intermediate shield, as well as runners-up fro the "Golden Goals" award. Two other clubs to split the spoils amongst themselves were Bradbank Sports who won intermediate division 2 and were runners-up in the Senior Shield, and Bookham who were runners-up in the same division but won the Senior Shield. Also meriting a mention were Hook Venturers who won the intermediate division 3 and were ruuners-up in both intermediate division 3 and junior division 2.

The Surrey County Cup competitions were less successful than last season, but the one high point was that of Bradbank Sports in winning the intermediate cup with an excellent all round team performace, this was all the more creditable coming just a few days after they had lost our own shield final, in which they also lost the services of their goalkeeper with a serious ligament problem.

In a season when misconduct generally showed an alarming increase, the majority of our clubs are to be congratulated on keeping our figures to a very low increase.

It is to be hoped that the coming season is equally as successful and that all the members of the League continue to enjoy playing in this competition and strive to spread the name of the League far and wide.   **Gordon Worsfold (Hon. General Secretary).**

<table>
<tr><td colspan="8">INTERMEDIATE DIVISION ONE</td></tr>
<tr><td></td><td>P</td><td>W</td><td>D</td><td>L</td><td>F</td><td>A</td><td>Pts</td></tr>
<tr><td>Holmesdale</td><td>22</td><td>14</td><td>6</td><td>2</td><td>46</td><td>24</td><td>34</td></tr>
<tr><td>Chessington & Hk U</td><td>22</td><td>14</td><td>5</td><td>3</td><td>56</td><td>25</td><td>33</td></tr>
<tr><td>Colliers Wood Utd</td><td>22</td><td>14</td><td>3</td><td>5</td><td>47</td><td>30</td><td>31</td></tr>
<tr><td>Coney Hall</td><td>22</td><td>10</td><td>6</td><td>6</td><td>55</td><td>30</td><td>26</td></tr>
<tr><td>Worcester Park</td><td>22</td><td>11</td><td>3</td><td>8</td><td>50</td><td>37</td><td>25</td></tr>
<tr><td>Greenside</td><td>22</td><td>10</td><td>3</td><td>9</td><td>40</td><td>31</td><td>23</td></tr>
<tr><td>Beaufoy United</td><td>22</td><td>10</td><td>3</td><td>9</td><td>37</td><td>37</td><td>23</td></tr>
<tr><td>Battersea Park Rov.</td><td>22</td><td>6</td><td>9</td><td>7</td><td>44</td><td>46</td><td>21</td></tr>
<tr><td>Monotype Sports</td><td>22</td><td>4</td><td>6</td><td>12</td><td>29</td><td>52</td><td>14</td></tr>
<tr><td>RAS Accra Utd</td><td>22</td><td>5</td><td>3</td><td>14</td><td>40</td><td>68</td><td>13</td></tr>
<tr><td>Corona</td><td>22</td><td>5</td><td>1</td><td>16</td><td>23</td><td>50</td><td>11</td></tr>
<tr><td>Kingswood Wand'rs</td><td>22</td><td>4</td><td>2</td><td>16</td><td>35</td><td>72</td><td>10</td></tr>
</table>

<table>
<tr><td colspan="8">INTERMEDIATE DIVISION TWO</td></tr>
<tr><td></td><td>P</td><td>W</td><td>D</td><td>L</td><td>F</td><td>A</td><td>Pts</td></tr>
<tr><td>Bradbank Sports</td><td>26</td><td>21</td><td>2</td><td>3</td><td>89</td><td>33</td><td>44</td></tr>
<tr><td>Bookham</td><td>26</td><td>18</td><td>5</td><td>3</td><td>76</td><td>29</td><td>41</td></tr>
<tr><td>Sutton Athletic</td><td>26</td><td>15</td><td>4</td><td>7</td><td>82</td><td>49</td><td>34</td></tr>
<tr><td>South Godstone</td><td>26</td><td>17</td><td>0</td><td>9</td><td>60</td><td>40</td><td>34</td></tr>
<tr><td>Crescent Rovers</td><td>26</td><td>14</td><td>4</td><td>8</td><td>59</td><td>38</td><td>32</td></tr>
<tr><td>Caius</td><td>26</td><td>14</td><td>2</td><td>10</td><td>51</td><td>48</td><td>30</td></tr>
<tr><td>Fetcham</td><td>26</td><td>11</td><td>5</td><td>10</td><td>73</td><td>68</td><td>27</td></tr>
<tr><td>Reigate Town</td><td>26</td><td>12</td><td>2</td><td>12</td><td>69</td><td>62</td><td>26</td></tr>
<tr><td>Merton Risley</td><td>26</td><td>9</td><td>5</td><td>12</td><td>47</td><td>50</td><td>23</td></tr>
<tr><td>Halliford</td><td>26</td><td>8</td><td>4</td><td>14</td><td>54</td><td>51</td><td>20</td></tr>
<tr><td>Strenue</td><td>26</td><td>6</td><td>4</td><td>16</td><td>41</td><td>74</td><td>16</td></tr>
<tr><td>Bletchingley</td><td>26</td><td>6</td><td>3</td><td>17</td><td>48</td><td>92</td><td>15</td></tr>
<tr><td>Oxted & District</td><td>26</td><td>4</td><td>3</td><td>19</td><td>41</td><td>97</td><td>11</td></tr>
<tr><td>Verdayne</td><td>26</td><td>4</td><td>3</td><td>19</td><td>33</td><td>92</td><td>11</td></tr>
</table>

(tables continued overleaf)

Int. Division 3	P	W	D	L	F	A	PTS
Hook Venturers	22	14	4	4	50	23	32
Sutton High	22	14	3	5	59	35	31
Eversley Rangers	22	13	5	4	58	37	31
A.F.C. Wandgas	22	12	4	6	48	29	28
Tadworth	22	8	9	5	36	30	25
St Andrews Res.	22	10	4	8	49	41	24
Warlingham	22	9	4	9	37	31	22
Woodmansterne	20	7	7	8	49	49	*20
Cheam Village War.	22	3	10	9	32	45	x17
Surbiton T. Utd	22	6	5	11	37	62	17
Ewell	22	4	1	17	30	72	9
Three Bridges 'A'	22	2	4	16	24	55	8

* - 1 pt deducted   x 1 pt awarded

Junior Div. 1	P	W	D	L	F	A	PTS
Coney Hall Res	22	18	2	2	56	19	38
Chessington Res	22	15	6	1	60	19	36
Worcester Pk Res	22	11	5	6	70	47	27
Beaufoy Utd Res	22	10	3	9	46	41	23
Crescent Rvrs Res	22	9	4	9	49	51	22
Holmesdale Res	22	9	4	9	41	50	22
Caius Res	22	8	5	9	45	42	21
Ras Accra U. Res	22	10	0	12	51	53	20
Greenside Res	22	7	4	11	43	49	18
Battersea P.R. Res	22	4	5	13	32	50	13
Springf. B.I. Res	22	6	1	15	28	71	13
Bookham Res	22	4	3	15	23	52	11

Junior Div. 2	P	W	D	L	F	A	PTS
Cobham 'A'	18	14	2	2	78	19	30
Sutton High Res	18	11	3	4	60	26	25
Bradbank Spts Res	18	9	3	6	54	35	21
Warlingham Res	18	9	3	6	42	39	21
St Andrews 'A'	18	7	5	6	33	28	19
Sutton Ath. Res	18	8	2	8	46	38	18
Cheam V.W. Res	18	7	1	10	34	42	15
Strenue Res	18	4	4	10	30	45	12
Bletchingley Res	18	4	2	12	23	59	10
Hersham RBL 'A'	18	4	1	13	15	84	90

Junior Div. 3	P	W	D	L	F	A	PTS
Chessington 'A'	20	14	4	2	75	23	x33
Merton Risley Res	20	14	4	2	59	21	32
Netherne 'A'	20	11	5	4	70	27	27
Vandyke 'A'	20	11	5	4	73	38	*26
Worcester Pk 'A'	20	11	2	7	55	34	24
Colliers Wd Res	20	9	2	9	39	37	20
Sth Godstone Res	20	7	1	12	44	58	15
Fetcham Res	20	6	3	11	41	75	15
Woodmansterne Res	20	5	2	13	34	62	12
Corona Res	20	4	3	13	32	87	11
Verdayne Res	20	2	1	17	15	75	5

* - 1 pt deducted   x 1 pt awarded

Junior Div. 4	P	W	D	L	F	A	PTS
Raynes Pk 'A'	20	19	1	0	85	17	39
Coney Hall 'A'	20	9	8	3	51	33	26
Chessington 'B'	20	11	2	7	58	39	24
Ewell Res	20	10	4	6	42	38	24
Battersea P.R. Res	20	8	2	10	45	48	18
Osted & D. Res	20	6	4	10	46	58	16
Tadworth Res	20	5	6	9	26	44	16
Eversley Rgrs Res	20	5	6	9	40	60	16
Holmesdale 'A'	20	5	6	9	39	67	16
Reigate Town Res	20	6	3	11	34	48	15
Halliford Res	20	3	4	13	38	52	10

INTERMEDIATE DIVISION ONE RESULT CHART 92-93

HOME TEAM	1	2	3	4	5	6	7	8	9	10	11	12
1. Battersea Park Rovers	*	2-1	1-1	1-1	4-1	6-1	1-1	0-0	1-1	0-0	4-1	1-5
2. Beaufoy United	1-1	*	0-1	0-3	2-1	2-0	0-3	3-2	5-1	2-0	W-L	2-5
3. Chessington & Hook Utd	3-0	4-1	*	5-1	2-1	3-0	2-1	0-0	4-1	2-1	4-1	2-3
4. Colliers Wood United	1-0	2-3	3-1	*	3-1	3-1	2-1	0-1	4-2	5-1	4-1	2-1
5. Coney Hall	2-2	1-0	0-0	1-2	*	2-1	3-1	1-2	5-0	1-1	7-1	4-1
6. Corona	1-4	0-4	1-4	0-1	1-6	*	0-1	0-2	0-1	2-1	5-2	0-0
7. Greenside	3-2	1-3	3-3	2-0	0-0	1-2	*	0-2	6-1	6-0	2-0	2-0
8. Holmesdale	0-0	2-1	2-2	2-0	0-7	2-1	2-0	*	5-0	4-2	3-0	1-1
9. Kingswood Wanderers	7-4	2-3	0-4	3-3	1-2	4-1	0-6	*	0-2	7-1	0-1	
10. Monotype Sports	1-7	1-1	1-2	2-2	2-5	3-2	2-0	2-2	3-1	*	1-2	1-2
11. R.A.S. Accra United	10-2	2-2	4-2	1-4	1-1	0-3	1-3	2-3	5-1	1-1	*	0-6
12. Worcester Park	4-1	3-1	0-5	2-2	1-2	1-0	1-2	2-3	5-1	3-1	3-4	*

INTERMEDIATE DIVISION TWO RESULT CHART 1992-93

HOME TEAM	1	2	3	4	5	6	7	8	9	10	11	12	13	14
1. Bletchingley	*	0-1	1-2	5-3	1-8	1-3	3-2	2-3	0-2	3-2	1-2	4-1	0-5	4-1
2. Bookham	6-2	*	2-1	2-1	1-0	2-2	3-1	W-L	2-1	2-0	2-0	4-2	5-2	10-0
3. Bradbank Sports	5-2	1-1	*	3-1	5-0	3-2	W-L	6-0	4-5	1-2	5-1	5-0	5-1	
4. Caius	2-1	2-1	0-5	*	2-3	4-2	4-3	1-1	2-1	3-0	2-1	1-3	2-1	3-1
5. Crescent Rovers	5-1	2-1	2-3	0-1	*	1-4	1-1	4-0	2-1	1-1	3-5	1-3	3-0	5-0
6. Fetcham	8-2	3-7	3-8	5-3	0-1	*	5-1	1-2	7-2	2-1	4-2	3-1	3-5	2-0
7. Halliford	9-0	1-4	1-2	0-1	0-1	2-2	*	1-1	2-1	1-3	1-0	3-1	2-3	8-1
8. Merton Risley	3-3	0-1	1-4	1-2	2-0	2-2	4-1	*	3-0	5-3	0-3	3-2	1-2	3-2
9. Oxted & District	4-4	0-9	3-4	1-1	1-2	3-3	2-6	2-0	*	2-5	2-7	4-2	1-5	3-0
10. Reigate Town	1-5	0-0	0-4	3-2	1-2	2-0	0-1	4-1	9-2	*	3-1	7-3	2-7	6-1
11. South Godstone	3-2	2-5	1-2	0-3	1-2	2-5	1-1	2-5	3-1	1-5	*	3-1	3-1	3-0
12. Strenue	0-0	2-1	1-1	2-0	1-1	2-5	3-1	1-5	1-2	*	0-1	0-2		
13. Sutton Athletic	4-1	2-2	1-2	4-2	3-3	4-2	2-0	4-4	6-0	3-1	2-3	9-1	*	1-1
14. Verdayne	7-0	2-2	1-6	0-3	1-5	2-2	1-3	3-2	3-2	1-4	0-1	2-4	0-5	*

INTERMEDIATE DIVISION THREE RESULT CHART 1992-93

HOME TEAM	1	2	3	4	5	6	7	8	9	10	11	12
1. A.F.C. Wandgas	*	6-2	5-2	0-3	0-1	5-1	2-0	2-3	1-1	3-2	1-0	5-1
2. Cheam Village Warriors	1-1	*	2-1	0-2	1-1	2-3	4-4	2-2	2-2	2-0	1-1	*1-1
3. Ewell	0-2	3-2	*	2-5	0-3	0-4	8-2	1-5	1-3	6-0	1-2	0-4
4. Eversley Rangers	1-0	2-2	7-0	*	1-1	2-2	W-L	2-5	2-2	3-2	1-0	5-2
5. Hook Venturers	0-1	3-1	1-0	4-1	*	0-1	7-2	2-1	2-1	3-0	5-1	
6. St Andrews Reserves	6-1	0-2	9-0	2-1	2-5	*	2-3	0-4	0-1	1-0	1-0	1-6
7. Surbiton Town United	2-2	3-2	1-2	5-2	2-2	1-4	*	2-1	2-0	2-1	1-3	2-4
8. Sutton High	0-5	3-0	3-1	2-3	3-2	2-1	4-1	*	3-0	2-0	1-1	4-1
9. Tadworth	1-0	2-1	6-0	1-1	0-1	3-0	0-2	*	1-2	2-1	2-2	
10. Three Bridges 'A'	0-3	1-1	0-0	2-5	0-2	1-4	1-1	3-5	1-2	*	1-3	4-3
11. Warlingham	1-1	3-0	3-1	1-4	3-2	1-1	4-0	2-3	2-3	2-0	*	4-1
12. Woodmansterne Sports	1-2	1-1	3-1	2-5	1-1	1-1	7-1	2-1	1-1	2-2	2-0	*

* - 1 pt to Cheam - Woodmamsterne fielded ineligible player

JUNIOR DIVISION ONE RESULT CHART 1992-93

HOME TEAM	1	2	3	4	5	6	7	8	9	10	11	12
1. Battersea Park Rovers Res	*	0-1	1-3	1-1	1-2	0-3	2-1	1-1	2-2	2-3	3-1	2-3
2. Beaufoy United Reserves	7-1	*	2-1	3-1	2-2	0-4	0-3	0-3	2-3	2-1	2-0	2-3
3. Bookham Reserves	2-2	1-3	*	0-1	0-0	1-2	0-4	1-1	2-1	W-L	3-1	1-5
4. Caius Reserves	3-1	1-1	7-3	*	0-1	1-4	0-2	1-1	5-2	2-0	5-4	1-1
5. Chessington & H. Utd Res	0-0	2-1	2-1	2-0	*	0-0	4-2	3-2	4-1	3-0	11-0	1-1
6. Coll Hall Reserves	1-5	3-2	2-0	4-2	2-1	*	4-0	3-2	3-0	3-0	1-0	0-0
7. Crescent Rovers Reserves	6-2	1-5	6-2	3-1	0-1	1-6	*	1-1	2-4	1-4	4-1	4-3
8. Greenside Reserves	3-1	2-4	W-L	0-3	0-4	0-2	1-2	*	5-2	1-6	4-0	4-5
9. Holmesdale Reserves	2-1	1-1	4-0	3-0	2-2	1-0	1-1	2-5	*	2-1	2-0	2-4
10. R.A.S. Accra Utd Reserves	2-0	2-1	5-1	4-3	2-4	3-4	5-1	2-6	L-W	*	6-1	3-2
11. Springfield Battersea I. Res	2-1	1-4	1-0	1-6	1-7	0-2	2-2	1-0	3-0	3-0	*	3-0
12. Worcester Park Res	1-3	5-1	2-1	1-1	1-4	0-3	2-2	5-1	7-4	11-2	8-2	*

Kingswood Wanderers withdrew - record expunged

JUNIOR DIVISION TWO RESULT CHART 1992-93

HOME TEAM	1	2	3	4	5	6	7	8	9	10
1. Bletchingley Reserves	*	W-L	3-1	1-1	2-3	W-L	2-6	1-5	0-4	2-7
2. Bradbank Sports Res	12-0	*	0-4	3-1	2-2	2-2	1-1	4-0	4-0	2-4
3. Cheam Village War. Res	2-1	3-4	*	2-4	3-0	0-2	5-1	0-5	0-3	6-1
4. Cobham 'A'	8-1	4-0	4-1	*	9-1	7-0	3-3	6-1	1-2	4-1
5. Hersham R.B.L. Reserves	2-1	2-5	2-1	0-10	*	0-1	0-4	0-10	0-2	0-7
6. St Andrews 'A'	2-2	1-3	L-W	1-2	4-0	*	1-0	4-4	4-3	3-1
7. Strenue Reserves	2-1	1-3	2-3	0-4	1-2	1-3	*	1-1	4-3	1-4
8. Sutton Athletic Reserves	1-5	4-6	5-1	0-2	4-1	1-2	1-0	*	0-3	3-0
9. Sutton High Reserves	1-0	2-1	5-1	1-2	17-0	3-3	6-0	0-3	*	3-1
10. Warlingham Reserves	2-1	4-2	1-1	1-6	1-0	1-0	2-1	2-2	2-2	*

Monotype Sports Reserves withdrew - record expunged

JUNIOR DIVISION THREE RESULT CHART 1992-93

HOME TEAM	1	2	3	4	5	6	7	8	9	10	11
1. Chessington & H. Utd 'A'	*	1-5	11-2	5-0	0-2	3-2	3-0	*1-1	4-0	4-2	4-0
2. Collier Wd Utd Res	0-1	*	3-1	6-1	1-3	0-3	2-4	3-7	6-1	3-1	3-4
3. Corona Reserves	1-4	1-1	*	4-0	0-8	2-6	4-3	1-2	2-2	0-2	0-4
4. Fetcham Reserves	2-4	2-0	3-4	*	0-3	0-17	2-5	4-2	6-2	3-1	4-1
5. Merton Risley Reserves	2-2	4-0	8-1	1-1	*	1-0	4-2	4-1	2-0	0-1	1-1
6. Netherne 'A'	2-2	0-2	0-0	9-3	2-2	*	6-1	1-3	3-0	6-1	2-2
7. South Godstone Reserves	1-4	0-1	8-1	1-2	3-2	2-3	*	2-2	2-1	W-L	2-3
8. Vandyke 'A'	1-1	0-0	12-1	4-4	4-0	2-4	8-1	*	7-1	5-3	2-4
9. Verdayne Reserves	0-12	0-1	1-6	1-0	2-3	L-W	3-1	1-3	*	0-2	0-3
10. Woodmansterne Sports Res	0-10	2-0	3-0	3-3	1-4	1-1	4-6	0-4	5-0	*	2-9
11. Worcester Park 'A'	L-W	1-2	6-1	2-1	0-3	0-3	3-0	2-3	8-0	2-1	*

JUNIOR DIVISION FOUR RESULT CHART 1992-93

HOME TEAM	1	2	3	4	5	6	7	8	9	10	11
1. Chessington & H. Utd 'B'	*	2-3	1-1	0-1	3-1	2-5	5-0	1-2	3-2	4-1	4-2
2. Coney Hall 'A'	1-3	*	2-2	1-1	W-L	1-1	2-2	1-4	3-1	4-0	3-1
3. Eversley Rangers Reserves	1-4	0-8	*	4-4	3-3	6-6	5-1	3-7	4-1	3-0	3-2
4. Ewell Reserves	5-2	2-2	W-L	*	6-1	3-1	5-1	0-3	0-5	0-0	1-2
5. Halliford Reserves	2-3	2-6	1-2	1-3	*	2-2	3-5	0-3	3-6	6-1	0-3
6. Holmesdale 'A'	2-7	4-1	2-1	1-2	0-4	*	3-2	1-4	1-1	3-3	1-6
7. Oxted & District Reserves	2-2	1-1	12-1	3-0	4-3	3-4	*	0-9	3-2	4-2	0-1
8. Raynes Park 'A'	2-1	2-2	3-0	6-1	W-L	12-0	4-0	*	5-2	2-0	7-2
9. Reigate Town Reserves	0-4	1-3	W-L	4-1	3-2	2-0	2-1	1-4	*	1-1	1-6
10. Tadworth Reserves	4-2	1-1	0-0	0-1	0-2	4-1	2-2	0-2	2-1	*	2-1
11. Battersea Park Rovers 'A'	2-5	3-6	3-1	1-3	2-2	1-1	2-0	2-4	2-1	1-3	*

SENIOR CUP 1992-93

First Round

Colliers Wood United (w/o) Busheymead (w'drew)	
Corona v Chessington & Hook United	0-3
Hook Venturers (w/o) Battersea Ironsides (w'drew)	
Warlingham v Halliford	2-1
Oxted & District v Merton Risley	0-4
Surbiton Town United v Battersea Park Rovers	1-9
Sutton Athletic v Sutton High	8-0
St Andrews Reserves (w/o) N.P.L. (w'drew)	
Cheam Village Warriors v Greenside	3-1
Bookham v Coney Hall	3-0

Second Round

South Godstone v Strenue	2-4
Bookham v Woodmansterne Sports	3-0
Bletchingley v Sutton Athletic	5-6(aet)
Battersea Park Rovers v Cheam Village War.	4-0
Ewell v R.A.S. Accra United	0-5
Monotype Sports v Merton Risley	4-1
Verdayne v Hook Venturers	1-2
Kingswood Wanderers v St Andrews Reserves	2-0
Eversley Rangers v Warlingham	0-2
Bradbank Sports v Crescent Rovers	2-0(aet)
Chessington & Hook United v Worcester Park	2-1
Reigate Town v Beaufoy United	1-4
A.F.C. Wandgas v Three Bridges 'A'	2-1
Fetcham (w/o) Morfax (withdrew)	
Colliers Wood United v Tadworth	5-0
Caius v Holmesdale	2-2(aet),3-5

Third Round

Strenue v Sutton Athletic	2-6
Bookham v Holmesdale	1-7
Chessington & Hook v Kingswood Wdrs	1-1,1-5
Monotype Sports v A.F.C. Wandgas	2-3
Battersea Park Rovers v Colliers Wood United	3-2
R.A.S. Accra United v Hook Venturers	0-1
Warlingham v Beaufoy Utd	1-1(aet),0-1
Bradbank Sports v Fetcham	1-4

Quarter-Finals

Holmesdale v Chessington & Hook Utd	5-0
A.F.C. Wandgas v Battersea Park Rovers	1-2
Beaufoy United v Hook Venturers	2-3
Sutton Athletic v Fetcham	2-3(aet)

Semi-Finals

Holmesdale v Battersea Park Rovers	1-2(aet)
Fetcham v Hook Venturers	1-4

Final: Battersea Park Rovers 1, Hook Venturers 0

JUNIOR CUP 1992-93

Coney Hall 'A' v Bookham Res	1-1*(aet)*,4-3		Cheam Village W. Res v Sutton Athletic Res		3-0

Coney Hall 'A' v Bookham Res 1-1*(aet)*,4-3
Warlingham Res v Netherne 'A' 0-1
Woodmansterne Res *(w/o)* Busheymead Res *(w'drew)*
Fetcham Res v Sutton High Reserves 1-8
Springfield Bat. I. 'B' v R.A.S. Accra Res 3-4*(aet)*
Raynes Park 'A' v Chessington & Hook Res 3-5
Hook Venturers Res *(w'drew)* Colliers Wd Res *(w/o)*
Holmesdale Res v Hersham 'A' 6-1*(H'dale expelled)*

Cheam Village W. Res v Sutton Athletic Res 3-0
Ewell Reserves v Oxted & District Res 4-2
Chessington & Hook Utd 'A' v Vandyke Res 4-3
Eversley Res v Holmesdale 'A' 1-7*(H'dale expelled)*
Worcester Park 'A' v Crescent Rovers Reserves 3-0
St Andrews 'A' v Merton Risley Reserves 1-3
Worcester Park Reserves v Tadworth Reserves 1-0

Second Round
Vandyke Reserves v Eversley Rgrs Res 0-5
Netherne 'A' v Corona Reserves 9-1
Hersham R.B.L. 'A' v R.A.S. Accra Utd Res 1-6
Colliers Wd Res v Woodmansterne Res 7-6*(aet)*
Caius Res v Chessington Res 2-2*(aet)*,0-2
Reigate Town Res v Worcester Park Res 0-15
Springfield Battersea I. 'A' v Ewell Reserves 0-2
Strenue Res v Chessington & Hook Utd 'B' 5-3

Cobham 'A' v Bradbank Res 4-4*(aet, B'bank expelled)*
Greenside Reserves v Coney Hall Reserves 1-6
Coney Hall 'A' v Sutton High Reserves 5-1
Sth Godstone Res v Battersea P.R. Res 3-3*(aet)*,1-4
Battersea Park Rvrs Res v Bletchingley Reserves 5-0
Chessington & Hook Utd 'A' v Worcester Pk 'A' 3-0
Cheam Village W. Res v Merton Risley Res 1-6
Halliford Res v Beaufoy United Reserves 1-6

Third Round
RAS Accra Utd Res v Eversley Rgrs Res 6-5*(aet)*
Netherne 'A' v Battersea Pk Rvrs Res 2-0*(aet)*
Chessington Res v Beaufoy United Reserves
Coney Hall Res v Battersea Park Rvrs 'A' 6-2*(aet)*

Merton Risley Res v Chessington & Hook 'A' 2-1
Strenue Reserves v Worcester Park Reserves 2-4
Ewell Res v Colliers Wood Utd Res 2-2*(aet)*,0-1
Cobham 'A' v Coney Hall 'A' 1-0

Quarter-Finals
Chessington & Hook Res v Cobham 'A' 1-2
Netherne 'A' v Coney Hall Reserves 3-6

RAS Accra Res v Colliers Wood United Reserves 3-1
Worcester P. Res v Merton Res 4-3*(ab. score stood)*

Semi-Finals
Coney Hall Reserves v Cobham 'A' 0-2

R.A.S. Accra Reserves v Worcester Park Reserves 0-8

Final: Cobham 'A' 1, Worcester Park Reserves 0

'ELLIS PRINTERS' LEAGUE SENIOR SHIELD
Verdayne *(w/o)* Morfax *(withdrew)*
Merton Risley v Crescent Rovers 0-9
Ewell v Bletchingley 1-5
Three Bridges 'A' v Bookham 0-3
Fetcham v Halliford 2-0
Tadworth v Woodmansterne Sports 4-0

Sutton High v Eversley Rangers 0-5
Warlingham *(w/o)* N.P.L. *(withdrew)*
South Godstone v Sutton Athletic 2-1
A.F.C. Wandgas v Cheam Village Warriors 4-3
Oxted & District v Caius 1-2
St Andrews Reserves v Hook Venturers 4-1

Second Round
Bookham v Strenue 5-2
Reigate Town v Bletchingley 0-5
Fetcham v St Andrews Reserves 4-0
South Godstone v Eversley Rangers 2-3

Bradbank Sports v A.F.C. Wandgas 2-0
Tadworth v Surbiton Town United 5-4*(aet)*
Verdayne v Warlingham 3-0
Caius v Crescent Rovers 2-6

Quarter-Finals
Bradbank Sports v Crescent Rovers 4-0
Bookham v Tadworth 4-2

Verdayne v Bletchingley 5-5*(aet)*,1-2
Fetcham v Eversley Rangers 4-2

Semi-Finals
Bookham v Fetcham 0-0*(aet)*,1-5

Bradbank Sports v Bletchingley 2-1

Final: Bookham 1, Bradbank Sports 0

ELLIS PRINTERS' INTERMEDIATE LEAGUE SHIELD
Worcester Park Res v Battersea P.R. Res 3-1
Greenside Reserves v Coney Hall Res 3-0
Hersham R.B.L. 'A' v Cheam Village Res 1-2
Strenue *(w/o)* Busheymead Res *(withdrew)*

Bookham Reserves v Caius Reserves 1-5
St Andrews 'A' v Holmesdale Reserves 3-6
R.A.S. Accra *(w/o)* Kingwood Wdrs Res *(withdrew)*
Crescent Rovers Res v Bradbank Sports Reserves 4-3

Second Round
Sutton Ath. Res v Caius Reserves 2-3
Bletchingley Res v Cobham 'A' 1-5
Strenue Res v Chessington & Hook Res 0-3
Cheam Village Res v R.A.S. Accra Utd Res 1-3

Crescent Rovers Res v Beaufoy United Res 1-2
Sutton High Res v Greenside Res 3-1*(Sutton expelled)*
Springfield Battersea Res v Worcester Park Res 2-7
Warlingham Reserves v Holmesdale Reserves 1-0

Quarter-Finals
Beaufoy United Res v R.A.S. Accra Res 6-2
Chessington Res v Greenside Reserves 5-0

Caius Reserves v Worcester Park Res 2-1
Warlingham Reserves v Cobham 'A' 1-3

Semi-Finals
Caius Reserves v Cobham 'A' 0-3

Chessington & Hook Utd Res v Beaufoy Utd Res 5-2

Final: Chessington & Hook United Reserves 3, Cobham 'A' 1

ELLIS PRINTERS' LEAGUE JUNIOR SHIELD
Sth Godstone Res v Chessington 'B' 3-3*(aet)*,2-1
Corona Reserves v Tadworth Reserves 2-8
Raynes Park 'A' v Netherne 'A' 3-1
Battersea P.R. 'A' v Vandyke 'A' 0-1

Eversley R. Res v Chessington 'A' 4-4*(aet)*,3-7
Oxted & District Reserves v Worcester Park 'A' 4-2
Holmesdale 'A' v Merton Res 0-8*(Merton expelled)*

Second Round
Ewell Reserves v Reigate Town Reserves 1-2
Colliers Wd Utd Res v Fetcham Reserves 1-3
Oxted & District Reserves v Raynes Park 'A' 1-0
Tadworth Reserves v Holmesdale 3-0

Coney Hall 'A' v Verdayne Reserves 9-1
Chessington & Hook 'A' v Woodmansterne S. Res 6-3
South Godstone Reserves v Vandyke 'A' 3-2
Halliford Res *(w/o)* Springfield B.I. 'B' *(w'drew)*

Quarter-Finals
Fetcham Reserves v South Godstone Res 0-1
Oxted & District Res v Tadworth Reserves 0-5

Halliford Res v Chessington 'A' 2-2*(H'ford expelled)*
Coney Hall 'A' v Reigate Town Reserves 3-0

Semi-Finals
Tadworth Reserves v Coney Hall 'A' 0-2

Chessington & Hook Utd 'A' v Sth Godstone Res 2-1

Final: Chessington & Hook United 'A' 2, Coney Hall 'A' 1

INTERMEDIATE DIVISION ONE CLUBS 1993-94

ASHTEAD
Secretary: Ralph Grange, 58 Leatherhead Rd, Ashtead, Surrey KT21 2SY (0372 276901).
Ground: Ashtead Rec., Barnett Wood Lane, Ashtead.　　　　　　**Colours:** Gold/black/black.
Directions: Epsom to Leatherhead road (A24), in Ashtead village turn right into Woodfield Lane, Barnett Wood Lane half mile on left, ground just along on left. Ashtead station 3 mins from ground. Bus 418 to The Woodman pub.

BATTERSEA PARK CORONA
Secretary: A Brown, 96 Ethelburga Tower, Rosenau Rd, Battersea SW11 4AB (071 252 8080).
Ground: Dundonald Rec, Avebury Rd SW1 (081 542 3282) *Reserves: Wimbledon Pk, Revelsoke Rd SW19.*
Colours: White/blue/white *(Reserves: All red, 'A': Grey/navy/navy).*
Directions: A298 to Merton, turn into Merton Hall Rd (opposite Nelson Hosp.), Avebury Avenue is 2nd right. Nearest Station is Wimbledon Chase. *For Wimbledon Park: A218 from Wandsworth (Merton Rd) - Revelsoke Rd is on right as road becomes Durnsford Rd. From Merton take A218 Haydens Rd which becomes Durnsford Rd - Revelstoke Rd on left where road becomes Merton Rd.*

BEAUFOY UNITED
Secretary: Derek Dalrymple, 54 Blythe House, Magee Str., Kennington, London SE11 5TY (071 793 7046).
Ground: Morden Park School Spts Centre, Hillcross Avenue, Morden.　　　　**Colours:** All blue
Directions: A3 to Shannaon Corner then A298, right into Grand Drive at 1st lights, 1st exit (Hillcross Ave.) at large island, ground on right after just over half a mile.

BOOKHAM
Secretary: Ian Waller, 8 Northumberland Rd, Bordon, Hants GU35 9TR (0420 487618).
Grnd: Crystie Rd, Recreation Grnd, Dorking Rd, Bookham (0372 459482).　　**Cols:** Amber/black/black.
Directions: M25 jct 9, A246 Guildford road, left into Leatherhead Rd 400yds after 'Jet' garage in Bookham, 1st left into Dorking Rd - ground 100yds on left. Bookham Station. Buses 408, 478, 479.

BRADBANK SPORTS
Secretary: J E Bergamin, 37 Cambridge Rd, Teddington, Middx TW11 8DT (081 977 3603).
Ground: Dundonald Rec (directions as Battersea Pk Corona above). **Colours:** All red *(Reserves: all blue).*

CHESSINGTON & HOOK UNITED
Secretary: Alan Warwick, 38 Hartfield Rd, Chessington, Surrey KT9 2PW (081 397 1843).
Ground: Chalk Lane, Chessington, Surrey (0372 729892).　　　　**Cols:** All blue *(Res: white/blue/blue).*
Directions: Chalky Lane is off A243 opposite Chessington World of Adventure Theme Park. BR to Chessington South station.

COLLIERS WOOD UNITED
Secretary: Tony Hurrell, 1 Inglewood, Pixton Way, Forestdale, Croydon CR0 9LN (081 651 3259).
Ground: Wibbundune Spts Ground, Robin Hood Way (A3) SW20 (081 942 8062)
Colours: Sky & navy/navy/sky.
Directions: On A3 (Robin Hood Way) between Robin Hood Gate and Raynes Park junctions; turn left immediately at 2nd footbridge from the Robin Gate junction.

CONEY HALL
Secretary: Bill Lennox, 1 Southway, Hayes, Kent BR2 7LR (081 462 7514).
Ground: Tiepigs Lane, Coney Hall, West Wickham, Kent (081 462 9103).　　　**Colours:** Red/black/black.
Directions: Gravel Hill continue along Kent Gate Way, across r'bout along Addington Village Rd and Addington Rd until next r'bout, continue ahead, 2nd left down Tiepigs Lane, ground on left before railway bridge.

CRESCENT ROVERS
Secretary: M D Bishop, 64 Wolsey Crescent, New Addington, Surrey CR0 0PF (0689 842996).
Ground: Southern Rail Sports Club, Mollison Drive, Wallington.　　　　**Colours:** Green/black/black.
Directions: A232 from central Croydon, take B271 Stafford Rd opposite Wilson School, cross A23 to 1st lights, left into Mollison Drive, ground 300yds on right. Bus 154 from central Croydon passes ground.

GREENSIDE
Secretary: E G Moon, 10 Curran Ave., Wallington SM6 7JW (081 669 7985).
Ground: Orchard Spts Centre, William Booth Rd, Anerley SE20 (081 778 3500).　　**Colours:** All green.
Directions: Ground off Anerley Rd (A214) almost oppisite Anerley BR station next to Old Town Hall.

PERRYWOOD SPORTS
Secretary: Michael Overmass, 94 Sandcross Lane, Reigate, Surrey (0737 243646).
Ground: Perrywood Spts & Social Club, Honeycrock Lane, Salfords (0737 763250).
Colours: Amber & black/black/black.
Directions: South on A23, Salfords is 5 miles beyond Redhill, left into Honeycrock Lane, ground entrance 1st right after railway bridge.

SOUTH GODSTONE
Secretary: Steve Scott-Douglas, 'Rowans', Eden Vale, East Grinstead, W. Sussex RH19 2JH (0342 314484).
Ground: Lagham Rd PF, Sth Godstone, Surrey (0342 892490).　　**Cols:** Red/blue/red *(res: all red)*
Directions: South from Godstone on A22 for about two and a half miles, as you enter South Godstone, 1st left into Harcourt Way, follow to end, pavillion immediately in front. 719 Green Line and 409 buses.

SUTTON ATHLETIC
Secretary: Mrs Diane Goff, 265 Malden Rd, Cheam SM3 8ET (081 715 5069).
Ground: Overton Rd Sports Ground, Sutton　　　　**Colours:** Red/blue/blue.
Directions: From Sutton BR take turning opposite station, Mulgrave Rd, Overton Rd 4th turning left, proceed to end of Overton Rd for ground.

WORCESTER PARK
Secretary: Laurie Burrage, 36 Lynwood Drive, Worcester Park KT4 7AB (081 330 1289).
Ground: Skinners Field, Green Lane, Worcester Park KT4 8AJ (081 337 4995).
Directions: Off A3 at New Malden r'bout onto A2043, 1st left under 2nd railway bridge into Green Lane. Entrance opposite Brookside Crescent. Adjacent to Worcester Park (BR) station.
Colours: Blue & white/white/blue.

INTERMEDIATE DIVISION TWO CLUBS 1993-94

A.F.C. WANDGAS
Secretary: B F Fry, Flat 2, 15 Effingham, Long Ditton, Surrey KT6 5JZ (081 398 9673).
Ground: Wandgas Spts Ground, Grafton Rd, Worcester Park　　　　**Colours:** Claret & blue/blue/claret.
Directions: A2043 Central Rd, Worcester Park going towards A3, under railway bridge and left up The Avenue, at top of hill go down other side - Grafton Rd - ground at crossroads with Cromwell Rd.

BLETCHINGLEY
Secretary: Andy Skinner, 'Motspur', Oxted Rd, Godstone, Surrey RH9 8AD (0883 743957).
Ground: Grange Meadow, Bletchingley (0883 742844).　　**Colours:** Green & yellow stripes/green/yellow.
Directions: A23 to Redhill, turn onto A25 Westerham Road, approx. 5 miles Bletchingley, 'Plough' PH on left, ground opposite.

CAIUS
Secretary: T Butler, 38 Hardington, Belmont Str., Chalk Farm NW1 8HN (071 485 6035).
Ground: Richardson Evans PF (081 228 6642).　　　　**Colours:** Sky/navy/navy.
Directions: Roehampton Vale on A3 at the Robin Hood Gate.

EVERSLEY RANGERS
Secretary: Malcolm Berks, 101 The Glade, Shirley, Croydon, Sutton (081 654 8821).
Ground: Harvington Rec., South Eden Park Rd, Beckenham.　　　**Cols:** Red & white (change: all white).
Directions: Upper Elmers End Rd (A214), under rail bridge at Eden Park, left onto A230 South End Park Rd, ground on left (Harvington Est.). BR to Eden Park station.

FETCHAM
Secretary: Howard Taylor, 53 Cock Lane, Fetcham, Surrey (0372 377557).
Ground: Cock Lane Rec., Fetcham, Surrey.　　　　**Colours:** All red *(Reserves: Blue/white/blue)*.
Directions: Turn into The Street at Tudor Motors Garage in village centre, Cock Lane 1st right - ground 400yds on right. From Leatherhead bus 462 to Fetcham, or 416 (limited time) to Cock Lane.

HALLIFORD
Secretary: Danny F Waite, 46 Halliford Rd, Sunbury, Middx TW16 6DR (0932 789286).
Ground: Kenyngton Rec.　　　　**Cols:** White (blue trim)/blue (white trim) *(Reverse for reserves)*.
Directions: M3 jct 1 (Sunbury Cross), 2nd exit on left Vicarage Rd, proceed down road, 1st turning past Beechwood Ave. (half mile), into Byron Way, follow road into Kenyngton Rec.

HINCHLEY WOOD UNITED
Secretary: Tony Arnold, 30 Cheshire Gdns, Chessington, Surrey KT9 2PR (081 397 9965).
Ground: Strenue Association, Lynwood Rd, Hinchley Wood (off Claygate Lane)(081 398 5374)
Colours: Sky & white/navy/navy *(Reserves: Blue & red/red/blue)*.
Directions: A3 southbound, bear left on Esher Rd (A309) directly after Aces of Spades underpass, right at 1st r'bout into Claygate Lane - Lynwood Rd turning off Claygate Lane (signposted Strenue Association).

HOOK VENTURERS
Secretary: Malcolm A Benham, 11 Ellingham Rd, Chessington, Surrey KT9 2JA (081 397 3638).
Ground: King Edward Rec., Hook Way, Chessington　　　　**Colours:** Sky/blue/blue.
Directions: BR from Waterloo to Surbiton station then 72 bus (stops outside ground). This bus also from Kingston BR station, or Hopper bus.

MERTON TOWN
Secretary: Fred G Brockwell, 28 Wordsworth Drive, Cheam, Surrey SM3 8HF (081 715 5052).
Ground: Merton Town Rec., Middleton Rd, Merton.
Previous Name: Merton Risley (pre'93) **Colours:** Red & black hoops/black/black *(Reserves: Navy & white)*.
Directions: Adjacent to St Helier BR station. Bus 93 to Central Rd from Morden tube; 5 mins from ground - turn right into Green Lane, Middleton Rd is 200yds on left, ground behind row of shops.

OXTED & DISTRICT
Secretary: Pete King, 2 The Greenway, Oxted, Surrey RH8 0JY (0883 716001).
Ground: Master Park, Oxted, Surrey (0883 712792).　　　　**Colours:** All red.
Directions: Rail to Oxted, bus 410 to Master Park. Or, A25 from Westerham or Redhill to Church Lane, Oxted. Ground quarter mile on left.

R.A.S. ACCRA UNITED
Secretary: George Wilson, 69a Perry Vale, Forest Hill, London SE23 2NJ (081 291 3659).
Ground: Pynners P.F., Dulwich Common　　　　**Colours:** All red *(Res: Yellow/black/black)*.
Previous Name: R.A.S. Knights (pre'92).
Directions: A205 Sth Circular to West Dulwich, ground on right 500yds past Dulwich College. BR to West Dulwich or Forest Hill.

REIGATE TOWN
Secretary: Mrs Anita Head, 82 The Crescent, Horley, Surrey RH6 7NU (0293 782084).
Ground: Reigate Heath, Flanchford Rd, Reigate　　　**Cols:** Green (white & black diamonds)/black/black.
Directions: A25 from Reigate towards Dorking, left at Black Horse into Flanchard Rd, grnd on right.

SUTTON HIGH
Secretary: Ian Daggett, 178 Stanley Park Rd, Carshalton Beeches, Surrey (081 661 6323).
Ground: University of London Spts Grnd, Motspur Park *(Reserves as Cheam Village page 415)*.
Directions: From Grand Drive left into Westway, left at end into West Barnes Lane. Over level crossing, ground on right. Motspur Park (BR).

VERDAYNE
Secretary: Andrew West, 11 Harrington Close, Beddingtom, Croydon CR0 4UN (081 680 5507).
Ground: Valley Spts, off White Knobs Way, Caterham　　　**Cols:** Grey (red trim)*(Res: Blue & yellow)*.
Directions: Thru Caterham on Godstone road, White Knobs Way on right just before A22 junction. Nb. Do not use Caterham bypass; no right turns on bypass.

INTERMEDIATE DIVISION THREE CLUBS 1993-94

CHARLWOOD
Secretary: Neil Maguire, 26 Birkdale Drive, Ifield, Crawley, West Sussex RH11 0TS (0293 512765).
Ground: The Recreation Ground, The Street, Charlwood   **Previous Lge:** Redhill & Dist. (champs 92-93).
Colours: Amber/black/black *(Reserves: Red & white/white/red).*
Directions: Gatwick Airport exit off M23, over 1st island, right at next for Redhill, join dual-c'way for 400yds, left at island to Charlwood (3 miles), pitch on left corner opposite Rising Sun. Via A23 to island at start of Gatwick. Straight over (signed Charlwood), then as above.

CHEAM VILLAGE WARRIORS
Secretary: Peter Clapton, 1 Hemmingford Rd, North Cheam, Surrey SM3 8HG (081 644 6894).
Grnd: Tattenham Way Rec., The Drive, Banstead **Cols:** Yel. & blue/blue/blue *(Res: Red & white/red/red)*
Directions: A217 from Sutton, right at Tattenham Way into Piquets Rise, left into The Drive, ground opposite. Banstead BR station. Buses 420 and 422 pass end of The Drive.

CHESSINGTON WHITE HART
Secretary: Alan Vincent, 38 The Causeway, Hook, Chessington, Surrey KT9 1DB (081 397 9633).
Grnd: Claygate Rec., Dalmore Ave., Claygate **Cols:** Green/white/green *(Res: Yellow/green/yellow)*
Directions: A3 southbound, left onto A309 Esher Rd, left signed Claygate (Woodstock Lane South), right into Red Lane then into St Leonards Rd, right onto High Street at end, immediate left into Hare Lane, Dalmore Avenue 1st left.

CHIPSTEAD 'A'
Ground & Directions: Corrigan Ave., Coulsdon - A23 to Coulsdon, into Chipstead Valley Rd at Red Lion, right at lights, up hill over railway bridge, left into Woodmansterne Rd, left into St Andrews Rd, 3rd left Alexander Rd leads into Whitehorn Ave. - Corrigan Ave. on left *(other details as per page 396).*

COBHAM 'A'
Secretary: Gerry Petit, 149 Bridge Rd, Chessington, Surrey KT9 2RT (081 397 0433).
Ground & Directions: Cobham Rec, Portsmouth Rd & Anvil Lane - opposite Police Station which is at junction of Portsmouth Rd & Northfield Rd *(other details as per page 396).*

RACAL DECCA
Sec: T J Hanlon, 86 Queens Drive, Surbiton, Surrey KT5 8PP (081 399 5319) *No calls after 9pm.*
Ground: Racal Decca Spts & Social Club, Old Kingston Rd, Tolworth (081 337 0519).
Colours: All blue *(Reserves: Red & black/black/black)*
Directions: A3 to Tolworth, Old Kingston Rd towards Epsom, left after 300yds (just after bridge), entrance to ground on left.

ST ANDREWS RESERVES *(details as per page 370)*

SOUTHSIDE
Secretary: Scott Mulholland, 26 The Alders, Aldrington Rd, London SW16 1TP (081 677 0854).
Ground: Cottenham Park, Raynes Park **Colours:** Sky & navy.
Directions: From Raynes Park BR station head towards Kingston, 2nd right (Durnham Rd), 4th left Melbury Gdns, ground 50yds on left.

TADWORTH
Secretary: M Lippett, 28 Rushmere Ct, The Avenue, Worcester Park, Surrey KT4 7EP (081 337 4987).
Ground: Tadworth Village Green **Cols:** Green & white stripes/gr./gr. *(Res: Green/green/black)*
Directions: From Burgh Heath Lights take A217 to large island, 3rd exit B2032 Dorking Rd, 1st left into Mill Rd B290 and park.

THORNTON HEATH ROVERS
Secretary: Ron Jones, 38a Brighton Rd, Coulsdon, Surrey CR5 2BA (081 668 4895).
Ground: Highbury Ave., Thornton Heath (081 764 5445) **Colours:** Black & white/black/red.
Directions: Thornton Hth BR station, left to clock tower, left into Parchmore Rd, left into County Rd after 1 mile (opposite Bricklayers Arms), 1st right Highbury Ave., ground on right.

THREE BRIDGES 'A'
Ground & Directions: Three Bridges Rec, Three Bridges Rd. Right out of Three Bridges BR station into Three Bridges Rd, Rec 1st left past 'Downs TV Shop'.

WARLINGHAM
Secretary: Stan Smith, 14a Abbey Rd, Selsdon, Surrey CR2 8NG (081 651 2439).
Grnd: Church Lane, Warlingham (0883 622943) **Cols:** White & black stripes.
Directions: Bus 403.

WOODMANSTERNE SPORTS
Secretary: David Pryor, 16 Tonbridge Close, Woodmansterne, Surrey SM7 3JD (0737 363330).
Ground: The Park, Woodmansterne Str., Woodmansterne (0737 350109). **Colours:** Gold/black/gold.
Directions: A2022 Purley-Epsom road, B278 Carshalton Rd to end, turn right past pub, clubhouse/car park on right.

JUNIOR SECTION 1993-94

Division One (Reserve teams): Ashtead, Battersea Park Corona, Beaufoy United, Caius, Chessington & Hook, Coney Hall, Crescent Rvrs, Greenside, Hinchley Wd Utd, RAS Accra Utd, Sutton High, Worcester Park.

Division Two (Reserve teams unless stated): Battersea Ironsides 'A', Bletchingley, Bookham, Bradbank Spts, Cheam V.W., Chessington & Hook 'A', Hersham RBL 'A', Merton Town, Netherne 'A', Racal Decca, Sutton Ath., Warlingham.

Division One (Reserve teams unless stated): Battersea Park Corona 'A', Chessington & Hook 'B', Colliers Wood Utd, Coney Hall 'A', Fetcham, Perrywood Spts, Raynes Park 'A', South Godstone, Vandyke 'A', Verdayne, Woodmansterne Spts, Worcester Park 'A'.

Division One (Reserve teams unless stated): AFC Wandgas, Charlwood, Chessington White Hart, Chipstead 'B', Crescent Rvrs 'A', Eversley Rangers, Halliford, Holmesdale 'A', Oxted & Dist., Reigate Town, Tadworth, Thornton Hth Rvrs.

REDHILL & DISTRICT LEAGUE

PREM. DIV.	P	W	D	L	F	A	PTS
Charlwood	22	18	2	2	67	17	38
Nutfield	22	17	3	2	96	35	37
Horley United	22	12	4	6	58	38	28
Godstone	22	12	3	7	50	43	27
Westcott '35	22	10	5	7	48	48	25
Nork Social	22	10	2	10	33	41	22
Smallfield	22	8	3	11	44	47	19
Holland Sports	22	7	4	11	37	39	18
South Park	22	7	4	11	32	53	18
Mickleham	22	5	6	11	29	50	16
Croydon United	22	4	3	15	36	76	11
Limpsfield Blues	22	1	3	18	23	66	5

DIV. ONE	P	W	D	L	F	A	PTS
Oddfellows	20	16	2	2	75	26	34
Walton Heath	20	15	3	2	70	20	33
Godstone Res.	20	13	2	5	59	29	28
Whytefeafe 'A'	20	12	3	5	60	37	27
Caterham Old Boys	20	10	2	8	43	29	22
Brockham	20	9	2	9	40	52	20
Beecham Research	20	6	1	13	36	61	13
Horley Utd Res.	20	6	1	13	46	73	13
Watsons	20	5	2	13	40	47	12
Westcott '35 Res.	20	5	0	15	30	82	10
Quadrant Spts	20	4	0	16	23	66	8

DIV. TWO	P	W	D	L	F	A	PTS
South Park Res.	22	16	6	0	81	29	38
Coulsdon Mitre	22	16	4	2	90	36	36
Oakside	22	15	3	4	75	37	33
Cheam Vil. War 'A'	22	11	3	8	42	41	25
Charlwood Res.	22	9	5	8	56	55	23
Griffin Albion	22	8	5	9	42	36	21
Woodland Albion	22	8	3	11	38	67	19
Croydon Utd Res.	22	6	6	10	58	60	18
Sth Godstone 'A'	22	8	2	12	34	52	18
Nork Social Res.	22	8	1	13	51	75	17
Warlingham 'A'	22	3	6	13	39	75	12
Woodmansterne 'A'	22	1	2	19	38	81	4

DIV. THREE	P	W	D	L	F	A	PTS
Rail Club '92	22	20	0	2	113	21	40
Merstham Newton	22	17	3	2	90	31	37
Caterham OB Res.	22	14	0	8	60	49	28
Bookham 'A'	22	11	4	7	71	46	26
Walton Heath Res.	22	11	2	9	56	46	24
Monotype Spts 'A'	22	9	5	8	44	57	23
Godstone 'A'	22	8	5	9	56	65	21
Horley Utd 'A'	22	7	3	12	46	58	17
Redhill R.B.L.	22	7	3	12	46	70	17
Warlingham 'B'	22	6	2	14	42	86	14
Quadrant Spts Res.	22	3	3	15	39	81	9
Limpsfield B. Res.	22	3	2	17	32	79	8

DIV. FOUR	P	W	D	L	F	A	PTS
Oddfellows Res.	22	16	2	4	59	30	34
Brockham Res.	22	16	1	5	76	40	33
Horley Utd 'B'	22	15	2	5	70	40	32
Holland Spts Res.	22	14	2	6	57	35	30
Godstone 'B'	22	8	3	11	50	50	19
Cheam Vil. War. 'A'	22	8	3	11	41	48	19
Oxted	22	7	5	10	44	56	19
South Park 'A'	22	7	4	11	42	61	18
Bletchingley 'A'	22	7	2	13	62	67	16
Redhill RBL Res	22	6	4	12	54	77	16
Bookham 'B'	22	5	5	12	41	57	15
Smallfield Res	22	6	1	15	37	72	13

DIV. FIVE	P	W	D	L	F	A	PTS
Waddon United	22	19	1	2	110	33	39
Nutfield Res.	22	15	1	6	78	40	31
Coulsdon Mitre Res.	22	15	1	6	62	34	31
Caterham OB 'A'	22	14	2	6	80	51	30
Woodmansterne 'B'	22	12	3	7	53	39	27
Merstham N'ton Res.	22	10	3	9	52	50	23
Mickleham Res.	22	10	3	9	62	60	23
Beechams R. Res.	22	6	4	12	35	48	16
Sth Godstone 'A'	22	6	4	12	38	71	16
Quadrant Spts 'A'	22	3	4	15	39	77	10
Westcott '35 'A'	22	4	2	16	33	76	10
Lingfield 'A'	22	4	0	18	38	87	8

MIDDLESEX ALLIANCE

PREM. DIV.	P	W	D	L	F	A	PTS
Chelsea Boys	20	15	3	2	76	29	48
Northolt Saints Res.	20	15	3	2	68	25	48
Pars	20	14	3	3	65	28	45
Feltham Town	20	11	2	7	40	49	35
J. & S.	20	9	3	8	66	35	30
New Inn '90	20	9	3	8	56	53	30
Assyrian	20	7	4	9	50	56	25
Talbot All Stars	20	6	2	12	38	63	20
Jubilee Motors	20	4	5	11	39	57	17
Vale	20	5	2	13	55	74	17
Associated Acad.	20	0	0	20	16	100	0

Senior Victory Cup Final:
Assyrian 1, Pars 0

DIV. ONE	P	W	D	L	F	A	PTS
Parkside (Ealing)	20	14	3	3	45	21	45
Talbot A.S. Res.	20	12	3	5	69	31	39
Northolt Saints 'A'	20	11	5	4	61	35	38
Hanworth R.B.L.	20	12	1	7	73	43	37
G.W.R.	20	12	1	7	39	33	37
Chiswick Homefields	20	10	2	8	76	71	32
Fishermans Arms	20	9	4	7	49	39	31
Ealing Athletic	20	5	5	10	45	49	20
N.C.R. Wanderers	20	3	3	14	36	87	12
Hanworth	20	2	5	13	35	63	11
Feltham T. Res.	20	3	2	15	20	76	11

Junior Victory Cup Final:
Talbot All Stars Res. 3, Hanworth R.B.L. 0

WEST MIDDLESEX COMBINATION

PREM. DIV.	P	W	D	L	F	A	PTS
Sandgate Old Boys	16	7	5	4	48	24	19
Rayners Lane 'A'	16	16	8	2	33	28	18
Black Bull	16	7	4	5	26	27	18
Spartan Rangers	16	7	3	6	26	34	17
Rutland Rovers	16	6	4	6	27	33	16
Gardeners Arms	16	6	3	7	36	28	15
Uxbridge Ivyleaf	16	4	6	6	31	36	14
Eastcote Regians	16	5	4	7	29	41	14
Ickenham Sports	16	4	5	7	32	37	13

DIV. ONE	P	W	D	L	F	A	PTS
Signcraft	18	13	2	3	58	26	28
F.C. Pronto	18	12	2	4	57	31	26
Ickenham Spts Res.	18	10	2	6	44	29	22
Stedfast United	18	9	4	5	52	44	22
Burleigh Athletic	18	7	5	6	36	37	19
Swan	18	6	5	7	41	40	17
Field End	18	5	5	8	36	41	15
Griffin Inn	18	4	5	9	31	57	13
Harefield Rangers	18	5	1	12	38	70	11
Ickenham United	18	3	1	14	23	41	7

DIV. TWO	P	W	D	L	F	A	PTS
Eastcote	20	16	3	1	56	29	35
Hanwell Wanderers	20	14	4	2	67	33	32
Prince of Wales	20	11	6	3	49	27	28
Ealing Rovers	20	10	5	5	65	36	25
Denham United	20	6	8	6	49	46	20
Harefield Wednesday	20	5	5	10	29	50	15
Signcraft Res.	20	6	3	11	42	46	15
North Hayes C.C.	20	4	5	11	24	37	13
Rutland Rvrs Res.	20	6	1	13	31	58	13
F.C. Pronto Res.	20	5	3	12	29	56	13
North Harrow	20	4	3	13	38	61	11

DIV. THREE	P	W	D	L	F	A	PTS
Rutland Rvrs 'A'	18	15	1	2	47	21	31
Stedfast Utd Res.	18	11	4	3	63	26	26
Nestles	18	8	3	7	36	22	19
Spartan Rgrs Res.	18	9	1	8	43	44	19
Swan Res.	18	7	4	7	52	42	18
Burleigh Ath. Res.	18	6	6	6	35	32	18
Nth Hayes CC Res.	18	7	2	9	31	41	16
Prince of Wales Res.	18	5	5	8	25	48	15
Uxb. Ivyleaf Res.	18	3	4	11	27	51	10
Eastcote Res.	18	3	2	13	27	59	8

CHARRINGTON CHILTONIAN LEAGUE

Chairman: Mr D Newell
Treasurer: Mr R G Woolman
Hon. Secretary: Mr R A Lipscombe,
31 Broughton Avenue, Aylesbury,
Bucks HP20 1NN (0296 394781).

A very successful campaign culminated with Eton Wick winning the Premier Division title after leading the table for most of the campaign. Finchampstead finished as runners-up with Slough Y.C.O.B. in third place. Broadmoor in their first season won the First Division championship and may provide some surprises in the Premier Division next season. Runners-up were Wooburn Athletic followed in third place by Mill End Sports.

In the Reserve Divisions, winners of Division One were Holmer Green followed by Slough Y.C.O.B. and Finchampstead. In Division Two, clear winners were Iver in their first season, followed by Mill End in runners-up position and Prestwood in third place.

This year's League Cup final was played at Chalfont St Peter between Finchampstead and Slough Y.C.O.B. The first game ended in a 1-1 draw with Slough Y.C.O.B. winning the replay 1-0 with a goal in the very last minute. In the Reserve League Cup final, Holmer Green met Wraysbury at Beaconsfield United In difficult conditions and on a poor pitch, Holmer Green won 5-0.

In outside cup competitions the League gained notable success with Eton Wick winning the Berks & Bucks Senior Trophy in its inaugural season by beating Sandhurst Town 2-1 at Newbury Town. In the Wycombe Senior Cup, Wooburn Athletic beat Martin Baker 3-0, and in the Wycombe Junior Cup, Holmer Green Reserves beat Beaconsfield Athletic by the same score. In the Reading Junior Cup final Letcombe Reserves lost 0-2 to Richfield Rovers, while in the Slough Town cup final Eton Wick beat Wraysbury, and Wooburn Athletic Reserves won the Maidenhead Junior Cup beating Finchampstead 'A'.

The League had a difficult start to the season losing Molins and Broomwade Sports before a ball was kicked, and also Chobham who were not released by the Surrey Premier League. Due to this, and the reduced number of league fixtures, it was decided that the first two rounds of the League Cup be played over two legs. Because of the bad weather in October this proved an unfortunate decision.

In an effort to link up with other leagues, the League have drawn up an agreement with the East Berks League for promotion and relegation. Discussions are due to take place in September regarding similar links with the Parasol Combined Counties League.

This season the League ran a representative side in the Middlesex competition and after the league stage qualified for the final in which they beat the Middlesex County League 2-1. Many thanks to Dave Russell and the few clubs that supported him.

R A Lipscombe, League Secretary

Eton Wick, League champions 1992-93, and promoted to the Parasol League. Photo - Gavin Ellis-Neville.

LEAGUE TABLES 1992-93

Premier Division	P	W	D	L	F	A	PTS
Eton Wick	24	19	1	4	66	22	58
Finchampstead	24	16	4	4	56	32	52
Slough Y.C.O.B.	24	16	1	7	56	30	49
Reading Town	24	11	5	8	38	23	38
Holmer Green	24	11	3	10	45	47	36
Wraysbury	24	10	4	10	38	35	34
Binfield	24	8	9	7	37	32	33
Martin Baker Spts	24	9	5	10	37	42	32
Stocklake	24	8	5	11	40	49	29
Letcombe	24	6	5	13	30	41	23
Brill United	24	7	2	15	40	58	23
Penn & Tylers G.	24	5	6	13	28	56	21
Prestwood	24	5	0	19	24	68	15

Division One	P	W	D	L	F	A	PTS
Broadmoor Staff	24	17	3	4	69	36	54
Wooburn Athletic	24	15	6	3	69	29	51
Mill End Sports	24	13	3	8	58	33	42
Henley Town	24	12	5	7	59	40	41
Drayton Wanderers	24	11	7	6	47	33	40
Denham United	24	11	5	8	43	36	38
Kodak (Harrow)	24	11	5	8	49	43	38
Chinnor	24	9	5	10	48	57	32
Hazells	24	9	3	12	50	55	30
Stokenchurch	24	8	5	11	40	49	29
Chalfont Wasps	24	5	5	14	31	56	20
Iver	24	4	6	14	30	64	18
Wallingford Utd	24	1	2	21	21	83	5

Reserve Div. 1	P	W	D	L	F	A	PTS
Holmer Grn Res.	26	18	5	3	85	30	59
Slough YCOB Res.	26	17	6	3	64	31	57
F'stead Res.	26	16	6	4	73	36	54
Wraysbury Res.	26	15	6	5	85	41	51
Wooburn Ath. Res.	26	12	3	11	67	55	39
Drayton W. Res.	26	7	14	5	51	42	35
Reading Town Res.	26	10	4	12	48	51	34
Eton Wick Res.	26	9	6	11	52	63	33
Penn & Tylers Res.	26	9	5	12	42	56	32
Martin Baker Res.	26	5	8	13	46	55	23
Binfield Res.	26	6	5	15	37	65	23
Stocklake Res.	26	6	4	16	47	78	22
Letcombe Res.	26	5	7	14	37	78	22
Henley Town Res.	26	5	5	16	35	88	20

Reserve Div. 2	P	W	D	L	F	A	PTS
Iver Res.	22	17	2	3	74	24	53
Mill End S. Res.	22	12	4	6	55	29	40
Prestwood Res.	22	12	2	8	49	60	38
Kodak Harrow Res.	22	12	1	9	52	36	37
Stokenchurch Res.	22	10	7	5	52	37	37
Broadmoor S. Res.	22	9	5	8	46	38	32
Chinnor Res.	22	9	4	9	48	45	31
Denham Utd Res.	22	8	5	9	51	55	*28
Wallingford Res.	22	7	2	13	42	60	23
Hazells Res.	22	7	2	13	27	53	23
Chalfont W. Res.	22	4	5	13	21	57	17
Brill Utd Res.	22	5	1	16	44	67	16

* - 1pt deducted

PREMIER DIVISION RESULTS

HOME TEAM	1	2	3	4	5	6	7	8	9	10	11	12	13
1. Binfield	*	3-1	0-2	L-W	2-2	1-2	3-1	3-3	6-2	0-0	1-1	1-3	2-1
2. Brill United	0-1	*	1-4	1-3	1-6	6-1	4-3	6-0	0-1	1-0	1-2	4-0	2-2
3. Eton Wick	0-0	6-1	*	1-3	4-0	2-0	5-0	2-0	3-0	0-1	3-0	2-1	5-0
4. Finchampstead	1-1	3-0	5-0	*	5-3	1-0	2-2	3-2	3-0	2-1	3-1	2-2	1-0
5. Holmer Green	2-2	4-0	0-4	0-4	*	0-2	0-2	4-0	4-0	1-0	3-2	3-3	1-0
6. Letcombe	0-1	1-2	1-2	1-3	0-3	*	3-2	0-0	1-4	1-1	0-1	2-2	3-0
7. Martin Baker Spts	3-1	2-1	0-4	2-1	4-1	0-0	*	2-0	2-1	0-0	3-1	1-1	1-2
8. Penn & Tylers	0-0	3-2	2-5	1-1	0-1	1-5	3-1	*	2-1	1-1	1-3	3-2	0-5
9. Prestwood	1-3	0-3	2-4	0-2	5-2	1-4	1-3	1-4	*	0-3	0-4	3-2	0-1
10. Reading Town	2-0	4-1	1-2	2-0	4-2	2-0	1-1	3-1	2-0	*	6-1	6-1	0-1
11. Slough Y.C.O.B.	2-1	5-0	1-2	4-2	3-0	2-0	1-0	3-0	5-0	2-1	*	5-0	1-3
12. Stocklake	1-1	3-1	3-2	3-4	0-1	3-2	3-1	1-0	0-1	0-1	1-2	*	1-0
13. Wraysbury	2-4	1-1	0-2	5-2	0-2	1-1	3-1	1-1	5-0	1-0	3-0	1-4	*

DIVISION ONE RESULTS

HOME TEAM	1	2	3	4	5	6	7	8	9	10	11	12	13
1. Broadmoor Staff	*	2-1	1-1	1-3	6-2	2-0	2-1	2-0	3-0	6-3	4-1	3-1	4-1
2. Chalfont Wasps	0-1	*	3-1	1-6	1-1	1-5	2-6	2-3	1-2	0-0	2-1	2-1	1-1
3. Chinnor	3-4	3-2	*	1-2	0-0	4-1	5-2	1-1	0-5	1-0	3-2	2-2	2-3
4. Denham United	0-1	3-1	0-1	*	1-1	3-2	1-1	2-1	3-2	3-0	0-1	4-1	1-2
5. Drayton Wanderers	3-4	1-0	3-2	2-1	*	1-2	4-0	2-2	2-0	1-2	1-2	2-0	1-1
6. Hazells	2-1	3-1	3-5	1-1	4-1	*	2-3	4-1	3-3	0-1	3-1	6-1	3-3
7. Henley Town	2-2	2-2	3-2	1-1	0-1	6-1	*	7-1	3-1	1-0	4-0	7-0	2-1
8. Iver	0-3	3-3	2-4	1-1	1-4	2-1	2-2	*	2-3	1-0	0-1	1-3	0-8
9. Kodak (Harrow)	2-6	0-2	4-1	2-0	0-3	3-1	1-1	3-1	*	2-3	2-2	6-1	1-1
10. Mill End Sports	3-0	6-0	2-2	3-1	1-3	5-0	2-0	3-1	1-1	*	6-1	6-0	2-4
11. Stokenchurch	4-3	1-1	4-1	1-3	1-1	5-1	2-1	1-1	2-3	1-3	*	1-1	1-2
12. Wallingford Utd	1-6	1-2	1-2	1-2	1-6	1-2	0-3	0-2	1-3	0-5	0-3	*	1-4
13. Wooburn Athletic	2-2	2-0	7-1	7-1	1-1	W-L	5-0	4-1	L-W	4-1	3-1	3-2	*

RESERVE DIVISION ONE RESULTS

HOME TEAM	1	2	3	4	5	6	7	8	9	10	11	12	13	14
1. Binfield Reserves	*	2-9	2-0	0-1	1-0	1-3	2-3	0-0	0-2	1-2	0-3	0-5	2-1	1-3
2. Drayton Wdrs Res.	2-2	*	3-1	2-2	1-1	0-4	3-0	2-3	0-0	0-0	1-2	0-1	2-1	1-1
3. Eton Wick Reserves	1-0	1-1	*	3-1	4-1	0-3	5-2	1-4	4-0	2-1	1-2	6-0	3-0	1-4
4. Finchampstead Res.	3-0	1-1	4-4	*	2-1	1-1	7-0	3-2	4-3	1-0	2-0	8-0	0-0	1-1
5. Henley Town Reserves	0-1	1-1	3-3	1-8	*	0-2	1-1	2-1	2-1	2-3	0-3	2-7	7-1	1-0
6. Holmer Green Res.	6-0	3-2	4-1	2-1	6-1	*	4-0	1-1	3-0	9-2	3-1	3-0	4-2	1-2
7. Letcombe Reserves	0-0	4-3	1-1	3-7	1-0	1-4	*	2-2	2-2	3-1	0-1	2-1	2-3	2-6
8. Martin Baker Reserves	0-4	3-3	2-2	1-2	1-1	2-2	3-2	*	1-2	0-1	1-1	6-1	2-3	1-2
9. Penn & Tylers Res.	2-2	1-2	5-4	0-2	1-0	0-3	3-1	1-3	*	2-2	4-2	2-2	0-2	1-0
10. Reading Town Res.	1-2	2-2	1-1	0-1	3-0	3-7	5-1	2-1	0-1	*	0-1	4-3	3-5	7-0
11. Slough Y.C.O.B. Res.	2-2	1-1	3-0	4-1	3-0	3-0	5-0	3-2	3-1	2-1	*	7-1	2-1	3-3
12. Stocklake Reserves	7-0	0-2	2-3	1-2	6-3	0-5	1-1	3-2	2-5	0-2	1-1	*	2-1	1-1
13. Wooburn Ath. Res.	6-1	4-2	9-0	1-4	10-3	2-2	3-3	2-1	2-1	1-2	2-3	3-0	*	2-1
14. Wraysbury Reserves	3-1	3-3	5-0	5-4	9-0	2-2	5-0	7-1	8-2	3-0	3-4	5-1	3-0	*

HOME TEAM	1	2	3	4	5	6	7	8	9	10	11	12
1. Brill Utd Reserves	*	4-1	3-4	1-1	0-1	1-4	1-6	0-1	0-6	3-4	0-3	5-0
2. Broadmoor S. Res.	3-2	*	0-0	1-2	2-4	1-0	2-2	1-5	2-3	5-0	2-2	3-2
3. Chalfont W. Reserves	0-4	1-1	*	1-0	3-9	0-2	0-2	2-0	L-W	0-0	1-1	0-5
4. Chinnor Reserves	3-1	1-1	5-1	*	2-2	2-1	1-2	2-3	2-5	4-3	3-0	3-2
5. Denham Utd Reserves	6-5	0-3	3-0	4-0	*	2-0	1-2	2-6	1-1	1-4	2-2	5-3
6. Hazells Reserves	2-5	0-3	1-2	1-8	W-L	*	2-2	3-1	2-2	0-2	3-1	2-2
7. Iver Reserves	10-0	4-1	7-1	2-1	5-1	1-2	*	1-0	3-2	7-0	5-1	3-1
8. Kodak Harrow Res.	W-L	2-4	3-0	4-5	3-1	4-1	1-1	*	2-3	7-2	1-3	4-0
9. Mill End S. Reserves	6-0	1-0	1-1	2-0	4-1	3-0	2-3	0-1	*	4-1	2-3	5-0
10. Prestwood Reserves	2-7	0-8	3-2	3-0	6-1	2-0	3-2	2-1	2-0	*	4-1	3-5
11. Stokenchurch Res.	2-1	3-1	6-2	1-1	2-2	5-1	1-3	1-0	1-1	1-1	*	8-0
12. Wallingford Reserves	2-1	0-1	1-0	4-2	2-2	5-0	0-2	2-3	4-2	1-2	1-4	*

LEAGUE CUP

First Round

Martin Baker Sports v Brill United	5-1,1-2	Broadmoor v Wooburn	2-2,2-2*(6-7 pens)*
Finchampstead v Chalfont Wasps	8-0,2-2	Holmer Green v Eton Wick	3-1,2-2
Binfield v Denham United	2-2,1-2	Stocklake v Mill End Sports	2-2,1-4
Iver v Reading Town	2-1,1-5	Hazells v Kodak (Harrow)	2-5,3-3
Letcombe v Drayton Wanderers	2-1,5-1	Henley Town v Wraysbury	1-5,0-8

Second Round

Wooburn Athletic v Martin Baker Spts	1-0,2-1	Wallingford United v Penn & Tylers Green	1-5,2-7
Finchampstead v Prestwood	4-0,2-2	Holmer Green v Denham United	1-0,2-0
Stokenchurch v Mill End Sports	1-5,0-1	Reading Town v Slough Y.C.O.B.	0-1,0-2
Kodak (Harrow) v Chinnor	3-1,3-1	Letcombe v Wraysbury	4-0,3-5

Quarter-Finals

Finchampstead v Holmer Green	4-1	Wooburn Athletic v Penn & Tylers Green	3-0
Mill End Sports v Slough Y.C.O.B.	1-1,1-2	Kodak (Harrow) v Letcombe	0-2

Semi-Finals

Wooburn v Finchampstead *(at Eton Wick)*	0-4	Slough Y.C.O.B. v Letcombe *(at Broadmoor S.)*	2-1

Final *(at Chalfont St Peter F.C.)*: Slough Y.C.O.B. 1, Finchampstead 0 *(after 1-1 draw)*.

RESERVES CUP

First Round

Martin Baker Res. v Stocklake Res.	0-1,0-1	Eton Wick Res v Penn & Tylers G. Res.	1-2,1-0
Hazells Res. v Stokenchurch Res.	1-0,2-4	Letcombe Res. v Iver Res.	3-2,1-3
Wallingford Res. v Wraysbury Res.	0-4,2-4	Binfield Res. v Holmer Green Res.	1-6,2-6
Drayton Wdrs Res. v Prestwood Res.	7-0,2-0	Denham United Res. *(w/o)* Brill Res. *(scr)*	
Slough Y.C.O.B. Res. v Chinnor Res.	3-1,5-1	Henley Town Res. v Reading Town Res.	1-6,2-2

Second Round

Stocklake Res. v Eton Wick Res.	2-2,3-6	Mill End Sports Res. v Stokenchurch Res.	3-1,1-1
Broadmoor Res. v Finchampstead Res.	4-2,2-3	Iver Res. v Wraysbury Res.	1-4,2-1
Wooburn Res. v Holmer Green Res.	2-6,11-4	Drayton Wdrs Res. v Chalfont Wasps Res.	3-0,6-0
Kodak Harrow Res. v Denham Utd Res.	2-3,1-4	Slough Y.C.O.B. Res. v Reading Town Res.	5-1,1-1

Quarter-Finals

Eton Wick Res. v Mill End Sports Res.	3-5	Broadmoor Staff Res. v Wraysbury Res.	0-3
Holmer Green Res. v Drayton Wdrs Res.	4-3	Denham Utd Res. *(scr)* Slough Y.C.O.B. Res. *(w/o)*	

Semi-Finals

Holmer Res. v Slough Y.C. *(at Prestwood)*	4-2	Mill E. Res. v Wraysbury Res. *(at Martin Bkr)*	2-2,2-6

Final *(at Beaconsfield Utd FC)*: Holmer Green Reserves 5, Wraysbury Reserves 0.

PREMIER DIVISION CLUBS 1993-94

BINFIELD

Chairman: Paul Hammerstone   **Manager:** T.B.A.
Secretary: Paul Hammerstone, 3 Knox Green, Binfield, Berks RG12 5HZ (0344 427179).
Ground: Stubbs Lane, Binfield, Berks.   **Local Press:** Bracknell News/ Times.
Seats: Yes   **Cover:** Yes   **Programme:** Sometimes   **Founded:** 1892.
Colours: All red   **Sponsors:** Churchill Financial Consultants.
Prev. League: Reading & Dist. (pre-1987). **Clubhouse:** Kitchen, bar, lounge, changing rooms, showers.
Hons: Chilt. Lg R-up 91-92 (Div 1 89-90, Lg Cup R-up 89-90), Reading Snr Cup R-up 91-92, Gt Western Comb. 46-47.

BRILL UNITED

Chairman: Mr S Shipperley   **Manager:** TBA.
Secretary: Mr P J Parker, 3 Norcotts Kiln, Brill, Aylesbury, Berks HP18 9TJ (0844 237651).
Ground: Brill Recreation Ground, Church Street, Brill, Aylesbury, Bucks (0844 237388).
Directions: Church Street is immediately behind Red Lion pub in village centre.
Seats: No   **Cover:** No   **Programme:** No   **Founded:** 1890.
Sponsors: Sun Inn, Brill   **Colours:** Black & white stripes/black/black
Prev. League: Oxon Snr/ Lord Jersey. **Clubhouse:** Bar, on ground.
Hons: Chilt. Lg Cup 86-87 (Div 1 R-up 90-91)   **Local Press:** Oxford Mail, Bucks Herald, Thame Gazette.

BROADMOOR STAFF

Chairman: Mr J W Sheppard   **Manager:** Mr P Long.
Secretary: Mr M A Roberts, 14 Hone Hill, Sandhurst, Camberley, Surrey (0252 879513).
Ground: Cricket Field Grove, Broadmoor Est., Crowthorne, Berks (0344 772612).   **Founded:** 1896.
Directions: Off M4 at A329(M) for Bracknell, follow signs to Crowthorne, first left Brookers Corner, ground on right at top of hill.
Seats: No   **Cover:** Yes   **Programme:** Yes   **Colours:** Red/white/white.
Local Press: Reading Evening Post, Reading Chronicle, Crowthorne/ Wokingham News.
Prev. League: Reading Senior.   **Clubhouse:** Broadmoor Staff Club.
Hons: Chiltonian Lg Div 1 92-93.

FINCHAMPSTEAD

Chairman: Mr Mike Husk **Manager:** Mr Mick Shaw.
Secretary: Mr M Husk, 16 Sadlers Lane, Winnersh, Wokingham, Berks (0734 785949).
Ground: Memorial Ground, Finchampstead (0734 732890). **Directions:** From Wokingham on A321, right onto B3016 to Greyhound pub, right onto B3348, ground 200yds on right.
Seats: No **Cover:** No **Programme:** Yes **Founded:** 1952.
Prev. League: Reading & Dist. **Clubhouse:** Club bar, sports bar, changing facilties.
Colours: Blue & white stripes **Hons:** Chilt. Lg 87-88 (R-up 92-93, Lg Cup R-up 88-89 92-93)
Local Press: Wokingham Times/ Wokingham News/ Reading Evening Post.

HENLEY TOWN

Chairman: Mr A R Bryan **Manager:** TBA
Secretary: Mr A Kingston, 50 Birdhill Ave., Reading, Berks RG2 7JU.
Ground: The Triangle Ground, Mill Lane, Henley-on-Thames, Oxon (0491 576463).
Directions: Leave Henley town centre on Reading Road (A4155), Mill Lane 1 mile on left before Motor Way Tyres. 10 mins walk from BR station.
Seats: No **Cover:** No **Prog.:** 25p (Editor: Tony Kingston) **Founded:** 1871.
Colours: White/black/black **Sponsors:** Bear Systems **Clubhouse:** Bar & function room.
Prev. Lges: Reading & Dist/ Spartan 31-52/ Gt Western Comb. 52-57/ Hellenic 57-71/ Ercol Snr.
Local Radio: Radio 210, Radio Oxford **Local Press:** Henley Standard, Reading Evening Post.
Hons: Oxon Snr Cup 03-04 10-11 12-13 13-14 46-47 (R-up 19-20 34-35), Hellenic Lg Div 1 63-64 67-68 (Benev. Cup 62-63 (R-up 61-62)), Spartan Lg Div 1 36-37 (Div 2 33-34), Ercol Snr Lg 78-79, Chiltonian Lg Div 1 87-88, Wycombe Snr Cup 78-79, Reading Snr Cup 78-79, Oxon Charity Cup 04-05 13-14 36-37 62-63 (R-up 02-03 09-1034-35 47-48), Bradley Charity Cup 38-39, Henley Hosp. Charity Cup(15)(R-up(7)).

HOLMER GREEN

Chairman: TBA **Manager:** Barry Hedley.
Secretary: Mr Bill Scholes, The Brambles, Penfold Lane, Holmer Green, Bucks HP15 6XS (0494 713867).
Ground: Holmer Green Sports Association, Watchet Lane, Holmer Green, Bucks (0494 711485).
Directions: From High Wycombe on A404 Amersham road, left at Hazlemere towards Gt Missenden, follow for one and a half miles (ignoring sign for Holmer Green), ground on left opposite 'Mandarin Duck'.
Seats: No **Cover:** No **Sponsors:** D & E Moulds. **Founded:** 1908.
Colours: Green & white **Prev. League:** Ercol Senior. **Programme:** Yes
Local Press: Bucks Free Press. **Clubhouse:** 2 bars open daily. Function room, hot food.
Hons: Chilt. Lg 84-85 85-86 (Res Div 1 92-93, Res Cup 92-93), Wyc. Snr Cup 91-92 (Jnr Cup R-up(res) 92-93).

MARTIN BAKER SPORTS & SOCIAL

Chairman: Mr B Gray **Manager:** Mr K Sibley.
Secretary: W Wright, C/O Hillside Cottage, Tilehouse Lane, Denham, Bucks UB9 5DD (0895 832977).
Ground: Martin's Field, Tilehouse Lane, Denham, Bucks (0895 833077).
Directions: Tilehouse Lane is second left on A412 from A40 London-Oxford route. Travelling from Watford, entrance is 150yds up Tilehouse Lane on right.
Seats: No **Cover:** No **Programme:** Yes **Founded:** 1961. **Cols:** White/navy
Prev. League: London Commercial. **Clubhouse:** Bar, with refreshments available.
Local Press: Uxbridge Gazette/ Slough Observer/ All Sport Weekly.
Hons: Wycombe Snr Cup R-up 92-93 **Sponsors:** Martin Baker Sports & Social Club.

PENN & TYLERS GREEN

Chairman: Mr A Prowse **Manager:** Mr D Russell.
Secretary: Mr R Dalling, 28 Baring Rd, Beaconsfield, Bucks HP9 2NE (0494 671424).
Ground: French School Meadow, Elm Road, Penn, Bucks (0494 671424).
Directions: Entrance on B474 Beaconsfield-Hazlemere road, almost opposite Horse & Groom pub.
Seats: No **Cover:** No **Programme:** Yes **Founded:** 1905.
Colours: Blue & white hoops **Local Press:** Bucks Free Press.
Prev. League: Wycombe Senior **Clubhouse:** Bar, 4 dressing rooms, 3 sets of showers.

PRESTWOOD

Chairman: M White **Manager:** C McDaid.
Secretary: N C Stansbury, 31 Colne Rd, High Wycombe, Bucks (0494 521792).
Ground: Prestwood Sports Centre, Honor End Lane, Prestwood, Great Missenden, Bucks (0240 65946).
Directions: From Chequers pub in village centre, ground half mile on left down road signed Gt Hampden.
Seats: No **Cover:** No **Programme:** Yes **Founded:** 1934.
Colours: Claret & sky. **Local Press:** Bucks Free Press/ Bucks Herald.
Clubhouse: On ground. **Prev. League:** Princes Risborough 34-36/ Wycombe 36-84.
Prev. Grnd: Prestwood Common (pre'80) **Hons:** Wycombe Lg 51-52 81-82 (Div 1 36-37).

READING TOWN

Chairman: Mr N Milne **Manager:** Mr R Ford.
Secretary: M Chalfield, 11 Goddard Close, Shinfield Village, Reading, Berks RG2 9DR.
Ground: Reading Town Spts Ground, Scours Lane, Tilehurst, Reading, Berks.
Directions: West side of Reading off the Oxford road.
Seats: Yes **Cover:** Yes **Programme:** Yes **Sponsors:** None **Founded:** 1968.
Colours: All red **Previous Names:** Reading Garage/ I.T.S. Reading Town.
Prev. Leagues: Reading & District. **Prev. Ground:** Kings Meadow Rd, Reading (pre'92).
Clubhouse: Yes **Local Press:** Reading Chronicle/ Reading Evening Post.

SLOUGH YOUTH CENTRE OLD BOYS

Chairman: Mr Edward Fletcher **Manager:** Mr Ian Dare.
Secretary: Mrs J Hughes, 14 Fairfield Lane, Farnham Royal, Bucks SL2 3BX (0753 643883).
Ground: Hatmill Community Centre, 112 Burnham Lane, Slough, Berks SL1 6LZ (0628 604760).
Directions: M4 jct 7, right at r'bout onto Bath Rd (A4), left at 2nd lights, ground quarter mile on right.
Seats: No **Cover:** No **Programme:** Yes **Founded:** 1941.
Cols: Sky & white stripes/white/sky **Sponsors:** Total Football.
Clubhouse: Bar, phone, toilets, food. **Prev. Lge:** Windor Slough & Dist./ East Berks.
Hons: Chiltonian Lg Cup 92-93, Slough Town Cup R-up 91-92
Local Press: Slough Observer, Slough Express, Maidenhead Advertiser.

STOCKLAKE SPORTS

Chairman: Mr Bob Hogg　　**Manager:** Mr P Harvey.
Secretary: Mr Tom Exton, 116 McBeth Drive, Aylesbury, Bucks (0296 415780).
Ground: Hayward Way, Aylesbury, Bucks (0296 23324).
Directions: Entering Aylesbury join A41 Bicester road, right into Jackson Way after 2 miles, 2nd left is Haywards Way.
Seats: No　　**Cover:** No　　**Programme:** Yes　　**Sponsors:** TBA　　**Founded:** 1966.
Colours: All yellow　　**Prev. Leagues:** Aylesbury Dist./ Wycombe Snr.
Change colours: All blue.　　**Clubhouse:** Bar, tea bar, games room, private bar.
Hons: Chiltonian Lg R-up 90-91　　**Local Press:** Bucks Herald/ Bucks Advertiser.

WOOBURN ATHLETIC

Chairman: Mr A R Nash　　**Manager:** Mr J Austin.
Secretary: Mr B Nash, 10 Philip Drive, Flackwell Heath, Bucks HP10 9JB (0628 523293).
Ground: Wooburn Park, Town Lane, Wooburn Green, Bucks (0628 819201/520772).
Directions: Turn off A4094 Loudwater-Maidenhead road down behind Wooburn church, left at T-junct, ground entrance straight ahead at right-hand bend in road.
Seats: No　　**Cover:** No　　**Sponsors:** Carlsberg.　　**Founded:** 1897.
Cols: Red/white　　**Local Press:** Bucks Free Press/ Star/ Maidenhead Advertiser　　**Programme:** Yes
Prev. Lge: Wycombe Ercol Senior　　**Clubhouse:** Wooburn WMC, 16 The Green, Wooburn Green.
Hons: Chiltonian Lg Div 1 R-up 92-93, Wycombe Snr Cup 92-93, Maidenhead Jnr Cup(res) 92-93.

WRAYSBURY

Chairman: Mr D W Hammond　　**Manager:** C Sherlock.
Secretary: Mr J Rice, 77 Grange Way, Iver, Bucks (0753 652780).
Ground: Memorial Ground, Wraysbury, Bucks (0784 482155).
Directions: From M4 jct 5 follow signs to Datchet, then Horton, then Wraysbury - left at George Hotel.
Seats: No　　**Cover:** No　　**Programme:** No　　**Founded:** 1902.
Colours: Green & white　　**Previous Name:** Coopers Payen.
Prev. League: Slough Windsor & Dist.　　**Clubhouse:** One minute walk from pitch.
Local Press: Slough Observer/ Windsor & Eton Espress.
Hons: Chiltonian Lg 86-87 88-89 89-90 (Lg Cup R-up 85-86 86-87 87-88 90-91, Reserves Cup R-up 92-93).

DIVISION ONE CLUBS 1993-94

CHALFONT WASPS

Chairman: T J Hooker　　**Manager:** TBA.
Secretary: A Figg, 47 Hillside Close, Chalfont St Peter SL9 0HN (0494 873289).
Ground: Playing Fields, Bowstridge Lane, Chalfont St Giles (0494 875050).
Directions: Turn off A413 thru village, first left, top of hill, first right.
Seats: No　　**Cover:** Yes　　**Programme:** No　　**Clubhouse:** Yes　　**Founded:** 1922.
Colours: Amber & black　　**Sponsors:** T.D.K. Motor Company.
Prev. League: Wycombe & District　　**Local Press:** Bucks Free Press, Bucks Examiner.

CHINNOR

Chairman: Mr J Walker　　**Manager:** TBA.
Secretary: Mr F Saulsbury, 86 Station Rd, Chinnor, Oxon OX9 4HA (0844 51073).
Ground: Playing Field, Station Rd, Chinnor, Oxfordshire (0844 52579).
Seats: No　　**Cover:** No　　**Programme:** No　　**Cols:** All blue　　**Founded:** 1884.
Prev. League: Ercol Senior　　**Clubhouse:** Excellent bar & social fac. overlooking ground.
Local Radio: Fox F/M, Oxford Radio　　**Local Press:** Bucks Free Press/ Thame Gazette/ Oxford Mail.

DENHAM UNITED

Chairman: Gerry Spencer　　**Manager:** Gary Marks (reserves: John Osborne).
Secretary: Colin Stevens, 18 The Dene, West Molesey, Surrey KT8 2HL (081 783 0433).
Ground: Oxford Road, Denhamw, Bucks (0895 238717).
Directions: Entering Uxbridge on A4020, ground is quarter mile on left after Denham roundabout.
Seats: No　　**Cover:** No　　**Programme:** Yes　　**Sponsors:** None　　**Founded:** 1905.
Colours: All blue (res: red/blue/red)　　**Local Press:** Berks & Bucks Advertiser, Uxbridge Gazette.
Prev. Lgs: Uxbridge & Dist./ W. Middx　　**Clubhouse:** Licensed bar, changing rooms and social area.

DRAYTON WANDERERS

Chairman: Mike Ash　　**Manager:** Roger Poulter.
Secretary: D Reader, 36 Shenley Ave., Ruslip Manor, Middx HA4 6BX (0895 675121).
Ground: Cowley Rec., Cowley High Rd, Cowley, Nr Uxbridge.
Directions: One and a half miles south of Uxbridge opposite Grand Union - follow signs for Heathrow/ W Drayton.
Seats: No　　**Cover:** No　　**Programme:** Yes　　**Clubhouse:** No　　**Founded:** 1964.
Colours: Blue & white stripes/navy　　**Sponsors:** Browne's Mini-Buses.
Prev. League: West Middx.　　**Previous Name:** Uxbridge Town (mid 80s-1992).
Hons: Chilt. Lg Div 1 85-86　　**Local Press:** West Drayton & Uxbridge Gazette.

HAZELLS

Chairman: D Gater　　**Ground:** Meadowcroft, Aylesbury, Bucks.
Secretary: Mr D Watkins, 21 Parker Walk, Meadowcroft, Aylesbury, Bucks HP19 3XS (0296 394721).
Directions: Ring-road to Weedon Rd, Meadowcroft 1st right in Weedon Rd, ground past houses after one mile.
Seats: No　　**Cover:** No　　**Programme:** No　　**Sponsors:** TBA　　**Founded:** 1886.
Colours: White/navy　　**Clubhouse:** Hazells Club, Oakfield Rd, Aylesbury.
Prev. Lges: Ercol Snr/ Hellenic 57-84　　**Local Press:** Bucks Advertiser, Bucks Herald.
Hons: Hellenic Lg 67-68 (R-up 66-67, Div 1 59-60 79-80, Prem Div Cup 80-81).

IVER

Chairman: Mr R Rankin　　**Manager:** Mr M Hodges.
Secretary: Mr S Law, 59 Grange Way, Iver, Bucks SL0 9NT (0753 819780).
Ground: Lea Barton, High Street, Iver, Bucks (0753 651248).　　**Directions:** A412 from Slough or Denham to Iver Heath, Iver turning to High Street, 2nd right past school Lea Barton to club car park.
Colours: Red, white & black/black/black　　**Programme:** Yes　　**Founded:** 1946.
Prev. Lge: Windsor Slough & Dist.　　**Clubhouse:** Members bar with full facilities.
Sponsors: AK Designs, E & E Construction **Local Press:** Slough Observer/ Slough Express.

KODAK (HARROW)

Chairman: TBA   **Manager:** TBA.
Secretary: Mr R D Langley, 610 Whitton Av., West Greenford, Middx UB6 0EE (081 423 2189).
Ground: Headstone Lane, Harrow View, Middx (081 427 2642).   **Directions:** Bus from Wealdstone, Nth Harrow or Rayners Lane stations to junction of Headstone drive and Harrow View. Ground 200yds on left.
Seats: No   **Cover:** Yes   **Programme:** No   **Sponsors:** Kodak   **Founded:** 1935.
Colours: Yellow/red/yellow   **Local Press:** Harrow Observer/ All Sport Weekly.
Prev. Leagues: West End AFA/ London Commercial. **Clubhouse:** Changing rooms, showers, bar and cafeteria.

SLOUGH HEATING

Chairman: P Healey   **Manager:** TBA.
Secretary: J Lake, 1 Hardymead Court, Kingsmead Rd, Loudwater, Bucks HP11 1JS (0494 464147).
Ground: Farnham Park.
Seats: No   **Cover:** No   **Programme:** No   **Founded:** 1923   **Colours:** All red.
Previous Lge: East Berks (pre'93)   **Local Press:** Slough Observer/ Slough Express.

SLOUGH IRISH SOCIETY

Chairman: W Fitzgerald   **Manager:** TBA.
Secretary: M Maloney, 51 Shaggy Calf Lane, Slough, Berks SL2 5HN (0753 528435).
Ground: King Georges Field.
Seats: No   **Cover:** No   **Programme:** No   **Founded:** 1975   **Cols:** Green/white.
Previous Lge: East Berks (pre'93)   **Local Press:** Slough Observer/ Slough Express.

STOKENCHURCH

Chairman: Mr D Errington   **Manager:** Mr R Thorne/ Mr M Dowding.
Secretary: Mrs B K Hunt, 'Deneholme', 4 Lowes Close, Stokenchurch, Bucks HP14 3TN (0494 482535).
Ground: Longburrow Park, Stokenchurch, Bucks HP14 3TQ (0494 482703).
Directions: From A40 High Wycombe/ Oxford Rd turn either just before or after Kings Arms Hotel. 100yds on behind hotel is Royal Oak pub - Park Road is down right hand side as you look at pub.
Seats: No   **Cover:** No   **Programme:** No   **Founded:** 1886.
Sponsors: Teal Furniture   **Colours:** Green & white/black/black
Clubhouse: Fleur-de-Lys   **Local Press:** Bucks Free Press/ Star.
Hons: Hellenic Lg R-up 56-57   **Prev. Lges:** Wycombe Comb./ Reading & Dist./ Hellenic 53-73.

VANSITTART WANDERERS

Chairman: **Manager:** TBA.
Secretary: D Kerby, 28 Denis Way, Cippenham, Slough, Berks SL1 5JP (0628 661030).
Ground: Slough Grammar School, Lascelles Rd.
Seats: No   **Cover:** No   **Programme:** No   **Founded:** 1989   **Cols:** White & sky
Prev. Lge: E Berks (champs 92-93)   **Local Press:** Slough Observer/ Slough Express.

WALLINGFORD UNITED

Chairman: Mr E L Townsend   **Manager:** Mr D Graham.
Secretary: Mr E Gniadek, 17 Offas Close, Benson, Wallingford, Oxon OX10 6NR (0491 838540).
Ground: Bull Croft, Wallingford, Oxon (0491 837173).
Directions: Centre of Wallingford near Blackstone Upper School.
Seats: No   **Cover:** Yes   **Programme:** Yes   **Sponsors:** Vantage   **Founded:** 1934.
Colours: Red/black/black & red   **Local Press:** Wallingford Herald/ Reading Ev. Post.
Prev. League: Reading & Dist.   **Clubhouse:** No (use adjacent Cross Keys pub).

Reserve Div. One 1993-94: Binfield, Drayton Wdrs, Finchampstead, Henley Town, Holmer Green, Iver, Martin Baker, Penn & Tylers Green, Prestwood, Reading Town, Slough Y.C.O.B., Stocklake, Wooburn Athletic.
Reserve Div. Two 1993-94: Brill United, Broadmoor Staff, Chalfont Wasps, Chinnor, Denham United, Hazells, Kodak (Harrow), Slough Heating, Slough Irish Society, Stokenchurch, Vansittart Wdrs, Wallingford Utd.

Eton Wick score their first in a 6-1 Division one thrashing of Brill United in November. Photo Gavin Ellis-Neville.

CEILING SYSTEM READING LEAGUE

President: L Summers
Chairman: John Dell
Hon. Secretary: David Jeanes,
6 Hawkesbury Drive, Fords Farm,
Calcot, Reading RG3 5ZP (0734 413926)

At the conclusion of another season, once again the Senior Section was closely contested. It took until the final league match for Woodley Arms to clinch the title from runners-up Mortimer. This match was a sombre affair, being a replayed game following an earlier abandonment due to the collapse and subsequent death of top local referee Graham Stockton.

The Berkshire Trophy Centre Senior Cup Cup final between Reading Exiles and Forest Old Boys saw Exiles finish worthy winners with a 3-0 victory. This final was the first of Exiles' cup successes as they went on to take the Reading Challenge Cup from Mortimer in an all-Reading League final.

The Berks & Bucks Senior Trophy also came close to a Reading League team, Woodley Arms being narrowly defeated by Parasol League side Sandhurst Town in the Semi-Finals.

This season has seen a number of representative matches with the League side conceding their first ever defeat in an exciting match for the annual Slevin Trophy against the Oxfordshire Senior League. In a close game which finished 1-1 after extra-time, the Oxfordshire team just got the better of Reading on penalties.

In the lower divisions, the Berkshire Trophy Centre Intermediate Cup was won by Forest Reserves, with the Junior final taken by Richfield Reserves. Richfield had an impressive season with the first team also winning the Evening Post Junior Cup.

Philip Lewis, Promotions Secretary.

SENIOR. DIV.	P	W	D	L	F	A	PTS
Woodley Arms	22	16	3	3	61	26	51
Mortimer	22	15	3	4	53	22	48
Reading Exiles	22	13	6	3	47	20	45
Forest Old Boys	22	10	8	4	47	20	38
Marlow United	22	10	7	5	49	33	37
South Reading	22	9	6	7	54	36	33
R.E.M.E.	22	10	1	11	62	65	31
Cookham Dean	22	8	4	10	35	42	28
West Reading	22	6	4	12	37	53	22
Newtown Henley	22	4	4	14	30	60	16
Tilehurst	22	2	6	14	20	53	12
Old Prestonians	22	3	0	19	28	93	9

PREM. DIV.	P	W	D	L	F	A	PTS
Reading Old Blues	20	12	4	4	51	24	40
Cleckendon	20	11	6	3	55	25	39
Reading University	20	10	5	5	57	40	35
Theale	20	9	5	6	64	41	32
Thames Valley	20	9	5	6	52	48	32
Berks County Spts	20	9	3	8	41	42	30
Ibis	20	8	5	7	46	43	29
Sonning	20	7	4	9	34	58	25
Earlbourne	20	6	5	9	30	43	23
C.S. Reading	20	4	4	12	36	56	16
Nettlebed United	20	0	4	16	21	67	4

DIV. 1 KENNET	P	W	D	L	F	A	PTS
AFC Maidenhead	22	15	4	3	81	23	49
Reading Exiles Res.	22	13	4	5	71	30	43
Pangbourne	22	11	9	2	61	22	42
Rabson Rovers	22	12	4	6	55	32	40
Cookham D. Res.	22	10	7	5	52	42	37
Emmbrook Sports	22	10	5	7	42	33	35
South Reading C.C.	22	10	4	8	48	49	34
Cantley Manor	22	8	4	10	48	48	28
West Reading Res.	22	8	1	13	44	70	25
Wargrave	22	6	3	13	42	76	21
Englefield	22	4	1	17	41	91	13
Bucklebury	22	2	0	20	29	98	6

DIV. 1 THAMES	P	W	D	L	F	A	PTS
Richfield Rovers	20	16	3	1	106	21	51
Unity	20	16	2	2	58	18	50
Forest O.B. Res.	20	12	4	4	56	31	40
Frilsham & Yatt.	20	11	2	7	57	44	35
Mortimer Res.	20	8	3	9	38	38	27
S.E.B. (Reading)	20	8	2	10	65	40	26
Finchampstead 'A'	20	7	4	9	32	47	25
Shinfield	20	7	1	12	43	66	22
St Bartholomews	20	5	0	15	19	72	15
Royal Mail	20	4	2	14	26	70	14
Compton	20	4	1	15	29	82	13

DIV. 2 KENNET	P	W	D	L	F	A	PTS
Sutton Exiles	20	14	5	1	97	31	47
Cox Green	20	15	4	1	81	19	*46
Marlow United Res.	20	11	1	8	65	45	34
Forest O.B. 'A'	20	10	4	6	39	39	34
Hurst	20	8	5	7	47	52	29
Westwood United	20	8	3	9	43	48	27
Newtown Hen. Res.	20	8	3	9	47	53	27
Goring United	20	7	4	9	35	42	25
Berks Co. S. Res.	20	4	4	12	38	66	16
British Telecom	20	2	6	12	19	68	12
Rides United	20	3	1	16	35	83	10
* - 3 points deducted							

DIV. 2 THAMES	P	W	D	L	F	A	PTS
Wallingford Ren.	20	17	1	2	78	32	52
Ibis Res.	20	13	2	5	67	39	41
Roundhead	20	12	2	6	47	43	38
Reading YMCA	20	11	4	5	64	40	37
Rabson Rvrs Res.	20	10	2	8	60	47	32
RBC (Nalgo) Sw.	20	9	4	7	45	38	31
Rifle Volunteer	20	8	3	9	56	50	27
Henley Wanderers	20	5	4	11	33	44	19
Tilehurst Res.	20	5	1	14	35	73	16
REME Apprentices	20	4	2	14	31	75	14
Sonning Sports	20	2	3	15	30	65	9

DIV. 3 KENNET	P	W	D	L	F	A	PTS
Woodley Town	20	18	1	1	107	32	55
Sonning Common	20	15	2	3	89	29	47
REME Res.	20	13	4	3	68	31	43
Theale Res.	20	11	2	7	54	47	35
Emmbrook S. Res.	20	9	3	8	50	43	30
Highmoor	20	7	5	8	42	45	26
Pangbourne Res.	20	8	2	10	48	53	26
Westwood Utd Res.	20	8	1	11	44	51	25
SEB (Reading) Res.	20	5	2	13	42	70	17
Calcot C.A.	20	2	2	16	24	97	8
A.R.M. Athletic	20	1	2	17	25	95	5

DIV. 3 THAMES	P	W	D	L	F	A	PTS
Woodley Arms Res.	20	16	1	3	91	26	49
Richfield Rvrs Res.	20	15	1	4	86	39	46
Peppard 'A'	20	14	4	2	60	16	46
Reading Univ. Res.	20	9	3	8	42	38	30
Ibis 'A'	20	8	1	11	35	53	25
Crowthorne Spts	20	8	0	12	41	55	24
Old Preston. Res.	20	7	2	11	46	53	23
Englefield Res.	20	7	1	12	41	83	22
Reading O.B. Res.	20	6	2	12	36	55	20
Reading Town 'A'	20	6	2	12	31	55	20
Goring United Res.	20	4	3	13	17	53	15

DIV. 4 KENNET	P	W	D	L	F	A	PTS
Caversham Park	18	15	2	1	91	24	47
Lower Earley	18	14	2	2	80	28	44
Earlbourne Res.	18	13	3	2	69	26	42
Hurst Res.	18	9	3	6	47	32	30
British T. Res.	18	9	0	9	46	60	27
Frilsham & Y. Res.	18	7	2	9	56	52	23
Sonning Res.	18	6	1	11	40	61	19
Ibis 'B'	18	3	2	13	30	81	11
ILM Social Club	18	3	0	15	33	74	9
Bucklebury Res.	18	2	3	13	23	77	9

DIV. 4 THAMES	P	W	D	L	F	A	PTS
Pegasus	20	17	1	2	95	16	52
Twyford & Rusc.	20	14	2	4	69	40	44
AFC M'head Res.	20	13	2	5	77	34	41
Wargrave Res.	20	12	4	4	63	25	40
Rockwell Collins	20	11	3	6	75	42	*33
Gladstone	20	9	3	8	51	50	30
Sonning Com. Res.	20	6	4	10	45	56	22
Nettlebed Utd Res.	20	5	3	12	30	67	18
Highmoor Res.	20	4	2	14	29	67	14
Shinfield Res.	20	3	2	15	21	95	11
Thameside	20	1	4	15	21	84	7

* - 3 points deducted

SENIOR DIVISION RESULTS

HOME TEAM	1	2	3	4	5	6	7	8	9	10	11	12
1. Cookham Dean	*	0-1	0-1	0-3	5-3	3-2	1-4	4-1	0-0	0-0	2-0	1-5
2. Forest Old Boys	0-0	*	0-0	2-2	4-0	5-1	0-3	1-2	1-1	4-1	6-2	1-0
3. Marlow United	2-4	0-1	*	3-1	2-1	6-2	1-1	3-2	2-3	3-3	0-0	0-2
4. Mortimer	2-1	2-0	1-1	*	4-0	2-1	1-2	4-1	4-2	0-1	2-1	1-2
5. Newtown Hanley	3-1	1-10	1-2	0-3	*	0-2	1-2	4-3	1-1	1-1	2-1	1-2
6. Old Prestonians	0-2	0-2	0-4	0-8	1-7	*	0-3	6-2	0-7	3-4	1-3	1-2
7. Reading Exiles	5-1	1-1	1-1	0-0	2-0	2-0	*	3-1	1-0	5-1	1-0	2-3
8. R.E.M.E.	4-1	1-1	1-4	1-4	4-2	9-1	0-6	*	4-3	6-0	3-1	4-3
9. South Reading	2-4	0-2	3-3	1-3	5-0	6-1	4-2	4-2	*	4-1	5-1	1-1
10. Tilehurst	0-2	0-0	1-6	A	1-1	1-2	0-0	2-5	0-1	*	1-4	1-3
11. West Reading	2-1	2-2	1-3	2-3	2-0	4-2	2-2	4-5	1-1	2-1	*	1-5
12. Woodley Arms	2-2	1-1	4-2	0-2	4-1	8-2	2-0	4-1	2-0	1-0	5-1	*

PREMIER DIVISION RESULTS

HOME TEAM	1	2	3	4	5	6	7	8	9	10	11
1. Berkshire County Sports	*	0-5	0-2	3-1	2-0	2-0	3-0	1-3	2-3	2-2	3-3
2. Checkendon Sports	5-0	*	6-4	3-1	4-1	5-0	1-1	6-5	1-1	2-0	1-1
3. C.S. Reading	2-3	1-1	*	2-2	1-2	5-1	2-2	1-7	1-3	1-5	2-7
4. Earlbourne	2-3	1-1	3-2	*	1-1	3-1	0-4	1-1	2-1	0-2	1-3
5. Ibis	4-3	4-3	2-1	2-2	*	3-2	2-3	1-3	4-1	4-0	5-1
6. Nettlebed United	2-5	1-3	0-0	1-3	2-2	*	0-4	1-5	0-1	2-6	2-7
7. Reading Old Blues	2-0	2-0	2-0	4-0	1-1	3-1	*	3-2	5-0	7-0	0-2
8. Reading University	3-2	1-0	5-2	1-0	5-3	0-0	3-1	*	1-3	2-3	1-3
9. Sonning	1-2	0-4	1-0	1-3	3-2	3-3	1-1	3-3	*	3-7	3-2
10. Thames Vale	2-2	0-0	4-6	0-4	3-1	3-1	4-3	2-2	5-1	*	2-3
11. Theale	0-3	1-4	0-1	7-0	2-2	4-1	2-3	4-4	10-1	2-2	*

'BERKSHIRE TROPHY CENTRE' SENIOR CUP 1992-93

First Round
Theale v Marlow United	5-2
C.S. Reading v Old Prestonians	7-1
Berkshire County Sports v Thames Vale	6-1
Sonning (w/o) Reading University	
Checkendon Sports v Nettlebed United	1-0
Newtown Henley v Cookham Dean	1-2
Earlbourne v Reading Old Blues	0-2

Second Round
Tilehurst v Berkshire County Sports	3-2
Ibis v Cookham Dean	2-3
West Reading v Theale	2-1
C.S. Reading v Mortimer	0-6
Reading Old Blues v Reading Exiles	1-5
R.E.M.E. v Woodley Arms	1-5
Checkendon Sports v Forest Old Boys	0-6
Sonning v South Reading	2-3

Quarter-Finals
Mortimer v Tilehurst	3-0
Cookham Dean v Woodley Arms	2-9
Reading Exiles v South Reading	4-2
West Reading v Forest Old Boys	3-4

Semi-Finals
Mortimer v Forest Old Boys	0-1
Reading Exiles v Woodley Arms	0-0 (3-2 on pens)

Final: Reading Exiles 3, Forest Old Boys 0

CLUB DIRECTORY

A.F.C. MAIDENHEAD
Secretary: Mrs D Saunders, 12 Crescent Court, 113 Crescent Rd, Reading RG1 5SJ (0734 261390).
Ground: Oaken Grove Park, Oaken Grove Rd, Maidenhead.
Colours: Green & white/white/green   **Reserves colours:** Red & black/black/black

A.R.M. ATHLETIC
Secretary: Mrs S Robertson, 10 Collis Str., Reading RG2 0AE (0734 314252).
Cols: White/navy/white & navy & red.   **Ground:** As South Reading (below)

BERKSHIRE COUNTY SPORTS
Secretary: Mark Harris, 41 Kerris Way, Earley, Reading RG6 2UW (0734 861015).
Grnd: Berkshire Co. Spts Club, Sonning Lane, Sonning.   **Cols:** All white *(Reserves: All blue)*.

BRADFIELD
Secretary: Edmund Muss, 32 Heath Rd, Southend, Bradfield, Reading RG7 6HD (0734 744548).
Ground: New Way, Southend, Bradfield.   **Colours:** All yellow

BRITISH TELECOM
Secretary: Paul Housego, 16 Wheelton Close, Lower Earley, Reading RG6 2YD (0734 664901).
Ground: Palmer Park, Wokingham Rd, Reading.
H.Q.: British Telecom Sports & Social Club, 14 London Rd, Reading RG1 5AD (0734 872390)
Colours: White & black stripes/black/black   **Reserves colours:** All royal.

BUCKLEBURY
Secretary: Anthony Kitchener, 1 Sagecroft Rd, Thatcham, Berks (0635 862321/41334).
Ground: Lower Rec. Ground, Bucklebury. **H.Q.:** The Blade Bone Inn, Bucklebury (0734 712326).
Colours: White/black/black   **Reserves colours:** Blue/white/blue

CALCOT COMMUNITY ASSOCIATION
Secretary: Mrs A Vasey, 3 Barclay Rd, Calcot, Reading RG3 7EL (0734 411132).
H.Q.: Calcot C.A.   **Colours:** Blue/maroon/blue   **Ground:** Calcot Rec., Highview, Calcot.

CANTLEY MANOR
Secretary: Nicholas Patterson, 11 Chatton Close, Lower Earley, Reading RG6 4DY (0734 876032).
Ground: Cantley Park, Milton Rd, Wokingham (0734 793188).
Colours: Red & white stripes/black/white **Change colours:** Sky & white/maroon/maroon.

CAVERSHAM PARK
Secretary: Carl Semonella, 10 Kirkham Close, Caversham Park Village, Reading RG4 0RD (0734 472252).
Colours: Red/black/black & red.   **Ground:** Clayfield Copse, Caversham Park

CHECKENDON SPORTS
Secretary: Ernie Smith, 10 Emmens Close, Checkendon, Reading RG8 0TU (0491 681575).
H.Q.: Four Horses, Checkendon, Reading RG8 0QS (0491 680325)
Ground: Checkendon P.F.   **Colours:** White/royal/white.

COMPTON
Secretary: Mick Pinfold, 11 Manor Cres., Compton, Newbury RG16 0NR (0635 578521).
Ground: Burrell Rd Rec., Compton.
Colours: Royal/white/royal   **H.Q.:** The Pavilion, Burrell Rd, Compton.

COOKHAM DEAN
Secretary: Rory Gavin, 14 Northfield Rd, Maidenhead SL6 7JP (0628 32997)
Ground: Alfred Major Rec., Hillcrest Ave., Cookham Rise, Maidenhead.
H.Q.: 0628 819423   **Colours:** Red/black/red.   **Res. cols:** Red & black hoops/black/red

COTSWOLD
Secretary: Stan Nichols, c/o 98 Royal Ave., Calcot, Reading (0860 419226).
Ground: As St Bartholomews (below)
Colours: Red & white/red/red & white   **Reserves colours:** Red & black/black/red & black.

COX GREEN
Secretary: Miss J Gigg, 6 Anstey Place, Burghfield Common RG7 3NQ (0734 835473).
Colours: Green/green/black   **Ground:** Desborough Pk, The Croft, Norden Rd, Maidenhead.

CROWTHORNE SPORTS
Secretary: James Athill, 26 Lodge Grove, Yateley, Camberley, Surrey GU17 7AD (0252 873925)
Ground: Morgan Rec., Wellington Rd, Crowthorne
Colours: White/black/black   **H.Q.:** Crowthorne Social Club, Wellington Rd.

C.S. READING
Secretary: Bob Davies, 54 Balmore Drive, Caversham, Reading RG4 8NN (0734 571608).
Ground: R.C.S.S.A. Club, James Lane, Burghfield.
Colours: Yellow/blue/yellow   **Change colours:** White & red/red/red.

EARLBOURNE
Secretary: Paul Sheppard, 48 Harvard Close, Woodley, Reading RG5 4UJ (0734 699908).
Ground: Woodford Park, Haddon Drive, Woodley, Reading RG5 4LY (0734 690356).
Cols: Red & blue stripes/black/black   **Res. colours:** Black & red stripes/black/black.

EMMBROOK SPORTS CLUB
Secretary: Glyn Webb, 1 Toutley Close, Emmbrook, Wokingham RG11 1JH (0734 788967).
Ground: Emmbrook Sports Ground, Lowther Road, Emmbrook, Wokingham (0734 780209).
Cols: Royal white hoops/royal/royal   **Reserves colours:** Black & white stripes.

ENGLEFIELD
Secretary: Mark Smyth, 19 Trelawney Drive, Tilehurst, Reading RG3 5WQ (0734 410485).
Grnd: Englefield S.C., Englefield Str., Englefield (off A4 Theale-Pangbourne road).   **Cols:** red/white/red.

FINCHAMPSTEAD 'A'   *(details as per page 420 except cols: yellow/black/black)*

FOREST OLD BOYS
Secretary: Bob Hulett, 10 Ramsbury Drive, Earley, Reading RG6 2RT (0734 663514).
Colours: Yellow & blue/blue/blue.   **Ground:** Woodford Pk, Haddon Drive, Woodley (0734 690356).

FRILSHAM & YATTENDON
Secretary: Brian Cannons, 2 Squash Court Cottage, Yattendon, Newbury RG16 0XT (0635 201357).
Ground: Frilsham P.F., Frilsham Common, Frilsham, nr Hermitage.
H.Q.: Yattendon Social Club, Yattendon Village Hall (0635 201847).
Colours: Blue/black/black   **Reserves colours:** Red/black/black

GLADSTONE (HORNCASTLE)
Secretary: Mike Stagg, 5 Vine Cres., Reading RG3 3LT (0734 507678).   **Grnd:** As West Reading (below)
H.Q.: Horncastle Pub, Bath Rd, Reading. **Colours:** Black & white stripes/black/black.

GORING UNITED
Secretary: Peter Jones, Bywater, Icknield Rd, Goring-on-Thames RG8 0DE (0491 872809).
Ground: Gardiners Recreation Ground, Upper Red Cross Rd, Goring.
H.Q.: Goring Social Club, High Street, Goring (0491 873105).
Cols: Yellow & green/green/yellow   **Reserves colours:** Blue/black/black.

HENLEY TOWN 'A' *(see page 420)*

HENLEY WANDERERS
Secretary: Robin Bishop, 3 Stirling Close, Caversham Park Village, Reading RG4 0SH (0734 470029).
Ground: As Henley Town 'A' (above)   **Colours:** Gold (royal trim)/royal/royal.

HIGHMOOR
Secretary: Chris Gallimore, 49 Westleigh Drive, Sonning Common, RG4 9LA (0734 722849).
Grnd: Highmoor Rec., Highmoor, Henley, Oxon.   **Cols:** All blue *(Reserves: Red & black/black/red)*.

HURST
Secretary: Mrs S Hicks, Rosevale, School Rd, Hurst RG10 0DR (0734 341541).
Ground: Hinton Rd, Hurst, Reading.   **Cols:** Tangerine/black/black *(Reserves: All blue)*.

IBIS
Secretary: Anthony McGrath, 25 Luscombe Close, Caversham, Reading RG4 0LG (0734 478161).
Ground: IBIS Sports Club, Scours Lane, Reading RG3 6AY (0734 424130).
Colours: Blue & white stripes/blue/blue **Reserves colours:** Claret/blue/blue.
'A' cols: Red & black stripes/black/black **'B' colours:** Yellow/blue/white.

I.L.M. SOCIAL CLUB
Secretary: Richard Smith, 3 Parthia Close, Katesgrove Lane, Reading RG1 2NQ (0734 502422).
Ground: Bulmershe, Woodlands Avenue, Earley, Reading.   **Colours:** Sky/blue/white
H.Q.: Hays Distribution, Theale, Reading RG7 4HN (0734 303636).   **Reserves cols:** Green/grey/white.

LOWER EARLEY
Secretary: Mr S Price, 50 Faygate Way, Lower Earley, Reading RG6 4DA (0734 864227).
Ground: Laurel Park, Marefield, Lower Earley (groundsman: 0734 875147).
H.Q.: Maiden Place Social Club, Maiden Place, Lower Earley, Reading (0734 268872)
Colours: All maroon   **Reserves colours:** Royal/white/white.

MARLOW UNITED
Secretary: Jayne Flint, 17 Stapleton Close, Marlow, Bucks (0628 474490).
H.Q.: Cross Keys, Marlow   **Ground:** Higginson Park/ Gossmore Park, Marlow.
Colours: Blue/blue/white   **Reserves colours:** Red & white/red/red.

MIDGHAM SPORTS
Secretary: S Flanagan, 4 Griffiths Close, Thatcham, Berks (0635 860363).
Ground: Victoria Park, Newbury   **Colours:** Red & black/black/black.

MORTIMER
Secretary: Steve Dell, 30 Croft Rd, Mortimer, nr Reading RG7 3TS (0734 333821).
Colours: Amber/black/black   **Grnd:** Alfred Palmer Mem. P.F., West End Rd, Mortimer.

NETTLEBED UNITED
Sec: Ian Gunn, 6 Belgravia Court, 53 Bath Rd, Reading RG3 2BL (0734 580308).   **Colours:** All sky
Grnd: Recreation Grnd, Watlington Rd, Nettlebed, Henley-on-Thames.   **Reserves cols:** White/navy/navy.

NEWTOWN HENLEY
Secretary: Mrs M Grant, 6 Peppard Lane, Henley-on-Thames, Oxon RG9 1NJ (0491 576457).
Ground: Harpsden Village, Nr Henley-on-Thames, Oxon.
Cols: Black & white stripes/black/black   **Res. colours:** Green & white hoops/white/white.

OLD PRESTONIANS
Secretary: Peter Bailey, 7 Myton Walk, Theale, Reading RG7 5EW (0734 323091).
Ground: Presentation College, 63 Bath Rd, Reading (0734 572861).
Colours: Black & white stripes/black/black   **Res. colours:** Claret/sky/sky.

PANGBOURNE
Secretary: Mr T McAllister, 2 Aston Ave., Pangbourne, Reading (0734 842104).
H.Q.: Pangbourne WMC (0734 842426)   **Ground:** Thames Ave. Rec., Pangbourne.
Colours: All royal   **Reserves colours:** Sky/sky/royal.

PEGASUS
Secretary: Barry Hoy, 24 Hadleigh Rise, Caversham Park Village, Reading RG4 0RW (0734 476434).
Colours: Sky/black/black   **Ground:** Emmer Green Rec. Ground.

PEPPARD 'A'
Grnd: Bishopswood Spts Centre, Horsepond Rd, Sonning Common (0734 722675) *(other details as page 401)*

R.B.C. (NALGO) SWEATSHOP
Secretary: Maurice Why, 83 St Michaels Rd, Tilehurst, Reading RG3 4RY (0734 425454).
H.Q.: Civic Offices, Civic Cte, Reading (390448/412)   **Grnd:** Palmer Pk, Wokingham Rd, Reading
Colours: Blue & white hoops/blue & red/blue & red   **Change cols:** Gold/black/black.

RABSON ROVERS
Secretary: Peter Parker, 103a Belmont Rd, Reading RG3 2UT (0734 585892).
Ground: Rabson Recreation Ground, Northumberland Ave., Reading.
H.Q.: South Reading Leisure Centre, Northumberland Ave., Reading (0734 864910).
Colours: Red/white/red.   **Change colours:** All sky.

READING EXILES
Secretary: L McDonald, 7 Oregon Ave., Tilehurst, Reading RG3 6RZ (0734 421465).
Ground: Holme Park Spts & Soc. Club, Sonning-on-Thames (0734 691305). (Opp. Reading Cricket Club).
Cols: Royal & white stripes/blue/blue   **Res. cols:** Navy & white/navy/navy

READING OLD BLUES
Secretary: Frank Glasspool, 17 Wyndham Cres., Woodley, Reading RG5 3AY (0734 692800).
Grnd: As Reading Exiles (above).   **Cols:** White & navy/navy/yellow *(Reserves: Yellow/blue/yellow).*

READING TOWN 'A'
Ground: Kings Meadow, Reading *(other details as page 420).*

READING UNIVERSITY
Secretary: Robert Cass, 80 London Rd, Reading (0734 753970 - Students Union).
H.Q.: Sports Federation Office, Students Union, P.O. Box 230, University of Reading RG6 2AZ.
Colours: Purple/black/purple   **Grnd:** Queens Drive, Reading Uni., Whiteknights.

READING Y.M.C.A.
Secretary: Wilf Fewtrell, 56 Waldeck Str., Reading RG1 2RE (0734 873593).
Ground: As SEB (below)
Cols: Red & black stripes/black/black   **H.Q.:** Marlborough House, Parkside Rd, Reading RG1

R.E.M.E. ARBORFIELD
Secretary: Peter Davies, 73 Chestnut Cres., Shinfield, Reading RG2 9HA (0734 884107).
Ground: Sports Pavilion, Biggs Lane, School of Electronic Eng., Arborfield (entrance by rocket).
Colours: Red/yellow/yellow   **Res. cols:** Grey/maroon/maroon   **'A' cols:** Red/white/red

RICHFIELD ROVERS
Secretary: Nigel Sawyer, 37 Brayford Rd, Reading RG2 8LT (0734 873613).
Ground: As Lower Earley (above)   **H.Q.:** Wallingford Arms, Caroline Str., Reading.
Colours: Red & white/red/red   **Reserves colours:** Yellow/blue/yellow.

RIDES UNITED
Secretary: H M Wathcham, 10 Goaters Rd, North Ascot, Berks (0344 886579).
Grnd: Rides Comm. Centre, Gorse Ride North, Finchampstead (0734 732852).   **Cols:** Red/blue/white

RIFLE VOLUNTEER
Secretary: Roy Martin, 23 Kent Close, Woosehill, Wokingham RG11 9AN (0734 891887).
Ground: Elizabeth Rd, Wokingham, Berks (off Norreys Ave.)   **Colours:** Green & black stripes/black/black

ROCKWELL COLLINS
Secretary: Steven Fahy, 133 Thirlmere Ave., Tilehurst, Reading (0734 418463).
Ground: As St Bartholomews (below)   **Colours:** Green & yellow/green/yellow.

ROUNDHEAD
Secretary: Eric Wise, 63 St Saviours Rd, Reading RG1 6EJ (0734 588426).
Grnd: As South Reading (below) **H.Q.:** Roundhead Pub (0734 588426).   **Cols:** Green & white/white/red.

ROYAL MAIL
Secretary: Reg Leadbetter, 27 Strathy Close, Tilehurst, Reading RG3 2PP (0734 425217)
Ground: Cintra Park, Cintra Ave., Reading.   **Cols:** Blue (red & white diamonds)/blue/blue
H.Q.: R.P.O.S.S.C., 6 Richfield Ave., Reading (0734 568157).   **Change colours:** All red

ST BARTHOLOMEWS
Secretary: Dave Hudson, 73 Cockney Hill, Tilehurst, Reading RG3 4HE (0734 451789).
Ground: Sol Joel Playing Field, Church Rd, Earley, Reading.
Colours: Red/black/red   **Change colours:** Blue/white/blue.

S.E.B. (READING)
Secretary: Philip Lewis, 21 Kent Rd, Reading RG3 2EJ (0734 575206).
H.Q.: Southern Electric Social Club, Vastern Rd, Reading.
Colours: Green & amber/green/green   **Grnd:** Christchurch Meadow, Reading Bridge, Reading.

SHINFIELD
Secretary: Chris Carne, 10 Linnet Close, Tilehurst, Reading RG3 5SR (0734 427914)
Ground: Millworth Lane, Shinfield, Reading.   **Colours:** All claret *(Reserves: All red).*

SONNING
Secretary: Mrs Valerie Backhouse, 35 Pound Lane, Sonning, Reading RG4 0XD (0734 697009).
Grnd: The Pavilion, King George VI Mem. P.F., Pound Lane, Sonning.   **Colours:** Red/white/red.

SONNING COMMON
Secretary: Sue Evans, 275 Gosbrook Rd, Caversham, Reading RG4 8DX (0734 482638).
Ground: Peppard Cricket Club, Peppard Common, Stoke Row Rd, Peppard.
H.Q.: The Butchers Arms, Sonning Common (0734 723101).
Cols: Red & white stripes/white/red   **Reserves colours:** Navy/white/red.

SONNING SPORTS
Secretary: Roger Prismall, 10 Churchill Cres., Sonning Common, Reading RG4 9RX (0734 724596).
Grnd: Palmer Park, Wokingham Rd, Reading   **H.Q.:** As Sonning FC (above)   **Cols:** Orange/red/red.

SOUTH READING
Secretary: Terry Darlow, Four Horseshoes P.H., 177 Basingstoke Rd, Reading RG2 0HX (0734 871604).
Grnd: Lower Whitley Rec., Basingstoke Rd, Reading **H.Q.:** Four Horsehoes (see sec.) **Cols:** red/white/red.

SOUTH READING C.C.
Secretary: Mike Gardner, 23 Buckland Rd, Reading RG2 7ST (0734 862859).
Colours: Orange/black/black   **Ground & H.Q.:** As Rabson Rovers (above)

SUTTON EXILES
Secretary: David Griffith, 54 Filey Rd, Reading RG1 3QQ (0734 665481).
Colours: Green/white/white   **Ground:** Reading Activities Centre, Crescent Rd.

THAMESIDE
Secretary: Chris Francis, 23 Coventry Rd, Reading RG1 3ND (0734 664630).
H.Q.: Cellulair, Bennet Rd, Reading (0734 861961).
Ground: As West Reading (below)   **Colours:** Red & blue stripes/blue/blue

THAMES VALLEY
Secretary: Mrs N Croshaw, 114 Severn Way, Tilehurst, Reading RG3 4HU (0734 429452).
Ground: As West Reading (above)   **Cols:** Green/white/white *(Reserves: White/blue/blue).*

THEALE
Secretary: Chris Sheppard, 11 Carron Close, Tilehurst, Reading RG3 4DS (0734 412859).
Ground: Englefield Rd. Rec., Theale   **H.Q.:** Crown Inn, Theale, Reading RG3 4SG (0734 302018).
Cols: Red & black stripes/black/black   **Res. colours:** Blue & black stripes/black/black.

TILEHURST
Secretary: Kevin McMahon, 48 School Rd, Tilehurst, Reading RG3 5AN (0734 415766).
Ground: Victoria Rec. Ground, Kentwood Hill, Tilehurst, Reading.
Cols: Black & white stripes/black & red/black   **Res. cols:** Black & white stripes/black/black.

TWYFORD & RUSCOMBE
Secretary: Miss M Bradbury, 4 Pennfields, Ruscombe, Twyford RG10 9BD (0734 345229).
Colours: Sky/navy/sky   **Ground:** Loddon Hall Rd Rec., Twyford (0734 345268)

UNITY
Secretary: Richard Weekes, 18 Pitcroft Ave., Earley, Reading RG6 1NH (0734 661680).
Ground: As SEB Reading (above).   **Colours:** Pale Amber/black/black.
H.Q.: Central Club, London Str., Reading (0734 574421).

WALLINGFORD RENEGADES
Secretary: Jason Marcham, 55 Wood Str., Wallingford, Oxon OX10 0AY (0491 36145).
Ground: Fairmile Spts & Social, Fairmile Hospital, Wallingford Rd, nr Cholsey.
Colours: All red   **Change colours:** Silver/red/red.

WARGRAVE
Secretary: Andy Dearing, 4 Longfield House, Longfield Rd, Twyford RG10 9AN (0734 343065).
Ground: Wargrave Recreation Ground, Recreation Rd, Wargrave.
Colours: White/royal/royal   **Change colours:** All royal.

WEST READING
Secretary: Mrs Susan Porton, 6 Hampstead Court, Grovelands Rd, Reading RG3 2QQ (0734 504034).
Ground: Prospect Park, Liebenrood Rd, Reading
Colours: Amber/black/black & amber   **H.Q.:** Spread Eagle Pub, Norfolk Rd, Reading

WESTWOOD UNITED
Secretary: Mrs Penny Brodie, 58 Devonshire Gdns, Tilehurst, Reading RG3 6FP (0734 424329).
Ground: Cotswold Sports Centre, Downsway, Tilehurst, Reading.
H.Q.: Westwood Club, Downsway, Tilehurst, Reading (0734 429865)
Cols: Green & white stripes/green/green   **Res. colours:** White & blue/white/blue.

WOODLEY ARMS
Secretary: Mrs D Ballard, 68 Howth Drive, Woodley, Berks RG5 3EG (0734 662289).
Ground: Woodford Park, Haddon Drive, Woodley, Berks RG5 4LY (0734 690356).
H.Q.: Woodley Arms P.H., Howth Drive, Woodley (0734 261810).
Cols: Yellow & black/black/black   **Reserves colours:** Yellow/black/black.

WOODLEY TOWN
Secretary: Mark Rozzier, 23 Welford Rd, Woodley, Reading RG5 4QS (0734 693235).
Ground: As Woodley Arms (above)   **Colours:** Navy, white & emerald/navy & white/navy.

'READING EVENING POST' READING SENIOR CUP 1992-93

First Round

Drayton Wanderers v Forest Old Boys	2-0	Reading Town v Old Prestonians	7-0
Finchampstead v Earlbourne United	9-1	Reading Exiles v Henley Town	2-1
Cookham Dean v Didcot Casuals	3-1	South Reading v Stokenchurch	1-0
Mill End v West Reading	2-0	Harwell v Woodley Arms	4-5
Hambleden v Wallingford United	3-2	Mortimer v Drayton	1-1,3-2
Tilehurst v Binfield	2-1	Ibis v Broadmoor Staff	1-4

Second Round

Broadmoor Staff v Reading Exiles	1-2	Mortimer v Mill End	2-1
South Reading v Thames Valley	3-0	Hambleden v Faringdon Town	0-5
Reading Town v Finchampstead	0-0,2-3	Drayton Wanderers v Letcombe	1-0
Cookham Dean v Woodley Arms	2-3	A.E.A. v Tilehurst	2-2,0-6

Quarter-Finals

Woodley Arms v Tilehurst	2-2,5-0	Finchampstead v Reading Exiles	0-4
South Reading v Drayton Wanderers	1-1,1-2	Mortimer v Faringdon Town	1-0

Semi-Finals

Mortimer v Drayton Wanderers	2-1	Woodley Arms v Reading Exiles	1-2

Final: Reading Exiles 3, Mortimer 1

ESSEX SENIOR LEAGUE

President: David Pond
Chairman: Robert Errington
Vice Chairman: Vernon Sitch
Treasurer: Margaret Errington
Hon. Secretary: David Wingrove, 8 Oak Piece,
North Weald, Epping, Essex CM16 6JJ (0992 522147).

THE ISLAND OF DREAMS

The success of the season was Canvey Island Football Club. The last side in British senior football to lose their 100% league record, they went on to surpass their own league record for successive wins at the season's start; fourteen in a row. They were worthy league champions and Challenge Cup winners, but the dream of all clubs at our level, reaching the F.A. Vase final at Wembley, was thwarted by Tiverton in Devon at the semi-final stage though they still managed to win at their impregnable fortress called Park Lane. Clubs from all over the country went away from Park Lane in the League and Vase, none getting the better of our champions - a memorable season for Jeff King and his lads.

The League race, having been won by Canvey, was nevertheless just as thrilling for the runners-up spot with Sawbridgeworth Town having to catch up on Bowers United, some 24 points ahead in April - they did it with nine wins, and, with the Herts Charity Shield and Challenge Cup runners-up under their belts, had their best ever season.

We welcomed Romford F.C., reformed after fourteen years out of football, and they brought a whole new meaning to the word 'support' with attendance records for league matches broken at various grounds during the season. Great Wakering Rovers joined having won all honours at intermediate level, and finished a very worthy seventh. Their match programme was not only adjudged to be best in the League but gained seventeenth place nationally in the Wirral Awards.

Southend Manor kept up their incredible record of having won every domestic competition they have entered since joining the League in 1985. This year it was the Essex Senior Trophy beating Jewson Eastern League Harwich & Parkeston 1-0, and to this was added the Harry Fisher Trophy for the second time in three years.

Sadly, for 1993-94 we have lost Woodford Town who formed the basis of Harlow Town (1993) Ltd, but we hope that this old club will soon be back on the map. Brentwood are in the process of building a new ground back in their town, and Eton Manor are groundsharing whilst their Roding Lane ground is brought up to Senior League standard. The League have a new Chairman, Robert Errington who has been associated with it since 1983, and Secretary, David Wingrove. The Fixture Secretary is now John Wiffen.

Robert Errington, Chairman

Canvey Island after securing 'The Double' by beating Sawbridgeworth in the League Cup. Photo - James Wright.

LEAGUE TABLES 1992-93

SEN. SECTION	P	W	D	L	F	A	PTS
Canvey Island	32	23	7	2	66	20	75
Sawbridgeworth T.	32	19	7	6	82	41	64
Bowers United	32	18	9	5	56	27	63
Burnham Ramblers	32	17	6	9	80	53	57
Basildon United	32	16	7	9	65	37	55
Brentwood	32	13	9	10	58	49	48
Gt Wakering Rvrs	32	13	8	11	50	43	47
Ford United	32	14	10	8	47	26	*46
Romford	32	12	9	11	48	42	45
Southend Manor	32	13	4	15	49	45	43
Concord Rangers	32	9	9	14	41	51	36
Maldon Town	32	8	10	14	45	59	34
East Ham United	32	10	4	18	46	67	34
Woodford Town	32	7	9	16	46	84	30
Eton Manor	32	7	8	17	32	75	29
Hullbridge Sports	32	7	6	19	38	70	27
Stansted	32	2	6	24	27	87	12

* - 6 points deducted

RES. SECTION	P	W	D	L	F	A	PTS
Sawbridgeworth Res.	26	17	6	3	59	32	57
Bowers Utd Res.	26	16	4	6	51	33	52
Basildon Utd Res.	26	15	6	5	67	32	51
Gt Wakering Res.	26	11	7	8	40	34	40
Hullbridge S. Res.	26	11	6	9	45	37	39
Brightlingsea Res.	26	12	3	11	49	46	39
East Thurrock Res.	26	9	7	10	44	46	34
Burnham Rbrs Res.	26	9	5	12	39	44	32
Southend Mnr Res.	26	9	5	12	37	54	32
Eton Manor Res.	26	8	7	11	44	45	31
Stansted Res.	26	8	6	12	56	69	30
Concord Rgrs Res.	26	7	5	14	41	46	26
Canvey Island Res.	26	6	6	14	26	47	24
Maldon Town Res.	26	5	5	16	34	67	20

SENIOR SECTION RESULTS

HOME TEAM	1	2	3	4	5	6	7	8	9	10	11	12	13	14	15	16	17
1. Basilton Utd	*	0-2	2-1	3-2	1-2	4-1	4-0	3-4	1-3	3-0	2-0	3-2	3-1	1-1	2-0	9-0	1-1
2. Bowers United	3-3	*	4-1	2-2	0-0	2-0	1-1	2-0	2-1	0-0	1-1	0-2	3-0	2-1	1-2	1-1	5-1
3. Brentwood	1-0	2-1	*	1-3	1-4	2-1	2-4	2-0	1-1	3-1	0-0	3-3	2-2	0-1	2-1	4-1	6-1
4. Burnham Ramblers	0-2	0-1	3-1	*	1-3	3-4	2-0	1-1	3-1	0-0	3-3	2-2	0-1	2-1	4-1	6-1	
5. Canvey Island	1-1	4-1	1-0	3-2	*	3-1	1-0	2-2	0-0	2-0	2-2	3-0	1-0	1-0	3-0	2-0	1-0
6. Concord Rangers	2-0	0-0	2-2	1-2	1-4	*	3-0	3-2	0-0	1-4	1-0	0-2	2-1	1-1	1-1	1-0	3-3
7. East Ham United	0-1	0-2	0-1	3-4	0-0	1-5	*	3-0	2-1	0-1	3-1	2-1	0-2	1-4	2-1	5-3	6-0
8. Eton Manor	1-1	0-2	0-2	0-5	0-3	0-0	1-1	*	1-2	2-2	0-0	1-1	2-1	2-4	2-1	1-0	1-3
9. Ford United	2-0	0-1	1-1	2-0	1-2	2-1	3-0	2-0	*	0-1	4-0	1-1	0-0	2-3	2-0	3-0	5-1
10. Gt Wakering Rovers	3-2	0-1	1-0	4-4	0-0	2-0	4-1	4-1	1-2	*	2-3	2-0	0-1	0-3	4-0	2-3	1-1
11. Hullbridge Sports	0-2	0-6	2-4	1-4	1-2	1-3	0-1	1-2	1-3	0-0	*	4-1	1-4	3-1		3-2	6-2
12. Maldon Town	1-4	0-1	2-2	2-2	1-6	2-2	1-0	0-1	0-0	2-2	4-1	*	3-2	1-1	0-1	5-0	0-3
13. Romford	0-0	0-2	1-1	0-0	0-2	0-1	3-1	5-1	2-0	2-1	2-1	2-2	*	2-2	3-4	2-2	2-0
14. Sawbridgeworth Town	1-1	4-3	4-0	1-1	1-0	3-0	4-0	3-2	3-1	3-1	4-0	4-0	1-4	*	1-5	1-0	4-4
15. Southend Manor	1-0	0-2	3-1	4-1	0-2	1-0	2-4	4-0	0-0	0-1	3-1	0-1	2-0	1-2	*	4-0	1-1
16. Stansted	0-3	1-3	0-4	1-3	2-6	1-1	5-2	1-1	0-0	1-1	0-1	0-2	0-1	0-4	0-3	*	1-1
17. Woodford Town	1-4	0-2	1-4	1-3	1-0	3-2	1-1	2-3	1-2	1-3	0-0	3-2	1-1	1-6	1-1	2-1	*

RESERVE DIVISION RESULTS

HOME TEAM	1	2	3	4	5	6	7	8	9	10	11	12	13	14
1. Basilton U. Res	*	3-0	6-0	3-0	5-2	3-1	6-2	2-2	3-1	4-0	5-0	2-2	1-5	4-0
2. Bowers Utd Res	3-2	*	5-2	2-1	1-0	2-4	2-3	2-1	2-0	3-2	3-0	4-1	4-1	4-0
3. Brightlingsea U. Res	1-0	1-2	*	2-1	0-1	1-0	3-1	6-2	1-1	0-1	1-0	0-1	5-1	3-2
4. Burnham Ramb. Res	1-2	0-0	0-5	*	1-1	0-2	4-0	1-2	3-0	0-0	4-2	1-2	3-2	2-4
5. Canvey Island Res	0-1	1-0	3-2	2-0	*	0-4	1-1	2-0	1-1	3-1		1-5	2-4	2-0
6. Concord Rgrs Res	1-2	1-2	3-2	0-4	1-0	*	0-3	1-1	1-1	0-1	1-3	1-3	4-0	3-3
7. East Thurrock U. Res	0-0	1-2	0-1	2-3	3-0	4-2	*	0-3	4-1	1-5	2-3	4-1	1-1	4-2
8. Eton Manor Res	3-3	0-0	2-1	1-1	4-1	2-0	1-1	*	5-0	0-1	1-2	2-3	1-1	3-2
9. Gt Wakering R. Res	1-1	1-2	4-0	1-0	0-0	1-1	0-0	4-1	*	2-0	3-1	1-2	2-0	2-1
10. Hullbridge Sports Res	0-3	3-1	3-0	0-1	0-0	3-2	0-2	3-2	0-2	*	5-0	1-1	0-0	0-3
11. Maldon Town Res	1-2	1-1	3-3	1-3	1-1	3-4	2-1	0-5	2-3	*	0-2	3-5	1-1	
12. Sawbridgeworth Res	2-1	1-1	1-5	1-1	3-2	0-0	0-0	4-1	3-1	5-0	*	2-0	2-0	
13. Southend Manor Res	3-2	2-3	0-1	0-2	2-0	1-0	1-0	1-0	0-2	2-2	0-0	1-2	*	3-0
14. Stansted Res	1-1	1-0	3-3	6-1	3-1	1-3	1-1	3-1	2-2	2-10	2-1	1-7	12-1	*

LEAGUE CUP

Preliminary Round
Southend Manor v Gt Wakering Rovers — 2-2,0-3

First Round

Bowers United v Maldon Town	3-2	East Ham United v Burnham Ramblers	1-2
Ford Utd v Romford	1-0 (Ford expelled)	Canvey Island v Eton Manor	6-0
Woodford Town v Sawbridgeworth Town	1-5	Basildon United v Stansted	2-0
Brentwood v Concord Rangers	2-0	Hullbridge Sports v Great Wakering Rovers	1-3

Quarter-Finals

Bowers United v Burnham Ramblers	3-4(aet)	Romford v Canvey Island	0-1
Sawbridgeworth Town v Basildon United	3-0	Brentwood v Great Wakering Rovers	3-2(aet)

Semi-Finals (Two Legs)

Sawbridgeworth T. v Brentwood	2-1,2-1	Burnham Ramblers v Canvey Island	0-3,0-0

Final (at Ford United FC, Saturday 1st May. Attendance: 450):
Canvey Island 3 (Jones 6 10, Mahoney 67), **Sawbridgeworth 1** (Liddle 40)
Canvey: Gary Harold, Scott Rogers, Eddie Carrick, Steve Hibbert, Steve Wiseman, Kevin Lee, Andy McDonald, Mark Dziadulewicz, Kevin Newbury, Andy Jones, Tony Mahoney. *Sawbridgeworth:* Mark Hardingham, Jason Lawes, Chris Quinn, Dave Williams, Dave Fawcett, Andy Lewis, Richard Head, Anthony Liddle, Mark Mower, Jason Scott, Gary Meadows. Subs: Lol Stapiton & Ally Hollison.

SENIOR SECTION TOP-SCORERS:
27 - Steve Harding (Burnham), 25 - Dave Stittle (Brentwood), 23 - Andy Jones (Canvey), 22 - Martin Lawrence (Southend Mnr), 19 - Tony Mahoney (Canvey), 16 - John Taylor (Bowers), 15 Gary Caldon (Maldon) Mark Mower & Tony Liddle (Sawbridgeworth), 13 - Howard Mackler (Gt Wakering), 12 - Jimmy Ablitt & Graham Stewart (Basildon) Andy Lewis (Sawbridgeworth) Billy Powell (East Ham) Robbie Nihill (Burnham), 11 - Len Cook (Brentwood) Barry Rainbird (Bowers) Wayne Toovey (Hullbridge), 10 - Maltese (Hullbridge) Risby (Eton Mnr) Shea (Fort) Flack & Ramsay (Gt Wakering) Mollison (Sawbridgeworth), Weeks (Southend Mnr). **Other Clubs' Top Scorer:** Romford: S Brock 8, Concord: K Lester 7, Stansted: L Russell 6, Woodford: N Taverner & M Stuart 5.

HARRY FISHER MEMORIAL TROPHY 1992-93

Preliminary Round
Southend Manor v East Ham United   5-5,2-1

Quarter-Finals

Eton Manor v Maldon Town	4-1	Southend Manor v Concord Rangers	1-0
Woodford Town v Ford United	1-1*(aet)*,0-1	Stansted v Hullbridge Sports	2-1

Semi-Finals

Eton Manor v Southend Manor	0-0,0-1	Ford United v Stansted	3-0*(Ford expelled)*

Final *(at East Ham United FC, Monday 3rd May)*:
Southend Manor 5 *(Weeks(3), Prue, Lawrence)* **Stansted 1** *(Ardley)*
Southend: Steve Whitmore, John Heffer, Danny Schneider, John Seaden, Neil Bailey, Matt Schneider, Gary Weeks, Alan Harding *(Man of the Match)*, Jimmy Prue, Martin Lawrence, Joey Jones. Subs: Desborough & Sullivan. *Stansted:* Turner, Evans, Robinson, Cole, Cuthbert, Hayes, Pritchard, Moore, Ardley, Wills, Russell. Subs: White, Rulton.

A jubilant Southend Manor after their second Harry Fisher Trophy win in three years. Photo - Paul Dennis.

RESERVE SECTION TOP-SCORERS:
28 - Clive Syrett (Basildon Res), 25 - Nicky Kemp (Sawbridgeworth Res), 24 Scott Ardley (Stansted Res), 13 - Wilson (Basildon Res), 11 - Purser (Concord Res) Jarvis (Hullbridge Res), 10 - Harvey & Buckingham (Bowers Res) Harney (Eton Manor Res), 9 - Rodway (Basildon Res) Cairns (Hullbridge Res).
Other clubs' leading scorers: Romford: S Brock 8, Concord: K Lester 7, Stansted: L Russell 6: Woodford: N Taverner & M Stuart 5.

RESERVE DIVISION CUP 1992-93

First Round

Concord Rangers Res v Stansted Res	4-0	Maldon Town Res v Bowers United Res	1-2
Hullbridge Sports Res v Basildon Utd Res	1-3	Brightlingsea Utd Res v Eton Manor Res	0-1
Sawbridgeworth Res v Southend Manor Res	0-2	Canvey Island *(bye)*	
East Thurrock Utd Res *(bye)*		Great Wakering Rvrs Res v Burnham Rblrs Res	1-4

Quarter-Finals

Concord Rangers Res v Bowers United Res	2-1	Basildon United Res v Eton Manor Res	3-0
Southend Manor Res v Canvey Island Res	2-3	Burnham Ramblers Res v East Thurrock Utd Res	2-1

Semi-Finals

Concord Rangers Res v Basildon Utd Res	1-3,2-8	Canvey Island Res v Burnham Ramblers Res	0-0,1-5

Final *(at Great Wakering Rovers FC, Saturday 24th April, Attendance: 157)*:
Basildon Utd Reserves 2 *(Syrett(2))*, **Burnham Ramblers 1** *(Taylor)*
Basildon: George, West, Reavill, Land, Gorbell, Thompson, Stokes, Rodway, Wilson, Syrett, Gould. Sub: Paul, Levitt. *Burnham:* Dennis, Pearson, Simmonds, Foster, Shaw, Duck, Dennerley, Taylor, Shaw, Glynn, S Simmonds. Subs: Snaith, Fry.

RESERVE DIVISION SHIELD 1992-93

First Round

Maldon Town Res v Stansted Rangers	2-3	Gt Wakering Rovers Res v Brightlingsea Res	4-2*(aet)*

Semi-Finals

Hullbridge Spts Res v Sawbridgeworth Res	1-3	Stansted Res v Great Wakering RoversRes	1-0

Final *(at Bishop's Stortford FC, Wednesday 5th May, Attendance: 85)*:
Stansted Reserves 3 *(Wood, Brown, Greenslade,* **Sawbridgeworth Town Reserves 1**
Stansted: O'Neill, Rulton, Wood, Cole, Cuthbert, Dixon, O'Brien, Brown, Wood, Wills, Nash. Subs: Greenslade.
Sawbridgeworth: Lacey, Stringer, Blanchard, Manning, Smith, Jelliman, Jarvis, Hastler, Kemp, Godfrey, Eyre. Subs: Dixon, O'Brien.

BASILDON UNITED

Chairman: Malcolm Carter   **Manager:** Vic Elson
Secretary: Trevor Thomas, 100 Littlecroft, South Woodham Ferrers, Essex CM3 5GQ (0245 323645).
Ground: Gardiners Close, Gardiners Lane, Basildon, Essex SS14 3AW (0268 520268).
Directions: A176 off Southend arterial (A127), left into Cranes Farm Road, proceed to end of duel carriageway, Gardiners Close on left at lights. Two and a half miles from Basildon BR station.
Seats: 400 **Cover:** Yes **Capacity:** 2,000 **Floodlights:** Yes **Founded:** 1967.
Colours: Amber & black **Change:** Sky & navy diamonds **Previous Name:** Armada Sports
Previous Leagues: Grays & Thurrock/ Gtr London 68-70/ Essex Snr 70-80/ Athenian 80-81/ Isthmian 81-91.
Record Gate: 4,000 v West Ham, ground opening 11/8/70 **Programme Editor:** Frank Ford.
Previous Ground: Grosvenor Park **Clubhouse:** Lunchtimes & evening **Nickname:** Bees.
Players progressing to Football League: Jeff Hull (Colchester), David Matthews & Steve Tilson (Southend), Jonathan Gould (Coventry City).
Hons: Isthmian Lg Div 2 83-83, Essex Snr Lg(4) 76-80 (Lg Cup 77-78, Reserve Cup 92-93).
Midweek Matches: Tuesday

BOWERS UNITED

Chairman: P Felham   **Manager:** Steve Wheeler
Secretary: E D Brown, 92 Quilters Straight, Fryerns, Basildon, Essex SS14 2SJ (0268 521201).
Ground: Crown Avenue, off Kenneth Rd, Pitsea, Basildon (0268 555583).
Directions: Turn into Rectory Rd from Old London Rd (B1464) at Pitsea Broadway into Kenneth Rd, right at top into Crown Avenue. One and a quarter miles from Pitsea (BR). Bus 523 to Rectory Rd, Bowers Guild.
Seats: 200 **Stand:** Yes **Capacity:** 2,000 **Floodlights:** Yes **Founded:** 1946.
Colours: Red & black **Change colours:** Blue/white/white.
Previous Ground: Gun Meadow, Pitsea.
Previous Leagues: Thurrock & Thameside Comb./Olympian. **Clubhouse:** Open every night.
Players progressing to Football League: Steve Tilson (Southend Utd).
Record Gate: 1,800 v Billericay Town, FA Vase. **Midweek Matches:** Wednesday.
Hons: Thurrock & Thameside Comb. 58-59/ Essex Snr Lg 80-81 (Div 1 Cup 90-91, Harry Fisher Mem. Tphy 91-92, Reserve Div R-up 92-93).

BRENTWOOD

Chairman: K J O'Neale   **Manager:** Derek Stittle
Secretary: C Harris, 56 Viking Way, Brentwood, Essex CM15 9HY (0277 219564).
Ground & Directions: As East Ham United FC (see below). **Founded:** 1955.
Colours: Sky & navy**Change colours:** All yellow **Programme:** Free with admission
Previous Names: Manor Ath. 55-70/ Brentwood Ath. 70-72. **Midweek Matches:**
Previous Grounds: King George, Hartswood/ 'Larkins', Ongar (pre-1992) **Nickname:** Blues
Previous Leagues: Romford & District/ Sth Essex Combination/ London & Essex Border/ Olympian.
Hons: Olympian Lg Cup 67-68, Essex Intermediate Cup 76-77, Essex Lg Cup 75-76 78-79 90-91.

BURNHAM RAMBLERS

Chairman: Gordon Brasted   **President:** R J Cole, Esq.
Secretary: Gordon Brasted, 6 Ramblers Way, Burnham-on-Crouch, Essex CM0 8LR (0621 782785).
Manager: John Wilson   **Assistant Manager:** T.B.A.
Ground: 'Leslie Field', Springfield Rd, Burnham-on-Crouch CM0 8TE (0621 784383).
Directions: On B1010 from South Woodham Ferrers, turn right half mile before town. 15 mins from Burnham (BR).
Seats: 300 **Stand:** Yes **Capacity:** 5,000 **Floodlights:** Yes **Founded:** 1900
Colours: Royal blue **Change colours:** Red
Nickname: Ramblers **Record Gate:** 1,500.
Previous Lges: N Essex/ Mid-Essex/Olympian/ SE Essex **Midweek matches:** Tuesday.
Previous Grounds: Wick Rd, Millfields/ Saltcourts (orig.) **Clubhouse:** Evenings & weekends
Programme: 36 pages **Editor:** Ron Bush (0621 783706).
Hons: Olympian Lg 65-66, Essex I'mediate Cup R-up 81-82, Essex Snr Lg Reserve Cup R-up 92-93.

CANVEY ISLAND

Chairman: W Overall   **Manager:** Jeff King.
Secretary: Mrs Frances Roche, 56 Harvest Way, Canvey Island SS8 9RP (0268 698586).
Ground: Park Lane, Canvey Island (0268 682991).
Directions: A130 from A13 or A127 at Sadlers Farm r'bout, 1 mile right through town centre, first on right past old bus garage. Bus 3 or 151 from Benfleet (BR) to stop after Admiral Jellicoe (PH).
Seats: None **Cover:** 250 **Capacity:** 2,500 **Floodlights:** Yes **Founded:** 1926.
Colours: Yellow **Change cols:** Red **Record Gate:** 3,250 v Tiverton, FA Vase SF 27/3/93
Programme Editor: John Nash **Nickname:** Gulls.
Previous Lges: Southend & Dist./ Thurrock & Thameside Comb./ Parthenon/ Metropolitan/ Gtr London 64-71.
Players progressing to Football League: Peter Taylor (Spurs, Crystal Palace & England).
Hons: FA Vase SF 92-93, Essex Snr Lg 86-87 92-93 (Lg Cup 83-84 92-93, Sportsmanship Award 83-84, Reserve Shield 91-92), Gtr London Lg(2) 67-69 (Lg Cup 68-69).

CONCORD RANGERS

Chairman: Jack Smith   **Manager:** Jack Welbourn.
Secretary: Robert Fletcher, 76 Eastwood Rd, Rayleigh, Essex (0268 770885).
Ground: Thames Road, Canvey Island (0268 691780). **Midweek Matches:** Tuesday.
Seats: No **Capacity:** 1,500 **Cover:** Yes **Floodlights:** Yes **Founded:** 1967.
Colours: Yellow/blue **Change colours:** Blue
Club Sponsor: Aspect Contracts.
Previous Lges: Southend & Dist Alliance/ Essex I'mediate (pre-1991) **Programme:** Yes
Record Gate: 1,500 v Lee Chapel North, FA Sunday Cup 89-90 **Previous Ground:** Waterside.
Hons: Essex I'mediate Lg Div 2 & Lg Cup, Southend Alliance. **Clubhouse:** Evenings & weekends.

Brentwood F.C. 1992-93. Back Row (L/R): Bradley Maltese, Danny Wye, Nicky Stagg, Murray Edwards, Richard Pike, Brendan Douglas, Kevin Gidea, Simon Benson. Front Row (L/R): Neil Slack, Steve Leslie, Stuart House, David Stittle, Lennie Cook. Photo - Richard Brock.

Canvey's Kevin Newbury beats Mark Short during the F.A. Vase Semi-Final at Tiverton. Photo - Dave West.

Woodford Town F.C. 1992-93. This famous old club have sadly resigned from the E.S.L. Photo - Gavin Ellis-Neville.

EAST HAM UNITED

Chairman: E H Whatmough   **Manager:** Reuben Gane.
Secretary: Rueben Gane, 108 Beccles Drive, Barking IG11 9HZ (081 594 7861).
Ground: Ferndale Spts Grnd, East Ham Manorway, Beckton E6 4NG (071 476 5514).
Seats: 150   **Capacity:** 2,500   **Nickname:** Hammers **Floodlights:** Yes   **Founded:** 1933.
Colours: Green, white & gold   **Change colours:** Claret & sky   **Programme:** Yes.
Record Gate: 4,250 - East Ham (inc George Best) v West Ham, friendly 15/2/76 at Terrance McMillan Stadium. 2,400 v Sutton United, FA Amateur Cup 14/11/53.
Previous Lges: Spartan, Metropolitan   **Previous Name:** Storey Athletic 1933-53
Previous Ground: Tilletts Farm (previous East Ham Utd, formed 1880 and played in Sth Essex Lge).
Hons: Metropolitan Lg, FA Vase QF, Essex Snr Tphy 76-77, Gtr London Lg Cup 69-70, London Jnr Cup 46-47.
Clubhouse: Evenings & weekends.   **Midweek Matchday:** Tuesday

ETON MANOR

Chairman: Reg Curtis   **Manager:** Barry Goldman
Secretary: George E Whiting, 69 John Walsh Tower, Montague Rd., Leytonstone E11 3ET (081 550 9618).
Ground: ******* At Roding Lane, Buckhurst Hill (081 504 9937). The ground is being rebuilt, and in the meantime the club are playing home games at Stansted F.C. (see page 436) *********
Nickname: Manor   **Founded:** 1901.
Programme Editor: Secretary   **Record Gate:** 12,000 v Romford, Essex Snr Cup Final 1938.
Colours: Sky   **Change colours:** White   **Midweek Matches:** Tuesday.
Previous Grounds: Temple Mills/ Walthamstow Avenue/ GUS/ Norwegian Ground, Barking.
Previous Name: Wilderness Leyton.   **Hons:** Essex Snr Cup R-up 37-38, London Lg 37-38 52-53 53-54 55-56, Essex Snr Lg Sportsmanship Award 75-76 (Div 1 Cup 90-91), Reserve Div Cup 91-92).
Clubhouse: Evenings (except Mondays).   **Previous Leagues:** London Metropolitan, Aetolian.

FORD UNITED

Chairman: J M Rowe   **President:** Stuart J Harmer
Vice Chairman: A Jones   **Manager:** Donal McGovern
Secretary: K D Dobson, 16 Tenby Court, Tenby Road, Walthamstow E17 7AT (071 521 9285).
Ground: Ford Spts & Soc. Club, Rush Green Rd., Romford (0708 745678).   **Directions:** On the A124 (Rush Green road) on left going towards Hornchurch. 2 miles from Romford (BR). Buses 173, 175 87, 106, 23.
Seats: 800   **Cover:** Yes   **Capacity:** 2,500   **Floodlights:** Yes   **Founded:** 1958
Cols: All royal blue **Change:** Yellow/red/yellow.   **Prog. Editor:** Colin Mynott (0268 281002).
Previous Names: Briggs Sports (founded 1934) & Fords Sports (founded 1934) merged in 1958.
Prev. Grnd: Victoria Rd (now Dagenham & Redbridge FC)   **Prev. Lges:** Spartan, Aetolian, Metropolitan
Nickname: Motormen   **Players progressing to Football League:** Les Allen (Spurs), Mick Flanagan (QPR, Charlton, Crystal Palace), Jim Stannard (Fulham, Southend, Millwall), Nicky Hammond (Arsenal, Swindon), Laurie Abrahams (Charlton), Doug Barton (Reading, Newport).
Record Gate: 58,000 Briggs Sports v Bishop Auckland, at St James Park, Newcastle, FA Amateur Cup.
Hons: FA Amateur Cup SF 53-54, London Snr Cup 55-56 56-57, Essex Snr Trophy 90-91 91-92, Essex Snr Cup 39-40 49-50 50-51 51-52, Spartan Lg 49-50 50-51 55-56 56-57 57-58, London Lg 36-37 38-39, Essex Elizabethan 59-60 60-61 70-71, Gtr London Lg 70-71, Essex Snr Lg 91-92 (Lg Cup 85-86), Sportsmanship Award 77-78 79-80 80-81).
Clubhouse: 4 bars, 2 dance halls, tea bar, snooker room.

GREAT WAKERING ROVERS

Chairman: Trevor Lovell   **Manager:** Ben Embery.
Secretary: Roger Sampson, 37 Lee Lotts, Gt Wakering, Southend-on-Sea, Essex SS3 0HA (0702 218794).
Ground: Burroughs Pk, Little Wakering Hall Lane, Gt Wakering, Southend-on-Sea SS3 0HQ (0702 217812).
Directions: 4a bus from Shoeburyness (BR), 4a or 4b from Southend. A127 past Southend signposted Gt Wakering, at Parsons Corner - Poynters Lane then into Star Lane, right to High Street, Little Wakering Hall Lane is half mile on left, ground 250 yds on left.
Seats: None   **Stand:** Due   **Capacity:** 1,500   **Floodlights:** No   **Founded:** 1919
Cols: Green & white stripes/white/green   **Change cols:** Red & yellow/white/white   **Nickname:** Rovers
Programme: Yes   **Editor:** N Johnson   **Midweek Matchday:** Tuesday
Previous Ground: Gt Wakering Rec.   **Record Gate:** 500 v Leyton Orient, friendly 18/7/92.
Previous Leagues: Southend & District/ Southend Alliance/ Essex Intermediate (pre-1992).
Players progressing to Football League: Les Stubbs (Chelsea), Jackie Bridge (Southend Utd).
Clubhouse: Self built, completed August 1989. Bar (capacity 150), boardroom, changing rooms.
Hons: Essex I'mediate Cup 91-92, Essex I'mediate Lg Div 2 91-92 (Div 3 90-91, Lg Cup 91-92), Essex Snr Lg Wirral Programme Award 92-93.

HULLBRIDGE SPORTS

Chairman: Brian Lloyd   **Manager:** Mark Lloyd
Secretary: Mrs G Adams, Hullbridge Spts & Social Club, Lower Rd, Hullbridge, Essex.
Ground: Lower Road, Hullbridge, Essex SS5 6BJ (0702 230420).
Directions: Turn into Rawreth Lane from A130 (left if arriving from Chelmsford), down to mini-r'bout, left, across next mini-r'bout, up hill, ground signed on right just past garage.
Seats: No   **Cover:** Yes   **Capacity:**   **Floodlights:** No   **Founded:** 1945
Colours: Royal blue & white/white/blue   **Change colours:** White/black.
Midweek matches: Tues/Thursday.   **Prog. Editor:** Mrs Lynne Ward.   **Sponsor:** Thermo Shield
Prev. Grounds: Pooles Lane Rec.   **Prev. Lges:** Southend & Dist./ Alliance/ Essex I'mediate
Honours: Essex Intermediate Snr Div Cup 87-88, Southend & District Lg Div 1 65-66 (Div 2 51-52, Div 3 56-57), French Cup 51-52, Essex Snr Lg Sportsmanship Award 91-92 92-93.
Clubhouse details: Lounge bar, function hall with bar & changing rooms - set in 16 acre land.

MALDON TOWN

Chairman: T.B.A.   **Manager:** Keith Hull.
Secretary: Ms Toni Morrant.
Ground: Fambridge Road, Maldon (0621 853762).
Directions: Half mile south of town on west side of Fambridge Road. Bus 92 from Chelmsford (BR).
Seats: 400   **Cover:** Yes   **Capacity:** 2,500   **Floodlights:** No   **Founded:** 1946.
Colours: Blue & white hoops   **Change colours:** Red & white hoops   **Programme:** Yes
Previous Lges: Eastern Counties, Essex & Suffolk Border.   **Hons:** Essex Snr Lg 84-85 (Sportsmanship 88-89), Essex & Suffolk Border Lg 55-56 (Cup 64-65), Essex Intermediate Cup 51-52.

East Ham United F.C. 1992-93. Photo - Gavin Ellis-Neville.

Great Wakering Rovers (stripes) pictured with their Leyton Orient opponents before their inaugural match as senior club. Photo - Gavin Ellis-Neville.

Maldon Town F.C. 1992-93. Neil Dobson, Nick Hawkins (trainer), Kevin Bird (captain), Paul Bardo, Danny Large, Everton Richards, Hales Eugene, Esmond Young, Graham Scales (Coach), Glen Bayliss. Front Row: Barry Winch, Laurie Staerck, Gary Caldon, Eddie Hawkins (Manager), Bon Large (Club Chairman), Trevor Thompson (Football Chairman), Toni Morrant (Secretary), Phil Douglas, Andy Dunsmuir, Mark Dorado.

ROMFORD

Chairman: Dave Howie **Manager:** Lyndon Lynch. **Press Officer:** Andy Adams (0708 347781).
Secretary: Bob Knightley, 7 Tulip Close, Harold Hill, Romford, Essex RM3 8BX (0708 374900).
Ground & Directions: As Hornchurch FC (see page 358) **Founded:** 1929 **Reformed:** 1992.
Colours: Gold/blue/gold **Change colours:** Blue/gold/blue **Nickname:** The Boro
Programme: 24 pages, 50p **Editor:** Ian Howitt **Club Shop:** Yes
Previous Grounds: Brooklands Sports Ground, Romford. **Midweek Matchday:** Tuesday.
Record Gate: 2,005 v Arsenal Celebrity XI, 28/5/92. **Sponsors:** Romford Recorder
Previous Leagues: None *(Original club: London 29-31/ Athenian 31-39/ Isthmian 45-59/ Southern 59-78)*
Local Newspapers: Romford Recorder, Post, Yellow Advertiser, Observer. **Clubhouse:** Yes
Hons: None *(Original club: FA Amtr Cup R-up 48-49, Southern Lg 66-67 (Div 1 R-up 59-60), Athenian Lg 35-36 36-37 (R-up 38-39), Essex Snr Cup 31-32 33-34 37-38 46-47, Essex Thameside Tphy 51-52 55-56 57-58).*

SAWBRIDGEWORTH TOWN

Chairman: Geoff Moore **Manager:** Don Watters
Secretary: Mr H T Annis, 15 Tunmeade, Harlow, Essex CM20 3HS (0279 425865).
Ground: Crofters End, West Road, Sawbridgeworth (0279 722039). **Nickname:** Robins.
Directions: Three quarters of a mile from station; up Station Road then West Road.
Seats: No **Capacity:** 1,500 **Cover:** 250 **Floodlights:** Yes **Founded:** 1890.
Colours: Red & black **Change colours:** Blue
Programme Editor: Ron Alder (0279 722360) **Previous Leagues:** Essex Olympian, Spartan 36-53.
Previous Grounds: Hyde Hall/ Pishiobury/ Hand & Crown.
Record Gate: 610 v Bishop's Stortford.
Hons: Essex Olympian Lg 71-72, Essex Snr Lg R-up 92-93 (Harry Fisher Mem. Cup 87-88, Lg Cup R-up 92-93, Reserve Div 91-92 92-93, Reserve Shield R-up 92-93), Herts Snr Tphy 90-91 (R-up 92-93), Herts Charity Shield 92-93, Uttlesford Charity Cup 92-93.

SOUTHEND MANOR

Chairman: Simon Dibley **Manager:** John Seaden.
Secretary: Dave Kittle, 15 Seymour Rd, Hadleigh, Benfleet, Essex SS7 2HB (0702 559581)
Ground: Southchurch Park Arena, Lifstan Way, Southend-on-Sea. (0702 615577)
Directions: A127 then A1159 for 1 mile turn right at second r-about at Rusty Bucket PH, due south for 1 mile – ground on right near sea front.
Seats: 500 **Cover:** Yes **Capacity:** 2,000 **Floodlights:** Yes **Founded:** 1955
Colours: Yellow, red & black **Change colours:** Black & white **Nickname:** The Manor
Programme: Yes **Sponsors:** Reeder Glazing **Midweek Matchday:** Wednesday
Record Attendance: 1,521 v Southend Utd, 22.7.91 (Floodlight inauguration).
Previous Leagues: Southend Borough Combination, Southend Alliance
Previous Grounds: Victory Spts/ Oakwood Rec. **Clubhouse:** Open every evening
Hons: Essex Snr Trophy 92-93, Essex Intermediate Cup 78-79, Essex Snr Lg 90-91 (Lg Cup 87-88, ESL Challenge Cup 89-90, Harry Fisher Mem. Tphy 90-91 92-93 (R-up 91-92)).
Soccer Line: 0891 88 44 27.

STANSTED

Chairman: Terry Shoebridge **Gen. Manager:** Alan Russell **Team Manager:** Roy Wood.
Secretary: P A G Heal, 28 Mountfitchet Rd, Stansted CM24 8NW (0279 812053)
Ground: Hargrave Sports Ground, Cambridge Rd, Stansted. (0279 812897)
Directions: B1383 north of Bishops Stortford on west side of Cambridge Rd. Stansted (BR) – 1/2 mile
Seats: 200 **Cover:** Yes **Capacity:** 2,000 **Floodlights:** Yes **Founded:** 1902
Colours: Blue/white/blue **Change colours:** White & black **Programme:** Yes
Midweek home matches: Thursday.
Record attendance: 828 v Whickham (FA Vase 83-84), 12,000 v Stamford (FA Vase Final at Wembley 83-84)
Previous Ground: Greens Meadow/Chapel Hill **Previous Leagues:** Spartan, London, Herts Co.
Honours: FA Vase 83-84, Essex Snr Lg 83-84 (Lg Cup 83-84, Harry Fisher Mem. Tphy 82-83 84-85 (R-up 92-93), Reserve Shield 92-93), East Anglian Cup 83-84, Courage Eastern Floodlight Comp 83-84.

East Ham United forward Simon Ayaoge makes a powerful run during the first-half of his side's 0-4 defeat at Sawbridgeworth on 27th February. Photo - Martin Wray.

Romford F.C. 1992-93. Back Row (L/R): Paul Tumpenny (Asst Manager), Davey Walker, John Burrows, Scott Rock, Steve Brock, Mark Brett, Roy Drake, Lyndon Lynch (Manager). Front: Hugh Stein, Mark Abbot, Naheed Bhatt, Simon Bumfrey, Lee Murcott, Trevor Pye, Andy Priest. Photo - Richard Brock.

Sawbridgeworth Town, who enjoyed perhaps their most prolific season ever. Photo - Gavin Ellis-Neville.

Southend Manor after winning the Essex Senior. Photo - Robert Errington.

ESSEX SENIOR LEAGUE TEN YEAR RECORD

	83/4	84/5	85/6	86/7	87/8	88/9	89/0	90/1	91/2	92/3
Basildon United	–	–	–	–	–	–	–	–	6	5
Bowers United	2	9	8	4	14	15	11	5	7	3
Brentwood	6	5	6	10	2	9	7	2	2	6
Brighlingsea Utd	16	12	11	17	11	1	1	–	–	–
Burnham Ramblers	–	–	12	6	13	4	8	3	13	4
Canvey Island	8	7	9	1	10	6	4	9	5	1
Chelmsford City Reserves	5	6	7	9	12	13	14	–	–	–
Coggeshall Town	17	16	17	–	17	14	–	–	–	–
Concord Rangers	–	–	–	–	–	–	–	–	11	11
East Ham United	14	15	16	16	15	16	16	14	15	13
East Thurrock United	12	13	5	5	5	2	3	8	3	–
Eton Manor	11	10	10	13	9	8	12	11	16	15
Ford United	10	8	3	12	6	3	9	7	1	8
Great Wakering Rovers	–	–	–	–	–	–	–	–	–	7
Halstead United	15	11	15	11	3	–	–	–	–	–
Heybridge Swifts	1	–	–	–	–	–	–	–	–	–
Hullbridge Sports	–	–	–	–	–	–	–	12	14	16
Maldon Town	13	1	4	15	16	17	15	13	17	12
Purfleet	–	–	–	3	1	–	–	–	–	–
Romford	–	–	–	–	–	–	–	–	–	9
Sawbridgeworth Town	7	14	14	8	8	11	5	4	4	2
Southend Manor	–	–	–	–	–	7	10	1	8	10
Stambridge	–	–	–	–	–	12	6	6	9	–
Stansted	4	3	13	14	7	5	13	10	12	17
Witham Town	3	2	1	2	–	–	–	–	–	–
Wivenhoe Town	9	4	2	–	–	–	–	–	–	–
Woodford Town	–	–	–	–	4	10	2	15	10	14
Woodford Town Reserves	–	–	–	7	–	–	–	–	–	–
No. of Clubs	**17**	**16**	**17**	**17**	**17**	**17**	**16**	**15**	**17**	**17**

Sawbridgeworth's Richard Head shoots in a 1-0 home beating of Stansted on 12th December. Photo - Martin Wray.

ESSEX & HERTS BORDER COMBINATION

EASTERN DIV.	P	W	D	L	F	A	PTS
Leyton Res	30	23	4	3	97	33	73
Dag. & Redb. Res	30	20	6	4	102	45	66
Wivenhoe T. Res	30	19	3	8	76	39	60
Braintree T. Res	30	16	2	12	71	42	50
Grays Ath. Res	30	15	5	10	59	43	50
Billericay T. Res	30	14	7	9	71	49	49
Collier Row Res	30	12	8	10	39	43	44
Ford United Res	30	12	7	11	58	56	43
Chelmsford C. Res	30	12	5	13	56	49	41
Tilbury Res	30	12	4	14	53	63	40
Witham Town Res	30	11	3	16	41	66	36
Tiptree Utd Res	30	8	5	17	32	62	29
Clapton Res	30	7	7	16	54	89	28
Aveley Res	30	7	7	16	48	84	28
Heybridge S. Res	30	5	10	15	57	83	25
Barkingside Res	30	4	3	23	46	114	15

WESTERN DIV.	P	W	D	L	F	A	PTS
Enfield Res	30	24	5	1	90	21	77
Bishop's S. Res	30	18	6	6	64	34	60
Boreham Wd Res	30	18	2	10	93	51	56
Ware Res	30	16	4	10	81	56	52
Hertford T. Res	30	15	5	10	57	44	50
Berkhamsted T. Res	30	15	5	10	54	45	50
Saffron W. Res	30	13	7	10	54	57	46
Hemel Hem. Res	30	13	2	12	54	65	44
Baldock T. Res	30	12	4	14	62	69	40
Cheshunt	30	11	5	14	58	62	38
Wingate & F. Res	30	10	5	15	60	71	35
Stevenage B. Res	30	8	7	15	56	77	31
Hoddesdon T. Res	30	7	7	16	46	68	28
Waltham Ab. Res	30	8	2	20	40	83	26
Tring Town Res	30	5	9	16	31	71	24
Royston Town Res	30	6	4	20	45	71	22

ESSEX INTERMEDIATE FOOTBALL LEAGUE

President: P.K. Byford **Chairman:** C.W. Rand
Hon. Secretary: R.F. Hurrell, 102 Falmouth Road, Springfield, Chelmsford, CM1 5JA (0245 256922)

When the final Senior game was played on Saturday 15th May in this long and extended season, all the issues had been resolved and the top flight saw a tight battle with the outcome not clear-cut until the final games. In the end it was the lads from Standard (Harlow) who accomplished another fine team effort to retain their title by eight points, whilst second place finally went to Writtle when they picked up a fine win at Rayleigh Town in their final game. On the relegation front it was a hard struggling season for Great Baddow Royal Engineers, (perhaps next season's change of name to Sandon Royals may bring them some luck), with the second relegation spot going to Rayleigh Athletic finishing one point behind a very disappointing Benfleet.

In Division 2 we had four teams early on battling for honours, but after Christmas Takeley fell away leaving the final push between the Shell Club, Hatfield Peverel and South Woodham Ferrers. An indifferent spell saw Shell lose their advantage as South Woodham overtook them and it was their title as they pipped Hatfield Peverel, enjoying their first season with us, by one point. Leaving this division and hoping to put next season to good use and rebuild will be Upminster and Caribbean International Sports who once again played some good and attractive football, but showed some indifferent discipline.

The tightest of all the division titles was in Senior Three with the final Saturday seeing any of four clubs in with a chance of honours and at this stage the challenge from Clavering ended with them gaining only a point from their final match. This took us to the final game of the season in mid-week when Danbury Trafford sat in third place entertained Great Baddow and a see-saw match finished with Danbury winners by the odd goal and sending them up as champions. It looked good early on for the home side, but a spirited fight back by the visitors saw the whole scenario change as Hambros Bank looked set for the championship with Broomfield the team to join them, but in the closing stages of a fine game Danbury Trafford hit back to clinch the title at their first attempt with Hambros Bank joining them in Division 2. With those teams left who just failed to gain promotion, next season will once again make division 3 very competitive which must surely be good news for the League.

Moving on to the Senior Cup Final, it was once again Hatfield Peverel taking second place to Kelvedon Hatch who at last, at the third attempt, lifted the cup. Hatfield Peverel had flown the League's flag in the final of the Essex Intermediate Cup, having had to beat some very good teams to get there. However, they failed at the final hurdle to a very impressive Canning Town to finish second best.

Phil Coultard (Publicity Secretary).

Standrad (Harlow) - Essex Intermediate League Champions 1992-93. Back Row (L-R): P.Bull (Manager), C.Roberts, K.Barry, S.Savidge, I.Richards, I.Bartram, A.Darvill. Front Row I.Beard, R.Stepleton, K.Gregory, M.Saunders, H.Cracknell. Photo - Martin Wray.

Senior Div. 1	P	W	D	L	F	A	PTS
Standard (Harlow)	24	17	4	3	74	37	38
Writtle	24	12	9	3	57	34	33
Stambridge	24	12	8	4	53	34	32
Kelvedon Hatch	24	11	9	4	48	26	31
Runwell Hospital	24	11	4	9	40	34	26
Rayleigh Town	24	10	6	8	44	38	26
O Chelmsfordians	24	9	4	11	42	56	22
Essex Police	24	6	9	9	48	50	21
Herongate Athletic	24	7	7	10	32	44	21
Harold Wood Ath.	24	6	7	11	37	46	19
Benfleet	24	5	6	13	38	63	16
Rayleigh Athletic	24	4	7	13	41	59	15
Gt Baddow Ryl Eng.	24	4	4	16	38	71	12

Reserve Div. 1	P	W	D	L	F	A	PTS
Writtle Res	24	17	4	3	69	18	38
Standrard Res	24	15	5	4	70	29	35
O Chelms. Res	24	14	7	3	59	25	35
Runwell Hos. Res	24	12	7	5	50	30	31
Kelvedon H. Res	24	12	4	8	47	30	28
Shell Club Res	24	11	4	9	47	40	26
Benfleet Res	24	10	4	10	45	52	24
Harold Wd A. Res	24	8	6	10	39	44	22
Rayleigh T. Res	24	8	5	11	33	33	21
Herongate A. Res	24	6	5	13	40	61	17
Gt Baddow RE Res	24	6	4	14	43	78	16
Ekco Spts Res	24	4	6	14	36	54	14
Stambridge Res	24	2	1	21	31	115	5

Senior Div. 2	P	W	D	L	F	A	PTS
S Woodham Ferrers	26	21	1	4	85	34	43
Hatfield Peverel	26	20	2	4	72	23	42
Shell Club	26	17	4	5	56	32	38
Ekco Sports	26	12	9	5	59	36	33
Takeley	26	12	7	7	50	31	31
S.C. Henderson	26	13	2	11	59	59	28
B S'ford Swifts	26	9	8	9	37	42	26
Mountnessing	26	9	5	12	40	45	23
Doddinghurst Olym.	26	8	6	12	39	52	22
White Notley	26	5	10	11	52	57	20
Basildon Town	26	7	6	13	34	49	20
Barnston	26	7	5	14	41	51	19
Caribbean I. Spts	26	4	4	18	40	65	12
Upminster	26	2	3	21	22	110	7

Reserve Div. 2	P	W	D	L	F	A	PTS
S Woodham F. Res	26	17	4	5	77	35	38
Hambros Bank Res	26	15	4	7	73	38	34
Takeley Res	26	13	7	6	49	32	33
Maldon St M. Res	26	12	7	7	67	53	31
S.C. Henderson Res	26	11	8	7	63	46	30
Caribbean Res	26	12	5	9	69	51	29
Doddinghurst Res	26	12	5	9	43	33	29
Springfield Res	26	12	5	9	45	49	29
B S'ford Sw. Res	26	11	5	10	62	43	27
Mountnessing	26	10	4	12	39	49	24
Essex Police Res	26	9	4	13	48	57	22
Ramsden Res	26	5	6	15	22	84	16
Eppingsale Res	26	3	6	17	48	83	12
Upminster	26	4	2	20	29	81	10

Senior Div. 3	P	W	D	L	F	A	PTS
Danbury Trafford	26	17	5	4	59	32	39
Hambros Bank	26	16	6	4	76	31	38
Broomfield	26	15	7	4	58	21	37
Clavering	26	15	6	5	75	28	36
Ongar Town	26	14	7	5	73	37	35
Hutton	26	11	8	7	55	35	30
Brentwood Manor	26	12	6	8	37	35	30
Great Baddow	26	12	3	11	44	41	27
Maldon St Mary's	26	8	6	12	37	55	22
Galleywood	26	9	3	14	39	60	21
Springfield	26	4	9	13	27	54	17
Eppingsale	26	5	1	20	24	77	11
A.F.C. Notley	26	4	3	19	34	91	11
Ramsden	26	3	4	19	29	70	10

Reserve Div. 3	P	W	D	L	F	A	PTS
Brentwood M. Res	26	19	2	5	59	23	40
Clavering Res	26	14	6	6	61	38	34
Barnston Res	26	13	7	6	47	27	33
A.F.C. Notley Res	26	14	4	8	44	36	32
Basildon Town Res	26	13	3	10	52	43	29
White Notley Res	26	13	1	12	58	50	27
Broomfield Res	26	11	5	10	43	42	27
Galleywood Res	26	7	11	8	49	53	25
Hatfield Pev. Res	26	10	5	11	36	40	25
Ongar Town Res	26	8	7	11	50	55	23
Hutton Res	26	8	4	14	35	45	20
Gt Baddow Res	26	8	3	15	50	78	19
Danbury Traff. Res	26	7	4	15	64	75	18
Rayleigh Ath. Res	26	5	2	19	42	85	12

SENIOR DIVISION ONE RESULT CHART 1992-93

HOME TEAM	1	2	3	4	5	6	7	8	9	10	11	12	13
1. Benfleet	*	2-6	3-2	2-2	1-1	2-3	2-3	2-2	2-4	1-2	1-1	1-6	1-1
2. Essex Police	0-1	*	6-1	2-1	1-1	2-2	1-1	1-1	0-1	2-2	1-4	2-3	1-4
3. Gt Baddow Royal Eng.	2-4	2-3	*	3-3	2-3	1-4	4-1	2-8	3-0	3-2	1-1	2-3	1-4
4. Harold Wood Athletic	1-2	3-5	3-1	*	2-3	2-1	1-3	6-1	2-2	1-2	0-1	0-4	1-1
5. Herongate Athletic	1-1	1-2	3-1	3-1	*	1-1	2-0	3-2	1-3	0-1	0-0	0-3	1-3
6. Kelvedon Hatch	4-2	1-1	4-1	3-0	2-0	*	1-2	1-1	1-0	1-1	1-0	2-3	2-2
7. Old Chelmsfordians	5-1	4-1	3-1	0-1	4-1	1-1	*	7-0	1-2	0-2	1-1	1-7	1-1
8. Rayleigh Athletic	2-3	2-3	0-2	0-1	1-3	2-2	1-2	*	2-2	2-0	2-2	0-2	4-5
9. Rayleigh Town	2-1	2-1	4-0	1-3	1-1	1-1	2-0	1-2	*	3-1	4-4	1-1	1-3
10. Runwell Hospital	3-0	2-0	3-0	1-0	2-2	0-3	7-0	2-1	2-1	*	1-3	1-2	0-3
11. Stambridge	3-2	3-3	0-0	3-0	3-0	1-0	5-1	2-3	0-3	3-2	*	4-0	3-2
12. Standard (Harlow)	4-0	4-3	5-2	1-1	5-0	0-5	7-0	2-2	3-2	2-0	3-2	*	3-5
13. Writtle	3-1	1-1	1-1	1-1	2-1	0-2	4-1	3-0	3-1	1-1	3-4	1-1	*

SENIOR DIVISION TWO RESULT CHART 1992-93

HOME TEAM	1	2	3	4	5	6	7	8	9	10	11	12	13	14
1. Barnston	*	4-1	2-4	3-2	0-2	1-2	1-3	1-1	1-3	1-0	1-3	2-4	5-0	3-3
2. Basildon Town	1-0	*	2-3	2-1	0-1	0-1	0-1	1-4	0-6	0-2	3-1	2-1	0-1	4-4
3. Bishop's Stortford Swifts	2-4	1-1	*	3-2	0-0	0-0	1-0	0-0	1-4	2-3	2-1	0-1	0-1	2-0
4. Caribbean International S.	1-1	3-3	3-0	*	1-2	2-3	L-W	3-0	1-2	2-4	1-3	0-6	4-2	2-2
5. Doddinghurst Olympic	1-3	2-2	1-3	2-0	*	4-7	1-3	2-1	1-2	1-3	4-4	2-2	1-0	2-2
6. Ekco Sports	3-1	2-1	1-1	4-0	3-0	*	1-2	3-0	2-2	1-3	6-4	1-1	1-1	2-2
7. Hatfield Peverel	0-1	4-0	2-0	2-0	3-1	3-3	*	5-1	5-0	3-2	4-1	2-2	12-0	3-0
8. Mountnessing	1-1	1-1	0-2	6-1	1-0	0-0	1-3	*	3-2	0-2	1-3	2-1	5-1	2-0
9. Shell Club	3-1	0-1	2-0	2-1	1-0	1-0	1-0	2-1	*	4-4	4-1	1-1	3-0	3-1
10. South Woodham Ferrers	2-1	3-4	4-2	5-1	3-2	3-1	3-1	3-2	3-1	*	4-0	2-0	10-0	3-1
11. Sporting Club Henderson	1-0	3-1	3-0	4-2	3-2	2-3	0-1	3-4	2-1	0-3	*	W-L	7-4	1-2
12. Takeley	2-0	0-0	1-1	3-1	1-0	3-5	1-0	0-0	2-0	2-3	*	7-2	2-1	
13. Upminster	2-1	0-4	1-3	2-4	1-1	0-5	0-2	0-2	0-1	0-8	2-4	0-4	*	2-3
14. White Notley	2-2	1-0	3-3	1-1	1-2	1-1	0-3	4-2	2-5	1-2	2-2	1-3	1-3	12-0

SENIOR DIVISION THREE RESULT CHART 1992-93

HOME TEAM	1	2	3	4	5	6	7	8	9	10	11	12	13	14
1. A.F.C. Notley	*	1-1	0-3	0-10	2-6	3-2	3-4	3-0	2-8	1-1	1-0	2-4	4-3	3-3
2. Brentwood Manor	3-0	*	1-0	2-0	0-2	1-0	3-0	0-0	2-5	2-3	2-1	1-0	2-1	1-0
3. Broomfield	3-1	2-0	*	2-2	0-1	3-1	0-1	3-0	2-1	1-1	1-1	2-1	6-0	3-0
4. Clavering	2-1	3-1	2-2	*	1-0	10-0	4-2	2-0	0-2	3-1	4-0	3-0	3-0	0-1
5. Danbury Trafford	3-1	2-0	1-3	0-0	*	3-1	4-1	4-3	2-2	1-1	3-1	1-1	1-0	2-1
6. Eppingsale	2-1	1-1	0-6	1-4	0-2	*	0-4	0-2	3-1	1-2	1-2	0-7	1-3	1-3
7. Galleywood	3-2	1-3	0-2	2-2	1-2	2-1	*	0-1	0-3	2-2	1-1	1-6	5-2	2-0
8. Great Baddow	6-1	3-1	0-3	3-1	1-5	3-0	5-0	*	2-0	2-4	0-3	1-4	2-0	4-0
9. Hambros Bank	8-0	2-0	0-0	1-5	3-0	3-0	2-1	2-0	*	1-0	10-2	3-3	4-0	4-1
10. Hutton	2-1	1-2	2-2	2-2	4-1	8-1	2-0	1-1	1-3	*	0-1	4-1	1-1	4-0
11. Maldon St Mary's	2-0	3-3	2-4	1-3	0-3	3-1	1-0	0-2	2-2	0-4	*	0-2	4-1	2-2
12. Ongar Town	8-0	2-2	1-1	2-1	1-1	1-0	7-2	1-2	2-0	2-0	2-1	*	5-1	2-2
13. Ramsden	3-1	0-1	2-1	0-2	1-3	1-2	1-2	1-3	1-2	1-6			*	1-1
14. Sprinfield	1-0	2-2	0-3	2-2	1-6	0-2	0-1	2-0	0-0	2-0	2-2	1-2	2-2	*

RESERVES DIVISION ONE RESULT CHART 1992-93

HOME TEAM	1	2	3	4	5	6	7	8	9	10	11	12	13
1. Benfleet Reserves	*	4-2	1-3	2-1	3-1	1-1	2-2	2-1	2-2	2-1	4-2	2-1	0-3
2. Ekco Sports	2-1	*	1-1	3-4	4-0	1-3	2-3	1-1	2-2	0-3	1-2	1-1	0-3
3. Great Baddow R.E. Res.	6-4	1-3	*	1-3	0-2	0-3	0-5	L-W	3-2	7-4	0-8	1-2	
4. Harold Wd Ath. Reserves	1-1	1-0	6-3	*	1-1	3-2	1-2	2-2	1-1	W-L	W-L	3-2	0-3
5. Herongate Ath. Reserves	2-1	3-3	2-2	3-1	*	1-2	0-4	1-0	1-2	0-1	7-1	2-7	2-4
6. Kelvedon Hatch Reserves	3-1	4-2	2-2	6-1	1-1	*	2-1	0-1	1-1	W-L	3-0	2-3	0-1
7. Old Chelmsfordians	3-1	1-0	3-0	1-0	3-0	1-0	*	3-1	1-0	2-2	9-0	1-3	2-2
8. Raleigh Town Reserves	2-0	1-0	4-0	2-2	2-2	1-2	1-1	*	0-2	0-1	3-0	0-4	1-2
9. Runwell Hospital Reserves	0-2	3-1	8-1	2-2	4-0	3-0	1-0	2-1	*		6-1	1-1	1-3
10. Shell Club Reserves	1-2	5-1	2-3	2-0	5-3	0-3	2-2	0-2	1-1	*	5-3	4-0	0-0
11. Stambridge Reserves	2-7	1-4	3-4	1-6	1-6	1-5	0-5	W-L	1-3	3-4	*	0-5	3-3
12. Standard (Harlow) Reserves	5-0	2-2	2-2	3-0	W-L	2-1	1-1	1-2	3-1	3-1	9-1	*	2-1
13. Writtle Reserves	3-0	4-0	1-0	1-0	9-0	2-1	1-1	5-0	0-1	4-0	9-1	1-2	*

RESERVES DIVISION TWO RESULT CHART 1992-93

HOME TEAM	1	2	3	4	5	6	7	8	9	10	11	12	13	14
1. Bishop's St. Swifts Res.	*	7-3	0-1	4-1	1-3	1-1	1-2	3-0	0-0	2-3	2-2	7-0	0-3	6-1
2. Caribbean I. Spts Res.	5-1	*	W-L	1-1	2-0	0-1	8-0	4-3	6-2	3-1	1-1	6-1	1-3	4-1
3. Doddinghurst O. Reserves	0-2	4-1	*	3-1		6-3	4-4	1-1	1-1	0-3	3-2	3-0	1-0	2-3
4. Eppingsale Reserves	1-2	2-7	1-1	*	0-2	1-4	2-7	0-3	7-0	1-3	3-1	0-5	2-3	3-1
5. Essex Police Reserves	1-5	3-4	0-0	4-4	*	0-3	3-1	0-1	3-2	6-4	3-3	1-1	3-1	2-3
6. Hambros Bank Reserves	3-2	3-3	0-4	4-1	2-0	*	5-4	3-0	11-0	1-4	0-1	1-1	2-1	3-0
7. Maldon St Mary's Res.	1-3	3-3	2-0	2-0	6-2	0-1	*	2-1	1-0	2-2	4-4	0-4	3-3	8-0
8. Mountnessing Reserves	2-4	W-L	1-2	2-2	0-0	0-6	0-1	*	1-1	1-3	4-0	3-0	1-3	2-1
9. Ramsden Reserves	1-0	4-2	L-W	4-3	2-3	0-5	1-3	1-6	*	0-6	1-8	0-2	0-0	1-0
10. Sth Woodham Ferrers Res.	1-1	1-0	3-2	5-3	3-0	1-1	2-1	1-2	11-0	*	0-2	L-W	2-2	2-1
11. S.C. Henderson Reserves	3-1	1-1	2-0	8-3	1-3	2-1	2-2	4-0	1-1	1-3	*	3-1	0-1	5-1
12. Springfield Reserves	2-2	2-0	2-1	1-1	4-2	3-2	0-2	3-1	4-0	1-5	1-3	*	2-2	3-1
13. Takeley Reserves	0-1	6-1	1-0	1-1	W-L	3-0	0-4	2-2	1-0	0-4	1-4	4-1	3-0	*
14. Upminster Reserves	3-2	0-3	0-4	5-2	2-4	0-7	2-2	L-W	L-W	1-4	2-2	0-2	1-2	*

RESERVES DIVISION THREE RESULT CHART 1992-93

HOME TEAM	1	2	3	4	5	6	7	8	9	10	11	12	13	14
1. A.F.C. Notley Reserves	*	1-1	3-2	1-4	1-2	3-0	2-1	1-3	L-W	1-0	1-1	1-0	3-1	
2. Barnston Reserves	1-0	*	0-0	2-1	0-1	3-0	1-1	4-0	4-1	0-0	2-0	3-3	5-1	4-0
3. Basildon Town Reserves	4-1	0-2	*	0-3	2-1	1-2	1-0	1-2	5-1	1-0	1-0	1-3	5-1	3-0
4. Brentwood Mnr Reserves	2-1	1-0	4-0	*	1-0	0-0	0-2	3-1	4-1	1-2	2-1	4-1	4-1	1-0
5. Broomfield Reserves	1-3	3-1	4-1	0-3	*	1-1	3-1	2-2	2-2	2-1	1-2	2-1	3-2	0-1
6. Clavering Reserves	1-2	0-1	5-2	1-4	7-0	*	4-3	3-3	10-1	W-L	2-1	6-0	2-0	0-3
7. Danbury Trafford Res.	3-5	1-2	3-6	1-4	0-3	3-4	*	2-4	2-6	1-3	2-3	2-1	10-2	0-5
8. Galleywood Reserves	0-2	1-0	1-1	0-0	0-0	1-1	4-4	*	4-2	3-3	1-1	1-1	2-3	2-6
9. Great Baddow Reserves	1-4	1-0	1-0	0-3	2-2	1-2	1-4	4-1	*	1-0	2-0	3-4	3-2	5-3
10. Hatfield Peverel Res.	0-0	2-2	1-2	2-0	2-1	0-2	2-4	2-4	3-2	*	1-3	1-3	4-2	2-3
11. Hutton Reserves	W-L	1-3	3-4	4-2	1-0	0-0	1-2	L-W	2-2	1-1	*	3-2	2-0	3-4
12. Ongar Town Reserves	1-2	2-2	1-4	0-1	1-2	2-2	3-3	3-1	3-2	1-2	5-3	*	3-1	2-0
13. Rayleigh Ath. Reserves	1-3	3-4	1-1	1-5	3-2	1-2	3-7	2-9	4-3	L-W	2-0	1-1	*	3-1
14. White Notley Reserves	7-0	3-0	0-3	1-2	1-5	2-4	2-2	2-1	5-1	1-2	2-0	2-0	3-2	*

LEAGUE (SENIOR) CUP 1992-93

First Round

Benfleet v Rayleigh Athletic	3-4
Basildon Town v Ramsden	8-3
Barnston v South Woodham Ferrers	3-3,0-1
Herongate Athletic v Mountnessing	3-0
White Notley v Maldon St Mary's	3-2
Clavering v Stambridge	3-5
Essex Police v Old Chelmsfordians	0-3
Standard (Harlow) v Eppingsale	4-3
Brentwood Manor v Doddinghurst Olympic	0-5

Second Round

Kelvedon Hatch v Takeley	3-2
Shell Club v Great Baddow	8-3
Springfield v Bishop's Stortford Swifts	2-1
Hutton v Rayleigh Town	0-1
Danbury Trafford v Runwell Hospital	0-3
Ekco Sports v Standard (Harlow)	1-2
Galleywood v Ongar Town	4-2
Sporting Club Henderson v Doddinghurst Ol.	10-0
A.F.C. Notley v Rayleigh Athletic	4-5
Stambridge v Basildon Town	4-0
Old Chelmsfordians v Broomfield	2-2,0-2
Upminster v Caribbean International Sports	0-4
South Woodham Ferrers v Writtle	2-1
Harold Wood Athletic v Herongate Athletic	0-3
Hatfield Peverel v Hambros Bank	2-0
Great Baddow Royal Engineers v White Notley	2-1

(continued on page 442)

(continued from page 441)

Third Round

Kelvedon Hatch v Rayleigh Athletic	2-0		Shell Club v Stambridge	1-0
Springfield v Broomfield	0-4		Rayleigh Town v Caribbean International Sports	5-2
Runwell Hospital v South Woodham Ferrers	5-3		Standard (Harlow) v Herongate Athletic	0-1
Galleywood v Hatfield Peverel	3-5		Sporting Club Henderson v Gt Baddow Royal E.	4-2

Quarter-Finals

Kelvedon Hatch v Shell Club	0-1		Broomfield v Rayleigh Town	2-4
Runwell Hospital v Herongate Athletic	1-0		Hatfield Peverel v Sporting Club Henderson	2-1

Semi-Finals

Kelvedon Hatch v Rayleigh Town	4-1		Runwell Hospital v Hatfield Peverel	0-3

Final: Kelvedon Hatch 2, Hatfield Peverel 0

RESERVES CUP

First Round

Old Chelmsfordians Res v Basildon T. Res	5-1		Standard (Harlow) Res v Springfield Reserves	4-0
Hatfield Peverel Res v Upminster Res	0-0,1-3		Barnston Reserves v Benfleet Reserves	2-1
Writtle Reserves v Maldon St Mary's Res	1-0		Essex Police Reserves v Shell Club Reserves	1-2
Hutton Reserves v Mountnessing Reserves	2-3		A.F.C. Notley Reserves v Takeley Reserves	4-1
Galleywood Reserves v Ekco Sports Reserves	4-3			

Second Round

Ongar Town Res v Old Chelmsfordians Res	3-7		White Notley Reserves v Great Baddow Reserves	4-0
Stambridge Reserves v S.C. Henderson Res	0-6		Sth Woodham Ferrers Res v Rayleigh Town Res	2-0
Kelvedon Hatch Res v Standard (Harlow) Res	2-4		Caribbean Int. Spts Res v Hambros Bank Res	0-1
Ramsden Reserves v Maldon St Mary's Res	1-9		Upminster Reserves v Barnston Reserves	1-0
Writtle Reserves v Eppingsale Reserves	5-1		Clavering Reserves v Shell Club Reserves	2-3
Mountnessing Reserves v A.F.C. Notley Res	4-0		Broomfield Res *(scr.)* Gt Baddow R.E. Res *(w/o)*	
Rayleigh Ath. Res v Danbury Trafford Res	2-1		Runwell Hospital Res v Brentwood Mnr Res	3-0
Herongate Athletic Res v Galleywood Res	2-3		Harold Wood Ath. Res v Doddinghurst Ol. Res	3-0

Third Round

Old Chelmsfordians Res v White Notley Res	2-0		S.C. Hendersons Res v S Woodham Ferrers Res	0-3
Standard (Harlow) Res v Hambros Bk Res	6-0		B.S. Swifts Reserves v Upminster Reserves	5-1
Writtle Reserves v Shell Club Reserves	1-2		Mountnessing Res v Gt Baddow R.E. Reserves	2-3
Rayleigh Ath. Res v Runwell Hospital Res	0-10		Galleywood Res v Harold Wood Athletic Reserves	1-3

Quarter-Finals

Old Chelms. Res v Sth Woodham Ferrers Res	4-1		Standard (Harlow) Reserves v B.S. Swifts Res	2-1
Shell Res v Gt Bad. RE Res	2-2*(GB expelled)*		Runwell Hospital Res v Harold Wood Ath. Res	0-1

Semi-Finals

Shell Club Res v Harold Wood Ath. Res	0-0,2-1		Old Chelmsfordians Res v Standard (Harlow) Res	2-3

Final: Standard (Harlow) Reserves 5, Shell Club Reserves 0

SENIOR DIVISION ONE CLUBS 1993-94

BENFLEET
Chairman: M Bumpus   **Manager:** D Dady.
Secretary: J Hunt, 29 Steli Ave., South Woodham Ferrers, Chelmsford CM3 5GH (0245 328622).
Ground: The Club House, Woodside Extension, Manor Rd, Benfleet, Rayleigh (0268 743957).
Colours: All sky   **Change colours:** Green/black/green.

ESSEX POLICE
Chairman: J A Dickinson   **Manager:** D C Murthwaite.
Secretary: K S Bevell, 68 The Fairway, Leigh-on-Sea, Essex SS9 4QS (0702 522936).
Ground: Police H.Q. (rear of Training School), Kingston Ave., Chelmsford (0245 267267).
Cols: Blue & white stripes/blue/red.   **Change colours:** White/blue/red.

HAROLD WOOD ATHLETIC
Chairman: A Adams   **Manager:** N Meekings.
Secretary: P Jones, 61 Juniper Way, Harold Wood RM3 0YQ (071 638 2323).
Ground: Harold Wood Recreation Park, Harold View, Harold Wood, Romford (0708 34882).
Colours: Claret & blue halves/claret/claret   **Change colours:** White/claret/claret.

HATFIELD PEVEREL
Chairman: R Windibank   **Manager:** C Wallington.
Secretary: C L Ballard, 3 Laburnum Way, Hatfield Peverel, Chelmsford CM3 2LP (0245 380132).
Ground: Strutt Memorial Field, Maldon Road, Hatfield Peverel.
Colours: Red/black/black   **Change colours:** Green/black/black.

HERONGATE ATHLETIC
Chairman: T Ardley   **Manager:** R Roser.
Secretary: B Sweeting, 64 Greenshaw, Brentwood CM14 4YH (0277 218190).
Ground: Adjacent to 77 Billericay Rd, Herongate, Brentwood CM13 3PU (0277 811260).
Colours: Yellow/black/yellow   **Change colours:** Red/white/white.

KELVEDON HATCH
Chairman: D L Hughes   **Manager:** R Bluck.
Secretary: R Balcombe, 22 Teesdale Rd, Leytonstone, London E11 1NQ (081 989 4977).
Ground: New Hall, School Rd, Kelvedon Hatch, Brentwood CM15 0DH (0277 372153).
Colours: All red   **Change colours:** All blue.

OLD CHELMSFORDIANS
Chairman: M McNally   **Manager:** C Eve.
Secretary: D Chandler, 8 Trotwood Close, Chelmsford CM1 4UZ (0245 442804).
Ground: Lawford Lane, Roxwell, Chelmsford CM1 2NS (0245 420442).
Colours: Red & black stripes/black/black   **Change colours:** White/black/black.

RAYLEIGH TOWN

Chairman: A G Mason   **Manager:** D Clarke.
Secretary: D H Medlock, 53 Hamilton Gdns, Hockley SS5 5BX (0702 203340).
Ground: London Road, Rayleigh (0268 784001) (on north side of A129 just west of Rayleigh).
Colours: White/blue/blue   **Change colours:** Blue/white/white.

RUNWELL HOSPITAL

Chairman: K G Bowles   **Manager:** R Saveall.
Secretary: B Hyde, 5 Redgate Close, Wickford SS11 8NG (0268 767509).
Ground: Runwell Hospital, Runwell Chase, Wickford SS11 7QE (0268 562967).
Colours: Yellow/blue/yellow   **Change colours:** All green.

SOUTH WOODHAM FERRERS UNITED

Chairman: J Oliver   **Manager:** K Pope.
Secretary: J Bird, 3 Gandalfs Ride, South Woodham Ferrers, Chelmsford CM3 5WX (0245 324139).
Ground: William de Ferrers Centre, Trinity Square.   **Prev. Grnd:** Saltcoats Pk, Ferrers Rd (pre-'93).
Colours: All blue   **Change colours:** Red/white/red.

STAMBRIDGE

Chairman: R Shepheard   **Manager:** G Hawes.
Secretary: A Hines, 62 Eanshall Ave., Prittlewell, Southend-on-Sea SS2 6NU (0702 330534).
Ground: Rochford Rd, Great Stambridge, Rochford SS4 2AX (0702 258988).
Cols: Gold (black trim)/black/gold & black   **Change cols:** Blue & white stripes/black/gold & black.

STANDARD (HARLOW)

Chairman: B Rye   **Manager:** P Bull.
Secretary: J Gotobed, 33 Whitewaits, Harlow CM20 3LL (0279 422799).
Ground: Standard Spts Ground, London Rd, Maypole Corner, Harlow (0279 417750).
Colours: White (green trim)/green/white   **Change colours:** Green & white hoops/white/green.

WRITTLE

Chairman: E R Gallacher   **Manager:** P Thrift.
Secretary: S M Turner, 39 Patching Hall Lane, Chelmsford CM1 4BT (0245 354896).
Ground: Playing Fields, Paradise Rd, Writtle, Chelmsford CM1 3HW (0245 420332).
Colours: White/black/black   **Change colours:** Blue/black/black.

SENIOR DIVISION TWO CLUBS 1993-94

BARNSTON A.F.C.

Chairman: R Walbanke   **Manager:** W Williams
Secretary: R Tyler, 52 Watts Close, Barnston, Dunmow CM6 1LT (0371 872017).
Ground: High Easter Road, Barnston, Dunmow CM6 1LZ.
Colours: All royal   **Change colours:** Yellow/royal/royal.

BASILDON TOWN

Chairman: P Cole   **Manager:** T Braney.
Secretary: D Lovell, 16 Poley Rd, Stanford-le-Hope SS17 0JJ (0375 679999).
Ground: Eversley Rd Rec., Crest Avenue, Pitsea, Basildon (0268 583076).
Cols: Blue (white trim)/blue/blue   **Change colours:** White (red trim)/white/red.

BISHOP'S STORTFORD SWIFTS

Chairman: P J Hunt   **Manager:** J Brace.
Secretary: P L Kitson, 18 Park Rd, Stansted CM24 8PB (0279 813107).
Ground: Silver Leys, Hadham Rd (A1250), Bishop's Stortford, Herts CM23 1MP (0279 658941).
Colours: All red   **Change colours:** All blue.

BROOMFIELD

Chairman: A Browning   **Manager:** C Harrison.
Secretary: C M Blackboro, 69 Wallasea Gdns, Springfield, Chelmsford CM1 5JY (0245 251481).
Ground: The Angel Meadow, Main Road, Broomfield, Chelmsford.
Colours: Red & black stripes/black/black   **Change colours:** White/black/black.

DANBURY TRAFFORD

Chairman: R N Ellis   **Manager:** D Chaplin.
Secretary: S A Rose, 'Shalamar', Struan Ave., Stanford-le-Hope SS17 8DG (0375 670160).
Ground: Eves Corner, Danbury, Chelmsford (0245 414515).
Colours: All royal   **Change cols:** Claret (blue pin-stripe)/claret/claret

DODDINGHURST

Chairman: A Smith   **Manager:** J Kiff.
Secretary: C Stanley, 4 Plane Tree Close, Chelmsford CM2 9HT (0245 281454).
Ground: Elmbridge School, Ongar.
Prev. Ground: Village Hall, Church Lane, Dod'hurst.   **Previous Name:** Doddinghurst Olympic
Colours: Yellow & green stripes/yellow/yellow   **Change colours:** White/green/yellow.

EKCO SOCIAL & SPORTS

Chairman: R E Westley   **Manager:** I Ness.
Secretary: M Lupton, 105 Vardon Drive, Leigh-on-Sea SS9 3SJ (0702 715521).
Ground: Thornford Gdns, Prittlewell, Southend-on-S. (0702 351641-off., 347602-clubhouse). On A1159.
Colours: Yellow (green trim)/green/yellow   **Change colours:** White (green trim)/green/yellow.

MOUNTNESSING

Chairman: D Pegram   **Manager:** D Brooks.
Secretary: K Gough, 302 Roman Rd, Mountnessing, Brentwood CM15 0TZ (0277 354835).
Ground: Warley Playing Fields, The Drive, Warley, Brentwood.
Colours: Red & black stripes/black/black   **Change colours:** White/black/black.

RAYLEIGH ATHLETIC

Chairman: M Jupe   **Manager:** P Keys.
Secretary: M Jupe, Poplar Lodge, Rayleigh Ave., Eastwood, Leigh-on-Sea SS9 3DN (0702 528136).
Ground: King George Playing Fields, Webster Way, Rayleigh SS6 8JQ.
Cols: Gold, black & white/black/black   **Change colours:** Silver grey/black/black.

SANDON ROYALS

Chairman: I Marshall   **Manager:** R Colman.
Secretary: D J Hamilton, 8 Douglas Close, Galleywood, Chelmsford CM2 8YD (0245 74694).
Ground: Sandon Sports Ground.
Prev. Name: Gt Baddow Ryl Engineers   **Prev. Grnd:** Springfield Hall Pk, Arun Close, Springfield (pre'93)
Colours: Royal/white/royal   **Change colours:** Red/white/royal.

SHELL CLUB

Chairman: K Thorogood   **Manager:** TBA.
Secretary: A C Gaskin, 13 Balmoral Ave., Corringham SS17 7PB (0375 641898).
Ground: Shell Club, Springhouse Rd, Corringham SS17 7QT (0375 673100).
Colours: Green & yellow/green/green   **Change colours:** Blue & white/red/red.

SPORTING CLUB HENDERSONS

Chairman: A Day   **Manager:** B A Smith.
Secretary: T Cooper, 62 Portchester Rd, Billericay CM12 0UQ (0277 659232).
Ground: Kenilworth Ave., Harold Park, Romford RM3 9NE (0402 342256).
Colours: White/red/red   **Change colours:** Red or blue/red/red.

TAKELEY

Chairman: M C Ellis   **Manager:** S Farndon.
Secretary: P Flawn, 13 Venmore Drive, Dunmow CM6 1HN (0371 872540).
Ground: Station Road, Takeley (adjacent to old railway bridge).
Colours: Sky/black/black   **Change colours:** Green & white hoops/green/green.

WHITE NOTLEY

Chairman: D Cleal   **Manager:** P Reade.
Secretary: D McKinley, 2 Ridlands Close, Tye Green, Cressing, Braintree CM7 8JD (0376 348820).
Ground: Oak Road, Faulkbourne, Witham (0376 519864).
Colours: Blue/white/blue   **Change colours:** White (green pinstripe)/green/green.

SENIOR DIVISION THREE CLUBS 1993-94

BRENTWOOD MANOR

Chairman: K O'Neale   **Manager:** D Platt.
Secretary: C Harris, 56 Viking Way, Pilgrims Hatch, Brentwood CM14 9HY (0277 219564).
Ground: Larkins Playing Field, Ongar Road, Pilgrims Hatch, Brentwood CM15 9JB (0277 210464)
Colours: All blue   **Change colours:** All amber.

CARIBBEAN INTERNATIONAL SPORTS

Chairman: J Thomas Snr   **Manager:** D Weeks.
Secretary: J Thomas Jnr, 47 Padnell Court, Chadwell Heath RM6 5HS (081 597 6066).
Ground: Little Heath Sports Ground (Chadwell Heath LTC), Hainault Rd, Little Heath, Romford.
Colours: Blue/blue/blue or white   **Change colours:** Yellow & green/green/yellow.

CLAVERING

Chairman: T K Oliver   **Manager:** P Isherwood.
Secretary: P A Flack, 7 Longley, Langley, Saffron Walden (0799 550428).
Ground: Jubilee Field Green, Clavering, Saffron Walden.
Colours: White (black trim)/black/black   **Change colours:** Green/black/green.

(A.F.C.) CRESSING

Chairman: R Crane   **Manager:** L Straiton.
Secretary: T Hammond, 125 Rayne Rd, Braintree CM7 7QD (0376 347519).
Ground: Cressing Spts & Social Club, Jeffrey Rd, Tye Green, Cressing, Braintree (0376 45521).
Cols: White/black/black (red tops)   **Change colours:** Yellow/black/yellow.

EPPINGSALE

Chairman: J H Corner   **Manager:** A Moretto
Secretary: I H Corner, 26 Rushkin Ave., Waltham Abbey EN9 3BP (0992 768696).
Ground: Stonards Hill P.F., Tidys Lane, Epping.
Colours: All sky   **Change colours:** White/black/red.

GALLEYWOOD

Chairman: D Wilson   **Manager:** D Blundell
Secretary: I M Gordon, 86 Keene Way, Galleywood, Chelmsford CM2 8NR (0245 492640).
Ground: Clarkes Field, Slades Lane, Galleywood, Chelmsford (on east side of B1007).
Colours: Orange/black/black   **Change colours:** All sky.

GREAT BADDOW

Chairman: J Cooper   **Manager:** J Clark.
Secretary: R W Royce, 50 Watchouse Rd, Galleywood, Chelmsford CM2 8PT (0245 264950).
Ground: Gt Baddow Rec., Baddow Rd, Chelmsford (0245 75899).
Colours: White/maroon/maroon   **Change colours:** Blue/blue/white.

HUTTON

Chairman: J Hall   **Manager:** P Garrett.
Secretary: L Rayner, 5 Surman Cres., Hutton, Brentwood (0277 225519).
Ground: Polo Fields, Hall Green Lane, Brentwood (0277 262257).
Colours: Yellow & green stripes/green/yellow   **Change:** Red/black/red & white

MALDON ST MARYS

Chairman: A Marchi   **Manager:** K Whiteley.
Secretary: C R Mawdsley, 51 Bramley Way, Maylandsea, Chelmsford CM3 6ER (0245 742646).
Ground: Marine Parade (Prom), Mill Rd, Maldon (0621 856166).
Cols: White (blue trim)/blue/blue   **Change:** Red & white stripes/black/black

ONGAR TOWN

Chairman: R C Salmon   **Manager:** T McManus.
Secretary: D V Jolly, 1 High Street, Great Bardfield CM7 4RF (0371 810897).
Ground: Love Lane Sports Ground, High Street, Ongar CM5 9BL (0277 363838).
Colours: All red   **Change colours:** All blue.

RAMSDEN

Chairman: J Hodges   **Manager:** D Moody.
Secretary: S H Howett, 63 Wainwright Ave., Hutton, Brentwood CM2 7EJ (0277 217022).
Ground: Nursery Sports Ground, Downham Rd, Ramsden Heath, Billericay.
Colours: White (maroon trim)/maroon/maroon   **Change colours:** Red/white/red.

SPRINGFIELD

Chairman: G Wilson   **Manager:** C Rice.
Secretary: N Digby, 578 Linnet Drive, Tile Kiln, Chelmsford CM2 8AW (0245 350260).
Ground: Pollards Meadow, Church Lane, Springfield, Chelmsford CM1 5SF (0245 492441).
Cols: Sky (navy trim)/black/black   **Change colours:** White (red trim)/red/red.

UPMINSTER

Chairman: S Hudson   **Manager:** P Adams.
Secretary: J Hatton, 35 Norfolk Rd, Romford RM2 5XH (0402 442041).
Ground: Upminster Hall Playing Fields, Hall Lane, Upminster (0222 20320).
Colours: Grey/black/black   **Change colours:** All red.

Reserve Division One 1993-94: Benfleet, Harold Wood Ath., Herongate Ath., Kelvedon Hatch, Maldon St Marys, Old Chelmsfordians, Rayleigh Town, Runwell Hosp., Sandon Royals, Shell Club, Sth Woodhams Ferrers Utd, Standard, Writtle.
Reserve Division Two 1993-94: Bishop's Stortford Swifts, Brentwood Manor, Caribbean Int. Spts, Clavering, Doddinghurst, Ekco, Essex Police, Mountnessing, Ramsden, Sporting Club Henderson, Springfield, Stambridge, Takeley.
Reserve Division Three 1993-94: A.F.C. Cressing, Barnston, Basildon Town, Broomfield, Danbury Trafford, Eppingscale, Galleywood, Gt Baddow, Hatfield Peverel, Hutton, Ongar Town, Rayleigh Ath., Upminster, White Notley.

First-half action in the League Cup in February as champions-elect Standard (hooped shirts) lose 0-1 at home to Herongate Athletic. Photo - Martin Wray.

MID-ESSEX LEAGUE

PREM. DIV.	P	W	D	L	F	A	PTS
Utd Glass Sports	22	17	2	3	55	22	53
Weir House	22	15	5	2	81	27	50
Boreham	22	13	3	6	64	30	42
Heybridge Sports	22	11	4	7	64	49	37
Southminster	22	10	5	7	46	38	35
Delafield	22	10	2	10	49	38	32
Roxwell	22	9	5	8	44	41	32
Crown Royals	22	8	3	11	50	62	27
Writtle Victoria	22	7	2	13	50	74	23
Braintree United	22	6	3	13	39	65	21
Outwood Common	22	5	4	13	38	46	19
Burnham Rblrs 'A'	22	1	1	20	19	107	4

Premier Division top-scorer:
Paul Hufton (United Glass Sports) 30

Divisional (Dave Strachan) Cup winners:
Braintree United

DIV. ONE	P	W	D	L	F	A	PTS
Tillingham Hotspur	22	17	4	1	83	33	55
Terling	22	13	6	3	54	29	45
Beacon Hill	22	12	5	5	66	45	41
Writtle 'A'	22	12	5	5	62	48	41
Marconi	22	10	2	10	63	43	32
Stock	22	8	6	8	36	47	30
St Margaret's	22	9	2	11	38	44	29
Shenfield	22	8	2	10	31	42	26
Estric	22	6	6	10	33	43	24
O Chelmsfordians 'A'	22	6	4	10	39	55	22
Sandon Sports	22	3	9	10	30	53	18
Latchingdon	22	1	3	18	18	71	6

Division One top-scorer:
Paul Welham (Beacon Hill Rovers) 21

Divisional Cup winners:
Estric

(Lower divisions on page 446)

DIV. TWO

	P	W	D	L	F	A	PTS
E.E.V.	22	16	3	3	70	27	51
Harold Wd Ath. 'A'	22	13	4	5	47	31	43
Boreham Res.	22	11	6	5	49	42	39
Writtle 'B'	22	11	3	8	32	32	36
Felsted United	22	10	2	10	71	54	32
Roxwell Res.	22	10	1	11	54	56	31
S. Woodham Fer. 'A'	22	8	5	9	47	50	29
Moulsham Lodge	22	9	2	11	39	50	29
Estric Res.	22	9	1	12	60	63	28
White Roding	22	8	2	12	43	57	26
Chemico	22	6	3	13	35	66	21
Outwood Cmn Res.	22	3	4	15	28	41	13

Division Two top-scorer:
Richard Gray (Estric Reserves) 28

Divisional Cup winners:
South Woodham Ferrers Utd 'A'

DIV. THREE

	P	W	D	L	F	A	PTS
Shelley Royals	26	22	4	0	92	22	70
Delafield Res.	26	16	5	5	65	36	53
Margaretting	26	15	2	9	73	51	47
O Chelmsfordians 'B'	26	13	5	8	53	41	44
Silver End Res.	26	13	4	9	44	42	43
Hullbridge Spts 'A'	26	12	5	9	63	61	41
Colestar	26	12	1	13	58	56	37
Abridge	26	10	4	12	55	59	34
Outwood Cmn 'A'	26	8	5	13	37	62	29
Anglia	26	7	5	14	40	49	26
Palace	26	7	5	14	64	73	26
Herongate Ath. 'A'	26	6	6	14	39	68	24
Mundon	26	6	4	16	40	69	22
Notley Hospital	26	5	5	16	55	83	20

Division Three top-scorer:
Mark Keeble (Shelley Royals) 39

Divisional Cup winners:
Colestar

DIV. FOUR

	P	W	D	L	F	A	PTS
Gidea Park Rangers	22	18	2	2	69	29	56
Rainsford	22	16	4	2	82	28	52
Stock United Res.	22	16	3	3	95	37	51
Charrington	22	14	3	5	69	32	45
Galleywood 'A'	22	8	6	8	38	35	30
Marconi Res.	22	9	3	10	60	57	30
Beacon Hill Rvrs Res.	22	8	5	9	46	57	29
Benfleet 'A'	22	7	3	10	47	54	24
Kelvedon Hatch 'A'	22	6	4	12	38	61	22
E.E.V. Res.	22	4	3	15	37	76	15
O Chelmsfordians 'C'	22	2	5	15	33	79	11
Outwood Cmn 'C'	22	2	2	18	27	94	8

Division Four top-scorer:
Chris Wood (Stock United Reserves) 29

Divisional Cup winners:
Stock United Reserves

DIV. FIVE

	P	W	D	L	F	A	PTS
Woodham Athletic	24	16	5	3	60	30	53
Heybridge Spts Res.	24	14	7	3	60	35	49
Old Brentwoods	24	13	6	5	75	37	45
Whitbread	24	12	7	5	60	35	43
Weir House Res.	24	13	2	9	63	41	41
Southminster Res.	24	11	8	5	56	41	41
Burnham Rblrs 'B'	24	7	8	9	61	50	29
Braintree Utd 'A'	24	7	8	9	45	50	29
Writtle 'C'	24	6	8	10	30	33	26
St Margarets Res.	24	8	1	15	32	64	25
Baddow	24	5	2	17	37	70	17
Harold Wd Ath. 'B'	24	3	4	17	42	77	13
A.F.C. Notley 'A'	24	3	4	17	37	84	13

Division Five top-scorer:
Mark Jiggins (Woodham Athletic) 31

Divisional Cup winners:
Weir House Reserves

DIV. SIX

	P	W	D	L	F	A	PTS
Tillingham H. Res.	24	21	0	3	149	35	63
S. Woodham Fer. 'B'	24	18	4	2	100	33	58
Benfleet 'B'	24	16	2	6	94	51	50
Ramsden 'A'	24	14	4	6	84	60	46
Shelley Royals Res.	24	14	1	9	91	48	43
Marconi 'A'	24	12	3	9	75	65	39
Springfield 'A'	24	11	2	11	66	52	35
Barnston 'A'	24	9	7	8	56	42	34
United C.C.	24	7	2	15	43	81	23
Outwood Cmn 'D'	24	4	6	14	38	102	18
Coval	24	3	3	18	33	94	12
Felsted Utd Res.	24	3	3	18	30	103	12
Latchingdon Res.	24	3	3	18	32	125	12

Division Six top-scorer:
Andrew Dowling (Tillingham Hotspur Reserves)

Divisional Cup winners:
Tillingham Hotspur Reserves

AYLESBURY & DISTRICT LEAGUE

(Established 1891, Sponsored by Aylesbury United Football Club)

PREM. DIV.

	P	W	D	L	F	A	PTS
Stone	24	19	4	1	92	33	40
Wing	24	17	3	4	75	26	37
Gawcott	24	14	7	3	69	40	35
Monks Risborough	24	16	2	6	77	43	34
Haddenham	24	11	8	5	69	31	30
Tring Corinthians	24	10	4	10	52	45	24
Waddesdon	24	10	4	10	56	52	24
Wendover Park	24	9	4	11	45	52	22
Long Marston	24	8	5	11	44	65	21
Royal Mail	24	7	3	14	46	64	17
Oving	24	2	5	17	37	99	9
Quainton	24	3	2	19	32	70	8
Council Sports	24	3	1	20	33	107	7

DIV. ONE

	P	W	D	L	F	A	PTS
Wendover	22	19	0	3	73	33	38
Bierton	22	17	2	3	78	27	36
Watermead	22	16	1	5	97	34	33
Haddenham Res.	22	14	1	7	67	32	29
Towersey	22	12	3	7	63	47	27
Stone Res.	22	11	1	10	69	55	23
Wingrave	22	11	0	11	62	60	22
Equitable Life	22	8	2	12	58	88	18
Chiltern Albion	22	7	2	13	54	66	16
Wing Res.	22	6	1	15	59	63	13
Stoke Mandeville	22	3	1	18	35	118	7
Oving Res.	22	0	2	20	26	118	2

DIV. TWO

	P	W	D	L	F	A	PTS
Waddesdon Res.	20	16	3	1	77	20	35
Twyford	20	16	0	4	64	25	32
Wendover Park Res.	20	12	4	4	51	30	28
Wendover Res.	20	13	0	7	70	57	26
Tring Corries Res.	20	9	5	6	43	31	23
Equit. Life Res.	20	9	3	8	61	43	21
Risborough Utd	20	8	2	10	39	48	18
Gawcott Res.	20	7	3	10	45	53	17
Long Marston Res.	20	4	0	16	33	64	8
Quainton Res.	20	4	0	16	35	76	8
Wingrave Res.	20	1	2	17	16	85	4

DIV. THREE

	P	W	D	L	F	A	PTS
Ay'bury W. Indians	18	14	2	2	94	25	30
Chiltern Rangers	18	14	1	3	53	24	29
Bricklayers Arms	18	12	3	3	41	27	27
Council Spts Res.	18	11	2	5	50	27	24
Bierton Res.	18	8	1	9	46	39	17
Sony Music	18	7	2	9	43	54	16
Risborough U. Res.	18	7	1	10	31	37	15
Ludgershall	18	4	6	8	37	44	14
Twyford Res.	18	2	0	16	30	84	4
Cuddington	18	2	0	16	21	85	4

minerva footballs

SOUTH MIDLANDS LEAGUE

Founded: 1922.

President: A G Joyce.   **Chairman: P Burns.**

Hon. Secretary: M Mitchell, 26 Leighton Court,
Dunstable, Beds LU6 1EW (Dunstable 667291)

TWO FAMOUS NAMES WIN TITLES

Oxford City won the South Midlands League championship for the first time last season, finishing twelve points clear of their nearest challengers Brache Sparta. City thus join the S.M.L.'s two previous champions, Thame United and Leighton Town, in the Diadora League for 1993-94.

The leadership battle in the Premier Division during the first half of the season was disputed between several clubs. Along with Oxford City, the following clubs were to hold top spot during the first three months of the campaign; Hoddesdon Town, Potters Bar Town, Wingate & Finchley, Arlesey Town, Brache Sparta. When Oxford City moved to the top during January, they would remain their for the rest of the season.

For Brache Sparta, the runners-up position represents their best performance in the top flight, but they were also denied an opportunity of lifting silverware by Biggleswade Town, who went on to defeat them 2-0 in the final of the O'Brien Butchers S.M.L. Trophy, played at Arlesey Town.

Biggleswade's season was dominated by Cup success; they also went on to lift the Huntingdonshire Premier Cup, Hinchinbrooke Cup and the Jesse Piggott Memorial Trophy. The League's other senior trophy, the O'Brien Butchers Premier Division Cup, was won by Luton Old Boys who defeated Hoddesdon Town 3-2 in the final at Welwyn Garden City.

At the opposite end of the table, spare a thought for luckless New Bradwell St Peter. They battled throughout a season which saw them fail to register a single victory.

In Division One, the season was completely dominated by the resurgence of Bedford Town. The Eagles gained promotion to the Premier Division in fine style and ended the campaign with an impressive tally of goals which included 101 at home in the League at their Allen Park base. With the prospect of moving to their new home before the start of the season, they appear to be headed on course for further glory in the future. Runners-up London Colney, in their first season in the League, held on gallantly, and their total of 99 points would have won the title in any other season.

(continued overleaf)

Bedford Town F.C. - the comprehensive Division One champions for 1992-93.

447

(continued from page 447)

In national competitions, Hoddesdon Town carried the S.M.L. flag into the last sixteen of the F.A. Vase before going down 2-3 at Bilston Town in the Fifth Round.

Only limited success came by way of the various county cup competitions. Division One side Caddington were the only winners, defeating rivals Shefford Town in the final of the Bedfordshire Intermediate Cup. London Colney and Biggleswade Town were beaten finalists in the Herts Charity Shield and Bedfordshire Premier Cup respectively.

Winslow United's striker Bernie McConnell's goalscoring exploits are worthy of a mention. He topped the leading scorers list for the third successive season, with 59 league goals. This brought his tally in league and cup competitions to an amazing 171 during this period.

Many matchday programmes continue to be of a very high standard. Hoddesdon Town achieved second place nationally in the Wirral Awards, with two other clubs, Langford and Sandy Albion, also featuring in the national top twenty.

The new season brings some exciting changes to the S.M.L. The League is pleased to welcome new sponsors, the Minerva Footballs Company who will be backing the S.M.L. for at least two seasons. The 1993-94 season also sees the restructuring of the League. Membership of the Premier Divsion is now restricted to clubs with floodlights. Clubs without floodlights, but whose facilties meet certain requirements, will form the new Senior Division.

Ground facilities continue to improve at many clubs. Both Buckingham Athletic and Potters Bar Town are due to have floodlighting completed during the summer, while several other clubs have plans to improve the standard of their facilities in the near future.

Five new sides join the League this season, and all will be competing in Division One. Eaton Bray (Luton District & South Beds League), Mercedes Benz, Scot and Milton Keynes County (North Bucks League), are joining the newly formed Houghton Town. Milton Keynes County will be playing at Wolverton Park, the former home of the now defunct Wolverton A.F.C.

In addition to Oxford City, the S.M.L. sees the departure of two other clubs. Ickleford failed to gain re-election at the end of the season, while Pirton after 21 seasons in the S.M.L. (the last twenty spent in the Premier Division), sadly folded during the close season.

Paul Gardner, League Historian & Statistician.

Biggleswade Town celebrate after beating Brache Sparta 2-0 at Arlesey Town to win the O'Brien Butchers South Midlands League Challenge Trophy. It was part of the club's hat-trick of Cup triumphs in 1992-93, the other successes coming in the Hinchinbrooke Cup and the Huntingdonshire Premier Cup. To cap a remarkable season, they also reached the final of the Bedfordshire Premier Cup. Photo - Gavin Ellis-Neville.

LEAGUE TABLES 1992-93

Premier Division	P	W	D	L	F	A	PTS
Oxford City	42	34	4	4	141	44	106
Brache Sparta	42	29	7	6	97	41	94
Arlesey Town	42	26	9	7	99	40	87
Wingate & Finchley	42	23	11	8	84	54	80
Hatfield Town	42	21	11	10	114	71	74
Hoddesdon Town	42	21	11	10	80	48	*71
Biggleswade Town	42	19	9	14	86	58	66
Shillington	42	19	9	14	63	58	66
Leverstock Green	42	19	7	16	62	62	64
Harpenden Town	42	18	9	15	67	47	63
Letchworth G.C.	42	18	8	16	79	63	62
M.K. Borough	42	18	8	16	77	65	x61
Potters Bar T.	42	17	9	16	81	82	60
Langford	42	14	13	15	75	63	55
Totternhoe	42	13	13	16	56	67	52
Luton Old Boys	42	15	7	20	57	75	x49
Buckingham Ath.	42	11	8	23	73	103	41
Pitstone & Iv.	42	11	5	26	50	99	38
Welwyn Gdn City	42	9	10	23	47	88	37
61 FC Luton	42	9	5	28	54	120	32
Pirton	42	4	8	30	32	115	20
New Bradwell St P.	42	0	7	35	20	131	7

* - 3pts deducted. x - 1pt deducted

Reserve Div. 1	P	W	D	L	F	A	PTS
London C. Res.	42	27	10	5	126	41	91
Arlesey T. Res.	42	24	10	8	99	44	82
Barton Rvrs Res.	42	24	9	9	68	37	81
Leighton T. Res.	42	27	5	10	100	46	+80
Potters B.T. Res.	42	24	7	11	107	63	79
Letchworth Res.	42	23	6	13	95	72	75
Langford Res.	42	22	5	15	81	66	x70
Leverstock Res.	42	17	13	12	80	66	64
Totternhoe	42	17	10	15	73	76	61
Hatfield Town Res.	42	19	6	17	101	74	*60
Shillington Res.	42	17	10	15	74	69	*58
Brache Sparta Res.	42	16	10	16	75	71	58
Biggleswade Res.	42	14	12	16	51	77	$54
Toddington Res.	42	13	10	19	78	79	49
Harpenden T. Res.	42	14	7	21	64	75	49
Pitstone Res.	42	13	7	22	60	94	46
Buckingham A. Res.	42	12	8	22	62	102	$44
Welwyn G.C. Res.	42	12	7	23	57	99	43
The 61 FC Res.	42	9	9	24	49	83	36
Pirton Res.	42	11	4	27	53	104	*34
M.K. Borough Res.	42	8	11	23	65	117	*32
Shefford T. Res.	42	7	8	27	58	121	29

* - 3pts deducted. x - 1pt deducted
+ - 6pts deducted. $ - 3pts awarded

Division One	P	W	D	L	F	A	PTS
Bedford Town	42	36	4	2	163	40	112
London Colney	42	32	3	7	127	36	99
Bedford United	42	26	7	9	114	64	85
Risborough Rgrs	42	25	9	8	86	55	84
Shenley & L'ton	42	24	10	8	98	56	82
Toddington Rvrs	42	24	8	10	102	56	80
Winslow United	42	21	8	13	117	62	71
Potters Bar C.	42	23	2	17	106	87	71
Caddington	42	22	3	17	88	78	69
Tring Athletic	42	18	12	12	83	72	66
Shefford Town	42	18	9	15	76	51	*60
Ashcroft	42	17	9	16	80	79	60
Ampthill Town	42	17	7	18	76	74	58
Stony Stratford	42	16	4	22	85	97	52
Delco Products	42	12	5	25	63	103	41
Sandy Albion	42	10	10	22	62	108	40
Cranfield United	42	9	11	22	59	94	38
Emberton	42	8	8	26	51	117	32
Flamstead	42	7	10	25	57	124	31
De Havilland	42	7	10	25	51	111	*28
Walden Rangers	42	7	4	31	44	129	25
Ickleford	42	4	5	33	46	145	17

* - 3 pts deducted

Reserve Div. 2	P	W	D	L	F	A	PTS
Oxford City Res.	34	24	7	3	103	32	*76
Ashcroft Res.	34	22	9	3	88	29	75
Bedford Utd Res.	34	19	9	6	85	50	66
Shenley Res.	34	16	9	9	84	64	57
Cranfield Res.	34	16	8	10	66	51	56
Stony S'ford Res.	34	16	6	12	80	56	54
Caddington Res.	34	14	11	9	70	57	x52
Tring Ath. Res.	34	14	9	11	57	52	51
Risboro. Rgrs Res.	34	14	7	13	60	54	49
Delco Res.	34	13	9	12	72	66	48
Winslow Utd Res.	34	14	5	15	88	91	47
Flamstead Res.	34	14	5	15	59	65	47
Potters B.C. Res.	34	11	8	15	77	85	41
De Havilland Res.	34	12	7	15	74	65	*40
Ampthill T. Res.	34	10	5	19	50	80	35
Sandy Albion Res.	34	3	8	23	44	97	17
Walden Rgrs Res.	34	5	5	24	40	110	*17
Ickleford Res.	34	4	3	27	40	133	15

* - 3pts deducted. x - 1pt deducted

PREMIER DIVISION RESULT CHART 1992-93

HOME TEAM	1	2	3	4	5	6	7	8	9	10	11	12	13	14	15	16	17	18	19	20	21
1. Arlesey T.	*	3-2	1-2	5-1	2-0	1-4	0-1	0-0	3-0	0-0	4-2	2-2	6-1	2-0	2-0	6-2	1-1	7-1	4-0	3-3	2-0	1-4
2. Biggleswade	0-2	*	2-4	1-1	1-2	0-0	2-2	0-2	1-1	2-2	2-1	2-2	4-0	0-1	3-0	4-0	3-0	2-2	4-0	4-0	5-1	5-2
3. Brache S.	2-1	3-0	*	6-1	2-2	5-5	2-4	1-1	3-0	3-2	1-1	3-0	7-0	1-3	4-0	1-0	1-0	1-0	2-1	2-1	1-1	0-0
4. Buck. Ath.	1-2	2-1	2-3	*	4-0	3-1	1-2	1-2	3-3	0-1	3-4	0-4	3-1	1-5	5-2	5-2	2-3	1-2	4-3	3-0	2-2	3-1
5. Harpenden	1-3	1-0	0-1	3-1	*	1-1	1-0	0-2	2-0	0-2	4-1	4-1	1-0	2-2	2-0	2-1	1-2	1-1	6-0	0-0	4-0	3-0
6. Hatfield	0-2	3-4	2-0	5-2	1-0	*	2-1	4-4	2-2	6-0	5-1	4-1	4-1	1-2	6-2	4-0	5-1	2-2	9-1	3-0	3-2	1-2
7. Hoddesdon	0-1	2-1	1-0	6-0	1-1	1-1	*	7-2	3-2	3-1	1-0	1-1	3-0	0-3	5-0	2-2	4-0	1-1	1-2	0-0	0-0	1-1
8. Langford	1-2	2-3	2-0	1-1	0-0	3-3	0-1	*	5-2	1-1	2-2	0-2	4-0	1-2	5-0	2-1	4-0	0-1	2-2	2-2	2-0	1-1
9. Letchworth	1-3	2-2	0-2	3-1	0-1	2-2	0-1	5-1	*	3-0	0-3	0-2	7-0	1-2	1-1	5-0	3-1	2-1	1-0	1-3	1-0	1-1
10. Leverstock	2-1	0-3	1-2	3-3	0-2	1-3	0-2	1-0	0-7	*	3-1	1-0	3-0	0-2	2-0	0-1	2-1	0-2	5-1	1-2	2-0	0-0
11. Luton O.B.	0-1	0-1	0-3	1-0	2-2	0-3	0-0	2-1	1-0	3-1	*	0-3	4-0	2-4	2-0	2-0	2-2	0-2	3-2	0-2	2-3	3-1
12. M.K. Borough	0-2	4-1	0-3	0-0	0-0	2-0	0-3	1-0	5-0	1-3	1-2	*	6-0	2-1	7-0	3-1	3-4	1-1	2-1	2-4	0-0	0-2
13. New Bradwell	0-5	0-1	0-4	1-1	0-4	1-4	0-1	1-5	0-3	0-5	1-2	1-4	*	2-3	1-1	1-6	1-6	1-1	1-1	0-3	0-1	2-2
14. Oxford C.	2-2	3-1	1-0	8-1	4-1	4-0	4-1	1-3	5-0	1-1	6-1	7-0	3-0	*	8-0	4-0	3-3	3-0	3-2	5-0	4-1	3-1
15. Pirton	1-1	0-3	0-2	0-1	3-0	0-3	0-0	1-1	2-2	0-3	2-1	1-2	1-0	1-3	*	0-2	0-2	2-4	1-3	0-2	3-2	0-5
16. Pitstone	0-7	0-3	0-6	2-1	0-4	0-4	0-5	0-0	0-1	0-1	0-1	2-0	0-0	2-3	3-1	*	2-3	1-1	2-1	3-0	1-1	4-0
17. Potters BT	0-1	3-0	1-4	3-1	2-1	2-2	6-1	1-0	0-2	1-1	3-0	2-2	5-1	2-7	3-0	3-1	*	4-3	0-1	2-3	2-4	0-5
18. Shillington	0-0	0-1	4-0	1-0	2-0	2-3	2-1	4-1	0-2	1-5	1-0	4-2	1-0	1-3	3-0	2-0	2-0	*	2-0	0-1	1-1	2-1
19. The 61 FC	0-5	2-5	0-2	2-4	0-7	1-0	2-5	0-3	1-5	0-2	2-2	0-2	3-2	2-4	4-2	0-1	2-6	1-0	*	2-1	4-2	2-2
20. Totternhoe	1-1	1-1	1-3	2-2	1-0	6-1	1-2	2-0	0-1	2-0	1-1	1-4	0-0	0-4	1-1	3-1	0-0	1-3	2-2	*	0-2	2-2
21. Welwyn GC	0-1	0-5	0-3	2-1	1-0	1-1	3-5	1-4	0-2	1-2	1-2	1-3	2-0	1-5	2-2	3-7	0-0	0-2	1-0	2-1	*	1-1
22. Wingate	2-1	2-1	1-1	4-1	3-1	5-1	2-0	4-3	0-5	3-0	1-0	1-0	1-0	2-0	4-2	4-0	1-1	4-0	3-1	1-0	2-1	*

DIVISION ONE RESULT CHART 1991-92

HOME TEAM	1	2	3	4	5	6	7	8	9	10	11	12	13	14	15	16	17	18	19	20	21	22
1. Ampthill Town	*	2-1	0-2	0-5	1-0	1-1	2-1	3-0	3-2	4-0	2-0	2-1	0-1	1-2	1-1	0-1	0-0	5-0	0-3	3-4	4-0	3-2
2. Ashcroft	3-2	*	1-5	1-2	2-3	0-1	0-0	1-1	1-1	3-3	3-0	4-3	2-3	3-1	2-1	3-1	0-3	2-1	4-5	0-2	1-0	0-2
3. Bedford T.	3-1	4-4	*	4-0	6-1	6-0	8-1	5-1	5-0	7-0	3-1	2-1	5-3	2-0	9-0	1-0	7-3	3-1	6-5	4-0	6-1	5-0
4. Bedford Utd	3-2	0-3	3-2	*	4-2	4-0	5-1	4-2	7-1	3-1	3-2	0-2	1-4	1-1	3-1	2-1	2-1	3-1	2-1	1-1	11-1	1-4
5. Caddington	2-0	5-0	2-3	3-4	*	4-0	3-2	2-1	2-1	0-0	8-2	0-4	3-6	1-4	3-0	1-2	1-2	4-3	1-0	2-4	3-0	0-4
6. Cranfield Utd	2-2	3-5	2-4	0-5	2-2	*	5-2	1-2	2-2	3-1	5-1	1-2	5-1	1-2	1-1	2-1	0-2	0-5	0-0	4-0	0-0	
7. De Havilland	1-3	2-3	0-3	3-2	1-6	2-1	*	3-4	1-1	0-1	4-1	0-2	3-1	0-2	3-1	1-0	1-1	3-1	0-2	1-1	0-0	1-2
8. Delco	0-5	0-1	0-3	2-2	2-1	1-0	1-0	*	3-0	9-2	5-0	0-5	2-0	0-1	2-4	0-5	3-5	1-3	2-3	1-5	3-2	1-5
9. Emberton	1-2	2-1	2-5	1-8	1-1	0-0	1-1	1-3	*	5-5	2-1	0-1	1-3	1-2	3-0	0-1	1-5	0-3	0-2	0-3	3-2	4-3
10. Flamstead	1-1	2-2	0-6	1-5	2-3	2-1	2-2	1-1	1-2	*	2-2	1-3	0-1	0-2	3-0	0-5	0-1	1-2	0-2	3-3	3-0	0-2
11. Ickleford	4-5	2-1	0-9	1-2	1-3	4-0	3-1	1-4	0-2	0-0	*	0-5	1-4	1-1	0-3	1-5	0-3	0-0	0-3	2-10	3-0	0-5
12. London C.	3-1	3-0	1-0	1-1	4-1	8-1	1-0	6-0	9-1	6-0	*	4-2	1-3	6-0	1-0	3-0	4-1	1-1	2-1	6-2	4-0	
13. Potters BC	7-2	1-2	0-4	5-3	2-0	3-2	3-3	3-3	5-1	4-2	2-5	*	4-2	2-0	4-3	1-3	2-0	1-4	0-1	6-1	6-1	
14. Risborough	4-2	1-4	0-0	1-0	0-1	2-1	2-2	1-0	2-0	2-1	4-2	1-0	5-1	*	3-0	4-2	2-2	4-0	2-2	4-0	3-2	1-7
15. Sandy A.	1-3	2-2	0-3	2-2	0-2	0-0	4-1	3-0	3-3	4-0	4-3	0-3	1-2	*	1-1	2-3	3-3	0-4	1-0	3-1	1-4	
16. Shefford	1-0	1-1	1-2	2-0	0-1	3-3	6-1	3-0	3-1	1-1	1-2	1-0	0-0	2-2	*	0-1	4-2	2-3	3-0	4-1	0-3	
17. Shenley	2-2	2-0	2-2	0-2	0-2	3-1	4-0	4-1	6-0	3-1	5-1	1-1	1-1	1-4	2-3	2-0	*	2-1	2-1	1-1	5-1	3-1
18. Stony Strat.	3-1	5-3	0-1	1-3	1-4	3-1	7-0	5-0	3-1	0-4	2-1	0-5	2-3	3-2	1-1	0-0	1-3	*	5-3	4-1	4-1	1-3
19. Toddington	2-0	0-2	0-1	1-1	1-0	3-0	2-2	0-0	4-0	1-4	4-0	2-1	4-2	4-2	5-1	2-2	1-1	2-1	*	2-3	3-0	2-2
20. Tring Ath.	2-1	0-5	0-0	1-1	2-4	1-1	4-3	3-0	4-1	1-2	5-2	1-3	1-0	0-0	7-2	1-1	0-4	2-4	1-0	*	2-2	2-0
21. Walden R.	1-3	1-3	1-4	0-2	0-1	3-2	3-3	2-0	1-2	5-4	1-0	1-0	0-4	0-4	0-3	0-3	5-3	1-5	0-1	*	0-0	
22. Winslow U.	1-1	1-1	2-3	0-1	4-0	2-0	7-0	4-2	5-1	11-0	6-0	1-3	3-0	1-1	7-1	0-1	3-3	5-2	1-3	2-2	1-2	*

RESERVE DIVISION ONE RESULT CHART 1992-93

HOME TEAM	1	2	3	4	5	6	7	8	9	10	11	12	13	14	15	16	17	18	19	20	21	22
1. Arlesey T.	*	0-1	1-0	2-2	5-2	3-2	0-2	6-1	3-0	1-2	3-1	2-1	5-0	6-0	5-0	1-0	0-0	1-1	4-2	1-0	2-2	1-1
2. Barton Rvrs	1-1	*	0-0	2-0	1-0	2-0	0-1	1-1	3-2	2-1	1-1	1-1	1-0	7-0	2-1	2-0	6-1	1-1	1-0	2-0	0-0	3-0
3. Biggleswade	0-2	1-0	*	1-2	4-0	2-1	1-3	2-1	0-2	2-1	0-0	1-1	P-A	1-1	2-1	1-6	3-1	5-0	1-0	1-4	0-1	3-3
4. Brache S.	1-4	0-1	4-0	*	3-1	1-4	4-2	0-2	0-2	1-1	1-0	2-2	5-3	2-0	1-4	1-2	2-2	2-1	3-0	1-2	1-4	2-2
5. Buck. Ath.	0-2	0-2	1-2	1-2	*	3-3	1-1	1-4	1-3	1-4	1-1	1-3	2-2	5-2	1-1	2-2	4-1	3-0	P-A	3-2	1-1	2-0
6. Harpenden	1-1	0-1	0-1	2-2	2-0	*	1-0	2-0	1-6	0-0	0-1	0-4	2-2	2-1	2-3	0-3	2-0	1-0	0-0	2-1	2-1	1-0
7. Hatfield	2-1	3-1	3-3	1-4	7-1	0-2	*	1-2	1-2	1-2	3-5	2-6	5-2	2-0	8-2	0-2	5-1	3-2	5-0	3-0	7-0	1-0
8. Langford	1-1	0-3	1-1	0-1	1-3	4-2	3-2	*	3-0	1-2	3-3	0-2	1-0	2-0	2-2	2-1	2-0	0-3	3-0	3-1	3-0	1-0
9. Leighton	1-1	0-2	4-0	3-0	4-0	2-1	1-3	5-1	*	5-1	4-0	3-3	3-0	1-1	2-0	1-2	7-0	4-0	3-0	1-0	3-0	2-1
10. Letchworth	4-1	0-2	5-1	3-3	5-0	2-1	0-1	3-2	0-2	*	5-4	2-4	4-1	3-1	2-1	4-3	0-1	3-2	0-1	3-2	3-0	0-1
11. Leverstock	3-0	3-0	1-1	3-1	5-0	1-1	1-1	0-3	0-5	*	2-0	1-1	4-0	3-0	1-3	3-2	4-1	4-3	5-1	3-3	0-1	
12. London C.	2-1	1-1	6-0	2-1	6-1	1-0	1-1	4-0	6-1	4-0	4-0	*	5-0	7-2	5-1	2-0	3-0	4-2	7-0	2-0	1-1	3-0
13. M.K. Boro.	1-6	1-1	5-4	0-4	0-2	1-4	6-2	1-4	3-1	2-1	1-1	3-3	*	4-1	1-1	2-2	2-1	4-2	2-1	1-2	0-1	2-1
14. Pirton	1-5	0-3	0-2	2-0	5-3	2-1	4-1	1-4	1-0	0-5	1-0	0-0	9-0	*	1-3	1-4	0-1	0-1	3-1	2-3	0-3	2-1
15. Pitstone	0-3	0-1	2-0	2-1	1-1	1-5	3-0	0-1	2-0	2-3	2-5	1-4	2-1	1-1	*	1-1	2-1	1-2	0-2	1-4	3-2	3-4
16. Potters BT	2-1	3-2	6-0	2-2	6-3	3-0	2-1	1-2	1-1	5-4	1-2	3-2	3-1	4-0	7-1	*	2-0	5-2	4-1	3-5	1-1	2-1
17. Shefford	2-2	3-1	0-0	2-1	2-3	4-3	1-7	0-4	1-4	3-3	1-1	1-0	2-2	0-2	1-2	4-3	*	2-3	2-0	2-2	3-4	2-3
18. Shillington	1-2	3-0	1-1	4-0	0-1	5-2	1-1	2-1	1-4	2-2	3-1	0-1	6-2	1-0	0-2	1-1	5-1	*	0-0	2-0	4-0	3-1
19. The 61 FC	0-6	0-3	0-0	0-0	1-4	1-2	2-0	1-2	0-1	0-1	0-0	0-1	3-0	4-1	1-0	5-4	6-0	3-3	*	4-0	3-1	1-1
20. Toddington	1-3	5-0	2-3	2-2	2-3	4-1	2-2	2-1	1-1	2-2	1-1	3-3	2-2	4-0	2-2	0-2	5-1	1-0	1-1	*	1-2	2-0
21. Totternhoe	0-3	1-3	1-1	1-2	3-0	3-0	2-1	3-4	1-3	4-0	2-1	2-1	4-3	2-1	1-1	1-0	5-2	2-2	2-2	1-0	*	2-2
22. Welwyn GC	0-1	2-1	4-0	0-5	1-0	1-6	0-6	1-7	0-4	0-2	1-3	0-8	4-1	1-2	3-1	1-2	3-2	0-0	5-0	2-2	3-2	*

RESERVE DIVISION TWO RESULT CHART 1992-93

HOME TEAM	1	2	3	4	5	6	7	8	9	10	11	12	13	14	15	16	17	18
1. Ampthill Town	*	2-1	1-1	2-1	2-1	0-3	1-2	3-5	5-2	0-3	3-1	2-4	1-1	1-5	0-4	2-3	4-3	1-0
2. Ashcroft	5-0	*	1-0	1-1	3-1	4-2	0-0	5-0	11-0	1-1	1-0	3-0	4-1	2-0	1-0	0-0	3-1	6-0
3. Bedford U.	2-0	5-2	*	4-0	1-1	2-2	4-1	2-2	3-1	4-1	4-1	0-6	3-2	2-2	2-1	3-1	6-1	4-0
4. Caddington	5-1	1-2	3-3	*	1-0	1-0	5-0	3-3	1-0	2-5	2-3	4-1	1-1	3-1	1-1	3-1	2-1	2-1
5. Cranfield	2-0	2-0	0-3	0-6	*	1-3	0-0	2-1	2-0	1-4	1-1	3-0	2-0	2-2	2-2	0-3	4-0	3-3
6. De Havilland	1-1	1-2	2-1	1-1	2-4	*	0-1	2-4	6-0	2-3	2-3	1-2	1-1	3-3	2-4	2-1	6-0	5-4
7. Delco	6-1	0-3	1-2	7-3	1-1	0-2	*	3-3	2-1	1-1	2-2	1-0	3-3	2-1	1-1	2-3	3-2	2-3
8. Flamstead	2-1	2-5	0-1	0-1	0-3	2-1	1-2	*	2-2	1-1	4-1	1-2	1-0	1-0	2-0	0-1	2-3	4-2
9. Ickleford	2-1	0-2	0-2	2-4	2-9	2-4	3-6	0-3	*	0-1	5-1	0-12	1-0	3-3	2-4	0-4	3-3	0-2
10. Oxford C.	3-2	1-1	6-3	3-0	3-0	3-1	1-0	6-0	*	3-0	3-0	3-1	7-0	3-0	1-1	6-0	9-0	
11. Potters BC	3-2	2-4	1-1	2-2	0-2	5-1	6-3	3-1	7-0	2-8	*	2-2	8-2	3-3	2-0	1-2	1-1	2-3
12. Risborough	0-1	1-1	3-2	1-1	1-0	4-1	1-1	0-1	1-2	0-0	*	1-1	2-0	1-2	2-2	3-1	0-4	
13. Sandy A.	1-4	1-3	1-1	0-2	1-4	2-2	1-6	5-1	3-2	0-4	4-7	0-1	*	3-3	1-5	1-0	1-2	2-6
14. Shenley	2-1	1-5	0-3	1-1	2-2	2-1	6-2	4-1	4-1	6-2	4-1	5-1	*	3-0	3-2	7-0	1-3	
15. Stony Strat.	1-1	2-2	0-3	2-0	0-2	1-5	3-0	2-0	8-1	1-3	4-1	3-1	4-2	1-2	*	3-0	6-0	5-1
16. Tring Ath.	2-0	1-1	0-4	2-2	3-5	0-0	4-3	1-0	2-0	0-0	0-2	0-1	3-0	2-2	2-1	*	4-2	1-2
17. Walden R.	1-1	0-3	2-2	2-5	0-1	0-5	1-3	1-4	1-2	0-4	3-1	4-1	2-1	0-2	1-3	0-0	*	0-3
18. Winslow	2-3	0-0	5-2	2-2	1-3	1-2	1-6	1-3	7-2	2-2	4-1	2-3	1-0	3-1	6-6	4-6	9-2	*

South Midlands League Premier (top) & Division One Ten Year Records

	83/4	84/5	85/6	86/7	87/8	88/9	89/0	90/1	91/2	92/3
Arlesey Town	–	–	–	–	–	–	–	–	–	3
Ashcroft Co-Op	7	14	16	–	–	–	–	–	–.	–
Biggleswade Town	–	–	–	–	15	15	5	3	3	7
Brache Sparta	–	16	–	–	–	16	14	18	7	2
Buckingham Athletic	–	–	–	–	–	–	–	–	18	17
Cranfield Utd	–	–	14	12	16	–	–	–	–	–
Eaton Bray Utd	3	1	8	11	–	–	–	–	–	–
Electrolux	–	–	–	–	8	14	8	10	–	–
Harpenden Town	–	–	–	–	–	–	–	7	12	10
Hatfield Town (Athletic)	5	–	–	–	–	–	–	–	–	5
Hoddesdon Town	–	7	9	3	5	5	4	9	6	6
Knebworth	–	4	6	15	17	–	–	–	–	–
Langford	–	–	15	13	3	1	16	13	10	14
Leighton Town	–	13	3	9	6	10	3	4	1	–
Letchworth Gdn City	–	–	–	–	–	–	–	6	14	11
Leverstock Green	–	–	–	–	–	–	–	–	8	9
Luton Old Boys	–	–	–	–	–	–	–	–	–	16
Milton Keynes Borough	–	–	10	4	11	18	12	19	2	12
New Bradwell St Peter	–	12	7	14	12	11	11	17	19	22
Oxford City	–	–	–	–	–	–	–	–	9	1
Pirton	2	9	11	8	13	12	13	14	16	21
Pitstone & Ivinghoe	–	–	–	–	–	8	1	16	15	18
Potters Bar Town	–	–	–	–	–	–	–	–	11	13
Royston Town	14	–	–	–	–	–	–	–	–	–
Selby	13	10	1	1	2	3	–	–	–	–
Shefford Town	1	3	5	16	10	17	19	–	–	–
Shillington	8	6	13	2	1	4	7	5	4	8
61 FC (Luton)	6	8	4	7	7	7	15	15	20	20
Stotfold	4	–	–	–	–	–	–	–	–	–
Thame United	–	–	–	–	–	2	2	1	–	–
Totternhoe	–	–	–	6	4	9	6	11	13	15
Vauxhall Motors	12	2	–	–	–	–	–	–	–	–
Walden Rangers	15	–	–	–	–	–	–	–	–	–
Waterlows (Dunstable)	10	15	–	–	–	–	–	–	–	–
Welwyn Garden City	11	11	2	10	9	6	10	12	17	19
Welwyn Garden Utd	–	–	–	–	–	–	18	–	–	–
Wingate (& Finchley)	–	–	–	–	–	–	–	8	5	4
Winslow United	9	5	12	5	14	13	17	20	21	–
Wolverton AFC	–	–	–	–	–	–	9	2	w/d	–
No. of Clubs	**15**	**16**	**16**	**16**	**17**	**18**	**19**	**20**	**21**	**22**
Ampthill Town	–	–	–	–	–	–	–	–	9	13
Ashcroft (Co-Op)	–	–	–	6	8	4	5	5	1	12
Bedford Town	–	–	–	–	–	–	–	–	4	1
Bedford United	–	–	–	–	–	–	10	10	3	3
Biggleswade Town	13	10	8	2	–	–	–	–	–	–
Biggleswade United	16	–	–	–	–	–	–	–	–	–
Brache Sparta	2	–	9	9	2	–	–	–	–	–
Buckingham Athletic	–	–	1	11	9	2	4	1	–	–
Caddington	–	–	–	4	3	3	3	6	19	9
Cranfield United	7	6	–	–	–	7	6	14	10	17
De Havilland	–	–	–	–	–	–	–	–	–	20
Delco Products	–	–	–	–	12	8	13	7	7	15
Electrolux	11	7	3	1	–	–	–	–	–	–
Emberton	–	–	–	–	–	–	–	–	18	18
Flamstead	–	–	–	–	–	–	–	8	16	19
Harpenden Town	9	13	4	12	11	12	1	–	–	–
Henlow	15	–	–	–	–	–	–	–	–	–
Ickleford	–	14	11	10	13	5	14	11	11	22
Knebworth	3	–	–	–	–	–	–	–	–	–
Langford	5	3	–	–	–	–	–	–	–	–
Leighton Town	4	–	–	–	–	–	–	–	–	–
London Colney	–	–	–	–	–	–	–	–	–	2
Luton Old Boys	–	–	–	–	–	–	–	–	2	–
Millford Villa	–	–	–	14	–	–	–	–	–	–
Milton Keynes Borough	–	1	–	–	–	–	–	–	–	–
Milton Keynes Town	–	–	–	–	6	–	–	–	–	–
Milton Keynes United	–	8	12	7	–	–	–	–	–	–
Mowlem	6	2	–	–	–	–	–	–	–	–
New Bradwell St Peter	1	–	–	–	–	–	–	–	–	–
Oxford City	–	–	–	–	–	–	–	3	–	–
Pitstone & Ivinghoe	12	11	5	5	1	–	–	–	–	–
Potters Bar Crusaders	–	–	–	–	–	–	–	4	14	8
Risborough Rangers	–	–	–	–	–	–	15	17	8	4
Sandy Albion	10	12	10	13	10	10	16	18	13	16
Shefford Town	–	–	–	–	–	–	–	13	17	11
Shenley & Loughton	–	–	–	–	–	–	8	2	5	5
Stony Stratford Town	–	–	–	–	5	11	7	16	20	14
Toddington Rovers	–	–	–	–	–	–	12	15	6	6
Totternhoe	8	5	2	–	–	–	–	–	–	–
Tring Athletic	–	–	–	–	–	9	9	12	12	10
Walden Rangers	–	9	7	3	4	6	11	9	15	21
Welwyn Garden United	14	4	6	8	7	1	–	–	–	–
Wingate	–	–	–	–	–	–	2	–	–	–
Winslow United	–	–	–	–	–	–	–	–	–	7
No. of Clubs	**16**	**14**	**12**	**14**	**13**	**12**	**16**	**18**	**20**	**22**

O'BRIEN BUTCHERS LEAGUE CHALLENGE TROPHY

Preliminary Round

Cranfield United v Ashcroft	2-5		Shenley & Loughton v Ickleford	7-1
Pitstone & Ivinghoe v Tring Athletic	1-3*(aet)*		Biggleswade Town v Emberton	6-0
Arlesey Town v Sandy Albion	4-0		Luton Old Boys v Oxford City	2-5
Langford v Ampthill Town	0-1		Wingate & Finchley v The 61 F.C. (Luton)	6-2
Letchworth Garden City v De Havilland	3-1		Shillington v Toddington Rovers	3-0
Buckingham Athletic v Risborough Rangers	1-3		Leverstock Green v Stony Stratford Town	4-1

First Round

Ampthill Town v Potters Bar Town	4-0		Hoddesdon Town v Hatfield Town	0-2
Welwyn Garden City v Risborough Rangers	2-1		Caddington v Walden Rangers	4-0
Leverstock Green v Totternhoe	4-3		Milton Keynes Borough v Arlesey Town	2-1
Ashcroft v Oxford City	2-6		Delco v London Colney	1-2
Shillington v Shefford Town	2-1*(aet)*		Flamstead v Bedford Town	1-5
Letchworth Garden City v Brache Sparta	3-5		Harpenden Town v Bedford United	0-1
Biggleswade Town v Tring Athletic	5-0		Winslow United v Shenley & Loughton	2-3*(aet)*
Wingate & Finchley v Potters Bar Crusaders	2-0		New Bradwell St Peter v Pirton	1-2

Second Round

Bedford United v Caddington	1-0		Leverstock Green v Oxford City	0-2
Shillington v Shenley & Loughton	2-3		Pirton v Brache Sparta	0-1
Wingate & Finchley v London Colney	2-3		Biggleswade Town v Hatfield Town	2-0
Bedford Town v Milton Keynes Borough	2-6		Ampthill Town v Welwyn Garden City	2-1

Quarter-Finals

Milton Keynes Boro. v Shenley & Loughton	0-1		Biggleswade Town v London Colney	3-1
Ampthill Town v Brache Sparta	0-3		Bedford United v Oxford City	1-3

Semi-Finals (2 legs)

Shenley & Loughton v Brache Sparta	1-1,0-2		Biggleswade Town v Oxford City	4-3,1-0

Final *(at Arlesey Town FC, Monday 3rd May)*: Biggleswade Town 2, Brache Sparta 0

Biggleswade captain Joe Caruso passes the O'Brien Challenge Trophy to a colleague. Photo - Gavin Ellis-Neville.

RESERVE CHALLENGE TROPHY

Preliminary Round

Letchworth Reserves v Toddington Reserves	2-1		Biggleswade Town Reserves v Oxford City Res.	3-2
Leighton Town Res. v Risborough R. Res.	2-1		Caddington Reserves v Walden Rangers Reserves	3-0
Barton Rovers Res. v The 61 FC Reserves	2-0		Welwyn Gdn City Res. v Potters Bar Town Res.	3-2
Hatfield Town Res. v Leverstock Green Res.	3-0		Milton Keynes Boro. Res. v Totternhoe Reserves	0-2

First Round

Barton Rovers Reserves v Pitstone Reserves	2-1		De Havilland Res. v Stony Strat. Res.	0-0*(aet)*,1-0
Arlesey Town Reserves v Flamstead Reserves	1-0		Shillington Reserves v Buckingham Athletic Res.	3-0
Hatfield Town Reserves v Sandy Albion Res.	9-2		Totternhoe Reserves v Shenley & Loughton Res.	1-0
Harpenden Reserves v Langford Reserves	1-2*(aet)*		Leighton T. Res. v London Col. Res.	1-1*(aet)*,0-1
Letchworth Res. v Tring Ath. Reserves	6-1		Potters Bar Crusaders Res. v Caddington Res.	7-0
Ashcroft Reserves v Bedford United Reserves	1-2		Ampthill Town Reserves v Delco Reserves	2-1
Cranfield Utd Reserves v Winslow Utd Res.	2-1		Welwyn Gdn City Res. v Pirton Reserves	2-1*(aet)*
Brache Sparta Reserves v Ickleford Reserves	9-0		Biggleswade Town Reserves v Shefford T. Res.	5-0

Second Round

Shillington Reserves v Potters Bar C. Res.	3-2		Langford Reserves v Welwyn Gdn City Reserves	3-0
Arlesey T. Res. v Letchworth Gdn City Res.	0-1		Biggleswade T. Res. v De Havilland Reserves	5-2
Totternhoe Res. v Brache Sparta Reserves	3-0		Bedford Utd Res. v London Colney Reserves	1-2
Hatfield Town Res. v Cranfield Utd Reserves	4-0		Ampthill Town Reserves v Barton Rvrs Reserves	1-2

Quarter-Finals

Totternhoe Reserves v Langford Reserves	4-0		Biggleswade T. Reserves v London Colney Res.	1-0
Hatfield Town Reserves v Barton Rvrs Res.	2-4		Letchworth Gdn City Reserves v Shillington Res.	2-0

Semi-Finals (2 legs)

Barton Rvrs Res. v Totternhoe Res.	1-0,1-0		Biggleswade Town Res. v Letchworth Res.	0-0,0-2

Final: Barton Rovers Reserves 2, Letchworth Garden City Reserves 1

O'BRIEN BUTCHERS PREMIER DIVISION TROPHY

Preliminary Round

Luton Old Boys v Pirton	3-1	Welwyn Garden City v Hatfield Town	1-2
Totternhoe v Leverstock Green	4-2	Milton Keynes Borough v Buckingham Athletic	3-1
Shillington v Biggleswade Town	2-4	Potters Bar Town v Pitstone & Ivinghoe	1-2

First Round

Arlesey Town v Brache Sparta	0-1	Wingate & Finchley v New Bradwell St Peter	4-2*(aet)*
The 61 F.C. (Luton) v Pitstone & Ivinghoe	2-0	Milton Keynes Borough v Luton Old Boys	1-1,1-5
Hatfield Town v Totternhoe	2-1	Letchworth Garden City v Langford	2-1*(aet)*
Harpenden Town v Hoddesdon Town	0-3	Biggleswade Town v Oxford City	1-0

Quarter-Finals

Wingate & Finchley v Biggleswade Town	2-0	Luton Old Boys v Brache Sparta	2-1
The 61 F.C. (Luton) v Hatfield Town	2-3	Letchworth Garden City v Hoddesdon Town	0-2*(aet)*

Semi-Finals

Wingate & Finchley v Luton Old Boys	2-4*(aet)*	Hoddesdon v Hatfield	3-3*(aet)*,1-2*(Hatfield expelled)*

Final *(Mon 17th May)*: Luton Old Boys 3, Hoddesdon Town 2

Kevin Breheney, captain of Luton Old Boys, collects the O'Brien Butchers Premier Division Trophy after a hard-fought final against Hoddesdon Town. Photo - Richard Brock.

PREMIER DIVISION CLUBS 1993-94

ARLESEY TOWN

Chairman: John Milton　　**President:** Maurice Crouch.
Secretary: John Albon, 13 St Johns Rd, Arlesey, Beds SG15 6ST (0462 731318).
Manager: Frank Reynolds　　**Asst Manager:** Paul Stump
Ground: Lamb Meadow, Hitchin Rd, Arlesey (0462 731448).
Directions: On main road thru village. From Hitchin, ground 200 yds past Biggs Wall on left.
Press Officer & Programme Editor: Tony Smith
Capacity: 8,000　　**Seats:** 120　　**Cover:** 1,000　　**Floodlights:** Yes　　**Founded:** 1891.
Programme: 12-16 pages, 50p
Cols: Sky & navy stripes/navy/navy　　**Change Colours:** All yellow　　**Nickname:** Blues.
Clubhouse: Members bar & function room. Open Lunchtimes & evening.
Midweek matchday: Tuesday　　**Record Gate:** 2,000 v Luton Res, Beds Snr Cup 1906
Previous Ground: Bury Meadow 1919-39.
Prev. Lges: Biggleswade & Dist./ Beds Co. (S. Mids) 22-26 27-28/ Parthenon/ London 58-60/ Utd Co's 33-36 82-92.
Players to progress to Football League: Roland Legate (Luton), Pat Kruse (Brentford, Leicester)
Local Press: Biggleswade Chronicle, Hitchin Gazette.
Hons: Utd Co's Lg 84-85 (KO Cup), Sth Mids Lg 51-52 52-53 (Chal. Cup 79-80, Championship Shield 64-65, F'lit Cup),
Beds Snr Cup 65-66 78-79.

BEDFORD TOWN

Chairman: Mike John　　**Vice Chairman:** D Donnelly　　**President:** Allen J Sturgess
Secretary: D E Garner, 14 Foxlease, Bedford (0234 262408).
Manager: Terry King　　**Asst Manager:** T Sullivan
Commercial Mgr: N/A　　**Press Officer:** Mrs Josie Meaney (0234 343239).
Ground: Meadow Lane, Cardington, Beds.
Directions: On A603 Bedford to Sandy road. Come off A1 at Sandy following signs to Bedford - ground on right. From
Bedford take Cardington Road out of town signposted Biggleswade and Sandy.
Capacity: 3,000　　**Seats:** 50　　**Cover:** 150　　**Floodlights:** Yes　　**Founded:** 1908
Colours: Blue/white/blue　　**Change Colours:** Red/white/red　　**Reformed:** 1989.
Midweek Matchday: Tuesday　　**Club Sponsors:** Kingston Windows　　**Nickname:** Eagles.
Club Shop: No, but scarves, ties, programmes etc are on sale in clubhouse.
Previous Grounds: Allen Park, Queens Park, Bedford (park pitch) 1991-93. *(predecessors: London Rd/ Gasworks/*
Queens Pk/ The Eyrie, Raleigh Street).
Record Attendance: 1,227 v Bedford Utd (at Allen Park), South Midlands League Division One, 26/12/91.
(predecessors: 18,407 v Everton, F.A. Cup 4th Round 12/2/66).
Previous Leagues: None *(predecessors: Utd Co's 08-39/ Southern 46-82).*
Programme: 20 pages, £2 with entry　　**Programme Editor:** Josie Meaney (0234 343239)
Record win: 9-0 v Ickleford & v Caddington
Record defeat: 1-5 v Toddington (Sth Mids Div. 1), 2-6 v Milton Keynes Boro. (Sth Mids Lge Cup).
Clubhouse: Normal pub hours. Good quality bar meals and snacks.
P.o.Y. 92-93: Vernon Pedley　　**Captain & Top Scorer 92-93:** Jason Reed.
Club record scorer: Jason Reed　　**Club record appearances:** Vernon Pedley.
Hons: South Mids Lg Div 1 92-93 *(predecessors: Southern Lg 58-59 (Div 1 69-70), Utd Co's Lg 30-31 32-33 33-34 (R-up*
11-12 12-13 13-14 29-30 31-32 34-35 36-37), FA Cup 4th Rd 63-64 65-66, FA Tphy SF 74-75).

BIGGLESWADE TOWN

Chairman: M Dorrington　　**Vice Chairman:** M Jarvis　　**President:** R Dorrington.
Secretary: G Arkwright, 21 Willsheres Road, Biggleswade, Beds SG18 0BU (0767 316992).
Manager: K Davidson　　**Physio:** R Ashcroft.
Ground: 'Fairfield', Fairfield Road, Biggleswade, Beds (0767 312374).
Directions: A1 North r'bout, left immediately after metal bridge into car park. 10 mins walk from Biggleswade (BR).
Capacity: 2,400　　**Seats:** 250　　**Cover:** 400　　**Floodlights:** Yes　　**Founded:** 1874
Colours: All green　　**Change:** White/green/green　　**Nickname:** Waders　　**Record Gate:** 2,000
Previous Leagues: Biggleswade & Dist. 02-20/ Bedford & Dist. 09-12/ Utd Co's (prev. Northants Lg) 20-39 51-55 63-
80/ Spartan 46-51/ Eastern Co's 55-63.
Previous Name: Biggleswade & District.　　**Clubhouse:** Open all matchdays. Filled rolls available.
Programme: 56 pages, with admission (extra copies available 50p each).
Captain 92-93: D Beddall　　**Top Scorer 92-93:** J Carvso, 53
P.o.Y. 92-93: Tim Chapman/ Nicky Holloway　　　　**Club Shop:** No.
Hons: Sth Mids Lg 23-24 (Div 1 52-53, Lg Cup 92-93, Prem. Div Tphy 91-92), Beds Snr Cup 02-03 07-08 46-47 51-52
61-62 62-63 66-67 73-74, Beds Premier Cup 22-23 27-28, Nth Beds Charity Cup 07-08 09-10 22-27 33-34(joint) 49-50
52-53 54-55 57-58 62-63 64-65 67-68 68-69 73-74 91-92, Utd Co's Lg Cup 63-64 73-74, Hunts Premier Cup 92-93,
Hinchingbrooke Cup 03-04 92-93, Jess Piggott Trophy 87-88 89-90 91-92 92-93.

BRACHE SPARTA

Chairman: Mr Roy Standring　　**President:** Mr Doug Smith.
Secretary: Mr Maurice Raymond Franklin, 62 Katherine Drive, Dunstable LU5 4NU (0582 661177).
Manager: Mr Kevin Millett.　　**Physio:** C E Jones.
Ground: **** *The Brache Sparta first team will be ground-sharing at Hitchin Town F.C. during 1993-94. See page 300 for*
ground details/directions ****. Foxdell Sports Ground, Dallow Road, Luton LU1 1UP (0582 20751).
Directions: Left off A505 to Dunstable into Chaul Lane at r'bout. Proceed across new relief road - ground entrance
adjacent to Foxdell Junior School.
Cover: 100　　**Seats:** 25　　**Capacity:** 400　　**Floodlights:** No　　**Founded:** 1960
Colours: White/navy/white　　**Change Colours:** All royal　　**Nickname:** None.
Midweek home maches: Wednesday　　**Previous League:** Luton & Dist.
Previous Ground: Crawley Green Road, Luton (public park).
Programme: 30 pages, £1　　　　**Players progressing to Football Lge:** None.
Hons: South Mids Lg R-up 92-93 (Div 1 R-up 83-84 87-88, Lg Cup R-up 75-76 80-81 92-93, Premier Div Cup R-up 91-92,
Reserve Div 2 R-up 75-76, Reserve Cup R-up 87-88), Luton & Dist. Lg 67-68 69-70 70-71 71-72, William Pease Trophy
66-67 67-68 70-71 71-72, Beds Intermediate Cup 71-72 (R-up 68-69 70-71), Beds Jnr Cup 82-83, Leighton Challenge
Cup R-up 69-70.

Jason Reed scores one of his two goals as Bedford Town defeat their Division One championship challengers London Colney. Photo - Neil Whittington.

Biggleswade Town F.C. 1992-93. Back Row (L/R): Darren Hutchinson, R Newman, Cliff Lamptey, Glen Crook, Peter Saunders, Sean Boyd, Gary Branch. Front: R Vye, Dean Beddall, Joe Caruso, Steve Winwood, Nick Holloway, Tim Chapman. Photo - Paul Dennis.

Brache Sparta, South Midlands League runners-up 1992-93. Photo - Gavin Ellis-Neville.

BUCKINGHAM ATHLETIC

Chairman: Mr Ron Ackerman   **President:** Mr Malcolm Macillop.
Secretary: Peter Hinson, 12 Badgers Way, Buckingham MK18 1AY (0280 816212).
Manager: Malcolm East.
Ground: Stratford Fields, Stratford Rd, Buckingham (0280 816945).
Directions: From Milton Keynes take the A422 Stony Stratford-Buckingham road – ground on left just before town centre. From Aylesbury, turn right at 1st r-about, across 2nd r-bout, left at 3rd – ground at bottom of hill on left.
Capacity: 1,500   **Seats:** No   **Cover:** 200   **Floodlights:** Yes   **Founded:** 1933
Colours: All sky   **Change Cols:** Red & white/white/red   **Nickname:** Swans
Midweek home matchday: Wednesday   **Previous Leagues:** North Bucks/ Hellenic.
Programme: 10 pages, 50p
Previous Names: None   **Previous Grounds:** None
Players progressing to Football League: None.
Hons: Sth Mids Lg Div 1 85-86 90-91 (R-up 88-89, Div 1 Cup 90-91), Nth Bucks Lg 84-85 (Lg Cup 83-84, Lg Shield 60-61), Berks & Bucks Jnr Cup 65-66, Buckingham Charity Cup 69-70 71-72.

HARPENDEN TOWN

Chairman: Alan King   **Manager:** Steve Woolfrey.
Secretary: Mark Revell, 65 New Park Drive, Hemel Hempstead, Herts HP2 4QZ (0442 62717).
Ground: Rothamsted Park, Amenbury Lane, Harpenden (0582 715724).
Directions: A1081 to Harpenden. Turn left/right at George Hotel into Leyton Road. Turn left into Amenbury Road, then left again (50yds) into 'Pay and Display' car park - the club entrance is signposted thru car park to opposite corner.
Capacity: 1,500   **Seats:** 25   **Cover:** 100   **Floodlights:** Yes   **Founded:** 1891
Colours: Yellow/blue/blue   **Change Colours:** Blue/yellow/yellow
Previous Grounds: None   **Previous Name:** Harpenden FC 1891-1908.
Programme: With admission   **Midweek home matchday:** Tuesday   **Nickname:** The Town
Previous Leagues: Mid-Herts/ Herts County.
Hons: Sth Mids Lg 61-62 64-65 (Championship Shield 67-68, Lg Cup 70-71, Div 1 89-90, Prem Div Tphy 89-90, Reserve Div 89-90), Herts Co. Lg 11-12 49-50 51-52 53-54 (Aubrey Cup 20-21 28-29 50-51 51-52), Mid-Herts Lg 09-10 20-21, Pratt Cup 06-07 08-09 10-11, Herts Jnr Cup 01-02 09-10 11-12 20-21 25-26, Herts I'mediate Cup 52-53, Herts Charity Shield 07-08, Bingham Cox Cup 1896-97 1902-03 09-10 20-21.

Harpenden Town 1992-93. Back Row (L/R): Kevin Haskins, Mark McDonald, Lee Attfield, Lee Bozier, Paul Cain, Kelvin Gregory, Steve Woolfrey (Manager). Front: David Hoiles, Steve McClelland, Justin Styles, Mark Underwood, Danny Johnson (Player-Coach), Glenn Bracey. Photo - Richard Brock.

HATFIELD TOWN

Chairman: Terry Edwards   **Vice Chairman:** Peter Robinson   **President:** Edward Rowley.
Secretary: Mrs Vivien Doctor, 1 Cloverland, Hatfield, Herts AL10 9ED (0707 269545).
Manager: Malcolm Doctor   **Asst Manager:** Lenny Brandon.
Coach: Laird Budge   **Physio:** Chris Berks.
Ground: Gosling Sports Park, Stanborough, Welwyn Garden City (0707 331056).
Directions: A1(M) jct 4 to r'bout, 1st exit A6129 towards Stanborough Lakes, right at next r'bout, ground 800 yds on right.
Capacity: 3,000   **Seats:** 50   **Cover:** 1,000   **Floodlights:** Yes   **Founded:** 1989
Colours: Blue/white/blue   **Change Colours:** All red   **Nickname:** Town
Previous Ground: Roe Hill Playing Fields, Briars Lane, Hatfield (pre-1992).
Midweek matchday: Wednesday   **Prev. Lges:** Mids Herts/ Herts Co. Snr (pre'92)
Programme: 20 pages, £1 with entry   **Editor:** Terry Edwards (0707 278319)   **Club Shop:** No.
Record Gate: 350 v Welwyn Garden City, South Midlands League Premier Division 27/1/93.
Record win: 9-1 v The 61 F.C.   **Record loss:** 1-6 v Totternhoe (both S. Mids Prem. 92-93)
Clubhouse: Sat 4.30-11pm, Wed 7-11pm. Hot & cold snacks.
Captain 92-93: Gary Durbridge   **Top Scorer 92-93:** Eamonn Rogers 25   **P.O.Y. 92-93:** Ray Kilby
Club record scorer: Eamonn Rogers   **Club record appearances:** Alan O'Neill.
Hons: Herts Co. Snr Lg 91-92 (Div 1 90-91, Div 2 89-90).

Hatfield Town F.C. 1992-93. Back Row (L/R): Laird Rudge (Coach), Lenny Brandon (Asst Manager), Mick Mountford, Dave Stephens, Eamonn Rogers, Gary Durbridge, Stuart Johnson, Simon Woolmer, Steve Gibbs, Malcolm Doctor (Manager). Front: Dave Pickstock, Adam Parker, Alan O'Neill, Ray Kilby, Mark Watts, Neil Drupers. Photo - Richard Brock.

HODDESDON TOWN

Chairman: Mr Elmer Elliott
Secretary: Mr Malcolm Owen, 7 The Red House, High Rd, Broxbourne, Herts EN10 7DE (0992 447613).
Manager: Ray Greenall   **Asst Manager:** Jim Briggs   **Coach:** John Walton.
Ground: 'Lowfield', Park View, Hoddesdon, Herts (0992 463133).
Directions: A10, A1170 and follow signs to town centre until left-hand fork signposted Broxbourne, right at 1st mini r-about into Cock Lane and 1st right is Park View. Ground on 200yds left opposite Park Rd.
Capacity: 3,000   **Seats:** 250   **Cover:** 250   **Floodlights:** Yes   **Founded:** 1879
Midweek home matchday: Tuesday   **Nickname:** Lilywhites or Lowfielders.
Colours: White/black/white   **Change Colours:** All yellow.
Record Gate: 3,500 v West Ham, friendly 1975.
Previous Leagues: East Herts 1896-1908 11-21/ Herts Co. 08-25/ Nth Middx District 10-22/ Spartan 25-75/ London Spartan 75-77/ Athenian 77-84.
Previous Grounds: Mancers Field 1879-99/ Essex Rd Arena 1953-54.
Programme: 72 pages (av.), 60p   **Programme Editor:** Mrs Jane Sinden (0767 631297).
Clubhouse: Bar and tea bar open at every game.
Top Scorer 92-93: Gary Cummins 30   **P.o.Y. 92-93:** Tony Tillbrook (players': David Wilson).
Captain 92-93: Paul Robbins   **Club record appearances:** Stuart Parker 508.
Hons: FA Vase 74-75 (1st winners), Sth Mids Lg Lg Cup 85-86 86-87 91-92 (Premier Div Tphy R-up 92-93), Spartan Lg 70-71 (R-up(3) 71-74, Div 1 35-36, Div 2 'B' 27-28, Lg Cup(2) 70-72), Herts Snr Cup(3) 1886-88 89-90, Herts Charity Shield(4) 47-48 70-72 78-79, Herts Snr Centenary Tphy 86-87, Sth Mids Floodlit Cup 89-90 (R-up 92-93), Waltham Hospital Cup 27-28, Perry Charity Cup(7), East Anglian Cup Group finalists 92-93.

Hoddesdon Town F.C. 1992-93. Back Row (L/R): Ray Greenall (Manager), Tony Tillbrook, Glenn Swaby, Wayne Morris, Phil Barnes, Martin Smith, Kelvin Williams, Gary Cummins, Dave Elliott, John Walton (Coach). Front: Jeff Cross, Mel Musa, Mark Kozak, Paul Robbins (Captain), David Wilson, Lee Browne.

LANGFORD

Chairman: Ian Chessum   **Vice Chairman:** Mick Quinlan   **President:** Ted Rutt.
Secretary: Frank Woodward, 2 North Lane, Gamlingay, Sandy, Beds SG19 3NT (0767 51022).
Manager/Coach: Alan Dunn   **Asst Mgr/Coach:** Phil Toyer   **Physio:** David Jenkins.
Press Officer: Secretary   **Commercial Manager:** David Binks.
Ground: Forde Park, Langford Road, Henlow SG16 6AF (0426 816106). *Freehold purchased Feb 1992.*
Directions: Halfway between Langford and Henlow on A6001 Hitchin to Biggleswade road. Bus 177 on main Hitchin-Biggleswade route stops right outside ground.
Capacity: 4,000   **Seats:** 100   **Cover:** 250   **Floodlights:** Yes   **Founded:** 1910.
Cols: Red & white   **Change Colours:** Blue &white   **Previous Lge:** Bedford & Dist. (pre-'51).
Record Gate: 450 v Q.P.R., 75th Anniversary and clubhouse opening, 22/8/85.
Previous Grounds: The Leys 10-37/ Bulls Meadow 37-53/ Langford Plyaing Field 53-84.
Programme: 38 pages, £1.75 with entry   **Editor:** Keith Mayhew (0462 314767)
Club Shop: Scarves, lapel badges and programmes available. Contact secretary.
Sponsors: Fine Stamps Ltd, A.H. Printers   **Midweek home matchday:** Tuesday   **Nickname:** Reds.
Record transfer fee paid: Nil   **Rec'd:** Undisclosed for Ian Phelan (Bedford T., Sept '91).
Clubhouse: Weekday evenings, matchdays 11am-11pm, Sun 12-3pm. Hot food on matchdays only. Function room with private bar available for hire.
Capt. 92-93: Mark Carter **Top Scorer 92-93:** Paul Charnock, 16   **P.O.Y. 92-93:** Brad Gillham/Guy Warmoth.
Hons: S Mids Lg 88-89 (Lg Cup 73-74 75-76, Prem. Div Tphy 88-89, O'Brien Div 1 Tphy 84-85), N Beds Charity Cup 27-28 30-31 69-70 75-76 86-87 92-93, Bedford & Dist. Lg 30-31 31-32 32-33, Bedford I'mediate Cup 68-69, Hinchingbrooke Cup 72-73.

Mark Thomas scores one of his two goals that gave champions-elect Oxford City a 2-1 victory at Langford. Photo - Neil Whittington.

LETCHWORTH GARDEN CITY

Chairman: John McNeillliey   **President:** Anthony Burrows   **Manager:** Mick Clements.
Secretary: Jane Bygrave, 151 Glebe Road, Letchworth, Herts SG6 1DX (0462 670471).
Ground: Baldock Road, Letchworth, Herts SG6 2GN (0462 684691).
Directions: Jct 9 (A6141) off A1M straight over large r-about, right at next r-about, ground on right. From Luton (A505) thru Hitchin, ground 3 miles after Hitchin. 2 miles from Letchworth (BR).
Capacity: 3,200   **Cover:** 400   **Seats:** 200   **Floodlights:** Yes   **Founded:** 1906
Colours: Blue/white   **Change Colours:** All red
Programme: 24 pages, 50p   **Midweek matchday:** Tuesday   **Nickname:** Bluebirds.
Previous Name: Garden City/ Letchworth Ath./ Letchworth Town
Previous Grounds: Letchworth Corner/ Garth Rd/ Cashio Lane.
Previous Leagues: Herts Co. 06-07/ Biggleswade 07-08/ Nth Herts 08-22/ S Mids 22-23 24-29/ Spartan 29-56/ Athenian 63-77/ Isthmian 77-90.
Players progressing to Football League: Imre Varadi, Keith Larner.
Hons: Herts Lg 11-12, Spartan Lg 29-30 35-36 51-52, Delphian Lg 57-58, Athenian Lg 74-75 (Mem. Shield 65-66 66-67), Herts Snr Cup 12-13 35-36 51-52, Herts Charity Shield 22-23 47-48 87-88 91-92, East Anglian Cup 76-77, Woolwich Cup 81-82, Hitchin Cup 81-82.

LUTON OLD BOYS

Secretary: Tim J Thomas, 10 Braceby Close, Luton, Beds LU23 2TP. (0582 579703)
Ground & Directions: As Dunstable F.C. (see Beazer Homes League section).
Colours: Red/black/black
Hons: Sth Mids Lg Premier Div Tphy 92-93 (Div 1 Tphy 91-92, Div 2 R-up 91-92)

MILTON KEYNES BOROUGH

Chairman: Martin Russell   **Vice Chairman:** Ray Jackson.
Secretary: Keith Jordan, 1 Langdale Close, Bletchley MK2 3QA (0908 368958).
Manager: Ray Richards   **Asst Manager:** Lional Marr.
Ground: Manor Fields, Bletchley, Milton Keynes (0908 375256)
Directions: Old A5 to Fenny Stratford, left at r-about, straight on at next r-about. 50 yds on turn left, proceed until Canal Bridge, then into Manor Fields
Capacity: 3,000   **Seats:** 160   **Cover:** 1,000   **Floodlights:** Yes   **Founded:** 1966.
Colours: Blue/white/blue   **Change Colours:** Yellow/sky/yellow   **Nickname:** Borough
Programme: 28 pages, 40p   **Editor:** Ernie Thompson   **Club Shop:** No.
Clubhouse: Two bars, open every day. Function room with 8ft satellite screen for major sporting events. Snack bar open matchdays.
Previous Ground: Denbigh (pre-1986)   **Previous Leagues:** Utd Co's Lg 70-79/ Hellenic 80-84.
Previous Name: Belsize   **Record Gate:** 767 v Leighton Town, S. Mids Lge 18/2/92.
Midweek home matchday: Tuesday   **Record win:** 11-0 v Winslow (A), S. Mids Lge, Feb '92.
Top Scorer 92-93: Terry Shrieves
Hons: Sth Mids Lg R-up 91-92 (Div 1 84-85, Premier Div Tphy 86-87).

POTTERS BAR TOWN

Chairman: John Robinson   **Vice Chairman:** Ian Curtis   **President:** Bert Wright
Secretary: Peter Waller, 26 Queen Annes Grove, Bush Hill Park, Enfield, Middx EN1 2JR (081 360 7859).
Manager/Coach: Alan Bolt   **Asst Manager:** Brian Goymer   **Physio:** John Garrett
Press Off.: Richard Brassett   **Commercial Manager:** Frank Bentley.
Ground: Parkfield Centre, The Walk, Potters Bar, Herts EN6 1QN (0707 654833).
Directions: M25 jct 24, enter Potters Bar along Southgate Rd (A111), at 1st lights right into the High St (A1000), half mile left into The Walk, ground 200 yds on right (opp. Potters Bar Cricket Club). BR to to Potters Bar - The Walk is directly opposite station - ground half mile up hill on left.
Capacity: 2,000   **Seats:** 25   **Cover:** 100   **Floodlights:** Yes   **Founded:** 1960
Colours: Red & Royal stripes/royal/royal   **Change colours:** White/red/red
Previous Leagues: Barnet & Dist. 60-65/ Nth London Comb. 65-68/ Herts Snr Co. 68-91.
Previous Names: Mount Grace Old Scholars/ Mount Grace (Potters Bar) until 1991.
Record Gate: 200 v Cockfosters, Herts Snr County League.
Previous Grounds: None.   **Nickname:** The Grace.
Programme: 16 pages, 50p   **Programme Editor:** Robert Brassett (081 443 0442).
Club Shop: Scarves, ties and old programmes from Robert Brassett (081 443 0442).
Club Sponsors: Welwyn Design Contractors/ Black Cat Video/ Pubal Tandoori Restaurant.
Midweek matchday: Tues or Wed.
Record win: 19-0 v Arkley, North London Combination 27/2/65.
Record defeat: 1-9 v Rolls Royce Engines, Herts County Aubrey Cup 10/1/70.
Clubhouse: Sat 12.30-11pm, Sun noon-3pm, Tues & Thurs 7.30-11pm, midweek matchnights 6-11pm.
Captain 92-93: Steve Foody   **Top Scorer 92-93:** Mark Trossell 25   **P.o.Y. 92-93:** Steve Duke
Club record scorer: Micky Gray 269   **Club record appearances:** Mick Holson 708 (60-89).
Hons: Herts Co. Lg 90-91 (Div 1 73-74 81-82, Aubrey Cup 90-91 (R-up 87-88, Div 3(res) 73-74, Reserve Div 2 88-89, Reserve Div 1 R-up 89-90, Reserve Cup R-up 75-76), FA Vase 3rd Rd 90-91, Herts I'mediate Cup 73-74, Barnet & Dist. Lg R-up 64-65 (Div 1 61-62, Div 2 R-up(res) 62-63, Div 3('A') 62-63), Barnet Jnr Cup 61-62, Nth L'don Comb. 67-68 (Div 1(res) 67-68, Div 2 R-up 65-66), Barnet Charity Cup 63-64 (R-up 64-65 68-69 70-71(res)), Potters Bar Charity Cup 76-77, Herts Snr Centenary Tphy SF 91-92, Herts Charity Shield SF 74-75 75-76, Sth Mids Lg Res Div 2 91-92, Mid-Herts Lg Div 1 R-up('A') 92-93 (Div 2('A') 87-88, Div 2 Cup('A') 84-85 87-88 (R-up 83-84 86-87), Div 4 R-up('B') 85-86, Reserve Shield('B') R-up 83-84), Mid-Herts Jnr Charity Shield('B') 76-77.

Gino Fraser of Potters Bar Town get in a cross despite the attentions of a Langford defender. Potters Bar won this home fixture in August by the game's only goal. Photo - Richard Brock.

SHILLINGTON

Chairman: Stan Burgdine   **President:** Brian Bowles.
Secretary: Aubrey J Cole, 32 Greenfields, Shillington, Hitchin, Herts SG5 3NX. (0462 711322).
Manager: Paul Stephens   **Physio:** Noel Lewis   **Press Officer:** Paul Stephens.
Ground: Playing Fields, Greenfields, Shillington, Hitchin SG5 3NX (0462 711757).
Directions: From Luton: A6 to Barton-le-Clay (by-pass), left at r'bout to Shillington via Higham Gobion. From Hitchin or Bedford turn off at 'Bird in Hand', Henlow Camp signposted Shillington. Five miles from Hitchin (BR).
Capacity: 600   **Seats:** 50   **Cover:** 100   **Floodlights:** Yes   **Formed:** 1946.
Colours: White/red/red   **Change Colours:** All yellow.
Midweek matchdays: Tuesday   **Record Gate:** 600 v Baldock Town.
Previous Lge: Luton & Dist. 1946-54   **Previous Ground:** Parsonage Lane.
Programme: £1 with admission.
Clubhouse: Open every evening and weekend lunctimes. Rolls available on matchdays.
Captain 92-93: Kevin Wright   **Top Scorer 92-93:** Tommy Doyle, 16   **P.o.Y. 92-93:** Albert Hunter
Hons: Sth Mids Lg 87-88 (R-up 64-65 86-87, Lg Cup 82-83 (R-up 64-65 65-66 84-85 91-92), Div 1 80-81 (R-up 75-76), Prem Div Tphy 87-88, Reserve Div 2 65-66, Reserve Shield/Tphy 68-69 79-80, Reserve Div R-up 80-81, Reserve Div 1 R-up 84-85 86-87 88-89), Beds Snr Cup R-up 63-64 64-65 (Jnr Cup 76-77), Barton Invitation Cup R-up 68-69 71-72, Houghton Regis Chall. Cup 85-86, Napier Electric Sportsmanship award 78-79.

WELWYN GARDEN CITY

Chairman: John Newman   **Manager:** Pat Maslen
Secretary: Richard Dunning, 38 Cowper Road, Welwyn Garden City, Herts AL7 3LS   (0707 334536).
Press Officer: Keith Browne.   **Physiotherapist:** Arthur Wood/ Derek Carlisle.
Ground: Herns Lane, Welwyn Garden City (0707 328470).
Directions: From A1 follow signs for industrial area. Take one-way system opposite Avdel Ltd (signed Hertford B195), take 2nd exit off one-way system. Ground 400 yards on left. One and a half miles from Welwyn GC (BR).
Capacity: 1,500   **Seats:** 40   **Cover:** 120   **Floodlights:** Yes   **Founded:** 1921
Cols: Maroon & blue/white/maroon   **Change Colours:** Yellow/blue/yellow
Midweek Matches: Tuesday   **Club Shop:** Yes   **Metal Badges:** Yes   **Nickname:** Citzens.
Programme: 24 pages, 50p   **Programme Editor:** Keith Browne (0707 251854).
Clubhouse: Open every night and weekend lunchtimes. Members Bar, function Hall. Steward: Ron Baird.
Record Gate: 600 v Welwyn Garden United.
Previous Ground: Springfields   **Previous Lges:** Spartan/ Metropolitan/ Gtr London
Best FA Vase year: 1st Rd 86-87.   **Best FA Cup year:** Prel. Rd replay 89-90.
Local Newspapers: Welwyn & Hatfield Times, Welwyn & Hatfield Herald & Post.
Hons: Herts Snr Centenary Tphy 84-85 (R-up 88-89), Herts Charity Shield 27-28 86-87 87-88 (R-up 48-49), Sth Mids Lg 73-74 (R-up 85-86, Div 1 69-70 81-82, Lg Cup R-up 74-75 81-82 88-89, Reserve Cup 85-86).

WINGATE & FINCHLEY

Chairman: Peter Rebak   **Vice Chairman:** L Black   **President:** H Whidden.
Secretary: Malcolm Graves, 28 Wise Lane, Mill Hill, London NW7 2RE (081 959 3825).
Manager: Martin Burt   **Asst Manager:** Jeff Bookman   **Coach:** Jeff Bookman.
Physio: Amos Shanaan   **Comm. Manager:** Steven Jacobs   **Press Off.:** Simon Martindale.
Ground: Bill Masters Stadium, Summers Lane, Finchley, London N12 (081 446 0906)
Directions: North Circular (A406) to jct with High Road Finchley (A1000), go north and Summers Lane is 200 yards on right - parking for 80 cars. Tube to East Finchley Station (Northern Line) and then 263 bus to Summers Lane. Buses 263 and and 17.
Capacity: 8,500   **Seats:** 500   **Cover:** 500   **Floodlights:** Yes   **Founded:** 1991
Colours: Blue/white/blue   **Change Colours:** All red   **Nickname:** Blues
Programme: 24 pages, 50p   **Editor:** Marc Morris (081 346 6215)   **Club Shop:** No.
Club Sponsors: Levy Gee
Record Gate: 9,555 - Finchley v Bishop Auckland, F.A. Amateur Cup QF 49-50.
Midweek home matchday: Tuesday   **Reserve's Lge:** Essex & Herts Border Comb. (West)
Record win: 9-0, Wingate v Sarratt, Herts County League Division One, 20/4/85.
Record defeat: 0-5, Wingate v Tudor Corinthians, Herts County League Division One, 13/4/85.
Clubhouse: Open during matches. Also tea-bar selling most refreshments.
Captain 92-93: Darren Curtis   **Top Scorer 92-93:** Marc Morris (35 in 44 games)
P.o.Y. 92-93: David Newman.
Club record scorer: Marc Morris 578   **Club record appearances:** Marc Morris 587 (1975-93).
Previous Names: Wingate (founded 1946), Finchley (founded late 1800s) merged in 1991.
Previous Grounds: Finchley FC: Long Lane 1874-84/ Green Man 84-94/ Woodhouse Lane 94-99/ Swan & Pyramids 99-1901/ Fallow Court 01-21/ Station Meadow 21-29. Wingate: Wingate Stadium 46-75/ Brickfield Lane, Arkley 75-91.
Prev. Lges: Finchley: London 02-12 14-1523-25 30-39/ Athenian 12-14 29-30 45-73/ Isth'n 73-91. Wingate: Middx 46-52/ London 52-62/ Delphian 62-63/ Athenian 63-75/ Barnet Yth, Hendon & Dist. Sunday 75-84/ Herts 84-89.
Hons: Finchley: London Snr Cup, London Charity Cup, FA Amtr Cup SF, Athenian Lg 53-54 (R-up 63-64 65-66), London Lg 36-37 (R-up 35-36, Div 2 06-07(jt with Enfield), Lg Cup 34-35, Park Royal Cup 37-38). Wingate: Middx Lg(2)(R-up(1), Lg Cup), London Lg R-up(2)(Lg Cup(1)), Middx Snr Cup SF, FA Vase QF 74-75, Athenian Lg Div 2 69-70, Herts Co. Lg Div 1 84-85 (Aubrey Cup 85-86), Herts I'mediate Cup 84-85, Herts Snr Tphy 86-87, Sth Mids Lg Div 1 R-up 89-90 (Lg Cup SF 89-90), Barnet Yth Lg 75-76, Pete Morrison Cup 82-83 83-84 (R-up 79-80 84-85), Hendon & Dist. Int. Div 79-80.

Shillington F.C. 1992-93. Photo - Gavin Ellis-Neville.

Two Welwyn Garden City defenders cannot prevent Bobby Hutchinson scoring an F.A. Cup goal for Wembley in the Preliminary Round at Vale Farm. Photo - Paul Dennis.

New Bradwell's S Hurst heads home in the 90th minute - his side are 1-0 up against Shillington and heading for their first win of 1992-93 (in this May fixture!) only to be foiled by a cruel injury-time equaliser. Photo - Gavin Ellis-Neville.

SENIOR DIVISION CLUBS 1993-94

AMPTHILL TOWN

Chairman: Richard Brown **President:** Gary Williams.
Secretary: Eric Turner, 34 Dunstable Street, Ampthill, Beds MK45 2JT (0525 403128).
Manager: Neil Rodney.
Ground: Woburn Road, Ampthill (0525 404440)
Directions: From Ampthill Town Centre follow signs to Woburn then 1st right into Ampthill Park.
Capacity: 1,500 **Seats:** 30 **Cover:** 400 **Floodlights:** No **Founded:** 1888.
Colours: Yellow/red/red **Change Colours:** Blue/black/black **Nickname:** Town
Previous Grounds: None **Previous Lges:** S Mids 51-65/ Utd Co's 65-91.
Midweek home matchday: Tuesday **Programme:** 16 pages, 50p with admission.
Hons: Sth Mids Lg 59-60 (C'ship Shield 58-59 59-60), North Beds Charity Cup 84-85.

A close shave for the Ampthill Town defence, but they still lose 0-3 at home to Premier Division high-fliers Brache Sparta in the League Challenge Trophy. Photo - Neil Whittington.

BEDFORD UNITED

Chairman: J W C Cleverley **President:** D Rostron **Manager:** Mark Smith
Secretary: Mike Jozwiak, 6 Tunstall Walk, Goldington, Bedford MK41 0AF (0234 342435).
Ground: Hillgrounds, Kempston.
Directions: M1 jct 13, A421 to Bedford, follow signs to Kempston at 1st r'bout, 2nd r'bout keep left, 3rd r'bout turn right, Hillgrounds is 1st left, ground half mile on left.
Capacity: 1,000 **Seats:** 25 **Cover:** 100 **Floodlights:** No **Founded:** 1957
Colours: White/white/blue **Change cols:** All blue or all red **Nickname:** United
Midweek home matches: Tuesday **Programme:** 24 pages, 50p.
Prev. Lge: Bedford & Dist. (pre'89) **Previous Name:** Printers Diemer Reynolds (pre'72)
Previous Ground: Fairhill, Clapham Rd (pre'93).
Record Gate: (at Fairhill) 852 v Bedford Town, South Midlands League Division One 26/12/92.
Hons: Beds Jnr Cup, Biggleswade KO Cup, Butcher Cup, Brittania Cup, Bedford Charity Cup.

LEVERSTOCK GREEN

President: L Bolino **Chairman:** R Saville
Secretary: S D Robinson, 11 Connaught Close, Hemel Hempstead, Herts HP2 7AB (0442 65734)
Manager: M Vipond **Asst Manager:** D Edwards **Press Officer:** B Barter.
Ground: Pancake Lane, Leverstock Green, Hemel Hempstead (0442 246280).
Directions: From M1 leave at A4147 to 2nd r-about. 1st exit to Leverstock Green, Pancake Lane is on left 300 yrds past the 'Leather Bottle' pub.
Seats: 25 **Cover:** 100 **Floodlights:** No **Founded:** 1907 **Nickname:** The Green.
Previous Leagues: West Herts (pre-1950)/Herts County 50-91.
Colours: Green & white/black/green **Change Colours:** Green & black/white/black
Programme: 24 pages, 50p **Clubhouse:** Yes.
Top scorer 92-93: C Gavin **P.O.Y. 92-93:** G Smith.
Players progressing to Football League: Dean Austin (Tottenham Hotspur).
Hons: Herts Centenary Tphy R-up 91-92, Herts Charity Shield R-up 91-92, Frank Major Tphy 1991.

Leverstock Green F.C. 1992-93. Back Row (L/R): Steve Rowley, Alan Edwards, Gary Broadridge, Vince Ryan, Gavin Smith, Tony Power, Mick Vipond (Manager). Front: John Mulvihill, Mike Bodger, Chris Brunt, Matthew Young, Colin Gavin, Mick Hopla, Andy Simpson. Photo - Paul Dennis.

LONDON COLNEY

Chairman: K Hull   **Vice Chairman:** M Chick   **President:** I Holt.
Secretary: W G Gash, 8 Whitehorse Lane, London Colney, Herts AL2 1JX (0727 823192).
Manager: S Seabrook/ H Wright   **Physio:** T Brown   **Press Officer:** S Buchanan.
Ground: Gotslandswick, London Colney (0727 22132).
Directions: From London Colney r'bout (junction of A414/A1081) take A414 towards Watford, after layby (300yds) turn left (hidden turning marked 'Sports Ground') and follow around to gates. Three miles from St Albans (BR). Buses 84 & 358.
Capacity: 1,000   **Cover:** 100   **Seats:** 30   **Floodlights:** No   **Founded:** 1907.
Colours: All royal   **Change Colours:** Yellow/black/yellow   **Nickname:** Blueboys
Programme: £1 with entry   **Previous Lges:** Mid Herts 1907-54/ Herts Co. 07-92.
Club Sponsors: Heath Construction   **Previous Ground:** Whitehorse Lane 07-75.
Clubhouse: Open after games. Hot food available.
Captain & P.o.Y. 92-93: Jim Franklin   **Top Scorer 92-93:** John Barber.
Hons: Sth Mids Lg Div 1 R-up 92-93 (Res. Div 1 92-93), Herts Co. Lg 56-57 59-60 86-87 88-89 (R-up 57-58 58-59, Aubrey Cup 21-22 22-23 56-57 58-59 81-82, Res. Div 1 87-88 88-89 89-90 91-92, Res. Cup 62-63 89-90 91-92 (R-up 70-71)), Herts Centenary Tphy 89-90 (R-up 90-91), Herts I'mediate Cup 58-59 74-75 82-83, Herts Charity Shield 61-62 (R-up 59-60), Herts Jnr Cup 54-55, Mid Herts Lg 91-92(res) (Div 1 22-23 53-54 54-55 89-90(res), Div 2 19-20 48-49, Div 3 81-82(res), Bingham Cox Cup 20-21 53-54 89-90(res) (R-up 91-92(res))), Mid Herts Benevolent Cup 27-28 29-30 48-49 (Benevolent Shield 51-52 52-53 53-54 54-55, Charity Cup 48-49), St Albans Playing Fields Cup 62-63 73-74 75-76 80-81, Frank Major Tphy 74-75 75-76.

London Colney F.C. 1992-93. Back Row (L/R): Terry Brown (Physio), Mick Wright (Manager), Carl Messel, Martin Main, Simon Dobbie, Paul Toms, Steve Murphy, Simon Marjoram, Mick McFarland, Steve Seabrook (Manager). Front: Greg Blundell, Gary McShane, Barry McCarthy, Steve Pattison, John Barbel, Desmond Sonner. Photo - Dave West.

NEW BRADWELL ST PETER

Chairman: Mr J E Haynes   **President:** Mr J P Booden.   **Manager:** Mr B Chapman
Secretary: Mr L Smith, 47 Rowle Close, Stantonbury, Milton Keynes MK14 6BJ (0908 319522).
Ground: Recreation Ground, Bradwell Road, New Bradwell, Milton Keynes MK13 7AT (0908 313835)
Directions: From M1 Jnt 14 go towards Newport Pagnell, left at 1st r-about into H3 (A422 Monks Way). Over 5 r-abouts, right at 6th island into V6 (Grafton St.), go right the way round (back on yourself) 1st island, 1st left, left at T-Junct, ground half mile on left (before bridge).
Nickname: Peters   **Seats:** 30   **Cover:** 100   **Floodlights:** No   **Founded:** 1902
Colours: Maroon & sky stripes/maroon/maroon   **Change Colours:** White/black/black
Previous Name: Stantonbury St James (predecessors were New Bradwell St James)/ Stantonbury St Peters (until merger with New Bradwell Corinthians in 1946).
Previous Grounds: Red Bridge (pre-1947)/ Mutual Meadow, Newport Rd.
Previous League: North Bucks   **Club Sponsors:** The Manulife Group.
Programme: 32 pages, £1 with entry   **Editor:** Mr K Felce (0908 312210).
Midweek home matchday: Wednesday
Clubhouse: Members only (a member can sign in 2 guests). Open every evening a weekend lunchtimes. No food available.
Captain 92-93: C Camozz   **Top Scorer 92-93:** K Brady   **P.o.Y. 92-93:** D Webb ('keeper)
Hons: Sth Mids Lg Div 1 76-77 83-84 (Reserve Div 2 R-up 76-77), Nth Bucks Lg 12-13 13-14 39-40 (R-up 48-49, Div 3 69-70, Div 3 Shield 69-70), Leighton Challenge Cup(5), Stantonbury Cup 84-85, Milton Keynes Referees Challenge Cup 84-85, Berks & Bucks Minor Cup 51-52. *Predecessors (New Bradwell St James):* Nth Bucks Lg(5) 1896-1901, Berks & Bucks Jnr Cup 00-01, Berks & Bucks Snr Cup R-up 01-02.

New Bradwell St Peter F.C. 1992-93. Photo - Gavin Ellis-Neville.

PITSTONE & IVINGHOE

Chairman: Harry Bowden   **President:** R Adlem   **Manager:** T.B.A.
Secretary: David Hawkins, 26 Glebe Close, Pitstone, Leighton Buzzard, Beds LU7 9AZ (0296 661456).
Ground: Pitstone Recreation Ground, Pitstone, Bucks (0296 661271)
Directions: Tring Rd from Dunstable, turn right for Ivinghoe, and continue through to Pitstone r-about; ground left then right. From Aylesbury - left at 'Rising Sun' in Aston Clinton, keep on that road to Pitstone r'bout; ground right then right.
Cover: 100   **Seats:** 25   **Capacity:** 500   **Floodlights:** No   **Founded:** 1958
Colours: Red & black stripes/black/black   **Change Colours:** Blue/blue/white.
Midweek home matches: Tuesday   **Previous Leagues:** Aylesbury/ West Herts.
Previous Grounds: None   **Previous Names:** Ivinghoe & Pitstone.
Programme: 16 pages, 50p   **Programme Editor:** I Travis.
Record gate: 350 v Leighton Town.
Clubhouse: Matchdays & Tuesday & Friday evenings
Hons: Sth Mids Lg 89-90 (Div 1 87-88, Lg Cup 88-89, Div 1 Cup 87-88, Reserve Div 2 R-up 85-86), Dunstable Alliance 73-74 75-76 76-77, Dunstable Premier Cup 74-75 76-77, Reading Jnr Cup 76-77 (R-up 75-76), Aspley Snr Cup 68-69, Aspley Jnr Cup 66-67, West Herts Chal. Cup 58-59, Marworth Cup 67-68, Roseberry Cup 67-68, Berks & Bucks Jnr Cup R-up 79-80(reserves).

RISBOROUGH RANGERS

Chairman: Jeff Galatin   **Manager:** Frank Carter
Secretary: Derrick J Wallace, 42 Ash Rd, Princes Risborough, Bucks HP27 0BQ (0844 345179)
Ground: Windsor's, Horsendon Lane, Princes Risborough (08444 274176)
Directions: Rear of Princes Risborough BR Station (Chiltern Line). A4010 from Aylesbury thru Princes Risborough, fork right onto A4009, left by thatched cottage, over railway bridge, immediate right ground 150 yds on right.
Capacity: 2,000   **Seats:** 25   **Cover:** 100   **Floodlights:** No   **Founded:** 1971
Colours: Red & white stripes   **Change Colours:** Blue & white stripes.
Programme: 30+ pages, £1 with entry   **Midweek home matchday:** Tuesday.
Previous League: Wycombe & Dist.   **Record Gate:** 1,200 v Showbiz XI.
Hons: Berks & Bucks Jnr Cup.

SHEFFORD TOWN

Chairman: M Dredge   **Manager:** Peter Hayes/ Eric Cummerbatch.
Secretary: Joe Gilmour, 61 Lucas Way, Shefford, Beds SG17 5DU (0462 812638).
Ground: Ivel Road, Shefford, Hitchin (0462 811038).
Directions: From Hitchin right at 3rd r'bout on A507 - ground 400 yds on left. From Bedford left at 3rd r'bout on A507 - ground 400 yds on left. From Ampthill right at lights, first right into Ivel Road.
Capacity: 1,000   **Seats:** 100   **Cover:** 100   **Floodlights:** No   **Founded:** 1946
Cols: Blue & white stripes/blue/blue   **Change Colours:** Black & white stripes/black/black
Programme: 30 pages, £1 with entry   **Midweek home matchday:** Tuesday or Wednesday.
Prev. Lges: S Mids 49-55/ Parthenon/ Utd Co's 58-62.   **Players progressing to Football Lge:** Pat Kruse.
Hons: Sth Mids Lg 53-54 54-55 83-84 (Div 1 82-83, Lg Cup 72-73).

SHENLEY & LOUGHTON

Chairman: Jim Gunn   **Life Vice-Pres.:** Len Willett   **Manager:** Simon Spooner
Secretary: Kath Graham, 29 Stafford Grove, Shenley Church End, Milton Keynes MK5 6AX (0908 502815).
Ground: Linceslade Grove, Loughton, Milton Keynes (0908 690668).
Directions: From M1 Jct 14 follow H6, Childs Way for 5 miles until V4 Watling Way (Knowlhill r-about), right to Loughton r-about, right along H5 Portway – 1st right Linceslade Grove.
Capacity: 550   **Cover:** 40   **Seats:** 25   **Floodlights:** No   **Founded:** 1947.
Colours: Blue & white/blue & white/blue   **Change:** Red multi/red/red
Programme: 8 pages, £1 with entry   **Midweek home matchday:** Wednesday.
Previous League: Nth Bucks   **Clubhouse:** Yes   **Record Gate:** 250 v Bedford Town.
Hons: Sth Mids Lg Div 1 90-91 (Lg Cup R-up 90-91), Stantonbury Cup R-up 90-91 (SF 91-92), Nth Bucks Lg.

Pitstone & Ivinghoe under heavy pressure in a 0-4 defeat at Oxford City on August 25th. Photo - Steve Daniels.

Nick Walker of Risborough Rangers powers in a second-half header at home to Emberton. Photo - Gavin Ellis-Neville.

THE 61 F.C. (LUTON)

Chairman: M Haynes   **Vice Chairman:** S Ledwidge   **President:** G B Mapp.
Secretary: R Everitt, 44 Somersby Close, Luton LU1 3XB (0582 485095).
Manager: R Everitt   **Physio:** D Everitt   **Comercial Mgr:** M Haynes
Ground: Kingsway, Beverley Road, Luton, Beds. (0582 582965)
Directions: M1 jct 11, A505 to Luton centre, right at 1st island, 1st left, Beverley Rd is 3rd left, entrance in Beverley Rd, approx 1.5 miles from Town Centre (watch for one-way stystem). All Luton to Dunstable buses pass ground - alight at Beech Hill Bowling Club. One mile from Leagrave (BR).
Capacity: 2,500   **Cover:** 100   **Seats:** 25   **Floodlights:** No   **Formed:** 1961
Colours: Sky/royal/royal   **Change:** Red/black/red   **Nickname:** Two Blues
Previous Grounds: None   **Previous Lges:** Luton & Dist. 61-72/ Hellenic 72-73.
Record Gate: 265 v Selby, Sth Midlands Lg Chal. Tphy final 1st leg, 16/4/88.
Programme: 8 pages, 20p   **Programme Editor:** Secretary   **Club Shop:** No.
Midweek home matchday: Wednesday
Clubhouse: Open every evening and weekend lunchtimes. Hot and cold snacks.
Captain 92-93: Pat Miller   **Top Scorer 92-93:** John Fogarty   **P.O.Y. 92-93:** Scott Woolley
Club record scorer: Sandor Simon   **Club record appearances:** Roger Smith 620.
Hons: Beds Snr Cup 83-84.

The 61 F.C. (Luton) 1992-93.

TODDINGTON ROVERS

Chairman: Hugh Geddes   **Vice Chairman:** Brian Horne   **President:** Peter Turner.
Secretary: Tony H Simmonds, 5 Manor Road, Toddington, Nr Dunstable, Beds LU5 6AH (0525 872786).
Manager: Steve Loasby   **Asst Manager:** Alan Loeasby   **Coach:** Roger King.
Physio: John Cullen   **Press Officer:** Colin Bryson.
Ground: Recreation Ground, Luton Road, Toddington, Nr Dunstable, Beds.
Directions: 1 mile to Toddington village centre from M1, take on-way street signposted Luton, ground 150yds on left. From A5 to Toddington via Knebworth, turn right in village centre, left after 200yds into Luton Road.
Seats: No   **Cover:** 100   **Nickname:** Rovers   **Floodlights:** No   **Founded:** 1894
Colours: Black & white stripes   **Change Colours:** Red & black stripes/black/black
Previous Grounds: Alma Farm, Dropshort 47-64.   **Club Shop:** No.
Previous Leagues: Luton & District South Beds 1894-1988.   **Nickname:** Rovers
Previous Name: Toddington Star.
Programme: 36 pages, 75p (includes admission & raffle)   **Editor:** Secretary
Sponsors: O'Neill Plant Hire   **Record Gate:** 160 v Silsoe, Luton & D. Lg 26/1/23.
Midweek home matchday: Tuesday
Record win: 11-0 v Luton St Marys 1981 **Record defeat:** 0-9 v Bidwell 1957
Clubhouse: Tea room available at ground. Club use Toddington Social & Services Club 600 yds available - cold food always available after matches.
Captain 92-93: Chris Tubb   **Top Scorer 92-93:** Andy McKay, 33   **P.O.Y. 92-93:** David Ashby
Club record scorer: David Ashby   **Club record appearances:** George Stewart, 1050.
Hons: Luton & District South Beds Lge R-up 57-58 58-59 63-64 (Div 1 29-30 30-31 31-32, Div 2 28-29 47-48, Div 3 26-27 47-48, Div 4 25-26), Luton News Cup R-up 80-81, Leighton Chall. Cup R-up 58-59, Beds Jnr Cup 30-31, Beds Intermediate Cup R-up 57-58 58-59 62-63. South Mids Lge Special Awards - Special Award 89-90, Napier English Electric Sportsmanship Tphy 91-92, Best ·Programme 92-93, Secretary of the Year 92-93.

TOTTERNHOE

Chairman: Jim Basterfield   **Vice Chairman:** John Power   **President:** Alf Joyce.
Secretary: Jim Basterfield, 41 Park Avenue, Totternhoe, Dunstable, Beds LU6 1QF (0582 667941)
Manager: Alex Butler   **Assistant Manager:** Paul Simmonds
Coach: Graham Dibsdall   **Physio:** Roy Mackerness.
Ground: Totternhoe Recreation Ground, Dunstable (0582 606738).
Directions: Turn off the main Dunstable to Tring Road B489. Ground on right as you enter the Totternhoe. Five miles from Leighton Buzzard (BR), 7 miles from Luton. Bus 61 Luton-Aylesbury.
Capacity: 1,000   **Seats:** 30   **Cover:** 200   **Floodlights:** No   **Founded:** 1906
Colours: All red   **Change Colours:** Blue & white hoops/blue/blue
Record Gate: 300 v Luton Town, clubhouse opening 13/10/82
Previous Grounds: None   **Previous League:** Luton & Dist. (pre-1958).
Programme: 16 pages, 80p with entry   **Club Sponsors:** Building Conservations   **Club Shop:** No.
Midweek home matchday: Tuesday   **Club Nickname:** Totts.
Record win: 11-0 v Commill Cars, 1961   **Record defeat:** 0-11 v Sandy Albion, 1963.
Clubhouse: Open evenings 8pm, Saturday after games, Sunday lunchtime. Sweets, confectionary, tea, coffee, soups at matches.
Capt. 92-93: Dermot Butler   **Top Scorer 92-93:** Martin Willmott   **P.O.Y. 92-93:** John Cook, Fergus Egan.
Club record scorer: John Waites, 48   **Club record appearances:** John Binding, 631.
Hons: Sth Mids Lg Div 1 61-62 (R-up 68-69 85-86), Beds Snr Cup R-up 69-70 86-87 91-92, Beds I'mediate Cup 77-78 (R-up 81-82), Luton & Dist. Lg 57-58.

TRING ATHLETIC

Chairman: Tony Pace   **President:** Paul Nichols
Secretary: Ralph Griffiths, 42 Bedgrove, Aylesbury, Bucks HP21 7BD (0296 26425).
Manager: Mick Eldridge   **Asst Manager:** Ray Brimson   **Coach:** Richard Vincent.
Ground: Miswell Lane, Tring, Herts.
Directions: Through Tring on main road towards Aylesbury, right just after Anchor PH into Miswell Lane, pitch approximately 500yds on right opposite Beaconsfield Road.
Seats: 25+   **Cover:** 100+   **Floodlights:** No   **Founded:** 1958   **Nickname:** Athletic
Colours: Red & black   **Change colours:** green.
Prev. Name: Tring Athletic & Youth.   **Prev. Grnd:** Pendley Spts Centre (Tring Town FC) 89-92.
Programme: 36 pages, 50p   **Programme Editor:** Secretary   **Club Shop:** No.
Midweek matchday: Wednesday   **Previous League:** West Herts 58-88.
Rec. win: 10-2 v Ickleford (A) 10/4/93   **Record defeat:** 2-7 v Buckingham Ath. (H) 1/10/82.
Players progressing to Football League: Peter Gibbs (Watford 'keeper in late seventies).
Clubhouse: Bar, open matchdays only. Crisps & filled rolls available.
Captain 92-93: Ged Keough   **Top Scorer 92-93:** Danny Glass   **P.O.Y. 92-93:** Grant Mosley.
Club record scorer: Ian Butler   **Club record appearances:** Alan Sheppard.

Tring Athletic F.C. 1992-93.

WINSLOW UNITED

Chairman: J B Robins   **Manager:** L Lamb.
Secretary: David F Ward, 29 Avenue Rd, Winslow, Buckingham MK18 3DH (0296 713202).
Ground: Winslow Recreation Ground, Elmfields Gate, Winslow (0296 713057)
Directions: A413 from Aylesbury to Winslow, in High Street turn right into Emerald Gate, ground 100yds on left opposite car park. From Milton Keynes take A421 to Buckingham, turn left thru Gt Horwood to Winslow, turn left off High Street into Emerald Gate.
Capacity: 2,000   **Cover:** 100   **Floodlights:** Yes   **Founded:** 1891.
Colours: Yellow/blue/blue   **Change Colours:** Red/black/black   **Club Shop:** No.
Record Gate: 720 v Aylesbury Utd, Berks & Bucks Snr Cup.
Previous Grounds: None   **Previous Leagues:** Leighton/ North Bucks.
Programme: 16 pages, £1 with entry   **Editor:** J Robins (0296 714206).
Midweek home matchday: Tuesday
Clubhouse: Open every evening except Wednesday. Full weekend opening. Youngers beers. Various snacks on matchdays.
P.O.Y. 92-93: S Searle   **Captain & Top Scorer 92-93:** B McConnell
Club record scorer: B McConnell
Hons: Sth Mids Lg R-up 75-76 (Div 1 74-75), Berks & Bucks Jnr Cup 67-68, Buckingham Charity Cup 29-30 32-33 66-67 67-68 73-74 74-75 77-78 79-80 81-82, Stantonbury Charity Cup 67-68 73-74 78-79 82-83 83-84 85-86, Leighton Challenge Cup 92-93.

Winslow United F.C. 1992-93. Photo - Bucks & Winslow Advertiser.

DIVISION ONE CLUBS 1993-94

ASHCROFT

Chairman: Neil Ludlow   **President:** Terry Gilmore   **Manager:** Steve Wyatt
Secretary: Neil Ludlow, 12 Tavistock Str., Luton, Beds LU1 3UR (0582 486802).
Ground: Vauxhall Motors Sports Ground, Luton (0582 413772).
Directions: M1 jct 10, follow airport signs, left at 1st r'bout, left at 2nd r'about, ground entrance on left.
Capacity: **Seats:**   **Cover:**   **Floodlights:** No   **Founded:** 1970
Cols: Blue & yellow/yellow/yellow   **Change Colours:** Purple/white/purple   **Programme:** No.
Previous Lg: Luton & Sth Beds   **Previous Name:** Ashcroft Co-op.
Previous Ground: Co-op Sports Ground, Stochingstone Rd.
Hons: Sth Mids Lg Div 1 91-92 (R-up 82-83, Div 1 Tphy R-up 91-92, Reserve Div 2 82-83 (R-up 92-93), Reserve Cup R-up 83-84), Luton & Sth Beds Lg 74-75 77-78 78-79 80-81 (R-up 79-80, Div 1 73-74, Div 2 R-up 71-72, William Pease Challenge Tphy 77-78 78-79 80-81 (R-up 79-80)), Beds Intermediate Cup R-up 83-84 (Jnr Cup 83-84 (R-up 73-74)), SOS Allen Tphy 80-81.

CADDINGTON

Chairman: Peter Spowage   **Hon. President:** David Pleat   **Manager:** Leigh Glenister
Secretary: John O'Brien, 25 Churchill Rd, Dunstable, Beds LU6 3LU (0582 696053).
Ground: Caddington Recreation Club, Manor Road, Luton (0582 450151).
Directions: On entering village turn into Manor Road (adjacent to shops and village green), proceed 500 metres; Clubhouse and ground on left side next to Catholic Church.
Capacity: Unknown   **Seats:** Not yet   **Cover:** Due   **Floodlights:** No   **Founded:** 1971.
Cols: Red & black hoops/black/red   **Change:** Blue (broad white stripe)/blue/blue.
Programme: Possibly 93-94   **Record Gate:** 150 v Barton Rvrs, Beds Snr Cup.
Prev. Names: Five Oaks/ The Oaks   **Prev. Lge:** Luton & Sth Beds Dist.   **Nickname:** The Oaks
Prev. Grnd: Stockwood Public Park   **Midweek home matchday:** Tuesday or Thursday.
Players progressing to Football League: Paul Kerling to professional football in Holland.
Hons: Beds Intermediate Cup 85-86 92-93, Luton & Sth Beds Dist. Lg 84-85 (Lg Cup 84-85), William Pease Cup 83-84.

CRANFIELD UNITED

Chairman: Roger Thompson   **Vice Chairman:** Jim Brandon   **President:** T.B.A.
Secretary: Paul Kilcoyne, 10 Springfield Way, Cranfield, Bedford MK43 0JN.
Manager: Trevor Evans   **Asst Manager:** Trevor Barnett   **Coach:** Ray Perry
Physio: Richard Kilcoyne   **Commercial Manager:** Brian Griffiths.
Ground: Crawley Road, Cranfield, Bedford MK43 0AA (0234 751444)
Directions: M1 jct 13 – A5140 to Bedford, 100 yds turn left, follow signposts to Cranfield, through village, left into Mill Rd, left into Crawley Rd, ground on left after houses. From Bedford – A5140, right at Marston Morteyne r'bout 'Happy Eater', left at T-junction into village, left into Crane Way, continue to ground on left.
Capacity: 3,000   **Seats:** 50   **Cover:** 150   **Floodlights:** Yes
Founded: 1904
Cols: Red & white stripes/red/red   **Change Colours:** Green/black/black   **Nickname:** United
Previous Leagues: Bedford & Dist. 04-32 61-76/ North Bucks 33-48/ South Midlands 49-60.
Previous Grounds: Various local pitches.
Clubhouse: Open every evening and weekend lunchtimes. Bingo Mondays. Tea/rolls available most weekends, hot food for special events. Parking for sixty cars.
Programme: 16 pages with admission   **Club Sponsors:** A J Dalkin   **Club Shop:** No.
Midweek home matchday: Wednesday
Record win: 13-0 v Woburn (H), 8/1/72   **Record defeat:** 1-11 v Bletchley (H), 14/1/56.
Captain 92-93: Chris Hyde   **Top Scorer 92-93:** Tom Brady 11   **P.o.Y. 92-93:** Steven Perry
Club record scorer: Mick Johnson 500+   **Club record appearances:** Mick Johnson 900+.
Hons: South Mids Lg Div 2 50-51 (Div 1 R-up 51-52, Cove Tphy R-up 85-86, Sportsmanship Award 77-78 85-86), Bedford & Dist. Lg R-up 74-75 (Div 1 67-68), Beds Snr Cup R-up 51-52, Stantonbury Cup 87-88, Beds Charity Cup R-up 64-65, Hinchingbrooke Cup R-up 92-93, Aubrey Tingay Cup R-up 1976, Beds Jnr Cup R-up 49-50, Beds Minor Cup 35-36, North Bucks Chall. Shield 48-49, Nth Bucks Lg Div 2 35-36.

DE HAVILLAND

Chairman: M J Hollis   **Manager:** P Long.
Secretary: Roy Ridgway, 85 Garden Ave., Hatfield, Herts AL10 8LH (0707 267327).
Ground: Comet Way, Hatfield (0707 263204/ 262665).
Directions: From south leave A1(M) at Hatfield turn, A1001 to Birchwood r'bout, 1st exit into car park. From north leave A1(M) at Welwyn G.C., A1001 to Birchwood r'bout and 4th exit into car park.
Capacity: **Seats:** None   **Cover:** No   **Floodlights:** No   **Founded:** 1934.
Colours: Blue & white/blue/red   **Change colours:** Red/red/black   **Nickname:** DH
Programme: Sometimes, 30p   **Previous League:** Herts Snr Co. (pre-1992)

DELCO

Chairman: Paul Shepherd   **President:** N Lee   **Manager:** S Howarth.
Secretary: Terry E Owen, 29 Elm Park Close, Houghton Regis, Dunstable, Beds LU5 5PN (0582 863273).
Ground: Delco Chassis Sports Ground (0582 695668)
Directions: On main A5 Trunk Rd to the North of Dunstable. Ground entrance is approximately 100yds south of traffic lights at Chalk Cutting.
Capacity: 2,000   **Seats:** 30   **Cover:** 80   **Floodlights:** No   **Founded:** 1934.
Colours: Red/white/red   **Change Colours:** Blue/white/blue.   **Nickname:** None
Programme: 12 pages, 50p   **Midweek home matchday:** Tuesday
Record Gate: 432 v Bedford Town.   **Previous Ground:** A.C. Delco Spts Ground.
Previous League: Luton & South Beds Dist./ Hellenic 69-73.
Previous Names: A.C. Sphinx 46-52/ A.C. Delco 52-85/ Delco Products 85-93.
Hons: William Pease Tphy R-up, SOS Allen Cup, Luton News Cup(3), Luton Lg Invitation Cup(2), Lorman Cup(4).

EATON BRAY

Chairman: Derek Jackson   **President:** Roy Bennett   **Manager:** Paul Reeves.
Secretary: Mark Holmes, 3 Alfred Str., Dunstable, Beds LU5 4HZ (0582 605204).
Ground: The Rye, Eaton Bray (0582 221443).
Directions: Follow A5 thru Dunstable past A.C. Delco, left onto Leighton Buzzard bypass, 1st left and follow signs to Eaton Bray, turn right 500yds ground on right.
Capacity: **Seats:** None   **Cover:** 30   **Floodlights:** No   **Founded:** 1989.
Cols: White (blue stripe)/blue/white   **Change Colours:** Sky/navy/white.   **Nickname:** None
Programme: 16 pages, 50p   **Midweek home matchday:** Thursday

EMBERTON

Chairman/Secretary: R L Dugdale, 9 Stone Court, West Lane, Emberton, Nr Olney, Bucks MK46 5ND (0234 711004).
Manager: Colin Hoyland   **Assistant Manager:** P York.
Physio: D Pinnock   **Commercial Manager:** C Campbell (0908 609926).
Ground: Hulton Drive, Emberton, Nr Olney, Bucks.
Directions: M1 jct 14 to Newport Pagnell, right onto A422 at 1st r'bout straight on north towards Olney. Emberton lies before Olney. Turn left at 2nd turning into village and 1st right Hulton Drive. Buses from Northampton, Bedford and Milton Keynes.
Capacity: 400   **Seats:** No   **Cover:** No   **Floodlights:** No   **Reformed:** 1968
Colours: Maroon/white   **Change colours:** Navy/white   **Nickname:** Rams
Previous Ground: Clifton Reynes (10yrs).
Previous Leagues: Rushden & District 66-85/ East Northants 85-91.
Programme: 12 pages, £1 with entry   **Editor:** Mr C Campbell (0908 609926)   **Club Shop:** No.
Sponsors: Dugdale Builders   **Record Gate:** 180 v Bedford T., Sth Mids Lg Div 1.
Midweek home matchday: Wednesday
Clubhouse: Matchdays. Tea, coffee, soft drinks, confectionary.
Captain & P.o.Y. 92-93: Paul Breeze   **Top Scorer 92-93:** W Botham.
Club record scorer: D Maloney 54   **Club record appearances:** R L Dugdale.
Hons: E Northants Lg 90-91 (R-up 86-87, Lg Cup 90-91), Rushden & Dist. Lg 84-85 85-86 (Lg Cup 84-85, Jnr Shield 79-80), Nth Bucks Lg Div 3 37-38, Haynes Tphy 69-70, Hamblin Cup 90-91, Stantonbury Cup R-up 92-93 (SF 91-92).

Emberton's Bob McKain pursues Frank Magnacavello in the 0-2 loss at Risborough Rangers. Photo - Gavin Ellis-Neville.

FLAMSTEAD

Chairman: Mr Alan Morrice   **Manager:** Tony Dumingan
Secretary: Mrs Susan Hayward, Greenways, Old Watling Str., Flamstead, St Albans, Herts AL3 8HN (0582 841213).
Ground: Friendless Lane, Flamstead, St Albans, Herts (0582 841307).
Ground Directions: From Dunstable Town Centre travel south on A5 Trunk Road towards the M1. Follow for approximately 3 miles then turn right opposite Hertfordshire Moat House Hotel. Ground and parking approximately half a mile on the corner of the first right turn.
Seats: None   **Cover:** None   **Floodlights:** No   **Founded:** 1962.   **Nickname:** None
Colours: White/red   **Change Colours:** Orange/black
Programme: 4 pages, 25p   **Midweek home matchday:** Tuesday.
Previous League: Luton & South Beds District.

HOUGHTON TOWN

Chairman: D McMorrow   **Manager:** P Rowe.
Secretary: Desmond Stewart, 9 Grove Rd, Houghton Regis, Dunstable, Beds LU5 5PD (0582 864286).
Ground: Houghton Town Associated Club, Park Rd North, Houghton Regis (0582 866128)
Directions: M1 jct 11, head towards Dunstable, right at island into Poynters Rd, straight over next island keeping left at small r'bout onto Park Rd North - ground on left 10yds before pelican crossing.
Capacity: **Seats:** None   **Cover:** No   **Floodlights:** No   **Founded:** 1993
Colours: All blue   **Change Colours:** All red
Programme: £1 with entry   **Midweek home matchday:** Tuesday.

MERCEDES BENZ

Chairman: Martin Parlett   **President:** Nigel Wells   **Manager:** Stuart Collard.
Secretary: Bob Flight, Mercedes (UK) Ltd, Mercedes Benz Centre, Tongwell, Milton Keynes, Bucks MK15 8BA (0604 764433).
Ground: The Barn, Pannier Place, Downs Barn, Milton Keynes, Bucks (0908 245158).
Directions: M1 jct 14, A509 for Milton Keynes, right onto H5 Portway at 1st island, right onto V9 Overstreet at 3rd island, 1st left into Downs Barn Boulevard, 2nd left into Pannier Place, ground at top of hill.
Capacity: 300   **Cover:** No   **Seats:** None   **Floodlights:** No   **Founded:** 1967.
Colours: All royal blue   **Change Colours:** All white   **Nickname:** Blues.
Programme: No   **Previous Lges:** Nth Bucks & Dist. (pre'93).
Midweek home matches: Tuesday   **Previous Ground:** Willen Rd, Newport Pagnell.
Hons: Nth Bucks Lg Div 1 90-91 (Premier Div Cup 92-93, Intermediate Tphy 91-92), Daimler-Benz Austrian International Tournament R-up 1990.

MILTON KEYNES COUNTY

Chairman: J Roscoe Snr   **President:** W Bilsom   **Manager:** J Roscoe Jnr.
Secretary: Edward Wright, 46 Conway Cres., Bletchley, Bucks MK3 6AR (0908 648066).
Ground: Wolverton Park, Old Wolverton Rd, Wolverton, Milton Keynes, Bucks (0908 312264).
Directions: North Milton Keynes turn off A5, 4th exit posted V5, over 2 islands and double mini-r'bout into Old Wolverton Rd, pass Galeon pub, turn right between the 2 bridges. Adjacent to Wolverton BR station.
Capacity: 4,500   **Cover:** Yes   **Seats:** Yes   **Floodlights:** Yes   **Founded:** 1992.
Cols: Blue & white/white/blue & white   **Change:** Green & white hoops/white/white **Nickname:** None.
Programme: Yes   **Previous Lges:** Nth Bucks & Dist. (pre'93).
Midweek home matches: Wednesday   **Previous Ground:** Rickley Park (council ground).
Previous Name: R.B.L. Bletchley.
Hons: Nth Bucks Lg Intermediate Div 1 92-93.

POTTERS BAR CRUSADERS

Chairman: Mr S Sandford   **President:** Mr J Metselar   **Manager:** Clive Eldridge.
Secretary: Linda Eldridge, 169 Ashwood Road, Potters Bar, Herts EN6 2QE (0707 646059).
Ground: King George V P.F., Mutton Lane, Potters Bar (0707 650764) *(Synthetic pitch).*
Directions: A1(M)/M25 to Bignalls Corner, follow signs to South Mymms, right into A111 (Mutton Lane). King George V playing fields 1 mile on the left. (Next to Furzefield Centre).
Capacity: 300   **Seats:** None   **Cover:** No   **Floodlights:** Yes   **Founded:** 1948
Colours: All Royal blue   **Change Colours:** Yellow (blue trim)
Programme: 14 pages, 50p   **Midweek home matchday:** Tuesday.
Previous League: Herts County County (pre-1990).

SANDY ALBION

Chairman: Brian Faulkner   **Vice Chairman:** Jeff Allen   **President:** Peter Brown
Secretary/Press Officer: Peter Francis, 6 Willow Rise, Sandy, Beds SG19 1AY. (0767 681615)
Manager: Ian Mulcahy   **Ground:** Rec. Grnd, Bedford Rd, Sandy (0767 680351).
Directions: Quarter mile off A1 junction at Sandy r-about. On B1042 road Bedford to Cambridge. Quarter mile from town centre, 5 mins walk from Sandy BR station.
Capacity: 2,000   **Seats:** None   **Cover:** No   **Floodlights:** No   **Founded:** 1909
Colours: White/black/black   **Change Colours:** Yellow & green
Programme: 40 pages, 30p   **Programme Editor:** Secretary   **Club Shop:** No.
Club Sponsors: King & Ayres   **Midweek home matchday:** Tuesday   **Nickname:** Albion.
Record win: 12-0 v Arlesey, 71-72   **Record defeat:** 0-10 v Potters Bar Crusaders.
Previous Grounds: **Previous Lge:** Bedford & Dist 1909-58
Clubhouse: Open two hours prior to kick-off on matchdays. Rolls, sweets, crisps, hot drinks.
Captain 92-93: Tony Whaymand   **Top Scorer & P.o.Y. 92-93:** Simon Braine (19 goals)
Club record scorer: Bruno Urtone, 131   **Club record appearances:** Bruno Urtone, Carlos Vincent (500+)
Players progressing to Football League: Richard Habin (Reading, Rotherham Utd, Doncaster Rovers).
Honours: Sth Mids Lg Div 1 59-60 (Chal. Tphy 80-81, Championship Shield 66-67), Hinchinbrooke Cup 59-60 74-75 76-77, Beds Jnr Cup 19-20, Nth Beds Charity Cup 21-22 35-36 78-79 (R-up 86-87), Beds I'mediate Cup 59-60, Jesse Piggott Trophy 90-91, Bedford Hosp. Cup 64-65.

Sandy Albion F.C. 1992-93.

SCOT

Chairman: Brian Greengrass   **Manager:** Peter Soper (Reserves: John McConnell).
Secretary: Thomas Hallford, 32 Browning Cres., Bletchley, Milton Keynes MK3 5AU (0908 640365).
Ground: Selbourne Ave., Bletchley, Milton Keynes (0908 372057).
Directions: Main roads to Bletchley then A421 Buckingham road, at Glen Garage right into Newton Rd, 2nd left into Selbourne Ave., through railway bridge to bottom of road.

Capacity:	**Seats:** None	**Cover:** No **Floodlights:** No **Founded:** 1968.

Colours: Blue (black stripe)/black/blue   **Change Colours:** All white
Prev. Grnd: Tattenhoe Lane, Bletchley   **Prev. Lges:** Nth Bucks & Dist./ Aylesbury & Dist.
Programme: Yes   **Midweek home matches:** Wednesday   **Nickname:** Scots.
Previous Names: None   **Hons:** Nth Bucks & Dist. Lg 91-92.

STONY STRATFORD TOWN

Chairman: R Gustafson   **Manager:** Perry Mercer
Secretary: Maurice J Barber, 26 Boundary Cres., Stony Stratford, Milton Keynes MK11 1DF (0908 567930).
Ground: Sports Ground, Ostlers Lane, Stony Stratford (0908 562267)
Directions: From Dunstable old A5, Watling Street, on approaching Bletchley continue on A5 loop road (Hinkley) to end of dual c'way to A422/A508 r'bout. First exit, thru lights, 2nd right into Ostlers Lane. From M1 jct 13 pick up A421 and join A5 (Hinkley) and proceed as above.
Capacity: 500+   **Seats:** None   **Cover:** No   **Floodlights:** No   **Reformed:** 1953
Previous Leagues: North Bucks & Dist./ Northampton Combination.
Colours: Sky/navy/navy   **Change Colours:** Red/black/red
Programme: 10 pages, £1 with entry   **Midweek matchday:** Tuesday.
Players progressing to Football Lge: George Henson (Northampton (in 1929), Wolves, Swansea, Bradford P.A. & Sheffield Utd).
Honours: Sth Mids Lg R-up 70-71 71-72

WALDEN RANGERS

Chairman: Mr M I Garrett   **Manager:** Cliff Bailey.
Secretary: Irene Oodian, 9 Garfield Court, Handcross Rd, Luton, Beds LU2 8JZ (0582 483090).
Ground: Breachwood Green Rec., Chapel Rd, Breachwood Green, Herts (0438 833332).
Directions: From Luton Airport roundabout (Eaton Green Rd)(away from Vauxhall/ IBC direction) take country road to Breachwood Green (2 miles). From Hitchin on A602, take country road to Preston (6 miles to Breachwood Green).
Floodlights: No   **Founded:** 1966
Colours: Blue/white/blue   **Change Colours:** Red/black/red

NORTH BUCKS & DISTRICT LEAGUE

PREM. DIV.	P	W	D	L	F	A	PTS
Stewkley	32	22	7	3	79	33	51
Leighton Athletic	32	23	4	5	105	35	50
Old Bradwell Utd	32	20	7	5	98	52	47
Scot	32	21	5	6	86	45	47
Newport Athletic	32	17	7	8	103	64	41
Westbury	32	17	7	8	64	38	41
Wicken Sports	32	16	5	11	65	42	37
Mercedes Benz	32	13	9	10	64	64	35
Silverstone	32	13	7	12	78	56	33
Earls Barton Utd	32	10	6	16	75	81	26
Roade	32	9	6	17	61	84	24
Marsh Gibbon	32	9	6	17	53	89	24
Potterspury	32	8	7	17	64	84	23
Steeple Claydon	32	6	8	18	40	80	20
Yardley Gobion	32	8	4	20	38	80	20
Padbury United	32	5	3	24	45	123	13
Deanshanger Ath.	32	4	4	24	46	114	12

I'MEDIATE DIV.	P	W	D	L	F	A	PTS
Milton Keynes Co.	30	25	3	2	117	31	53
Sherington	30	23	4	3	102	41	50
Great Horwood	30	13	7	10	56	43	33
Scot Res.	30	14	4	12	68	67	32
Tesco	30	11	9	10	59	53	31
Heath United	30	12	7	11	55	57	31
Leighton A. Res.	30	13	4	13	61	51	30
Abbey National	30	12	6	12	46	42	30
Syresham	30	13	3	14	57	61	29
Leedon Athletic	30	12	3	15	56	79	27
Willen Civil Serv.	30	11	3	16	48	65	25
Eaton United	30	10	4	16	54	63	24
Grendon Rangers	30	7	9	14	48	54	23
Hanslope	30	8	6	16	45	77	22
Audi-Volkswagen	30	9	3	18	33	70	21
Deanshanger Res.	30	8	3	19	46	97	19

DIV. ONE	P	W	D	L	F	A	PTS
Mercedes Benz Res.	28	24	2	2	99	36	50
O Bradwell U. Res.	28	20	2	6	104	45	42
Milton K. Dynamo	28	20	1	7	118	51	41
Wincanton	28	18	1	9	97	57	37
Roade Res.	28	16	2	10	74	56	34
Oldbrook	28	15	3	10	85	69	33
Silverstone Res.	28	15	2	11	67	58	30
Tingewick Sports	28	11	5	12	75	61	27
Earls Barton Res.	28	10	5	13	87	75	25
Stoke Bruerne Res.	28	10	5	13	49	67	25
Thornborough Ath.	28	10	3	15	45	69	23
Stewkley Res.	28	9	4	15	55	66	22
Yardley Gob. Res.	28	7	2	19	39	81	16
Stoke Hammond	28	2	3	23	22	154	7
Wicken Spts Res.	28	2	2	24	31	102	6

DIV. TWO	P	W	D	L	F	A	PTS
Potterspury Res.	28	21	3	4	75	42	45
Leighton Foxes	28	17	6	5	83	36	40
Leedon Ath. Res.	28	18	3	7	66	37	39
Abbey Nat. Res.	28	14	7	7	52	34	35
Padbury Utd Res.	28	16	2	10	72	53	34
Marsh Gibbon Res.	28	14	4	10	42	50	32
Dependable Couriers	28	12	6	10	71	59	30
Syresham Res.	28	11	5	12	63	57	27
Steeple Clay. Res.	28	10	5	13	61	77	25
Gt Horwood Res.	28	9	6	13	50	55	24
Grendon Rgrs Res.	28	9	4	15	58	66	22
MK Dynamo Res.	28	10	2	16	71	84	22
Tesco Res.	28	5	6	17	47	66	16
Hanslope Res.	28	4	7	17	40	76	15
Heath Utd Res.	28	6	2	20	37	96	14

CLUB PARTICULARS
(Tel. codes 0908 unless stated)

ABBEY NATIONAL
Ground: MK Spts Club, Woughton-on-the-Green
Secretary: M Burnside (0327 52095)

AUDI-VOLKSWAGEN
G: Willen, Newport Pagnell   S: M Winnett (612305)

DEANSHANGER ATHLETIC
G: Folly Rd, Deanshanger   S: Mrs Howe (562744)

EARLS BARTON UNITED
G: Northampton Rd   S: D Simpson (494389)

EATON UNITED
G: Denbigh Spts Grounnd, Bletchley
S: A Bryoka (644819)

GREAT HORWOOD
G: Castle Fields, Nash Rd, Gt Horwood
S: Mrs Whitehall (0296 713804)

GRENDON RANGERS
G: Grendon Rec   S: P Busby (0296 770369)

HANSLOPE
G: Castlethorpe Rd   S: L McLean (511267)

HEATH UNITED
G: Thrift Rd, Heath and Reach
S: P Palmer (0525 851428)

LEEDON ATHLETIC
G: Pages Park, Leighton Buzzard
S: K Paradowski (0525 384830)

LEIGHTON ATHLETIC
G: Memorial PF, Mentmore Rd, Leighton Buzzard
S: L Blair (0525 853680)

MARSH GIBBON
G: Edgott Rd   S: A Campbell (0869 277331)

NEWPORT ATHLETIC
G: North Crawley PF, Newport Pagnell
S: A Walker (320737)

OLD BRADWELL UNITED
G: Abbey Rd, Bradwell Village (312355)
S: A Walliker (318408)

PADBURY UNITED
G: Padbury PF   S: R Atkins (0582 882679)

POTTERSPURY
G: Meadow View   S: J Crampton (543266)

ROADE
G: Hyde Rd (0604 862814) D Curtis (0604 767015)

SHERINGTON
G: Perry Lane, Sherington   S: B Haynes (610673)

SILVERSTONE
G: Church Street, Silverstone
S: B Whitlock (0327 857080)

STEEPLE CLAYDON
G: Nth End Rd   S: Mrs Hammond (0296 730438)

STEWKLEY
G: Stewkley Rec   S: M Vaughn (0525 383267)

SYRESHAM
G: rear of Village Hall   S: B Archer (0280 850538)

TESCO
G: Bradwell Monk pub, Hodge Lea
S: J Beale (310943)

WESTBURY
G: Brackley Rd PF   S: J Grainge (0280 701107)

WICKEN SPORTS
G: St Johns Lane   S: D Fuller (569167)

WILLEN CIVIL SERVICE
G: The Pavillion, Willen   S: R Kerr (667691)

YARDLEY GOBION
G: School Lane, off Hesketh Rd, Yardley Gobion
S: R Hook (0604 708616610673)

BEDFORD & DISTRICT LEAGUE

PREM. DIV.	P	W	D	L	F	A	PTS
Cotton End Utd	24	18	5	1	90	34	41
Biggleswade Utd	24	17	3	4	69	33	37
Ickwell & Old Warden	24	12	6	6	51	39	30
Woburn	24	11	5	8	61	44	27
G.F. Sports	24	11	5	8	48	43	27
Clapham & Oakley S.	24	8	7	9	46	47	23
Wilshamstead	24	9	5	10	33	46	23
Dunton	24	9	4	11	46	36	22
Fairfield Social	24	8	6	10	48	51	22
Marston Shelton Rvrs	24	7	8	9	34	44	22
Flowerpot	24	7	4	13	31	59	18
Caldecote	24	5	3	16	38	67	13
Stevington	24	3	1	20	42	94	7

DIV. ONE	P	W	D	L	F	A	PTS
Elstow Abbey	24	18	2	4	74	32	38
Bromham United	24	17	2	5	81	22	36
Eaton Socon	24	13	7	4	53	26	33
Riseley Sports	24	13	5	6	58	36	31
Hunting Athletic	24	13	5	6	45	27	31
Henlow Italians	24	11	7	6	58	43	29
Wootton United	24	13	2	9	45	40	28
Ickwell & O. Res.	24	13	0	11	62	55	26
Campton	24	8	3	13	33	48	19
Lidlington Utd SC	24	5	4	15	46	76	14
Mogerhanger	24	5	1	18	32	72	11
Blunham	24	3	4	17	35	87	10
Pheasant	24	2	2	20	33	91	6

DIV. TWO	P	W	D	L	F	A	PTS
Brickhill Tigers	24	17	2	5	68	36	36
Bedford Telephones	24	14	4	6	61	31	32
Bedford N.E. Avenue	24	11	8	5	55	34	30
Biggleswade U. Res.	24	12	5	7	46	30	29
Newnham Sports	24	12	5	7	50	36	29
Renhold United	24	12	4	8	64	43	28
U.S.A.C.L.I.	24	11	3	10	58	56	25
Fairfield S. Res.	24	10	3	11	44	58	23
Westoning	24	7	5	12	54	73	19
St Cuthberts	24	4	8	12	35	56	16
Ampthill Athletic	24	6	4	14	26	55	16
Wilshamstead Res.	24	4	7	13	32	62	15
Henlow	24	5	4	15	26	49	14

DIV. THREE	P	W	D	L	F	A	PTS
Kempston Town	24	17	5	2	74	29	39
Ryl Oak Kempston	24	18	2	4	96	35	38
Bedford S.A.	24	16	2	6	70	36	34
Cotton End Res.	24	13	3	8	69	47	29
Eaton Socon Res.	24	12	4	8	58	47	28
Potton Utd Lions	24	10	7	7	48	40	27
Bromham Utd Res.	24	10	2	12	47	55	22
Clapham & O. Res.	24	8	4	12	56	63	20
Biggleswade T. 'A'	24	6	7	11	42	67	19
Caldecote Res.	24	7	4	13	44	63	18
Sandy Town	24	7	3	14	46	59	17
Marston Shelton Res.	24	4	8	12	50	66	16
Dunton Res.	24	1	3	20	27	120	5

DIV. FOUR	P	W	D	L	F	A	PTS
Bow Brickhill	24	19	2	3	97	30	40
Corinthians	24	16	5	3	63	31	37
Tempsford	24	16	4	4	80	42	36
Great Barford	24	15	4	5	71	29	34
Duke Inn Spts	24	13	5	6	64	37	31
Elstow Abbey Res.	24	12	1	11	47	45	25
Roxton	24	10	3	11	58	67	23
Sandy Town Res.	24	9	1	14	44	65	19
Westoning Res.	24	8	2	14	46	65	18
Campton Res.	24	8	0	16	28	63	16
Lidlington U. Res.	24	6	2	16	32	79	14
Bedford Albion	24	4	4	16	25	72	12
Haynes	24	2	3	19	25	75	7

DIV. FIVE	P	W	D	L	F	A	PTS
Hunting Ath. Res.	26	20	4	2	79	34	44
C.I.T.	26	18	3	5	74	23	39
Kempston Athletic	26	17	5	4	86	36	39
Renhold Utd Res.	26	14	6	6	61	34	34
Wootton Utd Res.	26	12	6	8	79	59	30
Turvey	26	13	2	11	57	41	28
Bk Horse Wootton	26	11	4	11	60	45	26
Woburn Res.	26	11	4	11	56	51	26
Kempston T. Res.	26	9	3	14	59	62	21
Cople Sports	26	8	4	14	50	91	20
Henlow Italians Res.	26	8	3	15	47	62	19
Mogerhanger Res.	26	5	6	15	36	77	16
Bow Brickhill Res.	26	7	2	17	35	79	16
Potton Lions Res.	26	2	2	22	23	108	6

HANWELL & DISTRICT WEDNESDAY LEAGUE

DIV. ONE	P	W	D	L	F	A	PTS
Datacab	12	9	2	1	49	18	20
Western Traders	12	8	2	2	45	22	18
Paddington Postal	12	7	1	4	31	30	15
Oaktown	12	6	1	5	27	24	13
Hayes & Southall PO	12	4	1	7	28	47	9
Immigration	12	1	3	8	16	33	5
London Fire Br. 'A'	12	0	4	8	12	34	4

DIV. TWO	P	W	D	L	F	A	PTS
Westbourne Park	14	10	1	3	63	27	21
District Line Utd	14	10	1	3	54	33	21
Kappa Travel Utd	14	6	4	4	40	35	16
London Fire Br. 'B'	14	6	2	6	40	46	14
Stewards	14	5	2	7	24	26	12
N.I.B. Athletic	14	5	2	7	36	49	12
A.A. London	14	4	1	9	26	50	9
District Line A.A.	14	3	1	10	34	51	74

DIV. THREE	P	W	D	L	F	A	PTS
Hayes Police	18	11	6	1	70	30	28
Royal Mail W12	18	13	2	3	62	25	28
United Airlines	18	11	2	5	78	28	24
Twickenham Postal	18	11	1	6	38	29	23
Royal Mail Feltham	18	9	2	7	57	38	20
London Golf Centre	18	7	2	9	42	40	16
Stewards Reserves	18	7	2	9	28	48	16
Golders Gn L.E.R.	18	7	0	11	36	55	12
Bush United	18	4	0	14	27	74	8
Chalk Fm Garage LT	18	1	1	16	15	86	3

EAST BERKSHIRE LEAGUE

DIV. ONE	P	W	D	L	F	A	PTS
Vansittart Wdrs	16	12	3	1	51	22	27
Slough Heating	16	11	2	3	43	22	24
Running Horse	16	10	2	4	42	26	22
Bracknell Boys Club	16	7	2	7	35	30	16
Cygnets	16	6	3	7	44	42	15
CBS (Bracknell)	16	5	4	7	36	38	14
Windsor Gt Park	16	3	3	10	23	43	9
Braywick Rovers	16	4	1	11	33	63	9
Spital Old Boys	16	2	4	10	30	51	6

DIV. TWO	P	W	D	L	F	A	PTS
Chalvey	22	19	1	2	69	27	39
Old Windsor	22	13	2	7	70	44	28
Windsor & Eton CC	22	10	5	7	56	34	25
Singh Sabha	22	10	5	7	51	37	25
Cippenham United	22	11	1	10	63	41	23
Slough Heating Res.	22	9	4	9	53	42	22
Vinsittart Res.	22	10	1	11	69	61	21
Iver Heath Rovers	22	8	5	9	39	42	21
Prince of Wales	22	8	5	9	40	43	21
Holyport	22	9	3	10	43	68	21
Slough Laurencians	22	4	1	17	39	77	9
Maidenhead Wdrs	22	3	2	17	23	99	8

'OBSERVER' CRAWLEY & DISTRICT LEAGUE

PREM. DIVISION	P	W	D	L	F	A	PTS
Edwards Sports	18	14	2	2	48	16	44
Longley	18	10	5	3	41	23	35
Thorn EMI	18	9	7	2	34	20	34
Thomas Bennett	18	10	2	6	49	35	32
Craw Post Office	18	6	4	8	38	37	22
Town Mead	18	7	1	10	30	37	22
Ifield 'A'	18	6	2	10	33	38	20
Rediffusion	18	4	6	8	24	41	18
Lower B Nuthurst	18	4	4	10	31	40	16
Bluebird Rangers*	18	3	1	14	26	67	7

* - 3pts deducted.

DIVISION ONE	P	W	D	L	F	A	PTS
Phoenix	22	15	4	3	53	21	49
Cherry Lane Ath.	22	15	3	4	81	42	48
Edwards Spts Res.	22	15	3	4	72	36	48
Crawley Down	22	12	6	4	67	46	42
B.O.C.	22	11	3	8	68	47	36
Thomas Ben. Res.	22	8	6	8	54	55	30
Charleston	22	8	2	12	55	65	26
Southgate Athletic	22	7	3	12	42	49	24
Faygate United	22	7	2	13	42	69	23
Furnace Green	22	5	7	10	45	53	22
Town Mead Res.	22	5	4	13	38	67	19
Rediffusion Res.	22	1	3	18	23	90	6

DIVISION TWO	P	W	D	L	F	A	PTS
Longley 'A'	26	21	3	2	79	36	66
Copthorne R. Res.	26	19	5	2	73	24	62
Brentford Electric	26	19	1	6	80	40	58
P.G.O. Res.	26	14	3	9	59	49	45
Worth Park Rgrs	26	14	2	10	93	62	44
Southgate A. Res.	26	12	3	11	49	53	39
Youngmans	26	10	5	11	73	56	35
Beehive Sports	26	11	1	14	79	83	34
Town Mead IV	26	9	5	12	50	88	32
Faygate Utd Res.	26	8	4	14	52	65	28
Stones	26	7	5	14	41	60	26
Crawley Sun	26	7	3	16	38	56	24
Phoenix 'A'	26	6	2	18	38	81	20
Horley T. Casual	26	2	4	20	42	93	10

The Middlesex Wanderers on tour in Holland. Back Row (L/R): Graham Allner (Manager), Paul Cavell, Stewart Brighton, Kevin Richardson, Colin Blewden, Steve Farrelly, Malcolm McKay, Gary Wager, John Askey, Martin Hardy, Jim Conway (Physio). Front: Gary Kerr, Jon Purdie, Paul Webb, Paul Richardson (Captain), Terry Robbins, Jason Broom, Richard Forsyth.

The Royal Navy F.A. Representative side. Photo - Eric Marsh.

President: G.E. Templeman.

Chairman: D.S.R. Gillard.

Hon. Secretary: D.J. Strudwick,
11 Welland Close, Durrington, Worthing, West Sussex
BN13 3NR (0903 267788).

SECRETARY'S REPORT

Such is the strength in depth of competition currently prevailing in the Beazer Homes League that five out of six of the League honours were not confirmed until the final day of season. It meant, of course, another afternoon on the motorway for the secretary in order to try and have the medals in the right place at the right time. But in reality, it also meant that the climax of the Beazer Homes League season could scarcely have been more dramatic.

"Top of the Bill", the premier division champions, Dover Athletic. The Kent club has been in the premier division for just five seasons. Having won the Southern Division championship in 1987-88 Athletic proceeded to make their mark in the top flight by finishing 6th, 1st, 4th and 2nd during the first four years. Not wishing to be the bridesmaid again this year, Dover set a blistering pace by gaining maximum points in ten of its first eleven fixtures. The club's first league defeat was not suffered until the 19th January when already sixteen victories were under their belt and only eight points (from four draws) had escaped the club's grasp.

It was this pace that eventually held Dover in good stead. Because, without being unkind to the remainder of the division, only a handful of clubs threatened their strangehold. During March and April Dover were able to ride a period when just two wins came from eleven matches played and still the championship was clinched by thirteen clear points. Evidence shows, therefore, that Dover were unquestionably the best allround team in the premier division. Their second championship in four years proved to be as popular as it was deserved.

Of the chasing pack only Hednesford Town and Trowbridge Town topped the table at any stage of the season. But it was Cheltenham Town who sneaked up on the rails with a victory at Waterlooville on the final Saturday to collect the silver medals. This was a rewarding performance after last year's relegation from the Football Conference. Corby Town, who appeared to be most people's favourite to mount the best challenge to Dover, finished third. Premier division freshmen Hednesford Town were fourth and Trowbridge, who spent longer than anyone in second spot during the year, finished fourth.

One of the division's other freshmen, newly promoted Weymouth, endured a wretched season and make an immediate return to the Southern section after gaining only five victories in a 40 match campaign. V.S. Rugby, too, return to a regional division after six seasons in the top flight.

Away from the premier division, two of the most eye-catching performances came from Salisbury City and Witney Town in the Southern division. Witney Town, playing in a new stadium, lost early games but did not lose again until New Year's Day. Two more reversals, though, were logged in the next four games. However, only two more defeats were registered in the next twenty fixtures. By now the problems of playing on a newly laid pitch had befallen the Marigolds. A tremendous backlog of fixtures had built up and the loss of four points in the club's final two games of a cramped schedule proved fatal to their promotion chances.

In the meantime, Salisbury (later to become Salisbury City to reflect Salisbury's new City status) had endured four defeats in their first nine fixtures. Only three wins had been earned in the club's opening eleven games. But after beating Erith & Belvedere on the 7th November Geoff Butler's men lost only four of their remaining thirty matches, dropping only eighteen points along the way.

But even these impressive statistics did not enable either club to catch Sittingbourne. The "Brickies" lost only four matches out of forty-two. The club's twelve drawn games, however, ensured that the race for the title went to the last week of the season. Witney's midweek draw at Buckingham reduced matters to a two-horse race on the last day. But Salisbury needed Sittingbourne to lose at Poole in order to take the championship. While City were drawing at Baldock Town, though, the "Brickies" won in Dorset 4-0 to take the title and a share of the Merit Cup (with Nuneaton Borough) for having scored most league goals; 102.

Dover Athletic, Premier Division Champions 1992-93. Back Row (L-R): B.Jennings (Physio), E.Avery (Res.Team Manager), J.Jackson, J.Bartlett, Tony Dixon, M.Munden, I.O'Connell, C.Browne, S.Cuggy, T.MacDonald, K.Raine (Scout), T.Terry (Physio). Front Row: N.Dent, R.Donker, R.Milton, S.Warner, N.Donn, C.Kinnear (Manager), B.Little, Tim Dixon, C.Blewden, D.Walker, M.Harrop.

Borough's goals enabled them to win the Midland division by five clear points. But it was only the 5-1 trouncing of Evesham United on the last day that finally clinched the gold medals. Until the previous week Barri, Gresley and Rushden & Diamonds could all have had a dramatic impact on where the honours would end up. But Barri's hopes receded with two midweek defeats at the hands of Gresley and Stourbridge. Stourbridge also wrecked Rushden's hopes by taking two points from them in the penultimate midweek. Having lost at home to Leicester on the last Saturday in April, Gresley galloped back into contention with that midweek win over Barri and another against Hinckley Town. Any hope of the title in their first season in the Beazer League was dashed, however, with a 3-1 defeat at Rushden on the final day. Borough, then, return to the premier division and by attracting a final home gate of 2,703, rekindled memories of past glories. Considering Sittingbourne's ability to attract over 3,000 for their clash with Gravesend & Northfleet, it could be said that the Champion clubs, in particular, will be forced to be reconded with next season. At this point it would be reprehensible to overlook the progress and development of Gresley Rovers. The club's response to three failed applications to join the competition in previous years has been nothing short of marvellous. Recent events revived memories of the Halesowen Town scenario a few years ago. And now both are in the premier division.

In the League cup, the Barclays Commercial Services Challenge Cup, holders Dover Athletic progressed to the final once again, albeit not too convincingly on occasions. Margate were dispatched in the first round only by a last minute extra-time goal. Canterbury, Gravesend and Crawley fell victim to the holders in subsequent rounds before Sudbury Town held Dover to a draw over the two legs of the semi-final only to be eliminated on the "away goals" rule.

Dover's opposition in the final, Stourbridge, mastered what appeared on paper to be a more difficult passage. Premier division Trowbridge, Hednesford and Halesowen were all defeated en route together with Midland division rivals Bilston Town and Rushden & Diamonds. In spite of Stourbridge's impressive run, however, it would not be unkind to say that Dover started the final as favourites to retain the Trophy. But a shock was in store. The League champions-elect were never allowed into their formidable stride in the first leg at Amblecote and went down 2-0. By the time the second leg came around Dover had been crowned champions, but only the most ardent of their fans would have predicted having an easy time redeeming the deficit. Stourbridge had shown enough in the first leg to suggest that they were not going to surrender lightly, if at all. Indeed, Stourbridge increased their lead with a first half goal. In a late rally Dover pulled two back, and also missed a penalty, before time ran out. Stourbridge had defeated the League champions. And as if to emphasise their victory further two Glassmen, Evron Wright and Andy Crannage collected the Barclays' "Man of the Match" awards in the two legs of the final.

Before leaving this domestic section of my report, it would be remiss of me not to mention the record breaking scoring exploits of Gravesend & Northfleet's Steve Portway. Steve bagged an astonishing 58 Beazer League and Barclays Commercial Services Cup goals. This is a Southern League record.

This year mixed fortunes were encountered in Football Association competitions with, perhaps, only one major success to enjoy. Gresley Rovers again achieved an excellent run in the F.A. Vase.

Rovers reached the semi-final after making the final itself two years ago. Unfortunately for the club, and everyone connected with the League, Gresley were drawn against the strongest side in the competition, the eventual winners, Bridlington Town. Rovers were beaten over two legs by the odd goal in five.

With five clubs (Bilston Town, Buckingham Town, Forest Green Rovers, Gresley and Newport I.O.W.) reaching the last sixteen of the competition, hopes were high for a repeat of Tamworth's success of three years earlier. Other than Gresley, only Bilston and Buckingham survived, and they themselves were knocked out in the quarter-finals by Canvey Island and Tiverton Town respectively.

With nine clubs in the F.A. Trophy first round thoughts of Dartford and Fareham Town's appearance in the semi-final, a few years ago, emerged. Unfortunately, however, this competition again proved to be an achilles heel for our clubs. Only Bashley, Dover, Gloucester and Nuneaton Borough progressed to round two. Although all were dismissed at this stage, mention must be made of Gloucester's stubborn resistance against Runcorn. It took the Conference club four attempts to eliminate their Beazer opposition. And Runcorn, remember, went all the way to Wembley.

By reaching the first round proper of the F.A. Challenge Cup, it could be said that six of our clubs reached their particular and ethereal Wembley. Salisbury fell to Marlow, after a replay. V.S. Rugby defeated Solihull Borough in similar fashion. Nuneaton twice surrendered the lead before going out to a last minute goal at Woking. Sutton Coldfield Town were unbelievably close to forcing a draw, at least, against Bolton Wanderers before going out by the odd goal in three. Personally, on my score-card, Sutton won on points. And judging by the most incredible ovation given to them by the Burnden Park supporters, it was a view well shared. Cheltenham, meanwhile, delivered a knock-out blow to St. Albans to earn a tie with Bournemouth in round two.

The Robins held the Cherries at the first attempt, but the League side proved too strong in a physical replay. In a similar pattern of games V.S. Rugby were sunk by Marlow. The draw for the third round established that Cheltenham and V.S. had missed out on trips to Blackburn Rovers and Tottenham Hotspur, respectively.

Football adminstration these days is sometimes a long way from events on the field, alone. A report of this kind, therefore, must not overlook the plethora of sources of assistance needed to support a competition at this level of the game. Our thanks for the help given to the League during the past six years by Beazer Homes Limited is only exceeded by our gratitude for the company's agreement to sign a further contract for three more years. Our particular thanks, therefore, are extended to Mr Dennis Webb, Beazer Homes Managing Director.

Through the good offices of David Nessling, a chairman of a member club, the League has enjoyed the benefit of having Barclays Commercial Services as sponsor of the League's challenge cup. As this agreement draws to a close we send our appreciation for this help and welcome aboard a replacement in the shape of Air Wair, the makers of Dr Marten's shoes. Our thanks here go to Max and Stephen Griggs. We hope that you will enjoy your (initial) three year association with the League. Thank you. I am pleased to say, also, that Barclays Commercial Services Limited has agreed in principle to maintain a liason with the League next season.

Kevin Baker at Sportique moves into his third year sponsoring the Manager of the Month awards. We know that this company has aided a large number of our clubs. In thanking Sportique, we hope that the mutual benefits of our association will continue to flourish.

It is "welcome time" for a number of clubs. Armitage, Clevedon Town and Tonbridge all join the complement for next season. They make up for the departures of Andover, Barri and Dartford. We wish these six clubs well in their future development.

We welcome back Farnborough Town. We are sorry that your re-entry into our competition is by way of relegation from the GM Vauxhall Conference, but trust that your stay with us will be as enjoyable as your last sojourn. Farnborough, of course, replace Dover Athletic, our worthy champions. I make no apology for mentioning their name again. I hope you will be at least as successful as the last club to be promoted from the Beazer Homes League, Bromsgrove Rovers, who finsihed runners-up in the Conference in their first season. Well done Rovers!!

D.J.Strudwick (Hon-Secretary)

BARCLAYS COMMERCIAL SERVICES
SOUTHERN LEAGUE CHALLENGE CUP

1st Round

Trowbridge	2;2
Stourbridge	2;6
Yate Town	1;1
Bilston	1;2
Hednesford	4;1
King's Lynn	0;0
Reddutch	3;1
Bridgnorth	0;0
Rushden	4;3
Atherstone	0;2
Wealdstone	2;0
Buckingham	5;1
Sutton C'field	2;2
Grantham	1;0
Burton A.	0;2
Gresley	1;3
R.C. Warwick	2;0
Leicester U.	2;4
Nuneaton	0;1
V.S. Rugby	0;0
Tamworth	0;3
Bedworth	0;2
Corby Town	7;6
Hinckley T.	1;0
Weston-s-M.	4;4
Newport AFC	4;1
Moor Green	1;0
Gloucester	0;3
Halesowen	3;4
Solihull	1;3
Evesham	1;2
Cheltenham	1;1
Hastings	1;1
Chelmsford	4;0
Bury Town	2;2
Dunstable	4;2
Cambridge	1;3
Sudbury	3;3
Burnham	2;1
Braintree	2;2
Salisbury	3;2
Havant	1;0
Fareham	2;3
Weymouth	2;0
Forest G.R.	0;2
Dudley T.	0;2
Barri	1;1
Witney T.	2;2
Poole T.	0;1
Andover	0;0
Dorchester	1;0
Bashley	1;2
Newport IOW	0;2
Waterlooville	1;3
Fisher	1;2
Crawley T.	4;5
Ashford	0;0
Gravesend	4;3
Erith & B.	w/o
Dartford	scr.
Canterbury	1;3
Sittingbourne	0;3
Margate	2;1
Dover Ath.	1;3

2nd Round

Bilston T.	1;0
Stourbridge	1;2
Hednesford T.	4
Redditch Utd	0
Rushden & D.	6
Buckingham T.	2
Sutton Coldfield	0;1
Gresley Rvrs	0;3
Leicester Utd	0
Nuneaton Boro.	3
Tamworth	2
Corby Town	0
Weston-s-Mare	1;2
Gloucester C.	1;3
Halesowen Town	2
Evesham Utd	1
Chelmsford	2;3
Dunstable	2;1
Sudbury Town	3
Braintree Town	1
Salisbury	1
Fareham Town	0
Forest Gn Rvrs	0
Witney Town	1
Poole Town	1
Bashley	4
Waterlooville	2
Crawley Town	3
Gravesend & N.	3
Erith & Bel.	2
Canterbury T.	1
Dover Athletic	3

3rd Round

Stourbridge	2
Hednesford	1
Rushden & D.	2
Gresley Rvrs	1
Nuneaton Boro.	2
Tamworth	1
Gloucester	2;1
Halesowen	2;2
Chelmsford	2;1
Sudbury	2;1
Salisbury	1
Witney Town	2
Bashley	1
Crawley Town	2
Dover Athletic	3
Gravesend & N.	0

Quarter-final

Stourbridge	2;4
Rushden	2;2
Nuneaton Boro.	0
Halesowen Town	5
Sudbury Town	4
Witney Town	1
Crawley Town	1
Dover Athletic	2

Semi-final

Stourbridge	2;2
1st leg at Stourbridge	
Halesowen Town	0;3
Sudbury Town	0;2
1st leg at Dover	
Dover Ath.	1;1

Final

Stourbridge	**2;1**
Dover Athletic	**0;2**

Preliminary Rd: Worcester 0;1 Cheltenham 2;6   Sudbury 1;7 Baldock 0;0   *(away goals rule applies throughout)*

Kent was certainly the place to be for scoring goals in in the Beazer Homes League Southern Division in 1992-93. Between them, Steve Portway of Gravesend & Northfleet, and Martin Buglione of Margate got over a hundred. Above we see the Portway (No. 10), the League's top marksman, in typically athletic action against Burnham. Photo - Alan Coomes. Below, Buglione receives a trophy from Margate chairman Gordon Wallis to mark his fiftieth goal of the campaign. Photo - Paul Bates.

BEAZER PREMIER LEAGUE ATTENDANCES

CLUB	Total	Games	Ave.	Highest		Lowest		Nos. of Gates over 1,000	2,000	3,000
Dover Athletic	28,501	20	1,425	2,093	v Cheltenham	1,022	v Burton Alb.	19	1	-
Weymouth	17,605	20	880	1,615	v Dorchester	568	v Chelmsford	5	-	-
Cheltenham Town	17,431	20	871	2,200	v Gloucester	474	v Chelmsford	4	1	-
Halesowen Town	14,365	20	718	988	v Dover	547	v Corby	-	-	-
Worcester City	14,136	20	706	1,037	v Cheltenham	484	v Waterlooville	2	-	-
Crawley Town	13,541	20	677	1,273	v Dover	421	v Dorchester	1	-	-
Chelmsford City	13,144	20	657	1,058	v Dover	512	v Bashley	1	-	-
Dorchester Town	12,848	20	642	3,027	v Weymouth	403	v Chelmsford	-	-	1
Hednesford Town	10,691	20	534	866	v Halesowen	343	v Waterlooville	-	-	-
Gloucester City	10,375	20	518	1,072	v Cheltenham	330	v Moor Green	1	-	-
Burton Albion	10,234	20	511	725	v Dover	323	v Dorchester	-	-	-
Hastings Town	10,087	20	504	1,774	v Dover	339	v Bashley	1	-	-
Trowbridge Town	8,300	20	415	626	v Dover	302	v Moor Green	-	-	-
Corby Town	7,647	20	382	497	v Burton Alb.	266	v Dorchester	-	-	-
VS Rugby	7,586	20	379	501	v Halesowen	260	v Waterlooville	-	-	-
Bashley	7,041	20	352	884	v Weymouth	125	v Hastings	-	-	-
Moor Green	6,859	20	342	559	v Solihull	211	v Waterlooville	-	-	-
Waterlooville	6,402	20	320	425	v Dorchester	212	v Hastings	-	-	-
Atherstone	6,260	20	313	520	v VS Rugby	227	v Corby	-	-	-
Solihull Borough	5,448	20	272	527	v Moor Green	161	v Corby	-	-	-
Cambridge City	5,366	20	268	404	v Cheltenham	162	v Weymouth	-	-	-

Dorchester Town's Avenue Stadium full to capacity. Photo - A.J. Milla.

Premier Division

| | P | HOME | | | AWAY | | | F | A | Pts |
		W	D	L	W	D	L			
DOVER ATHLETIC	40	16	3	1	9	8	3	65	23	86
CHELTENHAM TOWN	40	11	5	4	10	5	5	76	40	73
CORBY TOWN	40	9	8	3	11	4	5	68	43	72
HEDNESFORD TOWN	40	12	3	5	9	4	7	72	52	70
TROWBRIDGE TOWN	40	10	5	5	8	3	9	70	66	62
CRAWLEY TOWN	40	12	7	1	4	5	11	68	59	60
SOLIHULL BOROUGH	40	9	5	6	8	4	8	68	59	60
BURTON ALBION	40	8	4	8	8	7	5	53	50	59
BASHLEY	40	11	3	6	7	5	8	60	60	59
HALESOWEN TOWN	40	10	5	5	5	6	9	67	54	56
WATERLOOVILLE	40	10	4	6	5	5	10	59	62	54
CHELMSFORD CITY	40	9	7	4	6	2	12	59	69	54
GLOUCESTER CITY	40	6	7	7	8	4	8	66	68	53
CAMBRIDGE CITY	40	10	4	6	4	6	10	62	73	52
ATHERSTONE UNITED	40	9	5	6	4	9	7	56	60	50
HASTINGS TOWN	40	8	6	6	5	5	10	50	55	50
WORCESTER CITY	40	9	4	7	3	5	12	45	62	45
DORCHESTER TOWN	40	7	4	9	5	2	13	52	74	42
MOOR GREEN	40	7	2	11	3	4	13	58	79	36
V.S.RUGBY	40	5	5	10	5	1	14	40	63	36
WEYMOUTH	40	4	4	12	1	6	13	39	82	23

Atherstone United -3 points for fielding an ineligible player.
Bashley -3 points for fielding an ineligible player.
Weymouth -2 points for fielding an ineligible player.

Top League Goalscorers

J.Smith (Cheltenham Town)	29
R.Carter (Solihull Borough)	25
K.Bayliss (Gloucester City)	22
C.Burton (Solihull Borough)	22
P.Fishenden (Crawley Town)	22
G.Manson (Dorchester Town)	21
L. O'Connor (Hednesford Town)	21

THE PREMIER DIVISION RESULT CHART 1992-93

HOME TEAM	1	2	3	4	5	6	7	8	9	10	11	12	13	14	15	16	17	18	19	20	21
1. Atherstone	*	0-1	1-1	2-4	3-1	1-1	0-2	2-1	0-1	0-0	2-1	1-1	2-3	4-2	4-3	4-2	0-1	1-0	4-4	1-0	1-0
2. Bashley	2-1	*	0-1	1-1	5-3	1-3	1-1	1-3	0-2	2-1	0-3	4-3	2-1	0-1	6-1	2-0	1-1	2-0	3-0	2-0	1-0
3. Burton	1-1	2-0	*	2-0	2-0	0-3	1-2	3-1	4-0	0-0	0-3	1-1	0-0	1-5	1-2	0-2	4-2	1-2	0-2	2-0	1-0
4. Cambridge	0-3	1-1	1-0	*	3-1	0-3	1-2	6-4	3-1	1-2	6-3	0-3	0-0	3-1	4-4	1-3	3-2	2-1	2-1	3-2	0-0
5. Chelmsford	2-1	2-3	1-3	1-1	*	1-1	3-4	2-1	4-2	1-1	3-1	1-0	2-0	0-2	2-2	2-0	2-2	2-2	2-2	2-0	2-0
6. Cheltenham	2-2	1-2	0-0	2-0	5-1	*	0-1	3-2	3-1	1-1	4-0	2-1	0-1	1-1	1-0	1-3	1-0	1-0	5-0	2-2	4-1
7. Corby	2-3	5-2	1-1	1-0	2-0	3-0	*	3-0	2-2	1-0	1-1	1-1	1-1	2-2	2-0	2-2	0-0	1-3	3-1	4-0	1-2
8. Crawley	1-1	3-0	2-2	0-0	3-0	0-0	2-3	*	5-1	2-1	2-1	3-0	2-1	2-1	1-1	2-1	2-0	2-0	1-1	2-2	4-0
9. Dorchester	0-1	1-0	2-1	5-0	3-0	2-0	1-1	1-2	*	0-1	1-1	1-0	0-1	2-2	0-0	1-4	1-3	0-1	2-3	0-1	2-1
10. Dover	2-0	3-2	3-0	5-0	1-0	0-1	2-0	0-0	3-0	*	2-0	1-1	2-1	2-1	2-0	1-0	4-0	1-0	2-0	2-0	1-1
11. Gloucester	4-0	1-1	1-3	2-3	1-2	1-5	0-1	1-1	1-0	1-1	*	3-1	6-2	1-3	2-2	1-1	2-4	1-0	1-1	1-1	4-0
12. Halesowen	2-2	3-1	1-2	1-0	1-2	2-1	1-0	4-1	2-2	1-1	2-2	*	0-2	0-1	5-1	3-1	0-1	4-0	2-2	2-1	3-2
13. Hastings	0-0	0-0	3-0	1-1	1-1	2-1	1-2	2-0	3-2	1-1	0-1	1-4	*	1-2	1-0	5-1	0-1	2-1	0-2	5-2	1-1
14. Hednesford	1-1	4-1	3-0	1-1	3-2	1-0	4-2	3-1	0-1	1-2	0-3	3-2	*	5-1	0-1	2-1	2-0	3-1	1-1	1-3	
15. Moor Green	1-1	1-2	1-4	3-5	3-1	0-2	3-3	1-0	1-2	0-1	6-0	2-0	3-0	1-2	*	0-1	2-1	1-2	0-2	3-1	2-3
16. Solihull	5-0	0-1	2-2	0-0	1-2	1-1	0-1	2-2	1-0	1-2	1-3	2-3	1-1	3-0	3-2	*	4-0	1-0	2-1	4-2	2-1
17. Trowbridge	1-1	3-3	1-4	1-4	1-0	3-3	1-0	1-1	3-1	0-2	1-2	1-1	4-1	3-2	3-2	1-3	*	4-2	3-2	3-0	2-1
18. V.S.Rugby	1-1	1-2	0-1	2-0	0-1	0-5	1-2	1-2	4-1	1-1	0-1	1-3	1-1	1-2	2-1	3-3	2-3	*	1-0	1-1	1-0
19. Waterlooville	1-0	0-2	0-1	2-1	1-2	1-2	1-1	1-1	3-0	6-1	0-4	1-1	1-1	0-2	1-0	2-1	4-2	1-0	*	2-1	0-0
20. Weymouth	1-3	0-0	1-1	2-0	2-3	0-1	0-3	1-1	1-2	2-3	1-5	2-1	1-0	0-3	0-1	1-2	0-3	1-3	2-1	*	2-2
21. Worcester	2-1	3-0	0-0	2-1	2-2	2-4	2-1	1-2	1-4	1-2	2-0	1-0	2-0	0-0	0-2	3-0	0-5	0-0	1-3	2-0	*

Beazer Homes (Southern) League Premier Division Ten Year Records

	83/4	84/5	85/6	86/7	87/8	88/9	89/0	90/1	91/2	92/3
Alvechurch	16	15	4	8	7	14	21	–	–	–
Ashford Town	–	–	–	–	12	18	19	–	–	–
Atherstone United	–	–	–	–	–	–	6	15	13	15
Aylesbury United	–	–	8	3	1	–	–	–	–	–
Bashley	–	–	–	–	–	–	–	10	4	9
Basingstoke Town	–	–	15	16	–	–	–	–	–	–
Bath City	–	–	–	–	–	9	2	–	–	–
Bedworth United	11	12	10	12	14	22	–	–	–	–
Bromsgrove Rovers	–	–	–	2	4	10	10	5	1	–
Burton Albion	–	–	–	–	16	8	4	7	10	8
Cambridge City	–	–	–	6	3	5	8	3	5	14
Chelmsford City	3	9	2	5	19	–	18	18	18	12
Cheltenham Town	8	1	–	–	–	–	–	–	–	2
Corby Town	14	11	13	9	10	16	20	–	14	3
Crawley Town	–	3	6	13	6	12	15	19	17	=6
Dartford	1	–	–	4	2	2	3	13	6	w/d
Dorchester Town	19	–	–	–	11	13	14	11	11	18
Dover Athletic	–	–	–	–	–	6	1	4	2	1
Dudley Town	–	–	12	21	–	–	–	–	–	–
Enderby Town					(see Leicester United)					
Fareham Town	15	14	19	14	9	19	–	–	–	–
Farnborough Town	–	–	–	–	–	–	–	1	–	–
Fisher Athletic	2	8	3	1	–	–	–	–	21	–
Folkestone	7	7	9	22	–	–	–	–	–	–
Gloucester City	9	18	–	–	–	–	9	2	12	13
Gosport Borough	18	–	18	18	15	7	22	–	–	–
Gravesnd & Northfleet	4	13	20	–	–	–	7	21	22	–
Halesowen Town	–	–	–	–	–	–	–	8	8	10
Hastings Town	10	16	–	–	–	–	–	–	–	16
Hednesford Town	–	–	–	–	–	–	–	–	–	4
King's Lynn	6	2	14	20	–	–	–	–	–	–
Leamington	13	20	–	–	–	–	–	–	–	–
Leicester United	–	–	–	–	8	20	–	–	–	–
Merthyr Tydfil	–	–	–	–	–	1	–	–	–	–
Moor Green	–	–	–	–	–	15	11	16	9	19
Nuneaton Borough	–	–	–	–	21	–	–	–	–	–
Poole Town	19	–	–	–	–	–	–	17	20	–
Redditch United	–	–	–	7	18	21	–	–	–	–
Road Sea Southampton	–	5	16	–	–	–	–	–	–	–
Rushden Town	–	–	–	–	–	–	–	14	–	–
Salisbury	–	–	–	19	–	–	–	–	–	–
Shepshed Charterhouse	–	10	7	11	13	–	–	–	–	–
Solihull Borough	–	–	–	–	–	–	–	–	–	=6
Stourbridge	20	–	–	–	–	–	–	–	–	–
Sutton Coldfield Town	17	–	–	–	–	–	–	–	–	–
Trowbridge Town	–	19	–	–	–	–	–	–	7	5
V.S. Rugby	–	–	–	–	17	3	5	9	3	20
Waterlooville	–	–	–	–	–	17	16	20	15	11
Wealdstone	–	–	–	–	–	11	12	12	19	–
Welling United	12	6	1	–	–	–	–	–	–	–
Weymouth	–	–	–	–	–	17	22	–	–	21
Willenhall Town	–	4	11	15	20	–	–	–	–	–
Witney Town	5	17	17	17	22	–	–	–	–	–
Worcester City	–	–	5	10	5	4	13	6	16	17
No. of Clubs	20	20	20	22	22	22	22	22	22	22

Corey Browne puts over as cross as champions-elect Dover Athletic record a 2-0 home win against Gloucester City on February 27th. Gary Kemp is the covering defender.

ATHERSTONE UNITED

The Adders

Atherstone defender Gary Redgate (who has since departed for V.S. Rugby) tries to thwart Winston Whittingham of Grays Athletic during an F.A. Cup tie. Photo - Francis Short.

Chairman: Mr K Haskins   **Vice Chairman:** Mr P Barber   **President:** Mr C Culwick
Secretary: Keith Allen, 19 Hathaway Drive, Nuneaton CV11 6NU (0203 349989).
Manager: M Brookes   **Asst Manager:** L Spencer   **Physio:** D Looms
Press Officer: John Harman   **Commercial Manager:** Wendy Gretton
Ground: Sheepy Road, Atherstone, Warks CV9 1HG (0827 717829)
Directions: Half mile north of town centre on B4116 Twycross/Ashby road.
Capacity: 3,500   **Cover:** 1,000   **Seats:** 373   **Floodlights:** Yes   **Metal Badges:** Yes
Club Shop: Yes. Programmes, magazines, souvenirs etc. Contact John Harman (021 358 1681).
Colours: Red & white   **Change colours:** Yellow & blue
Club Sponsors: Lloyds Chemist.   **Previous Leagues:** West Midlands 1979-87
Midweek home matchday: Wednesday   **Reserve's Lge:** Ansells Midland Comb. Res. Div.
Record Attendance: 2,873 v V.S. Rugby, F.A. Cup 1st Round Proper 1987-88
Record win: 12-2 v Tipton Town (H), West Midlands (Regional) League Premier Division 86-87.
Record defeat: 0-5 v Solihull Borough (A), Southern League Premier Division 92-93.
Best F.A. Cup season: 2nd Rd Proper 1990-91 (lost 0-1 at Crewe Alexandra)
Record Fee Paid: £4,500 to Gloucester City for Gary Bradder, 1989.
Record Fee Received: £40,000 for Andy Rammell from Manchester United, September 1989.
Past Players who have progressed into The Football League: Andy Rammell (Manchester United).
Clubhouse: Normal hours, all usual facilities.
Record Goalscorer: Alan Bourton
Record Appearances: Lee Spencer
92-93 Captain: Steve Jackson
92-93 P.o.Y.: Paul Upton/ Robin Judd
92-93 Top scorer: Robin Judd.
Local Newspapers: Tamworth Herald (0827 60741), Evening Tribune, Atherstone Herald, Coventry Telegraph (0203 382251).
Local Radio Stations: Mercia Sound, CWR.
Honours: Southern Lg Midland Div 88-89, West Mids Lg 81-82 86-87 (Lg Cup 81-82, Premier Div Cup 86-87, Div 2 Cup (Reserves) 86-87), Walsall Snr Cup 83-84, Midland Comb. Reserve Division 87-88, Birmingham Snr Cup R-up 89-90, FA Tphy 1st Rd 88-89 91-92.

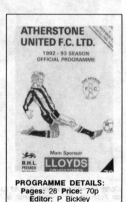

ATHERSTONE UNITED F.C. LTD.
1992 - 93 SEASON
OFFICIAL PROGRAMME

Main Sponsor
B.H.L. PREMIER
LLOYDS DRUGSTORES

PROGRAMME DETAILS:
Pages: 28 **Price:** 70p
Editor: P Bickley

BASHLEY

Bashley goalkeeper Nick Flower watches intently as Weymouth's Gareth Taylor puts on the under pressure during a 0-0 derby draw at the Wessex Stadium in December. Photo - Idris Martin.

Chairman: Trevor Adams   **Vice Chairman:** Murray Keen   **President:** Len Fairbrother
Secretary: Ray Murphy, Flat 10, Richmond Court, 122 Richmond Park Rd, Bournemouth BH8 8TH (0202 517607).
Manager: Trevor Parker   **Asst Manager:** Peter Moore   **Coach:** Sandy Baird
Commercial Mgr: David Groom   **Physio:** Kim Sturgess   **Newsline:** 0898 446 881.
Press Officer: Tony Adams (0425 613859)
Ground: Recreation Ground, Bashley, Hants BH25 5RY (0425 620280)
Directions: A35 Lyndhurst towards Christchurch, turn left down B3058 towards New Milton, ground on left in Bashley village. Half hour walk from New Milton (BR) station
Capacity: 4,250   **Cover:** 1,200   **Seats:** 200   **Floodlights:** Yes   **Metal Badges:** Yes
Colours: Yellow & black   **Change colours:** Blue & white.
Club Shop: Open matchdays
Club Sponsors: A.E. Insurance.
Previous Leagues: Bournemouth 50-83/ Hants 83-86/ Wessex 86-89.
Midweek home matchday: Wednesday   **Reserve's League:** Jewson Wessex Combination.
Record Attendance: 3,500 v Emley, F.A. Vase S.F. 1st Leg 1987-88
Best F.A. Cup season: 4th Qualifying Rd 1990-91 (lost 0-1 at Welling United)
Record Fee Paid: £7,500.
Record Fee Received: £5,000 from Havant Town for John Wilson, 1990.
Past Players who have progressed into The Football League: None
Clubhouse: Usual licensing hours. Snacks available.
Record Goalscorer: Colin Cummings
Record Appearances: John Bone
92-93 Captain: Sandy Baird
92-93 P.o.Y.: Gareth Hughes
92-93 Top scorer: Warren Patmore
Local Newspapers: Bournemouth Echo, Southern Pink, New Milton Advertiser.
Local Radio Stations: 2CR Solent, Ocean Sound.
Honours: Southern Lg Southern Division 89-90 (Lg Cup SF 89-90), Wessex Lg 86-87 87-88 88-89, Hants Lg Div 3 84-85, Hants Lg Combination 88-89, Russell Cotes Cup 88-89 90-91 92-93, FA Vase SF 87-88 (QF 88-89), FA Tphy 2nd Rd 91-92.

PROGRAMME DETAILS:
Pages: 36 Price: 70p
Editor: Dave Groom
(c/o Bashley F.C.)

BURTON ALBION

The Burton Albion defence are led a merry dance by Carlton Wynter in the 0-3 Premier Division defeat at Hastings Town. Photo - Jon Holloway.

Chairman: Jock Gordon   **Vice Chairman:** W Royall   **Secretary:** Tony A Kirkland, 40 Hurst Drive, Stretton, Burton-on-Trent DE13 0ED (0283 36510).
Manager: Brian Kenning   **Coach:** Alan Kurila   **Physio:** M Brown
Press Officer: David Twigg (0283 62013)   **Commercial Mgr:** C Bailey.
Ground: Eton Park, Princess Way, Burton-on-Trent DE14 2RU (0283 65938)
Directions: M1 - A50, turn right at island, left at next island. M42 - A38, take 2nd turn for Burton, right at island.
Capacity: 4,500   **Cover:** 2,500   **Seats:** 300   **Club Shop:** Yes   **Metal Badges:** Yes
Colours: All Yellow   **Change colours:** Red & white.
Sponsors: Inde Coope Burton Brewery Ltd.
Previous Leagues: West Mids 1950-58/ Southern 58-79/ Northern Premier 79-87
Midweek matchday: Tuesday   **Previous Ground:** Wellington Street 50-57.
Record Attendance: 5,860 v Weymouth, Southern Lg Cup Final 2nd leg, 1964 *(22,500 v Leicester City, F.A. Cup 3rd Rd 1984 - played at Derby County F.C.).*
Best F.A. Cup season: 3rd Rd Proper, 1955-56 and 1984-85. 1st Rd on nine occasions.
League clubs defeated in F.A. Cup: Halifax (55-56), Aldershot (84-85)
Record Fees - Paid: £21,000 to for R Jones and J Pearson (Kidderminster).
         Received: £60,000 for Darren Carr (Crystal Palace, 19889).
Past players progressing to Football League: Ray Russell (Shrewsbury 1954), David Neville (Rochdale 1955), Derek Middleton (York 1958), Tom McGlennon (Barrow 1959), Les Green & Tony Parry (Hartlepool 1965), George Hunter (Lincoln 1965), Stan Aston (Hartlepool 1966), David Jones (Newport 1968), Richie Barker & Jeff Bourne & Tony Bailey (Derby 1967 & 69 & 70), Maitland Pollock & Steve Buckley (Luton 1974), Peter Ward (Brighton 1975), Tony Moore (Sheffield Utd 1979), Carl Swan & Gary Clayton (Doncaster 1980 & 86), Richard Jobson (Watford 1982), Paul Haycock (Rotherham 1986), Alan Kamara (Scarborough 1987), Paul Groves (Leicester City 1988), Steve Cotterill & John Gayle (Wimbledon 1989), Darren Carr (Crystal Palace 1989), Darren Smith & Darren Roberts (Wolves 1990 & 92).
Clubhouse: 'The Football Tavern' - open pub hours. Full menu.
Steward: Brian Finch
Club Record Goalscorer: Ritchie Barker, 157
Club Record Appearances: Phil Annable, 567
92-93 Captain: Nigel Simms
92-93 P.o.Y.: Alan Kurila
92-93 Top scorer: Simon Redfearn.
Local Newspaper: Burton Daily Mail (0283 43311).
Local Radio: Radio Derby.
Honours: Southern Lg Cup 63-64 (R-up 88-89, Div 1 (Nth) R-up 71-72 73-74), Northern Premier Lg Challenge Cup 82-83 (R-up 86-87, Presidents Cup R-up 85-86 (SF 86-87), Birmingham Snr Cup 53-54 70-71 (R-up 86-87), FA Tphy R-up 86-87 (SF 74-75), GMAC Cup SF 86-87, Bass Charity Vase 81-82 85-86, Bass Challenge Cup 84-85, West Mids Lg R-up 53-54, Staffs Senior Cup 55-56.

PROGRAMME DETAILS:
Pages: 48 **Price:** 80p
Editor: David Twigg
(0283 62013)

CAMBRIDGE CITY

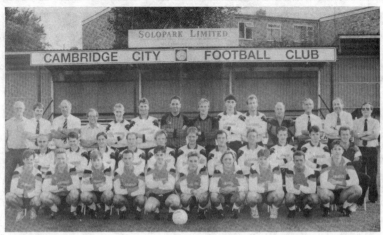

Cambridge City F.C. 1992-93.

Chairman: Dennis Rolph   **President:** Sir Neil Westbrook, CBE MA FRICS
Secretary: Stuart Hamilton, 55 Crowhill, Godmanchester, Huntingdon, Cambs (0480 412266).
Manager: Steve Fallon   **Asst Manager:** Peter Martin   **Physio:** Bill Brignell
Press Officer: Secretary   **Commercial Manager:** Jim Mills
Ground: City Ground, Milton Road, Cambridge CB4 1UY (0223 357973)
Directions: 50 yards on left from beginning of A1309, Cambridge to Ely Road. Half hour walk from Cambridge BR station.
Capacity: 5,000   **Cover:** 1,400   **Seats:** 400   **Floodlights:** Yes   **Metal Badges:** Yes
Club Shop: Yes, selling programmes, club history, badges, scarves, pennants, replica shirts etc. Contact Neil Harvey (0223 235991).
Colours: White/black/black   **Change colours:** All Sky
Club Sponsors: Chivers-Hartley.   **Previous Name:** Cambridge Town 1908-51.
Previous Leagues: Bury & Dist. 08-13 19-20/ East Anglian 08-10/ Southern Olympian 11-14/ Southern Amateur 1913-35/ Spartan 35-50/ Athenian 50-58.
Midweek matchday: Wednesday   **Reserve Team's League:** Jewson Eastern Counties.
Record Attendance: 12,058 v Leytonstone, F.A. Amateur Cup 1st Rd, 1949-50.
Best F.A. Cup season: 1st Rd Proper, v Ashford 1966, v Swindon 1946, v Walthamstow Ave. 1948.
Record Fee Paid: £7,000 for Andy Beattie (Barnet, 1991).
Record Fee Received: £15,500 for Kevin Wilkin (Northampton Town, 1991).
Players who have progressing to Football League: Ken Wright (West Ham 1946), Antonio Gallego (Norwich 1947), Alf Stokes (Watford 1961), Derek Weddle (Middlesbrough 1961), Dave Hicksen (Bury 1962), Bryan Harvey (Blackpool 1962), Robert Whitehead (Darlington 1962), George Cummins (Hull 1962), Reg Pearce & Dom Genovese (Peterborough 1963 & 88), Alan Banks (Exeter 1963), Tom Carroll (Ipswich 1966), Roy Jones (Swindon), Winston Dubose (Oldham).
Clubhouse: 11am-11pm Mon-Sat, 12-3pm & 7pm-10.30pm Sun. Bingo, Dances, Pool, Stag nights, Darts.
Club Record Scorer: Fred Barnard
Club Record Appearances: Mel Keenan
92-93 Captain: Steve Gawthrop
92-93 Top Scorer: Laurie Ryan
92-93 Players' P.o.Y.: Steve Gawthrop
92-93 Supporters' P.o.Y.: Andrew Jeffrey.
Local Press: Cambridge Evening News 35877
Local Radio: BBC Radio Cambridge
Honours: Southern Lg 62-63 (R-up 70-71, Southern Div 85-86, Div 1 R-up 69-70, Championship Cup 62-63), East Anglian Cup 30-31 35-36 42-43 43-44 45-46 47-48 59-60 64-65 75-76, Eastern Professional Floodlit Lg 65-66 72-73, Cambs Professional Cup 60-61 61-62 62-63 70-71 72-73 74-75, Cambs Invitation Cup 50-51 76-77 78-79 85-86 88-89 89-90, Spartan Lg 47-48 48-49 (R-up 49-50, Eastern Div Champs 45-46), Southern Amateur Lg 20-21 27-28 28-29 30-31 31-32, Bury & Dist. Lg 09-10 10-11 12-13 19-20, East Anglian Lg 09-10 39-40 40-41 41-42 42-43 44-45, A.F.A. Snr Cup 30-31 46-47 47-48(shared) 48-49 49-50, A.F.A. Invitation Cup 50-51, Hunts Premier Cup 62-63 64-65, Suffolk Senior Cup 09-10, F.A. Trophy 2nd Rd 86-87 87-88, F.A. Amateur Cup SF 27-28, Addenbrookes Hospital Cup 87-88, The Munns Youth Cup 82-83 83-84 84-85, Chiltern Youth League Cup R-up 75-76, South Mids Lg Youth Trophy 82-83, Robinson Cup 87-88 89-90, Jim Digney 89-90, Essex & Herts Youth Lg 89-90.

PROGRAMME DETAILS:
Pages: 28 **Price:** 50p
Editor: Dave Crane
(0223 233057)

CHELMSFORD CITY

Chelmsford City 1992-93. Back Row (L/R): Joe Sullivan (Manager), Peter Reed, Tony Rogers, Kevin Foster, Paul Gothard, Kurt Davidson, Wayne Hannigan, Liam Cutbush, Dean Crumpton, Terry Harris (Coach). Front: Matt Jones, Julian Hazell, David Jacques, Steve Mosely, Steve Restarick, Ian Brown, Gary Howard.

Chairman: Mr D P Wakeling
Secretary: Mr V A W Keeble, 13 Station Rd, Earls Colne, Colchester, Essex CO6 2ER (0787 222978).
Manager: Joe Sullivan   **Asst Manager:** N/A   **Coach:** Terry Harris
Press Officer: David Ward   **Physio:** Don Stewart   **Commercial Mgr:** Dave Seward.
Ground: The Stadium, New Writtle Street, Chelmsford CM2 0RP (0245 353052).
Directions: A1016 (Chelmsford) exit off A12, follow Colchester signs to 3rd r'bout, left (B1007, New London Rd), left at 2nd lights (signed County Cricket Ground), ground 100 yds on right. Residents only parking in New Writtle Street, but there is public car park next to ground (£1.30). 5 mins walk from Chelmsford (BR) station.
Capacity: 2,850 (Police limit)   **Seats:** 1,296   **Cover:** 1,700   **Metal Badges:** Yes
Club Shop: Yes, selling League & non-League programmes, badges, scarves, mugs etc. Contact Helen Williams or Rob Wigley via club.
Colours: White/claret/white.   **Sponsors:** TBA.
Change colours: Claret/white/claret.
Midweek home games: Monday   **Reserve Team's League:** Essex & Herts Border Comb.
Previous Name: None (Brentwood Town were incorporated in 1968).
Previous Leagues: None
Record Attendance: 16,807 v Colchester United, Southern League 10/9/49.
Best F.A. Cup season: 4th Rd Proper, 1938-39 (v Birmingham City). 1st Rd Proper on 25 occasions.
League clubs defeated in F.A. Cup: Darlington 38-39, Southampton 38-39, Oxford Utd 67-68.
Record win: 10-3 v Billericay Town (H), Essex Senior Cup, 4/1/93.
Record defeat: 2-10 v Barking (A), F.A. Trophy, 11/11/78.
Record Fee Paid: £10,000 for Tony Rogers (Dover Athletic, 1992).
           Received: £20,000 from Ian Brown (Bristol City, 1993).
Players progressing to Football League: Geoff Merton (Watford 1948), George Adams (Orient 1949), William O'Neill (Burnley 1949), Brian Farley & Sid McClellan (Spurs 1949), Oscar Hold (Everton 1950), Reuben Marden (Arsenal 1950), Cecil McCormack (Barnsley 1950), Les Dicker (Spurs 1951), Dave Sexton (Luton 1951), Wally Bellet & Robert Mason & Anthony Nicholas (Orient 1961 & 63 & 65), Robin Gladwin (Norwich 1966), Brian King (Millwall 1967), Peter Collins (Spurs 1968), John O'Mara (Bradford City 1974), Nigel Spink (Aston Villa 1977), Mark Dziadulewicz (Wimbledon 1979), Mervyn Cawston (Southend 1984), Phil Coleman (Exeter 1984), John Keeley & Adrian Owers (Brighton 1986 & 87), Ian Brown (Bristol City 1993).
Clubhouse: Open matchdays & every evening except Sunday (open Sunday lunchtimes). Pool, darts, satellite TV. Available for private hire. Playing facilities also available for private hire. Snacks served.
Club Record Goalscorer: Tony Butcher, 287 (1957-71).
Club Record Appearances: Derek Tiffin, 550 (1950-63).
92-93 Captain: Steve Mosely.
92-93 P.O.Y.: Ian Brown.
92-93 Top scorer: Tony Rogers, 26.
Local Newspapers: Essex Chronicle (0245 262421), Chelmsford Weekly News (0245 493444), East Anglian Daily Times (0473 230023).
Local Radio Stations: Essex Radio/Breeze AM, BBC Essex.
Hons: Southern Lg 45-46 67-68 71-72 (R-up 48-49 60-61 63-64 65-66, Southern Div 88-89, Lg Cup 45-46 59-60 (R-up 60-61), Merit Cup 71-72, Southern Lg War-Time (East) 39-40), Essex Professional Cup(5) 57-58 69-71 73-75, Essex Snr Cup 85-86 88-89 92-93, Non-League Champs Challenge Cup 71-72, E Anglian Cup 48-49, Eastern Co's Lg(3) 46-49 (Lg Cup 59-60), Eastern Floodlit Competition 66-67 74-75 77-78 81-82 82-83 86-87 (Cup 72-73 74-75), Metropolitan Lg 67-68 (Lg Professional Cup 67-68, Autumn Shield 70-71), Essex Snr Lg Cup 84-85 (Harry Fisher Memorial Tphy 88-89).

PROGRAMME DETAILS:
Pages: 32 **Price:** £1
Editor: Steve Dorrington
(0245 251667)

CHELTENHAM TOWN

Robins

Cheltenham Town on the defensive during their 1-0 win away to erstwhile Conference rivals Weymouth. Photo - Idris Martin.

Chairman: D J Deacon **President:** Vacant
Secretary: Reg Woodward, 3 Harveys Lane, Winchcombe, Glos GL54 5QS (0242 602261).
Manager: Lindsay Parsons **Asst Manager:** Peter Aitken **Coach:**
Press Officer: Arthur Hayward **Physio:** Billy Sabatella
Commercial Manager: P G Cook.
Ground: Whaddon Road, Cheltenham, Gloucestershire GL52 5NA (0242 513397).
Directions: M5 jct 10, A4019 through Cheltenham centre and join A46 Prestbury Road. Whaddon Rd turning on right. M5 jct 11, A40 into Cheltenham, join A46 Bath Road, follow through town and join Prestbury Road, Whaddon Rd on right. From London; A40 into Cheltenham and join A46 at Hewlett Rd then as above. Ground 1 mile from town centre and 2 miles from Cheltenham (BR).
Capacity: 5,000 **Cover:** 4,000 **Seats:** 1,000 **Floodlights:** Yes **Metal Badges:** Yes
Club Shop: Yes, selling souvenirs of all descriptions.
Colours: Red & white stripes **Change colours:** Blue
Sponsors: Gulf Oil.
Midweek home games: Tuesday **Reserve's Lge:** Neville Ovenden Football Comb.
Previous Leagues: Birmingham Combination/ Birmingham Lge/ Southern 35-85/ GMV Conference 85-92.
Record Attendance: 8,326 v Reading, FA Cup 1st Rd 56-57.
Best F.A. Cup season: 3rd Rd Proper 33-34 (lost 1-2 at Blackpool).
League clubs defeated in F.A. Cup: Carlisle United 33-34.
Record Fee Paid: £20,000 to Kidderminster Harriers (Kim Casey)
 Received: £45,000 from Derby County (Brett Angell).
Players progressing to Football League: Paul Tester (Shrewsbury), Brett Angell (Derby), Keith Knight (Reading), Peter Shearer (Bournemouth), Simon Brain (Hereford), Chris Burns (Portsmouth).
Clubhouse: Open every evening. 3 bars; clubroom, lounge, Robin's Nest. Open before and after Saturday matches. Nest & clubroom Available for private hire.
Club Record Scorer: Dave Lewis 290 (1970-83)
Club Record Apps: Roger Thorndale 701 (58-76)
92-93 Captain: Kevin Willetts
92-93 P.O.Y.: Steve Brown
92-93 Top scorer: Jimmy Smith 30.
Local Newspapers: Echo/ Western Daily Mail.
Local Radio Stations: Radio Glos.
Hons: Southern Lg 84-85 (Midland Div 82-83, Lg Cup 57-58 (R-up 68-69 84-85, Championship Shield 58-59, Merit Cup 84-85), Nth Glos. Snr Professional Cup(29), Midland Floodlit Cup 85-86 86-87 87-88.

PROGRAMME DETAILS:
Pages: 24 **Price:** £1
Editor: Paul Godfrey
(0242 517554)

CORBY TOWN

Corby's Town's Shaun Diver scores his side's winning goal against V.S. Rugby in a Beazer Homes League Premier Division match. With a very experienced team, Corby enjoyed a fine season. Photo - Mick Cheney.

Chairman: A Weatherall   **President:** H Hetterley.
Secretary: Roger Abraham, 68 Cornwall Rd, Kettering, Northants NN16 8PE (0536 522159).
Manager: Elwyn Roberts   **Asst Manager:** Stuart Carmichael
Commercial Mgr: Jimmy Kane.   **Physio:** Mick Mackie.
Ground: Rockingham Triangle Stadium, Rockingham Road, Corby NN17 2AE (0536 401007).
Directions: On northern outskirts of town at junction of A6003 and A6116, opposite entrance to Rockingham Castle grounds. One and a half miles from Corby (BR).
Capacity: 3,000   **Cover:** 1,150   **Seats:** 1,150   **Floodlights:** Yes   **Metal Badges:** Yes
Club Shop: Yes.
Colours: White/black/black   **Change colours:** All yellow.
Midweek home matchday: Monday
Previous Leagues: United Counties 35-52/ Midland 52-58.
Previous Name: Stewart & Lloyds 1935-48.
Previous Ground: Occupation Road 1935-85.
Sponsors: Corby District Council/ Noone & McGowan Stardust Centre/ Mr Bips.
Record Attendance: 2,240 v Watford, pre-season friendly 86-87. At Old Ground; 10,239 v P'boro, FA Cup 52-53.
Best F.A. Cup season: 3rd Rd 65-66 (lost to Plymouth). 1st Rd on five occasions; 54-55 63-66 67-68.
League clubs defeated in F.A. Cup: Luton Town 65-66.
Record Fees - Paid: £2,700 for Elwyn Roberts (Barnet)
                    Received: £20,000 for Matt Murphy (Oxford United).
Players progressing to Football League: Andy McCabe (Chesterfield 1955), Les Claimers (Leicester City 1956), Ken Brown (Nottm Forest 1956), Peter Kearns (Aldershot 1962), Norman Dean (Southampton 1963), Hugh Curran (Millwall 1964), Dixie McNeil & Andy McGowan & George Reilly (Northampton 1969 & 75 & 76), Phil Chard (Peterborough 1979), Trevor Morley (West Ham), J Flower (Sheffield Utd, Aldershot), Matt Murphy (Oxford United 1993).
Clubhouse: Open every day, usual club facilities.
Club Record Scorer: David Hofbauer 137 (1984-93)
Club Record Appearances: Derek Walker 600 (78-92).
92-93 Captain: Bryn Gunn
92-93 P.o.Y.: Bryn Gunn
92-93 Top scorer: Matt Murphy 20.
Local Newspapers: Northampton Evening Telegraph (0536 81111).
Local Radio Stations: BBC Radio Northampton, Hereward and KCBC.
Hons: F.A. Trophy 3rd Rd 86-87, UCL 50-51 51-52 (R-up 37-38), Midland Lg R-up 52-53, Southern Lg Midland Div R-up 90-91 (Merit Cup 63-64 90-91), Northants Snr Cup 37-38 39-40 50-51 62-63 75-76 82-83, Maunsell Cup 83-84, Midland Floodlit Cup 74-75, Evans Halshaw F'lit Cup 91-92, Anglia Floodlit Trophy 68-69 72-73, Chelmsford Invitation Cup 63-64 64-65 65-66(joint), Kettering & Dist Samaritan Cup 60-61(joint) 68-69, Wellingborough Charity Cup 50-51, Desborough Nursing Cup 48-49 50-51(joint), Bob Cumning Cup 85-86 86-87 87-88 88-89.

PROGRAMME DETAILS:
Pages: 32 **Price:** 60p
Editor: D Tilley

CRAWLEY TOWN

Crawley's Damian Webber arrives just too late to stop Danny Wyman making his pass during the away fixture at Hastings Town. Photo - Roger Turner.

Chairman: John Maggs   **President:** K Symons
Secretary: Stan Markham, 105 Winchester Road, Tilgate, Crawley RH10 5HH (0293 522371).
Manager: Ted Shepherd   **Asst Manager:** David Haining   **Commercial Mgr:** Andy Bell.
Ground: Town Mead, Ifield Avenue, West Green, Crawley (0293 21800).
Directions: M23 exit 10, A264 for Horsham, left at 2nd island, over mini r-about, right at next island into Ifield Avenue and ground 150 yards on right behind fire station. 10 mins walk from Crawley (BR).
Capacity: 5,600   **Cover:** 1,000   **Seats:** 250   **Floodlights:** Yes   **Metal Badges:** Yes.
Club Shop: Yes, selling programmes, metal badges, hats, scarves, mugs, replica kits. Contact Ian Hands.
Colours: Red/red/white   **Change colours:** Blue/blue/white or red.
Previous Leagues: Sussex County 1951-56/ Metropolitan 56-63
Midweek matchday: Tuesday   **Reserve Team's League:** Suburban.
Record Attendance: 3,427 v Horsham, FA Cup 4th Qualifying Round Replay 29/10/93.
Best F.A. Cup season: 3rd Rd Proper 91-92 (lost 0-5 at Brighton).
League Clubs defeated in F.A. Cup: Northampton Town 91-92.
Record win: 9-0 v Barry Town (A), Southern League 29/8/64.
Record defeat: 0-10 v Dartford (H), Mid-Surrey Professional Floodlit League 8/4/75.
Record Fee Paid: £5,000 to Wokingham Town for David Thompson, May 1992.
Record Fee Received: £15,000 from Hythe Town for Tommy Warrilow, February 1990
Players progressing to Football League: Ray Keeley (Mansfield 1968), Graham Brown (Mansfield 1969), Andy Ansah (Brentford 1987 (now Southend)), Brian Sparrow as coach to Wimbledon 1992.
Clubhouse: Weekday evenings 7-11pm, Saturday matchdays noon-2.30 & 4.45-6pm. Snacks available.
Club Record Goalscorer: Phil Basey
Club Record Apps: John Maggs 652.
92-93 Captain: Tony Vessey
92-93 P.o.Y.: Colin Caulfield
92-93 Top scorer: Paul Fishenden 28.
Local Newspapers: Crawley Observer (0293 526929), Crawley News (0293 526474).
Local Radio Stations: Radio Mercury, BBC Radio Sussex
Hons: Sussex Snr Cup(2) 89-91 (R-up 58-59), Sussex Intermediate Cup 26-27, Sussex Prof. Cup 69-70 (beat Brighton 1-0 in final), Southern Lg Southern Div R-up 83-84 (Merit Cup 70-71), Sussex Floodlit Cup(3) 90-93, Sussex Lg Div 2 R-up 55-56, Gilbert Rice Floodlit Cup 79-80 83-84, Southern Co's Comb. Floodlit Cup 85-86, Metropolitan Lg Chal. Cup 58-59, Mid-Sussex Snr 02-03, Montgomery Cup 25-26, F.A. Tphy 2nd Rd 85-86 87-88

PROGRAMME DETAILS:
Pages: 40 **Price:** £1
Editor: Ian Hands

DORCHESTER TOWN

The Magpies

Dorchester Town 1992-93. Back Row (L/R): Geoff Dine (Physio), Darren Powell, Gary Green, Gary Manson, Mark Cowley, Gavin Sandry, Jeremy Judd, Lee Bradford, Tony White, Duncan Brown, Bill Hall (Physio). Front Row: Steve Harris, Ben Rowe, Graham Waters, Tony Diaz, Paul Arnold (Manager), Gary Borthwick, David Peach, Paul Masters, Paul Young, Kieron Ryder. Photo - Jim Tamplin, Dorset Evening Echo.

Chairman: P J Aiken   **Vice Chairman:** C E Clark   **President:** J Pitfield
Secretary: Albert Miller, 29 Shaston Crescent, Dorchester DT1 2EB (0305 264843)
Manager: Paul Arnold   **Physio:** Geoff Dine
Commercial Manager: Keith Kellaway (0305 262451).
Ground: Avenue Stadium, Weymouth Avenue, Dorchester DT1 2RY (0305 262451).
Directions: At junction of southern bypass (A35) and Weymouth road (A354).
Capacity: 7,210   **Cover:** 4,000   **Seats:** 710   **Floodlights:** Yes   **Metal Badges:** Yes
Club Shop: Yes, selling replica shirts (£19.99/£24.99), club badges (£2.50/£2), bone china thimbles (£1.75), miniature bone china mugs (£1.75), porcelain lace plates (£19.95), bone china plate (£17.95), ashtrays (£3.25), hats (£2.50), mugs (£2.50), scarves (£3/£2.50).
Colours: Black & white stripes/black/black   **Change colours:** All sky blue
Previous Leagues: Dorset/ Western 1947-72.
Previous Grounds: Council Recreation Ground, Weymouth Avenue 1880-1929/ The Avenue Ground, Weymouth Avenue 29-90.
Midweek home games: Tuesday   **Reserve Team League:** Dorset Combination
Sponsors: Olds Motor Group
Record Attendance: 4,000 v Chelsea, official ground opening 1990. Competitive: 3,027 v Weymouth, Southern League Premier Division 26/12/92. *At old ground: 5,500 v York City, F.A. Cup Second Rd 1954).*
Best F.A. Cup season: 2nd Rd Replay 81-82 (lost 1-2 to A.F.C. Bournemouth after 1-1 draw). 2nd Rd 54-55 57-58, 1st Rd on seven occasions; 55-56 56-57 59-60.
League Clubs defeated in F.A. Cup: None.
Record win: 7-0 v Canterbury City (A), Southern League Southern Division 86-87.
Record defeat: 0-6 on four occasions: v Kettering 7/4/79, Cambridge City 2/9/89, Bath City 6/2/90.
Record Fees: Paid: £12,000 for Chris Townsend (Gloucester City, 1990)
          Received: £35,000 for Trevor Senior (Portsmouth, 1981)
Players progressing to The Football League: Len Drake (Bristol Rovers 1957), David Noake (Luton 1959), Mike Turner (Swindon 1961), Trevor Senior (Portsmouth 1981), David West (Liverpool 1983), Mike Squire (Torquay 1984), Jeremy Judd (Torquay 1984), Anthony White (Bournemouth 1985) + Graham Roberts (Spurs, Chelsea, Rangers, England) who progressed via Weymouth.
Clubhouse: Dorchester Lounge Club - access via main entrance to stadium. Cold food and snacks
Club Record Goalscorer: Dennis Cheney 61 (in one season)
Club Record Appearances: Trevor Townsend 377.
92-93 Captain: Gary Borthwick
92-93 P.o.Y.: Tony White
92-93 Top scorer: Gary Manson 20
Local Newspapers: Dorset Evening Echo, Western Gazette, Western Daily Press.
Local Radio Stations: Two Counties Radio (2CR Bournemouth).
Newsline (Magpies Hotline): 0839 664412.
Hons: Southern Lg R-up 79-80 (Div 1 (Sth) R-up 77-78, Lg Cup 86-87 (R-up 91-92), Western Lg 54-55 (R-up 60-61, Div 2 R-up 49-50), Dorset Snr Cup 50-51 60-61 67-68 68-69 71-72, Dorset Lg 37-38, FA Tphy 3rd Rd replay 71-72.

PROGRAMME DETAILS:
Pages: 32 **Price:** 80p
Editor: David Martin
(0305 264740)

FARNBOROUGH TOWN

Farnborough Town 1992-93. Back Row (L/R): David Coleman, Dean Coney, John Power, Gareth Howells, Roger Lapointe, Jamie Horton, Alan Morris (Physio). Centre: Ron Manville (Kit Mgr & groundsman), Robert Wilson, Jim Wigmore, Andy Bye (now Yeovil), Ian Savage, Peter Batey, Mark Jones, Steve Barker, Mike Savage (Coach). Front: Ken Ballard (Reserves' Mgr), David Leworthy, Simon Read, Ted Pearce (Manager), Brian Broome, Andy Rogers, Alan Taylor (Snr Coach, now Manager).

Chairman: Richard Molden   **President:** Maurice O'Brien.
Secretary: Terry Parr, 3 Cambrian Rd, Farnborough, Hants (0252 546387).
Manager: Alan Taylor   **Asst Manager:** Ken Ballard
Physio: Alan Morris   **Coach:** Mike Critchell/ Mike Savage.
Press Officer: Vince Curtis   **Commercial Mgr:** Graham Willis (0252 549328).
Ground: John Roberts Ground, Cherrywood Rd, Farnborough, Hants GU14 8UD (0252 541469).
Directions: M3 exit 4, A325 towards Farnborough, right into Prospect Avenue (club signposted), 2nd right into Cherrywood Rd, ground on right. 20-30 min walk from Farnborough Main, Farnborough North and Frimley BR stations. Whippet mini-bus route 19 passes ground.
Capacity: 4,900   **Cover:** 1,000   **Seats:** 500   **Floodlights:** Yes   **Metal Badges:** Yes.
Club Shop: Boro' Leisurewear shop sells all types of club leisurewear and matchballs (contact Commercial Manager (above)). Supporters Club shop sells old progs, scarves, badges etc (contact Sandy Turnball).
Colours: Yellow (blue sleeves)/blue/yellow   **Change colours:** White/sky/sky.
Previous Leagues: Surrey Snr 68-72/ Spartan 72-76/ Athenian 76-77/ Ithmian 77-89/ Alliance Premier (G.M.V. Conference) 89-90 91-93/ Southern 90-91.
Previous Grounds: Queens Road, Farnborough 68-76.
Club Sponsors: H.S.T. Services.
Midweek matchday: Tuesday   **Reserve Team's League:** None.
Record Attendance: 3,069 v Colchester United, G.M. Vauxhall Conference 9/11/91.
Best F.A. Cup season: 3rd Rd Proper replay 91-92 (lost 0-1 at West Ham United after 1-1 draw).
League Clubs defeated in F.A. Cup: Torquay United 91-92.
Record win: 11-0 v Chertsey Town (H), Spartan League 72-73.
Record defeat: 2-10 v Worplesdon (H), Surrey Senior League Division One 68-69.
Record Fee Paid: £6,000 to Runcorn for Mick Doherty.
Record Fee Received: £10,000 (+£7,000) from Crystal Palace for Dennis Bailey.
Players progressing to Football League: Dennis Bailey (Crystal Palace & Birmingham City), Paul Mortimer (Charlton Athletic), Tommy Jones (Aberdeen & Swindon Town), Allan Cockram (Brentford).
Clubhouse: Pub hours and matchdays. Hot pies, bar meals, crisps etc. Darts, pool, fruit machines & jukebox.
Club Record Goalscorer (career): Simon Read
Club Record Goalscorer (season): Simon Read 53, 88-89.
Club Record Appearances: Brian Broome.
92-93 Captain: David Leworthy.
92-93 P.o.Y.: David Leworthy.
92-93 Top scorer: David Leworthy.
Hons: Southern Lg 90-91, Ithmian Lg R-up 88-89 (Div 1 84-85, Div 2 78-79), Athenian Lg Div 2 78-79, Spartan Lg 72-73 73-74 74-75 (Lg Cup 74-75), London Spartan Lg 75-76 (Lg Cup 75-76), Hants Snr Cup 74-75 81-82 83-84 85-86 90-91, F.A. Trophy QF 92-93, F.A. Vase SF 75-76 76-77.

PROGRAMME DETAILS:
Pages: 38 **Price:** £1
Editor: Graham Willis
(0252 549328)

GLOUCESTER CITY

Gloucester City F.C. 1992-93. Back Row (L/R): B Tandy (Physio), R Baverstock, T Cook, T Callinan, P Bywater, S Crompton, M Buckland, S Abbley, B Hughes (Player-Coach), S Tregale (Physio), D Savory (Kit Manager). Front: R Jones, R Criddle, K Bayliss, W Noble, S Crouch, S Penny, G Kemp, M Fishlock.

Chairman: George Irvine **Vice Chairman:** John Beacham **President:** R F Etheridge
Secretary: Ken Turner, 24 Ladysmith Road, Cheltenham, GL52 5LQ (0242 522514).
Manager: Brian Godfrey **Asst Manager/Coach:** Brian Hughes.
Press Officer: John Beacham (0452 413758).
Physios: Bernard & Adrian Tandy
Commercial Manager: D Stallworthy (0452 421400)
Ground: Meadow Park, Sudmeadow Road, Hempsted, Gloucester GL2 6HS (0452 523883).
Directions: A40 to city centre towards historic docks, then Severn Road. Right into Hempsted Lane, and 2nd right again to Sudmeadow Road. Ground 50 yards on left.
Capacity: 5,000 **Cover:** 2,000 **Seats:** 560 **Club Shop:** Yes **Metal Badges:** Yes
Colours: All Yellow **Change colours:** White/white/red
Previous Leagues: Bristol & Dist. (now Western) 1893-96/ Gloucester & Dist. 97-1907/ Nth Glos. 07-10/ Glos. Nth Snr 20-34/ Birmingham Comb. 1935-39.
Previous Grounds: Longlevens 1935-1965/ Horton Road 65-86.
Previous Name: Gloucester Y.M.C.A.
Midweek home games: Tuesday **Sponsors:** Jewsons
Record Attendance: 10,500 v Spurs 1952 (at Meadow Park; 3,952 v Arsenal, July 1987)
Best F.A. Cup season: 2nd Rd Proper 89-90.
Record Transfer Fee: Paid: £25,000 S Fergusson (Worcester City)
Received: £25,000 Ian Hedges (A.F.C. Bournemouth, 1990)
Players progressing to The Football League: George Beattle & David Pugsley (Newport County 1950 & 53), John Boyd & Robert Etheridge & Charlie Cook (Bristol City 1950 & 56 & 57), David Jones (Leeds United 1954), Mike Johnson (Fulham 1958), William Teague & Rod Thomas (Swindon 1961 & 64), John Layton (Hereford 1974), Ian Main (Exeter 1978), Mike Bruton (Newport 1979), Mel Gwinnett (Bradford City 1984), Steve Talboys (Wimbledon, 1991).
Clubhouse: Open matchdays.
Club Record Goalscorer: Reg Weaver, 250
Club Record Apps: Stan Myers & Frank Tredgett in 1950s
92-93 Captain: Wayne Noble
92-93 P.o.Y.: Paul Bywater
92-93 Top scorer: Karl Bayliss.
Local Newspapers: Gloucester Citizen, Gloucester Express, Western Daily Press
Local Radio Stations: Severn Sound, BBC Radio Gloucestershire
Hons: Southern Lg R-up 90-91 (Lg Cup 55-56 (R-up 81-82), Midland Div 88-89), Glos Nth Snr Lg 33-34, Glos Snr Prof. Cup 37-38 49-58 65-66 68-69 70-71 74-75 78-79 79-80 81-82 82-83 83-84 90-91 92-93 (Snr Amtr Cup (Nth) 31-32), FA Tphy 3rd Rd 90-91.

PROGRAMME DETAILS:
Pages: 36 Price: 80p
Editor: Helen Lodge
& Debbie Dembny

GRESLEY ROVERS

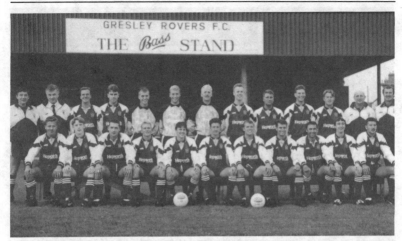

Gresley Rovers 1992-93. Back Row (L/R): Dick West (Reserves' Joint Mgr), Alan Titterton (Reserves' Joint Mgr), Brian Beresford, Mick Taplin, Lee Rippin, James Cheetham, Bob Aston, Stuart Evans, Richard Denby, Gil Land, Tony Marsden, Gordon Ford (Physiotherapist), Steve Dolby (Manager). Front: Neil Lovell, Matt Smith, Adam Stevens, Matthew Eames, Damon Whyatt, Dave Wardle, Craig Weston, Martin Dick, Paul Acklam, John Barry. Photo - Derrick Kinsey.

Chairman: Peter Hall   **Vice Chairman:** Dennis Everitt   **President:** Gordon Duggins.
Secretary: Neil Betteridge, 88 Midway Road, Midway, Swadlincote, Derbys DE11 7PG (0283 221881).
Manager/Coach: Steve Dolby   **Asst Manager:** Malcolm Campion   **Physio:** Gordon Ford.
Press Officer: Secretary   **Commercial Manager:** Frank McArdle.
Ground: Moat Ground, Moat Street, Church Gresley, Swadlincote, Derbys DE11 9RE (0283 216315).
Directions: Travel to A444 via either the A5, A38, A5121 or M42 North to Appleby Magna. On reaching A444 head for Castle Gresley. Turn onto A514 to Derby; at island take second exit (Church Street), then second left (School Street) then first left into Moat Street. Five miles from Burton-on-Trent (BR). Buses from Swadlincote and Burton.
Capacity: 2,000   **Cover:** 1,200   **Seats:** 400   **Floodlights:** Yes   **Metal Badges:** Yes
Club Shop: Yes - wide range of programmes and other merchandise. Contact Rachel Hall (0283 223545).
Cols: Red (white sleeves)/red/red   **Change colours:** All royal blue   **Sponsors:** T.B.A.
Previous Lges: Burton leagues 1892-95 97-98 1910-12 43-44/ Derbyshire Senior 1895-97 1902-03/ Leicestershire Senior 1898-1901 08-10 35-39 40-42 46-49/ Notts 01-02/ Midland 03-06/ Central Alliance 12-25 49-53 59-67/ Birmingham Combination 25-33 53-54/ Birmingham (now West Mids) 54-59/ Central Combination 33-35/ East Mids 67-75/ 75-92.
Previous Names: None
Prev. Grounds: Mushroom Lane, Albert Village   1882-95/ Church Str., Church Gresley 95-1909.
Midweek home matchday: Tuesday   **Reserve's Lge:** Ansells Midland Comb. (Res. Div.)
Record Attendance: 3,950 v Burton Albion, Birmingham (now West Mids) Lg Division One, 57-58.
Best F.A. Cup season: 1st Rd Proper 30-31 (lost 1-3 at York City).
League clubs defeated in F.A. Cup: None.
Record win: 23-0 v Holy Cross Priory, Leicestershire Junior Cup 1889-90.
Record defeat: 1-15 v Burton Crusaders, 1886-87.
Record fees received: £5,000 for Phil Gee (Derby County, 1985).
Players progressing to Football League: Phil Gee (Derby County).
Clubhouse: Inside ground, open Mon, Tues & Thurs evenings and matchdays. Variety of food available from tea bar on ground.
Club Record Goalscorer: Gordon Juggins 306.
Club Record Appearances: Dennis King 579.
92-93 Captain: Richard Denby
92-93 P.O.Y.: Stuart Evans
92-93 Top scorer: Martin Devaney
Local Newspapers: Burton Mail.
Hons: FA Vase R-up 90-91 (SF 92-93), West Mids Lg 90-91 91-92 (R-up 85-86 88-89, Lg Cup 88-89), Southern Lg Midland Div R-up 92-93, Derbys Snr Cup 87-88 88-89 89-90 90-91, Leics Snr Lg 46-47 47-48 (Lg Cup 46-47), Coalville Charity Cup 46-47, Derbys Divisional Cup 48-49, Bass Vase 10-11 28-28 30-31 48-49 49-50 66-67, Central Alliance 64-65 66-67 (Lg Cup 52-53), East Mids Regional Lg 67-68 69-70.

PROGRAMME DETAILS:
Pages: 36 **Price:** 70p
Editor: Brian Spare
(0332 862812)

HALESOWEN TOWN

Halesowen Town 1992-93 - Back Row (L/R): A Webb (Scout), M Hazlewood, C Guest, E Smith (Captain), A Rowe, I Bettles, M Martin, J Snape, R Massey, G Blackwell (Trainer). Front: A Patrick, A Bradley, F Bennett, L Yates, A Cooper, S Abell, S Hall (Asst Manager).

Chairman: Ron Moseley   **Vice Chairman:** Roger Wood   **President:** Laurence Wood.
Secretary: Stewart Tildesley, 83 Bloomfield Street, Halesowen B63 3RF (021 550 8443).
Manager: John Morris   **Asst Manager:** Alan Webb   **Coach:** Stuart Hall
Press Officer: Paul Floud (021 550 8999)   **Physio:** Gavin Blackwell.
Commercial Manager: David Berry   **Newsline:** 0898 122 910.
Ground: The Grove, Old Hawne Lane, Halesowen, West Midlands B63 3TB (021 550 2179).
Directions: M5 jct 3, A456 (signed Kidderminster) to 1st island turn right (signed A459 Dudley), left at 2nd island (signed A458 Stourbridge), at next island take 3rd left into Grammar School Lane, then Old Hawne Lane - ground 400 yds on left.
Capacity: 5,000   **Cover:** 1,420   **Seats:** 420   **Floodlights:** Yes   **Metal Badges:** Yes.
Club Shop: Yes, selling replica strips, T-shirts, waterproof tops, coats, scarves, programmes etc.
Colours: Blue/white/blue   **Change colours:** White/orange/orange.
Sponsors: D Berry & Co (Pipe Fitting Supplies) Ltd.
Previous Leagues: West Mids 1892-1905 06-11 46-86/ Birmingham Comb. 11-39.
Midweek home matchday: Tuesday   **Reserve's League:** Ansells Midland Comb. (Res. Div).
Record Gate: 5,000 v Hendon F.A. Cup 1st Rd Proper 1954. *(18,234 v Southall, 1986 FA Vase Final at Wembley).*
Best FA Cup year: 1st Rd 54-55 84-85 85-86(replay) 86-87 87-88(replay) 88-89 89-90 90-91 91-92(replay).
Record Fees - Paid: £5,000 for Richard Massey (Stourbridge, 1992)
           Received: £30,000 for Dean Spink (Aston Villa, 1989).
Players progressing to Football League: Arthur Proudler (Aston Villa), Cyril Spiers (Aston Villa), Billy Morris (Wolves), Dean Spink (Aston Villa), Stuart Cash (Nottm Forest), Andrew Pearce & Tim Clarke & Sean Flynn (Coventry).
Record win: 13-1 v Coventry Amateurs, Birmingham Senior Cup, 1956.
Record defeat: 0-8 v Bilston, West Midlands League, 7/4/62.
Clubhouse: (021 550 8907) 12-2.30 & 7-11pm daily (closes 10.30pm on Sundays). Cold snacks served.
Record Goalscorer: Paul Joinson 329
Record Appearances: Lee Joinson 544.
92-93 Captain: Eric Smith.
92-93 P.o.Y.: Shane Abell.
92-93 Top scorer: Malcolm Hazlewood.
Local Newspapers: Sports Argus, Express & Star, Birmingham Mail, Halesowen News, Stourbridge & Halesowen Chronicle.
Local Radio: B.R.M.B./BBC West Mids/Beacon.
Hons: Southern Lg Midland Div 89-90, W Mids Lg(5) 46-47 82-85 85-86 (R-up 64-65, Lg Cup 82-83 84-85), Birmingham Snr Cup 83-84 (R-up 51-52 67-68), Staffs Snr Cup 88-89 (R-up 83-84), FA Vase(2) 84-86 (R-up 82-83), Worcs Snr Cup 51-52 61-62 (R-up 87-88), FA Tphy 3rd Qual. Rd 69-70, Midland Comb. Res Div 89-90.

PROGRAMME DETAILS:
Pages: 44 **Price:** 70p
Editor: R Pepper &
C Shakespeare

HASTINGS TOWN

Steve Willard of Hastings Town (right) tackles David Scott during the first derby at the Pilot Field against Dover Athletic in the Beazer Homes League Premier Division. Photo - Roger Turner.

Chairman: Dave Nessling   **Vice Chairman:** Charles Pilbeam   **President:** David Harding
Secretary/Press Officer: R A Cosens, 22 Baldslow Road, Hastings TN34 2EZ (0424 427867).
Manager: Dean White   **Asst Manager:** Garry Wilson   **Physio:** Ray Tuppen
Newsline: 0891 664 356.
Ground: The Pilot Field, Elphinstone Road, Hastings TN34 2AX (0424 444635).
Directions: From A21 turn left at 1st mini-r'bout into St Helens Rd, left after 1 mile into St Helens Park Rd, this leads into Downs Rd, at end of Downs Rd (T-junction) turn left, ground 200yds on right. From town centre take Queens Road (A2101). Right at traffic lights into Elphinstone Road - ground 1 mile on right. One and a half miles from Hastings BR station - infrequent bus service from town centre to ground.
Capacity: 10,000   **Cover:** 1,750   **Seats:** 800   **Floodlights:** Yes   **Metal Badges:** Yes
Club Shop: Yes, selling replica kits, scarves, programmes, pens, key-rings etc.
Colours: All white   **Change colours:** All yellow   **Sponsors:** T.B.A.
Previous Lges: S. Eastern 04-05/ Southern 05-10/ Sussex Co. 21-27 52-85/ Sthern Amtr 27-46/ Corinthian 46-48.
Previous Name: Hastings & St Leonards Amateurs
Previous Ground: Bulverhythe Recreation Ground (until about 1976).
Midweek home matchday: Tuesday   **Reserve Team's League:** Winstonlead Kent Div 2.
Record Attendance: 2,248 v Arsenal, friendly 25/7/92. *Competitive: 1,774 v Dover Athletic, Southern League Premier Division 12/4/93.*
Best F.A. Cup season: 4th Qualifying Rd 85-86, lost 2-3 at Farnborough Town.
League clubs defeated in F.A. Cup: None.
Record Fees - Paid: £2,000 for Darren Hare (Dover)
                Received: £4,000 Peter Heritage and for Terry White (both Hythe Town).
Players progressing to Football League: Peter Heritage (Gillingham and Hereford United).
Clubhouse: Open matchdays and Tues, Thurs and Fri evenings from 7pm.
Club Record Goalscorer: Dean White 28
Club Record Apps:
92-93 Captain: Tony Burt
92-93 P.o.Y.: James Creed
92-93 Top scorer: Keith Miles 13.
Local Newspapers: Hastings Observer & Citizen (0424 854242), Evening Argus (0273 606799).
Local Radio Stations: Radio Sussex, Southern Sound.
Hons: FA Vase 5th Rd rep. 90-91, FA Amtr Cup 3rd Rd 38-39, Southern Lg Southern Div 91-92 (Div 2 R-up 08-09 (Div 2(B) 09-10)), Sussex Co. Lg R-up 21-22 25-26 (Lg Cup 80-81, Div 2 79-80 (R-up 59-60), Div 2 Cup 79-80), Sussex Snr Cup 35-36 37-38, AFA Snr Cup 37-38, Gilbert Rice F'lit Cup 89-90.

PROGRAMME DETAILS:
Pages: 44 **Price:** 80p
Editor: Tony Cosens
(0424 427867)

Nigel Barrows of Hednesford Town (right) cannot prevent Paul Henderson getting in a cross for Hastings Town. However, Hednesford won 2-1 in this battle between two newcomers to the Premier Division. Photo - Roger Turner.

Chairman: Mike Smith   **Vice Chairman:** John Baldwin   **President:** Ron Gray
Secretary: Bob Cooper, 59 Blewitt Street, Hednesford, Staffs WS12 4BD (0543 876114).
Manager: John Baldwin   **Asst Manager/Coach:** Tony Turner.
Physio: Don Drakeley
Press Officer: Alan Owen   **Commercial Manager:** Terry Brumpton
Ground: Cross Keys Ground, Hill Street, Hednesford (05438 422870). *A move to a new, adjacent, ground is planned to take place during the next two years.*
Directions: M6 junction 11 to Cannock, A460 to Hednesford. After 2 miles turn right opposite Shell garage, ground on right at bottom of hill.
Capacity: 4,000   **Cover:** 1,000   **Seats:** 400   **Floodlights:** Yes   **Metal Badges:** Yes
Club Shop: Yes.
Colours: White/black/black   **Change colours:** All yellow.
Sponsors: British Coal - Opencast Executive.
Previous Leagees: Walsall & District/ Birmingham Combination 08-15 45-53/ West Mids 19-39 53-72 74-84/ Midland Counties 72-74.
Previous Names: None - club the result of an 1880 amalgamation between West Hill and Hill Top.
Previous Ground: The Tins (behind Anglesey Hotel) until 1904.
Midweek home matchday: Monday   **Record Gate:** 10,000 v Walsall, FA Cup 1919-20.
Record Fees: Paid: £12,000 - Steve Burr (Macclesfield Town, 1991)
               Received: £6,000 - Steve Biggins (Shrewsbury Town).
Players progressing to Football League: Norman Allsop (West Bromwich Albion 1948), Ron Russon & George Heseltine & John Giles & Gordon Dyas (Walsall 1948 & 49 & 50 & 55), Dennis Jackson & Gordon Lee (Aston Villa 1954 & 55), Brian Horton (Port Vale 70), Steve Biggins (Shrewsbury 1977),
Vernon Allatt (Halifax Town 1979), Chris Brindley (Wolves 1986).
Clubhouse: Open every day with a matchday extension.
Club Record Scorer: Tosh Griffiths
Best F.A. Cup season: 1st Rd 19-20.
92-93 Captain: Mark Freeman
92-93 P.O.Y.: Joe O'Connor
92-93 Top scorer: Joe O'Connor.
Local Newspapers: Expess & Star (Wolverhampton 22351), Chronicle, Chase News, Hednesford Mercury.
Local Radio Stations: Radio West Mids, Beacon (Wolverhampton), Radio BRMB.
Club Hotline: 0891 12 29 35.
Hons: Welsh Cup R-up 91-92, FA Tphy 2nd Rd 2nd rep. 77-78, Southern Lg Midland Division R-up 91-92 (Lg Cup R-up 86-87), West Mids Lg 77-78 (R-up 83-84, Lg Cup 83-84), Birmingham Combination 09-10 50-51 (R-up 12-13 52-53), Staffs Senior Cup 69-70 73-74 (R-up 92-93), Birmingham Senior Cup 35-36.

PROGRAMME DETAILS:
Pages: 20 **Price:** 80p
Editor: Chris Southall

Formed: 1901

MOOR GREEN

The Moors

The main stand at the Moorlands.

Chairman: Brian Smith   **President:** Geoff Hood
Secretary: Martyn Davis, 22 Collingdon Ave., Sheldon, Birmingham B26 3YL (021 743 0991).
Manager: Bob Faulkner   **Asst Manager:** T.B.A.   **Coach:** T.B.A.
Press Officer: Peter Clynes (021 745 3262)   **Physio:** Steve Williams
Commercial Manager: Rory Lynas (021 777 8961).
Ground: 'The Moorlands', Sherwood Road, Hall Green B28 0EX (021 777 2727).
Directions: Off Highfield Road, which is off A34 (B'ham to Stratford). Hall Green & Yardley (BR) half mile away.
Capacity: 3,250   **Cover:** 1,200   **Seats:** 250   **Floodlights:** Yes   **Metal Badges:** Yes
Club Shop: Yes, selling scarves, mugs, stickers, programmes. Contact Craig Hochkins (021 745 3191).
Colours: Sky/royal/sky   **Change colours:** All yellow   **Sponsors:** Ansells.
Previous Leagues: (friendlies only 1901-21) Birmingham & Dist. A.F.A. 1908-36/ Central Amateur 36-39/ Birmingham Comb 45-54/ West Mids 54-65/ Midland Comb 65-83.
Previous Grounds: Moor Green Lane 1901-02/ numerous 02-22/ Windermere Road 1910-30.
Midweek home matchday: Tuesday   **Reserve Team's League:** None.
Best F.A. Cup season: 1st Rd Proper 1979-80 (lost 2-3 at Stafford Rangers).
Record Gate: 5,000 v Romford, FA Amtr Cup 1951 *(15,000 v Ajax in Olympic Stadium, Amsterdam).*
Record Fees - Paid: £1,000 for Adrian O'Dowd (Alvechurch).
       Received: £15,000 for Ian Taylor (Port Vale).
Players progressing to Football League: Herbert Smith & Ron Jefferies (Aston Villa 1947 & 50), Fred Pidcock (Walsall 1953), Peter Woodward (West Bromwich Abion 1954), Steve Cooper (Birmingham City 1983), Ken Barnes (Manchester City), Brian Mack (West Bromwich Albion), Paul Brogan (Mansfield Town), Ian Taylor (Pt Vale 1992).
Clubhouse: Two bars and dance floor. Open nightly and weekend lunchtimes.
92-93 Captain: G Clegg
92-93 P.o.Y.: P Brogan
92-93 Top scorer: D Fearon.
Local Newspapers: Solihull News (021 626 6635), Solihull Times (021 704 3338), Birmingham Post & Mail (021 236 3366), Express & Star (0902 319461).
Local Radio Stations: Radio WM, BRMB.
Hons: Southern Lg Midland Div R-up 87-88, Mids Comb 80-81 (R-up(4) 74-76 79-80 82-83, Div 1 85-86, Presidents Cup(2) 66-68 78-79), Mids Comb Challenge Cup 80-81 (R-up 69-70 82-83), Lord Mayor of B'ham Charity Cup 90-91, Mids F'lit Cup(2) 90-92, Tony Allden Tphy 81-82, B'ham Snr Cup 57-58, Worcs Snr Cup R-up 86-87, B'ham Jnr Cup 66-67, Worcs Jnr Cup 85-86, Solihull Charity Cup 85-86, Smedley Crook Memorial Cup 87-88, Central Amateur Lg 36-37 37-38 38-39, Verviers (Belg) Tphy 32-33 36-37, AFA Challenge Cup 38-39, AFA Snr Cup 26-27 35-36, Mids F'lit Yth Lg Cup R-up 87-88, B'ham County Yth Lg Cup R-up 83-84.

PROGRAMME DETAILS:
Pages: 52 **Price:** 60p
Editor: Peter Denham
(021 777 3356)

NUNEATON BOROUGH

The Boro' First, Reserve and Youth squads with their array of trophies after a highly successful 1992-93 campaign. Photo - Jim Jarvis.

Chairman: Howard Kerry **Vice Chairman:** Brendan Dodd.
Life President: Alf Scattergood.
Secretary: Peter Humphreys, 29 Amington Rd, Shirley, Solihull, West Mids (021 745 2031).
Manager: John Barton **Asst Manager:** Peter Eastoe **Physio:** Andy Cunningham
Press Officer: Gordon Chislett (0203 222106 office hrs)
Commercial Manager: Ray Dickinson (0203 491064/ 325281(office hrs)).
Ground: Manor Park, Beaumont Road, Nuneaton, Warks CV10 0SY (0203 342690/385738).
Directions: A444 to Nuneaton from M6 junction 3, 1st exit at 1st r-about, left at 2nd r-about then 2nd right into Greenmoor Road, turn right at the end and ground is on the left. From town centre ring-road ground is at the end of Queens Road. Parking for 100 cars at Manor Park School, Beaumont Rd, 50p each. Ground 1 mile from Nuneaton Trent Valley (BR) station.
Capacity: 5,000 **Cover:** 2,000 **Seats:** 600 **Floodlights:** Yes **Metal Badges:** Yes.
Club Shop: Yes. Numerous Boro' souvenirs, non-League & League programmes & fanzines. Current season programme exchanges welcome. Contact Andy Pace (0203 374043).
Colours: Royal & white stripes **Change colours:** Red & white **Sponsors:** Brew XI
Previous Leagues: Central Amateur 37-38/ B'ham Comb 38-52/ West Mids (B'ham) 52-58/ Southern 58-79 81-82/ GM Conference (Alliance Premier & Gola) 79-81 82-87.
Midweek home matchday: Tuesday **Reserves' League:** Ansells Midland Comb. (Res. Div.).
Record Gate: 22,114 v Rotherham, FA Cup 3rd Rd 1967 *(Best in Conference: 3,597 v Maidstone, 83-84).*
Best F.A. Cup season: 3rd Rd replay 66-67. 1st Rd on 18 occasions; 49-50 53-55 66-68 71-72 74-80 81-82 84-86 92-93.
League clubs defeated in F.A. Cup: Watford 53-54, Swansea Town 66-67, Oxford Utd 77-78.
Record Fees - Paid: £9,500 for Richard Dixey (Scarborough, 1981)
Received: £52,000 for Richard Hill (Northampton Town, 85-86).
Record win: 11-1 (45-46 & 55-56) **Record defeat:** 1-8 (55-56 & 68-69).
Players progressing to Football League: Richard Mason & Paul Culpin (Coventry 1946 & 85), Eric Betts (Walsall 1949), Frank Cruickshank (Notts Co. 1950), Ken Plant (Bury 1950), John Schofield (Birmingham 1950), Ron Howells (Wolves 1952), Frank Upton & Richard Hill (Northampton 1953 & 85), Ron Dickinson & Mike Gibson (Shrewsbury 1953 & 60), George Cattleugh (Watford 1954), Terry Wright (Barrow 1962), Mick Hartland (Oxford 1963), Ken Satchell & Barry Holbutt (Walsall 1965), Terry Bell (Hartlepool 1966), Alan Morton (Fulham 1970), Reg Edwards (Port Vale 1972), Kirk Stephens (Luton 1978), Trevor Peake (Lincoln 1979), Paul Sugrue (Manchester City 1980), Malcom Shotton & Tim Smithers (Oxford 1980), Dean Thomas (Wimbledon 1981), Paul Richardson (Derby 1984).
Clubhouse: Stewardess - Jackie Salisbury (0203 383152). Open every evening, weekebd lunchtimes and matchdays (inc Reserve & Youth). Vice Presidents Lounge under main stand. Members only.
Club Record Scorer: Paul Culpin 190.
Record Record Scorer in one season: Paul Culpin 55 (92-93).
Club Record Appearances: Alan Jones 545 (1962-74).
92-93 Captain: Gary Bradder.
92-93 P.o.Y.: John Symonds. **92-93 Top scorer:** Paul Culpin 55.
Local Newspapers: Hartland Evening News, Nuneaton Evening Telegraph, Neaton Weekly Tribune.
Local Radio: Mercia Sound, BBC CWR. **Boro' Newsline:** 0891 122 909.
Hons: F.A. Tphy QF 76-77(replay) 79-80 86-87, Alliance Premier Lge R-up(2) 83-85, Southern Lg R-up 66-67 74-75 (Midland Div 81-82 92-93, Lg Cup R-up 62-63, Merit Cup 92-93(joint)), Birmingham Lg 55-56 (Nth Div 54-55), Birmingham Comb. R-up 45-46 48-49 50-51, Birmingham Snr Cup 48-49 55-56 59-60 77-78 79-80 92-93 (R-up 52-53 66-67 90-91).

PROGRAMME DETAILS:
Pages: 36 **Price:** 70p
Ed.: Steve Packer + team
(0203 383152)

Formed: 1881   # SITTINGBOURNE   Brickies

Sittingbourne F.C. - Beazer Homes League Southern Division Champions 1992-93. Back Row (L/R): Dave Bourne, Jason Fenton, Tommy Warrilow, Andy Hough, Neil Emblen, Tim Hulme. Front: Rod De Khors, Jeff Ross, Leroy Ambrose, Phil Handford, Karl Elsey. Photo - V J Robertson.

Chairman: Mick Fletcher   **President:** E H Bennett.
Secretary: Ian Kingsworth, c/o Sittingbourne F.C.
Manager: John Ryan   **Coach:** Nicky Sparks   **Physio:** Kevin Manser
Youth Development & Community Liaison Officer: Carl Laraman.   **Newsline:** 0891 88 44 34.
Commercial Manager & Press Officer: Rob Kelly, c/o Sittingbourne F.C.
Ground: Central Park, Eurolink, Sittingbourne, Kent ME10 3SB (0795 475547. Fax: 0795 430776).
Directions: Through Sittingbourne on main A2, club signposted clearly and regularly from both east and west. 1 mile from Sittingbourne BR station.
Capacity: 8,000   **Cover:** 1,200   **Seats:** 200   **Floodlights:** 420 lux **Metal Badges:** Yes
Club Shop: Yes, selling match videos, action photos, college scarves, bar scarves, t-shirts, flat hats, bobble hats, badges, mugs, rosettes, tankards, pennants, car pennants & stickers, key rings, pens, coasters, replica home & away kits, club ties, programmes etc. Open matchdays, otherwise contact Ann Morrison (0795 664436) or Clive Phillips (0795 477108).
Colours: Red/black/red.   **Change colours:** All yellow.
Club Sponsors: Harrisons (team sponsors: Erith Building Supplies).
Previous Leagues: Kent 1894-1905 09-27 30-39 46-59 68-91/ South Eastern 05-09/ Southern 27-30 59-67.
Previous Names: Sittingbourne United 1881-86.
Previous Grounds: Sittingbourne Recreation Ground 1881-90/ Gore Court Cricket Ground 90-92/ The Bull Ground 1892-1990.
Midweek home matchday: Tuesday   **Reserve's League:** Hurst Electrical Kent Midweek.
Record Attendance: 5,951 v Tottenham Hotspur, friendly 26/1/93. *Competitive: 5,583 v Gravesend, F.A. Cup 1961 (at the Bull Ground).*
Best F.A. Cup season: Second Round Proper 25-26 (lost 0-7 at Swindon Town), 28-29 (lost 1-2 at Walsall). Also First Round Proper 26-27 30-31 62-63.
Record transfer fee paid: £15,000 for Phil Handford (Welling United, 1991).
Clubhouse: (0795 475577 - The Cabin). Open every day: 11am-3 & 7-11pm Mon-Fri (& non-match Sats), 11am-11pm matchdays Sats, noon-3 & 7-10.30pm Sun. Hot & cold food always available inc. full 3 course meals. Live music, discos & karaokes most weekends. Pool tables, darts, fruit machines (£100 jackpot). Head steward: Gary David.
92-93 Captain: Dave Ward
92-93 P.o.Y.: Neil Emblen
92-93 Top scorer: Dave Arter 30.
Local Newspapers: East Kent Extra.
Local Radio Stations: Invicta.
Hons: Southern Lg Southern Div 92-93, Kent Lg 1897-98 1902-03 57-58 58-59 75-76 83-84 90-91 (Lg Cup 25-26 58-59 73-74 80-81, Div 2 Cup 54-55 57-58 83-84 86-87 87-88), Kent Senior Cup 01-02 28-29 29-30 57-58, Kent Senior Shield 25-26 27-28 53-54, Kent Senior Trophy 89-90, Thames & Medway Cup 55-56 58-59, Thames & Medway Comination 02-03 07-08 11-12 24-25 25-26, Chatham Charity Cup 03-04 19-20. Kent Midweek Lg(res) 91-92 (Lg Cup 90-91). *Unbeaten in Kent Lg 90-91.*

PROGRAMME DETAILS:
Pages: 48 Price: £1
Editor: Rob Kelly
(c/o the club)

SOLIHULL BOROUGH

Solihull Borough F.C. 1992-92. Back Row (L/R): Phil Hawker, Keith Bertschin, Robert Hopkins, Recky Carter, Jan Mulders, Darrell Houghton, Ian Pinner, Paul Dyson, Clive Boxall, John Price, John Pearson. Front: Alan Ollis, Stuart Stokes, Robert Nayler, Lee Horrocks, Marc Coogan, Matt Nelson, Ian Stanners, Andy Canning, Oliver Latchford, Chris Burton. Photo - Dennis Ruddle, Birmingham Post & Mail.

Chairman: John Hewitson   **Vice Chairman:** T Stevens   **President:** Joe McGorian.
Secretary: John A France, 105 Coppice Walk, Cheswick Green, Shirley, Solihull B90 4HZ (05646 3011).
Manager: Ralph Punsheon   **Asst Manager:** M Tuohy   **Coach:** D Clements.
Physio: John Price   **Press Officer:** Richard Crawshaw (05646 2746).
Ground: Moor Green FC (see page 497). Solihull are groundsharing at Moor Green whilst awaiting planning permission for a stadium of their own
Directions & Capacity: See Moor Green   **Club Shop:** Yes   **Metal Badges:** Yes.
Colours: Red/white/red   **Change colours:** Yellow/black/black.
Sponsors: Mitchells & Butlers.   **Previous Leagues:** Mercian/ Midland Combination 69-91.
Previous Name: Lincoln F.C.   **Previous Grounds:** Widney Stadium, Solihull 65-88.
Midweek matchday: Wednesday   **Reserve's League:** Ansells Midland Combination.
Record Attendance: 1,360 v V.S. Rugby, F.A. Cup First Round 14/11/92. *At previous ground: 400 v Moor Green, Midland Combination Division Two, 1971.*
Best F.A. Cup season: First Round Proper replay 92-93 (lost 1-3 at V.S. Rugby after 2-2 draw).
League clubs defeated in F.A. Cup: None.
Record win: 6-1 v Hednesford Town (H), Southern League Midland Division 1991-92.
Record defeat: 1-7 v V.S. Rugby (A), Birmingham Senior Cup.
Record Fees - Paid: £2,500 for Chris Burton (from Kidderminster Harriers).
        Received: £30,000 for Andy Williams (from Coventry City).
Players progressing to Football League: Kevin Ashley (Birmingham City, Wolverhampton Wanderers), Andy Williams (Coventry City, Rotherham United, Leeds United, Notts County), Geoff Scott (Leicester City, Birmingham City, Stoke City), Danny Conway (Leicester City), Alan Smith (Leicester City, Arsenal), Dean Spink (Aston Villa, Shrewsbury Town).
Clubhouse: The Borough Club, Tanworth Lane, Shirley; opened June 16th 1990. Two bars, dance floor, meeting room available for hire. Open every night, Sunday and bank holiday lunchtimes. **Steward:** Mark Dumelow.
Club Record Goalscorer: D Badger
Club Record Appearances: D Badger.   **92-93 Captain:** Clive Boxall
92-93 P.O.Y.: Paul Dyson   **92-93 Top scorer:** Recky Carter 41.
Local Newspapers: Solihull Times, Solihull News, Sunday Mercury, Sports Argus.
Local Radio Stations: Radio WM, BRMB.
Hons: Southern Lg Midland Div 91-92, Midland Combination R-up 90-91 (Challenge Cup R-up 74-75 90-91, Presidents Cup R-up 69-70), Lord Mayor of Birmingham Charity Cup 91-92 92-93, Worcs Senior Cup R-up 92-93, F.A. Vase 5th Rd 74-75, F.A. Trophy 3rd Qualifying Rd 92-93.

PROGRAMME DETAILS:
Pages: 20 Price: 60p
Editor: Richard Crawshaw
(05646 2746)

Formed: 1880 **TROWBRIDGE TOWN** The Bees

Trowbridge Town's ground, which may be vacated in the not-too-distant future if the club's plans to relocate come to fruition. Photo - James Wright.

Chairman: A I Moore   **Vice Chairman:** C Belcher   **President:** A M Townley.
Secretary: Jeff Hooper, 8 Elm Close, North Bradley, Trowbridge BA14 0SF (0225 767187).
Manager: John Murphy   **Asst Manager:** Bob Baird   **Coach:** Pete Higgins.
Physio: P Barnes   **Press Officer:** A Meaden (0225 755752).
Commercial Manager: J Darawel.
Ground: County Way, Trowbridge, Wilts BA14 0DB (0225 752076).
Directions: On entering town, follow inner relief road (County Way) signs towards Frome, ground on left 100 yds past Ship Inn near Bradley Rd r'bout. Ground on right if entering from Frome.
Capacity: 5,000   **Cover:** 2,000   **Seats:** 250   **Floodlights:** Yes   **Metal Badges:** £1.55
Club Shop: Yes, selling hats, scarves, badges, mugs, sweaters, jumpers, replica kits, programmes.
Colours: Old gold/black/black   **Change colours:** All white.
Sponsors: Bowyers (Wiltshire) Ltd.
Previous Leagues: Somerset Senior/ Trowbridge & Dist/ Western 1892-98 1901-07 13-58/ Wiltshire/ Southern 58-81/ Alliance Premier (GMV Conference) 81-84.
Previous Name: Trowbridge F.C.
Previous Grounds: Timbrell Street 1880-87/ Flower Show Field 87-1923/ Bythesea Rd 23-34.
Midweek home matchday: Tuesday.   **Reserve Team's League:** None.
Record Attendance: 9,009 v Weymouth, F.A. 4th Qualifying Rd 49-50.
Best F.A. Cup season: 1st Rd replay (v Brighton) 47-48. 1st Rd 45-46 57-58 63-64.
Record win: 17-1 v Yeovil & Petters   **Record defeat:** 0-10 v Barnet.
Record Fees - Paid: £7,000 for John Freegard (Gloucester City, 1991).
    Received: £10,000 for Paul Compton (B'mouth), for Andy Feeley (Leicester City).
Players progressing to Football League: Alec Eisentrager (Bristol City 1950), Don Townsend (Charlton 1950), Cecil Dixon (Cardiff 1954), David Pyle & Jeff Meacham (Bristol Rovers 1955 & 87), Eric Weaver & Ken Skeen & Bryan Wade (Swindon 1961 & 64 & 85)), Paul Compton (Bournemouth 1980), John Layton (Newport 1984), Andy Feeley (Leicester 1984), Ray Cashley (Chester 1985).
Clubhouse: Open before and after games. Skittles, TV, pool, darts. Hot & cold pies and rolls.

92-93 Captain: Mike Kilgour
92-93 P.o.Y.: Paul Thorpe   **92-93 Top scorer:** Keith Knight.
Local Newspapers: Wiltshire Times (0225 777292), Bath Evening Chronicle, Western Daily Press.
Local Radio Stations: Radio Bristol, Wilts Radio, Wilts Sound.
Hons: F.A. Vase SF 90-91, F.A. Tphy 1st Rd rep 83-84, F.A. Amateurr Cup 2nd Rd 30-31, Southern Lg Southern Div R-up 90-91 (Lg Cup R-up 85-86), Western Lg(7) 27-28 29-30 38-40 46-48 55-56 (R-up 1892-93 1921-22 48-49 56-57, Lg Cup 56-57), Wilts Lg Div 2 11-12 30-31(jt)(R-up 03-04 06-07 08-09 19-20 88-89), Trowbridge & Dist Lg(3) 09-11 13-14, Wilts Snr Cup 1884-85 95-96(jt with Swindon T) 97-98 1921-22 25-26 33-34 37-38 (R-up 1886-87 89-90 92-93 96-97 1906-07 07-08 12-13), Wilts Prof. Shield(7) 45-47 49-50 68-70 72-73 92-93, Wilts F'lit Lg Cup 91-92, Bristol Charity Cup 25-26, Wilts Jnr Cup 10-11 12-13, Trowbridge & Dist Jnr Cup 19-20, Allen Palmer Cup 23-24 24-25(joint), Swanborough Cup 33-34 34-35 35-36(jt), Somerset Snr Lg 30-31 (R-up 11-12 33-34 35-36), Western Co's F'lit Lg Cup 80-81 85-86, Coronation Cup 92-93, Mid Wilts Yth u-17 Lg 91-92 (Lg Cup 91-92, u-16 91-92 (R-up 88-89), u-15 R-up 88-89, u-14 88-89), National Assn of Supporters Clubs u-16 champions 88-89.

PROGRAMME DETAILS:
Pages: 48 Price: 60p
Editor: A Meaden
(0225 752076)

WATERLOOVILLE

Waterlooville F.C. 1992-93, pictured at Aldershot before a Hampshire Senior Cup tie. Photo - Eric Marsh.

Chairman: F P Faulkner   **Vice Chairman:** K L Ashman   **President:** M Hibberd
Secretary: M C Richards, 124 Highbury Grove, Cosham, Portsmouth PO6 2RT (0705 263867).
Manager: Billy Gilbert/ Vince Hilaire   **Coach:** J Waugh.
Press Officer: **Physio:** Bill Pizey
Ground: Jubilee Park, Aston Road, Waterlooville PO7 7SZ (0705 263423 - office 254529).
Directions: Turn right off town by-pass (B2150) at Asda r-about. Dual carriage to next island, and return back towards town. Aston Road is first left. Nearest stations; Havant (4 miles), Cosham (5).
Capacity: 7,000   **Cover:** 1,500   **Seats:** 480   **Floodlights:** Yes   **Metal Badges:** Yes
Club Shop: Yes.
Colours: White/navy/white   **Change colours:** Yellow & green/green/yellow & green.
Previous Leagues: Waterlooville & Dist/ Portsmouth 38-53/ Hants 1953-71.
Sponsors: St Christophers Motor Group.
Previous Grounds: Convent Ground 10-30/ Rowlands Avenue Recreation Ground 30-63.
Midweek home matchday: Tuesday   **Reserve Team's League:** Wessex Combination.
Record Attendance: 4,500 v Wycombe Wanderers F.A. Cup 1st Rd 1976-77.
Best F.A. Cup season: 1st Rd 2nd replay v Northampton, 83-84. Also 1st Rd 68-69 76-77 88-89.
League clubs defeated in F.A. Cup: None
Record Fees: Paid: £4,000 for Paul Moody (Fareham)   **Received:** For Paul Moody (Southampton).
Players progressing to Football League: Phil Figgins (Portsmouth 1973), Paul Hardyman (Portsmouth 1983), Guy Whittingham (Portsmouth via Yeovil Town 1988), Paul Moody (Southampton 1991).
Clubhouse: Jubilee Club open for all games (1st team & Res).
92-93 Captain:
92-93 P.o.Y.:
92-93 Top scorer:
Local Newspapers: The News & Sports Mail.
Local Radio Stations: BBC Solent, Ocean Sound.
Hons: Southern Lg Div 1 Sth 71-72 (Lg Cup 86-87, R-up 82-83), Hants Lg R-up 69-70 (Div 2 59-60 64-65, Div 3 (East) R-up 53-54), Hants Snr Cup 69-70 72-73 84-85 (R-up 75-76 90-91), Russell Cotes Cup 88-89, Portsmouth Lg 49-50 50-51 51-52 (Div 2 46-47, Div 3 38-39), Portsmouth Snr Cup 68-69, Portsmouth Victory Cup 59-60 69-70, FA Tphy 2nd Rd 76-77, FA Amtr Cup 1st Rd 59-60.

PROGRAMME DETAILS:
Pages: 32 **Price:** 50p
Ed.: Universal Leisure Ltd

'THE NON-LEAGUE PLAYERS'
1993-94 EDITION

AVAILABLE DURING THE SEASON, WILL FEATURE DETAILS OF WATERLOOVILLE'S PLAYERS, AND INDEED THE PLAYERS OF ALL CLUBS IN THE TOP FOUR PYRAMID LEAGUES. FOR MORE DETAILS ON THIS PUBLICATION SEE THE ADVERT NEAR THE FRONT OF THIS DIRECTORY.

WORCESTER CITY

Worcester City's Steve Rutter prepares to celebrate a goal in the home fixture against Cambridge, but the ball was somehow cleared off the line. However, Worcester still won 2-1 in this their last game of the 1992-93 season. Photo - Worcester Evening News.

Chairman: Dr Michael Sorenson   **Vice Chairman:** N Collins   **President:** R H Mann
Secretary/Commercial Manager: Nigel Collins, c/o Worcester City F.C.
Manager: George Rooney   **Asst Mgr:** Graham Selby   **Coach:** Steve Bond.
Press Officer: None   **Physio:** Peter O'Connell   **Newsline:** 0898 884476.
Ground: St Georges Lane, Barbourne, Worcester WR1 1QT (0905 23003 (fax: 26668)).
Directions: M5 jct 6 (Worcester North), follow signs to Worcester, right at first lights, St Georges Lane is 3rd left. From South: M5 jct 6 (Worcester) A44 to Worcester, pass racecourse and follow A38 (towards Bromsgrove), ground on right. 1 mile from Foregate Street (BR) station.
Capacity: 4,749   **Cover:** 2,000   **Seats:** 1,223   **Floodlights:** Yes   **Metal Badges:** Yes
Club Shop: Yes, selling programmes and souvenirs. Contact John Hawkins (0905 20660).
Colours: Blue & white/blue/blue   **Change colours:** All red
Sponsors: Performance Print.   **Previous Grounds:** Severn Terrace/ Flagge Meadow.
Previous Leagues: West Mids (Birmingham) 1902-38/ Southern 38-79/ Alliance Premier 79-85.
Previous Names: Worcester Rovers, Berwick Rangers (merged in 1902).
Midweek home matchday: Monday   **Reserve Team's League:** No Reserves.
Record Attendance: 17,042 v Sheff Utd (lost 0-2), F.A. Cup 4th Rd 24/1/59.
Best F.A. Cup year: 4th Rd 58-59. 1st Rd (10) 05-06 25-26 28-29 50-51 57-58 60-61 78-79 82-84 87-88.
League clubs defeated in F.A. Cup: Millwall, Liverpool 58-59, Plymouth 78-79, Wrexham 82-83, Aldershot 83-84.
Record win: 18-1 v Bilston, Birmingham League 21/11/31.
Record defeat: 0-10 v Wellington, Birmingham League 29/8/20.
Record Fees - Paid: £8,500 for Jim Williams (Telford United, 1981)
           Received: £27,000 for John Barton (Everton, 1979).
Players progressing to Football League: John Goodwin (Birmingham 1946), Tom Brown (Portsmouth 1946), Gordon Medd (Birmingham 1946), Henry Horton (Blackburn 1947), Ron Baynham (Luton 1951), Arthur Lawless (Plymouth 1955), Harry Knowles & Peter King (1959 & 60), Keith Ball (Walsall 1965), John Fairbrother (Peterborough 1965), David Tennant (Lincoln 1966), Roger Davies (Derby 1971), Neil Merrick (Bournemouth 1974), John Barton (Everton 1978), James Williams (Walsall 1979), Andy Awford (Portsmouth 1988), Andy Preece (Wrexham 1990), Mark Gayle (Walsall 1991), Des Lyttle (Swansea 1992).
Clubhouse: Open every evening and Saturday and Sunday daytime. Cold snacks available.
Club Record Goalscorer: John Inglis 189 (1970-77).
Club Record Appearances: Bobby McEwan 596 (1959-75).
92-93 Captain: Stainton McKenzie.
92-93 P.o.Y: Mark Jones.   **92-93 Scorer:** Stewart Phillips 13.
Local Newspapers: Berrows Journal, Worcester Evening News, Worcester Source.
Local Radio Stations: Radio Wyvern & BBC Hereford & Worcester
Hons: Southern Lg 78-79 (Div 1 67-68, Div 1 Nth 76-77, Lg Cup R-up 45-46 59-60, Chal. Cup 39-40, Champs Cup 78-79), West Mids (B'ham) Lg(4) 13-14 24-25 28-30 (R-up(3) 31-34), Worcs Snr Cup(25) 07-14 28-30 32-33 45-46(jt) 48-49 55-59 60-61 62-63 64-65 69-70 77-78 79-80 81-82 83-84 87-88, B'ham Snr Cup 75-76, Staffs Snr Cup 76-77, Inter Lg Champs Cup 78-79, Welsh Cup SF 78-79, FA Tphy QF 69-70 73-74 80-81 81-82.

PROGRAMME DETAILS:
Pages: 32 **Price:** 70p
Editor: Julian Pugh
(0905 25844)

Midland Division

	P	HOME W	D	L	AWAY W	D	L	F	A	Pts
NUNEATON BOROUGH	42	12	4	5	17	1	3	102	45	92
GRESLEY ROVERS	42	15	1	5	12	5	4	94	55	87
RUSHDEN & DIA.	42	15	4	2	10	6	5	85	41	85
BARRI	42	13	1	7	13	4	4	82	49	83
NEWPORT A.F.C.	42	11	4	6	12	4	5	73	58	77
BEDWORTH UNITED	42	10	4	7	12	4	5	72	55	74
STOURBRIDGE	42	10	5	6	7	4	10	93	79	60
SUTTON COLDFIELD T.	42	12	2	7	5	7	9	82	78	60
REDDITCH UNITED	42	9	3	9	9	3	9	75	79	60
TAMWORTH	42	10	5	6	6	6	9	65	51	59
WESTON-SUPER-MARE	42	11	4	6	6	3	12	79	86	58
LEICESTER UNITED	42	11	4	6	5	5	11	67	67	57
GRANTHAM TOWN	42	10	4	7	6	5	10	60	73	57
BILSTON TOWN	42	11	5	5	4	5	12	74	69	55
EVESHAM UNITED	42	5	7	9	10	1	10	67	83	53
BRIDGNORTH TOWN	42	7	6	8	8	1	12	61	68	52
DUDLEY TOWN	42	6	6	9	3	5	13	56	89	38
YATE TOWN	42	6	6	9	3	5	13	56	89	38
FOREST GREEN R.	42	7	3	11	5	3	13	61	97	42
HINCKLEY BAY	42	6	6	9	3	5	13	56	89	38
KING'S LYNN	42	6	4	11	4	2	15	45	90	36
R.C. WARWICK	42	2	5	14	1	2	18	40	88	16

Top League Goalscorers

E.Wright (Stourbridge)	46
P.Culpin (Nuneaton Borough)	39
D.Draper (Bedworth United)	25
D.Withers (Barri)	24
J.Baker (Bilston Town)	23
T.Hall (Stourbridge)	23
D.Watkins (Rushden & Diamonds)	23

THE MIDLAND DIVISION RESULT CHART 1992-93

HOME TEAM		1	2	3	4	5	6	7	8	9	10	11	12	13	14	15	16	17	18	19	20	21	22
1.	Barri	*	1-2	2-1	1-2	3-1	3-1	2-0	0-1	1-2	1-0	2-0	3-1	4-1	1-4	3-1	0-1	2-1	0-2	3-3	2-0	3-0	3-1
2.	Bedworth	0-1	*	2-1	3-2	2-0	0-1	3-2	3-0	2-2	1-1	0-1	2-2	0-1	2-1	1-0	2-1	0-3	4-1	2-2	0-3	2-1	0-3
3.	Bilston	1-1	1-2	*	0-3	6-2	1-0	5-0	3-1	1-0	2-2	5-2	4-2	1-1	3-4	2-1	0-2	0-1	1-0	1-1	1-1	3-1	6-3
4.	Bridgnorth	2-4	0-2	0-0	*	0-0	1-0	4-1	1-0	1-4	0-1	3-0	3-0	0-1	1-2	4-2	2-1	2-2	0-6	2-3	0-0	1-1	1-1
5.	Dudley	1-3	0-3	2-2	2-1	*	0-2	1-0	0-2	2-5	1-0	2-0	0-1	0-1	1-3	3-2	1-2	1-2	1-0	4-2	4-1	5-1	1-1
6.	Evesham	3-4	1-0	3-2	2-3	0-0	*	1-2	2-2	0-2	5-2	7-1	0-4	2-2	0-2	2-2	1-1	1-2	2-2	0-3	1-1	3-1	0-3
7.	Forest Green	1-6	1-2	4-1	3-2	0-2	0-3	*	2-2	0-2	1-1	0-0	3-1	1-2	2-3	4-1	1-4	1-4	1-4	4-1	1-3	4-0	2-1
8.	Grantham	1-2	4-1	1-0	1-3	1-2	2-2	2-2	*	2-0	2-1	1-2	2-1	1-0	0-5	1-1	3-3	1-3	1-0	3-1	3-0
9.	Gresley	3-1	2-2	2-0	1-2	2-0	5-0	2-1	2-3	*	1-0	2-1	2-3	3-5	0-1	3-2	4-0	2-1	2-1	1-0	3-2	4-2	3-1
10.	Hinckley	1-2	2-2	3-1	1-0	6-3	1-5	1-1	2-0	1-2	*	0-2	1-2	3-4	1-5	2-0	0-2	0-0	1-1	1-1	0-0	1-2	3-1
11.	King's Lynn	0-2	1-3	0-3	0-0	2-2	1-2	3-1	1-3	1-4	2-2	*	2-0	1-1	0-2	0-3	4-1	0-1	1-5	3-2	4-1	0-2	4-2
12.	Leicester	2-2	0-2	0-0	2-1	1-3	5-2	5-0	3-1	3-2	0-1	0-0	*	1-2	1-2	2-2	2-3	4-0	3-1	2-1	1-0	3-1	4-0
13.	Newport	0-0	1-3	3-1	2-0	1-0	2-3	0-2	2-0	0-0	3-1	4-1	1-1	*	0-3	2-1	2-1	1-3	2-1	2-2	3-2	0-1	3-1
14.	Nuneaton	1-3	1-1	2-1	2-1	3-0	5-1	5-0	6-1	0-1	3-1	3-0	2-0	1-1	*	3-1	8-1	1-1	1-1	1-2	1-3	2-4	4-1
15.	R.C.Warwick	1-0	1-3	2-3	0-2	0-0	0-1	3-1	1-2	0-2	2-2	0-1	0-0	1-2	0-2	*	0-1	1-2	2-3	1-1	0-1	2-2	0-3
16.	Redditch	2-4	3-1	3-1	1-2	3-3	1-2	1-2	2-0	0-2	3-0	4-2	2-2	1-3	2-3	2-1	*	2-2	2-3	2-1	2-1	2-3	2-1
17.	Rushden	1-1	3-2	2-2	2-1	3-2	5-0	2-1	4-1	3-1	6-0	3-1	3-0	1-0	0-2	3-0	0-0	*	5-2	2-0	0-0	3-0	0-1
18.	Stourbridge	1-0	1-1	0-2	4-1	0-0	4-1	6-1	3-1	2-5	2-7	1-0	4-0	1-3	0-2	6-3	0-0	2-2	*	5-1	0-3	1-0	2-2
19.	Sutton C.T.	0-3	2-1	1-2	2-3	2-1	4-1	4-2	0-1	1-1	2-1	4-1	2-1	2-4	1-3	1-0	4-2	2-0	4-3	*	0-1	3-3	5-2
20.	Tamworth	0-1	0-1	1-1	3-2	1-2	1-2	1-1	0-0	1-1	5-0	3-0	3-4	4-3	0-0	1-0	2-1	4-1	5-2	2-1	*	0-1	3-0
21.	Weston	3-1	1-4	3-1	4-2	3-0	0-2	1-3	2-2	4-4	7-2	3-0	1-1	3-0	2-1	6-1	3-4	0-2	1-5	3-3	2-1	*	2-1
22.	Yate	0-1	0-3	3-2	1-0	2-5	1-0	0-2	2-2	2-3	5-0	1-0	1-0	0-2	3-1	3-0	4-0	0-3	3-2	0-3	1-1	2-0	*

Beazer Homes (Southern) League Midland Division Ten Year Records

	83/4	84/5	85/6	86/7	87/8	88/9	89/0	90/1	91/2	92/3
Alvechurch	–	–	–	–	–	–	–	20	21	–
Ashtree Highfield					(See Sandwell Borough)					
Atherstone United	–	–	–	–	4	2	–	–	–	–
Aylesbury United	5	2	–	–	–	–	–	–	–	–
Banbury United	18	17	17	12	10	16	21	–	–	–
Barri (ex-Barry Town)	–	–	–	–	–	–	5	6	4	4
Bedworth United	–	–	–	–	–	–	15	13	5	6
Bilston Town	–	–	7	18	17	13	17	14	12	14
Bridgend Town	16	–	–	–	–	–	–	–	–	–
Bridgnorth Town	12	10	8	14	11	17	12	17	17	16
Bromsgrove Rovers	3	6	1	–	–	–	–	–	–	–
Buckingham Town	–	–	–	13	12	–	–	–	–	–
Corby Town	–	–	–	13	12	–	–	–	–	–
Coventry Sporting	15	11	18	8	20	20	–	–	–	–
Dudley Town	4	1	–	–	8	9	9	19	22	17
Evesham United	–	–	–	–	–	–	–	–	–	15
Forest Green Rovers	11	14	14	9	9	12	10	18	19	19
Gloucester City	–	–	9	7	7	1	–	–	–	–
Grantham Town	–	–	10	11	3	5	14	9	13	13
Gresley Rovers	–	–	–	–	–	–	–	–	–	2
Halesowen Town	–	–	–	5	6	4	1	–	–	–
Hednesford Town	–	3	13	6	18	15	16	3	2	–
Hinckley Town	–	–	–	–	–	–	–	11	15	20
King's Lynn	–	–	–	–	13	19	13	8	14	21
Leamington	–	–	20	19	–	–	–	–	–	–
Leicester United	13	18	16	2	–	–	11	15	16	12
Merthyr Tydfil	8	12	3	3	1	–	–	–	–	–
Mile Oak Rovers & Youth	–	–	15	16	19	22	–	–	–	–
Milton Keynes City	19	–	–	–	–	–	–	–	–	–
Moor Green	6	4	19	4	2	–	–	–	–	–
Newport A.F.C.	–	–	–	–	–	–	–	7	10	5
Nuneaton Borough	–	–	–	–	–	6	3	5	6	1
Oldbury United	14	16	21	–	–	–	–	–	–	–
Paget Rangers	–	–	–	–	22	–	–	–	–	–
Racing Club Warwick	–	–	–	–	–	–	19	16	18	22
Redditch United	9	8	2	–	–	–	18	10	20	9
Rushden & Diamonds	–	–	–	–	–	–	–	–	–	3
Rushden Town	7	13	6	20	15	17	2	–	8	–
Sandwell Borough	–	–	–	–	–	14	22	–	–	–
Shepshed Charterhouse	2	–	–	–	–	–	–	–	–	–
Solihull Borough	–	–	–	–	–	–	–	–	1	–
Spalding United	–	–	–	–	–	8	6	22	–	–
Stourbridge	–	7	5	10	21	18	8	1	9	7
Stroud					(See Forest Green Rovers)					
Sutton Coldfield Town	–	9	12	17	5	10	7	12	3	8
Tamworth	20	–	–	–	–	3	4	4	7	10
Trowbridge Town	–	–	–	–	16	–	–	–	–	–
V.S. Rugby	10	5	4	1	–	–	–	–	–	–
Wellingborough Town	17	15	11	15	14	21	–	–	–	–
Weston-super-Mare	–	–	–	–	–	–	–	–	–	11
Willenhall Town	1	–	–	–	–	11	20	21	–	–
Yate Town	–	–	–	–	–	–	–	–	11	18
No. of Clubs	20	18	21	20	22	22	22	22	22	22

Beazer Homes League Secretary Dennis Strudwick presents the Beazer Homes League Midland Division runners-up trophy to Gresley Rovers skipper Richard Denby. Photo - Derrick Kinsey.

ARMITAGE '90

The stand at Armitage's ground. Photo - A J Earl.

Chairman: Daniel McMullan   **President:** S G Osborn
Secretary: F J Rought, 25 Lebanon Rd, Chase Terrace, Burntwood, Staffs (Tel: Ground - below).
Manager: Gary Haynes   **Coach:** A Hawksworth
Physio: M Howard.
General Manager: D McMullan   **Commercial Manager:** R Evans.
Ground: Kings Bromley Lane, Handsacre, Rugeley, Staffs WS15 4EB (0543 491077).
Capacity: 2,500   **Seats:** 300   **Cover:** 500   **Floodlights:** Yes
Colours: Green & white   **Change Colours:** Blue & white.
Sponsors: Armitage Shanks/ Bass Mitchell & Butlers.
Previous Names: None *(predecessors Armitage F.C., founded in 1915, ceased to operate in 1987).*
Previous League: Staffs Senior 90-91/ Midland Combination 91-93 *(predecessors: Staffs County/ West Midlands (Regional) 71-87).*
Record Gate: 800 v Notts County, friendly, August 1991.
Best F.A. Cup season: Not entered to date *(predecessors: 3rd Qualifying Rd).*
Best F.A. Vase season: Preliminary Rd 92-93 *(predecessors: 2nd Rd on two occasions).*
Best F.A. Trophy season: Not entered to date *(predecessors: 1st Qualifying Rd).*
Players progressing to Football League: P J Devlin (Notts County), D A Roberts (Wolves).
Clubhouse: Fully licensed Bar. Pool. Tea bar.
92-93 Captain: Chris Caulton.
92-93 P.o.Y.: Chris Caulton.
92-93 Top scorer: Jason Rhodes.
Local Newspapers: Burton Daily Mail, Lichfield Mercury.
Hons: Midlands Combination 92-93 (R-up 91-92), Walsall Snr Cup 91-92, Tony Allden Cup R-up 92-93 *(predecessors: West Midlands Lg Div 1 73-74, Walsall Snr Cup).*

PROGRAMME DETAILS:
Pages: 28 Price: 50p
Editor: C Bailey

BEDWORTH UNITED

Bedworth United 1992-93. S McGrory, A Piggon (Captain), J Rodwell, S Brown, R Battison, P Shields, T Emery. Front: S Ross, P Bowden, N Abderson, B Phillips (Manager - now Stafford Rangers), D Osborne, R Straw, T Smithers.

Chairman: Alan Robinson   **Vice Chairman:** Roy Whitehead   **President:** Harold Jones.
Secretary: Graham Bloxham, 43 Mount Pleasant Road, Bedworth, Nuneaton, Warks CV12 8EX.
Manager: Paul Thomas   **Asst Mgr:** Martin Sockett   **Press Officer:** Chairman
Ground: The Oval, Miners Welfare Park, Coventry Road, Bedworth CV12 8NN (0203 314302).
Directions: On B4113 Coventry to Bedworth road, less than 200yds from town centre next to swimming bath. One and a half miles from M6 junction 3.
Capacity: 7,000   **Cover:** 300   **Seats:** 300   **Floodlights:** Yes   **Metal Badges:** Yes
Club Shop: Yes, selling badges, programmes, shirts, hats, caps, club coats. Contact Tom Ison-Jacques (0203 314884).
Colours: Green & white   **Change colours:** Yellow   **Sponsors:** T.B.A.
Previous Leagues: Birmingham Comb. 47-54/ West Mids (at first Birmingham) Lg 54-72.
Previous Name: Bedworth Town 47-68   **Previous Ground:** British Queen Ground 11-39.
Midweek home matchday: Tuesday   **Reserve's Lge:** Ansells Midland Comb. (Res Div).
Record Attendance: 5,127 v Nuneaton Borough, Southern Lg Midland Division 23/2/82.
Best F.A. Cup season: 4th Qualifying Rd 1983/89/90
League clubs defeated in F.A. Cup: None.
Record win: 11-0   **Record defeat:** 1-10.
Record Fees - Paid: £1,750 for Colin Taylor (Hinckley Town, 1991-92)
         Received: £8,000 for I Hathaway (Mansfield Town, 1988-89).
Players progressing to Football League: Phil Huffer (Derby County 1953), Geoff Coleman (Northampton Town 1955), Ian Hathaway (Mansfield Town 1989).
Clubhouse: Social club open every day 7-11pm and weekend lunchtimes. Hot and cold bar food, pool, darts.
Club Record Goalscorer: Peter Spacey (1949-69)
Club Record Appearances: Peter Spacey.
92-93 Captain: Adrian Piggon
92-93 P.o.Y.: James Rodwell.
92-93 Top scorer: Martyn Twigger.
Local Newspapers: Bedworth Echo (312785/319548), Coventry Evening Telegraph (0203 633633)
Local Radio Stations: Mercia Sound, BBC CWR.
Hons: F.A. Trophy 2nd Rd 80-81, Birmingham Comb.(2) 48-50, Birmingham Snr Cup(3) 78-79 80-82, Midland Floodlit Cup 81-82 92-93.

'THE NON-LEAGUE PLAYERS'
1993-94 EDITION

AVAILABLE DURING THE SEASON, WILL FEATURE DETAILS OF BEDWORTH'S PLAYERS, AND INDEED THE PLAYERS OF ALL CLUBS IN THE TOP FOUR PYRAMID LEAGUES. FOR MORE DETAILS ON THIS PUBLICATION SEE THE ADVERT NEAR THE FRONT OF THIS DIRECTORY.

PROGRAMME DETAILS:
Pages: 24 **Price:** 50p
Editor: Peter Thompson
(Bedworth 311)

BILSTON TOWN

Bilston Town enjoyed a tremendous run in the F.A. Vase, but eventually bowed out in the Quarter-Finals at Canvey Island. Here they fall a goal behind to a header from the experienced Tony Mahoney. Photo - Roger Turner.

Chairman: Mr A Hickman   **President:** Dennis Turner MP.
Secretary: Mr Morris Baker, c/o Bilston Town F.C. (0902 491498).
Manager: Steve Bowater   **Asst Manager:** G Clarke   **Coach:** Michael Richards
Physio: Reg Pickering   **Press Officer:** Jeff Galloway (0902 491799).
Ground: Queen Street, Bilston WV14 7EX (0902 491498).
Directions: M6 junction 10, A454 towards Wolverhampton then pick up A563 towards Bilston and turn left into Beckett Street after a little over a mile, ground at bottom. 3 miles from Wolverhampton (BR), bus 45 from bus station passes ground. Buses 78 and 79 from Birmingham stop within quarter of a mile of ground.
Capacity: 4,000   **Cover:** 350   **Seats:** 350   **Floodlights:** Yes   **Metal Badges:** Yes
Club Shop: Yes, selling badges, pennants, key rings, pens, old and new non-League progs. Contact Paul Galloway, 4 Mervyn Rd, Bradley, Bilston, West Mids WV14 8DF.
Colours: Tangerine & white   **Change colours:** Blue & white   **Sponsors:** T.B.A.
Previous Names: Bilston Utd 1895-1932/ Bilston
Previous Ground: Pounds Lane 1895-1921.
Previous Leagues: Birmingham Comb. 07-21 48-54/ (Birmingham) West Mids 21-32 54-85.
Midweek home matchday: Tuesday   **Reserve Team's League:** N/A.
Record Attendance: 7,500 v Wolverhampton Wanderers, floodlight opening 1953. *Competitive: 7,000 v Halifax Town, F.A. Cup First Round 1968.*
Record win: 12-2 v Tipton Town   **Record defeat:** 0-8 v Merthyr Tydfil.
Best F.A. Cup season: 2nd Rd replay 72-73 (lost 0-1 at Barnet after 1-1 draw). Also 1st Rd 68-69.
League clubs defeated in F.A. Cup: None.
Record Fees - Paid: for Steve Gloucester.
    Received: From Southend United for Ron Poutney, 1975.
Players progressing to Football League: R Ellows (Birmingham), James Fletcher (Birmingham 1950), Stan Crowther (A Villa 1955), Ron Pountney (Southend 1975), K Price (Gillingham), Campbell Chapman (Wolves 1984).
Clubhouse: Open every night and weekend lunchtimes (normal pub hours). Usual club activities.
Club Record Scorer: Ron McDermott 78.
92-93 Captain: Jim Skidmore
92-93 P.o.Y.: Danny Williams
92-93 Top scorer: John Baker.
Local Newspapers: Express & Star, Evening Mail.
Local Radio Stations: Radio West Mids, WABC (Wol'ton), Beacon (Wol'ton), BRMB.
Honours: F.A. Tphy 2nd Rd 70-71 74-75, F.A. Vase QF 92-93, West Mids Lg 60-61 72-73 (R-up 22-23 70-71 73-74 74-75 75-76 84-85, Lg Cup 72-73 (R-up 65-66), Div 2 56-57), Birmingham Comb R-up 07-08 53-54, Staffs Senior Cup 57-58 59-60 60-61 61-62 (R-up 56-57 64-65 85-86), Birmingham Junior Cup 1895-96, Wednesbury Charity Cup 1981-81 81-82 82-83 84-85 (R-up 83-84).

PROGRAMME DETAILS:
Pages: 24 **Price:** 60p
Editor: J Galloway
(0902 491799)

BRIDGNORTH TOWN

Bridgnorth Town 1992-93. Back Row (L/R): Shaun Gilman, Jason Treharne, Mike Davidson, Peter Wilding, Carl Whitehouse, Paul Tester, Martin Lander, Trevor Beddow. Front: Steve Frisby, Danny Blocksidge, Larry Chambers, Mark Cornerford, Craig Hammond, Andy Taylor.

Chairman: Joe Heseltine **Vice Chairman:** Bernard Durnin **President:** Mike Williams
Secretary/Press Off.: Gordon Thomas, 7 Meadow Close, Oldbury Wells, Bridgnorth WV16 5HY (0746 765178).
Team Manager: Billy Ball **Asst Mgr:** Bob Macauley **Coach:** Bob Macauley
Physio: Carlton Leonard **Commercial Mgr:** Terry Brumpton (0902 671171).
Ground: Crown Meadow, Innage Lane, Bridgnorth, Salop WV16 6PZ (0746 762747/766064).
Directions: Follow signs for Shrewsbury (A458) over river bridge on by-pass, turn right for town centre at island, right at T-junction, 1st left into Victoria Rd, right at cross-road, follow road into Innage Lane, ground on left.
Capacity: 1,600 **Cover:** 700 **Seats:** 250 **Floodlights:** Yes **Metal Badges:** Yes
Club Shop: Yes, selling programmes, badges, pennants, pens, scarves and hats.
Colours: Blue/white/blue **Change colours:** All red. **Sponsors:** None.
Previous Name: St Leonards Old Boys (prior to the current club's formation in 1946).
Previous Leagues: Kidderminster & District (until 68)/ Midland Combination 68-83.
Midweek home matchday: Tuesday **Reserve's Lge:** Midland Combination (Reserve Div).
Record Attendance: 1,600 v South Shields, FA Vase 1976.
Best F.A. Cup season: 3rd Qualifying Rd 64-65.
League clubs defeated in F.A. Cup: None.
Record Fees - Paid: N/A **Received:** £10,000 for Delwyn Humphreys (to Kidderminster Harriers).
Players progressing to Football League: Roger Davies (Derby County).
Clubhouse: Open every evening and weekend lunchtimes. Darts, pool, fruit machines, dancehall. Hot meals on matchdays.
Club Record Scorer: Roger Davies 157 **Club Record Appearances:** Kevin Harris 426.
92-93 Captain: Larry Chambers **92-93 P.o.Y.:** Paul Evans.
92-93 Top scorer: Andy Taylor/ Danny Blocksidge.
Local Newspapers: Shropshire Star, Bridgnorth Journal, Express & Star.
Local Radio Stations: Beacon, BBC Radio Shropshire.
Honours: FA Vase 5th Rd 75-76, Midland Combination 79-80 82-83 (R-up 76-77 80-81, Lg Cup 78-79, Tony Allden Memorial Cup R-up), Kidderminster & District Lg, Shropshire Snr Cup 85-86, Shropshire County Cup 70-71 75-76 76-77 78-79 79-80, Welsh Amateur Cup 70-71, Shropshire Junior Cup - Bridgnorth are the only Shropshire side to have won all three county cups.

BRIDGNORTH Town Football Club

MIDLAND DIVISION

PROGRAMME DETAILS:
Pages: 24 **Price:** 60p
Editor: Terry Brumpton
(0902 671171)

CLEVEDON TOWN

The Clevedon Town side that won the Great Mills Western League championship under thus earned the club promotion to the Beazer Homes League Midland Division. A number of the players have now left the club and followed manager Terry Rowles to Taunton Town. Back Row (L/R): Jamie Ward, John Durham, Stuart Minall, Mark Stevens, Brendan Dowd, Ian Willmott, Gary Marshall. Front: Damon Palfrey, Wayne Morris, Nicky Brooks, Dave Ewens, Andy Perrett. Mascot: Master Perrett. Photo - James Wright.

President: Doug Hand   **Chairman:** B K Baker
Secretary: Mike Williams, 34 Robinia Walk, Whitchurch, Bristol BS14 0SH (0272 833835).
Manager: Steve Fahy   **Asst Manager:** T.B.A.   **Coach:** T.B.A.
Press Officer: Secretary   **Commercial Manager:** Keith Sheppard (c/o the club).
Ground: Hand Stadium, Davis Lane, Clevedon (0275 871636).
Directions: M5 Jct 20 - follow signs for Equestrian Centre; first left Central Way (at island just after motorway), 1st left Kenn Rd, 2nd left Davis Lane; ground half mile on right. Or from Bristol (B3130) left into Court Lane (opposite Clevedon Court), turn right after 1 mile, ground on left. Nearest BR station: Nailsea & Backwell. Buses from Bristol.
Seats: 300   **Cover:** 1,600   **Capacity:** 3,650   **Floodlights:** Yes   **Founded:** 1880
Club colours: Blue & white   **Change colours:** Yellow.
Midweek Matches: Wednesday
Reserve Team's League: Somerset Senior.
Previous Leagues: Weston & District/ Somerset Senior/ Bristol Charity/ Bristol & District/ Bristol Suburban/ Western 74-93.
Previous Grounds: Dial Hill (til early 1890's)/ Teignmouth Road (til 1991).
Previous Names: Clevedon F.C., Ashtonians (clubs merged in 1974).
Record Gate: 1,295 v Tiverton Town, Western League Premier Division 24/4/93 *(At Teignmouth Road: 2,300 v Billingham Synthonia, F.A. Amateur Cup, 52-53).*
Record win: 18-0 v Dawlish Town (H), Western League Premier Division 24/4/93.
Best F.A. Cup season: 1st Round Proper.
Best F.A. Amateur Cup season: 3rd Round Proper, 52-53.
Best F.A. Vase season: 5th Round, 92-93.
Clubhouse: Open every midday and evening, separate skittle alley on ground. Real ales. Tea bar within ground sells confectionary, crisps and hot and cold drinks.
92-93 Captain: Nicky Brooks.
92-93 P.O.Y.: Brendan Dowd.
92-93 Top scorer: Andy Perrett, 60.
Local Radio Stations: Radio Bristol
Local Newspapers: South Avon Mercury
Hons: Western Lg 92-93 (R-up 91-92, Lg Cup R-up 92-93), Bristol Charity Lg, Somerset Snr Cup 01-02 04-05 28-29 76-77, Somerset Snr Lg Div 1(reserves) 92-93.

PROGRAMME DETAILS:
Pages: T.B.A. **Price:** 50p
Editor: T.B.A.

Formed: 1893   # DUDLEY TOWN   The Robins

Dudley Town 1992-93. Back Row (L/R): Graham Thompson (Coach), Mick Washington (Asst Manager), John Street, Steve Moore, Mark Clifton, Neil Tomlinson, Chris Mason, Ian Scarr, Anton Day, Andy Harnett, Chris Field, Alan Edwards, Chris Marriott, Stuart Preece, Malcolm Woodbine (Manager). Front: Andy Hodgetts, Steve Field, Loy Stewart, Kevin Woodbine, Stuart Leeding, Gavin Whitehouse, Luke Yates, Phil Cartwright.

Chairman: Trevor Lester   **Vice Chairman:** Philip Edwards   **President:** N D Jeynes.
Secretary: Tony Turpin, 24 Andrew Drive, Short Heath, Willenhall WV12 5PP (0922 475541).
Manager: Malcolm Woodbine   **Coach:** Mick Washington   **Press Officer:** Secretary
Ground: The Round Oak Stadium, John Street, Brierley Hill, West Mids (0384 263478/78560).
Directions: From Dudley take the A461 towards Stourbridge for about 2 miles and on entering Brierley Hill turn right at lights onto on B4180 (John Str.), ground 200 yds on right. Two and a half miles from Stourbridge (BR).
Capacity: 3,000   **Cover:** 300   **Seats:** 234   **Floodlights:** Yes   **Metal Badges:** Yes
Club Shop: Yes, selling programmes and badges. Contact Frank Whitehouse.
Colours: Red/white/black   **Change colours:** All yellow.
Sponsors: Dudley Building Society/ Thornleigh Freight.
Previous Leagues: West Mids (previously Birmingham) 1898-1915 35-38 53-82/ Midland (Worcs) Combination 29-32/ Birmingham Combination 32-35 45-53.
Previous Grounds: The Sports Centre, Birmingham Rd 1936-85.
Midweek home matchday: Wednesday   **Reserves' League:** None.
Record Fee Received: £25,000 for Gary Piggott (West Bromwich Albion, March 1991).
Record Gate: 3,000 v West Bromwich Albion, pre-season friendly 1991. *(At old ground; 16,500 for the official opening (a representative game) in 1936).*
Best F.A. Cup season: 1st Rd replay 76-77 (v York).
League clubs defeated in F.A. Cup: None.
Record win: 8-0 v Banbury, 1965.
Players progressing to Football League: Albert Broadbent (Notts Co 1952), Joe Mayo (Walsall 1972), Ken Price (Southend 1976), Andy Reece (Bristol Rovers 1987), Russell Bradley (Nottm Forest 1988), John Muir (Doncaster 1989), Gary Piggott (West Bromwich Albion 1991).
Clubhouse: Dudley Town Sports & Social Club, John Street, Brierley Hill. Open nightly, all day Saturday and Sunday lunchtimes. Bar, lounge bar, ballroom, bowling green etc. Bar snacks available.
Club Record Scorer: Frank Treagust, 56 (47-48).
Club Record Appearances: Brendon Hackett & John Muir, 55.
92-93 Captain & P.o.Y.: Chris Field   **92-93 Top scorer:** Andy Hodgetts.
Local Newspapers: Express & Star, Dudley Evening Mail, Birmingham Post, Sunday Mercury.
Local Radio Stations: Beacon Radio, BRMB, BBC Radio West Midlands.
Honours: FA Trophy 2nd Rd 84-85, Southern Lg Midland Div 84-85, Birmingham Comb 33-34 (R-up 34-35 47-48), Midland (Worcs) Comb 31-32 (R-up 29-30 30-31), West Mids Lg Cp R-up 75-76 (Div 2 Cp R-up 80-81), Birmingham Senior Cp 85-86 (R-up 64-65 83-84), Worcs Senior Cp 45-46(joint)(R-up 84-85), Camkin Cp 64-65, Worcs Junior Cp 83-84.

PROGRAMME DETAILS:
Pages: 24 Price: 50p
Editor: T.B.A.

'THE NON-LEAGUE PLAYERS'
1993-94 EDITION

AVAILABLE DURING THE SEASON, WILL FEATURE DETAILS OF DUDLEY TOWN'S PLAYERS, AND INDEED THE PLAYERS OF ALL CLUBS IN THE TOP FOUR PYRAMID LEAGUES. FOR MORE DETAILS ON THIS PUBLICATION SEE THE ADVERT NEAR THE FRONT OF THIS DIRECTORY.

EVESHAM UNITED

The Robins

Evesham United 1992-93. Back Row (L/R): Tim Davies, Ricky Hooman, Micky Rivers, Chris Taylor, Sean Cotterill, Scott Crane, Jon Parry. Front: Neil Emms, Colin Day, Mick Brennan, Joe Rawle, Nigel Russell, Trevor Whittingham. Photo - Gavin Ellis-Neville.

Chairman: T.B.A.　　　　**Vice Chairman:** R H Stanley.　　　　**President:** M E H Davies
Secretary/Commercial Mgr: Mike J Peplow, 68 Woodstock Rd, St Johns, Worcester WR2 5NF (0905 425993).
Manager: John Busst　　　**Asst Manager:** Gary Webb　　　**Coach:** Mark Fogarty.
Physio: Ricky Harber　　　**Press Officer:** Graham Hill (0905 351653)
Ground: Common Rd, Evesham, Worcs WR11 4PU (0386 442303).
Ground Directions: From Evesham High Street turn into Swan Lane, continue down hill between Willmotts factory called Conduit Hill into Common Rd, ground 200yds down on right just before railway bridge. 5 minutes walk from Evesham BR station.
Seats: 350　　　**Capacity:** 2,000　　　**Cover:** 600　　　**Floodlights:** Yes　　**Metal Badges:** Yes
Club Shop: Yes, selling programmes, pennants, scarves and ties. Contact Darren Attwood c/o the club.
Colours: Red & white/red/red　　　**Change Colours:** Black & white/black/black
Club Sponsors: Safeway.
Midweek matches: Wednesday　　　**Reserves' League:** Midland Comb. Reserve Div.
Previous Name: Evesham Town　　　**Previous Ground:** The Crown Meadow (pre-1968).
Previous Lges: Worcester/ Birmingham Comb./ Midland Comb. 51-55 65-90/ West Midlands Regional 55-62.
Record Gate: 2,338 v West Bromwich Albion, friendly 18/7/92.
Record win: 11-3 v West Heath United.
Record Fee Paid: £1,500; to Hayes for Colin Day, 1992.
Record Fee Received: £5,000 for Simon Brain (to Cheltenham Town).
Players who have progressed to Football League: Billy Tucker, Gary Stevens (Cardiff 1977), Kevin Rose (Lincoln 1978), Andy Preece (Northampton 1986), Simon Brain (Hereford, via Cheltenham Town).
Clubhouse: Open matchdays and training nights. Food available in club and from tea hut on matchdays.
Club Record Scorer: Sid Brain.
Club Record Appearances: Rob Candy.
92-93 Captain: Sean Cotterill
92-93 P.o.Y: Sean Cotterill.
92-93 Top Scorer: Neil Emms.
Local Press: Evesham Journal (0386 765678), Worcester Evening News (0905 748200), Gloucester Echo.
Local Radio Stations: Radio Wyvern, BBC Hereford & Worcester.
Hons: F.A. Amateur Cup R-up 23-24, F.A. Vase QF 91-92, Worcs Snr Urn(2) 76-78 (R-up 90-91), Midland Comb.(6) 52-53 54-55 65-66 67-69 91-92 (Chal. Cup 53-54 87-88 91-92 (R-up(5) 54-55 71-72 83-84 88-90)), Worcs Comb. 52-53 54-55; B'gham Comb. R-up 30-31, Evesham Hosp. Cup 89-90, Tony Allden Mem. Cup 1973 1988 1992.

EVESHAM UNITED
FOOTBALL CLUB
COMMON ROAD, EVESHAM
THE ROBINS　　　1991-92
SPONSORED BY SAFEWAY

PROGRAMME DETAILS:
Pages: 24 Price: 50p
Editor: Graham Hill
(0905 351653)

FOREST GREEN ROVERS Rovers

Club captain Russell Wilton clears during the Centenary match against Portsmouth on 1st August 1992. Russell was also celebrating his testimonial season.

Chairman: Andy Coburn   **President:** G C Mills, MBE.
Secretary/Press Officer: Colin Peake, C/O Western Thermal Ltd, Unit 14, Springfield Business Centre, Stonehouse, Gloucestershire GL10 3SX (0452 523126).
Manager: Pat Casey   **Asst Manager:** John Evans   **Physio:** Adrian Tandy.
Ground: 'The Lawn', Nympsfield Road, Forest Green, Nailsworth, Glos. GL6 0ET (0453 834860).
Directions: About 4 miles south of Stroud on A46 to Bath. In Nailsworth turn into Spring Hill off mini r'bout - ground approximately 1 mile up hill on left. The nearest BR station is Stroud.
Capacity: 1,995   **Cover:** 800   **Seats:** 200   **Floodlights:** 138.4 lux
Club Shop: Yes - open matchdays.
Colours: Black & white stripes/black/red   **Change colours:** Red & white stripes/white/white.
Sponsors: Sheffield Insulations.
Previous Lges: Stroud & Dist. 1890-1921/ Glos Northern Snr 22-67/ Glos Co. 69-73 /Hellenic 73-82.
Previous Name: Stroud FC, 1989-92.
Previous Ground: None.
Midweek home matchday: Tuesday   **Youth Team's League:** Midland Floodlit Yth.
Record Attendance: 2,200 v Wolverhampton Wanderers, floolight inauguration 1981.
Best F.A. Cup season: 3rd Qualifying Rd 87-88.
League clubs defeated in F.A. Cup: None.
Players progressing to Football League: Graham Rogers (Newport County 1985), Mike England (Bristol Rovers 1985), Kevin Gill (Newport County 1985).
Clubhouse: (0453 833295). Bar and lounge, open every night.
Steward: Bob Cowley.
92-93 Captain: Russell Wilton
92-93 P.o.Y.: Gary French
92-93 Top scorer: Christian White 24 (18 in league)
Local Newspapers: Stroud News & Journal, Gloucester Citizen.
Local Radio Stations: Severn Sound, BBC Radio Gloucestershire.
Honours: FA Vase 81-82, FA Trophy 3rd Rd 90-91, Hellenic Lg 81-82, Stroud & Dursley Lg 02-03, Gloucestershire Northern Senior Lg 37-38 49-50 50-51, Gloucestershire Senior Cup 84-85 85-86 86-87, Gloucestershire Senior Amateur Cup (North) 26-27 45-46 71-72 75-76 77-78, Gloucestershire Senior Professional Cup 84-85 85-86.

'THE NON-LEAGUE PLAYERS'
1993-94 EDITION

AVAILABLE IN SEPTEMBER, WILL FEATURE DETAILS OF FOREST GREEN'S PLAYERS, AND INDEED THE PLAYERS OF ALL CLUBS IN THE TOP FOUR PYRAMID LEAGUES. FOR MORE DETAILS ON THIS PUBLICATION SEE THE ADVERT NEAR THE FRONT OF THIS DIRECTORY.

PROGRAMME DETAILS:
Pages: 24 **Price:** 60p
Editor: Keith Sheppard

GRANTHAM TOWN

Gingerbreads

The South Kesteven Sports Stadium, Grantham.

Chairman: Malcolm Pearce   **President:** The Baroness of Kesteven.
Secretary: Mr Pat Nixon, 2 Eskdale Road, Grantham, Lincs NG31 8EP (0476 64408).
Manager: Allen Crombie   **Asst Mgr:** Paul Buckthorp   **Physio:** Beverley Myers.
Ground: The South Kesteven Sports Stadium, Trent Road, Grantham, Lincs (0476 62011).
Directions: Midway between A1 and A52 on edge of Earlesfield Industrial Estate; from A1 take A607 to Earlsfield Ind. Est and continue into Trent Rd. From Nottingham on A52 thru Barrowby and turn right into Trent Rd. From Boston on A52 follow A607 across traffic lights to Trent Rd.
Capacity: 5,000   **Cover:** 1,750   **Seats:** 750   **Floodlights:** Yes   **Metal Badges:** Yes
Club Shop: Yes, selling programmes and club souvenirs.
Colours: Black & white stripes   **Change colours:** Yellow & blue
Sponsors: Malcolm Pearce Carpets.
Previous Leagues: Midland Amateur Alliance/ Central Alliance 11-25 59-61/ Midland Co's 25-59 61-72/ Southern 72-79/ Northern Prem. 79-85.
Prev. Name: Grantham F.C., pre-1980's   **Previous Ground:** London Road until October 1990.
Midweek home matchday: Tuesday   **Reserve Team's League:** None.
Record Attendance: 1,402 v Ilkeston Town, FA Cup Preliminary Rd 91-92 *(At London Road: 6,578 v Middlesborough, FA Cup 3rd Rd 1974).*
Best F.A. Cup season: 3rd Rd 1883-84 86-87 1973-74. Competition Proper on 23 occasions; 1877-79 80-81 83-88 1928-29 35-36 45-46 47-48 49-50 61-62 65-71 72-74 75-76.
League clubs defeated in F.A. Cup: Stockport 70-71, Rochdale 73-74.
Record win: 13-0 v Rufford Colliery (H), F.A. Cup Preliminary Rd 15/9/34.
Record defeat: 0-16 v Notts County Rovers (A), Midland Amateur Alliance 22/10/1892.
Record Fees - Paid: £8,500 for Gary Jones (Doncaster Rovers, 1989)
             Received: £20,000 for Gary Crosby (Nottingham Forest, 1987)
Players progressing to Football League: Archie Burgeon (Spurs 1930's), Syd Bycroft (Doncaster 1934), Ernest Morris (Halifax 1950), Peter Thompson & Robbie Cooke (Peterborough 1964 & 80), James Rayner (Notts County 1964), David Dall (Scunthorpe 1979), Nick Jarvis & Hugh Wood (Scunthorpe 1980), Devon White (Bristol Rvrs 1986), Terry Curran (Grimsby 1987), Gary Crosby (Nottm Forest 1987), Alan Kennedy (Wrexham 1987), Richard Wilson (Lincoln 1987).
Clubhouse: (0476 593506) Open evenings and weekends. Bar, darts, pool etc. Frequent live entertainment. Available for functions - contact Pete Credland (0476 74383).
Club Record Goalscorer: Jack McCartney 416
Club Record Appearances: Chris Gardiner 664.
92-92 Captain: Adrian Speed.   **92-92 Top scorer:** Dale Watkins 12.
92-92 P.o.Y.: Adrian Speed (Mgr's), Andy Bullimore (Players')
Local Newspapers: Grantham Journal (0476 62291), Nottingham Evening Post (0602 482000), Melton & Grantham Trader (0476 74433), Grantham Citizen, Lincolnshire Echo (0522 525252).
Local Radio Stations: Radio Lincolnshire, Lincs FM.
Hons: F.A. Tphy QF 71-72, Southern Lg R-up 73-74 (Div 1 Nth 72-73 78-79, Merit Cup 72-73), Midland Co's Lg(3) 63-64 70-72 (R-up 37-38 64-65 69-70, Lg Cup 68-69 70-71), Midland Amtr Lg 10-11 (Lg Cup R-up 10-11), Central All. 24-25 (Southern Div R-up 59-60), Lincs Snr Cup 1884-85 1936-37 (R-up(5) 34-36 39-40 45-47), Lincs Co. 'A' Cup(3) 53-54 60-62 (R-up 49-50 52-53 57-58), Lincs Co. Snr Cup 71-72 82-83 (R-up 80-81).

PROGRAMME DETAILS:
Pages: 36 **Price:** 70p
Editor: Ron Mole

HINCKLEY TOWN

Hinckley Town's famous chairman David Needham (ex-Nottingham Forest) pictured in his previous non-League post; as Kettering Town's manager in 1986 (fourth from left, front row). Photo - Malc Tompkins.

Chairman: David Needham **Vice Chairman:** Mike Sutton.
Secretary: Brian Edwards, 35 Woodbrook Rd, Loughborough, Leics (0509 233399).
Manager: John Martin **Physio:** Mark Moore.
Commercial Manager: Joyce Reid.
Ground: Leicester Road Sports Ground, Leicester Road, Hinckley, Leics (0455 615062).
Directions: From M69 junction 1 take A447 then A47 towards Leicester. Ground on A47 about 2 miles from town centre (half way between Earl Shilton and Hinckley).
Capacity: 2,000 **Cover:** 200 **Seats:** 200 **Floodlights:** Yes
Club Shop: Yes, selling programmes, books, vidoes, badges, mugs. Contact Mr Brian Blockley (0455 635148).
Colours: Claret & blue **Change colours:** Yellow. **Sponsors:** T.B.A.
Previous Name: Westfield Rovers 1958-66.
Previous Grounds: Westfield Playing Field 58-60/ Coventry Road Recreation Ground 60-68.
Previous Lges: Sth Leicester & Nuneaton Amtr/ Leics Snr 72-86/ Central Mids 86-88/ West Mids 88-90.
Midweek home matchday: Wednesday **Reserve Team's League:** Leicester & Dist.
Record Attendance: 2,000 v Real Sociedad, floodlight opening, 1986. *Competitive:* 1,022 v Nuneaton Borough, *Southern League Midland Division 1/1/91.*
Best F.A. Cup season: 4th Qualifying Rd 1988-89.
League clubs defeated in F.A. Cup: None.
Record win: 10-0 v Kettering Town Reserves, Central Midlands League B.E. Webbe Cup.
Record defeat: 0-10 v Barry Town, Southern League Midlands Division.
Record Fees - Paid: £1,600 for John Lane (V.S. Rugby) **Received:** £1,750 for Colin Taylor (Bedworth United).
Clubhouse: Bar with facilities for functions. Open matchdays and training nights (Tuesday & Thursday). Sandwiches available.
92-93 Captain: Paul Purser
92-93 P.o.Y.: Dennis Hewitt
92-93 Top scorer: Scott Kempin.
Local Newspapers: Hinckley Times (0455 238383), Leicester Mercury (512512).
Local Radio Stations: Radio Leicester.
Honours: FA Vase 3rd Rd 85-86, West Mids (Bank's) Lg 89-90, Central Midlands Lg 86-87 (R-up 87-88, B E Webbe Cup R-up 86-87 87-88, Gerry Mills Cup R-up 87-88), Leics Senior Lg R-up 83-84 (Div 2 72-73, Div 2 Cup 72-73), Leicestershire Challenge Cup 89-90 (R-up 90-91), Leics Senior Cup (Jelson Holmes) R-up 87-88, Leics Senior Cup 88-89, M & B Floodlit Cup 88-89, Midland F'lit Cup R-up 91-92.

HINCKLEY TOWN F.C.
v.
KINGS LYNN

OFFICIAL PROGRAMME
50p

PROGRAMME DETAILS:
Pages: 16 **Price:** 50p
Editor: Alan Mason

KING'S LYNN

The majestic main stand at the Walks Stadium. Photo - Paul Proctor.

Chairman: J Dollimore   **President:** Jim Chandler.
Secretary: John Franks, The Lyntons, Stamford Rd, Marholm, Peterborough PE6 7HX (0733 267272).
Manager: John Gidman   **Asst Manager/Coach:** Dominic McCallam.
Physio: Dave Betts.
Ground: The Walks Stadium, Tennyson Road, King's Lynn PE30 5PB (0553 760060).
Directions: At mini r-about arriving from A10/A47 take Vancouse Avenue. Ground on left after a quarter mile. Quarter mile from King's Lynn (BR), half mile from bus station.
Capacity: 8,200   **Cover:** 5,000   **Seats:** 1,200   **Club Shop:** Yes   **Metal Badges:** Yes
Colours: All royal blue (yellow trim)   **Change colours:** All yellow (blue trim)
Previous Leagues: Norfolk & Suffolk/ Eastern C'ties 35-39 48-54/ UCL 46-48/ Midland C'ties 54-58/ NPL 80-83.
Previous Name: Lynn Town   **Previous Ground:** None.   **Sponsors:** Skoda.
Midweek home matchday: Tuesday   **Reserve Team's League:** None.
Record Attendance: 12,937 v Exeter, FA Cup 1st Rd 50-51. *(44,916 saw the Cup tie at Everton (below)).*
Best F.A. Cup season: 3rd Rd 61-62 (lost 0-4 at Everton). Competition Proper on 14 occasions; 05-06 37-38 49-50 51-52 58-63 64-65 68-69 71-72 73-74 84-85.
League clubs defeated in F.A. Cup: Aldershot 59-60, Coventry 61-62.
Players progressing to Football League: Norman Rowe (Derby 1949), Brian Taylor & Polly Ward (Bradford Park Avenue 54 & 55), Tom Reynolds (Darlington 54), Graham Reed (Sunderland 55), Peter McCall (Bristol City 55), John Neal (Swindon 57), Tom Dryburgh (Oldham 57), John Hunter (Barrow 59), John Stevens (Swindon), George Catleugh (Watford), George Walters (Chesterfield 64), Peter McNamee (Notts County 1966), Wayne Biggins (Burnley & Manchester City), Jackie Gallagher (Peterborough 80), Andy Higgins (Rochdale 83), Neil Horwood (Grimsby 86), Darren Rolph (Barnsley 87), Mark Howard (Stockport 88).
Clubhouse: Normal hours, extension for matchdays.
Club Record Scorer: Mick Wright 1,152 (British Record)
Club Record Appearances: Malcolm Lindsay 321.
92-93 Captain: Clive Worthington.
92-93 P.o.Y.: Clive Worthington.
92-93 Top scorer: Dave Robinson.
Local Newspapers: Lynn News & Advertiser (0553 761188), Eastern Daily Press (0603 628311).
Honours: FA Amtr Cup R-up 1900-01, FA Tphy 2nd Rd 78-79, FA Vase 4th Rd 90-91, Southern Lg R-up 84-85 (Div 1 R-up 63-64), NPL Presidents Cup 82-83, Eastern Co's Lg 53-54 (R-up 49-50 52-53) (Lg Cup 53-54), Norfolk & Suffolk Lg(8)(R-up(6)), E Anglian Lg R-up(2), Norfolk Snr Cup(19) 1882-84 86-87 89-90 98-99 1907-08 23-25 31-32 33-34 36-37 38-39 51-52 53-58 (R-up(19)), Norfolk Prem. Cup 68-69(jt) 73-74, E Anglian Cup(4) 65-68 84-85 (R-up(3)), Eastern Prof. F'lit Lg 68-69.

PROGRAMME DETAILS:
Pages: TBA Price: TBA
Editor: TBA

LEICESTER UNITED

Leicester United's Chris Tonge heads in the first goal in the 2-1 home win against Bridgnorth Town in the Beazer Homes League Midland Division. Photo - Chris Monument.

Chairman: John Potter **Vice Chairman:** Gary Glover.
Secretary: Gary Glover, 19 Bachelor Rd, Fleckney, Leicester LE8 0BE (0533 403271).
Manager: Tommy Elliott **Asst Manager:** Chris Vernon **Coach:** Glen McNulty.
Physio: Brett Pruce **Commercial Manager/Press Officer:** Glen McNulty.
Ground: United Park, Winchester Road, Blaby, Leicester LE8 3HN (0533 778998).
Directions: 2 miles from junct 21 M1 & M69. 1st exit on approach road onto B582. Left at 1st r-about, right at next r-about (Everards Brewery) towards Narborough. Left at r-bout (Huntsman PH), through Whetstone village to next r-about, across A426 into Blaby, through lights and go 100 yds to next junction, right and ground on left immediately after residential area.
Capacity: 4,000 **Cover:** 1,300 **Seats:** 252 **Club Shop:** Yes **Metal Badges:** Yes
Cols: Red & white/black/red **Change colours:** All blue. **Sponsors:** T.B.A.
Previous Name: Enderby Town (1900-81). **Previous Ground:** George Street (until 1985).
Previous Leagues: Leics Senior 49-50 51-69/ East Mids 69-72.
Midweek home matchday: Tuesday **Reserve Team's League:** Ansells Midland Combination.
Record Attendance: 1,058 v Hinckley Town, 26/12/90.
Best F.A. Cup season: 1st Rd 77-78 (lost 1-6 at AP Leamington).
Best F.A. Trophy season: 3rd Rd replay 78-79 (lost 2-4 at Bishop Auckland).
Record Fees - Paid: £1,000
                Received: £22,500 for Keith Scott (Lincoln).
Players progressing to Football League: Richard Dixey (Burnley 1974), Cohen Griffith (Cardiff), Neil Lyne & Tony Loughlan (Nottm Forest), Dave Puttnam & Keith Scott (Lincoln), Graham Cross (Lincoln 1979), Robert Atkins (Sheffield Utd 1982).
Clubhouse: Open every day and evening. Meals available.
92-93 Captain: Steve Ross
92-93 P.o.Y.: Chris Tonge
92-93 Top scorer: Alan Liqorish.
Local Newspapers: Leicester Mercury. Oadby & Wigston Mail.
Local Radio Stations: Radio Leicester.
Honours: Southern Lg Midland Div R-up 86-87, Leics Senior Lg 62-63 64-65 66-67 (R-up 59-60 63-64 65-66 67-68 68-69, Div 2 58-59 (R-up 51-52)), East Mids Regional Lg 70-71 71-72 (Lg Cup 70-71), Leics Snr Cup 61-62 64-65 66-67 70-71 72-73 78-79, Leics Challenge Cup 78-79 79-80 86-87 87-88, Rolleston Charity Cup 92-93.

LEICESTER - UNITED

WELCOME TO

UNITED PARK

OFFICIAL
MATCHDAY PROGRAMME

PROGRAMME DETAILS:
Pages: 20 **Price:** 50p
Editor: T.B.A.

NEWPORT A.F.C.

Newport A.F.C. Back Row (L/R): P Towler, P Coyne, P Green, P Mason, G Brown, M Kendall, S Jones, S Lowndes. Front: J Lewis, C Williams, M Price, K Charles, L Jones, D Poretta.

Chairman: Mr David Hando   **President:** Brian Toms, MBE.
Secretary: Mike Everett, 66 Gibbs Rd, Newport, Gwent NP9 8AU (0633 280932).
Manager: Graham Rogers   **Asst Manager:** John Lewis   **Coach/Physio:** Tony Gilbert
Coach: David Williams   **Press Officer:** Wallace Brown (0633 265500).
Ground Directions & Ground details: As Gloucester City (see page 492).
Club Shop: Yes, selling metal badges, scarves, pennants, replica shirts, back issues of programme, sportswear, videos, mugs, bookmarks etc.
Colours: All amber   **Colours:** Green & white/green/green   **Sponsors:** TBA
Previous Leagues: Hellenic 89-90.
Previous Grounds: London Road, Moreton-in-the-Marsh 89-90.
Previous Names: None. Newport AFC were formed after the demise of Newport County in 1988-89.
Midweek matchday: Wednesday   **Reserve Team's League:** None.
Record Attendance: At Somerton Park: 2,354 v Moreton Town, friendly 13/8/90 (competitive game: 2,271 v Redditch Utd, Southern Lge 22/8/90). At Moreton: 594 v Pegasus Juniors, Hellenic Lge 19/8/89. At Gloucester: 810 v Sutton Utd, F.A. Cup 4th Qualifying Rd, 3/11/92. *Newport County had a crowd of 24,268 against Cardiff at Somerton Park in 1937.*
Best F.A. Cup season: 4th Qualifying Rd 92-93.
Best F.A. Trophy season: 1st Rd Proper 91-92.
Record win: 9-0 v Pontlottyn Blast Furnace (A), Welsh Cup 1/9/90.
Record defeat: 0-4 v Stourbridge (H), Beazer Homes Southern Lge Midland Div., 25/2/92.
Clubhouse: Open 2 hours before kick-off and three hours after (approx). Pasties available in club. Burgers, hot dogs, hot drinks etc available within ground.
Club Record Goalscorer: Chris Lilygreen.
Club Record Appearances: C Lilygreen, 181.
92-93 Captain: Mark Price
92-93 P.o.Y.: Linden Jones
92-93 Top scorer: Chris Lilygreen.
Local Newspapers: South Wales Argus, South Wales Echo.
Local Radio Stations: Red Dragon.
Honours: Hellenic Lg 89-90 (Lg Cup 89-90).

PROGRAMME DETAILS:
Pages: 20 **Price:** 80p
Editor: Wallace Brown
(0633 265500)

RACING CLUB WARWICK _{Racing}

Racing Club Warwick's Townsend Meadow Ground. Photo - Keith Clayton.

Chairman: Mr J Wright **Vice Chairman:** Mr E Jenkins.
Secretary: Patrick Murphy, 20 Dadglow Rd, Bishops Itchington, Leamington Spa CV33 0TG (0926 612675).
Manager: Malcolm Sockett **Asst Manager:** Len Derby
Press Officer: Secretary **Commercial Manager:** Robin Smith.
Ground: Townsend Meadow, Hampton Road, Warwick CV34 6JP (0926 495786).
Directions: On the B4095 Warwick to Redditch road (via Henley in Arden) next to owners' & trainers' car park of Warwick Racecourse. From M40 jct 15 (one and a half miles) take A429 into Warwick, left into Shakespeare Ave., straight over island, right at T-junction into Hampton Rd, ground 300yds on left. 2 miles from Warwick BR station.
Capacity: 1,000 **Cover:** 200 **Seats:** 200 **Floodlights:** Yes **Metal Badges:** Yes
Club Shop: Scarves, mugs, badges, programmes - contact Robin Lamb.
Colours: Gold/black/black **Change colours:** Red/white/white **Sponsors:** N/A.
Previous Leagues: Birmingham & West Midlands Alliance/ Warwickshire Combination/ West Midlands (Regional) 67-72/ Midland Combination 72-89.
Previous Name: Saltisford Rovers 1919-68/ Warwick Saltisford 68-70.
Midweek home matchday: Wednesday
Reserve Team's League: Ansells Midland Combination (Reserve Division).
Record Attendance: 1,000 v Halesowen Town, F.A. Cup 1987.
League clubs defeated in F.A. Cup: None.
Record Fees - Paid: £1,000 for Dave Whetton (Bedworth United)
     Received: £2,000 for Ian Gorrie (Atherstone Utd).
Record win: 9-1   **Record defeat:** 2-6.
Clubhouse: (0926 495786). Open every evening and and Fri/Sat/Sun & Mon lunchtimes.
Club Record Goalscorer: Steve Edgington.
Club Record Appearances: Steve Cooper 600.
92-93 Captain: Morton Titterton.
92-93 P.o.Y.:
92-93 Top scorer: Mark Hodgkinson/ Darren Deeley.
Local Newspapers: Warwick Advertiser, Leamington Courier, Coventry Evening Telegraph.
Local Radio Stations: BBC Radio Coventry.
Hons: F.A. Vase 4th Rd 77-78, Midland Combination 87-88 (R-up 88-89), Warwick Lg 33-34 34-35 35-36, Birmingham & West Mids Alliance 48-49, Birmingham & Dist Alliance Senior Cup 49-50, Leamington & Dist Lg 37-38 45-46 46-47 47-48, Leamington Hospital Cup 37-38 46-47, Warwick Cinderella Cup 35-36 36-37 37-38 38-39 46-47, T G John Cup 36-37, Leamington Junior Cup 38-39 46-47.

PROGRAMME DETAILS:
Pages: 20 **Price:** T.B.A.
Editor: Roger Redfern

Formed: 1900

REDDITCH UNITED

The Reds

Redditch United 1992-93. Back Row (L/R - players' names only): Kevin Seivwright, Justin Taylor, Paul Molloy, Ron Walker, Tony Donnelly, Micky Andrews, Paul Levy. Front: Barry Williams, Paul Snowball, Jimmy Williams, Michael Warner, Dennis Mulholland, Robert Smith. Photo - Keith Clayton.

Chairman: Mr R T Berry **President:** Bob Thompson.
Secretary: M A Langfield, 174 Harport Road, Redditch, Worcs B98 7PE (0527 26603).
Manager: Paul Hendrie **Asst Manager:** Colin Walsh **Physio:** Jack Chapman.
Commercial Mgr: Dave Roberts **Press Officer:** R Newbold (0527 27516).
Ground: Valley Stadium, Bromsgrove Road, Redditch B97 4RN (0527 67450).
Directions: Access 7 on town centre ring-road takes you into Bromsgrove Road (via Unicorn Hill) - ground entrance 400yds past traffic lights on right. Arriving from Bromsgrove take first exit off dual carriageway. Ground 400 yds from Redditch BR station and town centre.
Capacity: 9,500 **Cover:** 2,000 **Seats:** 400 **Floodlights:** Yes **Club Shop:** No.
Colours: Red & white stripes/red/red
Change colours: Black & white stripes/black/black.
Sponsors: Hermitage Windows & Conservatories.
Previous Leagues: Birmingham Combination 05-21 29-39 46-53/ West Midlands 21-29 53-72/ Southern 72-79/ GMV Conference (then Alliance Premier League) 79-80.
Previous Name: Redditch Town **Prev. Ground:** HDA Spts Ground, Millsborough Rd.
Midweek home matchday: Tuesday **Reserves' League:** Ansells Midland Comb. Res Div.
Record Attendance: 5,500 v Bromsgrove, league match 54-55.
Best F.A. Cup season: 1st Rd replay 71-72 (lost 0-4 at P'boro after 1-1 draw). Also 1st Rd 71-72.
League clubs defeated in F.A. Cup: None.
Record Fees - Paid: £3,000 for Paul Joinson
  Received: £42,000 for David Farrell (Aston Villa, 1991).
Players progressing to Football League: N Davis (Aston Villa), Hugh Evans (Birmingham 1947), Trevor Lewes (Coventry 1957), David Gilbert (Chesterfield 1960), Mike Tuohy (Southend Utd 1979), Neil Smith (Liverpool), David Farrell (Aston Villa 1992).
Clubhouse: Large clubroom and lounge boardroom. Open matchdays and for private hire. Food availsable on matchdays; hot dogs, burgers, chips etc.
92-93 Captain: Jimmy Williams.
92-93 P.o.Y.: Paul Molloy.
92-93 Top scorer: Chris Moss.
Local Newspapers: Redditch Indicator (0527 63611), Redditch Advertiser, Birmingham Evening Mail, Redditch Weekly Mail.
Local Radio Stations: BBC Hereford & Worcester.
Hons: F.A. Trophy 1st Rd 78-79, Southern Lg Div 1 Nth 75-76 (Midland Div R-up 85-86), West Mids (B'ham) Lg Southern Sect. 54-55, Birm. Comb. 13-14 32-33 52-53 (R-up 06-07 14-15 51-52), Staffs Snr Cup 90-91, Birm. Snr Cup 24-25 31-32 38-39 76-77, Worcs Snr Cup 1893-94 1930-31 74-75 76-77 (R-up 1888-89 1929-30 52-53 73-74), Worcs Jnr Cup 90-91.

PROGRAMME DETAILS:
Pages: 48 **Price:** 50p
Editor: Roger Newbold
(0527 27516)

520

RUSHDEN & DIAMONDS Russians

Rushden & Diamonds F.C. 92-93. Back Row (L/R): T Felton (Physio), Colin Waite, Junior Wilson, John Coe, Kevin Fox, Kevin Shoemake, John Flower, Darryl Page, Barrington Leslie, Mark Bushell, Billy Jeffrey. Front: Paul York, Ollie Kearns, Glenville Donegal, Andy Kirkup, Frank Belfon, Andy Peaks, Adie Mann.

Chairman: W M Griggs   **Vice Chairman:** A C Jones.
Joint Presidents: D Attley & C Jones.
Secretary: David Joyce, 54 Ferrestone Rd, Wellingborough, Northants NN8 4EJ (0933 279466).
Team Manager: Roger Ashby   **Coach:** Billy Jeffrey   **Physio:** Peter Brown
Press Officer/ Commercial Manager: Bernard Lake (0933 57968).
Ground: Nene Park, Station Rd, Irthlingborough, Northants (0933 650345).
Directions: On A6 approx. 350yds north of A45 junction over bridge.
Capacity: 3,500   **Cover:** 2,000   **Seats:** 2,000   **Floodlights:** Yes   **Metal Badges:** Yes
Club Shop: Yes, stocking football memorabilia etc. Contact Bernard Lake (number above).
Colours: Red/white/blue   **Change colours:** All white   **Sponsors:** Pittards Garner.
Previous Names: Irthlingborough Diamonds (formed 1946), Rushden Town (formed 1889) merged in 1992.
Previous Leagues: Rushden Town: Midland 1894-1901/ Utd Co's 01-04 19-56 61-83/ Central Alliance 61-83. *Irthlingborough Diamonds: Rushden Yth/ Rushden & District/ Kettering Amtr.*
Previous Ground: Rushden Town: Hayden Rd, Rushden (pre-1992).
Midweek home matchday: Tuesday   **Reserve Team's League:** Hereward Spts Utd Co's.
Record Attendance: 883 v Nuneaton Borough, League, 18/3/93. *Ground record: 2,470 Irthingborough Diamonds v Dagenham, F.A. Cup 1978*
Best F.A. Cup season: 4th Qualifying Round (as Rushden Town).
League clubs defeated in F.A. Cup: None
Record win: 6-0 home v Hinckley Town, Beazer Homes Midland Division 92-93.
Record win: 0-4 away v Leicester United, Beazer Homes Midland Division 92-93.
Record transfer fee paid: £8,000 for John Coe (V.S. Rugby, 1992).
Gordon Inwood.
Players progressing to Football League: From Rushden Town: Gordon Inwood (WBA 1949), Robert Peacock (Northampton 1957). *From Irthlingborough Diamonds: Scott Endersby (Ipswich, Tranmere, Swindon, Carlisle), Steve Brown & Dave Johnson (N'hampton).*
Clubhouse: Lounge facilities. Open matchdays only (at present). Crisps, rolls etc available.
Club Record Scorer: Glenville Donegal   **Record Apps:** Darryl Page
92-93 Captain & P.o.Y.: Jon Flower
92-93 Top Scorer: Glenville Donegal.
Local Newspapers: Northants Evening Telegraph (0536 81111), Chronicle & Echo (0604 231122), Herald & Post, Northants Citizen
Local Radio Stations: Radio Northampton, Radio Northampton 96.6, K.C.B.C.
Hons: Daventry Charity Cup 92-93, Campri Leisurewear Cup 92-93. As Rushden Town: Southern Lg Midland Div R-up 88-89, Utd Co's Lg(10) 02-03 26-27 29-30 31-32 34-38 63-64 72-73 (R-up(12) 01-02 24-25 28-29 30-31 33-34 38-39 49-50 62-63 71-72 77-79 82-83, Lg Cup(5) 33-35 36-38 46-47, Northants Snr Cup(9) 25-28 29-31 34-35 36-37 57-58 77-78, FA Amtr Cup 2nd Rd 1893-94, FA Tphy 3rd Qual Rd 69-70, FA Vase QF 89-90. *As Irthlingborough Diamonds: Utd Co's Lg 70-71 76-77 78-79 82-83 (KO Cup 78-79 80-81 (R-up 90-91)), Northants Snr Cup 80-81.*

RUSHDEN & DIAMONDS FOOTBALL CLUB

FOOTBALL SEASON PROGRAMME

R&D

PROGRAMME DETAILS:
Pages: 20 Price: 50p
Editor: Bernard Lake
(0933 57968)

SUTTON COLDFIELD TOWN

Sutton Coldfield Town F.C. 1992-93. Back Row (L/R): Keogh, Richardson, Belford, Adey, Smith, Clarke, Cooper (Coach). Centre: Glynn (Physio), Richards, Whitehouse, Cowdrill, Dale, Hadland, Sturgeon, Whittingham, Sharp (Asst Coach). Front: Biddle, Hunt, Wright (Manager), Shanahan (Secretary), Lockley (Chairman), Harrison (Vice Chairman), Carroll, Ling. Mascots: John Paul Shanahan, Michael Glynn.

Chairman: Gerry Shanahan　　**Vice Chairman:** Mike Harrison.
Secretary: Gerry Shanahan, 34 Shipton Road, Sutton Coldfield B72 1NR (021 354 5152).
Manager: Clive Perrins　　**Asst Manager:** N/A　　**Physio:** Brendon Glynn.
Press Officer: Bryan Turner　　**Commercial Manager:** Pete Young.
Ground: Central Ground, Coles Lane, Sutton Coldfield B72 1NL (021 354 2997/021 355 5475).
Directions: A5127 into Sutton, right at Odeon cinema (Holland Road), then first right into Coles Lane - ground 150 yds on left. 10 mins walk from Sutton Coldfield (BR), bus 104 from Birmingham.
Capacity: 4,500　　**Cover:** 500　　**Seats:** 200　　**Floodlights:** Yes　　**Metal Badges:** Yes
Club Shop: Yes, selling metal badges, scarves, hats, pens, rosettes, programmes. Contact via secretary.
Colours: Royal/white/royal　　**Change colours:** White/royal/white.
Previous Leagues: Central Birmingham/ Walsall Senior/ Staffs County/ Birmingham Combination 50-54/ West Mids (Regional) 54-65 79-82/ Midlands Combination 65-79.
Previous Grounds: Meadow Plat 1879-89/ Coles Lane (site of current ambulance station) 90-1919.
Reserve Team's League: Ansells Midland Combination Reserve Division.
Club Sponsors: Cox Jerome　　**Previous Name:** Sutton Coldfield F.C. 1879-1921.
Midweek home matchday: Wednesday
Record Attendance: 2,029 v Doncaster Rovers, F.A. Cup 80-81 (Receipts £2,727).
Best F.A. Cup season: 1st Rd 80-81 (lost 0-1 to Doncaster), 92-93 (1-2 at Bolton Wanderers).
Record Fees - Paid: £1,500 twice in 1991, for Lance Morrison (Gloucester) & Micky Clarke (Burton A.)
Received: £25,000 for Barry Cowdrill (WBA) 1979.
Players progressing to Football League: Arthur Corbett (Walsall 1949), Paul Cooper (Manchester City), Noel Blake (Leeds), Steve Cooper (Barnsley), Peter Latchford (WBA & Celtic), Mark Smith (Wolves), John Barton (Everton), Barry Cowdrill (WBA 1979), Colin Dryhurst (Halifax 1979), Dale Belford (Notts County 1987).
Clubhouse: Brick built lounge and concert room, fully carpeted and extensively decorated. Open daily, food available.
Club Record Goalscorer: Eddie Hewitt 288
Club Record Apps: Eddie Hewitt 465
92-93 Captain:
92-93 P.o.Y.: Dale Belford
92-93 Top scorer: Gary Smith 22.
Local Newspapers: Sutton Coldfield News, Sutton Observer.
Local Radio Stations: BRMB, Radio WM.
Honours: Southern Lg Midland Div R-up 82-83, West Mids Lg 79-80 (Lg Cup 80-81 81-82), Midland Comb.(2) 77-79 (R-up(2) 69-71, Lg Cup 69-70), Walsall Snr Lg 46-47, Walsall Snr Cup(3) 77-80 (R-up 80-81), Staffs Senior Cup R-up 89-90 (SF 84-85 86-87), Worcs Snr Cup SF 88-89, Walsall Challenge Cup R-up 46-47 47-48, Sutton Charity Cup 46-47 65-66 71-72 86-87 89-90 90-91, F.A. Trophy 1st Rd Replay 89-90, FA Amateur Cup 2nd Rd 70-71, Express & Star Cup 44-45.

PROGRAMME DETAILS:
Pages: 36 **Price:** 70p
Editor: T.B.A.

STOURBRIDGE

Stourbridge, Barclays Commercial Services League Cup winners 1992-93. Back Row (L/R): Evran Wright, Dave Nixon (Physio), Lee Young, Micky Williams, Nigel Barrows, Andy Crannage, Toby Hall, Steve Ingram, Alan Potter, Chris Smith (Kit Man). Front: Adrian Cooper, Richard Evans, John Horne, Chris Jones, Jason Lowe, Kevin Duckinworth. Photo by kind permission of the Stourbridge News & County Express.

Chairman: J C Driscoll **Vice Chairman:** G Taylor **President:** J L Guest.
Secretary/Press Off.: Hugh Clark, 10 Burnt Oak Drive, Stourbridge, West Mids DY8 1HL (00384 392975).
Manager: Neil Rioch **Asst Manager:** Alf Bowerman **Physio:** Dave Nixon.
Commercial Manager: Geoff Turner.
Ground: War Memorial Athletic Ground, High Street, Amblecote, Stourbridge DY8 4EB (0384 394040).
Directions: Take A491, signposted Wolverhampton, from Stourbridge ring-road - ground 300yds on left immediately beyond traffic lights and opposite 'Royal Oak' pub. Buses 245, 246 from Dudley, and 256 from Wolverhampton, pass ground. One mile from Stourbridge Town (BR).
Capacity: 2,000 **Cover:** 1,250 **Seats:** 250 **Floodlights:** Yes **Metal Badges:** Yes
Colours: Red & white stripes **Change colours:** Yellow & blue (new for 93-94).
Club Shop: Yes. Thousands of programmes and souvenirs. Contact Nigel Gregg.
Previous Leagues: West Midlandss (previously Birmingham) 1892-1939/ Birmingham Combination 45-53.
Previous Grounds: None **Previous Name:** Stourbridge Standard
Sponsors: Storm Ltd **Midweek home matchday:** Tuesday
Record Attendance: 5,726 v Cardiff City, Welsh Cup final 1st leg 1974.
Best F.A. Cup season: 4th Qual. Rd 3 times this century: v Arnold 67-68, v V.S. Rugby 84-85 & 85-86.
League clubs defeated in F.A. Cup: Crewe 1892-93, Burslem Port Vale 94-95, Burton Swifts 97-98.
Record Fee Received: £20,000 for Tony Cunningham (Lincoln City, 1979).
Players progressing to Football League: Doug Pinbley & Brian Farmer (Birmingham City 1946 & 54), Howard Edwards (Derby County 1947), James Pemberton (Luton Town 1947), Jack Boxley (Bristol City 1950), Antonio Rowley (Liverpool 1953), Colin Taylor & Keith Ball (Walsall 1958 & 72), Peter Clark (Stockport County 1965), Percy Freeman (West Bromwich Albion 1968), Chic Bates & Ray Harwood (Shrewsbury Town 1974), Les Lawrence (Shrewsbury Town 1975), Steve Cooper (Torquay 1978), Tony Cunningham (Lincoln 1979), Mel Gwinnet (Peterborough 1981).
Clubhouse: Open every evening from 8pm and Sunday lunchtimes.
Club Record Scorer: Ron Page, 269 **Club Record Appearances:** Ron Page 427.
92-93 Captain: Steve Ingram **92-93 Top scorer:** Evran Wright, 56.
92-93 P.o.Y.: Evran Wright/ Chris Jones. **Local Newspapers:** Stourbridge News & County Express, Express & Star, Dudley Evening Mail.
Local Radio Stations: Radio West Wids, B.R.M.B., Beacon.
Honours: Welsh Cup R-up 73-74, FA Trophy QF 70-71, Southern Lg Midland Div 90-91 (Lg Cup 92-93, Div 1 North 73-74, Merit Cup 73-74), West Mids (prev. Birmingham) Lg 23-24 (R-up 01-02 37-38 55-56 62-63, Div 2 R-up(res) 80-81), Birmingham Comb. R-up 51-52, Birmingham Snr Cup 49-50 45-46 75-76 (R-up 10-11 45-46 75-76), Worcs Snr Cup 04-05 05-06 19-20 21-22 23-24 27-28 49-50 67-68 80-81 (R-up 03-04 09-10 10-11 13-14 20-21 24-25 25-26 36-37 48-49 55-56 78-79), Herefordshire Snr Cup 54-55, Camkin Cup R-up 69-70, Camkin Presidents Cup 70-71, Albion Shield 43-44, Kidderminster Cup 1887-88, Keys Cup 37-38 62-63, Dudley Guest Hosp. Cup 1891-92, Worcester Charity Cup 1887-88, Worcs Comb. R-up 27-28, Worcester Jnr Cup R-up 27-28, Tillotson Cup R-up 39-40, Brierley Hill Lg R-up 44-45 (Lg Cup R-up 44-45), Brierley Hill Yth Lg Coronation Cup 56-57.

PROGRAMME DETAILS:
Pages: 32 **Price:** 60p
Editor: Secretary

TAMWORTH

Lambs or Town

Tamworth F.C. 1992-93: Back Row (L/R): Paul Wood (Manager), Robbie Ellison, Keith Russell, Adam Whitehouse, Dean Williams, Tony Eccleston, Ian Crawley, Steve Cartwright, Pete Nicholls (Yth Team Mgr), Frank Dwane (Physio). Front: Buster Kendall, Mark Smith, Tony Clarke, Darren Williams, Martin Bodkin, Ade Waters, Christos Demitros. Photo - Paul Barber.

Chairman: Malcolm Jones **Vice Chairman:** Bob Andrews **President:** Len Gendle.
Secretary: Rod A Hadley, 38 Godolphin, Riverside, Tamworth B79 7UF (0827 66786).
Manager: Paul Wood **Asst Manager:** Clive Lyons **Physio:** Frank Duane
Groundsman: Cliff Earp **Press Officer:** Mike Turner (0827 51689/ 60741).
Commercial Manager: Buster Belford.
Ground: The Lamb Ground, Kettlebrook, Tamworth, Staffs B79 1HA (0827 65798).
Directions: From town centre follow one-way road marked South into Kettlebrook Road - ground on right opposite railway arches. From M42 jct 10, A5 Watling Street to 'Bulls Head' at Two Gates traffic lights, left into Tamworth Road (A51), one mile to ground on left - entrance from car park at side of the Lamb Inn. 1 mile from Tamworth BR station.
Capacity: 2,500 **Cover:** 1,191 **Seats:** 391 **Floodlights:** Yes **Metal Badges:** Yes
Club Shop: Yes, selling lapel badges, pennants, balls, jumpers, T-shirts, sweat shirts, mugs, club comb & case, mirrors, caps, scarves, replica kits.
Colours: Red (white sleeves)/black/black **Change colours:** All yellow
Sponsors: Trisport.
Previous Leagues: Birmingham Combination 33-54/ West Midlands (initially Birmingham Lg) 54-72 84-88/ Southern 72-79 83-84/ Northern Premier 79-83.
Previous Names: None. **Previous Grounds:** Jolly Sailor Ground 33-34.
Midweek home matchday: Tuesday **Reserves' Lge:** Ansells Midland Comb. (Res Div).
Record Attendance: 4,920 v Atherstone Town, Birmingham Combination 3/4/48.
Best F.A. Cup season: 2nd Rd 69-70 (lost 0-6 at Gillingham). Also 1st Rd 66-67 70-71 87-88 90-91.
League clubs defeated in F.A. Cup: Torquay 69-70.
Record Fees - Paid: For Steve Cartwright (Colchester United, November 1988).
            Received: £5,000 for Steve Cartwright (Colchester, August 1988).
Players progressing to Football League: Peter Hilton (WBA 1949), Alan Godridge (Swansea 1950), W Ealing (Doncaster), Higgins (Fulham), P Weir (Cardiff), S Fox (Wrexham), Steve Cartwright (Colchester 1988).
Clubhouse: Registered club on ground open matchdays only, but club own the adjacent Lamb Inn which is open every day, normal licensing hours.
Club Record Goalscorer: Graham Jessop 195
Club Record Scorer in single season: Percy Vials 63 (33-37), Ray Holmes 60 (69-70).
Club Record Appearances: Dave Seedhouse 869.
92-93 Captain: Martin Bodkin.
92-93 P.o.Y.: Dean Williams.
92-93 Top scorer: Ian Crawley.
Local Newspapers: Tamworth Herald (0827 60741).
Local Radio Stations: Radio WM, BRMB Radio.
Hons: F.A. Vase 88-89, West Mids Lg 63-64 65-66 71-72 87-88 (R-up(2) 67-69, Div 2 55-56, Lg Cup(5) 64-66 71-72 85-86 87-88 (R-up 70-71)), Birmingham Snr Cup 60-61 65-66 68-69 (R-up 36-37 63-64), Staffs Snr Cup 58-59 63-64 65-66 (R-up 55-56 66-67 70-71), Midland F'lit Cup R-up 71-72 72-73, Camkin Cup 71-72 (R-up 70-71), Birmingham County Youth Cup 88-89.

PROGRAMME DETAILS:
Pages: 16 Price: 80p
Editor: Mike Turner
(0827 51689/60741)

V.S. RUGBY

Desolation for V.S. Rugby goalkeeper Derek Dudley, now with West Bromwich Albion, as he concedes a goal at Corby Town. Photo - Mick Cheney.

Chairman: Roy Gallimore.
Secretary: The Secretary, c/o V.S. Rugby F.C. (address as below).
Manager: Ron Bradbury   **Asst Manager:** Bob Stokley
Press Officer: T.B.A.   **Physio:** Paul Miller.
Ground: Butlin Road, Rugby, Warks CV21 3ST (0788 543692).
Directions: 1 mile walk from station. Ground off Clifton (B5414) on north side of Rugby.
Capacity: 6,000   **Cover:** 1,000   **Seats:** 240   **Floodlights:** Yes   **Metal Badges:** Yes
Club Shop: Yes.
Colours: Sky & navy blue stripes/navy/navy
Change colours: White (red trim)/white/white(red trim)
Sponsors: T.B.A.   **Previous Name:** Valley Sports/ Valley Sports Rugby.
Previous Leagues: Rugby & District 1956-63/ Coventry & Partnership/ North Warks 63-69/ United Counties 69-75/ West Midlands 75-83
Midweek matchday: Tuesday
Record Attendance: 3,961 v Northampton F.A. Cup 1984
Best F.A. Cup season: 1st Rd 84-85 85-86 86-87, 2nd Rd 87-88
League clubs defeated in F.A. Cup: None
Record Fees -   **Paid:** £3,500 R Smith, I Crawley, G Bradder
       Received: £15,000 T Angus (Northampton)
Players progressing to Football League: S Storer (Birmingham 1985), S Bicknell (Leicester), S Norris (Scarborough), T Angus (Northampton Town)
Clubhouse: Every night and weekend lunchtimes. Entertainment Saturday nights. Excellent facilities include Long Alley Skittles, darts and pool.
Club Record Goalscorer: Danny Conway, 124
Club Record Appearances: Danny Conway, 374
92-93 Captain:
92-93 P.o.Y.:
92-93 Top scorer:
Local Newspapers: Rugby Advertiser (0788 535363), Coventry Evening Telegraph (0203 633633), Rugby Observer (0788 535147).
Local Radio Stations: Mercia Sound, CWR
Club Newsline: 0891 884 497.
Hons: Southern Lg Midland Div 86-87 (Lg Cup 89-90), FA Vase 82-83, Midland F'lit Cup 84-85 89-90 (R-up 86-87), Birmingham Snr Cup 88-89 91-92, Utd Co's Lg Div 3 Cup 69-70. (all-time record FA Tphy win; 10-0 away to Ilkeston, Prelim. Rd 85-86.

PROGRAMME DETAILS:
Pages: 20 **Price:** 60p
Editor: Bob Pinks

IMPORTANT NOTE

AT THE TIME OF GOING TO PRESS, V.S. RUGBY FOOTBALL CLUB WERE IN THE HANDS OF THE LIQUIDATOR. ALTHOUGH THEY HAVE A PLACE IN THE MIDLAND DIVISION OF THE BEAZER HOMES LEAGUE, THEIR FUTURE IS UNDECIDED.

Weston-super-Mare enjoyed an excellent in the Vauxhall F.A. Trophy, the highlight of which was a 1-0 home win against Diadora League Premier Division side Windsor & Eton on 28th November. Here goalkeeper Glenn Thomas safely catches a Windsor corner. Photo - Paul Dennis.

President: D A Usher   **Chairman:** P T Bliss
Secretary: Geoff Milsom, 12 Greenland Road, Milton, Weston-s-Mare BS22 8JP (0934 413059).
Manager: Peter Amos   **Asst Manager:**   **Coach:** Keith Christie.
Physio: Terry Hardwell   **Press Officer:** Keith Refault.
Ground: Woodspring Park, Winterstoke Road, Weston-super-Mare BS23 2YG (0934 6355665/621618).
Directions: From North: M5 Jct 21, A370 into Weston until junction A371 on left (at Heron pub), take A371 over railway bridge to r'bout, take right-hand exit and follow to 3rd r'bout, bear left for 100yds - club on right. From South: M5 Jct 22, follow Weston signs for approx 7 miles, right at first r'bout (by Hospital), left at next r'bout, ground 1 mile on left. Twenty minutes walk from Weston-super-Mare (BR).
Seats: 250   **Cover:** 1,000   **Capacity:** 4,000   **Metal Badges:** Yes
Club Shop: Yes, selling programmes, club ties, pullovers, badges, scarves, pens, pennants, Sweat Shirts and T-shirts. Contact Mrs Aileen Milsom (0934 413059).
Club colours: White/blue/blue   **Change colours:** All yellow
Midweek matches: Tuesday   **Previous Name:** Borough of Weston-super-Mare.
Previous Grounds: The Great Ground, Locking Road 48-55, Langford Road 55-83.
Record Attendance: 958 v Bristol City, Somerset Premier Cup final, 22/4/1. At Langford Road: 2,500 v Bridgwater Town, FA Cup First Round Proper 1961-62.
Best FA Cup season: First Round Proper replay 1961-62 (lost 0-1 at Bridgwater Town).
Players progressing to Football League: Ian Maine, John Palmer.
Previous League: Western 1948-92.   **Club Sponsors:** Uphill Motor Company.
Record win: 11-0 v Paulton Rovers   **Record defeat:** 1-12 v Yeovil Town Reserves.
Clubhouse: Mon-Fri 7-11pm, Sat 12-11pm, Sun 12-3 & 7-11pm. 2 skittle alleys, 3 bars. Bar meals available and cooked meals on matchdays.
Club Record Goalscorer: Matthew Lazenby, 180
Club Record Appearances: Harry Thomas, 740.
92-93 Captain: Jon Bowering
92-93 P.O.Y.: Paul Elson.
92-93 Top scorer: Jon Bowering, Paul Elson, Matthew Lazenby - 14 each.
Local Newspapers: Bristol Evening Post, Western Daily Press.
Local Radio Stations: Somerset Sound.
Hons: Somerset Snr Cup 23-24 26-27, Western Lg 91-92 (R-up 76-77, Lg Cup 76-77 (R-up 89-90), Merit Cup 76-77 77-78), Somerset Snr Lg (Reserves) Div 1 87-88 (R-up 90-91), Div 2 R-up 85-86, Div 3 84-85).

'THE NON-LEAGUE PLAYERS'
1993-94 EDITION

AVAILABLE DURING THE SEASON, WILL FEATURE
DETAILS OF WESTON-SUPER-MARE'S PLAYERS, AND
INDEED THE PLAYERS OF ALL CLUBS IN THE TOP
FOUR PYRAMID LEAGUES. FOR MORE DETAILS ON
THIS PUBLICATION SEE THE ADVERT NEAR THE FRONT
OF THIS DIRECTORY.

PROGRAMME DETAILS:
Pages: 32 Price: 60p
Editor: Mrs Aileen Milsom
(0934 413059)

Formed: 1946

YATE TOWN

The Bluebells

Yate Town 92-93 - Back Row (L/R): James Hoytt, Richard Dunn, Howard Pitchard, Richard Bryant, Terry Stevenson, Mike Davis, Paul Harrison, Pete Jackson (Manager). Front: Gary Davis, Gary Jones, Kevin Thaws, Andy Fox, Martin Grimshaw, Bobby Brown. Photo courtesy of Phil Chilcott F.R.P.S..

Chairman: R G Hawkins   **Vice Chairman:** D A Phillips   **President:** R Hewetson.
Secretary: T M Tansley, 1 Tyning Close, Yate, Bristol BS17 4PN (0454 324305).
Manager: Peter Jackson   **Asst Mgr:** Bobby Brown   **Coach:** Bobby Brown
Press Officer: T.B.A.   **Physio:** Terry Leslie
Commercial Manager: Peter Last.
Ground: Lodge Road, Yate, Bristol BS17 5LE (0454 228103).
Directions: M4 jct 18, A46 towards Stroud, then A432 to Yate. Turn right at top of railway bridge into North Road, first left past traffic lights. Five miles from Bristol Parkway BR main line station, half mile from Yate BR station. Buses 329, X68 and 328.
Capacity: 2,000   **Cover:** 236   **Seats:** 236   **Floodlights:** Yes   **Metal Badges:** Yes
Club Shop: Yes, selling programmes, metal badges, pens, rosettes, shirts, key rings etc. Contact Secretary.
Colours: White/navy/white   **Change colours:** Red/whitered.
Sponsors: Carlsberg/ Tetley.
Previous Leagues: Gloucestershire County 68-83/ Hellenic 83-89.
Previous Name: Yate Y.M.C.A. 1946-70.
Previous Grounds: Yate Aerodrome 50-54/ Newmans Field 54-60/ Sunnyside Lane 60-84.
Midweek home matchday: Wednesday   **Reserve Team's League:** Bristol Suburban.
Record Attendance: 2,000 for Bristol Rovers v Bristol Rovers Past, Vaughan Jones testimonial 1990.
Record Fees - Paid: None.
            Received: £7,500 from York City for Darren Tilley, 1991.
Players progressing to Football League: Richard Thompson (Newport County & Exeter City), Phil Purnell (Bristol Rovers), Darren Tilley (York City), Steve Winter (Walsall).
Clubhouse: Open every night and weekend lunchtimes. Skittles, darts, pool, live entertainment.
Club Record Scorer: Kevin Thaws.
Club Record Appearances: Gary Hewlett.
92-93 Captain: Gary Hewlett.
92-93 P.o.Y.: Kevin Thaws.
92-93 Top scorer: Kevin Thaws.
Local Newspapers: Bristol Evening Post, Western Daily Press, North Avon Gazette.
Local Radio Stations: GWR, Radio Bristol.
Honours: F.A. Vase 5th Rd 91-92, Hellenic Lg(2) 87-89 (Div 1 R-up 84-85, Lg Skol Cup R-up 87-88), Glos Chal. Tphy 88-89 (R-up 78-79), Glos Snr Amtr Cup Sth 77-78 91-92(res) 92-93(res), Glos Snr Chal. Cup (Nth) R-up 89-90 92-93, Stroud Charity Cup R-up 74-75 81-82 84-85 (Sect. A Winners(6) 76-78 79-80 82-83 87-89), Berkeley Hosp. Prem. Cup(3) 73-75 80-81, S.W. Co's Sutton Vase 85-86.

PROGRAMME DETAILS:
Pages: 24 **Price:** 50p
Editor: Secretary

Southern Division

		HOME			AWAY					
	P	W	D	L	W	D	L	F	A	Pts
SITTINGBOURNE	42	16	4	1	10	8	3	102	43	90
SALISBURY CITY	42	16	2	3	11	5	5	87	50	88
WITNEY TOWN	42	13	6	2	12	3	6	77	37	84
GRAVESEND & N.	42	15	1	5	10	3	8	99	63	79
HAVANT TOWN	42	12	3	6	11	3	7	78	55	75
SUDBURY TOWN	42	13	4	4	7	7	7	89	54	71
ERITH & BELVEDERE	42	14	2	5	8	3	10	73	66	71
ASHFORD TOWN	42	12	3	6	8	5	8	91	66	68
BRAINTREE TOWN	42	13	3	5	7	3	11	95	65	66
MARGATE	42	9	4	8	10	3	8	65	58	64
WEALDSTONE	42	10	4	7	8	3	10	75	69	61
BUCKINGHAM TOWN	42	7	8	6	9	3	9	61	58	59
BALDOCK TOWN	42	7	7	7	8	2	11	59	63	54
POOLE TOWN	42	11	3	7	4	4	13	61	69	52
FAREHAM TOWN	42	9	6	6	5	2	14	67	65	50
BURNHAM	42	7	5	9	7	3	11	53	77	50
CANTERBURY CITY	42	10	4	7	2	6	13	54	76	46
NEWPORT IOW	42	4	9	8	5	7	9	44	56	43
FISHER ATHLETIC	42	5	4	12	3	5	13	38	98	33
ANDOVER	42	3	6	12	4	3	14	42	99	30
DUNSTABLE	42	5	4	12	0	10	11	42	92	29
BURY TOWN	42	4	2	15	4	3	14	46	119	29

Top League Goalscorers

S.Portway (Gravesend & Northfleet)	58
P.Smith (Sudbury Town)	34
M.Buglione (Margate)	31
S.Parnell (Sudbury Town)	27
L.McRobert (Ashford Town)	26
K.Clarke (Witney Town)	25

THE SOUTHERN DIVISION RESULT CHART 1992-93

HOME TEAM	1	2	3	4	5	6	7	8	9	10	11	12	13	14	15	16	17	18	19	20	21	22
1. Andover	*	1-1	2-1	0-5	0-2	1-2	2-0	3-3	2-2	1-1	1-4	3-0	2-2	0-1	0-0	1-4	0-1	0-5	0-3	0-3	0-2	0-5
2. Ashford	4-3	*	1-0	7-4	2-2	1-3	7-0	2-1	4-0	0-2	3-0	4-0	1-0	2-2	1-4	1-2	5-1	0-1	2-2	0-2	2-1	1-0
3. Baldock Town	3-2	3-3	*	1-1	2-1	1-2	2-1	5-1	1-1	3-0	0-2	0-0	2-2	2-4	0-3	1-0	4-3	0-0	1-1	0-3	3-4	1-2
4. Braintree	5-0	2-2	4-0	*	2-0	3-0	4-1	4-0	1-0	0-2	3-2	6-1	0-1	0-2	0-1	1-0	3-1	5-1	3-3	1-1	4-1	2-3
5. Buckingham	2-0	0-2	0-2	2-0	*	0-2	1-1	3-1	1-1	1-0	2-1	0-0	2-0	2-4	0-0	0-0	0-0	2-4	3-1	1-1	0-4	0-0
6. Burnham	1-1	2-0	3-2	1-2	0-3	*	1-2	2-2	1-1	1-0	2-0	1-2	0-5	2-1	1-3	1-1	3-0	0-0	2-3	3-2	1-3	2-6
7. Bury Town	1-2	1-4	0-2	0-4	2-0	2-2	*	1-1	2-1	2-7	1-4	2-3	2-7	0-4	0-5	0-2	1-4	0-3	2-3	3-2	0-4	3-2
8. Canterbury	2-3	3-2	0-0	2-1	0-4	0-2	1-0	*	2-2	1-2	3-0	2-0	2-3	0-0	5-1	1-0	1-0	1-2	1-5	3-1	3-0	1-1
9. Dunstable	1-3	1-2	0-3	1-7	2-3	2-0	5-1	0-5	*	1-3	2-0	0-0	2-3	1-2	1-1	1-1	0-3	1-0	1-1	1-6	2-1	0-1
10. Erith	4-0	2-6	2-1	1-3	1-0	4-1	3-2	6-1	2-0	*	3-2	1-0	1-4	0-2	1-0	2-1	2-0	2-3	1-0	1-1	1-1	2-0
11. Fareham	3-0	1-2	2-0	2-2	0-0	1-0	2-0	1-2	1-1	8-0	*	1-1	3-3	1-2	1-0	2-1	1-1	1-2	1-2	1-0	5-1	2-5
12. Fisher	1-3	2-1	1-2	2-0	1-3	1-2	3-0	0-0	4-0	1-0	1-6	*	0-4	1-4	0-5	2-2	1-3	2-2	1-1	0-4	0-1	0-1
13. Gravesend	5-0	3-1	0-1	4-0	3-4	4-1	4-1	4-0	3-0	3-5	0-1	2-1	*	4-3	2-0	0-1	2-0	2-0	3-3	2-0	3-0	2-1
14. Havant	1-0	0-3	1-0	3-2	3-2	1-1	0-1	1-0	4-1	0-0	2-0	6-0	3-2	*	1-2	1-1	3-1	0-2	2-1	0-2	4-2	1-3
15. Margate	1-0	0-4	0-2	2-5	1-0	4-0	0-2	1-0	2-2	2-0	3-1	1-3	2-0	2-0	*	1-1	3-1	3-5	0-0	0-0	1-2	1-2
16. Newport IOW	1-1	2-1	0-0	0-0	0-1	1-0	2-2	1-1	0-0	1-2	0-0	6-0	1-2	1-2	2-1	*	0-0	0-2	0-4	3-1	1-1	0-2
17. Poole	2-1	2-1	1-3	2-0	2-2	2-1	1-2	0-0	4-1	0-2	2-0	1-1	2-3	3-2	4-0	2-3	*	4-0	0-4	3-1	1-2	1-0
18. Salisbury	3-3	2-0	1-0	1-2	1-4	4-0	5-3	4-0	1-0	4-1	2-0	4-1	3-0	2-1	2-0	2-1	2-1	*	1-2	3-1	1-0	1-1
19. Sittingbourne	4-0	4-0	4-1	3-1	2-1	1-1	3-0	4-1	2-2	2-0	3-1	6-0	1-0	3-2	3-0	4-2	0-0	0-1	*	2-2	2-1	4-0
20. Sudbury	2-1	1-1	4-1	4-1	5-2	2-1	4-1	1-0	5-0	3-1	2-2	3-1	1-3	1-1	2-3	4-1	5-1	1-1	1-3	*	3-1	0-2
21. Wealdstone	5-0	2-3	0-3	2-1	3-4	1-2	3-1	3-1	2-0	2-2	4-1	2-0	3-0	1-0	1-2	1-4	0-0	2-1	4-3	2-2	*	0-1
22. Witney	1-0	2-2	1-0	3-1	2-1	2-0	0-0	1-0	2-2	2-1	1-0	3-0	7-0	1-0	1-2	5-0	2-0	1-1	0-1	1-1	1-1	*

Beazer Homes (Southern) League Southern Division Ten Year Records

	83/4	84/5	85/6	86/7	87/8	88/9	89/0	90/1	91/2	92/3
Addlestone & Weybridge T.	5	8	–	–	–	–	–	–	–	–
Andover	15	13	20	16	6	18	18	9	7	20
Ashford Town	8	17	18	2	–	–	–	5	9	8
Baldock Town	–	–	–	–	15	6	10	4	11	13
Bashley	–	–	–	–	–	–	1	–	–	–
Basingstoke Town	3	1	–	–	–	–	–	–	–	–
Braintree Town	–	–	–	–	–	–	–	–	4	9
Buckingham Town	–	–	–	–	–	16	3	1	5	12
Burnham	–	–	11	17	8	5	11	11	10	16
Bury Town	–	–	–	–	9	4	9	12	17	22
Cambridge City	10	15	1	–	–	–	–	–	–	–
Canterbury City	11	10	12	20	20	13	15	18	21	17
Chatham Town	14	16	19	9	21	–	–	–	–	–
Chelmsford City	–	–	–	–	–	1	–	–	–	–
Corinthian	–	–	5	14	18	22	21	21	–	–
Crawley Town	2	–	–	–	–	–	–	–	–	–
Dorchester Town	–	14	21	1	–	–	–	–	–	–
Dover Athletic	13	19	4	5	1	–	–	–	–	–
Dunstable	17	18	7	13	7	15	4	17	16	21
Erith & Belvedere	16	20	9	8	10	17	20	19	20	7
Fareham Town	–	–	–	–	–	–	12	20	19	15
Fisher Athletic	–	–	–	–	–	–	–	–	–	19
Folkestone Town	–	–	–	–	17	11	17	w/d	–	–
Gosport Borough	–	2	–	–	–	–	–	15	22	–
Gravesend & Northfleet	–	–	–	6	4	2	–	–	–	4
Hastings Town	–	–	3	4	12	7	8	7	1	–
Havant Town	–	–	–	–	–	–	–	–	3	5
Hillingdon Borough	7	4	–	–	–	–	–	–	–	–
Hounslow	20	–	–	–	16	8	19	–	–	–
Hythe Town	–	–	–	–	–	–	6	8	13	–
Margate	18	5	15	10	5	20	16	10	14	10
Newport Isle of Wight	–	–	–	–	–	–	–	14	15	18
Poole Town	6	3	17	18	14	3	2	–	–	14
Road Sea Southampton	1	–	–	–	–	–	–	–	–	–
Ruislip	–	–	8	19	19	22	–	–	–	–
Salisbury	9	6	2	–	3	9	5	3	12	2
Sheppey United	–	7	14	15	11	19	22	–	–	–
Sittingbourne	–	–	–	–	–	–	–	–	6	1
Sudbury Town	–	–	–	–	–	–	–	13	8	6
Thanet United						(See Margate)				
Tonbridge A.F.C.	4	12	6	7	13	21	–	–	–	–
Trowbridge Town	–	–	13	12	–	10	7	2	–	–
Waterlooville	12	9	10	11	2	–	–	–	–	–
Wealdstone	–	–	–	–	–	–	–	–	–	11
Weymouth	–	–	–	–	–	–	–	–	2	–
Witney Town	–	–	–	–	–	14	14	16	18	3
Woodford Town	19	11	16	3	–	–	–	–	–	–
Yate Town	–	–	–	–	–	–	13	6	–	–
No. of Clubs	15	16	14	12	14	13	12	16	18	20

Neighbours Sittingbourne and Gravesend & Northfleet, at the time vying for top spot in the Beazer Homes Southern Division, set a divisional record gate of over 3,000 when they met in a league fixture at Sittingbourne on Tuesday 23rd February 1993. Here Dave Bourne (centre of three Sittingbourne players) celebrates having just scored the only goal of the night. Photo - Paul Dennis.

ASHFORD TOWN

Ashford Town 1992-93. Back Row (L/R): M Hyham, A Morris, T Reynolds, L McRobert. Centre: G Sargeant (Physio), M Wakeman, M Stevens, A Pearson, S Weaver, A Lemoine, J Reilly, M Stanton, D Williams (Coach). Front: D Gear, J Wheeler, P McRobert, N Cugley (Manager), S Brignall, F Ovard, D Jordan. Mascot: M Williams (Mascot). Photo - Dereck West.

Chairman: Ernie A Warren　　　**Vice Chairman:** Roger C West　　**President:** Ashley M Batt.
Secretary/Press Officer: Alan G Lancaster, 128 Kingsnorth Road, Ashford, Kent TN23 2HY (0233 621325).
Manager: Neil Cugley　　　**Asst Manager/Coach:** Dave Williams
Commercial Manager: E A Warren (0233 634125).　　　　　　**Physio:** George Sergeant
Ground: The Homelands, Ashford Road, Kingsnorth, Ashford, Kent TN26 1NJ (0233 611838).
Directions: M20 jct 10, follow A2070 signs towards Brenzett & Lydd airport, dual carriageway to junction of old A2070, ground one mile on left through village of Kingsworth. 4 miles south of Ashford - special bus service leaves railway station at 13.35 (Saturday) and 18.35 (midweek matches).
Capacity: 3,200　　**Cover:** 1,250　　**Seats:** 500　　**Floodlights:** Yes　　**Metal Badges:** Yes
Club Shop: Yes, selling old programmes, pennants, scarves, gloves, hats. Contact Martin Simmons on club number matchdays only.
Colours: White & green stripes/white/green (white tops)　　　　**Change colours:** All royal.
Previous Leagues: Kent 30-59.　　　**Previous Ground:** Essella Park, Essella Rd 30-87.
Midweek home matchday: Tuesday　　　**Reserve Team's League:** Kent Midweek League.
Record Attendance: 6,525 (at Essella Park, previous ground), v Crystal Palace, FA Cup 1st Rd 1959.
Best F.A. Cup season: 2nd Rd 61-62 (lost 0-3 at home to QPR), 66-67 (0-5 at Swindon). Also 1st Rd 34-35 58-59 59-60 60-61 74-75.
League clubs defeated in F.A. Cup: None.
Previous Names: Ashford United/ Ashford Railway/ Ashford F.C.
Record Fees - Paid: £2,000 for Tim Hulme (Hythe Town, August 1988)
　　　　　　　Received: £25,000 for Jeff Ross & Dave Arter (Hythe Town, December 1990).
Record win: 10-1 v Barry Town, February 1964.
Record defeat: 0-8 v Crawley Town, November 1964.
Players progressing to Football League: Ollie Norris (R'dale 1961), Howard Moore (Coventry 1966), Tony Godden (WBA 1975).
Clubhouse: Open matchdays and for special functions. Licensed bar, pool, function room. Limited food available; sandwiches, sausage & chips, pie & chips etc.
Club Record Goalscorer: John Young 172
Club Record Apps: Peter McRobert 685.
92-93 Captain: Andy Pearson/ Carlton Wynter
92-93 P.o.Y.: Andy Pearson & Lee McRoberts (shared)
92-93 Top scorer:
92-93 Clubman o.Y: Steve Brignall.
Local Newspapers: Kentish Express (0233 623232), Ashford Citizen & Scene.
Local Radio Stations: Radio Kent, Radio Invicta.
Honours: FA Tphy SF 72-73, Southern Lg Southern Div R-up 86-87, Kent Lg 48-49 (R-up 31-32, Lg Cup 38-39), Kent Senior Cup 58-59 62-63 92-93.

PROGRAMME DETAILS:
Pages: 24 **Price:** 80p
Editor: Ernie Warren

BALDOCK TOWN

Baldock Town F.C. 1992-93. Back Row (L/R): Mark Radford, Steve Ward, Graham Golds, Simon Merrick, Andy Codd, Paul Brown, Cliff Spencer. Front: Tony Anglin, Marcelle Bruce, Ian Allinson, Keith Allinson, Keith Stanton, Kevin Phillips. Photo - Dave West.

Joint Chairmen: Ray Childerstone/ G D Watson-Challis   **Vice Chairman:** Tony J Bottomley
Secretary: C T Hammond, 2 Elmwood Court, High Str., Baldock, Herts SG7 6AY (0462 894253).
Manager: Rob Eagles   **Coach:** Dave Moseley   **Physio:** Fred Day.
Press Officer: David Hammond (0462 892797)   **Commercial Director:** Rob Eagles.
Ground: Norton Road, Baldock, Herts SG7 5AU (0462 895449).
Directions: Off A1(M) at Letchworth/Baldock sign, left to 3rd island, A505 to Baldock, Norton Road is left off A505, left past Orange Tree pub, ground on right after railway bridge. From North or East turn left into town, Hitchin Street, right into Norton then proceed as above. From Baldock station (Kings Cross to Royston line) - left down Icknelid Way and right into Norton Road.
Capacity: 3,000   **Cover:** 1,250   **Seats:** 250   **Club Shop:** No   **Metal Badges:** Yes
Colours: Red/white/red   **Change colours:** Yellow/blue/blue.
Sponsors: Baldock Insurance/ Ind Coope.
Previous Leagues: S Midlands 25-39 47-54 63-83/ Parthenon 54-59/ London 59-63/ United Counties 83-87.
Previous Ground: Bakers Close (until 1982).
Midweek home matchday: Tuesday   **Reserve Team's League:** Essex & Herts Border Comb.
Record Attendance: 1,200 v Arsenal, floodlight opening 1984.
Best F.A. Cup season: 4th Qualifying Round replay (lost 0-1 at Halesowen Town after 1-1 draw). 1991-92.
Record Fees - Paid: £2,000 for Colin Hull (Bishop's Stortford)
                Received: £1,000 for Ian Ferguson (Barnet).
Players progressing to Football League: Ian Dowie (Luton & West Ham), Alan Stewart (Portsmouth).
Clubhouse: Members' bar and seperate function room. Food available.
Club Record Goalscorer: Unknown.
Club Record Apps: Paddy Stanton 440
92-93 Captain: L Cullum
92-93 P.o.Y.: Marcelle Bruce.
92-93 Top scorer: Kevin Phillips.
Local Newspapers: Comet, Gazette, Herald.
Local Radio: Radio Bedfordshire, Chiltern.
Hons: FA Tphy 2nd Qual. Rd 90-91, FA Vase 5th Rd 83-84, United Counties Lg R-up 83-84 86-87, South Mids Lg 27-28 65-66 67-68 69-70 (R-up 53-54 82-83, Lg Cup 65-66 69-70, Div 1 49-50, Reserve Div 1 66-67), Herts Charity Cup 91-92, Herts Charity Shield 57-58 69-70, Wallspan Floodlit Cup 85-86, Hinchingbrooke Cup 86-87, TSI Floodlit Cup 88-89, Woolwich Equitable Building Society Cup 83-84, Herts Intermediate Cup 86-87.

PROGRAMME DETAILS:
Pages: 52 **Price:** T.B.A.
Editor: T.B.A.

BRAINTREE TOWN

Braintree Town F.C. 1992-93. Back Row (L/R): Duncan Coghlan, Mark Bewers, Dave King, John Bishop, Paul England, Paul Catley, Wayne Adcock. Front: Mark Cranfield, Neil Grice, Russell Tanner, Shane Bailey, Colin Sinclair, Gary Culling. Photo - Jon Weaver.

Chairman: George Rosling   **Vice Chairman:** Ivan Kibble   **President:** R F Webb.
Secretary: T A Woodley, 19a Bailey Bridge Road, Braintree, Essex CM7 5TT (0376 326234).
Manager: Frank Bishop   **Coach:** Denis Longhorn   **Physio:** Tony Last.
Press Officer: R F Webb (0376 325338)
Ground: Cressing Road Stadium, Clockhouse Way, Braintree, Essex (0376 345617).
Directions: Turn off A12 London to Yarmouth road at Witham and follow B1018 to Witham, follow Braintree bypass then signs for East Braintree Industrial Estates - floodlights visible behind 'The Sportsman' snooker club on left half a mile into town, entrance is next left in Clockhouse Way, then left again. 1 mile from Braintree & Bocking (BR). Bus 353 from Witham stops at 'The Sportsman'. Town centre is twenty minutes walk.
Capacity: 5,000   **Cover:** 1,500   **Seats:** 280   **Floodlights:** Yes   **Metal Badges:** £2.00
Club Shop: Yes, selling thousands of programmes, fanzines, handbooks, magazines, photos, memorabilia, newspapers, shirts, caps, mugs, jumpers, kit bags, club ties, teddy bears, scarves, pennants, club badges, bobble hats, key fobs, car stickers, rosettes, matchbooks, postcards. Contact Jon Weaver.
Cols: Yel. & white stripes/blue/yellow   **Change colours:** Red & black stripes/black/red.
Sponsors: Essex Electrical Wholesalers (Braintree) Ltd.
Previous Leagues: Spartan 28-35/ Eastern Counties 35-37 38-39 52-55 70-91/ London 45-52/ Suffolk Border 55-64/ Greater London 64-66/ Metropolitan 66-70/ North Essex.
Previous Names: Manor Works 1894-1918/ Crittall Ath. 18-68/ Braintree & Crittall Ath. 68-81/ Braintree FC 81-82.
Previous Grounds: Kings Head Meadow 1894-1902/ Spaldings Meadow, Panfield Lane 1902-24.
Midweek home matchday: Tuesday   **Best F.A. Cup season:** 4th Qual. Rd 69-70 85-86.
Record Attendance: 4,000 v Spurs, charity challenge match, May 1952.
Record Fees - Paid: £1,000 twice; for Gary Hollocks (Bury Town) and for Glenn Russell (Heybridge)
     Received: £1,000 Gary Nash (Bury Town).
Players progressing to Football League: J Dick (West Ham United), S Wright (Wrexham), J Cheesewright (Birmingham City), S Allen (Wimbledon - physio).
Record win: 12-0 v Thetford Town (H), Eastern Counties League 35-36.
Record defeat: 4-11 v Cambridge United, East Anglian Cup 63-64.
Clubhouse: Open every evening 7-11pm, Sunday lunchtimes noon-2pm and Saturday matchday lunchtimes. Full bar facilites, childrens games, darts, pool, video arcade, large satellite T.V. screen. Separate section for functions. Steward: Mrs Christine Thorogood.
Club Record Goalscorer: Chris Guy 211 (1983-90)
Club Record Appearances: Paul Young 524 (1966-77)
92-93 Captain: Paul England
92-93 P.O.Y.: Jimmy Thomas   **92-93 Top scorer:** Neil Grice.
Local Newspapers: Braintree & Witham Times (0376 551551).
Local Radio Stations: BBC Essex (103.5 fm), Essex Radio (102.6 fm).
Honours: Eastern Counties Lg 36-37 83-84 84-85 (R-up 86-87 87-88 88-89 90-91, Lg Cup 87-88 (R-up 35-36 74-75)), Essex County Lg R-up 37-38, London Lg (East) R-up 45-46 (Lg Cup 47-48(joint) 48-49 51-52 (R-up 49-50)), Metropolitan Lg Cup 69-70, Essex Elizabethan Tphy R-up 68-69, East Anglian Cup 46-47 68-69, Essex Senior Trophy 86-87 (R-up 90-91), Essex & Suffolk Border Lg 59-60 84-85 (Lg Cup 59-60), RAFA Cup 56-57, Gtr London Benevolent Cup 65-66, Worthington Evans Cup 62-63(joint) 71-72 (R-up 56-57 60-61 69-70 74-75 75-76), Eastern F'lit Cup 85-86, Anglian F'lit Lg 69-70.

PROGRAMME DETAILS:
Pages: 20 **Price:** 50p
Editor: Ron Webb
(0376 325338)

BUCKINGHAM TOWN

The Robins

Buckingham Town pictured before their F.A. Vase Quarter-Final against Tiverton Town on Saturday 27th February. Photo - Eric Marsh.

Chairman: Chris Lawrence　　**Vice Chairman:** Ernie Seaton　　**President:** Robin Taylor
Secretary: E J Seaton, 20 Glebe Road, Deanshanger, Milton Keynes MK19 6LT (0908 562875).
Manager: Mike Foster　　**Coach:** Keith Searle　　**Physio:** Willie Holman.
Press Officer: Phillip Cornwall　　**Commercial Manager:** None
Ground: Ford Meadow, Ford Street, Buckingham (0280 816257).
Directions: From town centre take Aylesbury (A413) road and turn right at Phillips Garage after 400yds. By public transport: train to Milton Keynes, then bus to Buckingham.
Capacity: 4,000　　**Cover:** 268　　**Seats:** 268　　**Floodlights:** Yes　　**Metal Badges:** Yes.
Club Shop: Yes, selling scarves, hats, badges and programmes. Contact Dave Newton at ground.
Colours: All red　　**Change colours:** All white.　　**Sponsors:** Ford Tingewick Garage.
Previous Lges: Aylesbury & Dist/ Nth Bucks/ Hellenic 53-57/ Sth Mids 57-74/ Utd Co's 74-86.
Midweek matchday: Tuesday　　**Reserve Team's League:** None.
Record Attendance: 2,451 v Orient, FA Cup 1st Rd 84-85.
Best F.A. Cup season: 1st Rd 84-85.
League clubs defeated in F.A. Cup: None.
Record Fees - Paid: £8,000 for Steve Jenkins (Wealdstone, 1992)
　　　　　　Received: £1,000 for Terry Shrieves (Kettering).
Players progressing to Football League: None.
Clubhouse: Open every evening 7-11pm (4-11pm on Sat) and weekend lunchtimes 12-3pm. Concert room with stage for hire, capacity 240. Bingo, dominoes, ladies and mens darts, pool, table tennis. Rolls ect available matchdays only.
92-93 Captain: Ian Bowyer
92-93 P.O.Y.: Mark Sherlock
92-93 Top scorer: David Draper
Local Newspapers: Buckingham Advertiser, MK Citizen, Herald & Post.
Local Radio Stations: Fox FM (102.6 fm).
Newsline: 0898 884 431.
Hons: FA Vase QF 90-91 92-93, Southern Lg Southern Div 90-91, Utd Co's Lg 83-84 85-86 (Div 1 R-up 75-76, Div 2 R-up 74-75, Lg Cup 83-84, Div 2 Cup R-up 74-75), Nth Bucks Lg(8) 24-25 28-29 33-34 35-37 38-39 48-49 49-50, Aylesbury & Dist. Lg 02-03, Berks & Bucks Snr Cup 83-84, Berks & Bucks Jnr Cup 02-03 48-49 (R-up 38-39 72-73), Berks & Bucks Minor Cup 32-33, Buckingham Snr Charity Cup(18) 32-33 35-36 37-38 47-50 52-55 72-73 75-77 78-79 80-81 83-87 (R-up 31-32 36-37 39-40 73-74 81-82).

PROGRAMME DETAILS:
Pages: 32 **Price:** TBA
Editor: Phillip Cornwall

Burnham F.C. 1992-93. Back Row (L/R): Mick Buckley, Martin Turner, Tim Cook, Andy Styles, James Davey. Centre: Colin Barnes (Manager), Steve Bunce, Nick Bettaccini, Eddie Hutchinson, Paul Brett, Lee Fryer, Colin Cooper (Physio). Front: Dave Lansley, Carl Lindo, Ronnie Nelson, Paul Grant, Steve Shaw.

Chairman: Malcolm Higton   **Vice Chairman:** D C Eavis   **President:** R J Laverick.
Secretary/Press Officer: M J Boxall, 39 Tockley Road, Burnham, Slough SL1 7DQ (0628 660265).
Manager: Colin Barnes   **Asst Manager:** Derek Clayton   **Coaches:** Dave Brown
Physio: Colin Cooper   **Commercial Manager:** T.B.A.
Ground: Wymers Wood Road, Burnham, Slough SL1 8JG (0628 602467/602697).
Directions: North west of village centre, 2 miles from Burnham BR station, 2 miles from M4 junction 7, 5 miles from M40 junction 2, 100yds north of Gore crossroads - fork right into Wymers Wood Rd and ground is immediately on right. Bee Line buses 66 and 68.
Capacity: 2,500   **Cover:** 250   **Seats:** 250   **Floodlights:** Yes
Club Shop: Yes, selling programmes and other club items. Contact Dale Hurman (0628 664399).
Colours: Blue & white   **Change colours:** All yellow.
Sponsors: Rep-Tech (Herpetological Supplies).
Previous Leagues: Sth Bucks & East Berks/ Maidenhead Intermediate/ Windsor, Slough & Dist./ Gt Western Comb. 48-64/ Wycombe Comb. 64-70/ Reading Comb. 70-71/ Hellenic 71-77/ Athenian 77-84/ London Spartan 84-85.
Previous Name: Burnham & Hillingdon 1985-87
Previous Ground: Baldwin Meadow (until 20's).
Midweek home matchday: Wednesday
Reserve Team's League: Suburban.
Record Attendance: 2,400 v Halesowen Town, F.A. Vase 2/4/83.
Best F.A. Cup season: 3rd Qualifying Rd.
League clubs defeated in F.A. Cup: None.
Best F.A. Trophy season: Third Qualifying Rd replay 89-90.
Record win: 18-0 v High Duty Alloys, 70-71
Record defeat: 1-10 v Ernest Turners Sports, 63-64.
Players progressing to Football League: None.
Clubhouse: Open every evening and weekend lunchtimes. Darts and pool, two bars, usual matchday food.
Club Record Scorer: Fraser Hughes 65, 69-70
92-93 Captain: Shane Chandler
92-93 P.o.Y.: Shane Chandler
92-93 Top scorer: Steve Bunce 27.
Local Newspapers: Slough Observer (0753 523355), South Bucks Express (0753 825111), Maidenhead Advertiser (0628 798048).
Local Radio Stations: Chiltern, Radio 210.
Hons: FA Vase SF 82-83 (QF 77-78), Athenian Lg R-up(2) 78-80, Hellenic Lg 75-76 (Div 1 R-up 72-73, Lg Cup 75-76, Div 1 Cup 71-72), London Spartan Lg 84-85 (Lg Cup 84-85), Reading Comb. Lg Cup 70-71 (All Champions Cup 70-71), Wycombe Comb. R-up(4) 65-67 68-70, various local cup competitions.

Burnham
Football
Club
EST. 1878

League

PROGRAMME DETAILS:
Pages: 24 Price: T.B.A.
Editor: Jon Adaway
(0628 603612)

BURY TOWN

Despite the attentions of two Bury Town defenders, Wayne Schweiso scores the first goal (Steve Portway got the other six!) for Gravesend & Northfleet in their 7-2 win at the Ram Meadow on 9th January. Photo - Clive Pearson.

Chairman: V J Clark   **Vice Chairman:** A J Hall   **President:** C Elsey.
Secretary: W M Parker, 18 Mill Lane, Barrow, Bury St Edunds IP29 5BS (0284 810679).
Manager: D Brooks   **Asst Manager:** C Buckle   **Coach:** Trevor Cox
Press Officer: A J Hall   **Physio:** John Chandler
Ground: Ram Meadow, Cotton Lane, Bury St Edmunds, Suffolk (0284 754721/754820).
Directions: Leave A45 at sign to <u>central</u> Bury St Edmunds, follow signs to town centre at exit r'bout, 1st exit into Northgate Street at next r'bout, left at 'T' junct. (2nd lights) into Mustow Street and left immediately into Cotton Lane - ground 350 yds on right, through 'Pay & Display' car park (n.b. fine for not displaying a 40p ticket is £15). 10 mins walk from station.
Capacity: 3,500   **Cover:** 1,500   **Seats:** 300   **Floodlights:** Yes   **Metal Badges:** Yes
Club Shop: Yes - contact Ian Pinches (0284 769440).
Colours: Blue/white/blue   **Change colours:** Red/black/red.
Sponsors: Greene King Plc.
Previous Lges: Norfolk & Suffolk/ Essex & Suffolk Border/ Eastern Co's 35-64 76-87/ Metropolitan 64-71.
Previous Names: Bury St Edmunds 1895-1902/ Bury Utd 02-06.
Previous Ground: Kings Road 1872-1978.
Midweek home matchday: Tuesday   **Reserves' Lge:** Jewson (Eastern Co's) Div 1.
Record Attendance: 2,500 v Enfield, F.A. Cup 3rd Qualifying Rd 1986. (At Kings Road, previous ground, 4,710 v King's Lynn, 1950).
Best F.A. Cup season: 1st Rd replay 68-69 (lost 0-3 at AFC Bournemouth after 0-0 draw).
League clubs defeated in F.A. Cup: None.
Record Fees - Paid: £1,500 for Mel Springett (Chelmsford 1990).
            Received: £5,500 for Simon Milton (Ipswich).
Players progressing to Football League: D Lewis (Gillingham, Preston), Larry Carberry (Ipswich & England), Terry Bly (Norwich 1956, Peterborough), Terry Pearce (Ipswich), Gary Stevens (Brighton, Spurs & England), Simon Milton (Ipswich 1990).
Clubhouse: Members'/Public Bars open at matchdays and evenings. Darts, pool, satellite TV, bar snacks, meeting facilities.
Club Record Goalscorer: Doug Tooley 58.
Club Record Appearances: Doug Tooley.
92-93 Captain: Trevor Collins.
92-93 P.o.Y.: Mark Barnard.
92-93 Top scorer: Trevor Collins.
Local Newspapers: East Anglian Daily Times (0473 230023), Bury Free Press (0284 768911).
Local Radio: BBC Radio Suffolk (0473 250000), S.G.R. Radio (0284 701511).
Honours: F.A. Vase QF 88-89, F.A. Trophy 2nd Rd 70-71, Eastern Counties Lg 63-64 (R-up 37-38, Lg Cup 61-62 63-64), Metropolitan Lg 65-66 (R-up 67-68 70-71, Lg Cup 67-68, Professional Cup 65-66), Suffolk Premier Cup 58-59 59-60 60-61 61-62 63-64 64-65 70-71 77-78, Suffolk Senior Cup 36-37 37-38 38-39 44-45 84-85.

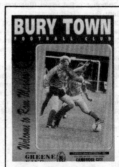

PROGRAMME DETAILS:
Pages: 40 **Price:** 50p
Editor: T.B.A.

CANTERBURY CITY

Canterbury City F.C. 1992-93. Back Row (L/R): Tony Pattenden (Physio), Les Hall (Manager), Paul Neat, Paul Bagley, Joe Radford, Julian Holmes, Paul Underwood, Willie Duncan (Reserve Manager), Bill Rose (Asst Physio). Front: Marc Hall, Mark Harrop, John Lineham, Jason Fenton, Stephen White, Graham Stonestreet, William Roffey. Photo - Eric Marsh.

Chairman: Derick J Owen   **President:** V H Heslop.
Secretary/Press Officer: Keith J Smith, 7 Knight Ave., London Rd Est., Canterbury, Kent CT2 0PZ (0227 456116).
Manager/Coach: Les Hall   **Asst Mgr:** Willie Duncan
Physio: Tony Pattenden   **Commercial Manager:** Joe Radford.
Ground: Kingsmead Stadium, Kingsmead Raod, Canterbury CT2 7PH (0227 762220).
Directions: A28 out of city centre into Military Road. At first r-about turn left into Tourtel Road, proceed to next r-about and head straight over into Kingsmead Road - stadium on right opposite Canterbury swimming pool. Half mile from Canterbury West (BR). Bus service 624 or 625 from Canterbury bus station - ask for Kingsmead crossroads.
Capacity: 3,000   **Cover:** 100   **Seats:** 100   **Floodlights:** Yes   **Metal Badges:** Yes
Club Shop: Programmes, souvenirs, clothing etc. Contact secretary.
Cols: Green & white/green/green   **Change colours:** Sky/navy/navy.   **Sponsors:** None.
Previous Leagues: Kent 47-59/ Metropolitan 59-60.
Previous Name: Canterbury Waverley   **Previous Grounds:** Wincheap Grove, Bretts Corner.
Midweek home matchday: Wednesday   **Reserve Team's League:** Winstonlead Kent Div 2
Record Attendance: 3,001 v Torquay, FA Cup 1st Rd 1964.
Record win: 10-0 v Deal Town   **Record defeat:** 0-9 v Corby Town.
Best F.A. Cup season: 1st Rd 64-65 (lost 0-6 to Torquay), 68-69 (lost 0-1 to Swindon).
Record Fees - Paid: £2,000 for Graham Knight (Maidstone United)
                Received: £2,000 for Dave Wiltshire (Gillingham).
Players progressing to Football League: Ron Gawler (Southend 1949), Arthur Hughes (Grimsby 1954), Arthur Nugent (Darlington 1956), John Richardson (Southport 1956), Tommy Horsfall (Cambridge Utd), Jimmy Murray (Wolves), Kenny Hill (Gillingham), Terry Norton (Brighton), Mark Weatherly (Gillingham), Pat Hilton (Brighton 1973), David Wiltshire (Gillingham 1974), Gary Pugh (Torquay 1984).
Clubhouse: Lounge bar open on 2pm matchdays. Tea bar sells burgers, pies, crisps, tea, coffee and soft drinks.
Club Record Goalscorer: Allan Jones
Club Record Appearances: John Carragher.
92-93 Captain: Kevin Smart.
92-93 P.o.Y.: Paul Bagley (supporters': Paul Underwood).
92-93 Top scorer: Paul Underwood 16.
Local Newspapers: Kentish Gazette (468181), Adscene (454545).
Local Radio Stations: Radio Kent, Invicta Radio.
Honours: FA Trophy 2nd Rd replay 74-75, Kent Lg Cup 49-50 (Div 2 (Reserves) 90-91, Div 2 Cup (Reserves) 89-90), Kent Senior Cup 53-54, Kent Senior Trophy 79-80, Kent Intermediate Cup 73-74, Kent Messenger Trophy, Frank Norris Memorial Shield.

PROGRAMME DETAILS:
Pages: 12 **Price:** 40p
Editor: Secretary

DUNSTABLE

Dunstable F.C. 1992-93. Back Row (L/R): G Kefford (Player-Coach), Neil Lane (now Arlesey Town), K Wheeler, I Edet, G Turner, K Thomas, G Hall, V Bittain, Steve Brinkman (Manager). Front: N Archell, C Campbell, R Camp, S Gyalog, P Coughlin, N Madden (Captain). Photo - Gavin Ellis-Neville.

Chairman: Alan Fieldhouse   **President:** Gerald Fox.
Secretary: Barry Hills (0582 665951).
Manager: Steve Brinkman   **Asst Manager:** Jim McCarthy
Press Officer: Secretary   **Physio:** Alex Webber
Commercial Manager: Steve Brinkman.
Ground: Creasey Park, Brewers Hill Road, Dunstable (0582 606691).
Directions: Brewers Hill Road runs west from A505 at north end of Dunstable at large traffic island; turn right after 150 yds. 5 miles from Luton (BR), buses 67 and 70 (from Luton) pass 200 yds from ground.
Capacity: 10,000   **Cover:** 750   **Seats:** 500   **Floodlights:** Yes   **Metal Badges:** Yes
Club Shop: Yes. New club shop planned to open during season.
Colours: All blue   **Change colours:** All red.
Sponsors: Fieldhouse & Husband.
Previous Leagues: Metropolitan 50-55 58-61 63-65/ Hellenic 55-58/ United Counties 61-63.
Previous Name: Dunstable Town.
Midweek home matchday: Tuesday   **Reserve Team:** No.
Record Attendance: 6,000 v Manchester United, Friendly 1974.
Best F.A. Cup season: 1st Rd 56-67 (lost 1-3 at Margate).
League clubs defeated in F.A. Cup: None.
Record Fees - Paid: £1,500 for Stuart Atkins (Wycombe 1979)
           Received: £20,000 for Kerry Dixon (Reading).
Players progressing to Football League: Bill Garner (Southend, Chelsea), Keith Barber (Luton 1971), Kerry Dixon (Reading 1980), Laurie Ryan (C'bridge Utd).
Clubhouse: (0582 63800). Large clubroom and bar.
92-93 Captain: Neil Maddon.
92-93 P.o.Y.: Steve Hunt.
92-93 Top scorer: Richard Camp.
Local Newspapers: Dunstable Gazette, Herald, Citzen.
Local Radio Stations: Radio Beds, Chiltern.
Honours: F.A. Trophy 3rd Qualifying Rd 2nd replay 71-72, Southern Lg Div 1 North R-up 74-75, Hellenic Lg R-up 57-58, Beds Senior Cup 1895-96 1956-57 59-60 79-80 82-83 85-86 86-87 87-88 88-89, Beds Premier Cup 80-81 82-83.

PROGRAMME DETAILS:
Pages: TBA **Price:** TBA
Editor: Harold Stew

ERITH & BELVEDERE

Erith & Belvedere F.C. 1992-93. Back Row (L/R): J Nohilly, M Hobbs, T Young, M Johnson, Harry Richardson (Manager), K Foster, P Battram, J Palmer. Front: J Leslie, M Dennehy, W Barlow, J Stinsen, H Hughton, G Brenton. Photo - Gavin Ellis-Neville.

Chairman: J McFadden **Vice Chairman:** R E Cowley **President:** L O'Connell.
Secretary: D Joy, 104 Overton Road, Abbey Wood, London SE2 9SE (081 311 0650).
Manager: Mick Springer **Asst Manager:** **Physio:** Ron Bates
Ground: Park View, Lower Road, Belvedere, Kent DA17 6DF (081 311 4444).
Directions: From Dartford bridge follow signs for Crayford to Erith and follow A206. Ground half mile from Erith Blackwall tunnel: head for Abbey Wood and on to Belvedere. Entrance in Station Road, adjoining Belvedere (BR) station. Bus No. 469.
Capacity: 1,500 **Cover:** 1,000 **Seats:** 500 **Floodlights:** Yes **Metal Badges:** Yes
Club Shop: Yes, selling programmes, badges and pens.
Colours: Blue & white **Change colours:** All red.
Previous Leagues: Kent 22-29 31-39 78-82/ London 29-31/ Corinthian 45-63/ Athenian 63-78.
Previous Names: Erith FC/ Belvedere & District FC (clubs amalgamated in 1922).
Midweek home matchday: Tuesday **Reserves' League:** Hurst Electrical Kent Midweek.
Record Attendance: 8,000 v Coventry City, F.A. Cup First Round Proper 1932.
Best F.A. Cup season: First Round Proper 24-25 32-33.
League clubs defeated in F.A. Cup: None.
Players progressing to Football League: Geoff Bray (Oxford Utd 1971), Tommy Ord (Chelsea 1972).
Clubhouse: Licensed social club open matchdays and weekends. Cold snacks available available, separate canteen provides hot food on matchdays.
92-93 Captain: John Glover **92-93 P.o.Y. & Top scorer:** John Leslie
Local Newspapers: Kentish Times, Kentish Independant.
Local Radio Stations: Radio Kent, Radio Thamesmead.
Honours: FA Amateur Cup R-up 23-24 37-38, FA Trophy 3rd Qualifying Rd 2nd replay 89-90, FA Vase 3rd Rd 76-77, Athenian Lg Div 1 R-up 70-71 (Lg Cup 73-74, Memorial Shield 67-68), Corinthian Lg R-up 62-63 (Lg Cup 47-48 48-49 49-50), Kent Lg 81-82 (Lg Cup R-up 81-82), London Senior Cup 44-45 (R-up 38-39), Kent Amateur Cup 23-24 47-48 65-66 66-67 68-69 69-70 (R-up 33-34 35-35 51-52 73-74), Bromley Hospital Cup 38-39, Kent Floodlit Lg R-up 67-68, Kent Intermediate Cup R-up 90-91, Kent Junior Cup 67-68, Essex & Herts Border Comb Cup 73-74, Kent County Yth Lg 90-91, Kent Yth Cup 87-88.

PROGRAMME DETAILS:
Pages: 30 **Price:** 50p
Editor: T.B.A.

FAREHAM TOWN

Back to 1987, and one of the happiest moments in Fareham Town's history - Malcolm Wilkes drills the ball past Scarborough goalkeeper Kevin Blackwell to put the Conference champions-elect out of the F.A. Trophy at the Third Round stage. Fareham went on to reach the Semi-Finals. Photo - Yorkshire Regional Newspapers.

Chairman: Michael K Jackson   **President:** Vacant.
Secretary: K F Atkins, 4 Cedar Close, Elson, Gosport PO12 4AT (0705 583049).
Manager: Roger Kent   **Asst Manager/Coach:** Paul Everest
Press Officer: M Willis   **Physio:** G Buckner
Ground: Cams Alders, Highfield Avenue, Fareham, Hants PO14 1JA (0329 231151).
Directions: From Fareham station follow A27 towards Southampton and take second left into Redlands Avenue. Turn right at Redlands Inn then left into Highfields Avenue.
Capacity: 5,500   **Cover:** 500   **Seats:** 450   **Club Shop:** Yes   **Metal Badges:** Yes
Colours: Red/white/red   **Change colours:** White/black/white.
Sponsors: Hellyers Coaches.
Previous Name: Fareham F.C.   **Previous Leagues:** Portsmouth 47-49/ Hants 49-79.
Previous Ground: Bath Lane.
Midweek home matchday: Wednesday   **Reserve Team:** None.
Record Gate: 2,650 v Wimbeldon, FA Cup 1965. *(at Southampton F.C.; 6,035 v Kidderminster Harriers, F.A. Trophy Semi Final Second leg 86-87).*
Best F.A. Cup season: 1st Rd replay 88-89 (lost 2-3 at home to Torquay after 2-2 draw).
League clubs defeated in F.A. Cup: None.
Record Fees - Paid: £1,000 for Peter Baxter (Poole)
           Received: £43,000 for David Leworthy (Spurs).
Players progressing to Football League: Ray Hiron (Portsmouth 1964), John Hold (A.F.C. Bournemouth), David Leworthy (Spurs 1984), Steve Claridge (A.F.C. Bournemouth 1984), Darren Foreman (Barnsley), Kevin Bartlett (Cardiff City 1986), Domenyk Newman (Reading 1990).
Clubhouse: Open every evening except Sundays.
92-93 Captain: Nigel Mottashed.
92-93 P.o.Y.: Miles Rutherford.   **92-93 Top scorer:** Robbie Taylor.
Local Newspapers: Portsmouth Evening News, Southampton Evening Echo.
Hons: F.A. Trophy S.F. 86-87, F.A. Amateur Cup 2nd Rd 63-64 66-67 73-74, Hants Lg(8) 59-60 62-67 72-73 74-75 (R-up 55-56 60-61 67-68 71-72 76-77 78-79, Div 2 R-up 52-53, Eastern Div 24-25, Div 3 East 49-50), Hants Snr Cup 56-57 62-63 67-68 92-93, Russell Cotes Cup(6) 64-65 72-77, Gosport War Memorial Cup, S.W. Co's Cup(2), Pickford Cup(2), Hants I'mediate Cup (reserves), F.A. Sunday Cup (as Fareham Centipedes) 74-75.

PROGRAMME DETAILS:
Pages: 36 Price: 50p
Editor: Roy Grant

'THE NON-LEAGUE PLAYERS'
1993-94 EDITION

AVAILABLE DURING THE SEASON, WILL FEATURE DETAILS OF FAREHAM TOWN'S PLAYERS, AND INDEED THE PLAYERS OF ALL CLUBS IN THE TOP FOUR PYRAMID LEAGUES. FOR MORE DETAILS ON THIS PUBLICATION SEE THE ADVERT NEAR THE FRONT OF THIS DIRECTORY.

FISHER '93

Fisher Athletic F.C. 1992-93. Back Row (L/R): Micky Wakefield (Manager), Femi Adedeja, Jimmy Jones, Danny Owen, Mark Bushell, Billy Reid, John Ugbah, Terry Back. Front: Richmond Donka, Lee Campbell, Darren Adams, Paul Bunter, Danny Davenport, Jason Huntley, Mark Beckett. Photo - Alan Coomes.

Chairman: James Webb   **President:** Lord Mellish of Bermondsey.
Secretary: M J Wakefield, 146 Layard Square, Drummond Rd, Bermondsey SE16 0JG (071 237 2819).
Manager: Mick Wakefield   **Asst Manager/Coach:** Ossie Bayram.
Press Officer: **Physio:** Joe Millar.
Commercial Manager: Bert Kite.
Ground: The Surrey Docks Stadium, Salter Road, London SE16 1LQ (071 231 5144. Fax: 231 5536).
Directions: 8 minutes walk from Rotherhithe (tube), 2 miles from London Bridge (main line). Buses 188, P11, P14.
Capacity: 5,300   **Cover:** 1,200   **Seats:** 400   **Floodlights:** Yes   **Metal Badges:** Yes
Club Shop: Yes.
Colours: Black & white stripes/white/black   **Change colours:** All red.
Previous Leagues: Parthenon/ West Kent/ Kent Amateur/ London Spartan 76-82/ Southern 82-87/ GMV Conference 87-91.
Midweek home games: Monday   **Reserve Team's League:** Suburban.
Record Gate: 4,283 v Barnet, GMV Conference 4/5/91.
Previous Name: Fisher Athletic 08-93.
Previous Ground: London Road, Mitcham.
Best F.A. Cup season: 1st Rd 84-85 (0-1 at home to Bristol City), 88-89 (0-4 at Bristol Rovers).
League Clubs Defeated in F.A. Cup: None.
Record Fees: Paid: £500 for Davis Regis.
          Received: Undisclosed.
Players progressing to The Football League: John Bumstead (Chelsea), Trevor Aylott (Bournemouth), Paul Shinners (Orient 1984), Dave Regis (Notts County - via Barnet).
Clubhouse: (071 252 0590). Luxury clubhouse, Vice-President's club, hot and cold food.
Club Record Scorer: Paul Shinners 205
Club Record Appearances: Dennis Sharp 720.
92-93 Captain:
92-93 P.o.Y.:
92-93 Top scorer:
Honours: Southern Lg 86-87 (R-up 83-84, Southern Div 82-83, Lg Cp 84-85, Championship Cup 87-88, Merit Cup), London Spartan Lg 80-81 81-82 (R-up 78-79, Senior Div 77-78, Div 2 R-up 76-77), Parthenon Lg 61-62 (Lg Cup 63-64 65-66), Kent Amateur Lg 73-74 74-75 (R-up 72-73), London Senior Cup 84-85 87-88 88-89, London Intermediate Cup 59-60 (R-up 75-76), Kent Senior Cp 83-84, Kent Senior Trophy 81-82 82-83, Surrey Intermediate Cup 61-62, FA Trophy 3rd Rd 3rd replay 87-88, FA Vase 2nd Rd replay 82-83.

PROGRAMME DETAILS:
Pages: 16 **Price:** 50p
Editor: Ken Wenham

Gravesend & Northfleet F.C. 1992-93. Back Row (L/R): Eric Rolls (Director), Denis Abboh, Mark Leahy, Jason Eede, Lee Graves, Lee Turner, Chris Fordred, Paul Lamb, Steve Portway, Dean Wells. Front: Ian Gibbs, Peter Coffill, Simon Ullathorne, Wayne Schweiso, Micky Cotter.

Chairman: L G F Ball   **Vice Chairman:** D F Hockley
Secretary: Bill Hornby c/o the club (H - 0474 363424).
Manager: Gary Aldous   **Asst Manager:** Peter Coffill
Coach: Peter Coffill/ Chris Weller   **Physio:** Micky Ward
Press Officer: Lionel R H Ball (0474 569985).
Ground: Stonebridge Road, Northfleet, Kent DA11 9BA (0474 533796)
Directions: From A2 take Northfleet/Southfleet exit (B262), follow to Northfleet then B2175 (Springhead Rd) to junction with A226, turn left (The Hill, Northfleet), road becomes Stonebridge Rd, ground is on right at bottom of steep hill after 1 mile - car parking behind for 400-500 cars. 2 mins walk from Northfleet BR station.
Capacity: 6,000   **Cover:** 5,000   **Seats:** 400   **Floodlights:** Yes   **Metal Badges:** Yes
Club Shop: Yes, selling various supporters' items (hats, scarves etc), other football memorabilia, extensive selection of programmes. Contact Mick Hills or Simon Merton via the club.
Colours: Red/white/red   **Change colours:** White/blue/white   **Sponsors:** T.B.A.
Previous Names: Gravesend Utd/ Northfleet Utd (merged in 1946).
Previous Leagues: Kent (as Gravesend Utd)/ Southern 1946-79/ Alliance Prem. 79-80.
Previous Ground: Central Avenue (as Gravesend United) *(Northfleet Utd alway played at Stonebridge Rd).*
Midweek home matchday: Tuesday   **Reserves' Lge:** Hurst Electrical Kent Midweek.
Record Attendance: 12,036 v Sunderland, F.A. Cup 4th Rd 62-63.
Best F.A. Cup season: 4th Rd Replay 1963 (lost 2-5 at Sunderland after 1-1 draw at home).
League clubs defeated in F.A. Cup: Exeter City, Carlisle United (both 62-63).
Record Fees -   Paid: £3,5000 for Dave Busby (Barrow, 1980).
              Received: £15,000 for Lee Smelt (Nottm Forest, 1980).
Record win: 8-1 v Clacton Town, Southern League 62-63.
Record defeat: 0-9 v Trowbridge Town (A), Southern League Premier Division 1991-92.
Players progressing to Football League: James Wilson (Chelsea 1947), Fred Pincott (Newport 1947), Stan Aldows & Herbert Hawkins (Orient 1950 & 51), Harry Gunning (West Ham 1952), John Hills (Spurs 1953), Norman Lewis (Newport 1954), Kevin Baron (Aldershot 1960), Roy Dwight (Coventry 1962), Robert Cameron (Southend 1963), Robert McNichol (Carlisle 1965), Alan Humphreys (Mansfield 1964), Barry Thornley (Brentford 1965), Pat Jeavons (Lincoln 1966), Barry Fry (Orient 1966), Barry Gordine (Sheffield Utd 1968), Tommy Baldwin (Brentford 1977), Lee Smelt (Nottm Forest 1980), Tom Warrilow (Torquay 1987)
Clubhouse: Fleet Social Centre open before and after all matches, Sat 7-11pm, Sun noon-2.30, Tues & Thurs 7-11pm. Hot and cold food available at tea bars on matchdays.
Club Record Goalscorer: Steve Portway, 61 (92-93).
Club Record Appearances: Ken Burrett 537.
92-93 Captain: Denis Abboh/ Wayne Schweiso.
92-93 P.O.Y.: Steve Portway (Young Player: Paul Lamb).
92-93 Top scorer: Steve Portway 61.
Local Newspapers: Gravesend & Dartford Reporter, Kent Evening Post, Gravesend Extra, Leader
Local Radio Stations: Invicta Radio, Radio Kent.
Hons: Southern Lg 57-58 (Div 1 Sth 74-75 (R-up 70-71 88-89), Lg Cup 77-78 (R-up 57-58), Champ'ship Cup 77-78), Kent Snr Cup 48-49 52-53 80-81 (R-up 47-48 76-77 90-91), Kent F'lit Cup 69-70 (R-up 72-73), Kent Snr Shield R-up 47-48 51-52, Kent I'mediate Cup R-up 87-88, Kent Yth Lg Cup 82-83 86-87, John Ullman Cup 82-83, FA Tphy 3rd Rd 88-89.

the Fleet Matchday Magazine 1992-93

BEAZER HOMES LEAGUE
Southern Division

PROGRAMME DETAILS:
Pages: 28 **Price:** £1
Editor: Lionel R H Ball
(0474 569985)

HAVANT TOWN

Havant Town F.C. 1992-93. Back Row (L/R): G Buckner (Physio), J Price, N Hards, S Tate, B Hewitt, S Riley, M Sherry, S McIntyre. Front: D Monteane, N Kerton, N Selby, C Webbe (Captain), J Webb, G Rutherford. Photo - V J Robertson.

Chairman: Ray Jones   **President:** George Jones.
Directors: Derek Pope, Paul Cummins, Ian Craig, Trevor Brock.
Secretary/Press Officer: Trevor Brock, 2 Betula Close, Waterlooville, Hants PO7 8EJ (0705 267276).
Manager: Tony Mount   **Physio:** Gary Buckner
Ground: West Leigh Park, Martin Road, West Leigh, Havant PO9 5TH (0705 470918).
Directions: Take B2149 to Havant off the A27 (B2149 Petersfield Rd if coming out of Havant). 2nd turning off dual carriageway into Bartons Road then 1st right into Martins Road. 1 mile from Havant BR station.
Capacity: 6,000   **Cover:** 1,500   **Seats:** 240   **Floodlights:** Yes   **Metal Badges:** Yes
Club Shop: Yes, selling various souvenirs and programmes.
Colours: Yellow   **Change colours:** Blue   **Sponsors:** Nynex Cablecomms.
Previous Leagues: Portsmouth 58-71/ Hants 71-86/ Wessex 86-91.
Previous Names: Leigh Park/ Havant & Leigh Park.
Previous Grounds: Front Lawn 1958-83.
Midweek home matchday: Monday   **Reserves' Lge:** Jewson Wessex Combination.
Record Attendance: 3,000 v Wisbech, F.A. Vase QF 85-86.
Best F.A. Cup season: Second Qualifying Round.
Record win: 10-0 twice; v Sholing Sports (H), F.A. Vase 4th Rd 85-86, v Portsmouth Royal Navy (H), Jewson Wessex League 90-91.
Record defeat: 1-7 v Camberley Town (H), F.A. Vase 3rd Rd 88-89.
Record Fees - Paid: £5,750 for John Wilson (Bashley, 1990)
         Received: £4,250 for Peter Cox (Gosport Borough, 1991).
Players progressing to Football League: Bobby Tambling (Chelsea).
Clubhouse: Open every day, lunchtime and evening. 2 bars, function suites, hot & cold food available.
Club Record Goalscorer: Unknown.   **Club Record Appearances:** Tony Plumbley.
92-93 Captain: Clint Webbe.   **92-93 P.o.Y.:** John Price.
92-93 Top scorer: Neil Selby 19.
Local Newspapers: News (Portsmouth)(0705 664488).
Local Radio Stations: Ocean Sound, Radio Solent.
Honours: FA Sunday Cup 68-69, FA Vase QF 85-86, Wessex Lg 90-91 (R-up 88-89), Hampshire Lg Div 3 72-73 (Div 4 71-72), Hampshire Senior Cup R-up 91-92, Hampshire Intermediate Cup, Hampshire Junior Cup, Russell Coles Cup 91-92, Portsmouth Senior Cup 83-84 84-85 91-92, Gosport War Memorial Cup 74-75 91-92 92-93, Southern Counties Floodlit Cup R-up 91-92, Hampshire Floodlit Cup 85-86, Portsmouth Lg.

PROGRAMME DETAILS:
Pages: 24 Price: 50p
Editor: Steve Cox
(0705 269072)

'THE NON-LEAGUE PLAYERS'
1993-94 EDITION

AVAILABLE DURING THE SEASON, WILL FEATURE DETAILS OF HAVANT TOWN'S PLAYERS, AND INDEED THE PLAYERS OF ALL CLUBS IN THE TOP FOUR PYRAMID LEAGUES. FOR MORE DETAILS ON THIS PUBLICATION SEE THE ADVERT NEAR THE FRONT OF THIS DIRECTORY.

MARGATE

Margate F.C. 92-93. Back Row (L/R): Tony Harwood, Paul Sawyer, Dave Lee, Stuart Reed, Adrian Clewlew, Kevin Hudson, Andy Allon, Mark Weatherley, Billy Plews, David Carr. Front: Peter Hansen, Shaun Pilbeam, Trevor Hand, Tim Page, Paul Golden, Peter Jarvis, Malcolm Smith, Ian Young. Photo - Paul Bates.

Chairman: Gordon Wallis **Vice Chairman:** Keith Piper **President:** Mr R W Griffiths
Secretary: K E Tomlinson, 65 Nash Road, Margate CT9 4BT (0843 291040).
Joint Managers: Mark Weatherley/ Andy Woolford
Press Officer: Chairman **Commercial Manager:** Cliff Egan
Ground: Hartsdown Park, Hartsdown Road, Margate CT9 5QZ (0843 221769).
Directions: A28 into Margate, turn right opposite hospital into Hartsdown Road, proceed over crossroads and ground is on left. Ten mins walk from Margate (BR).
Capacity: 6,000 **Cover:** 3 sides **Seats:** 400 **Floodlights:** Yes **Metal Badges:** Yes
Club Shop: Yes. Progs, books, magazines, fanzines, badges, scarves, car stickers, T-shirts, mugs, pens, key-rings, address books, tax disc holders, etc... Contact Paul Bates, 46 High Str., Minster, Ramsgate, Kent CT12 4BT (0843 821032).
Colours: Royal/white/royal **Change colours:** White or yellow.
Previous Grounds: Margate College/ Dreamland, Northdown Rd/ Garlinge.
Previous Leagues: Kent 11-23 24-28 29-33 37-38 46-59/ Southern 33-37. **Sponsors:** TBA.
Midweek home matchday: Tuesday **Reserve Team's League:** Kent Midweek Lg.
Previous Name: Thanet United 1981-89. **Record Gate:** 14,500 v Spurs, FA Cup 3rd Rd 1973.
Best F.A. Cup season: 3rd Rd 72-73 (lost 0-6 to Spurs), 36-37 (lost 1-3 at Blackpool).
League clubs defeated in F.A. Cup: Gillingham 29-30, Queens Park Rangers, Crystal Palace 35-36, Bournemouth & Boscombe Athletic 61-62, Swansea 72-73.
Record transfer fees paid: £3,750 for Neil Cugley (F'stone)
Record transfer fee received: Undisclosed for Martin Buglione (St Johnstone 92-93).
Players progressing to Football League: Pre-War; too numerous to mention, partly because Margate were Arsenal's nursery club between 1934 & 1938. Post-War: John Yeomanson (West Ham 1947), Doug Bing & George Wright (West Ham 1951), Tommy Bing (Spurs 1956), John Roche (Millwall 1957), Derek Hodgkinson (Manchester City 1961), Stan Foster (Crystal Palace 1961), John Fraser (Watford 1962), Robert Walker (Bournemouth 1965), Ken Bracewell (Bury 1966), Tom Jenkins & Ray Flannigan (Reading 1969-70),
Mel Blyth (Millwall 1978), Martin Buglione (St Johnstone 1992).
Clubhouse: Flexible hours, private functions, matchday facilities.
Steward: Pam & Mark Weatherly.
Club Record Goalscorer: Dennis Randall 66 (season 1966-67).
Club Record Appearances: Bob Harrop.
92-93 Captain: Phil Handford
92-93 P.o.Y.: Malcolm Smith
92-93 Top scorer: Martin Buglione, 53
Local Newspapers: Isle of Thanet Gazette, Thanet Times (0843 221313), Thanet Extra, Adscene.
Local Radio: Radio Kent, Invicta Radio.
Newsline: 0898 800 665.
Hons: Southern Lg 35-36 (Lg Cp 67-68 (R-up 61-62 74-75), Div 1 62-63 (R-up 66-67), Div 1 Sth 77-78, East Div R-up 33-34, Merit Cp 66-67 77-78, Midweek Sect. 36-37), Kent Lg(4) 32-33 37-38 46-48 (R-up 27-28 29-30 53-54 55-56 57-58, Div 2 37-38 53-54 56-57 89-90, Lg Cp 35-36 47-48 53-54 68-69), Kent Snr Cup(3) 35-37 74-75, Kent Snr Shield(8) 20-21 30-31 35-37 47-48 52-53 61-63, Kent F'lit Cp 62-63 66-67 75-76, Kent Jnr Cup 01-02, FA Tphy 3rd Rd rep 78-79.

PROGRAMME DETAILS:
Pages: 28 **Price:** 60p
Editor: Paul Bates
(0843 821032)

NEWPORT I.O.W.

Newport Isle of Wight F.C. 1992-93.

Chairman: K Lacey **Vice Chairman:** M Edwards **President:** W H J Bunday.
Secretary/Press Off.: Chris Cheverton, 127 Westhill Road, Ryde, Isle of Wight PO33 1LW (0983 567355).
Manager: Steve Mellor **Asst Manager:** Dave Wakefield **Coach:** Roger McCormack
Commercial Manager: Dave Hiscock. **Physio:** Steve Lambourne
Ground: St George's Park, St George's Way, Newport, Isle of Wight PO30 2QH (0983 525027).
Directions: Roads from all ferry ports lead to Coppins Bridge R-about at eastern extremity of town. Take Sandown/Ventnor exit, proceed to small r-about, St George's way is first exit (straight on), ground immediately visible on left. Five minute walk from Newport bus station; along Church Litten (past old ground), turn left then right at r-about.
Capacity: 5,000 **Cover:** 1,000 **Seats:** 300 **Floodlights:** Yes **Metal Badges:** Yes.
Club Shop: Yes, selling clothes, programmes and novelties. Contact M Reader at ground.
Colours: Royal & gold **Change colours:** White & red/black.
Previous Ground: Church Litten (previously Wells' Field) 1888-1989.
Previous Leagues: Isle of Wight 1896-1928/ Hants 28-86/ Wessex 86-90.
Midweek home matchday: Tuesday **Reserve Team's League:** Jewson Wessex Comb.
Record Attendance: 1,700 v Fulham (official ground opening). *(6,000 v Watford, FA Cup 1st Round 56-57, at Church Litten (old ground)).*
Record win: 14-1, home to Thornycroft Athletic, Hampshire League Division One, 22/12/45.
Record defeat: 2-11, home to Basingstoke Town, Hampshire League Division One, 12/10/68.
Best F.A. Cup season: 2nd Rd 35-36 45-46. 1st Rd another seven times; 45-46 52-55 56-59.
League clubs defeated in F.A. Cup: Clapton Orient 45-46.
Record Fees - Paid: £3,000 for Stuart Ritchie (Bashley, May 1991)
Received: £2,250 for Mick Jenkins (Havant, March 1992).
Clubhouse: Open normal licensing hours. 2 bars, full range of hot and cold bar snacks. Buffet inside ground.
Club Record Goalscorer: Eddie Walder. **Club Record Apps:** Jeff Austin 540 (69-80).
92-93 Captain: Mark Smith **92-93 P.o.Y.:** Andy Sampson **92-93 Top scorer:** Andy Sampson.
Local Newspapers (+Tel.Nos.): Portsmouth Evening News, I.O.W. County Press, Southampton Evening Echo.
Local Radio Stations: Solent, Isle of Wight Radio, Ocean Sound.
Honours: FA Vase 5th Rd 91-92, Wessex Lg R-up 89-90 (Comb. 91-92(reserves)), Hants Lg(11) 29-30 32-33 38-39 47-48 49-50 52-54 56-57 78-81 (R-up(7) 30-32 35-36 51-52 54-55 58-59 77-78, Div 2 R-up 70-71), Hants Snr Cup(7) 31-33 54-55 60-61 65-66 79-81, Russell Cotes Cup(3) 77-80, Pickford Cup(4) 47-50 52-53, Isle of Wight Snr (Gold) Cup(28) 29-30 35-36 37-38 39-40 44-47 48-49 52-54 55-56 57-58 65-66 67-68 70-76 77-79 80-81 86-88 89-90 91-93, Hants F'lit Cup 76-77 77-78, Isle of Wight Lg(4) 07-10 23-24, Hants I'mediate Cup 31-32, Hants Comb. Cup 38-39.

PROGRAMME DETAILS:
Pages: 32 Price: 60p
Editor: Peter Ranger
(0983 526144)

POOLE TOWN

Poole Town F.C. 1992-93. Back Row (L/R): A Turrell, C Sansom, A Morley, M Radburn, M Jones, A Coombes, A Trimby, D Reeks. Front: C Wilson, T Townsend, P Maloney, P Young, Mascot, C Morrison. Photo - Dennis Nicholson.

Chairman: Clive Robbins   **Vice Chairman:** Chris Reeves   **President:** Fred Yates
Secretary: Barry Hughes, 226 Malvern Road, Bournemouth, Dorset BH9 3BX (0202 536906).
Manager: Brian Chambers   **Asst Manager:** Eric Lisle   **Physio:** Dick Thomas.
Press Officer/Commercial Manager: Barry Hughes.
Ground: Poole Stadium, Wimborne Road, Poole BH15 2BP (0202 674747).
Directions: Near centre of Poole, behind Fire Station on A349. Adjacent to Poole station.
Capacity: 6,000   **Cover:** 2,300   **Seats:** 1,300   **Club Shop:** Yes   **Metal Badges:** Yes
Colours: Red & white stripes/red/white   **Change colours:** All blue.
Sponsors: Abba Roofing.
Previous Leagues: Hants 1903-04 05-10 11-14 20-23 29-30 34-35/ Western 23-26 30-34 35-39 46-57.
Midweek home matchday: Tuesday   **Reserve Team's League:** Dorset Combination.
Record Attendance: 11,155 v Watford, F.A. Cup First Round replay 1962-63.
Best F.A. Cup season: 3rd Rd Proper 1926-27 (lost 1-3 at Everton). 1st Rd 7 times; 26-29 46-47 62-63 66-67 83-84).
League clubs defeated in F.A. Cup: Newport County, 26-27
Record Fees - Paid: £5,000 for Nicky Dent (Yeovil Town, 1990).
             Received: £8,000 for Nicky Dent (Dover Athletic, 1992).
Players progressing to Football League: Derek Stround (Bournemouth & Boscombe Athletic 1950), Dave Lawrence (Bristol Rovers 1951), John Thomas (Bournemouth & Boscombe Athletic 1958), James Rollo (Oldham 1960), John Smeulders (AFC Bournemouth 1987), Bob Iles (Chelsea), Phil Ferns Jr (AFC Bournemouth), D Lyon (Southport).
Clubhouse: Open every evening & lunchtime.
Club Record Goalscorer: Tony Funnell
Club Record Appearances: Martyn Jones
92-93 Captain: Ashley Coobes
92-93 P.o.Y.: Andy Morley
92-93 Top scorer: Craig Wilson
Local Newspapers: Evening Echo, Gazette.
Local Radio Stations: Radio Solent, 2CR.
Honours: Southern Lg Div 1 R-up 61-62 (Southern Div R-up 88-89), Western Lg 56-57 (R-up 46-47 49-50 53-54 55-56, Lg Cup 54-55), Dorset Senior Cup 1894-95 96-97 1901-02 03-04 06-07 25-26 26-27 37-38 46-47 88-89, FA Trophy 1st Rd replay 69-70, FA Amateur Cup 2nd Rd 47-48 48-49.

PROGRAMME DETAILS:
Pages: 36 **Price:** 70p
Editor: T.B.A.

SALISBURY CITY

Salisbury City F.C. - Beazer Homes League Southern Division Runners-up 1992-93. Photo - Gavin Ellis-Neville.

Chairman: Mr P R McEnhill **President:** Mr L Whitmarsh.
Secretary: Sean Gallagher, 49 Sunnyhill Road, Salisbury, Wilts SP1 3JQ (0722 324932).
Manager: Geoff Butler **Coach:** Gordon Hobson **Trainer:** Conrad Parrott
Press Officer: David Macey (0264 774765/ 0831 395756) **Physio:** Ian Landon
Youth Development Officer: Kevin Jackson.
Commercial Manager: Geoff Butler, 52 Endless House, Salisbury (0722 26454).
Ground: Victoria Park, Castle Road, Salisbury SP1 3ER (0722 336689).
Directions: A345 (Amesbury) road north from city centre, Victoria Park is on the left 800 yds after the ring road. One mile from Salisbury (BR).
Capacity: 3,400 **Cover:** 1,000 **Seats:** 320 **Floodlights:** Yes **Metal Badges:** Yes
Club Shop: Yes.
Colours: White/black/black **Change colours:** All blue.
Sponsors: Dunlop Hiflex.
Previous Leagues: Western 47-68. **Previous Name:** Salisbury F.C. (pre-1992).
Midweek home matchday: Wednesday **Reserve Team's League:**
Record Attendance: 8,902 v Weymouth, Western League 1948.
Best F.A. Cup season: 2nd Rd 59-60, lost 0-1 at home to Newport County.
League clubs defeated in F.A. Cup: None.
Previous Ground: Hudson Field, Castle Rd, Salisbury.
Record Fees - Paid: £5,750 for Peter Loveridge (Dorchester Town, 1990)
         Received: £16,000 for Ian Thompson (A.F.C. Bournemouth, 1983).
Players progressing to Football League: Eric Fountain (Southampton 1948), Cyril Smith (Arsenal & Southampton 1948), Graham Moxham (Exeter 1975), Ian Thompson (Bournemouth 1983), Trevor Woods (Port Vale 1988), Denny Mundee (B'mouth 1988), Matthew Carmichael (Lincoln 1990).
Clubhouse: Small bar on ground. Main Supporters Club situated in Chatham Close, some 300yds from ground. Varied social facilities. Activities include snooker, darts, cribbage, television.
Two bars and a seperate function room. Supervisor: Mr Peter Wrigley.
Club Record Goalscorer: Allan Green 113 (Southern Lg)
Club Record Appearances: Barry Fitch 713.
92-93 Captain: Peter Loveridge
92-93 P.o.Y.: Mark Payne
92-93 Top scorer: Sean Sanders
Local Newspapers: Salisbury Journal, Southern Evening & Sports Echo, Western Gazette, Western Daily Press.
Local Radio Stations: Wiltshire Sound, Radio Solent, Spire F.M.
Club Information Line: Cityline, 0891 122 905 (Sponsored by Spire F.M.).
Honours: Southern Lg Southern Div R-up 85-86 92-93, Western Lg 57-58 60-61 (R-up 58-59 59-60 60-61 61-62 67-68, Div 2 47-48, Lg Cup 55-56), Hants Senior Cup 61-62 63-64, Alan Young Cup 59-60 60-61 62-63, Wilts Premier Shield 56-57 59-60 60-61 61-62 66-67 67-68 70-71 77-78 78-79, FA Trophy 1st Rd 85-86 90-91 91-92, FA Amateur Cup 2nd Rd 49-50.

PROGRAMME DETAILS:
Pages: 48 **Price:** 60p
Editor: David Macey
(0264 774765)

SUDBURY TOWN

Paul Smith, Sudbury Town's top-scorer last season. Photo - Francis Short.

Chairman: Phil Turner   **President:** H D J Yallop.
Secretary: David Webb, 6 Melford Road, Sudbury, Suffolk CO10 6LS (0787 372352).
Manager: Richie Powling   **Asst Mgr/Coach:** Graham Daniels. **Physio:** Tony Brightwell
Commercial Manager/Press Officer: Richie Powling, c/o the club (0787 370957).
Ground: Priory Stadium, Priory Walk, Sudbury, Suffolk (0787 379095).
Directions: Take Friars Street from town centre, pass cricket ground and continue to the 'Ship & Star'. Left into Priory Walk and continue to ground. Half mile and three quarters of a mile from bus and rail stations respectively.
Capacity: 5,000   **Cover:** 900   **Seats:** 300   **Club Shop:** Yes   **Metal Badges:** Yes
Colours: All yellow   **Change colours:** All red.
Sponsors: F.F.D.F.D.S. Transport/ Wheelers (Timber & Building).
Previous Leagues: Suffolk & Ipswich/ Essex & Suffolk Border/ Eastern Counties 55-90.
Previous Ground: Friar Street (until 1951).
Midweek home matchday: Tuesday   **Reserve Team's League:** Jewson Eastern Cos. Div 1.
Record Attendance: 4,700 v Ipswich Town, testimonial 1978.
Record Transfer Fee Received: For Steve McGavin (Colchester United, 1991).
Best F.A. Cup season: 3rd Qualifying Rd replay 74-75.
Players progressing to Football League: Gilbert Dowsett (Spurs 1952), John Taylor (Cambridge 1988), Steve McGavin (promoted with Colchester 1992).
Clubhouse: Open on matchdays and for other functions. Pool, darts, dancehall.
91-92 Captain: Andy Crane/ Graham Daniels.
91-92 P.o.Y.: Murray Osman.
91-92 Top scorer: Paul Smith.
Local Newspapers: Suffolk Free Press, East Anglian Daily Times.
Hons: FA Vase R-up 88-89 (SF 87-88 91-92), Eastern Counties Lg 73-74 74-75 75-76 85-86 86-87 88-89 89-90 (R-up 65-66 72-73 76-77 80-81 81-82 84-85, Lg Cup 69-70 76-77 82-83 86-87 88-89 89-90, Suffolk & Ipswich Lg 34-35 52-53, Suffolk Premier Cup 72-73 73-74 75-76 80-81 81-82 82-83 84-85 86-87 87-88 88-89 89-90 91-92 92-93, Suffolk Senior Cup 56-57 86-87, East Anglian Cup 85-86 91-92.

PROGRAMME DETAILS:
Pages: 24 Price: 50p
Editor: Brian Hender

TONBRIDGE A.F.C.

The Angels

Tonbridge's Russell Norris (left) outpaces Simon Colbron of Tunbridge Wells in the Boxing Day Winstonlead Kent League fixture at the Longmead Stadium. This derby, which is always keenly contested, finished 1-1. Photo - Alan Coomes.

Chairman: Ken Shellito **Vice Chairman:** Ken Jarrett.
Secretary: Steve Wardhaugh, 39 Badger Rd, Lordswood, Chatham, Kent ME5 8TY (0634 669154).
Manager: Phil Emblen **Physio:** Peter Battell **Coach:** Dave Boyton
Press Officer: Secretary **Commercial Manager:** Jim Lyon.
Ground: Longmead Stadium, Darenth Avenue, Tonbridge, Kent TN10 3JW (0732 352417/ 358868).
Directions: From Tonbridge BR station, through High Street, north up Shipbourne Rd (A227 Gravesend road) to 2nd mini-r'bout ('The Pinnacles' pub), left into Darenth Avenue, ground at bottom approx. 1 mile at far side of sports ground car park.
Seats: 202 **Cover:** 640 **Capacity:** 5,000 **Metal Badges:** Yes. **Shop:** Due 93-94.
Colours: Blue (white sleeves)/blue/blue **Change Colours:** All red.
Midweek matchday: Wednesday **Sponsors:** New Entreprises Coaches
Reserve Team's League: Winstonlead Kent Division Two.
Previous Leagues: Southern 48-89/ Kent 89-93.
Previous Ground: The Angel 48-80. **Previous Names:** Tonbridge Angels, Tonbridge F.C.
Record Gate: 1,463 v Yeovil Town, F.A. Cup 4th Qualifying Round 26/10/91. *At the Angel Ground: 8,236 v Aldershot, F.A. Cup 1st Round 1951.*
Players progressing to Football League: R Saunders, M McMcDonald, T Burns, I Seymour, G Moseley, T Morgan.
Clubhouse: Open Mon-Sat evenings and Sunday lunchtimes. Hot food on matchdays from burger bar.
Club Record Goalscorer: Unknown
Club Record Appearances: Mark Gillham, 520 to date.
92-93 Captain: Dave Boyton.
92-93 P.o.Y.: Danny Tingley.
92-93 Top scorer: Ian Mawson.
Local Newspapers: Kent Messenger.
Local Radio Stations: Invicta, Radio Kent.
Hons: Kent Lg Cup(2), Southern Lg Cup R-up(2)(SF(1)), Kent Snr Cup 64-65 74-75 (R-up(2)), Kent Snr Shield 51-52 55-56 57-58 58-59 63-64, FA Cup 1st Rd Proper 50-51 51-52 52-53 67-68 72-73.

'THE NON-LEAGUE PLAYERS'
1993-94 EDITION

AVAILABLE DURING THE SEASON, WILL FEATURE DETAILS OF TONBRIDGE'S PLAYERS, AND INDEED THE PLAYERS OF ALL CLUBS IN THE TOP FOUR PYRAMID LEAGUES. FOR MORE DETAILS ON THIS PUBLICATION SEE THE ADVERT NEAR THE FRONT OF THIS DIRECTORY.

PROGRAMME DETAILS:
Pages: 28 Price: 50p
Editor: Ian White

WEALDSTONE

Wealdstone F.C. 1992-93. Photo - Paul Dennis.

Chairman: Paul Rumens   **Vice Chairman:** Nick Dugard.
Secretary/Commercial Mgr: Ian Crossley, 9 Windermere Ave., Kempsham, Basingstoke, Hants (0256 59313).
Manager: Dennis Byatt   **Press Officer:** Steve Marshall.   **Newsline:** 0891 88 44 73
Ground: As Yeading F.C. (see page 309).
Metal Badges: Yes.   **Club Shop:** Yes
Colours: Blue & white quarters   **Change colours:** Yellow   **Sponsors:** T.B.A.
Previous Leagues: Willesden & Dist/ Middx Senior/ London 1911-14 19-32/ Spartan 22-28/ Athenian 28-64/ Isthmian 64-71/ Southern 71-79 81-82/ GMV Conference 79-81 82-88.
Previous Grounds: College Farm 10-22/ Lower Mead Stadium 22-91/ Vicarage Rd (Watford FC) 91-93.
Midweek home matchday: Wednesday   **Reserve Team's League:** N/A.
Record Attendance: 13,504 v Leytonstone F.A. Amateur Cup 1949.
Best F.A. Cup season: 3rd Rd 77-78 (0-4 at Q.P.R.). 1st Rd on 13 occasions 49-50 65-67 68-69 75-80 82-84 85-87.
League clubs defeated in F.A. Cup: Hereford Utd and Reading, 77-78.
Record Fees: Paid: £15,000 for David Gipp.
Received: £25,000 for Stuart Pearce (Coventry City).
Players progressing to Football League: Edward Smith (Chelsea 1950), Phil White (Orient 1953), Tom McGhee & John Ashworth (Portsmouth 1954 & 62), Charlie Sells (Exeter 1962), Eddie Dilsworth (Lincoln 1967), Colin Franks (Watford 1969), Stuart Pearce (Coventry 1983), Vinnie Jones (W'don 1986), Danny Bailey (Exeter 1989), Francis Joseph (Wimbledon & Brentford), Bobby Ryan.
Clubhouse: Yes, normal licensing hours.
Club Record Goalscorer: George Duck, 251
Club Record Appearances: Charlie Townsend, 514
92-93 Captain: Neil Cordice
92-93 P.o.Y.: P Tenkorang.
92-93 Top scorer: Dave Venables.
Local Newspapers: Harrow Observer, Watford Observer.
Local Radio: LBC, Capital, Greater London Radio, Radio Bedford.
Honours: FA Tphy 84-85, FA Amateur Cup 65-66 (R-up 67-68), GMV Conference 84-85, Southern Lg 81-82 (Div 1 South 73-74, Lg Cup 81-82), Athenian Lg 51-52 (R-up 52-53 58-59 60-61), Spartan Lg R-up 22-23, London Lg Div 2 12-13 (R-up 11-12), London Snr Cup 61-62(joint)(R-up 39-40, 51-52 60-61), Middx Snr Cup(10) 29-30 37-38 40-43 45-46 58-59 62-64 67-68, Capital League 84-85 86-87.

80p

WEALDSTONE
Season 1992/93
MATCHDAY PROGRAMME

PROGRAMME DETAILS:
Pages: 30+ Price: 80p
Editor: Roy Couch

WEYMOUTH

Weymouth F.C. 1992-93. Back Row (L/R): A Browne, M Brown, G Smith, S Weaver, T Cook, W Gibson, G Fullbrook, L Drake (then Manager). Front: I Down, S Pugh, D Keeling, J Diaz.

Chairman: Paul Cocks   **Vice Chairman:** Terry Nutman.
Secretary: T.B.A.
Manager: William Coldwell   **Asst Manager:** Anni Iannone **Physio:** Bob Lucas.
Commercial Manager: Fred Dunford.
Ground: Wessex Stadium, Radipole Lane, Weymouth, Dorset DT4 0TJ (0305 785558).
Directions: Arriving from Dorchester on A354, turn right following signs to Granby Industrial Estate at Safeway r'bout - ground on right as you enter estate.
Capacity: 10,000   **Cover:** All sides   **Seats:** 900   **Floodlights:** Yes   **Metal Badges:** Yes.
Club Shop: Operated by Andrew Millar at 4 Franklin Rd, Weymouth DT4 0JR (0305 772743). Progs & souvenirs.
Colours: Claret & blue   **Change colours:** White & blue
Previous Ground: Recreation Ground (until 1987).
Previous Lges: Dorset Lge/ Western 1907-23 28-49/ Southern 23-28 49-79/ Alliance Premier 79-89.
Midweek home matchday: Wednesday   **Reserve Team's League:** Dorset Combination
Record Attendance: 4,995 v Manchester Utd, ground opening, 21/10/87.
Best F.A. Cup season: 4th Rd 61-62, 0-2 at Preston. 1st rd on 29 occasions 25-27 48-50 51-54 55-57 58-59 60-62 63-66 67-70 71-72 73-79 80-83 84-86.
League clubs defeated in F.A. Cup: Merthyr 24-25, Aldershot 49-50, Shrewsbury Town 56-57, Newport County 61-62, Cardiff City 82-83.
Record Fees: Paid: £15,000 for Shaun Teale (Northwich)
             Received: £100,000 for Peter Guthrie (Spurs, 1988)
Players progressing to Football League: Reg Pickett & Brian Carter (Portsmouth 1949 & 56), Stan Northover (Luton 1950), Edward Grant (Sheffield United 1950), David Clelland (Scunthorpe 1950), Alex Corbett (Hartlepool 1953), William Holt (Barrow 1954), Alex Smith (Accrington 1961), Graham Bond, Terry Spratt, Andy Donnelly & Micky Cave (Torquay 1961, 65, 67 & 68), Peter Leggett (Swindon 1962), Ron Fogg (Aldershot 1963), Barry Hutchinson (Lincoln 1965), Terry Gulliver & Richard Hill (Bournemouth 1966 & 67), Alan Wool (Reading 1971), Alan Beer (Exeter 1974), Bob Iles (Chelsea 1978), Graham Roberts (Spurs 1980), Neil Townsend, Paul Morrell & John Smeulders (Bournemouth 1979, 83 & 84), Tony Agana (Watford), Andy Townsend & D Hughes (Southampton), S Claridge (Crystal Palace), B McGorry & Shaun Teale (Bournemouth), Tony Pounder & R Evans (Bristol Rvrs).
Clubhouse: Matchdays & functions. Hot & cold food available.
Club Record Goalscorer: W Farmer, Haynes. 275
Club Record Appearances: Tony Hobson 1,076
92-93 Captain: Steve Pugh
92-93 P.o.Y.: Ian Drewitt
92-93 Top scorer: Ian Drewitt, 13.
Local Newspapers (+Tel.Nos.): Dorset Evening Echo.
Local Radio Stations: 2CR (Bournemouth).
Honours: Alliance Premier Lg R-up 79-80 (Lg Cup 81-82), Premier Inter Lg Cup R-up 87-88 (QF 90-91), Southern Lg 64-65 65-66 (R-up 54-55 77-78, Lg Cup 72-73 (R-up 52-53 63-64 64-65 70-71 77-78), Southern Div R-up 91-92), Western Lg 22-23 (Div 2 33-34 36-37 (R-up 35-36 47-48)), Dorset Sen. Cup(24) 1893-94 98-1900 02-03 19-20 22-24 27-28 31-32 33-34 36-37 47-48 49-50 51-52 53-58 64-65 84-87 90-91, Mark Frowde Cup (12), FA Tphy 4th Rd rep. 76-77, FA Amateur Cup 1st Rd 1900.

PROGRAMME DETAILS:
Pages: 44 **Price:** 70p
Editor: Fred Danford
(784133)

WITNEY TOWN

An historic moment for Witney Town; their first goal at their new Oakey Park ground, headed home by Mark Gee in the 1-1 draw against Wealdstone on 8th September. Photo - Steve Daniels.

Chairman: Brian Constable   **President:** Vacant.
Secretary: Bob Watts, 16 Daubigny Mead, Brize Norton, Oxon OX18 3QE (0993 841210).
Manager: Andy Lyne   **Asst Mgr:** Peter Bridgewater   **Coach:** Ian Rundle
Press Officer: Adrian Bircher (0993 703257)   **Physio:** Roger Alder
Ground: Oakey Park, Down Rd, Curbridge, Witney, Oxon (0993 702549).
Directions: From West on A40; take B4047 at island past Burford, follow signs for Witney West & N.W. Industrial Estates, thru Minster Lovell to West Witney, right into Downs Rd, ground on right. From the East on A40, 2nd turn off to Witney and follow signs for South & S.W. Industrial Estates, right at r'bout to traffic lights, left and proceed to r'bout, straight over, signs to West Witney Industrial Estate, left at lights onto B4047, left into Downs Rd, ground on right. Nearest BR station is Oxford 12 miles away.
Capacity: 3,500   **Cover:** 1,224   **Seats:** 224   **Floodlights:** Yes   **Metal Badges:** Yes
Club Shop: Yes, selling programmes, t-shirts, sweatshirts, hats, scarves etc. Contact secretary.
Colours: Yellow/blue/yellow   **Change colours:** Blue/white/white.
Sponsors: West Oxon Motor Auctions.
Previous Leagues: Reading & Dist./ Oxfordshire Senior/ Hellenic 53-73.
Previous Name: Witney F.C.
Previous Ground: Marriotts Close, Welch Way - in Witney centre (pre-1992).
Midweek home matchday: Tuesday   **Reserve Team's League:** Hellenic (Res. Div.)
Record Attendance: 2,000 (approx) v Aston Villa, ground opening 1992. Competitive: 544 v Salisbury, F.A. 4th Qual. Rd 24/10/92. At Marriotts Close: 3,500 for Nottm Forest v West Bromwich Albion, Trevor Stokes benefit match 1965.
Best F.A. Cup season: 1st Rd 71-72 (lost 0-3 at home to Romford).
League clubs defeated in F.A. Cup: None.
Record Fees - Paid: £3,000 for Steve Jenkins (Cheltenham Town)
      Received: £5,000 for John Bailey (Worcester City).
Players progressing to Football League: Herbert Smith, Frank Clack (Birmingham City), Arthur Hall (Bristol Rovers 1959), David Moss (Swindon 1969), Jack Newman.
Clubhouse: Open evenings and all day Saturday. Hot food on matchdays.
92-93 Captain: Andy Leach
92-93 Top scorer: Kenny Clarke.
Local Newspapers: Witney Gazette (0993 704265), West Oxon Standard (0993 702175), Oxford Mail & Oxford Times (0865 244988).
Local Radio Stations: BBC Radio Oxford, Fox (FM) Oxford.
Hons: FA Tphy 2nd Rd 78-79, FA Amtr Cup 2nd Rd rep.(3) 66-67 71-73, Southern Lg Div 1 Nth 77-78, Hellenic Lg(8) 54-55 57-58 64-67 70-73 (R-up 53-54 67-68 69-70, Lg Cup(6) 56-57 63-65 69-70 71-73, Prem Div Benevolent Cup 59-60 63-64), Oxon Snr Lg(5) 28-30 31-32 51-53, Oxon Snr Cup(9) 1894-95 97-99 1952-53 54-56 58-59 70-71(jt) 72-73.

PROGRAMME DETAILS:
Pages: 40 **Price:** 50p
Editor: Adrian Bircher
(0993 703257)

SPORTIQUE 'MANAGER OF THE MONTH' AWARDS

MONTH	PREMIER DIVISION	MIDLAND DIVISION	SOUTHERN DIVISION
AUG.	John Murphy (Trowbridge)	Paul Hendrie (Redditch)	Keith Miller (Fareham)
SEP.	Brian Godfrey (Gloucester)	George Rooney (Nuneaton)	Gary Aldous (Gravesend)
OCT.	Vince Hilaire & Billy Gilbert (Waterlooville)	Steve Dolby (Gresley)	Keith Baker (Buckingham)
NOV.	John Morris (Halesowen)	Sammy Chung (Tamworth)	Richie Powling (Sudbury)
DEC.	Chris Kinnear (Dover)	Roy Chisholm (Barri)	Dennis Byatt (Wealdstone)
JAN.	Lindsay Parsons (Cheltenham)	Roger Ashby (Rushden)	Gary Aldous (Gravesend)
FEB.	Chris Kinnear (Dover)	John Barton (Nuneaton)	Geoff Butler (Salisbury)
MAR.	John Morris (Halesowen)	Steve Dolby (Gresley)	Rob Eagles (Baldock)
APR.	Trevor Parker (Bashley)	Roger Ashby (Rushden)	Geoff Butler (Salisbury)

SPORTIQUE PREMIER DIVISION MANAGER OF THE SEASON - CHRIS KINNEAR (DOVER ATHLETIC)

SPORTIQUE MIDLAND DIVISION MANAGER OF THE SEASON - JOHN BARTON (NUNEATON BOROUGH)

SPORTIQUE SOUTHERN DIVISION MANAGER OF THE SEASON - JOHN RYAN (SITTINGBOURNE)

Crunching Beazer Homes League Premier Division action - Chelmsford City's Tony Rogers expertly tackles a Halesowen Town players. Photo - Essex Chronicle.

UNIJET SUSSEX COUNTY LEAGUE

President: P H Strange
Chairman: Peter Bentley
Vice Chairman: L Ralph
Hon. Secretary: P Wells, 37 Bewley Rd,
Angmering BN16 4JL (0903 771146)

PEACEHAVEN'S DOMINATION CONTINUES

Peacehaven were indisputably team of the year. Having lifted both pre-season charity trophies, a unique achievement in itself, they also retained the League and Cup double, won the R.U.R. Charity Cup and the Brighton Charity Cup, defeating Littlehampton in the final, and reached the Fifth Round of the F.A. Vase thereby gaining a bonus award from Unijet, before losing by the only goal away to Gresley Rovers. League runners-up were Pagham, scoring 103 goals, with Wick third, the latter lifting the County Senior Cup for the first time in an all-County League final against Oakwood, the first such contested final for 28 years. Unijet marked this achievement with a special award.

In Division Two, Crowborough won the title for the first time defeating Stamco 3-2 in both clubs' last game of the season in front of a crowd declared to be 439. Crowborough acquired 84 points, a record for the Division, just two more than Stamco who will also being making their first appearance in Division One in 1993-94. East Grinstead were third and will join the other two at the higher level, when that Division is increased to twenty clubs, Midhurst being relegated after one season back in the top flight. Seaford Town and Haywards Heath Town will be relegated to Division Three, being replaced by Withdean, into senior football for the first time, and Storrington, returning after three seasons. Storrington were also runners-up in the Vernon Wentworth Cup. Steyning will be rejoining next season when Division Two will comprise eighteen teams. Nine applications were received for Division Three, and all appropriate clubs have been interviewed. The Division will next season comprise sixteen teams with three champions clubs joining; Edward Sports (Crawley League), Lingfield (Mid-Sussex League) and Sunallon (West Sussex League). Buxted retain the remaining vacant place.

The Reserve Section Premier Division was won by Peacehaven, who also won the Vernon Wentworth Cup of the Brighton, Hove & Worthing District F.A., and were seven points ahead of promoted Hassocks, whilst Burgess Hill Town defeated Worthing 3-2 in the Reserve Section Cup final held at Horsham Y.M.C.A. Reserve East was won by undefeated Stamco who also won the Hastings Intermediate Cup. Newhaven were runners-up while Worthing United won the Reserve Section West with Bosham runners-up. Youth Division East was won by Peacehaven completing a unique treble with their First and Reserve sides, Lewes being runners-up, while West was won by Burgess Hill Town with Worthing United runners-up. Peacehaven won the play-off at Arundel 2-0, and the same two sides contested the final of the Youth Section Cup at Oakwood, Peacehaven again winning this time by a single goal. In the final of the Sussex County F.A. Youth Cup, Lewes gained some consolation by defeating Oakwood 2-1 at Peacehaven.

Peter Bentley, League Chairman

Peacehaven & Telscombe F.C., Division One champions and League Cup winners 1992-93. Photo - Eric Marsh.

UNIJET SUSSEX COUNTY LEAGUE CUP 1992-93

Preliminary Round *(Played 28/8/92 - unless otherwise stated)*

Burgess Hill Town v Crowborough Ath.	3-0	Eastbourne Utd v Bexhill Town *(18/9/92)*	2-3
Midhurst & Easebourne v Saltdean *(19/9/92)*	1-2	Newhaven v Sidley United	2-0
Selsey v Chichester *(16/9/92)*	2-0*(aet)*		

First Round *(Played 23/9/92 - unless otherwise stated)*

Arundel v Horsham YMCA *(9/1/93)*	3-1	East Grinstead v Three Bridges *(21/10/92)*	1-0
Hailsham Town v Stamco	6-1	Langney Spts v Little Common A. *(15/9/92)*	4-1
Littlehampton Town v Broadbridge Heath	4-1	Newhaven v Bexhill Town *(13/10/92)*	3-2
Oakwood v Hassocks 2-2*(aet)*,3-2*(at O. 11/11/92)*		Peacehaven & Telscombe v Seaford Town	6-0
Portfield v Worthing Utd *(22/9/92)*	3-1	Redhill v Saltdean United *(29/9/92)*	3-1
Ringmer v Haywards Heath *(12/9/93)*	3-0	Selsey v Pagham	2-1
Shoreham v Burgess Hill T. *(12/12/92)*	0-2	Southwick v Eastbourne Town *(5/9/92)*	0-1
Whitehawk v Mile Oak	1-2	Wick v Lancing *(29/9 & 21/10/92)*	1-1*(aet)*,2-1

Second Round

Arundel v Wick *(26/1/93)*	2-1	East Grinstead v Ringmer *(21/11/92)*	0-2
Langney Spts v Burgess Hill Town *(6/2/93)*	4-0	Mile Oak v Eastbourne Town *(10/10/92)*	0-1*(aet)*
Oakwood v Hailsham Town *(17/2/93)*	3-2	Portfield v Newhaven *(5/12/92)*	0-1
Redhill v Peacehaven & Telscombe *(9/2/93)*	1-7	Selsey v Littlehampton Town *(4/11/92)*	1-4

Quarter-Finals

Arundel v Peacehaven & Telscombe *(20/2/93)*	1-4	Newhaven v Eastbourne Town *(5/1/93)*	2-0*(aet)*
Ringmer v Littlehampton Town *(5/12/92)*	1-2*(aet)*	Langney Sports v Oakwood *(23/2/93)*	1-0

Semi-Finals

Peacehaven & Tel. v Ringmer *(23/2/93)* At Langney Sports	3-1	Langney v Newhaven *(24 & 29/3/93)* 1-1*(aet)*,1-2*(aet)* Both games at Ringmer	

Final (at Burgess Hill Town FC, Friday 9th April)

Peacehaven & Telscombe v Newhaven	3-0	*(Man of the Match: Darren Newman - Peacehaven)*

Peacehaven attack during a 4-0 Division One win at Eastbourne Town on 25th August. Photo - Colin Stevens.

Pagham's Keith Pearson scores in the 5-2 home league win over Littlehampton in April. Photo - Colin Stevens.

DIVISION ONE 1992-93

	P	W	D	L	F	A	PTS
Peacehaven & Tel.	34	27	6	1	89	23	87
Pagham	34	25	5	4	103	32	80
Wick	34	25	3	6	81	35	78
Langney Sports	34	20	5	9	77	42	65
Whitehawk	34	18	9	7	55	32	63
Newhaven	34	16	5	13	63	51	53
Littlehampton T.	34	15	7	12	64	58	52
Oakwood	34	14	9	11	55	52	51
Three Bridges	34	14	6	14	50	50	48
Hailsham Town	34	13	6	15	64	53	45
Bexhill Town	34	10	6	18	43	61	36
Arundel	34	10	6	18	42	75	36
Portfield	34	8	10	16	39	60	34
Burgess Hill T.	34	7	8	19	39	59	29
Ringmer	34	8	5	21	44	73	29
Chichester City	34	8	5	21	41	85	29
Eastbourne Town	34	8	4	22	35	78	28
Midhurst & E.	34	5	5	24	26	91	20

Manager of the month awards

Aug	Mike Rogers (Newhaven)
Sept	Peter Cherry (Langney Sports)
Oct	Alan Pook (Peacehaven & Telscombe)
Nov	Carl Stabler (Pagham)
Dec	Butch Reeves (Whitehawk)
Jan	Alan Pook (Peacehaven & Telscombe)
Feb	Kevin Hotston (Littlehampton Town)
Mar	Alan Pook (Peacehaven & Telscombe)
Apr/May	Alan Pook (Peacehaven & Telscombe)

Manager of the Season:
Alan Pook (Peacehaven)

LEADING SCORERS (League matches only)
Mark Vickers (Pagham) 37
Mark Taylor (Peacehawk) 32
Andy Blythe (Newhaven) 22
Gavin Geddes (Wick) 22
Neil Darnley (Pagham) 22
Steve Guille (Peacehaven) 22

Roy Hayden Trophy: Peacehaven & Telscombe
Norman Wingate Trophy: Peacehaven & Telscombe

UNIJET SUSSEX COUNTY LEAGUE DIVISON ONE RESULTS 1992-93

HOME TEAM		1	2	3	4	5	6	7	8	9	10	11	12	13	14	15	16	17	18
1.	ARUNDEL	*	1-1	1-3	2-3	2-0	1-2	1-1	0-5	1-0	3-0	0-1	0-6	0-2	2-0	2-1	1-0	3-4	1-4
2.	BEXHILL TOWN	0-0	*	1-3	3-2	1-1	3-2	0-1	0-1	3-0	1-3	2-3	1-2	2-0	2-3	3-1	1-2	0-2	
3.	BURGESS HILL T.	4-1	0-2	*	2-3	2-0	0-0	2-0	2-2	3-0	0-2	1-1	1-2	0-3	1-2	3-2	0-2	1-2	2-3
4.	CHICHESTER CITY	2-0	0-0	3-0	*	6-1	1-1	0-6	1-2	0-2	0-2	1-1	0-6	1-2	0-1	3-1	1-1	1-3	1-5
5.	EASTBOURNE TOWN	2-2	0-3	2-2	4-0	*	1-4	3-4	2-1	0-1	1-0	1-2	0-2	0-4	1-0	1-1	1-3	2-1	2-5
6.	HAILSHAM TOWN	7-0	3-0	4-2	4-0	2-0	*	0-3	1-2	1-1	5-1	1-2	3-6	0-1	3-0	0-6	1-1	2-2	1-4
7.	LANGNEY SPORTS	4-2	1-1	2-0	7-0	5-0	1-0	*	5-3	4-0	2-1	1-2	1-0	0-1	2-3	2-1	4-0	0-3	4-2
8.	LITTLEHAMPTON	1-1	2-1	4-1	1-0	0-1	5-1	1-0	*	3-0	5-1	1-1	1-3	2-2	5-2	3-1	1-3	0-4	0-2
9.	MIDHURST & EASE.	0-3	1-4	0-0	4-1	1-1	0-4	2-3	0-1	*	1-0	2-3	1-7	0-3	2-2	0-2	0-5	1-3	0-2
10.	NEWHAVEN	3-1	5-1	3-1	2-1	2-1	1-0	2-2	1-1	8-0	*	2-0	2-4	0-2	1-2	3-0	3-1	3-1	1-1
11.	OAKWOOD	0-3	4-0	1-1	6-1	4-0	0-2	3-0	5-0	2-1	1-1	*	0-2	1-1	2-2	3-2	1-2	1-1	0-3
12.	PAGHAM	6-0	5-0	3-0	4-1	5-0	2-0	1-2	5-2	4-0	3-1	4-1	*	1-4	2-0	1-1	2-1	0-0	1-3
13.	PEACEHAVEN & T.	7-1	3-1	2-0	6-0	2-0	2-0	1-2	4-2	3-1	1-0	7-0	2-2	*	0-0	1-0	4-1	2-1	2-1
14.	PORTFIELD	1-1	1-2	2-1	0-3	2-3	2-2	2-2	1-3	2-2	1-0	0-2	2-6	*	4-0	0-1	1-2	0-2	
15.	RINGMER	1-3	0-1	1-1	1-1	1-0	0-5	0-3	0-3	5-0	1-2	0-2	1-4	1-4	1-1	*	3-2	1-5	1-4
16.	THREE BRIDGES	3-2	2-1	1-0	2-3	3-2	0-2	1-1	2-2	4-0	0-1	2-0	0-3	1-1	0-0	2-1	*	2-1	1-2
17.	WHITEHAWK	1-0	0-0	0-0	2-1	1-2	1-0	1-0	1-1	1-1	2-1	1-1	0-1	1-1	2-0	1-1	2-0	*	1-0
18.	WICK	0-1	3-0	2-0	1-0	4-1	2-1	3-2	3-0	4-1	4-3	3-1	2-2	0-1	1-1	2-3	1-0	1-0	*

Sussex County League Division One Ten Year Record

	83/4	84/5	85/6	86/7	87/8	88/9	89/0	90/1	91/2	92/3
Arundel	-	5	9	1	12	16	16	8	11	12
Bexhill Town	-	-	-	-	-	-	-	15	16	11
Burgess Hill Town	5	8	7	11	9	5	4	6	6	14
Chichester City	-	-	13	15	-	-	-	-	15	16
Eastbourne Town	10	3	3	5	4	15	15	16	12	17
Hailsham Town	9	14	11	14	6	4	13	13	8	10
Hastings Town Reserves	6	9	-	-	-	-	-	-	-	-
Haywards Heath Town	-	-	-	3	7	13	12	14	18	-
Horsham YMCA	11	11	15	13	16	-	-	-	-	-
Lancing	13	12	10	10	13	12	17	-	-	-
Langney Sports	-	-	-	-	-	10	3	3	2	4
Littlehampton Town	2	2	6	6	14	7	2	1	3	7
Midhurst & Eastbourne	12	15	14	16	-	-	-	-	-	18
Newhaven	-	-	-	-	-	-	-	-	10	6
Oakwood	-	-	-	-	-	-	17	-	9	14	8
Pagham	16	-	-	-	-	1	1	8	4	2
Peacehaven & Telscombe	7	10	5	7	8	8	5	2	1	1
Portfield	-	7	8	12	15	18	-	-	-	13
Redhill	-	-	-	-	-	11	18	-	-	-
Ringmer	8	13	16	-	-	-	10	12	9	15
Seaford Town	-	-	-	-	-	-	11	17	-	-
Selsey	-	-	-	-	11	9	14	18	-	-
Shoreham	-	-	12	8	10	14	9	11	17	-
Southwick	4	-	-	-	-	-	-	-	-	-
Steyning Town	3	1	1	-	-	-	-	-	-	-
Three Bridges	5	6	2	4	2	2	7	7	7	9
Whitehawk	1	4	4	2	5	3	6	10	13	5
Wick	14	16	-	9	3	6	1	5	5	3
No. of clubs competing	16	16	16	16	16	18	18	18	18	18

DIVISION TWO 1992-93

	P	W	D	L	F	A	PTS
Crowborough Ath.	36	26	6	4	98	34	84
Stamco	36	24	4	6	94	36	82
East Grinstead	36	21	10	5	78	40	73
Lancing	36	18	10	8	73	37	64
Worthing United	36	19	6	11	70	60	63
Horsham Y.M.C.A.	36	18	8	10	71	46	62
Shoreham	36	16	11	9	74	56	59
Hassocks	36	16	7	13	61	49	55
Mile Oak	36	14	10	12	69	65	52
Southwick	36	14	10	12	59	56	52
Selsey	36	12	3	21	55	65	39
Redhill	36	10	9	17	55	71	39
Little Common A.	36	10	8	18	42	77	38
Sidley United	36	9	8	19	57	80	35
Broadbridge Hth	36	9	8	19	43	84	35
Eastbourne Utd	36	9	6	21	48	76	33
Saltdean United	36	9	6	21	44	76	33
Seaford Town	36	8	5	23	38	79	29
Haywards Hth T.	36	7	7	22	49	91	28

Manager of the month awards

Aug	Brian Woolmer (Worthing United)
Sept	Graham Russell (Lancing)
Oct	Micky Reed (Stamco)
Nov	Micky Reed (Stamco)
Dec	Nick Greenwood/Peter Liddell (Hassocks)
Jan	Micky Reed (Stamco)
Feb	Roger Crouch (Crowborough Athletic)
Mar	Tony Gratwicke (Mile Oak)
Apr/May	Roger Crouch (Crowborough Athletic)

Manager of the Season:
Roger Crouch (Crowborough Athletic)

LEADING SCORERS
(League matches only)

Dean Kewley (Stamco) 33
Shaun Carey (Crowborough Athletic) 31
Nigel Waller (Worthing United) 25

UNIJET SUSSEX COUNTY LEAGUE DIVISON TWO RESULTS 1992-93

HOME TEAM	1	2	3	4	5	6	7	8	9	10	11	12	13	14	15	16	17	18	19
1. Broadbridge	*	1-5	2-5	1-1	0-0	3-2	0-0	0-1	0-1	1-2	4-3	4-3	3-2	0-3	1-0	1-0	2-3	0-0	1-5
2. Crowboro.	2-2	*	5-0	4-1	3-2	3-1	3-1	3-0	9-1	0-1	1-1	4-2	5-0	2-0	4-1	1-0	4-0	3-2	2-2
3. E Grinstead	5-0	2-3	*	5-1	2-1	4-0	3-2	2-1	5-0	3-2	1-1	1-0	1-1	3-0	1-2	1-1	0-0	1-0	5-0
4. E'bourne U.	1-1	2-2	1-1	*	1-3	4-0	1-6	0-1	0-0	2-0	2-4	3-1	2-1	1-2	2-1	2-0	2-1	0-1	0-1
5. Hassocks	1-2	1-0	0-2	6-4	*	2-0	0-0	3-5	2-3	3-1	1-2	1-0	3-0	3-4	1-2	1-1	0-0	1-2	2-3
6. Haywards H.	3-1	0-3	1-2	1-0	0-0	*	0-1	0-0	2-0	3-4	2-6	1-2	1-1	2-3	2-4	2-3	2-1	1-3	0-1
7. Horsham YM	2-0	0-1	1-0	3-0	1-1	8-1	*	0-0	0-0	0-3	2-0	6-0	4-0	3-1	2-2	5-1	2-2	1-2	1-3
8. Lancing	5-2	2-2	0-0	3-1	1-2	3-0	4-0	*	5-0	1-1	0-3	1-4	4-1	4-0	1-1	3-2	2-3	2-0	6-0
9. Little Cmn	0-0	0-2	1-1	3-0	1-4	1-4	2-2	1-1	*	1-3	2-3	0-4	4-2	3-1	1-1	2-0	1-3	1-4	1-3
10. Mile Oak	2-2	1-1	2-2	1-0	3-0	5-5	1-2	1-1	0-1	*	2-2	2-1	2-1	2-0	1-1	5-0	2-2	1-4	0-3
11. Redhill	0-2	1-2	1-3	2-0	0-4	2-2	1-3	0-2	3-4	3-4	*	3-0	1-2	4-1	0-3	3-0	2-1	2-4	1-1
12. Saltdean	1-4	1-6	1-3	2-1	1-3	2-4	1-0	1-3	1-0	3-2	0-0	*	3-0	1-2	2-4	1-1	2-2	0-4	1-3
13. Seaford	6-0	0-2	0-1	1-3	1-2	1-2	1-2	0-1	1-0	0-0	0-0	*	0-3	0-4	3-4	2-1	0-3	1-2
14. Selsey	2-0	1-2	1-3	0-1	0-1	4-0	1-2	3-3	2-0	4-3	0-0	0-1	1-2	*	4-0	3-3	0-1	0-1	1-2
15. Shoreham	1-0	1-2	1-2	3-2	0-0	2-2	1-2	2-1	5-1	2-2	3-2	3-2	5-0	2-4	*	3-1	1-1	2-2
16. Sidley	4-1	0-4	3-3	3-3	0-2	1-1	6-2	0-2	1-2	1-4	3-0	2-1	1-1	3-1	3-4	*	0-3	0-1	4-2
17. Southwick	3-1	3-1	2-2	1-3	2-3	4-1	1-2	1-1	0-0	0-1	0-0	1-3	2-0	2-2	1-4	*	4-4	3-0
18. Stamco	5-0	1-0	2-0	6-1	1-2	4-0	3-1	2-1	0-2	5-1	8-0	0-0	4-0	3-2	3-1	3-1	2-0	*	5-3
19. Worthing U.	5-1	0-2	1-3	3-0	1-0	3-1	2-1	1-1	1-1	2-1	1-2	4-1	2-1	0-3	3-1	3-0	3-1	*	

UNIJET SUSSEX COUNTY LEAGUE DIVISION TWO CUP 1992-93

First Round (Played on 12/12/92 unless stated otherwise)

Eastbourne United v Saltdean United	2-1	Haywards Hth Town v Sidley Utd (5/12/92)	1-3(aet)
Little Common Albion v Southwick	0-1		

Second Round

East Grinstead v Mile Oak (13/2/93)	1-3	Eastbourne United v Crowborough A. (23/1/93)	0-5
Horsham YMCA v Worthing Utd (30/1/93)	3-0	Redhill v Sidley United (6/2/93)	2-1(aet)
Seaford Town v Lancing (23/1/93)	0-2	Selsey v Broadbridge H. (16 & 30/1/93)	2-2(aet),3-2
Shoreham v Hassocks (17/2/93)	4-1	Southwick v Stamco (9/1/93)	1-2

Quarter-Finals

Horsham YMCA v Shoreham (23/2/93)	1-2	Redhill v Crowborough (23/2 & 16/3/93)	1-1(aet),1-1(aet, at East Grinstead, 3-1 pens)
Lancing v Stamco (10/3/93)	3-1	Selsey v Mile Oak (27/2/93)	0-1

Semi-Finals

Lancing v Shoreham (at Southwick 6/4/93)	1-0	Mile Oak v Redhill (at Burgess Hill 7/4/93)	4-1

Final (at Southwick, Mon. 3rd May): Lancing 1, Mile Oak 0 (Man of the Match: John Dutton - Lancing)

UNIJET SUSSEX COUNTY LEAGUE SUSSEX FIVES (5-A-SIDE)

AT WORTHING LEISURE CENTRE, MONDAY FEBRUARY 8th 1993
SPONSORED BY THE EVENING ARGUS AND PHONESPORT (SUSSEX SPORTSLINE)

GROUP 'A': Bexhill 0 Hailsham 1, Bexhill 1 Pagham 3, Hailsham 0 Worthing Utd 2, Pagham 2 Worthing Utd 2, Pagham 0 Hailsham 2, Worthing Utd 1, Bexhill 1

	P	W	D	L	F	A	PTS
Worthing United	3	1	2	0	5	3	4
Hailsham Town	3	2	0	1	3	2	4
Pagham	3	1	1	1	5	5	3
Bexhill Town	3	0	1	2	2	5	1

GROUP 'B': Langney 2 Stamco 2, Langney 2 Peacehaven 0, P'haven 1 Portfield 0, Stamco 1 Portfield 0

	P	W	D	L	F	A	PTS
Langney Sports	3	2	1	0	6	2	5
Stamco	3	2	1	0	6	3	5
Peacehaven & T.	3	1	0	2	2	5	2
Portfield	3	0	0	3	0	4	0

GROUP 'C': E Grinsead 3 Newhaven 0, E Grinstead 2 Hassocks 0, Wick 3 Hassocks 0, Newhaven 3 Hassocks 1, Wick 3 E Grinstead 2, Wick 2 Newhave 1

	P	W	D	L	F	A	PTS
Wick	3	3	0	0	8	3	6
East Grinstead	3	2	0	1	7	3	4
Newhaven	3	1	0	2	4	6	2
Hassocks	3	0	0	3	1	8	0

GROUP 'D': Crowboro. 2 Three Bridges 2, Crowboro. 3 Whitehawk 1, Littlehampton 1 Crowboro. 1, Littlehampton 2 Whitehawk 0, Littlehampton 3 Three Bridges 0, Whitehawk 2 Three Bridges 0

	P	W	D	L	F	A	PTS
Littlehampton T.	3	2	1	0	6	1	5
Crowborough Ath.	3	1	2	0	6	4	4
Whitehawk	3	1	0	2	3	5	2
Three Bridges	3	0	1	2	2	7	1

SEMIS: Worthing Utd 1, Wick 0
Littlehampton 1, Langney Spts 1 (1-0 pens)

FINAL: Littlehampton Town 3, Worthing Utd 1

DIVISION THREE 1992-93

DIVISION THREE 1992-93

	P	W	D	L	F	A	PTS
Withdean	26	18	5	3	69	21	59
Storrington	26	16	4	6	62	27	52
Bosham	26	15	4	7	52	51	49
Sidlesham	26	12	7	7	51	49	43
Forest	26	11	8	7	51	40	41
Hurstpierpoint	26	9	10	7	45	42	37
Ifield	26	10	7	9	44	43	37
St Francis Hos.	26	9	8	9	42	40	35
Lindfield Rgrs	26	9	6	11	38	43	33
Franklands Village	26	7	6	13	22	45	27
Shinewater Assn	26	6	7	13	39	49	25
East Preston	26	6	7	13	34	49	25
Buxted	26	6	6	14	45	66	24
Ferring	26	3	5	18	27	56	14

MANAGER OF THE MONTH

Aug	N/A
Sept	Graham Powell (Forest)
Oct	Dave Richardson (Lindfield Rangers)
Nov	Tony & Franco Massimo (Storrington)
Dec	Glen Morgan (St Francis Hospital)
Jan	Tony & Franco Massimo (Storrington)
Feb	Bob Collyere (Bosham)
Mar	Derek Tharme (Withdean)
Apr/May	Dave Richardson (Lindfield Rangers)

Manager of the Season:
Derek Tharme (Withdean)

LEADING SCORERS (League matches only)

David Agnew (Withdean) 24
Eamonn Searle (Storrington) 23
Simon Hatton (St Francis Hospital) 14
Des Lyons (Ifield) 14

UNIJET SUSSEX COUNTY LEAGUE DIVISON THREE RESULTS 1992-93

HOME TEAM		1	2	3	4	5	6	7	8	9	10	11	12	13	14
1.	BOSHAM	*	0-1	2-1	2-1	3-2	2-1	1-1	1-5	3-3	1-1	2-1	0-2	3-1	0-6
2.	BUXTED	0-2	*	1-0	3-3	1-3	1-2	1-1	1-5	2-4	4-1	5-3	1-2	3-3	0-7
3.	EAST PRESTON	1-4	0-2	*	2-1	1-1	0-1	5-0	2-3	3-1	1-1	2-3	0-0	0-2	3-3
4.	FERRING	0-1	2-2	1-2	*	1-1	0-1	1-1	0-2	0-2	0-2	1-2	2-2	1-0	0-4
5.	FOREST	6-1	3-1	1-0	3-2	*	1-0	4-2	2-2	0-0	3-0	3-0	3-3	1-5	1-2
6.	FRANKLANDS VIL.	0-3	1-2	1-1	3-2	2-1	*	0-4	0-4	1-2	0-0	1-1	2-1	1-1	0-0
7.	HURSTPIERPOINT	0-0	3-2	2-2	4-1	1-3	2-1	*	2-0	1-1	3-1	1-0	2-0	2-4	2-3
8.	IFIELD	1-4	2-1	3-1	2-1	0-0	0-1	1-1	*	0-2	1-1	2-1	2-2	1-5	1-3
9.	LINDFIELD RGRS	1-2	3-3	0-1	2-0	3-1	1-0	1-1	3-1	*	0-3	0-1	1-2	0-4	0-2
10.	ST FRANCIS HOS.	7-2	2-0	2-1	1-2	3-0	3-1	3-3	2-2	2-2	*	1-4	2-0	1-2	0-1
11.	SHINEWATER ASSN	1-6	2-2	1-1	1-3	0-0	1-1	1-2	1-2	2-3	1-2	*	7-1	1-1	0-1
12.	SIDLESHAM	2-4	7-4	3-1	3-1	2-5	2-1	2-1	3-2	4-2	1-1	3-3	*	0-1	0-0
13.	STORRINGTON	4-0	4-2	1-3	5-1	1-1	4-0	3-2	3-0	2-0	2-0	0-1	0-1	*	0-2
14.	WITHDEAN	2-3	1-0	9-0	3-0	4-2	6-0	1-1	0-0	2-1	3-0	3-0	1-3	0-4	*

UNIJET SUSSEX COUNTY LEAGUE DIVISION THREE CUP 1992-93

First Round *(Played 9/1/93 unless stated otherwise)*

Buxted v Ifield *(replay 6/2/93)*	3-3(aet),3-0	East Preston v Hurstpierpoint	1-5
Ferring v Bosham *(16/1/93)*	3-5	Forest v Withdean *(13/2/93)*	0-1
Franklands Vil. v Storrington *(6/2/93)*	2-1	Sidlesham v Lindfield Rangers	5-2

Second Round *(Played 20/2/93 unless otherwise stated)*

Buxted v Withdean	0-1	Franklands Village v Sidlesham *(6/3/93)*	1-0
St Francis Hospital v Bosham	0-1	Shinewater Association v Hurstpierpoint	0-2

Semi-Finals

Bosham v H'point *(at Lit'hampton 30/3/93)*	3-1	F. Vill. v Withdean *(at Horsham YM 5/4/93)*	1-1(aet)
		F. Vill. v Withdean *(at Southwick 24/4/93)*	1-0(aet)

Final (at Arundel FC, Thursday 29th April)

Franklands Village v Bosham   2-1   *(Man of the Match: Ian Rumble - Franklands Village)*

Withdean F.C. - Unijet Sussex County League Division Three Champions 1992-93. Photo - Colin Stevens.

FIRST DIVISION CLUBS 1993-94

ARUNDEL

President: Michael Monk   **Chairman:** Michael Peters   **Manager:** M Torode
Secretary/Press Officer: Peter Wells, 37 Bewley Road, Angmering BN16 4JL (0903 771146).
Ground: Mill Road, Arundel (0903 882548).
Directions: Into Arundel, look for Mill Road car park. 1 mile from Arundel (BR).
Seats: 100   **Cover:** Yes   **Capacity:** 2,200   **Floodlights:** 206 lux   **Founded:** 1889
Colours: Red/white/red   **Change colours:** All yellow   **Nickname:** Mulletts
Programme: Yes   **Programme Editor:** Secretary   **Admission:** £1.50
Midweek matchday: Tuesday.   **Record Gate:** 2,200 v Chichester, League 67-68
Previous Ground: Arun Park   **Previous League:** West Sussex.   **Club badges:** No.
Clubhouse: 2 bars, function room, pool, darts, phone, toilets, board room, tea bar.
Local Press: Arun Gazette   **92-93 Top Scorers:** Paul Bennett 9 (inc 1 for Littlehampton).
Hons: Sussex County Lg 57-58 58-59 86-87 (Lg Cup 86-87, Div 2 76-77, Reserve Section 78-79, Reserve Section Cup 78-79), Sussex RUR Charity Cup 68-69 72-73 78-79 79-80, Sussex Jnr Cup 07-08.

BEXHILL TOWN

President: Barry Woodcock   **Chairman:** Peter Eastham   **Manager:** J Lambert
Secretary: Mr E N Hughes, 5 Badgers Way, Hastings, East Sussex TN34 2QD (0424 427967).
Ground: The Polegrove, Brockley Rd, Bexhill-on-Sea, East Sussex (0424 220732).
Directions: At Little Common r'bout take 3rd exit to Cooden Sea Rd, left into Cooden Drive for one and a half miles, Brockley Rd on the right. Three quarters of a mile from Bexhill Central (BR).
Seats: 250   **Cover:** 250   **Capacity:** 2,000   **Floodlights:** No   **Founded:** 1926
Colours: Green & white   **Change colours:** Black & white   **Nickname:** Green Machine
Previous Name: Bexhill Town Athletic.
Programme: Yes   **Programme Editor:** Mr G Sully   **Admission:** £1.50/£1/50p
Record Gate: 2,000   **Clubhouse:** New clubroom and bar facilities
Local Press: Bexhill Observer   **92-93 Top Scorer:** Paul Balch 8.
Hons: S'sex Co. Lg 56-57 65-66 (Invit. Cup 55-56), S'sex RUR Char. Cup 57-58 73-74, S'sex Midweek Cup 25-26.

BURGESS HILL TOWN

President: Jack Lake   **Manager:** Ray McCarthy   **Chairman:** Roy McKey
Secretary: David McKechnie, 20 Junction Rd, Burgess Hill RH15 0JD (0444 241790).
Ground: Leylands Park, Burgess Hill, West Sussex RH15 8AW (0444 242429).
Directions: Wivelsfield Station (BR out of Victoria), turn right, first left, ground on right.
Seats: 100   **Cover:** Yes   **Capacity:** 2,000   **Floodlights:** Yes   **Founded:** 1882
Colours: Yellow/black/black   **Change colours:** Red/white   **Club badges:** No
Programme: Yes   **Midweek matchday:** Tuesday   **Admission:** £1.50   **Nickname:** Hillians
Record Gate: 600 v Carshalton A., FA Cup 3rd Qual. 1981.   **Sponsors:** J C Collins
Previous Lges & Grounds: None   **Clubhouse:** Bar & social facilities. Tea bar.
Local Press: Mid Sussex Times   **92-93 Top Scorer:** Paul Williams (now P'haven) 6.
Hons: Sussex County Lg 75-76 (Div 2 74-75, Lg Cup 90-91), Div 2 Cup 73-73, Reserve Section 76-77 77-78 91-92, Reserve Sect. East 77-78 82-83 84-85, Reserve Cup 82-83, Yth Sect. West 91-92, Sussex Fives 1980), Mid-Sussex Lg 00-01 03-04 39-40 46-47 56-57 (Div 2 03-04(res), Div 3 20-21 36-37, Div 4(res) 56-57, Montgomery Cup 39-40 56-57, Mowatt Cup 45-46, Sussex Snr Cup 1883-84 84-85 85-86, Sussex RUR Charity Cup R-up 91-92, Sussex I'mediate Cup 76-77, Sussex Jnr Cup 1889-90, Sussex Yth Cup 91-92.

CHICHESTER CITY

Manager: W Cronin   **President:** G Redford   **Chairman:** T Wallis
Secretary: J F Hutter, 28 Stockbride Gdns, Donnington, Chichester, West Sussex PO19 2QT (0243 785839).
Ground: Oaklands Park, Chichester (0243 785978).   **Press Officer:** T Wallis (0705 464438).
Directions: Half mile north of city centre adjacent to Festival Theatre. Turn into Northgate car park from Oaklands Way and entrance is beside Tennis and Squash club. 1 mile from Chichester (BR) - walk north through city centre.
Seats: 50   **Cover:** 500   **Capacity:** 2,500   **Floodlights:** No   **Founded:** 1873
Colours: White/black/white   **Change colours:** All yellow   **Nickname:** Lilywhites
Programme: Yes   **Editor:** T Wallis (0705 464438)   **Admission:** £1.50   **Metal Badges:** No
Record Gate: 2,500 v Dorchester, FA Cup 1960   **Previous Name:** Chichester FC (pre-1960)
Previous Grounds: New Park Rec. 1873-81/ Priory Park 1881-1956.
Best FA Cup year: 1st Round Proper 60-61 (lost 0-11 at Bristol City).
Clubhouse: Licensed, open matchdays and some evenings. Tea bar & boadroom. **Sponsors:** A.P.V. Anda.
Local Press: Chichester Observer   **Previous Lgs:** Chichester/ West Sussex 1886-1920
Midweek home matchday: Tuesday.   **92-93 Top Scorer:** Tom Pegler 17.
Hons: Sussex Co. Lg(5) 59-61 67-68 72-73 79-80 (Lg Cup 47-48 54-55 56-57 63-64, Div 2 R-up 84-85 90-91, Div 2 Cup 84-85 87-88 90-91, Invitation Cup 47-48 53-54 56-57 63-64), Sussex Snr Cup 25-26, Sussex RUR Charity Cup 60-61(jt) 63-64, Sussex I'mediate Cup 67-68, West Sussex Lg (reserves) 66-67 (Div 1 45-46), Chich. Charity Cup 73-74, G C Hillier Mem. Tphy 1984+85+88+89+90, Coronation Cup 1989+90, Simmonds Cup 46-47 49-50 64-65 66-67.

CROWBOROUGH ATHLETIC

President: Mr Peter Taylor   **Chairman:** Mr Barry Sykes
Secretary: David McKellow, 38 Cridge Drive, Crowborough, East Sussex TN6 2TJ   (0892 653122).
Manager: Roger Crouch   **Press Officer:** Peter Crisp (0892 655470).
Ground: Alderbrook Recreation Ground, Fermor Road, Crowborough (0892 661893).
Directions: Turn east off A26 at Crowborough. Cross traffic lights, through High Street, right into Croft Rd, continue into Whitehall Rd and Fermor Rd, Alderbrook is second right after mini-r'bout.
Seats: None   **Cover:** 200   **Capacity:** 1,000   **F'lights:** Due 93-94   **Founded:** 1894
Colours: White/navy/navy   **Change colours:** Red & yellow   **Nickname:** Crows.
Programme Editor: Peter Crisp (0892 655470)   **Sponsors:** Blackden Enterprises Ltd.
Previous League: Brighton   **Clubhouse:** Bar facilities & tea bar on matchdays
Midweek Matchday: Wednesday   **Local Press:** Kent & Sussex Courier.   **Club badges:** No.
Admission: £1   **Previous Grounds:** None
Record Gate: 439 v Stamco, Sussex County League Division Two 1/5/93.
92-93 Top Scorers: Shaun Carey 31, Richard Dorrill 20, Rod Harman 11, Darren Longley 11, Mark Moore 11.
Hons: Sussex Co. Lg Div 1 92-93 (Div 2 Cup 77-78, Div 3 R-up), Sussex Intermediate Cup 86-87.

Arundel F.C. 1992-93. Back Row (L/R): G Thornsett (Asst Manager), B Torode (Player-Manager), K Sawyer, T Turton, T Pulleybank, P Whittaker, D Stedman, K Pierce, P Wells (Physio/Secretary). Front: S Gibbs, D Vallis, K Platt (Captain), T Stedman, G Woolgar, K Stedman. Photo - Dave West.

Bexhill Town F.C. 1992-93. Back Row (L/R): Glen Sully, Jeff Collier, Dave Ward, Paul Balch, Dale Seymour, Jason Finch, John Lambert (Manager). Front: Richard Stonham, Cliff Marsh, Craig Willard, Gary Barker, Dave Montier, Matthew Dalton (Mascot), Graham Whybourne. Photo - Roger Turner.

Bexhill Town's Graham Matthews takes on the Ringmer defence at the Polegrove. Photo - Roger Turner.

EASTBOURNE TOWN

Chairman: Roger Addems   **Manager:** Pete Roberts.
Secretary: Roger Cooper, 81 St Philips Ave., Eastbourne, East Sussex (0323 734426).
Ground: The Saffrons, Compton Place Road, Eastbourne, East Sussex (0323 23734).
Directions: Turn south west off A22 into Grove Road (opposite BR station). Ground quarter mile on right.
Seats: 100   **Cover:** Yes   **Capacity:** 3,000   **Floodlights:** No   **Founded:** 1882
Colours: Yellow/blue/blue   **Changes:** White & black/white/white   **Nickname:** 'Bourne'
Programme Editor: Sid Myall (0323 728096)   **Admission:** £1.50/80p
Previous Leagues: Southern Amtr 07-46/ Corinthian 60-63/ Athenian 63-76.
Record Gate: 7,378 v Hastings U. 1953   **Prev. Ground:** Devonshire Park 1881-85   **Metal Badges:** Yes
Sponsors: Eastbourne Car Auctions   **Local Press:** Eastbourne Gazette & Herald Chronicle
Prev. Name: Eastbourne FC (pre-1970)   **Clubhouse:** Fully licensed bar. Board room. Tea bar.
92-93 Top Scorers: Roger Myall 8
Hons: Sussex County Lg 76-77, Sussex Snr Cup(12) 1889-91 93-95 98-1901 02-03 21-22 31-33 52-53, Sussex RUR Charity Cup 32-33 47-48 49-50, Southern Amtr Lg(2), AFA Snr Cup 21-22 24-25 (R-up 22-23 23-24), AFA Invitation Cup 69-70 (R-up 56-57 68-69 70-71).

EAST GRINSTEAD

President: Peter Paice   **Chairman:** Peter Cadman   **Mgr:** Mark Arnold
Secretary: Gary Bullen, 4 Churchfields, Nutley TN22 3NA (0825 713138).
Ground: East Court, East Grinstead (0342 325885).   **Press Officer:** Bruce Talbot (0293 543809).
Directions: A264 Tunbridge Wells road, turn off to right opposite Blackwell Farm Road, follow lane on left 200yds past rifle club.
Seats: None   **Cover:** 300   **Capacity:** 2,000   **Floodlights:** Yes   **Founded:** 1890
Colours: Gold/black/black   **Change colours:** Red/white/red   **Metal Badges:** Yes
Programme + Admission: £2   **Prog. Ed.:** Suart Ward (0342 327517)   **Nickname:** Wasps
Record Gate: 2,002 v Lancing 8/11/48   **Sponsors:** Rydon Construction.
Previous Lgs: Mid S'sex/ Sthern Amtr   **Midweek Matchday:** Wednesday.
Previous Grounds: West Street Cricket Ground/ King George's Field.
Clubhouse: Bar, kitchen (hot food on matchdays), darts, pool, dance floor, board room.
Local Press: East Grinstead Observer.
92-93 Top Scorers: Steve Norris 23, Gary Chandler 15 (inc 4 for Oakwood).
Hons: Sussex RUR Charity Cup 74-75, Sussex Lg Invitation Cup 51-52, Sussex Jnr Cup (jointly) 07-08.

HAILSHAM TOWN

President: M W Walker   **Chairman:** John Whippy   **Manager:** Mick French
Secretary/Press Officer: Derek York, 59 Anglesey Avenue, Horsebridge, Hailsham BN27 3BQ (0323 848024).
Ground: The Beaconsfield, Western Road, Hailsham, East Sussex (0323 840446).
Directions: A22 to Arlington Road, turn east, then left into South Road - left into Diplocks Way until Daltons. Four miles from Polegate (BR - Brighton-Eastbourne line); regular bus service from Eastbourne.
Seats: None   **Cover:** 300   **Capacity:** 2,000   **Floodlights:** Yes   **Founded:** 1885
Colours: Yellow & green   **Change colours:** Red   **Nickname:** None
Programme: Yes   **Programme Editor:** Secretary   **Admission:** £2
Previous League: E Sussex, Southern Comb.   **Previous Ground:** Western Rd Rec.
Record Gate: 1,350 v Hungerford, FA Vase Feb '89   **Metal Badges:** No.
Clubhouse: Hot and cold snacks. Open every evening, matchdays and Sundays, tea bar.
Local Press: Hailsham Gazette, Eastbourne Herald, Sussex Express
Midweek matchday: Wednesday.   **92-93 Top Scorers:** Barry Knight 17, Steve Marsh 10.
Hons: FA Vase 5th Rd 88-89, Sussex County Lg Div 2 R-up 80-81, Southern Co's Comb. 74-75, Sussex RUR Charity Cup, Sussex I'mediate Cup, Hastings Snr Cup, Sussex Jnr Cup, E Sussex Lg Cup, Hailsham Charity Cup.

LANGNEY SPORTS

President: Mr J Stonestreet   **Chairman:** Mr Len Smith   **Mgr:** Peter Cherry
Secretary: Mrs Jan Field, 38 Collingswood Close, Eastbourne, East Sussex BN23 6HW (0323 416476).
Ground: Priory Lane, Eastbourne, East Sussex (0323 766265).
Directions: A22 to Polegate, A27 to Stone Cross, right onto B32104 to Langney Shopping Centre, then left and first right. One mile from Pevensey & Westham (BR). Buses from Eastbourne.
Seats: None   **Cover:** 200   **Capacity:** 1,000   **Floodlights:** Yes   **Founded:** 1966
Colours: All red   **Change:** Blue & white/navy/navy   **Nickname:** None
Midweek Matchday: Tuesday
Programme: Yes   **Editor:** Tim Dawes (0323 764218)   **Admission:** £2/£1
Record Gate: 1,000+ v Crystal Palace, f'light opening 90-91.   **Sponsors:** Nobo Group Plc.
Clubhouse: Open every evening & lunchtime. Board room, matchday tea bar.
Previous League: Eastbourne & Hastings
Previous Grounds: Princes Park, Wartling Rd, Eastbourne/ Adjacent pitch.   **Metal Badges:** No
Local Press: Eastbourne Gazette & Herald
92-93 Top Scorers: Nigel Hole 20, Mick Green 13, Paul Stevens 10.
Hons: Sussex Co. Lg R-up 91-92 (Div 2 87-88, Lg Cup 89-90, Div 3 86-87, Div 3 Cup 86-87, 5-aside comp. 1990), Sussex I'mediate Cup 85-86, Eastbourne Challenge Cup 85-86 86-87.

LITTLEHAMPTON TOWN

President: Ian Cunningham   **Chairman:** B Suter   **Mgr:** Kevin Hotston
Secretary/Press Officer: Jim Owen, 24 Broadmark Ave., Rustington, West Sussex (0903 776832).
Ground: The Sportsfield, St Flora's Road, Littlehampton (0903 713944).
Directions: 10 minutes walk from Littlehampton station (BR) - turn left along Terminus Rd, continue through High Street and Church Rd to junction with St Flora's Rd (left).
Seats: 260   **Capacity:** 4,000   **Floodlights:** Yes   **Founded:** 1894
Colours: All gold   **Change:** Blue/whitewhite   **Nickname:** Marigolds
Programme Editor: Mr C Scrimshaw (0903 713466)   **Local Press:** Littlehampton Gazette
Record Gate: 4,000 v Northampton, FA Cup 1st Rd Proper 90-91   **Sponsors:** T.B.A.
Midweek Matches: Tuesday   **Club metal badges:** Yes   **Admission:** £1.50
Clubhouse: Sportsman (Private Club). Separate board room & tea bar.
92-93 Top Scorers: Steve Guille (subsequently transferred to Peacehaven) 15, Anton Romasz 11.
Hons: FA Vase SF 90-91, FA Cup 1st Rd 90-91, Sussex Co. Lg 90-91 (Lg 58-59(jt with Shoreham) 75-76 76-77 84-85 90-91 (R-up 91-92)), Sussex Snr Cup 73-74 (R-up 90-91).

Hailsham Town F.C. 1992-93. Back Row (L/R): Micky French (Manager), G Holder, P Charlton, S Chaytor-Grubb, G Richards, K Jeffrey, R Saunders, R Knight, G Bishop (Physio). Front: B Knight, S Marsh, N Ivemy, P Comber (Captain), S Lawrence, B Kenward. Photo - Roger Turner.

Littlehampton Town F.C. 1992-93, pictured before their F.A. Vase tie at Ash United. Photo - Eric Marsh.

Mark Bennett of Littlehampton Town (stripes) tussles with Hailsham's Barry Kenward. Photo - Roger Turner.

NEWHAVEN

President: **Chairman:** M Godden   **Manager:** M Rosers
Secretary: F D Dixon, 39 Southdown Avenue, Peacehaven, East Sussex BN10 8RX (0273 585514).
Ground: Fort Road, Newhaven, East Sussex (0273 513940).
Directions: A275 from Lewes, or A259 coast rd, to Newhaven 1-way system. 1 mile from Newhaven Town (BR).
Seats: 50   **Cover:** Yes   **Capacity:** 4,000   **Floodlights:** Yes   **Founded:** 1887
Colours: All red   **Change colours:** All white (blue flash)   **Nickname:** Dockers
Programme: Yes   **Editor:** Mike Taylor (0273 515232)   **Admission:** £1.50   **Metal Badges:** No
Previous Leagues: None (founder members of SCFL)   **Previous Name:** Newhaven Town.
Record Gate: 3,000   **Previous Ground:** None (Lewes FC temporarily 90-91)
Midweek Matchday: Tuesday   **Clubhouse:** Being redeveloped   **Sponsors:** Lojex.
Local Press: Evening Argus, Sussex Express   **92-93 Top Scorers:** Andy Blythe 22, Adie Chipper 16.
Hons: Sussex County Lg 53-54 (Div 2 71-72 90-91), Invitation Cup 48-49, Lg Cup R-up 92-93, Reserve Section East R-up 92-93), Sussex Snr Cup R-up 53-54.

OAKWOOD

President: R G Britts   **Chairman:** A T Bridges
Secretary: Gerry Martin, 'Singlegate', Tinsley Green, Crawley RH10 3NS (0293 882400).
Manager: Bryn Marshall   **Press Officer:** None
Ground: Tinsley Lane, Three Bridges, Crawley, West Sussex (0293 515742).
Directions: From A23 to Gatwick, take 1st set of lights into Manor Royal, pass next lights, over r'bout to warehouse marked Canon, turn right signposted Oakwood. Last clubhouse down lane. Two miles north of Three Bridges (BR).
Seats: 20   **Cover:** Yes   **Capacity:** 3,000   **Floodlights:** Yes   **Founded:** 1966
Colours: Red/white/red   **Change colours:** White/blue/white   **Nickname:** Oaks
Programme: Yes   **Editor:** A T Bridges (0293 533982)   **Admission:** £2
Previous Lgs: Crawley & Dist., Southern Co's Comb.   **Previous Ground:** Park pitches.
Record Gate: 367   **Midweek Matchday:** Wednesday   **Metal Badges:** Yes
Clubhouse: Pool tables, multidart boards, large bar area. Board room & tea bar.**Sponsors:** Bryant Homes
Local Press: Crawley Observer, Crawley News
92-93 Top Scorers: Paul Green 14.
Hons: Sussex Snr Cup R-up 92-93, Sussex Co. Lg Div 2 R-up 89-90 (Div 2 Cup 89-90, Div 3 84-85), Southern Comb. Cup 83-84.

PAGHAM

Chairman: John Allen   **Manager:** Vijay Korgaokar   **President:** A Peirce
Secretary/Press Officer: Mr Eric G Nunn, 8 West Drive, Aldwick, Bognor Regis PO21 4LY (0243 262879).
Ground: Nyetimber Lane, Pagham, West Sussex (0243 266112).
Directions: Turn off A27 Chichester by-pass (signposted A259 Pagham). Ground in village of Nyetimber. Three miles from Bognor (BR). Buses 260 & 240.
Seats: 200   **Cover:** 200   **Capacity:** 2,000   **Floodlights:** Yes   **Founded:** 1903
Colours: White/black/black   **Change colours:** Red & yellow   **Nickname:** None
Midweek Matchday: Tuesday
Programme: Yes   **Programme Editor:** Secretary   **Admission:** £2 & £1.
Record Gate: 1,200 v Bognor, 1971.   **Sponsors:** Viking Toyota.
Clubhouse: Members bar open matchdays and some evenings. Pool, darts etc. Board room. Tea bar.
Previous League: West Sussex   **Previous Grounds:** None   **Metal Badges:** No
Local Press: Bognor Observer
92-93 Top Scorers: Mark Vickers 37, Neil Darnley 22, Terry Withers 14 (8 for Littlehampton), Chrisr Sibley 13.
Hons: Sussex Co. Lg R-up 80-81 (Div 2 78-79 86-87, Lg Cup 88-89, Div 2 Cup 71-72 85-86, Res. Sect. West 80-81, Res Sect. Cup 80-81 87-88 88-89 90-91), Sussex F'lit Cup R-up 88-89, Sussex RUR Charity Cup 88-89, West Sussex Lg 65-66 68-69 69-70, Malcolm Simmonds Cup 67-68, Sussex I'mediate Cup 66-67.

PEACEHAVEN & TELSCOMBE

President: Mr W Parris   **Chairman:** Mr Jim Edwards   **Mgr:** P Edwards
Secretary/Press Officer: Mr Keith Parris, 12 Abbey Close, Peacehaven, E. Sussex BN10 7SD (0273 585173).
Ground: Piddinghoe Avenue, Peacehaven, East Sussex (0273 582471).
Directions: Arriving from Brighton on A259, cross r'bout and Piddinghoe Avenue is next left after 2nd set of lights - ground at end. From Newhaven Piddinghoe Avenue is first right after first set of lights. Three miles from Newhaven (BR). Peacehaven is served by Brighton to Newhaven and Eastbourne buses.
Seats: None   **Cover:** 250   **Capacity:** 3,000   **Floodlights:** Yes   **Founded:** 1923
Colours: White/black/black   **Change colours:** All sky   **Nickname:** The Tye
Programme: Yes   **Programme Editor:** Secretary
Local Press: Evening Argus/ Sussex Express
Record Gate: 1,420 v Littlehampton, League 11/5/91.   **Sponsors:** Brighton & Newhaven Fish Sales.
Previous Ground: Telscombe Tye   **Previous Leagues:** Lewes/ Brighton
Previous Names: Peacehaven Rangers merged with Telscombe Tye in 1923/ Peacehaven & Telscombe Cliffs (for one season only in early 1980's).
Midweek Matches: Wednesday   **Metal badges:** No   **Admission:** £1.50
Clubhouse: Bar open evenings and weekends, pool darts, hot and cold food available. Tea bar.
92-93 Top Scorers: Mark Taylor 32, Steve Guille 22 (including 15 for Littlehampton).
Hons: Sussex Co. Lg 78-79 81-82 82-83 91-92 92-93 (R-up 77-78 80-81 90-91, Lg Cup 91-92 92-93, Div 2 R-up 75-76, Div 2 Cup 75-76, Norman Wingate Tphy 82-83 91-92 92-93, Hayden Tphy 82-83 92-93, Div 2 Invitation Cup 69-70, Res. Sect. 83-84 92-93 (R-up 91-92), Res Sect. Cup 81-82 83-84 85-86 86-87 87-88, Res Sect East R-up 90-91), Sussex Snr Cup R-up 81-82, Sussex RUR Charity Cup 77-78 81-82 92-93 (R-up 80-81 89-90 90-91), Brighton Charity Cup 91-92 92-93, Vernon Wentworth 91-92 92-93, FA Cup 4th Qual. Rd 90-91, FA Vase 5th Rd 92-93.

Newhaven F.C. 1992-93. Back Row (L/R): Adie Chipper, Andy Blythe, Chris Harris, Martin Langley, Steve Rogers, Duncan Kneller, Andrew Rollings, Matthew Atkins. Front: Tony Towner, Stuart Corlett, Sean McFadden, Matthew Wiltshire, Glen Burville. Photo - Roger Turner.

Andy Webster heads away from Wick's Gavin Geddes in Oakwood's Sussex Senior cup final. Photo - Roger Turner.

Peacehaven's Mark Taylor challenges the Sittingbourne 'keeper in a 4-1 F.A. Vase win. Photo - Dennis Nicholson.

PORTFIELD

Manager: Steve White   **President:** C Newwell   **Chairman:** T Rustell
Secretary: Mr J Dowling, 36 St James Square, Chichester, West Sussex PO19 4NZ (0243 797044).
Ground: Church Road, Portfield, Chichester, West Sussex PO19 4HN (0243 779875)
Directions: A27 from Arundel to Chichester, take road to signposted city centre then 1st left (Church Rd) after supermarket r'bout. 1 mile from Chichester (BR).
Seats: 8   **Cover:** 200   **Capacity:** 2,000   **Floodlights:** Yes   **Founded:** 1896
Colours: Amber/black/black   **Change colours:** All white   **Nickname:** Field.
Programme Editor: T.B.A.   **Admission:** £1.50 & £1   **Metal Badges:** No.
Record Gate: Unknown   **Midweek Matchday:** Tuesday
Sponsors: Wadham Kenning.
Clubhouse: 2 bars, pool, snooker, pool, seating for 100, dance floor, darts, board room, tea bar selling hot & cold food.
Previous League: West Sussex.   **Local Press:** Chichester Observer
Previous Grounds: Downers (until 1952)/ Florence Road (until 1959).
92-93 Top Scorers: Adrian Miles 17.
Hons: Sussex Co. Lg Div 2 72-73 83-84 91-92 (Div 2 Cup 70-71 72-73, Reserve Sect. Cup 91-92, 5-aside comp. 1991), W Sussex Lg 46-47 48-49 (Malcolm Simmonds Cup 46-47), Sussex Jnr Cup 45-46, Benevolent Cup 46-47.

RINGMER

President: Sir G Christie   **Chairman:** Richard Soan
Secretary: Pam Howard, 39 Springett Avenue, Ringmer BN8 5HD (0273 813818).
Manager: B Smith   **Press Officer:** Alan Harper (0323 764263)
Ground: Caburn Pavillion, Anchor Field, Ringmer (0273 812738).
Directions: Turn into Springett Avenue opposite Ringmer village green. Anchor Field first left. Five miles from Lewes (BR).
Seats: No   **Cover:** Yes   **Capacity:** 1,000   **Floodlights:** Yes   **Founded:** 1910
Colours: Sky & navy blue   **Change colours:** All white   **Nickname:** None
Programme: Yes   **Editor:** Alan Harper (0323 764263)   **Entry:** £1.50/80p   **Club ties:** Yes.
Previous League: Brighton   **Previous Names:** None.   **Metal Badges:** No
Record Gate: 1,200 in FA Cup   **Previous Grounds:** None.
Midweek Matchday: Tuesday   **Clubhouse:** 2 bars, function room, board room, tea bar.
Local Press: Sussex Express   **92-93 Top Scorers:** Darren Brown 10.
Hons: FA Cup 1st Rd Proper 70-71 (lost 0-3 at Colchester Utd), Sussex Co. Lg 70-71 (Div 2 68-69, Div 2 Invitation Cup 66-67, Res. Sect. 80-81, Res. Sect. East 79-80 80-81 (R-up 89-90), Yth Section 87-88, Yth Section East 87-88), Sussex Snr Cup 72-73 (R-up 80-81), Sussex Jnr Cup 25-26.

STAMCO

Chairman: Leon Shepperdson   **President:** Mrs K Shepperdson
Secretary: Alan Ramsay, 8 Montgomery Rd, Hastings, East Sussex TN35 4LA (0424 712395).
Manager: Micky Reed   **Press Officer:** Michael James (0424 852926).
Ground: The Firs, Elphinstone Rd, Hastings, East Sussex (0424 434755).
Directions: Adjacent to Hastings Town F.C. - see page 495 for directions.
Seats: None   **Cover:** Yes   **Capacity:** 1,000   **Floodlights:** Yes   **Founded:** 1971
Colours: Blue/white/blue   **Change:** White/blue/white   **Metal Badges:** Yes
Programme: Yes   **Editor:** John Corneleus (0424 753242)   **Admission:** £1.50   **Nickname:** None
Record Gate: 527 v Hastings Town, Sussex Senior Cup 1992-93.
Previous Ground: Pannel Lane, Pett 1971-93.
Sponsors: Kenwood Pullen.
Previous Leagues: Southern Counties Combination/ East Sussex/ Hastings.
Clubhouse: Licensed bar, seating, pub games, tea bar.
Midweek Matchday: T.B.A.
Local Newspaper: Hastings Observer.   **92-93 Top Scorer:** Dean Kewley 33, Kevin Bevis 15.
Hons: Sussex Co. Lg Div 2 R-up 92-93 (Div 2 Cup R-up 89-90 90-91, Div 3 R-up, Div 3 Cup R-up, Reserve Section East 92-93), Hastings Snr Invitation Cup 89-90, Hastings Intermediate Cup 79-80 81-82 82-83 85-86 86-87 87-88.

Stamco F.C., Division Two Runners-up 1992-93. Back Row (L/R): Danny Sallows, Wayne Farrier, Dean Kewley, Gary Cawkill, Ian Menzies, Chris Clifford, Kevin Bevis. Front: Keith Blossom, Ted Harrison, Geoff Sallows, Paul Tuppenny, Colin Spray, Kevin Clee. Photo - Roger Turner.

THREE BRIDGES

President: Mr Jim Steele   **Chairman:** Mr O'Brien
Secretary: Mr Martin Clarke, 18 Mannings Close, Pound Hill, Crawley RH10 3TX (0293 883726).
Manager: Mr Bobby Nash   **Press Officer:** Mr Alf Blackler
Ground: Jubilee Field, Three Bridges, Crawley, West Sussex (0293 530540).
Directions: 200yds from Three Bridges (BR) - towards Crawley town centre.
Seats: None   **Cover:** 400   **Capacity:** 3,500   **Floodlights:** Yes   **Founded:** 1901
Colours: Amber & black   **Change colours:** All white   **Nickname:** None
Programme: Yes   **Editor:** Mark Stacy (0293 885864)   **Admission:** £1.50
Previous Lgs: Mid Sussex/ Redhill & District   **Previous Grounds:** None.
Record Gate: 2,000 v Horsham, 1948   **Midweek Matchday:** Tuesday   **Metal Badges:** No
Clubhouse: Bar, dance floor, pool, darts   **Sponsors:** Auto Body Care
92-93 Top Scorers: Andrew West 12.   **Local Press:** Crawley Observer, Crawley News
Hons: Sussex Co. Lg R-up 85-86 87-88 88-89 (Div 2 54-55, Invitation Cup 70-71, Div 2 Invitation Cup 62-63),
Sussex RUR Charity Cup 82-83.

WHITEHAWK

Manager: Butch Reeves   **President:** Ron Wiltshire   **Chairman:** Ken Powell
Secretary: John Rosenblatt, 25 Arundel Street, Brighton BN2 5TH (0273 680322).
Ground: The Enclosed Ground, East Brighton Park (0273 609736).
Directions: Follow Brighton seafront road towards Newhaven, turn inland (Arundel Road) opposite Marina, 3rd
right into Roedean Road, 1st left into Wilson Avenue. Three miles from Brighton (BR); take Newhaven, Eastbourne
or Saltdean bus to Marina, then as above.
Seats: None   **Cover:** 500   **Capacity:** 3,000   **Floodlights:** Yes   **Founded:** 1945
Colours: All red   **Change colours:** All blue   **Nickname:** Hawks
Midweek Matchday: Wednesday
Programme: Yes   **Editor:** Tony Kelly (0273 698203)   **Admission:** £1.50
Sponsors: Interplan.
Record Gate: 2,100 v Bognor Regis Town, FA Cup 4th Qualifying Rd replay 88-89.
Clubhouse: Licensed bar, pool, darts. Board room. Tea bar.
Previous League: Brighton Hove & Dist.   **Previous Grounds:** None   **Metal Badges:** No
Previous Name: Whitehawk & Manor Farm Old Boys (until 1958).
Local Press: Evening Argus   **92-93 Top Scorer:** Dale Mills 7.
Hons: Sussex Co. Lg 61-62 63-64 83-84 (Div 2 67-68 80-81, Lg Cup 82-83, Invitation Cup 60-61 69-70, Div 2 Cup
80-81), Sussex Snr Cup 50-51 61-62, Sussex RUR Charity Cup 54-55 58-59 90-91, Sussex I'mediate Cup 49-50,
Sussex Jnr Cup 48-49 51-52, Brighton Charity Cup 51-52 59-60 61-62 82-83 87-88 88-89, Worthing Charity Cup 82-83.

WICK

Chairman/Manager: Norman Cairns   **Press Off.:** Les Page (0903 260837)   **President:** M Hood
Secretary: C N Little, 4 Leeward Rd, Littlehampton, West Sussex BN17 6PG (0903 721962).
Ground: Crabtree Park, Coombes Way, Wick, Littlehampton, West Sussex (0903 713535).
Directions: A27 to Crossbush, left at Howards Hotel, after 1 mile cross level crossing, turn left into Coombes Way
next to Locomotive PH - ground at end. One and a half miles from Littlehampton (BR).
Seats: None   **Cover:** 200   **Capacity:** 2,000   **Floodlights:** Yes   **Founded:** 1892
Colours: Red & black   **Change colours:** Green & white
Programme: Yes   **Editor:** Les Page (0903 260837)   **Local Press:** Littlehampton Gazette.
Record Gate: 900.   **Sponsors:** T.B.A.   **Nickname:** Wickers
Prev. Grounds: Southfields Rec.   **Prev. Leagues/Names:** None   **Metal Badges:** No.
92-93 Top Scorer: Gavin Geddes 22, Ryan Gayler, Rod Wood 12.
Midweek Matches: Tuesday   **Clubhouse:** First floor. Capacity 120. Tea bar.
Admission: £1.50
Hons: Sussex Snr Cup 92-93, Sussex Co. Lg 89-90 (Lg Cup 87-88, Div 2 81-82 85-86, Div 2 Cup R-up 81-82,
Norman Wingate Tphy 88-89 90-91, Res. Sect West 87-88 90-91, Sussex 5-aside R-up 85-86), Sussex RUR Charity
Cup 89-90, Gilbert Rice F'lit Cup R-up 80-81 81-82, Sussex Jnr Cup 59-60, Brighton Charity Cup 85-86.

MERIT TABLE

Awards: 1st: £500 2nd: £400 3rd: £300

Win (W) = +5pts
Win by 5 or more goals (F) = +5pts
No goals against (N) = +5pts
Clean games - no cautions/sent-off (C) = +5pts
Cautions (B) = -5pts
Sendings-off (S) = -20pts

	W	F	N	C	B	S	PTS
Pagham	125	40	75	110	-85	0	265
Peacehaven & T.	135	20	80	115	-75	-20	255
Wick	125	10	55	115	-70	-20	215
Hailsham Town	65	15	50	120	-65	0	185
Whitehawk	90	5	55	120	-50	-40	180
Littlehampton T.	75	20	35	110	-70	-20	150
Three Bridges	70	5	35	115	-60	-20	145
Langney Sports	100	15	60	85	-125	0	135
Oakwood	70	10	30	100	-90	-40	80
Ringmer	40	10	25	105	-65	-40	75
Arundel	50	0	45	95	-105	-20	65
Newhaven	80	10	35	95	-115	-40	65
Burgess Hill T.	35	0	30	95	-105	0	55
Eastbourne Town	40	0	20	95	-115	0	40
Bexhill Town	50	0	35	90	-115	-20	40
Portfield	40	0	25	90	-110	-20	25
Midhurst & E.	25	0	20	90	-85	-40	10
Chichester City	40	5	20	95	-95	-60	5

DIV. ONE ATTENDANCES

Club	Agg.	Ave.	Best Gate
Hailsham T.	4107	241	530 v Langney 3/3/93
Peacehaven	3487	205	337 v W'hawk 12/4/93
Langney Spts	3455	203	400 v Hailsham 19/8/92
Littlehampton	3455	203	349 v Pagham 14/10/92
Pagham	2894	170	372 v Wick 21/8/92
Eastbourne T.	2855	168	427 v Hailsham 26/12/92
Newhaven	2367	139	364 v Hailsham 28/4/93
Midhurst	1855	109	180 v Chich C. 28/12/92
Wick	1854	109	240 v Pagham 31/3/93
Bexhill T.	1850	109	210 v Ringmer 28/12/92
Burgess Hill	1679	99	152 v P'haven 19/9/92
Chichester	1580	93	220 v Portfield 26/12/92
Ringmer	1578	93	190 v P'haven 18/8/92
Arundel	1570	92	227 v L'pton 26/12/92
Three Bridges	1524	90	189 v Oakwood 12/4/93
Whitehawk	1450	85	250 v Pagham 26/12/92
Portfield	1427	84	230 v Pagham 30/12/92
Oakwood	1403	83	389 v Three B. 28/12/92
	40390	**132**	

SECOND DIVISION CLUBS 1993-94

BROADBRIDGE HEATH

President: G W Manketelow   **Chairman:** K Soames   **Manager:** J Laker
Secretary: B P Nagle, The Briars, 59A Millfield, Southwater, Horsham RH13 7HT   (0403 730944).
Ground: Broadbridge Heath Sports Centre, Wickhurst Lane, Horsham (0403 65871).
Directions: Alongside A24, Horsham north/south bypass.
Seats: 300   **Cover:** 300   **Capacity:** 1,300   **F'lights:** Not full   **Founded:** 1919
Colours: All royal blue   **Change colours:** All red   **Nickname:** Bears
Programme: Yes   **Editor:** G Street (0403 240596)   **Admission:** £1   **Metal badges:** No
Previous Leagues: Horsham, West Sussex, Southern Co's Comb.   **Record Gate:** 240
Clubhouse: Bar. Kitchen serving meals, pool, darts, social club etc.   **Sponsors:** Badgers
Midweek matches: Tue or Wed   **Local Press:** West Sussex County Times.
92-93 Top Scorers: Martin Howes 10.   **Prev. Ground:** Guildford Rd, Broadbridge Heath.

Broadbridge Heath F.C. pictured before their F.A. Vase tie at Ash United on 6th September. They were unfortunate enough to lose 3-4 after extra-time. Photo - Eric Marsh.

EASTBOURNE UNITED

Chairman: Andrew Curry   **President:** C Philcox
Secretary: Maurice J Stevens, 21 Brookside Ave., Polegate, East Sussex BN26 6DL (0323 484644).
Manager: T Wood   **Press Officer:** Steve Dorling (0323 24541).
Ground: The Oval, Channel View Rd, Eastbourne, East Sussex (0323 269989).
Directions: To seafront and turn left. Turn left into Channel View Rd at Princes Park and ground 1st right. 2 miles from Eastbourne (BR).
Seats: 160   **Cover:** 160   **Capacity:** 3,000   **Floodlights:** Yes   **Founded:** 1894
Colours: White/black/black   **Change colours:** All tangerine   **Nickname:** The "U's"
Programme: Yes   **Editor:** Steve Dorling (0323 24541)   **Admission:** £1,50   **Metal Badges:** Yes
Record Gate: 11,000 **Previous Ground:** Lynchmere   **Previous Name:** Eastbourne Old Comrades
Previous Leagues: Sussex Co. 21-28 35-56/ Metropolitan 56-64/ Athenian 64-77/ Isthmian 77-92.
Clubhouse: Bar, lounge area, dancefloor, stage, tea bar, board room.
Local Press: Eastbourne Gazette + Herald, Evening Argus   **Midweek Matchday:** Tuesday
Players progressing to Football League: B Salvage, T Funnell, M French.
Sponsors: Plan-A-Head   **92-93 Top Scorers:** Neil Ivemy 14 (3 for Hailsham)
Hons: Sussex Co. Lg 54-55, Sussex Snr Cup(5) 60-61 62-64 66-67 68-69 (R-up 89-90), Sussex RUR Charity Cup 55-56, Metropolitan Lg Cup 60-61, Athenian Lg Div 2 66-67 (Div 1 R-up 68-69), Sussex I'mediate Cup 65-66 68-69.

Eastbourne United F.C. 1992-93. Photo - Gavin Ellis-Neville.

HASSOCKS

President: Maurice Boxall   **Chairman:** Jim Goodrum
Secretary: Bob Preston, 65 Oak Hall, Burgess Hill, West Sussex RH15 0DA (0444 245695).
Manager: Nick Greenwood/ Peter Liddell   **Press Officer:** Paul Elphick (0444 454492)
Ground: The Beacon, Brighton Rd, Hassocks (0273 846040)
Seats: None   **Cover:** None   **Capacity:**   **Floodlights:** No   **Founded:** 1902
Colours: Red/white/red   **Change colours:** All yellow.
Programme: Yes   **Editor:** Paul Elphick (0444 454492)   **Admission:** £1.50   **Metal Badges:** No.
Previous Leagues: Mid Sussex/ Brighton Hove & Dist./ Southern Co's Comb.   **Nickname:** Robins
Record Gate: 340 v Bognor Regis Town, Sussex Senior Cup 92-93. *At previous ground: 400 v Nottingham University, AFA Snr Cup January 1978.*
Midweek Matchday: Wednesday   **Clubhouse:** Clubroom, bar, kitchen.
Sponsors: Burgess Hill Glass   **Local Press:** Burgess Hill Times, Evening Argus
Previous Ground: Adastra Park, Hassocks (pre-1992).
92-93 Top Scorers: Steve Hards 22.
Hons: Sussex County Lg Div 3 91-92 (Res. Sect. East R-up 92-93), Southern Counties Comb. 76-77 (Lg Cup 79-80), Brighton Hove & Dist. Lg 71-72, Sussex Intermediate Cup 74-75 (R-up 80-81).

HORSHAM Y.M.C.A.

President: Gordon Head   **Chairman:** John Cashman   **Manager:** John Suter
Secretary/Press Off.: Bill Bower, 5 Patching Close, Ifield, Crawley, West Sussex RH11 0ES (0293 533831).
Ground: Gorings Mead, Horsham, West Sussex (0403 252689).
Directions: At end of lane at rear of Horsham F.C. (see page 359). Half mile from Horsham (BR).
Seats: 100   **Cover:** 200   **Capacity:** 800   **Floodlights:** Yes   **Founded:** 1898
Colours: White/black/red   **Change colours:** All red   **Nickname:** "YM's"
Programme: Yes   **Editor:** B Denyer (0403 741401)   **Metal Badges:** No (ties + jumpers)
Record Gate: 600 v Horsham, FA Cup   **Previous Ground:** Lyons Field, Kings Rd   **Admission:** £1.50
Clubhouse: Bar, kitchen, main hall, bar, committee room.
Previous League: Horsham & District/ Brighton Hove & District/ Mid Sussex.
Sponsors: Principal Copiers/ Swift Surveying Services Ltd.   **Midweek Matchday:** Tuesday
Local Newspaper: West Sussex County Times
92-93 Top Scorers: Duane Read 14, Barry Burden 14.
Hons: Sussex Co. Lg Div 2 65-66 82-83 (Lg Cup 81-82, Invitation Cup 66-67 67-68, Div 2 Invitation Cup 59-60 61-62, Reserve Section West R-up).

Horsham Y.M.C.A. 1992-93. Back Row (L/R): Gary Barnes, Doug Cashman, Darren Benn, Terry Botting, Gary Pike, Richard Tween, Peter Durrant. Front: Warren Tilley, Steve Best, Michael Faird, Barry Burden, Dave Smith, Duane Reed. Photo - Roger Turner.

LANCING

President: R G Steele   **Chairman:** R J Brown   **Manager:** G Russell
Secretary: J Chisnall, 15 Orchard Way, Lancing, West Sussex BN15 9ED (0903 763048).
Press Officer: John Rea (0903 761142).
Ground: Culver Road, Lancing, West Sussex (0903 764398).
Directions: Third turning left north of Lancing station (BR).
Seats: 350   **Cover:** 350   **Capacity:** 2,400   **Floodlights:** Yes   **Founded:** 1941
Colours: Yellow/blue/yellow   **Change colours:** All red   **Nickname:** Yellows
Programme: Yes   **Editor:** John Rea (0903 761142)   **Sponsors:** Churchill Windows.
Previous Name: Lancing Athletic   **Previous Ground:** Croshaw Rec, Sompting.
Local Press: Lancing Herald, Evening Argus.
Previous League: Brighton Hove & Dist.   **Metal Badges:** No.
Record Gate: 2,591 v Tooling, FA Amtr Cup 22/11/47. At Culver Road: 2,340 v Worthing 25/10/52.
Midweek Matches: Wednesday   **Clubhouse:** Run by Sussex F.A. Tea bar   **Admission:** £1.50p
92-93 Top Scorers: Mark Wakefield (10 for Southwick), Mark McGilvray 15, Gary Salter 12.
Hons: Sussex Co. Lg R-up 49-50 64-65 (Div 2 57-58 69-70 (R-up 82-83), Div 2 Cup 81-82 92-93, Invitation Cup), Sussex RUR Charity Cup 65-66, Brighton Lg 46-47 47-48, Sussex Intermediate Cup 46-47, Brighton Charity Cup 83-84 84-85 86-87.

LITTLE COMMON ALBION

Chairman/Manager: K E Cherry **President:** Councillor Ivor Brampton.
Secretary: Mrs M Cherry, 11 Bidwell Avenue, Bexhill-on-Sea, East Sussex TN39 4DB (0424 217191).
Ground: Little Common Rec., Pear Tree Lane, Little Common, East Sussex (0424 35861)
Directions: A259 from Brighton.
Seats: None **Cover:** 250 **Capacity:** **Floodlights:** No **Founded:** 1960
Colours: Claret & blue **Change colours:** White & blue **Nickname:** Common
Programme: Yes **Editor:** Chas Tibbutt (0424 713757) **Admission:** £1.50 **Metal Badges:** No.
Record Gate: 251 **Clubhouse:** Bar, clubroom, tea bar **Midweek Matchday:** Wednesday
Local Newspapers: Bexhill Observer **Previous League:** East Sussex
Sponsors: D Scotcher.
92-93 Top Scorers: John Chapman 7.
Hons: E Sussex Lg(2) 75-77 (Lg Cup 76-77), Hastings I'mediate Cup 76-77, Hawkhurst Chal. Cup 75-76 76-77, Sussex Minor Cup 75-76, Sussex Co. Lg P.G. Cunningham Sportsmanship Award 92-93.

MIDHURST & EASEBOURNE

Chairman: Robert Boxall **President:** Andy Robertson.
Secretary: E S Dummer, 14 Nine Acres, June Lane, Midhurst, West Sussex GU29 9EP (0730 813887).
Manager: Simon Gibson **Press Officer:** Rex Lane (0730 812839).
Ground: Rotherfield, Dodsley Lane, Midhurst, West Sussex (0730 816557)
Directions: Ground one mile out of Midhurst on London Road.
Seats: 60 **Cover:** 200 **Capacity:** 800 **Floodlights:** No **Founded:** 1946
Colours: All royal blue **Change colours:** All red **Nickname:** None
Programme: Yes **Editor:** Secretary **Admission:** £1.50 **Metal Badges:** No.
Record Gate: 300 in local Gingell Cup, 1989.
Clubhouse: Clubhouse with canteen and bar, capacity 80.
Previous Grounds: None **Sponsors:** Frankform European.
Local Press: Midhurst & Petworth Observer. West Sussex Gazette
Previous Leagues: West Sussex 46-79/ Southern Co's Combination 79-81.
92-93 Top Scorers: Andrew Claydon 6, Derek Curwood 6.
Hons: Sussex Co. Lg Div 2 R-up 81-82 91-92 (Div 2 Cup 88-89), Southern Co's Comb. Div 2 80-81 (Chal. Cup 80-81), W Sussex Lg 67-68 76-77 79-80 (Div 1 55-56 62-63 64-65, Malcolm Simmonds Cup 59-60 73-74 77-78 79-80, Bareham Tphy 70-71), Sussex I'mediate Cup(5) 54-57 62-63 77-78.

MILE OAK

Manager: Tony Gratwicke **Chairman:** R A Kearly **President:** D Bean
Secretary: C D Brown, 19 The Crescent, Southwick, West Sussex BN42 4LB (0273 591346).
Ground: Mile Oak Recreation Ground, Graham Avenue, Mile Oak (No telephone).
Directions: From A27 take Mile Oak Road or Locks Hill & Valley Road to Chalky Road, ground 500yds on right along Graham Avenue which runs up valley from centre of Chalky Road.
Seats: None **Cover:** Yes **Capacity:** **Floodlights:** No **Founded:** 1960
Colours: All tangerine **Change colours:** All white **Nickname:** The Oak
Programme: Yes **Editor:** C Tew (0273 881696) **Admission:** £1.50 **Metal Badges:** No
Previous Leagues: Southern Counties Combination/ Brighton Hove & District
Record Gate: 175 **Previous Ground:** Victoria Rec., Portslade.
Midweek Matchday: Tuesday **Clubhouse:** Mile Oak Pavillion; Hall and tea bar.
Sponsors: Lancing Glass Works Ltd **92-93 Top Scorers:** Gavin Tanner 14, Neil Roberts 12.
Local Press: Brighton Evening Argus, Shoreham Herald
Hons: Sussex Co. Lg Div 3 R-up 91-92 (Div 2 Cup R-up 92-93), Southern Counties Combination 86-87, Brighton Hove & District Lg 80-81, Vernon Wentworth Cup 85-86, Sussex Intermediate Cup R-up 88-89.

REDHILL

President: Vacant **Chairman:** Mr Alan Thurlbeck.
Secretary: Mr Neil Hoad, 'Braeside', 2b Earlswood Rd, Redhill, Surrey RH1 6HE (0737 766726).
Joint Mgrs: J Fears/ P Duffell **Press Officer:** Ray Summerfield.
Ground: Kiln Brow, Three Arch Road, Redhill, Surrey (0737 762129).
Directions: On left hand side of A23, two and a half miles south of Redhill.
Seats: 100 **Cover:** 100 **Capacity:** 3,100 **Floodlights:** Yes **Founded:** 1894
Cols: Red & white stripes/white/red **Change colours:** White/black. **Metal Badges:** Yes
Record Gate: 1,200 v Crystal Palace & All Star XI, Brian Medlicott Testimonial 1989
Programme: Yes **Editor:** Ricky Kidd (0293 772792) **Admission:** £2 **Nickname:** Reds
Sponsors: Pink's Gym.
Previous Leagues: East West Surrey/ Spartan 09-10/ Southern Suburban/ London 21-23/ Athenian 23-84.
Local Newspaper: Surrey Mirror & The Independent.
Previous Grounds: Memorial Sports Ground 1894-1986.
Clubhouse: Social club, bar, canteen, board room, club shop, tanoy, toilets.
92-93 Top Scorers: Ricky Kidd 15.
Hons: FA Amtr Cup SF 25-25, FA Cup 1st Rd 57-58, Athenian Lg 24-25 83-84 (Lg Cup 69-70 70-71), Surrey Snr Cup 28-29, Gilbert Rice F'lit Cup 80-81, Sussex County Lg Div 2 Cup 91-92, Southern Co's Comb. Cup 90-91.

SALTDEAN UNITED

Chairman: Trevor Clarke **Manager:** G Green **President:** Jim Bower
Secretary: I S Fielding, 40 Rowan Way, Rottingdean, Brighton BN2 7FP (0273 304995).
Ground: Hill Park, Combe Vale, Saltdean, Brighton (0273 309898).
Directions: A259 coast road east from Brighton to Saltdean Lido, left into Arundel Drive West, and Saltdean Vale to bridle path at beginning of Combe Vale. Club 200yds along track.
Seats: 50 **Cover:** Yes **Capacity:** 2,000 **Floodlights:** No **Founded:** 1967
Colours: Red & black **Change colours:** Blue & black **Nickname:** Tigers
Programme: Yes **Editor:** T Clarke (0273 309898) **Admission:** £1.50 **Metal Bagdes:** Yes
Record Gate: 250 **Previous Grounds:** None **Sponsors:** Sunley
Clubhouse: Licensed bar, lounge, juke box, video games, board room, tea bar.
Previous League: Brighton Hove & Dist. **Local Press:** Brighton Evening Argus.
92-93 Top Scorer: Dave Woolgar 8. **Hons:** Sussex Co. Lg Div 3 88-89.

Lancing F.C., Division Two Cup winners 1992-93. Back Row (L/R): Graham Russell (Manager), Max Blann (Kit Manager), Gary Salter, Darren Woods, Tim Fletcher, John Dutton, Steve Barber, Mark Collins, Richard Whittington, Peter Towell (Trainer). Front: Clive Towell, Mark McGilvray, Brian Jones (Joint Manager), Vic Gretton (Captain), Alan Herbert (now Worthing United), Dave Funnell.

Little Common Albion F.C. 1992-93. Photo - Colin Stevens.

Redhill's top-scorer Ricky Kidd challenges Martin Wood, but the Sidley United goalkeeper wins the ball, and his side the match by three goals without reply. Photo - Colin Stevens.

SELSEY

Chairman: Derek Longworth   **Manager:** D Kew/ G Peach   **President:** Roy Glew
Secretary: Mr D C Lee, 29 Malthouse Cottages, West Wittering, West Sussex (0243 513788).
Press Officer: Mr P Emms. **Ground:** High Street Ground, Selsey, Chichester, West Sussex (0243 603420)
Directions: B2145 from Chichester to Selsey, turn right by Fire Station. Regular buses from Chichester.
Seats: 50   **Cover:** Yes   **Capacity:** 2,250   **Floodlights:** Yes   **Founded:** 1923
Colours: Blue/white/blue   **Change colours:** White/red/red   **Metal Badges:** No
Programme Editor: Mrs D Hayers (0243 604013)   **Admission:** £1.50   **Nickname:** Blues
Midweek Matchday: Wednesday   **Record Gate:** 750-800 v Chichester or Portfield, 1950's
Clubhouse: Bar, hospitality room, lounge, toilets, kitchen. **Sponsors:** Allslade Welding & Fabrications Ltd
Local Newspapers: Chichester Observer, Evening Argus, Portsmouth Evening News.
92-93 Top Scorers: Shaun Leggett 12.   **Previous Leagues:** Chichester & Dist./ West Sussex.
Hons: Sussex Co. Lg R-up 89-90 (Div 2 63-64 75-76 (R-up 86-87), Div 2 Cup 86-87 (R-up 84-85), Div 2 Invitation Cup 63-64, Sussex 5-aside 88-89), Sussex Snr Cup R-up 63-64, Sussex I'mediate Cup 58-59, Sussex Jnr Cup(Reserves) 76-77, West Sussex Lg 54-55 55-56 57-58 58-59 60-61 (Malcolm Simmonds Cup 55-56 56-57 57-58 58-59).

Selsey F.C. 1992-93. Photo - Gavin Ellis-Neville.

SHOREHAM

President: Mr Alf Bloom   **Chairman:** Mr John Bell.
Secretary: Mr Glen Hilton, 67 Test Rd, Sompting, West Sussex BN15 0EP (0903 763024).
Manager: B Donnelly   **Press Officer:** Mr Michael Wenham (0273 596009).
Ground: Middle Road, Shoreham-by-Sea, West Sussex (0273 454261).
Directions: Half mile from Shoreham-by-Sea (BR) - east across level crossing, up Dolphin Road, ground 150yds on right. Or, A27 to Southlands Hospital - south down Hammy Lane, left at end, ground opposite.
Seats: 20   **Cover:** 1 stand   **Capacity:** 1,500   **Floodlights:** Yes   **Founded:** 1892
Colours: Blue & white   **Change colours:** Red & white   **Nickname:** Musselmen
Programme: Yes   **Editor:** Mr M Wenham (0273 596009)   **Admission:** £1.50
Previous League: West Sussex   **Midweek Matchday:** Wednesday   **Metal Badges:** No
Record Gate: 1,342 v Wimbledon (floodlight opening 1986).
Sponsors: Len German Wholesalers.   **Previous Ground:** Buckingham Park (pre-1970)
Local Press: Shoreham Herald   **Clubhouse:** Seats 70. Bar, pool, darts, tea bar.
92-93 Top Scorers: Lee Butler 18, Francis Haren 14, Simon Pierce 11.
Hons: Sussex Co. Lg 51-52 52-53 77-78 (R-up 34-35, Div 2 61-62 76-77 84-85, Div 2 Cup 74-75 82-83, Invitation Cup 57-58), Sussex Snr Cup 01-02 05-06, Sussex F'lit Cup R-up 89-90, Sussex RUR Charity Cup 02-03 05-06, Vernon Wentworth Cup 86-87.

Shoreham F.C. 1992-93. Back Row (L/R): P Dolner (Physio), G Hilton (Secretary), J Bell (Chairman), J Gregory, J Byatt, D Howarth, C Cheeseman, W Newington, L Murphy, P Croft (then Manager), L Butler, P Burchell. Front: S Berrett, S Pierce, H Lillie, N Mahoney, F Haren, A Dawes. Photo - Dennis Nicholson.

SIDLEY UNITED

President: Tibby Adams   **Chairman/Press Off.:** Peter Snow (0424 210974)
Manager: Steve Johnson   **Secretary:** Jasper Yevell, 3 Mendip Gdns, Hastings, E. Sussex (0424 433951).
Ground: Gullivers Sports Ground, North Road, Glovers Lane, Sidley, Bexhill-on-Sea (0424 217078).
Directions: From Brighton on A259 to Bexhill bypass traffic lights, left into London Road, continue into Sidley, right into Glovers Lane and 1st left into North Road. One mile from Bexhill (BR).
Seats: None   **Cover:** 150   **Capacity:** 1,500   **Floodlights:** No   **Founded:** 1906
Colours: Royal & sky blue   **Change colours:** All red   **Nickname:** Blues
Programme: Yes   **Editor:** Mr Peter Snow (0424 210974)   **Admission:** £1.20 (50p OAP)
Previous Leagues: East Sussex/ Hastings & District   **Metal Badges:** Yes
Record Gate: 1,300 in 1959   **Previous Grounds:** None.   **Sponsors:** J Burke
Midweek Matchday: Tues/ Weds   **Clubhouse:** Large bar area & function room. Tea bar.
Local Press: Bexhill Observer, Bexhill News
92-93 Top Scorers: Carl Bune 21, Wayne Grant 10, Dale Seymour 10 (4 for Bexhill and 5 for Rinmger).
Hons: Suss. Co. Lg Div 2 58-59 64-65 (Div 2 Invit. Cup 57-58), Suss. I'mediate Cup 47-48, Suss. Jnr Cup 24-25.

Sidley United F.C. 1992-93.

SOUTHWICK

Chairman: Roy Pollard   **President:** Dr D W Gordon, MBBS Dr.COG
Secretary: Peter Hallett, 10 Hawkins Close, Shoreham-by-Sea, West Sussex BN43 6TL (0273 594349).
Manager: Micky Fogden   **Press Officer:** Paul Symes (0273 594142).
Ground: Old Barn Way, off Manor Hall Way, Southwick, Brighton BN43 4NT (0273 591744).
Directions: Five minutes walk from either Fishergate or Southwick BR stations. By A27 from Brighton take 1st left after 'Southwick' sign to Leisure Centre. Ground adjacent.
Seats: 220   **Cover:** 1,220   **Capacity:** 3,500   **Floodlights:** Yes   **Founded:** 1882
Colours: Red & black stripes/black/black **Change Colours:** Yellow/red/red
Record Gate: 3,200 v Showbiz side 1971 **Midweek matchday:** Tuesday   **Metal Badges:** Yes.
Programme: Yes   **Editor:** Paul Symes (0273 594142)   **Sponsors:** Market Cars/ Lada Cars.
Previous Leagues: West Sussex 1896-1920/ Sussex County 20-52 54-84/ Metropolitan 52-54/ Combined Counties 84-85/ Isthmian 85-92.   **Previous Grounds:** Croft Avenue/ The Green/ Oldfield Crescent.
Players progressing to Football League: Charles & William Buttenshaw (Luton 1948).
Best FA Cup season: 1st Rd Proper 74-75 (lost 0-5 at AFC Bournemouth).   **Nickname:** Wickers
Best FA Amtr Cup season: 3rd 28-29   **Best FA Vase season:** 3rd Rd 79-80 85-86
Local Newspaper: Evening Argus (0273 606799), Shoreham Herald (0273 455104), Adur Herald.
Clubhouse: Weekdays noon-3 & 6-11pm, all day Saturday, normal hrs Sunday. Members bar & boardroom with private bar. Snacks on matchdays from tea bar.   **92-93 Top Scorer:** Mark Wakefield (now Lancing) 10.
Hons: Isthmian Lg Div 2 Sth 85-86, Sus. Co. Lg 25-26 27-28 29-30 47-48 68-69 74-75 (R-up(9) 23-24 28-29 36-37 39-40 70-71 76-77 78-80 82-83, Lg Cup 77-78, Div 1 Invit. Cup 65-66, Div 2 R-up 65-66), Combined Co's Lg R-up 84-85, Sus. Snr Cup 1896-97 1910-11 12-13 24-25 27-28 29-30 30-31 36-37 47-48 67-68, Sus. RUR Charity Cup(10) 1896-97 08-09 10-11 24-26 27-30 37-38 76-77, W. Sus. Lg 1896-97 97-98 1908-09 10-11, Sus. Jnr Cup 1891-92.

Southwick F.C. 1992-93. Photo - Mr J Harrison.

STEYNING TOWN

President: R Head　　　　　　　　**Chairman:** I Kennett
Secretary: G Lean, 60 Shooting Field, Steyning, West Sussex (0903 879144).
Manager: B Paine　　**Asst Manager:** T Hatchett　　　　**Coach:** C Hutchings.
Ground: The Shooting Field, Steyning, West Sussex (0903 812228).
Directions: A27 east then A283 turn off - town centre turning at r'bout, right into Church Street, straight into Church Lane, straight into Shooting Field, ground on left by Grammar School. Bus 10 from Shoreham-by-Sea BR station stops at end of road.
Seats: None　　**Cover:** 400　　　　**Capacity:** 2,000　　**Floodlights:** Yes　　**Club Shop:** No.
Colours: Red/white/red　　　　　　**Change colours:** All blue　　　　　　　**Founded:** 1900
Midweek home matchday: Wednesday　　**Record Gate:** 1,100 v Halesowen Town, FA Vase QF 84-85.
Previous Leagues: Sussex County 64-86/ Wessex 86-88/ Combined Counties 88-93.
Programme: 28 pages, 50p　　　　　　**Programme Editor:** B Owen (0403 253371).
Record win: 15-0 v Battle, 1968　　　**Record defeat:** 1-11 v Littlehampton Town, 1991.
Record transfer fee paid: Nil　　　　**Received:** £1,000 for Paul Walker (Wokingham, 1989).
Clubhouse: Tues-Fri 7-11pm, Sat 12-3 & 4.30-11pm, Sun 12-3 & 7-10.30pm. Snacks available.
Captain & P.o.Y. 92-93: M Salter　　　**Top Scorer 92-93:** P Barnard, 15.
Club record scorer: D Deans, 42　　　**Club record appearances:** N Manvell, 800.
Hons: FA Vase QF 84-85, Sussex Snr Cup 85-86 88-89, Sussex Co. Lg 84-85 85-86 (Lg Cup 77-78 83-84 85-86, Div 2 Invitation Cup 65-66, Reserve Section West 88-89), Sussex RUR Charity Cup 79-80, Vernon Wentworth Cup 33-34, Sussex Jnr Cup 01-02 37-38.

STORRINGTON

President: D Medhurst　　　　　　**Chairman:** A Massimo.
Secretary: K Dalmon, 4 End Cottages, Storrington Rd, Amberley, Arundel, West Sussex BN18 9LX (0798 831887).
Manager: A Massimo/ F Massimo　　　　　　**Press Officer:** T Brookes.
Ground: Recreation Ground, Pulborough Road, Storrington (0903 745860).
Directions: Turn west on A283 (off A24). Ground opposite pond to the west of the village
Seats: None　　**Cover:** Yes　　**Nickname:** Swans　　**Floodlights:** No　　**Founded:** 1920
Colours: All blue　　　　　　**Change colours:** White/navy/navy
Metal Badges: No
Programme: Yes　　**Editor:** T.B.A.　　　　　　**Previous Leagues:** Worthing/ W Sussex.
Previous Grounds: No　　　　**Sponsors:** The White Horse, The Square, Storrington
Clubhouse: Clubroom with bar, dressing rooms & toilets
Local Newspapers: Chanctonbury Herald, Horsham County Times.
92-93 Top Scorer: Eamonn Searle 23.
Hons: Sussex Co. Lg Div 3 R-up 92-93, Worthing Lg(3).

WITHDEAN

Chairman: Keith Turrell　　　　　　**President:** Graham Spicer
Secretary: Dave J Gunstone, 285 Brighton Rd, Lancing, West Sussex BN15 8JR (0903 750063).
Manager: Derek Tharme.
Ground: Withdean Stadium, off Valley Drive, Brighton (0703 551638).
Directions: Off main London - Brighton road.
Seats: 1,000　　**Cover:** Due　　**Capacity:** 10,000　　**Floodlights:** No　　**Founded:** 1984.
Colours: Red/blue/blue　　　　**Change Colours:** All white　　　　**Metal Badges:** No.
Clubhouse: Pub on ground
Programme Editor: Dave Bull.
Previous Leagues: Brighton Hove & District
Previous Ground: Council pitch.
Local Newspaper: Brighton Evening Argus　　　　　　**Midweek Matchday:**
92-93 Top Scorer: David Agnew 24, Geoff Kirzynowski 11.
Sponsors: Express Computers Consultants Ltd.
Hons: Sussex Co. Lg Div 3 92-93 (Div 3 Cup 91-92).

WORTHING UNITED

President: Ken Higson　　　　　　**Chairman:** Mr L Newbon
Secretary: Mr B A Withers, 23 Westlands, Rustington, West Sussex BN17 6RT (0903 725900).
Manager: Mr Brian Woolmer　　　　　　**Press Officer:** Mr Brian Woolmer.
Ground: Beeches Avenue, Lyons Way, Worthing, West Sussex (0903 234466).
Directions: From west on A27, Beeches Avenue is 4th left past Barn Hill r'bout. From east take 2nd left past lights at Downlands Hotel and proceed to Beeches Avenue - go to and follow concrete road to cap park.
Seats: 100　　**Cover:** 500　　**Capacity:** 1,000　　**Floodlights:** No　　**Founded:** 1948
Colours: Sky & white　　　　**Change colours:** All white　　　　**Nickname:** None
Programme: Yes　　**Editor:** N Woolmer (0903 772698)　　**Sponsors:** Tinsley Robor.
Previous Name: Wigmore Athletic　　**Previous Grounds:** Harrison Road, Worthing.
Previous Leagues:
Midweek Matches:　　　　　　**Record Gate:** 180 v Northwood, FA Vase 3rd Rd 91-92.
Clubhouse: Bar (capacity 80), refreshment facilities (tea bar).　　　　**Metal badges:** Yes
Admission: £1.50 (75p OAP & children).
Local Newspapers: Worthing Herald.
92-93 Top Scorers: Nigel Waller 25, Steve Gurney 20.
Hons: Sussex Co. Lg Challenge Cup 74-75 (Invitation Cup 59-60, Div 2 52-53, Div 2 Invitation Cup 59-60, Div 3 89-90, Reserve Section West 92-93, 5-aside comp. R-up 1993), Sussex Jnr Cup 49-50.

DIV. TWO MERIT TABLE

Win (W) = +5pts
Win by 5 or more goals (F) = +5pts
No goals against (N) = +5pts
Clean games - no cautions/sent-off (C) = +5pts
Cautions (B) = -5pts
Sendings-off (S) = -20pts

	W	F	N	C	B	S	PTS
Stamco	130	25	70	135	-40	-20	300
Horsham Y.M.C.A.	90	20	55	145	-50	0	260
Crowborough Ath.	130	25	60	130	-80	0	255
East Grinstead	105	25	55	125	-65	0	245
Mile Oak	70	10	30	130	-65	0	175
Hassocks	80	5	60	115	-65	-20	175
Worthing United	95	10	30	140	-60	-40	175
Lancing	90	20	70	95	-105	0	170
Little Common A.	50	0	40	115	-70	0	135
Broadbridge Hth	45	0	35	135	-60	-20	135
Redhill	50	5	35	115	-85	-20	100
Shoreham	80	10	35	100	-110	-20	95
Sidley United	45	5	5	115	-85	0	85
Southwick	70	0	50	120	-70	-100	70
Haywards Hth T.	35	5	20	100	-95	-40	25
Saltdean United	45	0	45	75	-135	-20	10
Selsey	60	0	35	60	-170	-20	-35
Eastbourne Utd	45	0	25	80	-170	-40	-60
Seaford Town	40	5	25	70	-205	-40	-105

DIV. TWO ATTENDANCES

Club	Agg.	Ave.	Best Gate
Hassocks	2465	137	346 v H. Hth 26/12/92
E Grinstead	2183	121	265 v Crowb. 26/12/92
Sidley Utd	2052	114	284 v Little C 26/12/92
Crowborough	1974	110	439 v Pagham 14/5/93
Southwick	1947	108	541 v Shoreham 1/1/93
Eastbourne U.	1811	101	260 v Seaford 12/4/93
Redhill	1719	96	130 v E Grinst. 27/4/93
Lancing	1642	91	117 v Worthing 12/4/93
			& v Shoreham 1/5/93
Horsham YM	1528	85	114 v Lancing 19/9/92
Haywards H.	1398	78	205 v Hassocks 12/4/93
Stamco	1296	72	119 v Crowboro. 6/3/93
Mile Oak	1278	71	175 v S'wick 26/12/92
Seaford T.	1205	67	126 v E'b. Utd 28/12/92
Selsey	1026	57	101 v Saltdean 1/5/93
Shoreham	1025	57	182 v S'wick 13/4/93
Saltdean U.	1009	56	85 v Shoreham 24/4/93
Worthing Utd	958	53	138 v Lancing 26/12/92
Little Cmn A.	914	51	150 v Sidley 12/4/93
Broadbridge H.	893	50	110 v Horsham
			YMCA 26/12/92
	28323	83	

DIV. THREE MERIT TABLE

Win (W) = +5pts
Win by 5 or more goals (F) = +5pts
No goals against (N) = +5pts
Clean games - no cautions/sent-off (C) = +5pts
Cautions (B) = -5pts
Sendings-off (S) = -20pts

	W	F	N	C	B	S	PTS
Withdean	90	20	80	100	-30	-40	220
Shinewater Assn	30	5	15	125	-5	0	170
Forest	55	10	35	110	-20	-20	170
Hurtpierpoint	45	0	25	115	-20	0	165
St Francis Hos.	45	5	30	105	-30	0	155
Sidlesham	60	5	20	105	-35	0	155
Bosham	75	5	20	100	-30	-20	150
Storrington	80	15	45	80	-50	-40	130
Ifield	50	10	20	90	-45	0	125
Lindfield Rgrs	45	0	25	100	-35	-20	115
Franklands V.	35	0	25	90	-35	-20	95
East Preston	30	5	15	85	-50	-20	65
Ferring	15	0	5	85	-45	0	60
Buxted	30	5	15	85	-75	0	60

P.G. CUNNINGHAM SPORTSMANSHIP TROPHY

Club	%
Little Common Albion	80.00
Stamco	78.88
Broadbridge Hth/ Sidley United	76.94
Whitehawk	76.76
Horsham Y.M.C.A.	75.83
Hailsham Town	74.41
Crowborough Athletic	74.16
Bexhill Town	73.52
Wick	72.94
Hassocks	72.77
Eastbourne Town	72.64
Worthing United	72.50
Three Bridges	72.35
Mile Oak	71.94
Pagham/ Portfield	71.76
Ringmer	71.17
Southwick	71.11
Littlehampton/ Peacehaven & T.	70.88
East Grinstead/ Lancing	70.83
Redhill	69.72
Arundel/ Chichester City	69.11
Midhurst & Easebourne	67.35
Shoreham	67.22
Langney Sports/ Oakwood	65.88
Saltdean United	65.83
Haywards Heath Town	65.00
Seaford Town/ Selsey	64.16
Burgess Hill Town/ Newhaven	63.52
Eastbourne United	59.16

DIV. THREE SPORTSMANSHIP

Club	%
Shinewater Association	78.07
Forest	77.30
Franklands Village	74.61
St Francis Hospital	73.84
Lindfield Rangers	72.30
Hurstpierpoint	71.53
Buxted	69.61
Storrington	69.23
East Preston/ Ferring	68.46
Withdean	67.69
Sidlesham	67.30
Bosham	65.38
Ifield	65.00

THIRD DIVISION CLUBS 1993-94

BOSHAM

President: D G Phillips   **Chairman:** M Maiden   **Manager:** R L Collyer
Secretary: R D Probee, 39 Arnold Way, Bosham, West Sussex PO18 8NJ (0243 572570).
Ground: Walton Lane, Bosham, West Sussex PO18 8QF (0243 574011).
Directions: Half mile from Bosham (BR) - walk south down station road, over A27 r'bout, left at T-junction, ground entrance 50 yds on left.
Seats: None   **Cover:** 50   **Capacity:** 2,000   **Floodlights:** No   **Founded:** 1901
Colours: Red/white/red   **Change colours:** White/black/white   **Nickname:** Robins
Programme: Yes   **Programme Editor:** Secretary   **Admission:** None   **Metal Badges:** No
Previous Leagues: Chichester & Dist Jnr/ Chichester & Bognor/ Chichester & Dist./ West Sussex
Midweek Matchday: Tuesday.   **Sponsors:** None.
Clubhouse: Lounge bar, open evenings & weekends. Tea bar.
92-93 Top Scorers: Steve Clapp (inc one for Pagham).
Local Press: Portsmouth News, Chichester Observer.
Hons: Sussex Co. Lg Div 3 R-up 84-85 (Div 3 Cup 84-85 (R-up 92-93), Reserve Sect. West R-up 92-93), Sussex Jnr Cup 55-56, West Sussex Lg 77-78 (Div 2 56-57), Chichester & Dist. Jnr Lg 06-07, Chichester & Bognor Lg 11-12 12-13 (Lg Cup 11-12), Chichester & Dist. Lg 53-54 55-56, Chichester Charity Cup 55-56.

BUXTED

President: C S Winter   **Chairman:** K Isted   **Manager:** P Neal
Secretary: P J Durrant, 'Haven', Station Rd, Isfield, East Sussex TN22 5XB (0825 750449).
Ground: Buxted Recreation Ground (0825 812431).
Directions: A272 to Buxted, first right into Framfield Rd opposite Buxted Inn, ground 500 yds on right.
Seats: None   **Cover:** No   **Floodlights:** No   **Founded:** 1918   **Nickname:** The Bux.
Colours: Red/black/black & red   **Change colours:** Blue & white stripes/blue/blue
Programme: Yes   **Editor:** K Isted (0825 763593)   **Sponsors:** T.B.A.
Previous Leagues: Brighton Hove & District/ Mid Sussex.   **Admission:** None
Clubhouse: Pavillion with social area and bar, Tea bar.
Local Newspapers: The Courier, Sussex Express
Previous Grounds: None   **92-93 Top Scorers:** Tim Pierce 9.

EAST PRESTON

President: Greg Stanley   **Chairman:** D Cooper   **Mgr:** R Finneran.
Secretary: K Freeman, 41 Ambersham Cres., East Preston, West Sussex BN16 1AJ (0903 771158).
Ground: Roundstone Rrecreation Ground, East Preston, West Sussex (0903 776026).
Directions: 1 mile from Angmering (BR). A259 from Worthing to Roundstone Hotel (6 miles), turn south over level crossing, 1st right is Roundstone Drive.
Seats: None   **Cover:** Yes   **Capacity:**   **Floodlights:** No   **Reformed:** 1966
Colours: White/black/black   **Change:** Green/sky/yellow   **Nickname:** None
Programme: Early & late season   **Sponsors:** Focus.
Previous Lges: Worthing/ W Sussex .   **92-93 Top Scorer:** Mark Loten 11.
Clubhouse details: 4 dressing rooms, licensed bar, kitchen   **Metal Badges:** No
Local Press: Littlehampton Gazette.
Hons: Sussex Co. Lg Div 3 83-84 (Div 3 R-up 90-91, Div 3 Cup 87-88), West Sussex Lg 77-78 80-81 81-82 82-83 (Malcolm Simmonds Cup 80-81 82-83), Vernon Wentworth Cup 80-81.

EDWARDS SPORTS

Chairman: M Weever   **Manager:** C Lenson.
Secretary: Mr McQueenie, 119 Trefoil Cres., Crawley RH11 9EY (0293 549666).
Ground: Edwards Sports Ground, Ifield, Crawley.
Directions: Follow signs to Ifield off A23, over mini-r'bout to Ifield Ave., 3rd left into Ifield Green.
Seats: None   **Cover:** Yes   **Prev. Lge:** Crawley & Dist. (pre-1993)   **Floodlights:** No
Colours: Red & black/black/black   **Hons:** Crawley & District Lg 92-93.

Forest F.C. 1992-93. Photo - Colin Stevens.

FOREST

Chairman: Michael Robinson   **Manager/Press Off.:** Graham Powell (0403 273169)
Secretary: Mrs Sandra Robinson, 51 Cook Road, Horsham RH12 5GJ (0403 62513).
Ground: Roffey Sports Social Club, Spooners Road, Roffey, Horsham, West Sussex (0403 210223).
Directions: Spooners Road is off the main Crawley Road, approx 100yds from the Star Public House heading towards Crawley.
Seats: No   **Cover:** 250   **Capacity:** 1,000   **Floodlights:** No   **Founded:** 1958
Colours: Blue & white   **Change colours:** Yellow & green   **Metal Badges:** No.
Programme: Yes   **Programme Editor:** Graham Powell (0403 273169)
Previous Leagues: Crawley/ Southern Co's Comb./Mid Sussex **Midweek Matchday:**
Local Newspapers: West Sussex County Times.   **Previous Ground:** Forest Boys School.
Sponsors: Roffey Sports & Social Club   **Record Gate:** Unknown.   **Nickname:** None
Clubhouse: 2 large bars, 3 snooker tables, bar billiards, dart, board room, tea bar.
92-93 Top Scorers: Colin Johnson 13, Michael Fairs 11 (including 5 for Horsham Y.M.C.A.).
Hons: Mid Sussex Snr Charity Cup 76-77 84-85 85-86 86-87 89-90, Sussex I'mediate Cup 87-88.

FRANKLANDS VILLAGE

President: J Rutherford   **Chairman:** P Gaston
Secretary: Mr N J Worsfold, Flat 3, 5 Sydney Rd, Haywards Heath, West Sussex RH16 1QQ (0444 415331).
Manager: P Batchelor   **Press Officer:** Mr R Collins.
Ground: Hardy Memorial Playing Fields, Franklands Village, Haywards Heath, West Sussex (0444 440138).
Directions: A272 Haywards Heath to Uckfield Road turn left at Birch Service Station which leads down to the village.
Seats: No   **Cover:** 400 sq ft.   **Capacity:** N/A   **Floodlights:** No   **Founded:** 1956
Colours: All royal blue   **Change colours:** Gold & black   **Nickname:** None.
Programme: Yes   **Editor:** Mrs L Worsfold (0444 416475)   **Midweek Midweek:** Wednesday
Previous Leagues: Mid Sussex/ Crawley/ Brighton Hove & District/ Southern Counties Combination.
Clubhouse details: Franklands Village Social Club. Bar, function room, pool, snooker room, games room, committe room, darts, television, tea bar.
Local Newspapers: Mid Sussex Times.
Previous Grounds: None   **Record Gate:** 500   **Admission:** N/A   **Metal Badges:** No
Sponsors: Abacus.   **92-93 Top Scorer:** Mark Read 8.
Hons: Brighton Lg 76-77 78-79, Sussex Co. Lg Div 3 R-up (Div 3 Cup 88-89 92-93), Southern Counties Combination 82-83, Mid Sussex Charity Cup 79-80 80-81 82-83 88-89, Sussex Intermediate Cup 88-89.

HAYWARDS HEATH TOWN

Manager: Grant Paskins   **President:** Tony Lander   **Chairman:** R Hatt.
Secretary: Stan Barnes, 'Fairfields', London Rd, Hassocks, West Sussex BN6 9NE (0444 235192).
Ground: Hanbury Park Stadium, Allen Road, Haywards Heath, West Sussex (0444 412837).
Directions: A272 to Haywards Heath town centre. At Sussex r'bout, north on B2078 (Hazelgrove Road), first right into New England Road, 4th right into Allen Road which leads to ground. 1 mile from Haywards Heath (BR).
Seats: 490   **Cover:** 490   **Capacity:** 5,000   **Floodlights:** Yes   **Founded:** 1888
Colours: White (blue trim)/blue/blue   **Change colours:** All yellow   **Nickname:** Bluebells
Programme: Yes   **Editor:** Pat Bucknell (0444 457726)   **Admission:** £1.50   **Sponsors:**
Previous Leagues: Mid Sussex/ Metropolitan 52-61.   **Metal Badges:** No.
Previous Grounds: Muster Green/ Haywards Heath Recreation Ground/ Victoria Park.
Previous Names: Haywards Heath Junior/ Haywards Heath Excelsoir/ Haywards Heath FC 1895-1988.
Record Gate: 4,000 v Horsham, Metropolitan League, 1952.
Local Newspaper: Mid Sussex Times   **Clubhouse:** Bar, small dance floor, pool.
92-93 Top Scorer: Graham Hatt 11.
Hons: Sussex Snr Cup 57-58, Sussex RUR Charity Cup 66-67 74-75 75-76, Sussex Co. Lg 45-46 49-50 50-51 69-70 (R-up 74-75, Lg Cup 72-73), Mid Sussex Lg 11-12 19-20 22-23 23-24 24-25, Montgomery Cup 19-20 22-23 24-25.

HURSTPIERPOINT

President: **Chairman:** W Marchant   **Manager:** Steve Chambers
Secretary/Press Officer: Paul Joun, 16 Church Close, Burgess Hill, West Sussex RH15 8EZ (0444 247183).
Ground: The Pavilion, Fairfield Recreation Ground, Cuckfield Rd, Hurstpierpoint, Sussex (0273 834785).
Directions: At Hurst crossroads (mini r'bout) proceed north into Cuckfield Rd (B2117) for 1km. Entrance to ground between houses Nos 158 & 160.
Seats: None   **Cover:** No   **Floodlights:** No   **Nickname:** The Point **Founded:** 1886
Colours: Blue & black stripes/blue/blue   **Change:** Yellow/green/yellow.
Programme: Yes   **Editor:** Matthew Bosher (0273 835290)   **Midweek Matchday:** Tuesday
Previous Leagues: Mid Sussex/ Brighton Hove & District/ Southern Counties Combination.
Clubhouse: Facilities for refreshments including licenced premises and tea bar.
Local Newspapers: Mid Sussex Times, West Sussex County Times   **Metal Badges:** No
92-93 Top Scorer: Mark Stafford 13, Daniel Bryan 11.   **Sponsors:** Picket & White.

IFIELD

President: D Whinder   **Chairman:** B Crossley   **Manager:** T.B.A.
Secretary: R S Anderson, 15 Sissington Close, Pound Hill, Crawley (0293 886215).
Ground: Ifield Green, Rusper Rd, Ifield, Crawley (0293 536569).
Directions: From Ifield BR station follow Ifield Drive, 2nd left into Rudgwick Rd, turn right, ground 600 yds on left.
Seats: None   **Cover:** No   **Nickname:** None   **Floodlights:** No   **Founded:**
Cols: Red & white stripes/black/black   **Change colours:** Blue & white stripes   **Metal Badges:** No
Programme: Yes   **Editor:** Geoff Thornton (0293 531911)   **Midweek Matchday:** Wednesday
Previous Leagues: Mid Sussex 73-74/ Crawley & Dist.
Clubhouse: Located within football and sports field. Two changing rooms & showers, referee's changing room & shower, bar, kitchen.
Local Press: Crawley News, Crawley Observer   **Sponsors:** Jardine DFS Air Cargo.
92-93 Top Scorer: Des Lyons 14.
Hons: Mid Sussex Snr 73-74, Crawley Premier Lg 73-74, Crawley Snr Cup 83-84.

LINDFIELD RANGERS

Manager: Mr Dave Richardson **Chairman:** Squadron Ldr B F Ryan **President:** N Fisk
Secretary: Mr P Fisk, Dormer Cottage, 64 Oathall Rd, Haywards Heath (0444 412112).
Press Officer: R Tilford (0825 763737). **Ground:** Underhill Lane, Clayton, East Sussex.
Directions: A23 from Brighton to Pycombe Garage, right onto Burgess Hill Rd, at bottom of Pycombe Hill turn right into ground.
Seats: None **Cover:** No **Nickname:** None **Floodlights:** No **Founded:** 1983.
Colours: Red/white/red **Change colours:** Blue & white hoops **Metal Badges:** No
Programme: **Midweek Matchday:** **Sponsors:** Trident Copiers.
Previous Leagues: Crawley & District/ Mid Sussex (pre-1991).
Previous Ground: Hickmans Lane, Lindfield. **Clubhouse:** Tea bar.
92-93 Top Scorers: Paul Mann 5. **Hons:** Mid Sussex Lg 90-91

LINGFIELD

Chairman: M Thomsett **Manager:** D Moore.
Secretary: A Munns, 109 Saxbys Lane, Lingfield, Sussex RH7 6DP (0343 833735).
Ground: Godstone Rd, Lingfield (0342 834269). **Hons:** Mid-Sussex Lg 92-93.
Seats: None **Cover:** Yes **Clubhouse:** Yes **Capacity:** 1,000 **Floodlights:** No
Colours: Scarlet & amber stripes/black/yellow **Prev. Lges:** Sussex County/ Mid-Sussex

ST FRANCIS HOSPITAL

Chairman: Phil Gaffney **Manager:** Glen Morgen.
Secretary: Mr E Toner, 3 Catkin Way, Haywards Heath RH16 5TU (0444 457798).
Ground: Colwell Lane, Haywards Heath.
Seats: None **Cover:** None **Capacity:** 300 **Floodlights:** No **Founded:** 1890.
Colours: Green & white/white/white **Change:** Blue & yellow stripes **Nickname:** Saints
Previous Grounds: None **Local Newspaper:** Mid Sussex Times. **Metal badges:** No
Programme: Yes **Editor:** Glen Morgen (0444 454016) **Admission:** None
Sponsors: D Gander Builders **Previous League:** Mid Sussex (pre-1992). **Record Gate:** 250
Clubhouse: St Francis Hospital Clubhouse. Bar, changing rooms, tea bar, boardroom.
Hons: Sussex Intermediate Cup R-up.

SEAFORD TOWN

President: J V Tanner **Chairman:** Fred Gillman **Mgr:** Dave Shearing.
Secretary: Mick Webster, 113 Lexden Drive, Seaford, East Sussex BN25 3JF (0323 899218).
Ground: Crouch Gardens, East Street, Seaford, East Sussex (0323 892221).
Directions: Enter Seaford on A259 and turn into Warwick Road (opposite Library), continue into East Street. Ground along Crouch Lane (by phone box). Third of a mile from Seaford (BR).
Seats: 50 **Cover:** 50 **Capacity:** 1,000 **Floodlights:** No **Founded:** 1889
Colours: All red **Change colours:** All blue **Metal Badges:** No **Nickname:** Town
Programme: Yes **Editor:** Secretary **Sponsors:** T.B.A. **Previous Name or Grounds:** None.
Previous Leagues: S'sex 01-02/ Mid S'sex 02-52/ S'sex Co. 52-78/ Southern Co's Comb./ Brighton Hove & Dist.
Midweek Matches: Tuesday **Record Gate:** 800 v Brighton & H.A. 16/8/89.
Clubhouse: Tea Bar, Licensed bar. Pool, darts **Admission:** £1
Local Newspapers: Seaford Gazette, Sussex Express.
92-93 Top Scorers: Sherriff Anjourin 10.
Hons: Sussex Co. Lg Invitation Cup 58-59 (Div 2 88-89 (R-up 63-64), Div 3 85-86, Div 3 Cup 85-86), Sussex Jnr Cup 09-10, Brighton Lg Div 1 80-81, Sussex RUR Charity Cup R-up 73-74, Montgomery Cup 35-36 38-39.

SHINEWATER ASSOCIATION

President: A Rose **Chairman:** S Courtney **Manager:** A Walsh/ K Rogers.
Secretary: B Dowling, 79 Harebeating Drive, Hailsham, East Sussex BN27 1JE (0323 442488).
Press Officer: A Holman/ A Walsh. **Ground:** Shinewater Lane, Langney, Eastbourne, East Sussex.
Seats: None **Cover:** None **N'name:** The Shine **Capacity:** 2,000 **Floodlights:** No
Colours: Sky/navy/navy **Change colours:** All yellow **Admission:** None
Programme Editor: Secretary **Previous Leagues:** East Sussex.
Sponsors: British Gas **Midweek Matchday:** TBA **Metal Badges:** No
Previous Grounds: None **Local Press:** Eastbourne Herald, Eastbourne Gazette.
Record Gate: 98 **Clubhouse:** Brick building housing bar andtea bar.
Top Scorer 92-93: Gary Callingham 11 **Hons:** East Sussex Lg 91-92, Eastbourne Chal. Cup 91-92.

SIDLESHAM

Manager: P Cleverley **President:** Cyril Cooper **Chairman:** Roy Parker
Secretary: Mr Peter Turner, 14 Ashurst Close, North Bersted, Bognor Regis PO21 5UJ (0243 867970).
Ground: The Recreation Ground, Sidlesham, West Sussex (0243 641538).
Directions: Signposted Hunston/Selsey (B2145) - from r'bout travel south towards Selsey for four miles; ground on right between houses.
Seats: None **Cover:** 100 **Nickname:** None **Floodlights:** Yes **Reformed:** 1946.
Colours: Yellow & green stripes/black/black **Change colours:** All- blue
Programme: Yes **Editor:** Mr Patrick Phillips (0243 603028)
Previous Grounds: None. **Midweek Matchday:** Wednesday
Local Press: Chichester Observer **Previous Leagues:** West Sussex (pre-1991).
Clubhouse: Large bar, separate function room, snooker room, board room, tea bar (food).
Metal Badges: No **Sponsors:** T.B.A. **Record Gate:** 120 **92-93 Top Scorer:** Joe Laidlaw 11.
Hons: Sussex Co. Lg Div 3 Cup 91-92, West Sussex Lg Malcolm Simmonds Cup 78-79 90-91, Sussex I'mediate Cup 90-91.

SUNALLON

Manager: M Roberts **Chairman:** B Goring.
Secretary: D Roberts, 6 Foxley Chase, Horsham, West Sussex RH12 4AX (0403 260033).
Ground: Meadowlands, North Heath Lane, Horsham, West Sussex (0403 253814).
Directions: Into Horsham on Warnham Rd, left at lights, over mini-r'bout into North Heath Lane, ground on left.
Seats: None **Cover:** None **Floodlights:** No **Colours:** Yellow/blue/blue
Previous Leagues: West Sussex (pre-1993)**Hons:** West Sussex Lg 92-93.

UNIJET SUSSEX COUNTY LEAGUE RESERVE & YOUTH SECTIONS

Reserve Prem.	P	W	D	L	F	A	PTS
Burgess Hill Town	30	19	6	5	55	26	63
Peacehaven & T.*	30	19	5	6	66	27	62
Portfield *	30	17	9	4	79	36	60
Horsham YMCA	30	16	7	7	52	33	55
Pagham	30	15	7	8	56	42	52
Peacehaven Res	30	20	8	2	82	29	68
Hassocks Res	30	18	7	5	75	39	61
Portfield Res	30	18	4	8	68	29	58
Langney S. Res	30	17	2	11	57	31	53
Burgess H. Res	30	15	7	8	56	40	52
Worthing Res	30	14	4	2	69	54	46
Ringmer Res	30	11	8	11	55	50	41
Pagham Res	30	11	7	12	49	52	40
Bognor R.T. Res	30	12	3	15	69	66	39
Wick Res	30	12	3	15	56	71	*39
Horsham YM Res	30	10	8	12	38	56	38
Lit'hampton Res	30	10	5	15	42	55	35
Arundel Res	30	8	5	17	31	80	29
Lewes Res	30	8	5	17	42	90	29
Oakwood Res	30	7	5	18	33	63 *+26	
E'bourne T. Res	30	7	3	20	53	70	+24

Reserve East.	P	W	D	L	F	A	PTS
Stamco Res	26	17	9	0	72	21	*60
Newhaven Res	26	17	6	3	71	26	57
E Grinstead Res	26	15	6	5	48	26	51
Whitehawk Res	26	13	6	7	58	x35	45
Frank. Vill. Res	26	12	6	8	49	51	42
Hailsham T. Res	26	11	4	11	58	52	37
Sidley Utd Res	26	8	7	11	45	44	31
Crwoborough Res	26	8	6	12	40	54	30
Haywards H. Res	26	9	3	14	&33	52 *+30	
Saltdean U. Res	26	8	5	13	45	66	29
E'bourne U. Res	26	8	2	16	32	63+ +26	
Seaford T. Res	26	7	3	16	47	68	24
Little Cmn Res	26	5	9	12	27	50	24
Bexhill T. Res	26	6	4	16	46	63	22

Reserve West	P	W	D	L	F	A	PTS
Worthing U. Res	26	18	4	4	70	36	58
Bosham Res	26	17	5	4	67	32	56
Lancing Res	26	15	6	5	70	35	51
Steyning T. Res	26	14	5	7	51	37	47
Mile Oak Res	26	13	6	7	59	52	45
E Preston Res	26	12	7	7	43	42	*43
Broadbridge H. Res	26	12	3	11	51	48	39
Southwick Res	26	9	7	10	45	38	34
Chichester Res	26	9	4	13	59	58	31
Selsey Res	26	8	7	11	39	38	31
Midhurst & E. Res	26	8	6	12	34	45	30
Shoreham Res	26	5	6	15	46	56	21
Storrington Res	26	3	6	17	29	88	15
Ferring	26	2	2	22	29	87	+8

* - Match awarded - unfulfilled fixture
+ - Match not played - points to opponents
& - 2 goals deducted from total scored because of
ineligible player.
x - 2 goals added to total scored, as above.

Youth East	P	W	D	L	F	A	PTS
Peacehaven Yth	24	21	3	0	116	14	66
Lewes Yth	24	20	3	1	71	14	63
Shinewater Yth	24	14	5	5	69	26	47
Bexhill T. Yth	24	14	2	8	61	43	44
Little Cmn Yth	24	13	2	9	66	35	41
Langney S. Yth	24	11	2	11	62	50	35
Whitehawk Yth	24	9	4	11	40	56	31
Hailsham T. Yth	24	8	5	11	46	71	29
Ringmer Yth	24	8	4	12	57	72	28
Buxted Yth	24	7	4	13	57	78	25
Newhaven Yth	24	4	2	18	25	75	14
Saltdean U. Yth	24	3	4	17	27	101	13
E'bourne T. Yth	24	2	4	18	15	77	10

Youth West	P	W	D	L	F	A	PTS
Burgess Hill Yth	26	19	6	1	85	25	63
Worthing Utd Yth	26	18	5	3	91	39	59
Worthing Yth	26	17	5	4	88	37	56
Lindfield Rgrs Yth	26	16	3	7	76	49	51
Steyning T. Yth	26	16	3	7	54	37	51
Lit'hampton Yth	26	14	3	9	71	44	45
Midhurst & E. Yth	26	12	2	12	77	42	38
Chichester Yth	26	11	3	12	59	61	36
Forest Yth	26	10	3	13	64	81	34
Shoreham Yth	26	10	4	12	42	56	34
Wick Yth	26	9	3	14	86	87	30
Storrington Yth	26	7	1	18	59	91	22
Hassocks Yth	26	1	1	24	24	132	4
Selsey Yth	26	1	0	25	18	113	3

YOUTH SECTION PLAY-OFF (at Arundel)
Peacehaven & Tel. v Burgess Hill Town	2-0

YOUTH SECTION CUP FINAL (at Whitehawk)
Peacehaven & Tel. v Burgess Hill Towm	1-0

RESERVE SECTION CUP 1992-93

First Round (19-9-92 unless stated)
Crowborough Athletic v Wick	2-3
East Preston v Sidley United	3-2(aet)
Ferring v Eastbourne Town	0-5
Franklands Village v Lewes (10/10/92)	0-2
Hailsham Town v Southwick	3-1
Haywards Heath Town v Littlehampton Town	1-6
Mile Oak v Langney Sports	1-3
Ringmer v Steyning Town	1-0
Seaford Town v Bognor Regis (17/10/92)	1-6
Selsey v Hassocks	0-3
Storrington v Bexhill Town	2-1

Second Round (17-10-92 unless stated)
Burgess Hill Town v Little Common (6/2/93)	5-1
East Grinstead v Hassocks (3/2/93)	4-0
East Preston v Peacehaven & Tel. (5/12/92)	3-2
Eastbourne U. v Arundel (7/11/92)	0-3
Hailsham Town v Ringmer	6-4(aet)
Horsham Y.M.C.A. v Stamco	1-4
Langney Sports v Whitehawk	1-2
Lewes v Chichester City (12/12/92)	4-2
Littlehampton v Broadbridge Hth (9/1/93)	2-3
Midhurst & Easebourne v Worthing (5/12/92)	1-4
Pagham v Lancing (12/12/92)	4-1
Portfield v Newhaven (9/1/93)	3-1
Shoreham v Oakwood (14/11/92)	4-3(aet)
Storrington v Eastbourne Town	1-4
Wick v Bosham (rep: 19/12/92)	1-1(aet),0-2
Worthing Utd v Bognor Regis (12/12/92)	2-4

Third Round (13-2-93 unless stated)
Bosham v Worthing (23/1/93)	2-6
Broadbridge Heath v Burgess Hill Town	0-1
East Preston v Bognor Rgis (16/1/93)	2-1
Lewes v Stamco	2-1
Pagham v East Grinstead	3-3
Portfield v Hailsham (23/1 & 6/2/93)	3-3(aet),2-1
Shoreham v Arundel (5/12/92)	1-3
Whitehawk v Eastbourne Town	3-0

Quarter-Fin. (20-2-93 unless stated)
Burgess Hill v Arundel (27/2/93)	2-1(aet)
East Grinstead v Lewes	2-1
Portfield v Whitehawk	6-0
Worthing v East Preston	4-0

Semi Finals (18-3-93 unless stated)
Burgess Hill v E Grinstead (at Ringmer)	2-0
Portfield v Worthing (at Wick 25/3/93)	1-2

Final (Thurs 22nd April at Horsham Y.M.C.A.)
Burgess Hill T. Reserves v Worthing Reserves 3-2
(Man of the Match: Nigel Nash, Burgess Hill Town)

RESERVE SECTION PREMIER DIVISION RESULTS 1992-93

HOME TEAM	1	2	3	4	5	6	7	8	9	10	11	12	13	14	15	16
1. Arundel Reserves	*	3-1	0-0	1-1	0-3	0-4	3-1	3-2	2-1	1-1	1-1	0-4	1-3	0-3	1-3	0-4
2. Bognor Regis Town Res.	6-0	*	1-1	6-2	1-3	2-1	3-2	2-2	7-2	8-2	1-0	3-5	1-0	1-2	3-4	1-4
3. Burgess Hill Town Res.	1-1	1-0	*	2-0	3-3	0-1	1-0	5-1	3-0	2-1	1-1	1-1	2-1	2-0	0-1	2-1
4. Eastbourne Town Reserves	4-0	2-3	0-4	*	3-1	3-1	0-4	7-1	2-2	2-4	1-2	3-3	1-3	2-4	1-4	2-3
5. Hassocks Reserves	7-0	3-0	4-1	4-1	*	2-0	1-0	5-0	1-0	1-1	3-2	4-2	0-1	3-1	2-2	4-3
6. Horsham Y.M.C.A. Res.	0-2	1-0	1-5	1-2	0-6	*	0-0	2-0	3-1	2-2	1-1	3-2	0-1	1-3	2-1	2-2
7. Langney Sports Reserves	6-0	3-1	0-2	2-0	2-3	1-2	*	2-1	3-1	1-0	0-0	1-2	1-0	1-0	4-1	4-1
8. Lewes Reserves	1-0	3-1	3-1	3-2	3-2	0-1	0-5	*	2-4	3-1	4-1	2-3	0-0	0-4	0-7	4-2
9. Littlehampton Town Res.	0-5	1-2	3-2	1-0	0-0	2-2	0-1	6-1	*	4-0	0-0	0-2	2-1	0-0	4-1	0-3
10. Oakwood Reserves	0-1	3-1	1-3	W-L	1-4	0-0	3-1	2-0	2-3	*	1-1	1-4	1-2	2-0	2-0	1-2
11. Pagham Reserves	1-2	3-3	1-4	2-1	4-1	4-2	1-3	3-0	0-1	6-0	*	0-2	0-3	0-4	3-2	2-1
12. Peacehaven & T. Reserves	7-0	2-1	1-1	2-0	5-0	1-1	3-0	2-2	3-1	3-0	3-0	*	2-0	1-1	6-0	2-1
13. Portfield Reserves	3-0	5-1	5-1	1-0	0-0	4-1	1-0	12-2	2-0	4-1	1-2	1-1	*	2-2	2-1	6-1
14. Ringmer Reserves	4-1	2-3	1-3	2-6	0-2	0-0	1-2	1-1	3-0	3-0	1-4	1-1	2-1	*	4-4	2-4
15. Wick Reserves	6-2	1-5	2-1	0-3	1-1	2-3	0-6	3-0	1-0	W-L	1-3	1-6	1-2	1-2	*	2-1
16. Worthing Reserves	2-1	3-1	5-1	4-2	2-2	7-0	0-1	1-1	1-3	1-0	4-1	0-1	2-1	2-2	2-3	*

RESERVE SECTION EAST RESULTS

HOME TEAM	1	2	3	4	5	6	7	8	9	10	11	12	13	14
1. Bexhill Town Reserves	*	2-3	2-3	1-2	1-1	3-5	0-1	5-0	0-5	2-1	3-2	1-3	2-5	1-3
2. Crowborough Athletic Res.	1-2	*	1-3	1-2	1-1	1-0	4-0	0-0	0-3	6-0	3-2	0-3	0-3	1-1
3. East Grinstead Reserves	3-2	4-2	*	6-1	0-1	2-0	2-0	0-0	2-1	1-1	3-1	W-L	0-0	6-0
4. Eastbourne United Res.	1-1	1-2	0-2	*	1-5	2-1	1-1	1-0	2-5	1-3	4-0	1-0	1-3	0-5
5. Franklands Village Res.	3-1	3-3	0-0	3-2	*	3-2	0-3	3-1	0-2	4-0	6-4	0-1	2-2	1-0
6. Hailsham Town Reserves	1-5	5-1	6-3	1-2	4-0	*	0-3	2-2	2-1	4-1	2-1	1-1	2-2	4-2
7. Haywards Hth Town Res.	2-1	1-2	2-2	W-L	2-3	3-1	*	1-3	2-7	3-0	0-4	2-0	0-3	0-6
8. Little Common Albion Res.	3-2	1-1	0-2	3-0	2-2	0-3	1-5	*	0-2	1-1	0-0	1-1	1-1	0-3
9. Newhaven Reserves	2-0	3-1	1-0	W-L	4-0	4-1	0-0	3-0	*	5-1	7-1	2-2	2-2	2-2
10. Saltdean United Reserves	2-1	5-1	2-1	5-2	1-2	1-3	4-0	4-1	3-1	*	1-5	2-4	1-1	2-4
11. Seaford Town Reserves	3-3	0-2	0-1	1-0	2-4	1-3	3-1	3-2	1-3	2-2	*	5-4	1-3	1-2
12. Sidley United Reserves	0-3	2-2	1-3	3-4	4-1	4-4	3-0	0-2	1-1	2-0	5-3	*	0-2	1-3
13. Stamco Reserves	7-1	3-1	3-0	7-0	6-0	2-0	W-L	4-1	2-2	1-1	4-0	1-0	*	3-1
14. Whitehawk Reserves	1-1	4-0	0-0	3-0	2-1	2-1	2-1	1-2	1-3	8-1	0-1	0-0	2-2	*

RESERVE SECTION WEST RESULTS

HOME TEAM	1	2	3	4	5	6	7	8	9	10	11	12	13	14
1. Bosham Reserves	*	0-0	2-2	2-2	9-1	4-3	1-0	0-1	3-1	1-1	2-0	3-2	9-1	5-1
2. Broadbridge Hth Reserves	3-5	*	2-1	1-2	5-0	1-4	0-1	3-1	1-1	2-1	3-1	0-1	3-1	2-4
3. Chichester City Reserves	0-1	0-3	*	0-0	9-1	3-3	3-2	3-4	1-5	1-4	1-3	2-3	5-1	2-3
4. East Preston Reserves	1-0	1-5	1-3	*	3-1	2-3	1-0	1-0	2-1	2-1	2-0	1-3	2-2	1-1
5. Ferring Reserves	2-3	1-3	0-5	L-W	*	2-4	1-0	1-3	0-3	1-4	1-4	0-1	4-1	0-2
6. Lancing Reserves	3-2	3-1	2-2	3-2	4-0	*	1-0	1-2	0-1	1-1	3-3	3-4	10-0	1-1
7. Midhurst & Ease. Res.	0-3	1-0	4-1	3-3	4-3	0-3	*	0-0	2-2	1-4	2-1	4-3	1-0	1-3
8. Mile Oak Reserves	2-1	4-2	1-3	2-0	5-3	0-3	2-1	*	2-3	7-5	5-1	1-3	4-2	2-2
9. Selsey Reserves	0-1	1-3	1-4	2-0	2-2	0-0	0-0	1-2	*	2-2	0-1	0-0	4-0	1-2
10. Shoreham Reserves	1-2	0-1	1-3	2-2	5-1	0-3	0-2	1-1	2-3	*	2-2	1-2	1-2	1-6
11. Southwick Reserves	1-2	8-1	4-2	0-2	1-0	0-2	1-1	1-1	1-2	4-1	*	0-1	4-0	2-0
12. Steyning Town Reserves	1-2	1-2	2-1	1-2	3-1	2-3	1-1	2-2	2-0	3-1	0-0	*	4-0	4-0
13. Storrington Reserves	2-2	2-2	0-1	1-5	2-2	1-4	4-1	2-3	3-2	0-4	1-1	1-1	*	0-7
14. Worthing United Reserves	1-2	3-2	5-1	5-1	2-1	1-0	4-2	5-2	2-1	1-0	1-1	6-1	2-0	*

Eastbourne United's Jimmy Chater (right) brings the ball away from Marc Agostinelli of Selsey. United lost 1-2 at home in this Division Two fixture, one of their first after their return to the County League. Photo - Gavin Ellis-Neville.

UNIJET WEST SUSSEX LEAGUE

PREM. DIVISION	P	W	D	L	F	A	PTS
Sunallon	24	18	3	3	78	30	39
Lancing & Sompting	24	16	4	4	50	26	36
South Bersted	24	15	5	4	61	24	35
North Holmwood	24	17	1	6	62	31	35
London & E Sports	24	13	3	8	83	53	29
Steyning Old Gr.	24	10	5	9	52	45	25
Cowfold	24	10	2	12	40	55	22
S.B. Sports	24	8	4	12	50	50	20
Barns Green	24	7	3	14	37	51	17
West Chiltington	24	4	8	12	22	53	16
Rustington	24	5	5	14	34	53	15
Henfield	24	6	3	15	38	72	15
Old Collyerians	24	2	4	18	35	99	8

DIVISION ONE	P	W	D	L	F	A	PTS
Swan	24	19	5	0	90	22	43
Roffey	24	17	3	4	80	30	37
Oving Social C.	24	16	2	6	62	41	34
Stedham United	24	13	3	8	58	41	29
Milland	24	11	3	10	44	46	25
Horsham Olympic	24	9	4	11	61	63	22
Ifield Res.	24	9	4	11	42	57	22
Emsworth	24	10	2	12	40	56	22
Warnham	24	9	3	12	32	41	21
Lurgashall	24	8	4	12	46	56	20
Lavant	24	7	5	12	43	71	19
Worthing B.C.O.B.	24	5	3	16	48	58	13
Eastergate Utd	24	1	3	20	27	91	5

DIV. 2 SOUTH	P	W	D	L	F	A	PTS
Wittering Utd	24	18	2	4	76	35	38
Chichester Hos.	24	17	4	3	67	38	38
South Bersted Res.	24	15	2	7	57	33	32
Petworth	24	9	10	5	64	45	28
Maple Leaf Rgrs	24	11	6	7	59	54	28
Bracklesham	24	11	3	10	45	40	25
Rogate	24	9	5	10	39	31	23
Sidlesham Res.	24	7	6	11	49	53	20
Angmering	24	6	8	10	41	62	20
Lancing & S. Res.	24	6	6	12	40	48	18
Pulborough	24	7	3	14	37	61	17
Fernhurst Spts	24	6	3	15	42	65	15
Amberley	24	3	4	17	21	72	10

DIV. 2 NORTH	P	W	D	L	F	A	PTS
Billingshurst	22	13	5	4	48	27	31
Shipley	22	13	4	5	50	29	30
Alford	22	13	3	6	53	29	29
Capel	22	11	6	5	46	34	28
Partridge G.	22	10	4	8	38	42	24
N. Holmwood Res.	22	9	4	9	51	46	22
Ciba-Geigy	22	9	2	11	44	39	20
Ashington Rvrs	22	8	3	11	42	50	19
Wisborough G.	22	7	4	11	44	44	18
Steyning O.G.	22	7	4	11	34	47	18
Ockley	22	5	5	12	36	67	15
Slinford	22	2	6	14	19	51	10

DIV. 3 CENTRAL	P	W	D	L	F	A	PTS
Liss Ath. Res.	20	16	1	3	71	28	33
Northchapel S.	20	13	4	3	86	42	30
Lodsworth	20	13	1	6	54	41	27
Milland Res.	20	11	3	6	39	35	25
Fittleworth	20	12	0	8	58	34	24
Shipley Res.	20	7	4	9	41	52	18
Stedham Utd Res.	20	7	3	10	50	58	17
Barns Green Res.	20	6	4	10	45	55	16
East Dean	20	5	1	14	45	74	11
Pulborough Res.	20	4	2	14	26	68	10
Watersfield	20	4	1	15	29	57	9

DIV. 3 SOUTH	P	W	D	L	F	A	PTS
Clymping	22	14	6	2	70	24	34
Bognor Motors	22	11	9	2	51	30	31
Southbourne Spts	22	9	10	3	55	40	28
Ford United	22	10	5	7	63	53	25
Emsworth Res.	22	10	4	8	53	41	24
Oving S C Res.	22	8	6	8	39	39	22
East Preston 'A'	22	9	4	9	47	55	22
Hunston	22	7	6	9	54	47	20
Yapton	22	6	6	10	37	65	18
Bilsham Utd	22	5	6	11	34	48	16
Corinthians	22	6	2	14	40	67	14
Tavern Villa	22	4	2	16	40	74	10

DIV. 3 NORTH	P	W	D	L	F	A	PTS
Sunallon Res.	22	18	1	3	108	17	37
Horsham Baptists	22	15	4	3	64	23	34
Rudgwick	22	15	3	4	58	22	33
Roffey Res.	22	15	2	5	76	37	32
Seelec Delta	22	12	3	7	67	44	27
Forest Res.	22	9	4	9	35	32	22
East End Utd	22	8	5	9	53	49	21
Cranleigh 'A'	22	6	5	11	40	61	17
Broadbridge H. 'A'	22	6	2	14	39	61	14
Warnham Res.	22	6	2	14	34	66	14
Friends Prov.	22	4	1	17	34	98	9
Roffey Ath.	22	1	2	19	19	117	4

DIV. 4 NORTH	P	W	D	L	F	A	PTS
Sunallon 'A'	24	19	1	4	93	26	39
Horsham Trinity	24	19	1	4	86	30	39
Henfield Ath. Res.	24	14	3	7	63	47	31
Cowfold Res.	24	11	5	8	42	37	27
Partridge G. Res.	24	12	2	10	62	57	26
Horsham Oly. Res.	24	10	5	9	41	40	25
Rudgwick Res.	24	8	6	10	40	46	22
Capel Res.	24	8	3	12	73	67	21
Newdigate	24	8	5	11	46	61	21
Rusper Village	24	8	4	12	40	52	20
Bell Spartans	24	7	4	13	56	78	18
Ciba-Geigy Res.	24	5	3	16	40	104	13
O. Collyerians Res.	24	4	2	18	35	72	10

DIV. 4 CENTRAL	P	W	D	L	F	A	PTS
Harting	24	20	3	1	60	10	43
Alford Res.	24	15	4	5	67	28	34
Billingshurst 'A'	24	14	5	5	75	40	33
Lodsworth Res.	24	13	6	5	70	47	32
Graffham	24	13	3	8	78	51	29
W. Chiltington Res.	24	10	7	7	67	42	27
Plaistow & K.	24	11	1	12	55	63	23
Fittleworth Res.	24	10	1	13	61	62	22
Loxwood	24	8	1	15	54	59	17
Upper Beeding	24	6	4	14	53	92	16
Lurgashall Res.	24	4	6	14	41	76	14
Cocking	24	4	5	15	42	82	13
Petworth Res.	24	3	3	18	37	99	9

DIV. 4 SOUTH	P	W	D	L	F	A	PTS
Aldwick Athletic	20	15	2	3	80	32	32
Slindon	20	13	3	4	74	44	29
Aldingbourne	20	13	2	5	95	38	28
Broadwater Saints	20	9	5	6	46	41	23
Boxgrove	20	8	4	8	40	44	20
Angmering Res.	20	8	3	9	57	37	19
Wittering Utd Res.	20	8	3	9	33	38	19
Rustington	20	7	3	10	32	57	17
Chichester H. Res.	20	5	3	12	36	68	13
Clymping Res.	20	4	4	12	39	86	12
Lavant Res.	20	3	2	15	36	83	8

DIV. 5 SOUTH	P	W	D	L	F	A	PTS
South Bersted 'A'	22	19	2	1	103	23	40
Aldwick Ath. Res.	22	16	3	3	69	28	35
Southbourne Res.	22	12	4	6	52	34	28
G.C.R.I.	22	12	3	7	61	54	27
Ambassadors	22	10	4	8	54	56	24
Rustington 'B'	22	10	2	10	52	48	22
Aldingbourne Res.	22	8	3	11	49	48	19
Bilsham Utd Res.	22	8	2	12	61	64	18
A.W. Mundham	22	7	3	12	34	65	17
Amberley Res.	22	7	2	13	36	69	16
Yapton Res.	22	7	1	14	31	58	14
Boxgrove Res.	22	1	2	19	33	88	4

(tables continued overleaf)

DIV. 5 CENTRAL	P	W	D	L	F	A	PTS
Fernhurst S. Res.	22	16	2	4	82	39	34
Watersfield Res.	22	14	4	4	76	34	32
Ashington R. Res.	22	14	4	4	89	43	32
Northchapel S. Res.	22	12	5	5	82	62	29
Wisborough G. Res.	22	10	6	6	74	44	26
Billingshurst 'B'	22	11	4	7	70	47	26
Alford 'A'	22	8	5	9	55	54	21
Ambassadors Res.	22	8	3	11	56	61	19
Horsham Bapt. Res.	22	7	3	12	51	80	17
Plaistow & K. Res.	22	5	2	15	43	86	12
Graffham Res.	22	4	3	15	43	77	11
Petworth 'A'	22	2	1	19	22	116	5

DIV. 5 NORTH	P	W	D	L	F	A	PTS
Seelec Dalta Res.	24	21	2	1	92	29	44
East End Utd Res.	24	16	4	4	66	28	36
Roffey 'A'	24	16	2	6	75	37	34
Nth Holmwood 'A'	24	15	2	7	83	37	32
Broadbridge H. 'B'	24	14	2	8	57	37	30
Horsham Bapt. 'A'	24	12	4	8	62	44	28
Partridge G. 'A'	24	12	4	8	62	58	28
Horsham Try. Res.	24	9	4	11	54	61	22
Sunallon 'B'	24	7	5	12	50	70	19
Ockley Res.	24	7	1	16	53	78	15
Slinfold Res.	24	4		16	24	58	12
Horsham Olym. 'A'	24	5	0	19	29	80	10
Barns Green 'A'	24	0	2	22	20	110	2

CLUB DIRECTORY

A.W. MUNDHAM
Secretary: A Clarke, 54 Windsor Rd, Chichester PO19 2XL (0243 774609).
Ground: Oaklands Park, Chichester. **Colours:** White.

ALDINGBOURNE
Secretary: J L Cooke, 7 Bala Cres., Felpham, Bognor Regis PO22 8LY (0243 827857).
Grnd: Aldingbourne PF, Olivers Meadow, Westergate, Chichester (0243 542940) **Cols:** Yellow *(Res: white)*

ALDWICK ATHLETIC
Secretary: D P Bolland, 'Hanith', 60 Barrack Lane, Aldwick, Bognor Regis PO21 4DD (0243 267200).
Grnd: Avisford Park, Rose Green, Bognor Regis **Cols:** Red & white stripes *(Reserves: blue).*

ALFORD
Secretary: A Erricker, Pond Cottage, Loxwood Rd, Alford, Cranleigh, Surrey GU6 8HP (0483 752317).
Ground: Alford Spts Ground (0483 753132). **Colours:** White *(Res: red)*

AMBASSADORS
Secretary: Mrs M J Pink, 34 Kendal Close, Littlehampton, West Sussex BN17 6SZ (0903 731820).
Ground: Avisford Park, Rose Green, Bognor Regis. **Colours:** Royal blue.

AMBERLEY
Secretary: Mrs S M Joad, 63 White Horses Way, Littlehampton BN17 6NJ (0903 722232).
Ground: Storrington Rd, Amberley. **Colours:** Yellow.

ANGMERING
Secretary: G Anscombe, 5 Mill Close, Rustington, Littlehampton BN16 3HR (0903 776886).
Ground: Palmer Rd Rec., Angmering Village **Colours:** Red

ASHINGTON ROVERS
Secretary: R M Vine, 91 Stone Lane, Worthing, West Sussex BN13 2BD (0903 267047).
Ground: Church Lane Rec., Ashington. **Colours:** Blue.

BARNS GREEN
Secretary: D J Strudwick, 25 Hornbeam Close, Horsham RH13 5NP RG4 0RD (0403 66718).
Ground: Barns Green PF, Horsham (Southwater 730473) **Colours:** Yellow *(Res: red).*

BELL SPARTANS
Secretary: M Foreman, 61 Pilgrims Walk, West Worthing BN13 1RJ (0903 692900).
Ground: Horsham Park (0403 68561). **Colours:** Red & black stripes

BILLINGSHURST
Secretary: D S Glaysher, 10 Groomsland Drive, Billingshurst RH14 9HA (Billingshurst 782300).
Ground: Station Rd (Res & 'A' Lower Station Rd), Billingshurst. **Cols:** Blue & white stripes.

BILSHAM UNITED
Secretary: A K Misselbrook, Walene, Bilsham Rd, Yapton, Arundel BN18 0JN (0903 552715).
Grnd: King George V PF, Yapton (res: Southfields Rec., Littlehampton). **Cols:** Blue & white stripes.

BOGNOR MOTORS
Secretary: B P Irish, 24 Hillsboro Rd, Bognor Regis PO21 2DX (0243 822482).
Ground: Avisford Park, Rose Green, Bognor Regis **Colours:** White.

BOXGROVE
Secretary: D R Westbrook, 1 The Glebe, Tangmere, Chichester PO20 6HD (0243 775546).
Ground: Boxgrove Spts Field, The Street, Boxgrove (0243 786611). **Colours:** Yellow *(Res: navy)*

BRACKLESHAM
Secretary: T I Sadler, 19 Saxon Meadow, Tangmere, Chichester PO20 6GA (0243 784052)
Ground: Stocks Lane, East Wittering **Colours:** Green.

BROADWATER SAINTS
Secretary: B Harris, 37 Twyford Rd, Worthing BN13 2NP (0903 260274).
Ground: Broadwater Green, Ardsheal Rd, Worthing **Colours:** Green.

CAPEL
Secretary: Mrs S Burlinson, 24 Littlehaven Lane, Roffey, Horsham RH12 4JA (0403 68930).
Ground: Recreation Grnd, The Street, Capel, Dorking, Surrey **Colours:** Yellow.

CHICHESTER HOSPITALS
Secretary: J Edwards, 78 Chatsworth Rd, Chichester PO19 2YJ (0243 533269).
Ground: Sports Field, Graylingwell Hospital **Colours:** Black & white stripes *(Res: red).*

CIBA-GEIGY
Secretary: A Crisp, Computer Services, Ciba-Geigy, Wimblehurst Rd, Horsham RH12 3LD (0403 52273).
Grnd: Ciba-Geigy Spts & Social Club, Parsonage Rd, Horsham (0403 60943) **Colours:** Blue.

CLYMPING
Secretary: Mrs J Bethell, 17 Potters Mead, Wick, Littlehampton BN17 7HZ (0903 715423).
Ground: Church Lane, Clymping (0903 724877). **Colours:** Blue *(Res: red).*

COCKING
Secretary: D P Waller, 25 The Croft, Cocking, Midhurst GU29 0HQ (Midhurst 814440).
Ground: Bell Lane, Cocking.   **Colours:** Red

CORINTHIANS
Secretary: J Shacklady, 23 Wainscott Rd, Southsea, Portsmouth, Hants PO4 9NN (0705 730198).
Grnd: Bourne Comm. School, Park Rd, Southbourne   **Cols:** Amber.

COWFOLD
Secretary: Mrs D E Brockbank, 2 Oakfield Cottages, Bolney Rd, Cowfold, Horsham RH13 8AA (0403 864498).
Ground: Cowfold Rec, Bolney Rd, Cowfold.   **Colours:** Navy blue

EAST DEAN
Secretary: P A Cooper, 1 Park Farm Cottages, Racton, Chichester PO18 9DP (0903 374278).
Ground: Gasson Meadow, East Dean (Singleton 750)   **Colours:** Blue.

EAST END UNITED
Secretary: N D Painting, 113 Heath Way, Horsham RH12 5XQ (0403 55723).
Grnd: Bennetts Field PF, Horsham   **Colours:** Black & white stripes *(Res: Sky & white stripes)*.

EASTERGATE UNITED
Secretary: A Ebling, 12 Park Rd, Yapton, Arundel BN18 0JE (0903 863161).
Ground: Eastergate Rec., Eastergate, Chichester   **Colours:** Red *(Res: blue).*

ELMER BEACH
Secretary: A J Ide, Flat 2, 43 West Str., Bognor Regis PO21 1XB (0243 860868).
Ground: King George V PF, Summerley Lane, Felpham, Bognor Regis.   **Colours:** Red.

EMSWORTH
Secretary: L Wade, 2 Cumberland Ave., Emsworth, Hants PO10 7UH (Emsworth 375526).
Grnd: Horndean Rd Rec, Emsworth (Emsworth 372330).   **Cols:** Black & white stripes *(Res: red)*

FERNHURST SPORTS
Secretary: G Puttick, Raemar, Hill House Hill, Headley Rd, Liphook, Hants GU30 7PX (Liphook 723347).
Grnd: Church Rd Rec, Fernhurst (Haslemere 642302).   **Colours:** Green *(Res: red).*

FERRING
Secretary: Malcolm Gamien, 46 Sunningdale Rd, Durrington, Worthing BN12 2NE (0903 263655).
Ground: Glebelands, Greystoke Rd, Ferring (0903 53618).   **Colours:** Blue.

FITTLEWORTH
Secretary: G B Rapson, 6 Greatpin Croft, Fittleworth, Pulborough RH20 1HX (Fittleworth 470).
Ground: Fittleworth Rec (Fittleworth 781)   **Colours:** Green.

FORD UNITED
Secretary: K M Fletcher, PE Dept, HM Prison Ford, Arundel BN18 0BX.
Ground: H.M. Prison, Ford.   **Colours:** Red.

FRIENDS' PROVIDENT
Secretary: D Spence, Flat 4, Simons Ct, Station Approach, Leatherhead, Surrey KT22 7TE (0372 386165).
Ground: Pixham End, Pixham Lane Dorking (0306 889020)   **Colours:** Sky blue.

GLASSHOUSE CROPS RESEARCH INSTITUTE
Sec: T J Elliott, Horticulture Res. International, Worthing Rd, Littlehampton BN17 6LP (0903 715804)
Ground: Southfields Rec, Littlehampton.   **Colours:** Red & black stripes

GRAFFHAM
Secretary: C Cobbold, 1 Hurlands Cottages, Selham, Petworth (Lodsworth 605).
Ground: Graffham Rec.   **Colours:** Black & white stripes *(Res: white).*

HARTING
Secretary: D G Matthews, 51 Madeline Rd, Petersfield, Hants GU31 4AL (0730 60715).
Ground: War Memorial PF, South Harting   **Colours:** White (green pinstripes)

HENFIELD ATHLETIC
Secretary: R Knight, 9 Lower Faircox, Henfield BN5 9UT (Henfield 492293).
Ground: Henfield Common (Henfield 492990)   **Colours:** Red.

HORSHAM BAPTISTS
Secretary: Miss J R Nichols, 71 Clarence Rd, Horsham RH13 5SL (0403 53498).
Ground: Horsham Park (0403 68561)   **Colours:** White.

HORSHAM OLYMPIC
Secretary: W H Lipyeat, 6 Swindon Rd, Horsham RH12 2HD (0403 51274).
Ground: Dutchell's Copse, Rusper Rd, Horsham   **Colours:** Green *(Res: red).*

HORSHAM TRINITY
Secretary: B Knight, 9 Sycamore Ave., Roffey, Horsham RH12 4TP (0403 56046).
Ground: Victory Rd Rec, Horsham.   **Colours:** Green *(Res: sky).*

HUNSTON UNITED
Secretary: R Netley, 51 Leodgars Way, Hunston, Chichester PO20 2PE (0243 786073).
Ground: Main Road, Hunston, Chichester.   **Colours:** Black & white hoops

LANCING & SOMPTING ROYAL BRITISH LEGION
Secretary: R D George, 12a Freshbrook Rd, Lancing BN15 8BL (0903 761879).
Ground: Croshaw Ground, Bounstone Lane, Lancing   **Colours:** Gold.

LAVANT
Secretary: S J Massey, 57 Garland Square, Tangmere, Chichester PO20 6JF (0243 532730).
Ground: Lavant Village Green *(Res: Raughmere Park, Lavant).*   **Colours:** Yellow.

LISS ATHLETIC
Secretary: A Ridding, Imberdown, Woodlands, Liss, Hants GU33 7EZ (Liss 894007).
Ground: Newman Collard PF, Hill Brow Rd, Liss (Liss 894022).   **Colours:** Yellow.

LODSWORTH
Secretary: G Boardman, 6 Yew Tree Place, Liss, Hants GU33 7ET (Liss 893773).
Ground: Lodsworth Rec (Lodsworth 583)   **Colours:** Blue (amber trim)*(Res: Yellow (blue trim)*

LONDON & EDINBURGH SPORTS
Secretary: P Stone, Windsor Cottage, Mouse Lane, Steyning BN44 3DG (0903 879800).
Grnd: The Warren, Warren Rd, Worthing - entrance Hill Barn Lane (0903 201323)   **Cols:** Blue

LOXWOOD
Secretary: R Blackwell, 7 Forge Way, Billingshurst, RH14 9LJ (Billingshurst 783439).
Ground: Flitchfold, Plaistow Rd, Loxwood (Loxwood 753185)   **Colours:** White.

LURGASHALL
Secretary: Mrs A E Wilson, 10 Greengate Cottages, Lurgashall, Petworth GU28 9ES (Northchapel 683).
Ground: Glebe Rd, Lurgashall   **Colours:** Red.

MAPLE LEAF RANGERS
Secretary: P Cotten, 22 Cypress Ave., Worthing BN13 3PS (0903 268476).
Grnd: Worthing Leisure Centre, Shaftesbury Ave., Worthing (0903 502237)   **Colours:** White.

MILLAND
Secretary: G Bray, 12 Carterlands Corner, Milland, Liphook, Hants (Milland 203).
Grnd: Spts Grnd, North End Cross Rds, Milland, Liphook, Hants   **Cols:** Red *(Res: blue & white)*

NEWDIGATE
Secretary: A Roberts, 10 Nursery Close, Markham Park, Capel, Dorking, Surrey RH5 5JU (0306 711585).
Ground: Brows Field, Trigg Str., Newdigate, Dorking (Newdigate 566)   **Colours:** White & blue.

NORTHCHAPEL SPORTS
Secretary: D G Dabbs, 13 Valentines Lea, Northchapel, Petworth GU28 9HY (Northchapel 721).
Grnd: Northchapel Village Green   **Cols:** Wine *(Res: Sky & navy stripes).*

NORTH HOLMWOOD
Secretary: E E Adams, 24 Carterdale Cottages, Capel, Dorking, Surrey RH5 5ES (0306 712395).
Grnd: Meadowbank Rec, Mill Lane Dorking *(Res: Big Fld, Kiln Lane Brockam)*   **Cols:** Yellow *(Res: sky).*

OCKLEY
Secretary: L P Figg, Village Hall Cottage, Stane Str., Ockley, Dorking, Surrey RH5 5SY (0306 712408).
Ground: The Village Green, Stane Lane, Ockley   **Colours:** White.

OLD COLLYERIANS
Secretary: D P Bussey, 35 Goose Green Chase, Horsham RH12 5ZX (0403 69575).
Ground: Collyers VI Form Coll., Hurst Rd, Horsham   **Cols:** Blue & black stripes *(Res: red).*

OVING SOCIAL CLUB
Secretary: R G C Dorey, 19 High View Rd, Eastergate, Chichester PO20 6XB (0243 542086).
Ground: Village PF, Highfield Lane, Oving, Chichester   **Colours:** Silver *(Res: tangerine)*

PARTRIDGE GREEN
Secretary: J G Gamble, 8 Little Oak, Partridge Green, Horsham RH13 8JY (0403 710598).
Grnd: King George V PF, Partridge Gn *('A': Ashurst Rec, School Lane, Ashurst)*   **Cols:** Green & white

PETWORTH
Secretary: K A Lintill, 22 Littlecote, Petworth GU28 0EF (Petworth 42948).
Grnd: Petworth Pk, Midhurst Rd (Petworth 43743)   **Cols:** Red & black stripes *('A': White (black trim)*

PLAISTOW & KIRDFORD
Secretary: A Simmonds, Boughs, Rickmans Lane, Plaistow, Billinghurst RH14 0NT (Plaistow 344).
Ground: Floxfield, Plaistow   **Colours:** Blue *(Res: yellow).*

PULBOROUGH
Secretary: C Cox, 8 Cousins Way, Pulborough RH20 2TB (Pulborough 875127).
Ground: Rectory Lane Rec, Pulborough (Pulborough 873020)   **Colours:** Red.

ROFFEY
Secretary: V A Searle, 46 Bostock Ave., Roffey, Horsham (0403 62387).
Grnd: Roffey Rec, Leith View Rd, Horsham (0403 60775)*('A': Bennetts Rd PF, Horsham)*   **Cols:** Blue

ROFFEY ATHLETIC
Secretary: S P Reeves, 2 Rangers Lodge, Oakhill Rd, Horsham RH13 5LF (0403 53178).
Ground: Horsham Park (0403 68561)   **Colours:** White.

ROGATE
Secretary: P H Collins, 6 Terwick Rise, Rogate, Petersfield, Hants GU31 5DE (0730 821456).
Ground: North Street Rec, Rogate, Petersfield (0730 821347)   **Colours:** Maroon

RUDGWICK
Secretary: J Houston, 15 The Copse, Southwater, Horsham RH13 7UG (Southwater 732620).
Ground: King George V Playing Field, Bucks Green   **Colours:** White *(Res: claret & blue)*

RUSPER VILLAGE
Secretary: R Harlow, Elsinore, Horsham Rd, Rusper, Horsham RH12 4PR (0293 871495).
Ground: Rusper PF, High Str., Rusper   **Colours:** Blue & white stripes.

RUSTINGTON
Secretary: G F Hixon, 2 Jubilee Ave., Littlehampton BN16 3NB (0903 787436).
Grnd: Jubilee Avenue Rec, Rustington (0903 770495)   **Colours:** Blue

S.B. SPORTS
Secretary: K T Yeates, 101 Upton Rd, Worthing BN13 1BY (0903 262818).
Ground: S.B. Ground, Dominion Way, Worthing   **Colours:** Blue & white.

SEELEC DELTA
Secretary: B F Burdfield, 13 Fairfield Drive, Dorking, Surrey RH4 1JQ (0306 884260).
Ground: Seeboard Spts Grnd, London Rd, Dorking   **Colours:** Blue *(Res: yellow).*

SHIPLEY
Secretary: R Jones, 20 Beechings, Henfield, BN5 9XB (Henfield 493027).
Ground: Dragons Green, Shipley (on A272) **Colours:** Red *(Res: Yellow)*

SLINDON
Secretary: Mrs K Collier, 10 Woodgate Park, Woodgate, Chichester PO20 6QP (0243 545154).
Ground: Mill Rd Rec, Slindon. **Colours:** Blue

SLINFOLD
Secretary: A Haines, 11 Charrington Way, Broadbridge Heath, Horsham RH12 3TJ (0403 56250).
Ground: Cherry Tree Farm, Hayes Lane, Slinfold **Colours:** Red & black.

SOUTH BERSTED
Secretary: P Curran, 4 Shearwater Drive, North Bersted, Bognor Regis PO22 9QP (0243 830008).
G: Jubilee PF, Chalcraft Lane, Nth Bersted *('A': Hampshire Ave, Bognor)* **C:** Red *(Res: white, 'A': blue)*

SOUTHBOURNE SPORTS
Secretary: D Wiesner, 41 Elm Park Rd, Havant, Hants PO9 2AD (0705 475948).
Ground: Bourne Park, Park Rd, Southbourne **Colours:** Sky *(Res: green).*

STEDHAM UNITED
Secretary: G Baigent, c/o Stedham Collins & Spts Club, The Street, Stedham, Midhurst (0730 813458).
Ground: Sports Field, Stedham (0730 813458) **Colours:** Claret (Blue trim)*(Res: blue)*

STEYNING OLD GRAMMARIANS
Secretary: Mrs M J Bryant, 5 Thornscroft, Steyning BN44 3RP (0903 815824).
Ground: Steyning Grammar School, Shooting Field, Steyning **Colours:** Blue.

SWAN
Secretary: R Warner, 55 Woodlea Rd, Worthing (0903 203910).
Ground: Northbrook Park, Carisbrook Rd, Worthing **Colours:** Green, white & black.

TAVERN VILLA
Secretary: M Davies, 15 Sycamore Rd, North Bersted, Bognor Regis PO22 9LD (0243 862322).
Ground: West Meads PF, West Meads, Bognor Regis **Colours:** Blue & white stripes.

UPPER BEEDING
Secretary: R Patmore, 36 Saltings Way, Upper Beeding, Steyning BN44 3JH (0903 814560).
Ground: Memorial PF, High Str., Upper Beeding **Colours:** Yellow.

WARNHAM
Secretary: N P Taylor, 8 Vale Drive, Horsham RH12 2JX (0403 58765).
Ground: Warnham Court Sch., Church Str., Warnham **Colours:** Sky *(Res: claret & blue).*

WATERSFIELD
Secretary: N Lamb, 123 Clun Rd, Littlehampton BN17 7EP (0903 714304).
Ground: Alban Head PF, Watersfield **Colours:** Blue

WEST CHILTINGTON
Secretary: J T Jones, Quincys, Mill Rd, West Chiltington, Pulborough RH20 2PZ (0903 812371).
Ground: Mill Rd Rec, West Chiltington **Colours:** White *(Res: blue).*

WISBOROUGH GREEN
Secretary: T Fallows, Stane House, Kirdford Rd, Wisborough Green RH14 0DD (Wisborough Green 700283).
Grnd: Wisborough Green Village Green (Wisborough Green 700474) **Colours:** Green & white hoops

WITTERING UNITED
Secretary: D W Vine, 23 Mill Gardens, West Wittering, Chichester PO20 8PR (0243 672600).
Ground: Sports Field, Rookwood Rd, West Wittering **Colours:** Red.

WORTHING BOYS CLUB OLD BOYS
Secretary: Mrs S Woolgar, 21 Acacia Ave., Worthing BN13 2JB (0903 266519).
Ground: The Bowl, Pond Lane, Worthing **Colours:** Red.

YAPTON
Secretary: Mrs B Goss, 61 Hazel Rd, Bognor Regis (0243 866741).
Ground: King George V PF, Yapton, Arundel **Colours:** Red *(Res: red & blue stripes)*

WORTHING & DISTRICT LEAGUE

With no support to follow that of Ketchen King, the League had no main sponsor for 1992-93. The Premier Division lost Swan and Lancing & Sompting R.B.L. Reserves to the West Sussex League, and Becket through disbandment, but the total number of teams rose to 45 with Manor Athletic returning from the West Sussex League and new sides in A.F.C. Egremont, East Preston 'C', Lamb Durrington and Taulk-King Finance. Additionally, Manor Reserves broke away to form Radnor Rovers, and Southwick Rangers renamed themselves A.F.C. Lion.

A sequence of nine matches from January 2nd that produced seven wins and two draws earned Northbrook the Premier Division championship for the first time in their 41 years, denying early season favourites Eurotherm who also had the disappointment of semi-final defeats in both the Charity Cup and Mike Smith Trophy.

Division One winners Lyle would have been the sole unbeaten side in League games had they not lost their final fixture to runners-up Cissbury Athletic.

J.F.P. led Division Three for most of the season yet finished just one point ahead of A.F.C. Egremont, the latter having to win their final game by a four-goal margin to pip Royal Mail on goal difference which they did with an 8-3 win over B.T.R. brakes who were playing their 13th game in 29 days.

In contrast, a last-match five goal success was not forthcoming for Sussex Police in their bid to win Division Two in which Manor Athletic led for almost the entire season until securing only two points from their last four games.

Laurie Claydon

PREM. DIVISION	P	W	D	L	F	A	PTS
Northbrook	18	12	3	3	39	19	27
Eurotherm	18	11	3	4	42	21	25
Sompting	18	9	5	4	53	37	23
West Tarring WMC	18	9	3	6	54	40	21
Russell Bourne	18	6	8	4	37	30	20
St Theresa's	18	6	5	7	26	36	17
S.B. Sports Res.	18	6	3	9	43	38	15
Worthing Civic	18	5	3	10	39	50	13
The Wigmore	18	5	2	11	26	51	12
Rustington Res.	18	3	1	14	27	64	7

(lower Divisions overleaf)

583

DIVISION ONE	P	W	D	L	F	A	PTS
Lyle	20	15	4	1	63	23	34
Cissbury Athletic	20	11	7	2	53	26	29
Inland Revenue	20	10	6	4	49	32	26
Tabernacle	20	11	3	6	46	29	25
Montre United	20	10	5	5	52	38	25
AFC Lion	20	9	4	7	45	37	22
Durrington Ath.	20	8	5	7	38	34	21
Worthing United 'B'	20	7	2	11	41	39	16
East Worthing	20	3	2	15	34	63	8
Sompting Res.	20	2	4	14	26	99	8
Storrington P.	20	2	2	16	33	60	6

CUP FINALS

'Eschmanns' Charity Cup: Rustington Res 5, West Tarring W.M.C. 3 (aet)
Mike Smith Trophy: Tabernacle 2, Durrington Ath. 1
Ernie Walmesley Mem. Cup: Lyle 6, Montre Utd 0
Croshaw Cup: Sompting Res. 3, Worthing BCOB Res. 2
'A & M Trophies' Benevolent Cup: Sussex Police 4, Maple Leaf Res. 0
Div 3 KO Trophy: AFC Egremont 4, Royal Mail 2
Suttle Shield 'A' Comp.: Sompting 5, SB Spts Res. 1
Sportsmanship Cup: Tabernacle.

WALL BROS CARPETS TEAMS OF THE MONTH:
Sep: Manor Ath., **Oct:** Durrington Ath., **Nov:** E. Preston 'C', **Dec:** Sussex Police, **Jan:** Northbrook, **Feb:** Tabernacle, **Mar:** Lyle.

DIVISION TWO	P	W	D	L	F	A	PTS
Dolphin Sports	22	17	2	3	75	26	36
Manor Athletic	22	15	4	3	92	39	34
Sussex Police	22	16	2	4	80	36	34
L & S RBL 'B'	22	11	4	7	54	46	26
Ldn/Edin Spts Res	22	11	1	10	68	56	23
Worthing BCOB Res	22	10	2	10	69	48	22
St Theresa's Res	22	8	5	9	39	56	21
Maple Leaf Res.	22	9	2	11	71	59	20
Inland Revenue Res	22	9	2	11	56	65	20
W.Tarring WMC Res	22	4	3	15	32	91	11
Angmering 'B'	22	4	1	17	41	95	9
SB Sports 'A'	22	3	2	17	40	100	8

DIVISION THREE	P	W	D	L	F	A	PTS
J.F.P.	22	14	6	2	61	24	34
AFC Egremont	22	15	3	4	73	35	33
Royal Mail	22	14	5	3	71	35	33
East Preston 'C'	22	11	5	6	61	33	27
B.T.R. Brakes	22	11	5	6	76	64	27
Lamb Durrington	22	11	4	7	54	41	26
Taulke-King Finance	22	10	4	8	52	41	24
Worthing Civic Res	22	6	6	10	47	52	18
Storr'n Priory Res	22	7	2	13	40	84	16
Radnor Rovers	22	3	6	13	30	66	12
Eurotherm Res	22	4	2	16	37	60	10
L & S R.B.L. 'C'	22	1	2	19	16	83	4

EAST SUSSEX LEAGUE

Chairman: J Ades, Esq
President: J E Davey, Esq

Formed in 1896, the League operated just one division until 1959, but since has grown by amalgamation and expansion to its present constitution of two intermediate and eight junior divisions accommodating some 112 teams.

The demise of a long-standing member club plus the departure of clubs up the Pyramid to both the Unijet Sussex County and F.C.N. Music Kent Leagues meant that it was one of the most inexperienced premier divisions for many years. Therefore, it was no surprise when Wadhurst United, one of the more established sides, went to the top early on and stayed there to the end. They took the title by ten clear points by virtue of conceding the least goals in the division whilst also being its highest scorers. Hollington United finished as runners-up for the second consecutive season but achieved a more significant double by retaining the League Challenge Cup, the first club to do so for nearly forty years.

In the other divisions, five teams that had been promoted as champions took the titles of their new divisions. Amongst these were Heathfield Hotspurs who conpleted the league season with a 100% record. Changing fortunes have seen Punnetts Town, who left the top division eight years ago and dropped as far as division four, bounce back almost as rapidly winning promotion for the past three years including taking the division one and two titles in successive years.

Success in the Sussex Intermediate Cup has eluded a member club since 1965 and even Eastbourne Rose & Crown were unable to repeat their previous season's victory in the Sussex Junior Cup. However, East Hoathly did reach the semi-final stage.

The league's representative sides fared better in the county F.A.'s Inter-League competitions: The Intermediate side lifting the trophy for the third time in six years after defeating the Mid-Sussex League in the final; the Junior team also reached their final but against opposition from the same league were unsuccessful.

P F **High**, Hon. Secretary, Hastings & District F.A.

PREM. DIVISION	P	W	D	L	F	A	PTS
Wadhurst United	18	13	3	2	47	25	42
Hollington United	18	10	2	6	45	32	32
Wadhurst TOC H.	18	10	1	7	41	37	31
Hertsmonceux	18	7	4	7	35	30	25
Rock-a-Nore	18	6	6	6	31	34	24
E'bourne Fishermen	18	7	2	9	42	40	23
Polegate	18	6	4	8	34	45	22
Bodiam	18	6	3	9	35	40	21
Hawkhurst United	18	5	4	9	30	43	19
Willingdon	18	3	5	10	27	41	14

DIVISION ONE	P	W	D	L	F	A	PTS
Punnetts Town	18	13	0	5	49	29	39
Burwash	18	12	2	4	45	23	38
Rye United Res.	18	9	3	6	39	24	30
Westfield	18	8	6	4	37	25	30
Icklesham Casuals	18	7	4	7	26	28	25
The J.C.Tackleway	18	7	2	9	36	43	23
Ninfield United	18	5	4	9	30	36	19
Sandhurst	18	5	3	10	26	50	18
Old Hastonians	18	5	2	11	23	47	17
Hastings Rangers	18	3	6	9	31	37	15

DIVISION TWO	P	W	D	L	F	A	PTS
Langney Spts Res.	20	17	1	2	63	35	52
Shinewater Res.	20	14	3	3	69	24	45
Tenterden S.M. Res.	20	12	2	6	53	34	38
Mountfield United	20	10	2	8	50	37	32
Mayfield	20	8	3	9	37	48	27
Northiam '75	20	8	2	10	39	48	26
Cranbrook Town	20	6	4	10	35	37	22
Magham Down	20	7	1	12	38	47	22
Claverham	20	4	8	8	29	37	20
Hooe Sports	20	5	3	12	39	65	18
Wadhurst Utd Res.	20	2	5	13	26	66	11

DIVISION THREE	P	W	D	L	F	A	PTS
E'bne Rose & Crown	20	18	1	1	82	19	55
Peche Hill Select	20	15	4	1	70	24	49
Ticehurst	20	12	4	4	60	29	40
Hollington U. Res.	20	11	3	6	57	43	36
Battle Rangers	20	11	1	8	60	50	34
Pebsham-Sibex	20	8	2	10	54	43	26
Iden	20	7	3	10	54	63	24
Old Centmodians	20	7	1	12	41	52	22
Hawkhurst U. Res.	20	6	3	11	28	61	16
Polegate Res.	20	4	0	16	30	72	12
Blacklands	20	0	0	20	13	100	0

DIVISION FOUR	P	W	D	L	F	A	PTS
Robertsbridge U.	22	13	4	5	70	45	43
Hillcrest	22	12	5	5	84	60	41
Beach	22	13	1	8	79	55	40
Hellingley Hosp.	22	11	5	6	62	29	38
Bexhill Athletic	22	12	2	8	62	56	38
Travaux	22	11	2	9	60	48	35
Ninfield U. Res.	22	10	5	7	51	45	35
Rye United 'A'	22	9	4	9	55	62	31
East Hoathly	22	9	3	10	62	50	30
Westfield Res.	22	8	3	11	58	82	27
Shinewater 'A'	22	3	2	17	31	84	11
Hastings Rgrs Res.	22	2	2	18	33	91	8

DIVISION SEVEN	P	W	D	L	F	A	PTS
Heathfield Spurs	22	22	0	0	88	23	66
Beckley '92	22	14	2	6	69	37	44
O Centmodians Res.	22	12	4	6	55	29	40
Durgates	22	12	4	6	54	36	40
Tenterden S.M. 'A'	22	10	1	11	41	51	31
Tack United	22	8	3	11	60	48	27
Cranbrook T. Res.	22	8	3	11	37	38	27
Claverham Res.	22	8	3	11	49	66	27
Burwash Res.	22	8	2	12	41	63	26
Westfield 'A'	22	7	2	13	42	64	23
Northian '75 Res.	22	4	3	15	39	75	15
Icklesham C. Res.	22	4	3	15	31	76	15

DIVISION FIVE	P	W	D	L	F	A	PTS
Old Town Ebne	22	18	2	2	81	25	56
Hurst Green Vil.	22	15	4	3	74	26	49
Wittersham	22	13	2	7	65	37	41
St Vincents	22	12	3	7	65	33	39
Willingdon Res.	22	11	5	6	53	43	38
Heathfield Utd	22	9	5	8	51	59	32
O Hastonians Res.	22	8	3	11	61	65	30
Herstmonceux Res.	22	8	1	13	57	71	*22
Pevensey & Westham	22	5	6	11	41	67	21
Catsfield	22	5	5	12	56	88	20
Redgrove	22	4	3	15	38	90	15
Little Cmn A. 'A'	22	4	1	17	40	78	13

DIVISION EIGHT	P	W	D	L	F	A	PTS
Rolvenden	20	17	1	2	95	20	52
E. Hoathly Res.	20	13	0	7	79	53	39
Broad Oak Utd	20	11	3	6	98	66	36
Herstmonceux 'A'	20	12	3	7	59	31	*36
Pebsham-Sibex 'A'	20	9	4	7	46	35	31
Hellingly H. Res.	20	8	4	8	45	51	28
Magham Down Res.	20	8	2	10	53	78	26
Mayfield Res.	20	8	1	11	50	59	25
Pevensey & W. Res.	20	7	0	13	42	52	21
Ticehurst Res.	20	6	0	14	38	83	18
Hillcrest Res.	20	2	0	18	34	111	6
Old King John - Record expunged.							

DIVISION SIX	P	W	D	L	F	A	PTS
Sedlescombe	22	20	1	1	110	34	61
Nelson Tigers	22	16	3	3	89	26	51
Pebsham-Sibex Res.	22	13	6	3	81	25	45
Frant	22	12	4	6	80	52	40
Battle Rgrs Res.	22	11	3	8	77	66	36
Silverhill Rgrs	22	10	2	10	49	56	32
Wadhurst T.H. Res.	22	8	4	10	52	55	28
Staplecross	22	6	3	13	41	68	21
Seeboard (Hastings)	22	5	3	14	48	79	18
J C Tackleway Res.	22	5	2	15	42	94	17
Hawkhurst U. 'A'	22	4	3	15	30	92	15
Travaux Res.	22	2	6	14	32	88	12

DIVISION NINE	P	W	D	L	F	A	PTS
Firehills	20	17	1	2	97	33	52
Sedlescombe Res.	20	15	1	4	47	31	46
Rob'bridge Res.	20	13	2	5	67	38	41
Staplecross Res.	20	9	3	8	51	38	30
Bexhill AAC Res.	20	9	3	8	62	50	30
H'field Spurs Res	20	9	1	10	49	43	28
Mountfield U. Res.	20	9	0	11	59	73	27
Bohemia United	20	7	2	11	49	60	23
O Hastonians 'A'	20	5	4	11	35	44	19
Punnetts Town Res.	20	6	0	14	54	86	18
J C Tackleway 'A'	20	2	1	17	30	104	7
* - 3pts deducted							

PREMIER DIVISION CLUBS 1993-94

BODIAM
Secretary: Mrs M Ennis, The Maltings, Woodbury Rd, Hawkhurst, Kent TN18 4DD (0580 752803).
Ground: Bodiam Sports Field   **Colours:** Claret/sky/sky.

BURWASH
Secretary: Mr K Bray, 7 Mayview Close, Broad Oak, Heathfield TN21 8SL (0435 864628).
Ground: Swan Meadow Ham Lane, Burwash.   **Colours:** Blue & black stripes/black/blue

EASTBOURNE FISHERMEN
Secretary: Mrs I Bennett, 106a Foxglove Rd, Eastbourne BN23 8BX (0323 762672).
Ground: Eastbourne VI Form College, Kings Drive, Eastbourne   **Colours:** Yellow/blue/yellow.

HERSTMONCEUX
Secretary: Mr D A Page, 2/3 Corner Cottage, West End, Herstmonceux BN27 4NG (0323 833152).
Ground: Lime Cross.   **Colours:** Blue & white/blue/blue.

HOLLINGTON UNITED
Secretary: Mr K S Dullaway, 10 Swynford Drive, St Leonards-on-Sea, East Sussex TN38 9NE (0424 852894).
Ground: Gibbons Mem. Field, Wishing Tree Rd, St Leonards-on-Sea.   **Colours:** All royal blue.

POLEGATE
Secretary: Mrs G C Smith, 193 Priory Rd, Langney, Eastbourne BN23 7TB (0323 760684).
Ground: Polegate Rec.   **Colours:** Red & white/red & black/red & black.

PUNNETTS TOWN
Secretary: Mr M E Kent, 11 North Str., Punnetts Town, Heathfield TN21 9DT (0435 830374).
Ground: Punnetts Town Rec.   **Colours:** Sky & black/black/black

ROCK-A-NORE
Secretary: Mr H J Veness, 39 Royal Terrace, St Leonards-on-Sea TN37 6QH (0424 427500).
Ground: Tilekiln PF, Ingleside, St Leonards   **Colours:** All sky.

WADHURST TOC H.
Secretary: Mr D Mallion, 27 Queens Cottages, Wadhurst TN5 6RN (0892 783363).
Ground: Sparrows Green PF, Wadhurst   **Colours:** White/black/black.

WADHURST UNITED
Secretary: Mr J Barnes, 2 Crossways, High Street, Flimwell, Wadhurst TN5 7PB (0580 87620).
Ground: Washwell Lane, Wadhurst.   **Colours:** White/black/black.

DIVISION ONE CLUBS 1993-94

HAWKHURST UNITED
Secretary: Mr D D Saunders, 55 Cranford Rd, Tonbridge, Kent TN10 4HQ (0732 361398).
Ground: King George V PF, The Moor, Hawkhurst   **Colours:** Red & white/white/red.

ICKLESHAM CASUALS
Secretary: Mr D Mayne, 12 Mill Lane, Hastings TN35 4LJ (0424 812214).
Ground: Icklesham Rec.   **Colours:** Green & white quarters/black/green.

LANGNEY SPORTS 'A' *(See page 560)*

BURWASH
Secretary: Mr E H Cocksedge, 10 Stocks Meadow, Ninfield, Battle TN33 9JD (0424 892035).
Ground: Ninfield Rec. **Colours:** Yellow (green pinnstripe)/green/yellow.

RYE UNITED RESERVES *(See Kent County League section)*

SANDHURST
Secretary: Mrs S Kerry, 'Mount Pleasant', Cranbrook, Kent TN18 5LN (0580 850313).
Ground: Sandhurst PF, Sandhurst, Kent. **Colours:** Blue & white/blue/blue.

SHINEWATER ASSOCIATION RESERVES *(See page 576)*

THE JUNIOR CLUB TACKLEWAY
Secretary: Mr A M Brown, 42 St Thomas's Rd, Hastings TN34 3LQ (0424 444391).
Ground: Sandhurst PF, The Ridge, Hastings. **Colours:** Yellow/black/black.

WESTFIELD
Secretary: Mr J M Drinkwater, 28 Churchfield, Hastings TN35 4SN (0424 754032).
Ground: Westfield Parish Field **Colours:** Green & yellow/black/black

WILLINGDON
Secretary: Mr D Roderick, 30 Freeman Ave., Eastbourne BN22 9NT (0323 506685).
Ground: Willingdon Rec. **Colours:** All green.

DIVISION TWO CLUBS 1993-94

CLAVERHAM
Secretary: Mr G Wenham, 10 Martindale Close, St Leonards-on-Sea TN37 7SW (0424 753604).
Ground: Claverham Comm. College, Nth Trades Rd, Battle **Colours:** Maroon & sky stripes/sky/maroon.

CRANBROOK TOWN
Secretary: Mr G J Holmes, 'Elim', New Rd, Cranbrook, Kent TN17 3LE (0580 712653).
Ground: Big Ball Field, Waterloo Rd, Cranbrook **Colours:** Blue & black stripes/black/black.

EASTBOURNE ROSE & CROWN
Secretary: Mr F Woods, 10 North Ave., Old Town, Eastbourne BN20 8RD (0323 649986).
Ground: Eastbourne VI Form College, Kings Drive, Eastbourne **Colours:** Amber/black/black.

HASTINGS RANGERS
Secretary: Mrs L J Major, 404 Bexhill Rd, St Leonards-on-Sea TN38 8AS (0424 446796).
Ground: Bulverhythe PF, Bexhill Rd, St Leonards. **Colours:** Red/black/black.

MAGHAM DOWN
Secretary: Mr B W Brady, 79 Shakespeare Walk, Langney, Eastbourne BN23 7PN (0323 765802).
Ground: Red Lion Field, Magham Down. **Colours:** Black & white stripes/black/black.

MAYFIELD
Secretary: Mr D G Baldock, 15 Southmead Close, Mayfield TN20 6UJ (0424 873460).
Ground: King George V PF, Mayfield. **Colours:** Gold/black/black.

MOUNTFIELD UNITED
Secretary: Mr G R Brooman, 27 Fair Lane, Robertsbridge TN32 5AT (0580 880759).
Ground: Riverhall, Mountfield. **Colours:** White (red trim)/white/red.

NORTHIAM '75
Secretary: Mr Mr F Francis, 23 Goddens Gill, Northiam, Rye TN31 6QE (0797 252365).
Ground: The Playing Field, Main Str., Northiam, Rye **Colours:** All yellow.

OLD HASTONIANS
Secretary: Mr P A King, 5 Gilbert Rd, St Leonards-on-Sea TN38 0RH (0424 428057).
Ground: Sandhurst PF, The Ridge, Hastings **Colours:** Red/black/black.

PECHE HILL SELECT
Secretary: Mr M Delpeache, 17 Burry Rd, St Leonards-on-Sea TN37 6QW (0424 431317).
Grnd: Tilekiln PF, Ingleside, St Leonards-on-Sea **Cols:** Red & black stripes/white/white.

TICEHURST
Secretary: Mr A A Stanbridge, 'Tilsmore', Tilsmore Rd, Heathfield TN21 0XU (0435 866750).
Ground: Bell Field, Pickeforde Lane, Ticehurst **Colours:** Amber/black/amber.

DIVISION THREE CLUBS 1993-94

BATTLE RANGERS
Secretary: Mr A Bashford, 6 Hoath Hill, Mountfield TN32 5LN (0580 880053).
Ground: Battle Rec. **Colours:** Green/black/green.

BEACH
Secretary: Mr T H Walker, 74 Beach Rd, Eastbourne BN22 7AB (0323 723542).
Ground: Hampden Park, Eastbourne. **Colours:** Red/white/blue & red.

HILLCREST
Secretary: Mr C Banfield, 7 Emmanuel Rd, Hastings TN34 3LB (0424 424228).
Ground: Hillcrest Sch., Rye Rd, Hastings **Colours:** Amber/black/black.

HOOE SPORTS
Secretary: Mrs P Baker, 1 Sawpits, Hooe, Battle TN33 9HR (0424 892880).
Ground: Hooe Rec. **Colours:** Green & black stripes/black/black.

IDEN
Secretary: Mr G B Say, 18 Parkwood, Iden, Rye TN31 7XE (0797 280495).
Ground: Iden Playing Field. **Colours:** Tangerine/black/black.

OLD CENTMODIANS
Secretary: Mr K Edwards, 5 St Marys Terrace, Battle TN33 0BU (0424 774059).
Ground: Bulverhythe PF, Bexhill Rd, St Leonards-on-Sea. **Colours:** All blue

PEBSHAM-SIBEX
Secretary: Mr K Fuller, 28 Alma Villas, St Leonards-on-Sea TN37 6QU (0424 442229).
Ground: Buxton Drive, Sidley. **Colours:** Sky/navy/navy

ROBERTSBRIDGE UNITED
Secretary: Mrs A Hardy, 43 Coronation Gdns, Hurst Green, Etchingham TN19 7PH (0580 860543).
Ground: Robertsbridge Rec. **Colours:** Black & white stripes/black/black.

Plus the Reserve sides of: *Hawkhurst Utd, Hollington Utd & Wadhurst Utd.*

DIVISION FOUR CLUBS 1993-94

BEXHILL AMATEUR ATHLETIC CLUB
Secretary: Mr M Hyland, 18 Heather Close, Langney, Eastbourne BN23 8DF (0323 765479).
Ground: The Downs, Little Common Rd, Bexhill-on-Sea **Colours:** All red.

BLACKLANDS
Secretary: Mr H Rich, 64 Hughenden Rd, Hastings, TN34 3TE (0424 439622).
Ground: Tilekiln PF, Ingleside, St Leonards-on-Sea **Colours:** Red & white/white/white.

EAST HOATHLY
Secretary: Mr T Ginno, 106 Sorrel Drive, Eastbourne BN23 8BJ (0323 768920).
Ground: East Hoathly War Mem. PF **Colours:** All white.

HELLINGLY HOSPITAL
Secretary: Mr L Mansbridge, 63 LOndon Rd, Hailsham BN27 3DD (0323 846498).
Ground: Hellingly Hospital. **Colours:** Black & white stripes/black/black.

HURST GREEN VILLAGE '89
Secretary: Mrs M Goldfinch, 'Woodmans Cottage', Little Iridge Farm, Hurst Green TN19 7PX (0580 860418).
Ground: Drewetts Field, Hurst Green. **Colours:** Blue & white hoops/blue/blue.

OLD TOWN EASTBOURNE
Secretary: Mr R Lade, 78 Brodrick Rd, Hampden Park, Eastbourne BN22 9NS (0323 505641).
Ground: Hindland PF, Polegate. **Colours:** Blue & black stripes/black/black.

TRAVAUX
Secretary: Mr D Andrews, Flat 3, 23 East Ascent, St Leonards-on-Sea TN38 0DS (0424 460773).
Ground: Tilekiln PF, Ingleside, St Leonards-on-Sea **Colours:** Sky & white stripes/black/sky.

WITTERSHAM
Secretary: Mr C K Packham, 3 Forge Meads, Wittersham, Nr Tenterden, Kent TN30 6PE (0797 270239).
Ground: Wittersham Spts Ground **Colours:** Green & white/white/black.

Plus the Reserve sides of: *Ninfield Utd, Polegate, Westfield,* **and the 'A' side of:** *Rye Utd.*

DIVISION FIVE CLUBS 1993-94

CATSFIELD
Secretary: Mr M J Davey, Lower Hill Farm, Watermill Lane, Bexhill-on-Sea TN39 5JB (0424 830477).
Ground: Catsfield PF **Colours:** Amber/black/amber.

HEATHFIELD HOTSPURS
Secretary: Mr B V Hemsley, 6 Uplands Ct, Burwash Rd, Heathfield TN21 8SP (0435 864623).
Ground: Tower Rec, Tower Str., Heathfield **Colours:** Apple green/dark green/apple green.

HEATHFIELD UNITED
Secretary: Mr D C Wright, 3 Geerswood Cottages, Ghyll Rd TN21 0AH (0435 866696).
Ground: Comm. Centre, Sheepsetting Lane, Heathfield **Colours:** Yellow/blue/yellow.

NELSON TIGERS
Sec.: Mr D J Weller, Flat 1, 33 High Str., Hastings TN34 3ER (0424 423280 'The Lord Nelson').
Ground: Bulverhythe PF, Bexhill Rd, St Leonards-on-Sea **Colours:** Black & yellow/black/yellow

PEVENSEY & WESTHAM
Secretary: Mr N Coombes, 2 Trossachs Close, Eastbourne BN23 8HA (0323 460997).
Ground: Pevensey Rec. **Colours:** Blue & claret/claret/claret & blue.

SEDLESCOMBE
Secretary: Mr G Buss, 39 East View Terrace, Sedlescombe, Battle TN33 0PY (0424 870432).
Ground: Oaklands Park, Sedlescombe, Battle **Colours:** Red & black stripes/black/black.

Plus the Reserve sides of: *Hastings Rgrs, Herstmonceux, Old Hastonians (playing at Bulverhythe PF, St Leonards) and Willingdon,* **and the 'A' side of:** *Shinewater Association.*

DIVISION SIX CLUBS 1993-94

BECKLEY '92
Secretary: Mr M J Wreford, c/o Manroy Engineering, Hobbs Lane, Beckley, Rye TN31 6TS (0892 529109).
Ground: Jubilee Field, Beckley, Rye **Colours:** White/black/white.

CASTLE
Secretary: Mr R B Woollven, 10 Grand Ave., Bexhill-on-Sea TN40 2PH (0424 733104).
Ground: Little Common Rec. **Colours:** Yellow & green/green/yellow.

DYNAMO C.E.F.
Secretary: Mr S Millard, 2 Harlequin Gdns, St Leonards-on-Sea TN37 7PF (0424 752537).
Ground: Sandhurst PF, The Ridge, Hastings **Colours:** Coral & purple/purple/purple

FRANT
Secretary: Mr B Akehurst, 'Winster Cottage', Stonecross, Crowborough TN6 3SJ (0892 662741).
Ground: Church Field, Main Rd, Frant **Colours:** Black & white stripes/black/black.

SEEBOARD (HASTINGS)
Secretary: Mr J G Vidler, 1 Ravine Close, Hastings TN34 2BH (0424 426570).
Ground: Bulverhythe PF, Bexhill Rd, St Leonards-on-Sea **Colours:** White/blue/blue & white.

SILVERHILL RANGERS
Secretary: Mrs C A Clark, 150 Athelstan Rd, Hastings TN35 5JE (0424 422265).
Ground: Bulverhythe PF, Bexhill Rd, St Leonards-on-Sea   **Colours:** Sky & white/black/black.

STAPLECROSS
Secretary: Mr M A Chandler, 3 Cricketers Field, Staplecross, Robertsbridge TN32 5QQ (0580 830871).
Ground: Gate House Farm, Lordine Lane, Staplecross   **Colours:** All blue.

Plus the Reserve sides of: *Battle Rgrs, Pebsham-Sibex, The J.C. Tackleway, Wadhurst TOC H,* **and the 'A' side of:** *Little Common Albion.*

DIVISION SEVEN CLUBS 1993-94
DURGATES
Secretary: Mr C E Baker, 3 Orchard Cres., Horsmonden, Kent BN12 8LB (0424 722649).
Ground: Bayham Rd, Tunbridge Wells   **Colours:** White/blue/white.

ROLVENDEN
Secretary: Mr K Sims, 26 Sparkeswood Ave., Rolvenden, Cranbrook TN17 4LX (0580 241351).
Ground: Gatefield.   **Colours:** Blue/blue/yellow.

TACK UNITED
Secretary: Mr R Acland, Flat 4, Stamford Court, Harold Rd, Hastings TN35 5PE (0424 426400).
Ground: Benenden, Kent   **Colours:** Red & black stripes/black/black.

Plus the Reserve sides of: *Burwash, Claverham, Cranbrook Town, East Hoathly, Old Centmodians, Travaux,* **and the 'A' sides of:** *Hawkhurst Utd, Tenterden & St Michaels, Westfield.*

DIVISION EIGHT CLUBS 1993-94
BROAD OAK UNITED OLD BOYS
Secretary: Mr B Hart, 'Wheatsheaves', Street End Lane, Broad Oak, Heathfield TN21 8RY (0435 862676).
Ground: Tower Rec, Tower Str., Heathfield   **Colours:** Yellow/black/black.

FIREHILLS
Secretary: Mrs S Medhurst, 5 Playden Gdns, Hastings TN34 2SH (0424 434084).
Grnd: Bulverhythe PF, Bexhill Rd, St Leonards-on-Sea   **Cols:** Green & white stripes/white/green.

Plus the Reserve sides of: *Hellingly Hosp., Icklesham Cas., Magham Down, Mayfield, Northiam 75, Pevensey & Westham, Robertsbridge Utd, Sedlescombe,* **and the 'A' sides of:** *Herstmonceux, Pebsham-Sibex.*

DIVISION NINE CLUBS 1993-94
BOHEMIA UNITED
Secretary: Mr H D Chapman, 25 Magdalen Rd, St Leonards-on-Sea TN37 6EP (0424 439403).
Ground: Sandhurst PF, The Ridge, Hastings.   **Colours:** Blue/white/blue.

Plus the Reserve sides of: *Bexhill A.A.C., Castle, Heathfield Hotspurs, Heathfield Utd, Hillcrest, Mountfield Utd, Old Town E'bourne, Punnetts Town, Ticehurst, Wadhurst Utd,* **and the 'A' sides of:** *Old Hastonians (playing at Bulverhythe PF, St Leonards), The J.C. Tackleway.*

LEAGUE CHALLENGE CUP

First Round

Bexhill A.A.C. v The J.C. Tackleway	2-4	Burwash v Rock-a-Nore	1-6
Eastbourne Fishermen *(w/o)* Sandhurst *(scr)*		Eastbourne Rose & Crown v Herstmonceux	2-1
Hastings Rangers v Willingdon	0-4	Hollington United v Punnetts Town	5-0
Old Hastonians v Peche Hill Select	1-2	Wadhurst Toc H v Hawkhurst United	2-9
Westfield v Ninfield United	2-3		

Second Round

Bodiam v Hawkhurst United	5-1	Hollington Utd v Rye Utd Res.	2-2*(aet)*,3-2
Icklesham Casuals v Old Town Eastbourne	4-5	Langney Spts 'A' v The Junior Club Tackleway	0-2
Peche Hill Select v Ninfield United	2-0	Rock-a-Nore v Eastbourne Rose & Crown	0-2
Wadhurst United v Polegate	1-3	Willingdon v Eastbourne Fishermen	2-1

Quarter-Finals

Bodiam v Hollington United	1-5	Peche H.S. v Ebne Rose & Crown	2-2*(aet)*,1-2
The Jnr Club Tackleway v Old Town Ebne	0-3	Willingdon v Polegate	3-2

Semi-Finals

Willingdon v Hollington United	0-2	Eastbourne Rose & Crown v Old Town Eastbourne	0-0

Final *(at Hailsham Town FC, Fri 7th May)*: Eastbourne Rose & Crown 1 *(Lee Salmon 14m)*, Hollington Utd 0

OTHER EAST SUSSEX LGE FINALS

TALBOT KENT CUP (DIVS 2 & 3):
Langney 'A' 3, Ebne Rose & Crown 2 *(at Hailsham)*

PERCY CHAMBERS CUP (DIVS 4 & 5):
Hurst Green Village 3, Travaux 2 *(at Wadhurst Utd)*

FRED EADE CUP (DIVS 6 & 7):
Sedlescombe 2, Nelson Tigers 1 *(at Wadhurst Utd)*

PRESIDENTS CUP (DIVS 8 & 9):
Rolvenden 2, Herstmonceux 'A' 0 *(at Wadhurst Utd)*

HASTINGS & DIST. F.A. FINALS

SENIOR INVITATION CUP:
Bexhill Town 1, Stamco 0 *(at Hastings Town)*

INTERMEDIATE CHALLENGE CUP:
Stamco Reserves 5, Bodiam 0 *(at Hastings Town)*

JUNIOR CHALLENGE CUP:
Heathfield Hotspurs 5, Firehills 3 *(at Hastings T.)*

VETERANS INVITATION CUP:
Battle Rangers 1, Westfield 0 *(at Hastings Town)*

UNIJET MID-SUSSEX LEAGUE

President: Ken Somerville.
Chairman: Allen D Washer.
Vice President: Brian Hall.

The Unijet Mid-Sussex League, formed in 1900, is one of six intermediate leagues that feed into the Unijet Sussex County League.

Being in the heart of Sussex, the majority of the pitches used come under the control of local and parish councils, whom in turn determine the availability of the playing surfaces. The past season has been a particularly difficult one with many games postponed through the bad weather, but nevertheless, with a few exceptions the league programme was completed by the end of April.

Dominating the championship were two clubs, Lingfield and Plumpton Athletic, and the former being the more consistent, became champions and as such were accepted into the Sussex County League for 1993-94. Plumpton Athletic had the satisfaction of winning the Senior Montgomery Challenge Cup. Division One was closer with three teams fighting for promotion, and it was perhaps appropriate that Nutfield, who reached the final of the Sussex Junior Cup, and Chailey, who reached the Semi-Final, were successful. For the third season running, D.M.S. Cuckfield have become champions (Division Four) to continue their meteoric rise, and Barcombe have become champions for a second consecutive year (Division Six).

Five new clubs have been accepted into the League bringing the total to 58. Two divisions to arrange football for all 118 teams.

Peter Strange, Hon. Secretary.

PREM. DIVISION	P	W	D	L	F	A	PTS
Lingfield	24	19	3	2	78	24	60
Plumpton Ath.	24	16	3	5	69	23	51
Wealden	24	13	5	6	57	36	44
Maresfield Village	24	12	3	9	33	34	39
Leftovers Sports	24	11	5	8	51	32	38
Crawley Down Utd	24	11	4	9	51	43	37
Cuckfield	24	7	8	9	39	53	29
Pease Pottage Vil.	24	8	4	12	35	42	28
Newick	24	8	4	12	35	60	28
Lewes Rovers	24	7	3	14	45	66	24
Southwater	24	5	7	12	38	41	22
Lindfield	24	4	8	12	34	50	20
Wisdom Sports	24	6	1	17	22	73	19

DIVISION ONE	P	W	D	L	F	A	PTS
Nutley	24	17	3	4	72	26	54
Chailey	24	16	5	3	48	27	53
Felbridge	24	16	4	4	52	27	52
Village of Ditchling	24	13	5	6	67	31	44
Handcross Village	24	12	4	8	63	48	40
Clayton	24	11	7	6	46	36	40
Ashurstwood	24	10	5	9	67	46	35
Leftovers Spts Res.	24	9	5	10	43	52	32
Uckfield Town	24	8	3	13	40	54	27
Heath Pilgrims	24	6	4	14	57	69	22
Wivelsfield Green	24	6	4	14	41	61	22
Ardingly	24	4	2	18	31	81	14
Forest Row	24	1	3	20	21	90	6

DIVISION TWO	P	W	D	L	F	A	PTS
Linfield Rgrs Res.	24	16	5	3	74	33	53
Ansty	24	16	5	3	83	47	53
Bolney Rovers	24	13	3	8	56	38	42
Plumpton Ath.Res.	24	11	5	8	50	32	38
West Hoathly	24	11	5	8	42	39	38
Southwater Res.	24	11	3	10	45	48	36
Wisdom Sports Res.	24	10	3	11	62	54	33
Buxted Res.	24	10	3	11	54	63	33
E.Grinstead 'A'	24	8	3	13	43	45	27
Fairwarp	24	7	5	12	65	69	26
Leftovers Sports 'A'	24	7	4	13	38	64	25
Oakwood 'A'	24	7	4	13	49	78	25
Turners Hill	24	4	2	18	25	66	14

DIVISION THREE	P	W	D	L	F	A	PTS
St.Francis Hosp.Res.	26	19	5	2	104	32	62
Horley Athletico	26	17	5	4	79	32	56
Sovereign Finance	26	14	6	6	59	34	48
Ringmer 'A'	26	14	4	8	72	47	46
Horsted Keynes	26	11	7	8	58	48	40
Balcombe	26	11	5	10	63	48	38
Maresfield Vill.Res.	26	10	7	9	56	54	37
Danehill	26	8	8	10	52	54	32
Cuckfield Res.	26	8	8	10	44	52	32
Lewes Rovers Res.	26	9	3	14	58	73	30
Ashurstwood Res.	26	8	5	13	56	57	29
Franklands Vil.'A'	26	7	7	12	38	57	28
Crawley D. Utd Res.	26	7	4	15	36	70	25
Groombridge	26	1	2	23	21	132	5

DIVISION FOUR	P	W	D	L	F	A	PTS
DMS Cuckfield	22	18	2	2	89	19	56
Lingfield Res.	22	16	3	3	79	24	51
Crowborough Ath 'A'	22	13	2	7	80	37	41
E.Grinstead Mariners	22	11	4	7	37	37	37
Hartfield	22	11	2	9	56	42	35
Pease Pot. V. Res.	22	10	4	8	53	40	34
Hurstpierpoint 'A'	22	9	3	10	58	59	30
Lindfield Res.	22	7	7	8	41	53	28
Village of D. Res.	22	6	5	11	35	53	23
Newick Res.	22	6	2	14	44	68	20
Southwater 'A'	22	6	1	15	48	95	19
Forest Row Res.	22	1	1	20	14	107	4

DIVISION FIVE	P	W	D	L	F	A	PTS
Woodcock Ath.	22	18	2	2	83	21	56
St.Francis Hosp.'A'	22	16	2	4	55	27	50
Bridgeview	22	13	3	6	54	33	42
Uckfield Town Res.	22	10	6	6	55	53	36
Heath Pilgrims Res.	22	9	2	11	53	54	29
Clayton Res.	22	8	4	10	49	46	28
Wivelsfield G. Res.	22	8	3	11	39	54	27
Wisdom Sports 'A'	22	7	3	12	48	59	24
Staxil Burgess Hill	22	7	1	14	42	61	22
Scaynes Hill Utd	22	5	6	11	34	49	21
Leftovers Sports 'B'	22	6	3	13	35	61	21
Crawley Down Lions	22	5	5	12	35	66	20

DIVISION SIX	P	W	D	L	F	A	PTS
Barcombe	24	19	2	3	95	20	59
Felbridge Res.	24	18	2	4	83	38	56
Wealden Res.	24	15	3	6	65	31	48
Chailey Res.	24	13	4	7	52	38	43
Ansty Res.	24	12	2	10	53	47	38
West Hoathly Res.	24	10	7	7	50	48	37
Handcross Vill.Res.	24	8	6	10	46	54	30
Buxted 'A'	24	7	7	10	47	51	28
Lindfield 'A'	24	8	4	12	36	67	28
Turners Hill Res.	24	7	4	13	28	49	25
Cuckfield 'A'	24	6	3	15	46	60	21
Ardingly Res.	24	4	3	17	34	82	15
Ashurstwood 'A'	24	3	5	16	27	77	14

DIVISION SEVEN	P	W	D	L	F	A	PTS
Sovereign F. Res.	26	19	2	5	88	36	59
DMS Cuckfield Res.	26	18	2	6	64	36	56
Nutley Res.	26	16	5	5	80	35	53
Maresfield Vill.'A'	26	16	4	6	74	43	52
Horsted Keynes Res.	26	14	2	10	97	54	44
Bridgeview Res.	26	13	4	7	74	52	43
Hartfield Res.	26	12	6	8	65	58	42
Uckfield Town 'A'	26	12	2	12	49	61	38
Fairwarp Res.	26	10	3	13	66	61	33
Vill./Ditching 'A'	26	9	6	11	52	52	33
Barcombe Res.	26	6	7	13	51	81	25
Lewes Rovers 'A'	26	5	3	18	37	108	18
Wealden 'A'	26	4	2	20	38	83	14
Balcombe Res.	26	2	4	20	17	92	10

PREMIER DIVISION RESULT CHART 1992-93

HOME TEAM		1	2	3	4	5	6	7	8	9	10	11	12	13
1.	Crawley Down United	*	3-0	3-0	2-4	1-1	2-3	1-2	3-1	2-7	2-1	3-0	5-1	5-1
2.	Cuckfield	4-4	*	1-1	4-3	2-2	1-1	1-2	1-0	L-W	1-7	1-1	2-5	2-0
3.	Leftovers Social Club	3-1	1-2	*	3-1	3-0	1-1	5-1	1-3	3-1	2-2	1-1	1-0	5-0
4.	Lewes Rovers	3-0	3-2	0-5	*	2-2	1-5	1-2	1-1	1-2	1-3	4-1	3-4	1-5
5.	Lindfield	3-0	3-3	3-2	1-1	*	2-3	1-2	4-0	2-2	1-4	0-0	2-3	0-1
6.	Lingfield	0-1	6-2	3-0	6-2	2-0	*	0-1	7-1	2-1	3-2	4-1	2-0	3-0
7.	Maresfield Village	2-3	0-0	1-0	5-0	0-0	2-3	*	3-2	2-0	0-5	1-0	1-1	1-0
8.	Newick	1-1	2-2	0-2	3-2	2-0	1-7	1-0	*	0-1	1-4	3-1	2-4	2-4
9.	Pease Pottage Village	1-1	1-2	4-2	4-1	5-1	1-3	1-0	2-3	*	0-2	2-3	1-1	0-1
10.	Plumpton Athletic	2-1	5-0	4-0	3-1	2-3	2-3	3-1	7-0	1-1	*	0-0	0-2	2-0
11.	Southwater	0-2	0-3	1-1	1-2	4-2	0-2	1-0	1-2	3-1	0-2	*	2-3	1-1
12.	Wealden	3-0	3-1	0-2	5-2	4-1	1-1	4-2	1-1	5-0	0-1	1-1	*	1-2
13.	Wisdom Sports	0-5	0-2	0-7	1-5	2-0	0-8	1-2	1-3	1-3	0-5	0-5	1-5	*

DIVISION ONE RESULT CHART 1992-93

HOME TEAM		1	2	3	4	5	6	7	8	9	10	11	12	13
1.	Andingly	*	2-6	0-2	3-3	1-2	0-2	4-0	1-6	3-0	1-4	1-0	0-3	1-2
2.	Ashurst Wood	5-0	*	2-2	1-2	1-3	9-1	2-2	7-3	3-0	1-4	3-4	1-1	4-1
3.	Chailey	4-2	1-0	*	2-0	1-1	4-0	0-3	3-2	4-2	0-0	3-1	2-0	3-1
4.	Clayton	3-1	0-4	1-2	*	0-1	4-0	1-3	4-4	3-0	4-2	2-1	1-1	2-1
5.	Felbridge	5-2	2-0	1-0	1-1	*	3-1	5-0	2-0	3-1	0-1	1-1	1-1	3-2
6.	Forest Row	0-1	1-1	1-2	0-3	0-3	*	0-4	4-4	1-1	0-2	0-2	2-5	1-2
7.	Handcross Village	5-3	2-2	1-2	2-0	3-0	6-1	*	1-1	4-1	1-3	6-0	3-2	5-0
8.	Heath Pilgrims	6-0	1-7	1-3	0-1	3-4	4-2	2-2	*	0-2	2-5	3-1	2-4	8-2
9.	Leftovers Social Club Res.	6-1	5-4	1-1	1-1	2-1	3-0	2-1	3-2	*	1-3	1-1	2-4	3-1
10.	Nutley	5-2	4-1	4-0	2-3	1-3	9-2	6-0	3-0	7-0	*	W-L	2-1	2-2
11.	Uckfield Town	5-0	0-1	1-4	0-4	3-1	6-1	2-3	4-1	1-1	1-2	*	1-5	0-8
12.	Village of Ditchling	5-0	4-0	1-1	3-3	0-3	10-1	4-2	4-0	3-0	1-0	1-2	*	3-0
13.	Wivelsfield Green	2-2	1-2	1-2	1-1	2-3	2-0	5-4	0-2	0-5	1-1	2-3	2-1	*

DIVISION TWO RESULT CHART 1992-93

HOME TEAM		1	2	3	4	5	6	7	8	9	10	11	12	13
1.	Ansty	*	4-3	3-1	3-1	1-1	5-3	4-4	4-0	8-1	2-2	4-3	4-2	3-3
2.	Bolney Rovers	3-2	*	2-3	4-0	6-2	1-1	3-0	1-3	2-1	4-0	1-1	2-2	1-3
3.	Buxted Reserves	2-3	4-1	*	6-1	5-1	3-1	3-6	W-L	2-2	2-5	3-0	1-3	3-2
4.	East Grinstead 'A'	4-2	1-2	3-0	*	4-2	1-2	L-W	3-1	1-1	2-1	4-2	2-0	4-4
5.	Fairwarp	6-7	4-3	4-4	4-3	*	10-0	1-1	1-4	7-3	4-2	3-1	2-3	1-6
6.	Leftovers Social Club 'A'	1-6	0-3	3-1	W-L	4-3	*	2-3	1-5	5-1	2-3	1-1	2-1	0-1
7.	Lindfield Rangers Reserves	0-2	1-0	10-0	2-0	3-1	1-1	*	4-0	4-4	6-0	2-1	2-0	3-2
8.	Plumpton Athletic Reserves	1-3	2-1	3-0	W-L	0-0	1-4	2-2	*	6-1	1-2	2-0	1-1	3-2
9.	Oakwood 'A'	1-3	2-3	1-3	1-6	2-1	4-2	1-7	2-2	*	2-3	1-0	0-2	3-2
10.	Southwater Reserves	1-1	0-2	1-1	3-1	W-L	4-2	0-2	6-2	1-2	*	1-2	0-1	4-1
11.	Tunners Hill	0-4	2-3	0-4	2-0	3-1	2-1	1-4	0-3	0-3	0-3	*	0-1	0-6
12.	West Hoathly	2-1	0-1	5-1	2-2	2-4	0-0	2-1	2-2	6-4	0-7	4-2	*	0-3
13.	Wisdom Sports Reserves	1-4	0-4	3-2	W-L	2-2	3-0	1-5	2-3	2-5	6-1	7-2	0-1	*

DIVISION THREE RESULT CHART 1992-93

HOME TEAM		1	2	3	4	5	6	7	8	9	10	11	12	13	14
1.	Ashurst Wood Reserves	*	2-5	7-1	2-4	3-4	3-1	3-1	0-2	0-1	3-1	2-3	2-5	0-1	0-0
2.	Balcombe	3-0	*	5-0	2-0	1-2	4-1	4-1	3-3	3-0	1-3	2-4	2-1	2-2	2-1
3.	Crawley Down Utd. Res.	1-5	2-0	*	2-0	1-1	6-0	1-1	0-2	1-3	4-1	0-0	0-2	0-8	1-3
4.	Cuckfield Reserves	2-2	0-0	1-3	*	1-0	1-0	7-0	1-1	2-2	1-1	2-1	3-4	1-2	1-3
5.	Danehill	1-1	2-3	2-5	3-4	*	3-3	4-1	0-1	3-1	0-0	1-1	3-2	4-3	0-0
6.	Franklands Village 'A'	0-1	1-1	1-1	1-1	2-0	*	8-0	0-6	0-4	1-1	5-0	3-1	0-6	0-2
7.	Groombridge	0-10	1-1	2-1	1-3	1-4	1-2	*	0-5	1-6	1-4	1-4	1-5	0-10	0-3
8.	Horley Athletico	1-1	3-2	6-0	7-0	3-1	2-3	12-0	*	3-1	3-1	1-6	5-1	2-2	1-0
9.	Horsted Keynes	0-3	3-1	3-1	3-2	3-3	0-2	4-0	0-1	*	6-2	0-1	W-L	5-5	3-3
10.	Lewes Rovers Reserves	9-3	1-3	6-3	4-0	3-5	3-1	2-1	1-2	1-3	*	7-5	1-6	1-4	1-3
11.	Maresfield Village Reserves	0-0	4-1	4-1	1-1	2-1	2-1	6-1	1-2	2-2	2-3	*	0-3	2-7	1-1
12.	Ringmer 'A'	3-1	4-2	L-W	7-1	3-3	1-1	4-2	3-2	3-3	2-0	2-2	*	4-1	4-0
13.	St Francis Hospital Res.	5-0	2-0	2-0	0-0	2-1	6-0	10-2	3-1	2-2	7-0	4-1	5-1	*	2-1
14.	Sovereign Finance	3-2	1-0	5-0	0-5	4-1	1-1	9-1	1-1	2-2	3-0	3-1	3-1	2-3	*

DIVISION FOUR RESULT CHART 1992-93

HOME TEAM		1	2	3	4	5	6	7	8	9	10	11	12
1.	Crowborough Athletic 'A'	*	2-3	3-3	10-1	8-1	3-1	L-W	8-1	1-0	4-3	6-1	2-1
2.	D.M.S. Cuckfield	2-0	*	5-0	11-1	6-1	2-0	3-0	2-2	1-2	2-1	7-1	2-0
3.	East Grinstead Mariners	3-1	0-3	*	3-0	0-4	3-1	1-3	1-0	1-0	0-3	3-0	3-0
4.	Forest Row Reserves	0-4	0-5	2-2	*	1-3	1-2	2-5	0-7	0-2	0-3	2-4	1-6
5.	Hartfield	3-0	4-1	0-2	5-0	*	3-5	1-3	0-3	6-0	2-1	6-1	1-2
6.	Hurstpierpoint 'A'	3-3	2-2	3-4	5-0	1-5	*	5-2	0-2	6-5	6-3	3-5	0-2
7.	Lindfield Reserves	1-6	1-6	2-2	7-1	0-0	3-1	*	1-1	3-3	0-0	2-3	3-3
8.	Lingfield Reserves	3-2	2-3	3-0	4-0	2-0	5-2	7-0	*	6-0	7-0	9-1	6-0
9.	Newick Reserves	2-6	0-5	0-2	10-0	2-5	1-3	4-2	2-2	*	L-W	5-9	3-2
10.	Pease Pottage Reserves	2-1	0-2	5-1	4-0	2-1	2-2	2-2	L-W	3-1	*	7-0	3-3
11.	Southwater Reserves	2-6	1-10	0-5	4-0	0-3	3-4	0-1	2-4	1-2	5-9	*	0-1
12.	Village of Ditchling Res.	1-4	0-6	1-1	1-2	2-2	0-3	2-0	0-3	4-0	1-5	3-3	*

DIVISION FIVE CHART 1992-93

HOME TEAM	1	2	3	4	5	6	7	8	9	10	11	12	13
1. Bridgeview	*	3-0	3-2	2-0	5-0	8-0	0-0	2-0	3-0	1-5	1-5	5-1	1-3
2. Burgess Hill Rangers	1-6	*	2-1	3-1	*	*	4-0	2-7	2-3	2-1	0-3	3-3	*
3. Clayton Reserves	1-2	*	*	4-0	4-3	3-3	2-2	0-2	4-0	2-4	5-1	1-2	2-2
4. Crawley Downs Lions	2-2	*	1-5	*	3-2	3-2	3-1	0-1	1-4	1-2	3-3	1-4	0-4
5. Heath Pilgrims Reserves	2-1	2-0	2-3	4-4	*	9-0	2-1	2-3	3-0	5-0	3-2	3-5	1-7
6. Leftovers Social Club 'B'	0-1	*	1-3	6-2	1-1	*	4-3	1-0	3-1	1-1	0-2	0-1	0-3
7. Scaynes Hill United	3-3	2-0	1-1	1-0	1-3	3-2	*	1-4	1-2	1-1	3-2	2-0	0-4
8. St Francis Hospital 'A'	0-1	*	2-1	2-2	0-1	5-2	2-1	*	3-1	9-2	2-1	4-2	3-2
9. Staxill (Burgess Hill)	3-2	5-0	0-3	2-4	1-2	1-4	2-3	1-4	*	3-6	6-3	4-1	1-3
10. Uckfield Town Reserves	2-3	*	4-1	3-0	4-3	3-2	4-2	2-4	2-2	*	4-1	3-3	2-2
11. Wisdom Sports 'A'	2-4	1-3	5-3	6-4	2-3	1-0	2-2	2-4	1-3	1-1	*	1-2	1-5
12. Wivelsfield Green Reserves	0-3	*	4-1	0-0	2-1	1-2	2-2	2-1	3-4	0-2	2-3	*	1-8
13. Woodcock Athletic	2-1	6-3	4-0	9-1	5-1	4-1	3-0	0-1	2-1	6-1	2-1	3-1	*

N.B. Burgess Hill Rangers' record was expunged and is shown for interest only.

DIVISION SIX RESULT CHART 1992-93

HOME TEAM	1	2	3	4	5	6	7	8	9	10	11	12	13
1. Ansty Reserves	*	4-1	4-1	0-5	W-L	1-3	1-0	4-1	3-3	5-0	3-2	1-0	2-2
2. Andingly Reserves	2-1	*	2-2	2-4	2-4	2-3	5-1	0-6	0-3	2-2	1-5	1-1	2-6
3. Ashurst Wood 'A'	0-3	3-4	*	2-2	0-4	0-2	2-2	1-4	2-1	0-2	0-2	1-2	1-3
4. Barcombe	3-0	3-0	13-0	*	6-1	2-0	4-1	2-0	3-2	10-0	1-1	4-0	6-1
5. Buxted 'A'	5-1	4-1	2-3	5-2	*	1-1	3-1	1-1	0-3	3-5	1-4	0-4	2-2
6. Chailey Reserves	2-0	8-1	5-1	1-0	1-1	*	3-1	1-2	2-2	4-1	2-0	2-1	4-2
7. Cuckfield 'A'	4-0	6-1	2-2	1-6	2-3	2-2	*	1-2	4-1	2-3	1-0	0-4	2-3
8. Felbridge Reserves	3-7	5-1	5-1	1-0	4-3	4-1	5-2	*	3-3	10-0	3-1	2-1	7-2
9. Handcross Village Res.	3-2	3-1	2-0	1-5	1-1	3-0	2-6	1-2	*	1-3	1-0	0-5	1-4
10. Lindfield 'A'	4-2	1-2	2-1	0-3	0-0	2-1	2-3	0-2	1-3	*	3-3	1-4	2-0
11. Tunners Hill 'A'	1-5	2-0	1-2	0-5	1-0	1-4	2-0	0-6	0-0	3-1	*	0-1	1-3
12. Wealden	3-2	3-1	6-0	0-4	1-1	6-0	3-2	3-4	4-3	2-0	6-0	*	1-1
13. West Hoathly Reserves	1-2	2-0	2-2	1-2	5-2	2-0	1-0	2-1	3-3	1-1	0-0	1-4	*

DIVISION SEVEN RESULT CHART 1992-93

HOME TEAM	1	2	3	4	5	6	7	8	9	10	11	12	13	14
1. Balcombe Reserves	*	0-3	0-7	1-4	0-6	0-2	1-5	0-2	0-3	0-4	1-6	1-1	0-5	1-2
2. Barcombe Reserves	1-1	*	1-4	1-6	1-1	1-1	4-1	5-0	1-2	2-3	0-1	0-3	2-2	2-0
3. Bridgeview Reserves	6-2	5-0	*	3-0	1-3	2-2	1-1	8-3	3-2	2-2	2-1	3-4	3-2	2-1
4. D.M.S. Cuckfield Reserves	1-0	3-3	1-0	*	7-3	3-4	2-0	2-0	0-1	0-3	1-1	2-1	4-2	1-2
5. Fairwarp Reserves	5-0	7-2	3-2	2-4	*	1-4	1-3	L-W	3-1	1-1	0-5	2-3	3-3	4-0
6. Hartfield Reserves	1-1	2-4	0-6	1-3	2-4	*	3-4	3-0	2-2	3-2	2-4	3-4	1-1	8-4
7. Horsted Keynes Reserves	5-1	14-2	2-2	0-1	5-2	4-1	*	15-0	1-3	4-2	3-5	2-6	0-1	5-4
8. Lewes Rovers 'A'	1-1	6-2	4-5	0-5	3-7	1-1	1-9	*	1-4	3-2	2-5	2-3	0-7	2-3
9. Maresfield Village 'A'	6-1	1-1	7-1	4-1	1-0	2-3	3-2	5-4	*	2-5	2-4	2-1	0-0	2-1
10. Nutley Reserves	6-1	4-1	7-2	1-2	3-0	0-2	2-2	3-0	2-2	*	4-0	2-0	2-0	6-4
11. Sovereign Finance Res.	6-1	5-3	3-1	1-2	3-1	0-2	3-0	6-1	3-1	1-1	*	6-0	3-1	4-3
12. Uckfield Town 'A'	0-1	3-5	0-3	0-5	3-2	3-4	0-3	4-0	2-6	0-4	1-0	*	W-L	2-0
13. Village of Ditchling 'A'	4-0	3-1	1-1	1-2	4-2	1-5	4-1	1-2	0-3	0-3	1-9	3-3	*	2-1
14. Wealden 'A'	0-2	3-3	2-1	1-2	0-2	1-3	1-6	2-2	1-7	1-6	0-3	0-2	*	1-3

MONTGOMERY CHALLENGE CUP

First Round

Felbridge v Ashurst Green	1-5	Oakwood 'A' *(scr)* v Lingfield Rgrs Reserves *(w/o)*	
Uckfield Town v Cuckfield	3-5	Nutfield v Leftovers Sports	2-2,1-4
Handcross Village v Lingfield	2-2,2-1	Plumpton Athletic *(bye)*	
Crawley Down Utd v Village of Ditchling	5-5,0-5	Buxted Reserves v Wivelsfield Green	3-0
Forest Row v Lindfield	6-3	Chailey v Lewes Rovers	1-0
Heath Pilgrims v Wisdom Sports	1-4	Pease Pottage Village v Southwater	5-1
Wealden v East Grinstead Reserves	4-2	Clayton v Newick	0-2
Fairwarp v West Hoathly	2-5	Ardingly v Maresfield Village	1-6

Second Round

Ashurst Wood v Lindfield Rangers	2-1	Cuckfield v Nutley	2-3
West Hoathly v Maresfield Village	1-1,2-7	Handcross Village v Plumpton Athletic	2-3
Village of Ditchling v Buxted Reserves	7-1	Forest Row v Chailey	1-6
Wisdom Sports v Pease Pottage	1-2	Wealden v Newick	2-1

Quarter-Finals

Ashurst Wood v Nutley	2-1	Plumpton Athletic v Village of Ditchling	5-3
Wealden v Maresfield Village	2-3	Chailey v Pease Pottage 0-1 *(Pease Pottage expelled)*	

Semi-Finals

Ashurst Wood v Plumpton Athletic	0-3	Chailey v Maresfield Village	2-0

Final: Plumpton Athletic 1, Chailey 0

MOWATT CHALLENGE CUP

First Round

Southwater Reserves v Danehill	0-4	Plumpton Athletic Reserves v Oakwood 'A'	3-0
Heath Pilgrims v Bolney Rovers	2-4	Wivelsfield Green v Village of Ditchling	1-4
Lindfield Rgrs Res. v Nutley	1-0	Clayton v Handcross Village	2-1
East Grinstead 'A' v Uckfield Town	3-1	Groombridge v Horley Athletico	0-5
Leftovers Reserves v Forest Row	4-1	Anst v St Francis Hospital Reserves	1-0
Ahurst Wood v Chailey	1-0	Lewes Rovers *(w/o)* Feletchling Athletic *(scr)*	
Buxted Reserves v Turners Hill	7-0	Ringmer 'A' v Newick	6-2
Ardingly v Felbridge	1-4	Wisdom Sports Reserves v Fairwarp	1-2
(continued overleaf)			

(continued from page 591) **Second Round**

Plumpton Ath. Reserves v Danehill	1-0	
Lindfield Rgrs Reserves v Clayton	1-3	
Leftovers Reserves v Ansty	6-6,2-1	
Buxted Reserves v Ringmer 'A'	9-4	

Bolney Rovers v Village of Ditchling	1-3
East Grinstead 'A' v Horley Athletico	4-4,5-4
Ashurstwood v Lewes Rovers Reserves	3-2
Felbridge v Faiwarp	3-2

Quarter-Finals

Clayton v East Grinstead 'A'	1-2
Leftovers Reserves v Ashurst Wood	0-1

Plumpton Athletic Res. v Village of Ditchling	1-0
Buxted Reserves v Felbridge	3-0

Semi-Finals

Ashurst Wood v Buxted Reserves	5-2

Plumpton Ath. Reserves v East Grinstead 'A'	1-3

Final: Ashurst Wood 3, East Grinstead 'A' 1

EDGAR GERMAN CHALLENGE CUP Preliminary Round

Bolney Rovers v Lewes Rovers Reserves	1-5
Buxted Reserves v Groombridge	6-1

D.M.S. Cuckfield v Ansty	4-4,2-6

First Round

Fletchling Athletic *(scr)* Ringmer 'A'	0-4
Horley Athletico v Forest Row Reserves	5-1
Newick Reserves v Danehill	0-4
Plumpton Ath. Res v Balcombe	2-2,3-2
Franklands Vil. Res v Crawley Down U. Res.	5-1
Southwater Res. v Ashurst Wood Reserves	0-1
West Hoathly v Fairwarp	4-0
Crowborough Ath. 'A' v Turners Hill	2-3

Oakwood 'A' v Leftovers Reserves	3-4
Lindfield Reserves v St Francis Hosp. Res	4-0
Horsted Keynes v Lingfield Reserves	5-0
Maresfield Village Res v Wisdom Spts Res.	1-2
Cuckfield Reserves v Hurstpierpoint 'A'	5-0
Lewes Rovers Reserves v Lindfield Rgrs Res.	0-5
Hartfield v Ansty	2-4
Sovereign Finance v Buxted Reserves	3-2

Second Round

Ringmer 'A' v Leftovers S.C. 'A'	3-2
Danehill v Horsted Keynes	1-0
Franklands Village 'A' v Cuckfield Reserves	1-3
West Hoathly v Ansty	0-3

Horley Athletico v Lindfield Reserves	4-0
Plumpton Athletic Res. v Wisdom Spts Res.	5-1
Ashurst Wood Res v Lindfield Rgrs Res.	3-3,2-5
Turners Hill v Sovereign Finance	1-2

Quarter-Finals

Ringmer 'A' v Horley Athletico	1-4
Cuckfield Reserves v Lindfield Rgrs Res.	3-0

Danehill v Plumpton Athletic Reserves	3-1
Ansty v Sovereign Finance	3-2

Semi-Finals

Horley Athletico v Danehill	3-0

Cuckfield Reserves v Ansty	0-1

Final: Ansty 2, Horley Athletico 0

SOMERVILLE CHALLENGE CUP Preliminary Round

Cuckfield Green Res v Wivelsfield G. Res.	3-1
Ashurst Wood 'A' v Southwater 'A'	3-2
Buxted 'A' v Bridgeview	1-3

Hurstpierpoint 'A' v Scaynes Hill	4-0
Heath Pilgrims Reserves v Forest Row Reserves	5-1

First Round

Woodcock Athletic v Lindfield Reserves	2-0
Clayton Reserves v Staxil Burgess Hill	2-1
Hurstpierpoint 'A' v Crowborough Ath. 'A'	5-3
Ansty Reserves v Wisdom Sports 'A'	3-0
Village of Ditchling v D.M.S. Cuckfield	0-2
Ashurst Wood 'A' v Heath Pilgrims Reserves	2-4
Newick Reserves v Bridgeview Reserves	1-2
Felbridge Reserves v Hartfield	3-1

Lingfield Reserves v Crawley Down Lions	17-3
Ardingly Reserves v St Francis Hosp. 'A'	1-4
Wealden Reserves v Handcross Village Reserves	5-0
Pease Pot. Village Res v West Hoathly Reserves	2-3
Cuckfield 'A' v East Grinstead Mariners	0-2
Burgess Hill Rangers v Leftovers S.C. 'B'	1-2
Turners Hill Reserves v Uckfield Town Reserves	0-3
Chailey Reserves v Barcombe	2-1

Second Round

Woodcock Athletic v Lindfield Reserves	1-2
Hurstpierpoint 'A' v Wealden Reserves	1-4
D.M.S. Cuckfield v East Grinstead Mariners	3-1
Bridgeview v Uckfield Town Reserves	2-0

Clayton Reserves v St Francis Hospital 'A'	0-3
Ansty Reserves v West Hoathly Reserves	1-0
Heath Pilgrims Res v Leftovers S.C. 'B'	1-2
Felbridge Reserves v Chailey Reserves	4-1

Quarter-Finals

Lingfield Reserves v St Francis Hospital 'A'	2-0
D.M.S. Cuckfield *(w/o)* Leftovers S.C. 'B' *(scr.)*	

Wealden Reserves v Ansty Reserves	4-3
Bridgeview v Felbridge Reserves	1-4

Semi-Finals

Lingfield Reserves v Wealden Reserves	3-0

D.M.S. Cuckfield v Felbridge Reserves	3-2

Final: D.M.S. Cuckfield 4, Lingfield Reserves 0

STUBBINS CHALLENGE CUP First Round

D.M.S. Cuckfield v Horley Athletico	4-2
St Francis H. Reserves v Forest Hill Res.	10-0
Balcombe v Pease Pottage Village Res.	1-2
Lewes Rovers Reserves v Groombridge	1-0
Sovereign Finance v Danehill	4-0
Southwater 'A' v Staxill Burgess Hill	2-0
Newick Reserves v Burgess Hill Rangers	1-3
Ringmer 'A' v Ashurst Wood Reserves	1-2

Village of Ditchling Res. v Cuckfield Res.	2-2,0-5
Crawley Down U. Reserves v Hurstpierpoint 'A'	1-2
Leftovers Social Club Reserves v Hartfield	0-1
Lindfield Reserves v Franklands Village 'A'	2-4
Uckfield T. Res. v Crowborough A. Res.	3-3,2-2,2-4
Lingfield Reserves v East Grinstead Mariners	4-0
Wisdom Sports 'A' v Horsted Keynes	1-5
Maresfield Village Reserves *(bye)*	

Second Round

Cuckfield Reserves v D.M.S. Cuckfield	1-3
Pease Pottage Vill. Reserves v Hartfield	2-1
Sovereign Finance v Crowborough A. Res.	4-1
Burgess Hill Rgrs v Horsted Keynes	1-6

St Francis Hospital Res. v Hurstpierpoint Res.	9-3
Lewes Rvrs Reserves v Franklands Village 'A'	2-1
Southwater 'A' v Lingfield Reserves	1-6
Ashurst Wood Reserves v Maresfield Vil. Res.	6-2

Quarter-Finals

D.M.S. Cuckfield v St Francis Hospital Res.	1-3
Sovereign Finance v Lingfield Reserves	3-2

Pease Pottage Reserves v Lewes Rvrs Reserves	0-3
Horsted Keynes v Ashurst Wood Reserves	1-0

Semi-Finals

St Francis H. Res. v Lewes Rvrs Reserves	3-1

Sovereign Finance v Horsted Keynes	2-4

Final: St Francis Hospital Reserves 2, Horsted Keynes 0

STRATFORD CHALLENGE CUP Preliminary Round

Wivelsfield Green Reserves v Woodcock Ath.	0-1	Staxill Burgess Hill v Buxted 'A'	1-1,2-4
Crawley Hill Lions v Cuckfield 'A'	0-2	Maresfield Village 'A' v Balcombe Reserves	3-1

First Round

Barcombe v Woodcock Athletic	4-2	Handcross Village Reserves v Wisdom Spts 'A'	2-3
Horsted Keynes Reserves v Lindfield 'A'	2-0	Ashurst Wood 'A' v Fairwarp Reserves	2-5
Burgess Hill Rangers v Hartfield Reserves	1-2	Buxted 'A' v Lewes Rovers 'A'	7-2
Sovereign Reserves v Scaynes Hill	5-3	D.M.S. Cuckfield Reserves v Cuckfield 'A'	2-4
Nutley Reserves v Maresfield Village 'A'	5-0	Uckfield Town Reserves v West Hoathly Res.	3-3,1-4
Felbridge Reserves v Village of Ditchling 'A'	7-0	Wealden Reserves v Turners Hill Reserves	4-1
Bridgeview Reserves v Heath Pilgrims Reserves	3-5	Clayton Reserves v St Francis Hospital 'A'	0-4
Ansty Reserves v Leftovers Social Club 'B'	4-2	Ardingly Reserves v Chailey Reserves	2-4

Second Round

Barcombe v Wisdom Sports 'A'	1-2	Horsted Keynes v Fairwarp Reserves	1-2
Hartfield Reserves v Buxted 'A'	6-0	Sovereign Finance Res. v Cuckfield 'A'	7-0
Nutley Reserves v West Hoathly Reserves	2-1	Felbridge Reserves v Wealden Reserves	0-5
Heath Pilgrims Res. v St Francis Hos. 'A'	0-6	Ansty Reserves v Chailey Reserves	6-1

Quarter-Finals

Wisdom Sports 'A' v Fairwarp Reserves	5-0	Hartfield Reserves v Sovereign Finance Reserves	0-4
Nutley Reserves v Wealden Reserves	5-1	St Francis Hospital 'A' v Ansty Reserves	5-1

Semi-Finals

Barcombe v Sovereign Finance	2-1	Nutley Reserves v St Francis Hospital	0-5

Final: Barcombe 2, St Francis Hospital 'A' 0

MALINS CHALLENGE CUP First Round

Chailey Reserves v Ansty Reserves	3-0	Sovereign Finance Reserves v West Hoathly Reserves	0-4
Wealden 'A' v Ashurst Wood 'A'	2-3	Hartfield Reserves v Handcross Village Reserves	3-6
Buxted 'A' v Maresfield Village 'A'	1-1,3-2	Cuckfield 'A' v Uckfield Town 'A'	4-2
Nutley Reserves v Balcombe Reserves	9-0	Lewes Rovers Res. v Balcombe Reserves	3-6

Second Round

Chailey Reserves v Sovereign Finance Res.	2-1	Ashurst Wood 'A' v Handcross Village Reserves	2-0
Felbridge Reserves v Buxted 'A'	2-2,3-0	Fairwarp Reserves v Cuckfield 'A'	0-3
Nutley Reserves v Lindfield 'A'	3-1	Barcombe Reserves v D.M.S. Cuckfield Reserves	3-1
Ardingly Reserves v Village of Ditchling 'A'	2-1	Bridgeview Reserves v Horsred Keynes Reserves	4-1

Quarter-Finals

Chailey Reserves v Ashurst Wood 'A'	2-2,3-2	Felbridge Reserves v Cuckfield 'A'	3-2
Nutley Reserves v Barcombe Reserves	5-0	Ardingly Reserves v Horsted Keynes Reserves	2-0

Semi-Finals

Chailey Reserves v Felbridge Reserves	3-3,2-1	Nutley Reserves v Ardingly Reserves	6-0

Final: Nutley Reserves 1, Chailey Reserves 0

VETERANS CUP First Round

Pease Pottage Village (w/o) Cuckfield (scr.)		Barcombe v Southwater	0-4
Newick v Lewes Rovers	5-2	Plumpton Athletic (w/o) Ansty (scr.)	
Oakwood v Nutley	1-0		

Quarter-Finals

Wisdom Sports v Ardingly	2-4	Village of Ditchling (w/o) Pease Pottage Village (scr.)	
Southwater (w/o) Newick (scr.)		Plumpton Athletic v Oakwood	1-3

Semi-Finals

Ardingly v Village of Ditchling	2-3	Soothwater v Oakwood	1-0

Final: Southwater 3, Village of Ditchling 1

PREMIER DIVISION CLUBS 1993-94

CHAILEY
Secretary: Mr D Foord, Broomfields Farm Cottage, South Chailey, Lewes BN8 4QJ (0273 890085).
Ground: Chailey Rec. **Colours:** Red/white/red.

LEFTOVERS SPORTS CLUB
Secretary: Miss K Wheeler, 10 Kennedy Ave., East Grinstead RH19 2DE (0342 301335).
Ground: Kings Centre, Moat Rd, East Grinstead **Colours:** Blue/black/black.

LEWES ROVERS
Secretary: Mrs P Barker, 14 Caburn Cres., Lewes BN7 1NR (0273 476784).
Ground: Cooksbridge Rec. **Colours:** All yellow.

MARESFIELD VILLAGE
Secretary: Mr T Gee, 1 Park View Rd, Uckfield TN22 1JP (0825 764496).
Ground: Maresfield Rec. **Colours:** White/black/black.

NEWICK
Secretary: Mrs J Brown, 1 Arkendale, Felbridge RH19 2QU (0342 313531).
Ground: King George V Rec., Newick **Colours:** White/blue/white.

NUTLEY
Secretary: Mr K Funnell, 21 Selhurst Rd, Woolingdean, Brighton BN2 6WE (0273 308127).
Ground: Fords Green, Nutley. **Colours:** Sky/navy/navy.

PEASE POTTAGE VILLAGE
Secretary: Mr R Cornock, 41 Selsey Rd, Broadfield, Crawley RH11 9HP (0293 515112).
Ground: Finches Field, Pease Pottage **Colours:** Green & white/black/green.

PLUMPTON ATHLETIC
Secretary: Mrs Chris Brimicombe, 10 Hollycroft, East Chiltington BN7 3AZ (0273 890697).
Ground: King George VI PF, Plumpton **Colours:** Blue & white stripes/blue/red.

SOUTHWATER
Secretary: Mrs Lynda McPherson, Hopedene, Green Close, Southwater RH13 7HA (0403 730265).
Ground: Village Centre, Pevensey Rd *(or Church Lane)* **Colours:** Red & black/black/red.

WEALDEN
Secretary: G Pope, c/o 10 Cleve Close, Framfield, Uckfield TN22 5PQ (0825 890632).
Ground: Framfield Rec., Uckfield **Colours:** White & blue/blue/white.

DIVISION ONE CLUBS 1993-94

ANSTY
Secretary: Mrs J Bealey, 34a Old Shoreham Rd, Brighton BN1 5DD (0273 883210).
Ground: Deaks Lane, Ansty (0444 454010) **Colours:** Yellow/blue/blue.

ASHURST WOOD
Secretary: A Goold, 5 Chestnut Close, East Grinstead RH19 3UW (0342 317533).
Ground: Hammerwood Rd Rec, Ashurst Wood **Colours:** Red/black/red.

CLAYTON
Secretary: Mr John Bushell, 36 Victoria Close, Burgess Hill RH15 9QS (0444 245940).
Ground: Belmont Ground, Belmont Rd, Hassocks **Colours:** Red & blue/blue/blue.

FELBRIDGE
Secretary: Mr J McCuffie, 5 Waterside, East Grinstead RH19 3XS (0342 325969).
Ground: Crawley Down Rd, Felbridge **Colours:** All yellow.

HANDCROSS VILLAGE
Secretary: Mr P Sinclair, 2 Warren Cottages, Horsham Rd, Handcross RH17 6DJ (0444 400621).
Ground: Handcross Rec. **Colours:** Amber & black/black/black.

HEATH PILGRIMS
Secretary: Mrs Angela Broad, 7 Orchard Close, Scaynes Hill RH17 7PQ (0444 242643).
Ground: Victoria Park, Haywards Heath. **Colours:** Claret & grey/grey/grey.

LINDFIELD
Secretary: Mr J Phipps, 33 Triangle Rd, Haywards Heath RH16 4HN (0444 415240).
Ground: Lindfield Common **Colours:** Green/white/green.

UCKFIELD TOWN
Secretary: Mr D Nelson, 24 Lealands Court, The Drive, Uckfield TN22 2AG (0825 766125).
Ground: Victoria Pleasure Ground, Uckfield **Colours:** Red/black/black.

VILLAGE OF DITCHLING
Secretary: Mrs J Jenner, 21 Blackthorns, Hurstpierpoint, West Sussex (0273 833930).
Ground: Ditchling Rec., Lewes Rd, Ditchling (0273 843423) **Colours:** Red/white/red.

WISDOM SPORTS
Secretary: Mr B Menzies, 15 Augustines Way, Haywards Heath RH16 3JQ (0444 456016).
Ground: Isle of Thorns, Haywards Heath **Colours:** Red/white/red.

WIVELSFIELD GREEN
Secretary: Mr B Truran, 17 Kemps, Hurstpierpoint BN6 9UF (0273 834513).
Ground: Wivelsfield Green Rec. **Colours:** Green/black/green.

Plus the Reserve sides of: *Leftovers Sports Club, and Lindfield Rangers (see page 576).*

DIVISION TWO CLUBS 1993-94

ARDINGLY
Secretary: Mr D Cole, 9 College Rd, Ardingly RH17 6TU (0444 892102).
Ground: Ardingly Rec. **Colours:** Blue & white stripes/blue/blue.

BOLNEY ROVERS
Secretary: Mr J Faulkner, 14 Bankside, Bolney, West Sussex (0444 881701).
Ground: Bolney Rec. **Colours:** Sky & navy stripes/white/blue.

FOREST ROW
Secretary: Mr Townsend, 49 Forest View Rd, East Grinstead RH19 4AW (0342 328202).
Ground: Memorial Ground, Chapel Lane, Forest Row **Colours:** Yellow & green/green/green.

HORLEY ATHLETICO
Secretary: Mr P Woodburn, 16 Michael Cres., Horley, Surrey RH6 7LH (0293 784668).
Ground: Horley Youth Centre, Court Lodge, Horley **Colours:** Red/black/black.

WEST HOATHLY
Secretary: Mr D Dibble, 37 Forest View Rd, East Grinstead RH19 4AW (0342 312797).
Ground: West Hoathly Rec. **Colours:** Claret & blue/claret/claret.

Plus the Reserve sides of: *Buxted (see page 574), Hassocks (page 567), Hurstpierpoint (page 575), Plumpton Ath., St Francis Hospital (page 576), Southwater, Wisdom Sports.*

DIVISION THREE CLUBS 1993-94

BALCOMBE
Secretary: Mr C Tester, 145 St Marys Drive, Pound Hill, Crawley RH10 3BG (0293 537103).
Ground: Balcombe Rec. **Colours:** Red/black/red.

D.M.S. CUCKFIELD
Secretary: Mr M Robson, 14 Wheatsheaf Lane, Cuckfield RH17 5TZ (0444 441064).
Ground: Hickmans Lane *(or Whitemans Green)*, Cuckfield **Colours:** Green/white/green.

FAIRWARP
Secretary: Mr J Lazenby, 'Androse', 19 Old Forge Lane, Fairwarp TN22 3EW (0825 712188).
Ground: Fairwarp Sports Field **Colours:** Green/white/green.

HORSTED KEYNES

Secretary: Mr A V Barker, 36 Challoners, Horsted Keynes RH17 7DT (0825 790036).
Ground: Horsted Keynes Rec.   **Colours:** Blue & white/blue/blue.

SOVEREIGN FINANCE

Secretary: Mr S Etherington, 81 Newlands Cres., East Grinstead (0342 312231).
Ground: East Court, East Grinstead   **Colours:** Yellow/red/yellow.

TURNERS HILL

Secretary: Mr M Purcell, 24 Bourg de Peage Ave., East Grinstead RH19 3YE (0342 301323).
Ground: Turners Hill Rec.   **Colours:** Claret/white/claret.

Plus the Reserve sides of: *Lingfield (see page 576), Maresfield Village,* **and the 'A' sides of:** *East Grinstead (page 560), Leftovers S.C., Oakwood (page 562), Ringmer (page 564, playing at Ringmer Community College).*

DIVISION FOUR CLUBS 1993-94

A.F.C. PEACEHAVEN

Secretary: Mr A Mills, 121 Horsham Ave., Peacehaven BN10 8DT (0273 585577).
     Ground: Sports Park, Piddington Avenue, Peacehaven.

DANEHILL

Secretary: Mr D Weeding, 27 Oak Tree Cottages, Danehill RH17 790113 (0825 790113).
Ground: Isle of Thorns, Chelwood Gate.   **Colours:** Blue & yellow/blue/yellow.

JARVIS BROOK

Secretary: Mr C Frampton, 11 Windsor Place, Jarvis Brook, Crowborough TN6 2HU   (0892 661413).
Ground: Limekiln PF, Palesgate, Crowborough

ROTHERFIELD

Secretary: Mr R Paige, 8 Brook Cottages, New Rd, Rotherfield TN6 3JT (0892 852931).
Ground: Rotherfield Sports Ground, Rotherfield

WOODCOCK ATHLETIC

Secretary: Mr S Duly, 'The Shieling', Woodcock Hill, Felbridge RH19 2RD (0342 410474).
Ground: Danehill Rec.   **Colours:** All green.

Plus the Reserve sides of: *Ashurst Wood, Crawley Down Village, Cuckfield, Lewes Rovers,* **and the 'A' sides of:** *Crowborough Ath. (see page 558), Franklands Village (page 575), St Francis Hospital (page 576).*

DIVISION FIVE CLUBS 1993-94

BARCOMBE

Secretary: Mr R Hepple, 20 Grantham Bank, Barcombe BN8 5DJ (0293 400576).
Ground: Barcombe Rec.   **Colours:** Yellow & black/black/yellow.

BRIDGEVIEW

Secretary: Mr W Richards, 15 Beckett Way, Malling, Lewes BN7 2EB (0273 478215).
Ground: Malling Comm. Centre, Spences Lane, Lewes   **Colours:** Orange/black/black.

EAST GRINSTEAD MARINERS

Secretary: Mr R Connor, 'The Ship Inn', Ship Str., East Grinstead RH19 4EG (0342 312089).
Ground: Imberhorne Sch., Imberhorne Lane, East Grinstead   **Colours:** White/black/black.

GROOMBRIDGE

Secretary: Mr A Tamkin, 40 Erskine Park Rd, Rusthall, Tunbridge Wells, Kent TN4 8UR (0892 541041).
Ground: The Tanyard, Corsley Rd, Groombridge.   **Colours:** Sky/navy/navy.

HARTFIELD

Secretary: Mr B Moore, 19 Post Horn Lane, Forest Row RH18 5DD (0342 823571).
Ground: Town Croft, Hartfield   **Colours:** White (black trim)/black/white.

Plus the Reserve sides of: *Felbridge, Lindfield, Newick, Pease Pottage Village, Village of Ditchling,* **and the 'A' sides of:** *Hurstpierpoint, Southwater.*

DIVISION SIX CLUBS 1993-94

SCAYNES HILL

Secretary: Mr J Jeremiah, 7 Hillcrest Rd, Scaynes Hill RH17 7PJ (0444 831437).
Ground: Scaynes Hill Rec.   **Colours:** Red/black/red.

STAXIL (BURGESS HILL)

Secretary: Mr C Rogers, 143 Maples Drive, Burgess Hill RH15 8DE (0444 243487).
Ground: Fairfield Rd Rec, Burgess Hill   **Colours:** Yellow/blue/blue.

Plus the Reserve sides of: *Clayton, D.M.S. Cuckfield, Forest Row, Heath Pilgrims (playing at Barn Cottage, Haywards Heath), Sovereign Finance, Uckfield Town, Wealden, Wivelsfield Green,* **and the 'A' side of:** *Wisdom Sports (playing at Victoria Park, Haywards Heath),* **and the 'B' side of:** *Leftovers S.C.*

DIVISION SEVEN CLUBS 1993-94

DORMANSLAND ROCKETS

Secretary: Mr S Hendry, 5 Locks Meadow, Dormansland, Surrey RH7 6AW (0342 884446).
     Ground: Colin Anderson PF, Wilderwick Rd, Lingfield, Surrey.

Plus the Reserve sides of: *Ansty, Chailey, Handcross Village, Turners Hill, West Hoathly,* **and the 'A' sides of:** *Buxted (playing at Highhurst Rec), Crawley Down Village, Cuckfield (playing at Whitemans Green), Lindfield,* **and the 'B' side of:** *Hassocks.*

DIVISION EIGHT CLUBS 1993-94

The Reserve sides of: *Ardingly, Bridgeview, Fairwarp, Hartfield, Horsted Keynes, Nutley,* **and the 'A' sides of:** *Ashurst Wood, Lingfield, Maresfield Village, Uckfield Town, Village of Ditchling.*

DIVISION NINE CLUBS 1993-94

HAYWARD RANGERS

Secretary: Mr M Sutherland, 19 Samphire Close, Broadfields, Crawley RH11 9EN (0293 618152).
Ground: Barn Cottage, Haywards Heath.

Plus the Reserve sides of: *Barcombe, Balcombe, Danehill, Jarvis Brook, Rotherfield, Scaynes Hill,* **and the 'A' sides of:** *Lewes Rovers (playing at Convent Field), Plumpton Athletic, Wealden,* **and the 'B' side of:** *Maresfield Village.*

UNIJET BRIGHTON, HOVE & DISTRICT LEAGUE

PREM. DIVISION	P	W	D	L	F	A	PTS
AFC Falcons	20	16	2	2	83	19	50
Endsleigh	20	15	4	1	70	19	49
American Express	20	11	2	7	60	41	35
Midway	20	11	2	7	57	48	35
Old Varndeanians	20	9	4	7	36	45	31
Brighton B.B.O.B.	20	7	3	10	37	51	24
Rottingdean '89	20	5	8	7	32	42	23
Stanmer Athletic	20	7	1	12	30	46	22
Legal & General	20	5	3	12	25	50	18
Preston Village	20	4	3	13	25	63	15
Portslade Athletic	20	2	4	14	19	50	10

DIVISION ONE	P	W	D	L	F	A	PTS
Patcham (1903)AFC	20	16	2	2	62	11	50
Uni. of Sussex	20	15	2	3	68	25	47
Grenadier	20	12	1	7	62	37	37
Hanover	20	12	1	7	56	37	37
Hassocks 'A'	20	10	3	7	45	40	33
Withdean Res.	20	8	3	9	44	32	27
Ericsson	20	8	1	11	38	60	25
Hurstpierpoint Res.	20	6	2	12	39	51	20
Brighton Insurance	20	6	2	12	39	67	20
Brighton Electricity	20	4	1	154	24	78	13
AMP Connectors	20	4	0	16	23	62	12

DIVISION TWO	P	W	D	L	F	A	PTS
AFC Bensleys	20	14	1	5	60	41	43
Hartwells Athletic	20	13	2	5	70	39	41
Sussex County Rgrs	20	12	5	3	53	28	41
International Factors	20	12	3	5	58	35	39
Alliance & Leicester	20	12	2	6	55	31	38
American Ex. Res.	20	10	3	7	59	41	33
Uni. of Sussex Res.	20	8	4	8	52	53	28
Hove County	20	6	2	12	31	46	20
Burgess Hill Ath.	20	6	1	13	41	54	19
Dray & Sons	20	2	2	16	21	80	8
Shoreham United	20	2	1	17	27	79	7

DIVISION THREE	P	W	D	L	F	A	PTS
The Hollingbury	18	17	0	1	92	25	51
Barclays Bank	18	12	3	3	65	37	39
Brighton Rangers	18	7	5	6	37	37	26
Madison Tigers	18	7	4	7	37	40	25
Portslade Ath Res.	18	6	3	9	38	47	21
Adur Athletic	18	6	2	10	26	41	20
AFC Falcons Res.	18	5	3	10	48	54	18
Rottingdean '89 Res.	18	4	6	8	32	59	18
Saltdean Utd 'A'	18	4	5	9	31	46	17
Midway Res.	18	4	5	9	28	48	17

DIVISION FOUR	P	W	D	L	F	A	PTS
Lower Bevendean	20	16	0	4	76	37	48
Shannon	20	13	2	5	46	32	41
Clarendon Church	20	10	4	6	57	45	34
Brighton Telephones	20	10	3	7	48	43	33
Montpelier Villa	20	8	6	6	54	29	30
Brighton P.O.Youth	20	9	3	8	46	37	30
Grenadier Res.	20	9	3	8	51	55	30
SX County Rgrs Res.	20	6	3	11	35	50	21
O Varndeanians Res.	20	6	2	12	38	67	20
Legal & Gen. Res.	20	4	4	12	22	49	16
Hove Streamline U.	20	3	2	15	46	75	11

DIVISION FIVE	P	W	D	L	F	A	PTS
AFC Peacehaven	20	15	2	3	75	30	47
Patcham Res.	20	13	1	6	64	32	40
Sunblest Rangers	20	12	2	6	53	40	38
The Mile	20	11	4	5	67	42	37
Hassocks 'B'	20	8	3	9	51	62	27
B'ton Rangers Res.	20	8	2	10	41	48	26
Old Toll Gate	20	8	2	10	32	53	26
Lwr Bevendean Res.	20	7	3	10	48	52	24
Burgess Hill A. Res.	20	6	3	11	40	67	21
B'ton Electricity Res.	20	5	3	12	36	51	18
Queens Park Bupa	20	2	5	13	31	62	11

DIVISION SIX	P	W	D	L	F	A	PTS
Stanmer Ath. Res.	14	13	1	0	66	18	40
Portslade Ath. 'A'	14	7	5	2	38	24	26
B'ton B.B.O.B. Res.	14	6	3	5	30	32	21
B'ton Tele. Res.	14	5	4	5	47	36	19
Southern Rgrs O.B.	14	5	3	6	39	39	18
Shoreham Utd Res.	14	4	3	7	23	32	15
Jaycee Sports	14	3	3	8	27	36	12
B'ton Insurance Res.	14	2	0	12	21	74	6

DIVISION SEVEN	P	W	D	L	F	A	PTS
Erib E.T.L.	16	12	1	3	46	28	37
Woodingdean (Sat)	16	10	2	4	58	30	32
Sussex Panthers	16	8	3	5	59	44	27
B'ton P.O. Yth Res.	16	8	3	5	62	48	27
Norton & Wiston	16	7	3	6	52	40	24
Lion & Unicorn	16	6	2	8	48	54	20
SX County Rgrs 'A'	16	3	6	7	30	27	15
Nurdin & Peacock	16	5	0	11	35	72	15
Legal & General 'A'	16	2	2	12	11	58	8

DIVISION 6 & 7 SUPPLEMENTARY TROPHY

GROUP ONE	P	W	D	L	F	A	PTS
Stanmer Ath Res.	8	7	0	1	52	10	21
Woodingdean (Sat)	8	7	0	1	36	11	21
B'ton P.O. Yth Res.	8	4	1	3	29	22	13
B'ton Telephones Res.	8	3	2	3	17	18	11
Sussex Panthers	8	3	1	4	27	25	10
SX County Rgrs 'A'	8	2	4	2	9	16	10
Lion & Unicorn	8	2	3	3	16	23	9
B'ton Insurance Res.	8	1	1	6	10	25	4
Legal & Gen. Res.	8	0	2	6	2	48	2

GROUP TWO	P	W	D	L	F	A	PTS
Shoreham Utd Res.	7	5	0	2	15	10	15
Southern Rgrs O.B.	7	4	1	2	24	14	13
Brighton B.B.O.B.	7	4	1	2	24	15	13
Erib Etl	7	3	1	3	17	20	10
Nurdin & Peacock	7	3	0	4	16	18	9
Jaycee Sports	7	2	2	3	13	17	8
Norton & Wiston	7	2	1	4	13	19	7
Portslade Ath. 'A'	7	1	2	4	12	21	5

GOSPORT & FAREHAM LEAGUE

DIV. ONE	P	W	D	L	F	A	PTS
Ferndale	14	12	0	2	64	12	24
Royal F.C.	14	8	3	3	41	23	19
Fareport	14	7	2	5	45	27	16
Rowner Rec.	14	6	4	4	46	36	16
Bridgemary	14	6	3	5	48	34	15
Stoke Select	14	6	3	5	37	30	15
Lee Athletic	14	2	0	12	15	103	4
Turnpike	14	1	1	12	23	54	3

Division Two Champions: A.F.C. Castle

WINSTONLEAD
KENT LEAGUE

President: D.D. Baker
Chairman: P.C. Wager
Vice-Chairman: E.V. Ward
Hon. Secretary: A.R. Vinter, The Smithy,
The Square, Chilham, Canterbury, Kent CT4 8BY (0227 730884)

The team of the season and champions of the Winstonlead Kent League division one were Tonbridge FC, taking the title from the 1991/92 champions Herne Bay who finished their season in the runners-up place after an exciting finish in the last few months of the campaign. At the start of April, Herne Bay were eight points behind Tonbridge FC with five games in hand and it looked likely that the title would be regained by the side from Winch's Field especially after a run of nine wins. But a dramatic loss of form that saw Herne Bay lose vital matches handed the title to Tonbridge for the first time in their history. The hopes of Tonbridge FC regaining their Beazer Homes League status now rest with their committee. Tonbridge had been relegated from the Southern Division four seasons ago and have always made it known that they have wished to rejoin the higher grade of football. Elsewhere in the League, throughout the season, we have seen some remarkable peformances which include the efforts of Sheppey United who finished in third place behind Tonbridge FC and Herne Bay with the best "away" record of all the clubs, sixteen wins and two draws. They also managed a spell during the season of not conceeding for ten consecutive league games to equal the record of Whitstable Town in 1990/91. Deal Town, who finished fourth, scored a record of 128 league goals, beating their 1992/93 record of 119, from their forty matches played. They also recorded the biggest win of the season when they defeated Tunbridge Wells (away) by eleven goals to one (the previous week they beat the same side at home by eight goals to two).

A good season was had by Alma Swanley, Chatham Town and Danson Furness United as they all finished well and with high placings which gives them all a good platform for the new season. The biggest disappointment must have been for Faversham Town, last seasons runners-up to Herne Bay, who finished their campaign a lowly fifteenth place. At the bottom, Crockenhill and Corinthian have to face re-election when it comes to the A.G.M. Certainly for Corinthian this is a position that two years ago you would not have thought possible, but after relegation from the Southern League they have slipped badly.

In division two, Dover Athletic completed a notable "double" for the club, their first team having won the Southern League Premier title, by winning the division two championship from Herne Bay, Hastings with third.

In the respective divisional league cups, Ramsgate triumphed over Beckenham Town in an exciting final by a goal to nil and the same score applied in the division two final as Tonbridge FC beat Canterbury City to complete a club double. The Kent Senior Trophy was won by Cray Wanderers who defeated Whitstable Town in the final by a goal to nil at Gillingham's Priestfield Stadium, whilst the Kent Intermediate Cup Final saw Bromley overcome Dover Athletic by three goals to one. Efforts from the Winstonlead Kent League sides in the F.A. Cup saw Deal Town reach the third qualifying round before losing to Ashford Town from the Beazer Homes Southern League, and Tunbridge Wells progressed to the fourth round of the F.A. Vase before going out to Hoddesdon Town from the Campri League.

Overall, the 1992/93 season in the Winstonlead Kent League has been a successsful one for all the clubs with many looking forward to the new season with recharged legs and a continuation of sponsorship from Winstonlead Cables Ltd..
Paul Rivers (Press Officer)

Tonbridge F.C., Winstonlead Kent League Champions. Back Row: Steve Campfield, Mark Gillham, Gary Julians, Steve Gibbons, Ian Mawson, Steve Clark, Richard Hardy. Front Row: Danny Woods, Tony Booth, Dave Boyton, Steve Hearn, Danny Tingley, Peter Jarvis. Photo - Roger Turner.

LEAGUE TABLES 1992-93

DIV. ONE	P	W	D	L	F	A	PTS
Tonbridge AFC	40	27	9	4	107	39	90
Herne Bay	40	26	6	8	96	44	84
Sheppey United	40	24	9	7	65	29	81
Deal Town	40	24	7	9	128	58	79
Alma Swanley	40	24	4	12	93	65	76
Chatham Town	40	19	11	10	79	52	68
Danson Furness U.	40	18	13	9	58	40	67
Thamesmead Town	40	17	9	14	62	56	60
Beckenham Town	40	17	8	15	64	60	59
Whitstable Town	40	18	4	18	77	64	58
Slade Green	40	15	13	12	71	60	58
Ramsgate	40	17	5	18	78	76	56
Folkestone Invicta	40	16	5	19	78	95	53
Tunbridge Wells	40	13	6	21	66	102	45
Faversham Town	40	11	10	19	44	71	43
Greenwich Borough	40	12	5	23	49	75	41
Cray Wanderers	40	10	8	22	64	79	38
Kent Police	40	10	7	23	56	121	37
Darenth Heathside	40	9	7	24	54	104	34
Corinthian	40	6	8	26	50	95	26
Crockenhill	40	6	8	26	56	108	26

DIV. TWO	P	W	D	L	F	A	PTS
Dover Ath. Res.	26	21	3	2	81	23	66
Herne Bay Res.	26	20	2	4	78	27	62
Hastings T. Res.	26	16	1	9	73	39	49
Beckenham T. Res.	26	14	5	7	54	41	47
Canterbury C. Res.	26	12	5	9	62	58	41
Thamesmead Res.	26	10	7	9	47	39	37
Whitstable T. Res.	26	10	4	12	40	57	34
Tonbridge Res.	26	9	6	11	44	49	33
Darenth H. Res.	26	10	3	13	34	44	33
Folkestone I. Res.	26	7	4	15	36	58	25
Chatham T. Res.	26	7	3	16	48	59	24
Deal Town Res.	26	6	5	15	43	66	23
Cray Wdrs Res.	26	6	4	16	32	70	22
Ramsgate Res.	26	4	8	14	27	69	20

DIVISION ONE RESULT CHART 1992-93

HOME TEAM	1	2	3	4	5	6	7	8	9	10	11	12	13	14	15	16	17	18	19	20	21
1. Alma Swanley	*	2-1	2-5	4-2	2-0	1-2	2-3	7-2	0-6	1-0	4-2	1-0	0-1	3-2	0-5	1-2	2-1	2-2	2-5	6-1	6-0
2. Beckenham T.	1-0	*	2-0	3-1	2-0	4-1	1-1	2-1	1-3	4-0	3-4	0-1	3-1	1-2	6-0	0-0	1-0	1-0	2-3	0-2	1-0
3. Chatham Town	1-0	2-2	*	3-1	1-0	5-3	2-0	3-3	4-2	0-1	4-0	0-1	1-1	4-0	1-0	1-0	0-2	3-1	0-2	1-1	3-0
4. Corinthian	1-2	0-0	1-1	*	4-1	2-1	1-4	0-1	0-7	1-2	1-7	2-2	1-3	0-3	3-4	2-3	0-2	1-1	1-3	1-1	2-3
5. Cray Wanderers	0-1	1-2	1-4	1-1	*	6-0	3-2	2-0	2-5	0-3	2-0	2-3	2-1	5-2	7-2	0-4	0-1	1-2	0-4	1-1	1-3
6. Crockenhill	0-6	1-2	1-4	2-3	2-2	*	1-2	2-2	1-6	3-0	7-1	1-4	1-4	1-2	1-0	0-1	2-2	1-2	3-5	2-2	0-2
7. Danson Furness	0-0	0-0	0-0	1-1	0-2	4-1	*	1-0	1-0	3-0	2-2	2-1	0-1	0-1	4-1	0-1	0-0	2-1	2-2	2-1	3-2
8. Darenth Heath.	1-7	3-0	1-6	2-1	0-0	1-1	0-3	*	1-3	1-4	2-3	0-3	0-1	1-4	2-0	0-3	0-2	1-3	1-3	6-3	4-3
9. Deal Town	2-3	1-0	1-1	1-3	3-2	4-3	1-3	3-1	*	5-0	6-2	3-3	4-3	5-0	2-1	1-4	2-2	1-1	0-0	8-2	3-1
10. Faversham Town	2-3	1-1	1-3	1-1	1-1	0-0	2-1	2-0	0-2	*	0-3	3-0	0-1	2-2	1-2	0-5	3-3	1-1	2-3	0-2	3-0
11. Folkestone Inv.	1-2	1-1	1-3	1-1	1-1	0-0	2-1	2-0	0-2	1-1	*	4-0	0-3	0-0	1-5	3-4	2-3	1-0	0-5	1-4	1-1
12. Greenwich Boro	1-2	1-2	4-1	0-1	1-0	0-0	0-1	1-1	0-4	1-0	2-4	*	0-3	2-3	1-1	0-2	2-4	0-2	0-3	0-2	4-2
13. Herne Bay	2-2	4-1	1-1	4-0	5-1	4-0	1-1	8-0	3-1	4-2	0-3	0-2	*	5-0	3-1	0-2	2-1	4-3	3-1	4-1	1-3
14. Kent Police	2-5	3-1	2-2	2-0	0-8	3-5	1-1	3-4	0-5	0-2	2-6	3-0	1-1	*	2-2	0-2	2-2	0-4	0-5	2-0	1-7
15. Ramsgate	1-2	2-1	3-2	2-1	2-2	5-3	3-1	4-1	1-1	4-0	0-2	4-2	0-3	4-1	*	0-1	1-2	1-0	2-2	4-0	1-0
16. Sheppey United	0-1	0-1	1-1	5-3	0-2	2-0	0-0	1-1	2-2	1-0	1-2	1-0	0-1	3-0	2-0	*	2-0	0-0	1-1	1-0	1-1
17. Slade Green	1-1	1-1	1-1	1-4	3-3	4-0	1-3	3-1	1-4	1-2	3-3	0-2	1-3	5-2	2-1	0-0	*	1-0	3-0	2-3	5-1
18. Thamesmead T.	3-2	1-1	0-5	3-2	3-2	0-0	2-2	0-2	0-0	4-1	3-1	2-1	3-1	4-2	4-1	1-2	0-0	*	0-3	4-0	1-0
19. Tonbridge	2-0	4-0	3-0	4-1	3-0	1-0	0-0	2-2	4-2	6-0	3-0	5-0	0-0	5-0	1-4	2-1	2-2	3-0	*	1-1	2-1
20. Tunbridge Wells	1-3	4-3	1-3	1-0	3-0	4-0	0-2	1-3	1-11	1-1	5-2	0-4	1-4	5-1	4-3	1-2	1-3	0-4	2-4	*	3-1
21. Whitstable Town	1-3	6-2	5-0	3-0	0-0	5-1	2-0	3-1	1-3	0-0	5-2	4-0	0-2	4-0	2-1	1-2	1-0	0-1	1-0	2-0	*

DIVISION TWO RESULT CHART 1992-93

HOME TEAM	1	2	3	4	5	6	7	8	9	10	11	12	13	14
1. Beckenham Town Reserves	*	1-1	3-0	2-1	2-1	4-1	0-4	2-2	3-2	5-2	1-0	1-0	4-3	7-1
2. Canterbury City Reserves	1-1	*	2-4	4-2	3-0	2-1	0-1	2-3	5-1	3-1	3-1	3-2	3-1	5-1
3. Chatham Town Reserves	0-0	11-0	*	7-0	3-0	3-3	2-3	0-4	2-0	1-3	0-1	1-3	3-1	0-3
4. Cray Wanderers Reserves	1-4	1-2	3-1	*	1-4	2-2	0-3	1-0	2-8	1-1	4-2	0-0	2-1	1-4
5. Darenth Heathside Reserves	0-6	0-0	3-0	3-0	*	2-1	0-3	0-3	0-6	0-2	3-1	2-0	2-0	5-0
6. Deal Town Reserves	1-1	2-7	4-1	4-0	1-2	*	1-4	2-0	1-7	0-4	4-0	1-3	1-2	2-2
7. Dover Athletic Reserves	7-2	1-0	3-1	2-0	4-0	4-0	*	5-1	0-2	4-2	5-0	5-1	2-2	6-1
8. Folkestone Invicta Reserves	1-2	4-1	3-2	1-1	1-1	1-4	0-2	*	2-4	0-1	1-0	0-1	0-4	2-1
9. Hastings Town Reserves	5-0	7-2	2-0	2-3	2-0	3-0	1-3	6-3	*	1-2	3-0	2-1	2-0	2-0
10. Herne Bay Reserves	2-1	1-1	8-0	3-0	1-0	5-1	1-3	4-0	4-0	*	7-0	3-2	4-1	1-0
11. Ramsgate Reserves	2-1	3-3	1-3	0-3	0-4	3-3	1-1	1-1	3-2	0-6	*	2-2	2-2	1-0
12. Thamesmead T. Reserves	0-1	4-1	3-3	4-1	1-2	0-4	6-1	2-0	0-1	2-2	*	2-2	0-0
13. Tonbridge A.F.C. Reserves	1-0	3-2	2-0	4-1	0-0	1-3	2-1	2-0	0-0	1-4	4-0	2-2	*	1-5
14. Whitstable Town Reserves	2-0	1-6	1-0	2-1	2-1	2-0	1-1	3-2	1-3	2-5	1-1	0-2	4-2	*

DIVISION ONE CUP 1992-93

First Round

Slade Green v Corinthian	2-3	Folkestone Invicta v Whitstable Town	2-1(aet)
Alma Swanley v Chatham Town	1-0	Kent Police v Ramsgate	3-3(aet),2-3
Darenth Heathside v Sheppey United	0-1		

Second Round

Beckenham Town v Crockenhill	2-1	Folkestone Invicta v Faversham Town	0-4
Deal Town v Corinthian	8-0	Thamesmead Town v Tonbridge A.F.C.	3-1
Alma Swanley v Cray Wanderers	2-1	Herne Bay v Tunbridge Wells	3-2
Danson Furness Utd v Ramsgate	0-1	Sheppey United v Greenwich Borough	0-1

Third Round

Beckenham Town v Faversham Town	1-0	Deal Town v Thamesmead Town	2-0
Alma Swanley v Herne Bay	1-4	Ramsgate v Greenwich Borough	2-0

Semi-Finals

Beckenham Town v Deal Town	2-0(aet)	Herne Bay v Ramsgate	1-2(aet)

Final (at Whitstable Town F.C., Saturday 24th April): Ramsgate 1, Beckenham Town 0.

DIVISION TWO CUP 1992-93

First Round

Thamesmead Town Res v Canterbury C. Res	1-2	
Hastings Town Res v Deal Town Reserves	5-3	
Tonbridge A.F.C. Res v Dover Ath. Res	4-2*(aet)*	
Chatham Town Res v Ramsgate Reserves	3-1	
Folkestone Invicta Res v Cray Wdrs Reserves	2-0	
Darenth Heathside Res v Beckenham Res	2-2*(aet)*,0-3	

Second Round

Canterbury C. Reserves v Chatham T. Res	3-1
Folkestone Invicta Res v Tonbridge AFC Res	0-2
Hastings Town Res v Herne Bay Reserves	1-0
Whitstable Town Res v Beckenham Town Res	3-0

Semi-Finals

Tonbridge A.F.C. Res v Whitstable Town Res	2-0
Canterbury City Res v Hastings Town Res	0-0*(aet)*,4-3

Final *(at Herne Bay F.C., Wed 5th May)*: Tonbridge A.F.C. Reserves 1, Canterbury City Reserves 0

KENT LEAGUE DIVISION ONE TEN-YEAR RECORD

	83/4	84/5	85/6	86/7	87/8	88/9	89/0	90/1	91/2	92/93
Alma Swanley	13	11	1	3	12	6	5	8	5	5
Beckenham Town	8	4	15	15	8	17	12	14	14	9
Chatham Town	-	-	-	-	-	19	16	12	19	6
Corinthian	-	-	-	-	-	-	-	-	13	20
Cray Wanderers	4	5	14	10	7	7	18	2	18	17
Crockenhill	6	16	3	2	19	13	15	15	16	21
Danson Furness United	-	-	-	-	15	14	17	18	20	7
Darenth Heathside	12	8	4	9	11	4	10	13	21	19
Deal Town	9	12	18	16	16	2	4	5	3	4
Faversham Town	10	7	6	17	2	3	1	6	2	15
Folkestone Invicta	-	-	-	-	-	-	-	-	-	16
Greenwich Borough	-	6	7	1	1	16	6	17	9	16
Herne Bay	7	13	11	5	18	20	14	3	1	2
Hythe Town	3	2	12	11	5	1	-	-	-	-
Kent Police	14	15	9	18	6	12	11	19	11	18
Metropolitan Police (Hayes)	-	9	13	14	13	15	19	20	w/d	-
Ramsgate	16	17	8	4	10	9	20	10	10	12
Sheppey United	2	-	-	-	-	-	-	21	6	3
Sittingbourne	1	3	2	6	4	5	2	1	-	-
Slade Green	11	14	17	12	14	10	9	9	8	11
Thamesmead Town	-	-	-	-	-	-	-	-	17	8
Thames Polytechnic	-	-	10	13	17	18	13	16	15	-
Tonbridge A.F.C.	-	-	-	-	-	-	-	3	4	1
Tunbridge Wells	5	1	5	7	9	11	7	11	12	14
Whitstable Town	15	10	16	8	3	8	8	7	7	10
Number of clubs	**16**	**17**	**18**	**18**	**19**	**20**	**20**	**21**	**22**	**21**

Thamesmead Town 2, Greenwich Borough 1 - 31/8/92. S Davis of Greenwich rises high to head against the Thamesmead woodwork - Kevin Prosser and Evans Cook are unable to stop this effort. Photo - Gavin Ellis-Neville.

ALMA SWANLEY

Chairman: Mike Dougherty   **President:** Margaret Isley.
Secretary: Ron Moore, 11 Oaklands Close, West Kingsdown, Kent TN15 6EA (0474 85215).
Manager: Franny Fitzpatrick   **Asst Manager:** John Mears   **Press Officer:** Dave Clark.
Ground: Green Court Road, Crockenhill, Kent (0322 666120).
Directions: From junction of M25 & M20 follow signs for Swanley. Left at Crockenhill turning, then first right after motorway crossing. 500 yards from Swanley (BR).
Seats: 100   **Cover:** 200   **Capacity:** 1,500   **Floodlights:** No   **Founded:** 1963.
Colours: Red & black   **Change Colours:** Red/white/red   **Nickname:** Alma.
Midweek matchday: Tuesday   **Record Gate:** 1,500 v Enfield, London Snr Cup 76-77.
Sponsors: Hanover Park Group PLC   **Previous Lges:** Gtr London 65-71/ L'don Spartan 75-82
Programme: 12 pages, 20p   **Programme Editor:** Mike Dougherty
Clubhouse: Open daily day.   **Previous Ground:** Swanley Rec.   **Hons:** Spartan 73-74
(Lg Cup 73-74, Benevolent Cup 73-74), Kent Snr Tphy 75-76, Kent Lg 85-86 (Lg Cup 88-89 (R-up 90-91)).

BECKENHAM TOWN

Chairman: Les Chandler.   **Vice Chairman:** B Hollaway.
Secretary: Peter Palmer, 107 Wentworth Rd, West Croydon, Surrey CR0 3HZ (081 689 2134).
Manager: Kevin Sugrue   **Asst Manager:** Bob Chilvers
Ground: Eden Park Avenue, Beckenham, Kent (081 650 1066).
Directions: M25, A21 to Bromley then follow signs to Beckenham. Ground 1 mile west of town off A214, 2 mins walk from Eden Park (BR) station - trains from London Bridge. Bus 264.
Seats: 120   **Cover:** 120   **Capacity:** 4,000   **Floodlights:** Due   **Reformed:** 1971.
Colours: Red/red/white   **Change Colours:** White/black/black   **Nickname:** Reds.
Midweek matchday: Wednesday   **Record Gate:** 692 v Greenwich Borough, League 1988.
Sponsors: F M Conway Ltd   **Prev. Ground:** Stanhope Grove, Beckenham (60 yrs)
Previous Leagues: South East London Amtr 71-73/ Metropolitan 73-75/ London Spartan 75-82.
Programme: 6 pages, 50p   **Programme Editor:** Bob Chilvers (081 301 2624)
Club Shop: Yes - contact secretary.
Captain 92-93: J Spiers   **P.O.Y. & Top Scorer 92-93:** R Bennett.
Clubhouse: All day opening at weekends. Hot & cold food, teas, coffees on matchdays. Bar and dance area. Pool tables and fruit machines.
Hons: London Spartan Lg Cup R-up 77-78 78-79, Kent Snr Tphy R-up 81-82, Kent Lg Cup R-up 84-85 92-93 (Div 2 Cup R-up 90-91).

Beckenham Town F.C. 1992-93.

CHATHAM TOWN

Chairman: P Enright   **President:**
Secretary: Brian Burcombe, 4 Hallwood Close, Parkwood, Rainham, Kent ME8 9NT (0634 363419).
Manager: Barry Zilwood   **Asst Manager:** Les Warren.
Ground: Maidstone Road Sports Ground, Maidstone Road, Chatham, Kent (0634 812194).
Directions: M2, A229 Chatham turn-off, follow signs to Chatham, ground one and a half miles on right opposite garage. 1 mile from Chatham (BR).
Seats: 500   **Cover:** 1,000   **Capacity:** 5,000   **Floodlights:** Yes   **Founded:** 1882.
Colours: Red & white hoops/black   **Change Colours:** Yellow & green   **Nickname:** Chats.
Midweek matchday: Tuesday   **Record Gate:** 5,000 v Gillingham, 1980.
Sponsors: Topps Scaffolding   **Previous Ground:** Great Lines, Chatham 1882-90.
Previous Lges: Southern (several spells)/ Aetolian 59-64/ Metropolitan 64-68/ Kent (Sev. spells).
Programme: 12 pages, 50p   **Programme Editor:** Trevor Busby
Clubhouse: Matchdays and functions   **Previous Names:** Chatham FC/ Medway FC (1970s).
Hons: Kent Lg(9) 1894-95 03-05 24-25 26-27 71-72 73-74 76-77 79-80 (R-up 02-03 23-24 25-26 70-71 74-75 80-81, Lg Cup 71-72 76-77 (R-up(3)), Thames & Medway Comb.(5) 1896-97 04-06 19-20 23-24, FA Cup QF (beat Nottm Forest 2-0 en route) 1888-89, FA Tphy 3rd Rd 70-71, Kent Snr Cup 1888-89 1904-05 10-11 18-19, Kent Snr Shield 19-20.

CORINTHIAN

Chairman: R J Billings Jnr.   **Manager:** Tony Sitford
Secretary: Mr Ron Brown, 10 Pincroft Wood, New Barn, Longfield, Kent DA3 7HB (0474 707186).
Ground: Gay Dawn, Valley Road, Fawkham, Nr Dartford, Kent DA3 8LZ (0474 7559).
Directions: A2 off Longfield, take Fawkham Road - ground one mile on left. Or, A20 to Fawkham Green then ground one and a half miles on right. One and a quarter miles from Longfield (BR).
Seats: 134   **Cover:** 175   **Capacity:** 2,000   **Floodlights:** Yes   **Founded:** 1972.
Colours: Green & white hoops/white   **Change Colours:** All blue   **Nickname:** None.
Midweek matchday: Tuesday   **Record Gate:** 480 v Spurs, friendly 1979.
Sponsors: None   **Clubhouse:** Bar, kitchen, large lounge.
Programme: 12 pages, 30p   **Programme Editor:** TBA
Previous Grounds: None.   **Previous League:** Southern 85-91.
Captain 92-93: John Stinson   **P.o.Y. 92-93:** Ray Walker (goalkeeper).
Hons: Essex AFA Snr Cup 82-83, Kent Snr Tphy 83-84 86-87, Fort Lauderdale International Tournament 84-85, Kent Intermediate Cup 89-90 90-91.

Corinthian's Mark Miller (hoops) fends off Simon Clark during a game at Darenth Heathside on 20th January. Photo - Alan Brown.

CRAY WANDERERS

Chairman: Bob Bell   **President:** Mr W Faulkner
Secretary: Mr Kerry Phillips, 15 Watling Street, Bexleyheath, Kent DA6 7QJ (0322 554108).
Manager: Eddie Davies   **Asst Manager:** John Dunbar.
Coach: Patsy Carolan   **Press Officer:** Greg Mann (081 318 6888).
Ground: Oxford Road, Sidcup, Kent (081 300 9201).
Directions: Between Sidcup High Street and Footscray High Street; from A20 turn off for Footscray, left at lights, Oxford Rd is 3rd left. Three quarters of a mile from Sidcup (BR) station - Kentish bus 492 from Dartford and Sidcup station passes top of Oxford Rd - 30 mins service on Saturdays.
Seats: 106   **Cover:** 300   **Capacity:** 2,000   **Floodlights:** Due   **Founded:** 1860.
Colours: Amber & black   **Change Colours:** Navy & white   **Nickname:** Wands.
Midweek matchday: Tuesday   **Record Gate:** 1,523 v Stamford, F.A. Vase QF 80-81.
Record win: 15-0 v Sevenoaks, 1894-95   **Record defeat:** 1-11 v Bromley, 20-21.
Sponsors: Quality Homecare   **Club Record Scorer:** Keith Collishaw, 272.
Programme: 20 pages, 50p   **Editor:** Greg Mann (081 318 6888)   **Club Shop:** No.
Previous Leagues: Kent Amtr/ West Kent/ Southern Suburban/ London 20-34 51-59/ Aetolian 59-64/ Gtr London 64-66/ Metropolitan 66-71/ London Metropolitan 71-75/ London Spartan 75-78.
Previous Grounds: Star Lane/ Tothills/ Twysden/ Fordcroft/ Grassmeade, St Mary Cray.
Clubhouse: Open pub hours (freehouse). Hot & cold food available.
Captain 92-93: Ian Jenkins   **P.o.Y. 92-93:** Pat Brown   **Top Scorer 92-93:** Phil Collins.
Hons: London Lg(2) 56-58 (Lg Cup 54-55), Aetolian Lg 62-63 (Lg Cup 63-64), Gtr London Lg 65-66 (Lg Cup(2) 64-66), Metropolitan Lg Cup 70-71 (Amtr Cup(2) 66-68), London Spartan Lg(2) 76-78, Kent Lg 01-02 80-81 (R-up 79-80 90-91, Lg Cup 83-84), Kent Snr Tphy 92-93, Kent Amtr Cup(4) 30-31 62-65.

CROCKENHILL

Chairman: Alan Parker   **Secretary:** A Cloke (0322 665804).
Manager: Tim Kite   **Asst Manager:**
Ground: 'Wested', Eynsford Road, Crockenhill, Kent (0322 662097).
Directions: Just off M25 junction 3, off Swanley by-pass. Just over a mile from Swanley (BR). Bus 477.
Seats: 100   **Cover:** 100   **Capacity:** 1,500   **Floodlights:** No   **Founded:** 1946.
Colours: Red/white/black   **Change Colours:** All blue   **Nickname:** Crocks.
Midweek matchday: Tuesday   **Record Gate:** 800 v Maidstone, Kent Amtr Cup 1948.
Sponsors: Erith Sports   **Previous Lges:** Kent Amtr/ Aetolian 59-64/ Gtr London 64-68
Programme: Sometimes   **Players progressing to Football Lge:** Tony Cascarino.
Clubhouse: Friday & Saturday nights and matchdays. On-ground licensed bar.
Hons: Kent Lg 82-83 (R-up 84-85), Kent Snr Tphy 80-81, Kent Amtr Cup R-up, West Kent Snr Cup, Sevenoaks Charity Cup.

DANSON FURNESS UNITED

President: Steve Brown   **Secretary:** D Skeel (081 464 8571).
Manager: Alan Sutherland   **Asst Manager:** Dave Hamer
Ground & Directions: As Alma Swanley FC (see page 600).   **Founded:** 1991.
Colours: Sky/navy/white   **Change Colours:** All red   **Nickname:** None.
Midweek matchday: Tuesday   **Record Gate:** 350 v Newport I.O.W., FA Vase 1980.
Previous Names: Danson (Bexley Borough)(founded 1941), Furness United. Clubs merged in 1991.
Previous Grounds: Randell Down Road 41-53/ Eltham Road 53-60/ Crook Log, Brampton Road 60-92.
Prev. Lges: Sidcup & Dist./ S.E. London Amtr/ London Spartan 82-87. *Furness: Sth London Alliance (pre-1991).*
Programme: 8 pages, 20p   **Editor:** Fabio Rossi.   **Club Sponsors:** S H E Printers
Clubhouse: Matchdays and functions   **Hons:** S.E. Amtr Lg Cup R-up 60-61.

DARENTH HEATHSIDE

Chairman: Brian Smith.   **Press Officer:** Martin Wiseman (0689 833083).
Secretary: A J Kingshott, 67 Avondale Rd, Bromley, Kent BR1 4HS (081 460 4834).
Joint Managers: Clayton Hart/ Graham Smith.   **Coach:** John Johns.
Ground: The Heathside Club, Horton Road, South Darenth, Dartford, Kent (0322 863554).
Directions: Turn east off A225 (Dartford-Farningham) into Station Rd at brick railway bridge near Farningham Road BR station. Ground at bottom of Station Rd near large viaduct diagonally opposite 'The Sun'. Farningham Rd station (trains from London Victoria) is half mile away. Buses 14 & 15 from Dartford.
Seats: 140   **Cover:** 140   **Capacity:** 2,000   **Floodlights:** No   **Founded:** 1951.
Colours: Blue & white   **Change Colours:** All red   **Nickname:** None.
Midweek matchday: Tuesday   **Previous Name:** Heathside Sports.
Clubhouse: Open matcdays one and a half hours before kiv-off until about two and a half hours after match. Also open (bar from 9pm) Tuesday training nights. Hot & cold snacks available matchdays.
Previous Lges: Local Lges (Dartford, Sidcup) 51-65/ Gtr London 68-71/ London Spartan 75-78.
Record Gate: 900 v Jimmy Hill's International XI, club's Silver Jubilee match, 1976.
Record win: 9-1 v Riverside Sports, Kent Amateur Cup 71-72 (in Kent League: 7-0 v Ramsgate 80-81).
Record defeat: 0-8 twice; v Canvey Island, Gtr London Lge 69-70, & v Herne Bay, Kent Lge 92-93.
Programme: 8 pages, 25p   **Editor:** Martin Wiseman (0689 833083)   **Club Shop:** No.
Record Scorer (in one season): Dean Bowey 28 (89-90).   **Record Appearances:** John Martinez 516.
Captain 92-93: Various   **Top Scorer & P.o.Y.:** Lee Annett 26 (Lge & Cup).
Hons: Kent Lg Cup R-up 80-81 85-86 (Div 2 Cup R-up 78-79), Kent I'mediate Cup 74-75 (Minor Cup 57-58 59-60 62-63).

DARTFORD

Chairman: Dave Skinner   **Vice Chairman:** Dick Mace.
Secretary/Press Officer: Mike Brett-Smith, 83 Wellcome Ave., Dartford, Kent DA1 5JL (0322 277243).
Manager: Tony Durman   **Asst Manager:** Alan Carrington   **Coach:** Dave Wadhams.
Physio: Terry Skelton   **Commercial Manager:** Steve Irving.
Ground: Cray Wanderers F.C. (see page 601).
Colours: White/black/white   **Change colours:** Red/white/red   **Founded:** 1888   **Nickname:** Darts
Previous Leagues: Kent 1894-96 97-98 99-1902 09-14 21-26/ Southern 1896-98 99-1900 27-81 82-84 86-92/ GMV Conference 1981-84 84-86.
Midweek home games: Wednesday   **Reserve Team:** No.
Programme: 28 pages, 60p   **Editor:** Secretary.   **Club Shop:** Open matchdays. Progs, souvenirs, ties, handbooks, fanzines etc. Mail order; Norman Grimes (0322 271664 - evenings).
Sponsors: National Power.   **Record Gate:** 11,004 v Leyton Orient FA Cup 1st Rd 48-49
Rec. win: 11-1 v Faversham, Kent Snr Cup.   **Record defeat:** 0-10 v Guildford C., Southern Lge 1947.
Previous Grounds: Brent Rec/ Lowfield Street/ Summers Meadow 1906-1914/ Watling Street 21-92.
Best F.A. Cup season: 3rd Rd Proper 1935-36 (v Derby), 1936-37 (v Darlington).
League Clubs Defeated in F.A. Cup: Cardiff (1935), Exeter (1961) Aldershot (1968)
Record Fees: Paid: £6,000 for John Bartley (Chelmsford City, 1988)
           Received: £25,000 for Andy Hesenthaler (from Watford, via Redbridge Forest)
Players progressing to Football Lge: Riley Cullum (Charlton 1947), Ted Croker (Charlton 1948), Frank Coombs (Bristol C. 1949), James Kelly (Gillingham 1951), Tom Ritchie (Grimsby 1958), Dave Underwood (Watford 1960), Derek Hales (Luton 1972), Archie Cross (Arsenal), Andy Hesenthaler (Watford via Redbridge F.).
Clubhouse: Club have use of Conservative Club adjacent to ground on matchdays. Day membership available on production of match ticket/DFCSA membership card.
92-93 Captain: Andy Prutton   **92-93 P.o.Y.:** Not awarded   **92-93 Top scorer:** Leo Fortune-West.
Hons: Southern Lg(4) 30-32 73-74 83-84 (R-up(3) 80-81 87-89, Eastern Dib 30-31, Southern Div 80-81, Lg Cup(3) 76-77 87-89 (R-up 79-80 83-84 89-90), Championship Shield(3) 83-84 87-89), Kent Snr Cup(9) 30-33 34-35 47-48 69-70 72-73 86-88 (R-up 1893-94), Kent F'lit Cup(3) 64-66 70-71, Kent Lg Cup 24-25, Inter Lg Chal. 1974 (beat Boston Utd 5-3 on agg.), FA FA Tphy R-up 73-74.

DEAL TOWN

Chairman: John H Ullman   **Vice Chairman:** Bill Bennett.
Secretary: Jim Nokes, 51 Celtic Road, Deal, Kent CT14 9EF (0304 36847).
Manager/Coach: Jim Nokes   **Physio:** Dave Dadd
Press Officer: Bill Bennett   **Commercial Manager:** Dave Clements (0304 368776).
Ground: Charles Sports Ground, Mill Road, Deal, Kent (0304 375623).
Directions: A258 through Walmer, left into Cornwell Road, continue into Hamilton Road, veer left into Mill Rd, follow round to right into Manor Road, right into St Leonards Road, ground 100 yards on right. 1 mile from both Walmer and Deal BR stations. Local buses stop near ground.
Seats: 150   **Cover:** 500   **Capacity:** 2,000   **Floodlights:** Yes   **Founded:** 1908.
Colours: All yellow   **Change Colours:** Black & white hoops   **Nickname:** Town.
Midweek matchday: Tue or Wed   **Record Gate:** 4,000 v Billy Wright showbiz XI, Feb '61.
Clubhouse: Matchdays & functions. Bar. Tea bar with hot & cold food.   **Sponsors:** T.B.A.
Programme: 20 pages, 30p   **Editor:** Dave Clements (0304 368776)   **Club Shop:** No.
Previous Grounds: None   **Prev. Lges:** Aetolian 59-63/ Southern 63-66/ Gtr London 66-71
Record win: 11-1 v Tunbridge Wells (A), Feb'93   **Record defeat:** 0-10 v Tunbridge Wells (A), May'86.
Club Record Scorer: Jim Nokes   **Club Record Appearances:** Alan Barton.
Captain 92-93: Colin Gilmore   **Top Scorer & P.o.Y. 92-93:** Joe Brayne (51 goals).
Hons: Kent Lg 52-53 (R-up 88-89, Lg Cup 55-56 81-82 (SF 88-89 89-90), Kent Snr Tphy R-up 82-83 90-91, Gtr London Lg Cup 67-68, Aetolian Lg R-up 59-60.

Cray Wanderers F.C. 1992-93. Back Row (L/R): B Faulkner (Chairman), P Carolan (Coach), S Wright, R Welch, M Loveday, P Brown, S Hutchins, P Collins, C Hanlon, E Davies (Manager). Front: P Hewitt, R Valence, A Dodds, S Paris, M Scott, J Mummery, D Adams.

Ramsgates' Gary Hammond (right) gets in a shot before Peter Menditta of Darenth Heathside can get in his tackle. Photo - Alan Coomes.

Deal Town F.C. 1992-93, pictured before their F.A. Cup tie at Croydon. Back Row (L/R): Dave Dadd (Physio), Andy Bigginton, Dave Dixon, Colin Gilmore (Captain), Joe Brayne, Dave Waring, John Ridgeon, Andy Ward, Paul Cureton, Jim Nokes (Manager/Secretary). Front: Paul Roberts, Andy Young, Stiggy Meadows, Simon Bryant, Richard Edwards. Photo - Dave West.

FAVERSHAM TOWN

Chairman: Terry Rowland **Vice Chairman:** Cllr B Vaughan **President:** Mr R W B Neame
Secretary: K F Hammond, 8 Sherwood Close, Faversham, Kent ME13 7QS (0795 535612).
Manager: Hugh Stinson **Asst Manager:** Steve Wren **Physio:** Andy Potterton.
Coach: Bob Mason **Commercial Manager:** Chris Turner.
Ground: Shepherd Neame Stadium, Salters Lane, Faversham, Kent (0795 532738).
Directions: On A2 (Canterbury road) just west of town.
Seats: 350 **Cover:** 1,500 **Capacity:** 2,000 **Floodlights:** Yes **Founded:** 1901.
Colours: White/navy/red **Change Colours:** Red/white/blue **Nickname:** Town.
Midweek matchday: Tuesday **Record Gate:** 1,400 v Sheppey Utd, 1949.
Sponsors: Shepherd Neame. **Clubhouse:** Matchdays, Tue/Wed/Thurs. Snacks sold.
Programme: 8 pages with entry **Programme Editor:** C Young.
Reserves' Lge: Canterbury. **Previous Ground:** Gordon Square 1946-58
Previous Leagues: Aetolian 59-64/ Metropolitan 64-71/ Athenian 71-76.
Rec. win: 8-0 v Greenwich B., Aug'89 **Record defeat:** 0-9 v Sittingbourne, Jan '82.
Club Record Scorer: Tony Rudd 43. **Club Record Appearances:** Bob Mason.
Captain 92-93: Bob Mason **P.o.Y. 92-93:** Gary Chiltenden **Top Scorer 92-93:** Tony Rudd.
Hons: Kent Lg 69-70 70-71 77-78 89-90 (R-up 87-88, Lg Cup 70-71 90-91 (R-up 82-83)), Kent Snr Tphy 76-77 77-78 (R-up 87-88 88-89), Kent Amtr Cup 56-57 58-59 71-72 72-73 73-74.

FOLKESTONE INVICTA

Chairman: T R Guiver **Secretary:** B Goodsell (0233 633120).
Manager: Gary Stanliforth **Asst Manager:** Terry Collins **Coach:** Curly Russell
Ground: The New Pavilion, Cheriton Road, Folkestine, Kent CT20 5JU (0303 57461).
Directions: On the A20 behind Presto foodstore, midway between Folkestone Central and Folkestone West BR stations.
Seats: 900 **Cover:** 3,500 **Capacity:** 4,000 **Floodlights:** Yes **Founded:** 1946.
Colours: Amber & black/black/black **Change Colours:** Red & white/white/red **Nickname:**
Midweek matchday: Tuesday **Previous Lges:** Kent County (pre-1991). **Sponsors:**
Rec. Gate: 1,211 v Brighton, friendly 26/9/91. *Ground record; 7,801 Folkestone v Margate, Kent Snr Cup 1958.*
Programme: Yes **Previous Ground:** South Rd, Hythe (pre-1991).
Clubhouse: Yes **Hons:** Kent Lg Div 2 90-91.

GREENWICH BOROUGH

President: T H M Edwaards **Chairman:** B Thompson.
Secretary: Ms Denise Richmond, 7 Castlecombe Rd, Mottingham, London SE9 4AU (081 851 4169).
Manager: Dave Waight **Asst Manager:** Doug Francis
Ground: Harrow Meadow, Eltham Green Rd, Eltham, London SE9 (081 850 3098).
Directions: South Circular (A205) to Yorkshire Grey pub, ground opposite. 1 mile from both Eltham and Kidbrooke BR stations.
Seats: 50 **Cover:** 50 **Capacity:** 2,500 **Floodlights:** Yes **Founded:** 1928.
Colours: Red & black **Change Colours:** Black & white **Nickname:** Boro.
Midweek matchday: Tuesday **Previous Ground:** Erith & Belvedere F.C. 1992-93.
Record Gate: 2,000 v Charlton, floodlight opening, 1978.
Record defeat: 0-8 v Faversham Town, August 1989.
Sponsors: Pelgary Ltd **Previous Name:** London Borough of Greenwich.
Previous Leagues: South London Alliance/ Kent Amateur/ London Spartan 77-84.
Programme: 8 pages, 20p **Programme Editor:** Denise Richmond. **Clubhouse:** Yes.
Hons: London Spartan Lg 79-80 (Lg Cup 82-83), Kent Lg 86-87 87-88 (Lg Cup 84-85 86-87), Kent Snr Tphy 84-85, FA Vase 5th Rd 89-90.

HERNE BAY

Chairman: M Todd **Vice Chairman:** R Todd. **President:** J Hodkinson
Secretary: S Connolly, 60 Ivanhoe Rd, Herne Bay, Kent CT6 6EQ.
Manager: Tom Sampson **Coach:** K Lissenden **Physio:** J Hodkinson.
Ground: Winch's Field, Stanley Gardens, Herne Bay, Kent (0227 374156).
Directions: Leave A299 at Herne Bay r'bout, 2nd left, 1st left. Half mile from Herne Bay (BR); down Station Approach, 1st right (Spencer Road), 2nd right.
Seats: 250 **Cover:** 1,500 **Capacity:** 5,000 **Floodlights:** Yes **Founded:** 1886.
Colours: Blue & white stripes/blue **Change Colours:** White (claret trim) **Nickname:** The Bay.
Midweek matchday: Tuesday **Previous Ground:** Memorial Park 1886-1953.
Record Gate: 2,303 v Margate, FA Cup 1970. **Clubhouse:** Open most evenings and matchdays.
Sponsors: Herne Bay Snooker Club, Waterways Caravan Park.
Previous Lges: Kent Amtr/ Thanet/ East Kent/ Aetolian 59-64/ Athenian 64-74.
Programme: 28 pages, 35p **Programme Editor/Press Officer:** T.B.A.
Captain 92-93: Neil Brown **P.o.Y. 92-93:** Lol Wright **Top Scorer 92-93:** Steve Tapp.
Hons: Kent Lg 91-92 (R-up 92-93, Div 2 62-63 63-64, Lg Cup R-up 78-79, Div 2 Cup 53-54), Kent Snr Tphy 78-79, Kent Amtr Cup 57-58 (R-up 58-59 63-64 68-69 72-73), Aetolian Lg Div 2 62-63 63-64 (Lg Cup R-up 62-63, Div 2 Cup 62-63 63-64), Athenian Lg Div 2 70-71 (Lg Cup 66-67), Kent Amtr Lg Cup 53-54 54-55, Thames & Medway Comb. Cup R-up 61-62, FA Cup 4th Cup Qual. Rd 70-71 86-87.

KENT POLICE

Chairman: P Hermitage **President:** P Condon, Chief Constable.
Secretary: J C Bateman, Christmas Cottage, Lavender Square, Hawkhurst TN18 4DX (0622 681740).
Manager: Duncan McLachlan **Asst Mgr/Coach:** Staurt McFaden **Press Officer:** Secretry
Ground: Police H.Q., Sutton Rd, Maidstone, Kent (0622 690690).
Directions: Leave Maidstone on Hastings Road, then onto A274 to Rye Road.
Seats: 40 **Cover:** 60 **Capacity:** 3,000 **Floodlights:** No **Founded:** 1951.
Colours: Royal blue **Change Colours:** Blue & white **Nickname:** None.
Midweek matchday: Tues/Wed. **Record Gate:** Unknown.
Sponsors: **Previous League:** Kent Amateur.
Programme: 6 pages, £1 with entry **Programme Editor:** Secretary.
Clubhouse: Use HQ bar on matchdays. New changing room/ refreshment facilities adjacent to pitch.
Hons: Kent Lg R-up 69-70 (Lg Cup 69-70).

Faversham Town F.C. 1992-93. Back Row (L/R): Andy Potterton (Trainer), Tony Rowland (Chairman), Paul Brinchley, Phil Sainsbury, Bobby Mason (Captain), Scot Davenport, Stuart Legg, Matthew Rochester, Micky Denley (Manager). Front: Mark Gannon, Andy Maxsted, Tony Rudd, Gary Chittenden, Simon Read, Jimmy Marsh, Mark Valler. Photo - Richard Brock.

Greenwich Borough F.C. 1992-93. Back Row (L/R): D Waight (Manager), G Daniels, G Payne, V Barton, J Hindmarsh, D Levy, S Bevis (Physio), T Joyce (Coach). Front: A Penford, S Leibo, S Kitt, S Davis, P Challis (Captain), E Evans, K Randall, M Edwards. Photo - Gavin Ellis-Neville.

Herne Bay F.C. 1992-93, pictured before their F.A. Cup tie at Camberley Town. Photo - Eric Marsh.

RAMSGATE

Chairman: R Lawson   **Vice Chairman:** C Payne   **President:** M Breach.
Secretary/Press Officer: Tom Atkins, 8 Manston Rd, Ramsgate, Kent CT11 0RB (0843 595632).
Manager/Coach: Lennie Lee   **Asst Manager:** Lester Smith   **Physio:** Paul Wheeler.
Commercial Manager: Mick Beier.
Ground: Southwood Stadium, Prices Avenue, Ramsgate, Kent (0843 591662).
Directions: From London on A229, A253 into Ramsgate - left into Netherhill at r'bout, right into Ashburnham Rd, right into Southwood Rd. 15 mins walk from Ramsgate BR station; walk thru Warre Recreation Ground, along St Lawrence High Str., left at 'White Horse', follow Southwood Rd and turn right into Prices Avenue.
Seats: 400   **Cover:** 600   **Capacity:** 5,000   **Floodlights:** Yes   **Founded:** 1946.
Colours: Red/white/white   **Change Colours:** White/blue/blue   **Nickname:** Rams.
Midweek matchday: Tuesday   **Record Gate:** 5,200 v Margate, 56-57.
Sponsors: British Gas.   **Club Record Scorer:** Mick Williamson.
Clubhouse: Open matchdays & private functions. Two bars, two pool tables, darts. Hot & cold food on matchdays.
Programme: 20 pages   **Programme Editor:** Ivor Thomas   **Club Shop:** No.
Previous Name: Ramsgate Athletic.   **Previous Leagues:** Southern 59-75.
Captain 92-93: Cliff Stokes   **P.o.Y. 92-93:** Marcus Newton   **Top Scorer 92-93:** Lennie Lee
Hons: Kent Lg 49-50 55-56 56-57 (Lg Cup 48-49 92-93), Kent I'mediate Cup 54-55, Kent Snr Cup 63-64, Thames & Medway Cup 60-61, Kent Snr Shield 60-61, Kent Floodlit Tphy 69-70, Kent Snr Tphy(2) 87-89.

Ramsgate F.C. 1992-93. Photo - Paul Bates.

SHEPPEY UNITED

Chairman: Dave Whitton   **Secretary:** P Bailey (0795 474474).
Ground & Directions: As Faversham Town FC (see page 604).   **Founded:** 1890.
Colours: Red & white/white   **Change colours:** All blue
Midweek matchday: Tuesday   **Nickname:** Islanders or Ites.
Previous Name: Sheppey Athletic.   **Programme:** 16 pages, 20p
Previous Ground: Botany Road, St Georges Avenue, Sheerness (pre-1992).
Record Gate: 4,000 v Sittingbourne, Kent Senior Trophy 1927 (at Botany Road).
Previous Leagues: Southern 1894-1901 84-91/ Kent 01-27 32-59 72-84/ Aetolian 59-64/ Gtr London 64-65/ Metropolitan Lg 65-71.
Players progressing to Football League: E C Harper (England, Blackburn, Spurs, Preston).
Hons: Kent Lg(6) 05-07 27-28 72-73 74-75 78-79 (R-up 03-04 04-05 77-78 83-84, Lg Cup 75-76 78-79, Div 2(reserves) 32-33 84-85 (R-up 1894-95 1979-80)), Thames & Medway Comb. 08-09 12-13 22-23 25-26 28-29 55-56, Kent Amtr Cup 45-46 51-52, Kent Snr Shield 77-78, Kent Snr Cup R-up(3), Gtr London Lg 64-65, FA Cup 6th Qual. Rd 19-20, FA Tphy 1st Rd Proper 85-86.

Sheppey United F.C. 1992-93. Back Row (L/R): Keith Lissenden (Physio, now Herne Bay), John Roseman (Asst Manager), Martin Osborne, Mark Rees, Ian Crouch, Brett Walker, David Brown, Jason Ash, David Monteith, Tom Sampson (Manager, now Herne Bay). Front: Steve Hearn, Karl Rolls, Terry Martin, Mark Dryden, Colin Ford, Gary Allen, Steve Talbot. Photo - Kent Messenger.

SLADE GREEN

President: William Dudley   **Chairman:** Brian Smith.   **Manager:** Tod Dowling
Secretary: Bruce Smith, 15 Gumping Rd, Orpington, Kent BR5 1RX (0689 858782).
Asst Manager: Tony Carley   **Coach:** John Hibbert   **Physio:** Ron Mitchell
Ground: The Small Glen, Moat Lane, Slade Green, Erith, Kent (0322 351077).
Directions: Off A206 between Erith & Dartford. 400 yards from Slade Green BR station. Buses 89 & B13.
Capacity: 3,000   **Seats:** 100   **Cover:** 400   **Floodlights:** Yes   **Founded:** 1946.
Colours: White & green   **Change Colours:** All yellow   **Nickname:** The Green
Midweek matchday: Tuesday   **Previous Name:** Slade Green Athletic 46-86.
Previous Leagues: Dartford 46-52/ Kent Amateur 52-62/ Greater London 62-64.
Record Gate: 3,000 v Millwall, friendly 25/7/92.   **Rec. win:** 14-0 v Island Social, Kent Amtr Lge 1953.
Rec. defeat: 1-6 thrice; v Herne B., Kent Snr Cup 55-56. v Whitstable, Kent Lg 83-84. v Alma Swan., Kent Lg 89-90.
Programme: 24 pages, with admission   **Prog. Editor/Press Officer:** Robert Smith (0322 287982).
Club Record Scorer: Colin Dwyer   **Club Record Appearances:** Colin Dwyer.
Captain 92-93: Melvyn Phillips   **Top Scorer 92-93:** Peter Copeland 24   **P.o.Y. 92-93:** Graham Hall.
Hons: Kent Snr Tphy 91-92 (R-up 80-81), Kent Lg Cup 82-83, Kent Amtr Lg 52-53 60-61 (Lg Cup 60-61), Kent Intermediate Cup 61-62, Kent Benevolent Cup 46-47, West Kent 60-61 65-66, Dartford Lg R-up 48-49 (Lg Cup 47-48 (R-up 46-47)), Erith Hospitals Cup 46-47 48-49, Gtr London Lg R-up 68-69, Plumstead Challenge Cup 48-49.

THAMESHEAD TOWN

Chairman: B Morris   **Vice Chairman:** K Dunsmore.
Secretary/Comm. Mgr: Paul Bayne, 9 Bayliss Ave., Thamesmead, London SE28 8NS (081 311 1276).
Manager: Mick Watts   **Asst Manager:** Tony Pruce   **Physio:** Stuart Bevis.
Coach: Steve Kemp   **Press Officer:** Matthew Panting.
Ground: Bayliss Avenue, Thamesmead, London SE28 8NS (081 311 4211).
Directions: From Abbey Wood (BR) north east along Harrow Manor Way, into Crossway at 3rd r'bout, Bayliss Av. is 3rd right (Bexley bus 272 stops in Crossway near Bayliss Av. By road: From Dartford tunnel A2 to London, exit Danson Interchange and follow signs for Thamesmead and Abbey Wood. From Blackheath tunnel exit on south side and follow signs to Woolwich, to Plumstead and then to Thamesmead.
Seats: 125   **Cover:** 125   **Capacity:** 400   **Floodlights:** Yes   **Founded:** 1970.
Colours: Green & black   **Change Colours:** All red   **Nickname:** The Mead.
Midweek home matchday: Tues/Wed   **Previous Ground:** Meridian Ground, Greenwich.
Clubhouse: Mon-Fri 6-11pm, Sat 12-11pm, Sun 12-3 & 7-10.30pm. Double bar, lounge, dancefloor, children's games room, video machines, hot & cold food.
Prev. Lge: London Spartan 80-91.   **Record Gate:** 400 v Wimbledon, ground opening 1988.
Programme: Free with admission   **Club record appearances:** Delroy D'Oyley.
Captain 92-93: Philip Miles   **Top Scorer & P.o.Y. 92-93:** Dean Bowey.
Hons: Spartan Lg Div 3 79-80 (Lg Cup 84-85 86-87), I'mediate champs 85-86), Kent I'mediate Cup 83-84. 4 promotions, and 9 trophies (inc London FA and Kent FA Cups) in progress thru Spartan I'mediate Divs, 1980-87.

TUNBRIDGE WELLS

Chairman: R J Bonny   **Vice Chairman:** P C Wager.
Secretary: P C Wager, 46 Mereworth Rd, Tunbridge Wells, Kent TN4 9PL (0892 24182).
Manager: Mark Higgs   **Asst Manager:** Tony Atkins   **Coach:** Roger Pitchfork
Press Officer: R Bonny (0892 31898).   **Commercial Mgr:** Norman Sales.
Ground: Culverden Stadium, Culverden Down, Tunbridge Wells, Kent TN4 (0892 20517).
Directions: Leaving town on main Tonbridge road (A26), turn left opposite 'Red Lion' pub - ground half mile. 1 mile from Tunbridge Wells Central (BR). Served by any Tunbridge Wells-Tonbridge bus - alight at St Johns.
Seats: 350   **Cover:** 1,000   **Capacity:** 5,000   **Floodlights:** Yes   **Founded:** 1886.
Club Shop: Yes, selling programmes, badges etc.   **Reformed:** 1967.
Colours: Red & white   **Change Colours:** All blue   **Nickname:** Wells.
Midweek matchday: Tuesday   **Record Gate:** 967 v Maidstone United, FA Cup 1969.
Sponsors: Private Patients Plan.   **Clubhouse:** Open matchdays and as required.
Programme: 12 pages, 30p   **Programme Editor:** Secretary.
Prev. Names: None. *predecessors:* T. Wells FC 1886-1910 47-50/ T. Wells Rgrs 03-09 63-67/ T. Wells Utd 51-62.
Previous Grounds: Down Lane 1906/ Combley Park 06-10/ Swiss Cottage 06-14/Down Farm 19-39/ St Johns 47-50/ Eridge Road 50-51.
Record win: 10-0 v Deal (H), May'86   **Record defeat:** 1-11 v Deal Town (H), 20/2/93.
Record Scorer: John Wingate 150   **Club Record Appearances:** Tony Atkins 386.
Captain 92-93: Carl Wells   **P.o.Y. 92-93:** Richard Tucker   **Top Scorer 92-93:** John Wingate 20.
Hons: Kent Lg 84-85 (R-up 68-69, Lg Cup 74-75 77-78 85-86 87-88), Kent Snr Tphy R-up 85-86 91-92.

WHITSTABLE TOWN

Chairman: Joe Brownett   **Vice Chairman:** Peter Dale   **President:** James Lambie.
Secretary: Mrs Sylvia J Davis, 5 Old Bridge Rd, Whitstable, Kent CT5 1RJ (0227 265646).
Manager: Wayne Godden   **Asst Manager:** John Crabbe   **Physio:** Andy Harman
Ground: Belmont Road, Belmont, Whitstable, Kent (0227 266012).
Directions: From Thanet Way (A299), left at Tescos r'bout and down Millstrood Rd - ground at bottom of road, 400yds from Whitstable (BR) station. Car park at Grimshall Rd entrance.
Capacity: 2,000   **Cover:** 1,000   **Seats:** 500   **Floodlights:** Yes   **Founded:** 1885.
Colours: Red/white/red   **Change colours:** Yellow/black
Midweek matchday: Tuesday   **Nickname:** 'Oystermen', 'Reds', or 'Natives'.
Sponsors: D & J Tyres   **Club Shop:** Proposed for 1993-94.
Programme: 48 pages, 50p   **Prog. Editor/Press Offiver:** Paul Rivers (0227 773050).
Record win: 18-0 v Greenstreet (H), Faversham & District Lge 20-21.
Record defeat: 0-10 v Sittingbourne (A), F.A. Cup 1st Qualifying Round 1962-63.
Record Gate: 2,500 v Gravesend & Northfleet, F.A. Cup 3rd Qualifying Rd, 19/10/87.
Clubhouse: Social & recreation purposes, open all matchdays. Bar. Hot food & drinks at tea-bar.
Prev. Names: Whitstable Utd (pre-1886)/ Whitstable Swifts 93-95/ Whitstable Town 95-1905/ Whitstable FC 08-66.
Prev. Grnds: Saddleton's Field 1885-94/ Westmeads (Cromwell Rd) 94-95/ Joy Lane 95-1908/ Church Rd 08-09.
Prev. Lges: E. Kent 1897-1909/ Kent 09-59/ Aetolian 59-60/ Kent Amtr 60-62 63-64/ Seanglian 62-63/ Gtr London 64-67/ Kent Premier 67-68 (also in New Brompton, Thanet and Faversham & Dist. Lges over the years).
Captain 92-93: Geoff Record   **Top Scorer 92-93:** Gary Pullen   **P.o.Y. 92-93:** Dave Linstrem
Club record scorer: Barry Godfrey   **Club record appearances:** Frank Cox 429 (1950-60).
Hons: Kent Lg Div 2 27-28 33-34 49-50 (Lg Cup 79-80 (R-up 89-90 91-92)), Kent Amtr Lg East 60-61, Kent Amtr Cup 28-29, Kent Snr Tphy R-up 78-79 89-90 92-93, Gtr London Lg Cup R-up 65-66, Kent Amtr Cup 28-29.

Slade Green F.C. 1992-93, with the Kent Senior Trophy, won the previous season. Back Row (L/R): Paul Copley, Ron Mitchell (Physio), Ray Gibbs, Sean Bristow, Craig Townsend, Tony Carley (Asst Manager), Colin Hart, Dave Clark, John Maloney, Mark White, Tony Elliott, Steve Nicholson, Martin Whiteman, Darren Martin. Front: Lee Allchorn, Graham Hall, Jason Head, Tod Dowling (Manager), Teddy John, Melvyn Phillips (Captain), Peter Coupland.

Thamesmead Town F.C. 1992-93. Back Row (L/R): Colin O'Keefe, Terry Malin, Kevin Prosser, Steve Allen, Evans Cook, John Moore, Warren Leach, Mick Watts (Manager). Front Row: Martin Dennis, Paul Manchester, Stuart White, Phil Miles (Captain), Dean Bowey, Les Baldwin. Photo - Gavin Ellis-Neville.

Tunbridge Wells F.C. 1992-93. Back Row (L/R): Peter Littlechild (Trainer), Dave Brereton, Richard Tucker, Alan Hall, Mark Irvine, Phil Hassell, Simon Colbran. Front: Steve Benton, Carl Wells, John Wingate, Tony Atkins (Captain), Dan Rusha, Andy Mills. Photo - Roger Turner.

KENT COUNTY FOOTBALL LEAGUE

Premier: A.E.Farmer.
Chairman: C.T.C.Windiate
Press Officer: J.C.Mugridge,
14 Cherry Tree Road, Tunbridge Wells, Kent TN2 5QA
(0892 521578)

SEVENOAKS TOWN TAKE TITLE

The premier division introduced at the start of the season and incorporating teams from both the Eastern and Western regions was won by Sevenoaks Town with Aylesford Paper Mill runners-up. Sevenoaks Town also reached the final of the Kent County F.A. Intermediate Challenge Shield, but were beaten 3-2 by Eastern Region first division Headcorn in a close fought tie played at the ground of Tonbridge AFC.

In the FCN Music Inter Regional Challenge Cup final, played at Priestfield Stadium, Gillingham, Oakwood, last year's beaten finalists, made amends winning with two Digby Kennard goals against Teynham & Lynsted who were unable to score. Another club to do well in the County Cups was Western Region second division Strood County, who reached the final of the Kent Junior Cup group A and beat South London Football Alliance premier division Segas Bromley by 3-1.

Rob Dobereiner, manager of Platt United, won the Manager of the Year Award and the club, having played in excess of forty league and cup games, won £480 sponsorship money by having one of the best disciplinary records during the season and being runners-up in the second division. Talks with the Winstonlead Kent League in respect of the Pyramid of football progressed during the season and an agreement has new been made between both parties for promotion and relegation between the Winstonlead Kent League first division and the premier division to commence immediately following the completion of the 1995/96 season. In the interim county league sides will be asked to improve the standards of their grounds and facilities.

FCN Music indicated, mid-way through the season, that they did not wish to take up their option for continued sponsorship following the end of the 1992/93 season and consequently the league will no longer be known as the FCN Music Kent County League. The league and FCN Music are parting on amicable terms and the union between them has been very successful ensuring that a high profile has been achieved and maintained. Despite numerous approaches to many likely sources a new sponsor has not yet been found and the League will revert to its title of Kent County League for the start of 1993/94. General secretary John Mugridge also gave in his notice at the commencement of last season and was replaced by Tony Scott. John is maintained his contact with the League as appointed press officer.

J.C.Mugridge (Press Officer)

Sevenoak Town - Kent County League Champions 1992-93 - Back Row (L-R): Ray Miles, Ian Gaston, Lee Phillips, David Barton, Mick Miles (Manager), Neil Hamilton, Ian Godgrey, Paul Salako, Martin Weller. Front row: Mark Giles, Ross Campbell, Steve MacKenzie, Robin Jenner, Andre Pignault, Peter Harrington. Photo: John Mugridge.

PREM. DIVISION

PREM. DIVISION	P	W	D	L	F	A	PTS
Sevenoaks Town	26	16	6	4	65	37	54
Aylesford P.M.	26	13	8	5	56	35	47
Knockholt	26	13	6	7	57	37	45
Scott Spts & Soc.	26	13	4	9	50	44	43
Oakwood	26	9	11	6	47	42	38
Stansfeld O&B	26	8	12	6	45	40	36
Teynham & Lynsted	26	8	11	7	49	49	35
Lordswood	26	7	11	8	38	38	32
Otford United	26	8	7	11	48	53	31
New Romney	26	9	4	13	31	42	31
Thames Poly	26	8	6	12	51	63	30
Greenways	26	7	6	13	48	57	27
VCD Athletic	26	6	6	14	43	53	24
Woodnesborough	26	6	4	16	34	72	22

EASTERN DIV.1

EASTERN DIV.1	P	W	D	L	F	A	PTS
Lydd Town	24	19	4	1	88	25	61
Tenterden	24	15	3	6	68	28	48
Rye United	24	14	3	7	58	38	45
Headcorn	24	13	5	6	54	46	44
Bromley Green	24	12	4	8	66	44	40
Hythe United	24	12	2	10	41	46	38
Uni. of Kent	24	10	2	12	48	56	32
White Lion	24	9	4	11	51	58	31
Broomfield Utd	24	7	6	11	45	56	27
Kennington	24	7	5	12	37	52	26
Snowdon C.W.	24	7	4	13	43	66	25
Knatchbull	24	6	2	16	34	66	20
Houchin Rovers	24	2	2	20	41	93	8

WESTERN DIV.1

WESTERN DIV.1	P	W	D	L	F	A	PTS
Ex Blues	20	14	2	4	47	28	44
Ten Em Bee	20	12	3	5	51	33	39
Edenstone	20	10	4	6	44	34	34
Bearsted	20	8	7	5	39	25	31
Westerham	20	9	3	8	58	44	30
Rushall	20	7	6	7	38	39	27
Colts '85'	20	7	4	9	39	40	25
Borough United	20	7	4	9	36	37	25
Phoenix Sports	20	6	3	11	30	43	21
Sutton Athletic	20	4	6	10	26	49	18
Moonshot	20	4	2	14	24	60	14

WEST RES. DIV.1

WEST RES. DIV.1	P	W	D	L	F	A	PTS
Stansfeld	14	11	0	3	41	13	33
Otford United	14	9	1	4	33	20	28
Scott Sports	14	7	3	4	35	31	24
VCD Athletic	14	7	2	5	23	23	23
Sevenoaks Town	14	5	4	5	28	26	19
Lordswood	14	6	1	7	21	20	19
Bearsted	14	2	3	9	17	37	9
Edenstone	14	2	0	12	17	45	6

EASTERN DIV.2

EASTERN DIV.2	P	W	D	L	F	A	PTS
New Romney Res.	22	15	5	2	80	27	50
Walmer Rovers	22	15	2	5	57	39	47
Lydd Town Res.	22	15	1	6	64	30	46
Uni. of Kent Res.	22	13	4	5	73	26	43
Kennington Res.	22	11	4	7	60	40	37
Sturry	22	10	4	8	45	38	34
Knatchbull Res.	22	9	3	10	40	57	30
Folkestone Inv. A	22	9	1	12	54	56	28
Bromley Green Res	22	7	1	14	47	73	22
Castle Tavern	22	7	1	14	41	91	22
Teynham Res.	22	4	2	16	32	72	14
Royal George	22	2	2	18	28	72	8

WESTERN DIV.2

WESTERN DIV.2	P	W	D	L	F	A	PTS
Strood County	24	16	6	2	80	37	54
Platt United	24	16	6	2	68	39	54
AFC Egerton	24	17	2	5	75	30	53
Wellcome (Sat.)	24	15	4	5	69	44	49
Paddock Wood T.	24	15	0	9	64	49	45
Edenbridge Utd	24	12	2	10	44	45	38
Fleetdown United	24	11	3	10	53	34	36
Eltham Palace	24	7	5	12	49	52	26
Halstead	24	8	2	14	49	69	26
Eynsford	24	5	6	13	44	66	21
Chislehurst	24	7	0	17	41	71	21
Tonbridge Invicta	24	4	4	16	33	78	16
St.Georges	24	2	2	20	31	86	8

WESTERN DIV.3

WESTERN DIV.3	P	W	D	L	F	A	PTS
Empire	24	18	0	6	80	38	54
Sherwood Pk. C.A.	24	17	2	5	85	49	53
Snodland	24	13	4	7	62	47	43
N.P.I.	24	12	6	6	56	63	42
Dunton Green	24	12	5	7	70	55	41
Nomads	24	11	6	7	65	43	39
Joyce Green	24	11	4	9	56	46	37
Tonbridge Rangers	24	8	3	13	46	72	27
Wickham Park	24	6	7	11	41	62	25
Chipstead	24	7	3	14	45	62	24
Swanscombe Utd	24	7	1	16	48	70	22
Halls	24	6	4	14	39	62	22
Old Bexleians	24	4	3	17	43	67	15

WEST RES. DIV.2

WEST RES. DIV.2	P	W	D	L	F	A	PTS
Greenways	14	10	3	1	51	16	33
Westerham	14	8	2	4	44	20	26
Rushall	14	8	1	5	36	26	25
Oakwood	14	7	1	6	38	32	22
Aylesford P.M.	14	6	2	6	39	27	20
Thames Poly	14	5	3	6	30	30	18
Borough United	14	3	3	8	32	58	12
Colts '85'	14	1	1	12	18	79	4

F.C.N MUSIC INTER-REGIONAL CHALLENGE CUP Preliminary Round

Castle Tavern v Knatchbull	0-3	Broomfield United v Tenterden & St Michaels	3-4
Edenbridge United v Bearsted	2-1	Eynsford v Borough United	3-1
Fleetdown United v Ex-Blues	1-6	Phoenix Sports v Colts '85	5-1
St Georges (Wrotham) v Edenstone	3-5	Strood County v Halsted	2-1

First Round

Chislehurst v Rushall	3-3(aet),1-5	Edenbridge United v Edenstone	1-2
Ex Blues v A.F.C. Egerton	2-0	Folkestone Invicta 'A' v Kennington	0-3
Headcorn v Snowdown Colliery Welfare	4-0	Houchin Rovers v Hythe United	3-2
Knatchbull v White Lion (Cheriton)	4-3	Lydd Town v Sandwich Sports	8-0
Rye United (w/o) Dymchurch (withdrew)		Moonshot Ath. v Eltham Palace	2-2(ab.),3-0
Strood County v Platt United	3-3,1-2	Sturry v Bromley Green	0-2
Ten Em Bee v Paddock Wood Town	3-1	Tenterden & St Mich. v Ryl George (F'stone)	3-1
Tonbridge Invicta v Phoenix Sports	0-6	University of Kent v Walmer Rovers	3-1
Westerham v Eynsford	4-1	Wellcome (Saturday) v Sutton Athletic	2-2,2-1

Second Round

Ex Blues v New Romney	3-2	Headcorn v Edenstone	1-2
Houchin Rovers v Ten Em Bee	1-5	Kennington v Teynham & Lynsted	0-3
Knockholt v Aylesford Paper Mill	1-6(aet)	Lordswood v Westerham	5-0
Lydd Town v Knatchbull	8-0	Moonshot Athletic (expelled) Oakwood (w/o)	
Phoenix Sports v Thames Polytechnic	2-4	Rye United v Otford United	0-2
Scotts Spts & Soc. v V.C.D. Athletic	2-2,2-1	Stansfeld O & B Club v Rushall	2-1
Sevenoaks Town v Greenways	4-3	Tenterden & St Michaels v Platt United	1-2
University of Kent v Woodnesborough	5-2	Wellcome (Saturday) v Bromley Green	1-6

Third Round

Edenstone v Sevenoaks Town	6-2	Lordswood v Bromley Green	0-2
Lydd Town v University of Kent	5-0	Oakwood v Ex Blues	2-1
Otford United v Scott Sports & Social	2-3	Stansfeld Oxford & B. Club v Platt Utd	1-1,1-2(aet)
Teynham & Lynsted v Ten Em Bee	2-0	Thames P. v Aylesford	1-1(ab in et),2-2(TP away gls)

Quarter Finals

Bromley Green v Scott Sports & Social	0-1	Edenstone v Thames Polytechnic	1-3
Lydd Town v Teynham & Lynsted	1-4	Oakwood v Platt United	2-0

Semi Finals

Thames Polytechnic v Oakwood	1-2	Teynham & Lynsted v Scotts Sports & Social	3-1

Final (at Gillingham FC): Oakwood 2, Teynham & Lynsted 0

Headcorn F.C., of the Eastern Region First Division, with the Kent Intermediate Challenge Shield that they won at Tonbridge by beating Premier Division Sevenoaks Town 3-2. Photo - John Mugridge.

Tenterden & St Michaels F .C. 1992-93. Back Row (L/R): M Light (Manager), V Edgar, A Douglas, D Rooney, A Garner, R Pope, N Hall, D Sivyer, R Oliver (Physio). Front: C Wright, D Light, S Finnis, D Brookes, P Stubbins, I Ramsden. Photo - Dave West.

Oakwood F.C., Inter-Regional Challenge Cup winners 1992-93. Back Row (L/R): Sean Gentle, Greg McLachlan, Rob Moore, Mark Lane, Darren Brocklett, Andy Skinner, Matt Broadway, Digby Kennard. Front: Mark Butcher, Chris Humphrey, Steve Megson (Captain), Simon Broadway (Mascot), Graham Humphrey, Simon Brown. Photo - John Mugridge.

PREMIER DIVISION RESULT CHART 1992-93

HOME TEAM	1	2	3	4	5	6	7	8	9	10	11	12	13	14
1. Aylesford P.M.	*	1-1	2-2	3-0	1-2	4-1	1-0	2-2	1-2	1-4	3-2	2-3	4-1	4-3
2. Greenways	0-3	*	4-0	3-2	3-2	1-1	1-2	2-1	1-2	1-1	0-1	2-2	0-5	8-0
3. Knockholt	1-1	3-0	*	3-1	2-1	1-1	2-1	1-2	1-2	4-0	3-0	3-0	2-2	3-1
4. Lordswood	1-1	3-2	2-2	*	2-1	0-0	3-0	0-2	2-1	0-0	2-2	5-3	3-1	0-2
5. New Romney	0-2	3-1	0-3	0-2	*	2-0	3-1	1-0	3-2	4-3	2-2	0-2	0-1	1-0
6. Oakwood	0-2	1-0	0-5	1-1	3-0	*	1-0	5-2	3-3	2-2	2-2	4-1	1-1	3-0
7. Otford United	0-3	4-3	2-2	1-0	3-1	3-3	*	3-4	3-3	1-1	1-1	6-1	1-3	2-1
8. Scott Sports & Social	0-0	1-4	2-3	2-1	2-0	3-1	3-2	*	1-2	1-1	2-4	2-2	4-3	3-2
9. Sevenoaks Town	2-1	2-0	3-1	1-1	2-0	2-3	2-2	2-1	*	2-1	4-2	2-2	4-1	8-1
10. Stansfeld O & B	2-2	7-3	3-1	1-1	3-3	0-0	2-0	2-1	1-4	*	3-1	1-1	1-1	3-2
11. Teyham & Lynsted	1-1	4-3	4-1	2-2	0-0	2-2	2-1	0-1	1-1	2-1	*	3-4	6-3	0-3
12. Thames Poly	3-4	0-1	1-5	2-0	2-1	0-3	4-5	0-1	2-5	1-0	1-1	*	3-0	9-2
13. VCD Athletic	1-3	5-2	0-2	1-1	0-1	4-2	2-3	1-2	0-1	0-0	2-3	2-2	*	0-1
14. Woodnesborough	1-4	2-2	2-1	1-4	0-0	1-4	1-1	0-5	2-1	1-2	1-1	3-0	1-3	*

EASTERN FIRST DIVISION RESULT CHART 1992-93

HOME TEAM	1	2	3	4	5	6	7	8	9	10	11	12	13	14
1. Bromley Green	*	3-3	3-5	5-1	5-0	2-1	2-1	0-4	0-2		1-1	0-2	0-4	9-1
2. Broomfield United	3-3	*	4-4	4-3	0-2	2-3	2-2	2-4	1-1		2-4	0-3	0-3	2-3
3. Headcorn	2-1	2-0	*	3-2	3-2	4-4	5-1	1-5	1-2		4-2	4-1	2-0	3-0
4. Houchin Rovers	0-5	0-2	1-3	*	3-9	1-2	0-2	0-4	3-5		2-2	2-4	2-2	6-2
5. Hythe United	3-7	1-2	0-1	1-0	*	1-0	2-1	0-3	0-3		2-1	0-2	3-0	1-0
6. Kennington	2-3	2-2	1-1	0-3	0-2	*	3-2	3-3	0-4		2-0	0-4	2-3	1-1
7. Knatchbull	2-1	1-3	0-2	6-2	1-1	1-4	*	1-8	1-2		2-1	0-2	1-3	2-1
8. Lydd Town	2-1	8-2	2-0	6-3	4-0	4-0	2-3	*	2-0		5-0	0-0	4-2	5-0
9. Rye United	1-2	3-1	1-1	5-2	4-2	1-3	4-1	3-4	*		6-1	1-1	3-0	1-4
10. Sandwich Sports										*				
11. Snowdown C.W.	0-4	1-0	3-0	5-2	1-2	1-0	2-1	2-2	4-1		*	0-3	2-3	3-4
12. Tenterden	0-1	0-3	4-0	7-0	1-1	3-2	6-1	1-4	0-1		10-2	*	7-1	3-1
13. University of Kent	1-5	0-3	5-1	4-2	0-1	0-1	4-0	1-3	2-3		3-3	4-3	*	1-0
14. White Lion	3-3	0-2	2-2	5-1	4-5	4-1	4-1	0-0	2-1		5-2	0-1	5-2	*

WESTERN FIRST FIRST DIVISION RESULT CHART 1992-93

HOME TEAM	1	2	3	4	5	6	7	8	9	10	11
1. Bearsted	*	0-2	2-0	1-1	0-1	6-3	1-0	1-1	3-0	1-1	4-1
2. Borough United	0-0	*	3-2	2-2	2-3	1-2	0-1	4-2	1-1	2-1	3-2
3. Colts '85'	1-0	3-3	*	4-2	3-1	1-1	3-3	1-2	7-1	2-1	1-4
4. Edenstone	2-1	2-1	3-2	*	3-0	2-0	2-3	2-5	1-1	2-3	5-1
5. Ex-Blues	2-2	1-0	2-0	2-1	*	4-1	5-0	2-1	4-1	4-1	4-3
6. Moonshot	2-1	0-4	2-4	0-1	1-3	*	2-1	0-4	1-1	0-3	1-2
7. Phoenix Sports	2-5	0-2	2-3	1-3	1-0	5-0	*	2-2	1-1	2-1	0-3
8. Rusthall	3-3	2-1	2-2	0-2	0-0	2-1	1-3	*	3-2	1-1	4-2
9. Sutton Athletic	0-3	2-1	3-0	2-4	1-4	1-6	3-1	2-1	*	0-1	2-2
10. Ten Em Bee	3-3	6-2	1-0	3-2	4-1	6-1	3-2	2-1	3-0	*	2-0
11. Westerham	0-2	5-2	2-0	2-2	3-4	8-0	3-0	6-1	2-2	7-5	*

EASTERN SECOND DIVISION RESULT CHART 1992-93

HOME TEAM	1	2	3	4	5	6	7	8	9	10	11	12	13
1. Bromley Green Reserves	*	4-1	3-0	0-2	2-5	2-2	1-3	5-2		2-5	3-0	2-4	0-4
2. Castle Tavern	1-4	*	5-4	2-5	3-4	1-4	2-8	3-2		5-2	1-0	3-9	2-2
3. Folkstone Invicta 'A'	3-5	10-1	*	4-1	3-1	0-1	3-3	4-0		2-3	4-2	2-1	3-4
4. Kennington Reserves	6-3	10-0	3-1	*	1-1	1-4	1-4	2-2		1-0	3-3	1-2	5-1
5. Knatchbull Reserves	4-3	2-3	2-1	1-3	*	4-3	0-3	2-2		0-1	4-1	3-2	0-5
6. Lydd Town Reserves	3-2	3-0	2-1	0-4	7-0	*	0-1	2-1		6-0	8-1	2-0	1-3
7. New Romney Reserves	9-1	2-1	6-2	3-3	4-0	3-1	*	2-0		5-1	9-0	2-2	5-1
8. Royal George	1-2	0-1	0-2	2-5	1-2	1-7	0-3	*		1-5	4-1	1-5	5-2
9. Sandwich Sports Reserves									*				
10. Sturry	6-1	4-1	1-2	2-1	0-0	2-1	2-2	4-1		*	6-1	0-0	1-2
11. Teyham Reserves	2-1	1-3	1-2	0-2	4-1	1-2	1-1	6-1		3-0	*	0-6	2-3
12. University of Kent Reserves	4-0	8-1	7-0	2-0	4-2	1-2	3-1	5-0		0-0	5-0	*	2-2
13. Walmer Rovers	6-1	3-1	4-1	3-0	1-2	1-3	2-1	2-1		1-0	3-2	2-1	*

WESTERN DIVISION TWO RESULT CHART 1992-93

HOME TEAM	1	2	3	4	5	6	7	8	9	10	11	12	13
1. AFC Egerton	*	4-0	5-0	1-1	3-2	3-1	3-1	3-0	4-2	3-	7-1	7-2	3-1
2. Chislehurst	1-2	*	2-3	2-1	2-1	2-4	3-4	1-4	2-4	3-2	1-3	1-3	1-3
3. Edenbridge United	0-4	6-1	*	1-1	3-1	2-1	1-0	1-3	2-2	4-0	1-3	1-0	1-5
4. Eltham Palace	4-2	1-2	0-1	*	3-1	2-1	2-4	7-2	1-1	3-1	3-3	3-0	1-6
5. Eynsford	0-2	3-2	0-4	4-4	*	2-1	6-2	0-5	1-1	3-3	2-2	3-1	2-2
6. Fleetdown United	3-1	2-0	1-0	1-0	2-0	*	3-3	2-3	1-1	3-2	0-1	5-1	2-2
7. Halstead	1-3	1-3	3-4	2-1	3-2	0-5	*	2-5	2-4	3-1	2-3	3-2	2-4
8. Paddock Wood Town	2-1	3-1	3-2	2-0	1-3	0-5	0-2	*	1-2	3-0	0-2	6-1	4-3
9. Platt United	1-6	6-1	1-0	3-2	3-1	1-0	4-2	5-2	*	2-1	3-3	4-2	6-2
10. St. Georges	0-4	1-2	1-2	1-4	4-3	1-5	2-3	0-5	0-3	*	0-6	2-2	1-5
11. Stood County	2-2	7-2	4-1	4-1	7-0	2-1	4-1	2-3	2-2	8-2	*	1-0	6-1
12. Tonbridge Invicta	2-1	0-5	2-4	4-3	1-1	2-1	3-3	0-5	1-5	1-5	1-3	*	2-2
13. Wellcome (Sat.)	2-1	3-1	2-0	3-1	5-3	3-2	1-0	4-2	0-2	5-0	1-1	4-0	*

WESTERN DIVISION THREE RESULT CHART 1992-93

HOME TEAM	1	2	3	4	5	6	7	8	9	10	11	12	13
1. Chipstead	*	2-3	1-2	4-2	1-2	4-0	0-4	2-1	1-3	2-4	5-0	1-3	6-4
2. Dunton Green	3-1	*	5-4	2-0	2-4	2-4	4-2	4-2	7-2	3-1	1-1	6-1	4-0
3. Empire	3-0	3-1	*	6-1	3-2	6-2	1-3	2-3	4-1	4-3	2-3	5-0	2-3
4. Halls	1-0	6-3	0-4	*	2-0	2-3	4-0	1-3	1-1	3-0	1-4	3-5	0-1
5. Joyce Green	4-4	1-1	1-3	2-3	*	1-2	2-1	4-3	1-0	2-1	1-2	1-2	4-0
6. N.P.I.	2-2	4-2	0-2	2-2	1-5	*	3-1	3-2	3-1	3-1	2-2	0-0	2-1
7. Nomads	5-2	2-2	1-0	5-1	3-3	3-3	*	3-1	0-0	4-0	1-4	5-0	4-0
8. Old Bexleians	1-3	0-3	0-4	2-2	3-6	1-3	2-2	*	1-2	1-2	2-3	2-2	2-3
9. Snodland	3-1	2-2	0-3	5-2	2-1	4-1	3-1	5-0	*	4-0	2-3	5-3	2-0
10. Swanscombe United	4-0	2-3	1-6	3-0	1-0	4-6	3-6	4-0	2-4	*	2-3	5-0	3-3
11. Sherwood Park C.A.	7-1	4-3	2-4	1-0	2-3	13-3	4-1	0-5	5-4	6-0	*	4-1	2-3
12. Tonbridge Rangers	1-2	5-2	3-4	4-0	2-2	0-2	0-7	4-3	3-5	3-1	1-2	*	3-1
13. Wickham Park	0-0	2-2	2-3	2-2	2-4	2-2	1-1	0-3	2-2	4-1	1-8	4-0	*

WESTERN RESERVE DIV. 1 RESULT CHART 1992-93

HOME TEAM	1	2	3	4	5	6	7	8
1. Bearsted Reserves	*	1-2	0-2	1-6	1-2	2-1	0-2	2-2
2. Edenstone Reserves	2-3	*	1-2	1-8	6-3	0-4	0-6	1-2
3. Lordswood Reserves	1-0	2-1	*	0-1	0-1	3-1	0-3	5-1
4. Otford United Reserves	4-2	1-0	2-1	*	2-3	4-1	0-4	1-0
5. Scott Sports Reserves	2-2	6-3	2-1	3-0	*	3-3	1-2	2-1
6. Sevenoaks Town Reserves	0-0	4-0	5-3	1-1	2-2	*	2-3	1-0
7. Stansfeld Reserves	7-0	2-0	1-0	1-2	5-4	1-2	*	4-1
8. VCD Athletic Reserves	4-3	1-0	1-1	2-1	3-1	4-1	1-0	*

WESTERN RESERVE DIVISION TWO RESULT CHART 1992-93

HOME TEAM	1	2	3	4	5	6	7	8
1. Aylesford P.M. Reserves	*	9-1	8-0	0-2	0-0	7-0	1-2	3-1
2. Borough United Reserves	4-3	*	6-2	2-2	6-4	2-4	1-3	0-5
3. Colts '85' Reserves	2-3	4-4	*	2-8	0-6	0-7	2-0	1-6
4. Greenways Reserves	5-0	9-3	3-1	*	3-0	1-1	3-3	3-1
5. Oakwood Reserves	6-1	2-0	7-2	0-5	*	4-1	2-0	1-3
6. Rusthall Reserves	2-0	6-0	3-0	1-4	4-1	*	3-1	2-0
7. Thames Poly Reserves	2-2	3-1	6-2	0-3	2-4	4-1	*	1-1
8. Westerham Reserves	0-2	2-2	12-0	2-0	5-1	2-1	4-3	*

PREMIER DIVISION CLUBS 1993-1994

AYLESFORD PAPER MILLS
Secretary: Mr Casey, 10 Ragstone Court, Ditton, Aylesford, Kent ME20 6AJ (0732 849476)
Ground: Cobdown, Station Road, Ditton, Nr. Maidstone (0622 717771) **Founded:** 1979
Colours: Red & white stripes/red/red **Change Colours:** Black & white stripes/black/black

GREENWAYS
Secretary: Mr W Miller, 14 Cygnet Gardens, Northfleet, Kent DA11 7DN (0474 560913)
Ground: Blue Circle Spts Ground, via Springhead Road, Northfleet (0474 534625) **Founded:** 1965
Colours: All red **Change Colours:** All blue

HYTHE UNITED (1992)
Secretary: Mr S Walker, 4 Kingfisher Ave., Hythe, Kent CT12 6RD (0303 264470)
Ground: Reachfields, Fort Rd, Hythe (0303 264932) **Founded:** 1992
Colours: White/red/red **Change Colours:** Blue & white/blue/blue.

KNOCKHOLT
Secretary: Mrs I Bryant, 4 Blair Court, The Knoll, Beckenham, Kent BR3 2JJ (081 650 7389)
Ground: Knockholt Village Club, Main Road, Knockholt (0959 532346) **Founded:** 1967
Colours: Red/black/black **Change Colours:** Grey & black/black/black

LORDSWOOD
Secretary: Mr S Lewis, Sunnybrook, Gorsewood Road, Hartley, Longfield (0474 708233)
Ground: Lordswood Spts & Social Club, North Dane Way, Walderslade (0634 669138) **Founded:** 1968
Colours: Amber/black/black **Change Colours:** White/black/black

NEW ROMNEY
Secretary: Mr H Payne, 'Stonecrop', Grand Parade, Littlestone, New Romney, Kent TN28 8NQ (0679 66425)
Ground: Station Road, New Romney (0679 64858) **Founded:** 1895
Colours: All blue **Change Colours:** White/blue/blue

OAKWOOD
Secretary: Mr P Mannering, 24 Ellenswood Close, Otham, Maidstone, Kent ME15 9QA (0622 862482)
Ground: Honey Lane, Otham, Maidstone **Founded:** 1924
Colours: All red **Change Colours:** White/white/red

OTFORD UNITED
Secretary: Mr R Gulliver, 22 Berwick Way, Sevenoaks, Kent TN14 5EY (0732 459064)
Ground: Recreation Ground, High Street, Otford **Founded:** 1900
Colours: Amber/black/black **Change Colours:** Red/black/black

SCOTT SPORTS & SOCIAL
Secretary: Mr R Taylor, 24 Sun Lane, Gravesend, Kent DA12 5HG (0474 332208)
Ground: Scott Sports & Social Club, Nelson Road, Northfleet (0474 336456) **Founded:** 1927
Colours: Black & white stripes/black/black **Change Colours:** Blue & white hoops/white/blue

SEVENOAKS TOWN
Secretary: Mr E Diplock, 23 Holly Bush Lane, Sevenoaks, Kent TN13 3TH (0732 454280)
Ground: Greatness Park, Seal Road, Sevenoaks (0732 741987) **Founded:** 1883
Colours: Red & black/black/black **Change Colours:** Tangerine/black/tangerine.

STANSFELD OXFORD & BERMONDSEY CLUB

Secretary: Mr A Rigby, 70 Roundtable Road, Bromley, Kent BR1 5LG (081 698 5641)   **Founded:** 1897
Ground: St James Squash & Leisure Club, Marvels Lane, Grove Park SE12 (081 851 3522)
Colours: Blue & yellow stripes/blue/blue   **Change Colours:** All red.

TEYNHAM & LYNSTED

Secretary: Mr M Ashworth, 74 Harold Road, Sittingbourne, Kent ME10 3AJ (0795 423986)
Ground: Frognal Lane, Teynham, Off A2   **Founded:** 1961
Colours: Sky & white stripes/maroon/sky   **Change Colours:** Red & black/black/black

THAMES POLYTECHNIC

Secretary: Derek A Ingram, 8 St Josephs Close, Orpington, Kent BR6 9TY (0689 977162)
Ground: University of Greenwich, Avery Hill Rd   **Founded:** 1888.
Colours: Yellow/green/green   **Change Colours:** White & green/white/white.
Previous Lge: Kent (pre-1992)   **Previous Ground:** Kidbrooke Lane, Eltham (pre-1993)

VICKERS CRAYFORD/DARTFORD ATHLETIC

Secretary: Mr R Bond, 97 Birkbeck Road, Sidcup, Kent DA14 4DJ (081 300 9943)
Ground: Oakwood, Old Road, Crayford (0322 524262)   **Founded:** 1916
Colours: Green & white hoops/white/white   **Change:** Yellow/black/black.

WOODNESBOROUGH

Secretary: Mr G Hunt, Hillcross Farm, Eastry, Sandwich, Kent CT13 0NY (0304 611311)
Ground: "Hillborough", Woodnesborough Road, Eastry (0304 614721)   **Founded:** 1961
Colours: Yellow/blue/blue   **Change Colours:** All blue

EASTERN FIRST DIVISION CLUBS 1993-1994

BROMLEY GREEN

Secretary: Mr A Barham, 218 Cheriton High Street, Folkestone, Kent (0303 277240)
Ground: T.B.A.   **Founded:** 1930
Colours: All green   **Change Colours:** Orange/black/orange.

BROOMFIELD UNITED

Secretary: Mr J Edgington, 4 Damerham Close, Canterbury, Kent CT2 7SB (0227 452323)
Ground: Bridge Recreation Ground, Patrixbourne Road, Bridge, Nr Canterbury   **Founded:** 1925
Colours: Red & white stripes/black/red & black   **Change Colours:** Sky blue/black/navy

HEADCORN

Secretary: Mr A Purvis, 5 Newlands, Bridewell, Ashford, Kent (0233 631365)
Ground: Grigg Lane, Off Oak Lane, Headcorn   **Founded:** 1920
Colours: Ambler/black/black   **Change Colours:** All blue

HOUCHIN ROVERS

Secretary: Mrs S Blackmore, 3 Goat Lees, Faversham Rd, Kennington, Ashford, Kent TN25 4PH (0233 639843).
Ground: Bybrook Road, Kennington (0233 624233).   **Founded:** 1962
Colours: Blue & white/navy/sky   **Change Colours:** Grey/black/black.

KENNINGTON

Secretary: Mr R Lancaster, 'Totternhoe', Goat Lees, Faversham Road, Kennington, Ashford (0233 624858)
Ground: Spearpoint Rec. Grnd, opposite Spearpoint Hotel, The Ridge, Kennington   **Founded:** 1880
Colours: Amber   **Change Colours:** All red

KNATCHBULL

Secretary: Mr D Howie, 13 Charminster, Washford Farm, Ashford, Kent TN23 2UH (0233 611207)
Ground: Hatch Park, Off A20, Mersham, Nr. Ashford   **Founded:** 1981
Colours: White/white/maroon   **Change Colours:** Maroon/white/maroon

LYDD TOWN

Secretary: Mr P Sisley, 52 Skinner Road, Lydd, Kent TN29 9HP (0679 21194)
Ground: The Rype, Manor Road, Lydd   **Founded:** 1885
Colours: Red/green/green   **Change Colours:** All green

MILTON ATHLETIC

Secretary: Mr P Duffin, 18 Hales Rd, Tunstall, Sittingbourne, Kent ME10 1SR (0795 471260)
Ground: U.K.P. Sports Ground, Gore Court Rd, Sittingbourne (0795 477047)   **Founded:** 1926.
Colours: Sky/navy/navy   **Change Colours:** Red/white/white.

NEW ROMNEY RESERVES *(details as per page 613)*

RYE UNITED

Secretary: Mr S Williams, 'Grovewood', Grove Lane, Iden, East Sussex TN31 7PX (0797 280509)
Ground: Rye Football and Cricket Salts   **Founded:** 1938
Colours: Red & black/black/red & black   **Change Colours:** All white

SNOWDOWN COLLIERY WELFARE

Secretary: Mrs A Norton, 26 Burgess Road, Aylesham, Canterbury, Kent (0304 841706)
Ground: Spinney Lane, Aylesham, Canterbury (0304 840278)   **Founded:** 1907
Colours: Black & white stripes/black/black   **Change Colours:** Green & yellow/green/green.

TENTERDEN & ST MICHAELS

Secretary: Mr S Stevens, Kent House, Ashford Rd, St Michaels, Tenterden (0580 762703).
Ground: The Recreation Ground, Tenterden.   **Founded:** 1890
Colours: Blue & white/navy/black   **Change Colours:** Maroon/sky/maroon

UNIVERSITY OF KENT

Secretary: Mrs I Simmonds, Sports Federation, Sports Centre, University of Kent, Canterbury, Kent CT2 7NL
(0227 768027)
Ground: The Playing Fields, University of Kent, Canterbury   **Founded:** 1967.
Colours: Black & white stripes/black/black   **Change Colours:** Red/black/black

John Featherstone of Empire F.C. Three times winner of on the 'Manager of the Month' award, he guided Empire to the Western Region Third Division title and the final of the Western Region Junior Cup. Photo - John Mugridge.

New Romney F.C. 1992-93. Photo - Dave West.

Tenterden & St Michaels captain David Brookes receives the Weald of Kent Charity Shield from Mr W Manklow after a 6-0 win at home to New Romney in the 22nd May final. Photo - Dave West.

WALMER ROVERS

Secretary: Mr B Skinner, 131 Downs Rd, Deal, Kent CT14 7TF (0304 361832)
Ground: Harke Wood, Dover Rd, Walmer (0304 374160)   **Founded:** 1959.
Colours: All blue   **Change Colours:** All red.

WHITE LION (CHERITON)

Secretary: Mr R Matthews, 41 Brambley Cres., Folkestone, Kent CT20 3PU (0303 276151)
Ground: Cheriton Recreation Ground, Weymouth Rd, Folkestone   **Founded:** 1990
Colours: Red/blue/red   **Change Colours:** All green.

WESTERN FIRST DIVISION CLUBS 1993-1994

A.F.C. EGERTON

Secretary: Mr S Parkes, 48 Oakdene Rd, St Mary Cray, Orpington, Kent BR5 2AN (0689 821737).
Ground: St Mary Cray Rec, Park Rd, St Mary Cray, Orpington   **Founded:** 1971
Colours: Blue/blue/white   **Change Colours:** White/blue/blue.

BEARSTED

Secretary: Mr J Scannel, 24 Fauchons Lane, Bearsted, Maidstone, Kent (0622 39072)
Ground: Bearsted Green, The Street, Bearsted   **Founded:** 1895
Colours: White/white/blue   **Change Colours:** Blue & yellow/blue/blue

BOROUGH UNITED

Secretary: Mr M G Bennett, 29a Princes Road, Dartford, Kent DA1 3HJ (0322 270231)
Ground: Dartford Sports & Social Club, Darenth Road, Dartford   **Founded:** 1945
Colours: Blue/navy/navy   **Change Colours:** Yellow/navy/yellow

COLTS '85

Secretary: TBA.   **Founded:** 1985
Ground: Swanmead Sports Ground, Swanmead Way, off Cannon Lane, Tonbridge (0732 350473)
Colours: Blue/white/blue   **Change Colours:** White/white/blue

EDENSTONE

Secretary: Mrs C Jones, 84 Southlands Road, Bromley, Kent BR2 9QS (081 290 6034)
Ground: The Grove Sports Club, Oakley Road, Bromley   **Founded:** 1965
Colours: Blue/white/white   **Change Colours:** Silver grey/black/grey

EX BLUES

Secretary: Mr M Harvey, 29 Crown Lane Bromley, Kent BR2 9PG (081 464 4815)
Ground: 118 Pickhurst Rise, Off Pickhurst Lane, Hayes, West Wickham, Kent (081 777 9904)
Colours: White/blue/blue   **Change Colours:** All blue   **Founded:** 1945

PHOENIX SPORTS

Secretary: Mr A Pearson, 4 Gainsborough Avenue, Dartford, Kent (0322 228625)
Ground: Phoenix Sports Ground, May Road East, Barnehurst.   **Founded:** 1895
Colours: Red & white/black/red   **Change Colours:** Green/red/red.

PLATT UNITED

Secretary: Mr G Broad, The Lilacs, Rowhill Rd, Hextable, Kent BR8 7RL (0322 662452).
Ground: Stonehouse Field, Longmill Lane, Platt   **Founded:** 1930
Colours: White/blue/white   **Change Colours:** Red/blue/red.

RUSTHALL

Secretary: Mr R Forbes, 27 Ashenden Walk, Tunbridge Wells, Kent TN2 3HR (0892 545075)
Ground: Jockey Farm, Newington Road, Rusthall   **Founded:** 1899
Colours: All green   **Change Colours:** Claret & blue/sky/sky.

STROOD COUNTY

Secretary: Mrs A Potter, 37 Darnley Road, Strood, Kent ME2 2EY (0634 716299)
Ground: Riverside Spts Ground, The Esplanade, Rochester   **Founded:** 1979
Colours: White/blue/white   **Change Colours:** Red/black/black

TEN EM BEE

Secretary: Mr David Barnard.
Ground: Old Bromley Road Playing Fields, Old Bromley Road (081 460 0652)   **Founded:** 1975
Colours: Green/black/black   **Change Colours:** Green/white/green.

WESTERHAM

Secretary: Mr A Noad, 25 Croydon Road, Westerham, Kent (0959 62658)
Ground: King George Playing Fields, Costells Meadow, off Quebec Avenue, Westerham (0959 61106)
Colours: Red/black/black   **Change Colours:** Green/black/black   **Founded:** 1888

LOWER DIVISION CONSTITUTIONS 1993-94

Eastern 2nd	Western 2nd	Western 3rd	Western 4th:	Western Res. Div.
Bishopsbourne	Chislehurst	Chipstead	Aylesford	Aylesford PM Res.
Bond Sports	Edenbridge U.	Dunton Green	Belvedere	Bearsted Res.
Bromley Gn Res.	Eltham Palace	Halls	Greenways Res.	Borough Utd Res.
F'stone Inv. 'A'	Empire	Joyce Green	Hawkenbury	Colts '85 Res.
Headcorn Res.	Eynsford	N.P.I.	Lordswood Res.	Edenstone Res.
Hythe U. Res.	Fleetdown U.	Snodland	Maidstone Inv.	Fleetdown Utd Res.
Kennington Res.	Halstead	St Georges (W'ham)	Old Bexleians	Joyce Green Res.
Knatchbull Res.	Moonshot Ath.	Swanscombe Utd	Otford Utd Res.	Nomads Res.
Lydd Town Res.	Paddock Wd T.	Tonbridge Inv.	Scott S. & S.I Res.	Oakwood Res.
New Romney 'A'	Sherwood Park C.A.	Tonbridge Rgrs	Sevenoaks T. Res.	Phoenix Spts Res.
Ryl George (F'stone)	Sutton Athletic	Wickham Park	Stansfeld O&B Res	Platt Utd Res.
St Margarets	Wellcome (Sat.)		VCD Athletic Res.	Rusthall Res.
Sturry			Westerham Res.	Thames Poly Res.
Tenterden SM Res.				
Teynham & L. Res.				
Uni. of Kent Res.				

'D. & J. TYRES' KENT YOUTH LEAGUE

NORTHERN	P	W	D	L	F	A	PTS
V.C.D Athletic	24	21	3	0	92	16	45
Maidstone Invicta	24	18	3	3	105	36	39
Gillingham (N)	24	12	8	4	48	32	32
Charlton Ath.	24	13	5	6	53	32	31
Danson Furness U.	24	11	7	6	58	47	29
Tonbridge Angels	24	11	5	8	40	36	27
Erith & Belvedere	24	12	3	9	51	48	27
Dartford	24	9	4	11	47	44	22
Thamesmead Town	24	5	5	14	33	61	15
Corinthian	24	5	4	15	29	66	14
Phoenix Sports	24	3	5	16	25	73	11
Cray Wanderers	24	4	2	18	38	72	10
Fisher Athletic	24	3	4	17	29	85	10

SOUTHERN	P	W	D	L	F	A	PTS
Gillingham (S)	24	20	2	2	111	20	42
Dover Athletic	24	18	4	2	95	33	40
Ashford Town	24	16	4	4	71	41	36
Whitstable Town	24	13	3	8	57	38	29
Chatham Town	24	12	4	8	46	42	28
Sittingbourne	24	12	4	8	42	51	28
Margate	24	12	1	11	65	61	25
Herne Bay	24	7	2	15	31	50	16
Ramsgate Athletic	24	6	4	14	31	57	16
Folkestone Invicta	24	6	3	15	31	62	15
Lordswood	24	6	1	17	26	66	13
Deal Town	24	5	2	17	33	74	12
Faversham Town	24	6	0	18	33	87	12

RESULT CHARTS 1992-93

NORTHERN SECTION		1	2	3	4	5	6	7	8	9	10	11	12	13
1.	Charlton Athletic	*	4-0	4-1	1-3	2-1	2-0	9-1	0-1	0-5	6-0	1-1	1-4	1-3
2.	Corinthian	0-2	*	4-2	3-7	1-2	1-5	1-0	0-3	1-6	0-1	2-2	3-1	1-3
3.	Cray Wanderers	0-3	2-1	*	2-3	0-5	2-4	3-2	0-1	2-3	3-1	1-2	1-5	1-2
4.	Danson Furness United	0-1	6-2	3-1	*	2-7	1-2	5-0	1-2	2-2	4-1	2-0	2-1	1-5
5.	Dartford	1-4	1-1	2-3	1-3	*	2-2	2-1	1-3	1-4	4-0	1-4	0-2	1-2
6.	Erith & Belvedere	2-2	0-0	5-3	1-2	1-4	*	4-1	3-2	0-8	4-1	5-1	1-0	1-3
7.	Fisher Athletic	1-2	1-1	3-3	2-2	0-1	2-4	*	1-3	2-5	2-1	2-2	1-0	0-5
8.	Gillingham (N)	0-0	2-1	3-2	2-2	2-2	5-1	7-3	*	3-4	1-1	2-0	1-0	2-2
9.	Maidstone Invicta	3-5	9-0	3-1	4-4	4-2	1-0	10-1	3-0	*	1-3	2-0	9-3	2-2
10.	Phoenix Sports	0-2	1-4	2-2	2-2	1-4	1-2	0-0	1-1	0-8	*	5-2	1-2	0-5
11.	Thamesmead Town	1-1	0-1	4-2	1-2	0-1	0-3	2-1	0-0	0-6	6-1	*	2-3	2-6
12.	Tonbridge Angels	2-0	1-1	1-0	1-1	1-1	2-1	4-1	2-2	0-2	3-1	1-0	*	1-4
13.	Vickers Cray. Dartford A.	4-0	4-0	6-1	3-0	1-0	2-0	9-0	2-0	4-1	5-0	10-1	0-0	*

SOUTHERN SECTION		1	2	3	4	5	6	7	8	9	10	11	12	13
1.	Ashford Town	*	3-2	3-0	3-3	10-1	3-2	2-1	6-0	4-0	2-1	2-1	1-1	2-2
2.	Chatham Town	2-4	*	5-1	0-3	2-1	1-2	2-4	2-0	3-2	3-2	2-1	1-0	2-1
3.	Deal Town	0-8	3-3	*	2-6	1-2	3-2	1-3	1-3	4-1	4-3	0-2	2-3	1-3
4.	Dover Athletic	5-0	3-0	6-0	*	7-0	7-1	2-2	1-0	5-1	3-3	2-1	6-2	4-4
5.	Faversham Town	1-4	0-3	3-2	2-7	*	0-4	1-3	7-1	4-0	0-7	0-1	1-2	1-0
6.	Folkestone Invicta	1-2	1-1	1-3	2-5	2-1	*	2-3	1-1	2-1	1-5	3-2	0-2	1-1
7.	Gillingham (S)	5-0	0-1	3-0	5-0	9-0	11-0	*	6-1	4-0	5-1	13-0	5-0	4-0
8.	Herne Bay	1-3	1-0	4-1	1-2	1-2	0-1	1-3	*	0-1	2-0	3-0	0-1	1-3
9.	Lordswood	2-4	1-0	1-0	1-6	2-0	2-0	1-4	1-1	*	1-0	1-2	2-3	1-5
10.	Margate	3-1	5-6	4-1	0-5	5-1	2-0	1-4	4-0	4-1	*	3-2	4-0	3-2
11.	Ramsgate Athletic	4-0	1-1	1-1	3-4	2-0	2-2	0-5	2-0	2-4	*	1-1	0-1	1-1
12.	Sittingbourne	2-2	1-1	3-0	0-3	5-2	2-1	1-6	4-3	3-1	2-1	3-1	*	1-4
13.	Whitstable Town	1-2	3-1	1-2	2-1	5-1	2-1	1-6	0-1	6-2	3-0	4-0	3-0	*

ALDERSHOT & DISTRICT LEAGUE

SENIOR DIV.	P	W	D	L	F	A	PTS
Bordon	22	14	3	5	66	37	45
Yateley Green	22	13	4	5	53	38	43
Frimley Town	22	12	6	4	77	37	42
Yateley	22	12	3	7	63	41	39
Monteagle Arms	22	13	0	9	54	45	39
Four Marks	22	9	8	5	51	35	35
Liphook	22	9	7	6	59	49	34
Tongham	22	9	3	10	63	45	30
Border Sports	22	9	3	10	48	50	30
Bass Alton T. 'A'	22	4	4	14	26	67	16
Fleet Spurs Res.	22	4	3	15	28	62	15
Covies Res.	22	0	4	18	20	102	4

DIV. ONE	P	W	D	L	F	A	PTS
Airborne United	20	18	1	1	105	25	55
Hale	20	17	0	3	70	13	51
Aldershot P.O.	20	9	6	5	51	43	33
Frimley Town Res.	20	10	2	8	55	50	32
Hartley Wintney 'A'	20	8	6	6	51	53	30
Yateley Gn Res.	20	8	4	8	43	47	28
Fleet Spurs 'A'	20	8	2	10	42	47	26
Yateley Res.	20	7	2	11	32	53	23
Admel	20	5	3	12	36	62	18
Bordon Res.	20	2	3	15	36	76	9
Tongham Res.	20	2	3	15	28	60	9

DIV. TWO	P	W	D	L	F	A	PTS
Crookham Rovers	22	16	4	2	82	22	52
Binsted	22	15	1	6	82	50	46
Keogh	22	14	3	5	70	32	45
Pyestock	22	12	7	3	54	30	43
Liphook Res.	22	10	7	5	65	39	37
Border Spts Res.	22	10	4	8	49	44	34
Froyle	22	9	7	6	47	52	34
Anchor Normandy	22	8	4	10	60	64	28
Lindford Ryl Exch.	22	8	1	13	51	81	25
Courtmoor	22	5	1	16	55	89	16
Rowledge	22	2	3	17	30	81	9
Heath End Wdrs 'A'	22	1	2	19	26	87	5

DIV. THREE	P	W	D	L	F	A	PTS
Yateley 'A'	20	17	3	0	57	24	54
Puttenham	20	13	3	4	57	26	42
Alton United	20	13	1	6	51	39	40
Headley	20	12	1	7	67	52	37
Sandhurst T. 'A'	20	11	3	6	59	27	36
Four Marks Res.	20	11	3	6	47	34	36
Old Dean	20	11	1	8	59	41	34
Hartley Wintney 'B'	20	5	1	14	33	69	16
Hale Res.	20	4	1	15	42	59	13
Aldershot C.C.	20	3	1	16	24	68	10
Crondall	20	0	2	18	20	77	2

DIV. FOUR	P	W	D	L	F	A	PTS
Yateley 'B'	18	16	2	0	63	22	50
Kings	18	14	3	1	98	25	45
Farnham Athletic	18	9	2	7	78	51	29
Yateley Green 'A'	18	7	5	6	43	33	26
Eversley	18	7	4	7	47	44	25
Courtmoor Res.	18	7	2	9	41	59	23
Fleet Spurs 'B'	18	6	4	8	48	48	22
Lindford R.E. Res.	18	5	3	10	46	64	18
Tongham 'A'	18	5	2	11	56	80	17
Queens Head	18	0	1	17	28	122	1

'MOREYS' ISLE OF WIGHT LEAGUE

DIV. ONE	P	W	D	L	F	A	PTS
Oakfield	22	17	3	2	54	12	54
Shanklin	22	14	5	3	49	26	47
Wootton Bridge Spts	22	13	3	6	57	47	42
Ryde Sports Res.	22	12	4	6	59	25	40
Seaview	22	11	4	7	50	32	37
Sandown	22	9	3	10	49	44	30
E. Cowes V.A. Res.	22	9	1	12	43	48	28
Ventnor	22	5	7	10	27	39	22
Brighstone	22	6	4	12	22	39	22
Brading Town Res.	22	7	1	14	26	53	22
Binstead C.O.B.	22	6	3	13	21	43	21
Carisbrooke Utd	22	3	2	17	28	75	11

DIV. TWO	P	W	D	L	F	A	PTS
Northwood	22	15	3	4	85	20	48
Cowes Spts Res.	22	13	5	4	73	43	44
St Helens	22	12	6	4	65	39	42
Bembridge	22	12	1	9	56	48	37
Haylands	22	9	5	8	51	49	32
Osborne Coburg	22	7	6	9	50	42	27
West Wight Res.	22	6	9	7	42	48	27
Medina	22	7	5	10	35	45	26
Newport IOW 'A'	22	6	6	10	31	50	24
Wootton	22	6	6	10	32	63	24
Niton	22	5	5	12	39	75	20
Yarmouth Town	22	3	5	14	25	61	14

COMB. ONE	P	W	D	L	F	A	PTS
Ryde Sports 'A'	28	22	1	5	82	27	67
Oakfield Res.	28	20	5	3	85	29	65
Shanklin Res.	28	16	4	8	74	36	52
Wootton Bdge Res.	28	13	8	7	66	55	47
Binstead Res.	28	13	6	9	61	43	45
Ventnor Res.	28	13	4	11	52	43	43
Northwood Res.	28	11	5	12	54	49	38
Sandown Res.	28	10	7	11	62	55	37
Cowes Sports 'A'	28	12	1	15	60	60	37
Seaview Res.	28	11	4	13	44	60	37
E. Cowes V.A. 'A'	28	9	4	15	68	75	31
Carisbrooke Res.	28	9	5	14	59	74	*31
St Helens Res.	28	9	3	16	53	69	30
Brading T. 'A' Res.	28	8	5	15	37	64	*28
Wootton	28	2	2	24	27	146	*7

DIV. THREE	P	W	D	L	F	A	PTS
Brading Youth	27	24	0	3	144	28	*71
Westlands	27	21	3	3	107	32	66
Central Park	27	17	1	9	103	48	52
Plessey	27	14	4	9	65	51	46
Calbourne	27	14	3	10	80	55	45
Wroxall	27	14	0	13	82	65	42
Red Star Spartans	27	9	5	13	58	89	32
Smallbrook	27	7	3	17	49	81	24
Shanklin Youth	27	2	2	23	30	159	8
Newchurch	27	1	3	23	24	122	6

COMB. TWO	P	W	D	L	F	A	PTS
Newport IOW 'B'	28	21	4	3	85	23	67
Bembridge Res.	28	20	3	5	91	36	63
Medina Res.	28	18	4	6	74	46	*57
Plessey Res.	28	17	6	5	75	43	x50
Brading Yth Res.	28	16	1	11	64	47	49
Osborne Cob. Res.	28	14	2	12	61	50	*43
Brighstone Res.	28	13	3	12	68	64	42
Haylands Res.	28	13	2	13	75	64	*40
Yarmouth T. Res.	28	11	3	13	71	52	35
Niton Res.	28	9	5	14	58	64	32
Calbourne Res.	28	9	5	14	66	90	32
Westlands Res.	28	9	4	15	54	69	31
West Wight 'A'	28	6	4	18	54	85	22
Smallbrook Res.	28	6	2	20	32	66	20
Wroxall Res.	28	2	4	21	30	137	10

* - 1pt deducted
x - 7pts deducted

The Isle of Wight side that hosted the 'Island Games' in July 1993. They finished joint fifth/sixth in a tournament that also included Jersey, Isle of Man, Greenland, Aland, Anglesey, Gibraltar and Shetland. Back Row (L/R): Shaun North, Andy Sampson, Malcolm Cole, John Simpkins, Andy Watson, Andy Butler. Centre: Kevin McArthur, Shaun Flux, Mark Deacon, Bruce Long, Kevin Thorne, Brian Brockwell, Roy Maskell, John Richards. Front: Glyn Taylor, Nigel Stevens, Steve Legg, Greg Jacobs (Mascot), Neil Berridge, Garry Sperry, Mark Hutton. Photo - Dave West.

TIMBER & BUILDING MATERIALS

JEWSON

EASTERN COUNTIES LEAGUE

President: Derek I. Needham
Secretary: Colin Lamb,
3 Land Close, Clacton-on-Sea, Essex Co16 8UJ (0255 436398)

1992-93 saw the League start with a new officer: Merlin Saddleton, having responsibility for ground standards.

The opening day of season 1992-93: August 22, saw defending champions Wroxham beat Halstead 3-0. Tiptree United's trend of not winning on the opening day of the season, dating back to the 1985-86 season, continued as they drew 1-1 at home to Great Yarmouth. Division one champions Diss Town went down 1-3 to Chatteris Town in their opening premier division game, whilst the other promoted club, Fakenham Town, drew 0-0 against Cornard. Newcomers to the Legaue, Stanway Rovers, drew 2-2 away to Swaffham Town. Diss would record ther first premier division victory the following Saturday against Fakenham, 2-0. The latter side's first premier division success came a month later in their 9th match versus Tiptree. Stanway's first ECL win came on August 25th against Woodbridge.

On September 12, Wroxham's Matthew Metcalfe netted all 5 in his side's 5-3 win over Cornard. Metcalfe would go on to end the season the League's leading marksman with 50 goals. September 13, saw the first managerial casualty when Great Yarmouth, with just one draw from their opening six games, sacked joint managers Brian Cockrill and John Cogger. The Bloaters would go undefeated in their first six games under new manager Mel Antcliffe and would end the season with a run of 10 unbeaten games. On September 22, Cambridge City Reserves became only the second club in the League's history to score six goals at home in a league match and lose, beaten 6-7 by Mildenhall Town. Four days later Sudbury Town Reserves beat Bury Town Reserves 9-1, away. Debutant Julian Knight got a hat-trick, as did Marty Thorpe. On September 29, Newmarket Town became the sole Jewson survivors in the F.A. Cup, 3rd Qualifying Round, after beating Baldock 6-2 in their 2nd Qualifying Round replay. One day on, Soham's Adrian Bullett, who would end the season as division one's leading marksmen hit six in his side's 8-1 home win against Warboys. By the end of September Harwich & Parkeston led the premier division, narrowly ahead of Wisbech Town and Wroxham. Sudbury Wanderers headed division one, from Hadleigh & Stanway Rovers. Wanderers would in fact retain the top slot for the remainder of the season, securing the championship on April 24th in a 2-2 draw versus Cambridge City Reserves.

On October 10th, Newmarket beat Diadora premier division side Grays Athletic to progress into the 4th Qualifying Round of the F.A. Cup. On October 17th, the 2nd Round of the League Cup was drawn live on BBC Radio Suffolk by secretary Colin Lamb and the station's head of sport Charles Collins, the first time a Jewson cup draw had been made on radio. On October 21st, Ely City

Wroxham captain Stuart Larter receiving the League Championship Cup, plus a match football for their April premier division club of the month award, from League President Derek Needham.

manager Alan Biley stood down through work commitments, succeeded by Steve Clark. Three days later, Newmarket's run in the F.A. Cup ended, beaten 2-0 by Hayes. October 24th also saw Stowmarket Town become the 4th Club to complete 1,500 Jewson League matches, drawing 0-0 against Tiptree. October 25th saw Brightlingsea United, with only three draws from their nine games, part company with manager Graham Carter. New boss Chris Dolby however would fare little better, and by the end of the season the club would have a third manager in Frank Thompson, and would go until April 12th before recording the first of only two victories (against Tiptree) and end in bottom slot and be relegated. On October 27th, Felixstowe Town included two sets of brothers: Gary and Neal Stanbridge and Richard and David Barber versus Lowestoft. By the end of October, Wisbech Town, unbeaten in 16 games, headed division one from Wroxham & Harwich. The Fenmen would retain top slot until April 3rd. Division one leaders Sudbury Wanderers, were also unbeaten in the league, and led from Stanway and Hadleigh.

On November 5th it was reported that Thetford Town manager David Low had resigned; the Norfolk club having achieved only one win in their first season after being relegated. Mr Low was succeeded by Gary Hughes. He fared no better and resigned in early March. Ian Prior took over the reins for the remainder of the season in a caretaker capacity. By the end of the season, Thetford would have won just two of their 36 games and would finish in bottom slot. In early November Haverhill Rovers appointed a lady physio, Joyce Gronow. November 7th, saw Sudbury Wanderers play their first match under their newly installed floodlights, beating Downham 4-0. The same day, 17-year-old Duncan Begg scored both Felixstowe's goals in a 2-2 draw against Norwich United, on his ECI debut. During the week commencing November 9th, Histon reported appointing Tom Finney manager in succession to Roy Johnson. Cornard manager Keith Martin also resigned that week and was succeeded by the club's reserve manager Clive Hesketh, assisted by Don James. On November 17th, Sudbury Wanderers equalled the division's highest margin of victory, when they beat a flu-weakened Swaffham side 11-0. The win saw them establish a new divisional record for the number of league games unbeaten from the start of a season, bettering the 12 match sequence of Norwich United in 1990-91. Wanderers would in fact go unbeaten in their initial 17 games. However, after the 11-0 defeat the Pedlars manager Adrian Hewitt resigned. He was succeeded by Barry Cooke. Also, on November 24th, Wisbech Town beat Gorleston 9-1, Ian Williams and Mark Garwood both getting hat-tricks. Despite losing their first league match of the season on the 28th November to Harwich (their 20th league match), Wisbech Town still headed the premier division, from Worxham and Harwich. In division one, Sudbury Wanderers, still unbeaten, led from Hadleigh and Stanway.

On December 5, Warboys Town played their first home match under their newly installed floodlights, beating Long Sutton 4-0. On December 19th, Lowestoft Town became the League's last survivors in the F.A. Vase, winning their 3rd Round tie versus Walthamstow Pennant 1-0. The same day, Newmarket Town notched their first away win at Wellelsey Road, Great Yarmouth, since season 1973-74. Halstead, who were then lying third from bottom, appointed Keith Martin manager in succession to Adrian Webster. On Boxing Day, Hadleigh Chairman Peter Vardon found himself having to run the line for 85 minutes of the game against Bury Reserves, after one of the appointed linesmen went ill. By the end of December Wisbech were still in pole position in the premier division, from Wroxham and Cornard. In division one, Sudbury Wanderers, still unbeaten, led from Hadleigh & Soham Town Rangers.

On January 4th, Watton United, with only two wins from their 25 league games, relieved manager Mick Simmons of his duties, appointing Tony Ship as caretaker boss until the end of the season. On January 9th, Cornard United's 17 match unbeaten run (Started 30/09 versus Stowmarket) ended when they were beaten 4-2 by Newmarket Town. On January 16th, Jewson involvement in the F.A. Vase ended when Lowestoft Town were beaten 4-1 away by Newport (IOW). It was the first time since 1983-84 that the League would not have representation in the 5th Round. The match also marked the beginning of a remarkable decline for Lowestoft, who would only win two of their following 22 games. On January 23rd, Sudbury Wanderers' record unbeaten 17 match start to a season ended when they went down 5-3 away to Soham. At the end of January there had been no change in the top three places in the premier division. In division one, Sudbury Wanderers still led. Soham had however overtaken Hadleigh to move into second slot.

In the final week in February, Stowmarket joint managers Doug Wade and Geoff Porter resigned and were succeeded by Trevor Wardlaw. At the end of February, Wisbech and Wroxham still held the top two places in the premier division. Fakenham were up to third. Sudbury Wanderers and Soham were still first and second in division one, with Woodbridge third.

On March 2nd, Newmarket Town's run of nine games without conceding a goal (started 12/01 v March) ended, Tiptree's Chris Guy the man ending that run, but the Jockeys still won the match 4-2. The League Cup semi-finals were contested on March 6th, Cornard and Wroxham beating Wisbech and Newmarket respectively. On March 13th, Chatteris Town, recorded their highest score since season 1976-77, beating Harwich & Parkeston 6-1. March 16th, saw the first 1,000+ crowd of the season, when 1,011 turned up at Trafford Park for the Wroxham verses Wisbech match, which Wroxham won 1-0. 1,023 packed Fenland Park for the return on Apri 10th, Wroxham's 3-1 win giving them a double over Wisbech and virtually securing them the title. On March 20th, Haverhill Rovers ended a run of six matches without a win, during which time they scored just one goal, by thumping Cornard 9-3, their highest-ever score at home in the League in 29 years of membership. The same day, Harwich & Parkeston became the 18th club to complete 1,000 Jewson matches, going down 3-1 away to Wroxham. One week later, Soham beat Thetford Town 9-1. At the end of March, Wisbech led Wroxham on goal difference, with the Norfolk club having two matches in hand, with Cornard third. Sudbury Wanderers were still heading division one. Soham were second, Woodbridge third.

On April 3rd, Swaffham striker Peter Blackmuir netted all five in his side's 5-3 away win over Mildenhall. April 3rd also saw a change in leadership of the premier division. Wroxham beat Brightlingsea 1-0, the goal coming in injury time, whilst Wisbech drew 2-2 against Tiptree and that saw the Norfolk club on top, a position they would not relinquish, losing only one of their remaining eight league games, whilst Wisbech could only win three of their final seven games and ended up pipping Newmarket Town for runners-up slot, on goal difference, but the Jockeys third place was their best placing since 1966-67 when they were runners-up. On April 10th, Soham's opening goal in their 5-2 win over Ipswich Wanderers, set a new record for the highest number of goals scored in the division, bettering the record 105 of Diss Town in 1981-82. Soham's final tally would be 119 (Cambridge City Reserves would also score over 100 goals - 104). On April 17th, Wroxham beat Watton United in an all Jewson Norfolk Senior Cup final. On April 24th, Gorleston became the 5th side to complete 1,500 Jewson League games, drawing 1-1 with Brightlingsea. The same day Wisbech Town became the 19th side to complete 1,000 Jewson League games, beating Felixstowe Town 3-0. Wroxham the League Cup final on April 27th, beating Cornard 6-0, and four days later retained their championship with a 4-0 win over Histon, thus completing a remarkable treble. On the same day, Halstead recorded their highest-ever Jewson home league victory beating Watton United 9-1, Colin Sinclair getting five.

At the other end of the table, Brightlingsea United had been relegated in early April. At one stage Watton or Halstead, looked likely to go down with them, but a great show of form saw both erode the gap on the teams above them and draw Histon, March and Brantham into the battle, with Brantham, who only managed two wins in their final 12 league games, ultimately ending in the second relegation slot.

In division one, the battle for the second promotion place rested between Soham Town Rangers and Woodbridge. The two met on April 17th, Woodbridge winning 3-1. Soham won their final match against King's Lynn, and that left Woodbridge needing four points fromt their final three games to become runners-up. However, defeats versus Sudbury Wanderers and Somersham, (the latter club, after taking one point from their initial five games), won 21 and drew two of their remaining 31 games, left the Woodpeckers having to beat Swaffham by a 37 goal margin. They won 5-0, but that left Soham runners-up on goal difference.

At the bottom, with Huntingdon United having resigned in the 1992 close season, only Thetford were eleigible to be relegated. However, their continued memebership was assured when King's Lynn withdrew their reserve side. Although, no clubs from the League's four feeder leagues are seeking promotion, leaving two vacancies, an application from a new club, West Norfolk Athletic, ground-sharing at "The Walks" with King's Lynn, was turned down.

Clubs with new managers going into 1993-94 include: Brantham, Graham Warren replacing Keith Norton; Gorleston; Paul Tong the new incumbent, March Town United who have appointed former WBA & Ipswich player and former Warboys Town manager Tony Godden as successor to Clive Death; Thetford Town, Dave Brooks their new manager; Warboys have appointed ex-Peterborough and Kettering player Robbie Cooke player/manager and Wotton United, who have appointed Chris Watts and Steve Bunting joint managers. Two men going it alone are Neil Farlie at Haverhill and Alan Dilloway at Hadleigh, after Steve Hubbard and Les Tibbott stood down from their respective positions as joint managers.

Colin Lamb (League Secretary).

Division one champions Sudbury Wanderers receiving the league division one cup from Mr Sam Lawrence and league president Derek Needham.

621

JEWSON EASTERN COUNTIES LEAGUE TABLES 1992-93

PREM. DIVISION	P	W	D	L	F	A	PTS
Wroxham	42	32	4	6	106	36	100
Wisbech Town	42	28	6	8	109	48	90
Newmarket Town	42	27	9	6	87	37	90
Cornard United	42	22	9	11	99	68	75
Diss Town	42	24	2	16	65	52	74
Harwich & Parkes.	42	20	10	12	75	51	70
Fakenham Town	42	19	10	13	68	50	67
Norwich Unietd	42	16	14	12	66	57	62
Felixstowe T.	42	15	12	15	66	62	57
Gorleston	42	16	9	17	64	89	57
Great Yarmouth T.	42	16	8	18	41	60	56
Tiptree United	42	15	8	19	64	76	53
Stowmarket Town	42	14	9	19	54	59	51
Haverhill Rovers	42	14	8	20	65	80	50
Halstead Town	42	14	8	20	60	83	50
Chatteris Town	42	15	4	23	64	73	49
Lowestoft Town	42	12	12	18	55	56	48
March Town Utd	42	13	9	20	56	67	48
Watton United	42	12	8	22	51	84	44
Histon *	42	10	13	19	60	90	42
Brantham Ath.	42	8	12	22	47	73	36
Brightlingsea Utd	42	2	12	28	35	104	18

* - 1pt deducted - ineligible player.

FIRST DIVISION	P	W	D	L	F	A	Pts
Sudbury Wand.	36	26	5	5	96	37	83
Soham Town Rgrs	36	24	4	8	119	45	76
Woodbridge Town	36	24	4	8	82	40	76
Hadleigh United	36	19	9	8	95	59	66
Clacton Town	36	20	6	10	78	53	66
Somersham Town	36	21	3	12	68	52	66
Cambridge City Res.	36	16	7	13	104	77	55
Ely City	36	14	11	11	59	48	53
Long Sutton Ath.	36	15	8	13	69	75	53
Stanway Rovers	36	15	6	15	73	76	51
Ipswich Wanderers	36	14	6	16	63	72	48
Mildenhall Town	36	14	5	17	76	98	47
Sudbury Town Res	36	13	7	16	70	72	46
Warboys Town	36	10	12	14	63	72	42
King's Lynn Res.	36	11	5	20	49	63	38
Downham Town	36	11	4	21	64	84	37
Swaffham Town *	36	12	4	20	58	97	36
Bury Town Res.	36	6	1	29	46	122	19
Thetford Town	36	2	3	31	24	114	9

* - 6pts deducted for not fulfilling fixtures

E.C.L. PREMIER DIVISION RESULT CHART 1992-93

HOME TEAM	1	2	3	4	5	6	7	8	9	10	11	12	13	14	15	16	17	18	19	20	21	22
1. Brantham	*	0-0	3-2	0-2	1-0	1-1	0-0	1-1	0-0	1-1	1-3	3-0	3-2	1-2	1-3	0-3	1-4	2-4	6-1	3-2	0-1	1-2
2. Bright'sea	1-1	*	1-5	0-2	0-2	0-3	1-5	1-1	1-2	1-2	1-4	0-4	2-2	1-0	0-0	0-3	2-2	1-6	1-3	0-0	2-2	0-1
3. Chatteris	0-0	2-1	*	1-2	3-1	1-3	3-0	1-2	1-3	0-1	6-1	0-0	1-2	1-2	4-1	1-2	2-3	3-2	4-0	2-0	1-1	1-2
4. Cornard U.	2-0	4-2	3-0	*	1-2	0-0	2-1	4-3	2-0	0-1	1-1	4-1	2-1	7-1	1-2	3-0	2-1	5-0	1-1	1-1	2-0	
5. Diss Town	1-0	4-1	5-1	3-1	*	2-0	0-2	2-0	2-1	5-0	1-2	4-1	0-0	2-0	1-0	0-2	3-1	1-0	2-1	1-0	0-4	1-2
6. Fakenham T.	4-0	4-0	1-1	0-2	2-1	*	1-3	0-0	1-0	6-0	3-1	1-1	2-1	1-3	1-1	2-1	0-2	2-1	3-1	4-1	1-2	3-2
7. Felixstowe	1-1	1-0	2-1	3-4	1-2	2-0	*	2-1	2-0	5-0	1-1	2-2	0-0	0-2	1-1	0-3	2-2	0-1	0-0	2-3	2-2	0-2
8. Gorleston	1-0	2-2	1-2	4-3	2-1	1-1	3-1	*	1-1	4-0	0-4	4-3	2-1	0-5	3-1	2-4	2-1	1-1	1-1	0-3	1-5	
9. Gt Yarmouth	2-1	2-1	1-0	2-2	0-1	2-1	1-5	1-0	*	2-1	1-0	1-2	0-3	0-5	2-1	2-3	0-3	1-0	0-3	3-1	0-1	0-2
10. Halstead T.	1-0	2-2	3-1	1-6	1-2	2-1	1-1	4-1	0-0	*	0-4	2-1	1-2	1-1	0-1	3-1	3-3	4-0	1-1	9-1	1-3	0-5
11. Harwich & P.	2-0	3-1	3-0	1-1	2-0	0-2	3-1	3-1	0-0	2-2	*	1-2	0-2	3-0	1-2	1-0	1-2	2-2	3-0	2-1	3-0	1-2
12. Haverhill	3-2	4-1	2-0	9-3	2-0	0-1	1-1	4-1	3-0	2-3	0-5	*	1-1	0-0	1-0	0-3	0-0	1-0	1-2	2-1	1-2	0-4
13. Histon	3-2	2-0	3-4	2-2	2-6	0-0	1-1	0-3	2-2	1-0	2-4	4-2	*	0-3	1-1	1-4	1-1	1-1	1-5	2-3	1-3	0-4
14. Lowestoft	0-1	1-1	0-2	1-1	0-1	2-1	1-2	0-2	4-0	0-2	1-1	3-1	0-0	*	2-1	1-1	1-1	2-5	0-0	1-3	0-1	
15. March T.U.	3-0	3-0	0-1	3-0	1-1	2-1	1-3	0-2	0-2	2-1	2-3	3-0	2-3	1-0	*	0-0	2-0	1-4	1-3	2-1	5-0	1-2
16. Newmarket	2-1	2-1	3-2	4-2	5-0	0-0	3-0	0-0	0-1	4-0	3-0	2-1	3-1	3-3	0-0	*	2-2	2-0	2-3	2-0	2-0	0-0
17. Norwich Utd	1-1	4-0	2-1	1-3	2-3	1-2	2-1	1-2	3-1	0-3	1-2	3-1	1-0	1-1	2-0	0-0	*	1-0	3-1	1-1	0-2	1-1
18. Stowmarket	2-2	1-1	1-0	3-1	1-0	2-1	0-3	5-1	1-0	3-1	0-0	1-1	1-2	1-0	3-0	0-1	0-2	*	2-0	1-2	1-3	1-1
19. Tiptree U.	4-1	0-4	0-1	0-0	1-0	1-4	2-3	0-1	1-1	2-1	1-2	2-1	6-2	3-3	2-4	0-2	1-1	0-0	*	3-1	1-0	0-2
20. Watton Utd	2-1	2-0	1-2	2-5	1-2	2-0	0-4	5-3	1-1	1-0	1-0	1-2	3-3	2-1	1-2	1-1	2-0	0-3	*		0-1	1-5
21. Wisbech T.	4-1	5-1	6-0	4-3	4-0	2-3	3-0	9-1	1-2	2-1	1-1	5-1	5-1	3-1	4-1	2-2	4-1	4-0	3-1	3-0	*	1-3
22. Wroxham	2-3	6-0	4-0	5-3	1-0	3-1	5-0	5-1	0-1	3-0	3-1	4-1	2-1	2-0	1-1	2-4	0-3	5-1	1-0	3-0	1-0	*

E.C.L. DIVISION ONE RESULT CHART 1992-93

HOME TEAM	1	2	3	4	5	6	7	8	9	10	11	12	13	14	15	16	17	18	19
1 Bury Town Reserves	*	3-3	0-5	1-6	0-3	1-5	2-1	1-5	1-3	1-4	0-5	2-3	1-4	1-9	0-6	2-1	3-1	4-1	0-3
2. Cambridge City Reserves	4-1	*	0-1	3-0	5-1	6-5	1-4	1-1	1-0	6-7	1-3	5-2	4-0	4-1	1-3	7-1	2-0	4-2	1-2
3. Clacton Town	6-3	3-2	*	2-0	0-1	1-2	1-1	4-0	2-2	2-0	2-1	0-1	3-2	2-1	0-5	4-0	2-0	2-2	2-0
4. Downham Town	3-1	2-4	1-2	*	5-2	0-6	2-0	1-4	2-1	5-4	0-1	1-1	5-0	4-1	1-1	2-3	4-2	3-2	0-1
5. Ely City	2-1	1-1	2-0	3-2	*	1-1	0-0	1-0	2-2	5-3	1-2	0-1	1-1	0-0	0-2	2-0	6-0	1-2	1-2
6. Hadleigh United	5-0	6-3	1-1	2-1	2-2	*	2-0	2-0	3-0	3-1	0-1	2-2	1-1	5-1	4-3	3-2	3-0	1-2	1-1
7. Ipswich Wanderers	5-2	1-4	0-1	1-1	3-0	1-3	*	2-0	1-1	3-1	0-5	3-2	2-1	3-1	2-3	1-0	7-1	3-4	1-5
8. King's Lynn Reserves	4-0	0-2	1-3	3-1	0-2	4-0	1-2	*	1-2	1-3	0-6	2-0	0-1	1-1	1-2	0-1	0-0	1-0	1-2
9. Long Sutton Athletic	2-1	4-2	3-1	3-2	1-1	3-3	1-1	3-3	*	0-3	0-5	2-4	4-1	1-2	2-1	2-1	3-1	4-2	2-3
10. Mildenhall Town	2-1	2-1	3-3	3-0	3-2	2-1	2-3	3-3	0-5	*	4-4	4-1	0-1	3-2	1-7	3-5	1-0	0-0	0-5
11. Soham Town Rangers	3-1	4-2	3-1	7-1	2-1	3-0	5-2	7-0	1-1	4-1	*	2-3	4-0	1-1	5-3	1-2	9-1	8-1	1-3
12. Somersham Town	2-0	2-0	2-0	3-0	2-1	2-3	2-1	1-0	2-3	5-0	2-4	*	4-0	2-1	0-1	2-0	3-0	2-0	2-0
13. Stanway Rovers	4-2	6-4	3-4	4-1	0-3	1-6	1-0	4-2	4-1	7-0	3-1	1-1	*	6-1	1-3	5-2	1-0	0-2	4-2
14. Sudbury Town Reserves	2-3	1-7	5-2	1-0	0-1	3-0	4-5	2-1	3-2	3-2	2-1	6-2	2-0	*	0-1	2-2	4-1	2-2	2-3
15. Sudbury Wanderers	3-2	2-2	1-2	4-0	3-3	1-1	4-0	2-1	3-1	1-0	1-0	4-0	2-0	1-1	*	0-2	3-1	3-2	1-0
16. Swaffham Town	2-0	1-6	0-5	1-1	1-5	3-0	6-0	0-3	2-4	1-3	1-3	3-2	1-0	0-11	*		5-3	2-2	1-4
17. Thetford Town	2-1	3-3	1-7	0-6	0-1	1-6	1-4	0-1	0-1	1-3	0-5	0-1	0-0	1-3	0-4	*		0-3	0-4
18. Warboys Town	2-4	2-2	2-2	3-0	0-0	2-2	2-0	1-2	4-0	3-3	2-2	2-1	2-1	1-1	0-1	1-2	3-2	*	1-2
19. Woodbridge Town	1-0	2-2	2-0	4-1	1-1	3-5	0-0	0-2	6-0	3-2	2-0	1-0	4-2	0-2	0-1	5-0	2-0	4-1	*

JEWSON SPORTSMANSHIP TROPHY 1992-93: Woodbridge Town
(previous winners: 88-89: Brantham Athletic, 89-90: Lowestoft Town, 90-91: Woodbridge Town, 91-92: Woodbridge Town.

JEWSON FAIR PLAY TROPHY 1992-93: Thetford Town
(previous winners: 91-92: Stowmarket Town.

JEWSON EASTERN COUNTIES LEAGUE CUP 1992-93

Preliminary Round *(Attendances in parentheses)*

Downham Town v Lowestoft Town *(83)*	0-2	
March Town United v Mildenhall Town *(120)*	1-0	
Newmarket v Brantham *(75 & 72)*	1-1*(aet)*,4-1	
Stanway v Somersham *(37 & 72)*	1-1*(aet)*,2-4	
Woodbridge Town v Sudbury Town Res. *(80)*	0-2	
Ely City v Fakenham Town *(56)*	2-3	
Norwich United v Thetford Town *(32)*	3-0	
Sudbury Wanderers v Diss Town *(102)*	1-3	
Warboys Town v Gorleston *(66)*	0-1	

First Round

Chatteris Town v Tiptree United *(72)*	3-1	Clacton Town v Soham Town Rgrs *(79)*	0-1	
Cornard United v Histon *(55)*	4-1	Fakenham Town v Norwich United *(136)*	0-2	
Felixstowe Town v Gorleston *(83)*	2-1	Hadleigh U. v Diss Town *(145 & 159)*	3-3*(aet)*,2-6	
Halstead Town v Somersham Town *(140)*	2-1	Haverhill Rovers v Bury Town Reserves *(56)*	4-2	
Ipswich Wanderers v Swaffham Town *(43)*	1-0	Long Sutton Athletic v Cambridge C. Res. *(35)*	0-7	
Lowestoft Town v King's Lynn Res. *(121)*	2-1	March Town United v Wroxham *(90)*	0-3	
Newmarket T. v Harwich & Parkeston *(102)*	3-1	Stowmarket Town v Watton United *(73)*	1-0	
Sudbury T. Res. v Brighlingsea U. *(52)*	5-1	Wisbech Town v Great Yarmouth Town *(400)*	5-0	

Second Round

Cambridge City Reserves v Wroxham *(68)*	1-3	Cornard United v Ipswich Wanderers *(53)*	1-0	
Halstead T. v Norwich U. *(120 & 40)*	2-2*(aet)*,0-1	Haverhill Rovers v Soham Town Rangers *(52)*	3-4	
Lowestoft Town v Felixstowe Town *(98)*	1-3	Newmarket Town v Sudbury Town Reserves *(69)*	6-0	
Stowmarket Town v Chatteris Town *(105)*	3-0	Wisbech Town v Diss Town *(308)*	3-1	

Quarter-Finals

Cornard United v Felixstowe Town *(83)*	2-1	Newmarket Town v Soham Town Rangers *(261)*	1-0
Wisbech Town v Stowmarket Town *(423)*	2-1	Wroxham v Norwich United *(378)*	4-0

Semi-Finals

Cornard United v Wisbech Town *(131)*	2-1	Newmarket Town v Wroxham *(208)*	0-2

Final *(at Diss Town FC, Tues 27/4/93)*: Wroxham 6, Cornard United 0 *(att: 585)*.

Midfield action from Soham Town Rangers' 4-3 2nd Round win at Haverhill on 5th December. Photo - Clive Pearson.

Wroxham captain Stuart Larter receives the League Cup from Jewson Marketting Manager Les Morrell.

JEWSON EASTERN LEAGUE ATTENDANCES 1992-93

Club	Games	Total	Ave		Best Gate 92-93
Brantham Athletic	25	1,350	54	140	(12/4 - League v. Harwich)
Brightlingsea Utd	23	2,125	92	167	(26/8 - League v. Harwich)
Chatteris Town	25	2,799	112	425	(26/8 - League v. Wisbech)
Cornard United	26	2,934	95	238	(3/3 - Suf. Prem. C. v Sudbury)
Diss Town	22	3,748	170	398	(17/11 - League v. Wisbech)
Fakenham Town	27	5,407	200	354	(1/9 - League v Norwich Utd)
Felixstowe Town	27	2,203	82	148	(27/10 - League v. Lowestoft)
Gorleston	28	3,858	138	300	(26/12 - League v. Gt Yarmouth)
Gt Yarmouth Town	22	2,664	121	344	(12/4 - League v. Gorleston)
Halstead Town	29	4,176	144	220	(25/8 - League v. Tiptree)
Harwich & Parkeston	33	6,580	199	342	(29/9 - League v. Brightlingsea)
Haverhill Rovers	27	2,052	76	179	(12/4 - League v. Newmarket)
Histon	26	2,076	80	150	(3/3 - Camb. Cup v. C'bridge City)
Lowestoft Town	26	3,865	149	325	(24/11 - FA Vase v. Yarmouth)
March Town Utd	25	3,612	144	900	(12/4 - League v. Wisbech)
Newmarket Town	33	4,599	139	651	(24/10 - FA Cup v. Hayes)
Norwich United	28	2,307	70	225	(6/20 - Norf Snr v. Wroxham)
Stowmarket Town	25	2,579	103	186	(26/8 - League v. Harwich)
Tiptree United	22	2,003	72	172	(13/10 - EA Cup v. Colchester)
Watton United	25	2,037	81	175	(13/10 - League v. Wroxham)
Wisbech Town	29	12,346	426	1,023	(10/4 - League v. Wroxham)
Wroxham	28	5,984	213	1,011	(16/3 - League v. Wisbech)

Division One

Club	Games	Total	Ave		Best Gate 92-93
Bury Town Reserves	18	897	50	87	(29/9 - League v. Sudbury Res)
Cambridge C. Reserves	19	1,014	53	89	(19/12 - League v. Soham)
Clacton Town	20	1,793	90	112	(17/3 - League v Woodbridge)
Downham Town	23	1,939	84	185	(25/8 - League v. K.Lynn Res)
Ely City	24	1,705	71	260	(12/4 - League v. Soham)
Hadleigh Utd	23	2,895	126	340	(22/1 - League v. Woodbridge)
Ipswich Wdrs	19	1,351	71	253	(12/4 - League v. Woodbridge)
King's Lynn Res.	18	1,213	67	160	(10/11 - League v. Downham)
Long Sutton Ath.	21	1,007	48	71	(14/9 - League v Warboys)
Mildenhall Town	19	1,717	90	163	(20/2 - League v. Soham)
Soham Town Rgrs	20	2,261	113	276	(17/4 - League v. Woodbridge)
Somersham Town	23	1,377	60	138	(12/4 - League v. Warboys)
Stanway Rovers	20	1,092	55	104	(4/9 - League v. Soham)
Sudbury Town Reserves	21	1,492	71	129	(12/4 - Lge Cup v. Sudbury Wdrs)
Sudbury Wanderers	22	2,019	92	248	(20/4 - League v. Woodbridge)
Swaffham Town	18	1,366	76	182	(1/9 - League v. K.Lynn Res)
Thetford Town	19	1,135	60	110	(12/3 - League v. Stanway)
Warboys Town	22	1,668	76	174	(26/12 - League v. Somersham)
Woodbridge Town	29	3,470	120	302	(29/9 - League v. Hadleigh)

The above includes Jewson League and League Cup matches and, where notified, FA Cup, FA Vase, East Anglian Cup, Eastern Floodlit Competition and County Cup ties. Attendance totals; Premier Division - 81,304 (581 matches - average gate: 140), Division One - 31,411 (398 matches - average gate: 79), Total - 112,715.

PREMIER DIVISION - TEN YEAR RECORD

	83/84	84/85	85/86	86/87	87/88	88/89	89/90	90/91	91/92	92/93
Braintree Town	1	1	6	2	2	2	3	2	-	-
Brantham Athletic	11	16	16	19	20	17	8	19	17	21
Brightlingsea Utd	-	-	-	-	-	-	-	-	20	22
Bury Town	13	9	4	3	-	-	-	-	-	-
Chatteris Town	10	15	19	15	7	19	21	21	19	16
Clacton Town	21	17	22	12	12	18	20	12	21	-
Colchester U. Res.	3	7	2	7	14	-	-	-	-	-
Cornard United	-	-	-	-	-	-	-	8	3	4
Diss Town	-	-	-	-	-	-	-	-	-	5
Ely City	20	18	20	22	22	20	-	-	-	-
Fakenham Town	-	-	-	-	-	-	-	-	-	7
Felixstowe Town	14	14	12	17	17	11	13	13	13	9
Gorleston	7	11	13	18	18	10	5	17	12	10
Gt. Yarmouth Town	9	3	3	6	4	5	6	18	14	11
Halstead Town	-	-	-	-	-	-	14	3	9	15
Harwich & Parkes.	-	21	17	14	13	14	4	5	6	6
Haverhill Rovers	17	20	14	13	10	7	15	4	8	14
Histon	16	8	10	21	5	6	7	10	15	20
Lowestoft Town	4	4	11	9	8	12	18	9	11	17
March Town Utd.	15	6	7	4	1	4	9	15	10	18
Newmarket Town	12	19	21	16	15	16	17	20	7	3
Norwich United	-	-	-	-	-	-	-	-	4	8
Saffron Walden T.	6	-	-	-	-	-	-	-	-	-
Soham Town Rang.	18	12	18	20	21	21	-	-	-	-
Stowmarket Town	19	10	8	10	19	8	11	11	2	13
Sudbury Town	5	2	1	1	3	1	1	-	-	-
Thetford Town	22	22	15	23	16	9	2	14	22	-
Tiptree United	8	13	5	5	11	15	19	16	16	12
Watton United	-	-	-	8	9	13	16	6	18	19
Wisbech Town	2	5	9	11	6	3	10	1	5	2
Wroxham	-	-	-	-	-	-	12	7	1	1
Teams Competing	**22**	**22**	**22**	**23**	**22**	**21**	**21**	**21**	**22**	**22**

PREMIER DIVISION STATISTICS

LEAGUE STATISTICS			1992/93 STATISTICS	
Club	**Season Joined**	**Championships or Best Placing**	**Leading Appearances League & Lge. Cup**	**Leading Goalscorers League & Lge. Cup**

Brantham	1978/79 15	4th - 1983	43 - Paul Smythe
			41 - Jason Burman
			38 - Darren Howell
			  - Nigel Crouch
				7 - Dave Ellis
				6 - Ian Gedny
				5 - Terry Clark
				  - Nigel Crouch
				  - Adrian Harris

Brightlingsea	1990/91 2	20th - 1992
		Div 1 runners-up
		1991
			41 - Lloyd Pentney
			33 - Neil Turner
			29 - Shaun Duffett
				6 - Shaun Duffett
				  - Dave Gray
				3 - Julian Hazell
				  - Steve Gray

Chatteris	1966/67 27	3rd - 1968	44 - * Tim Gale
			  - * Steve Hudson
			43 - Tim Hudson
				12 - Steve Hudson
				   - Rob Rickard
				9 - Kevin Malle

Cornard Utd	1989/90 4	3rd - 1992 Div 1 1990	47 - * Micky Stratton - * Andy Smiles 44 - Ricky Cornish	29 - Andy Smiles 25 - Scott Young 16 - Micky Stratton
Diss Town	1988/89 5	5th - 1993 Div 1 1992	46 - Gary Smith 44 - Jason Carter - Jason Fletcher	16 - Steve Miles 15 - Jason Fletcher 10 - Paul Warne
Fakenham Town	1988/89 5	7th - 1993 Div 1 runners-up 1992	44 - * Paul Dungar - * Mark House 43 - Shaun Freestone	16 - Simon Barnes 15 - Kevin Topping 13 - Shaun Freestone

Felixstowe	1976/77 17	8th - 1983	45 - * Danny Catermole
			  - * Micky Smith
			43 - Nicky Baker
				18 - Nigel Wallis
				14 - Tony Gayfer
				6 - Stuart Swift
				  - Mark Keeley

Gorleston	1935/36 18 1969/70 24	1953, 1973 1980, 1981	43 - Sean Trail 42 - Steve King 39 - Paul Gibbs	11 - Martin Woolsey 9 - Colin Danby 7 - Paul Gibbs
Gt. Yarmouth	1935/36 51	1969	42 - Mark Vincent 41 - Paul Casey 35 - Ray Goodson	8 - Peter Monro 5 - Ray Goodson 4 - Mark Grealey

Halstead	1988/89 5	3rd - 1991
		Div 1 runners-up
		1988/89
			40 - Dave Streetley
			39 - James Goodwin
			33 - Mark Elliott
				14 - Colin Sinclair
				7 - Dave Streetley
				5 - Mark Elliott
				  - Gary Bright
				  - Neale Dakin

Harwich	1935/36 2 1938/39 19 1984/85 9	1935 (Jt)	43 - Gary Hudson - John Kemp 41 - George Patten	22 - Glen Hepburn 21 - John Kemp 9 - Dave Lee

Haverhill	1964/65 29	1979	44 - * Lee Fish
			  - * Andy Ince
			42 - Alex Banthorpe
				12 - Andy Ince
				10 - Brian Abbery
				  - Simon Stoten

Histon	1965/66 28	4th - 1975	34 - Paul Cordy
			33 - Dave Brown
			32 - Vince Garner
			  - Vince Kempton
				10 - Nigel Foster
				9 - Darren Hayward
				5 - Gary Haylock
				  - Mark Shelford
				  - Salvatore Maoirana

Lowestoft	1935/36 51	1936, 1938 1963, 1965-68 1970-71, 1978	44 - * Paul Mobbs 41 - Paul Barker - Micky Chapman	11 - Paul Barker 10 - Micky Chapman 9 - Gary Tuttle

March Town	1954/55 39	1988	44 - * Andy Clenshaw
			42 - Neil Tipper
			40 - Clive Death
			  - Mark Clenshaw
				10 - Clive Death
				9 - Neil Tipper
				  - Mark Wales

Newmarket	1937/38 8
	1959/60 34
		2nd - 1967	48 - * Kevin Crisp
			  - * Martin Marris
			47 - Richard Skelly
			  - Peter Lindsay
				30 - Jerry Rose
				13 - Kevin Crisp
				9 - John McLean

Norwich United	1989/90 4	4th - 1992
		Div 1 Winners
		1991
			47 - * Paul Hartle
			45 - Rob Musgrave
			44 - Darren Gill
			  - Nicky Twaits
				10 - Kelly Barth
				9 - Darren Gill
				  - Micky Money

	LEAGUE STATISTICS			1990-91 STATISTICS	
Club	Season Joined		Championships or Best Placing	Leading Appearances League & Lge. Cups	Leading Goalscorers League & Lge. Cups
Stowmarket	1952/53	41	2nd - 1992	45 - * Nigel Vincent 43 - Mark Clarke - Craig Oldfield - Simon Morris	11 - Simon Cutting 7 - Craig Oldfield 6 - Nigel Vincent
Tiptree	1979/80	14	1982	43 - Julian Lamb 42 - Chris Guy 41 - Nicholas Lee	10 - Chris Guy - Julian Lamb 9 - Lee Sonnex
Watton	1986/87	7	8th - 1987	43 - * Mark Bond 42 - Tim Warner - Chris Watts	12 - Steve Rumblow 11 - Mark Blockwell - Tommy Taylor - George Wilson
Wisbech	1950/51 1970/71	2 23	1972 & 1977 & 1991	45 - Dave Massingham - Mel Mattless 44 - Martyn Lindsay - Ian Williams	32 - Ian Williams 18 - Mark Garwood 17 - Jackie Gallagher
Wroxham	1988/89	5	1992, 1993	47 - * Adrian Harris - * Stu Larter - * Ryan Lemmon	50 - Matthew Metcalfe 24 - Darren Prior 9 - Mark Halsey

* - Denotes ever-present in Jewson League/ Jewson League Cup.

LEADING SCORERS 1992-93

Premier Division

50 - Matthew Metcalfe (Wroxham)
32 - Ian Williams (Wisbech Town)
30 - Jerry Rose (Newmarket Town)
29 - Andy Smiles (Cornard United)
- Mark Argent (Histon - 25 for Camb C Res)
25 - Scott Young (Cornard United)
24 - Darren Prior (Wroxham)
22 - Glen Hepburn (Harwich & Park.)
21 - John Kemp (Harwich & Park.)
18 - Mark Garwood (Wisbech Town)
- Nigel Wallis (Felixstowe)
17 - Jackie Gallagher (Wisbech)
16 - Stephen Miles (Diss Town)
- Micky Stratton (Cornard Uld)
15 - Jason Fletcher (Diss Town)
- Kevin Topping (Fakenham T.)

Division One

32 - Adrian Bullett (Soham Town Rgrs)
28 - Darren Theobald (Soham Town Rgrs)
24 - Donny Davis (Hadleigh United)
- Dean Jeffries (Clacton Town)
23 - Tony Gill (Woodbdge - 11 for Hadleigh)
22 - Adam Crofton (Sudbury Wdrs)
- Karl Simper (Ely City)
21 - Brendan Doe (Somersham Town)
- Chris Rose (Soham Town Rgrs)
- Micky Wayman (Long Sutton Ath.)
20 - Paul Keys (Hadleigh Utd)
17 - Simon Dumican (Mildenhall T.)
19 - Spencer Breeze (Ipswich Wdrs)
16 - Simon Fryatt (Woodbridge Town)
15 - James Russell (Cambridge C. Res.)

Individual Scoring Feats:

6 goals: Adrian Bullett (Soham) 30/9/92 v. Warboys Town.
5 goals: Matthew Metcalfe (Wroxham) 12/9/92 v. Cornard.
: Peter Blackmuir (Swaffham) 3/4/93 v. Mildenhall Town.
: Colin Sinclair (Halstead) 1/5/93 v. Watton Utd.
4 goals: Paul Keys (Hadleigh Utd) 12/9/92 v. Thetford Town.
: Stuart Swift (Felixstowe Town) 12/9/92 v. Gt Yarmouth Town.
: Jason Fletcher (Diss) 20/10/92 v. Hadleigh Utd. (League Cup).
: Neil Donohue (Cambridge C. Res.) 31/10/92 v. Stanway Rovers.
: Dean Jeffries (Clacton Town) 7/11/92 v. King's Lynn Reserves
: Mark Argent (Cambridge C. Res.) 14/11/92 v. Hadleigh United.
: Jerry Rose (Newmarket Town) 9/1/93 v. Cornard Utd.
: Brendan Doe (Somersham Town) 20/2/93 v. Stanway Rovers.
: Simon Whiting (Stanway Rovers) 27/2/93 v. Downham Town.
: Matthew Metcalfe (Wroxham) 24/4/93 v. Halstead.

There were a total of 70 hat-tricks recorded during the season 1992-93, 30 in the Premier Division, and 40 in Division One. Glen Hepburn (Harwich); Mark Garwood (Wisbech), Matthew Metcalfe (Wroxham), and Tony Gill (Hadleigh/ Woodbridge) each hit three.

MONTHLY AWARDS 1992-93

Month	Premier Division Club of the Month	Division One Club of the Month	Good Conduct
Aug/Sept	Harwich & Parkeston	Sudbury Wanderers	Clacton Town
October	Lowestoft Town	Soham Town Rgrs	Swaffham Town
November	Harwich & Parkeston	Cambridge City Res.	Soham Town Rgrs
December	Cornard United	Soham Town Rgrs	Halstead Town
January	Wroxham	Woodbridge Town	Long Sutton Ath.
February	Newmarket Town	Woodbridge Town	Felixstowe Town
March	Wroxham	Somersham Town	Mildenhall Town
April	Wroxham	Sudbury Wanderers	Haverhill Rovers

PREMIER DIVISION CLUBS 1993-94

CHATTERIS TOWN

Chairman: A Parish   **President:** J Chambers   **Manager:** Lester Kent/ Dave Simmons
Secretary: Anthony Summers, 41 The Elms, Chatteris, Cambs PE16 6JN (0354 692062).
Ground: West Street, Chatteris (0354 692139).
Directions: Entering Chatteris on A141 from Huntingdon turn right into West Street after by-pass roundabout.
Seats: 250   **Cover:** 400   **Capacity:** 2,000   **Floodlights:** Yes   **Founded:** 1920.
Colours: All white   **Change colours:** Red & black   **Nickname:** Lillies.
Previous League: Peterborough   **Midweek Matches:** Wednesday   **Pennants:** Yes.
Clubhouse details: Bar & tea bar.   **Record Gate:** 2,000 v March Town Utd, League 5/5/88.
Programme: 12 pages, 20p   **Previous Ground:** First Drove
Matchday food & drink: Tea, coffee, cold drinks, confectionary, burgers, hotdogs, sandwiches, soup, rolls.
Players progressing to Football League: Andy Rogers (Reading, Southend, Plymouth), Dave Gregory (Plymouth).
Honours: Eastern Counties Lg Cup 67-68, Peterborough Premier Lg(3).

CORNARD UNITED

Chairman: Dave Nickells
Secretary: R J Powell, 14 North Rise, Great Cornard, Sudbury, Suffolk CO10 0DE (0787 371671).
Manager: Clive Hesketh   **Asst Manager:** Don James   **Coach:** A Row.
Ground: Blackhouse Lane Sportsfield, Great Cornard, Suffolk (0787 376719).
Directions: Left off r'bout on A134. Follow signs for Country Park - ground is immediately opposite along Blackhouse Lane.
Seats: 250   **Cover:** Yes   **Capacity:** 2,000   **Floodlights:** Yes   **Founded:** 1964.
Colours: Blue & white/white/blue   **Change colours:** White/black/black.   **Pennants:** Yes.
Previous Leagues: Bury St Edm. & Dist. 66-71/ Colchester 71-78/ Essex & Suffolk Border 78-89.
Record Attendance: 330 v Sudbury Town, Eastern Floodlit League 4/2/92.
Midweek Matches: Tuesday   **Prog.:** 16 pages, 30p **Programme Editor:** M Vincent
Clubhouse details: Open matchdays   **Local Newspaper:** Suffolk Free Press.
Matchday food & drink: Tea, coffee, cold drinks, confectionary, hotdogs, burgers, soup, sandwiches, rolls.
Honours: Eastern Co's Lg Div 1 89-90 (Lg Cup R-up 92-93), Essex & Suffolk Border Lg 88-89 (Lg Cup 88-89), Suffolk Snr Cup 89-90.

DISS TOWN

Chairman: D A Tebble   **President:** R A Gooderham   **Manager:** Bill Punton.
Secretary: R S Upson, Bamburgh House, Brewers Green Lane, Diss, Norfolk IP22 3QP (0379 642923).
Ground: Brewers Green Lane, Diss (0379 651223).
Directions: Just off B1066 Diss-Thetford road, near Roydon School. One and a half miles from Diss (BR).
Seats: 260   **Cover:** Yes   **Capacity:** 2,000   **Floodlights:** Yes   **Founded:** 1886.
Colours: Tangerine/black   **Change colours:** White/navy/tangerine.   **Pennants:** Yes.
Previous Leagues: Norwich & District/ Norfolk & Suffolk 35-64/ Anglian Combination 64-82.
Midweek Matches: Tuesday   **Previous Ground:** Roydon Road 1886-1982.
Record Gate: 1,528 v Wimborne, FA Vase QF 29/2/92   **Nickname:** Tangerines.
Programme: 10 pages, 30p   **Programme Editor:** G Enderby
Clubhouse details: Open evenings (except Sunday), Sat/Sun lunchtimes, and matchdays.
Matchday food & drink: Tea, coffee, cold drinks, confectionary, burgers, hotdogs, soup, rolls.
Players progressing to the Football League: Alec Thurlow (Man City), Mervyn Cawston (Norwich), Trevor Whymark (Ipswich), Clive Stafford (Colchester).
Honours: Eastern Co's Lg Div 1 91-92, FA Vase QF 91-92, Anglian Comb. 76-77 78-79 (R-up 74-75, Div 1 67-68 73-74, Lg Cup 67-68 79-80 81-82), Norfolk & Suffolk Lg R-up 55-56 (Applegate Cup 56-57 57-58(joint)(R-up 55-56)), Norfolk Jnr Cup 1891-92.

FAKENHAM TOWN

Chairman: Tony Fisher   **President:** B E Woodhouse   **Manager:** Nolan Keeley
Secretary: E V Linnell, 40 Warren Avenue, Fakenham, Norfolk NR21 8NP (0328 855445).
Ground: Barons Hall Lawn, Norwich Road, Fakenham (0328 862939).
Directions: Adjacent to Police Station in Norwich Road.
Seats: 80   **Cover:** 300   **Capacity:** 1,500   **Floodlights:** Yes   **Founded:** 1884.
Colours: Amber & black   **Change colours:** Red & white   **Club Shop:** Yes.
Previous Leagues: Anglian Comb.   **Midweek Matchday:** Tuesday.
Record Gate: 1,000 v Norwich City, floodlight inauguration.
Clubhouse details: Bar, colour TV and pool table.
Matchday food & drink: Tea, coffee, cold drinks, confectionary, soup.
Programme: 32 pages (Barnes Print), 20p **Local Newspapers:** Fakenham & Wells Times.
Players progressing to the Football League: Nolan Keeley (Scunthorpe & Lincoln).
Honours: Norfolk Snr Cup 70-71 72-73 73-74 91-92, Eastern Co's Lg Div 1 R-up 91-92, Anglian Comb. Cup 78-79.

FELIXSTOWE TOWN

Chairman: Dave Ashford   **President:** TBA   **Manager:** Paul Adams.
Secretary: Norman Howlett, 139 Ashcroft Rd, Ipswich, Suffolk (0473 749137).
Ground: Dellwood Avenue, Felixstowe (0394 282917).
Directions: A45 to Felixstowe. Turn right at 3rd r'bout then 1st left - ground 100 yds on left. 5 mins from Felixstowe (BR) and town centre.
Seats: 200   **Cover:** 200   **Capacity:** 2,000   **Floodlights:** Yes   **Founded:** 1890.
Colours: Red/white & black   **Change:** Blue & white/black   **Nickname:** Seasiders.
Prev. Leagues: Essex & Suffolk Border/ Ipswich & Dist.   **Midweek Matches:** Wednesday
Record Attendance: 1,500 v Ipswich Town, floodlight inauguration 25/1/91.
Programme: 16 pages, 30p   **Programme Editor:** P Griffiths.
Clubhouse details: Bar, snack bar, TV, darts, pool table.   **Local Newspaper:** East Anglia Daily Times.
Matchday food & drink: Tea, coffee, cold drinks, confectionary, hotdogs, burgers, soup, rolls.
Honours: Suffolk Senior Cup 66-67 74-75.   **Club Shop:** Yes **Enamel Badges & Pennants:** Yes.

GORLESTON

Chairman: A Norton   **President:** J Jones   **Manager:** Paul Tong.
Secretary: Kevin Antcliffe, 62 Englands Lane, Gorleston, Gt Yarmouth, Norfolk NR31 6BE (0493 668475).
Ground: Emerald Park, Woodfarm Lane, Gorleston, Great Yarmouth (0493 602802).
Directions: On Magdalen Estate - follow signs to Crematorium, turn left and follow road to ground. Five and a half miles from Great Yarmouth Vauxhall (BR).
Seats: 100   **Cover:** 5,000   **Capacity:** 5,000   **Floodlights:** Yes   **Founded:** 1884.
Colours: Green & white   **Change colours:** All white.   **Nickname:** Greens.
Prev. Ground: Recreation Ground.   **Prev. Leagues:** Norfolk & Suffolk/ Anglian Comb.
Midweek Matchday: Tuesday.   **Record Gate:** 4,473 v Orient, FA Cup 1st Rd 29/11/51.
Prog.: 30p (Ed.: D Benson)   **Clubhouse:** Bar, colour TV, pool table, darts, snacks.
Matchday food & drink: Tea, coffee, cold drinks, confectionary, burgers, hotdogs, soup, rolls.
Past players progressing to the Football League: Billy Bailey (Wolves & England), Dave Stringer (Norwich), R Carter (Aston Villa), D Carter (Man City), A Brown (Charlton, S Morgan (Cambridge).
Honours: Eastern Co's Lg 52-53 72-73 79-80 80-81 (R-up 82-83, Lg Cup 55-56 (R-up 91-92)), Norf. Snr Cup(13)(R-up(24)), Anglian Comb. 68-69, Norf. & Suf. Lg(7) 20-21 25-26 29-30 31-35, E Anglian Lg 52-53(res.).

GREAT YARMOUTH TOWN

Chairman: Colin Smith   **President:** Derek Needham   **Manager:** Mel Antcliffe.
Secretary: Michael Capon, 16 Orchard Way, Fleggburgh, Gt Yarmouth, Norfolk NR29 3AY (0493 369530).
Ground: Wellesey Recreation Ground, Wellesey Road (0493 842936).
Directions: Just off Marine Parade, 200 yds north of Britannia Pier. Half a mile from Vauxhall (BR).
Seats: 500   **Cover:** 2,100   **Capacity:** 3,600   **Floodlights:** Yes   **Founded:** 1897.
Colours: Amber & black/black   **Change colours:** White/blue   **Nickname:** Bloaters.
Previous Leagues: Norfolk & Suffolk   **Midweek Matches:** Tuesday   **Club Shop:** No.
Record Attendance: 8,944 v Crystal Palace, FA Cup 1st Rd 52-53.   **Pennants:** Yes
Record Victory: 13-0 v Cromer, FA Cup 1st Qualifying Rd 52-53.   **Prog.:** 20 pages, 50p
Clubhouse details: (0493 8443373). Dancehall, Committee Room, darts, pool.
Matchday food & drink: Tea, coffee, cold drinks, confectionary, hotdogs, burgers, soup, sandwiches, rolls.
Local Newspapers: Yarmouth Mercury (844201), Eastern Football News (Norwich 283111).
Players progressing to the Football League: Roy Hollis (Norwich), Mel Blyth & Nolan Keeley (Scunthorpe), Steven Davy (West Ham), Kevin Ready (Aston Villa), Gary Butcher (Blackburn).
Honours: Eastern Co's Lg 68-69 (R-up 56-57 67-68 77-78 78-79, Lg Cup 37-38 74-75 80-81), East Anglian Cup(3), Norfolk Snr Cup(12)(R-up(22)), Norfolk Premier Cup(twice shared), Norfolk & Suffolk Lg 13-14 26-27 27-28, FA Vase SF 82-83, FA Cup 2nd Rd(2)(1st Rd(1)), Anglian Comb. Cup 65-66(res), E Anglian Lg 56-57(res).

HALSTEAD TOWN

Chairman: M Gage   **President:** T Burrett   **Manager:** Keith Martin.
Secretary: Michael Gage, 3 Bois Hall Gdns, Halstead, Essex CO2 2HX (0787 475110).
Ground: Rosemary Lane, Halstead, Essex (0787 472082).
Directions: A131 Chelmsford to Braintree - follow signs to Halstead. In Halstead, 1st left after Police Station, then 1st right, and first left to ground.
Seats: 492   **Cover:** 500   **Capacity:** 2,000   **Floodlights:** Yes   **Founded:** 1879.
Colours: White & black   **Change colours:** Red & white
Previous Lges: Nth Essex/ Halstead & Dist./ Haverhill/ Essex & Suffolk Border/ Essex Snr 80-88.
Previous Grounds: Three Gates 1879-1948, Coggeshall Pieces, Ravens Meadow, King George Playing Field.
Record Attendance: 4,000 v Walthamstow Avenue, Essex Senior Cup 1949.
Clubhouse details: Open evenings and matchdays.   **Programme:** 30p   **Editor:** D Osborne.
Matchday food & drink: Tea, coffee, cold drinks, confectionary, burgers, hotdogs, sandwiches, rolls.
Players progressing to the Football League: Steve Allen (Wimbledon Physio).
Midweek Matches: Tuesday   **Local Newspaper:** Halstead Gazette.
Hons: Eastern Co's Lg Div 1 R-up 89-90, Knight F'llt Cup R-up 90-91, Ess.&Suff. Border Lg(3) 57-59 77-78 (R-up 49-50 54-55 60-61, Lg Cup(3) 57-59 73-74), Ess. Snr Lg Cup R-up 79-80, Ess. Jnr Cup 01-02 46-47 (R-up 00-01).

HARWICH & PARKESTON

Chairman: Paul Revell   **President:** J Whitmore   **Mgr:** Martin Head/ Chris Dolby
Secretary: Graham Firth, 24 Glebe Close, Wix, Essex CO11 2SD (0255 870805).
Directions: Main road into Dovercourt. 600 yds from Dovercourt (BR).
Ground: Royal Oak, Main Road, Dovercourt, Harwich (0255 503649).
Seats: 350   **Cover:** 1,000   **Capacity:** 5,000   **Floodlights:** Yes   **Founded:** 1877.
Colours: Black & white stripes/black   **Change colours:** Yellow   **Nickname:** Shrimpers.
Previous Lges: Eastern Co's 35-37 38-64/ Essex County 37-38/ Athenian 64-73 83-84/ Isthmian 73-83.
Midweek Matches: Tuesday   **Previous Ground:** Phoenix Field, Seafront.
Record Attendance: 5,649 v Romford, FA Amateur Cup 4th Rd 19/3/38.   **Club Shop:** Yes
Newsline: 0898 664 250.   **Pennants & Enamel Badges:** Yes
Clubhouse details: Open every day. Dances, bingo, darts, pool, function room.
Matchday food & drink: Tea, coffee, cold drinks, confectionary, hotdogs, burgers, soup.
Players progressing to the Football League: I Gillespie (C Palace, Ipswich), G Waites, K Sanderson.
Prog.: 20 pages, 30p (Ed.: A Schooler)   **Local Paper:** Harwich & Manningtree Standard.
Honours: FA Amateur Cup R-up 1898-99 1952-53, FA Vase QF 90-91, Eastern Counties Lg 35-36(joint)(Lg Cup 35-36 36-37), Essex County Lg 37-38, Athenian Lg Div 1 R-up 65-66 (Div 2 64-65, Lg Cup 64-65), Essex Senior Cup 1898-99 1936-37, Essex Senior Trophy 89-90, AFA Senior Cup 35-36 36-37, Worthington Evans Cup 80-81.

HAVERHILL ROVERS

Chairman: R Esdale   **President:** R C Carter   **Manager:** Neil Farlie.
Secretary: C Davies, 8 Helions Park Avenue, Haverhill, Suffolk CB9 8BL (0440 705472).
Ground: Hamlet Croft, (0440 702137).   **Directions:** Centre of Haverhill.
Seats: 200   **Cover:** 200   **Capacity:** 3,000   **Floodlights:** Yes   **Founded:** 1886.
Colours: All red   **Change colours:** All yellow   **Prev. League:** Essex & Suffolk Border.
Record Attendance: 1,537 v Warrington Town, FA Vase QF 86-87.   **Nickname:** Rovers.
Midweek Matches: Tuesday   **Programme:** 24 pages, 30p (**Editor:** R Esdale)
Clubhouse details: Open matchdays and function. Country & Western evening Saturday.
Matchday food & drink: Tea, coffee, cold drinks, confectionary, burgers, hotdogs.
Local Paper: Haverhill Echo.   **Players progressing to the Football League:** R Wilkins (Colchester).
Honours: Eastern Co's Lg 78-79 (Lg Cup 64-65), E & S Border Lg 62-63 63-64, East Anglian Cup 90-91.

Jason Fletcher shoots wide for Diss in a 0-5 defeat at Newmarket Town on 9th February. Photo - Martin Wray.

Haverhill Rovers F .C. 1992-93. Back Row (L/R): S Hubbard (Joint Manager), A Salter, A Ince, A Banthorpe, S Stoten, S Martin, S Brown, S Henderson, L Fish,   D Franklin (Physio). Front: M Manning, P Blackburn, B Abery, N Farlie (Joint Manager), A Thomas. Photo - Richard Brock.

Haverill player-manager Neil Farlie clears the danger at Stowmarket on 19th September. Photo - Richard Brock.

HISTON

Chairman: Gareth Baldwin   **President:** G P Muncey   **Manager:** Tom Finney
Secretary: Pauline Dobbyne, 21 Gresley Lodge, Old North Rd, Royston SG8 5AG (0763 244798).
Ground: Bridge Road, Impington, Cambridge (0223 232301).
Directions: Leave A45 northern Cambridge bypass on B1049 (signposted Histon and Cottenham). Ground half a mile on right. 5 miles from Cambridge (BR). Bus No. 104.
Seats: 250   **Cover:** 200   **Capacity:** 2,250   **Floodlights:** Yes   **Founded:** 1904.
Colours: Red (white stripes)/red/black   **Change colours:** All blue.
Previous Leagues: Cambridgeshire 04-48/ Spartan 48-60/ Delphian 60-63/ Athenian 63-65.
Midweek Matches: Tuesday   **Previous Name:** Histon Institute 04-51.
Programme: 16 pages, 50p   **Prog. Editor:** Kevin Woollard.
Record Gate: 2,400 v K. Lynn, FA Cup.   **Local Newspaper:** Cambridge Evening News.
Clubhouse details: Bar/lounge open Tues-Sun evenings, Sun lunctimes and matchdays.
Matchday food & drink: Tea, coffee, cold drinks, confectionary, soup, rolls.
Honours: Eastern Co's Lg Cup 90-91, Cambridge Invitation Cup 77-78 79-80 (R-up 50-51 52-53 53-54), Spartan Lg Div 1 (East) 50-51, Cambs Chal. Cup, Cambs Lg Section 'A'.

LOWESTOFT TOWN

Chairman: Roy Harper   **President:** S Matley   **Manager:** Colwyn Rowe.
Secretary: Terry Lynes, 156 Denmark Road, Lowestoft, Suffolk NR32 2EL (0502 564034).
Ground: Crown Meadow, Love Road, Lowestoft (0502 573818).
Directions: Just off A12, 10 mins walk from Lowestoft (BR).
Seats: 466   **Cover:** 500   **Capacity:** 4,000   **Floodlights:** Yes   **Founded:** 1890.
Colours: Blue & white   **Change colours:** Yellow/red/yellow   **Nickname:** Blues.
Previous Leagues: Norfolk & Suffolk   **Midweek Matches:** Tuesday   **Metal Badges:** Yes
Record Attendance: 5,000 v Watford, FA Cup 1st Rd 9/12/67.
Programme: 20 pages, 30p   **Programme Editor:** T Lynes
Clubhouse details: Pub hours
Matchday food & drink: Tea, coffee, cold drinks, confectionary, hotdogs, burgers, soup.
Honours: Eastern Co's Lg(8) 35-36(joint) 37-38 62-63 64-65 67-68 69-71 77-78 (Lg Cup(7) 38-39 54-55 65-67 68-69 75-76 83-84), Norf. & Suffolk Lg(8) 1897-99 1900-04 28-29 30-31, Suffolk Prem. Cup(5) 66-67 71-72 74-75 78-80, Suffolk Snr Cup(10) 02-03 22-24 25-26 31-32 35-36 46-49 55-56, E Anglian Cup(10), FA Cup 1st Rd 26-27 38-39 66-67 77-78, Anglian Comb. (Reserves) 77-78 79-80 (Lg Cup 76-77), E Anglian Lg (Reserves) 57-58 63-64.

MARCH TOWN UNITED

Chairman: Geoff Allen   **President:** D Wilkinson   **Manager:** Tony Godden.
Secretary: C R Woodcock, 24 Grounds Avenue, March, Cambs PE15 9BG (0354 54817).
Ground: GER Sports Ground, Robin Goodfellows Lane, March (0354 53073).
Directions: 5 mins from town centre, 10 mins from BR station.
Seats: 500   **Cover:** 2,000   **Capacity:** 4,000   **Floodlights:** Yes   **Founded:** 1885.
Club colours: Yelow/blue   **Change colours:** Blue & black stripes/white.
Previous Ground: The Avenue (prior to 1946).   **Nickname:** Hares
Previous Leagues: Peterborough/ Isle of Ely/ Utd Co's 48-54.
Midweek Matches: Tuesday   **Record Gate:** 7,500 v King's Lynn, FA Cup 1956.
Clubhouse: On ground, seating 150.   **Programme:** 30p   **Prog. Editor:** S Snell c/o Secretary
Matchday food & drink: Tea, coffee, cold drinks, soup, sandwiches, rolls.
Local Newspapers: Cambs Times, Fenland Advertiser, Peterborough Evening Telegraph.
Honours: Eastern Co's Lg 87-88 (Lg Cup 60-61), Utd Co's Lg 53-64, FA Cup 1st Rd 53-54 (lost to Brentford) 77-78 (to Swindon), Cambs Invitation Cup 54-55, East Anglian Cup 53-54(jt with Barking).

NEWMARKET TOWN

Chairman: K Sheppard   **President:** M J Nicholas   **Manager:** David Pinkowski.
Secretary: Mr John E How, 25 Highwood Cres., Gazeley, Newmarket, Suffolk CB8 8RU (0638 750852).
Ground: Cricketfield Road, off New Cheveley Road, Newmarket (0638 663637).
Directions: 400 yds from Newmarket (BR) - turn right into Green Road, right at crossroads New Cheveley Road - ground at top on left.
Seats: 200   **Cover:** 150   **Capacity:** 3,000   **Floodlights:** Yes   **Founded:** 1877.
Colours: Yellow/navy/blue   **Change:** Red/black/red   **Nickname:** Jockeys.
Previous Name: Newmarket FC.   **Prev. Grounds:** The Severals 1877-78/ Sefton Lodge 1878-85
Prev. Lges: Bury Snr/ Ipswich Snr/ Essex & Suffolk Border/ Utd Co's 34-37/ Eastern Co's 37-52.
Record Attendance: 2,701 v Abbey Utd (now Cambridge Utd), FA Cup 1st Qualifying Rd 1/10/49.
Best F.A. Cup year: 4th Qualifying Rd 92-93 (lost 0-2 at home to Hayes).
Midweek Matches: Tuesday   **Clubhouse details:** Matchdays only.
Programme: 30p   **Programme Editor:** G Eales.
Matchday food & drink: Tea, coffee, cold drinks, confectionary, burgers, hotdogs, soup, sandwiches, rolls.
Players progressing to the Football League: Mick Lambert (Ipswich), M Wright (Northampton), G Tweed (Coventry), R Fuller (Charlton).
Honours: Suffolk Snr Cup 34-35, Cambs Invitation Cup 58-59, Cambs Challenge Cup 21-22 26-27, Cambs Snr Lg, 19-20, Ipswich Snr Lg 30-31 31-32 32-33 33-34, Peterborough Lg 57-58.

NORWICH UNITED

Chairman: John Hilditch   **President:** Michael Miles   **Manager:** Paul Chick.
Secretary: Mick Alexander, Plantation Park, Plantation Rd, Blofield, Norwich NR13 4PL (0263 721943).
Ground: Plantation Road, Blofield, Norwich, Norfolk NR13 4PL (0603 716963).
Directions: Half a mile from Blofield village.
Seats: 100   **Cover:** Yes   **Capacity:** 3,000   **Floodlights:** Yes   **Founded:** 1903.
Club colours: Yellow & blue   **Change colours:** Red   **Metal Badges:** Yes
Programme: 12 pages, 40p   **Programme Editor:** Secretary   **Pennants:** Yes
Midweek Matches: Tuesday   **Previous Leagues** Anglian Comb.   **Nickname:** Planters.
Previous Ground: Gothic Club, Heartsease Lane, Norwich (until end of 90-91).
Record Attendance: 401 v Wroxham, League match, 2/10/91.
Clubhouse details: All facilities.   **Local Newspaper:** Eastern Counties Newspapers.
Matchday food & drink: Tea, coffee, cold drinks, confectionary, hotdogs, burgers, soup, sandwiches, rolls.
Honours: Eastern Co's Lg Div 1 90-91 (R-up 89-89, Lg Cup 91-92), Anglian Combination 88-89.

SOHAM TOWN RANGERS

Chairman: C J Murfitt   **President:** B E Owers   **Manager:** Adrian Davis.
Secretary: Wendy Gammon, 32 Broad Piece, Soham, Cambs CB7 5EL (0353 722139).
Ground: Julius Martins Lane, Soham, Cambs (0353 720732).
Directions: A142 between Newmarket and Ely - Julius Martins Lane.
Seats: 200   **Cover:** Yes   **Capacity:** 2,000   **Floodlights:** Yes   **Founded:** 1947.
Colours: Green/white   **Change colours:** Blue/yellow/black   **Nickname:** Town or Rangers.
Previous Lges: Peterborough & Dist.   **Record Gate:** 3,000 v Pegasus, FA Amateur Cup 1963.
Previous Names: Soham Town and Soham Rangers amalgamated in 1947.
Prog.: With entry, Ed.: Secretary   **Previous Ground:** Soham Rangers: Brook Street 1919-47.
Midweek Matchday: Wednesday   **Clubhouse:** General bar, Stud Bar, Lounge Bar.
Local Newspapers: Ely Standard, Newmarket Journal, Cambridge Evening News.
Hons: Eastern Co's Lg Div 1 R-up 92-93, P'boro. Lg(3), *6-0 win v renowned Pegasus in '63 Amtr Cup.*

Soham Town Rangers - Division One runners-up 1992-93. Back Row (L/R): Mick Mann (Manager), Darren Theobald, Richard Goodson, Lee Brooks, Phil Hubbard, Dean Shipp, Chris Rose, Dave Huggett (Asst Mgr). Front: Phil Coulson, Mark Leonard, James Pullar (now Cambridge City), Adrian Bullett, Trevor Claxton, Eddie Partridge, Mick Drury (Trainer). Photo - Dave West.

STOWMARKET TOWN

Chairman: John Kerry   **President:** David Hunting   **Manager:** Trevor Wardlow.
Secretary: John Doward, Deepland House, Stowupland, Stowmarket, Suffolk IP14 1LD (0449 612003).
Ground: Green Meadows Stadium, Bury Road, Stowmarket (0449 612533).
Directions: Take Bury Street from lights in town centre - continue r'bout, ground on right. 880 yds from Stowmarket (BR).
Seats: 200   **Cover:** 450   **Capacity:** 2,000   **Floodlights:** Yes   **Founded:** 1883.
Colours: Gold & black   **Change colours:** Red   **Nickname:** Stow
Midweek Matches: Wednesday   **Previous League:** Essex & Suffolk Border **Club Shop:** Yes
Record Gate: 3,800 v Romford, FA Amtr Cup 1st Rd 15/12/51.   **Pennants & Metal Badges:** Yes.
Programme: 20 pages, 30p   **Programme Editor:** John Gillingham
Local Press: E. Anglian, Bury Free Press **Previous Names:** Stowmarket Corinthians, Stowmarket FC
Clubhouse: Bar, meeting rooms, kitchen, entertainment Saturdays, snooker.
Matchday food & drink: Tea, coffee, cold drinks, confectionary, hotdogs, burgers, soup, sandwiches, rolls, ice cream, cream cakes.
Players progressing to Football League: Craig Oldfield (Colchester), Les Tibbett & Brian Klug (Ipswich).
Honours: Eastern Co's Lg R-up 91-92, Suffolk Premier Cup(4), Suffolk Snr Cup(10), Suffolk Jnr Cup.

Stowmarket Town F.C. 1992-93: Back Row (L/R): Geoff Porter (Joint Manager), Martin Bennett, Nigel Vincent, Cameron Smith, Steve Wade, Simon Cutting, Craig Oldfield, Martin Philbrough, Doug Wade (Joint Manager), Dean Francis. Front: Simon Morris, Adrian Hunt (Captain), Graham Pooley, David Thompson, Mark Clarke, Roger Aldis, Jimmy Sharpe (Trainer). Photo - Richard Brock.

SUDBURY WANDERERS

Chairman: N Smith   **President:**   **Manager:** M Mills.
Secretary: Brian Tatum, 4 Beaconsfield Close, Sudbury, Suffolk CO10 6JR (0787 375840).
Ground: Brundon Lane, Sudbury, Suffolk (0787 376213).
Directions: From Sudbury centre follow Halstead/Chelmsford signs for about 1 mile. Take 1st right after railway bridge at foot of steep hill, and 1st right after sharp lefthand bend.
Seats: 200   **Cover:** 150   **Capacity:** 2,500   **Floodlights:** Yes   **Founded:** 1958
Midweek Matchday: Tuesday   **Prog.:** With entry   **Colours:** Yellow
Nickname: Wanderers
Record Attendance: 248 v Woodbridge Town, Jewson Eastern Counties League Division One 20/4/93.
Clubhouse: Matchdays/ training nights.   **Matchday food & drink:** Hot & cold drinks, confectionary.
Hons: Eastern Co's Lg Div 1 92-93, Ess. & Suff. Border Lg(2) 89-91 (R-up 88-89), Suffolk Snr Cup 90-91.

TIPTREE UNITED

Chairman: F Byles   **President:** L Foakes   **Manager:** Steve Sutton.
Secretary: Peter G Fidge, 77 Chelmer Road, Chelmsford, Essex CM2 6AA (0245 353667).
Ground: Chapel Road, Tiptree, Essex (0621 815213).
Directions: Enter town on B1023 - Chapel Road is left at second crossroads. 3 miles from Kelverdom (BR). Served by Eastern National Colchester to Maldon bus.
Seats: 150   **Cover:** 250   **Capacity:** 2,500   **Floodlights:** Yes   **Founded:** 1933.
Club colours: Red & white   **Change colours:** White.   **Nickname:** Jam Makers.
Midweek Matchday: Tuesday.   **Previous Lges:** Essex & Suffolk Border/ Essex Snr 71-79
Record Attendance: 1,289 v Spurs, floodlight inauguration Dec 1990.
Programme: 30 pages, 30p   **Programme Editor:** Secretary
Local Newspapers: Colchester Evening Gazette, Essex County Standard.
Clubhouse details: Sports Hall & licensed bar, snooker, pool, darts, badminton. Open every day.
Matchday food & drink: Tea, coffee, cold drinks, confectionary, burgers, hotdogs, soup.
Honours: Essex Snr Tphy 80-81, Eastern Co's Lg 81-82 (Lg Cup 81-82 84-85), Essex Snr Lg R-up 75-76 77-78, Harwich Charity Cup(4).

WATTON UNITED

Chairman: Dick Jessup   **President:** Malcolm Warner
Manager: Chris Watts/ Steve Bunting.
Secretary: Tim Warner, 9 Spinney Close, Beech Road, Beetley, Dereham NR20 4EZ (0362 860016).
Ground: Dereham Road, Watton, Norfolk (0953 881281).
Directions: On A1075 towards Dereham about half a mile from junction with B1108.
Seats: 50   **Cover:** 150   **Capacity:** 2,000   **Floodlights:** Yes   **Founded:** 1888.
Colours: All white   **Change colours:** Green/black/green   **Nickname:** Brecklanders.
Midweek Matches: Tuesday   **Previous Leagues:** East Anglian/ Anglian Comb.
Record Gate: 1,200 v Norwich C., floodlight opener 1985.
Programme: 25p   **Programme Editor:** Rick Neave   **Clubhouse:** Watton 881281
Matchday food & drink: Tea, coffee, cold drinks, confectionary, burgers, soup, sandwiches, rolls.
Players progressing to Football League: Chris Watts & Robert Taylor (Norwich).
Honours: Anglian Comb. 66-67 67-68 85-86 (Lg Cup 66-67 69-70).

WISBECH TOWN

Chairman: M E Davis   **President:** J W A Chilvers   **Vice Chairman:** A Buchan.
Secretary: M E Davis, Ely House, 158 Lynn Road, Wisbech, Cambs PE13 3EB (0945 583567).
Manager: J Gallagher/ K Rudd.   **Newsline:** 0898 446 887.
Ground: Fenland Park, Lerowe, Wisbech, Cambs (0945 584176).
Directions: On Lerowe Road, a right turn off the A47 Lynn Road. 20 mins walk from town centre, irregular bus service to Wisbech from Peterborough or March.
Seats: 258   **Cover:** 3,000   **Capacity:** 7,500   **Floodlights:** Yes   **Founded:** 1920.
Colours: Red/white   **Change colours:** Blue/white.   **Nickname:** Fenmen
Previous Lges: Peterborough/ Utd Co's 35-50/ Eastern Co's 50-52/ Midland 52-58/ Southern 58-70.
Previous Grounds: Wisbech Park 20-21, Waisoken Rectory 21-22, Harecroft Road 22-47.
Record Attendance: 8,044 v Peterborough Utd, Midland Lg 25/8/57.   **Metal Badges:** Yes.
Midweek Matchday: Tuesday.   **Clubhouse:** Open every day.   **Pennants:** Yes
Matchday food & drink: Tea, coffee, cold drinks, confectionary, burgers, hotdogs, soup, sandwiches, rolls.
Programme: 36 pages, 40p   **Programme Editor:** Secretary   **Club shop:** Yes
Honours: FA Cup 2nd Rd 57-58 (1st Rd(5) 45-46 58-60 64-66), FA Vase SF 84-85 85-86, Southern Lg Div 1 61-62, Utd Co's Lg(4) 46-48 49-50 61-62(reserves) (R-up 48-49, Lg Cup 35-36 (R-up 46-47)), Midland Lg R-up 57-58, Eastern Co's Lg 71-72 76-77 90-91 (R-up 70-71 73-74 83-84 92-93, Lg Cup 50-51 70-71 71-72 (R-up 73-74 76-77 86-87), Cambs Invitation Cup(8) 52-53 55-56 57-58 74-76 81-83 91-92, East Anglian Cup 87-88 (R-up 40-41 48-49), Peterborough Lg 24-25 27-28 28-29 31-32 32-33, Peterborough Snr Cup 32-33 76-77 89-90.

WROXHAM

Chairman: T Jarrett   **President:** L King   **Manager:** Bruce Cunningham.
Secretary: Chris Green, 24 Keys Drive, Wroxham, Norfolk NR12 8SS (0603 783936).
Physio: G Christmas   **Press Officer:** Chris Green   **Commercial Manager:** Tom Jarrett
Ground: Trafford Park, Wroxham (0603 783583).
Directions: Arriving from Norwich turn left at Castle PH and keep left to ground. Two and a half miles from Hoveson (BR). Buses 722, 724 and 717.
Seats: 50   **Cover:** 250   **Capacity:** 2,500   **Floodlights:** Yes   **Founded:** 1892.
Colours: Blue/white   **Change colours:** All white.   **Nickname:** Yatchtsmen.
Previous League: Anglian Comb.   **Midweek Matchday:** Tuesday.
Record Attendance: 1,011 v Wisbech, Eastern Co's Lg Premier Division 16/3/93.
Programme: 24 pages, with entry   **Programme Editor:** Chris Green
Local Newspapers: North Norfolk, Eastern Football (Norwich 28311).
Clubhouse details: Bar, pool, darts etc.
Matchday food & drink: Tea, coffee, cold drinks, confectionary, burgers, hotdogs, soup, sandwiches, rolls.
Honours: Eastern Co's Lg 91-92 92-93 (Div 1 88-89, Lg Cup 92-93 (R-up 90-91)), Norfolk Snr Cup 92-93, Anglian Comb. (5)(Lg Cup (6)).

Sudbury Wanderers - Division One champions 1992-93. Back Row (L/R): Robert Sims, Steve Day, Jason Haygreen, Andrew Fenwick, Adam Crofton, Trevor Irvine, Colin Pearce. Front: Gary Harvey, Warren Dave, Chris King, Lee Wilson, Richard Codling, Glen Birch. Photo - Richard Brock.

Tiptree United F.C., at Vicarage Road for their F.A. Cup tie against Wealdstone. Photo - Paul Dennis.

Wisbech Town - Jewson Eastern Counties League runners-up 1992-93.

DIVISION ONE CLUBS 1993-94

BRANTHAM ATHLETIC

Chairman: Alan Clarke   **President:** D White   **Manager:** Graham Warren.
Secretary: Dave Baldwin, 20 Brooklands Road, Brantham, Essex CO11 1RP (0206 392757).
Ground: B.A.S. Club, New Village, Brantham, Manningtree, Essex (0206 392506).
Directions: Leave A12 at B1070 junction signposted Manningtree. Ground just off A137.
Seats: 100   **Cover:** 200   **Capacity:** 1,500   **Floodlights:** Yes   **Founded:** 1887.
Colours: Blue & white   **Change colours:** Red & black   **Pennants:** Yes.
Midweek Matches: Wednesday   **Previous League:** Essex & Suffolk Border.
Programme: 24 pages, 25p   **Record Gate:** 1,500 v VS Rugby, FA Vase 5th Rd 82-83.
Clubhouse details: Open daily, licensing hours. 2 bars, dancing, snooker, pool, refreshments.
Matchday food & drink: Tea, coffee, cold drinks, confectionary, burgers(after), chips(after), soup, rolls.
Honours: Suffolk Senior Cup, Essex Border Lg(4), Essex & Suffolk Border League Cup(2), Suffolk Premier Cup, Jewson Sportsmanship Award 88-89.

BRIGHTLINGSEA UNITED

Chairman: Graham Steady   **Manager:** Frank Thompson.
Secretary: H J Beere, 108 Regent Road, Brightlingsea, Essex CO7 0NZ (0206 303122).
Ground: North Road, Brightlingsea, Essex (0206 304199).
Directions: B1027 Colchester-Clacton, B1029 from Thorrington Cross - follow Church Road into town, left into Spring Road, left into Church Road. Nearest station; Colchester then bus 78 to Brightlingsea.
Seats: 50   **Cover:** 250   **Capacity:** 2,000   **Floodlights:** Yes   **Club Shop:** Yes.
Colours: Red/white   **Change colours:** All blue   **Nickname:** Oystermen.
Previous Leagues: Tendring Hundred, Essex & Suffolk Border, Essex Senior 1972-90.
Midweek Matches: Wednesday   **Record Gate:** 1,200 v Colchester, friendly 68-69.
Programme: 24 pages, 30p   **Prog. Editor:** M Cole (0206 304430)   **Founded:** 1887
Clubhouse details: Open matchdays and all evenings bar Sunday.
Matchday food & drink: Tea, coffee, cold drinks, confectionary, hotdogs, sandwiches, rolls.
Local Newspapers: Essex County Standard, Evening Gazette.
Honours: Essex Snr Lg 88-89 89-90 (Harry Fisher Mem. Tphy 89-90 (R-up 88-89), Lg Cup R-up 78-79), Eastern Co's Lg Div 1 R-up 90-91, Essex & Suffolk Border Lg Prem. Div Cup 71-72, Harwich Charity Cup 87-88, Worthington Evans Cup 76-77 77-78 78-79.

BURY TOWN RESERVES (See page 535 for full details)

CAMBRIDGE CITY RESERVES (See page 485 for full details)

CLACTON TOWN

Chairman: Fred Lawrence   **President:** R Manning   **Manager:** Dave Reynolds.
Secretary: George Betts, 15 Hill Rd, Gt Clacton, Essex CO15 4EN (0255 474427).
Ground: The Rushgreen Bowl, Rushgreen Road, Clacton-on-Sea (0255 432590).
Directions: A133 to Clacton, at r'bout right into St Johns Rd, 4th left Cloes Lane, 3rd right Rushgreen Rd, ground approximately half mile on right. From B1027 take main Jaywick turn off (Jaywick Lane), then 2nd left (after about a mile) into Rushgreen Rd. Ground 400 yds. 2 miles from Clacton (BR), buses 3, 5 or 5a to Coopers Lane/Rushgreen Rd.
Seats: 200   **Cover:** Yes   **Capacity:** 2,500   **Floodlights:** Yes   **Founded:** 1892.
Colours: Royal blue   **Change colours:** All red   **Club Shop:** Yes
Previous Grounds: Clacton Stadium, Old Road 06-87/ Gainsford Av (temp).   **Metal Badges:** Yes.
Midweek Matches: Tuesday   **Pennants:** Yes.
Record Attendance: 3,505 v Romford, FA Cup 1st Qualifying Rd 1952 (at Old Road).
Previous Leagues: Eastern Co's 35-37 38-58/ Southern 58-64.
Programme: 40 pages, 30p   **Local Paper:** Clacton Gazette   **Nickname:** Seasiders.
Clubhouse details: Licensed club. Open 7-11pm Mon-Sat, 12-3pm Sat-Sun.
Matchday food & drink: Tea, coffee, cold drinks, confectionary, burgers, hotdogs, soup, rolls.
Players progressing to Football League: Vivian Woodward (Spurs, Chelsea, England), Mick Everitt (Arsenal, Northampton), Christian McLean (Bristol Rovers).
Honours: Southern Lg Div 1 59-60, Eastern Co's Lg R-up 36-37 53-54 64-65 74-75 (Lg Cup 73-74), East Anglian Cup 53-54, Worthington Evans Cup 56-57 67-68 74-75, FA Cup 1st Rd (v Southend) 60-61.

DOWNHAM TOWN

Chairman: John Fysh   **President:** T G Barker   **Manager:** Kevin Bunn.
Secretary: B Connor, 02, Bungalow, Windsor Street, Downham Market, Norfolk PE38 9EG (0366 383179).
Ground: Lynn Road, Downham Market, Norfolk (0366 388424).
Directions: One and a quarter miles from Downham Market (BR) - continue to town clock, turn left and ground is three quarters of a mile down Lynn Road.
Seats: None   **Cover:** Yes   **Capacity:** 1,000   **Floodlights:** Yes   **Founded:** 1881.
Colours: Red & white   **Change colours:** Yellow/navy   **Nickname:** Town
Midweek Matches: Tuesday   **Previous Leagues:** Peterborough
Record Attendance: 292 v Diss Town, Jewson League Division One 1991/92.
Clubhouse: Open matchdays   **Programme:** By Barnes Promotions, with entry
Matchday food & drink: Tea, coffee, cold drinks, confectionary, hotdogs, burgers, soup, sandwiches, rolls.
Honours: P'boro Lg(5) 62-63 73-74 78-79 86-88, Norfolk Senior Cup 63-64 65-66 (R-up(3) 66-69).

ELY CITY

Chairman: Roger Pauley   **President:** Doug Unwin   **Manager:** Steve Clark.
Secretary: Derek Oakey, 37 Fordham Road, Soham, Nr Ely, Cambs CB7 5AH (0353 722141).
Ground: Unwin Sports Ground, Downham Road (0353 662035).
Directions: A10 Ely by-pass turn off for Downham. 3 miles (approx) from Ely (BR).
Seats: 50   **Cover:** 150   **Capacity:** 1,500   **Floodlights:** Yes   **Founded:** 1885
Colours: All red   **Change colours:** Sky/royal   **Midweek Matches:** Tuesday
Previous Leagues: Peterborough/ Central Alliance 58-60.   **Nickname:** Robins
Record Gate: 220 v Cambridge Utd, Hunts Premier Cup 15/11/88.   **Metal Badges:** Yes
Clubhouse details: Open matchdays   **Local Press:** Ely Standard (0353 667831). **Programme:** 20p
Matchday food & drink: Tea, coffee, cold drinks, confectionary, hotdogs, burgers, sandwiches, rolls.
Hons: Cambs Snr Cup 47-48, Eastern Co's Lg R-up 69-70 (Lg Cup 79-80), FA Cup 1st Rd 54-55 (2-6 v Torquay).

HADLEIGH UNITED

Chairman: Peter Vardon   **Manager:** Alan Dilloway.
Secretary: R Pett, 9 Fullers Close, Hadleigh, Suffolk IP7 5AS (0473 827242).
Ground: Millfield, Duke Street, Hadleigh, Suffolk (0473 822165).
Directions: Follow signs to Hadleigh off A12. Duke Street is off the High Street - turn by Library.
Seats: None   **Cover:** 100   **Capacity:** 2,000   **Floodlights:** Yes   **Founded:** 1892.
Colours: White/navy/white   **Change:** Yellow/white/yellow   **Programme:** 20p
Midweek Matches: Wednesday.   **Previous League:** Suffolk & Ipswich (pre-1991).
Record Gate: 340 v Woodbridge Town, Jewson Eastern Counties League Division One 22/1/93.
Clubhouse details: Open matchdays, Fridays & Sundays.
Matchday food & drink: Tea, coffee, cold drinks, confectionary, soup, rolls.
Honours: Suffolk & Ipswich Lg(5)(Lg Cup(4)), Suffolk Senior Cup(3).

IPSWICH WANDERERS

Chairman: J Barker   **President:**   **Manager:** Brian Swift.
Secretary: Keith Bassett, 15 Heathercroft Road, Ipswich, Suffolk IP1 6QG (0473 748458).
Ground: Humberdoucey Road, Ipswich, Suffolk (0473 728581).
Directions: A12 north of Ipswich Rushmere Golf Club. Players Road into Humberdovey Lane.
Seats: None   **Cover:** Yes   **Capacity:** 2,000   **Floodlights:** No   **Founded:** 1983.
Colours: Blue/blue/white   **Change colours:** Red & black/red/red.
Nickname: Wanderers.
Previous Leagues: Little David Sunday   **Previous Names:** Loadwell Ipswich.
Midweek Matches: Wednesday   **Record Gate:** 276 v Woodbridge, Jewson Lg 18/3/91.
Programme: With admission   **Clubhouse details:** Bar, refreshments.
Matchday food & drink: Tea, coffee, cold drinks, confectionary, burgers, hotdogs, sandwiches, rolls.
Local Newspapers: East Anglian Daily Times, Evening Star.

LONG SUTTON ATHLETIC

Chairman: P Childs   **President:** V W Day   **Manager:** B L Wilson.
Secretary: Simon Caney, Plot 1, Mansion Site, Daniels Cottage, Lng Sutton, Spalding, Lincs (0406 26542).
Ground: London Road, Long Sutton, Spalding, Lincs (0406 364208).
Directions: On left hand side of A17 entering village from Wisbech or King's Lynn.
Seats: None   **Cover:** 100   **Capacity:** 1,000   **Floodlights:** Yes   **Founded:** 1922.
Colours: Black & white stripes/black   **Change colours:** All blue.   **Nickname:** Magpies
Previous League: Peterborough.   **Prev. Name:** Long Sutton Town 1922-55. **Programme:** 20p
Clubhouse: Open matchdays.   **Record Gate:** 537 v Grimsby, friendly.
Matchday food & drink: Tea, coffee, cold drinks, pies, pasties, sandwiches.
Local Press: Wisbech Standard, Spalding Guardian, Lincs Free Press.   **Midweek Matchday:** Tuesday.
Honours: Lincs Junior Cup 85-86 (R-up 87-88), Lincs 'B' Snr Cup 88-89, TSLB Challenge Cup 88-89.

MILDENHALL TOWN

Chairman: B Brigden   **President:** J E Butcher   **Manager:** Mark Goldsack.
Secretary: B W Hensby, 14 Sanderling Close, Mildenhall, Suffolk IP28 7LF (0638 715772).
Ground: Recreation Way, Mildenhall, Suffolk (0638 713449).
Directions: Next to swimming pool/car, quarter of a mile from town centre.
Seats: None   **Capacity:** 2,000   **Midweek Matchday:** Tuesday   **Founded:** 1890.
Club colours: Amber/black   **Change colours:** All white   **Nickname:** Town or yellows.
Previous Leagues: Bury & District/ Cambs Lg 2B, 1B & Premier.
Record Attendance: 350 v Norwich City, friendly 22/7/89.
Programme: Free with admission   **Editor:** D Isaac   **Clubhouse:** Open matchdays & functions.
Matchday food & drink: Tea, coffee, cold drinks, confectionary, sandwiches, rolls.
Local Newspapers: Bury Free Press, Newmarket Journal, Cambridge Evening News.
Honours: Suffolk Junior Cup 1899-1900.

SOMERSHAM TOWN

Chairman: David Hardy   **President:** Jack Marjason   **Comm. Mgr:** Norman Ward (0487 840181).
Secretary: John Lyon, 'Molineux' 1 Asplins Avenue, Needingworth, Huntingdon PE17 3SX (0480 464411).
Manager: Norman Hudson   **Asst Manager:** John Scarborough   **Physio:** Alan Magnus
Ground: West End Ground, St Ives Road, Somersham, Cambs (0487 843384).
Directions: On A604 St Ives to Somersham on right as you enter town.
Seats: None   **Cover:** 200   **Capacity:** 1,500   **Floodlights:** Yes   **Founded:** 1893.
Colours: All amber   **Change colours:** Sky/navy/sky   **Midweek matchday:** Tuesday.
Previous League: Peterborough & Dist.   **Record Gate:** 538 v Norwich City, floodlight inauguration 19/11/91.
Programme: 76 pages, 30p   **Programme Editor:** Dave Hardy (0487 840441)
Sponsors: T S Frozen Foods   **Clubhouse:** Open Friday, Sat/Sun lunchtimes.
Matchday food & drink: Tea, coffee, cold drinks, confectionary, rolls.
Local Newspapers: Hunts Post, Cambs News, Citizen Express, St Ives Weekly.
Honours: Hunts Snr Cup 72-73, P'boro Snr Cup 84-85, Hinchingbrooke Cup 54-55.

STANWAY ROVERS

Chairman: Alan Buck   **Manager:** Alan Smith   **President:**
Secretary: Richard Degville, 5 Old Heath Road, Colchester, Essex CO3 4AU (0206 792599).
Ground: 'Hawthorns', New Farm Road, Stanway, Colchester, Essex (0206 578187).
Directions: Take turn off marked Stanway off A12. Turn right and go over flyover, left at r'bout, 1st right into Villa Rd, after 25 yards turn left into Church Rd, 200 yards on left into New Farm Rd, ground 400 yards on left.
Seats: None   **Cover:** Yes   **Capacity:** 1,500   **Floodlights:** No   **Founded:**
Colours: Green/white/black   **Change colours:** Yellow/black/black   **Nickname:** Rovers.
Record Attendance: 104 v Soham Town Rangers, Eastern Counties League Division One 4/9/92.
Previous League: Essex & Suffolk Border (pre-1992).
Programme: Yes   **Clubhouse:** Normal licensing hours.
Midweek matchday: Tuesday.   **Local Newspaper:** Essex County Standard.
Honours: Essex Intermediate Cup R-up 89-90 90-91, Essex & Suffolk Border Lg R-up 91-92.

SUDBURY TOWN RESERVES (See page 547 for full details)

SWAFFHAM TOWN

Chairman: R Goldsmith   **President:**   **Manager:** Barry Cook.
Secretary: David Ward, 2 Princes Street, Swaffham, Norfolk PE37 7BX (0760 722516).
Ground: Shoemakers Lane, Swaffham, Norfolk (0760 722700).
Seats: None   **Cover:**   **Capacity:** 2,000   **Floodlights:** Yes   **Founded:** 1892.
Colours: Black & white stripes/black/black.   **Change:** Yellow/black/yellow.
Nickname: Pedlars
Midweek Matchay: Tuesday.   **Previous Leagues:** Dereham, Anglian Combination
Record Attendance: 250 v Downham Town, Jewson Eastern Co's League Cup 3/9/91.
Clubhouse details: Open Tuesday, Thursday, Saturday & Sunday lunchtimes & evenings.
Matchday food & drink: Tea, coffee, cold drinks, confectionary, rolls (occasionally).
Programme: 36 pages, 30p   **Hons:** Norfolk Snr Cup(2), Anglian Comb. 89-90 (Div 1 88-89).

THETFORD TOWN

Chairman: M Bailey   **President:** F Huson   **Manager:** David Brooks.
Secretary: John Wordley, 4 Claxton Close, Thetford, Norfolk IP24 1BA (0842 762530).
Ground: Mundford Road, Thetford, Norfolk (0842 766120).
Directions: On Mundford Road, signposted via Lynn, Downham Market on A143 of A11.
Seats: 400   **Cover:** 400   **Capacity:** 2,000   **Floodlights:** Yes   **Founded:** 1964.
Colours: Claret/blue   **Change colours:** White (red pin stripe)/black
Previous Leagues: Norfolk & Suffolk   **Midweek Matches:** Tuesday   **Club Shop:** Yes.
Local Press: Thetford & Watton Times, Bury Free Press.   **Programme:** 28 pages, 30p
Clubhouse details: Bar, teas, refreshments, light meals.   **Pennants:** Yes.
Matchday food & drink: Tea, coffee, cold drinks, confectionary, hotdogs, burgers, sandwiches, rolls.
Record Gate: 394 v Diss Town, Norfolk Snr Cup 23/1/91.
Players progressing to Football League: Dick Scott (Norwich City, Cardiff City), Kevin Seggie (Leeds United), Simon Milton (Ipswich Town).
Honours: Eastern Co's Lg R-up 89-90, Norfolk & Suffolk Lg 54-55, Norfolk Snr Senior Cup 47-48 90-91.

WARBOYS TOWN

Chairman: Trevor Chamberlain   **President:** G C Bowd   **Manager:** Robbie Cook.
Secretary: R O Erigland, 39 High Street, Warboys, Huntingdon PE17 2TA (0487 822312).
Ground: Sports Field, Forge Way, off High Street, Warboys, Cambs (0487 823483).
Directions: Access through Forge Way, half way along south side of High Street.
Seats: None   **Cover:** 200   **Capacity:** 2,000   **Floodlights:** Yes   **Founded:** 1885.
Colours: Red/white   **Change colours:** Blue & maroon/blue   **Nickname:** Witches.
Midweek Matches: Tuesday   **Previous Leagues:** Utd Co's/ Peterborough & Dist.
Record Attendance: 500 v Ramsey Town, Hunts Senior Cup Semi Final.
Programme: 12 pages, 20p   **Programme Editor:** M England
Local Newspaper: Hunts Post (0480 411481).
Clubhouse: Bar, lounge, function hall. Open every evening & Sunday lunchtime. Various entertainments.
Matchday food & drink: Tea, coffee, cold drinks, confectionary, sandwiches, rolls.
Past Players progressing to Football League: Alex Chamberlain (Ipswich, Everton, Colchester).
Honours: Utd Co's Lg Div 2 R-up, P'boro Lg R-up(2), P'boro Snr Cup, Hunts Snr Cup.

WOODBRIDGE TOWN

Chairman: K Dixon   **President:** J Coates   **Manager:** David Dixon/ Les Simmons
Secretary: Ralph Coxall, 5 Orchard Close, Woodbridge, Suffolk IP12 1LD (0394 387839).
Ground: Notcutts Park, Seckford Hall Road, Woodbridge, Suffolk (0394 385308).
Directions: Turning into Woodbridge off last r'bout from Lowestoft, or 1st r'bout from Ipswich. Take 1st turning left and 1st left again. Drive to ground at end of road on left.
Seats: None   **Cover:** 250   **Capacity:** Unknown   **Floodlights:** Yes   **Founded:** 1885.
Colours: Black & white stripes/white/white   **Change colours:** Yellow/navy.
Nickname: The Bridge or Woodpeckers.
Midweek Matches: Wednesday   **Previous Leagues:** Suffolk & Ipswich
Record Gate: 3,000 v Arsenal, floodlight inauguration 2/10/90.
Local Newspapers: East Anglian Daily Times.
Programme: 36 pages, 20p   **Programme Editor:** K Dixon
Clubhouse details: Visitors bar, lounge bar, function hall.
Matchday food & drink: Tea, coffee, cold drinks, confectionary, hotdogs, soup, burgers, sandwiches, rolls. Also small cooked meals after match.
Honours: Suffolk Senior Cup(3).

Hadleigh United F.C. 1992-93. Back Row (L/R): Graham Skinner (Physio), R Davis, M Mulley, P Keys, P Kutchins, A Brown, M Bailey, L Tibbott, A Dilloway (Manager). Front: T O'Neill, T Parkin, K Tilley, A Callaghan, P Tynan, S Coonan, T Gill. Photo - Gavin Ellis-Neville.

Somersham Town F.C. 1992-93. Photo - Gavin Ellis-Neville.

Stanway Rovers F.C. 1992-93. Back Row (L/R): Graham Bird (Coach), Robbie Free, Alan Day, Gary Matthews, Simon Whiting, Paul Duley, Paul Keaney, Danny King, Martin Fowles (Physio), Mark Vincent, Alan Smith (Manager). Front: Paul Palmer, Paul Addison, Phil Eley, David Smith, Gary Bright, Richard Handley. Photo - Dave West.

'FREEMAN KERSHAW' CAMBRIDGESHIRE LEAGUE

PREMIER A	P	W	D	L	F	A	PTS
Philips UK	28	18	6	4	61	30	60
Steeple Bumpstead	28	14	7	7	58	34	49
Bassingbourn	28	14	6	8	50	32	48
Over Sports	28	12	8	8	50	39	44
Great Shelford	28	11	7	10	47	39	40
Gamlingay	28	11	7	10	54	52	40
Godmanchester Rvrs	28	10	8	10	51	43	38
Waterbeach	28	10	7	11	47	51	37
West Wratting	28	9	9	10	44	44	36
Cherry Hinton	28	9	8	11	34	36	35
Linton Granta	28	10	4	14	42	66	34
Haslingfield	28	9	6	13	36	59	33
Fulbourn Institute	28	9	5	14	58	63	32
Soham T. Rgrs Res.	28	9	3	16	29	50	30
Cottenham United	28	7	5	16	44	67	26

DIVISION 1A	P	W	D	L	F	A	PTS
Debden	24	19	4	1	87	35	61
Linton Granta Res.	24	12	7	5	64	49	43
Hardwick	24	13	4	7	60	52	43
Eternit	24	12	4	8	53	46	40
Fulbourn I. Res.	24	11	4	9	55	55	37
Abington Utd	24	11	3	10	56	47	36
Comberton Utd	24	9	5	10	48	46	32
Gt Shelford Res.	24	10	1	13	30	40	31
Schering	24	9	2	13	55	54	29
Balsham	24	6	10	8	42	39	28
Thurlow	24	9	1	14	54	56	28
Cherry Hinton Res.	24	6	4	14	42	62	22
Fowlmere	24	2	5	17	21	86	11

LEAGUE CUP: Steeple Bumpstead
PREMIER A 5-aside: Haslingfield
PREMIER B 5-aside: Foxton
DIV. 1 Play-off 4/5/93: Over Res 3, Debden 2 (aet)
Play-off 30/4/93: Earith U. 2, Linton 1 (after 2-2)
DIV. 2 A: Cambridge Univ. Press, **B:** Girton Utd
DIV. 2 Play-off 8/5/93: Girton Utd 4, C.U.P. 2

PREMIER B	P	W	D	L	F	A	PTS
Foxton	30	24	3	3	128	37	75
Longstanton	30	19	6	5	66	38	63
Newmarket Res	30	17	5	8	69	42	56
Histon Res	30	17	5	8	81	55	56
Sawston Rovers	30	16	8	6	54	33	56
Bluntisham	30	16	6	8	72	40	54
Orwell	30	13	5	12	65	68	44
Philips UK Res	30	12	5	13	56	65	41
Somersham Res	30	11	5	14	47	53	38
Haddenham	30	10	4	16	39	54	34
Whittlesford	30	9	7	14	51	70	34
T.S.B.Rangers	30	9	3	18	34	74	30
Steeple Bump Res	30	6	6	18	31	69	24
Willingham	30	5	8	17	32	58	23
Purbeck	30	4	10	16	35	73	22
St.Ives Town Res	30	5	8	17	29	60	20

DIVISION 1B	P	W	D	L	F	A	PTS
Over Spts Res.	22	15	4	3	63	27	49
Earith United	22	13	3	6	39	25	42
Ely City Res.	22	10	5	7	39	38	35
Papworth	22	10	4	8	50	40	34
Fordham	22	9	6	7	62	45	33
Milton	22	8	6	8	43	39	30
Burwell	22	8	2	12	50	69	26
Littleport Town	22	8	2	12	39	58	26
Wicken Amateurs	22	7	4	11	39	44	25
Soham United	22	7	4	11	41	51	25
Barton Mills	22	7	3	12	31	45	24
Camden United	22	4	9	9	35	51	21

DIV. 3 A: Great Chishill, **B:** Napp Sports
DIV. 3 Play-off 4/5/93: Gt Chishill 2, Napp Spts 0
DIV. 4 A: Mott McDonalds, **B:** Somersham Town 'A'
DIV. 4 Play-off 29/4/93: Somersham 3, Mott McDonalds 1
DIV. 5 A: Elmdon, **B:** Marshalls Sports
DIV. 5 Play-off 24/4/93: Elmdon 3, Marshalls Spts 2

Champions Philips (UK) score the first in their home win over Bassingbourn on 17th April. Photo - Martin Wray.

'WESTSIDE' EASTERN JUNIOR ALLIANCE

(UNDER-18's LEAGUE - TABLES ARE FINAL - NOT ALL GAMES PLAYED)

N.E. SECTION	P	W	D	L	F	A	PTS
Brantham Ath.	21	14	4	3	68	23	46
Colchester Utd	22	13	6	3	59	26	45
R.S.S.C. Ransomes	22	12	8	2	61	23	44
Wivenhoe Town	22	13	5	4	57	23	44
Whitton United	22	11	4	7	55	39	37
Stowmarket Town	22	9	8	5	56	27	35
Stanway Rovers	21	7	7	7	55	33	28
Felixstowe T.	22	8	2	12	40	38	26
Long Melford	22	7	4	11	38	53	25
Halstead Town	22	5	4	13	34	48	19
Woodbridge T.	22	4	3	15	29	85	15
Clacton Town	22	0	1	21	13	147	1

S.W. SECTION	P	W	D	L	F	A	PTS
Runwell Hospital	18	16	1	1	79	10	*52
Caribbean Int.	17	12	5	1	47	21	*44
Gt Wakering Rvrs	16	9	3	4	52	21	30
Standard Harlow	16	9	1	6	48	33	28
Herongate Ath.	15	9	0	6	51	31	27
Hullbridge Spts	20	8	3	9	37	39	27
Barkingside	18	7	1	10	42	48	*25
Braintree Town	17	6	3	8	39	41	21
Woodford Town	18	5	1	12	29	70	16
Canvey Island	18	4	3	11	35	63	15
Sawbridgeworth	18	0	1	17	9	91	1

Lge Cup Final 2/5/93: Ransomes 2, Gt Wakering 0

LOVEWELL BLAKE ANGLIAN COMBINATION FOOTBALL LEAGUE

Chairman: A.J.Dickerson Esq,

Hon.Secretary: J.C.Harpley,
4 Harlington Avenue, Hellesdon, Norwich, NR6 5LJ

MULBARTON WIN EXCITING TITLE RACE

Another new name was added to the 96-years-old Sterry Trophy when in their last game, which they had to win to clinch the title, Mulbarton United. defeated 3rd-placed Blofield United 2-0 thus pipping Carrow AFC by one point for the premier division championship.

This was one of the most enthralling seasons we have had for sometime in the premier division, Ashlea made all the running during September, October and November and were looking capable of maintaining the top spot, having gone 12 games without defeat, but then in December, surprisingly lost to Wymondham Town & Coltishall HV after two very hard games with Beccles Town in the knock-out cup, which they also lost and from then on, never recovered their early season form, finally finishing 4th.

Coltishall HV took over the leadership in December and January, but they could not hold off the challenge coming from Carrow AFC and Mulbarton United, the latter two battled for the title right up to the final games.

Wortwell continued their see-saw performance between the premier and division one. Having gained promotion to the premier last season, they struggled this term and were relegated again to division one; Great Yarmouth Reserves, who have spent the past 11 seasons in the premier, now join Wortwell in division one. Coming up from division one are the two Jewson League reserve teams, Wroxham and Diss. They both quickly filled the top two places early on and stayed there all season, Wroxham Reserves finishing five points clear of Diss Reserves. In this division, Hempnall failed to stop their decline and return to the Junior sections after eight seasons in the top flight; going down with them are Harleston Town; regrettably, Fred Coleman their secretary is calling it a day, after 30 years with the club. After 20 years in the Junior sections, Thorpe Village have regained Senior status by winning division two and joining them is another Jewson League reserve team, Fakenham.

In the Norfolk Senior Cup there were some notable successes against Jewson League opposition. Horsford and St. Andrews disposed of Swaffham Town and Downham Town respectively in the first round, whilst the biggest upsets were the defeat of Diss Town by Reepham Town and Lakeford defeating Great Yarmouth Town.

In the senior knock-out cup Beccles Town produced some exciting football in reaching the final, but disappointed at the last hurdle, going down 3-0 to Blofield United.

J.C.Harpley (General Secretary).

Mark Jones (11) wins a tackle for Mulbarton United as the champions-elect win 5-0 at Wymondham Town on 2nd February. Photo: Martin Wray.

PREMIER DIV.	P	W	D	L	F	A	PTS
Mulbarton Utd	30	22	4	4	86	32	48
Carrow	30	20	7	3	96	43	47
Blofield United	30	16	7	7	71	47	39
Ashlea	30	16	7	7	60	46	39
Dereham Town	30	13	10	7	50	41	36
Coltishall HV 85	30	14	7	9	56	45	35
Lakeford Rangers	30	13	6	11	52	53	32
Overstrand	30	11	5	14	61	51	27
Horsford United	30	10	6	14	44	66	26
Beccles Town	30	11	3	16	52	54	25
St Andrews	30	11	3	16	60	64	25
Newton Flotman	30	8	8	14	33	50	24
Wymondham Town	30	9	6	15	40	60	24
Kirkley	30	10	2	18	53	67	22
Gt Yarmouth Res.	30	6	6	18	25	64	18
Wortwell	30	5	3	22	23	79	13

DIV. ONE	P	W	D	L	F	A	PTS
Wroxham Res.	30	24	2	4	94	34	50
Diss Town Res.	30	20	5	5	71	33	45
Loddon United	30	18	6	6	67	38	42
Mattishall	30	16	4	10	81	44	36
Bradenham	30	13	6	11	66	55	32
Brandon Town	30	12	7	11	60	56	31
Gorleston Res.	30	13	5	12	52	58	31
Wymondham O.B.	30	10	10	10	53	56	30
Oulton Broad	30	11	6	13	56	59	28
Hellesdon	30	9	9	12	46	64	27
Watton Utd Res.	30	8	10	12	40	63	26
Reepham Town	30	11	2	17	43	65	24
Norwich Union	30	9	5	16	43	53	23
Lowestoft T. Res.	30	7	9	14	54	74	23
Hempnall	30	4	11	15	42	64	19
Harleston	30	3	7	20	33	85	13

DIV. TWO	P	W	D	L	F	A	PTS
Thorpe Village	30	21	6	3	94	37	48
Fakenham T. Res.	30	20	5	5	105	36	45
Lakenheath	30	16	6	8	75	51	38
North Walsham	30	14	7	9	50	34	35
Caister United	30	13	8	9	61	43	34
Poringland Wdrs	30	12	7	11	52	56	31
Town Hall Scrips	30	11	8	11	67	65	30
Wells Town	30	11	7	12	49	53	29
Scole United	30	11	6	13	64	76	28
Sprowston Wdrs	30	12	3	15	59	68	27
Stalham	30	8	11	11	52	69	27
Thetford Rovers	30	11	4	15	44	62	26
Mundford	30	8	8	14	49	72	24
Bungay Town	30	10	2	18	60	84	22
Holt United	30	7	7	16	41	65	21
Aylsham Wanderers	30	5	5	20	43	94	15

PREMIER DIVISION RESULT CHART 1992-93

HOME TEAM	1	2	3	4	5	6	7	8	9	10	11	12	13	14	15	16
Ashlea	*	4-1	1-3	1-1	2-1	2-1	3-1	4-0	6-4	1-1	4-1	2-1	3-1	2-1	1-1	4-2
Beccles	0-3	*	1-1	2-3	2-3	2-3	4-0	4-0	3-2	1-2	0-1	0-1	1-0	1-3	2-3	1-2
Blofield Utd	1-2	3-1	*	1-1	2-3	3-0	2-1	6-2	4-1	2-1	0-2	2-2	4-3	4-0	3-0	0-2
Carrow	0-0	3-2	4-1	*	1-1	0-0	5-2	5-2	4-3	3-3	5-1	5-2	4-2	6-1	7-0	4-3
Coltishall	3-2	1-0	1-4	3-2	*	2-2	3-1	1-2	4-3	0-2	2-6	3-1	1-0	1-2	1-2	6-0
Dereham Town	2-2	2-2	2-2	0-0	2-2	*	1-0	3-2	4-2	2-0	0-1	2-0	2-0	4-2	2-0	2-2
Gt Yarmouth Res.	2-2	1-2	1-0	0-3	1-1	1-0	*	1-2	1-4	1-4	0-2	0-0	0-1	0-4	2-1	1-0
Horsford	4-2	0-3	1-2	4-6	0-0	3-1	2-2	*	1-0	2-2	1-6	0-3	1-2	3-1	1-0	2-1
Kirkley	0-1	3-0	2-3	3-2	2-0	3-2	0-1	1-1	*	3-1	1-0	0-1	0-1	3-0	4-1	0-2
Lakeford Rgrs	3-0	1-5	1-2	1-4	0-2	3-2	1-0	1-0	2-1	*	2-2	2-1	3-3	3-1	1-2	3-0
Mulbarton Utd	3-0	6-1	1-1	0-3	2-0	4-0	2-1	3-0	11-1	5-1	*	4-0	2-2	2-1	2-0	4-1
Newton Fl'man	0-1	0-1	1-1	0-1	1-1	0-1	0-0	0-0	1-3	1-4	2-2	*	1-0	3-1	1-0	0-0
Overstand	1-1	1-3	2-1	0-4	1-3	0-1	5-0	0-0	5-1	4-1	2-3	7-3	*	2-4	3-0	4-0
St.Andrews	2-0	2-3	4-1	1-7	0-0	0-2	7-0	6-3	2-1	2-0	1-2	1-2	2-2	*	6-0	2-2
Wortwell	0-3	0-3	1-5	2-4	1-5	0-3	2-0	3-2	2-2	1-1	0-1	2-3	0-6	1-0	*	2-1
Wymondham T.	5-1	1-1	2-5	1-2	0-0	1-1	0-2	0-2	1-0	2-0	0-5	4-2	2-1	2-3	1-0	*

DIVISION ONE RESULT CHART 1992-93

HOME TEAM	1	2	3	4	5	6	7	8	9	10	11	12	13	14	15	16
Bradenham	*	5-1	2-0	1-1	3-1	6-1	3-3	2-1	3-0	3-0	1-1	1-6	1-2	5-0	2-7	2-4
Brandon Town	2-0	*	2-2	1-2	2-3	3-0	0-2	2-3	2-2	5-0	1-3	1-0	4-3	6-0	0-3	2-0
Diss Town Res.	3-2	1-0	*	2-1	1-0	3-0	8-1	3-2	1-1	3-2	3-0	5-0	1-0	5-0	0-4	4-2
Gorleston Res.	2-1	1-3	1-5	*	5-0	1-3	2-2	0-4	2-0	2-5	2-0	2-7	2-1	4-0	1-3	1-1
Harleston	1-5	0-5	1-3	0-2	*	2-3	2-1	0-1	4-2	0-7	0-3	1-3	0-1	0-0	2-7	2-2
Hellesdon	0-0	2-1	4-2	1-4	2-2	*	2-2	0-3	2-3	1-1	3-1	2-1	1-0	5-1	2-3	3-3
Hempnall	4-4	1-2	3-1	0-3	1-1	1-1	*	0-2	1-2	4-1	1-2	0-0	4-0	1-4	1-3	1-2
Loddon United	2-1	1-1	0-0	1-1	2-1	1-1	3-1	*	6-3	0-2	3-1	3-2	3-0	5-1	2-2	2-3
Lowestoft T. Res.	4-1	6-1	0-4	2-3	7-0	3-0	1-1	1-3	*	0-7	2-2	2-2	2-2	1-1	0-4	1-2
Mattishall	2-1	1-3	1-2	1-1	1-1	4-1	0-0	2-1	6-1	*	3-0	4-2	6-0	3-1	0-1	0-2
Norwich Union	0-1	3-0	2-3	1-2	2-0	0-0	3-0	0-1	4-2	0-7	*	0-2	4-5	1-1	1-2	4-0
Reepham Town	0-1	2-4	1-0	1-0	3-2	0-1	2-2	1-4	2-1	3-2	1-0	*	5-2	1-4	4-1	
Watton Utd Res.	2-3	3-3	1-1	1-3	0-3	4-1	0-0	0-0	0-0	1-2	2-2	3-0	2-5	*	1-0	2-0
Wroxham Res.	5-0	2-0	5-0	4-2	4-1	3-4	6-0	3-2	3-1	4-1	4-1	0-1		1-1	*	1-0
Wymondham O.B.	3-3	1-1	1-2	4-0	2-2	1-1	4-1	2-1	2-5	1-3	1-2	4-2	2-0	0-2	0-2	*

SENIOR KNOCK-OUT CUP 1992-93 First Round (12th September)

Blofield Utd v Lowestoft T. Res.	4-1
Carrow v Oulton Broad	4-0
Dereham Town v Wroxham Reserves	4-2
Hempnall v Brandon Town	3-7
Kirkley v Diss Town Reserves	2-5
Newton Flotman v Lakeford Rangers	1-0
Norwich Union v Harleston Town	1-5
St Andrews v Gorleston Reserves	0-1
Beccles v Mulbarton	3-4(replay ordered),1-0
Coltishall H.V. '85 v Overstrand	2-3
Hellesdon v Bradenham	4-2
Horsford United v Watton United Reserves	5-2
Loddon United v Ashlea	0-3
Mattishall v Great Yarmouth Town Reserves	0-3
Reepham Town v Wymondham Old Boys	2-3(aet)
Wymondham Town v Wortwell	4-0

Second Round (10th October)

Carrow v Dereham Town	3-2
Horsford United v Harleston Town	4-3(aet)
Newton Flotman v Brandon Town	1-0
Wymondham Town v Beccles Town	1-4
Diss Town Reserves v Blofield United	0-4
Gorleston Reserves v Wymondham Old Boys	2-4
Overstrand v Hellesdon	2-1
Great Yarmouth Town Reserves v Ashlea	1-2

(continued opposite)

Quarter-Finals *(21st November)*

Blofield United v Carrow	3-0	Ashlea v Beccles Town	3-3*(aet)*,2-3*(aet)*
Newton Flotman v Horsford United	2-1	Wymondham Old Boys v Overstrand	1-1*(aet)*,0-4

Semi-Finals *(19th December)*

Newton Flotman v Blofield United	0-3	Overstrand v Beccles Town	0-1*(aet)*

Final *(at Wroxham F.C., Tues 23rd March)*: Blofield United 3, Beccles Town 0

Brandon Town F.C. Back Row (L/R): D Kent (Manager), K Rutherford, W Farthing, R Barnard, P Wharf, I Gray, S Nouncer, D Rolph (Trainer), R Darkings. Front: D Halls (Coach), M Darkings, G Stephenson, P Webster, S Duke, K Ayms, M Cooper. Photo - Martin Wray.

Norwich Union F.C. Back Row (L/R): Linesman, M Goodson, C Ainley, M Swinnerton, P Stevens, A Tick, P Gustovitch, S Baddley, M Yeomans. Front: Mascot, C Alford, C Masey, A Lincoln, R Atherton. Photo - Martin Wray.

Brandon attack in the second-half but lose 1-3 at home to Norwich Union on 16th January. Photo - Martin Wray.

CLUB DETAILS

ASHLEA
Ground: Pitch 1, Normaston Park, Lowestoft.　　　**Secretary:** E Peek (0502 568716).

BECCLES TOWN
Ground: College Meadow, Beccles (0502 712016).　　　**Secretary:** J Humby (0502 713776).

BLOFIELD UNITED
Ground: Great Yarmouth Road, Blofield.　　　**Secretary:** G Hambling (0603 716893).

BRADENHAM
Ground: Bradenham Village Green.　　　**Secretary:** R Ayers (0603 762575).

BRANDON TOWN
Ground: Remenbrance PF, Church Rd, Brandon (0842 813177).　　　**Secretary:** C Marchant (0842 812123).

CARROW
Ground: Lakenham Cricket Ground, Norwich.　　　**Secretary:** P Bugdale (0603 483283).

COLTISHALL H.V.
Ground: Rectory Road, Coltishall.　　　**Secretary:** Mrs Batch (0603 400065).

DEREHAM TOWN
Ground: Recreation Ground, Commercial Rd, Dereham.　　　**Secretary:** M Henman (0362 692242).

HARLESTON TOWN
Ground: Recreation Ground & Memorial Leisure Centre, off Wilderness Lane, Harleston (0379 85088) **Secretary:** F Coleman (0379 853815).

HELLESDON
Ground: Coronation Playing Fields, Hellesdon (603 427675).　　　**Secretary:** J Watson (0603 868937).

HEMPNALL
Ground: Bungay Road, Hempnall.　　　**Secretary:** R Youngman (0508 44237).

HORSFORD UNITED
Ground: St Faiths Sports Centre, St Faiths (0603 898069)　　　**Secretary:** S Hare (0603 897819).

KIRKLEY
Ground: Walmer Rd Rec., Lowestoft (0502 513549)　　　**Secretary:** P Gant (0502 589619).

LAKEFORD RANGERS
Ground: Cringleford Rec. Ground, Oakfields, Cringleford, Norwich.　　　**Secretary:** R Watling (0603 898440).

LODDON UNITED
Ground: George Lane, Loddon (0507 28497).　　　**Secretary:** A Cook (0508 28115).

MATTISHALL
Ground: Mattishall PF, South Green.　　　**Secretary:** R Kaye (0362 850489).

MULBARTON UNITED
Ground: Mulberry Park, Mulbarton.　　　**Secretary:** J Eastell (0508 70832).

NEWTON FLOTMAN
Ground: Newton Flotman Village Centre, Grove Way.　　　**Secretary:** N Harrod (0603 746507).

NORWICH UNION
Ground: Pinebanks, School Lane, off Harvey Lane, Thorpe.　　　**Secretary:** C McCulloch (0603 402242).

OVERSTRAND
Ground: Sports Ground, High Street, Overstrand (0263 788287) **Secretary:** R Rounce (0263 513715).

OULTON BROAD
Ground: Normaston Park, Lowestoft.　　　**Secretary:** D Rackham (0502 563353).

REEPHAM TOWN
Ground: Stimpsons Piece Rec., Reepham.　　　**Secretary:** D Norris (0603 870634).

ST ANDREWS
Ground: Thorpe Rec., Laundry Lane, Thorpe (0603 300316).　　　**Secretary:** I Bishop (0603 720737).

WORTWELL
Ground: Wortwell PF (opposite Bell pub).　　　**Secretary:** I Fisher (0379 608401).

WYMONDHAM OLD BOYS
Ground: Browick Rd Rec., Wymondham.　　　**Secretary:** M Musk (0953 603421).

WYMONDHAM TOWN
Ground: Kings Head Meadow, Wymondham (0953 607326).　　　**Secretary:** M Utting (0953 453146).

(See Jewson Eastern Counties League section for details of Reserve sides)

WIMPEY HOMES
ESSEX & SUFFOLK BORDER LEAGUE

President: B R Tatum Esq.
Hon. Secretary: K G Bulow Esq.,
13 Kingswood Road, Mile End, Colchester CO4 5JX Tel: 0206 851733

PREM. DIVISION	P	W	D	L	F	A	PTS
Little Oakley	30	20	5	5	87	39	65
Alresford Colne Rgrs	30	19	6	5	71	36	63
West Bergholt	30	17	7	6	62	30	58
Stowmarket T.Res.	30	17	6	7	64	37	57
Dedham Old Boys	30	16	5	9	57	36	53
Haverhill Rvrs Res.	30	14	2	14	44	44	44
H. & Parkeston Res	30	12	7	11	54	73	43
Sudbury (Lucas) Ath.	30	11	5	14	51	65	38
Boxted Lodgers	30	11	5	14	45	59	38
Long Melford	30	10	5	15	42	60	35
Clacton Town Res.	30	10	4	16	61	62	34
Gas-Recreation	30	10	4	16	56	83	34
Kelvedon Social	30	8	9	13	60	65	33
St.Johns(Clacton)	30	9	6	15	49	60	33
Felixstowe T. Res.	30	8	6	16	52	72	30
Mistley United	30	4	6	20	30	64	18

DIVISION TWO	P	W	D	L	F	A	PTS
Foxash Social	26	19	4	3	86	35	61
Woods West End	26	15	2	9	80	50	47
Great Bentley	26	14	4	8	63	39	46
Bures United	26	13	7	6	56	39	46
Silver End	26	14	3	9	57	39	45
Alresford C.R. Res.	26	11	7	8	52	45	40
Cavendish	26	11	4	11	69	63	37
Mersea Island Res*	26	10	7	9	58	63	37
Gas-Recreation Res.	26	10	5	11	43	53	35
St.Johns(Clacton)Res	26	10	3	13	53	77	33
Earls Colne	26	8	6	12	47	63	30
Boxted Lodgers Res	26	8	5	13	52	60	29
Wormingford Wand.	26	4	3	19	35	84	15
Walton Town	26	4	2	20	27	68	14

* - Three points awarded.

DIVISION ONE	P	W	D	L	F	A	PTS
Mersea Island	30	23	3	4	72	36	72
Sudbury Wdrs Res.	30	20	5	5	83	37	65
Tiptree Heath	30	17	8	5	52	24	59
Stanway Rvrs Res.	30	14	6	10	51	49	48
Halstead Town Res.	30	13	4	13	58	53	43
Anchor Press	30	11	8	11	43	42	41
Cornard Utd Res.	30	10	10	10	47	42	40
Brantham Ath. Res.	30	11	6	13	45	49	39
Rowhedge	30	12	3	15	42	49	39
Weeley Athletic	30	12	3	15	69	77	39
West Bergholt Res.	30	11	4	15	57	62	37
Royal London	30	10	7	13	55	61	37
Bramston CML	30	10	7	13	50	57	37
Long Melford Res.	30	10	7	13	39	52	37
Lawford Lads	30	11	3	16	64	54	36
Little Oakley Res.	30	1	4	25	25	108	7

DIVISION THREE	P	W	D	L	F	A	PTS
Hedinghams United	26	18	4	4	82	39	58
Kelvedon Soc. Res.	26	17	5	4	71	30	56
Tiptree Heath Res.	26	17	3	6	90	38	54
Bramston CML Res	26	14	4	8	75	49	46
Anchor Press Res	26	14	3	9	71	52	45
St.Osyth	26	15	0	11	62	58	45
Rowhedge Res	26	12	4	10	57	44	40
Dedham O.B. Res	26	9	9	8	54	43	36
Sudbury(Lucas) Res.	26	10	5	11	52	52	35
Coggeshall Town	26	9	2	15	43	61	29
Severalls Ath.	26	8	2	16	36	57	26
Mistley Utd Res	26	6	6	14	46	64	24
Lawford Lads Res	26	6	5	15	35	55	23
Bures Utd Res	26	1	0	25	26	158	3

PREMIER DIVISION RESULT CHART 1992-93

HOME TEAM	1	2	3	4	5	6	7	8	9	10	11	12	13	14	15	16
Alresford Colne Rangers	*	2-2	1-3	2-1	1-1	1-0	4-1	1-2	0-0	1-2	3-0	3-0	3-1	2-2	2-0	1-1
Boxted Lodgers	0-2	*	2-0	1-0	2-1	1-1	2-3	1-0	0-2	0-2	2-2	1-0	2-0	1-3	2-3	1-2
Clacton Town Reserves	0-3	4-0	*	1-1	2-2	6-2	2-4	3-0	2-4	1-2	0-2	3-2	0-0	2-1	3-4	0-4
Dedham Old Boys	1-0	1-2	3-1	*	4-2	2-3	6-3	2-1	3-0	1-1	1-0	6-1	1-2	1-3	2-0	1-3
Felixstowe Town Reserves	1-3	0-6	1-2	0-3	*	0-4	2-3	5-1	2-7	0-4	5-1	1-0	4-2	2-2	3-4	1-2
Gas-Recreation	4-5	2-4	4-3	0-3	2-3	*	2-2	1-2	4-3	1-5	3-1	2-0	3-2	0-4	3-3	1-3
Harwich & Parkeston Res.	0-4	1-1	2-1	3-1	1-7	0-3	*	2-1	4-4	0-2	0-0	2-2	2-1	1-2	2-5	0-5
Haverhill Rovers Reserves	1-2	2-1	2-1	2-0	4-0	2-0	4-1	*	1-0	1-3	2-0	3-2	3-1	3-1	0-2	0-3
Kelvedon Social	1-4	5-0	4-3	2-2	4-1	2-2	2-4	1-2	*	1-5	2-3	2-2	2-4	2-2	1-0	1-2
Little Oakley	2-1	10-1	1-4	2-3	4-1	5-0	1-1	2-1	3-0	*	2-1	4-2	1-3	7-1	2-2	2-6
Long Melford	1-3	1-3	0-7	0-2	3-1	1-3	2-3	1-1	3-0	2-2	*	1-0	2-1	0-4	1-3	1-1
Mistley United	0-4	1-1	2-1	0-1	0-2	3-0	0-1	1-1	0-2	0-5	1-4	*	0-6	0-1	0-0	1-3
St.Johns(Clacton)	1-2	2-4	1-3	1-1	0-0	4-0	2-2	3-1	1-1	3-2	2-5	1-0	*	4-2	1-4	0-1
Stowmarket Town Reserves	0-1	1-0	4-1	0-1	1-1	7-1	2-3	2-1	1-0	0-0	2-1	1-1	5-0	*	3-1	1-0
Sudbury (Lucas) Athletic	3-5	3-2	1-1	0-3	0-3	2-3	0-2	1-0	3-3	1-3	1-2	0-5	4-0	0-5	*	0-3
West Bergholt	5-5	3-0	3-1	0-0	0-0	4-2	3-1	1-0	2-2	0-1	0-1	3-4	0-0	0-1	0-1	*

DIVISON ONE RESULT CHART 1992-93

HOME TEAM	1	2	3	4	5	6	7	8	9	10	11	12	13	14	15	16
Anchor Press	*	3-0	0-1	2-2	1-0	2-1	1-0	2-1	2-3	1-0	2-3	1-2	1-1	0-0	1-2	3-1
Bramston CML	1-2	*	1-0	0-0	3-2	2-0	3-0	0-1	3-1	0-1	3-0	2-3	1-6	0-5	6-5	3-1
Brantham Athletic Reserves	1-4	0-0	*	2-0	0-3	3-2	3-1	3-0	0-1	0-0	2-3	0-1	1-0	1-2	0-3	5-2
Cornard United Reserves	1-1	1-1	1-0	*	0-0	0-2	3-1	3-1	1-1	2-0	3-3	0-1	0-2	0-2	4-0	0-1
Halstead Town Reserves	2-3	1-1	1-3	4-0	*	2-1	6-1	4-0	0-1	0-4	1-5	3-1	0-3	2-2	3-3	2-1
Lawford Lads	0-3	1-2	1-1	2-2	0-4	*	5-0	6-0	1-3	2-0	3-2	0-1	1-2	0-1	6-2	8-1
Little Oakley Reserves	1-1	2-5	3-3	1-6	1-8	1-3	*	1-2	1-7	0-2	0-4	0-0	1-5	0-0	0-3	3-1
Long Melford Reserves	2-1	2-2	2-3	3-3	2-0	3-2	3-0	*	0-1	3-1	2-2	0-2	0-0	0-0	4-1	1-1
Mersea Island	2-0	2-1	3-3	0-3	3-0	2-0	6-1	2-1	*	3-2	1-0	6-1	3-1	1-0	2-1	4-1
Rowhedge	2-0	1-0	1-1	0-1	1-2	6-4	3-2	1-0	0-0	*	3-1	2-4	0-1	0-2	4-2	1-2
Royal London	1-1	1-4	1-3	0-2	2-4	2-2	3-0	0-2	1-4	2-3	*	0-0	3-3	2-3	2-0	3-1
Stanway Rovers Reserves	2-0	1-1	3-0	1-4	4-0	2-1	5-0	0-1	1-2	1-0	1-3	*	1-4	1-2	4-4	3-2
Sudbury Wanderers Reserves	6-2	4-2	2-1	1-1	1-0	2-1	5-0	4-1	3-2	2-1	7-0	4-1	*	0-2	5-1	2-1
Tiptree Heath	1-1	2-2	3-0	1-0	1-2	2-3	2-1	3-0	0-1	1-2	2-1	1-1	1-1	*	4-1	2-0
Weeley Athletic	2-2	2-0	2-1	6-3	4-0	0-4	5-2	4-2	2-4	4-0	1-3	4-1	3-2	0-2	*	1-2
W.Bergholt Reserves	1-0	3-1	3-0	1-3	1-2	1-2	5-1	0-0	6-1	6-1	0-0	2-2	5-4	1-3	4-1	*

DIVISION TWO RESULT CHART 1992-93

HOME TEAM	1	2	3	4	5	6	7	8	9	10	11	12	13	14
Alresford C.R. Reserves	*	3-3	1-2	0-1	3-1	1-3	1-0	1-1	3-2	1-1	1-0	5-1	2-1	3-0
Boxted Lodgers Reserves	0-2	*	0-4	4-3	0-1	0-3	1-2	0-2	2-0	6-0	3-3	2-0	4-3	2-3
Bures United	4-4	1-1	*	3-1	2-2	1-4	4-1	1-0	1-3	1-1	0-1	3-0	1-5	3-1
Cavendish	4-4	2-0	0-3	*	4-1	2-1	0-3	1-4	4-1	11-2	1-4	2-0	3-0	7-2
Earls Colne	3-2	4-1	1-2	2-2	*	3-6	1-2	3-2	4-4	4-3	3-1	3-0	1-4	2-1
Foxash Social	1-1	8-2	1-1	4-2	2-0	*	2-0	3-2	5-0	5-2	2-4	2-0	5-3	7-1
Gas Recreation Reserves	0-0	4-1	3-3	6-4	3-2	3-1	*	2-2	0-3	2-0	1-0	1-1	2-2	0-1
Great Bentley	1-0	3-2	2-0	0-3	3-0	1-1	2-0	*	5-1	3-0	4-2	5-2	3-4	3-1
Mersea Island Reserves	3-1	2-2	1-1	3-1	2-2	1-1	5-1	3-3	*	6-4	1-7W-L	0-3	5-0	
St.Johns (Clacton) Reserves	1-3	1-5	4-3	2-2	5-1	1-6	4-2	1-3	2-1	*	1-0	1-0	2-3	4-2
Silver End	2-1	1-1	0-2	5-1	3-0	0-3	1-0	2-0	4-1	0-3	*	5-2	2-1	5-2
Walton Town	3-4	1-5	0-2	1-4	1-1	0-3	2-3	2-1	2-4	0-3	2-1	*	0-3	2-0
Woods-West End	4-1	3-1	2-3	7-3	4-1	3-4	6-0	4-2	2-3	5-1	2-2	3-2	*	2-0
Wormingford Wanderers	3-4	1-4	0-5	1-1	1-1	1-3	4-2	0-6	3-3	2-4	1-2	2-3	2-1	*

DIVISION THREE RESULT CHART 1992-93

HOME TEAM	1	2	3	4	5	6	7	8	9	10	11	12	13	14
Anchor Press Reserves	*	6-2	5-1	2-0	1-1	2-3	0-5	4-3	5-1	0-2	1-2	4-1	1-2	2-1
Bramston CML Reserves	2-1	*	11-4	6-2	2-2	2-3	1-1	4-0	1-3	0-2	2-1	1-1	2-1	5-0
Bures United Reserves	1-7	0-4	*	1-5	3-7	2-7	0-2	0-4	0-7	1-9	0-15	1-2	1-4	1-7
Coggeshall Town	2-5	2-4	0-1	*	3-2	0-4	2-4	1-1	0-5	1-3	0-1	3-0	5-1	0-3
Dedham Old Boys Reserves	2-2	1-1	8-1	0-5	*	0-0	3-3	1-2	1-1	3-0	3-2	1-3	1-1	0-2
Hedingtons United	3-4	5-1	11-0	3-2	2-1	*	1-0	6-2	3-3	6-2	3-2	1-0	1-1	1-2
Kelvedon Social Reserves	2-0	3-2	2-1	2-0	3-2	2-2	*	6-1	6-1	5-1	7-0	3-2	3-1	2-3
Lawford Lads Reserves	0-2	0-2	8-0	2-3	0-0	0-3	0-2	*	2-1	1-1	2-4	0-1	1-0	1-2
Mistley United Reserves	2-4	0-1	4-1	0-2	1-3	2-3	1-1	0-0	*	1-1	0-3	3-1	2-5	1-3
Rowhedge Reserves	4-0	0-3	8-1	1-2	2-3	2-0	1-0	4-0	1-1	*	4-1	1-2	2-1	2-2
St.Osyth	2-5	5-4	3-1	1-0	2-1	1-2	3-1	2-1	2-5	2-1	*	2-0	3-1	1-1
Severalls Athletic	4-2	1-6	7-3	1-2	0-3	2-4	0-2	1-2	1-0	1-3	0-1	*	4-2	0-3
Sudbury (Lucas) Athletic Reserves	3-3	0-3	5-0	1-1	1-4	2-1	1-3	1-1	6-0	2-0	2-0	3-0	*	4-3
Tiptree Heath Reserves	1-3	5-3	6-1	7-0	0-1	2-4	1-1	4-1	8-1	5-0	8-1	1-1	7-1	*

ESSEX & SUFFOLK BORDER PREMIER DIVISION 1993-94

ALRESFORD COLNE RANGERS
Secretary: R Wood, 33 Broomfield Crescent, Wivenhoe, Colchester (0206 822983).
Ground: Ford Lane, Alresford, Colchester.
Colours: Red & black quarters/black/black & red   **Change Colours:** Yellow/black/black.

BOXTED LODGERS
Secretary: G R Scott, 6 Home Dale Cottages, Boxted CO4 5SJ (0206 272596).
Ground: Boxted Sports & Social Club, Cage Lane, Boxted, nr Colchester (0206 271969).
Colours: White (Royal trim)/Royal/white   **Change Colours:** Royal or yellow/navy or royal/royal or white

CLACTON TOWN RESERVES *(see page 634)*

DEDHAM OLD BOYS
Secretary: H G Martin, 16 Southfield Close, Colchester, Essex CO4 4QH (0206 842531).
Ground: Old Grammar School, Recreation Ground, Dedham, Essex.
Colours: Red & white stripes/black/black   **Change Colours:** Blue & white stripes/blue/black.

FELIXSTOWE TOWN RESERVES *(see page 627)*

GAS RECREATION
Secretary: G McKillop, 'Four Seasons', Mumford Close, West Bergholt, Colchester CO6 3HY (0206 241501).
Ground: British Gas Sports Club, Bromley Road, Colchester, Essex (0206 860383).
Colours: Red & black stripes/black/black   **Change Colours:** All blue.

HARWICH & PARKESTON RESERVES, HAVERHILL ROVERS RESERVES *(see page 628)*

KELVEDON SOCIAL
Secretary: G Riseley (0376 520635).   **Ground:** The Playing Field, The Chase, High Street (0376 572240).

LITTLE OAKLEY
Secretary: D Chopping, 1 Laurel Avenue, Dovercourt, Essex CO12 4HP (0255 553025).
Ground: Little Oakley Club, Memorial Ground, Little Oakley (0255 880370).
Colours: Blue/navy/blue   **Change Colours:** Red/black/black & white

LONG MELFORD
Secretary: G Berry (0787 77761).
Ground: 'Stonylands', New Road, Long Melford, Suffolk (0787 312187).
Colours: white & black stripes/white/black & white   **Change Colours:** Red/black/black & white.

ST JOHN'S (CLACTON)
Secretary: C Garrod, 20 Gilders Way, Clacton-on-Sea, Essex CO16 8UU (0255 434621).
Ground: Eastcliff Sports Ground, Dulwich Road, Holland-on-Sea (0255 814874)
Colours: Red/black/black   **Change Colours:** Green & white hoops/green/black.

STOWMARKET TOWN RESERVES *(see page 631)*

SUDBURY (LUCAS) ATHLETIC
Secretary: R Sievey (0787 311859)   **Ground:** Lucas Spts Club, Alexandra Rd, Sudbury (0787 881143).

SUDBURY WANDERERS RESERVES *(see page 632)*

WEST BERGHOLT
Secretary: P Thompson, 54 Erle Way, West Bergholt CO6 3LH (0206 241227).
Ground: Rear of Orpen Hall, Lexden Road, West Bergholt (0206 240180).
Colours: Sky blue/navy/navy   **Change Colours:** Red/black/red.

Lower Division Constitutions for 1992-93:

Division 1:
Anchor Press, Bramston CML, Brantham Athletic Reserves, Cornard United Reserves, Foxash Social, Halstead Town Reserves, Long Melford Reserves, Mersea Island, Mistley United, Rowhedge, Royal London (Colchester), Stanway Rovers Reserves, Tiptree Heath, Weeley Athletic, West Bergholt Reserves, West End United.

Division 2:
Alresford C.R. Reserves, Boxted Lodgers Reserves, Bures United, Cavendish, Earls Colne, Gas Recreation Reserves, Great Bentley, Hedinghams United, Kelvedon Social Reserves, Lawford Lads, Little Oakley Reserves, Mersea Island Reserves, St Johns (Clacton) Reserves, Silver End United, Tiptree Hth Reserves

Division 3:
Anchor Press Reserves, Bradfield Rovers, Bramston CML Reserves, Coggeshall Town, Dedham Old Boys Reserves, Finchingfield Rovers, Hadleigh United Reserves, Lawford Lads Reserves, Mistley United Reserves, Rowhedge Reserves, St Osyth, Severalls Athletic, Walton Town, Wormingford.

West Bergholt F.C. 1992-93. Back Row (L/R): R Storey (Manager), I Booth, N Diplock, N Bloomfield, J Chapman (Captain), C Howitt, D Simmonds. Front: S McKiliop, M Clark, G Bethall, P Nuttall, J Lumb, R Woodall. Photo - Martin Wray.

Alresford Colne Rangers F.C. 1992-93. Back Row (L/R): Gene Evers, Paul Bennett, Tony Green, Peter Cook, Michael Caulderbank, Andy Corton, Adam Deveaux. Front: Dale Chaplin, Wayne Parsons, Jason Beer, Keith Shepherd, Matt Bennett, Brian Dunn. Photo - Richard Brock.

BRITISH SUGAR
SUFFOLK & IPSWICH LEAGUE

Patron: W C A Snook
President: G Harper.
Chairman: P M Cocker.
Vice Chairman: G Whight.
Hon. Secretary: Alan Gorham,
179 Cauldwell Hall Road, Ipswich, Suffolk IP4 5DA (0473 723685).

With the League's administrators beginning to turn their attention to Friday 15th September 1993 which will be the launch of the League's centenary year, the Senior Division completed what was perhaps its most interesting season in the near one hundred year history.

Whitton United, having seemed to be locked in battle all season with Haughley United, suffered a 0-1 defeat at Westerfield on 13th March and almost unnoticed Stutton, for the first time in their history, topped the Senior Division and started the most exciting six weeks of football that anyone can remember.

On the penultimate Saturday of the season Whitton, having put together five successive wins since the Westerfield defeat, travelled to Stutton and continued their winning run with a single goal success thus ensuring that both sides needed a victory in their last matches to lift the championship. On the vital day Stutton were the visitors at Old Newton and had to make do with a point. With the local B.B.C. Radio giving the scores from both matches, Whitton were visiting early season rivals Haughley United and clinched the silverware with a fine 5-0 victory. With their second string picking up the Intermediate 'A' title, Whitton finished the season as 'Senior Club of the Year'.

The League's major knock-out cup, which is played for by both Senior and Junior clubs in a competition run on an F.A. Cup formula, was won by Grundisburgh. This was their third win in five years meeting this term first-time finalists Melton St Audrys who were at the wrong end of a 0-4 defeat. A major interest in the competition was a record number of wins by Junior clubs over Senior clubs. Saxmundham Sports, second in Division One and thus heading for next season's Senior Division, had two of these successes, firstly defeating Walsham-le-Willows and then knocking out holders Framlingham Town by 4-2. The other three victories were all recorded by Newbury United. 'Junior Club of the Year', Newbury were Division Two champions, won the Suffolk County Junior Cup and also the League's McNeil Giant Killer awards for the following results; they began with an outstanding 10-2 success over Willis Corroon and continued with wins over Needham Market and Senior Division champions Whitton United, before losing to a fourth Senior club, Melton St Audrys, in the Semis, but only by 5-2 after they had had their goalkeeper sent off in the latter stages of the first half.

After eleven seasons with the Tolly Cobbold and Pubmaster organisations, the League will start the new season with a new sponsor at the masthead. The eleven year period has been one of good ideas, much excitement and continuing improvement in the League's administration. It was of course during this period that the League became one of the first competitions to computerise. So as we welcome a new sponsor, we also replace the computer. The software is being completely updated and it is with these signs of forward thinking that we are joining British Sugar Plc planning together to reach our centenary. **Alan Gorham, Hon. Secretary.**

Senior Division	P	W	D	L	F	A	PTS
Whitton United	30	21	6	3	75	26	48
Stutton	30	21	4	5	72	27	46
Grundisburgh	30	17	10	3	68	36	44
Westerfield	30	17	7	6	61	37	41
Haughley United	30	17	7	6	65	43	41
B. Sugar F. Ath.	30	17	2	11	59	46	36
Halesworth Town	30	13	4	14	50	45	30
Framlingham Town	30	11	6	13	39	44	28
Melton St Audrys	30	11	4	15	44	52	26
B.T. Research	30	11	4	15	46	63	26
Needham Market	30	9	6	15	58	60	24
Old Newton United	30	9	6	15	35	46	24
Stonham Aspal	30	7	7	16	44	53	21
Walsham-le-Willows	30	9	2	19	27	67	20
Willis Corroon	30	5	5	20	35	83	15
R.S.S.C. Ransomes	30	4	2	24	42	92	10

Division One	P	W	D	L	F	A	PTS
Achilles	26	19	4	3	79	19	42
Saxmundham Town	26	17	4	5	56	25	38
Stanton	26	14	7	5	74	39	35
Crane Sports	26	12	7	7	48	34	31
Wenhaston	26	12	6	8	55	42	30
Ipswich Athletic	26	11	8	7	41	31	30
Fisons	26	10	6	10	38	37	26
Coplestonians	26	9	6	11	42	42	24
Elmsett	26	7	10	9	40	61	24
Walton United	26	6	7	13	34	50	19
Bramford Utd	26	7	5	14	33	58	19
Leiston	26	6	5	15	33	60	17
Elmswell	26	5	5	16	35	67	15
Ipswich Exiles	26	5	4	17	21	64	14

SENIOR DIVISION RESULTS 1992/93

HOME TEAM	1	2	3	4	5	6	7	8	9	10	11	12	13	14	15	16
1. B.T. Research	*	1-5	0-2	1-4	0-1	0-3	0-4	1-7	2-2	3-2	5-4	0-2	4-0	3-5	3-4	1-1
2. B.S. Fonnereau	3-1	*	2-0	1-4	3-2	1-1	6-1	1-1	1-2	3-2	2-1	1-2	3-0	0-1	0-3	2-0
3. Framlingham Town	1-0	4-1	*	0-2	1-0	0-2	3-1	4-2	1-0	4-0	1-1	0-4	1-3	0-0	1-2	2-5
4. Grundisburgh	3-2	1-2	0-0	*	1-1	3-2	2-2	2-1	2-2	1-0	4-2	0-3	1-0	4-4	0-0	6-0
5. Halesworth Town	0-2	1-2	3-2	2-3	*	2-5	2-1	2-1	1-0	6-2	5-2	0-1	1-0	1-2	1-3	0-0
6. Haughley United	0-1	2-0	1-1	2-2	1-1	*	1-1	5-0	2-3	4-1	2-1	0-3	2-0	3-2	0-5	2-0
7. Melton St Audrys	0-2	1-4	4-1	2-2	1-0	3-0	*	1-2	1-0	3-1	2-0	2-2	0-1	0-3	1-3	3-4
8. Needham Market	2-1	0-2	0-1	3-2	2-2	3-3	0-1	*	2-0	0-1	3-1	0-4	0-3	1-2	3-3	1-1
9. Old Newton Utd	1-2	2-0	0-1	0-3	0-4	1-3	3-0	2-1	*	2-2	0-1	1-1	2-0	1-2	1-3	2-0
10. R.S.S.C. Ransomes	0-3	2-3	0-4	2-3	1-4	1-2	3-2	2-6	0-2	*	1-3	3-5	4-1	1-2	0-2	5-2
11. Stonham Aspal	1-1	1-2	0-0	1-2	2-0	1-2	1-0	1-1	0-0	4-2	*	1-3	5-0	0-0	0-2	2-2
12. Stutton	0-2	2-0	4-1	0-3	1-2	1-2	3-0	4-2	3-1	3-1	3-2	*	7-0	1-1	0-1	2-0
13. Walsham-le-Will.	0-1	2-1	0-0	0-4	0-1	3-4	2-1	1-6	1-1	4-2	0-4		*	1-0	1-4	1-0
14. Westerfield Utd	4-1	3-4	3-1	0-0	3-0	1-1	0-1	6-3	3-1	3-1	2-0	1-2	3-0	*	1-0	3-1
15. Whitton United	1-1	2-1	1-0	1-1	3-1	1-2	1-2	1-0	3-1	1-1	4-2	0-0	4-0	4-0	*	4-1
16. Willis Corroon	1-2	1-3	3-2	0-3	0-4	1-6	0-3	0-5	1-2	7-1	0-3	0-2	2-1	1-1	1-9	*

Grundisburgh forward Dale Vince (left) gets past a desperate lunge by a Haughley defender in his side's 3-2 home win on 5th December. Photo - Martin Wray.

Needham Market F.C. 1992-93. Back Row (L/R): A Sparkes (Asst Mgr), P Dennison, J Wilcox, K Jameson, A Manning, T Hewitt, N Francis (Manager), S Mortimer, I Crick (Asst Manager). Front: P Tingley, G Hurren, A Grogan, M Grogan, P Hatcher. Photo - Martin Wray.

Framlingham Town 1992-93. Back Row (L/R): G Sharman, P Sharman, D Hessey, R Grobbett, D Woodlands, A Llewellyn (Manager). Front: T Hearing, G French, M Holdiss, K Read, R Mayhew, B Tysoe. Photo - Martin Wray.

SUFFOLK & IPSWICH LEAGUE SENIOR DIVISION 1993-94

ACHILLES
Secretary: Leonard Goddard, 8 Fishbane Close, Ipswich, Suffolk IP3 0SE (0473 726517).
Ground: Pauls S.C., Stonelodge Lane, Ipswich, Suffolk.
Colours: Red/black.   **Change Colours:** Yellow/red/black.

BRITISH SUGAR FONNEREAU ATHLETIC
Secretary: Nigel Spurling, 16 Thanet Rd, Ipswich, Suffolk IP4 5LB (0473 716018).
Ground: British Sugar Plc, Sproughton Road, Ipswich, Suffolk.
Colours: All royal blue   **Change Colours:** All white.
Previous Names: Silent Youth/ Fonnereau Ath./ YMCA Fonnereau Ath.

B.T. RESEARCH
Secretary: Richard Field, 26 Harvesters Way, Martlesham Heath, Ipswich, Suffolk IP5 7UP (0473 610663).
Ground: The Hollies, Straight Road, Bucklesham.
Colours: Yellow/blue/blue   **Change Colours:** All red.
Previous Names: British Telecom   **Programme Editor:** Julian Catt (0473 252239).

FRAMLINGHAM TOWN
Secretary: Mrs Fiona Whatling, 46 College Rd, Framlingham, Woodbridge IP13 9ES (0728 723524).
Ground: Sports Field, Badlingham Road, Framlingham, Woodbridge, Suffolk.
Colours: Green & white/white/white   **Change Colours:** Maroon & blue/blue/blue.

GRUNDISBURGH
Secretary: Malcolm Harris, 70 Post Mill Gardens, Grundisburgh, Woodbridge IP13 6UP (0473 35422).
Ground: The Playing Field, Grundisburgh, Woodbridge.
Colours: All rblue   **Change Colours:** Red/red/black.

HALESWORTH TOWN
Secretary: John Stannard, 87 Bedlingfield Cres., Halesworth IP19 8ED (0986 873529).
Ground: Playing Fields, Dairy Hill, Bungay Road, Halesworth.
Colours: White/navy/red   **Change Colours:** Maroon & royal/royal/royal.

HAUGHLEY UNITED
Secretary: Paddy Durren, 15 Bixly Ave., Haughley, Stowmarket, Suffolk IP14 3PE (0449 673768).
Ground: British Sugar Plc, Sproughton Road, Ipswich, Suffolk.
Colours: All white   **Change Colours:** Red/white/red.

MELTON ST AUDRYS
Secretary: Paul Drake, 23 Clifford Rd, Ipswich, Suffolk IP4 1PJ (0473 213604).
Ground: St Audrys Hospital Sports Field, Melton, Nr Woodbridge, Suffolk.
Colours: Red/black/black   **Change Colours:** Grey & white stripes/black/black.
Programme Editor: Michael Milbourne (Woodbridge 380146).

NEEDHAM MARKET
Secretary: Ian Croft, 30 Masefield Rd, Stowmarket, Suffolk IP14 1TH (0449 676517).
Ground: Barretts Lane, Needham Market, Suffolk.   **Programme Editor:** Alan Parson (0449 720468).
Colours: Red/red/black   **Change Colours:** Green/green/grey.

OLD NEWTON UNITED
Secretary: John Thorndyke, 13 Winchester Close, Stowmarket, Suffolk IP14 1SH (0449 675653).
Ground: Playing Field, Church Road, Old Newton.
Colours: Amber/amber/blue   **Change Colours:** All blue.
Programme Editor: Rob Atherton (0449 673105).

SAXMUNDHAM TOWN
Secretary: Mrs Eileen Pearse, 118 Saxton Rd, Saxmundham, Suffolk IP17 1EF (0728 602490).
Ground: Carlton Park, Saxmundham   **Colours:** Gold/black   **Change Colours:** All red.

STONHAM ASPAL
Secretary: Eric Cousins, 2 Holly Green, Mickfield, Stowmarket, Suffolk IP14 5LH (0449 711884).
Ground: Delsons Meadow, Three Crossways, Stonham Aspal.
Colours: Blue/blue/white   **Change Colours:** All yellow.

STUTTON
Secretary: Michael Coombs, 4 Crowcroft Glebe, Nedging Tye, Ipswich, Suffolk IP7 7LH (0449 741200).
Ground: Hall Park, Stutton.   **Programme Editor:** Ivan Ransby (0473 47645).
Colours: White/black/black   **Change Colours:** Gold/black/black.

WALSHAM-LE-WILLOWS
Secretary: Vincent Butcher, Shirvin, Willow Close, Badwell Ash IP31 3DT (0359 259720).
Ground: Walsham Sports Club, Sumner Road, Walsham-le-Willows.   **Programme Editor:** Julie Smith.
Colours: Blue/blue/navy   **Change Colours:** White/navy/blue.

WESTERFIELD UNITED
Secretary: Mrs Jan Mitchell, 12 Fairfield Rd, Ipswich, Suffolk IP3 0LD (0473 714692).
Ground: S.E.H. Sports Centre, Humber Doucy Lane, Rushmere.
Colours: All blue   **Change Colours:** Red & black stripes/black/red.

WHITTON UNITED
Secretary: David Gould, 7 Karen Close, Ipswich, Suffolk IP1 4LP (0473 253838).
Ground: King Geore V Playing Field, Norwich Road, Ipswich, Suffolk.
Colours: Green & white hoops/white/green **Change Colours:** Blue/white/green.
Previous Name: Whitton FC   **Programme Editor:** Ian Vernau (0473 680592).

DIVISION ONE 93-94: Bramford Utd, Coplestonians, Crane Spts, Elmsett Spts, Ipswich Ath., Leiston, Newbury Utd, Nicholians Loco., Ransomes, Rushmere Ath., Stanton, Walton Utd, Wenhaston Utd, Willis Corroon.

Grundisburgh with the Mick McNeil Cup after beating Melton St Audrys at Willis Coroon. Photo - Martin Wray.

Westerfield United F.C. 1992-93. Back Row (L/R): A Burrows (Manager), D Smith, M Keinzley, A Smye, P Deacon, G Osborne, S Smith, D Burrows. Front: D Dedswell, P Keinzley, R Osborne, C King, S Jay, D Gordon, D Godfrey. Photo - Martin Wray.

Walsham-le-Willows 1992-93. Back Row (L/R): D Bailey, C Whiting, C Arnold, K Abrahams, C Soares (Manager), D Foster, S Gooch, N Smith. Front: C Wilson, A Goddard, M Jackson, T Bowling, M Howlett. Photo - Martin Wray.

'MOTORSPARES' BURY ST EDMUNDS & DIST. LGE

DIV. ONE	P	W	D	L	F	A	PTS
St Edmunds '65	18	14	1	3	61	15	29
Lakenheath Res.	18	13	2	3	72	34	28
Cockfield Utd	18	12	2	4	68	31	26
Bury Town 'A'	18	10	2	6	57	32	22
Thurston	18	9	3	6	63	44	21
Sporting '87	18	10	1	7	52	40	21
Pot Black Utd	18	5	2	11	39	78	12
Thomas Ridley	18	4	3	11	29	51	11
Hundon	18	4	2	12	30	62	10
Beck Row	18	0	0	18	12	89	0

DIV. TWO	P	W	D	L	F	A	PTS
Wanderers S.C.	26	21	3	2	125	35	45
Newbury Utd Res.	26	20	1	5	81	31	41
Hepworth	26	17	4	5	74	42	38
Old Burians	26	15	3	8	64	38	33
Eastgate Ath.	26	13	3	10	70	68	29
Next Installs	26	12	4	10	59	53	28
T.K. Landscapes	26	12	3	11	76	59	27
Priors Inn	26	7	7	12	43	69	21
Lakenheath 'A'	26	7	6	13	44	60	20
Eastbury	26	7	6	13	40	61	20
Barons	26	9	1	16	51	74	19
Brandon Town Res.	26	5	5	16	37	60	15
Cockfield U. Res.	26	5	5	16	47	81	15
Tostock '85	26	6	1	19	33	114	13

DIV. THREE	P	W	D	L	F	A	PTS
Wickhambrook	26	26	0	0	137	21	52
Ixworth	26	20	1	5	109	43	41
Silver Spoon	26	19	1	6	97	43	39
Advanced Air	26	18	3	5	96	55	39
Barrow	26	17	2	7	94	48	36
Helmsman	26	14	2	10	85	70	30
Cadogan Arms	26	10	1	15	48	62	21
Sporting '87 Res.	26	7	7	12	47	70	21
Royal Mail	26	7	4	15	64	79	18
Rangers	26	7	4	15	53	87	18
Lucky Break	26	6	4	16	40	95	16
Beck Row Res.	26	5	5	16	42	94	15
Form St Martin	26	5	3	18	42	83	13
Hundon Res.	26	2	2	22	31	135	6

First-half action from the Bury League fixture in May between the top two, Lakenheath Reserves and St Edmunds '65. The former recorded a 3-0 home win, but the latter took the title. Photo - Martin Wray.

'TREADFIRST' HALSTEAD LEAGUE

PREMIER DIV.	P	W	D	L	F	A	PTS
Ashdon United	18	16	0	2	67	19	32
H.M.P.	18	10	4	4	53	25	24
Finchingfield Rvrs	18	9	5	4	55	32	23
Red Lion	18	9	3	6	46	26	21
Drum	18	9	1	8	64	37	19
Glemsford	18	6	1	11	34	48	13
Kedington	18	6	1	11	24	48	13
Halstead Colts	18	5	2	11	21	46	12
Withersfield	18	5	2	11	33	71	12
Clare	18	4	3	11	25	70	11

DIV. ONE	P	W	D	L	F	A	PTS
Gosfield	20	17	1	2	87	31	35
Hedingham Res.	20	14	3	3	78	33	31
Ashdon Utd Res.	20	12	3	5	61	27	27
Sudbury Luc. A. 'A'	20	11	3	6	66	43	25
Border Athletic	20	8	7	5	51	34	25
Cavendish Res.	20	9	4	7	43	38	22
Hempstead Utd	20	8	2	10	61	62	18
H.M.P. Res.	20	3	5	12	35	50	11
Yeldham	20	4	2	14	30	73	10
Belchamps Utd	20	2	3	15	18	66	8
Toppesfield Utd	20	3	2	15	23	96	8

DIV. TWO	P	W	D	L	F	A	PTS
Finchingfield Res.	22	17	4	1	71	21	38
Leighs	22	14	5	3	79	30	33
Pebmarsh	22	13	3	6	55	25	29
H/Bumpstead	22	12	3	7	64	48	27
Glemsford Res.	22	12	3	7	41	34	27
Bardfield	22	12	2	8	69	45	26
Halstead S.C.	22	11	3	8	74	60	25
Kedington Res.	22	7	6	9	39	49	20
Five Bells	22	6	2	14	42	65	14
Gosfield Res.	22	3	3	16	29	84	9
Clare Res.	22	3	2	17	33	85	8
Border Ath. Res.	22	2	2	18	21	71	6

HEREWARD SPORTS
UNITED COUNTIES LEAGUE

Chairman: T N Bates
Hon. Secretary: R J Gamble, 8 Bostock Avenue, Northampton

TREBLE CHANGE FOR ROTHWELL

The 1992-93 season was dominated by Rothwell Town, who after a number of seasons during which they were strong title contenders but never carried off the crown, finally came good in spectacular fashion by making a clean sweep of the domestic prizes.

The Bones ended their 93 year quest for the major honour, the league championship, with a 1-0 win at Stotfold in their penultimate match. That ended a battle royal between Rothwell and 1992 kings Northampton Spencer, who put up a spirited defence of their title, in deed at the end of February they looked likely winners again, but they were unable to match Rothwell's consistency during the run in. Raunds had to settle for third place, with a heavy late season programme of fixtures taking its toll on the Shopmates, who were unable to play on their Kiln Park ground for three months during the winter, due to drainage problems. Potton and Cogenhoe had topped the division during the season but although they were the most potent attacking sides they couldn't keep their challenges going right to the end.

At the other end of the table, Brackley finished bottom for the second season running, going through their 42 match programme without a win and conceding a record 210 goals. Despite this nightmare campaign the Churchill Way club remain in the top flight for 1993-94. Two long established senior clubs, Wellingborough and Desborough, also had seasons they would rather forget.

In Division One, Ford Sports' goal-hungry side lifted the crown, their first honours as league members. The Motormen stayed the course better than Higham who were the only side in the league to go through the season unbeaten at home. These two dominated the division although Peterborough City had made a flying start back in the lower grade only to fall apart after losing manager Jan Czarnecki to Ramsey in October. City folded at the end of the season while also bowing out of the league are basement side Towcester who managed just one win in their 34 games and they, like Brackley, conceded over two hundred goals! Towcester will play in the Central Northants Combination next term.

The knockout cup was notable for Higham's giant killing exploits - they beat three Premier sides, Wellingborough, Long Buckby and Kempston en route to the semi-finals where they were beaten by Rothwell, who went on to win the trophy for a second season running - Rothwell had been the last club to retain the cup back in 1972! Daventry were Rothwell's opponents in the final, and like Stotfold a year earlier they found that an away draw at Cecil Street wasn't enough, Rothwell's 3-1 second leg triumph at Elderstubbs gave them a 5-3 aggregate victory.

The treble was completed by Rothwell's Benevolent Cup success. The Bones beat Ford Sports 4-2 to lift this trophy for the first time, Fords having earlier surprised holders Northampton Spencer at Kingsthorpe Mill in the semi-final.

Rothwell also carried the league banner with distinction in the FA Vase, reaching the 5th Round before losing 2-1 to eventual winners Bridlington, a last minute goal proving decisive in extra time. The Bones had earlier ousted some impressive sides including Armitage, Wisbech and Knowsley,

Rothwell Town - Hereward Sports United Counties League Champions 1992-93. Photo: Eric Marsh.

potential winners all. Bourne also had a fine Vase run before bowing out at Peacehaven in a 3rd Round replay. In the FA Cup Raunds were our most successful representatives. They reached the 3rd Round Qualifying and on the way they won 2-0 at Northwich, the first ever win by one of our clubs against Conference opposition in the competition.

On the county cup front, Eynesbury made it three successive victories in the Huntingdonshire Senior Cup, beating Warboys 4-2 in the final, while Mirrlees Blackstone collected their first major honour in the Lincs Senior Cup 'A', surprising Bourne 2-1 in the final. Kempston reached their second successive Bedfordshire Senior Cup final, losing 5-4 on penalties to Leighton after two goals had been shared, while Olney collected their first ever county honour, the Berks & Bucks Intermediate Cup, won with a 2-0 final defeat of Faringdon. Completing the county successes, the Raunds second string retained the Northants Junior Cup with a 4-3 win over Perkins Sports.

The league will have one new club in membership for 1993-94, Vanaid having been promoted from the Northampton Town League, the first club to porgress from the junior pyramid.

Jeremy Biggs (Press Liaison Officer)

Bourne's Mark Schiavi nets his side's second goal at Stamford - Robbie Cooke looks on and Shaun Greetham is the unfortunate keeper! Photo: Gavin Ellis-Neville.

Olney forward Andy Kerchington and Sharnbrook defender Bolton chase the ball. Olney won 3-1. Photo: Martin Wray.

PREM. DIVISION	P	W	D	L	F	A	PTS
Rothwell Town	42	30	8	4	97	28	98
Northampton S.	42	29	6	7	96	37	93
Raunds Town	42	28	6	8	93	41	90
Potton United	42	26	7	10	107	56	85
Daventry Town	42	24	7	11	91	60	79
Cogenhoe United	42	23	9	10	101	56	78
Stewart & L.	42	24	6	12	97	62	78
Bourne Town	42	22	6	14	94	59	72
Eynesbury R.	42	22	6	14	92	71	72
Long Buckby	42	19	6	17	91	65	63
Boston	42	17	7	18	80	74	58
Stamford	42	18	3	21	81	76	57
Spalding United	42	17	4	21	66	70	55
Newport Pagnell T.	42	15	9	18	65	79	54
Kempston R.	42	14	11	17	60	60	53
Mirrlees Blackst.	42	14	8	20	69	82	50
Stotfold	42	15	3	24	90	82	48
Wootton Blue C.	42	11	10	21	51	76	43
Holbeach Utd	42	12	3	27	59	91	39
Desborough T.	42	5	10	27	61	127	25
Wellingborough T.	42	4	8	30	44	143	20
Brackley Town	42	0	3	39	20	210	3

Premier/Div 1 Fairplay Award: Olney Town
Reserve Divs Fairplay Award: Newport Pagnell

DIVISION ONE	P	W	D	L	F	A	PTS
Ford Sports	34	27	3	4	134	48	84
Higham Town	34	22	9	3	97	28	75
Bugbrooke St M.	34	21	4	9	78	43	67
Ramsey Town	34	18	10	6	76	49	64
Whitworths	34	14	8	12	68	49	50
Burton Park Wdrs	34	13	11	10	60	52	50
St Ives Town	34	13	9	12	72	52	48
Cottingham	34	13	9	12	70	64	48
Olney Town	34	12	11	11	61	38	47
Thrapston Vent.	34	12	9	13	61	70	45
Peterborough City	34	13	5	16	70	78	44
Harrowby Utd	34	11	10	13	57	60	43
O.N. Chenecks	34	10	11	13	69	61	41
Blisworth	34	11	7	16	51	67	40
Sharnbrook	34	11	6	17	64	74	39
British Timken	34	9	9	16	68	100	36
Irchester Utd	34	6	6	22	58	95	24
Towcester Town	34	1	1	32	18	204	4

Reserve Div 1 champions: Rushen & Diamonds
Reserve Div 1 runners-up: Rothwell Town
Reserve Div 2 champions: Burton Park Wdrs
Reserve Div 2 runners-up: Newport Pagnell
Reserve K.O. Cup winners: Rushden & Diamonds
Reserve K.O. Cup runners-up: Eynesbury Rvrs

HEREWARD SPORTS UNITED COUNTIES LEAGUE RESULT CHART 1992-93

HOME TEAM	1	2	3	4	5	6	7	8	9	10	11	12	13	14	15	16	17	18	19	20	21	22
1. Boston	*	1-5	9-0	1-1	2-0	0-1	1-5	2-2	1-0	2-1	1-0	1-1	0-5	2-2	1-2	0-1	4-1	2-3	0-1	2-1	4-0	1-1
2. Bourne	1-1	*	14-0	0-1	2-2	4-0	5-2	1-0	2-1	2-0	3-0	4-1	2-1	0-1	0-1	1-2	1-0	2-1	1-2	3-2	1-0	3-0
3. Brackley	0-4	1-7	*	0-5	1-4	1-1	0-4	0-6	0-3	0-12	1-1	0-2	1-5	0-2	2-11	0-1	1-2	1-5	0-5	0-3	1-3	1-2
4. Cogenhoe	6-1	0-0	5-0	*	2-5	9-1	3-1	3-2	1-1	2-1	4-1	0-1	3-1	0-1	1-1	0-0	2-1	3-0	0-2	1-3	5-3	0-2
5. Daventry	1-2	2-6	5-0	3-1	*	6-0	0-1	1-0	1-1	1-1	2-0	1-1	2-0	2-2	3-1	0-1	1-0	1-0	1-0	8-0	1-1	
6. Desborough	1-4	0-1	6-0	3-3	1-2	*	0-5	1-3	2-2	1-2	2-2	0-4	1-2	0-3	1-3	0-2	4-1	1-3	1-4	0-4	2-2	2-2
7. Eynesbury	0-4	4-1	5-1	1-2	1-2	5-1	*	2-1	1-1	2-1	0-0	3-3	2-0	1-2	3-2	0-4	3-2	2-1	3-2	1-6	5-1	1-1
8. Holbeach	3-2	2-1	8-0	0-1	2-3	3-5	0-5	*	1-3	2-2	2-0	1-3	1-3	0-3	0-2	0-2	1-3	2-1	3-4	0-3	2-3	1-1
9. Kempston	0-1	1-1	4-0	1-3	4-3	4-0	0-1		*	0-0	4-5	1-0	0-0	0-3	0-1	1-1	0-0	1-0	1-0	3-2	5-0	1-1
10. Long Buckby	1-0	5-0	4-1	3-1	0-1	2-3	6-1	1-2	1-0	*	2-1	10-1	0-2	2-2	1-3	0-0	2-1	1-3	0-1	3-1	2-3	1-1
11. Mirrlees B.	1-4	1-1	4-1	1-4	1-4	5-1	0-2	3-1	2-0	3-1	*	2-2	0-3	2-2	0-3	1-3	1-3	0-3	5-1	2-0	4-1	2-0
12. Newport P.	0-3	0-3	0-1	1-5	1-2	3-3	2-4	3-1	1-2	2-1	4-3	*	1-1	2-2	0-1	0-2	2-1	0-3	4-0	1-1	3-1	3-0
13. N'pton Sp.	1-0	3-2	3-0	1-1	3-1	2-1	1-0	5-0	1-2	4-2	2-1	5-0	*	2-0	1-0	0-0	2-2	3-1	0-2	3-1	3-0	4-0
14. Potton	2-2	3-2	9-0	0-1	6-3	3-2	2-0	2-0	5-3	1-2	2-3	3-1	2-4	*	1-1	0-1	5-1	3-1	3-0	4-3	4-0	1-0
15. Raunds	4-0	2-1	4-1	0-0	1-2	4-3	1-1	0-1	2-0	1-2	1-0	2-0	2-2	0-3	*	2-1	1-0	3-0	2-2	5-0	2-0	3-0
16. Rothwell	4-0	3-1	7-0	0-3	4-2	8-0	1-1	4-0	2-1	4-1	0-0	2-1	1-2	3-0	3-5	*	5-0	4-1	1-0	3-1	2-0	1-0
17. Spalding	2-0	0-3	4-0	2-0	4-2	4-1	3-1	4-2	1-2	0-1	2-0	1-0	0-2	1-2	1-2	1-2	*	3-1	0-2	1-3	3-0	3-2
18. Stamford	2-1	1-2	4-1	1-4	3-0	2-2	1-4	4-0	5-3	2-3	0-3	1-2	1-0	4-2	2-3	1-1	2-0	*	1-2	2-1	1-0	2-1
19. Stewart & L.	3-2	2-2	14-2	3-2	2-2	2-0	1-0	3-0	0-0	2-1	5-0	2-1	0-1	3-2	1-2	1-1	2-4	4-4	*	3-6	6-0	2-1
20. Stotfold	4-2	3-0	4-0	2-2	2-4	3-3	0-3	1-2	3-0	1-3	3-4	1-2	1-3	1-3	0-3	0-1	1-2	3-2	0-1	*	6-0	1-2
21. Wellingboro'	3-7	2-5	2-2	3-6	1-2	1-1	2-4	1-0	0-3	3-4	2-2	0-0	0-6	1-4	0-1	1-7	0-0	1-6	0-4	1-7	*	1-1
22. Wootton BC	2-3	3-0	4-0	2-5	2-1	2-0	1-1	0-1	2-0	2-3	0-3	2-0	1-4	0-5	0-4	0-2	2-2	1-0	3-1	1-2	2-2	*

HEREWARD SPORTS UNITED COUNTIES LEAGUE DIVISION ONE RESULT CHART 1992-93

HOME TEAM	1	2	3	4	5	6	7	8	9	10	11	12	13	14	15	16	17	18
1. Blisworth	*	0-3	3-5	1-1	1-3	1-3	0-2	4-5	1-1	1-1	2-2	1-0	2-4	2-0	0-2	2-0	6-1	2-0
2. British Timken	1-5	*	1-5	3-5	1-0	1-4	2-4	2-11	4-2	3-3	0-3	0-3	1-3	0-0	2-1	3-3	9-0	0-5
3. Bugbrooke St Michaels	1-1	2-1	*	1-2	4-1	3-1	2-0	0-5	5-1	2-0	1-3	3-1	1-1	2-0	1-2	4-3	9-0	0-0
4. Burton Park Wanderers	2-1	3-3	0-1	*	1-1	0-3	6-2	1-0	6-1	0-0	1-1	0-1	0-1	1-3	4-1	2-2	3-0	1-0
5. Cottingham	2-1	4-1	0-2	0-0	*	2-3	2-0	0-3	3-1	3-2	0-0	8-2	2-4	0-0	1-1	4-2	9-0	4-2
6. Ford Sports	6-1	5-1	3-2	5-1	2-2	*	3-1	2-1	6-1	3-2	4-2	6-1	3-1	4-3	3-3	4-1	8-1	0-3
7. Harrowby United	1-3	1-2	5-3	1-1	2-2	0-1	*	0-1	4-2	0-1	2-1	2-2	1-1	1-1	0-3	0-4	4-1	3-1
8. Higham Town	3-0	5-0	2-1	0-0	2-2	6-2	1-1	*	3-0	1-1	2-1	1-0	3-2	2-1	1-2	2-0	15-0	2-0
9. Irchester United	4-0	2-2	0-3	2-6	0-1	1-6	1-4	1-2	*	1-4	1-0	1-3	1-1	0-1	1-4	1-2	13-0	1-0
10. O.N. Chenecks	0-1	3-4	1-3	3-3	4-2	2-3	3-1	1-0	2-2	*	1-1	1-4	2-3	3-3	6-0	2-5	5-0	1-1
11. Olney Town	3-0	1-1	2-1	0-1	2-1	0-1	3-2	1-1	1-1	2-2	*	1-2	0-0	0-1	3-1	1-1	11-0	4-0
12. Peterborough City	1-3	1-6	0-2	1-1	3-2	1-8	1-1	0-1	2-3	2-1	1-1	*	1-2	2-1	4-2	2-2	9-0	2-4
13. Ramsey Town	4-0	4-4	2-0	5-1	4-1	2-2	1-3	1-1	5-2	2-1	2-1	0-4	*	0-4	1-1	4-0	5-1	1-1
14. St Ives Town	0-1	3-1	0-1	3-1	1-2	1-3	2-2	1-2	3-3	1-1	1-0	4-1	2-3	*	1-4	3-0	8-1	2-1
15. Sharnbrook	1-3	6-2	1-2	2-3	1-2	0-7	1-1	0-1	5-3	0-1	1-3	3-1	3-1	2-5	*	1-1	6-0	0-2
16. Thrapston Venturas	0-0	2-2	0-2	3-0	2-2	0-5	0-0	1-4	2-0	1-2	1-3	4-3	0-4	3-2	2-1	*	4-2	4-2
17. Towcester Town	0-0	0-1	1-4	0-3	6-1	0-15	1-4	0-7	0-3	0-5	0-3	0-4	0-1	3-1	0-2	1-4	*	1-2
18. Whitworths	5-1	1-1	0-0	1-0	4-1	1-0	1-2	1-1	4-1	3-2	2-1	2-5	0-0	2-2	6-2	0-2	11-0	*

PREMIER DIVISION - TEN YEAR RECORD

	83/84	84/85	85/86	86/87	87/88	88/89	89/90	90/91	91/92	92/93
Ampthill Town	10	20	14	21	-	-	-	-	-	-
APV Peterborough City	-	-	-	-	15	17	13	11	11	-
Arlesey Town	11	1	9	15	9	14	9	18	10	-
Baker Perkins					(See APV Peterborough City)					
Baldock Town	2	8	3	2	-	-	-	-	-	-
Boston	-	-	-	-	-	-	-	-	8	11
Bourne Town	4	10	17	20	21	20	4	1	4	8
Brackley Town	-	16	16	11	14	2	20	20	24	22
Buckingham Town	1	3	1	-	-	-	-	-	-	-
Burton Park Wanderers	-	-	-	-	-	-	17	22	-	-
Cogenhoe United	-	-	-	-	11	16	5	8	12	6
Daventry Town	-	-	-	-	-	-	-	-	14	5
Desborough Town	18	6	15	13	7	11	16	7	18	20
Eynesbury Rovers	16	17	20	17	16	12	21	3	7	9
Hamlet Stewarts & Lloyds					(See Stewarts & Lloyds)					
Holbeach United	15	18	10	8	20	3	1	13	23	19
Irthlingborough Diamonds	7	4	4	4	13	4	12	14	17	-
Kempston Rovers	-	-	-	16	19	19	22	15	15	15
Long Buckby	8	2	7	9	10	9	10	9	16	10
Mirrlees Blackstone	-	-	-	-	-	18	8	12	6	16
Newport Pagnell Town	12	12	21	-	-	-	-	-	-	14
Northampton Spencer	-	-	11	12	8	13	7	5	1	2
Potton United	5	7	6	1	4	1	14	4	13	4
Raunds Town	14	13	13	6	3	6	3	6	2	3
Rothwell Town	13	15	12	18	2	5	2	2	3	1
St Neots Town	19	19	18	19	18	-	-	-	-	-
Spalding United	-	-	-	7	1	-	-	-	21	13
Stamford	3	5	10	12	7	-	15	21	20	12
Stevenage Borough	6	-	-	-	-	-	-	-	-	-
Stewart & Lloyds	17	11	2	5	6	15	11	17	9	7
Stotfold	-	14	19	3	5	10	6	10	5	17
Wellingborough Town	-	-	-	-	-	-	19	16	22	21
Wootton Blue Cross	9	9	8	14	17	8	18	19	19	18
No. of clubs competing	19	20	21	21	21	20	22	22	24	22

LEAGUE KNOCKOUT CUP 1992-93

Preliminary Round
Stewart & Lloyds 6 *(McGowan 2, Hamill, Wilkinson, Martin 2)*, Holbeach Utd 2 *(Bailey, Secker)*
Cogenhoe Utd 7 *(Heslop, Leonard, Cunningham 5)*, O.N. Chenecks 0
Ramsey Town 3 *(Ding, Gannon, Barron)*, Burton Park Wanderers 2 *(Milne, Hauser)*
Newport Pagnell Town 3 *(Norris, Bearman 2)*, Peterborough City 0
Towcester Town 0, Higham Town 3 *(Day, Lord, Medlin)*
Bourne Town 2 *(Appleby, Lawrence)*, Potton United 0
Brackley Town 3 *(Brown, Paul, Pickwick)*, Irchester United 0
Olney Town 3 *(Sands, Halsall, Cockerell)*, Sharnbrook 2 *(Woods, C Bolton)*

First Round
Bugbrooke St Michaels 2 *(Gunn, Robinson)*, Blisworth 1 *(Woolgar)*
Mirrless Blackstone 0, Raunds Town 6 *(Field, Keeble, Genovese, Westley 3)*
Ford Sports 1 *(Hough)*, Boston 4 *(Cook 2, Kent, Own Goal)* AET
Stotfold 6 *(O'Brien, M P Bennett 2, Walker 3)*, Whitworths 1 *(Burrows)*
Cottingham 0, Harrowby United 2 *(Scotcher, North)*
Wootton Blue Cross 2 *(Sawyer 2)*, Long Buckby 2 *(Pacey, M Walker)* AET
British Timken 1 *(R Brown)*, Rothwell Town 4 *(Bates 2, McDonald, Own Goal)*
Stamford 3 *(Edey 3)*, Eynesbury Rovers 5 *(Bryant, Brown 2, O'Keeffe, Lindsay)* AET
Desborough Town 3 *(Taylor, Marlow, March)*, Northampton Spencer 1 *(Sandy)*
St Ives Town 1 *(Claridge)*, Olney Town 2 *(Sands, Cockerell)*
Higham Town 7 *(Christie, Dodson 2, Medlin, G Smith, Hill 2)*, Wellingborough Town 0
Spalding United 4 *(Hepburn, Keeble, Gregory)*, Thrapston Venturas 1 *(James)*
Stewart & Lloyds 4 *(Leech, Ringrose, Martin, Own Goal)*, Cogenhoe United 2 *(Forbes, Shelswell)*
Bourne Town 1 *(Cooke)*, Kempston Rovers 1 *(King)* AET
Newport Pagnell Town 2 *(Ewart, Smith)*, Brackley Town 1 *(R Hoyte)*
Ramsey Town 1 *(Kilby)*, Daventry Town 4 *(Pearce, Reynolds 2, Shields)*
Replays:
Long Bucky 3 *(McFarlane, Henry, Keech)*, Wootton Blue Cross 2 *(Troughton, Cashin)*.
Kempston Rovers 1 *(Farrar)*, Bourne Town 0

Second Round
Bugbrooke St Michaels 0, Kempston Rovers 3 *(Newton, King 2)*
Desborough Town 0, Stewart & Lloyds 2 *(Bogle, Ringrose)* AET
Spalding United 2 *(Grogan, Own Goal)*, Olney Town 1 *(Wrighting)*
Eynesbury Rovers 1 *(O'Keeffe)*, Daventry Town 5 *(Reynolds, Geary 2, Donovan 2)*
Harrowby United 0, Rothwell Town 3 *(Sheerin, McIlroy 2)*
Higham Town 2 *(Abrahart, Lord)*, Long Buckby 1 *(M Walker)* AET
Raunds Town 2 *(Torrance, Keeble)*, Newport Pagnell Town 0
Stotfold 1 *(M Bennett)*, Boston 4 *(Robinson, Rawcliffe, Baines 2)*

Quarter Finals
Spalding United 0, Rothwell Town 2 *(Sheerin, O'Keefe)*
Kempston Rovers 1 *(Holmes)*, Higham Town 1 *(Lord)* AET
Raunds Town 4 *(Torrance 2, Keeble, Westley)*, Stewart & Lloyds 0
Daventry Town 5 *(Pearce, McGrath, Geary, Donovan)*, Boston 1 *(Vaughan)*
Replay:
Higham Town 4 *(Medlin, G Smith 3)*, Kempston Rovers 0

Semi Finals
Higham Town 1 *(G Smith)*, Rothwell Town 2 *(Akeredolu, O'Keefe)*
Daventry Town 2 *(S Williams, Donovan)*, Raunds Town 1 *(Westley)* AET

Final
1st Leg
Rothwell Town 2 *(Murphy 2)*, **Daventry Town** 2 *(McGrath, Donovan)*
Rothwell: Liquorish, Wills, Hornby, Murphy, Bates, Sheerin, McDonald, O'Keefe, Edwards, Davies, Akeredolu.
Subs: McHutchison, McIlroy.
Daventry: Stoker, C Waldock, Pearce, Ashenden, Reynolds, Wall, D Williams, Murphy, McGrath, Geary, Donovan.
Subs: Gwilliam, Humphries.

2nd Leg
Daventry Town 1 *(Ashenden)*, **Rothwell Town** 3 *(Murphy, McDonald 2)*
Daventry: Stoker, Minchin, Pearce, S Williams, Reynolds, Ashenden, Geary, Murphy, McGrath, Donovan, Wall.
Subs: Parks, Humphries.
Rothwell: Liquorish, Wills, Geoghegan, Murphy, Bates, Sheerin, McDonald, O'Keefe, Edwards, Davies, Akeredolu.
Subs: McHutchison, McIlroy.

BENEVOLENT CUP 1992-93

Semi Finals
Northampton Spencer 1 *(Calvert)*, Ford Sports 2 *(Blakeman, Own Goal)* 2
Rothwell Town 2 *(Kenney)*, Higham Town 1 *(Smith)*

Final
Rothwell Town 4 *(Sheerin, O'Keefe, Wills, Murphy)*, **Higham Town** 2 *(Brough, Calvey)*
Rothwell: Liquorish, Wills, Hornby, Robertson, Bates, Sheerin, McDonald, O'Keefe, Murphy, Davies, Akeredolu.
Subs: McHutchison, Kenney.
Higham: Beauchamp, Blakeman, Hough, Green, Lester, Fuller, Smith, Brough, Haynes, Navas, McKay. Subs:
O'Neill, Calvey.

LEADING SCORERS 1992-93

PREMIER DIVISION		Club	League	KO Cup	Ben. Cup	Total
Joey Marton		Stewart & Lloyds	42	3	-	45
Shaun Keeble		Raunds Town	33	3	-	36
Jamie Cunningham		Cogenhoe United	29	5	-	34
Chris Goodchild		Long Buckby	32	-	-	32
Darren Edey		Stamford	26	3	-	29
Darren King		Kempston Rovers	26	3	-	29
Roy Boon		Potton United	28	-	-	28
Ray Seekings		Potton United	27	-	-	27
Kevin McGuire		Northampton Spencer	26	-	-	26
Danny Nicholls		Wootton Blue Cross	26	-	-	26
James Westley	Raunds (inc 2 lge for Wellingboro.)		21	5	-	26
Terry O'Keefe		Rothwell Town	21	2	2	25
Robbie Cooke		Bourne Town	23	1	-	24
Jason O'Connor		Holbech United	23	-	-	23
Steve Forbes		Cogenhoe United	20	1	-	21
Paul Murphy		Rothwell Town	17	3	1	21
Neil Donovan		Daventry Town	15	5	-	20
Nick Keeble		Spalding United	19	1	-	20
Steve Marshall	Eynesbury (inc 10 for Peterboro C.)		19	-	-	19
Adam Sandy		Northampton Spencer	18	1	-	19
Dave Torrance		Mirrlees Blackstone	19	-	-	19
Dave Albone		Potton United	18	-	-	18
Adrian Marlow		Desborough Town	17	1	-	18
Gary Walker		Stotfold	14	3	-	17
Mark Hipwell		Stamford	16	-	-	16
Les Lawrence		Bourne Town	15	1	-	16
Gary Baines		Boston	13	2	-	15
Lloyd Glennon		Wellingborough Town	15	-	-	15
Adrian Sheerin		Rothwell Town	12	2	1	15
Lee Bearman		Newport Pagnell Town	12	2	-	14
Chris Cook		Boston	14	2	-	14
Scott Kent	Spalding (inc 8 Lge, 1 KO Cup for Boston)		13	1	-	14
Ian Locke		Mirrlees Blackstone	14	-	-	14
Richard McGrath		Daventry Town	11	3	-	14
Ian Pearce		Daventry Town	12	2	-	14
Bobby Smith		Newport Pagnell Town	13	1	-	14
Julian Capone		Raunds Town	13	-	-	13
Steve McIlroy		Rothwell Town	11	2	-	13
Jason Meeds		Eynesbury Rovers	13	-	-	13
Mark Winwood		Potton United	13	-	-	13
Mick Bennett		Stotfold	11	1	-	12
Matthew Burrows		Long Buckby	12	-	-	12
Paul Hucker		Stamford	12	-	-	12
Jon Inwood		Northampton Spencer	12	-	-	12
Pat O'Keeffe		Eynesbury Rovers	10	2	-	12
Danny Reilly		Eynesbury Rovers	12	-	-	12
Dave Scotney		Bourne Town	12	-	-	12

DIVISION ONE		Club	League	KO Cup	Ben. Cup	Total
Neil Brough	Ford Sports (inc 2 Lge for Daventry)		54	-	1	55
Jim Barron	St Ives T. (inc 17 Lge, 1 KO Cup for Ramsey)		27	1	-	28
Steve Medlin		Higham Town	24	3	-	27
Dave Botterill		Bugbrooke St Michaels	21	-	-	21
Andy Calvey		Ford (inc 6 Lge for N. Pagnell)	18	-	1	19
Mark James		Thrapston Venturas	18	1	-	19
Neil Tilley		Burton Park Wanderers	19	-	-	19
Russell Brown		British Timken	17	1	-	18
Stuart Kilby		Ramsey Town	16	1	-	17
Clive Woodland		Olney Town	17	-	-	17
Chris Crotwell		Ramsey (inc 8 for P'boro C.)	16	-	-	16
Sean Dodson		Higham Town	14	2	-	16
Rod Hough		Ford Sports	16	-	-	16
Rob McKay		Ford Sports	16	-	-	16
Grant Smith		Higham Town	10	5	1	16
Andy Evans		O.N. Chenecks	15	-	-	15
Steve Whitehead		Whitworths	15	-	-	15
Chris Bolton		Sharnbrook	13	1	-	14
Dean Hendry		Peterborough City	14	-	-	14
Shay O'Riordan		Bugbrooke St Michaels	14	-	-	14
Gary Petts		Thrapston Venturas	14	-	-	14
Mark Shiels		St Ives Town	14	-	-	14
Paul Geary		St Ives Town	12	-	-	12
Darren Wilkins		Whitworths	12	-	-	12

HAT-TRICKS 1993-94

PREMIER DIVISION

Five Goals
Joey Martin (Stewart & L.) v Brackley 2/3/93
Jason O'Connor (Holbeach) v Brackley 6/3/93
Dave Scotney (Bourne) v Brackley 27/3/93
Chris Goodchild (L. Buckby) at Brackley 22/4/93

Four Goals
Joey Martin (Stewart & L.) at Brackley 6/10/92
Chris Goodchild (L. Buckby) v Eynesbury 29/9/92
Nicky Keech (L. Buckby) v N. Pagnell 5/12/92
Jamie Cunningham (Cogenhoe) at Brackley 5/1/93
Shaun Keeble (Raunds) v Stotfold 24/4/93

Three Goals
Joey Martin (Stewart & L.) v Mirrlees B. 18/8/92
Ray Seekings (Potton) v Stotfold 18/8/92
Scott Kent (Boston) at Brackley 22/8/92
Gary Baines (Boston) v Spalding 25/8/92
Darren King (Kempston) v Wellingboro. 25/8/92
Jason Meeds (Eynesbury) at Desborough 5/9/92
Mark Livermore (Stotfold) at Desboro. 22/9/92
Robbie Cooke (Bourne) v Eynesbury 23/9/92
Roy Boon (Potton) v Daventry T. 3/10/92
Ian Locke (Mirrlees B.) at Desboro. 10/10/92
Robbie Cooke (Bourne) at Brackley 24/10/92
Carlton Grogan (Spalding) v Holbeach 24/10/92
Paul Shields (Daventry) v Wellingboro. 28/10/92
Paul Hucker (Stamford) v Potton U. 7/11/92
Paul Shields (Daventry) at Kempston 14/11/92
Adrian Sheerin (Rothwell) at Eynesbury 28/11/92
Matthew Burrows (L. Buckby) v N. Pagnell 5/12/92
Steve Forbes (Cogenhoe) v Desborough 5/12/92
Chris Goodchild (L. Buckby) v N. Pagnell 5/12/92
Nick Green (Cogenhoe) v Desborough 5/12/92
Darren King (Kempston) v Brackley 5/12/92
Roy Boon (Potton) v Spalding 12/12/92
Steve Forbes (Cogenhoe) at Wootton 12/12/92
Bobby Smith (N Pagnell) v Mirrlees B. 12/12/92
Kevin McGuire (N. Spencer) at Mirrlees 20/1/93
Chris Goodchild (L. Buckby) v Bourne 30/1/93
Shaun Keeble (Raunds) at Long Buckby 13/2/93
Shaun Keeble (Raunds) v Boston 16/2/93
Dave Albone (Potton) v Brackley 20/2/93
Roy Boon (Potton) v Brackley 20/2/93
Roy Boon (Potton) at Raunds 23/2/93
Richard Marsh (Desboro.) v Brackley 23/3/93
Joey Martin (Stewart & L.) v Wellingboro. 27/2/93
Steve Farr (Stewart & L.) v Brackley 2/3/93
Steve Wilkinson (Stewart & L.) v Brackley 2/3/93
Darren Gibbons (Boston) v Brackley 13/3/93
Danny Reilly (Eynesbury) v Brackley 16/3/93
Fred McDonnell (Boston) at Desboro. 23/3/93
Joey Martin (Stewart & L.) v Holbeach 23/3/93
Ku Akeredolu (Rothwell) at Wellingboro. 27/3/93
Robbie Cooke (Bourne) v Brackley 27/3/93
Joey Martin (Stewart & L.) v Stamford 27/3/93
Steve Marshall (Eynesbury) at Stamford 6/4/93
Milton Graham (Bourne) at Wellingboro. 8/4/93
Shaun Keeble (Raunds) at Brackley 8/4/93
James Westley (Raunds) at Brackley 8/4/93
Jamie Cunningham (Cogenhoe) v N. Spencer 12/4/93
Lloyd Glennon (Wellingboro.) at Brackley 12/4/93
Matthew Burrows (L. Buckby) at Brackley 22/4/93
Adam Sandy (N. Spencer) at Wootton BC 24/4/93
John McLean (Eynesbury) at Boston 1/5/93

DIVISION One

Nine Goals
Neil Brough (Ford) at Towcester 12/4/93

Eight Goals
Neil Brough (Ford) v Towcester 26/12/92

Six Goals
Dave Botterill (Bugbrooke) v Towcester 6/2/92

Five Goals
Nick Shelton (Irchester) v Towcester 20/3/93
Steve Medlin (Higham) v Towcester 3/4/93
Jason Cole (Olney) v Towcester 10/4/93

Four Goals
Steve Whitehead (Whitworths) v Towcester 5/9/92
Andy Evans (ON Chenecks) v Sharnbrook 17/10/92
Jim Barron (Ramsey) v Blisworth 31/10/92
Chris Bolton (Sharnbrook) v British Tim. 31/10/92
Russell Brown (Brit. Tim.) at Ramsey 12/12/92
Jim Barron (St Ives) v P'boro City 13/2/93
Jon Ogden (Sharnbrook) at St Ives 27/2/93
Neil Brough (Ford) at P'boro City 10/4/93
Clive Woodland (Olney) v Towcester 10/4/93
Neil Brough (Ford) v Blisworth 20/4/93

Three Goals
Les Webster (Chenecks) v Towcester 25/8/92
Carl Pask (Cottingham) v Whitworths 29/8/92
Mark James (Thrapstons) v Whitworths 1/9/92
Sean Dodson (Higham) at Brit. Tim. 5/9/92
Steve Farthing (Sharnbrook) v Irchester 5/9/92
Mark James (Thrapston) at Bugbrooke 5/9/92
Steve Medlin (Higham) at Brit. Tim. 5/9/92
Dave Botterill (Bugbrooke) at Brit. Tim. 12/9/92
Neil Tilley (Burton PW) at Irchester 3/10/92
Warren Everdell (St Ives) at Towcester 17/10/92
Neil Tilley (Burton PW) at Brit. Tim. 17/10/92
Steve Medlin (Higham) v Ford 31/10/92
Neil Brough (Ford) v Irchester 14/11/92
Jim Barron (Ramsey) v Thrapston 28/11/92
Jim Barron (Ramsey) v Brit. Tim. 12/12/92
Neil Brough (Ford) at Sharnbrook 12/12/92
Rod Hough (Ford) at Sharnbrook 12/12/92
Neil Brough (Ford) at Cottingham 19/12/92
Sammy Pigott (Harrowby) v Irchester 16/1/93
Tony Burt (Brit. Tim.) v Towcester 13/2/93
Lee Jones (Brit. Timken) v Towcester 13/2/93
Shay O'Riordan (Bugbrooke) v Irchester 13/2/93
Chris Crotwell (Ramsey) v Burton PW 20/2/93
Andy Randall (Higham) v Brit. Tim. 27/2/93
Wayne Sutton (Burton PW) at Towcester 13/3/93
Chris Foster (Irchester) v Towcester 20/3/93
Neil Brough (Ford) at Irchester 27/3/93
Sean Dodson (Higham) v Towcester 3/4/93
Andy Evans (Chenecks) v Brit. Tim.) 12/4/93
Shay O'Riordan (Bugbrooke) at Towcester 20/4/93
Jeff Horwell (Brit. Tim.) at P'boro. C. 24/4/93
Gary Edwards (Blisworth) v Higham 8/5/93.

LEAGUE KNOCKOUT CUP

Five Goals
Jamie Cunningham (Cogenhoe) v Chenecks 12/9/92
Three goals
Gary Walker (Stotfold) v Whitworths 12/9/92
Darren Edey (Stamford) v Eynesbury 19/9/92
James Westley (Raunds) at Mirrlees 27/10/92
Grant Smith (Higham) v Kempston 13/3/93

1992-93 RESULTS ANALYSIS

	PREMIER DIVISION	DIVISION ONE
Biggest Home Win	Bourne 14, Brackley 0 *(27/3/93)*	Higham 15, Towcester 0 *(3/4/93)*
Biggest Away Win	Brackley 0, L. Buckby 12 *(22/4/93)*	Towcester 0, Ford Spts *(12/4/93)*
Highest Score Draw	Stewart & L. 4, Stamford 4 *(27/3/93)*	Ramsey 4, British Tim. 4 *(12/12/92)*
Highest Aggregate	Stewart & L. 14, Brackley 2 *(2/3/93)*	Higham 15, Towcester 0 *(3/3/93)*
		Towcester 0, Ford Spts 15 *(12/4/93)*
Longest Unbeaten Run	14 games - Raunds Town	18 games - Higham Town
" run without win	42 - Brackley Town	29 - Towcester Town
Most consecutive wins	9 - Northampton Spencer	9 - P'boro C./ Ford Spts
Most consecutive draws	3 - Bourne/ Desborough/ Wootton Blue Cross	4 - ON Chenecks
" " defeats	16 - Brackley Town	28 - Towcester Town
" " scoring games	21 - Daventry Town	21 - Ford Sports
" " without scoring	6 - Brackley Town	8 - Towcester Town
" " matches conceding	42 - Brackley Town	28 - Towcester Town
" " not conceding	5 - Bourne/ Raunds	5 - Bugbrooke St Michaels

PREMIER DIVISION CLUBS 1993-94

BOSTON

Chairman: Mick Vines   **Secretary:** Clive Atkinson, 66 Hessle Ave., Boston, Lincs (0205 351094)
Manager: Percy Freeman   **Asst Manager:** Dick Creasey
Ground: Tattershall Road, Boston, Lincs (0205 65470).
Directions: A52 Grantham - Sleaford, 2nd left into Brothertoft Road, Argyle Street to bridge, immediately over left into Tattershall Road, ground three quaters of a mile.
Capacity: 6,000   **No. seats:** 450   **Covered Accom:** 950   **Floodlights:** Yes
Programme: 16 pages, 25p   **Editor:** Andy Sandall   **Press Officer:** Pete Massam
Club Colours: Blue & white   **Change Colours:** All white
Clubhouse: Open matchdays and special functions.   **Previous Ground:** Mayflower.
Year formed: 1963   **Nickname:** Poachers   **Midweek matchday:** Tuesday
Record Gate: 2,700 v Boston Utd, FA Cup 1970.   **Previous Lges:** Lincs/ Central All. 65-66/ Eastern Co's 66-68/ Mids 68-82/ Northern Co's East 82-87/ Central Mids 87-91.
Players progressing to Football League: Julian Joachim (Leicester City).
Honours: Midland Co's Lg 74-75 78-79 80-81 (Lg Cup 76-77), Lincs Snr 'A' Cup (5), Central Mids Lg.
Club Captain 1992-93: Jamie Ireland   **Player of the Year 1992-93:** Brendan McDaid.
Leading Scorers 1992-93: Gary Baines 15, Chris Cook 14, Scott Kent 9.
Leading Appearances 1992-93: Brendan McDaid 45, Jamie Ireland 38, Jason Vaughan 37.

BOURNE TOWN

Chairman: Geoff Charnock   **President:** Ray Ferrer
Secretary: Jim Hornby, 6 Godwin Close, Bourne, Lincs PE10 9YE (0778 423958).
Manager: Mark Mitchell   **Asst Manager:** Jimmy Jackson
Ground: Abbey Lawn, Abbey Road, Bourne, Lincs (0778 422292).
Directions: In market place take Spalding Road, ground 500 yds on right
Capacity: 3,000   **No. seats:** 300   **Covered Accom:** 750   **Floodlights:** Yes
Programme: 24 pages, 30p   **Eds.:** Don Mitchell/ Alan Gout   **Press Officer:** Don Mitchell
Club Colours: White & maroon   **Change Colours:** White
Local Press: Stamford Mercury, Lincs Free Press, Peterborough Evening Telegraph, Bourne Local.
Clubhouse details: Small, open matchdays and specific events
Year formed: 1883   **Nickname:** The Wakes   **Midweek matchday:** Wednesday
Record Attendance: 3,000 v Chelmsford, FA Tphy 1970   **Previous Ground:** Cricket Field.
Previous Leagues: Peterborough/ UCL 47-56/ Central Alliance 58-61/ Midland Counties 61-63.
Players to progress to Football League: Peter Grummit (Nottm Forest), Shaun Cunnington (Wrexham, Grimsby, Sunderland), David Palmer (Wrexham).
Major Honours: Utd Co's Lg 68-69 69-70 71-72 90-91 (KO Cup 69-70, Benevolent Cup 90-91), Lincs Snr 'A' Cup 71-72 (R-up 92-93), Central Alliance Division 1 South 59-60, Lincs Intermediate Cup 85-86.
Club Captain 1992-93: Paul Langford   **Player of the Year 1992-93:** Steve Appleby
Leading Scorers 1992-93: Robbie Cooke 24, Les Lawrence 16, Dave Scotney 12.
Leading Appearances 1992-93: Steve Appleby 45, Gary Clipston 44, Paul Langford 43.

BRACKLEY TOWN

Chairman: Kim Golding   **President:** Miss C Billingham
Secretary: Don Webb, 32 Bridge Str., Brackley, Northants NN13 5EW (0280 704780).
Manager: Don Watts   **Asst Manager:** Chris Possinger.
Ground: St James Park, Churchill Way, Brackley, Northants (0280 704077).
Directions: Churchill Way, east off A43, south end of town
Capacity: 3,500   **No. seats:** 400   **Covered Accom:** 50   **Floodlights:** Yes
Programme: No   **Press Officer:** Pat Ashby
Local Newspapers: Brackley Advertiser, Banbury Guardian, Herald & Post.
Club Colours: Red, black & white   **Change Colours:** All yellow
Clubhouse details: Lounge & main hall. Open all week
Year formed: 1890   **Nickname:** Saints   **Midweek matchday:** Tuesday
Record Attendance: 600 v Kettering, Northants Senior Cup 1989
Previous Leagues: Banbury & District/ North Bucks/ Hellenic 77-83.
Previous Grounds: Banbury Road, Manor Road, Buckingham Road (upto 1974).
Players to progress to Football League: Jon Blencowe (Leicester)
Hons: UCL 88-89 (Div 1 83-84), N'hants Snr Cup R-up, Buck'ham Charity Cup, Hellenic Lg Div 1 Cup 82-83.
Club Captain 1992-93: Steve Wilkes   **Player of the Year 1992-93:** Tim Harris.
1992-93 Top Scorers: Kevin Blencowe 4, Jim Lawrence 4.
1992-93 Leading Appearances: Andy Lester 25, Tim Harris 23, Jim Lawrence 23, Steve Wilkes 23

COGENHOE UNITED

Chairman: Derek Wright   **President:** Steve Brockwell
Secretary: Mick Marriott, 14 Kiln Corn Close, Cogenhoe, Northants NN7 1NX (0604 890043).
Asst Manager: Stuart Robertson   **Manager:** Dave Conlon
Ground: Compton Park, Brafield Rd. Cogenhoe (0604 890521).
Directions: Turn off A428 at Brafield-on-the-Green, first turn right to Cogenhoe or A45 to Billing Aquadrome. Carry on, take second Cogenhoe turn on left.
Capacity: 5,000   **No. seats:** 100   **Covered Accom:** Yes   **Floodlights:** Yes.
Programme: 24 pages with admission   **Editor/ Press Officer:** Mick Marriott
Club Colours: Sky blue   **Change Colours:** Red & black.
Clubhouse: Bar & changing room block, open all week   **Hons:** UCL Div 1 R-up, Daventry Charity Cup.
Year formed: 1967   **Nickname:** Cooks   **Midweek matchday:** Tuesday
Record Attendance: 1,000 v Eastenders XI   **Previous League:** Central Northants Combination
Players to progress to Football League: Darren Bazeley (Watford), Darren Harmon (Notts Co., Shrewsbury, Northampton), Matt Murphy (Oxford Utd), Gary Leonard (Northampton).
Local Newspapers: Chronicle & Echo, Northants Evening Telegraph.
Club Captain 1992-93: Neil Heslop   **Player of the Year 1992-93:** Steve Hair
1992-93 Leading Scorers: Jamie Cunningham 34, Steve Forbes 21, Steve Knibb 10.
92-93 Leading Apps: Steve Hair 43, Stuart Pepper 38, Jamie Cunningham 37, Neil Westland 37, Neil Worker 37.

Bourne Town F.C. 1992-93. Photo - Gavin Ellis-Neville.

Stamford 1, Bourne Town 2 on Easter Monday; Bourne's Dave Scotney gets a good view of the ball thanks to Clive Foster's challenge. Photo - Gavin Ellis-Neville.

Steve Forbes' shot threads its way through the defenders and into the net to help Cogenhoe to a 5-1 win at Newport Pagnell. Photo - Neil Whittington.

DAVENTRY TOWN

Chairman: Ray Humphries   **President:** Des Johnson.
Secretary: David Hirons, 53 Arnoll Cres., Daventry, Northants NN11 5AZ (0327 71461).
Manager: Willie Barrett   **Asst Manager:** Russ Ashenden.
Ground: Elderstubbs Farm, Leamington Way, Daventry, Northants (0327 706286).
Directions: Adjacent to A45 by-pass.
Capacity: 2,000   **Seats:** 250   **Cover:** Yes   **Floodlights:** Yes   **Founded:** 1886.
Programme: 16 pages   **Editor:** Gavin Hanna   **Press Officer:** Cliff Farthing
Local Newspapers: Daventry Weekly Express, Herald & Post.
Club colours: Black & white stripes   **Change colours:** All red.
Midweek Matchday: Tuesday   **Nickname:** None.
Record Attendance: 350 v Ford Sports 1991.   **Clubhouse:** Large Bar.
Previous Leagues: Northampton Town, Central Northants Combination.
Hons: UCL Div 1(2)(Lg Cup R-up 92-93, Highest Aggregate Cup), Northants Junior Cup(3).
Players Progressing to Football League: Martin Aldridge (Northampton).
Club Captain 1992-93: Gary Wall   **Player of the Year 1992-93:** Neil Donovan
1992-93 Leading Scorers: Neil Donovan 20, Richard McGrath 14, Ian Pearce 14.
1992-93 Leading Appearances: Shane Geary 48, Ian Pearce 48, Andy Stoker 47.

DESBOROUGH TOWN

Chairman: Bryan Walmsley   **President:** Ernie Parsons.
Secretary: John Lee, 85 Breakleys, Daventry, Northants NN14 2PT (0536 760002).
Manager: Colin Neill   **Asst Manager:** Steve Coe.
Ground: Waterworks Field, Braybrooke Rd, Desborough (0536 761350).
Directions: Half a mile west of A6 following signs for Braybrooke.
Capacity: 8,000   **No. seats:** 250   **Covered Accom:** 500   **Floodlights:** Yes
Prog.: 20 pages with entry   **Editor:** Robert Bindley   **Press Officer:** John Lee
Local Newspapers: Evening Telegraph, Northants Post, Chronicle & Echo, Harborough Mail.
Club Colours: All blue   **Change Colours:** Old yellow.
Clubhouse details: Lounge & main hall, 2 bars, games room. Open every evening, weekend lunchtimes.
Year formed: 1896   **Nickname:** Ar Tarn   **Midweek matchday:** Tuesday
Record Attendance: 8,000 v Kettering   **Previous Leagues:** None.
Players progressing to Football League: Wakeley Gage (Northampton, Chester, Peterborough and Crewe), Jon Purdie & Campbell Chapman (Wolves), Andy Tillson (Grimsby, QPR & Bristol Rvrs).
Hons: Utd Co's (Prev. Northants) Lg 00-01 01-02 06-07 20-21 23-24 24-25 27-28 48-49 66-67 (R-up 02-03 10-11 19-20 22-23 79-80 (Div 2 10-11(Res) 28-29(Res) (R-up 09-10(Res) 26-27(Res) 51-52(Res)), KO Cup 77-78), Northants Snr Cup 10-11 13-14 28-29 51-52.
Club Captain 1992-93: Simon Morrice   **Player of the Year 1992-93:** Simon Morrice
1992-93 Leading Scorers: Adrian Marlow 18, Sean McPolin 11, Richard Marsh 11.
1992-93 Leading Appearances: Andy McEachran 40, Adrian Marlow 36, Richard Marsh 35.

EYNESBURY ROVERS

Chairman: Ian Kavanagh   **President:** W Stephenson
Secretary/Press Officer: Deryck Irons, 12 Hadleigh Close, Bedford MK41 8JW (0234 268111).
Manager: Alan Day   **Asst Manager:** John McLean
Ground: Hall Road, Eynesbury, St Neots (0480 474041).
Directions: Approx 2 miles from A1, on South side of St Neots urban area, near Ernulf School.
Capacity: 3,000   **No. seats:** 270   **Covered Accom:** 270   **Floodlights:** Yes
Programme: 24 pages, 30p   **Editor:** Patrick Worrall
Local Newspapers: Hunts Citizen, Cambridge Evening News, St Neots Weekly News.
Club Colours: Royal blue & white   **Change Colours:** All yellow.
Clubhouse details: Large bar, capacity 150, committee room
Year formed: 1897   **Nickname:** Rovers   **Midweek matchday:** Tuesday
Record Gate: 5,000 v Fulham 1953   **Previous Lges:** Sth Mids 34-39/ UCL 46-52/ Eastern Co's 52-63.
Players to progress to Football Lge: Chris Turner (P'boro, Luton, Cambridge), Denis Emery (P'boro)
Hons: UCL Div 1 76-77, Hunts Snr Cup(12) 13-14 46-47 48-51 54-55 56-57 69-70 84-85 90-93, Hunts Premier Cup 50-51 90-91, Hinchingbrooke Cup(7) 46-47 48-52 57-58 66-67, Cambs Invitation Cup 61-62, E Anglian Cup R-up 90-91 91-92, Scott Gatty Cup 35-36 56-57 84-85 89-90, Hunts Jnr Cup 21-22 26-27, S Mids F'lit Cup 90-91(Res).
Club Captain 1992-93: Dave Jackson   **Player of the Year 1992-93:** Howard Keir
1992-93 Leading Scorers: Jason Meeds 13, Pat O'Keeffe 12, Danny Reilly 12.
1992-93 Leading Appearances: Howard Keir 42, Warren Brown 38, Mick McCreanor 38, Pat O'Keeffe 34.

HOLBEACH UNITED

Chairman: Alan Mitchell   **President:** J King
Sec.: John Crunkhorn, The Old Nurseries, Bakers Corner, High Rd, Whaplode, Spalding, Lincs (0406 22540).
Manager: Steve Evans   **Assistant Manager:** Peter Harrison.
Ground: Carters Park, Park Road, Holbeach (0406 24761).
Directions: Second left at traffic lights in town centre, 220 yds down road on left. From King's Lynn; sharp right at traffic lights.
Capacity: 4,000   **No. seats:** 200   **Covered Accom:** 450   **Floodlights:** Yes
Programme: 20 pages, 30p   **Editor:** Alan Wright   **Press Officer:** Ian Lovell
Local Newspapers: Lincs Free Press, Spalding Guardian, Peterborough Evening Telegraph.
Club Colours: Old gold & black   **Change Colours:** Blue & white
Clubhouse details: Large enough to hold dances. Lounge & kitchen, open every night.
Year formed: 1929   **Nickname:** Tigers   **Midweek matchday:** Wednesday
Record Attendance: 4,094 v Wisbech 1954.   **Previous Name:** Lily Whites.
Previous Leagues: Peterborough/ Utd Co's 46-55/ Eastern Co's 55-62/ Midland Co's 62-63.
Players progressing to Football League: Peter Rawcliffe (Lincoln).
Major Honours: Utd Co's Lg 89-90 (KO Cup(2), Benevolent Cup), Lincs Snr Cup 'A'(3), Lincs Senior Cup 'B', FA Cup 1st Rd Proper 82-83 (lost 0-4 v Wrexham at Peterborough).
Captain 1992-93: Dean Elston   **Player of the Year 1992-93:** Peter Rawcliffe.
1992-93 Leading Scorers: Jason O'Connor 23, Linden Secker 7, Wayne Garner 6.
1992-93 Leading Appearances: Linden Secker 41, Andy Crunkhorn 40, Dean Elston 34, Danny Hussey 34.

KEMPSTON ROVERS

Chairman: W E Gwilt **President:** H Gilbert
Secretary: Alan Scott, 25 King William Rd, Kempston, Bedford MK42 7AT (0234 854875).
Manager: Alan Wright **Assistant Manager:** Bobby Folds.
Ground: Hillgrounds Rd, Kempston, Bedford (0234 852346).
Directions: M1 junction 13 to Bedford, ground opposite Sainsburys in Kempston.
Capacity: 2,000 **No. seats:** 100 **Covered Accom:** 250 **Floodlights:** Yes
Programme: 48 pages, 30p **Editor/Press Officer:** Alan Scott.
Local Newspapers: Bedfordshire Times, Herald & Post.
Club Colours: Red, white & black **Change Colours:** Yellow.
Clubhouse details: Bar & Lounge, built 1986, extended 1989
Year formed: 1884 **Nickname:** Walnut Boys **Midweek matchday:** Tuesday
Record Attendance: unknown **Previous League:** Sth Mids 27-53.
Previous Grounds: Hillgrounds Road, Bedford Road.
Hons: Utd Co's Lg 73-74 (R-up 56-57 59-60 (Div 2 55-56 (R-up 67-68), KO Cup 57-58 59-60 76-77), Beds Senior Cup(3)(R-up 92-93).
Club Captain 1992-93: Richard Evans **Player of the Year 1992-93:** Stuart Holmes.
1992-93 Leading Scorers: Darren King 29, Dave Farrar 11, Steve Newton 9.
1992-93 Leading Appearances: Andy Watt 45, Martin Baker 42, Darren King 38.

LONG BUCKBY

Chairman: Ted Thresher **President:**
Secretary: Dave Austin, 6 Jubilee Close, Long Buckby NN6 7NP (0327 843286).
Manager: Mick Emms **Asst Manager:** Les Thurbon
Ground: Station Rd, Long Buckby (0327 842682).
Directions: On Daventry - Long Buckby road. 400 yds from station (Northampton - Rugby line).
Capacity: 1,000 **No. seats:** 200 **Covered Accom:** 200 **Floodlights:** Yes
Programme: 16 pages, 20p **Editor/Press Officer:** Rod Bryor
Local Newspapers: Chronicle & Echo, Daventry Weekly News.
Club Colours: Sky & navy **Change Colours:** All red.
Clubhouse details: Bar & concert room.
Year formed: 1945 **Nickname:** Bucks **Midweek matchday:** Tuesday
Record Attendance: 750 v Kettering Town, Northamptonshire Senior Cup Final 1984.
Previous Name: Long Buckby Nomads 1936.
Previous Leagues: Rugby & District, Central Northants Combination.
Past Players to progress to Football League: Gary Mills (Nottingham Forest, Derby, Notts County, Leicester), Vince Overson (Burnley, Birmingham), Des Waldock (Northampton), Steve Norris (Scarborough, Carlisle, Halifax, Chesterfield).
Honours: UCL KO Cup 84-85 (UCL Div 2 70-71 71-72, Div 3 69-70, Div 2 KO Cup 71-72), Northants Snr Cup R-up.
Club Captain 1992-93: Chris Goodchild **Player of the Year 1992-93:** Simon Henry
1992-93 Top Scorers: Chris Goodchild 32, Matt Burrows 12, Nicky Keech 11.
1992-93 Leading Appearances: Mark Walker 41, Simon Henry 39, Peter Walker 39.

MIRRLEES BLACKSTONE

Chairman: Bill Sewell **President:**
Secretary: Derek Hall, 67 Ringwood, South Bretton, Peterborough PE3 9SR (0733 332074).
Manager: Steve Blades **Press Officer:** Ian McGillivray
Ground: Lincoln Road, Stamford (0780 57835).
Directions: A6121 Stamford to Bourne road, 2nd left past MB works.
Capacity: 1,000 **No. seats:** 100 **Covered Accom:** Yes **Floodlights:** Yes
Programme: 20 pages, 20p **Editor:** Kevin Boor
Local Newspapers: Stamford Mercury, Herald & Post, Peterborough Evening Telegraph.
Club Colours: Blue & white **Change Colours:** Red & white.
Clubhouse details: Open evenings, lunchtimes & matchdays.
Year formed: 1920 **Nickname:** Stones **Midweek matchday:** Tuesday
Record Gate: 700 v Glinton.
Previous Leagues: Peterborough Works/ Peterborough/ Stamford & District.
Previous Names: Rutland Ironworks/ Blackstone (until 1975).
Players to progress to Football League: Craig Goldsmith (Peterborough, Carlisle), Alan Neilson (Newcastle & Wales).
Hons: UCL Div 1 R-up 87-88 (Benevolent Cup R-up), Lincs Snr Cup 'A' 92-93.
Captain 1992-93: Stan Hardy **Player of the Year 1992-93:** Eric Bolster/ Shaun Burke.
1992-93 Leading Scorers: Dave Torrance 19, Ian Locke 14, Stan Hardy 7.
1992-93 Leading Appearances: Eric Bolster 43, Dave Torrance 43, Stan Hardy 41.

NEWPORT PAGNELL TOWN

Chairman: Ernie Print **President:** Ken Inch.
Secretary: John Anderson, 29 De Ferneus Drive, Raunds, Northants NN9 6SU (0933 623734).
Manager: Alan Milne **Asst Manager:** Terry Ashton.
Ground: Willen Road, Newport Pagnell (0908 611993).
Directions: Adjacent to A442 Newport Pagnell by-pass.
Capacity: 2,000 **Seats:** 100 **Cover:** 100 **Floodlights:** Yes **Founded:** 1963.
Prog: 20 pages **Editor:** Jim Bean **Press Officer:** Barry Cook.
Clubhouse: Open every evening **Local Newspapers:** Milton Keynes Citizen.
Club colours: Green & white **Change colours:** Yellow & black
Previous Leagues: Nth Bucks/ Sth Mids 71-73 **Nickname:** Swans
Hons: UCL Div 1 81-82 (R-up 91-92, Div 1 Cup 77-78).
Captain 1992-93: Paul Beattie **Player of the Year 1992-93:** Paul Beattie.
1992-93 Leading Scorers: Lee Bearman 14, Bobby Smith 14, Tony Hamilton 8.
1992-93 Leading Appearances: Les Caves 42, Paul Beattie 37, Gary Hartwell 37, Andy Page 37.

NORTHAMPTON SPENCER

Chairman: Graham Wrighting   **President:** Barry Rumford
Secretary: Cliff Dadds, 10 Wakefield Rd, Kingsthorpe, Northampton NN2 7RU (0604 714640).
Manager: Gary Sargent   **Asst Manager:** Keith Bowen
Ground: Kingsthorpe Mill, Studland Rd, Northampton NN3 1NF (0604 718898).
Directions: Turn off Kingsthorpe Rd at traffic lights into Thornton Rd, 1st right into Studland Rd, ground at end.
Capacity: 2,000   **No. seats:** 100   **Covered Accom:** 350   **Floodlights:** Yes
Programme: 40 pages   **Programme Editor/Press Officer:** Andy Goldsmith
Local Newspapers: Chronicle & Echo, Northampton Post, Northants Advertiser.
Club Colours: Yellow & green   **Change Colours:** White & green
Clubhouse details: Large lounge and bar, open matchdays
Year formed: 1936   **Nickname:** Millers   **Midweek matchday:** Tuesday
Record Attendance: 800, English Schools Semi-Final 1991, Kingsthorpe v Erith.
Previous League: Northampton Town   **Previous Name:** Spencer School Old Boys.
Previous Grounds: Dallington Park 1936-70, Duston High School 70-72.
Players to progress to Football League: Paul Stratford (Northampton), Wakeley Gage (Northampton, Chester, Peterborough, Crewe)
Hons: Utd Co's Lg 91-92 (R-up 92-93), Div 1 84-85, KO Cup & R-up, Benev. Cup 91-92), N'hants Snr Cup R-up
Club Captain 1992-93: Paul Jelley   **Player of the Year 1992-93:** Tim Agutter.
1992-93 Leading Scorers: Kevin McGuire 26, Adam Sandy 19, John Inwood 12.
1992-93 Leading Apps: Tony Calvert 44, Tim Agutter 43, John Arundel 43, Paul Jelley 43.

POTTON UNITED

Chairman: Claude Munns   **President:** Peter Hutchinson.
Secretary: Derek Inskip, 3 Bellevue Close, Potton, Beds SG19 2QA (0767 260355).
Manager: Andy Lloyd   **Asst Manager:** Mark Humphrey   **Coach:** Dave Earl
Ground: The Hollow, Biggleswade Road, Potton (0767 261100).
Directions: Outskirts of Potton on Biggleswade Road (B1040). Three and a half miles from Sandy (BR). United Counties buses from Biggleswade.
Capacity: 2,000   **Seats:** 180   **Cover:** 250   **Floodlights:** Yes   **Founded:** 1943
Programme: 48 pages, 30p   **Pogramme Editor/ Press Officer:** Keith Mayhew
Local Newspapers: Biggleswade Chronicle, St Neots Weekly News.
Club Colours: Blue & white   **Change Colours:** Yellow & black   **Nickname:** Royals
Clubhouse details: Large (capacity for 100), opened 1985.   **Midweek matchday:** Tuesday
Record Attendance: 470 v Hastings Town, FA Vase 1989
Previous Lges: Sth Mids 46-55/ Central Alliance 56-61 **Previous Ground:** The Recreation Grnd until 1947.
Hons: Utd Co's Lg 86-87 88-89 (KO Cup 72-73, Benevolent Cup 89-90), Beds Snr Cup(5) 47-49 63-64 75-76 77-78, Wallspan Floodlit Cup 87-88, Hinchingbrooke Cup 51-52 84-85 89-90 90-91 91-92, Hunts Premier Cup 89-90, Beds I'mediate Cup 43-44, Nth Beds Charity Cup(9) 58-60 65-67 70-72 85-86 87-88 89-90, FA Vase 5th Rd 89-90.
Club Captain 1992-93: Dave Albone   **Player of the Year 1992-93:** Mark Scott.
1992-93 Leading Scorers: Roy Boon 28, Ray Seekings 27, Dave Albone 18.
1992-93 Leading Appearances: Dave Albone 42, Mark Scott 42, Mark Humphrey 41, Ray Seekings 41.

RAUNDS TOWN

Chairman: George Hagan   **President:** R Woods
Secretary: Frank Matson, 44 Holmes Avenue, Raunds, Northants NN9 6SX (0933 624765).
Manager: Keith Burt   **Asst Manager:** Glen Burdett
Ground: Kiln Park, Brick Kiln Road, Raunds (0933 623351).
Directions: Take Raunds turning at r'bout on A605 and ground is first left.
Capacity: 3,000   **No. seats:** 100   **Covered Accom:** 1,000   **Floodlights:** Yes
Prog.: 48 pages 30p (Wirral Club survey National Winner 1993 - Runner-up 1992 - UCL winner since 1989).
Press Officer & Programme Editor: Mick Jones
Local Newspapers: Northants Evening Telegraph, Wellingborough Post, Chronicle & Echo.
Colours: Red & black   **Change Colours:** White.   **Clubhouse:** On ground, open every day
Year formed: 1896   **Nickname:** Shopmates   **Midweek matchday:** Tuesday
Record Attendance: 1,500 v Crystal Palace, ground opening 23/7/91.
Previous Leagues: Rushden & District, Central Northants Combination.
Previous Grounds: Greenhouse Field (until 1948), The Berristers (1948-91).
Players to progress to Football League: Greg Downs (Norwich, Coventry, Birmingham, Hereford).
Hons: UCL Div 1 82-83 (KO Cup 90-91), Northants Snr Cup, Northants Jnr Cup 92-93(Reserves)
Club Captain 1992-93: Tony Boatswain   **Player of the Year 1992-93:** Ashley Carr.
1992-93 Leading Scorers: Shaun Keeble 36, James Westley 24, Julian Capone 13.
1992-93 Leading Appearances: Simon Field 46, Ashley Carr 45, Gary Torrance 45.

ROTHWELL TOWN

Chairman: Stuart Andrews   **President:** Jack Covington.
Secretary: Roger Barratt, 18 Norton Street, Rothwell, Northants (0536 711244).
Manager: Jack Murray   **Asst Manager:** Graham Simmonds
Ground: Cecil Street, Rothwell (0536 710694).
Directions: Enter Rothwell on A6, turn into Bridge Street at Midland Bank, turn 3rd left into Tresham Street, ground is at top. Three miles from Kettering (BR); Rothwell is served by Kettering to Market Harborough buses.
Capacity: 3,000   **No. seats:** 460   **Covered Accom:** 700   **Floodlights:** Yes
Programme: 20 pages, 20p   **Programme Editor/Press Officer:** Peter Bradley
Local Newspapers: Northants Evening Telegraph, Chronicle & Echo.
Club Colours: Blue & white.   **Change Colours:** Red & white
Clubhouse: Large Sportsmans Bar, 'Top of the Town Ballroom', lounge for 200.
Year formed: 1896   **Nickname:** Bones   **Midweek matchday:** Tuesday
Record Attendance: 2508 v Irthlingborough 1971   **Previous Name:** Rothwell Town Swifts.
Previous Leagues: Kettering Amateur, Leicestershire Senior, Central Alliance 56-61.
Players progressing to Football Lge: Lee Glover (Nottm F., Barnsley & Scotland u-21), Matty Watts (Charlton)
Hons: UCL 92-93 (KO Cup(6), Div 2(2) 52-54, Div 2 Cup(2) 52-54, Benevolent Cup 92-93), Northants Lg 1899-1900, Northants Snr Cup(3)
Club Captain 1992-93: Adrian Sheerin   **Player of the Year 1992-93:** Nigel Bates.
1992-93 Leading Scorers: Terry O'Keefe 25, Paul Murphy 21, Adrian Sheerin 15.
1992-93 Leading Appearances: Nigel Bates 50, Danny Liquorish 50, Adrian Sheerin 49.

SPALDING UNITED

Chairman: Rod Quinton
Secretary: Howard Williamson, 26 Rembrant Way, Spalding, Lincs (0775 711165).
Manger: Martin Henderson   **Asst Manager:** Dave Arnold
Ground: Sir Halley Stewart Field, Winfrey Avenue, Spalding (0775 724957).
Directions: Town centre off A16, adjacent to bus station. 250 yds from Spalding (BR).
Capacity: 7,000   **Seats:** 350   **Cover:** 2,500   **Floodlights:** Yes   **Founded:** 1921
Programme: 16 pages   **Editor:** Jack Grimwood   **Press Officer:** Ray Tucker
Club Colours: Blue & white   **Change Colours:** Red & white
Clubhouse details: Open matchdays, and events.   **Midweek matchday:** Tuesday
Record Attendance: 6,972 v Peterborough, FA Cup 1952.   **Nickname:** Tulips
Previous Leagues: Peterborough/ Utd Co's 31-55 68-78 86-88/ Eastern Co's 55-60/ Central Alliance 60-61/ Midland Co's 61-68/ Northern Co's East 82-86/ Southern 88-91.
Players progressing to Football League: Carl Shutt (Sheffield Wednesday, Bristol City, Leeds).
Local Newspapers: Lincs Free Press, Spalding Guardian, Peterborough Evening Telegraph.
Hons: Utd Co's Lg 54-55 74-75 87-88 (R-up 50-51 51-52 52-53 72-73 75-76, KO Cup 54-55), Northern Co's East Lg 83-84, Lincs Snr Cup 52-53, Lincs Snr 'A' Cup 87-88, Lincs Snr 'B' Cup 50-51, Evans Halshaw F'lit Cup 89-90.
Club Captain 1992-93: Glen Nitley   **Player of the Year 1992-93:** Mick Smith
Leading Scorers 1992-93: Nick Keeble 20, Carlton Grogan 9, Ian Shooter 8.
Leading Appearances 1992-93: Jeremy Moulds 45, Mick Smith 44, Nick Keeble 41.

STAMFORD

Chairman: Arthur Twiddy
Secretary/Press Officer: Andrew Eason, 36 Queens Walk, Stamford, Lincs (0780 54510).
Manager: Chris Corby   **Asst Manager:** Mick Reilly
Coach: Stuart Chiverton   **Commercial Mgr:** Bob Ford/ George Bennett
Ground: Wothorpe Road, Stamford, Lincs (0780 63079).
Directions: Off A43 Kettering Rd, 1 mile east of A1. 200 yds from station.
Capacity: 5,000   **No. seats:** 250   **Covered Accom:** 1,250   **Floodlights:** Yes
Programme: 40 pages, 50p   **Editor:** Andrew Eason   **Club Shop:** Dave Salisbury (0780 52377)
Local Newspapers: Stamford Mercury, Peterborough Evening Telegraph, Herald & Post.
Club Colours: Red & blue   **Change Colours:** All white
Year formed: 1896   **Nickname:** Daniels   **Midweek matchday:** Tuesday
Record Attendance: 4,200 v Kettering, FA Cup 1953.
Previous Leagues: Peterborough/ Northants (UCL) 08-55/ Central Alliance 55-61/ Midland Co's 61-72.
Players to progress to Football League: Alan Birchenall (Chelsea, Crystal Palace, Leicester), Reg Chester (Aston Villa), Teddy Tye (Chelsea), Gerry Fell (Brighton, Southend, Torquay, York), Campbell Chapman (Wolves), Steve Collins (Peterborough), Keith Alexander (Grimsby, Stockport, Lincoln), Andy Tillson (Grimsby, QPR, Bristol Rovers), Brian Stubbs (Notts Co.), Domenico Genovese (Peterborough).
Hons: FA Vase 79-80 (R-up 75-76 83-84), Utd Co's Lg 75-76 77-78 79-80 80-81 81-82 (KO Cup 51-52 75-76 79-80 81-82 85-86, Northants Lg 11-12, Lincs Snr 'A' Cup 78-79 82-83, Lincs Snr 'B' Cup 51-52 53-54, Hinchingbrooke Cup, William Scarber Mem. Cup 70-71 82-83 85-86 88-89, Stamford Chal. Cup 89-90, Lincs Jnr Cup 48-49.
Club Captain 1992-93: Simon Daws   **Player of the Year 1992-93:** Jason Walker.
1992-93 Leading Scorers: Darren Edey 29, Mark Hipwell 16, Paul Hucker 12.
1992-93 Leading Appearances: Darren Edey 43, Jasin Walker 43, Simon Daws 41.

STEWART & LLOYDS

Chairman: John Hamill
Secretary: Phil Mackay, 207 Rockingham Road, Kettering, Northants NN16 9JA (0536 410840).
Manager: Kevin Byrne
Ground: Recreation Ground, Occupation Road, Corby (0536 401497).
Directions: On Occupation Rd at rear of Stewart & Lloyds Leisure Club, next to old Corby Town F.C. ground.
Capacity: 1,500   **No. seats:** 100   **Covered Accom:** 200   **Floodlights:** Yes
Programme: 8 pages with admission   **Programme Editor/Press Officer:** Dave Foster
Clubhouse details: Licensed bar.   **Local Press:** Northants Evening Telegraph
Club Colours: Yellow & blue   **Change Colours:** Red & white
Year formed: 1935   **Nickname:** None   **Midweek matchday:** Tuesday
Record Attendance: Unknown   **Previous Leagues:** Kettering Amateur
Previous Name: Hamlet Stewart & Lloyds (until 1992).
Players to progress to Football League: Andy McGowan (Northampton), Willie Graham (Brentford)
Hons: UCL R-up 85-86 (KO Cup, Div 1(2) 73-75, Div 1 Cup(2) 73-75, Div 2(Res) 76-77, Div 2 KO Cup(2) 75-77)
Club Captain 1992-93: P J Hamill   **Player of the Year 1992-93:** Joey Martin.
1992-93 Leading Scorers: Joey Martin 45, Steve Farr 11, Steve Wilkinson 10.
1992-93 Leading Appearances: P J Hamill 46, Graham Leech 46, Mike McConnell 45.

STOTFOLD

Chairman: Gerry Watson   **President:** Charlie Hyde
Secretary: Bill Clegg, 12 Common Rd, Stotfold, Hitchin, Herts SG5 4BX (0462 730421).
Manager: Ian Allinson   **Asst Manager:** Tony Anglin
Press Officer: Julie Longhurst   **Physiotherapists:** J Page, I Taylor.
Ground: Roker Park, The Green, Stotfold (0462 730765).
Directions: A507 from A1, right at lights, right at T-jct. A507 from Bedford via Shefford, left at lights, right at T-jct.
Capacity: 5,000   **Seats:** 50   **Cover:** 300   **Floodlights:** Yes   **Nickname:** Eagles
Programme: 32 pages   **Editor:** Keith Mayhew   **Price:** With admission
Local Newspapers: Comet, Biggleswade Chronicle.
Club Colours: Amber & black   **Change Colours:** Sky blue
Clubhouse details: Clubroom, bar, dressing rooms, physio room.   **Midweek matchday:** Tuesday
Year formed: 1904, reformed 1945   **Record Attendance:** 1,000 v Letchworth Town, FA Vase.
Previous Leagues: Biggleswade & District/ North Herts/ South Midlands 51-84.
Hons: Utd Co's Lg KO Cup R-up 91-92 (Res Div 1 87-88), Sth Mids Lg 80-81 (R-up 55-56 57-58 58-59 59-60 63-64 65-66 77-78, Div 1 53-54, Chal. Tphy 81-82, Beds Snr Cup 64-65, Beds Premier Cup 81-82, Beds I'mediate Cup 58-59, Nth Beds Charity Cup 55-56 56-57 61-62 81-82 87-88 90-91, Beds Colts Lg 88-89.
Club Captain 1992-93: Steve Vessey   **Player of the Year 1992-93:** Steve Vessey/Dave Chellew.
1992-93 Leading Scorers: Gary Walker 17, Mick Bennett 12, Mark Whelan 9.
1992-93 Leading Appearances: Gary Walker 43, Steve Vessey 41, Dave Chellew 35.

WELLINGBOROUGH TOWN

Chairman: Mike McNamee **President:** Corville Brown.
Secretary/Press Officer: Mike Walden, 5 Fernie Way, Wellingborough, Northants NN8 3LB (0933 279561).
Manager: Martin Potton
Ground: Dog & Duck, London Rd, Wellingborough (0933 223536).
Directions: 200 yds off A45 by-pass, by Dog & Duck public house. 1 mile from Wellingborough (BR).
Capacity: 5,000 **Seats:** 300 **Cover:** 500 **Floodlights:** Yes **Founded:** 1867
Programme: 16 pages, 30p **Editor:** Nick Dzyka
Local Newspapers: Northants Evening Telegraph, Chronicle & Echo.
Colours: Blue & gold **Change Colours:** All red **Clubhouse details:** On ground, full facilties.
Nickname: Doughboys **Midweek matchday:** Tuesday **Record Attendance:** 4,013 v Kettering
Previous Leagues: Midland 1895-97 98-1901/ Southern 01-05 79-82/ Northants (Utd Co's) 19-34 36-56 61-68/ Central Alliance 56-61/ Metropolitan 68-70/ West Mids 70-71.
Players to progress to Football League: Phil Neal (N'hampton, L'pool & Eng.), Fanny Walden (Spurs & Eng.).
Major Honours: UCL(3), Metropolitan Lg 69-70, Northants Senior Cup(7).
Club Captain 1992-93: Mark Cowper **Player of the Year 1992-93:** Lloyd Glennon
1992-93 Leading Scorers: Lloyd Glennon 15, Brian Clarke 4.
1992-93 Leading Appearances: Lloyd Glennon 42, Mark Cowper 33, Mark Buckby 30.

WOOTTON BLUE CROSS

Chairman: B Keens **President:** J Clarke
Secretary: Trevor Templeman, 67 Glenwoods, Newport Pagnell, Bucks MK16 0NG (0908 611053).
Manager: Ken Goodeve **Asst Manager:** Neil Simms.
Ground: Weston Park, Bedford Rd, Wootton (0234 767662).
Directions: 4 miles south of Bedford on main road through village, at rear of Post Office.
Capacity: 2,000 **No. seats:** 50 **Covered Accom:** 500 **Floodlights:** Yes
Programme: 12 pages, 20p **Press Officer & Programme Editor:** Trevor Templeman.
Local Newspapers: Bedfordshire Times, Bedford Herald, Beds Express, Beds On Sunday.
Club Colours: Blue & white **Change Colours:** All white
Clubhouse: Main hall, bar, darts, pool, bingo. Open every evening, Sat & Sun lunchtimes
Year formed: 1887 **Nickname:** Blue Cross **Midweek matchday:** Tuesday
Record Attendance: 838 v Luton Town, Beds Premier Cup 1988
Previous Leagues: Bedford & District, South Midlands 46-55.
Players to progress to Football League: A Biggs (Arsenal).
Hons: Utd Co's Lg Div 2 67-68 69-70 (KO Cup 82-83, Div 2 Cup 64-65), Sth Mids Lg 47-48 (R-up 49-50), Beds Snr Cup 70-71, Hinchingbrooke Cup(5).
Club Captain 1992-93: Des Ewart **Player of the Year 1992-93:** Alan Brown.
1992-93 Leading Scorers: Danny Nicholls 26, Paul Cashin 6, Alan Sawyer 6.
1992-93 Leading Appearances: Brendan Quill 42, Jamie Hawthorn 38, Alan Brown 37, Leo Conroy 37, Des Cook, Danny Nicholls 37.

DIVISION ONE CLUBS 1993-94

BLISWORTH

Chairman: Pete Edwards **Manager:** Gary Knibbs
Secretary: Terry Jeyes, 33 Buttmead, Blisworth, Northampton NN7 3DQ (0604 858750).
Ground: Blisworth Playing Field, Courteenhall Rd, Blisworth (0604 858024).
Directions: Courteenhall Rd off A43.
Capacity: 1,000 **Seats:** None **Cover:** None **Floodlights:** No **Clubhouse:** Yes
Colours: Yellow & green **Change:** White & blue **Programme:** 8 pages with admission
Previous Leagues: Central Northants Combination **Honours:** Northants Junior Cup
Club Captain 1992-93: Wayne Humphries **Player of the Year 1992-93:** Darren Andrews.
1992-93 Leading Scorers: Paul Andrews 8, Gary Edwards 5, John Frost 4, Wayne Humphries 4.
1992-93 Leading Appearances: Darren Andrews 31, Gary Edwards 30, Wayne Humphries 25, Ian Lovell 25.

BRITISH TIMKEN

Chairman: A Watts **Manager:** Derek Lary **Asst Manager:** Darren Taylor
Secretary: Gary Duff, 10 Oriel Row, Stefan Hill, Daventry, Northants NN11 4SP (0327 705362).
Ground: Braunston Rd, Daventry (0604 581588). **Programme:** 16 pages, with admission.
Directions: A45 from Northampton to outskirts of Daventry, works entrance at top of Braunston Road.
Capacity: 2,500 **Seats:** 150 **Cover:** Yes **Floodlights:** No **Clubhouse:** Yes
Previous Leagues: None **Hons:** UCL Div 1 (Div 2, Div 2 Cup, Benevolent Cup)
Club Captain 1992-93: Wayne Brown **Player of the Year 1992-93:** Wayne Brown
1992-93 Leading Scorers: Russell Brown 18, Wayne Brown 10, Tony Burt 8.
1992-93 Leading Appearances: Wayne Brown 33, Andy Joseph 30, Russell Brown 28, Tony Burt 28.

BUGBROOKE ST MICHAELS

Chairman: John Curtis **Manager:** Nick Verity **Asst Manager:** Tony Bonner.
Secretary: Roger Geary, 31 Kislingbury Rd, Bugbrooke, Northampton NN7 3QG (0604 831678).
Ground: Birds Close, Gayton Rd, Bugbrooke (0604 830707).
Directions: A45 Northampton to Daventry road, turn onto B4525 (Banbury Lane) at Kislingbury, turn left to Gayton, ground on left.
Capacity: 1,500 **Seats:** None **Cover:** Yes **Floodlights:** Yes **Nickname:** Badgers
Founded: **Programme:** 8 pages **Clubhouse:** Yes
Club colours: Blue & yellow **Change colours:** Yellow & navy
Previous Leagues: Central Northants Combination **Major Honours:** Northants Junior Cup
Club Captain 1992-93: Mark Brown **Player of the Year 1992-93:** Dale Williams.
1992-93 Leading Scorers: Dave Botterill 21, Shay O'Riordan 14, Jamie Elliott 8.
1992-93 Leading Appearances: Mark Brown 36, Mike Dillon 34, Dale Williams 34.

Stamford F.C. 1992-93. Photo - Gavin Ellis-Neville.

Wootton Blue Cross F.C. 1992-93. Photo - Dave West.

Blisworth's John Woolgar (left) shields the ball from Burton Park Wanderer Neil Tilley. Photo - Martin Wray.

BURTON PARK WANDERERS

Chairman: Bernard Lloyd   **Manager:** Ian Lawson.
Secretary: Stuart Coles, 5 Southgate Drive, Kettering, Northants (0536 520349).
Ground: Latimer Park, Polwell Lane, Burton Latimer (0536 725841).
Directions: Entering Burton Latimer, turn off A6 Station Rd and right into Powell Lane; ground on the right.
Capacity: 1,000   **Seats:** 100   **Cover:** 150   **Floodlights:** No   **Founded:** 1961
Local Newspapers: Northants Evening Telegraph, Northants Post.
Club Colours: Green & yellow   **Change Colours:** Red & black
Prog: 16 pages with entry   **Nickname:** The Wanderers   **Midweek matchday:** Tuesday
Record Attendance: 253 v Rothwell, May 1989   **Previous Leagues:** Kettering Amateur
Past Players to progress to Football League: Shaun Wills (Peterborough)
Major Honours: UCL Div 1 R-up, Benevolent Cup R-up
Club Captain 1992-93: Ian Milne   **Player of the Year 1992-93:** Neil Tilley.
1992-93 Leading Scorers: Neil Tilley 19, Wayne Sutton 10, Frank Hauser 8.
1992-93 Leading Appearances: Darren Vowden 34, Dave Chandler 33, John Sadler 32, Neil Tilley 32.

COTTINGHAM

Chairman: Mike Beadsworth   **Manager:** Neil Newlands   **Asst Manager:** Vinny Keefe
Secretary: Lindsay Brownlie, 30 Bancroft Rd, Cottingham, Market Harborough LE16 8XA (0536 771009).
Ground: Berryfield Rd, Cottingham (0536 770051).
Directions: One and a half miles from Corby on A427 turn right to Cottingham. At junction of B670 turn left; Berryfield Road 200 yds on right.
Capacity: 1,000   **No. of seats:** None   **Covered Accommodation:** Yes
Floodlights: No   **Programme:** No   **Clubhouse:** Bar & changing rooms
Club colours: White & navy blue   **Change colours:** Blue, white & green.
Previous Leagues: East Mids Alliance, Kettering Amateur, Market Harborough
Major Honours: UCL Div 1 runners-up, Northants Junior Cup
Club Captain 1992-93: Neil Pask   **Player of the Year 1992-93:** Ian McLuckie.
92-93 Top Scorers: Terry Bates 9, Mick Ward 8, Ian McLuckie 7, Dave Rogers 7.
1992-93 Leading Appearances: Ian McLuckie 30, Neil Pask 29, John Sneddon 26.

FORD SPORTS

Chairman: Dave Taylor   **Manager:** Gary Graham   **Asst Manager:** Jim Henderson.
Secretary: David Hirons, 53 Armull Cres., Daventry, Northants (0327 71461).
Ground: Royal Oak Way South, Daventry (0327 709219).
Directions: Enter Daventry on A45 or A361 and follow signs for Royal Oak Way
Capacity: 1,000   **Seats:** Yes   **Covered Accommodation:** Yes
Floodlights: Yes   **Programme:** 12 pages   **Clubhouse:** Yes
Club colours: All blue   **Change colours:** All red.
Previous Leagues: Central Northants Combination
Club Captain 1992-93: Richard Green   **Player of the Year 1992-93:** Richard Haynes.
1992-93 Leading Scorers: Neil Brough 53, Rod Hough 16, Rob McKay 16.
1992-93 Leading Appearances: Rob McKay 37, Richard Green 35, Brian Blakeman 35.
Hons: UCL Div 1 92-93 (Benevolent Cup R-up 92-93, Highest Aggregate Goalscoring Trophy 92-93).

HARROWBY UNITED

Chairman: Chris Whitehead   **Manager:** Barry Shaw   **Assistant Mgr:** Pete Down
Secretary: Jack Gardner, 14 Wong Gdns, Harrowby, Grantham, Lincs (0476 590822).
Ground: Harrowby Playing Fields, Harrowby Lane, Grantham (0476 590822).
Directions: From A1 take B6403, go past A52 roundabout, past Ancaster turn and take road to Harrowby. Continue into Grantham, ground on right opposite Cherry Tree public house.
Capacity: 1,500   **No. of seats:** 100   **Covered Accommodation:** Yes.
Floodlights: No   **Programme:** 12 pages   **Clubhouse:** Yes
Club colours: Blue & white   **Change colours:** Red & white.
Previous Leagues: Mids Regional Alliance, East Mids, Lincolnshire, Grantham.
Hons: Utd Co's Lg Div 1 91-92 (Benev. Cup R-up 91-92), Mids Regional All. Lg & Cup, Lincs Snr 'B' Cup(2).
Club Captain 1992-93: Darren Hallene   **Player of the Year 1992-93:** None
1992-93 Leading Scorers: Dennis Jenas 10, Sammy Piggott 10, Chris North 6.
1992-93 Leading Appearances: Darren Hallcro 33, Gary Bredan 26, Neil Gardner 23, Steve Pearson 23.

HIGHAM TOWN

Chairman: Phil Palmer   **Manager:** Gary Savage   **Asst Manager:** Alan Strickland
Secretary: Chris Ruff, 27 Queensway, Higham Ferrers NN9 8BU (0933 58862).
Ground: Vine Hill Drive, Higham Ferrers (0933 57501).
Directions: From Kettering 1st right on A6 after A45 junction to St Neots. From Bedford, 3rd left after A45 junction to Northampton
Capacity: 1,000   **No. of seats:** Nil   **Covered Accommodation:** 100
Floodlights: No   **Programme:** 12 pages   **Clubhouse:** Yes
Colours: Sky blue & navy   **Change colours:** White & black   **Previous Lge:** Rushden & Dist.
Hons: UCL Div 1 R-up 92-93, Northants Lg 21-22 22-23, Northants Snr Cup 21-22, Maunsell Cup.
Club Captain 1992-93: Mark Newton   **Player of the Year 1992-93:** Steve Broadhurst.
1992-93 Leading Scorers: Steve Medlin 27, Shaun Dodson 16, Grant Smith 16.
92-93 Leading Apps: Stuart Abrahart 41, James Keeney 41, Steve Broadhurst 40, John Sellers 40, Grant Smith 40.

IRCHESTER UNITED

Chairman: Geoff Cotter   **Manager:** Alan Ambridge/ Martin Batley.
Secretary: P Mayhew, 25 Finedon Street, Burton Latimer, Northants, (0536 723341).
Ground: Alfred Street, Irchester (0933 312877).
Directions: Off Rushden Road to Wollaston Road, next to recreation ground.
Capacity: 1,000   **No. of seats:** None   **Covered Accommodation:** Yes
Floodlights: No   **Programme:** No   **Clubhouse:** Yes
Club colours: Claret & white   **Change colours:** Yellow & black
Previous Leagues: Rushden & District   **Hons:** Northants Lg Div 2 30-31 31-32.
Club Captain 1992-93: Glen Finch   **Player of the Year 1992-93:** Andy Cotter.
1992-93 Leading Scorers: Chris Foster 10, Steve Raybould 7, Nick Shelton 7.
1992-93 Leading Appearances: Darren Drage 33, Glen Finch 32, Keith Hacker 31.

NORTHAMPTON O.N. CHENECKS

Chairman: John Wilson **Manager:** Tony Pancoust.
Secretary: John Goodger, 74 Beech Avenue, Northampton NN3 2JG (0604 717224).
Ground: Billing Road, Northampton (0604 34045).
Directions: South ring road, exit A43 Kettering, left at lights, top of hill, ground 200 yds on right.
Capacity: 1,350 **Seats:** Yes **Covered Accommodation:** Yes
Floodlights: No **Prog.:** 16 pages with entry **Clubhouse:** Yes
Club colours: All blue **Change colours:** All red
Previous Leagues: Northampton Town **Hons:** UCL Div 1 77-78 79-80.
Club Captain 1992-93: John Paver **Player of the Year 1992-93:** Keith Garraway
1992-93 Leading Scorers: Andy Evans 15, Keith Garraway 10, Chris Smith 10
1992-93 Leading Appearances: Chris Smith 35, Trevor Cadden 35, Andy Evans 30.

NORTHAMPTON VANAID

Chairman: Rob Clarke **Manager:** Richard Underwood **Asst Manager:** Mick Calvert.
Secretary: Tony Loveday, 28 Rickyard Rd, The Arbours, Northampton NN3 3RR (0604 412502).
Ground: Fernie Fields, Moulton, Northampton.
Directions: R'bout at Lumbertub pub take turn to Moulton 1st right.
Capacity: 700 **Seats:** 20 **Covered Accommodation:** Yes
Floodlights: No **Programme:** Yes **Clubhouse:** Yes
Club colours: White/black/blue **Change colours:** Red, navy/blue.
Previous Lges: Northampton Town (pre-1993)
Club Captain 1992-93: Stuart Prior **Player of the Year 1992-93:** Jessel Dore

OLNEY TOWN

Chairman: Peter Shipton **Manager:** Alan Byron **Asst Manager:** Barry Simons
Secretary: Andrew Baldwin, 49 Midland Road, Olney, Bucks MK46 4BP (0234 711071)
Ground: East Street, Olney (0234 712227)
Directions: Enter Olney on A509 from Wellingborough, 100yds on left enter East St, ground 200 yds on left.
Capacity: 2,000 **No. of seats:** None **Covered Accommodation:** Yes
Floodlights: No **Programme:** 32 pages **Clubhouse:** Yes
Club colours: White & black **Change colours:** Green & yellow.
Prev. Lges: Nth Bucks, Rushden & Dist. **Hons:** UCL Div 1 72-73, Berks & Bucks I'mediate Cup 92-93
Club Captain 1992-93: Paul Banks **Player of the Year 1992-93:** Clive Woodland.
1992-93 Leading Scorers: Clive Woodland 17, Jason Cole 10, Adrian North 7.
1992-93 Leading Appearances: Russell Ward 35, Adrian North 34, Mark Lancaster 33, Gary Little 33.

RAMSEY TOWN

Chairman: Ian Cooper **Manager:** Jan Czarnecki **Asst Manager:** Steve Grys
Secretary: Mike Baldwin, 19 Slade Close, Ramsey, Cambs PE17 1LF (0487 814084).
Ground: Cricketfield Lane, Ramsey (0487 814218)
Directions: 100 yds off B1040 Ramsey to Warboys road.
Capacity: 1,000 **No. of seats:** None **Covered Accommodation:** Yes
Floodlights: Yes **Programme:** 12 pages **Clubhouse:** Yes
Club colours: Amber & black **Change colours:** Red & white.
Previous Leagues: Peterborough & District **Honours:** UCL Div 1, Hunts Senior Cup(3).
Club Captain 1992-93: Gary Richardson **Player of the Year 1992-93:** Ian Edmonds
1992-93 Leading Scorers: Jim Barron 18, Stuart Kilby 17, Chris Crowtell 8.
1992-93 Leading Appearances: Lional Ding 30, Ian Edmonds 29, Stuart Kilby 28.

ST IVES TOWN

Chairman: Mick Tacchi **Manager:** Tony Coulson **Asst Manager:** Neil King.
Secretary: Jim Stocker, 23 Townsend Rd, Needingworth, St Ives, Cambs PE17 3SE (0480 492680).
Ground: Westwood Rd, St Ives, Cambs (0480 63207) **Directions:** Adjacent to St Ives Sports Centre.
Capacity: 5,000 **Seats:** Yes **Covered Accommodation:** Yes
Floodlights: Yes **Programme:** 8 pages **Clubhouse:** Bar and entertainment room.
Club colours: White & black **Change colours:** Sky & navy
Previous Leagues: Peterborough, Cambs **Major Honours:** Hunts Senior Cup(8).
Club Captain 1992-93: Warren Everdell **Player of the Year 1992-93:** Ian Brown.
1992-93 Leading Scorers: Mark Shiels 14, Paul Geary 12, Jim Barron 10.
92-93 Leading Appearances: Warren Everdell 35, Paul Geary 30, Mark Shiels 28.

SHARNBROOK

Chairman: Peter Butler **Manager:** Dick Williams **Asst Manager:** Jim Donaldson
Secretary: Rob Stanton, 4 Towns End Rd, Sharnbrook, Beds (0234 782052).
Ground: Lodge Rd, Sharnbrook (0234 781080).
Directions: Second sign to Sharnbrook from Rushden on A6, under railway bridge, right at T-junction, left past church, right into Lodge Road.
Capacity: 1,000 **No. of seats:** None **Covered Accommodation:** Yes
Floodlights: No **Programme:** 12 pages **Clubhouse:** Yes
Cols: Maroon & white **Change colours:** White & black. **Previous Leagues:** Bedford
Club Captain 1992-93: Steve Guerin **Player of the Year 1992-93:** Steve Farthing.
1992-93 Leading Scorers: Chris Bolton 14, Steve Farthing 11, Adrian Allebone 7.
1992-93 Leading Appearances: Steve Guerin 34, Steve Smith 33, Adrian Allebone 27, Steve Farthing 27.

THRAPSTON VENTURAS

Chairman: David Morson   **Manager:** Gary Petts   **Asst Manager:** Mark James.
Secretary: Derek Pickard, 9 Springfield Ave., Thrapston, Northants (08012 734102)
Ground: Chancery Lane, Thrapston, Northants (08012 732470).
Directions: Chancery Lane off A605 in town centre.
Capacity: 1,000   **No. of seats:** Yes   **Covered Accommodation:** Yes
Floodlights: No   **Programme:** Yes   **Clubhouse:** Yes
Club colours: Blue & white   **Change colours:** Yellow & black
Previous Leagues: Kettering Amateur   **Major Honours:** Northants Junior Cup
Club Captain 1992-93: Paul Wainwright   **Player of the Year 1992-93:** Eugene Emanuel
92-93 Leading Scorers: Mark James 19, Gary Petts 14, John Frost 4, Neil Mattinson 4, Clive Roberts 4.
92-93 Leading Appearances: Ian Woolley 33, Eugene Emanuel 32, Mark James 32.

WELLINGBOROUGH WHITWORTHS

Chairman: B Jarvis   **Manager:** Ian Young   **Asst Manager:** Mick Thompson.
Secretary: Ron Edwards, 15 James Rd, Wellingborough NN8 2LR (0933 227765).
Ground: London Road, Wellingborough, Northants (0933 227324).
Directions: Off London Road at Dog & Duck public house
Capacity: 700   **No. of seats:** None   **Covered Accommodation:** Yes
Floodlights: No   **Programme:** No   **Clubhouse:** Yes
Club colours: Blue & white   **Change colours:** Green & white
Previous Leagues: East Midlands Alliance, Rushden & District
Club Captain 1992-93: Steve Grant   **Player of the Year 1992-93:** Steve Grant.
1992-93 Leading Scorers: Steve Whitehead 15, Darren Wilkins 12, Lee Burrows 11.
1992-93 Leading Apprearances: Steve Grant 34, Barrie Price 30, Lee Burrows 26.

Olney Town striker Gary Sands lines up a shot in the 3-1 home win over Sharnbrook. Photo - Martin Wray.

Irchester forward Andy Larkins (left) on the ball against the now defunct Peterborough City. Photo - Martin Wray.

PEARL ASSURANCE
PETERBOROUGH & DISTRICT LEAGUE

PREM. DIVISION	P	W	D	L	F	A	PTS
Perkins Sports	34	26	4	4	109	33	82
Ortonians	34	24	5	5	91	34	77
Deeping Rangers	34	22	6	6	86	31	72
March T. Utd Res.	34	20	10	4	98	40	70
Molins	34	20	8	6	82	31	68
Eye United	34	20	7	7	79	45	67
Wisbech T. Res.	34	15	8	11	68	41	53
Alconbury	34	14	4	16	55	65	46
Oundle Town	34	13	5	16	71	69	44
Moulton Harrox	34	12	6	16	42	57	42
Chatteris T. Res.	34	12	5	17	54	81	41
Stamford Belvedere	34	12	3	19	53	74	39
Thomas Cook	34	11	3	20	45	64	36
Leverington Spts	34	10	6	18	55	86	36
Peterborough BRAD	34	7	8	19	30	62	29
Pinchbeck Utd	34	8	4	22	47	96	28
Whittlesey Utd	34	7	4	23	45	69	25
Brotherhoods	34	4	2	28	31	163	14

DIVISION ONE	P	W	D	L	F	A	PTS
Hotpoint	28	21	2	5	87	33	65
Outwell	28	19	1	8	86	41	58
Deeping R. Res.	28	16	4	8	68	46	52
Ryhall	28	15	5	8	62	43	50
Pearl	28	14	4	10	71	49	46
Ortonians Res.	28	14	3	10	71	40	45
Holbeach U. Res.	28	13	5	10	59	46	44
Manea United	28	13	2	13	68	82	41
Thurlby United	28	13	4	11	54	60	*40
Newage	28	11	5	12	68	63	38
Juventus	28	11	5	12	52	59	38
Stilton	28	8	4	12	45	64	28
Pinchbeck U. Res.	28	6	4	18	34	71	22
Crowland	28	6	2	20	38	77	20
Peterborough Rov.	28	4	2	22	36	124	14
* - 3 points deducted.							

Perkins Sports - Premier Division champions 1992-93. Back Row (L/R): D Brown, M Rayment, S Zeuchuk, A Smith, S Keir, N Papworth (Manager), K Ventus. Front: P Pavey, L Adams, M Graham, C Woollard, P Gauntlett, B Fisher. Photo - Martin Wray.

Ortonians F.C. - Premier Division runners-up 1992-93. Back Row (L/R): D Hart (Trainer), S Hubbard, A Jackson, M Harvey, T Smith, M Shortland, N Wilson, C Wingrove, E Brookes (Manager). Front: F Davison, C Strickle, M Wilson, M Talbot, S Ball, S Gavigan. Photo - Martin Wray.

PETERSBOROUGH & DISTRICT LEAGUE CLUBS

(Tel. codes 0733 unless stated)

ALCONBURY
Ground: Rec. Field, Gt North Rd
Secretary: P Dixon (0480 413272)

BROTHERHOODS
G: Lincoln Rd, Peterborough   S: J Lilley (570172)

CROWLAND TOWN
G: Snowden Field, Thorney Rd
S: Mrs Atkinson (211431)

DEEPING RANGERS
G: Outgang Rd, Market Deeping
S: J Sandall (0780 346006)

EYE UNITED
Lindisfarne Rd, Eye (222094)   P Mitchell (261586)

HOTPOINT
G: Ringwood, Bretton   S: A Andrews (342897)

JUVENTUS
Chestnut Ave., Dogsthorpe   K Woods (526961)

LEVERINGTON SPORTS
G: Church Rd   S: N Missin (0945 582234)

MANEA UNITED
G: Park Rd, Manea   S: P Hawes (0354 78355)

MOLINS
Bretton Way, Nth Bretton   F Hestleton (268544)

MOULTON HARROX
G: Broad Lane   S: H Childs (0406 23849)

NEWAGE
G: Empingham Rd, Stamford
S: T Brookes (0780 51407)

ORTONIANS
G: Bushfield Spts Centre, Orton
S: P Spridgeon (0778 342011)

OUNDLE TOWN
G: Station Rd (0832 274188)
S: M Smith (0832 272013)

OUTWELL SWIFTS
The Nest, Wisbech Rd   Mrs Luckett (0945 773012)

PEARL ASSURANCE
G: Splash Lane, Castor   S: R Young (576461)

PERKINS SPORTS
G: Oxney Rd, Peterboro.   S: R Wells (344232)

PETERBOROUGH B.R.A.D.
G: B.R. Spts Grnd, Maskew Ave., off Lincoln Rd
(66301)
S: P Goodhand (572517)

PETERBOROUGH ROVERS
G: Fulbridge Rd   S: Mrs Starkey (0327 270836)

PINCHBECK UNITED
G: Knight Str., Pinchbeck S: C Clow (0775 85330)

RYHALL UNITED
G: Meadows PF, Ryhall   S: R Young (0780 66618)

STAMFORD BELVEDERE
G: Queen Eleanor Sch., Green Lane
S: K Rawlings (0780 62577)

STANGROUND UNITED
G: Lawson Ave.   S: G Bullivant (342177)

STILTON UNITED
G: High Str., Stilton   S: J Wayland (241097)

THOMAS COOK
Thorpe Wood, Peterboro.   S Gallagher (330400)

THURLBY UNITED
G: Lawrence Park   S: A Pfielderer (0778 393739)

WHITTLESEY UNITED
G: Manor Field, Station Rd, Whittlesey
S: T Bass (203087)

CENTRAL NORTHANTS COMBINATION

PREM. DIVISION	P	W	D	L	F	A	PTS
Milton	26	20	4	2	78	20	64
Woodford United	26	19	4	3	99	33	61
Yardley United	26	17	2	7	91	48	53
Harpole	26	12	6	8	82	55	42
Heyford Athletic	26	11	7	8	67	48	40
Moulton	26	12	3	11	51	44	39
Brington	26	8	12	6	52	48	36
Kislingbury	26	11	3	12	52	51	36
West Haddon	26	10	3	13	53	63	33
Braunston (-1pt)	26	10	4	12	63	87	33
Northants Police	26	9	1	16	55	62	28
Brown Brothers	26	6	6	14	44	69	24
Brackley Town Res.	26	5	4	17	28	94	19
Long Buckby A.	26	2	1	23	33	126	5

'BRAYBROOKE RACING'
HUNTINGDONSHIRE LEAGUE

DIVISION ONE	P	W	D	L	F	A	PTS
St Neots Town	22	20	1	1	121	25	61
Yaxley	22	19	0	3	79	26	57
Huntingdon Utd	22	16	5	1	75	12	53
Brampton	22	11	3	8	63	52	36
Buckden	22	10	4	8	48	44	34
Needingworth	22	9	4	9	40	36	31
B R J	22	9	3	10	76	70	30
Hemingford	22	7	3	12	46	56	24
Offord	22	7	2	13	41	63	23
Great Paxton	22	6	1	15	37	83	19
Hilton	22	3	2	17	23	92	11
Fenstanton	22	1	0	21	19	109	3

NORTHAMPTON TOWN LGE

PREM. DIVISION	P	W	D	L	F	A	PTS
Pitsford Eagles	26	20	4	2	95	29	44
N'pton Vanaid	26	19	2	5	84	32	40
Northampton Park	26	19	1	6	75	46	39
Rosebery Rangers	26	16	5	5	82	35	37
Queens Park WMC	26	16	2	8	74	36	34
Queen Eleanor	26	14	4	8	70	33	32
Bective Wdrs (-1)	26	12	5	9	48	40	30
Crusaders	26	11	7	8	55	35	29
Wootton (-2)	26	8	3	15	42	67	17
St Georges OB (+1)	26	5	5	16	48	77	16
Duston United	26	5	6	15	40	82	16
St Mary's	26	4	7	15	30	82	15
Delapre Old Boys	26	4	2	20	17	91	10
Strollers	26	2	1	23	19	88	5

EAST NORTHANTS LEAGUE

PREM. DIVISION	P	W	D	L	F	A	PTS
Fox Sports	18	15	1	2	78	25	31
Royal Oak	18	15	1	2	53	25	31
Weavers Old Boys	18	8	2	8	37	40	18
Emberton Res.	18	8	2	8	31	48	18
Finedon Volta	18	7	3	8	31	39	17
Rushden Park	18	5	5	8	29	32	15
Lavendon Sports	18	6	2	10	36	49	14
Rushden St Peters	18	6	1	11	33	37	13
Wollaston Victoria	18	5	2	11	33	49	12
Wanderers	18	4	3	11	33	49	11

Alconbury F.C. 1992-93. Photo - Martin Wray.

Ortonian T Smith gets in a cross closely watched by Scott Symonds of Peterborough BRAD. Photo - Martin Wray.

Deeping Rangers F.C. 1992-93. Back Row (L/R): P Bentley, A Fouracres, N Reeve, N Burles, K Webber, D Lowins, D Tarrant, G Prince. Front: J Paste, R Tansley, M Gray, V Garmary, D Woods, S White. Photo - Martin Wray.

SPORTSWORLD EAST MIDLANDS ALLIANCE

Chairman: J Shooter.

Hon. Secretary: W Morris,
30 Exeter Street, Kettering.

DANESHOLME WIN FIRST TITLE

The rains of Autumn and early winter 1992 caused havoc with the league programme programme causing wholesale postponements and leaving a backlog equivalent to six full weeks of fixtures before the turn of the year. In February 1993 it became evident that all the matches could not be completed by the end of the season, and a decision was made that all the divisions would be resolved on a formula, the number of points obtained being declared as a percentage against the number of games each team had played by 8th May. In the event, despite a determined effort when more evening matches than planned were played, 23 games in the four divisions were outstanding by the final date.

Nevertheless an exciting season overcame much of the pre-Christmas frustration, with the championship of three of the four divisions only being decided in the last few days of competition. In the County Division, Corby Strip Mills appeared to be home and dry by early April, but as they stumbled, fellow Corby side Danesholme produced a sustained winning run, starting with a convincing 2-0 victory over their nearest rivals on 22nd April. Five further wins in the next sixteen days ensured the title, their first championship since being promoted to the top division in 1984. The two Corby sides finished well clear of the following fourteen clubs, Gretton being their nearest challengers some twelve points behind. But as Corby dominated the top two places it was woe for Kettering based clubs, Barton Seagrave and Avondale/Harlequin who finished in the last two and face Intermediate Division football next season.

There was some consolation for Strip Mills as their Reserve team swept to the top of the Intermediate Division, just ahead of the stylish Wellingborough Grammarians. The winners however cannot be promoted to the County Division, leaving the promotion spot to the Wellingborough club. Division One was also a two-horse race, with Wellingborough AFC 2000 and Wilbarston gaining the honours, and it is a matter of regret that the former have decided to leave the League. Wilbarston, however, will sample the higher division for the first time ever in 1993-94. The Division Two championship was never in doubt as Corby Earlstree carried everything before them to lead four fellow Corby sides in the final table.

League Cup competitions sponsored by R. Griggs & Co. 'Dr Martens' Ltd saw Brixworth All Saints gain a 'double' double. The first team retained the Munton Cup for the second year in succession, whilst the Reserves picked up the Doug Fairey Cup, a competition for the League's Reserve sides. In the Munton Cup final, played on the ground of Kettering Town F.C., Brixsworth gained the ascendancy over Weldon with a five goal burst in the last twenty minutes of an entertaining game to win by six goals to one. For more than an hour the losers more than held their own, but persistence by Brixsworth paid off, and all out attack saw a decisive victory once they got their noses in front. However, it needed a replay for their Reserve team to gain a 2-0 win against Gretton Reserves, a fine reward for a team which had struggled against relegation all season. The Airwair Cup for Division One and Two clubs was easily taken by Corby Valley who showed little mercy for fellow Corby side, Hartlepool Candle, with a 5-1 win on the ground of Corby Town F.C.

It is with deepest regret that we record the death of W.E. (Ted) Robins, a great stalwart of both the E.M.F.A. and the Northamptonshire F.A. in October. The ninety year old had been connected with the League as a player, Club Secretary, League Official since 1927. For the last twenty years Ted was League President, following an equal length of service as Chairman. A member of the County Association, he was a Vice-President of that organisation. We sadly miss his wisdom, but recall the great devotion and dedication he afforded to football in Northamptonshire.

Walter Morris, Hon. Secretary

County Division

	P	W	D	L	F	A	%
Corby Danesholme	26	20	5	1	75	19	86.4
Corby Strip Mills	28	21	5	2	93	28	83.9
Gretton	28	15	5	8	66	46	62.5
Kettering Nomads	30	14	6	7	55	41	61.7
Brixsworth	28	14	5	9	60	46	58.9
Weldon	23	11	4	8	52	34	56.5
F.C. Fisher	27	12	5	10	64	56	53.7
Medbourne	28	13	4	11	59	60	53.6
Grampian Assoc.	30	12	7	11	56	53	51.7
Kettering Generals	28	9	6	13	46	70	42.9
Corby Pegasus	29	9	4	16	45	80	37.9
Corby Locomotives	28	6	9	13	44	63	37.5
Stanion United	30	7	7	16	36	51	35.0
Rothwell Corinth.	30	6	7	17	39	62	31.7
Barton Seagrave	29	6	5	18	40	76	29.3
Kett. Avondale/Harl.	28	4	5	19	33	79	23.2

Intermediate Division

	P	W	D	L	F	A	%
Corby Str. M. Res.	23	15	5	3	47	22	76.1
Wellingboro. Gram.	24	16	4	4	59	26	75.0
Corby St Brendans	26	18	2	6	74	39	73.8
Corby FC Maple	26	15	2	9	56	50	61.5
Geddington WMC	25	12	4	9	62	35	56.0
Irthlingboro. Rgrs	26	12	4	10	51	51	53.9
Gretton Res.	25	11	4	10	41	38	52.0
Stanwick Rvrs	26	10	6	10	46	50	50.0
Kett. Reflections	25	9	5	11	63	55	46.0
Corby D'holme Res.	26	10	2	14	43	46	42.3
Brixworth Res.	25	6	5	14	34	62	34.0
Kett. Orchard Park	26	6	4	16	37	66	30.8
Rothwell Cor. Res	26	6	2	18	32	58	26.9
Corby Loco. Res.	26	5	3	18	45	94	25.0

WEST MIDLANDS (REGIONAL) LEAGUE

(Est. 1889 as Birmingham & Dist. League)

Chairman: R H Juggins.

Hon. Secretary: K H Goodfellow,
11 Emsworth Grove, Kings Heath,
Birmingham B14 6HY (021 624 3186)

Oldbury United, League Champions 1992-93, with the championship shield.

PREM. DIV.	P	W	D	L	F	A	PTS
Oldbury United	36	24	8	4	80	39	80
Chasetown	36	23	11	2	66	28	80
Paget Rangers	36	21	7	8	84	54	70
Rocester	36	20	9	7	71	41	69
Stourport Swifts	36	19	9	8	69	38	66
Ilkeston Town	36	19	8	9	73	38	65
Rushall Olympic	36	17	7	12	61	53	58
Wednesfield	36	14	10	12	58	47	52
Alvechurch	36	14	5	17	58	65	47
West Brom. Town	36	13	6	17	55	86	45
Pelsall Villa	36	10	12	14	60	54	42
Blakenall	36	9	13	14	57	75	40
Willenhall Town	36	12	4	20	49	69	40
Hinckley Athletic	36	11	6	19	56	68	39
Halesowen Harriers	36	8	9	19	44	62	33
Cradley Town	36	9	6	21	42	71	33
Oldswinford	36	9	6	21	39	80	33
Westfields	36	8	6	22	56	85	30
Lye Town	36	7	8	21	47	72	29

DIV. ONE	P	W	D	L	F	A	PTS
Knypersley Victoria	36	26	3	7	105	34	81
Darlaston	36	25	6	5	69	27	81
Lichfield	36	23	6	7	75	42	75
Ettingshall H.T.	36	20	11	5	69	34	71
Gornal Athletic	36	17	8	11	75	52	59
Cannock Chase	36	16	4	16	50	59	52
Wolverhampton Utd	36	14	7	15	60	69	49
Great Wyrley	36	12	12	12	44	53	48
Tividale	36	14	5	17	76	67	47
Hill Top Rangers	36	13	8	15	58	62	47
Donnington Wood	36	12	11	13	67	77	47
Malvern Town	36	12	10	14	56	71	46
Oldbury Utd Res.	36	10	13	13	52	67	43
Moxley Rangers	36	11	11	14	48	53	41
Ludlow Town	36	10	9	17	55	78	39
Wolverhampton Cas.	36	11	5	20	57	72	38
Tipton Town	36	9	11	16	42	63	38
Gornal Sports	36	7	6	23	42	75	27
Wem Town	36	4	6	26	39	84	18

DIV. TWO	P	W	D	L	F	A	PTS
Rushall O. Res.	32	23	4	5	87	42	73
Bloxwich Strollers	32	23	2	7	99	39	71
Chasetown Res.	32	21	5	6	81	28	68
Rocester Res.	32	20	6	6	104	49	66
Manders	32	20	5	7	83	40	65
Blackheath Elec.	32	17	5	10	69	56	56
Mitchells & Butlers	32	14	9	9	70	53	51
Hinckley Ath. Res.	32	14	9	9	57	48	51
Lye Town Res.	32	14	5	13	61	71	47
Albright & Wilson	32	13	5	14	53	62	44
Oldsinford Res.	32	10	4	18	40	67	34
Halesowen H. Res.	32	9	6	17	49	86	32
Cradley Town Res.	32	8	4	20	38	68	28
Wolves Cas. Res.	32	7	5	20	44	87	26
Park Rangers	32	6	5	21	34	80	23
Cheslyn Hay	32	4	6	22	44	87	18
Tividale Res.	32	5	3	24	38	88	18

YOUTH DIV.	P	W	D	L	F	A	PTS
Hereford United	26	23	1	2	108	15	70
Birmingham City	26	20	3	3	81	25	60
Boldmere St Mich.	26	17	2	7	61	37	50
Lye Town	26	15	3	8	61	39	48
Hinckley Town	26	15	1	10	79	55	46
Pelsall Villa	26	13	4	9	62	52	43
Oldswinford	26	10	5	11	38	46	35
Blakenall	26	10	3	13	44	58	33
Chasetown	26	8	3	15	41	59	27
Redditch United	26	7	4	15	51	72	25
Wednesfield	26	6	4	16	34	66	22
Hinckley Athletic	26	6	5	15	45	81	22
Oldbury United	26	7	1	18	35	83	22
Rushall Olympic	26	4	3	19	30	83	15

PREMIER DIVISION RESULT CHART 1992/93

HOME TEAM	1	2	3	4	5	6	7	8	9	10	11	12	13	14	15	16	17	18	19
1. Alvechurch	*	3-4	2-1	2-4	0-2	0-3	1-0	2-0	3-0	4-0	0-1	1-4	2-2	2-2	1-5	0-2	0-1	4-2	2-1
2. Blakenall	0-1	*	1-1	2-3	1-1	1-3	0-2	2-1	1-7	2-2	2-4	1-1	2-0	0-0	1-1	1-1	1-2	1-1	4-1
3. Chasetown	3-1	4-1	*	2-0	3-0	1-0	0-0	2-0	1-1	2-0	1-0	1-1	3-2	2-1	1-0	0-0	3-0	4-2	2-0
4. Cradley Town	1-2	1-2	2-3	*	1-2	2-3	2-2	1-2	1-5	0-1	1-0	0-4	0-1	1-3	2-2	0-0	3-2	2-1	2-1
5. Halesowen H.	0-3	5-6	2-0	0-1	*	0-3	1-1	1-1	0-0	1-0	2-2	1-1	1-0	1-1	3-0	1-2	9-0	1-0	1-2
6. Hinckley Ath.	1-1	3-1	1-3	4-1	6-3	*	1-2	2-0	0-2	1-0	2-4	0-0	1-3	1-2	2-2	2-2	2-2	2-3	0-3
7. Ilkeston T.	0-2	3-1	1-1	5-0	2-0	1-1	*	5-1	1-3	8-1	2-0	2-0	1-1	0-1	2-2	2-1	9-0	1-2	2-1
8. Lye Town	2-3	1-1	0-0	0-1	3-1	2-1	1-3	*	1-3	1-1	3-2	2-3	1-2	2-1	1-2	1-4	3-1	3-5	2-2
9. Oldbury United	1-0	1-3	1-1	3-3	4-1	2-0	2-1	1-2	*	3-2	2-0	3-0	2-2	2-1	2-1	3-2	3-2	3-1	2-1
10. Oldswinford	2-0	1-3	1-1	3-2	3-0	3-2	0-2	4-2	0-3	*	1-4	0-3	0-3	0-2	2-1	0-1	2-1	1-1	3-3
11. Paget Rangers	4-1	4-1	0-0	2-0	3-0	4-2	5-0	2-1	1-1	2-0	*	4-1	3-4	4-4	1-1	1-1	2-4	5-4	3-2
12. Pelsall Villa	1-4	3-3	2-3	2-2	3-1	2-0	0-1	1-1	0-2	7-1	0-1	*	0-2	0-3	1-1	2-2	0-0	7-0	1-3
13. Rocester	3-1	2-2	0-2	3-0	3-1	1-2	3-2	1-1	1-0	1-1	3-0	0-0	*	3-0	0-0	4-1	2-1	5-3	6-1
14. Rushall Olym.	2-1	2-0	1-2	1-1	2-0	3-1	0-0	2-1	0-3	6-2	1-3	1-0	1-2	*	1-2	2-1	0-3	2-1	2-2
15. Stourport Sw.	4-1	2-1	1-1	2-1	1-0	4-0	0-1	1-0	1-3	2-0	1-2	0-0	3-1	4-0	*	4-2	6-0	2-1	1-2
16. Wednesfield	1-0	1-2	0-1	2-0	2-2	1-2	1-3	2-1	1-1	0-1	2-2	2-1	2-1	1-3	0-1	*	4-0	4-0	4-1
17. West Brom Town	3-3	2-2	0-4	1-0	1-0	3-1	0-3	2-0	1-2	3-1	0-3	1-4	1-1	1-5	2-4	2-2	*	3-1	4-0
18. Westfields	1-3	0-0	2-3	0-1	0-0	2-0	2-3	3-3	2-2	2-0	2-3	4-2	0-2	4-1	0-4	0-2	1-3	*	1-2
19. Willenhall T.	2-2	5-1	2-4	1-0	1-0	2-1	1-0	2-1	1-2	1-0	1-3	1-3	0-1	0-2	0-1	0-2	0-2	1-2	*

West Mids League Premier Division Ten Year Record

	83/4	84/5	85/6	86/7	87/8	88/9	89/90	90/1	91/2	92/3
Alvechurch	-	-	-	-	-	-	-	-	-	9
Armitage	8	19	20	19	-	-	-	-	-	-
Atherstone United	3	3	3	1	-	-	-	-	-	-
Bilston Town	17	2	-	-	-	-	-	-	-	-
Blakenall	18	18	15	20	12	1	4	14	4	12
Brereton Social	16	14	10	14	-	-	-	-	-	-
Chasetown	19	16	17	9	5	9	10	2	5	2
Cradley Town	20	-	-	-	-	-	-	-	14	16
Darlaston	-	-	-	-	-	-	-	-	4	-
GKN Sankey	15	11	7	11	16	-	-	-	-	-
Gresley Rovers	4	8	2	4	4	2	3	1	1	-
Halesowen Harriers	-	-	-	7	6	3	9	10	10	15
Halesowen Town	1	1	1	-	-	-	-	-	-	-
Harrisons	-	-	4	10	11	12	12	-	-	-
Hednesford Town	2	-	-	-	-	-	-	-	-	-
Hinckley Athletic	14	9	8	8	10	14	6	5	15	14
Hinckley Town	-	-	-	-	-	7	1	-	-	-
Ilkeston Town	-	-	-	-	-	-	-	7	-	6
Lye Town	5	12	6	13	3	8	5	9	9	19
Malvern Town	12	17	12	6	7	10	13	21	16	-
Millfields (see West Bromwich Town)										
Oldbury United	-	-	-	2	2	6	8	3	7	1
Oldswinford	7	10	14	17	18	19	18	18	19	17
Paget Rangers	-	-	-	-	-	4	11	17	2	3
Pelsall Villa	-	-	-	-	-	-	-	15	12	11
Rocester	-	-	-	-	-	11	2	11	6	4
Rushall Olympic	13	13	11	12	9	5	14	12	8	7
Shifnal Town	9	20	13	-	-	-	-	-	-	-
Stourport Swifts	-	-	-	-	-	21	15	13	3	5
Tamworth	-	7	9	5	1	-	-	-	-	-
Tipton Town	-	5	19	18	15	20	21	22	-	-
Tividale	11	6	16	15	13	13	19	20	-	-
Wednesfield (Social)	10	4	5	3	8	16	7	6	17	8
West Bromwich Town	-	-	-	-	-	18	20	8	13	10
Westfields	-	-	-	-	14	17	17	19	18	18
Willenhall Town	-	-	-	-	-	-	-	-	11	13
Wolverhampton Casuals	-	-	-	-	-	15	16	16	-	-
Wolverhampton United	6	15	18	16	17	-	-	-	-	-
No. of clubs competing	20	20	20	20	18	21	21	21	19	19

DIVISION ONE RESULT CHART 1992/93

HOME TEAM	1	2	3	4	5	6	7	8	9	10	11	12	13	14	15	16	17	18	19
1. Cannock Chase	*	0-2	1-1	0-5	1-0	2-0	2-0	2-0	2-1	1-2	3-1	1-2	0-1	2-3	0-1	1-0	1-1	1-0	0-2
2. Darlaston	0-2	*	4-0	0-2	2-1	0-3	2-0	1-1	0-0	2-1	2-1	2-0	4-0	3-0	4-2	2-0	3-2	3-1	
3. Donnington W.	5-2	2-2	*	2-0	0-4	3-2	1-2	2-2	0-2	1-1	2-4	3-3	2-2	2-2	4-3	1-4	3-2	1-2	3-1
4. Ettingshall	0-3	5-1	3-1	*	1-1	2-2	1-1	2-0	1-1	3-1	3-0	3-3	2-0	1-1	1-3	3-2	2-0	1-1	1-0
5. Gornal Ath.	4-0	2-0	4-3	1-3	*	3-0	0-1	2-2	1-2	0-1	1-0	5-0	1-1	3-0	4-0	3-2	4-3	2-3	0-3
6. Gornal Sports	3-0	0-2	1-0	2-6	1-2	*	2-2	6-0	0-1	2-4	2-1	2-2	0-2	3-6	1-3	0-3	2-1	2-3	0-2
7. Great Wyrley	1-0	0-0	2-2	1-1	2-2	0-0	*	2-2	1-4	0-5	1-2	1-4	1-0	2-3	0-0	2-3	1-0	1-1	0-1
8. Hill Top Rgrs	0-3	0-2	4-1	1-4	1-2	2-1	1-2	*	3-1	1-4	4-2	1-2	1-4	4-0	3-0	2-1	3-1	3-1	0-0
9. Knypersley V.	5-0	1-4	0-1	1-1	3-1	6-0	3-0	1-0	*	0-1	4-0	2-0	6-1	4-0	3-2	1-3	2-1	3-2	7-1
10. Lichfield	5-2	1-5	0-2	0-1	2-1	3-1	1-1	0-1	1-3	*	4-1	1-1	4-1	2-0	2-0	3-2	3-2	2-0	4-3
11. Ludlow Town	1-2	1-0	3-1	0-3	2-2	0-2	1-3	1-1	1-7	1-1	*	2-0	2-2	2-5	3-3	2-2	5-1	0-3	0-1
12. Malvern Town	0-1	0-5	2-2	0-2	2-1	3-1	0-3	2-2	1-7	0-2	3-0	*	0-0	1-1	1-3	3-1	4-0	2-4	2-4
13. Moxley Rangers	2-0	0-1	3-4	1-2	1-3	1-0	2-3	1-1	0-2	0-0	1-1	0-1	*	3-3	2-0	2-3	3-0	1-1	2-0
14. Oldbury U. Res.	2-2	0-1	0-0	0-0	1-3	3-1	2-2	2-0	1-0	1-3	1-1	1-2	1-2	*	1-1	2-3	1-0	2-1	2-2
15. Tipton Town	2-2	0-1	3-0	0-0	4-4	1-1	0-2	3-1	0-5	1-4	1-4	1-1	0-1	0-1	*	0-0	1-0	2-1	0-0
16. Tividale	2-4	0-0	2-4	0-1	0-0	4-1	1-2	1-5	1-2	0-1	2-1	1-2	2-1	5-1	3-0	*	4-0	5-2	3-1
17. Wem Town	2-4	1-2	1-1	1-0	0-2	1-0	1-0	0-2	2-4	0-2	1-2	2-2	3-4	2-2	1-1	1-3	*	4-2	2-4
18. Wolves Cas.	1-2	0-2	1-2	1-2	0-1	0-0	2-0	0-3	0-3	4-2	3-4	1-2	0-0	3-1	1-3	4-3	4-0	*	1-2
19. Wolves Utd	2-1	0-1	3-5	2-1	5-4	0-1	0-2	2-2	0-7	0-3	1-2	3-2	1-1	0-0	2-0	4-3	2-2	2-3	*

DIVISION TWO RESULT CHART 1992/93

HOME TEAM	1	2	3	4	5	6	7	8	9	10	11	12	13	14	15	16	17
1. Albright & Wil.	*	2-1	2-3	2-1	4-1	3-0	1-1	0-4	1-3	1-1	3-4	0-2	3-2	0-3	1-1	2-0	2-0
2. Blackheath E.	1-4	*	0-2	1-3	4-2	2-1	2-0	2-0	8-3	1-0	3-5	3-1	4-1	1-0	4-1	2-1	2-3
3. Bloxwich Str.	1-1	1-2	*	2-0	5-0	3-0	5-0	5-1	7-0	4-0	3-2	3-1	1-0	2-6	0-3	3-0	4-0
4. Chasetown Res.	7-1	4-0	4-1	*	4-0	2-1	3-0	3-0	1-0	2-1	4-1	8-0	5-1	4-0	1-2	2-1	1-1
5. Cheslyn Hay	0-1	1-4	2-1	3-5	*	1-1	4-2	0-1	1-2	2-3	2-2	1-3	1-1	3-3	3-4	1-1	0-2
6. Cradley T. Res.	2-1	2-1	1-2	1-4	2-1	*	2-3	2-2	4-4	2-4	1-2	1-3	1-1	0-2	0-1	2-0	1-2
7. H'sowen H. Res.	0-3	0-1	1-8	1-1	5-0	3-0	*	2-2	1-3	0-4	2-9	5-1	1-2	3-1	1-5	3-1	1-1
8. Hinckley A. Res.	1-2	3-2	5-1	1-1	8-1	1-0	2-1	*	1-1	2-3	0-0	2-1	1-0	1-4	1-3	0-0	2-1
9. Lye Town Res.	1-0	3-3	5-2	2-0	2-1	1-0	1-2	0-3	*	0-2	1-4	1-0	2-1	2-0	1-3	9-2	1-3
10. Manders	4-0	1-2	0-3	1-0	3-1	1-2	4-0	1-1	6-1	*	2-1	3-0	4-0	3-3	2-2	5-0	5-1
11. Mitchells & B.	2-1	0-0	1-3	1-1	3-1	1-2	0-0	2-2	3-1	1-1	*	4-0	3-1	1-3	1-1	4-1	5-1
12. Oldswinford Res.	0-2	1-3	0-1	0-3	1-1	2-1	4-3	0-1	1-1	0-4	1-1	*	1-0	0-1	5-3	0-2	1-0
13. Park Rangers	4-1	1-1	0-9	0-4	3-2	1-2	1-1	1-4	0-2	1-4	0-2	0-3	*	1-4	1-3	0-3	3-1
14. Rocester Res.	6-3	5-5	2-2	2-2	3-1	7-0	7-0	4-0	5-1	2-1	5-1	3-1	2-2	*	1-2	4-1	7-2
15. Rushall O. Res.	4-2	3-0	0-2	0-0	2-1	4-1	5-0	4-2	3-2	0-1	3-0	4-0	3-0	1-4	*	7-0	4-1
16. Tividale Res.	1-3	0-1	0-4	2-0	1-3	0-2	2-5	1-3	2-4	1-3	1-2	0-0	1-3	3-2	2-3	*	5-1
17. Wolves C. Res.	1-1	2-2	0-6	0-1	1-3	3-1	1-2	0-0	1-1	4-6	3-2	2-7	1-2	0-3	2-3	4-3	*

YOUTH DIVISION RESULT CHART 1992/93

HOME TEAM	1	2	3	4	5	6	7	8	9	10	11	12	13	14
1. Birmingham C.	*	6-0	0-2	1-0	1-0	6-2	3-2	5-2	4-0	3-1	3-3	5-0	6-0	3-1
2. Blakenall	2-3	*	2-3	4-1	0-4	2-1	0-2	0-0	5-0	2-2	0-2	3-2	2-1	1-0
3. Boldmere S.M.	2-2	3-0	*	1-4	1-2	5-1	3-2	2-1	2-0	3-0	3-1	2-1	3-2	5-1
4. Chasetown	0-1	2-1	2-1	*	0-4	2-3	1-3	2-0	7-0	1-3	1-1	0-3	3-1	3-2
5. Hereford United	1-1	9-1	5-1	3-0	*	6-0	10-0	5-1	3-1	5-2	3-1	8-0	7-0	6-0
6. Hinckley Ath.	0-3	4-2	2-0	1-1	2-3	*	2-9	3-2	1-4	0-0	2-5	3-3	0-2	1-2
7. Hinckley Town	0-2	0-2	2-1	3-0	0-2	6-2	*	3-3	6-0	1-0	5-0	4-3	9-0	2-1
8. Lye Town	2-1	1-1	0-3	5-0	1-0	1-2	5-0	*	2-1	2-1	4-0	4-2	5-2	3-0
9. Oldbury United	1-0	1-5	1-7	6-2	0-2	2-6	1-3	1-4	*	1-3	0-3	1-0	4-2	0-4
10. Oldswinford	1-3	2-0	0-1	3-1	0-4	3-2	4-2	0-5	1-3	*	3-2	2-2	1-0	3-0
11. Pelsall Villa	1-7	2-0	2-0	3-3	0-4	5-0	5-1	1-3	1-2	2-1	*	5-3	9-1	4-1
12. Redditch Utd	1-2	3-2	3-4	3-1	1-5	2-2	4-3	4-1	5-1	0-0	2-3	*	0-2	3-1
13. Rushall Olympic	0-5	0-1	1-1	1-4	0-5	3-3	1-3	0-1	3-2	1-2	0-1	3-1	*	2-2
14. Wednesfield	1-5	4-6	0-2	1-0	1-2	2-0	0-8	0-3	2-2	0-0	0-0	5-0	3-2	*

RESERVE DIVISION CONSTITUTION 1993-94

13 Teams (to replace Division Two):
Chasetown Reserves, Cradley Town Reserves, Halesowen Harriers Reserves, Hinckley Athletic Reserves, Lye Town Reserves, Moxley Rangers Reserves (new to League), Oldbury United Reserves (moved from Division One), Pelsall Villa Reserves (new to League), Rocester Reserves, Rushall Olympic Reserves, Tividale Reserves, Walsall Wood Reserves (new to League), Wolverhampton Casuals Reserves.

YOUTH DIVISION CONSTITUTION 1993-94

13 Teams:
Birmingham City, Blakenall, Boldmere St Michaels, Brierley Hill Town (formerly Oldswinford), Chasetown, Hereford United, Hinckley Athletic, Hinckley Town, Lye Town, Oldbury United, Pelsall Villa, Redditch United, Wednesfield.

PREMIER DIVISION CUP 1992-93

First Round

Westfields v Blakenall	1-1,3-3,1-2	Stourport Swifts v Rushall Olympic	2-0
Wednesfield v Ilkeston Town	0-1		

Second Round

Stourport Swifts v Blakenall	2-0	Chasetown v Lye Town	2-0
Cradley Town v Willenhall Town	2-0	Pelsall Villa v Hinckley Athletic	2-2,1-2
Oldbury United v Alvechurch	2-0	Ilkeston Town v Rocester	3-1
Paget Rangers v Halesowen Harriers	2-0	Oldswinford v West Bromwich Town	0-2

Quarter Finals

Stourport Swifts v Chasetown	4-3	Hinckley Athletic v Cradley Town	2-1
Oldbury United v Ilkeston Town	2-1	Paget Rangers v West Bromwich Town	2-0

Semi-Finals

Stourport Swifts v Hinckley Athletic	0-1,3-1	Oldbury United v Paget Rangers	2-1,1-3

Final: Stourport Swifts 1, Paget Rangers 0

DIVISION ONE CUP 1992-93

First Round

Moxley Rangers v Ludlow Town	0-1	Lichfield v Tividale	1-3
Wolverhampton Utd v Ettingshall Holy Trin.	3-1		

Second Round

Cannock Chase v Darlaston	1-2	Gornal Athletic v Oldbury United Reserves	4-0
Hill Top Rangers v Malvern Town	2-0	Great Wyrley v Knypersley Victoria	0-3
Gornal Sports v Ludlow Town	3-2	Donnington Wood v Wolverhampton United	3-1
Tividale v Wem Town	6-1	Tipton Town v Wolverhampton Casuals	1-3

Quarter Finals

Darlaston v Tividale	0-1	Hill Top Rangers v Knypersley Victoria	0-2
Gornal Sports v Gornal Athletic	0-2	Donnington Wd v Wolverhampton Cas.	1-1,2-1 *(aet)*

Semi-Finals

Tividale v Donnington Wood	2-1,3-3	Gornal Athletic v Knypersley Victoria	1-1,4-4,1-0

Final: Gornal Athletic 2, Tividale 0

DIVISION TWO CUP 1992-93

First Round

Chasetown Reserves v Rushall Olympic Res.	1-2	Rocester Reserves v Albright & Wilson	0-2

Second Round

Lye Town Reserves v Oldswinford Reserves	2-6	Hinckley Athletic Reserves v Park Rangers	5-1
Halesowen H. Res. v Mitchells & Butlers	2-2,0-3	Rushall O. Reserves v Wolverhampton Cas. Res.	6-1
Cradley Town Reserves v Cheslyn Hay	3-1	Albright & Wilsons v Bloxwich Strollers	2-2,3-4
Manders v Blackheath Electrodrives	4-2	Tividale Reserves	bye

Quarter Finals

Mitchells & Butlers v Oldswinford Reserves	4-0	Rushall O. Reserves v Hinckley Athletic Reserves	1-4
Manders v Tividale Reserves	3-0	Bloxwich Strollers v Cradley Town Reserves	4-0

Semi-Finals

Manders v Mitchells & Butlers	0-0,5-3	Hinckley Ath. Res. v Bloxwich Strollers	1-1,2-2,1-5

Final: Manders 2, Bloxwich Strollers 1

Manders F.C. - Division Two Cup Winners 1992-93. Back Row (L/R): G Mood, I Davies, S Corbett, J Simpson, R Everitt, S Astley, M Farmer. Centre: G Sands, N Birch, M Ecclestone (Asst Manager), T Stokes, E Edwards (Physio), P Deam. Front: J Webb, R Myatt, R Nicholls, C Rooney.

YOUTH DIVISION CUP 1992-93

First Round

Chasetown Yth v Hereford United Yth	2-1	Rushall Olympic Yth v Wednesfield Yth	1-3
Boldmere St M. Yth v Oldswinford Yth	3-1	Hinckley Athletic Yth v Birmingham City Yth	1-9
Redditch Utd Yth v Pelsall Villa Yth	2-1	Oldbury United Yth v Blakenall Yth	6-4
Hinckley Town Yth	bye	Lye Town Yth	bye

Quarter Finals

Redditch Utd Yth v Hinckley Town Yth	2-4	Wednesfield Yth v Birmingham City Yth	0-0,0-6
Lye Town Yth v Oldbury United Yth	6-2	Boldmere St Michaels Yth v Chasetown Yth	1-3

Semi-Finals

Hinckley Town Yth v Lye Town Yth	1-2,2-0	Chasetown v Birmingham	2-2,0-2(B'gham expelled)

Final: Hinckley Town Youth 1, Chasetown Youth 0

Gornal Athletic captain Stephen Worley with the Division One after the final victory against Tividale. Photo: Mark Wood.

Premier Division action in February as Ilkeston Town (white shorts) record a 2-0 victory against visiting Paget Rangers. Photo - Colin Stevens.

PREMIER DIVISION CLUBS 1993-94

ALVECHURCH

Chairman: Neil Hughes   **Vice Chairman:** Kevin Hilde   **President:** Geoff Turton
Secretary: Roy Yardley, 11 Brandon Rd, Alvechurch, Worcs B48 7PE (021 445 2950).
Manager: Lee Shaw   **Asst Manager:** Mick Preece   **Coach:** Mick Preece.
Ground: Lye Meadow, Redditch Rd, Alvechurch, Worcs (021 445 2929).
Directions: M42 jct 2, left for Alvechurch (A441) at 1st island, pass right thru Alvechurch - ground on left half mile after village. 10 mins walk from Alvechurch BR station. Birmingham-Redditch buses pass ground.
Seats: 300   **Cover:** 700   **Capacity:** 3,000   **Floodlights:** Yes   **Founded:** 1992
Colours: Gold/black/gold   **Change colours:** All white
Previous Name: None *(predecessors, Alvechurch F.C., founded 1929, folded in 1992. All italicised historical entries below apply to this previous club).*
Previous Grounds: None *(predecessors: The Meadows (pre-1957)).*
Previous Leagues: None *(predecessors: Midland Comb. 61-73/ West Mids 73-78/ Southern 78-92).*
Programme: 12 pages   **Programme Editor:** Secretary   **Club Shop:** No.
Club Sponsors: Quazer Sports   **Record Gate:** *1,600 v Enfield, F.A. Amtr Cup 1964.*
Nickname: The Church.   **Midweek home matchday:** Wednesday
Record win: *7-1 v Redditch Utd*   **Record defeat:** *1-8 v Halesowen Town.*
Record transfer fee paid: £3,000 for Peter Gocan (Worcester City)
Received: £28,000 for Andy Comyn (Aston Villa, 1990).
Best F.A. Cup year: Not entered to date *(predecssors: 3rd Rd 73-74 beating Exeter en route. Also 1st Rd 71-72).*
Players progressing to Football League: *Derek Newman (Southampton 1964), John Mason (Peterborough 1966), Colin Brazier (Wolves 1975), Ron Green (Walsall 1977), Richard Kelly (Walsall 1979), Sean O'Driscoll (Fulham 1979), Alan Smith (Leicester 1982 (now Arsenal & England)), Neil Cusack (Leicester 1987), David Kelly (Walsall 1982), Brian Palgrave (Walsall 1984), Andy Comyn (Aston Villa 1990).*
Clubhouse: Open midweek 7.30-11pm, matchdays and noo-2.30pm Sundays. Full range of food.
Captain 92-93: Mick Jones   **Top Scorer 92-93:** Matthew Pugh   **P.O.Y. 92-93:** Martin Hallam.
Club record scorer: *Graham Allner*   **Club record appearances:** *Kevin Palmer.*
Hons: *Southern Lg 80-81 (Midland Div R-up 81-82, Lg Cup 82-83, Championship Match 80-81), West Mids Lg 73-74 74-75 75-76 76-77 (R-up 77-78, Lg Cup 73-74 74-75 77-78, Midland Comb. 62-63 64-65 66-67 71-72 (R-up 63-64 65-66 66-67 68-69 72-73, Lg Cup 64-65 65-66 67-68 68-69 71-72), Worcs Snr Cup 72-73 73-74 76-77, B'gham Snr Amtr Cup 73-74, B'gham Jnr Cup 65-66 67-68, Border Counties F'lit Cup 75-76.*

BLAKENALL

President: F Rowley   **Chairman:** P Laneston
Secretary: David Birch, 64 Wimperis Way, Great Barr, Birmingham B43 7DF (021 360 3574).
Manager: Andy Keeling   **Press Officer:** F Rowley (0384 408025).
Ground: Red Lion Ground, Somerfield Rd, Bloxwich, Walsall, West Mids (0922 405835).
Directions: M6 jct 10, follow signs for Walsall centre. At 1st lights turn left (about 200yds from Motorway junction) into Bloxwich Lane. Keep following this lane to the 'T' junction and turn right into Leamore Lane, at this island turn left into Somerfield Road. Ground is approx. 400yds on the right.
Seats: Nil   **Cover:** 400   **Capacity:** 2,000   **Floodlights:** Yes   **Founded:** 1946.
Colours: Blue & white stripes/blue/blue   **Change colours:** All red
Clubhouse: Yes   **Programme:** 16 pages 25p
Previous Leagues: Bloxwich Comb./ Staffs County/ Midland Comb. 60-79.
Hons: Midland Comb. 76-77, Walsall Snr Cup (6)

BRIERLEY HILL TOWN

Chairman: A Purchase   **Vice Chairman:** A Hingley.
Secretary/Press Officer: D G Dew, 148 King William Street, Amblecote, Stourbridge (0384 376902).
Manager: S Daniels   **Asst Manager:** T Hotheridge.   **Coach:** G Fullwood.
Ground: The Dell Sports Stadium, Bryce Rd, Pensnett, Brierley Hill, West Mids (0384 77289).
Directions: At lights in the Brierley Hill High Street turn into Bank Street by Police Station. Proceed over bridge into Pensnett Road, ground three quarters of a mile on left Paddy's Garage. Main entrance 120yds in Bryce Road.
Seats: 300   **Cover:** 300   **Capacity:** 5,000   **Floodlights:** Yes   **Founded:** 1955
Colours: Blue   **Change colours:** Yellow   **Club Shop:** No.
Programme: 20 pages, 50p   **Programme Editor:** Secretary
Previous Name: Oldswinford F. & S.C. 1955-93.
Previous Leagues: Kidderminster (eight seasons)/ Staffs County (South)(seven seasons).
Previous Grounds: Cottage Street, Brierley Hill (four seasons)/ South Road, Stourbridge (seventeen seasons)/ Swinford Common, Stourbridge (two seasons).
Club Sponsors: Various   **Record Gate:** 800 v Wolverhampton Wdrs, friendly.
Midweek matchday: Mon or Wed.   **Nickname:** Lions.
Record transfer fee paid: Nil   **Received:** From Wolves for Neil Edwards.
Clubhouse: Open Mon, Wed & Fri. Hot foods & drinks on matchdays - Best hot dogs in the Midlands!
Captain 92-93: Morgan Brookes   **Top Scorer 92-93:** A Kelly
Hons: West Mids Lg Prem. Div Cup R-up 84-85 (Div 1 80-81 (Div 1 Cup 80-81)).

PHOTOS OPPOSITE:
Top: Chasetown F.C. - Premier Division runners-up 1992-93. Back Row (L/R): D Shelton, D Langston, A Walsh, A Withington, T Dixon, G Smith, S Hyden. Front: J Rose, A Cox, D Ansell, P Hill, T Jones, M Malcolm. Photo - James Wright.

Bottom: Oldswinford F.C., who have now changed their name to Brierley Hill Town. Back Row (L/R): Terry Hotheridge (Asst Manager), P Probert, S Cookson, C Thomas, A Harnett, M Pugh, A Convy, P Blackham, Roger Holden (Sponsor), Steve Daniels (Manager). Front: L Shaw, A Kelly, J Hughes, J McLaren, L Hardwick, F Salmon. Photo - James Wright.

CHASETOWN

Chairman: G Rollins **Vice Chairman:** A Purcell **President:** A Scorey.
Secretary: J T Bacon, 67 Hill St., Chasetown, Walsall WS7 8XU (0543 672462).
Manager: Mervyn Rowe **Asst Manager:** T Jones **Coach:** John Newell
Physio: E Highfield. **Commercial Manager/Press Officer:** D M Shelton.
Ground: The Scholars, Church Street, Chasetown (0543 62222/684609).
Directions: Follow Motorways M5 or M6 and follow signs for A5. A5 to Whitehorse Road/Wharf Lane, left into Highfields Rd (B5011), left into Church Street, ground at end just beyond church. Buses 394 or 395 from Walsall.
Seats: 120 **Cover:** 250 **Capacity:** 2,000 **Floodlights:** Yes **Founded:** 1954.
Colours: All blue **Change colours:** Red & black/black/red
Programme: 24 pages, 40p **Programme Editor:** David Shelton (0543 6822222)
Club Shop: Yes, selling jumpers, sweatshirts, T-shirts, programmes, ties, enamel badges, bannerettes, pens, key fobs. Contact David Shelton (0543 6822222).
Prev. Grnd: Burntwood Rec Cte (pre'83) **Previous Name:** Chase Terrace Old Scholars 54-72.
Record Gate: 659 v Tamworth, F.A. Cup 2nd Qualifying Rd 1/10/88.
Previous Leagues: Cannock Yth/ Lichfield & District/ Staffs County.
Club Sponsors: Halso Petroleum **Midweek home matchday:** Tuesday **Nickname:** Scholars
Record win: 14-1 v Hanford, Walsall Snr Cup
Record defeat: 1-8 v Telford United Reserves, West Mids (Regional) Lge Division One.
Clubhouse: Mon-Fri 7.30-11pm, Sat 11am-11pm, Sun 8-10.30pm. Basic snacks, but club caterers available on request.
Captain 92-93: D Ansell **Top Scorer 92-93:** T Dixon 29.
Club record scorer: T Dixon 142 **Club record appearances:** A Cox 427 (+10 sub).
Hons: West Mids Lg R-up 90-91 92-93 (Lg Cup 89-90 90-91, Div 1 77-78 (R-up 73-74 74-75 75-76 80-81 82-83), Div 1 Cup R-up 80-81 82-83, Div 2 R-up 87-88, Div 2 Cup R-up 86-87), Walsall Snr Cup 90-91 92-93, Staffs Snr Cup R-up 91-92.

CRADLEY TOWN

Chairman: C Pickett   **Vice Chairman:** R Kirton   **President:** W Forrest
Secretary: A Hill, 51 Meres Road, Halesowen, West Midlands B63 2HL (0384 69585).
Ground: Beeches View Avenue, Cradley, Halesowen, Cradley Heath (0384 69904).
Directions: M5 Jct 3, take A456, right at 2nd Island, 2nd left and follow to end, left, left at next T-junction, left again after 20yds (Beeches Rd East), 1st left (Abbey Rd), right at end, ground 50yds on left. Nearest BR station is Cradley Heath.
Seats: 100   **Cover:** 600   **Capacity:** 1,500   **Floodlights:** Yes   **Founded:** 1948.
Cols: Red & black stripes/white/white   **Change colours:** Yellow/green/yellow   **Nickname:** Lukes
Previous Name: Albion Haden United   **Previous Grounds:** None.
Previous Leagues: Metropolitan/ Brierley Hill/ Kidderminster/ West Mids Amtr/ Midland Comb. 71-82.
Programme: 12 pages, 50p   **Programme Editor:** Secretary   **Club Shop:** No.
Club Sponsors: Paper Plane   **Record Gate:** 1,100 v Aston Villa, friendly.
Midweek home matchday: Tuesday   **Reserve team's League:** Division Two.
Record win: 9-0   **Record defeat:** 1-9
Record transfer fee paid: Nil   **Received:** For J Williams (Swansea City, 1992).
Clubhouse: Pub hours. Bar snacks.   **Club record scorer:** R Stafford.
Captain 92-93: A Davis   **Top Scorer 92-93:** G Foster   **P.o.Y. 92-93:** M Clarke
Hons: Midland Comb. Div 2 72-73 (R-up 75-76 77-78, Presidents Cup 74-75 75-76, Invitation 72-73), Metropolitan Lg 70-71, Wednesbury Charity Cup 90-91, Dudley Guest Hosp. Cup 71-72 72-73 75-76 90-91.

Cradley Town F.C. Back Row (L/R): Alan Potts, Dave Townsend, Kevin Beasley, Brenton Hanson, Steve Carter, Jos Mulville, Gavin Burborough. Front: Neil Moore, Darrol Sherwood, Lee Burford, Gary Foster, Ian Broom, Peter Slowey, Marcus Slowey. Photo - James Wright.

DARLASTON

Chairman: A Schofield
Secretary: Raymond J Fisher, 72 Brackenfield Rd, Great Barr, Birmingham B44 (021 360 9904).
Ground: City Ground, Waverley Rd, Darlaston (021 5264423).
Directions: M6 Jct 10, onto A454 towards Willenhall, left at lights outside 'Lane Arms' into Bentley Road North, follow this down hill and over the railway and canal bridges to traffic lights. Cross over the lights into Richards Street and along into Victoria Rd, 1st right into Slater Street and ground on left but entrance is next left in Waverley Rd.
Seats: Yes   **Cover:** Yes   **Programme:** Yes   **Clubhouse:** Yes   **Floodlights:** No
Colours: Sky & navy stripes/blue/blue   **Change colours:** All yellow   **Founded:** 1874.
Previous Leagues: Birmingham Jnr pre-1908/ Birmingham Combination 08-11 28-54/ West Mids 11-28.
Hons: W Mids Lg Div 1 R-up 91-92 92-93, B'ham Snr Cup 72-73, B'ham Jnr Cup 07-08, B'ham Comb. 10-11 37-38 45-46.

HALESOWEN HARRIERS

Secretary: Brian P Beasley, 69 Bower Lane, Quarry Bank, West Mids DY5 2DU (0384 62124).
Manager: D Beasley   **Asst Manager:** T Argent
Coach: M Gwynne   **Physio:** D Bowen.
Ground: Hayes Park, Park Rd, Colley Gate, Halesowen (0384 896748).
Directions: On A458 Birmingham to Stourbridge Road (B'ham 10 miles, Stourbridge 4 miles) - main bus route. M5 Jct 3 (towards Kidderminster), right at 1st island (towards Dudley), turn left at island (towards Stourbridge), straight over next island then 3 miles to ground on left-hand side, 200yds past Park Lane. Just over a mile from Lye BR station.
Seats: 350   **Cover:** 500   **Capacity:** 4,000   **Floodlights:** Yes   **Founded:** 1961
Colours: White   **Change colours:** Sky.   **Club Shop:** No.
Programme: 24-28 pages   **Editor:** The Editor, H.H.F.C. (0384 896741).
Previous League: Festival (Sunday)   **Sponsors:** A Page (Building Merchants)
Previous Grounds: Birmingham parks 61-70/ Halesowen Town FC 70-84 (both whilst in Sunday football).
Record Gate: 750; friendlies v Walsall and Wolves in 1985. Competitive; 450 v Lye, Lge 1988.
Nickname: Lilywhites   **Midweek home matchday:** Tuesday or Wednesday.
Record win: 12-1 v Lichfield & v Malvern Town, 1986.
Record defeat: 2-8 v Frickley Athletic (A), F.A. Cup 2nd Qualifying Rd 26/9/92.
Record transfer fee paid: £750 to Oldswinford for L Booth, 1991.
Clubhouse: Open every evening (possibly every lunchtimes from July '93). Limited range of hot ssnacks, but full cold snack kitchen.
Captain & P.o.Y. 92-93: Steve Brain   **Top Scorer 92-93:** Ian Perry
Hons: West Mids Lg Div 1 85-86 (Div 2 84-85, Div 2 Cup 84-85), Inter City Bowl 67-68 68-69, Festival Lg(5)(R-up(9)), FA Sunday Cup SF 79-80, Midland Sunday Cup, Birmingham Sunday Cup.

HINCKLEY ATHLETIC

Chairman: M Voce   **Vice Chairman:** R Mayne   **President:** D Loakes.
Secretary: Mr J Colver, 22 Begonia Drive, Burbage, Hinckley, Leics LE10 2SW (0455 230263).
Manager: J Hanna   **Asst Manager:** B Nally   **Coach:** F Harrison
Physio: T Baker   **Comm. Manager:** P Williamson   **Press Officer:** A Gibbs.
Ground: Middlefield Lane, Hinckley. Leics (0455 613553).
Directions: A47 Coventry Road towards Hinckley. Keep on Inner Ring Road to lights at top of Upper Bond Street at junction of Ashby Road/Derby Road. Turn left and ground is at the bottom of Middlefield Lane. Two miles from Hinckley (BR).
Seats: 300   **Cover:** 1,000   **Capacity:** 5,000   **Floodlights:** Yes   **Founded:** 1889
Club colours: Red/black/red   **Change colours:** All blue   **Club Shop:** No.
Programme: 24 pages   **Editor:** B Todd (0455 846856).
Previous Ground: Hollywell Lane, London Rd (pre'40)
Previous Leagues: Leicestershire & Northants/ Leics Senior/ Birmingham Combination 14-39 47-54/ West Mids (Reg.) 54-59/ Southern 63-64.
Previous Names: Hinckley AFC, Hinckley Town, Hinckley United.
Best FA Cup season: 2nd Rd Proper 54-55 (lost 1-2 at Rochdale), 62-63 (2-7 at Queens Pk Rgrs).
Best FA Trophy season: 1st Qualifying Rd 69-70 72-73 73-74.
Best FA Vase season: 76-77 77-78 78-79 89-90.
Record Gate: 5,410 v Nuneaton Borough, Birmingham Combination 26/12/49.
Players progressing to Football League: John Allen (Port Vale).
Club Sponsors: Vend Fabrics   **Midweek home matchday:** Tuesday   **Nickname:** Robins.
Clubhouse: Social club with lounge, games room, and concert room. Open each evening, Sunday lunch and matchdays. Hot & cold food available (0455 615012).
Captain 92-93: N Stanborough   **Top Scorer 92-93 & P.o.Y. 92-93:** S Sinden
Hons: Leics Snr Cup 1899-1900 00-01 09-10 82-83, Leics Snr Lg 1896-97 97-98 99-1900 08-09 09-10 13-14, Birmingham Comb. 23-24 26-27 (R-up 22-23), West Mids (Reg.) Lg R-up 82-83, Birmingham Snr Cup 54-55(jt with Brush Sports), Leics Challenge Cup 57-58 58-59 59-60 60-61 61-62 67-68.

Hinckley Athletic F.C. 1992-93. Photo - Colin Stevens.

ILKESTON TOWN

Chairman: Paul Millership   **President:** Robert Lindsay
Secretary: Mr Anthony Cuthbert, 8 Darwin Road, Long Eaton, Nottingham NG10 3NW (0602 731531).
Manager: Danny Boyes   **Asst Manager:** John Bartlett   **Press Officer:** John Richards
Ground: New Manor Ground, Awsworth Rd, Ilkeston (0602 324094).   **Floodlights:** Yes
Directions: M42 to M1 jct 23A, continue on M1 to jct 26, exit left onto A610 towards Ripley, take 1st exit signed Awsworth and Ilkeston (A6096), continue thru Awsworth, right at top of hill into Newtons Lane (signed Cotmanhay & Heanor) - ground half mile on left before canal bridge. Or, A38 to Derby centre, A52 for Nottm to M5 jct 25, then follow as above from M1 jct 26. Rail to Nottingham or Derby then bus to Ilkeston. Ground about 1 mile from town centre.
Capacity: 3,000   **Seats:** 170   **Cover:** 570   **Floodlights:** Yes   **Reformed:** 1945.
Colours: Red/white/red   **Change colours:** White/black/black   **Nickname:** Robins.
Programme: 32 pages, 50p   **Programme Editor:** Mick Capill (0602 324257).
Club Shop: Yes, selling shirts, T-shirts, jumpers, caps, badges, programmes, scarves, 'Team Talk' magazine. Contact Roger Rosser or Janice Straw (0602 292537). Programme swaps welcome.
Record Gate: 1,641 v Alfreton Town, Derbys Snr Cup final 2nd leg 11/5/93. *At old ground: 9,800 v Rochdale, F.A. Cup 1st Rd 1951.*
Previous Leagues: Midland 1894-1902 25-58 61-71 73-82/ Central Alliance 47-61/ Central Mids 82-90.
Best FA Cup season: 1st Rd 51-52 (lost 0-2 at home to Rochdale), 56-57 (1-5 at home to Blyth).
Sponsors: Manor House Furnishing   **Previous Ground:** Manor Ground, Manor Rd (pre-1992).
Midweek home matchday: Tuesday   **Reserve team's League:** Mids Regional Alliance.
Record win: 14-2   **Record defeat:** 1-11
Record transfer fee paid: Nil   **Received:** £11,750 for Chris Brookss (Luton Town, 1992).
Clubhouse: Open Wed-Fri 7-11pm, Sat-Sun noon-3 & 7-11pm, and Mon or Tue if there is a match. Snacks behind bar. Large tea bar open matchdays 2-5pm. (6.30-9pm for night games).
Captain 92-93: Paul Fletcher   **Top Scorer 92-93:** Simon Osborne
P.O.Y. 92-93: John Humphreys (Players' choice: Simon Osborne, Supporters': Jason Campbell).
Hons: West Mids Lg Div 1 91-92 (Lg Cup 91-92), Central Mids Lg Cup 87-88, Midland Lg 67-68 (R-up 1898-99), Central All. 52-53 53-54 54-55 (R-up 47-48 55-56), Derbys Snr Cup 1894-95 95-96 96-97 97-98 1948-49 52-53 55-56 57-58 62-63 82-83 92-93.

Ilkeston Town F.C. 1992-93. Back Row (L/R): Jeff Wooley, Larry Burrell, Jamie Kay, Steve Aldridge, Alan Rigby (Trainer), Paul Fletcher, Jason Campbell, Graham Harrod, Kenny Burns, Danny Boyes (now Manager). Front: Lee Edwards, Nigel Bailey, Bill Fossey (then Manager), John Humphreys, David Bevon, Simon Osborne.

KNYPERSLEY VICTORIA

Chairman: A Farr   **Vice Chairman:** P Leese   **President:** G Quinn.
Secretary: P H Freeman, 30 Caton Crescent, Milton, Stoke-on-Trent ST6 8XQ (0782 543123).
Manager: R Horton   **Asst Mgr:** E Mountford   **Coach:** E Mountford
Physio: N Gregory   **Press Officer:** J Shenton.
Ground: Tunstall Road, Knypersley, Stoke-on-Trent, (0782 522737/ 513304).
Directions: M6 Jct 15 join A500, 4th exit, pick up A527, follow through Tunstall, Chell, to Biddulph. Ground is situated on A527 just before Biddulph. From M6 jct 18 follow signs to Holmes Chapel then Congleton. A527 Congleton to Biddulph. Bus 61 Congleton-Tunstall passes ground.
Seats: 160   **Cover:** Yes   **Capacity:** 850   **Floodlights:** Yes   **Founded:** 1969.
Colours: Blue/maroon/blue   **Change Colours:** All maroon   **Nickname:** Vics.
Previous Ground: None   **Record Gate:** 1,100 v Pt Vale, friendly '89.
Programme: 16-18 pages, 50p.   **Editor:** J Shenton (S-o-T 517962)   **Club Shop:** No.
Previous Leagues: Leek & Moorlands 69-78/ Staffs Co. (North) 78-83/ Staffs Senior 83-90.
Club Sponsors: Charlton Solicitors.   **Record transfer fee paid:** £1,000 M Biddle (Congleton, 1993)
Midweek home matchday: Tues/Thurs   **Reserve team's League:** Staffs Alliance.
Record win: 10-0 v Clancey Dudley   **Record defeat:** 0-9 v Meir K.A.
Clubhouse: Open from 1pm on Saturdays and 7pm weekdays. Burgers, hot dogs, crisps etc at games.
Captain & P.o.Y. 92-93: T Stanway   **Top Scorer 92-93:** J Burndred, 36
Club record scorer: J Burndred   **Club record appearances:** M Gosling, 450.
Hons: West Mids Lg Div 1 92-93, Staffs Snr Lg 84-85 (Lg Cup 84-85 85-86), Staffs Co. Lg R-up 79-80, Staffs FA Vase 83-84 86-87, Sentinel Cup 86-87, Leek & Moorlands Lg 72-73 (Div 2 71-72).

Knypersley Victoria - West Midlands (Regional) League Division One champions 1992-93. Photo - Staffordshire Sentinel.

LYE TOWN

Chairman: W Homer   **President:** G Ball   **Comm. Manager:** Terry Brumpton.
Secretary: Mrs A Ball, 79 Aretha Close, Crestwood Park, Kingswinford, West Mids DY6 8SW (0384 79038).
Manager: Ian Cole   **Asst Manager:** Ron Corbett   **Physio:** Harry Hill.
Ground: Stourbridge Road, Lye (0384 422672).
Directions: On A458 Birmingham-Stourbridge road about 400yds after lights/crossroads at Lye. From M5 jct 3 take road marked Kidderminster as far as lights at bottom of Hagley Hill, right at island, 3rd turn off at next island, 3rd turn off at crossroads/lights, left, ground about 400yds on left. Quarter mile from Lye (BR).
Seats: 100   **Cover:** 600   **Capacity:** 5,000   **Floodlights:** Yes   **Founded:** 1930.
Colours: White/red/red   **Change Colours:** All sky   **Nickname:** Flyers.
Programme: 28 pages, 40p   **Programme Editor:** Dave Liley
Clubhouse: Yes (0384 822672).   **Previous Leagues:** Midland Combination 31-39.
Record Gate: 6,000 v Brierley Alliance.   **Hons:** West Mids Lg R-up 76-77 78-79 79-80 80-81 (Prem. Div Cup 75-76), Midland Comb. 35-36 (R-up 32-33 34-35 37-38), B'ham Snr Cup R-up 80-81.

Lye Town F.C. 1992-93. Back Row (L/R): Home, Cooper, Wingfield, Williams, Stafford, Shaw, Hill. Front: Stokes, Gilbert, Homer, Taylor, Gore, Godwin. Photo - James Wright.

OLDBURY UNITED

Chairman: Roger Fennell   **Vice Chairman:** Ken Harris.
Secretary: Michael Stanley, 32 Junction St., Oldbury, Warley, West Mids B69 3HD (021 544 5091).
Manager: Jeff Allard   **Asst Mgr:** Kevin Hadley   **Physio:** Tony Dandy
Press Officer: Martin Scott   **Commercial Manager:** Eddie Winkett.
Ground: The Cricketts, York Road, Rowley Regis, Warley, West Midlands (021 559 5564).
Directions: M5 jct 2, follow Blackheath & Halesowen signs, first left at lights and fourth left into York Road (turning before motorway flyover), ground 200yds on left. One and a half miles from Sandwell & Dudley and Rowley Regis BR stations. Bus 404 from West Bromwich, Oldbury and Blackheath.
Seats: 300   **Cover:** 1,000   **Capacity:** 3,000   **Floodlights:** Yes   **Founded:** 1958
Cols: All blue (white flashes/trim)   **Change colours:** All yellow (blue flashes/trim)
Previous Names: Queens Colts 58-62/ Whiteheath Utd 62-65.   **Nickname:** Cricketts
Record Gate: 2,200 v Walsall Wood, Walsall Snr Cup Final 1982.
Prev. Lges: Oldbury 58-62/ Warwick & W Mids All. 62-65/ Worcs (later Midland) Comb. 65-82/ Southern 82-86.
Previous Grounds: Brittana Park 61-63/ Newbury Lane (Oldbury Stadium) 63-78.
Players progressing to F'ball Lge: C Gordon, L Conoway, J Scott, R O'Kelly, G Nardiello, Dakin, T Reece.
Programme: 24 pages, 50p   **Programme Editor:** Secretary
Club Shop: No, but club metal badges, polo shirts and jumpers can be obtained from secretary.
Midweek home matchday: Tuesday   **Club Sponsors:** Beswick Paper Group, Oldbury.
Record win: 10-1 v Blakenall   **Record defeat:** 1-9 v Moor Green.
Record transfer fee paid: Nil   **Received:** £10,000 for Colin Gordon (Swindon, 1985).
Clubhouse: Mon-Fri 7.30-11pm, Sat-Sun 12-2.30 (12-11pm Sat matchdays). Hot dogs, pies, burgers, cobs and hot drinks available from kitchen on matchdays only.
Captain 92-93: Mark Wakefield   **Top Scorer 92-93:** Neil Hesson, 21   **P.O.Y. 92-93:** Mick Guest.
Hons: West Mids Lg 92-93, Staffs Snr Cup 87-88, Midland Comb. R-up 78-79 (Presidents Cup 72-73(res), Div 3 R-up 82-83(res), Chal. Vase 82-83(res)), Walsall Snr Cup 82-83, B'ham Snr Amtr Cup, Oldbury Lg Div 2 61-62, Worcs Snr Urn 86-87, Sandwell Charity Cup 86-87.

PAGET RANGERS

Chairman: R R Ruddick   **President:** E Angelides
Secretary: Ian T Price, 24 Biddulp Court, Braemar Rd, Sutton Coldfield, West Mids B73 6LN (021 355 7072).
Manager: Keith Shrimpton   **Commercial Manager:** Paul Vanes.
Ground: Springfield Road, Walmley, Sutton Coldfield (021 3151563).*** *Important note - move to new ground imminent with possible groundshare at Sutton Coldfield Town. Check before travelling ***.*
Directions: From B'gham & Gravelly Hill I'change (M6 Jct 6) via A38 Tyburn Rd & B4148 Eachelhurst Rd, over narrow rail bridge, Walmley Rd, thru village, 500yds on right Springfield Rd. Ground 50yds past church on right before petrol station. 2 miles from Sutton Coldfield (BR). Bus 114 from B'ham, 71 114 & 165 from Sutton.
Seats: 300   **Covered:** 300   **Capacity:** 3,500   **Floodlights:** Yes   **Founded:** 1938
Colours: Gold/black/gold   **Change colours:** All red
Programme: 24 pages, 30p   **Programme Editor:** W Dudley
Clubhouse: 6 evenings/week & weekend lunchtimes. Regular weekend entertainment, plus darts, pool etc.
Previous Grnd: Pype Hayes Pk 38-46.   **Record Gate:** 2,000 v A Villa, F'light opening 1971.
Previous Lges: Birmingham Suburban/ Central Amtr/ Mids Comb. 50-81/ Southern 86-88.
Players progressing to Football League: John Gittens (Southampton for £10,000).
Hons: West Mids Lg R-up 91-92 (Lg Cup 91-92), Midland Comb.(6) 59-61 69-71 82-83 85-86 (R-up 77-78, Lg Cup 59-60 66-67, Div 1 Cup 70-71, Div 3 82-83(res)), B'ham Jnr Cup 51-52, Walsall Snr Cup 85-86.

PELSALL VILLA

Chairman: C V Dolphin   **Vice Chairman:** J H Gough   **President:** B J Hill
Secretary: Gareth J Evans, 72 St Pauls Crescent, Pelsall, Walsall WS3 4ET (0922 693114).
Manager: Reg Priest   **Asst Mgr/Coach:** P Stone   **Physio:** M Gascoigne
Press Officer: C V Dolphin   **Commercial Manager:** C V Dolpin.
Ground: The Bush, Walsall Rd, Heath End, Pelsall, Walsall (0922 682018 or 692748 matchdays only).
Directions: M6 jct 7 marked A34 B'gham. Take A34 towards Walsall to 1st island, turn right (marked Ring Road), cross two islands. At large island at bottom of hill take last exit marked Lichfield, up hill, cross next island to lights. Continue to next set of lights and turn left (B4154 Pelsall). Go over railway bridge to Old Bush house on right (next to Pelsall Cricket and Sports Club).
Seats: 124   **Cover:** 124   **Capacity:** 2,000   **Floodlights:** Yes   **Reformed:** 1961.
Colours: Red & black/white or black/white or black   **Change colours:** Blue/yellow/white
Programme: 32 pages, 40p   **Programme Editor:** Secretary   **Club Shop:** No.
Previous Grounds: None   **Previous League:** Staffs County (South) 61-81.
Club Nickname: Villians   **Record Gate:** 1,800 v Aston Villa 28/11/91.
Midweek home matchday: Monday
Record win: 7-0 v Westfields   **Record defeat:** 1-7
Record transfer fee paid: £800 for Dean Walters (Blakenall, 1992).
Received: £2,000 for Phil Wood (Halesowen, 1993).
Best F.A. Cup season: 3rd Qualifying Rd 92-93 (lost 2-4 at Gainsborough Trinity).
Best F.A. Vase season: 5th Rd 92-93 (lost 0-1 at Buckingham Town).
Clubhouse: Mon-Fri 7.30-11pm, Sat noon-11pm, Sun noon-3 & 7.30-10.30pm. Hot & cold meals.
Captain 92-93: K Gough   **Top Scorer 92-93:** A Horne   **P.o.Y. 92-93:** Dean Walters 47.
Club record scorer: K Gough 180   **Club record appearances:** K Gough 353.
Hons: West Mids Lg Div 1 Cup 88-89 (R-up 89-90, Div 2 Cup R-up 83-84), Walsall Snr Cup R-up 89-90 92-93, Wednesbury Charity Cup 67-68 68-69 69-70 73-74 88-89 89-90 (R-up 66-67 70-71 72-73 87-88 90-91 92-93), D Stanton Shield(2) 73-75 (R-up 75-76), Sporting Star Cup 76-77 (R-up 61-62), Staffs Co. (Sth) Lg R-up 68-69 (Div 1(res) 83-84, Prem Div Tphy(res)89-90), Rugeley Charity Cup 78-79 (R-up 69-70), Bloxwich Charity Cup(2) 81-83, Staffs Jnr Cup 68-69, Cannock Chase Charity Cup 63-64, Edge Cup 83-84, Ike Cooper Tphy R-up 89-90.

Pelsall Villa, who enjoyed their best ever season in 1992-93.

ROCESTER

Chairman: Mr D Hill
Secretary: Mr Gilbert Egerton, 23 Eaton Road, Rocester, Uttoxeter, Staffs ST14 5LL (0889 590101).
Manager: Frank Northwood   **Reserves' Mgr:** Dave Price   **Coach:** Darren Heyes
Commercial Mgr: Mr M Harper   **Press Officer:** Ian Cruddas (0889 564173).
Ground: The Rivers Field, Mill Street, Rocester, Uttoxeter, Staffs (0889 590463).
Directions: From A50 r'bout adjoining Little Chef restaurant at Uttoxeter take B5030 towards Rocester and Alton Towers, right into Rocester village after 3 miles over narrow bridge, in village centre bear right at sharp left-hand bend into Mill Str., ground 500yds on left just past former cotton mill.
Seats: 200   **Cover:** 500   **Capacity:** 4,000   **Floodlights:** Yes   **Founded:** 1876
Colours: Amber/black/black   **Change colours:** All sky blue   **Nickname:** Romans
Programme: 36/40 pages, 50p   **Programme Editor:** Barry Smith (0889 563989).
Club Shop: Yes, selling mostly programmes and a few Rocester souvenirs. Contact Ian Cruddas (0889 564173).
Record Transfer Fee Paid: £1,000 for Paul Ede (from Burton Albion, September 1989).
Record Transfer Fee Received: £8,000 for Tony Hemmings (from Northwich Victoria, March 1991).
Players progressing to Football League: George Shepherd (Derby County), Mark Sale (Birmingham).
Record Gate: 1,026 v Halesowen Town, FA Vase 4th Rd January 1987 (at Leek Town FC).
Previous Lges: Ashbourne/ Leek & Moorland/ Cheadle & Disrtist/ Uttoxeter Amateur/ Stafford 53-57/ Staffs County Nth 57-84/ Staffs Senior 84-87.
Previous Ground: Mill Street, Rocester (early 1900s-1987).
Midweek home matchday: Tuesday   **Sponsors:** H.K.B. Steels Ltd, Tipton.
Record win: 14-0 (twice)   **Record defeat:** 0-9.
Clubhouse: On matchdays (normal licensing hours) and other special events. Hot drinks and snacks during games.
Captain 92-93: Guy Hall   **Top Scorer 92-93:** Paul Ede   **P.o.Y. 92-93:** Cory Johnson 15.
Club record scorer: Mick Collins   **Club record appearances:** Peter Swanwick.
Hons: West Mids Lg R-up 89-90 (Div 1 87-88, Div 1 Cup 87-88), Staffs Snr Lg(2) 85-87, Staffs FA Vase 85-86 87-88.

RUSHALL OLYMPIC

Chairman: John Burks   **Vice Chairman:** Trevor Westwood   **President:** Brian Greenwood.
Secretary: Peter Athersmith, 46 Blakenall Lane, Leamore, Walsall (0922 711735).
Manager: Alan Deeley   **Asst Manager:** Cliff Painter   **Coach:** Cliff Painter
Physio: Claude Guest   **Press Officer:** Darren Stockall (0922 379153).
Ground: Dales Lane, off Daw End Lane, Rushall, Nr Walsall (0922 641021).
Directions: From Rushall centre (A461) take B4154 signed Aldridge. Approx., 1 mile on right, directly opposite Royal Oak Public House, in Daw End Lane. Ground on right. Two miles from Walsall (BR) station.
Seats: 200   **Cover:** 200   **Capacity:** 2,500   **Floodlights:** Yes   **Founded:** 1951
Colours: Amber/black/black   **Change colours:** White/red/red   **Nickname:** Pics.
Programme: 16 pages, 20p   **Programme Editor:** Darren Stockall (0922 379153)
Previous Grounds: Rowley Place 51-75/ Aston University 76-79.
Previous Leagues: Walsall Amateur 52-55/ Staffs County (South) 56-78.
Players progressing to Football League: Lee Sinnott (Watford), Lee Palin (Villa, Nottm F, Bradford).
Record Gate: 2,000 v Leeds United Old Boys, charity match 1982.
Club Sponsors: W.M. Print   **Midweek home matchday:** Tuesday
Record win: 7-1   **Record defeat:** 0-6 v Bilston, F.A. Vase.
Clubhouse: Excellent bar/lounge, kitchen, adjoining large refreshment facilities. Bar open every night 8-11pm, Saturday matchdays before and after game, Sunday noon-2.30pm.
Captain 92-93: Stuart Watkiss   **Top Scorer & P.o.Y. 92-93:** Steve Taylor.
Club record scorer: Graham Wiggin   **Club record appearances:** Brian Greenwood.
Hons: West Mids Lg Div 1 79-80, Walsall Amtr Lg Div 1 55-56 (Div 2 52-53, Snr Cup 54-55 55-56, Jabez Cliff Cup 55-56), Staffs Co. Lg Div 1 60-61 61-62 62-63 64-65 (Div 2 56-57), Walsall Charity Cup 52-53, Walsall Chal. Cup 54-55 56-57, Walsall Memorial Charity Cup 55-56 56-57 57-58 58-59 59-60 60-61 61-62, W Preston Chal. Cup 56-57, Cannock & Dist. Charity Cup 56-57, Wednesbury Snr Cup 58-59 59-60 60-61, Sporting Star Cup 59-60 60-61(joint) 64-65 65-66 67-68, J W Edge 62-63 66-67, Walsall Snr Cup 64-65, Lichfield Charity 64-65 66-67, Staffs Yth Cup 81-82.

STOURPORT SWIFTS

Chairman: Chris Reynolds   **Vice Chairman:** Trevor Roberts   **President:** Roy Crowe.
Secretary: John McDonald, 65 Princess Way, Stourport-on-Severn (0299 822088).
Coach: John Holmes.   **Joint Managers:** Phil Mullen/ Pat Lynch
Physio: John Kane.   **Commercial Manager:** Peter Longmore.
Press Officer: Dave Watts (0299 823349).
Ground: Walshes Meadow, off Harold Davis Drive, Stourport-on-Severn (0299 825188).
Directions: Follow one-way system through Stourport sign posted Sports Centre. Go over River Severn Bridge, turn left into Harold Davies Drive. Ground is at rear of Sports Centre. Nearest rail station is Kidderminster.
Seats: 250   **Cover:** 200   **Capacity:** 2,000   **Floodlights:** Yes   **Founded:** 1882.
Colours: Black & gold/black/black   **Change colours:** All Red
Nickname: Swifts.
Previous Leagues: Kidderminster/ Worcester/ Midland Combination.
Programme: 40 pages, 50p   **Editor:** Dave Watts (0299 823349)   **Club Shop:** No.
Club Sponsors: T. & J. Joinery   **Record Gate:** 4,000 v Birmingham, charity match.
Midweek home matchday: Tuesday   **Reserve team's League:** Kidderminster.
Record win: 10-0   **Record defeat:** 1-7
Clubhouse: Clubhouse open matchdays. Hot snacks available. Licensed bar.
Captain 92-93: Nigel Laker   **Top Scorer 92-93:** Simon Marsh 33   **P.o.Y. 92-93:** Adam Micholls.
Club record scorer: Norman Laker   **Club record appearances:** Vaughan Little.
Hons: West Mids Lg Div 1 R-up 87-88 (Premier Div Cup 92-93, Div 2 Cup R-up 82-83), Worcs Snr Urn 92-93.

WEDNESFIELD

Chairman: R Thomas   **Vice Chairman:** J Massey
Secretary: James Highfield, 6 Soberton Close, Wednesfield, West Mids WV11 2QX (0902 724771).
Manager: K Howells   **Asst Mgr/Coach:** K Hall   **Physio:** M Andrews
Commercial Mgr: D Clayton   **Press Officer:** J Massey (0902 781819).
Ground: Cottage Ground, Amos Lane, Wednesfield, Wolverhampton (0902 735506).
Directions: From Wolverhampton on the A4124 Wednesfield Rd. Stay on road right through Wednesfield until island. Leave island at first exit (Wood End Rd), left after about 200yds into Amos Lane. Ground is on right, approx. 400yds along. 3 miles from Wolverhampton BR station. Bus 559 to Wood End or 560 to Red Lion.
Seats: 148   **Cover:** 250   **Capacity:** 1,000   **Floodlights:** Yes   **Founded:** 1961.
Colours: Red & white stripes/black/black **Change colours:** Green & yellow stripes/green/yellow
Programme: New for 93-94, 50p   **Programme Editor:** T.B.A.   **Club Shop:** No.
Record Gate: 480 v Burton Albion, FA Cup 1981.
Previous Ground: St Georges PF 61-76
Previous Name: Wednesfield Social 61-89.
Previous League: Wolverhampton & District Amateur 61-76.
Club Sponsors: Ansells   **Midweek home matchday:** Tuesday   **Nickname:** Cottagers.
Clubhouse: Evenings 7-11pm. Food (burgers, chips etc) on 1st team matchdays.
Captain 92-93: M Sankey   **Top Scorer 92-93:** M Swann   **P.o.Y. 92-93:** K Harris
Hons: West Mids Lg Div 1 76-77 (R-up 77-78).

WEST BROMWICH TOWN

Chairman: A Brown   **President:** R Langford   **Founded:** 1962
Secretary: Kenneth Jones, 24 Wilow Ave., Wednesfield, Wolverhampton WV11 1DP (0902 728416).
Ground & directions: As Willenhall Town FC (see overleaf).   **Programme:** Yes
Colours: Yellow (blue trim)/blue/yellow (blue trim)   **Change colours:** Red/white/red.
Previous Name: Millfields F.C.

WESTFIELDS

Chairman: Steven Knight   **Vice Chairman:** Roy Williams   **President:** Denis Hartland
Secretary/Press Officer/Comm. Mgr: Andy Morris, 17 Fayre Oaks Green, Kings Acre, Hereford (0432 264711).
Manager: Gary Stevens   **Asst Manager:** Sean Edwards   **Coach:** Phil Dean
Ground: Thorn Lighting, Holme Lacy Rd, Rotherwas, Hereford (0432 268131, club-410548).
Directions: Proceed 1 mile south from Hereford on A49, left in Home Lacy Rd at Broadleys Inn, proceed 1 mile to Thorn Lighting Rotherwas, ground on the right on Rotherwas Ind. Estate. 2 miles from Hereford (BR).
Seats: 100   **Cover:** 200   **Capacity:** 2,000   **Floodlights:** Yes   **Founded:** 1966
Colours: Maroon & sky   **Change colours:** Sky & white
Previous Grounds: Widemarsh Common 66-73/ King George Playing Fields 73-74.
Previous Leagues: Herefordshire Sunday 66-74/ Herefordshire 72-74/ Worcester & Dist. 74-77.
Programme: 16 pages, 30p   **Programme Editor:** Secretary   **Club Shop:** No.
Club Sponsors: Hereford Times   **Record Gate:** 1,057 v Hereford Utd, t'monial 1980.
Midweek home matchday: Tuesday   **Reserve team's League:** Herefordshire.
Record win: 11-0 v Coventry Sporting   **Record defeat:** 0-7 v Pelsall Villa.
Record transfer fee paid: Nil   **Received:** £2,000 for Alex Sykes (Mansfield, 1992).
Nickname: The Fields   **Clubhouse:** Evenings 7-11pm, matchdays 12-11pm. Bar snacks.
Captain 92-93: Chris Dzioba   **Top Scorer 92-93:** Paul Burton   **P.o.Y. 92-93:** Marc Priday
Club record scorer: Brian Preece   **Club record appearances:** Phil Powell/ Mark Tabb.
Hons: West Mids Lg Div 1 86-87 (Div 2 R-up 83-84 (Div 2 Cup 79-80 83-84))), Herefordshire Snr Cup 85-86 88-89 91-92 (Yth Cup 92-93), Kington Chall. Cup 83-84 85-86 86-87 89-90, Kington Invitation Cup 84-85 85-86 86-87, Presteigne Ottway Cup 78-79 81-82 84-85, Worcs Jnr Cup 79-80, Wye Guild Cup 74-75 77-78, Hereford Sunday Lg 75-76 76-77 (Div 1 71-72, Div 2 76-77, Div 3 75-76, Prem Div Cup 75-76 76-77, Div 1 Cup 73-74 74-75, Div 3 Cup 72-73), Stuart Brown Cup 67-68.

Westfields F.C. 1992-93. Back Row (L/R): Alec Irvine, Phil Dean (Coach), Gary Stevens (Player-Manager), Andy Kingston, Chris Dzioba, Marc Pridal, Peter Wallace, Anthony Rivett, Dave Taylor, Sean Edwards (Assistant Manager), Andy Morris (Chief Executive), Eric Richards (Committee). Front: Simon Shakeshaft (Physiotherapist), Paul Burton, Ashley Botwood, Rob Weaver, Kevin Davies, Jon Dallow, Darren Preece.

WILLENHALL TOWN

Chairman: J Williams   **Vice Chairman:** G L Mills.
Secretary: Fred Rhodes c/o The club: Noose Lane, Willenhall, Willenhall (605132-club, 636586-off.).
Manager: Chris Robinson   **Asst Manager/Coach:** Barry Stobart.
Physio: John Porter   **Press Officer/Commercial Manager:** Dave Norton.
Directions: Noose Lane is off the main A454 Walsall to Wolverhampton road. 3 miles from jct 10 (M6) - follow signs for Wolverhampton for 2 miles, Keyway dual c'way to lights at Neachells Lane, turn rights at these lights, first right again into Watery Lane and left at island into Noose Lane. Two and a half miles from Wolverhampton (BR). Buses 525, 526, 529.
Seats: 324   **Cover:** 500   **Capacity:** 5,000   **Floodlights:** Yes   **Founded:** 1953
Colours: All red   **Change colours:** All blue   **Midweek home matchday:** Monday.
Programme: 40 pages, 40p   **Editor:** M Skitt (0902 636586).
Club nickname: The Reds   **Club sponsors:** Wolverhampton & Dudley Brewery.
Record win: 11-0   **Record defeat:** 1-6.
Reserve team's league: Floodlit Lge   **Record transfer fee received:** £5,000.
Record transfer fee paid: £2,000 for Gary Stevens (Cheltenham, 1981).
Record Gate: 3,454 v Crewe Alexandra, FA Cup 1st Rd 1981.
Previous Leagues: Wolverhampton/ Staffs County/ West Mids 75-82/ Southern 82-91.
Previous Grounds: Farmers Field, Spring Lane 53-55/ Memorial Park 55-74/ Marstons Spts Grd 74-75.
Club Shop: Yes, selling programmes, rosettes, key rings and badges.
Clubhouse: Open Mon-Thurs 12-3 & 7-11pm, Fri-Sat 11am-11pm, Sun 12-2 & 7-10.30pm.
Captain & P.o.Y. 92-93: Darren Wright   **Top-scorer 92-93:** Ade Edwards.
Club record scorer: Gary Matthews   **Club record appearances:** Gary Matthews.
Hons: FA Vase R-up 80-81, West Mids Lg 78-79 (Div 1 75-76, Prem. Div Cup 79-80, Div 2 Cup 78-79(res)), Birmingham Snr Cup R-up 82-83, J W Hunt Cup 73-74.

DIVISION ONE CLUBS 1993-94

BLOXWICH STROLLERS

Secretary: George A Llewellyn, 7 Birchover Road, Walsall WS2 8TU (0922 614595).
Manager: Leigh Taylor   **Assistant Manager:** Gavin Stanton.
Ground & Directions: Blakenall FC (see page 678).
Colours: White/red/red   **Change colours:** All yellow   **Founded:** 1888.
Programme: Yes   **Programme Editor:** Neil Morris.
Previous Leagues: Walsall/ Birmingham Combination 13-32/ West Mids 52-55/ Bloxwich Combination/ West Mids Metropolitan/ Staffs Co. (Sth)/ Midland Combination (pre-1988).
Previous Grounds: The Red Lion (originally)/ T P Riley Community Centre, Lichfield Rd (pre'87).
Previous Name: Little Bloxwich Strollers   **Top Scorers 92-93:** Ricky Watson & Jason Marsden.
Hons: Birmingham Comb. 24-25 (R-up 22-23), West Mids Lg Div 2 R-up 92-93 (Div 2 Cup R-up 92-93), Staffs Co. Lg Sth, Edge Cup, Lg Shield 84-85, Walsall Challenge Cup 92-93, Walsall Charity Cup, Staffs Jnr Cup, Walsall Lg.

CANNOCK CHASE

Chairman: P Lomas   **Vice Chairman:** P Walsgrove   **President:** W Longmore
Secretary: Mark Clementson, 79 Stafford Rd, Huntington, Cannock, Staffs WS12 4NU (0543 425418).
Manager: Alan Dennison.
Ground: West Cannock Spts Centre, Bradbury Lane, Hednesford WS12 4EP (0543 422141).
Directions: From Cannock take A34 towards Stafford, right into Pye Green Rd half mile from town centre (park and Leisure Centre on left), thru 2 sets of lights across island, after 3 miles right into Broadhurst Green, ground 1 mile down hill on right.
Seats: None   **Cover:** 50   **Capacity:** 2,000   **Floodlights:** No   **Founded:** 1968.
Colours: White/black/red   **Change Colours:** Red/red/black   **Nickname:** The Prog
Programme: Yes   **Editor:** Peter Lomas (0543 570118)   **Club Shop:** No.
Previous Leagues: Cannock Chase 68-76/ Mid Staffs 76-78/ Staffs Co. (Sth) 78-84/ Staffs Snr 84-86.
Previous Grounds: Hednesford Park 68-79/ Heath Hayes F.C. (goundshare) 79-80.
Club Sponsors: Betaprint Press Ltd   **Midweek home matchday:** Wednesday
Captain 92-93: Paul Slater   **Top Scorer 92-93:** Keith Kelly   **P.O.Y. 92-93:** Craig Machin.
Club record scorer: Keith Kelly   **Club record appearances:** P Walsgrove 800.
Clubhouse: Open matchdays.   **Hons:** W Mids Lg Div 1 Cup R-up 91-92.

CHESLYN HAY

Chairman: Mr L Lazenby   **Vice Chairman:** Mr J Randall   **Founded:** 1984.
Secretary: Mr Ivor Osborne, 16 Littlewood Lane, Cheslyn Hay, Walsall WS6 7EJ (0922 414755).
Ground: As Great Wyrley F.C. (see above).
Colours: Blue & white hoops/blue/blue   **Change:** Scarlet & red stripes/black/black
Programme: Yes   **Editor:** Secretary   **Club Shop:** Not yet   **Nickname:** The Hay
Previous Grounds: Lucas Sports 84-88/ Rushall Community Centre 88-89/ Cheslyn Hay Rec. 89-90/ Harrison M.W. ground (on opposite side of Hazel Lane) 90-91).
Previous Leagues: Bloxwich Combination 84-88/ Staffs County (South) 88-90.
Midweek home matchday: Tuesday   **Record Gate:** 91 v Albright & Wilson, League Aug '91.
Record win: 8-1 v Mitchells & Butlers Reserves, 14/1/89.
Record defeat: 1-8 v Hinckley Athletic Reserves, 5/12/92.
Clubhouse: Evenings & matchdays.   **Hons:** Bloxwich Comb. Lg Cup 86-87 87-88.
Captain 92-93: Gary Osborne   **Top Scorer 92-93:** Kevin Shuck, 9   **P.O.Y. 92-93:** Paul Dennis.
Club record scorer: Gary Osborne, 52   **Club record appearances:** Gary Osborne, 252.

DONNINGTON WOOD

Chairman: D Roberts   **Manager:** P Woods
Secretary: G Vater, 33 Sunbury Drive, Trench, Telford, Salop TF2 7EA (0952 612273).
Ground: Duke Street Playing Fields, St Georges, Telford.
Directions: M54 jct 4 (Telford East). From island take B5060 Priorslee Rd, follow to r'bout junction with A5. Left, follow road to next island, right B5061 to Wellington, 2nd right - St Georges and continue along Stafford Street, to mini island, straight over into Gower Street, second right Duke Street, 100yds to car park. Take lane on far side of car park down to ground.
Seats: No   **Cover:** Yes   **Capacity:**   **Floodlights:** No   **Founded:** 1910.
Colours: White (green trim)/green/green   **Change colours:** All blue.
Programme: Yes (Editor - B Harvey 0952 583002)   **Hons:** West Mids Lg Div 1 R-up 76-77.

ETTINGSHALL HOLY TRINITY

Chairman: Richard Platt   **Vice Chairman:** David Caddick   **President:** David Gadd.
Secretary: Graham Mills, 27 Ashen Close, Sedgley, Dudley, West Mids DY3 3UZ (0902 662222).
Manager: Graham Mills   **Asst Manager:** Dave Caddick.
Physio: Ty Jones   **Press Officer:** Peter James (0902 762564).
Ground: Aldersley Stadium, Aldersley Rd, Tettenhall, Wolverhampton (0902 751171).
Directions: From central Wolverhampton take A41 (Tettenhall Rd) for just over a mile, right into Lower Str., right into Aldersley Rd, ground on right. From M54 jct 2, A49 toward Wolverhampton, right into Oxley Moor Rd and follow signs to Aldersley stadium.
Seats: 500   **Cover:** 500   **Floodlights:** Yes   **Club Shop:** No   **Founded:** 1920.
Colours: Green/white   **Change colours:** Red/blue   **Nickname:** Trins.
Previous League: Wednesbury Church & Chapel (early 1900s)/ Bilston Youth (1950s)/ Wolverhampton & District Amateur (1960s)/ Staffs County (South).
Previous Grounds: Compton Park (4 years)/ Bilston Town F.C. 89-92.
Programme: 25 pages, 50p   **Programme Editor:** Peter James (0902 762564).
Midweek home matchday: Wednesday   **Sponsors:** K Phones/ Direct Batteries/ D.K.B. Electric.
Captain 92-93: Colin Nicklin   **Top Scorer 92-93:** Ian Bosworth.
P.O.Y. 92-93: Ian Bosworth and Warren Waterfield (joint).
Hons: West Mids Lg Div 1 Cup R-up 85-86 (Div 2 R-up 84-85, Sporting Award 85-86), Staffs Co. Lg R-up 82-83 (Lg Shield 82-83 83-84, Ike Cooper Cup 82-84 83-84, Sporting Club Award 81-82), Wolverhampton & District Amateur Lg 80-81 (Div 1 65-66, Div 2 64-65, Div 1/2 Cup 64-65 65-66, A H Oakley Cup 80-81), J W Hunt Cup 82-83 83-84 (R-up 79-80), Wolverhampton Cup 83-84 (R-up 82-83).

GORNAL ATHLETIC

Chairman: Ken Taylor
Secretary: Paul Westwood, 18 The Close, Lower Gornal, Dudley DY3 2JY (0902 664209).
Manager: John Gwinnell   **Coach:** Ian Clark.
Ground: Garden Walk Stadium, Lower Gornal, Dudley, West Midlands (0384 52285).
Directions: From Dudley take A459 to Sedgley past the Burton Rd Hospital. 1st on left at the Green Dragon public house on the B4175 (Jews Lane). Follow the road until you come to the Old Bull's Head, turn left into Rednall Road, 2nd left to Garden Walk.
Seats: None   **Cover:** 500   **Capacity:** 3,000   **Floodlights:** No   **Founded:** 1945.
Colours: Yellow/green/yellow   **Change colours:** All sky   **Club Shop:** No.
Previous Name: Lower Gornal Ath.   **Previous Lge:** Midland Comb. 51-63   **Nickname:** Peacocks
Record transfer fees received: £1,500 for Gary Bell and for George Andrews both to Cardiff City, 1965.
Captain 92-93: Stephen Worley   **P.O.Y. 92-93:** Paul Wells   **Top Scorer 92-93:** David Lowe 17.
Hons: West Mids Lg Div 1 R-up 83-84 (Div 1 Cup 92-93), Birmingham Vase 91-92.

Gornal Athletic - Division One Cup winners 1992-93. Photo - James Wright.

GORNAL SPORTS

Secretary: Stephen Parsonage, 16 Stanton Avenue, Woodsetton, Derby DY1 3RR (0902 676598).
Ground & Directions: Gornal Athletic FC (see above).   **Founded:** 1979.
Colours: All red   **Change colours:** White/black/black   **Hons:** W Mids Lg Div 2 R-up 91-92.

GREAT WYRLEY

Chairman: F Titley   **Manager:** F Dinham
Secretary: D Catchpole, 3 Briar Close, Pye Green, Hednesford, Cannock, Staffs WS12 4EY (0543 425883).
Ground: Hazelbrook Ground, Hazel Lane, Gt Wyrley (0922 410366).   **Clubhouse:** Yes
Directions: A34 thru Gt Wyrley until you get to Star Public House, left into Hazel Lane. Ground is on the left. **N.B.** Please park on tarmac road at side of ground.
Seats: No   **Cover:** Yes   **Floodlights:** No   **Programme:** Yes   **Founded:** 1960.
Colours: Red/black/black   **Change Colours:** All blue   **Hons:** W Mids Lg Div 2 82-83.

HILL TOP RANGERS

Chairman: Mr J Scott
Secretary: Mrs A Scott, 46 James Watt St., Hill Top, West Bromwich B71 2AJ (021 556 3597).
Manager: Paul Allen   **Asst Manager:** Mark Williams   **Coach:** Dave Scott
Physio: J Scott   **Press Officer:** Mrs S Allen.
Ground & Directions: Darlaston F.C. (see page 680).   **Founded:** 1980.
Colours: Yellow/black/yellow   **Change Colours:** Red/navy/red   **Club Shop:** No.
Previous Grounds: The Jesson 1980/ Hydes Rd 81-84/ Red House Park 84-87.
Previous Leagues: West Bromwich & Dist. 80-84/ West Mids Metropolitan 84-86/ Mercian F.A. 86-88.
Programme: 16 pages, 30p   **Programme Editor:** Secretary
Midweek home matchday: Mon/Wed   **Record Gate:** 165 v Darlaston, W Mids Lg Div 1 12/4/94.
Record win: 15-0 v Ham Baker 7/1/84 (Cup) & v Minworth 18/10/86 (League).
Record defeat: 1-9 v West Bromwich Athletic 28/11/81 (Cup match, West Brom a Div higher).
Clubhouse: Open 1 hour prior to match and about 2 hours after. Beefburgers, pies, hot dogs, hot drinks etc available from food bar.
Captain & P.O.Y. 92-93: Mark Williams   **Top Scorer 92-93:** Kevin Hemmings.
Club record scorer: Dean Cadman 175   **Club record appearances:** Dave Scott 399.
Hons: West Mids Lg Div 2 89-90, West Mids Metropolitan Lg R-up 85-86, Mercian F.A. 86-87, West Bromwich District Charity Cup.

LICHFIELD

Chairman: C Clarke   **Ground:** Shortbutts Lane, Lichfield, Staffs (0543 262246).
Secretary: M Cohen, 5 Mesnes Green, Lichfield, Staffs WS14 9AB (0543 255497).
Directions: From A5 proceed to island at A5127 Birmingham Rd, right into Shortbutts Lane, ground on left approx. 300 yds after railway bridge.
Seats: No   **Cover:** Yes   **Floodlights:** No   **Clubhouse:** Yes   **Founded:** 1966.
Colours: All royal blue   **Change colours:** All red   **Programme:** Yes
Hons: Walsall Chal. Cup 66-67, Lichfield Charity Cup.

LUDLOW TOWN

Chairman: A Cade **Manager:** Steve Mulliner **Founded:** 1890.
Secretary: Alan Cade, Haybridge, Burway Lane, Ludlow, Shropshire SY8 1DT (0584 872783).
Ground: The Riddings, Riddings Road, Ludlow, Shropshire (0584 875103).
Directions: From Kidderminster road A4117; straight over r'bout into Henley Rd, 2nd left into Sandpits Rd, follow road for a quarter mile until road bears round to the left into Ridding Road - ground immediately on right.
Seats: No **Cover:** 150 **Floodlights:** No **Clubhouse:** Yes **Programme:** No
Cols: Red (white pin stripes)/black/black (red tops) **Change colours:** Royal blue/white/royal
Previous League: Kidderminster. **Hons:** Wes Mids Lg Div 1 Cup 90-91, Presteigne-Otway Cup 90-91.

MALVERN TOWN

Chairman: R C Tandy **President:** R H Mann **Manager:** Martyn Day
Secretary: G F Knapper, 27 Alexandra Lane, Malvern, Worcs WR14 1JF (0684 574861).
Ground: Langland Stadium, Langland Avenue, Malvern, Worcs (0684 574068).
Directions: From Worcester take main road to Malvern. When reaching Malvern turn left at 1st lights into Pickersleigh Ave., follow to Langland Arms Pub on left, left into Madresfield Rd, 2nd left into Langland Ave., ground 100yds on right. 1 mile from Malvern (BR).
Seats: 140 **Cover:** 310 **Capacity:** 4,000 **Floodlights:** Yes **Founded:** 1947.
Colours: Claret & blue/white/sky **Change colours:** White/black/claret.
Prog: 12 pages 20p (special matches) **Programme Editor:** Dave Liley
Clubhouse: 2 bars, large dance area **Previous League:** Midland Comb. 55-79.
Hons: Worcester/ Midland Comb. 55-56. **Record Gate:** 1,221 v Worcester, FA Cup

MANDERS

Chairman: Colin Greatrix **Sec:** Barry Hall, 10 Miles Meadow Close, Willenhall WV12 5YE (0922 409017).
Manager: Tom Stokes **Asst Manager:** Martin Eccleston **Physio:** Eddie Edwards.
Ground & Directions: Wednesfield FC (see page 685) **Founded:** 1935.
Colours: White/red/red **Change colours:** Green/black/black **Reformed:** 1988.
Previous League: Wolverhampton & District Works.
Previous Grounds: Cannock Rd Sports Ground/ Ashmore Park/ Wednesfield High School.
Nickname: Paintmen. **Clubhouse:** Normal licensing hrs (maybe shut Wed. evening).
Captain 92-93: Paul Dearn **Top Scorer 92-93:** Jason Simpson **P.o.Y. 92-93:** Steve Astley.
Honours: West Mids Lg Div 2 Cup 92-93, JW Hunt Cup(3), Wolverhampton Charity Cup 76-77 79-80 83-84.

MOXLEY RANGERS

Chairman: C Aldritt **Sec:** Ian Beddow, High Str., Moxley, Wednesbury, WS10 8RX (0902 498251).
Ground: Darlaston Community Sports & Social Club, Hall Street, Darlaston (021 526 5217).
Directions: M6 jct 10, A454 Wolverhampton Rd towards Bilston, approx. 2 miles to island, round island towards Bilston, 1st left into Darlaston Lane, over canal bridge, 2nd left into Hall Str., ground 50yds on right.
Colours: All red **Change:** Black & white/black/black **Clubhouse:** Yes **Founded:** 1966.

STAFFORD TOWN

Manager: Chris Curtiss **Secretary:** Ian Clark, 21 Cull Avenue, Stafford ST16 3UX (0785 49640).
Ground: Rowley Park Stadium, Averill Rd, Stafford (0785 51060 - 223741 after home games)
Directions: Approaching Stafford northbound on M6 leave at junction 13 and travel towards town on A449, travel past Garth Hotel on right into Rising Brook (High School on left), Rowley Park Stadium is signed 200yds after school. Turning left left into Westway the entrance drive, Averill Rd is then 2nd right. From Cannock/Lichfield via A513 then turn left at the bottom of Radford Bank via Silkmore Lane to Rising Brook.
Founded: 1974 **Programme:** Yes **Colours:** All red **Change colours:** All blue.
Previous Ground: Riverway, Stafford **Previous Names:** Stafford Town 74-90/ Stafford M.S.H.D. 90-92.
Previous League: Staffs Snr (pre'93) **Hons:** Staffs Snr Lg R-up 91-92

Stafford Town, who join this summer from the Staffordshire Senior League. Photo - Staffordshire Newsletter.

TIPTON TOWN

President: W Powell   **Chairman:** H C Hackett   **Vice Chairman:** D Fisher.
Secretary: John A Cross, 1 Moreton Close, Tipton, West Mids DY4 0DG (021 556 3566).
Manager/Press Off.: Mick Henley   **Asst Manager:** Steve Mills   **Coach:** Mel Perry.
Physio: John Pope   **Commercial Manager:** Graham Bunch.
Ground: Tipton Recreation & Community Centre, Wednesbury Oak Rd, Tipton (021 556 5067/ 502 5534).
Directions: M5 jct 2, A4123 towards Dudley/ Wolverhampton turning right at junction with A4037 - ground on right adjacent to Dales (ASDA) superstore about 2 miles further on. From M6 jct 9 take A461 through Wednesbury and proceed to Ocker Hill, Tipton turning right at island towards Bilston and Wolverhampton, next left at lights - ground 50yds on lefy. On 245 bus route.
Seats: 150   **Cover:** 150   **Capacity:** 2,000   **Floodlights:** No   **Formed:** 1948
Cols: Black & white stripes/black/red   **Change colours:** All blue   **Nickname:** None
Previous Grounds: Jubilee Park 48-66/ Lee, Howe & Co. Ltd Works Ground 66-70.
Prev. Lge: Wolverhampton Amateur 48-66. **Record Gate:** 1,300 v Wolves, friendly 1/8/88.
Programme: 20 pages, 25p   **Programme Editor:** Secretary   **Club Shop:** No.
Sponsors: Status Systems/ Tipton & Coseley
Midweek home matchday: Wednesday   **Reserve team's League:** Staffs County (South).
Record win: 8-1 v Brewood   **Record defeat:** 2-12 v Bilston Town.
Record transfer fee paid: Nil   **Received:** £1,000 for Steve Bull (West Brom.).
Clubhouse: Weekdays 7-11pm, Sats 12-11pm. Bar food, microwave meals, cold sandwiches.
Captain & P.o.Y. 92-93: Mark Hudson   **Top Scorer 92-93:** Lee Rollason, 11.
Club record scorer: Graham Lappage   **Club record appearances:** Mick Henley, 600.
Hons: West Midlands Lg Div 1 83-84 (R-up 76-77, Div 1 Cup 83-84), Birmingham Challenge Vase 86-87, Wednesbury Charity Cup 74-75 75-76 79-80 80-81.

TIVIDALE

Chairman: Don Ashton   **President:** Lord Peter Archer.
Secretary: D Aston, 18 Hollies Rd, Tividale, Warley, West Mids B69 1SX (0384 239206).
Manager: Terry Jones   **Asst Mgr:** Kevin Mullinder   **Coach:** M Dunning/A James.
Physio: J Cotton/K Nicklin   **Comm. Mgr:** T Jones   **Press Officer:** T Clark.
Ground: The Beeches, Packwood Rd, Tividale, Warley, West Midlands B69 1UL (0384 211743).
Directions: Dudley Port Station to Burnt tree, left towards Birmingham, ground 1 mile on right. Or, M5 jct 2, follow Dudley signs A4123, after approx 2 miles turn left into Regent Rd and left again into Elm Terraces, first left into Birch Crescent. Packwood Rd is second left - ground at end of cul-de-sac.
Seats: 200   **Cover:** 1,000   **Capacity:** 3,500   **Floodlights:** Yes   **Founded:** 1954
Colours: Yellow   **Change colours:** Red   **Nickname:** Dales
Programme: 40 pages, £1.75 with entry   **Programme Editor:** Robert Shinfield (0384 241154),
Previous Ground: City Road.   **Record Gate:** 2,400 v Telford United, FA Cup.
Club Sponsors: Richmond Insurance   **Players progressing to Football Lge:** G Hughes, L May.
Midweek home matchday: Tuesday   **Reserve team's League:** Div. Two.   **Club Shop:** No.
Record transfer fee paid: Nil   **Received:** £3,000 for Leroy May (Hereford, 1993).
Clubhouse: Mon-Fri 8-11pm, Sat 12-11pm, Sun 12-3 & 8-10.30. Cobs, rolls, sandwiches available.
Captain 92-93: Paul Whitehead   **Top Scorer 92-93:** Leroy May   **P.o.Y. 92-93:** Scott Hall
Hons: W Mids Lg Div 1 72-73 (Prem. Div Cup 76-77, Div 1 Cup 72-73), Wednesbury Charity Cup 76-77.

WALSALL WOOD

Manager: Michael Speake
Secretary: Stuart J Rousell, 6 Pool Green, Aldridge, Walsall WS9 0JH (0902 58041).
Ground: Oak Park, Lichfield Rd, Walsall (0543 361084).
Directions: Off A461 Walsall-Lichfield Rd, 4 miles from Walsall town centre and 100yds south of junction with A4152 Aldridge-Brownhills. If travelling via M6/M5 exit motorway at jct 7 (Post House) and continue on A34 towards Walsall before joining A4148 which connects with the A461. 4 miles from Walsall (BR) station - regular buses pass ground.
Capacity: 3,000   **Seats:** 400   **Cover:** 400   **Floodlights:** Yes   **Founded:** 1928.
Colours: Red/black/red   **Change colours:** All blue   **Programme:** Y
Previous Grounds: None   **Previous Leagues:** Mids Comb. 51-92/ Staffs Snr 92-93.
Previous Names: Walsall Wood, Walsall Sportsco merged in 1982 to form Walsall Borough. Name later reverted.
Record Gate: 800 v Aston Villa, 1980.
Clubhouse: Evenings, matchdays and Sunday lunchtimes. Darts, pool, juke box. Hot snacks on matchdays.
Hons: Midland Comb. 51-52 (R-up 53-54 54-55 57-58 58-59 60-61, Lg Cup 54-55 60-61 (R-up 56-57 58-59)), B'ham Jnr Cup 76-77. *Walsall Sportsco: Mids Comb. Lg Cup 79-80.*

WEM TOWN

Chairman: G Sage
Secretary: Mrs Beverley Hoyle, 24 Coseley Ave., Telford Estate, Shrewsbury SY2 5UP (0743 358818).
Ground: Bowensfield, Wem, Salop (0939 33287).
Directions: M54 jct A42 for Newport and Whitchurch, in Newport take the B5062 to High Ercall, then B5063 to Shawbury and Wem. Entering Wem carry on to T-junction, right under rail bridge. Continue to T-junction by church, right, then left turning for Whitchurch opposite the White Lion, continue for a quarter mile and turn left at the Hawkestone Pub into Pyms Rd; ground 2nd left.
Seats: No   **Cover:** Yes   **Floodlights:** No   **Clubhouse:** No   **Founded:** 1921.
Colours: All sky   **Change colours:** White/black/black   **Programme:**

Tipton Town F.C. 1992-93. Back Row (L/R): Steve Mills (Asst Manager), Gavin Caw, Lee Rollaston, Kevin Warner, Mazhar Iqbal, Craig Phillips (Asst Manager), Dave Burns, John Pope (Trainer), Mick Henley (Manager). Front: Ray Thomas, Trevor Beech, Martin Sibley, Stuart Mole, Ian Duffield, Kevin Steventon. Photo - James Wright.

Tividale F.C. - Division One Cup finalists 1992-93. Photo - Mark Wood.

WOLVERHAMPTON CASUALS

Chairman: G Jones   **President:** Clive Hammond   **Manager:** Horace Crutchley
Secretary: Michael J Green, 63 St Philip's Ave., Pennfields, Wolverhampton WV3 7GD (0902 333677).
Ground: Brinsford Lane, Coven, Wolverhampton (0902 782314).
Directions: Onto M54 from M6 North, at jct 2 turn right (A449 to Stafford). Ground half a mile, turn right into Brinsford Lane. 2 miles from Billbrooke (BR). Stafford-Wolverhampton buses pass ground.
Seats: 50   **Cover:** 50   **Capacity:** 2,000   **Floodlights:** No   **Founded:** 1896
Colours: Green/white/green   **Change colours:** White/black/white
Programme: 28 pages, 30p   **Programme Editor:** G Smith
Previous Name: Staffs Casuals (pre-1981) **Previous Ground:** Aldersley Stadium.
Clubhouse: Bar and snacks, open Tues, Wed, Thurs, Sat, Sun & alternative Mon.
Players progressing to Football League: David Heywood (Wolves).
Prev. Lges: B'gham AFA, W'hampton Amtr   **Hons:** W Mids Lg Div 1 R-up(3) 85-88 (Div 1 Cup 85-86).

WOLVERHAMPTON UNITED

Chairman: T Pritchard
Secretary: Philip Taylor, 15 Burbage Close, Fallings Park, Wolverhampton WV10 9YG (0902 725513).
Ground: Prestwood Rd Spts Centre, Prestwood Rd West, Wednesfield (0902 730881).
Directions: Situated between Nos. 44 and 46 Prestwood Rd West, approached by way of a drive between the two houses. From Wolverhampton centre Ring Road, follow round to Stafford Str. (A449), join Cannock Rd (A460), after 1 mile bear right into Victoria Road, cross over into Thorneycroft Lane/Prestwood Rd West - ground on right 200yds from pedestrian crossing.
Seats: 200   **Cover:** Yes   **Programme:** Yes   **Clubhouse:** Yes   **Founded:** 1976.
Colours: Old gold/black/gold   **Change colours:** Red & black/Black/Red
Hons: West Mids Lg Div 1 76-77 (R-up 81-82).

KIDDERMINSTER & DISTRICT LEAGUE

PREM. DIV.	P	W	D	L	F	A	PTS
Brint Chainwire	24	14	4	6	65	36	46
Bewdley Town	24	14	4	6	68	42	46
Ludlow Colts	24	13	4	7	64	36	43
Wyre Forest	24	13	2	9	64	38	41
Bandon	24	11	6	7	59	46	39
County Sports	24	9	6	9	38	36	33
Woofferton	24	9	4	11	47	51	31
Netherton Lib.	24	9	4	11	42	52	31
Cradley Heath	24	9	4	11	39	51	31
Two Gates	24	9	2	13	35	54	29
Highley Welfare	24	7	7	10	40	50	28
Stourport Sw. Res.	24	7	3	14	37	71	24
Parkdale Rovers	24	5	4	15	30	65	19

DIV. ONE	P	W	D	L	F	A	PTS
Forest '90	24	18	3	3	110	42	57
Dunn Bank Rvrs	24	17	4	3	83	35	55
Gilt Edge	24	14	4	6	53	36	46
Wordsley Star	24	15	1	8	57	48	46
Chaddesley	24	14	1	9	79	48	43
Springvale Rvrs	24	12	2	10	72	67	38
Ludlow Town Res.	24	9	3	12	56	68	30
Enville Ath. Res.	24	8	5	11	40	47	29
Brint C'wire Res.	24	7	6	11	39	48	27
Kinver	24	6	4	14	36	65	22
Worths	24	6	3	15	47	71	21
Wordsley	24	5	4	15	35	54	19
Bache Arms	24	5	0	19	31	106	15

DIV. TWO	P	W	D	L	F	A	PTS
Bewdley T. Res.	26	18	3	5	96	37	57
Edgecliff Eagles	26	16	8	2	93	43	56
Quarry Bank Labour	26	16	5	5	94	51	53
Dudley Snooker	26	16	2	8	84	47	50
Clee Hill United	26	14	4	8	87	59	46
Shakespeare Inn	26	13	4	9	61	54	*40
Blackheath El. Res.	26	11	6	9	67	51	39
Areley Kings	26	11	3	12	65	71	36
Parkdale Rvrs Res.	26	8	6	12	49	58	30
Quarry Bank Celtic	26	9	3	14	69	87	30
Cleobury Town	26	8	4	14	54	71	28
Steelstock	26	5	2	19	50	106	17
Cradley Hth Res.	26	5	2	19	40	107	17
Adam Carpets	26	5	2	19	53	127	17
* - 3pts deducted							

DIV. THREE	P	W	D	L	F	A	PTS
Horn & Trumpet	26	21	4	1	114	30	67
Highley Wel. Res.	26	18	4	4	89	38	58
Coppertops	26	18	3	5	103	34	57
Interlink	26	17	4	5	83	42	55
Clent	26	16	2	8	84	35	50
Ian Walker Group	26	14	5	7	77	56	47
Kinver Res.	26	10	3	13	38	69	33
Burlish Olympic	26	9	5	12	63	59	32
Dunsdale	26	9	4	13	67	91	31
Furnace Sports	26	9	3	14	71	78	30
Broadway Utd	26	10	2	14	70	84	*29
Cleobury T. Res.	26	3	3	20	25	79	12
Broughton Shoes	26	3	1	33	28	103	10
Stourport Rangers	26	3	1	22	45	165	10
* - 3pts deducted							

'MARSTONS' BURTON-ON-TRENT & DISTRICT F.A.

'Pedigree' Premier Division

	P	W	D	L	F	A	PTS
New Inn	20	17	3	0	75	18	54
Winshill	20	17	2	1	64	17	53
Uttoxeter	20	14	2	4	48	33	44
Stapenhill Res.	20	8	5	7	46	45	29
Barton United	20	8	3	9	40	32	27
B.T.R. Rolleston	20	7	3	10	55	37	24
Newhall Utd Res.	20	7	3	10	38	43	24
Bass	20	6	4	10	37	40	22
Coton	20	6	2	12	48	62	20
Marstons	20	2	4	14	26	70	10
Rosliston Albion	20	0	5	15	11	93	5

'B.T.R.' Division Two

	P	W	D	L	F	A	PTS
Linton Villa	20	16	2	2	83	16	50
Rangmore	20	15	2	3	91	22	47
BRT Rolleston Res.	20	15	2	3	60	25	47
Monks Bridge	20	9	3	8	61	45	30
Barton Utd Res.	20	8	5	7	48	44	29
Dowty Woodville	20	9	2	9	40	49	29
Repton Cas. Res.	20	7	2	11	33	56	23
Burton Fire Station	20	6	3	11	31	77	21
Brown & Sharpe	20	5	3	12	44	64	18
Derby Inn	20	2	5	13	31	65	11
Marston Res.	20	1	5	14	28	85	8

'Double Diamond' Division One

	P	W	D	L	F	A	PTS
Repton Casuals	18	15	2	1	69	15	47
M.T.G.	18	14	2	2	66	24	44
Brenstar	18	13	2	3	71	28	41
Prince Arthur	18	12	1	5	61	33	37
Robirch	18	6	6	6	31	35	24
Burton Caribbean	18	6	1	11	29	38	19
Nethersdale St Peters	18	5	2	11	29	51	17
Overseal St Matthews	18	4	3	11	48	50	15
Winshill Res.	18	4	2	12	22	79	14
Rosliston Alion Res.	18	0	1	17	21	93	1

'White Shield' Division Three

	P	W	D	L	F	A	PTS
Silver Jubilee	20	17	1	2	106	30	52
Woodville New Inn	20	16	2	2	87	28	50
Copper Hearth	20	14	1	5	77	37	43
Dosthill Boys Club	20	9	3	8	53	55	30
Stretton	20	9	2	9	42	57	29
Burton Roebuck	20	7	6	7	44	52	27
Drakelow	20	7	4	9	52	55	25
Barton Royal Oak	20	6	5	9	58	63	23
Bass Res.	20	4	4	12	29	59	16
Pirelli	20	5	0	15	45	75	15
Burton Oak & Ivy	20	2	0	18	27	105	6

WOLVERHAMPTON & DIST. AMATEUR LEAGUE

	P	W	D	L	F	A	PTS
Claregate Dynamo	20	16	2	2	84	30	34
Rovers Pk Village	20	15	3	2	72	26	33
Wednesfield C.A.	20	14	0	6	67	37	28
Paget Arms	20	12	0	8	57	30	24
East Park Maestro	20	10	1	9	49	44	21
Orton Vale	20	7	5	8	43	42	19
Amat United	20	7	2	11	55	45	16
Anglo-Italian	20	7	2	11	42	41	16
Claregate Ravens	20	5	4	11	31	47	14
Mossley Y.C.	20	6	1	13	27	62	13
Walsall Manor	20	1	0	19	13	135	2

PREMIER CUP
Winners: Rovers Park Village
Runners-up: Claregate Dynamo

LGE CUP Group A	P	W	D	L	F	A	PTS
Wednesfield C.A.	3	3	0	0	16	6	6
Rovers Pk Village	3	2	0	1	9	7	4
Claregate Ravens	3	1	0	2	3	5	2
Anglo-Italian	3	0	0	3	2	12	0

LGE CUP Group B	P	W	D	L	F	A	PTS
East Park Maestro	5	3	2	0	13	5	8
Claregate Dynamo	5	3	1	1	16	6	7
Amat United	5	3	1	1	13	11	7
Orton Vale	5	2	1	2	17	14	5
Paget Arms	5	0	2	3	4	11	2
Mossley Y.C.	5	0	1	4	3	12	1

Final won by Wednesfield C.A.

A.H. OAKLEY CUP:
Winners: Rovers Park Village
Runners-up: Orton Vale.

ANSELLS MIDLAND
FOOTBALL COMBINATION

President: P Fellows
Chairman: L Wathen
Hon. Secretary: L W James JP, 175 Barnett Lane,
Kingswinford, West Mids DY6 9QA (0384 273459)

ARMITAGE GO ONE BETTER

The Premier Division title went to Armitage '90 who went one better than the previous season under a new managerial team of Danny McMullan and Garry Haynes. Their joy was increased after the end of the season when they were admitted to the Beazer Homes League.

The main challengers to their title hopes for much of the season were Sandwell Borough who fell away badly towards the end of the campaign to finish fifth. Stratford Town lost fewer games than any other side in the division, only four, but thirteen draws show why they finished only third. Like Sandwell, they will start the new season with a new manager after John Busst moved to Evesham United. In the end it was left to Stapenhill to provide the main threat to Armitage when they embarked on a stunning run from Christmas losing just one game in the final month of the season. That 0-1 defeat at Stratford on May Day finally handed the title to Armitage with three games to play.

The Challenge Cup was won for the first time by Stapenhill who beat Highgate United 2-0 in the final at Boldmere with goals from Walker and Barnes, who scored in every round. Stapenhill were also the division's top scorers with 105 goals, including the top two victories in the league; 8-0 v Mile Oak and 11-0 v Alcester Town.

The Division One title was won by an impressive Wellesbourne side who finished a full ten points clear of Kings Heath. Kenilworth Town threatened their hopes at one stage, but an impressive run in the Birmingham County Vase when they became the first Combination club to win the competition, and a number of postponements, weighed heavy at the end of the season and they fell away.

The Presidents Cup saw Kings Heath again in the bridesmaid's role as they went down 0-2 to local rivals Kings Norton Ex-Servicemen. At the bottom of Division One, spare a thought for Ledbury Town '84 who failed to collect a single point before Christmas, but rallied with a young side to get sixteen after. They still finished bottom, but the youngsters learned a lot.

Division Two saw Ansells, newcomers to the League, win the title by eight clear points. From the time they started winning their games in hand there was little doubt where the championship was heading. Coleshill Reserves led the table before falling away, whilst Shirley Town started the season in fine fettle before slipping badly in mid-season, then surged back to claim runners-up spot scoring an incredible 142 goals in the process, many of them scored by the prolific Junior McKeon.

The Challenge Vase was won by newcomers Colletts Green who had an excellent first season in the league. They beat Thimblemill Rec 1-0 in a closely contested final at Pershore. Green also finished third in the league and reached the final of the Worcestershire Junior Cup in their first season of entering.

(continued overleaf)

League Chairman Mr Lewis Wathen (centre left) presents the League Championship Shield to Chris Caulton the Armitage captain. Photo - Burton Mail.

Tamworth Reserves were the team of the season in the Reserve Division collecting a league and cup double and recording a fourteen point gap between themselves and runners-up Nuneaton Borough Reserves. Paul Wood, manager for most of the season, was justly rewarded by being promoted to first team boss.

For the second successive season the 'Ansells Combination Monthly Magazine' held its own 'Programme of the Year' award with a new name assured on the shield kindly donated by the Moor Green F.C. programme shop after Hinckley F.C. merged with Barwell Athletic to form Barwell F.C. A total of 29 clubs entered with some surprising omissions, but in third place was newcomers Meir K.A.'s excellent issue edited by Steve Osborne with assistance from Barry Smith and Stan Tooth. In second place came another excellent issue from Sherwood Celtic, edited by Phil Smith, and in first place - the club is different but the editor remains the same; Alan Mason, last season with Hinckley F.C. - winners Barwell F.C. All three issues come highly recommended.

Three clubs have been promoted to the Premier Division for 1993-94, subject to ground improvements being carried out. The clubs have placed a bond with the League and will not be promoted should the work not be carried out. In come Division One champions Wellesbourne, Kings Heath, returning after just one season in the lower flight, and, somewhat surprisingly Division Two champions Ansells. Moving downward are the bottom two Alcester Town and Barlestone St Giles.

Promoted from Division Two to Division One are runners-up Shirley Town and third placed Colletts Green, with Ledbury Town moving in the opposite direction. Also promoted are Monica Star in place of Marston Green who tendered their resignation due to problems with their home ground at Hurley Daw Mill. Sutton Coldfield Town Reserves come into Division Two playing at the Gas Ground, Pershore Town taking their place in the Reserve Division.

The Combination has gone from strength to strength with an unprecedented demand from new clubs wishing to join, so much so that the Management Committee has decided to form a new division to accomodate all the new clubs. Five clubs joining Division Two from the Coventry Alliance are Sphinx, Jaguar-Daimler, G.P.T., Massey-Ferguson and Alvis, whilst four clubs are switching to the new Division Three from the West Midlands (Regional) League; Mitchells & Butlers, G.E.C. Electrodrives (Blackheath), Albright & Wilson and Park Rangers. Rugby Town join Division Two from the Coventry & North Warwick League, and into Division Three come Alveston from the Stratford Alliance, Bilston Community College from the Staffs County (South) League and Continental Star.

One famous name from the past, Shifnal Town, are on the way back and will play in the Premier Division alongside another famous club, Shepshed Albion, who are taking a step down and can only enhance the quality of the competition.

Steve Davies, Editor 'Ansells Combination Monthly Magazine'.

PREM. DIV.	P	W	D	L	F	A	PTS
Armitage '90	38	26	6	6	91	32	84
Stapenhill	38	25	4	9	105	45	79
Stratford Town	38	21	13	4	70	33	76
Sandwell Borough	38	21	9	8	89	47	72
Pershore Town '88	38	21	8	9	74	38	71
West Mids Police	38	20	10	8	77	39	70
Coleshill Town	38	21	6	11	63	44	69
Boldmere St M.	38	17	12	9	74	48	63
Knowle	38	15	10	13	70	71	55
Barwell	38	14	12	12	63	70	54
Northfield Town	38	13	12	13	58	59	51
Meir K.A.	38	9	12	17	47	60	39
Mile Oak R. & Y.	38	9	9	20	37	72	36
Studley B.K.L.	38	7	14	17	39	71	35
Chelmsley Town	38	7	13	18	51	75	34
Highgate United	38	8	10	20	47	80	34
Bloxwich Town	38	5	11	22	28	74	26
Barlestone St G.	38	5	5	28	40	104	20
Alcester Town	38	3	10	25	30	102	19

DIV. TWO	P	W	D	L	F	A	PTS
Ansells	40	32	4	4	137	41	100
Shirley Town	40	29	5	6	142	57	92
Colletts Green	40	27	5	8	122	52	83
Monica Star	40	26	5	9	104	41	83
Coleshill Town Res.	40	24	3	13	92	57	75
Fairfield Villa	40	22	8	10	96	60	74
Enville Athletic	40	20	9	11	93	67	69
Meir K.A. Res.	40	20	9	11	75	57	69
Archdales	40	15	12	13	87	78	57
Holly Lane	40	16	9	15	90	82	57
Swift P.P.	40	17	5	18	78	67	56
Pershore T. Res.	40	15	10	15	76	59	55
Thimblemill Rec.	40	16	7	17	86	78	55
Burntwood Town	40	15	6	19	65	75	51
Kenilworth T. Res.	40	13	10	17	65	89	49
Studley BKL Res.	40	12	8	20	67	86	44
Earlswood Town	40	10	5	25	65	110	35
Wigston Fields Res.	40	7	6	27	49	119	27
Barlestone SG Res.	40	6	4	30	42	168	22
Wellesbourne Res.	40	6	2	32	42	133	20
Dudley Spts Res.	40	3	6	31	45	141	15

DIV. ONE	P	W	D	L	F	A	PTS
Wellesbourne	40	27	8	5	89	41	89
Kings Heath	40	24	7	9	100	44	79
Kenilworth Town	40	23	7	10	86	49	76
West Heath United	40	23	4	13	92	64	73
Handrahan Timbers	40	19	10	11	66	52	67
Kings Norton Ex-S.	40	20	6	14	71	54	66
Southam United	40	17	13	10	66	45	64
Becketts Sporting	40	17	13	10	69	61	64
Sherwood Celtic	40	19	6	15	76	63	63
W.M. Fire Service	40	18	7	15	71	58	61
Badsey Rangers	39	16	8	15	64	62	56
Hams Hall	40	15	11	14	68	68	56
Solihull B. Res.	40	15	10	15	65	64	55
Marston Green	40	14	8	18	69	75	50
Wilmcote	40	12	10	18	67	85	46
Polesworth N.W.	40	12	8	20	68	95	44
Triplex	40	11	10	19	41	57	43
Dudley Sports	40	11	3	26	55	84	36
Wigston Fields	39	9	8	22	57	80	35
Upton Town	40	9	8	23	45	84	35
Ledbury Town	40	5	1	34	31	130	16

RES. DIV.	P	W	D	L	F	A	PTS
Tamworth Res.	42	33	3	6	143	53	102
Nuneaton B. Res.	42	27	7	8	117	58	88
Bromsgrove R. Res.	42	26	9	7	141	58	87
Boldmere SM Res.	42	25	7	10	73	48	82
Burton Albion Res.	42	24	9	9	105	66	81
Sutton C'field Res.	42	24	7	11	112	72	79
Atherstone Utd Res.	42	21	7	14	83	75	70
Gresley Rovers Res.	42	19	9	14	93	74	66
Halesowen T. Res.	42	19	2	21	99	103	59
Kidderminster Res.	42	17	7	18	107	94	58
Bridgnorth T. Res.	42	17	7	18	66	73	58
Hednesford T. Res.	42	16	9	17	92	96	57
Shepshed A. Res.	42	17	3	22	92	107	54
Stratford T. Res.	42	14	8	20	66	87	50
Leicester Utd Res.	42	13	10	19	87	102	49
Barwell Res.	42	12	10	20	48	77	46
R.C. Warwick Res.	42	13	7	22	75	115	46
Evesham Utd Res.	42	11	7	24	79	120	40
V.S. Rugby Res.	42	12	4	26	69	116	40
Redditch Utd Res.	42	8	11	23	57	101	35
Sandwell B. Res.	42	7	11	24	60	104	32
Witney Town Res.	42	8	4	30	55	123	28

HOME TEAM	1	2	3	4	5	6	7	8	9	10	11	12	13	14	15	16	17	18	19	20
1. Alcester Town	*	0-4	1-3	1-4	2-0	0-3	2-2	0-3	2-4	2-3	1-3	2-1	1-3	0-0	1-2	0-5	1-1	1-5	2-2	0-1
2. Armitage '90	3-1	*	7-0	4-2	3-0	0-0	4-0	2-1	2-1	0-0	4-2	1-0	3-1	4-2	0-1	4-3	2-2	1-3	4-0	1-0
3. Barleston St.Giles	2-3	0-6	*	3-5	0-2	2-5	1-2	2-2	0-1	2-0	2-3	2-1	2-1	0-2	0-0	2-3	0-4	0-2	1-2	1-8
4. Barwell	1-0	0-1	2-1	*	0-0	4-1	1-1	1-1	1-2	0-2	3-2	2-2	1-1	0-0	2-2	1-0	2-2	1-0	2-5	0-0	0-2
5. Bloxwich Town	2-2	0-4	0-1	1-2	*	0-1	1-4	1-1	0-1	0-0	2-0	1-1	1-1	2-1	0-0	0-3	0-4	0-4	0-2	1-6
6. Boldmere St.Michaels	6-0	3-2	3-0	4-1	3-2	*	1-2	1-0	1-1	4-1	6-0	1-2	1-1	2-2	1-0	3-1	1-2	1-1	0-0	2-4
7. Bolehall Swifts	5-0	0-1	2-1	2-2	6-0	1-1	*	2-2	1-3	2-3	2-2	1-1	2-0	4-2	0-6	1-1	0-2	0-3	3-0	0-3
8. Chelmsley Town	0-0	1-6	1-1	2-2	1-1	1-3	0-3	*	2-3	2-2	3-2	2-2	5-0	0-3	0-3	4-1	3-2	0-2	0-0	0-1
9. Coleshill Town	2-0	1-0	3-0	2-1	0-1	2-2	0-0	2-0	*	4-1	2-2	2-0	0-2	3-1	3-1	1-6	2-3	3-0	1-1	0-1
10. Highgate United	5-0	1-2	0-0	2-1	2-1	0-2	0-5	2-2	0-2	*	0-1	1-3	6-1	0-1	2-2	0-5	0-5	1-1	2-1	1-1
11. Knowle	0-0	2-1	3-1	2-2	2-2	1-0	2-1	5-2	0-2	1-0	*	1-1	5-2	4-1	3-2	2-5	3-1	0-2	1-2	1-3
12. Mier K.A.	1-1	0-3	4-1	2-2	3-0	2-2	0-1	2-2	1-2	1-0	3-1	*	1-0	0-2	1-2	3-0	1-3	0-1	2-2	2-2
13. Mile Oak Rovers	2-0	0-2	4-1	1-3	2-0	2-1	0-3	3-0	0-2	0-0	1-4	0-1	*	1-1	0-4	0-3	0-2	2-0	2-0	0-0
14. Northfield Town	2-0	1-2	3-2	4-0	1-1	1-1	2-0	0-1	2-1	4-0	2-1	4-1	2-1	*	1-1	1-1	1-5	1-1	3-0	3-3
15. Pershore Town '88	4-0	1-1	5-1	2-3	2-0	3-4	3-2	2-1	3-1	5-1	3-1	2-0	3-1	1-0	*	1-0	2-0	1-0	1-2	1-0
16. Sandwell Borough	3-1	0-0	4-2	1-2	3-1	0-0	1-2	3-1	1-0	6-0	3-3	3-2	0-0	5-0	2-1	*	4-1	0-0	3-2	2-1
17. Stapenhill	11-0	1-0	3-2	5-0	1-0	2-1	2-1	4-2	3-0	4-1	3-1	3-0	8-0	5-2	1-1	1-3	*	1-2	2-0	3-4
18. Stratford Town	1-1	1-1	3-0	5-1	2-2	4-1	0-1	2-2	2-1	3-1	1-0	2-0	1-1	1-1	1-0	2-1	1-0	*	0-0	1-1
19. Studley BKL	1-1	0-4	0-0	3-4	1-2	0-1	3-2	1-0	1-2	0-3	2-2	1-1	1-1	1-0	2-2	1-2	1-6	3-3	*	1-4
20. W.Mids. Police	2-1	1-2	4-1	0-3	2-1	1-1	0-0	4-0	1-1	1-1	3-2	3-0	3-1	0-0	1-2	1-0	0-1	1-2	4-0	*

HOME TEAM	1	2	3	4	5	6	7	8	9	10	11	12	13	14	15	16	17	18	19	20	21
1. Badsey Rangers	*	1-1	6-1	2-1	3-2	1-1	0-2	7-0	1-1	1-0	2-5	1-1	0-3	3-3	4-0	1-0	1-2	1-2		0-0	1-2
2. Becketts Sporting	3-2	*	0-1	0-0	1-1	3-0	3-3	4-1	3-1	6-1	2-1	3-0	2-2	2-0	1-1	0-2	1-4	4-3	2-0	2-2	0-6
3. Dudley Sports	1-2	1-2	*	3-4	0-1	0-1	0-1	4-1	2-1	2-1	0-2	2-5	0-2	4-2	2-3	1-3	1-0	2-1	3-2	2-2
4. Hams Hall	1-1	0-1	2-0	*	3-0	2-1	2-0	6-0	2-3	2-0	3-2	1-3	0-3	1-0	3-1	0-2	2-4	2-2	2-2	0-0	0-3
5. Handraham Tim.	3-0	1-1	2-0	2-0	*	3-1	0-2	2-1	3-0	3-0	3-1	2-2	0-0	1-0	1-1	1-1	3-1	1-3	7-1	2-2	1-0
6. Kenilworth T.	5-1	0-0	0-3	5-1	1-0	*	1-2	3-0	2-0	6-1	3-0	2-2	2-2	1-0	3-1	3-3	4-1	0-1	3-2	2-2	1-0
7. Kings Norton E.S.	1-2	2-1	4-1	3-1	0-1	0-2	*	2-1	4-3	2-2	3-1	1-1	0-1	1-4	1-1	1-3	1-3	0-1	1-0	0-3
8. Ledbury T.'84	0-2	1-3	1-7	2-4	1-2	0-4	1-2	*	2-3	2-1	0-4	1-0	1-0	1-2	3-2	0-3	0-5	0-1	1-1	1-3	1-4
9. Marston Green	1-3	1-2	4-1	2-1	1-1	1-5	2-4	2-1	*	2-2	0-2	1-0	6-2	2-0	0-2	2-3	2-0	1-2	0-2	1-4	2-2
10. Polesworth N.W.	3-1	5-5	5-1	2-2	1-3	1-5	0-5	3-0	3-1	*	2-3	4-0	1-1	2-0	1-0	1-2	1-2	2-0	3-2	2-0	0-0
11. Sherwood Celtic	5-0	1-3	3-0	4-2	3-0	1-2	2-0	2-1	2-1	2-0	*	2-1	2-7	2-2	3-1	1-0	1-5	5-1	1-1	1-1	1-3
12. Solihull B.Res	0-2	4-0	3-2	0-0	1-5	1-0	1-2	6-1	1-4	1-1	1-3	*	0-0	3-1	0-1	2-3	4-2	0-2	1-0	2-2	1-0
13. Southam Utd	1-1	1-1	2-0	0-1	3-0	1-3	2-2	3-1	0-1	3-1	0-0	2-2	*	2-0	2-0	0-3	1-0	2-0	7-1	0-2
14. Triplex	2-0	0-2	2-1	0-0	2-4	1-2	1-0	1-0	2-2	2-0	0-2	1-1	*	0-0	1-3	2-2	0-2	3-0	1-1	1-1
15. Upton Town	1-2	0-0	3-2	2-2	1-1	1-2	0-4	1-1	1-6	1-2	0-0	2-1	2-0	1-0	*	1-2	2-1	0-3	2-1	3-0	1-3
16. Wellesbourne	2-1	2-0	3-4	4-1	3-1	2-1	5-0	0-0	4-1	3-1	1-1	1-2	1-0	2-0	*	2-0	3-1	3-2	3-3	2-2
17. W. Heath Utd	2-1	4-1	2-3	1-1	3-0	0-2	1-0	6-1	1-1	5-1	1-0	1-2	2-0	1-3	4-1	1-4	*	2-1	2-3	2-0	3-1
18. W.M. Fire Serv.	1-2	1-1	1-0	1-1	1-2	2-1	1-4	6-0	2-2	4-1	2-3	3-2	1-2	0-0	5-1	0-0	1-3	*	4-2	3-0	1-0
19. Wigston Fields	0-1	3-0	0-0	2-3	1-1	1-1	1-2	3-0	0-2	4-2	1-1	0-1	1-1	3-1	6-3	0-3	1-6	3-3	*	3-0	2-4
20. Wilmcote	0-2	2-1	0-0	4-2	4-0	3-5	0-3	4-1	2-2	1-5	1-0	1-2	1-5	2-0	5-1	3-5	2-1	1-2	4-1	*	2-5
21. Kings Heath	4-2	1-2	4-1	1-3	1-0	2-1	0-1	7-0	4-3	9-2	3-0	1-2	7-1	1-0	2-0	2-0	1-1	2-0	2-0	1-2	*

N.B. Badsey Rangers v Wigston Fields not played.

HOME TEAM	1	2	3	4	5	6	7	8	9	10	11	12	13	14	15	16	17	18	19	20	21
1. Ansells	*	1-0	9-0	2-1	3-2	6-0	7-1	1-0	5-0	2-0	7-3	1-2	1-2	4-4	3-5	5-1	1-0	4-0	3-0	8-0	6-0
2. Archdales'73	2-2	*	4-2	3-0	2-2	2-0	4-0	0-1	1-1	2-2	1-1	1-2	1-3	2-1	2-2	0-2	1-2	2-2	4-1	2-2	5-1
3. Barlestone SG Res	0-3	1-2	*	0-7	1-5	3-0	0-5	1-0	0-4	2-2	1-1	2-2	1-5	3-1	1-9	0-7	2-0	1-4	1-3	2-8	2-2
4. Coleshill Res.	4-4	2-0	6-0	*	3-2	7-1	4-3	3-1	0-0	0-2	1-4	0-2	1-0	0-1	0-5	2-0	1-2	4-0	4-2	1-0	3-1
5. Colletts Green	3-4	8-1	6-0	3-4	*	1-1	5-0	3-1	2-2	2-0	5-3	2-3	1-1	1-0	5-1	3-1	1-0	4-2	3-0	2-0	3-0
6. Dudley S. Res	1-2	1-5	2-1	2-3	1-3	*	1-1	1-4	1-2	1-5	2-5	1-1	0-3	0-2	0-3	1-1	2-3	4-5	3-0	1-0	2-4
7. Earlswood T.	0-7	1-3	7-2	1-3	0-6	3-2	*	0-3	2-2	3-5	2-4	3-2	0-4	0-3	1-3	0-0	3-1	5-1	0-1	1-0
8. Enville Ath.	1-3	4-1	4-2	1-3	0-3	4-2	7-0	*	1-2	3-9	2-1	1-0	1-5	2-1	1-1	1-1	3-1	0-0	2-1	5-5	1-0
9. Fairfield Villa	2-0	5-2	3-0	0-1	0-5	4-3	2-1	1-2	*	2-2	9-0	0-1	4-1	5-2	0-5	1-0	3-2	1-2	3-0	8-0	1-0
10. Holly Lane '92	1-1	1-3	5-2	0-3	3-4	11-1	3-2	1-1	0-3	*	3-0	0-2	2-4	3-2	3-2	2-4	2-0	2-3	0-1	1-0
11. Kenilworth Res.	0-3	1-1	5-0	3-2	0-5	3-0	2-2	1-1	3-4	2-2	*	3-1	0-0	1-1	0-5	3-0	1-3	2-0	1-2	1-3	0-5
12. Meir K.A. Res.	0-4	2-2	8-1	1-0	1-2	6-0	2-1	3-3	0-5	1-1	5-0	*	1-2	2-0	0-2	4-1	2-1	2-1	2-0	1-2	0-1
13. Monica Star	0-3	4-1	8-0	1-2	4-1	5-1	3-0	0-2	1-0	6-1	0-0	3-1	*	0-1	1-3	1-1	1-0	4-1	7-1	2-0	5-0
14. Pershore Res.	1-2	1-2	6-0	2-1	1-1	3-1	2-3	1-1	1-2	1-1	2-3	1-1	1-2	*	3-0	1-1	0-1	4-1	0-0	5-1	2-1
15. Shirley Town	1-2	2-3	10-1	1-3	2-1	6-1	4-3	5-4	2-1	3-0	1-1	6-0	3-1	1-3	*	6-1	5-1	4-0	4-0	4-1	5-1
16. Studley BKL Res.	1-2	3-0	2-3	1-0	0-1	6-1	1-4	1-9	2-2	7-3	2-0	1-0	1-4	2-3	1-3	*	2-3	1-4	3-1	4-1	1-1
17. Swift P.P.	0-1	1-2	3-0	4-0	1-2	1-1	3-1	1-1	2-3	1-2	0-2	1-4	1-1	2-3	4-4	0-2	*	1-4	5-1	3-0	6-1
18. Thimblemill Rec	1-2	2-2	3-0	1-1	3-2	9-0	3-1	0-3	4-4	1-1	1-0	0-0	2-3	2-0	0-5	0-1	3-1	*	4-1	4-1	4-0
19. Wellesbourne Res	0-7	1-6	1-2	0-6	2-6	2-1	1-4	0-4	0-3	1-2	0-2	2-0	0-4	0-6	2-4	2-3	2-4	1-3	*	4-1	1-2
20. Wigston F. Res.	1-4	2-8	1-2	1-5	0-3	1-1	2-0	2-0	1-1	1-4	0-2	1-3	0-3	3-3	1-4	0-0	1-6	6-5	0-2	*	0-1
21. Burntwood	1-2	5-2	1-0	0-1	1-3	5-1	1-1	1-3	3-1	1-0	5-1	1-1	1-0	1-1	6-3	3-1	1-1	2-1	5-1	5-0	*

CHALLENGE CUP 1992-93

First Round

Armitage '90 v Boldmere St Michaels	2-1	Bloxwich Town v Wellesbourne	0-1
Coleshill Town v Bolehall Swifts	3-0	Hams Hall v Northfield Town	0-2
Ledbury Town v Dudley Spts	0-0(aet),0-3	Studley B.K.L. v Mile Oak Rovers & Yth	1-0
Triplex v Wigston Fields	3-4	West Midlands Police v Meir K.A.	2-1

Second Round

Badsey Rangers v Wigston Fields	2-1	Barlestone St Giles v Kenilworth Town	2-4
Becketts Sporting Club v Northfield Town	1-2	Chelmsley Town v Dudley Sports	4-3
Handraham Timbers v Sandwell Borough	0-6	Highgate United v Marston Green	4-2
Kings Heath v West Heath United	3-8(aet)	Kings Norton Ex-Serv. v West Mids Police	6-5(aet)
Knowle v Barwell	5-2	Polesworth North Warwick v Pershore Town '88	0-4
Sherwood Celtic v Southam United	0-1	Stratford v Upton Town	4-1
West Mids Fire Service v Wellesbourne	1-2	Wilmcote v Stapenhill	0-4
Armitage '90 v Alcester Town	5-0	Studley B.K.L. v Coleshill Town	2-0

Third Round

Armitage '90 v Studley B.K.L.	2-0	Chelmsley Town v West Heath United	3-1
Highgate United v Kings Norton Ex-Service	3-2	Kenilworth Town v Badsey Rangers	3-1
Northfield Town v Stapenhill	0-2	Sandwell Borough v Knowle	1-2
Southam v Stratford (at Stratford)	1-6	Wellesbourne v Pershore Town '88	4-8(aet)

Quarter Finals

Highgate United v Stratford Town	1-0(aet)	Kenilworth Town v Armitage '90	1-4
Stapenhill v Knowle	4-2	Pershore v Chelmsley Town	1-1(aet),3-2(aet)

Semi-Finals

Highgate Utd v Armitage '90	3-1(aet)	Pershore Town '88 v Stapenhill	1-4

Final (at Boldmere St Michaels, Wednesday 5th May): Stapenhill 2, Highgate United 0

Stapenhill players at their presentation night proudly displaying the Challenge Cup and the Premier Division runners-up shield. Back (L/R): Ken Hulland (Trainer), Brian Beresford, Steve Adcock, Bob Sykes (Manager), John O'Hare Snr (Guest), Dave Bolton, Ian Pearsall, Steve Warren, Ian Pitt, Mark Deaville, Richard Walker, Paul Adams (Secretary). Front: Paul Mable, Adey Sharp, Dave Carlin, Martin Walton, John Wayte (Asst Manager), Mark Barnes, John O'Hare Jnr. Photo courtesy of the Burton Mail.

PRESIDENTS CUP 1992-93

First Round

Dudley Sports v West Mids Fire Service	0-2	Handraham Timbers v Becketts Sporting Club	3-1
Ledbury Town '84 v Kings Heath	0-2	Sherwood Celtic v Kenilworth Town	1-4
Wilmcote v West Heath United	2-1		

Second Round

Badsey Rangers v Hams Hall	2-1	Polesworth N.W. v Kings Norton Ex-Service	0-1
Solihull Boro. Reserves v Wilmcote	2-5(aet)	Southam United v Kenilworth Town	2-3
Triplex v Wellesbourne	2-4(aet)	Upton Town v West Midlands Fire Service	2-3
Wigston Fields v Kings Heath	2-3	Handraham Timbers v Marston Green	2-1

Quarter Finals

Kenilworth Town v Wilmcote	4-1	Kings Heath v Handrahan Timbers	3-1
West Mids Fire Service v Badsey Rgrs	2-3(aet)	Kings Norton Ex-S. v Wellesbourne	1-1(aet),2-1(aet)

Semi-Finals

Badsey Rangers v Kings Heath	0-1	Kings Norton Ex-Service v Kenilworth Town	4-1

Final (at Solihull Borough F.C., Tuesday 18th May): Kings Norton Ex-Service 2, Kings Heath 0 (aet)

CHALLENGE VASE 1992-93

First Round

Burntwood Town v Dudley Spts Reserves	4-1	Holly Lane '92 v Ansells		1-6
Pershore Reserves v Fairfield Villa	0-1	Swift P.P. v Shirley Town		2-3(aet)
Wellesbourne Res. v Thimblemill Rec	3-5	Wigston Fields v Archdales '73		1-3

Second Round

Ansells v Burntwood	3-0	Colletts Green v Coleshill Town Reserves	6-0
Enville Athletic v Archdales '73	2-3(aet)	Meir K.A. Reserves v Wythall	2-1
Monica Star v Kenilworth Town Res.	0-2	Shirley Town v Fairfield Villa	3-0
Studley BKL Res. v Barlestone S.G. Res.	2-0	Thimblemill Rec v Earlswood Town	3-0

Quarter Finals

Archdales '73 v Colletts Green	0-5	Meir K.A. Res. v Kenilworth Town Reserves	4-2
Studley B.K.L. Reserves v Ansells	1-0	Thimblemill Rec v Shirley Town	4-2

Semi-Finals

Studley B.K.L. Res. v Thimblemill Rec	1-4(aet)	Meir K.A. Res. v Colletts Green	3-3(aet),2-6

Final (at Pershore Town '88 F.C., Wednesday 12th May): Colletts Green 1, Thimblemill Rec 0

CHALLENGE TROPHY 1992-93

First Round

Barwell Reserves v Nuneaton Boro. Res.	1-2	Bridgnorth Town Res. v Halesowen Town Res.	5-0
Bromsgrove Rvrs Res. v Burton Albion Res.	2-1	Evesham Utd Res. v Stratford Town Reserves	3-0
Leicester U. Res. v Hednesford Res.	3-8(aet)	Tamworth Reserves v Gresley Rovers Reserves	3-2
V.S. Rugby Res. v Kidderminster H. Res.	3-4		

Second Round

Armitage '90 Res. (scr) Sandwell Res. (w/o)		Bridgnorth Res. v Bromsgrove Rovers Res.	2-1
Kidderminster Res. v Boldmere S.M. Res.	7-6(aet)	Nuneaton Borough Res. v Atherstone Utd Res.	1-0
RC Warwick Res. v Sutton C.T. Res.	4-4(aet),2-0	Shepshed Albion Res. v Redditch Utd Res.	3-1
Tamworth Reserves v Hednesford T. Reserves	1-0	Witney Town Res. v Evesham United Reserves	1-3

Quarter Finals

R.C. Warwick Res. v Kidderminster H. Res.	5-0	Evesham Res. v Nun. B. Res. 3-3(aet, N'ton removed)	
Sandwell Boro. Res. v Bridgnorth T. Res.	0-1	Tamworth Reserves v Shepshed Albion Reserves	8-0

Semi-Finals

Tamworth Reserves v Evesham Utd Reserves	4-1	R.C. Warwick Res. v Bridgnorth Town Res.	2-3(aet)

Final (at Redditch Utd F.C., Tuesday 11th May): Tamworth Reserves 2, Bridgnorth Town Reserves 0

MIDLAND COMBINATION PREMIER DIVISION 10-YEAR RECORD

	83/4	84/5	85/6	86/7	87/8	88/9	89/0	90/1	91/2	92/3
Alcester Town									13	20
Armitage '90									2	1
Ashtree Highfoeld				(see Sandwell Borough)						
Barlestone St Giles									17	19
Barwell										11
Bloxwich Town			5	16	19		7	15	20	18
Boldmere St Michaels	10	4	1	4	2	1	1	12	9	8
Bolehall Swifts				20	12	11	8	16	10	9
Chelmsley Town						13	13	18	15	16
Chipping Norton Town	14									
Cinderford Town	16									
Coleshill Town	2	17	11	18	7	16	16	8	12	7
Evesham United	8	13	13	13	5	3	3	3	1	
Highgate United	4	6	12	9	17	10	11	9	4	17
Hinckley						9	12	10	19	
Hurley Daw Mill	7	14	14							
Kings Heath	15	18	20	15	10	12	15	13	18	
Kings Norton Ex-Service								21		
Knowle (North Star)	20	20	16	14	14	14	18	14	16	10
Leamington					15					
Meir K.A.										13
Mile Oak Rovers & Youth	12	1					19	17	21	14
New World		5	15							
Northfield Town	11	16	4	6	9	6	2	6	11	12
Paget Rangers	6	3	2	2					6	4
Pershore Town										
Polesworth North Warwick		7	9	11	16	15	14	20		
Princes End United					12	8	4	9	19	
Racing Club Warwick	5	10	10	3	1	2				
Sandwell Borough	18	12	19	10	3			4	5	5
Shirley Town						18				
Smethwick Highfield				(see Sandwell Borough)						
Solihull Borough	13	2	7	7	11	17	10	2		
Southam United	19	19	17	17						
Stapenhill							4	7	8	2
Stratford Town	9	9	6	1	4	7	5	5	14	3
Streetley Celtic							20			
Studley Sporting	1	15	18	19						
Studley B.K.L.										15
Walsall Borough/Wood	17	11	8	8	13	8	17	11	7	
West Midlands Police	3	8	3	5	6	5	6	1	3	6
Wilmcote					18					
No. of clubs competing	**20**	**20**	**20**	**20**	**19**	**18**	**20**	**21**	**21**	**20**

PREMIER DIVISION CLUBS 1993-94

ANSELLS

Manager: Bernard Cronin **Secretary:** D Cronin (021 351 7074).
Ground: Ansells Sports Club, Aldridge Rd, Perry Barr, Birmingham (021 356 4296).
Directions: Coming from city centre Aldridge Rd is a right turn (just before Perry Barr stadium) off the main Birmingham to Walsall road. Ground entrance almost immediately on right.
Capacity: T.B.A. **Seats:** T.B.A. **Cover:** T.B.A. **Floodlights:** No
Previous League: Birmingham Works (pre-1992).
Clubhouse: Large Social Club.
Hons: Midland Combination Div 2 92-93, Birmingham Works Lg (numerous occasions).

BARWELL

Chairman: David Laing **Vice Chairman:** Roger Goadby.
Secretary: Mr Roger Goadby, 4 Elm Tree Drive, Burbage, Hinkley, Leics LE10 2TX (0455 632682).
Manager: David Callow **Asst Manager:** Paul Shackleton
Physio: Viv Coleman. **Press Officer:** Mervyn Nash.
Ground: Kirkby Rd, Barwell, Leics (0455 843067).
Directions: M42 jct 10 (Tamworth Services), A5 towards Nuneaton, sharp left signed Market Bosworth after 11 miles (400m after Longshoot Motel), left for Barwell at 3rd island (3 miles), right onto B581 after half mile to Barwell centre (1 mile), turn left opposite Nat West bank and immediately right into Kirkby Rd - entrance to Barwell Spts & social Club 400m on right. From M69 jct 1 take B4109 towards Hinckley, right at lights after one and a half miles into Brookside, at end after 1 mile left onto Burbage Rd, left signed Leicester (A47) at 2nd lights, after Rugby Club take next left for Barwell, half mile to town centre - over mini-r'bout and Kirkby Rd is 50yds on right. BR to Hinckley station - bus station is 200yds away via Station Rd - take Leicester bus and Barwell is 1st village en route (two and a half miles).
Capacity: 2,500 **Seats:** 140 **Cover:** 750 **Floodlights:** Yes **Founded:** 1992.
Colours: Yellow/green/yellow **Change colours:** Black & white stripes/black/black.
Previous Names: Barwell Athletic F.C., Hinckley F.C. - amalgamated in 1992.
Previous Ground: Barwell Athletic: None. Hinckley: groundshare at Hinckley Athletic (pre-1992).
Previous Leagues: Barwell Athletic: Leicestershire Senior. Hinckley: Central Midlands 86-88.
Programme: 36 pages, 50p **Editor:** Alan Mason (Curzon Publications - 0533 625354).
Club Sponsors: Cleartherm **Midweek home matchday:** Tuesday
Nickname: Canaries. **Clubhouse:** Evenings & lunchtimes. Snacks available.
Captain 92-93: Carl Williams **Top Scorer 92-93:** Joey Aitchison **P.o.Y. 92-93:** Syd Warren
Club record scorer: Joey Aitchison **Club record appearances:** Kevin Johnson.
Hons: Barwell Athletic: Leics Snr Lg Tebbutt Brown Cup 91-92.

BLOXWICH TOWN

Manager: John Dyas. **Founded:** 1977.
Secretary: S Clarke, 10 Sandhill Str., Bloxwich, Walsall WS3 2JH (0922 405635 - messages).
Ground: Abbey Park, Glastonbury Crescent, Bloxwich, Walsall. (0922 77640)
Directions: A34 Walsall-Bloxwich, then west onto A4124. Ground 2-3 miles on right, s.p. Mossley Estate.
Capacity: 1,000 **Seats:** 50 **Covered:** 200 **Floodlights:** No **Nickname:** Kestrels
Midweek Matches: Tues/Thurs **Previous Name:** Bloxwich FC.
Colours: All royal blue **Change Colours:** All yellow
Programme: 16 pages 20p **Programme Editor:** Ken Moseley
Hons: Bloxwich Comb.(2), Staffs Co. Lg Div 1, Walsall Snr Cup R-up 86-87, Invitation Cup 89-90, Midland Combination Div 1 89-90, Alan Peck Cup (3).

BOLDMERE ST MICHAELS

Manager: Alan Parsons
Secretary: John Shaw, 176 Springthorpe Rd, Erdington, Birmingham B24 0SN (021 350 5869).
Ground: Church Road, Boldmere, Sutton Coldfield (021 373 4435).
Directions: A38 & A5127 from City towards S. Coldfield, left at Yenton lights onto A452 (Chester Rd), Church Rd is 6th turning on the right. 400yds from Chester Road (BR).
Capacity: 2,500 **Seats:** 100 **Covered:** 100 **Floodlights:** Yes **Nickname:** Mikes.
Midweek matches: Tues/Thurs **Previous Leagues:** West Mids 49-63. **Founded:** 1882
Colours: White/black/black **Change Colours:** All yellow (black trim)
Programme: 28 pages, 30p **Programme Editor:** Dave Tolley (021 382 7130)
Clubhouse: Bar & lounge, every evening and four lunchtimes
Hons: Birmingham AFA 36-37, Birmingham AFA Snr Cup, FA Amtr Cup SF 47-48, AFA Snr Cup 47-48, Central Amtr Lg 48-49, Midland Comb.(3) 85-86 88-90 (Challenge Cup 77-78 89-90, Tony Allden Memorial Cup 78-79 88-89 91-92, Challenge Trophy 86-87).
Players who progressed to Football League: John Barton (Everton, Derby County), Kevin Collins (Shrewsbury), Jack Lane (Birmingham City, Notts Co.), John Lewis (Walsall), Don Moss (Cardiff, C Palace), Harry Parkes (Aston Villa), Wally Soden (Coventry).

BOLEHALL SWIFTS

President: Dennis Baker **Chairman:** Howard Harper
Manager: Colin Middleton.
Secretary: John Boyce, 99 Falcon, Wilnecote, Tamworth, Staffs B77 5DW (0827 261428).
Ground: Rene Road, Bolehall, Tamworth (827 62637).
Ground: A51 signs south to Bolebridge island, left under railway arches into Armington Rd, 4th left into Leedham Ave, fork right, Rene Rd, ground on right
Capacity: 2,000 **Seats:** None **Cover:** 600 **Floodlights:** No **Founded:** 1953
Midweek matches: Tuesday **Previous League:** Staffs County **Nickname:** Swifts
Colours: White/black/black **Change Colours:** Royal blue/navy/white.
Programme: Yes **Programme Editor:** W Gould
Clubhouse: Large Social Club with lounge. Open every evening and lunchtimes.
Hons: Midland Combination Div 2 84-85 (Challenge Vase 84-85), Ernie Brown Memorial Cup R-up 91-92 92-93.

Barwell F.C. 1992-93.

CHELMSLEY TOWN

Manager: Bill Cox.
Secretary: M J Harris, 149 Wyckham Road, Castle Bromwich, Birmingham (021 747 4589).
Ground: The Pavilion, Coleshill Road, Marston Green, West Midlands (021 779 5400).
Directions: A452 Chester Rd towards N.E.C., right into Coleshill Heath Rd, right into Coleshill Rd (s.p. Marston Green). Ground on right (s.p. Chelmsley Hospital). 10 mins walk from Marston Green (BR).
Capacity: 2,500   **Seats:** 50   **Cover:** 200   **Floodlights:** No   **Founded:** 1927
Midweek matches: Tuesday   **Prev. Lges:** Handsworth/ B'ham Yth O.B./ Mercian.
Colours: Sky & white stripes/sky/sky   **Change Colours:** Yellow/black/black
Programme: 24 pages 30p   **Programme Editor:** Terry Stanners
Previous Name: Christchurch (pre 1969)   **Previous Ground:** Coleshill Hall Hospital, Selly Oak
Clubhouse: One room bar and clubroom   **Record Gate:** 3,000 v A Villa Old Stars, charity game.
Players who have progressed to Football League: Bob Peyton (Port Vale)
Hons: B'ham Yth Committee Champions & B'ham Vase R-up 90-91, Handsworth Lg, Mercian Lg(3), Mids Comb 87-88 (Presidents Cup 77-78, Invitation Cup 77-78 87-88).

COLESHILL TOWN

Manager: Robert Nimmons.   **Founded:** 1894.
Secretary: C Burns, 49 Circus Ave., Chelmsley Wood, Birmingham B37 7NG (021 770 9513).
Ground: Pack Meadow, Packington Lane, Coleshill, Birmingham B46 3JQ (0675 63259).
Directions: A446 to A4117 towards Coleshill, Packington Lane forks from A4117, south of village and ground is 150 yds on right. M6 jct 4, 1 mile away.
Capacity: 3,000   **Seats:** 50   **Cover:** 50   **Floodlights:** Yes   **Nickname:** Coalmen.
Midweek matches: Tues/Thurs   **Record Gate:** 1,000.
Colours: All maroon   **Change Colours:** Green/white/green
Clubhouse: Bar open 7 nights a week. Bar manager resident.   **Programme:** 30p, **Editor:** Mavis Gordon
Players who have progressed to Football League: Gary Shaw (Aston Villa, Walsall)
Hons: Mercian Lg 75-76, Walsall Snr Cup 82-83 (R-up 83-84), Midland Comb. R-up 83-84 (Div 2 69-70 (R-up 74-75), Invitation Cup 1970, Presidents Cup R-up(2) 67-69).

Coleshill Town F.C. 1992-93. Photo - James Wright.

HIGHGATE UNITED

Manager: Mick Neville   **Founded:** 1947.
Secretary: Geoff Read, 23 Southam Rd, Hall Green, Birmingham B28 8DQ (021 777 1786).
Ground: The Coppice, Tythe Barn Lane, Shirley, Solihull B90 1PH (021 744 4194).
Directions: A34 from City through Shirley, fork right B4102 (Tanworth Lane), half mile then right into Dickens Heath Rd, then first right and the ground is on the left. 100yds from Whitlocks End (BR).
Capacity: 5,000   **Seats:** 250   **Covered:** 750   **Floodlights:** Due   **Nickname:** The Gate
Midweek matches: Tuesday   **Record Gate:** 4,000 v Enfield, FA Amtr Cup QF '67.
Colours: All red   **Change Colours:** All white   **Programme:** 30p, **Editor:** Terry Bishop
Clubhouse: Members Club open Tues, Wed, Thurs & Sat
Players progressing to Football League: John Gayle (W'ledon), Keith Leonard (A Villa, P Vale), Geoff Scott (Leic.)
Hons: Midland Comb.(3) 72-75 (Div 2 66-67 68-69 71-72, Lg Cup(5) 72-74 75-77 84-85 (R-up 78-79 92-93), Presidents Cup 70-71 85-86), Tony Allden Mem. Cup 74-75, Invit. Cup 68-69 71-72 85-86, West Mids All. 63-64, Birmingham Snr Cup 73-74 (SF 91-92).

KINGS HEATH

Manager: Barry Hancocks   **Founded:** 1964.
Secretary: D Ellis, 2 Willsbridge Covert, Druids Heath, Birmingham B14 5YD (021 459 7444)
Ground: As Shirley Town F.C. (see Division One).
Previous Names: Horse Shoe F.C./ Kings Heath Amateur.
Cols: Gold shadow stripes/black/gold   **Change Colours:** All red   **Nickname:** The Kings
Programme: 12 pages   **Programme Editor:** M Kite
92-93 Top Scorer: Mark Averill 32.
Players progressing to Football League: Geoff Scott (Stoke, Leicester, Birmingham).
Hons: Midland Combination Div 1 R-up 92-93 (Div 2 R-up 82-83, Presidents Cup R-up 79-80 81-82 92-93), Birmingham Challenge Vase R-up 86-87.

Kings Heath F.C. - Division One runners-up 1992-93. Back Row (L/R): Andrew Kite, Mark Simpson, Steve Ellis, Mark Averill, Richard Flynn, Kevin Hallett, Andrew Walker, Robert Trindel, Mark Cartwright. Front: Andrew Lloyd, Anthony McGann, Shaun Lawless, Perry Deakin, John Price, Anthony Forletta, Clive Seeley.

KNOWLE

Manager: Peter Christoforou   **Founded:** 1926.
Secretary: R Gardner, 11 Runcorn Close, Chelmsley Wood, Birmingham B37 6QX (021 770 9273).
Ground: Hampton Rd, Knowle, Solihull (0564 779807).   **Directions:** A41 Warwick Rd from City, left at Wilsons Pub into Hampton Rd, ground 200 yds on right. 1 mile from Dorridge (BR). Buses from Solihull.
Capacity: 3,000   **Seats:** 72   **Cover:** 200   **Floodlights:** No   **Nickname:** Robins.
Midweek matches: Wednesday   **Record Gate:** 1,000 in FA Vase 1980.
Programme: 20 pages, 25p   **Editor:** Dave Radburn
Colours: Red/white/red   **Change Colours:** Yellow/black/yellow
Previous Name: Knowle North Star 80-87   **Previous Ground:** Bentley Heath Village
Clubhouse: Seating for 60, tea bar   **Previous Lges:** Birmingham Yth O.B./ Birmingham Alliance.
Players who have progressed to Football League: Guy Russell (Birmingham City)
Hons: B'gham Jnr Cup R-up 70-71, FA Vase QF 81-82, Midland Combination Div 2 R-up 68-69.

MEIR K.A.

Manager: Des Reaney   **Vice Chairman:** Michael McDonnel.
Secretary: Stanley Tooth, 29 Colclough Road, Meir, Stoke-on-Trent ST3 6DH (0782 310145).
Manager: Des Reaney   **Asst Manager:** Michael Collins   **Coach:** Terry Lees.
Press Officer: Graham Birks   **Commercial Manager:** Barry Smith.
Ground: Stanley Park, Hilderstone Road, Meir Heath, Stoke-on-Trent (0455 613553)
Directions: M6 jct 14, A34 to Stone, A520 from Stone, right (B5066) at Meir Heath, ground on right. 2 miles from Blythe Bridge (BR).
Capacity: 5,000   **Seats:** 400   **Cover:** 1,000   **Floodlights:** No   **Founded:** 1976.
Colours: Old gold/black/black   **Change colours:** All blue.   **Nickname:** Kings.
Previous Ground: Normacot Rec.   **Previous Name:** Station Shoulder of Mutton.
Programme: 24 pages 50p   **Programme Editor:** Steve Osborne
Midweek home matchday: Wednesday   **Previous Leagues:** Staffs Alliance/ Staffs Snr 84-92.
Record win: 6-0   **Record loss:** 1-5   **Clubhouse:** Built in 1982, open matchdays. Hot food.
Club Record Scorer: W J Anderson   **Club Record Appearances:** David Preston, 500+
Captain 92-93: David Preston   **P.o.Y. 92-93:** Scott Reaney   **Top Scorer 92-93:** Adam Hope.
Hons: Staffs Snr Lg 91-92.

MILE OAK ROVERS & YOUTH

Manager: Colin Burton **Founded:** 1958.
Secretary: Keith Wakelin, 45 Reindeer Rd, Fazeley, Tamworth, Staffs B78 3SN (0827 251026).
Ground: Recreation Groundd, Price Ave., Mile Oak, Tamworth (0827 289614). **Directions:** South on A5 Watling Str. from Mile Oak Hotel, take 3rd right, ground 200yds on right. 2 miles from Tamworth (BR).
Capacity: 2,500 **Seats:** 60 **Cover:** 300 **Floodlights:** Yes **Nickname:** Oaks
Midweek matches: Wednesday **Record attendance:** 780 v Tamworth, 18.3.89
Colours: Yellow & blue stripes/blue/blue **Change Colours:** All yellow
Clubhouse: Large bar with separate lounge **Programme:** 25p, **Editor:** Keith Wakelin
Previous Leagues: Trent Valley/ Midlamd Combination 70-85/ Southern 85-89.
Players who have progressed to Football League: Keith Downing (Notts C, Wolves), Tony Coton (Birmingham, Watford), John Gayle (Wimbledon), Kevin Francis & Martyn Taylor (Derby), Colin Robinson (Shrewsbury, Birmingham, Hereford)
Hons: Mid Comb 84-85 (Pres. Cup 73-74, Tony Allden Mem. Cup 84-85, Invit. Cup 73-74), Birmingham Jnr Cup, Fazeley Charity Cup 91-92.

NORTHFIELD TOWN

Manager: Tom Owens **Founded:** 1966.
Secretary: Monty Patrick, 38 Pensford Rd, Northfield, Birmingham B31 3AG (021 475 2057).
Ground: Shenley Lane, Selly Oak, Birmingham B29 (021 478 3900).
Directions: A38 from City, past Selly Oak, opposite Woodlands/Royal Orthopaedic Hospital turn right into Whitehill Lane, right at end into Shenley Lane. Ground on right. One and a half miles from Northfield (BR).
Capacity: 3,500 **Seats:** None **Cover:** Yes **Floodlights:** No **Nickname:** The Cross
Midweek Matches: Tues/Thurs **Clubhouse:** Brick built clubhouse. (021 478 3870).
Colours: Yellow/blue/yellow **Change Colours:** Blue & yellow/blue
Record Gate: 3,300, Charity match, 1967 **Programme:** 24 pages 25p, **Editor:** Eric Rough.
Previous Names: Allens Cross/ Cross Castle Utd/ Northfield Town Amateur/ Northfield FC.
Players who have progressed to Football League: Clive Whitehead (WBA), Colin Brazier (Wolves, Walsall), Mark Rees (Walsall), Carlton Palmer (WBA, Sheffield Wed)
Hons: Midlands Comb. 61-62 75-76 (Div 2 61-62(res) 63-64, Chal. Cup 56-57 (R-up 63-64 86-87), Presidents Cup 61-62 80-81), Tony Allden Mem. Cup 1977, Birmingham Snr Amtr Cup 74-75, Lord Mayor of Birmingham Charity Cup R-up 92-93, Birmingham Jnr Cup 1958, 1962, Birmingham Co. Yth Cup(3) 69-72, Worcs Co. Yth Cup(4).

PERSHORE TOWN '88

Chairman: Mr A Bradstock **Vice Chairman:** Mr C Scarrett.
Secretary: Mr A J Barnett, 8 Croft Cottages, Cropthorne, Nr Pershore, Worcs WR10 3LX (0386 860243).
Manager: Colin Shepherd **Asst Manager:** Kenneth Gwynne.
Trainer: Mr M Palfrey **Press Officer:** Mr C Millward.
Ground: King George XI Playing Fields, High Street, Pershore, Worcs (0386 556902).
Seats: 120 **Cover:** 120 **Capacity:** 4,000 **Floodlights:** Yes **Founded:** 1988.
Colours: Blue & white stripes/blue/blue **Change colours:** Yellow/green.
Previous Grounds: None **Previous Leagues:** None.
Previous Names: None (formed in 1988 my the amalgamation of three Pershore sides).
Programme: 20 pages, 50p **Editor:** Mr T Conway (0386 554390)
Club Shop: In the process of being set up. Club ties and jumpers already available.
Club Sponsors: Martin Stevens **Midweek home matchday:** Tuesday **Nickname:** The Town
Record Gate: 295 v Stourport Swifts, Worcs Snr Urn Final 2nd Leg, 92-93.
Record win: 10-0 **Record defeat:** 1-4 v Stapenhill (H), Chal. Cup SF 92-93.
Record transfer fee paid: Nil **Received:** Undisclosed for Simon Judge (Worcester, 92-93).
Clubhouse: Open every evenings and matchdays. Coffee, tea and rolls always available. New function room, the Abbey Suite, just opened.
Captain 92-93: Ian Maitland **Top Scorer 92-93:** Alan Pountian **P.O.Y. 92-93:** Ian Aldington.
Hons: Midland Combination Div 2 89-90, Worcs Jnr Cup 90-91, Bob Biggart Cup(2) 90-92, Worcs Snr Urn R-up 92-93.

Pershore Town '88 F.C. 1992-93. Back Row (L/R): Garry Hughes, John Judge (Trainer), Simon Judge, Ian Maitland, Melvyn Langford, Mark Davis, Chris Wyres, David Clasen, Neil Annis, John Fryer, Colin Shepherd (Manager). Front: Stephen Payne, Mark Buckley, Stephen Hodgson, Stephen Turner, Ian Aldington, Kenneth Gwynne (Asst Manager). Photo - Gavin Ellis-Neville.

SANDWELL BOROUGH

Manager: Paul Molesworth.   **Founded:** 1918.
Secretary: Ken Jones, 19 Henn Drive, Tipton, West Mids DY4 9NN (021 557 9429).
Ground: Oldbury Sports Centre, Newbury Lane, Oldbury (021 552 1759).
Directions: Follow A4123 B'ham-Wolverhampton Rd, past island at jnt 2 M5, after half mile turn left into Newbury Lane and stadium is on the right. 2 miles from Sandwell & Dudley (BR).
Capacity: 3,000   **Seats:** 200   **Cover:** 600   **Floodlights:** Yes   **Nickname:** Trees
Midweek Matches: Wednesday   **Previous Grnd:** Londonderry, Smethwick 18-81
Colours: Green & white stripes/green/green   **Change Colours:** Amber & black
Record Gate: 950 v Halesowen T., FA Cup 1987
Programme: 12 pages 25p   **Programme Editor:** R Unitt.
Previous Leagues: B'ham Suburban/ Central Amtr/ Worcs (Midlands Comb.) 48-88/ Southern 88-90.
Previous names: Smethwick Town, Smethwick Highfield, Ashtree Highfield
Clubhouse: Licensed bar overlooking pitch. Open everyday
Players who have progressed to Football League: Andy Micklewright (Bristol Rov, Bristol City, Swindon, Exeter), Gary Bull (Southampton, Cambridge Utd)
Hons: Mids Comb. Chal. Cup R-up(5) 49-50 51-53 67-68 74-75, Chal. Tphy R-up 88-89, Pres. Cup 79-80 (R-up 76-77), Div 2 R-up 79-80), B'ham Jnr Cup.

SHEPSHED ALBION

Chairman: David Heap   **Vice Chairman:** Mr M Clayton.
Secretary: Mrs C J Blackhouse, 39 Ploughmans Drive, Shepshed, Leics (0509 508917).
Manager: Bill Fossey   **Press Officer:** Maurice Brindley (0509 267922)
Ground: The Dovecote, Butthole Lane, Shepshed, Leics (0509 502684).
Directions: M1 junction 23, A512 towards Ashby, right at first lights, right at garage in Forest Street, right into Butthole Lane opposite Black Swan. Five miles from Loughborough (BR).
Capacity: 5,000   **Cover:** 1,500   **Seats:** 209   **Floodlights:** Yes   **Founded:** 1890
Colours: Black & white   **Change colours:** All green   **Nickname:** Raiders.
Previous Leagues: Leics Senior 07-16 19-27 46-50 51-81/ Midland Counties 81-82/ Northern Counties (East) 82-83/ Southern 83-88/ Northern Premier 88-93.
Previous Names: Shepshed Albion 1890-1975/ Shepshed Charterhouse 75-91.
Midweek home matchday: Tuesday   **Record Attendance:** 1,672.
Best F.A. Cup season: 1st Rd 82-83 (lost 1-5 at Preston North End).
Rec. fee paid: £2,000 for Doug Newton   **Received:** £10,000 for John Deakin.
Players progressing to Football League: Neil Grewcock (Burnley 1984), Gordon Tucker (Huddersfield 1987), Devon White (Bristol Rovers 1987), John Deakin (Birmingham City).
Clubhouse: Accomodates 120 in main room, 50 in others.
Club Record Scorer: Jeff Lissaman   **Club Record Appearances:** Austin Straker 300.
92-93 Captain: Mick Collins   **92-93 P.o.Y.:** Gary Statham.
Honours: Southern Lg Midland Division R-up 83-84, Northern Counties (East) Lg 82-83 (Lg Cup 82-83), Midland Counties Lg 81-82 (Lg Cup 81-82), Leics Senior Lg 10-11 20-21 78-79 79-80 80-81 (R-up 21-22, Div 2 53-54 65-66 77-78, Div 2 Cup 77-78), Leics Senior Cup 77-78 79-80 81-82 83-84 84-85 85-86 87-88, FA Vase SF 78-79, Loughborough Charity Cup 92-93, FA Tphy 1st Rd Replay 85-86 89-90.

SHIFNAL TOWN

Chairman: Mr D Adams   **Vice Chairman:** Mr R Owen   **President:** Mr R Arnold
Secretary: Mr D Growcott, 4 Idsall Cres., Shifnal, Shropshire, TF11 8ES (0952 461466).
Manager/Coach: Ken Jones   **Asst Manager:** M Humphries
Commercial Mgr: D Chandler   **Press Officer:** Mr G Davies (0952 460326).
Ground: Phoenix Park, Coppice Green Lane, Shifnal, Shropshire.
Directions: M54 jct 3, A41 towards Newport, 1st left for Shifnal (3 miles), in Shifnal take 1st right, and sharp right again up Coppice Green Lane, ground 800yds on left past Idsall School. 1 mile from Shifnal BR station.
Seats: 40   **Cover:** 300   **Capacity:** 3,000   **Floodlights:** No   **Founded:** 1964
Colours: Red/white/black   **Change colours:** Yellow/green   **Nickname:** None.
Midweek home matchday: Tuesday   **Previous Grounds:** Admirals Park 80-85
Previous Leagues: Wellington (East Dist.) 64-69/ Shropshire County 69-77 85-93/ West Midlands 77-85.
Programme: None at present   **Record win:** 10-1 v Malvern, 82-83   **Record loss:** 1-6
Club Shop: No   **Sponsors:** Associated Cold Stores & Transport Ltd.
Record Gate: 1,002 v Bridgnorth Town, F.A. Vase 3rd Rd 83-84 (at Admirals Park).
Clubhouse: Not on ground but in Newport Rd, Shifnal. Open Mon-Fri 7.30-11pm, noon-11pm Sat matchdays, noon-2.30 & 7.30-11pm Sat non-matchdays, Sun noon-3 & 7.30-11pm.
Captain 92-93: Mark Rix   **Top Scorer 92-93:** John Powell.
P.o.Y. 92-93: Dean Yates   **Club record scorer:** Steve Kelly.
Hons: West Mids Lg 80-81 81-82 (Div 1 78-79), Shropshire Snr Cup 80-81 90-91 92-93.

STAPENHILL

Chairman: Bob Hutchinson   **Vice Chairman:** Ken Hulland   **President:** Don Wood.
Secretary: Paul Adams, 5 Mayfield Drive, Stapenhill, Burton-on-Trent DE15 9D6 (0283 31024).
Manager: Bob Sykes   **Asst Manager:** John Wayte   **Physio:** Ken Hulland.
Ground: Edge Hill, Maple Grove, Stapenhill, Burton-on-Trent (0283 62471).
Directions: Three miles from Burton on A444 Measham Rd, turn right (coming from Burton) at Copperhearth Public House into Sycamore Rd, Maple Grove is 5th left. 3 miles from Burton-on-Trent (BR) - use buses 22, 23, 38 from opposite station.
Capacity: 2,000   **Seats:** 50   **Covered:** 200   **Floodlights:** Yes   **Founded:** 1947.
Midweek matches: Wednesday   **Record Gate:** 2,000 v Gresley, Derbys Snr Cup final 88-89.
Colours: Red/white/red   **Change Colours:** Blue/white/blue   **Nickname:** Swans.
Previous League: Leics Snr 58-89   **Previous Name:** Stapenhill Waterside Community Centre.
Sponsors: K C Hulland Builders   **Clubhouse:** In ground. Pub hours. Matchday tea bar.
Record win: 11-0 v Alcester Town (H), Midland Combination Premier Division, 1992-93.
Record defeat: 0-7 v Bridgnorth Town, F.A. Vase.
Captain 92-93: Steve Adcock   **Top Scorer 92-93:** Brian Beresford 35   **P.o.Y. 92-93:** Ian Pearsall
Record scorer: Brian Beresford 119   **Record appearances:** Ian Pearsall 130.
Hons: Midland Combination R-up 92-93 (Div 1 89-90, Challenge Cup 92-93), Leics Snr Lg 59-60 86-87 88-89 (Tebbutt Brown Cup(2) 87-89), Leics Snr Cup 69-70 86-87, Derby Snr Cup R-up 88-89 91-92.

Shepshed Albion, pictured on May 5th before beating Barrow Town 1-0 to win the 1993 Loughborough Charity Cup at Loughborough Dynamo F.C. Photo - James Wright.

Shifnal Town F.C., at Shrewsbury for the Shropshire Senior Cup final in which they beat Ellesmere 2-0 on 10th May. Back Row (L/R): M Humphries (Asst Manager), M Flavell, A Sullivan, D Nock, M Rix, J Powell, G Loxley, D Smith, W Grainger (Trainer), D Adams (Chairman). Front: T Bennet, D Yates, J Roberts, K McKenzie, D Sturrock, R Finney.

Stapenhill F.C. - Midland Combination Challenge Cup winners 1992-93.

STRATFORD TOWN

Manager: Alan Campbell. **Founded:** 1944.
Secretary: P W Gardner, 17 Trevelyan Crescent, Stratford-upon-Avon, Warks CV37 9LL (0789 68432).
Ground: Masons Road, off Alcester Road, Stratford-upon-Avon, Warks (0789 297479).
Directions: Follow Alcester signs from Town and Masons Rd is on the right past railway bridge. 400 yards from Stratford-on-Avon (BR).
Capacity: 4,000 **Seats:** 200 **Covered:** 200 **Floodlights:** Yes **Nickname:** The Town
Midweek Matches: Tues/Thurs **Clubhouse:** Open 7 nights & Sunday lunch.
Colours: Tangerine/black/tangerine **Change Colours:** Silver/maroon/maroon
Programme: Yes **Programme Editor:** P Gardner **92-93 Top Scorer:** Richard Landon, 37.
Previous Name: Stratford Town Amateur **Previous Lges:** W Mids 57-70/ Hellenic 70-75.
Record Gate: 484 v Aston Villa, Birmingham Snr Cup, Oct 1984
Players who have progressed to Football League: Martin Hicks (Charlton, Reading), Roy Proverbs (Coventry, Bournemouth, Gillingham)
Hons: Midland Comb 56-57 86-87 (Chal. Cup 86-87 88-89 (R-up 55-56), Chal. Vase 81-82, Jack Mould Tphy 81-82, Tony Allden Mem. Cup 86-87, B'ham Snr Cup 62-63.

Stratford Town. Back Row (L/R): Andrew Beechey, Gary Roberts, Easton Shaw, Andy Clarke, Paul Alderidge, Dave Roberts, Mark Robinson, Carl Bannister. Front: Nick Ballinger, Jim Kernick, Ron Malcolm, Pete Frain, John O'Brien, John Mitchell. Photo - Gavin Ellis-Neville.

STUDLEY B.K.L.

Chairman: D Robinson **Manager:** Ray Richards/ John Adams **Founded:** 1971.
Secretary: Gary Shepherd, 38 Lightoak Close, Walk Wood, Redditch, Worcs B97 (0527 546639).
Ground: 'Beehive', BKL Spts Ground, Abbeyfields, Birmingham Rd, Studley, Warks (0527 24780).
Colours: Sky/navy/navy **Previous Name:** B.K.L. Works **Nickname:** Bees.
Previous League: Redditch & South Warwickshire Sunday Combination 71-87.
Hons: Midland Comb. Div 1 91-92 (Chal. Cup R-up 91-92, Presidents Cup R-up 91-92, Div 2 Cup 87-88), Smedley Crooke Charity Cup 90-91 91-92.

WELLESBOURNE

Manager: Stuart Dixon. **Founded:** 1932
Secretary: R Burns, 32 St Peters Rd, Wellesbourne, Warks CV36 9PD (0789 840301).
Ground: The Sports Field, Loxley Road, Wellesbourne (0789 841878).
Programme: Yes **Colours:** All blue
Hons: Midlands Comb. Div 1 92-93 (Presidents Cup 91-92, Invitation Cup 92-93).

WEST MIDLANDS POLICE

President: Chief Constable R Hadfield OBE
Chairman: Asst Chief Constable D G Ibbs MBE **Vice Chairman:** Superintendent M Hale.
Secretary: B H Nunn, 98 Griffins Brook Lane, Bournville, Birmingham B30 1QG (021 476 5223).
Manager: Colin Brookes **Coach:** Dave Scriven.
Asst Manager: Bryan Dorrian **Press Officer:** Tony Pearson.
Ground: Police Spts Ground, 'Tally Ho', Pershore Road, Edgbaston, Birmingham B5 7RN (021 472 2944).
Directions: 2 miles south west of city on A441 Pershore Road. Ground is on the left 50yds past Priory Road lights (Warks County Cricket Ground). 3 miles from Birmingham New Street (BR) - buses 41, 45 & 47 from city.
Capacity: 2,500 **Seats:** 50 **Covered:** 200 **Floodlights:** Yes **Founded:** 1974
Midweek matches: Tues/Thurs. **Programme:** Averages 8 pages **Editor:** Derek Carter.
Colours: Red/black/black **Change Colours:** Yellow/green/green.
Previous Names: Birmingham City Police (founded 1938), West Mids Constabulary - merged in 1974.
Previous Leagues: B'ham Wednesday 28-38/ Mercian 46-53/ B'ham Works 53-69.
Record Gate: 1,072 v Sudbury Town, FA Vase QF 29/2/92. **Record win:** 9-3 **Record defeat:** 1-10.
Clubhouse: Complex of 3 bars including snooker room, ballroom, kitchen. Hot & cold food. Open all day.
Hons: FA Vase QF 91-92, Mids Comb 90-91 (Chal. Cup 74-75 (R-up 85-86)), Tony Allden Mem. Cup 75-76 (R-up 91-92), B'ham Jnr Cup, Worcs Snr Urn 84-85 90-91 91-92 (R-up 81-82 85-86), National Police Cup(12) 61-65 66-67 69-70 73-76 80-81 87-88 91-92 (R-up(6) 67-68 70-72 76-78 88-89), Aston Villa Cup 60-61 64-65 65-66.

DIVISION ONE CLUBS 1993-94

ALCESTER TOWN

Chairman: Raymond Hodgetts   **Secretary:** M Sealey (0527 501724)   **Manager:** Bob Wragg
Ground: Conway Playing Fields, St Faiths Road, Alcester (763356) *** *N.B. The club may well move back to their old ground, at Stratford Rd, before or during the 1993-94 season ***.*
Seats: No   **Cover:** Yes   **Clubhouse:** Yes   **Programme:** Yes   **Floodlights:** No
Previous Name: Alcester Juniors 27-53.   **Nickname:** The Town **Founded:** 1927
Colours: Red & black hoops/black/red & black   **Change Colours:** Blue & white hoops
Record Gate: 402 v Evesham Utd, Aug. Bank Holiday '91.   **Previous Ground:** Stratford Road (until 1991)
Prev. Lges: Redditch & Dis. 27-31 38-62/ Stratford All. 31-38/ Warks Comb. 62-65/ Worcester Comb. 65-85.
Players progressing to Football League: Percy Freeman (West Bromwich Albion), Paul West (West Brom. 1990).
Hons: Midland Comb. Div 1 90-91 (Div 2 R-up 71-72, Presidents Cup 69-70 90-91, Invitation Cup 90-91), B'gham Co. Vase R-up 89-90, Redditch & Dist. Lg 29-30 30-31 (Police Cup 30-31), Stratford Alliance 32-33 33-34 (R-up 34-35).

Alcester Town - who return to Division One after two years in the top flight. Photo - Gavin Ellis-Neville.

BADSEY RANGERS

Chairman: A Stallard   **Vice Chairman:** G Brooks   **President:** A W Sparrow.
Secretary: M J Loram, 39 Synehurst, Badsey, Evesham, Worcs WR11 5UI (0386 832040).
Manager: Alex Ogg   **Asst Manager:** Max Green   **Comm. Mgr:** Mrs L Rogers
Ground: Badsey Recreation Ground, Sands Lane, Badsey, Evesham (0386 830867).
Directions: B4035 from Evesham to Badsey (2 miles), right into Synehurst by Lloyds Bank, thru village, left into School Lane after 'Wheatsheaf', next right into Willersey Rd, Sands Lane is 1st left - ground at end on left. Bus service negligable
Seats: 50   **Cover:** 250   **Capacity:** 3,000   **Floodlights:** No   **Founded:** 1890
Cols: Red & black stripes/black/black   **Change colours:** Tangerine/white/tangerine.
Previous Grounds: Aldington Pastures, Aldington, Evesham 1890-1920.
Prev. Lges: N Cotswold & Vale of Evesham 1893-1902/ Worcester (time out in Stratford All. and Central Amtr) 03-89.
Programme: 20 pages, 50p   **Programme Editor:** Mrs L Rogers (0386 49602).
Club Shop: No, but a small book published to celebrate club centenary in 1990 is available for £3.50 from club secretary. It is a historical record of the club. **Rec. Gate:** 2,500 v Evesham, Worcester Infirmary Cup final 1949.
Sponsors: Goodalls (Vauxhall)   **Record win:** 24-0 v Essex House 4/10/02   **Record defeat:** 3-19
Clubhouse: Tea bar sells tea, coffee, soup, confectionary, rolls, crisps, pies, pasties, hot-dogs etc.
Captain 92-93: Andy Clarke   **Top Scorer 92-93:** Eamon Dooey   **P.o.Y. 92-93:** Dave Trotman
Hons: Mids Comb. Div 1 R-up 91-92 (Div 2 90-91), Jack Mould Tphy R-up 91-92 *(plus scores of local competition honours that are all listed in the official club history).*

Badsey Rangers F.C. 1992-93. Back Row (L/R): Dave Trotman, Gerald Bearcroft, Malcolm Bennett, Andy Clarke (Captain), Nick Stanley, Eamonn Dooey, Glenn Burrow, Max Green (Asst Manager). Front: Geoff Cowley, Jonathan Gregory, Martin Scaembri, Greg Press.

BARLESTONE ST GILES

Manager: John Farrington   **Secretary:** R Williamson (0530 62278).
Ground: Barton Road, Barlestone, Nuneaton.   **Nickname:** Saints.
Colours: Gold/black/black   **Previous League:** Leics Snr (until 1991)

BECKETTS SPORTING CLUB

Chairman: Mr A Sinnot   **Manager:** Mick Adams
Secretary: Roy Waters, 115 Trimpley Rd, Bartley Green, Birmingham B32 3PH (021 422 1087).
Asst Manager: Paul Sly   **Coach/Physio:** Kelvin Hardman
Ground: Beckett's Farm, Chapel Lane, Wythall, Near Birmingham B47 (0564 822890).
Directions: M42 jct 3, A435 towards Birmingham, 1 mile on dual c'way to Beckett's island (Beckett's Farm Shop on left), left (signed Headley Heath) into Middle Lane, left after 200yds at Wythall Cemetry into Chapel Lane, ground 100yds on left. 1 mile from Wythall BR station.

Seats: None	**Cover:** 100	**Capacity:** 200 **Floodlights:** No	**Founded:** 1980
Colours: Black & white		**Change colours:** Green & white	**Nickname:** Bulls.
Previous Grounds: None		**Previous Lges:** Sth Birmingham 80-82/ Mercian AFA 82-89.	
Programme: To start 93-94		**Midweek Matchday:** Wednesday	**Club Shop:** No.
Sponsors: Rowans Catering Ltd		**Record Gate:** 200, Birmingham Vase SF 91-92.	
Record win: 13-0 v Stapenhill Reserves, Midland Comb. Div 1 91-92.			**Record defeat:** 0-6.

Clubhouse: Open Saturday afternoon & evening, Sunday morning & afternoon and for midweek games. Pies, pasties, sandwiches, tea, coffee, crisps, nuts etc.
Captain & P.O.Y. 92-93: Andy May   **Top Scorer 92-93:** Colin Allbright.
Club record scorer: Mark Brown   **Club record appearances:** Colin Allbright.
Hons: Midland Combination Div 2 R-up 90-91, Mercian AFA 88-89 (Div 1 83-84), Sth Birmingham Lg 80-81 81-82, Birmingham Co. FA Vase SF 91-92.

COLLETTS GREEN

Manager: Adrian Green   **Secretary:** P Golding (0684 568799)
Ground: Victoria Park, Malvern
Directions: A few minutes walk from Malvern Link (BR) station.
Cover: Yes   **Floodlights:** Yes.
Prev. Name: Three Nuns (pre-1992)   **Prev. League:** Worcester Sunday (pre-1992).
Top Scorer 92-93: Philip Slade 33.
Hons: Midland Combination Challenge Vase 92-93, Worcs Junior Cup R-up 92-93.

DUDLEY SPORTS

Chairman: J Forrest   **Vice Chairman:** M Webster   **President:** H Branney
Secretary: Mrs Joan Forrest, 39 Smallshire Way, Wordsley, West Mids DY8 4XQ (0384 378558).
Manager: Kevin Blabber   **Asst Manager:** Steve Mason   **Coach:** M Webster
Physio: D Hemmings   **Press Officer/Commercial Manager:** Steve Lawrence.
Ground: High Ercal Avenue, Brierley Hill, West Mids (Brierley Hill 71260).
Directions: Just off A461 Dudley-Stourbridge Rd; coming from S'bridge, left after Silver Lane P.O.

Seats: None	**Cover:** 200	**Capacity:** 2,000 **Floodlights:** No	**Founded:** 1978
Colours: Red/black/red		**Change colours:** All blue	**Club Shop:** No.
Previous League: Birmingham Works		**Sponsors:** R's Tool Hire	**Nickname:** Pie Men
Programme: 12 pages, 50p		**Programme Editor:** Steve Lawrence (0384 230123)	
Midweek home matchday: Tuesday		**Record Gate:** 700 v Polesworth, B'ham Vase Oct '89.	
Record win: 10-1 v Alcester Town		**Record defeat:** 1-6 v Badsey Rangers.	

Clubhouse: Open weekday evenings 7-11pm, all day Sat, Sun 12-2 & 7-10.30pm. Large club with function room and snooker rooms. Hot food available.
Captain 92-93: Les Prosser   **Top Scorer 92-93:** A Osborne/ S Bennett
P.O.Y. 92-93: Steve Mason
Club record scorer: Paul Shinton   **Club record appearances:** John Pearson.
Hons: Birmingham Works Lg 80-81, Midland Combination Presidents Cup 90-91, Bass Cup, W.B.A. Shield, Black & White Cup, Aston Villa Shield.

HAMS HALL

President: E J Parkes   **Chairman:** A S Lakin.
General Mgr/Press Officer: Bob Ringrose, 6 Holly Drive, Hurley, Atherstone, Warks CV9 2JY (0827 872747).
Manager: Kevin Hateley   **Asst Manager:** Steve Ridsdill.
Physio: Martin Johnson   **Commercial Manager:** Phil Haseley.
Ground: Hams Hall Generating Station, Lea Marston, Sutton Coldfield B76 0BG (0675 462071 - mess. only).
Directions: M42 jct 9, A446 signed Coleshill, Water Orton & M6, 1st left main gate of power station. Rail to Water Orton BR station.

Seats: None	**Cover:** 700	**Capacity:** 2,000 **Floodlights:** No	**Founded:** 1930
Colours: White/black/black		**Change colours:** Sky & navy	**Nickname:** Powermen
Previous Grounds: None.		**Previous Lges:** Sutton Amtr 32-79/ Mercian FA 79-89.	
Programme: 24 pages, free		**Programme Editor:** Press Officer	**Club Shop:** No.
Club Sponsors: Powergen		**Rec. Gate:** 800 - A. Villa Shield 1986 (at Villa Park)	
Midweek home matchday: Wednesday			

Clubhouse: Open after matches and Monday, Wednesday & Saturday evenings. Fresh cobs available.
Club record scorer: Ken Taylor 151   **Club record appearances:** Arthur Lakin 363.
Captain 92-93: Craig Smith   **Top Scorer 92-93:** Ken Taylor 17   **P.O.Y. 92-93:** Richard Antiss.
Hons: Midland Combination Div 2 R-up 91-92, Jack Mould Trophy 92-93, Ernie Brown Cup 92-93, Walsall Challenge Cup 88-89, Fazeley Charity Cup 92-93, Mercian Lg Aston Villa Shield 85-86. Many honours in Sutton Amateur Lg.

HANDRAHAN TIMBERS

Chairman: E J Smith **President:** W J Handrahan
Secretary: Stuart Fereday, 93 Millfield Cres., Kidderminster (0562 820385).
Manager: Mitchell Woods **Asst Manager:** Phillip McNally
Press Officer: E J Smith (0384 295394).
Ground: The Mile Flat Sports Ground, Mile Flat, Wallheath, Kingswinford, West Mids (0381 484755).
Cover: 50 **Seats:** None **Floodlights:** No **Nickname:** Timbers **Founded:** 1982.
Colours: Red/white/red **Change colours:** Sky/navy/navy **Club Shop:** No.
Previous Grounds: None **Previous Leagues:** Staffs County Lg (South) 82-86.
Programme: Occasionally **Clubhouse:** Teas only. **Record win:** 9-0
Sponsors: W J Handrahan & Son **Midweek home matchday:** Wednesday **Record defeat:** 0-6.
Captain & P.o.Y. 92-93: Roy Moran **Top Scorer 92-93:** Paul Baker.
Club record scorer: Paul Baker **Club record appearances:** Jonathan Role.
Hons: Wednesbury Charity Cup 91-92, J W Hunt Cup 92-93.

Handrahan Timbers F.C. 1992-93.

KENILWORTH TOWN

Manager: John Clark **Founded:** 1936
Secretary: Richard Brooks, 33 Suncliffe Drive, Kenilworth, Warks CV8 1FH (0926 57728).
Ground: Gypsey Lane (off Rouncil Lane), Kenilworth, Warks (0926 50851).
Seats: No **Cover:** Yes **Clubhouse:** Yes **Floodlights:** No **Programme:** 50p
Colours: Blue/white/blue **Previous Name:** Kenilworth Rangers (pre-1992).
92-93 Top Scorer: Nigel Clarke 38 **Hons:** Birmingham Challenge Vase 92-93.

KINGS NORTON EX-SERVICEMEN

President: M T Hickey **Founded:** 1982
Sec: Eric Talbot, C/O Kings Norton Ex-Service Club, 185a Pershore Rd, Cotteridge B30 3DJ (021 459 1403).
Ground: Highgate Utd FC (see page 700).
Colours: All royal blue **Change colours:** White (blue trim)/royal/white
Programme Editor: S Jesic **Previous Ground:** Becketts Farm, Wythall.
Hons: Midland Comb. Div 2 R-up 85-86 (Presidents Cup 92-93, Challenge Vase R-up 84-85), Solihull Charity Cup R-up 84-85, Smedley Crooke Charity Cup 87-88 (R-up 89-90).

MONICA STAR

Manager: Tony Carter **Founded:** 1977.
Secretary: Nigel Peters, 10 Ravensdale Road, Small Heath, Birmingham B10 9HU (021 772 6871).
Ground: As Chelmsley Town (page 699). **Colours:** Red/black/red
Prev. Ground: The Glades, Lugtrout Lane, Solihull (pre-'92) **Top Scorer 92-93:** David Stokes 39.

OLTON ROYALE ·

Manager: Derek Attwood. **Founded:** 1969.
Secretary: Brian D Fox, 189 Kingshurst Road, Northfield, Birmingham B31 2LL (021 475 4465).
Ground: Bay Tree Farm, Middle Lane, Wythall, Near Birmingham (0564 826612).
Colours: All red **92-93 Top Scorer:** Andrew Williams 34.
Previous Name: West Heath United (1969-93).
Hons: Midland Combination Div 2 R-up 84-85, Smedley Crooke Charity Cup 92-93.

POLESWORTH NORTH WARWICK

Manager: David Wright.
Secretary: E Guild, 43 Station Road, Polesworth, Tamworth, Staffs B78 1BG (0827 893690).
Ground: North Warwick Sports Ground, Hermitage Hill, Tamworth Road, Polesworth (892482).
Seats: 50 **Capacity:** 1,000 **Floodlights:** No **Founded:** 1966 **Nickname:** Poles
Colours: Green & white hoops/green/yellow **Change colours:** Tangerine & black
Previous League: Mercian. **Clubhouse:** Bar, tea room and refreshments.
Hons: Midland Combination Challenge Cup 83-84 (Presidents Cup(2) 82-84), Birmingham Jnr Cup 83-84, Ernie Brown Cup 91-92.
Players progressing to Football League: Dave Tunnicliffe (Birmingham City).

SHERWOOD CELTIC

Manager: Mark Foggerty. **Founded:** 1982
Secretary: Mark Askey, 96 Newborough Road, Shirley, Solihull B90 2HF (021 744 4591).
Ground: As Knowle F.C. (See page 700). **Colours:** Gold/green/gold **Programme:** Yes
Previous Ground: Becketts Farm, Wythall (pre-'92) **Hons:** Fazeley Charity Cup R-up 92-93.

SHIRLEY TOWN

Manager: Pete Sysum.
Secretary: N Charles, 13 Ardley Rd, Kings Heath, Birmingham (021 441 2326).
Ground: Shirley Stadium, Tile House Lane, Shirley, Solihull (021 744 1560).
Directions: A34 B'gham to Shirley, right onto B4025 towards Shirley (BR) - ground one and a half miles on left.
Colours: All red **Previous League:** B'ham Comb. 35-38. **Founded:** 1926
Top Scorer 92-93: Junior McKeon 64 **Hons:** Midland Combination Division 2 R-up 92-3.

SOLIHULL BOROUGH RESERVES *(See page 500 for other details)*

Manager: Ron Mason **Ground:** Borough Club, Tanworth Lane, Shirley, Solihull (021 745 6758)

SOUTHAM UNITED

Manager: Ollie Berry **Founded:** 1905.
Secretary: R J Hancocks, 18 Warwick Road, Southam, Leamington Spa CV33 0HN (0926 813483).
Ground: Banbury Road Ground, Southam, Leamington Spa (0926 812091).
Directions: On righthand side of A423 Banbury Road heading south from Southam.
Seats: No **Cover:** Yes **Nickname:** Saints **Clubhouse:** Yes
Colours: Yellow/black/black **Previous League:** Coventry & North Warks.
Hons: Mids Comb. Div 3 80-81 (Div 2 R-up 82-83, Chal. Vase 80-81).

UPTON TOWN

Chairman: John Cook **Vice Chairman:** Bill Jones **President:** Steve Goode.
Secretary/Press Officer: Don Roberts, 6 Gardens Close, Upton-on-Severn, Worcs WR8 0LT (0684 593439).
Manager: Alan Kealy **Coach:** Keith Aingel **Physio:** A Pugh.
Commercial Manager: Les Wadley.
Ground: Malvern Town F.C. (See page 689). **Founded:** 1904
Colours: Green & white **Change:** Red & black stripes **Nickname:** Emeralds
Programme: 16 pages, 50p **Editor:** Graham Hill (0905 351653) **Club Shop:** No.
Sponsors: D.G. Car & Van Hire **Prev. Ground:** Old Street, Upton-on-Severn (pre'92)
Previous Leagues: Malvern 04-71/ Worcester & Dist. 72-85/ Kidderminster 85-88.
Midweek home matchday: Tuesday **Record Gate:** 300 v Archdales, County Cup SF March 1990.
Record win: 13-1 **Record defeat:** 0-17.
Clubhouse: Evenings 7.30-11pm, Saturday matchdays 12.30-11pm. Food (hamburgers etc), tea, coffee, squash available on matchdays.
Captain 92-93: Mark Davies **Top Scorer 92-93:** Paul Newman 14 **P.o.Y. 92-93:** Mark Walker
Club record scorer: Paul Buckley **Club record appearances:** Keith Aingel.
Hons: Midland Combination Div 2 89-90 (Jack Mould Tphy 89-90, Presidents Cup R-up 89-90), Worcs Jnr Cup 73-74 88-89 (R-up 74-75), Worcs Minor Cup 24-25 86-87.

WEST MIDLANDS FIRE SERVICE

Chairman: Mr R Jefferies **President:** Chief Fire Officer.
Secretary: Mr J Clarke, 51 Stonebury Ave., Coventry CV5 7FW (0203 467997).
Manager: Ian Green **Asst Manager:** Clive Mason.
Ground: 'The Glades', Lugtrout Lane, Solihull (021 705 8602).
Directions: M42 jct 5, A45 towards B'ham Airport, leave at next junction and at island take 1st exit (Catherine de Barnes Lane) - ground half mile on left. Nearest station is Birmingham International. No buses pass ground.
Seats: None **Cover:** 150 **Floodlights:** No **Club Shop:** No **Founded:** 1947
Colours: All red **Change colours:** White/navy/navy **Previous Grounds:** None.
Previous Leagues: Birmingham A.F.A. (pre-1986).
Programme: 12 pages, 25p **Editor:** J Kempson (0922 408464)
Sponsors: Contract Fire Sytems Ltd **Record defeat:** 1-14 v West Heath United.
Midweek home matchday: Tues/Thurs **Nickname:** None.
Clubhouse: No. **Club record appearances:** Brian Farrell.
Captain 92-93: Sean Moore **Top Scorer 92-93:** Lee Sketchley **P.o.Y. 92-93:** T.B.A.
Hons: Midlands Combination Div 2 87-88 (Jack Mould Trophy 87-88), Fire Services National Cup 89-90, Fire District Cup 90-91.

WILMCOTE

Manager: Martin Skipp **Founded:** 1971.
Secretary: Mrs Jennifer Smith, 2 Wavensmere Cottage, Wootten Wawen, Solihull B95 6BS (Henley-in-Arden 794552).
Ground: The Patch, Wilmcote Men's Club, Aston Cantlow Road, Wilmcote, Stratford (0789 297895).
Directions: Wilmcote signs off A34, right at T-junction opposite garage; ground on right.
Seats: No **Cover:** Yes **Clubhouse:** Yes **Programme:** No **Nickname:** Cote.
Colours: Yellow/green/yellow **Previous League:** Stratford Alliance.
Players progressing to Football League: Steve Mardinbrow (Coventry City), John Smith (WBA).

DIVISION TWO CLUBS 1993-94

ALVIS

Manager: Adrian Newbury.
Secretary: D A Leslie, 9 Stephenson Close, Milverton, Leamington Spa CV32 6BS (0926 336700).
Ground: Alvis Spts & Social Club, Green Lane, Finham, Coventry.
Previous League: Coventry Alliance (pre-1993).

ARCHDALES '73

Manager: Martin Stephens   **Colours:** Red/white/red   **Founded:** 1934
Secretary: R T Widdowson, 37 Mayfield Avenue, Worcester WR3 8LA (0905 27866).
Ground: Windermere Drive, Worcester (0905 51410)   **Nickname:** Dales

BURNTWOOD

Manager: Martin Daley   **Secretary:** D Cox (0543 671060).
Ground: Memorial Institute, Rugeley Rd, Burntwood.

COLESHILL TOWN RESERVES *(See page 699)*

EARLSWOOD TOWN

Chairman: J J Jones   **Vice Chairman:** D G Barr   **President:** R Taylor.
Secretary: J Jones, 22 Antony Road, Shirley, Solihull B90 2NX (021 745 3397).
Manager: G Ashford   **Coach:** G Whitehouse.
Commercial Manager: D McKever   **Press Officer:** John Sharpe (021 444 7979)
Ground: Malthouse Lane, Earlswood, Solihull (05646 3989).
Directions: Follow signs to Earlswood, pass between Lakes and into Malthouse Lane, ground half mile on left. Train to 'The Lakes' station - ground adjacent.
Seats: None   **Cover:** 100   **Capacity:** 1,000   **Floodlights:** No   **Founded:** 1968
Colours: Red/black/red   **Change colours:** Green & yellow   **Nickname:** Earls
Previous League: Mercian.   **Previous Ground:** Lady Lane, Earlswood 68-75.
Programme: 20 pages, 40p   **Programme Editor:** John Sharpe (021 444 7979).
Club Shop: Yes. Club programmes, enamel badges etc available. Contact John Sharpe - number above.
Club Sponsors: Earlswood Garage   **Record Gate:** 500 v A. Villa Old Star, charity game 1991.
Midweek home matchday: Wednesday   **Clubhouse:** Open matchdays. Bar. Food available.
Captain 92-93: Mark Johnson   **P.o.Y. 92-93:** Mark Logan
Top Scorer 92-93: Chris Johnson   **Club record appearances:** J Jones.

ENVILLE ATHLETIC

Manager: David Pell   **Colours:** All sky blue   **Founded:** 1890
Secretary: Graham Hingley, 24 Bramley Way, Blossom Hill, Bewdley, Worcs DY12 2PU (0299 400745).
Ground: Hall Drive Ground, Hall Drive, Enville, Stourbridge (Kinver 872368).
Reserve Team's League: Kidderminster & District.
Clubhouse: Yes   **Cover:** No   **Hons:** B'ham Co. FA Vase QF 91-92.

FAIRFIELD VILLA

Chairman: P Eades   **Vice Chairman:** J Rea   **President:** L J Hill.
Secretary: C W Harris, 7 Churchill Road, Catshill, Bromsgrove B61 0PE (0527 31049).
Manager: Cliff Hughes   **Asst Manager:** K Smith   **Coach:** R Hughes.
Press Officer: Secretary   **Physio:** S Kings/ C Waldron.
Ground: Recreation Ground, Stourbridge Road (B4091), Fairfield, Bromsgrove (0527 77049).
Capacity: 500   **Seats:** None   **Floodlights:** No   **Founded:** 1902   **Reformed:** 1959
Colours: Red/black/black   **Change colours:** White & green   **Nickname:** Villa.
Previous Grounds: None   **Previous Lges:** Bromsgrove 59-69/ Kidderminster 70-84.
Sponsors: Richards Packages   **Club Shop:** No   **Programme:** No.
Clubhouse: Evenings 8-11pm, matchdays, Sun noon- & 8-10.30pm. Sandwiches available.
Captain 92-93: P Webb   **Top Scorer 92-93:** P Cotterill   **P.o.Y. 92-93:** M Smith
Club record scorer: Brian Preece   **Club record appearances:** Phil Powell/ Mark Tabb.
Hons: Bromsgrove Lg 69-70, Kidderminster Lg 81-82 83-84, Malvern Invitation Cup 77-78, Worcs Junior Cup 77-78, Smedley Crooke Charity Cup R-up 91-92.

G.P.T. (COVENTRY)

Manager: Fred Robinson.
Secretary: C P Bevan, 85 Gainford Rise, Friars Mead, Coventry, West Mids (0203 459708).
Ground: G.E.C. Sports Ground, Allard Way, Copsewood, Coventry.
Previous League: Coventry Alliance (pre-1993).

HOLLY LANE '92

Chairman: Tom McCosh   **Vice Chairman:** Harry Parks   **President:** George Harvey.
Secretary: R G Ashton, 19 Grange Road, Erdington, Birmingham B24 0DG (021 350 2352).
Manager: Derek Stevens   **Asst Manager:** Chris Eustace   **Coach:** Paul Snowball.
Ground: Holly Sports & Social, Holly Lane, Erdingtpn, Birmingham B24.
Seats: None   **Floodlights:** No   **Founded:** 1992   **Programmes:** Yes   **Club Shop:** No.
Colours: Yellow/black   **Change colours:** All green   **Nickname:** None.
Record win: 11-1   **Record defeat:** 3-7.
Midweek home matchday: Thursday   **Clubhouse:** Open all day Saturday, snacks available.
Captain 92-93: Michael Haly   **Top Scorer & P.o.Y. 92-93:** William Roche.
Club record appearances: Derek Hill.

JAGUAR-DAIMLER

Secretary: David Jenkin, 178 Holbrook Lane, Coventry, West Mids CV6 4BY (0203 688435).
Ground: Jaguar Sports & Social Club, Middlemarch Rd, Coventry.
Previous League: Coventry Alliance (pre-1993).

LEDBURY TOWN '84

Chairman: Mr C Bloise **Vice Chairman:** Mr D Skyers **President:** Mr C Hutchings
Secretary: Mrs J Phillips, Th Newtons, Much Marcle, Ledbury (0531 84382).
Manager: Ralph Tyler **Ground:** New Street, Ledbury.
Seats: 50 **Cover:** 50 **Capacity:** 200 **Floodlights:** Yes **Founded:** 1966
Colours: Black & white **Change colours:** Blue & black
Sponsors: Hills of Ledbury **Clubhouse:** Yes, on ground.

MASSEY-FERGUSON

Manager: Frank McDermott
Secretary: C Richards, Binley, Coventry, West Midlands CV3 2FE (0203 458695).
Ground: Massey-Ferguson Sports Ground, Banner Lane, Tile Hill, Coventry.
Previous League: Coventry Alliance (pre-1993).

MEIR K.A. RESERVES

Manager: Brian Wilding *(See page 700 for other club details)*

RUGBY TOWN

President: John Dean **Chairman:** Paul Moss
Manager: Barry Collinson. **Secretary:** Mick O'Toole
Ground: East Warwickshire College *(*** N.B. The club will probably be on a new ground for 93-94 ****).*
Previous Names: Rugby Town/ Rugby Irish - clubs merged in 1992.
92-93 Captain: J Whiteside **Previous League:** Coventry & North Warwick 1992-93.

Rugby Town F.C., who make a welcome return to senior football in 1993-94.

SPHINX

Manager: W Hollywood.
Secretary: C Jones, 29 The Farmstead, Stoke Aldermoor, Coventry, West Mids CV3 1EB (0203 442439).
Ground: Sphinx Sports Ground, Sidderley Ave., Stoke Aldermoor, Coventry.
Previous League: Coventry Alliance (pre-1993).

STUDLEY B.K.L. RESERVES

Manager: Glenn Adams *(See page 704 for other club details)*

SUTTON COLDFIELD TOWN RESERVES

Manager: Terry Bent **Ground:** The Gas Ground. *(See page 523 for other club details)*

SWIFT P.P.

Manager: T.B.A. **Founded:** 1982.
Secretary: Tony Moogan, 6 George Arthur Rd, Saltley, Birmingham B8 1LW (021 328 9720).
Ground: Alvechurch F.C. *(See page 678).*
Colours: White (red trim)/white/red **Previous League:** Birmingham Works.
Previous Ground: Shirley Town F.C. (pre-'92)/ Wythall Park, Silver Street, Wythall (Wythall F.C.) 92-93.

THIMBLEMILL R.E.C.

Manager: Peter Gardiner **Programme:** Yes **Founded:** 1964.
Secretary: G M Houten, 68 Gower Road, Lapal, Halesowen, West Mids B62 9BT (021 442 3357).
Ground: Thimblemill Recreation, Thimblemill Road, Smethwick, Warley (021 429 2459).
Colours: White (blue trim)/white/navy blue
Hons: Midland Combination Challenge Vase R-up 92-93 (Challenge Cup QF 91-92).

RESERVE DIVISION CONSTITUTION 1993-94

1. Atherstone Utd Res.
2. Barwell Res.
3. Boldmere St Mich. Res.
4. Bridgnorth Town Res.
5. Bromsgrove Rovers Res.
6. Burton Albion Res.
7. Evesham Utd Res.
8. Gresley Rovers Res.
9. Halesowen Town Res.
10. Hednesford Town Res.
11. Kidderminster H. Res.
12. Leicester Utd Res.
13. Nuneaton Borough Res.
14. Pershore Town '88 Res.
15. Redditch Utd Res.
16. Shepshed Albion Res.
17. Stratford Town Res.
18. Tamworth Res.
19. V.S. Rugby Res.

Wilmcote F.C. of Division One. Photo - Gavin Ellis-Neville.

The Enville Athletic 'keeper tips over a cross in a 2-1 home win over Kenilworth Reserves. Photo - James Wright.

Kenilworth Town Reserves, who will play in Division Three next season. Photo - Keith Clayton.

DIVISION THREE CLUBS 1993-94

ALBRIGHT & WILSON

Secretary: Stephen Smith, 68 Forest Road, Oldbury, Warley B68 0EF (021 421 3211).
Ground: Albright & Wilson Spts Club, Tat Bank, Oldbury, Warley (021 552 1048).
Directions: A4034 Oldbury Road from M5 jct 2; right at island along A457 Smethwick Road, second right into Stone Street and continue to Tat Bank.
Colours: All sky **Change colours:** Gold/black/black   **Founded:** 1935.
Previous League: West Midlands (Regional) (pre-1993).

ALVESTON

Secretary: K Unitt, 47 Luddington Rd, Stratford-upon-Avon, Warks CV37 9SG.
Ground: Home Guard Club, Main Street, Tiddington, Stratford-upon-Avon.
Previous League: Stratford Alliance (pre-1993).

ANSELLS RESERVES *(see page 698)*

BARLESTONE ST GILES RESERVES *(see page 706)*

BILSTON COMMUNITY COLLEGE

Chairman: Mr Earl Laird   **Manager:** Brian Waldron.
Secretary: M J Baker, 88 Magness Cres., Short Heath, Willenhall, Staffs WV12 4QW (0902 630364).
Ground: Bilston Town F.C. *(see page 508)*
Colours: All navy   **Change:** Green & gold/green.   **Programme:** No.
Previous League: Staffs County (South) (pre-1993)
Previous Ground: Springvale Spts & Social Club, Millfields Rd, Bilston (pre-1993).
Hons: Staffs County (South) Lg 89-90 90-91 91-92 92-93, J W Hunt Charity Cup 90-91.

BLACKHEATH ELECTRODRIVES

Chairman: Mr G Ellison   **Vice Chairman:** Tony Brookes   **Manager:** Bob Homer.
Secretary/Press Officer: Mr Tito Martire, 10 Marshwood Croft, Halesowen B62 0EZ (021 422 3449).
Ground & Directions: Electrodrives Sports Ground, Cakemore Road, Rowley Regis, Warley (021 559 1500).
A4123 towards B'ham from M5 jct 2, right at 'Hen & Chickens' (B4169) - ground half mile on left 100 yds before works entrance in Cakemore Rd.
Seats: Nil   **Cover:** Nil   **Capacity:** 2,000   **Floodlights:** No   **Formed:** 1920.
Colours: All red   **Change colours:** All blue   **Nickname:** "G's"
Previous Lge: Birmingham Works 20-88.   **Previous Name:** Blackheath Electromotors (pre-1992).
Programme: No   **Club Shop:** No   **Sponsors:** Electrodrives.
Midweek home matchday: Wednesday   **Reserve team's League:** Kidderminster.
Record win: 11-0 v Smethwick   **Record defeat:** 1-7 v Cheslyn Hay.
Clubhouse: Nearby. Snack bar on ground.
Captain 92-93: Mark Lovatt   **Top Scorer 92-93:** Kevin Davies   **P.o.Y. 92-93:** Ian Mills
Club record scorer: Paul Birch   **Club record appearances:** Mark Lovatt.

CONTINENTAL STAR

Secretary: Noel O'Donnell, 555 Kingsbury Rd, Erdington, Birmingham B24 9NJ (021 384 2277).
Ground: Magnet Centre, Park Approach, Erdington, Birmingham.
Previous League: Birmingham Works (pre-1993).

DUDLEY SPORTS RESERVES *(see page 706)*

ENVILLE ATHLETIC RESERVES *(see page 709)*

KENILWORTH TOWN RESERVES *(see page 707)*

MITCHELLS & BUTLERS

Chairman: L Linford   **Manager:** T Malanaphy.
Secretary: Mr Ian R Burford, 141 Cape Hill, Smethwick, West Mids B66 4SH (021 565 2143).
Asst Manager: P Walsh   **Coach:** M Shaw   **Physio:** J McGowan.
Ground: City Road, Edgbaston, Birmingham (021 420 1576/429 2469(club)).
Directions: From Birmingham City centre follow Broad Street down Five Ways island, go under island into Hagley Rd, right into Sandon Rd after approx one and a half miles, right at 1st lights into City Road. From M5 jct 1, left at 2nd island onto A457, after 3rd set of lights 1st right into Shenstone Road, right at 'T' junction into City Road - ground entrance 100 yds on left. Buses 82, 87, 88 & 89 from Birmingham centre - alight at Summerfield Park and take 1st left into City Road.
Seats: Nil   **Cover:** 50   **Capacity:** 500   **Floodlights:** No   **Founded:** 1871
Colours: Navy & sky   **Change colours:** All red   **Nickname:** Brewers.
Previous Grounds: Winson Street 1877/ The Oval, Cape Hill 1888.
Previous Names: Birmingham St George/ Mitchells St George.
Previous Leagues: Football Alliance/ Birmingham Works (pre-1985).
Programme: No   **Club Shop:** No   **Club Sponsors:** V.T. Plastics/ Stevetone.
(Recent) Record Gate: 450 v Birmingham City, friendly.
Midweek home matchday: Tuesday   **Reserve team's League:** Staffs Co. (South).
Captain 92-93: P Bannister   **Top Scorer & P.o.Y. 92-93:** T Breen.
Club record scorer: R Cox/ D Jessop.   **Clubhouse:** Open after matches. Cold food available.
Hons: Staffs Chal. Cup twice (including 1-0 win over West Brom in final at Stoke in 1888), WBA Shield 82-83 83-84, B'ham Wks Lg Div 1 82-83 (Div 4(res) 82-83), M & B Cup 82-83, Sandwell Charity Cup 84-85.

PARK RANGERS

Chairman: B Leishenring **President:** D Gallear.
Secretary: Peter Worwood, 3 Speedwell Close, Aldridge, West Mids WS9 0DL (0922 56385).
Commercial Manager/Press Officer: N Willis (0384 74374).
Ground: Tividale Community Centre, Lower City Road, Tividale, Warley, West Mids (021 544 8332).
Directions: A4123 towards Dudley from M5 jct 2; Lower City Road is on right opposite 'Huntsman' pub and ground is signposted 300yds on right. 126 bus from Dudley or Birmingham. Nearest BR station is Dudley Port.
Seats: None **Cover:** No **Capacity:** 1,000 **Floodlights:** No **Founded:** 1968
Colours: All red **Change colours:** Yellow/black/black.
Previous Leagues: West Midlands Metropolitan/ Staffs County (South)/ West Mids (Regional) 91-93.
Programme: 24 pages, free **Editor:** N Willis (0384 74374) **Club Shop:** No.
Sponsors: Aldridge Electrical **Midweek home matchday:** Tuesday
Record win: 11-1 v Bearwood Am. **Record defeat:** 0-9 v Bloxwich Strollers.
Nickname: Salamanders **Clubhouse:** Yes. Food for special matches only.
Captain 92-93: Peter Robinson **Top Scorer 92-93:** Jason Marsden 8 (in 8 games)
P.o.Y. 92-93: Tommy Bergin **Club record scorer:** Pat Hoban.
Hons: Albion Shield 68-69, West Mids Metropolitan Lg Div 1 North 70-71, Jennings Invitation Cup 73-74, Ike Cooper Cup 90-91.

STAPENHILL RESERVES *(see page 702)*

WELLESBOURNE RESERVES *(see page 704)*

WEST MIDLANDS POLICE RESERVES *(see page 704)*

WILMCOTE RESERVES *(see page 708)*

'MITCHELLS & BUTLERS' COVENTRY ALLIANCE

PREM. ONE	P	W	D	L	F	A	PTS
Folly Lane	22	15	5	2	47	24	35
G.P.T. (Coventry)	22	14	4	4	58	32	32
Sphinx (-2pts)	22	12	6	4	58	33	28
Massey-Ferguson	22	11	6	5	49	27	28
Triumph	22	12	4	6	45	43	28
Stockingford	22	10	5	7	61	38	25
Nun Griff	22	8	4	10	51	52	20
Bulkington	22	6	5	11	19	30	17
Jet Blades	22	6	4	12	29	41	16
Bermuda	22	5	5	12	28	53	15
A.E.I. Rugby	22	5	3	14	39	57	13
Alvis	22	2	1	19	18	80	5

PREM. TWO	P	W	D	L	F	A	PTS
Arley	22	17	1	4	88	14	35
Dunlop	22	16	2	4	60	19	34
Highway	22	13	4	5	68	36	30
Christ the King	22	13	3	6	55	30	29
Clifton	22	11	6	5	47	33	28
Coventry Colliery	22	10	4	8	50	34	24
Jaguar-Daimler	22	8	4	10	41	45	20
President Kennedy	22	6	7	9	33	43	19
Woodlands	22	8	3	11	44	72	19
Wytherley	22	5	3	14	29	46	13
Stringers	22	3	4	15	29	80	10
Bourton	22	1	1	20	16	106	3

ALLIANCE 1	P	W	D	L	F	A	PTS
Folly Lane	22	17	3	2	67	24	37
Whitnash	22	14	5	3	57	33	33
Massey-Ferg. Res.	22	15	2	5	49	26	32
Nuneaton Ex-Serv.	22	11	4	7	44	29	26
G.P.T. Res.	22	10	4	8	44	41	24
Binley Woods	22	10	3	9	42	40	23
Nueaton Griff	22	9	3	10	37	35	21
Brico	22	8	3	11	33	38	19
Sphinx Res.	22	7	4	11	46	54	18
MSA Phildown	22	6	3	13	28	45	15
Bulkington Res.	22	5	3	14	34	59	13
Alvis Res.	22	0	3	19	17	74	3

ALLIANCE 2	P	W	D	L	F	A	PTS
Stockton	22	18	0	4	89	37	36
Finham	22	15	5	2	86	36	35
Peugeot	22	13	3	6	54	40	29
Meadway	22	12	4	6	67	50	28
Shilton	22	10	5	7	66	42	25
Jet Blades Res.	22	10	4	8	65	46	24
Cov. University	22	7	7	8	54	54	21
Massey-Ferg. 'A'	22	7	4	11	44	71	18
Stockingford Res.	22	7	3	12	41	62	17
Cov. Colliery Res.	22	7	1	14	44	76	15
Highway	22	3	5	14	24	49	11
Wytherley	22	1	3	18	20	87	5

SUBURBAN 1	P	W	D	L	F	A	PTS
Newman	22	17	4	1	77	31	38
Brooklands	22	17	0	5	94	33	34
Foleshill	22	13	7	2	46	30	33
Coundon	22	14	2	6	53	32	30
Balsall	22	11	3	8	45	34	25
B. Tachbrook	22	9	3	10	41	49	21
Wolston	22	9	2	11	45	59	20
A.E.I. Rugby Res.	22	7	5	10	39	52	19
Longford	22	7	4	11	35	40	18
Brico Res.	22	6	4	12	33	43	16
Jaguar-Daimler Res.	22	1	4	17	30	66	6
Dunlop Res. (-2pts)	22	2	3	17	29	77	5

SUBURBAN 2	P	W	D	L	F	A	PTS
Stockton Res.	20	15	3	2	56	20	33
Arley Res.	20	14	4	2	76	28	32
G.P.T. 'A'	20	13	1	6	55	35	27
Fillongley	20	9	4	7	52	38	22
Folly Lane Res.	20	9	3	8	36	36	21
Radford	20	8	4	8	36	41	20
Canley Social	20	7	3	10	46	53	17
Cov. Univ. Res.	20	5	5	10	39	41	15
Christ the King Res.	20	5	4	11	37	54	14
Meriden	20	5	0	15	36	80	10
Shilton Res.	20	3	3	14	29	59	9

SUBURBAN 3	P	W	D	L	F	A	PTS
Coundon Res.	20	16	2	2	73	26	34
Bermuda Res.	20	15	3	2	69	26	33
B. Tachbrook Res.	20	13	2	5	56	37	28
MSA Phildown Res.	20	9	4	7	37	35	22
Wolston Res.	20	7	4	9	32	43	18
Pres. Kennedy Res.	20	8	2	10	32	52	18
A.E.I. Rugby 'A'	20	5	5	10	50	59	15
Balsall Res.	20	6	2	12	46	60	14
Peugeot Res.	20	5	4	11	34	46	14
Cov. Univ. 'A'	20	5	2	12	33	64	12
Unity	20	4	4	12	30	56	12

SUBURBAN 4	P	W	D	L	F	A	PTS
Clifton Res.	22	18	3	1	94	31	39
Lewis	22	12	7	3	51	25	31
Longitchington	22	11	4	7	63	49	26
Bedlam	22	11	4	7	54	47	26
Bulkington 'A'	22	11	4	7	52	44	26
Radford Res.	22	10	5	7	74	58	25
Pheasant	22	9	6	7	56	35	24
Fillongley Res.	22	10	3	9	51	50	23
Peugeot 'A'	22	6	4	12	41	53	16
Christ the King 'A'	22	5	4	11	42	75	14
Meriden Res.	22	2	3	17	33	80	7
Bourton	22	3	1	18	28	95	7

EVERARDS BREWERY
LEICESTERSHIRE SENIOR LEAGUE

President: J M Elsom
Chairman: Peter Henwood
Hon. Secretary: David Jamieson,
48 King George Rd, Loughborough LE11 2PA (0509 267912).

PREM. DIVISION	P	W	D	L	F	A	PTS
Holwell Sports	34	23	6	5	115	43	75
Friar Lane OB	34	22	7	5	85	30	73
Oadby Town	34	23	4	7	85	45	73
Anstey Nomads	34	21	5	8	103	46	68
St Andrews S.C.	34	19	8	7	66	30	65
Burbage OB	34	17	5	12	71	56	56
North Kilworth	34	16	7	11	60	68	55
Birstall United	34	15	7	12	76	65	52
Highfield Rangers	34	14	8	12	46	51	50
Leics Constabulary	34	14	7	13	64	66	49
Syston St Peters	34	11	8	15	55	75	41
Lutterworth Town	34	11	7	16	54	63	40
Newfoundpool WMC	34	11	7	16	41	67	40
Ibstock Welfare	34	9	6	19	52	65	33
Downes Sports	34	9	4	21	50	78	31
Pedigree Petfoods	34	8	4	22	43	95	28
Houghton Rangers	34	6	4	24	32	89	22
Narboro. & L'thorpe	34	2	6	26	28	94	*10

* - 1pt deducted.

DIVISION ONE	P	W	D	L	F	A	PTS
Barrow Town	34	26	2	6	92	27	80
Sileby Town	34	24	5	5	81	37	77
Cottesmore Amtrs	34	23	3	8	91	50	72
Kirby Muxloe SC	34	22	4	8	85	39	70
Thringstone	34	19	6	9	94	54	63
Asfordby Amtrs	34	18	8	8	105	54	62
Fosse Imps	34	18	5	11	70	44	59
Quorn	34	16	7	11	67	60	55
Ravenstone	34	15	7	12	68	71	52
Loughboro. Dynamo	34	11	8	15	68	72	41
Anstey Town	34	13	2	19	51	68	41
Harborough T.I.	34	13	2	19	60	93	41
Hillcroft	34	11	2	21	55	82	35
Leicester YMCA	34	9	5	20	59	102	32
Earl Shilton Alb.	34	6	8	20	51	89	26
Huncote S & S	34	7	5	22	38	92	26
Aylestone Park OB	34	8	2	24	55	114	26
Whetstone Ath.	34	4	5	25	37	79	17

Barrow Town - Division One champions 1992-93. Photo - James Wright.

TEBBUTT BROWN (LEICS SENIOR LEAGUE) CUP 1992-93

Preliminary Round

Ibstock Welfare v Downes Sports	0-0,1-2
Newfoundpool WMC v Syston St Peters	0-1
Asfordby Amateurs v Quorn	4-2
Kirby Muxloe SC v Fosse Imps	2-3

First Round

Premier Division

Anstey Nomads v Houghton Rangers	5-2
Birstall Utd v Narborough & Littlethorpe	3-0
Friar Lane Old Boys v Burbage Old Boys	2-0
Highfield Rangers v Pedigree Petfoods	5-3
Leics Contabulary v Downes Sports	4-1
Oadby Town v North Kilworth	2-0
St Andrews v Lutterworth	2-2,1-1,2-1
Syston St Peters v Holwell	2-2,4-4,2-4

Division One

Asfordby Amateurs v Fosse Imps	3-0
Aylestone Park Old Boys v Earl Shilton Albion	2-3
Cottesmore Amateurs v Barrow Town	1-3
Huncote S. & S. v Leicester Y.M.C.A.	2-1
Sileby Town v Hillcroft	2-1
Ravenstone v Loughborough Dynamo	2-0
Thringstone M.W. v Anstey Town	6-1
Whetstone Athletic v Harborough Town Imperial	2-1

Second Round

Premier Division

Birstall United v Highfield Rangers	3-0
Friar Lane Old Boys v Oadby Town	2-0
St Andrews S.C. v Leics Constabulary	3-0
Holwell Sports v Anstey Nomads	4-0

Division One

Barrow Town v Sileby Town	2-0
Huncote S. & S. v Whetstone Athletic	2-2,0-2
Ravenstone v Earl Shilton Albion	1-5
Thringstone M.W. v Asfordby Amateurs	0-0,1-3

Quarter Finals (open to all teams)

Earl Shilton Albion v Birstall United	1-3
St Andrews S.C. v Barrow Town	2-0
Thringstone M.W. v Holwell Sports	1-1,1-2
Whetstone Athletic v Friar Lane O.B.	1-1,1-6

Semi-Finals

Holwell Sports v Friar Lane Old Boys	5-2
Birstall United v St Andrews S.C.	2-3

Final: St Andrews Social Club 2, Holwell Sports 0

PREMIER DIVISION CLUBS 1993-94

ANSTEY NOMADS
Secretary: Andy Coleman, 14 Church Lane, Anstey, Leicester LE7 7AF (0533 363191).
Ground: Cropston Road, Anstey, Leicester (0533 364868).
Directions: Anstey Lane from Leicester to Anstey, right at r'bout into Cropston Rd. 1 mile from London Road (BR).
Seats: None   **Cover:** 100   **Capacity:** 2,500   **Floodlights:** No   **Founded:** 1945.
Cols: Red & white stripes/black/black   **Record Gate:** 4,500 v Hayes, FA Amtr Cup 53-54.
Programme: 12-14 pages, 25p   **Hons:** Leics Snr Lg 51-52 53-54 81-82 82-83 (Div 2 73-74).

BARROW TOWN
Secretary: Nick J Freeman, 1 Beacon Drive, Loughborough, Leics LE11 2BD (0509 212853).
Ground: Riverside Park, Meynell Road, Quorn, Leics (0509 620650).
Colours: Red (white pin stripe)/black/red
Hons: Leics Snr Lg Div 1 92-93, Loughborough Charity Cup 92-93.

BIRSTALL UNITED
Secretary: Bob Garrard, 58 Halstead Rd, Mountsorrel, Leicester LE12 7HF (0533 376886).
Ground: Meadow Lane, Birstall (671230)   **Directions:** Off Wanlip Lane, Birstall.   **Floodlights:** Yes.
Colours: White/navy/white   **Hons:** Leics Snr Lg Div 2 76-77.

BURBAGE OLD BOYS
Secretary: Mrs S Taylor, 8 Brockhurst Avenue, Burbage, Leics LE10 2HG (0455 633916).
Colours: Blue/white/royal   **Ground:** Britannia Rd, Burbage, Leics.
Hons: Leics Snr Lg Div 1 91-92.

COTTESMORE AMATEURS
Secretary: K Nimmons, 17 Redwing Close, Oakham, Rutland LE15 6DA (0572 724582).
Ground: Main Street, Cottesmore, Rutland (0572 813486).   **Colours:** Green/black/green.

DOWNES SPORTS
Secretary: Stuart Millidge, 25 Elizabeth Rd, Hinckley, Leics LE10 0QY (0455 635808).
Colours: All tangerine   **Ground:** 259 Coventry Rd, Hinckley (0455 635186).

FRIAR LANE OLD BOYS
Secretary: T J Knibbs, 75 Brighton Avenue, Wigston Fields, Leicester LE18 1JB (0533 888928).
Ground: Knighton Lane East, Leicester (0533 833629).
Directions: Between A50 Welford Rd and Saffron Lane near Sports Centre.
Seats: None   **Cover:** 250   **Capacity:** 3,500   **Floodlights:** No   **Founded:** 1961.
Colours: Black & white stripes/black/red
Record Gate: 1,325 v Stamford, FA Vase Semi Final April 1975.
Hons: FA Vase SF(2) 74-76, Leics Snr Lg(7) 70-72 73-78 (R-up 92-93, Div 2 69-70), Leics Snr Cup(3) 73-75 91-92

HIGHFIELD RANGERS
Secretary: M Christian, 18 Blanklyn Avenue, Leicester LE5 5FA (0533 734002).
Ground: Gleneagles Ave., Rushey Mead, Leicester (0533 660009)
Directions: A6 to Leicester, 2nd left at Birstall r'bout into Watermead/Troon Way, right at 2nd lights, 1st left.
Colours: Yellow/black/yellow   **Previous League:** Central Mids (until 1992).

HOLWELL SPORTS
Secretary: Mrs C W Warner, 40 Klondyke Way, Asfordby, Melton Mowbray, Leics LE14 3TW (0664 812010).
Ground: Welby Road, Asfordby Hill, Melton Mowbray, Leics (0664 812663)
Directions: One and a half miles out of Melton Mowbray on A607 to Loughborough.
Previous Name: Holwell Works   **Cols:** Green & gold/green/green & gold   **Floodlights:** Yes.
Hons: Leics Snr Lg 11-12 86-87 91-92 92-93 (Div 1 84-85, Tebbutt Brown Cup R-up 92-93), Leics Snr Cup 54-55 56-57 57-58.

IBSTOCK WELFARE
Secretary: R A Wilkinson, 6 Valley Rd, Ibstock, Leicester LE67 6NY (0530 260744).
Ground: The Welfare, Leicester Road, Ibstock (0530 260656).   **Colours:** All red.

LEICESTERSHIRE CONSTABULARY
Secretary: Mrs Judith Leacy, 6 Lena Drive, Groby, Leicester LE6 0FJ (0530 243110).
Colours: Yellow/green/green   **Ground:** Police WQ, St Johns, Enderby (0533 482198).

Dean Culpin rolls in Anstey Nomad's final goal in a 4-2 win over Cottesmore in the Second Round of the Jelson Leicestershire Senior Cup on 7th November. Photo - Rob Ruddock.

LUTTERWORTH TOWN

Secretary: B J Davies, 20 Riverside Rd, Lutterworth, Leics LE17 4BP (0455 554652).
Ground: Hall Lane, Bitteswell, Lutterworth, Leics (0455 554046)
Directions: M6 jct 1 or M1 jct 20, follow A426 through Lutterworth; Bitteswell signposted one and a half miles on beyond town.
Seats: None   **Cover:** None   **Capacity:** 3,000   **Floodlights:** Yes   **Founded:** 1890.
Previous Ground: Dunley Way (pre-1991) **Programme:** 24 pages with admission.
Colours: White/navy/navy
Clubhouse: Normal licensing hours   **Hons:** Leics Snr Lg 90-91 (Div 2 80-81).

NEWFOUNDPOOL W.M.C.

Secretary: Mrs C J Nixon, 6 Oakleigh Avenue, Glen Parva, Leicester LE12 9TH (0533 779332).
Ground: Meadow Lane, Birstall (0533 673965).   **Colours:** Green & yellow stripes/green/green & yellow.
Directions: Off Wanlip Lane, Birstall. First of two ground in Meadow Lane.
Hons: Leics Snr Lg 65-66 69-70 (Div 2 82-83), Leics Snr Cup 68-69.

NORTH KILWORTH

Secretary: R Bell, High Street, North Kilworth, Lutterworth, Leics LE17 6ET (0858 464048)(Steve Bell).
Ground: Rugby Road, North Kilworth, Lutterworth, Leics (0858 880890).
Colours: All blue   **Hons:** Leics Snr Lg Div 2 R-up 91-92.

OADBY TOWN

Secretary: D P Collins, 26 Hill Way, Oadby, Leics LE2 5YG (0533 713557).
Ground: Invicta Park, Wigston Road, Oadby, Leics (0533 715728)
Directions: Oadby is four miles south of Leicester on A6. From Oadby church in town centre follow signs for Wigston; ground three quarters of a mile on left.
Seats: None   **Cover:** 200   **Capacity:** 2,000   **Prog:** 20 pages   **Founded:** 1939.
Colours: All red   **Clubhouse:** Matchdays only
Hons: Leics Snr Lg 63-64 67-68 68-69 72-73 (Div 2 51-52), Leics Snr Cup 62-63 63-64 75-76 76-77 80-81.

ST ANDREWS SOCIAL CLUB

Secretary: Martin Wilson, 3 Ainsdale Rd, Western Park, Leicester LE3 0UD (0533 858227).
Ground: Canal Street, Old Aylestone, Leicester (0533 839298).
Directions: Aylestone Rd at rear of Granby Street School.
Colours: Black & white/black/red   **Hons:** Leics Snr Lg 89-90 (Tebbutt Brown Cup 92-93).

SYSTON ST PETERS

Secretary: Alan Walton, 73 Broad Str., Syston, Leicester (0533 696773).
Ground: Memorial Ground, Necton Street, Syston, Leics (0533 695922).
Directions: A607 Leicester-Melton Mowbray road, on entering Syston take 1st fork left into Broad Street after railway bridge. Necton Street is third left.
Colours: Red & black stripes/black/black   **Hons:** Leics Snr Lg 61-62 (Div 2 60-61).

WIGSTON FIELDS

Manager: Don Ludden   **Reserves' Manager:** Stewart Ryan/ Nick Smith.
Secretary: Malc Jelley, 35 Copinger Road, Aylestone Park, Leicester LE2 6LF (0533 838475).
Ground: Windsor Avenue, Glen Parva, Leicester (0533 771039).   **Nickname:** Fields
Colours: All red   **Founded:** 1947   **Previous League:** Leics Snr/ Midland Comb. 91-93.
Clubhouse: Yes   **Cover:** No.

DIVISION ONE CLUBS 1992-93

ANSTEY TOWN

Secretary: G Ford, Hollow Rd, Anstey, Leics LE7 7FR (0533 364170).
Ground: Leicester Road, Thurcaston (0533 368231)   **Colours:** All blue

ASFORDBY AMATEURS

Secretary: Miss Sue Johnson, 61 Swallowdale Rd, Melton Mowbray, Leics LE13 0AU (0664 68690).
Ground: Hoby Road Sports Ground, Asfordby, Melton Mowbray (0664 434545).
Colours: Green/black/black

AYLESTONE PARK OLD BOYS

Secretary: Brendon Tyrrell, 8 Melbourne Close, Kibworth, Beauchamp, Leicester LE8 0JP (0533 793136).
Ground: Dorset Avenue, Fairfield Estate, Wigston, Leics (0533 775307)
Colours: All red.   **Floodlights:** Yes.

BLABY & WHETSTONE ATHLETIC

Secretary: Mrs S C Morris, 10 Winchester Road, Blaby, Leics LE8 3HJ (0533 773208).
Ground: Blaby & Whetstone Boys Club, Warwick Road, Whetstone (0533 864852).   **Colours:** All blue

EARL SHILTON ALBION

Secretary: Paul Groom, 46 Grass Acres, Leicester LE3 2UQ (0533 890485).
Ground: Stoneycroft Park, New Street, Earl Shilton, Leics (0455 842056).
Colours: All green   **Hons:** Leics Snr Lg Div 2 68-69 79-80 88-89, Leics Snr Cup 72-73.

FOSSE IMPS

Secretary: I V Colbourne, 55 Harrowgate Drive, Birstall, Leics LE4 3GQ (0533 671424).
Ground: Co-op Grnd, Birstall, Leicester (0533 674059)   **Colours:** Red/white/black

HARBOROUGH TOWN IMPERIAL

Secretary: Gary Waterfield, 4 Lindsey Gdns, Market Harborough, Leics LE16 9JF (0858 431620).
Ground: Imperial Park, Northampton Road Sports Ground, Market Harborough, Leics.
Colours: Red & black stripes/black/black **Hons:** Leics Snr Lg Div 1 83-84.
Previous Ground: St Mary's Road (until 1992).

HILLCROFT

Secretary: Bruce Parry, 43 Blenheim Rd, Birstall, Leicester LE4 4FP (0533 677293).
Ground: Lawrence Park, Gipsy Lane, Leicester (0533 461209)   **Colours:** Yellow & blue/blue/blue.

HOUGHTON RANGERS

Secretary: J P Silver, Red Roofs, 41 Main Street, Houghton-on-the-Hill, Leics LE7 9GE (0533 433951).
Ground: Weir Lane, Houghton-on-the-Hill, Leics (0533 419551).
Colours: Blue/white/white   **Hons:** Leics Snr Lg Div 2 90-91.

HUNCOTE SPORTS & SOCIAL

Secretary: D Russell, 72 Sycamore Way, Littlethorpe, Leics LE9 5HU (0533 841952).
Ground: Enderby Lane, Thurlaston, Leics (0455 24430).   **Colours:** All blue.

KIRBY MUXLOE S.C.

Secretary: R Pallett, 184 Blackbird Road, Leicester LE4 0AF (0533 626020).
Ground: Ratby Lane, Kirby Muxloe (0533 393201)   **Colours:** All blue.

LEICESTER Y.M.C.A.

Secretary: C W Chappell, 132 South Knighton Road, Leicester LE2 3LQ (0533 702721).
Ground: Belvoir Drive, Aylestone, Leicester (0533 440740)   **Colours:** Red/white/red

LOUGHBOROUGH DYNAMO

Secretary: R M Hutchinson, 3 Wythburn Close, Loughborough, Leics LE11 3SZ (0509 266092).
Ground: Nanpanton Sport Ground, Loughborough (0509 612144).
Colours: Gold/black/gold.   **Clubhouse:** Yes   **Cover:** Yes   **Programme:** Yes.

NARBOROUGH & LITTLETHORPE

Secretary: B Garner, 7 Riverside Court, Station Rd, Littlethorpe, Leics LE9 5LU (0533 867362).
Ground: Leicester Road, Narborough (Near M1 bridge) (0533 751855).
Directions: M1 jct 21, follow signs to Narborough (2 miles).
Colours: All blue   **Hons:** Leics Snr Lg Div 2 81-82.

QUORN

Secretary: W L Caunt, 64 Wood Lane, Quorn, Leics LE12 8DB (0509 414213).
Ground: Warwick Avenue, Quorn, Leics (0509 620490). *N.B. this ground has been sold and must be vacated by Christmas - the club will move to a new ground during the 93-94 season.*
Directions: A607 Leicester-Melton Mowbray road, on entering Syston take 1st fork left into Broad Street after railway bridge. Necton Street is third left.
Colours: Red/white/red   **Hons:** Leics Snr Cup 53-54.

RAVENSTONE

Secretary: Robert Brooks, 17 Ashland Drive, Coalville, Leics LE67 3NH (0530 833269).
Ground: Ravenslea Estate, Ravenstone, Leics.
Directions: A607 Leicester-Melton Mowbray road, on entering Syston take 1st fork left into Broad Street after railway bridge. Necton Street is third left.
Programme: 20 pages, 50p with entry   **Prev. Lge:** Nth Leics (pre-1992)   **Cover:** No.
Colours: Yellow & blue/blue/yellow.

SILEBY TOWN

Secretary: G Clarke, 123 Highgate Road, Sileby, Leics LE12 7PW (0509 813503).
Ground: Memorial Park, Seagrave Road, Sileby, Leics (0509 816104)
Colours: All blue.   **Hons:** Leics Snr Lg Div 1 R-up 92-93.

THRINGSTONE MINERS WELFARE

Secretary: Paul A Nelson, 30 Bardon Rd, Coalville, Leics (0530 838694).
Ground: Homestead Road, Thringstone (0530 223367).
Colours: Gold/black/gold.   **Hons:** Leics Snr Lg 84-85 (Div 2 71-72).

UNITED COLLIERIES

Secretary: John Meason, 29 Standard Hill, Coalville, Leics LE67 3HN (0530 810941).
Ground: Station Rd, Bagworth.
Previous Names: Bagworth Colliery/ Ellistown Colliery - clubs merged in 1993.
Colours: Yellow/royal/royal.

LEICESTER & DISTRICT LEAGUE

PREM. DIVISION	P	W	D	L	F	A	PTS
Saffron Dynamoes	26	18	4	4	83	32	58
G E C	26	17	6	3	80	30	57
Croxton Kerrial *	26	17	1	8	67	40	49
Uppingham Town	26	16	4	7	61	36	49
Cosby United	26	13	2	11	66	47	41
Greetham	26	12	5	9	53	53	41
Blaby United	26	11	6	9	55	62	39
British Shoe	26	9	11	6	54	44	38
Birstall RBL	26	9	7	10	48	52	34
Glenfield Town	26	10	0	16	41	56	30
Dunton Bassett	26	8	5	13	43	57	29
Stoney Stanton	26	8	4	14	41	52	28
Thurmaston	26	3	3	20	30	98	12
Thurnby Utd *	26	2	2	22	38	101	5

8 - 3pts deducted.

DIVISION ONE	P	W	D	L	F	A	PTS
G & D United	28	20	6	2	102	26	66
Syston Town	28	19	6	3	87	32	63
City Gas	28	16	4	8	75	40	52
Sapcote United	28	15	6	7	88	62	51
South Golding	28	14	7	7	84	49	49
Epworth	28	12	10	6	53	41	46
County Hall	28	13	6	9	70	46	45
Heather	28	12	6	10	61	53	42
Flackney	28	11	6	11	64	88	39
Newbold Jubilee	28	10	5	13	58	69	35
Frisby United	28	8	4	16	52	65	28
Tungstone	28	8	4	16	51	65	28
Dainite	28	4	5	19	35	86	17
Welby Ln.	28	3	5	20	39	87	14
Apollo	28	4	2	22	26	136	14

'BREW XI' NUNEATON & DIST. AMATEUR LEAGUE

'Brew XI' Premier Division

	P	W	D	L	F	A	PTS
Attleborough Libs	21	15	2	4	61	23	*49
Collycroft Spts	21	13	5	3	64	18	*46
Raiders	21	9	8	4	58	34	&34
N'ton Griff & Coton	21	8	6	7	55	40	30
Attleborough Labour	21	8	5	8	36	39	29
Nuneaton Ex-Service	21	7	6	8	40	43	&26
Woodlands W.M.C.	21	6	4	11	45	63	22
Brooklyn P.M.C.	21	0	0	21	28	122	0

* - 2pts awarded
& - 1pt deducted

'Shiltons of Coventry' Division One

	P	W	D	L	F	A	PTS
Newdigate Spts	18	17	1	0	71	29	52
Haunchwood Inst.	18	13	1	4	55	27	40
3M Sports	18	12	0	6	56	29	36
Collycroft S. Res.	18	11	0	7	44	36	36
Raiders Res.	18	10	2	6	44	34	*29
Att. Libs Res.	18	9	1	8	61	48	28
Att. Labour Res.	18	5	0	13	32	63	&18
Nuneaton Co-op Spts	18	5	1	12	42	56	16
Horseshoes Inn	18	3	1	14	28	48	10
Coton Liberals	18	1	1	16	30	89	4

& - 3pts awarded   * - 3pts deducted

ANSELLS BIRMINGHAM WORKS & COMBINATION

PREM. DIV.

	P	W	D	L	F	A	PTS
Continental Star	18	14	3	1	55	16	31
Ansells (Aston)	20	12	4	4	62	38	28
Kwik Save	17	10	3	4	40	26	23
Civil Service Spts	19	8	4	7	29	43	20
Swan Sports	17	7	6	4	59	28	20
Hamstead Social	20	7	4	9	41	40	18
Monica Star Res.	16	4	6	6	23	32	14
Blackheath Town	18	5	3	10	38	47	13
Harborne Harriers	18	4	5	9	35	65	13
Wonder Vaults	19	3	5	13	24	50	9
Smethwick Rangers	16	2	5	9	25	46	9

Singh Bros withdrew - records expunged

DIV. ONE

	P	W	D	L	F	A	PTS
Shere Punjab	12	7	2	3	30	21	16
Greenman (Crofton)	12	6	3	3	37	26	15
Oakland	11	4	3	4	27	30	11
Tudor Webasto	11	1	2	8	22	39	4

N.T. Minerva withdrew - records expunged

DIV. TWO

	P	W	D	L	F	A	PTS
Holly Lane S. & S.	20	16	1	3	104	25	33
Continental S. Res.	19	15	1	3	62	27	31
Ansells (Perry Bar)	20	10	5	5	65	57	25
Lucas Marston Green	18	10	3	5	62	40	23
Swan Sports 'A'	16	8	3	5	57	43	19
F.C.S. Laser	17	5	5	7	36	43	15
Zion	15	5	3	7	34	56	13
Bantry Rovers	19	5	2	12	41	56	12
Green Star	18	3	4	11	31	59	10
Cornerstone Emman.	15	2	4	9	32	63	8
Gilby United	15	1	1	13	27	86	3

DIV. THREE

	P	W	D	L	F	A	PTS
Lozells G.M.A.	12	7	3	2	55	22	17
Engine White Star	12	7	3	2	27	17	17
The Bear XI	12	6	3	3	41	18	15
Singh Bros 'A'	12	3	5	4	25	20	11
Tudor Webasto Res.	12	3	3	6	16	30	9
Langley Oak	12	4	1	7	22	42	9
James Upton	12	2	2	8	21	58	6

Cabrizzi International withdrew - records expunged

WORCESTER & DISTRICT LEAGUE

PREM. DIV.

	P	W	D	L	F	A	PTS
Cooksons	26	17	3	6	58	29	37
Tewkesbury YMCA	26	16	4	6	73	43	36
Golden Cross	26	14	3	9	72	43	31
Chequers Fladbury	26	13	5	8	53	48	31
Inkberrow	26	11	8	7	47	33	30
Malvern Rangers	26	12	5	9	58	51	29
Ross United	26	12	4	10	53	44	28
Droitwich	26	11	4	11	57	56	26
Feckenham United	26	7	8	11	50	45	22
St Richards O.B.	26	9	4	13	58	84	22
Hereford Lads Club	26	7	7	12	48	52	21
Hallow W.M.C.	26	7	6	13	31	51	20
Malvern Radar	26	9	1	16	41	69	19
Littleton	26	5	2	19	33	86	12

PREMIER DIVISION CLUBS
(Tel. codes 0905 unless stated)

CHEQUERS FLADBURY
Ground: Station Rd Rec
Sec: M Anderson (0386 870540)

COOKSONS
G: Checketts Lane, Droitwich Rd, Worcester
S: T Goodwin (420916)

DROITWICH
G: Salwarpe Valley PF   S: S Duggan (774854)

FECKENHAM UNITED
G: Mill Lane   S: M Hawkes (0527 893341)

GOLDEN CROSS
G: Charford PF, Churchfields, Bromsgrove
S: C Stenton (0527 73059)

HALLOW W.M.C.
G: Hallow PF, Main Rd   S: D Lowe (58996)

HEREFORD LADS CLUB
G: Widemarsh Common   S: A Morrison (354652)

INKBERROW
G: Sands Rd PF   S: G Keir (0527 404359)

LITTLETON
G: Five Acres, Pebworth Rd, Nth Littleton
S: M Malin (0386 858313)

MALVERN RADAR
G: Victoria Pk PF, Malvern Link
S: S Harness (0684 576012)

MALVERN RANGERS
G: As Malvern Radar   S: B Burge (0684 574005)

ROSS UNITED
G: Ross-on-Wye Spts Centre, Wilton Rd
S: M Davies (0989 65426)

ST RICHARDS OLD BOYS
G: King George PF, Salwarpe, Droitwich
S: J Ricketts (554428)

TEWKESBURY Y.M.C.A.
G: Vineyard PF, Gloucester Rd
S: T Neather (0684 297023)

DIV. ONE

	P	W	D	L	F	A	PTS
B.S.K.	20	17	2	1	84	26	36
Kempsey	20	13	1	6	43	37	27
Perrywood	20	11	3	6	52	37	25
Barbourne	20	11	3	6	49	43	23
Pershore T. 'A'	20	9	1	10	41	45	19
Tewkesbury Res.	20	8	2	10	41	53	18
Pershore	20	8	2	10	25	49	18
Martley	20	7	1	12	44	49	15
Upton Town Res.	20	6	3	11	34	46	13
Nelson	20	5	3	12	31	47	13
Avondale	20	4	1	15	22	43	9

DIV. TWO

	P	W	D	L	F	A	PTS
Bromsbury	24	19	3	2	87	32	41
Ashchurch	24	19	2	3	74	29	40
County Sports	24	17	2	5	65	24	34
Hallow W.M.C. Res.	24	14	5	5	59	34	33
All Blacks	24	12	3	9	53	37	27
Powick	24	9	6	9	65	52	24
Tewkesbury 'A'	24	11	2	11	52	52	24
Malvern Res.	24	10	3	10	47	53	23
Comer Green	24	6	7	10	25	33	19
Malvern V.	24	6	2	15	41	67	14
Cromwells	24	5	2	17	56	90	12
Vine Athletic	24	3	4	17	33	89	10
West Malvern	24	2	1	20	27	94	5

REFUGE ASSURANCE
STAFFORDSHIRE SENIOR LEAGUE

President: P Keller

Chairman: F Askey   **Vice-Chairman:** A Key

Secretary: J K Johnson, 149 St Nicholas Ave.,
Norton, Stoke-on-Trent ST6 8JW (0782 534866)

Stafford Town, who last season lost out on goal difference, were firm favourites to take their first title with champions Redgate Clayton expected to do well. Fancied outsiders were Norton United while Walsall Wood, from the Midland Combination, were not expected to go all the way. Before the season got started the League were surprised and disappointed to receive the resignation of Stafford Rangers Reserves, leaving the it with an odd club.

Yet again the early pacesetters were Audley but in September they relinquished pole position never to regain it. Norton took over, and with the exception of one week in January, kept it until the final game of the season. Milton United promised much, but invariably failed against teams they were expected to do well against, too many draws yo-yoing them up and down the table. Staffordshire Police deposed Norton in January, but from that date they went downwards, losing eight of the last twelve games to end in a disappointing mid-table position.

One team who made excellent progress through the season were Goldenhill Wanderers, a mediocre first quarter was followed by an undefeated run of thirteen games, during which they held the leaders and obtained wins at Redgate and Stafford, earning praise for the quality of their football. The young teams fielded by Leek CSOB always gave 100% effort, but although finishing a creditable eighth needed an older head on occasions. Despite lacking this factor they twice defeated Walsall Wood at Oak Park, ending Walsall's interest in the cup at the first hurdle.

Last season's re-elected clubs were again struggling to make an impression. Hanford hit the foot of the table mid September and thereafter never vacated the spot. Ball Haye Green did have a three-pronged tussle with Rists United, Eccleshall and Brereton Social before finally joining Hanford in the re-election zone.

As the season entered its final quarter, Norton were strongly entrenched at the top of the table. 23 games had gone and United were still unbeaten in league and cup, then all of a sudden the balloon burst. Defeats in consecutive weeks saw them dismissed from two cup competitions and this bad run continued with a barren spell in the league. Drawn games at Heath Hayes and Leek were followed by reverses at Brocton and Walsall Wood. The title chase was no longer a one horse race. Stafford Town and Redgate were back in the reckoning, while Norton's destiny was no longer in their own hands. As the season wore on Stafford cracked, and only Redgate Clayton stood in Norton United's way.

Four games to play from which full points were a necessity; Norton having completed their fixtures could only sweat it out, and it was at this point that Redgate's ability to score vital goals at the death came to the fore. At Brereton Social they got the only goal thirty seconds from time while it was even closer against Brocton; a penalty in injury time.

The final game arrived, away to Stafford Town, who with just three games to go were themselves contemplating top honours. Redgate turned on the style and had the game won by half-time. If only for their efforts over the last few games, where nothing less than victory was good enough, the 'Gate' earned their honour.   **J K Johnson, Hon. Secretary**

Redgate Clayton F.C., Staffordshire Senior League Champions. Photo - Staffs Sentinel.

FINAL TABLE	P	W	D	L	F	A	PTS
Redgate Clayton	32	25	4	3	99	30	79
Norton United	32	24	6	2	74	30	78
Stafford Town	32	22	4	6	89	36	70
Walsall Wood	32	18	6	8	61	38	60
Milton United	32	17	6	9	59	45	57
Goldenhilll Wdrs	32	14	11	7	61	46	53
Brocton	32	16	4	12	62	50	52
Leek C.S.O.B.	32	13	7	12	60	52	46
Staffs Police	32	11	9	12	55	55	42
Congleton Hornets	32	12	5	15	55	72	41
Heath Hayes	32	10	8	14	37	55	38
Audley	32	10	5	17	40	66	35
Brereton Social	32	8	4	20	46	71	28
Eccleshall	32	7	6	19	40	60	27
Rists United	32	6	7	19	41	66	25
Ball Haye Green	32	5	7	20	36	78	22
Hanford	32	3	3	26	29	94	12

RESULT CHART

HOME TEAM	1	2	3	4	5	6	7	8	9	10	11	12	13	14	15	16	17
1. Audley	*	2-1	0-4	1-4	2-0	3-0	1-1	3-2	0-1	2-4	0-1	2-3	0-4	2-0	1-2	1-3	2-0
2. Ball Haye Green	2-3	*	0-2	2-3	0-2	2-0	1-1	0-1	0-2	1-2	1-1	0-3	2-7	2-2	0-5	0-5	1-0
3. Brereton Social	0-0	5-0	*	1-0	2-3	2-4	1-2	1-1	1-1	0-2	1-2	0-2	0-1	1-3	0-1	1-7	4-2
4. Brocton	2-1	1-1	1-4	*	5-2	2-2	1-4	2-1	0-1	1-0	3-0	3-0	3-1	2-4	2-2	3-1	1-3
5. Congleton Hornets	5-2	1-0	2-0	4-3	*	4-0	1-3	3-0	1-0	0-7	1-4	1-2	1-1	3-1	2-3	1-1	2-2
6. Eccleshall	2-3	1-2	2-2	1-3	4-1	*	1-1	5-0	4-0	2-1	1-2	0-2	0-2	2-1	1-2	0-1	1-2
7. Goldenhill Wanderers	1-2	1-2	7-2	1-1	2-0	0-0	*	4-2	6-2	2-1	0-0	2-2	0-5	1-1	5-4	3-0	1-1
8. Hanford	1-2	0-7	2-1	1-6	6-1	0-2	0-2	*	2-2	0-1	0-2	2-4	2-3	0-1	0-1	1-3	1-2
9. Heath Hayes	2-1	3-1	4-2	0-1	1-1	1-1	4-1	2-1	*	1-1	0-1	2-2	0-1	1-1	0-5	4-3	2-2
10. Leek C.S.O.B.	1-0	0-0	5-0	1-4	0-2	5-1	0-3	4-0	4-0	*	1-2	0-0	1-5	3-2	0-3	3-1	0-1
11. Milton United	2-1	1-1	4-2	3-0	2-1	2-0	2-1	5-0	1-0	1-1	*	0-0	1-4	7-1	2-4	1-2	3-5
12. Norton United	4-0	1-0	3-2	3-1	3-2	2-1	2-0	5-1	4-1	4-4	3-1	*	0-0	1-0	3-0	4-1	2-1
13. Redgate Clayton	6-0	5-2	5-2	1-0	7-0	4-1	1-2	5-1	2-1	5-0	5-1	0-1	*	3-1	1-1	2-2	4-1
14. Rists United	0-1	5-2	0-2	0-2	2-4	1-1	0-1	0-0	1-3	1-2	3-1	1-4	1-3	*	1-1	1-1	2-4
15. Stafford Town	4-0	5-1	2-0	0-2	3-1	4-1	1-1	9-0	5-0	4-2	3-0	0-1	1-3	2-1	*	5-0	4-3
16. Staffs Police	1-1	6-2	1-2	3-0	2-2	1-0	1-1	2-0	1-0	2-2	0-3	1-4	1-2	0-3	1-2	*	1-1
17. Walsall Wood	3-0	3-0	2-0	1-0	2-0	2-0	4-1	4-2	1-0	1-2	1-1	1-0	0-1	4-0	2-1	0-0	*

LEAGUE CUP RESULTS 1992-93

First Round
Walsall Wood v Leek C.S.O.B.   3-4

Second Round
Brereton Social v Milton United	1-1,1-7		Brocton v Eccleshall	1-1,1-0
Goldenhill Wanderers v Rists United	3-1		Hanford v Congleton Hornets	1-4
Norton United v Heath Hayes	1-0		Redgate Clayton v Ball Haye Green	4-0
Staffordshire Police v Audley	1-6		Leek C.S.O.B. v Stafford Town	0-1

Third Round
Brocton v Audley	4-2		Milton United v Norton United	3-4
Redgate Clayton v Goldenhill Wdrs	1-1,1-0		Stafford Town v Congleton Hornets	6-0

Semi-Finals
Brocton v Redgate Clayton 1-1,2-2 *(away g/s)*   Stafford Town v Norton United   0-1

Final *(Eastwood Hanley FC, 26/4/93)*: Brocton 2, Norton United 1

Brocton F.C. - pictured before their League Cup final win over Norton. A penalty three minutes from time gave them their first silverware since joining the League. Norton could have no complaints for it was a penalty that had given them the cup twelve months earlier. Photo - Colin Stevens.

AUDLEY
Ground: Old Road, Bignall End. **Prog.:** Yes **Founded:** 1985
Secretary: Alan Smith, Frensham, Newfold Cres., Brown Edge, Stoke-on-Trent ST6 8QZ (0782 782108).
Manager: Terry Greer **Colours:** Red/navy/red **Hons:** Lg Cup 89-90

BALL HAYE GREEN
Ground: Rear Balle Haye Green WMC, Leek. **Founded:** 1880
Secretary: Michael Naylor, 27 Wallbridge Close, Leek ST13 8HZ (0538 383711). **Prog.:**
Manager: Peter Booth **Colours:** Green & white/green/green **Hons:** Lg Cup R-up 89-90

BRERETON SOCIAL
Ground: Armitage Lane, Rugeley (0889 585526). **Founded:** 1899
Secretary: David J Rowley, 32 Lodge Rd, Brereton, Rugeley WS15 1HG (0889 583000).
Manager: Michael Morris **Colours:** Red & white/red/red &white **Prog.:** Yes

BROCTON
Ground: Rowley Park Stadium, Stafford (0785 51060). **Prog.:** Yes **Founded:** 1937
Secretary: T J Homer, 124 John Street, Chadsmoor, Cannock WS11 2HR (0543 571964).
Manager: T R Cook **Colours:** Green & white/white/green & white **Hons:** Lg Cup 92-93.

CANNOCK TOWN
Chairman: Gary Richards **Manager:** Robert Brookes **Founded:** 1991
Secretary: John Bradbury, 10 South Close, Cannock WS11 1EH (0543 503877) **Prog.:** Yes
Ground: Littleton Miners Welfare Centre, Avon Rd, Cannock (on left of left of A460 200yds from town centre).
Cover: No **Capacity:** 1,000 **Floodlights:** No **Clubhouse:** Yes
Colours: Black & green/black/black. **Change colours:** Yellow/blue/yellow.
Prev. Lge: Staffs Co. Lg (South) 91-93 **Hons:** Staffs Co. (Sth) Lg R-up 92-93 (Premier Cup 92-93, Div 1 91-92), Bloxwich Charity Cup 92-93, Walsall Challenge Cup R-up 91-92 92-93.

CONGLETON TOWN HORNETS
Ground: Booth Street, Congleton (0260 274460). **Founded:** 1896
Secretary: David Wilcock, 9 Maxwell Road, Congleton, Cheshire CW12 3HY (0260 276347).
Manager: Alan Hughes **Colours:** Black & white/black/black.

ECCLESHALL
Ground: Pershall Park, Near Eccleshall. **Founded:** 1971
Secretary: Jed C Atkins, 30 School Road, Eccleshall ST21 6AS (0785 851016). **Prog.:** Yes
Manager: Barry Lowe **Colours:** Green & white/green/green **Hons:** Champs 89-90.

GOLDENHILL WANDERERS
Ground: Shelford Road, Sandyford (0782 811977). **Founded:** 1885
Secretary: Michael J Goodwin, 4 Russell Place, Sandyford ST6 5LS (0782 824838). **Prog.:** Yes
Manager: Bryan Finney **Colours:** Blue/white/blue **Hons:** Lg Cup R-up 85-86

HANFORD
Ground: Trentmill Road, Hanley. **Founded:** 1959
Secretary: Ian Bradbury, 9 Frenchmore Grove, Lightwood, Longton ST3 7SF (0782 341877).
Manager: Ken Hughes **Colours:** All red **Prog.:**

HEATH HAYES
Ground: Newlands Lane, Heath Hayes. **Founded:** 1965
Secretary: Peter J Francis, 191 Hednesford Road, Heath Hayes (0543 274212).
Manager: Dennis Killbride **Colours:** Blue & white/blue/blue **Prog.:** Yes

LEEK C.S.O.B.
Ground: Leek Town FC (see Northern Premier League). **Founded:** 1945
Secretary: Neil Ogden, 11 Moorfields, Leek ST13 5LU (0538 384281).
Manager: Chris McMullin **Colours:** Red/white/white **Prog.:** Yes

MILTON UNITED
Ground: Leek Road, Milton End. **Founded:** 1985
Secretary: Maurice Sherratt, 3 Clifford Avenue, Norton Green (0782 533775). **Prog.:** Yes
Manager: Barry Flint **Colours:** Blue & white/white/white **Hons:** Lg R-up 84-85 (Lg Cup 87-87 88-89).

NORTON UNITED
Ground: Community Drive, Smallthorne (0782 838290). **Founded:** 1989
Sec.: Dennis Vickers, 86 Ford Green Road, Smallthorne, S.-on-T. ST6 1NX (0782 822727) **Prog.:** Yes
Manager: Neil Dundas **Colours:** Red & black/black/black
Hons: Lg R-up 92-93 (Lg Cup 91-92 (R-up 92-93)).

PARKWAY CLAYTON
Ground: As Newcastle Town FC (see Bass North West Counties Lge) **Founded:** 1964
Sec: Trevor Wilson, 6 Clough Hall Drive, Talke, S.-on-T. ST7 1UT (0782 784212) **Prog.:** Yes
Manager: Glyn Chamberlain **Colours:** Blue/white/blue.

REDGATE CLAYTON
Ground: Northwood Lane, Clayton, Newcastle-under-Lyme (0782 717409). **Founded:** 1969
Directions: M6 jct 15, left for Newcastle, past Post House Hotel, ground on right at 1st r'bout.
Secretary: Roger Farr, 9 Winnipeg Close, Trentham ST4 8UE (0782 641334). **Prog.:** Yes
Manager: Brian Nettleton **Colours:** Red/blue/red **Nickname:** Gate
Previous Name: Manor Park **Prev. Grounds:** St Josephs College 84-87/ Oldfields Spts Grnd
Hons: Champs 87-88 91-92 92-93 (Lg Cup 90-91 (R-up 87-88 91-92)), Walsall Snr Cup 87-88, Staffs Vase 91-92.

RISTS UNITED
Ground: Lower Milehouse Lane, Newcastle-under-Lyme (0782 563366). **Founded:** 1956
Secretary: Graham Michael Rutter, 46 James Street, Wolstanton ST5 0BX (0782 619567).
Manager: Stephen Smith **Colours:** All green **Prog.:** Yes

STAFFORDSHIRE POLICE
Ground: Silkmore Lane, Stafford (0785 58386). **Prog.:** Yes **Founded:** 1953
Secretary: Chris Haines, Police House, Blythe Bridge Rd, Caverswall, Stoke-on-Trent ST11 9ET (0782 397678).
Manager: Peter Dent **Colours:** Red/black/red **Hons:** Lg Cup 87-88 (R-up 86-87)

Norton United - runners-up in the Staffordshire Senior League and League Cup. Photo - Colin Stevens.

Staffordshire Police, pictured in front of the smart pavillion at Silkmore Lane.

A sad farewell to Marston Green F.C. who have been forced to resign their place in the Midland Combination because of problems with their ground at Hurley Daw Mill. Back Row (L/R): Russell Roberts, Andy Packer, Paul Forman, Andre Marriner, Les Carroll, Mark Hunt, Steve Grady, Des Seivwright, Beau Chambers. Front: Tim Stacey, Pat Dunne, Dave Keen, Martin Edwards, Mark Hodson, John Brimble.

STAFFORDSHIRE
COUNTY LEAGUE (SOUTH)

President: Mr W Davis   **Vice-Chairman:** Mr R Smart

Secretary: Mr A Payne,
7 Norton Canes, Cannock WS11 3QZ (0543 279080)

Bilston Community College claimed their fourth successive Premier Division title, in the final week of the season, after trailing runners-up Cannock Town for eight months of the campaign. The college club also had an extended run in the Walsall Senior Cup, which ended at the semi-final stage in a thrilling match with Pelsall Villa. Cannock Town did, however, have the satisfaction of beating the new champions in the final of the Premier Trophy, at Chasetown on 11th May.

In the most exciting finish to Division One for many years, Mahal took the title on goal difference from West Bromwich B.H. Mahal lost in their last game of the season, but surprisingly so did West Brom, to 'wooden spoonists' Rocket Pool. Cup specialists Rugeley Athletic won the Divisional Cup, the Ike Cooper Trophy, beating Mahal in the final.

Of the external cup competitions, G.E.C. Stafford collected the Penkridge Charity Cup, Cannock Town won the Bloxwich Charity Cup and West Bromwich B.H. won the West Bromwich Charity Cup.

This season the League will officially become part of the Pyramid, being a regional feeder to the West Midlands (Regional) League. This will go some way, we hope, to untangling the 'pyramuddle' that has existed in Staffordshire for far too long. The announcement has caused, as expected, an exodus of clubs who fear that if they do not move now they may not have a club good enough to do so for a good while. The League has, therefore, dissolved Division One for this season and is catering only for a Premier Division of sixteen clubs.

Alan Payne, League Secretary

PREM. DIV.	P	W	D	L	F	A	PTS
Bilston Com. C.	20	16	2	2	71	16	34
Cannock Town	20	14	3	3	63	34	31
Toll End Wesley	20	11	3	6	44	18	25
Brownhills Town	20	11	2	7	54	35	24
G.E.C. Stafford	20	11	1	6	57	35	23
Beechdale	20	10	3	7	44	37	23
Sikh Hunters	20	6	5	9	35	52	17
Lichfield Res.	20	7	2	11	39	57	16
Tipton Sports	20	5	3	12	28	47	13
Tipton Town Res.	20	3	2	10	32	80	8
Bloxwich Town Res.	20	1	4	15	14	70	6

Hawkins Sports *(withdraw - record expunged)*

DIV. ONE	P	W	D	L	F	A	PTS
Mahal	16	11	1	4	53	22	23
West Brom B.H.	16	9	5	2	47	29	23
Moxley Rgrs Res.	16	7	3	6	27	18	17
Mitchells & B. Res.	16	6	4	6	22	27	16
Walsall Wood Res.	16	7	2	7	28	34	16
Rugeley Athletic	16	4	7	5	26	28	15
Toll End Wes. Res.	16	4	5	7	33	44	13
Clancey Dudley	16	3	5	8	31	41	11
Rocket Pool	16	3	4	9	21	45	10

PREMIER DIVISION RESULT CHART 1992-93

HOME TEAM		1	2	3	4	5	6	7	8	9	10	11	12
1.	Bilston Community College	*	5-0	4-0	4-2	3-1	*	8-1	3-0	4-0	6-0	1-0	3-2
2.	Bloxwich Town Reserves	0-0	*	2-2	2-2	0-9	5-2	0-5	0-0	0-7	4-1	0-4	0-5
3.	Brownhills Town	2-1	5-0	*	0-8	2-3	*	2-0	1-3	3-0	12-1	1-3	4-0
4.	Cannock Town	2-7	4-1	2-1	*	2-1	*	2-0	4-1	5-0	5-2	2-1	5-1
5.	G.E.C. Stafford	1-4	1-0	1-3	6-0	*	4-1	1-1	2-5	4-0	4-1	2-0	4-1
6.	Hawkins Sports	*	*	2-8	*	7-2	*	*	*	*	0-4	2-6	4-3
7.	Lichfield Reserves	0-6	4-0	1-7	2-8	2-1	*	1-3	3-0	5-1	0-5	0-3	
8.	Sikh Hunters	1-4	2-1	1-2	1-2	1-4	*	4-4	*	1-1	4-3	0-5	0-5
9.	Tipton Sports	0-2	3-2	0-3	1-2	3-1	*	3-1	3-3	*	2-4	1-3	0-4
10.	Tipton Town Reserves	2-5	3-1	0-3	0-3	3-7	6-0	0-6	3-4	1-1	*	1-2	2-4
11.	Toll End Wesley	0-0	5-0	5-0	1-1	1-2	*	1-0	3-0	1-3	1-1	*	3-0
12.	Walsall M.A. *(Beechdale)*	2-1	3-1	1-1	2-2	3-2	*	2-3	1-1	1-0	1-4	3-1	*

N.B. Hawkins Sports withdrew - record expunged and shown for interest only.

DIVISION ONE RESULT CHART 1992-93

HOME TEAM		1	2	3	4	5	6	7	8	9
1.	Mahal	*	0-3	3-1	5-2	3-1	4-0	1-2	9-1	3-3
2.	Mitchells & Butlers Res.	0-1	*	0-1	1-1	0-0	1-0	1-8	0-1	3-2
3.	Moxley Rangers Reserves	0-2	0-1	*	2-1	1-1	9-0	1-2	1-0	4-3
4.	Toll End Wesley Reserves	3-6	2-3	2-1	*	3-2	3-3	2-2	2-1	3-3
5.	Rugeley Athletic	3-2	2-2	0-3	4-1	*	2-2	2-1	2-0	1-1
6.	Walsall Wood Reserves	2-1	1-2	1-0	4-1	2-1	*	2-3	2-1	3-1
7.	West Bromwich B.H.	1-4	4-2	0-0	3-4	3-3	3-0	*	4-4	2-1
8.	Clancey Dudley	0-7	1-1	1-2	3-2	1-1	3-2	1-1	*	3-5
9.	Rocket Pool	0-2	3-2	1-1	1-1	1-2	0-4	2-7	4-0	*

PREMIER TROPHY 1992-93

First Round

Cannock Town v Tipton Sports	7-0
Sikh Hunters v Bloxwich Town Reserves	3-1
Brownhills Town v Tipton Town Reserves	4-1

Quarter-Finals

Lichfield Reserves v Cannock Town	1-4
Walsall M.A. v Brownhills Town	0-2
Bilston Community College v G.E.C. Stafford	4-0
Toll End Wesley v Sikh Hunters	1-3

Semi-Finals

Cannock Town v Sikh Hunters	4-2
Brownhills Town v Bilston Community College	0-1

Final *(at Chasetown F.C. Tuesday 11th May 1993)*:
Cannock Town 3 *(Terry Brown 2, Paul Westwood)*, Bilston College 1 *(Loxley Brown)* Att: 222.

'IKE COOPER TROPHY' (DIVISION ONE CUP)

Group One
Rocket Pool 2, Mitchells & B. Res. 1
Rocket Pool 1, Toll End Wesley Res. 4
Clancey Dudley 4, Toll End W. Res. 3
Mitchells & B. Res. 2, Clancey Dudley 0
Mahal 1, Toll End Wesley Res. 2
Mahal 2, Clancey Dudley 1
Clancey Dudley 2, Rocket Pool 0
Mahal 5, Mitchells & Butlers Res. 0
Mahal 2, Rocket Pool 2
Mitchells & B. Res. 2, Toll End Res. 1

Group Two
Moxley Rgrs Res. 1, West Bromwich B.H. 3
Walsall Wood Res. 2, West Bromwich B.H. 0
Rugeley Ath. 3, Moxley Rangers Res. 2
Walsall Wood Res. 2, Moxley Rgrs Res. 1
Rugeley Ath. 3, West Bromwich B.H. 1
Walsall Wood 1, Rugeley Athletic 1

	P	W	D	L	F	A	PTS
Mahal	4	2	1	1	10	5	5
Toll End Wes. Res.	4	2	0	2	10	8	4
Clancey Dudley	4	2	0	2	7	7	4
Mitchells & B. Res	4	2	0	2	5	8	4
Rocket Pool	4	1	1	2	5	9	3

	P	W	D	L	F	A	PTS
Rugeley Athletic	3	2	1	0	7	4	5
Walsall Wood Res.	3	2	1	0	5	2	5
West Bromwich B.H.	3	1	0	2	4	6	2
Moxley Rgrs Res.	3	0	0	3	4	8	0

Semi-Finals
Rugeley Ath. v Toll End Wesley Res. 4-0 Walsall Wood Res. v Mahal 3-3(4-5 on pens)

Final *(at Yates Social F.C. Tuesday 18th May 1993):*
Rugeley Athletic 2 *(Steve Friberg, Glyn Baker)*, Mahal 0 *(attendance: 44)*

CLUB DIRECTORY

BEECHDALE

Chairman: Mark Neville **Manager:** Gary Blland **Founded:** 1984
Secretary: Mr S Platt, 14 Beddows Rd, Walsall (0922 723908)
Ground: Pleck Park, Walsall.
Directions: M6 jct 9, A461 towards Walsall, left at 1st lights into Montford Rd - entrance straight ahead.
Cover: No **Capacity:** 500 **Floodlights:** No **Clubhouse:** Yes **Programme:** No.
Colours: Blue & white/blue **Change colours:** Yellow & blue.
Previous Name: Walsall M.A. (pre-1993)
Hons: Staffs Co. (Sth) Lg Div 1 R-up 90-91 (Lge Shield 91-92, Edge Cup 90-91, Ike Cooper Tphy R-up 90-91).

BROWNHILLS TOWN

Chairman: Alan Payne **Manager:** Tim Wall **Founded:** 1957
Secretary: Mr C Kelly, School House, St Marks Rd, Shire Oak, Brownhills (0543 374193)
Physio: Steve Hughes **Trainer:** Paul Gibson.
Ground: Jubilee Park, Hanney Hay Rd, Hammerwich, Brownhills.
Directions: A5 Watling Street from Cannock towards Lichfield, thru lights by Chasewater Amusement Park, Hanney Rd 1st left after next lights.
Cover: No **Capacity:** 800 **Floodlights:** No **Programme:** 32 pages, 25p
Colours: Sky & white/blue/blue **Change colours:** Red & white/red
Clubhouse: Hospitality lounge only
Hons: Staffs Co. (Sth) Lg Div 1 R-up 91-92 (Lge Shield R-up 91-92), Cannock Charity Cup 90-91.

CLANCY

Chairman: W Mole **Founded:** 1971
Secretary: Mr P Wright, 35 Halesowen Rd, Warley, West Mids B65 5NA (0384 481518)
Ground: Ashtree Park, Hickmans Ave., Cradley Heath.
Directions: M5 jct 2, A4034 Oldbury Rd to Blackheath, right onto A4100 High Street (Powke Lane), left at island onto Garratts Lane, over lights into Reddal Hill Rd, Hickmans Ave is 1st right, ground entrance on right.
Cover: No **Capacity:** 800 **Floodlights:** No **Clubhouse:** No **Programme:** No.
Colours: Red/white/black **Change colours:** Blue/white/black.

G.E.C. STAFFORD

Chairman: Mr Clinton/ Mr Simmonds **Manager:** Kevin Downey **Founded:** 1965
Secretary: Mr R Daly, 17 Beechmount Rise, Wildwood, Stafford ST17 4QR (0785 54543).
Ground: G.E.C. Stychfields, Salt Ave., Stafford
Directions: M6 jct 13, A449 to Stafford, right into Hayrick Rd after railway bridge, right then left into Salt Avenue.
Cover: No **Capacity:** 1,000 **Floodlights:** No **Clubhouse:** Yes **Programme:** No.
Colours: Blue & white hoops/blue **Change colours:** Gold/black/black.

MAHAL

Secretary: Mr S S Pal, 1 St Georges (off Perry Str.), Smethwick, West Mids B66 1DN (021 565 4556)
Ground: Wood Lane Playing Fields, Romilly Ave., Handsworth Wood, Birmingham.
Directions: M5 jct 1, A41 to Handsworth, A4040 to Handsworth Wood, left at island into Handsworth Wood Rd, follow road to right then 2nd left into Romilly Ave., ground on left.
Cover: No **Capacity:** 300 **Floodlights:** No **Clubhouse:** No **Programme:** No.
Colours: Red & black stripes/black **Change colours:** Red & navy/navy **Founded:** 1979.
Hons: Staffs Co. (Sth) Lg Div 1 92-93 (Edge Cup R-up 91-92, Ike Cooper Tphy R-up 92-93).

ROCKET POOL

Chairman: Mr W Hollyhead **Founded:** 1989
Secretary: Mr J Baer, 122 Rocket Pool Drive, Bilston WV14 8BD (0902 496928)
Ground: Bilston College, Westfield Rd, Bilston.
Directions: From Bilston town centre take A41 towards Wolverhampton, right at island into Hadley Rd, 2nd left (Bailey Rd), 1st right (Wolsey Rd), left into Lambeth Rd - ground entrance straight ahead.
Cover: No **Capacity:** 500 **Floodlights:** No **Clubhouse:** No **Programme:** No.
Colours: Green & white/white **Change colours:** Red/black.

RUGELEY ATHLETIC

Chairman: Gerald Williscroft   **Founded:** 1981
Secretary: Mr D J Rowley, 32 Lodge Rd, Brereton, Rugeley, Staffs WS12 1HG (0889 583000)
Ground: St Augustines, Bryons Lane, Rugeley.
Directions: A51 from Lichfield to Rugeley town centre, right at island onto the Uttoxeter road, right at next island, ground 50yds on left - Mansfield House car park.
Cover: No   **Capacity:** 800   **Floodlights:** No   **Clubhouse:** Mansfield House.
Colours: All royal blue   **Change colours:** Green & white/green
Programme: 32 pages, 30p   **Hons:** Staffs Co. (Sth) Lg Div 1 82-83, Penkridge Charity Cup 86-87.

SIKH HUNTERS

Chairman: Jasbinder Singh   **Manager:** Ron Parker   **Founded:** 1964
Secretary: Mr A S Moore, 20 Proffitt Close, Ryecroft, Walsall WS2 9BD (0922 644471)
Ground: West Midlands College, Gorway, Walsall.
Directions: M6 jct 9, A454 Walsall ring road, left onto A34 towards Walsall, 1st left and left again into Gorway Rd, college entrance 100yds ahead.
Cover: No   **Capacity:** 800   **Floodlights:** No   **Clubhouse:** No   **Programme:** No.
Colours: Green & yellow/green   **Change colours:** Blue/black.
Hons: Staffs Co. (Sth) Lg R-up 90-91 (Div 1 89-90).

TIPTON SPORTS & SOCIAL

Chairman: Mr H Lucas   **Manager:** Wally Twist   **Founded:** 1964
Secretary: Miss W Baker, 42 Ambleside Close, Bradley, Bilston, West Mids WV14 0SN (0902 497404)
Ground: Coneygre Rd, Tipton.
Directions: M5 jct 2, A4123 Birmingham New Rd to Burnt Tree island, A461 Coneygre Rd, ground entrance 200yds on left between terraced house and new Estate on left.
Cover: No   **Capacity:** 500   **Floodlights:** No   **Clubhouse:** Yes   **Programme:** No.
Colours: Sky/navy   **Change colours:** Green & white/navy.
Hons: Staffs Co. Lg (Sth) Div 1 88-89.

TOLL END WESLEY

Chairman: Mr S Page   **Manager:** A Cartwright/ M Smith   **Founded:** 1905
Secretary: Mr B Walker, 23 Gospel Oak Rd, Ocker Hill, Tipton, West Mids DY4 0DR (021 556 7711).
Ground: Union Locks, Josiah Rd, Willenhall.
Directions: M6 jct 10, A454 to Willenhall, thru town centre, straight on towards Wolverhampton, entrance on right just before island on main A454 dual c'way.
Cover: No   **Capacity:** 500   **Floodlights:** No   **Programme:** No.
Clubhouse: Hospitality lounge & bar.
Colours: Red & black/black   **Change colours:** White/black.
Hons: Staffs Co. Lg (Sth) R-up 88-89 91-92 (Div 1 R-up 87-88, Edge Cup 91-92, Ike Cooper Tphy R-up 91-92).

WEST BROMWICH B.H.

Chairman: Clive Peel   **Programme:** No   **Founded:** 1985
Secretary: Mr M Peel, 120 Old Meeting Str., West Bromwich B70 9SW (021 553 4833)
Ground: As Park Rangers F.C. (see page 713).
Colours: Yellow/blue   **Change colours:** White/black
Hons: Staffs Co. (Sth) Lg Div 1 R-up 92-93, West Bromwich Charity Cup 92-93.

STAFFORDSHIRE
COUNTY LEAGUE (NORTH)

President: T Myatt   **Chairman:** F Askey   **Vice-Chairman:** J T Phillips
Secretary: J K Johnson, 149 St Nicholas Ave.,
Norton, Stoke-on-Trent ST6 8JW (0782 534866)

FINAL TABLE	P	W	D	L	F	A	PTS
Cheadle Rovers	34	26	3	5	108	33	53
Wolstanton Utd	34	24	3	7	85	33	51
Redgate C'ton Res.	34	22	7	5	85	35	51
Florence	34	21	6	7	90	53	48
Oakamoor	34	19	6	9	86	57	44
Chell	34	19	4	12	87	60	42
Stallington	34	16	9	9	83	48	41
Audley Res.	34	15	7	12	59	51	37
Rists United Res.	34	14	8	12	69	57	36
Stone Old Alleynians	34	14	6	14	65	59	34
Foley	34	12	9	13	59	53	33
Goldenhill W. Res.	34	10	9	15	47	60	29
Eccleshall Res.	34	9	5	20	57	89	23
Norton A.G.	34	8	6	20	45	98	22
Abbey Hulton Utd	34	6	6	22	35	84	18
Vale Juniors	34	6	5	23	37	107	17
Hanley Town Res.	34	6	4	24	36	87	16
Cheadle Old Boys	34	5	5	24	44	113	15

LEAGUE CUP 1992-93

First Round
Florence 1, Cheadle Rovers 0
Rists Utd Res. 3, Redgate Clayton Res. 2

Second Round
Cheadle Old Boys 0, Stallington 5
Chell 0, Audley Res. 1
Eccleshall Res. 0, Florence 0
rep: Florence 4, Eccleshall Res. 0
Foley 1, Rists Utd Res. 1
rep: Rists Utd Res. 4, Foley 1
Goldenhill Wdrs Res. 5, Oakamoor 0
Hanley Town Res. 1, Stone Alleynians 0
Vale Juniors 1, Norton A.G. 1
rep: Norton A.G. 4, Vale Juniors 1
Wolstanton Utd 3, Abbey Hulton Utd 1

Third Round:
Audley Res. 2, Norton A.G. 1
Florence 0, Rists Utd Res. 0
rep: Rists Utd Res. 0, Florence Res 0
(Florence won 5-4 on pens)
Goldenhill Wdrs Res. 1, Stallington 1
rep: Stallington 5, Goldenhill W. Res. 0
Hanley Town Res. 1, Wolstanton Utd 2

Semi-Finals
Audley Res. 0, Wolstanton Utd 0
rep: Wolstanton Utd 4, Audley Res. 0
Florence 2, Stallington 3

Final: Stallington 3, Wolstanton Utd 1

HEREFORD TIMES
HEREFORDSHIRE LEAGUE

President: Colin Shepherd, MP

Chairman: H J Handley   **Vice-Chairman:** M Magor

Hon. Secretary: W E Morris,
26 Brookside, Tupsley, Hereford HR1 2RW (273814)

The League had an excellent 94th season. Hinton won both the County F.A. Senior Cup and Charity Bowl competitions against opposition from teams in the more senior West Midlands (Regional), Hellenic and Mid-Wales leagues. The strength of the League Premier Division, however, was demonstrated by Hinton being beaten in the final of the League Senior Cup by Ewyas Harold.

All divisions were closely contested, especially Division One where the three top clubs all finished with the same number of points.

W E Morris, League Secretary

PREM. DIV.	P	W	D	L	F	A	PTS
Hinton	22	17	1	4	77	30	35
Bromyard	22	15	4	3	49	22	34
Fownhope	22	11	5	6	40	36	27
Woodville	22	9	8	5	66	54	26
Colwall	22	12	2	8	49	42	26
Pegasus Jnrs Res.	22	8	5	9	34	38	21
Thorn Lighting	22	8	5	9	35	42	21
Ewyas Harold	22	8	4	10	52	41	20
Westfields Res.	22	7	6	9	43	44	20
Wellington	22	6	5	11	27	47	17
Golden Valley	22	3	4	15	32	74	10
Weston	22	2	3	17	29	63	7

DIV. THREE	P	W	D	L	F	A	PTS
Hinton Colts	22	16	3	3	75	31	35
Ewyas Harold Res.	22	16	2	4	76	32	34
Great Western	22	13	4	5	53	33	30
Bringsty	22	12	4	6	56	35	28
Dorstone	22	12	4	6	49	36	28
Woofferton	22	10	2	10	40	31	22
Weston Res.	22	10	2	10	40	41	22
Colwall Res.	22	9	4	9	41	54	22
Woodville Res.	22	6	4	12	41	59	16
Pencombe	22	4	5	13	29	52	13
Staunton	22	2	4	16	32	75	8
Hereford Lads C. Res.	22	1	4	17	27	80	6

DIV. ONE	P	W	D	L	F	A	PTS
Burghill	20	15	0	5	73	35	30
Bromyard Res.	20	12	6	2	55	18	30
Sutton United	20	14	2	4	48	28	30
Leominster Utd	20	11	3	6	35	22	25
Civil Service	20	9	3	8	45	38	21
Fownhope Res.	20	9	1	10	45	39	19
Leintwardine	20	6	4	10	30	39	16
Hereford Sports	20	7	2	11	31	58	16
Holme Lacy	20	5	3	12	38	47	13
Pegasus Colts	20	6	1	13	28	57	13
Ledbury T. Res.	20	2	3	15	27	74	7

DIV. FOUR	P	W	D	L	F	A	PTS
Bulmers	20	19	0	1	84	27	38
Pembridge	20	14	2	4	60	28	30
P.O. Sports	20	13	3	4	72	35	29
Civil Service Res.	20	8	4	8	49	42	20
Leominster Town	20	8	4	8	53	50	20
Orleton	20	7	4	9	45	46	18
Newtown	20	5	7	8	44	58	17
West St Reg.	20	6	3	11	36	49	15
Three Elms	20	5	2	13	37	68	12
Bosbury	20	4	3	13	36	74	11
Wellington Colts	20	4	2	14	30	69	10

DIV. TWO	P	W	D	L	F	A	PTS
Stoke Prior	22	17	1	4	82	34	35
Hereford Tiles	22	16	2	4	72	27	34
Richards Castle	22	14	2	6	53	36	30
Walford	22	11	3	8	71	55	25
Kingstone	22	11	3	8	61	47	25
Tupsley	22	11	2	9	62	58	24
Wellington Res.	22	9	3	10	46	50	21
Dymock	22	7	6	9	55	60	20
Ross United	22	6	7	9	48	44	19
Credenhill	22	8	3	11	64	65	19
Tram	22	5	1	16	37	84	11
Putson	22	0	1	21	19	110	1

DIV. FIVE	P	W	D	L	F	A	PTS
Shobdon	20	19	1	0	85	19	39
Leom. Town Colts	20	14	3	3	54	26	31
Kingstone Res.	20	9	5	6	39	34	23
Bromyard Colts	20	9	3	8	41	34	21
Eardisley	20	9	3	8	38	31	21
Kington Colts	20	8	4	8	47	36	20
Holme Lacy Res.	20	6	7	7	38	48	19
Shellack	20	8	1	11	40	56	17
Hereford Spts Res.	20	5	6	9	31	42	16
Painters	20	2	3	15	31	60	7
R.H.M. Ledbury	20	2	2	16	25	83	6

SENIOR CUP 1992-93

First Round

Fownhope v Bromyard	2-2,3-1
Wellington v Colwall	3-2
Weston v Woodville	1-2
Thorn Lighting v Pegasus Juniors Reserves	1-2

Quarter-Finals

Hinton v Wellington	2-0
Fownhope v Westfields Reserves	3-2
Woodville v Golden Valley	8-0
Pegasus Juniors Reserves v Ewyas Harold	1-2

Semi-Finals

Woodville v Hinton	6-6,3-3,1-3
Ewyas Harold v Fownhope	3-1

Final: Ewyas Harold 1, Hinton 0

JUNIOR CUP 1992-93

First Round

Sutton United v Wellington Reserves	4-2
Credenhill v Fownhope Reserves	0-2
Dymock v Burghill	1-8
Putson v Hereford Sports	0-3
Stoke Prior v Ross United	5-3
Ledbury Town Reserves v Walford	1-1,2-4
Leominster United v Richards Castle	5-0

Second Round

Fownhope Reserves v Hereford Tiles	1-2
Sutton United v Bromyard Reserves	0-3
Kingstone v Leintwardine	3-4
Pegasus Jnrs Colts v Leominster United	4-6
Walford v Tupsley	6-1
Tram v Stoke Prior	2-4
Civil Service v Burghill	1-4
Hereford Sports v Holme Lacy	1-4

(continued opposite)

Quarter-Finals

Stoke Prior v Leintwardine	4-2	Holme Lacy v Walford	3-2
Hereford Tiles v Bromyard Reserves	4-0	Burghill v Leominster United	2-1

Semi-Finals

Holme Lacy v Stoke Prior	3-4	Burghill v Hereford Tiles	2-3

Final: Hereford Tiles 1, Stoke Prior 0

F.W. PETERSON CUP First Round

Woofferton v P.O. Sports	4-2	Painters v Three Elms	1-0
Bringsty v Bulmers	3-2		

Second Round

Ewyas Harold Reserves v Hinton Colts	4-2	Hereford Spts Res. v Hereford Lads Club Res.	4-3
Leominster Town v Orleton	7-0	Pencombe v Colwall Reserves	3-5
Eardisley v Wellington Colts	1-1,0-5	R.H.M. Ledbury v Dorstone	1-4
Shobdon v Bringsty	4-5	Newtown v Woofferton	2-6
Painters v West St Regs	0-2	Woodville Reserves v Leominster Colts	3-0
Pembridge v Kington Colts	2-0	Civil Service Reserves v Staunton	2-3
Sellack v Great Western	2-7	Weston Reserves v Bosbury	9-0
Bromyard Colts v Kingstone Reserves	2-5		

Third Round

Staunton v Kingstone Reserves	1-3	Ewyas Harold Reserves v Woodville Reserves	1-2
Colwall Reserves v Hereford Sports Res.	0-2	Dorstone v Great Western	1-1,0-4
Leominster Town v Bringsty	1-5	West St Regulars v Woofferton	0-3
Weston Reserves v Pembridge	4-3	Holme Lacy Reserves v Wellington Colts	0-1

Quarter-Finals

Woodville Reserves v Bringsty	2-4	Wellington Colts v Kingstone Reserves	0-0,0-3
Woofferton v Great Western	0-2	Hereford Sports Reserves v Weston Reserves	1-3

Semi-Finals

Weston Reserves v Kingstone Res.	0-0,2-4	Great Western v Bringsty	1-1,1-2

Final: Kingstone Reserves 3, Bringsty 0

PREMIER DIVISION RESULT CHART 1992-93

HOME TEAM	1	2	3	4	5	6	7	8	9	10	11	12
1. Bromyard	*	5-2	1-0	1-0	6-0	1-4	2-0	4-0	1-1	3-1	2-0	2-2
2. Colwall	0-2	*	3-1	0-3	7-1	1-6	2-1	5-0	1-0	1-3	1-3	5-4
3. Ewyas Harold	2-3	1-2	*	2-2	0-1	2-3	2-0	4-2	2-0	4-1	12-1	4-6
4. Fownhope	1-0	2-5	1-3	*	4-2	2-1	1-0	3-0	0-0	1-2	2-2	2-2
5. Golden Valley	3-2	1-2	2-2	1-3	*	1-5	0-1	0-0	1-2	2-4	1-2	1-3
6. Hinton	1-2	3-2	2-0	2-3	8-0	*	3-1	5-2	7-1	2-0	4-0	4-5
7. Pegasus Juniors Reserves	0-2	0-2	2-3	2-2	7-1	1-6	*	3-2	4-2	2-2	1-0	1-1
8. Thorn Lighting	0-0	1-0	2-1	1-0	2-2	2-2	0-1	*	1-2	2-1	2-1	7-5
9. Wellington	2-2	1-1	2-1	1-2	3-6	1-3	0-1	0-5	*	2-1	2-1	1-2
10. Westfields Reserves	1-2	1-3	1-1	1-2	4-1	1-2	2-2	1-1	1-1	*	4-2	3-3
11. Weston	1-2	2-3	2-3	2-3	2-2	1-2	0-1	0-2	1-2	3-5	*	2-2
12. Woodville	1-4	1-1	2-2	6-1	5-3	1-2	3-3	2-1	3-1	2-3	5-1	*

DIVISION ONE RESULT CHART 1992-93

HOME TEAM	1	2	3	4	5	6	7	8	9	10	11
1. Bromyard Reserves	*	5-2	2-1	2-2	5-0	6-3	2-0	5-1	0-0	8-1	2-2
2. Burghill	1-5	*	4-2	4-1	5-2	5-3	6-1	3-0	0-1	13-2	2-3
3. Civil Service	2-1	0-5	*	0-3	7-1	3-1	9-0	3-2	1-7	1-0	1-3
4. Fownhope Reserves	0-6	5-2	3-0	*	4-0	1-2	4-0	0-1	0-2	0-2	4-2
5. Hereford Sports	0-3	2-3	0-8	1-4	*	2-1	3-1	3-2	0-1	1-0	2-4
6. Holme Lacy	0-0	0-4	0-1	3-1	2-3	*	7-1	2-1	1-1	0-1	2-3
7. Ledbury Town '84 Reserves	1-1	1-5	2-2	3-2	2-2	1-6	*	0-3	5-1	1-3	2-3
8. Leintwardine	1-1	1-4	0-0	4-6	3-3	3-1	4-2	*	0-1	1-0	2-2
9. Leominster United	1-2	3-0	0-1	2-1	0-2	1-1	3-1	1-0	*	4-1	0-2
10. Pegasus Juniors Colts	0-1	0-2	3-3	2-4	0-2	5-2	6-2	0-1	1-5	*	0-6
11. Sutton United	2-0	1-3	1-0	1-0	3-2	4-1	2-1	2-0	3-0	0-1	*

DIVISION TWO RESULT CHART 1992-93

HOME TEAM	1	2	3	4	5	6	7	8	9	10	11	12
1. Credenhill	*	6-1	0-5	0-3	13-0	2-3	4-2	2-4	2-1	1-5	1-9	2-2
2. Dymock	2-7	*	0-6	5-2	1-1	2-5	2-2	2-1	9-1	3-2	2-3	0-2
3. Hereford Tiles	3-2	2-2	*	0-0	6-0	0-2	4-1	1-4	8-1	4-1	2-0	5-1
4. Kingstone	4-1	3-1	1-2	*	6-1	1-4	2-0	2-6	2-2	2-1	4-4	8-1
5. Putson	2-3	0-3	2-5	0-5	*	0-3	0-7	1-6	2-4	1-6	0-1	0-3
6. Richards Castle	1-2	2-2	1-0	2-1	4-1	*	1-0	1-2	3-1	7-4	2-1	2-1
7. Ross United	4-4	2-2	1-3	1-0	6-1	2-2	*	2-2	4-0	1-2	2-1	3-1
8. Stoke Prior	3-2	2-3	2-1	5-0	11-0	5-1	2-0	*	6-1	6-3	3-1	3-1
9. Tram	1-4	3-1	1-3	6-7	3-1	3-2	2-0	0-1	*	2-4	1-3	1-3
10. Tupsley	4-1	1-6	3-5	1-5	5-1	3-2	3-3	1-0	5-1	*	3-3	2-0
11. Walford	4-3	5-4	1-4	4-2	6-4	2-1	2-2	7-2	9-0	2-3	*	2-5
12. Wellington Reserves	2-2	2-2	1-3	0-1	3-0	1-2	4-3	1-6	5-2	2-0	5-1	*

DIVISION THREE RESULT CHART 1992-93

HOME TEAM	1	2	3	4	5	6	7	8	9	10	11	12
1. Bringsty	*	3-2	2-1	2-0	0-3	1-4	5-0	1-0	1-1	3-0	6-1	2-2
2. Colwall Reserves	3-4	*	2-2	1-6	1-0	2-3	2-0	2-0	4-3	2-1	0-0	0-4
3. Dorstone	2-3	2-1	*	0-5	0-3	2-2	3-0	4-1	4-2	2-0	4-3	1-0
4. Ewyas Harold Reserves	6-0	2-2	0-2	*	6-1	3-3	4-0	4-1	9-1	1-0	2-1	3-0
5. Great Western	1-1	2-2	2-3	3-1	*	2-0	3-0	2-0	3-1	3-0	3-0	2-0
6. Hinton Colts	2-0	8-1	4-4	5-0	1-0	*	6-1	7-0	4-2	4-2	5-0	1-3
7. Lads Club	1-7	1-5	1-5	2-4	4-4	1-3	*	0-4	3-2	2-3	1-2	2-2
8. Pencombe	2-1	1-2	1-0	2-3	1-1	2-3	3-3	*	2-2	0-3	2-2	0-3
9. Staunton	0-5	1-2	1-1	3-4	0-9	1-4	5-1	3-5	*	3-1	0-2	0-3
10. Weston Reserves	1-1	3-1	2-1	1-8	9-0	2-3	2-1	0-0	3-0	*	2-1	1-0
11. Woodville Reserves	0-6	6-1	1-4	2-3	2-5	1-3	3-3	5-1	2-2	3-0	*	1-4
12. Woofferton	3-2	2-3	1-2	0-2	1-2	1-0	3-0	2-1	2-0	2-3	2-3	*

DIV. FOUR RESULTS

		1	2	3	4	5	6	7	8	9	10	11
1.	Bosbury	*	1-4	0-4	1-3	3-2	0-2	2-3	2-7	1-3	4-1	1-1
2.	Bulmers	6-3	*	6-2	8-0	2-1	7-1	3-2	4-2	6-0	7-1	3-2
3.	Civil Service Reserves	6-1	1-2	*	3-3	2-2	2-0	1-3	2-0	2-4	3-4	3-1
4.	Leominster Town	5-5	3-2	3-1	*	2-2	2-2	0-1	1-2	6-2	4-0	4-3
5.	Newtown	2-2	1-3	1-1	4-1	*	2-7	1-1	1-6	4-3	4-2	5-2
6.	Orleton	5-0	1-4	1-1	1-6	6-1	*	1-2	0-2	1-2	2-2	3-2
7.	Pembridge	5-1	1-2	3-1	3-2	4-2	5-0	*	4-3	3-0	5-1	6-1
8.	P.O. Sports	9-1	2-3	6-1	3-2	2-2	4-1	3-1	*	4-1	4-0	3-2
9.	Three Elms	2-4	0-4	0-4	3-4	2-2	2-7	3-2	4-4	*	3-4	1-0
10.	Wellington Colts	2-3	1-3	2-4	2-1	2-4	0-4	0-5	2-2	3-1	*	0-4
11.	West St Regulars	2-1	2-5	0-5	2-1	5-1	0-0	1-1	1-4	3-1	2-1	*

DIV. FIVE RESULTS

		1	2	3	4	5	6	7	8	9	10	11
1.	Bromyard Colts	*	1-1	4-0	4-0	1-2	2-2	2-1	2-1	4-3	5-0	1-6
2.	Eardisley	1-0	*	1-1	9-3	2-0	0-2	0-2	4-0	0-0	2-0	1-2
3.	Hereford Sports Reserves	0-0	3-0	*	1-1	1-2	0-4	0-1	2-1	8-0	2-4	0-4
4.	Holme Lacy Reserves	1-0	3-1	4-4	*	2-0	1-1	2-3	2-2	2-0	3-1	1-6
5.	Kingstone	1-3	3-2	1-1	0-0	*	1-1	2-2	6-3	3-0	3-0	0-5
6.	Kingstone Colts	4-1	0-2	2-0	4-4	2-5	*	0-3	4-1	10-0	3-1	2-3
7.	Leominster Town Colts	4-1	1-2	5-2	2-1	1-1	1-0	*	4-3	4-1	7-1	2-2
8.	Painters	0-4	2-3	1-1	1-1	1-4	6-2	1-3	*	2-3	1-3	0-6
9.	R.H.M. Ledbury	1-2	2-4	2-3	2-4	3-1	1-4	1-5	0-3	*	4-6	0-7
10.	Sellack	3-2	3-1	1-2	4-1	1-3	1-0	1-3	3-2	2-2	*	2-4
11.	Shobdon	3-2	3-2	4-0	3-2	3-1	3-0	3-0	3-0	9-0	6-3	*

PREMIER DIVISION CLUBS
(Tel. codes 0432 unless stated)

BROMYARD TOWN Sec: D Harding (0885 482774)
Ground: Delahey Meadow

COLWALL RANGERS
G: Walwyn Rd   **S:** P Butler (0684 40747)

EWYAS HAROLD UNITED
G: Ewyas Harold Rec   **S:** D Manning (0981 240372)

FOWNHOPE
G: Malt House   **S:** P Davies (0432 850605)

GOLDEN VALLEY
G: Kingstone School   **S:** J Price (0981 250712)

HINTON
G: Broomy Hill, Hereford   **S:** G Hemmington (342312)

THORN LIGHTING   **S:** Mrs Rutherford (271258)
G: Thorn Lighting, Rotherwas

WELLINGTON   **S:** M Perkins (71523)
G: Wellington PF, Hereford (71455)

WESTFIELDS RESERVES
G: City Spts Club, Granstand Rd, Hereford

WESTON
G: Weston Rec   **S:** C Holmes (0989 81511)

WOODVILLE   **S:** B James (0989 62376)
G: Ross-on-Wye Spts Centre (0989 63696)

'PERKINS ENGINES' SHROPSHIRE COUNTY LEAGUE

PREM. DIVISION

	P	W	D	L	F	A	PTS
Shifnal Town	24	18	3	3	85	18	57
Little Drayton Rgrs	24	15	3	6	62	55	48
Admaston Juniors	24	14	4	6	45	28	46
Snailbeach WS (-2pts)	24	11	6	7	46	33	36
Ellesmere Rangers	24	11	3	10	51	40	36
Meole Brace	24	11	3	10	45	38	36
Wellington Amateurs	24	11	3	10	35	40	36
Albrighton S & S	24	9	7	8	37	39	34
Oakengates Town	24	9	4	11	50	57	31
Madeley Town	24	8	1	15	47	52	25
St Georges Town	24	8	1	15	35	59	25
Tibberton	24	5	2	17	29	74	17
Newport	24	4	4	16	30	64	16

PREMIER DIVISION 93-94
(Tel. codes 0952 unless stated)

ADMASTON
G: Leegomery, Telford   **S:** D Donaldson (603873)

ALBRIGHTON S. & S.
G: Loak Rd, Albrighton   **S:** J Rhoden (0902 372730)

BELLE VUE OLD BOYS
G: Springfield, Shrewsbury   **S:** P Pugh (0743 367544)

BROSELEY ATHLETIC
G: Birchmeadow, Broseley   **S:** L Price (883678)

CHURCH STRETTON TOWN
G: Russells Meadow   **S:** K Hartley (0694 724281)

ELLESMERE RANGERS
G: Beech Grove   **S:** J Edge (0691 623587)

LITTLE DRAYTON RGRS S: B Garratt (0630 654618)
G: Greenfields Spts Grnd, Market Drayton

MADELEY TOWN
G: Sutton Hill, Madeley   **S:** M Terry (501362)

MEOLE BRACE   **S:** L Rowlinson (0743 248962)
G: Church Rd, Meole Brace, Shrewsbury

NEWPORT
G: Shukers Field, Newport   **S:** Mrs Henry (825006)

OAKENGATES TOWN   **S:** Mrs Hickman (78282)
G: Off School Grove, Oakengates, Telford

STAR ALUMINIUM
G: Stourbridge Rd, Bridgnorth   **S:** D Rymer (727542)

SNAILBEACH WHITE STAR
G: The Coates   **S:** V Jones (0743 722672)

ST GEORGES TOWN
G: Sutton Hill, Telford   **S:** B Rouse (618204)

TIBBERTON
G: Tibberton PF   **S:** G Fallows (630363)

WELLINGTON AMATEURS
G: As Admaston (above)   **S:** G Richards (463155)

DIVISION ONE

	P	W	D	L	F	A	PTS
Belle Vue Old Boys	16	12	4	0	54	14	40
Star Aluminium	16	12	3	1	52	14	39
Church Stretton T.	16	7	3	6	43	36	24
Telford Juniors	16	7	2	7	31	37	23
St Martins	16	7	1	8	34	36	22
Weston Rhyn Utd	16	5	4	7	21	31	19
Weston United	16	5	3	8	33	34	18
Column	16	4	4	8	24	44	16
Broseley Colts	16	0	2	14	18	64	2

DIVISION ONE 93-94
(Tel. codes 0952 unless stated)

BROSELEY COLTS
G: Birchmeadow, Broseley   **S:** E Fielding (882336)

COLUMN
G: Springfield, Shrewsbury   **S:** J Dyas (0743 240640)

DONNINGTON PARK *(newly promoted)*

HADLEY KEYS *(newly promoted)*

HANWOOD UNITED *(newly promoted)*

HEATH HILL
G: Doseley Rd, Dawley   **S:** J Sheward (590047)

ST MARTINS
G: Rhyn Park Sch., St Martins, Oswestry
S: D Stokes (0691 772699)

TELFORD JUNIORS
G: Doseley Rd, Dawley   **S:** A Bucknell (503090)

WESTON RHYN UNITED
G: Weston Rhyn Rec   **S:** C Mottram (0691 661648)

WESTON UNITED
G: Weston-under-Lizzard Spts Grnd
S: P Sylvester (76308)

SPECTRE HELLENIC LEAGUE

Chairman: N A S Matthews
Vice Chairman: A B Cooke
Hon. Secretary: T G Cuss, 7 Blenheim Rd,
Kidlington, Oxford OX5 2HP (0867 55920)

WOLLEN SPORTS EMULATE MILTON UNITED

For the second time in three years the Premier Division was won by a club promoted the previous season. Wollen Sports followed in the footsteps of Milton United, taking the championship by nine points from Moreton Town and Milton United, the former taking runners-up spot by virtue of a better goal difference.

Sadly, however, the achievements of Wollen Sports were overshadowed by the failure of two clubs, Moreton Town and Didcot Town, to complete their fixtures until Saturday 12th June. The match referee had abandoned the original fixture at Moreton Town after three players had been sent off and there were unsubstantiated allegations that two of the dismissed players were in possession of knives and threatening violence. The order to replay the fixture at Moreton on 8th May was not complied with by Didcot Town, and the League eventually were able to have the fixture played on June 12th. I am told that this is a record late for a league fixture played under the jurisdiction of the Football Association.

The Premier Division Challenge Cup was won by Moreton Town who defeated Bicester Town in the final with a last minute goal. Bicester Town can consider themselves unfortunate to be runners-up.

In their second season in the League, Tuffley Rovers from Gloucestershire are champions of Division One winning the League by ten clear points from West Oxfordshire rivals North Leigh. A revived Wallingford Town finished third. Tuffley completed a Division One League and Cup double by winning the Division One Challenge Cup 3-1 against Purton. The Reserve Section was won by Oxfordshire club Headington Amateurs by a solitary point from Swindon Supermarine, whilst Cirencester Town defeating Wallingford Town 5-2 in the Reserve Section Challenge Cup final.

The long road to Wembley for the F.A. Cup was short but relatively sweet. Banbury United, Cinderford Town, Abingdon United, Rayners Lane and Shortwood United all embarked on the long journey at the end of August. Cinderford Town, Abingdon United and Rayners Lane progressed to the next round, the Abingdon club securing an excellent victory over Beazer Homes League Poole Town. The First Qualifying Round saw the demise of Abingdon United, but Cinderford and Rayners Lane made further progress. The Wembley trail ended in the Second Qualifying Round with Cinderford losing at Cheltenham Town and Rayners Lane to St Albans City.

In the F.A. Vase, Almondsbury Picksons pulled off an excellent 4-1 win over the holders, Wimborne Town. Two of our more fancied clubs were unfortunate in meeting the in-form Tiverton Town who were ultimately the losing finalist. By mid-December our interest in the Vase was over.

The annual representative match against the Army Football Association, due to be played at Almondsbury in October, was postponed due to pitch conditions.

In outside competitions, Banbury United reached the final of the Oxfordshire Senior Cup, but lost in extra-time. Cinderford were finalists in the Gloucestershire Challenge Trophy and Wollen Sports were finalists in the Wiltshire Senior Cup. **Trevor Cuss, League Secretary**

Moreton Town F.C., Premier Division runners-up and League Cup winners 1992-93. Photo - Gavin Ellis-Neville.

PREM. DIV.	P	W	D	L	F	A	PTS
Wollen Sports	34	25	4	5	75	31	79
Moreton Town	34	22	4	8	70	43	70
Milton United	34	21	7	6	67	33	70
Cirencester Town	34	20	8	6	54	28	68
Cinderford Town	34	15	10	9	64	44	55
Almondsbury Pick.	34	15	7	12	62	50	52
Shortwood United	34	12	10	12	63	59	46
Swindon Super.	34	11	13	10	46	43	46
Bicester Town	34	12	9	13	45	45	45
Rayners Lane	34	13	4	17	53	63	43
Banbury United	34	10	10	14	50	66	40
Fairford Town	34	8	13	13	55	48	37
Headington Am.	34	10	6	18	40	67	36
Kintbury Rangers	34	9	8	17	35	51	35
Abingdon United	34	9	7	18	49	67	34
Wantage Town	34	8	8	18	47	70	32
Pegasus Juniors	34	7	9	18	52	76	30
Didcot Town	34	6	9	19	42	94	27

DIV. ONE	P	W	D	L	F	A	PTS
Tuffley Rovers	30	25	2	3	90	24	77
North Leigh	30	21	4	5	113	43	67
Wallingford Town	30	17	9	4	84	47	60
Lambourn Sports	30	16	6	8	73	61	54
Purton	30	17	3	10	64	53	54
Kidlington	30	13	9	8	49	41	48
Yarnton	30	12	4	14	48	60	40
Cheltenham Saras	30	12	2	16	48	47	38
Carterton Town	30	11	4	15	58	63	37
Clanfield	30	9	10	11	47	66	37
Highworth Town	30	9	6	15	48	62	33
Wootton Bassett T.	30	8	6	16	40	53	30
Bishops Cleeve	30	9	3	18	44	76	30
Cirencester Utd	30	8	4	18	41	78	28
Chipping Norton T.	30	7	5	18	51	82	26
Easington Sports	30	5	5	20	34	76	20

RESERVE DIV.	P	W	D	L	F	A	PTS
Headington Am.	21	15	2	4	64	22	47
Swindon Super.	21	15	1	5	53	21	46
Wantage Town	21	14	2	5	62	30	44
Wollen Sports	21	13	3	5	54	29	42
Milton United	21	11	5	5	57	33	38
Bicester Town	21	12	2	7	50	30	38
Cirencester Town	21	11	3	7	59	38	36
Cheltenham Saras	21	10	5	6	51	34	35
North Leigh	21	9	6	6	47	35	33
Wallingford Town	21	9	5	7	59	42	32
Kidlington	21	9	5	7	41	38	32
Abingdon United	21	9	2	10	42	37	29
Fairford Town	21	9	2	10	40	38	29
Carterton Town	21	8	5	8	45	44	29
Almondsbury Pick.	21	8	3	10	32	36	27
Highworth Town	21	8	2	11	31	47	26
Didcot Town	21	7	3	11	37	47	24
Kintbury Rangers	21	5	3	13	34	52	18
Yarnton	21	5	2	14	36	91	17
Cirencester United	21	3	4	14	26	71	13
Clanfield	21	1	8	12	17	57	11
Easington Sports	21	2	3	16	17	82	9

PREMIER DIVISION RESULT CHART 1992-93

HOME TEAM	1	2	3	4	5	6	7	8	9	10	11	12	13	14	15	16	17	18
1. Abingdon United	*	1-3	0-1	0-3	3-1	0-1	4-3	1-1	2-2	0-0	0-2	0-2	1-1	2-2	3-3	1-3	2-0	2-3
2. Almondsbury P.	1-2	*	1-1	3-0	2-0	1-3	4-2	1-1	1-1	2-1	1-1	1-4	2-1	2-3	4-1	1-2	4-0	1-3
3. Banbury United	3-1	0-4	*	0-1	0-6	1-1	3-1	3-1	1-1	1-2	2-5	2-1	4-4	2-5	1-0	2-3	1-2
4. Bicester Town	4-3	1-0	2-2	*	1-1	0-2	2-2	3-1	3-2	3-0	2-6	1-2	2-0	0-1	1-2	0-0	1-1	0-1
5. Cinderford T.	2-0	2-1	1-1	4-2	*	0-0	7-0	2-3	4-2	2-0	0-2	1-0	3-1	4-0	1-1	2-0	3-3	4-0
6. Cirencester Town	2-0	2-4	3-0	3-2	2-0	*	1-0	2-0	1-1	2-0	0-0	2-1	1-1	2-1	1-2	3-0	0-2	3-2
7. Didcot Town	0-3	2-2	1-1	2-1	0-0	1-4	*	3-1	0-2	0-0	0-2	2-3	3-2	1-5	0-3	1-1	0-0	0-1
8. Fairford Town	2-0	3-0	2-2	0-2	0-0	0-0	7-1	*	1-2	1-2	1-1	3-3	7-1	5-1	0-0	1-2	2-2	1-3
9. Headington Am.	4-1	0-1	0-1	1-1	3-2	1-1	1-3	0-1	*	2-4	0-4	0-4	1-6	0-1	1-0	2-2	3-2	1-3
10. Kintbury Rgrs	1-2	1-1	0-0	2-0	2-3	0-2	2-4	2-1	1-0	*	0-4	0-1	1-1	1-2	2-1	0-0	3-1	1-1
11. Milton United	3-4	1-1	0-1	2-0	3-0	2-4	2-0	2-0	2-1	1-0	*	0-2	2-0	2-1	2-2	2-0	0-0	2-1
12. Moreton Town	1-2	0-1	2-1	1-0	2-2	0-1	7-2	2-2	3-0	3-2	1-4	*	6-2	2-1	4-5	0-1	2-0	2-2
13. Pegasus Jnrs	5-2	3-1	4-1	1-1	0-0	1-2	2-2	1-1	2-1	3-0	1-4	0-5	*	1-1	1-2	2-2	5-1	0-1
14. Rayners Lane	2-1	1-3	1-0	0-3	2-0	0-2	4-0	1-1	0-1	2-1	1-2	1-2	4-2	*	1-2	3-0	2-1	2-4
15. Shortwood Utd	0-2	2-5	4-4	0-2	1-1	7-0	0-0	1-2	2-1	0-1	1-3	7-1	2-1	*	1-1	2-1	2-3
16. Swindon S'marine	1-1	1-2	2-3	0-0	2-2	3-0	2-2	1-0	3-0	2-1	1-1	0-1	1-0	3-1	1-1	*	5-0	0-4
17. Wantage Town	3-2	2-1	1-3	0-1	2-3	1-0	3-4	0-3	0-1	1-2	5-3	1-3	4-0	2-0	0-0	3-3	*	1-1
18. Wollen Sports	2-1	0-2	2-1	0-0	2-0	1-0	5-0	2-1	5-0	0-1	2-0	0-1	2-0	5-1	5-0	1-0	4-1	*

DIVISION ONE RESULT CHART 1992-92

HOME TEAM	1	2	3	4	5	6	7	8	9	10	11	12	13	14	15	16
1. Bishops Cleeve	*	3-4	0-1	3-1	1-2	2-3	2-1	3-1	1-0	3-4	0-3	0-3	1-2	0-0	2-1	4-2
2. Carterton Town	2-0	*	3-1	3-0	1-2	1-3	7-0	1-1	0-0	3-5	1-5	1-2	0-5	0-2	0-1	3-1
3. Cheltenham Saras	1-3	2-0	*	4-0	3-2	4-0	2-0	3-2	0-1	0-1	0-2	2-0	0-1	2-4	1-1	4-1
4. Chipping Norton	2-2	0-3	2-1	*	0-1	5-1	0-4	2-2	0-3	1-4	1-0	7-0	2-4	1-7	0-0	2-5
5. Cirencester Utd	4-1	4-3	1-3	0-1	*	1-1	1-1	4-1	2-3	0-1	0-11	0-1	0-1	1-6	3-3	2-3
6. Clanfield	1-1	0-1	3-1	3-2	4-0	*	0-3	3-3	1-1	1-1	1-0	0-4	0-7	1-3	1-5	3-2
7. Easington Sports	0-1	1-1	2-1	2-1	1-2	0-2	*	0-1	1-4	3-7	1-1	0-4	2-3	2-2	2-1	0-1
8. Highworth Town	3-0	1-5	3-2	2-3	2-1	1-2	4-0	*	0-3	2-3	0-2	0-3	2-3	2-2	3-0	2-2
9. Kidlington	4-1	4-2	3-2	4-1	2-1	1-1	3-0	1-1	*	2-2	1-3	1-1	0-3	1-1	1-0	1-3
10. Lambourn Sports	4-1	1-3	1-2	2-2	1-1	2-6	4-1	2-1	4-0	*	1-5	1-3	1-2	2-2	2-1	1-3
11. North Leigh	7-1	5-3	3-1	3-2	8-3	5-1	8-1	1-2	3-0	4-4	*	5-1	4-1	4-2	3-2	1-2
12. Purton	3-1	2-0	2-1	6-3	7-0	4-1	3-3	1-3	2-1	0-2	2-8	*	0-5	3-4	1-1	3-0
13. Tuffley Rovers	6-0	4-0	2-1	6-1	3-0	1-1	3-1	3-0	2-0	1-2	3-2	0-1	*	7-1	0-0	6-0
14. Wallingford Town	4-1	4-4	3-1	1-1	0-1	1-1	2-0	4-1	2-2	6-1	4-1	2-1	2-3	*	5-2	1-2
15. Wootton Bassett	3-5	0-3	1-2	3-2	2-1	1-0	3-1	3-0	1-1	1-3	1-4	0-1	0-2	0-1	*	1-2
16. Yarnton	4-1	4-0	0-0	3-6	0-2	2-2	2-1	0-2	0-1	1-4	1-1	1-0	0-1	0-3	1-2	*

730

PREMIER DIVISION CUP 1992-93

Preliminary Round

Almondsbury Picksons v Milton United	3-1
Kingsbury Rangers v Headington Amateurs	0-1

First Round

Rayners Lane v Moreton Town	1-2
Wantage Town v Almondsbury Picksons	4-3
Bicester Town v Abingdon United	2-1
Shortwood United v Pegasus Juniors	4-2
Didcot Town v Fairford Town	4-0
Swindon Supermarine v Cirencester Town	1-0
Headington Amtrs v Cinderford Town	1-0
Wollen Sports v Banbury United	2-0

Second Round

Moreton Town v Didcot Town	4-0
Bicester Town v Headington Amateurs	1-0
Wantage Town v Swindon Supermarine	2-1
Shortwood United v Wollen Sports	0-3

Semi Finals

Moreton Town v Wantage Town *(at Cirencester Town)*	1-0
Bicester Town v Wollen Sports *(at Abingdon United)*	2-0, 0-0,1-0

Final *(at Banbury United)*: Moreton Town 2, Bicester Town 1

FIRST DIVISION CUP 1992-93

First Round

Highworth Town v Bishops Cleeve	0-0,0-2
Lambourn Sports v Purton	2-3
Tuffley Rovers v Chipping Norton Town	2-1
Clanfield v Yarnton	0-1
Wootton Bassett Town v Cirencester United	2-0
Wallingford Town v Kidlington	3-1
North Leigh v Carterton Town	2-1
Cheltenham Saracens v Easington Sports	2-1

Second Round

Purton v Wallingford Town	2-1
Tuffley Rovers v North Leigh	5-2
Bishops Cleeve v Wootton Bassett	3-3,2-2,0-3
Cheltenham Saracens v Yarnton	1-2

Semi Finals

Wootton Bassett Town v Purton *(at Clanfield & Swindon Supermarine)*	0-0,1-2
Tuffley Rovers v Yarnton *(at Carterton Town)*	1-0, 0-0,1-0

Final *(at Moreton Town)*: Tuffley Rovers 3, Purton 1

In last season's Directory the Hellenic League result grids were published incomplete. We know that some readers like to have a complete record, so the 1991-92 results grids are printed in full below. Our thanks go to Malcolm Clarke for plugging the gaps.

PREMIER DIVISION RESULT CHART 1991/92

HOME TEAM	1	2	3	4	5	6	7	8	9	10	11	12	13	14	15	16	17	18
1. Abingdon United	*	0-1	1-3	2-0	2-1	1-0	4-0	0-2	1-4	3-2	0-1	2-0	1-0	10-0	0-1	1-1	1-2	0-2
2. Almondsbury P.	2-0	*	1-0	2-2	6-0	4-1	0-4	0-1	0-2	3-2	3-0	1-1	1-1	6-2	1-0	6-1	1-2	3-2
3. Banbury United	1-2	1-2	*	0-0	2-0	4-1	3-2	0-1	1-1	2-2	0-1	1-4	1-2	3-1	4-1	1-1	5-6	4-0
4. Bicester Town	1-2	1-1	1-3	*	4-0	1-0	1-0	0-1	1-0	1-0	2-0	0-0	0-0	1-1	1-1	2-2	0-1	0-0
5. Bishops Cleeve	2-4	0-1	1-3	0-4	*	0-1	0-2	0-0	2-2	4-4	1-2	1-3	0-2	0-2	1-0	0-0	0-2	0-2
6. Carterton Town	0-2	1-2	0-1	1-4	1-1	*	2-2	0-3	1-1	1-3	0-2	3-2	2-1	0-1	1-1	0-3	1-5	0-4
7. Cinderford Town	0-0	2-0	3-1	1-1	2-0	3-1	*	0-1	2-1	1-2	3-1	1-1	1-1	1-0	4-1	1-1	2-1	1-1
8. Cirencester Town	3-2	3-2	0-0	2-1	6-0	1-1	1-0	*	2-2	3-0	3-0	2-0	1-1	5-0	4-3	6-0	4-2	1-2
9. Didcot Town	1-0	1-2	1-2	5-0	4-3	4-1	1-2	0-1	*	1-1	0-3	3-1	4-1	4-1	2-1	3-0	2-3	3-0
10. Fairford Town	0-1	1-2	3-0	2-0	2-1	2-2	1-5	1-1	0-1	*	2-2	6-0	5-1	9-0	4-1	3-1	0-4	1-1
11. Headington Amtrs	0-2	0-2	2-0	0-1	2-2	1-2	2-2	3-4	0-2	2-2	*	3-2	2-4	4-1	2-2	5-1	1-2	1-4
12. Kintbury Rgrs	1-3	0-0	2-0	2-2	4-1	3-0	0-2	0-2	1-1	1-4	0-1	*	1-2	0-1	1-3	4-1	1-2	0-4
13. Milton United	1-2	0-0	4-0	5-1	3-0	2-1	3-0	1-1	1-0	2-1	1-1	0-3	*	5-1	5-0	3-0	2-3	2-1
14. Moreton Town	1-2	1-2	2-4	2-1	2-3	2-0	2-2	0-3	1-3	2-1	1-1	0-3	1-2	*	3-2	1-4	2-4	0-4
15. Pegasus Juniors	2-2	2-0	3-0	3-4	10-0	5-2	1-2	0-4	3-1	2-4	2-0	1-2	1-1	5-1	*	0-2	2-4	2-0
16. Rayners Lane	1-3	3-2	2-3	1-2	6-1	1-3	2-3	1-1	1-0	2-1	5-0	2-2	2-5	2-1	1-3	*	0-4	0-2
17. Shortwood United	5-0	1-1	1-3	2-1	3-0	1-0	1-0	1-4	5-2	0-0	2-1	2-2	1-3	3-1	2-0	3-0	*	0-0
18. Swindon Athletic	0-0	0-3	0-1	2-2	3-0	1-2	3-1	2-1	4-8	2-1	2-2	2-0	6-0	1-1	3-2	0-0	1-2	*

DIVISION ONE RESULT CHART 1991/92

HOME TEAM	1	2	3	4	5	6	7	8	9	10	11	12	13	14	15	16	17
1. Cheltenham Saracens	*	0-2	0-2	9-2	3-0	1-0	3-1	6-2	1-1	4-1	5-0	2-2	4-0	0-3	3-0	1-2	0-1
2. Chipping Norton	0-0	*	3-0	4-2	3-1	2-1	1-1	1-1	0-2	0-2	3-0	2-3	3-1	1-2	0-4	4-1	1-0
3. Cirencester Utd	2-0	0-2	*	2-0	1-0	4-1	3-2	2-1	0-5	0-3	1-0	2-2	4-0	1-2	0-2	1-1	6-1
4. Clanfield	0-2	3-2	0-0	*	4-1	1-2	3-1	1-1	0-1	0-0	3-0	2-2	0-1	1-1	0-1	1-1	0-1
5. Easington Spts	2-4	1-0	4-2	3-1	*	2-1	5-2	1-6	0-3	1-0	2-5	0-5	1-2	0-3	0-4	1-0	1-4
6. Highworth Town	1-4	2-0	3-1	5-0	4-0	*	1-1	1-2	2-3	0-0	2-0	0-2	6-0	2-5	0-1	2-4	0-0
7. Kidlington	1-1	1-2	5-3	0-0	3-1	1-1	*	2-3	2-1	1-3	6-0	1-1	0-3	0-3	0-3	2-2	2-1
8. Lambourn Sports	1-6	3-3	1-1	1-1	1-4	2-2	4-1	*	2-1	1-3	2-1	2-1	2-2	1-2	0-2	0-3	3-2
9. North Leigh	7-1	4-1	2-1	3-2	0-1	2-3	2-1	4-0	*	3-1	7-1	4-0	6-1	2-1	2-4	4-1	4-0
10. Purton	1-0	8-1	1-1	3-1	1-2	1-1	1-4	1-0	2-1	*	1-0	0-3	2-1	1-1	2-2	2-0	2-1
11. Supermarine	1-1	3-0	0-3	0-4	3-1	0-2	0-2	0-2	0-0	0-2	*	0-3	1-1	2-4	0-3	1-1	2-1
12. Tuffley Rovers	1-1	2-1	3-1	2-0	3-0	4-0	4-1	4-0	1-1	1-0	10-0	*	2-0	2-4	2-2	5-1	11-0
13. Wallingford T.	0-1	0-7	1-1	2-0	0-2	2-3	2-2	6-1	1-5	2-0	0-1	0-2	*	0-2	1-7	5-0	1-1
14. Wantage Town	1-1	1-1	4-3	9-0	3-1	2-3	4-1	1-0	5-1	2-1	3-1	0-0	5-1	*	1-1	3-0	2-1
15. Wollen Sports	4-3	4-0	2-0	4-1	7-1	1-1	5-0	6-1	2-1	3-1	5-1	4-3	3-0	1-2	*	4-0	2-1
16. Wootton Bassett	0-2	3-3	0-0	1-1	3-1	3-0	3-0	1-3	1-1	1-0	2-0	2-3	3-1	1-2	1-2	*	0-2
17. Yarnton	4-1	0-1	4-1	1-1	1-0	3-1	1-1	2-3	0-1	2-2	1-0	0-6	1-3	1-0	0-1	2-2	*

HELLENIC LEAGUE PREMIER DIVISION TEN YEAR RECORD

	83/4	84/5	85/6	86/7	87/8	88/9	89/0	90/1	91/2	92/3
Abingdon Town	5	11	4	1	2	-	-	-	-	-
Abingdon United	4	6	7	6	4	3	3	7	6	15
Almondsbury Picksons	1	10	17	-	-	-	7	10	3	6
Avon (Bradford)	16	-	-	-	-	-	-	-	-	-
Banbury United	-	-	-	-	-	-	-	8	10	11
Bicester Town	8	14	15	14	10	6	6	3	9	9
Bishops Cleeve	-	-	-	-	16	10	16	14	18	-
Carterton Town	-	-	-	-	-	-	-	12	17	-
Cinderford Town	-	-	-	-	-	-	-	-	5	5
Cirencester Town	-	-	-	-	-	-	-	-	2	3
Clanfield	11	18	-	-	-	-	-	-	-	-
Didcot Town	9	17	-	-	5	8	15	4	7	18
Fairford Town	14	8	13	15	8	4	5	2	11	12
Hazells Club (Aylesbury)	17	-	-	-	-	-	-	-	-	-
Headington Amateurs	-	-	-	-	-	-	12	5	12	13
Hounslow	-	5	3	2	-	-	-	9	-	-
Kintbury Rangers	-	-	-	-	-	15	8	11	14	14
Maidenhead Town	12	13	18	-	-	-	-	-	-	-
Milton United	-	-	-	-	-	-	-	1	4	2
Moreton Town	2	2	9	8	12	7	13	17	16	4
Morris Motors	-	9	14	7	14	-	-	-	-	-
Newport A.F.C.	-	-	-	-	-	-	1	-	-	-
Northwood	13	-	-	-	-	-	-	-	-	-
Pegasus Juniors	-	-	11	12	17	5	9	15	13	17
Penhill					(See Swindon Athletic)					
Rayners Lane	6	12	6	13	13	13	11	13	15	10
Ruislip Park	-	-	-	-	-	-	18	-	-	-
Sharpness	-	4	1	5	7	2	4	-	-	-
Shortwood United	-	1	2	3	3	11	2	6	1	7
Supermarine	7	3	5	11	15	14	17	-	-	-
Swindon Athletic	-	-	-	9	6	9	10	16	8	-
Swindon Supermarine	-	-	-	-	-	-	-	-	-	8
Thame United	3	16	10	17	9	-	-	-	-	-
Viking Sports	-	-	-	4	11	17	-	-	-	-
Wallingford Town	10	15	12	16	18	16	-	-	-	-
Wantage Town	15	7	16	18	-	12	14	18	-	16
Wollen Sports	-	-	-	-	-	-	-	-	-	1
Yate Town	-	-	8	10	1	1	-	-	-	-
No. of clubs competing	17	18	18	18	18	17	18	18	18	18

PREMIER DIVISION CLUBS 1993-94

ABINGDON UNITED

President: R Barlow FJMI   **Chairman:** P Evans   **Manager:** G Clark
Secretary: Terry Hutchinson, 41 Austin Place, Abingdon, Oxon OX14 1LT (0494 452559).
Press Officer: W Fletcher (0235 520255).
Ground: Northcourt Road, Abingdon OX14 1PL (0235 520255).
Directions: From north (Oxford) leave A34 at Abingdon north sign and Northcourt Rd is 1st major turning after r'bout. From South, East or West leave Abingdon on A4183 and turn left into Northcourt Rd after 1 mile. 2 miles from Redley (BR)
Seats: 52   **Cover:** 120   **Capacity:** 2,000   **Floodlights:** Yes   **Founded:** 1946
Colours: Yellow/blue/yellow   **Change colours:** White/red/white.
Previous leagues: North Berks
Programme: 30p   **Programme Editor:** W Fletcher, ACJI (0235 20255).
Record Gate: 500 v Abingdon Town, Berks & Bucks Senior Cup 1989-90.
Clubhouse: Two bars, membership 350. Open normal hours. New Clubhouse summer 1989.
Honours: N Berks Lg 53-54 (Lg Cup R-up 53-54, Charity Shield 52-53), Hellenic Div 1 R-up 76-77 81-82 (Lg Cup R-up 89-90, Div 1 Cup 65-66 81-82 (R-up 66-67), Berks & Bucks Snr Cup R-up 83-84.

ALMONDSBURY PICKSONS

Secretary: D W Winstone, 4 St Michaels Close, Winterbourne, Bristol BS17 1NS (0454 773771).
Ground: Oaklands Park, Almondsbury, Bristol (0454 612220/201343).
Directions: Adjacent to M5 junction 16 - follow A38 Thornbury - ground first left. 4 miles from Bristol Parkway (BR).
County bus services to Thornbury, Stroud and Gloucester.
Seats: None   **Cover:** No   **Capacity:** 2,000   **Floodlights:** Yes   **Founded:** 1897
Colours: Blue/white/blue   **Change colours:** Red/black/black.
Record Gate: Hellenic Cup Final replay 89-90.
Previous Leagues: Bristol Weslyan/ Bristol Suburban/ Bristol Premier Comb./ Glos Co.
Previous Names: Almondsbury/ Almondsbury Greenway/ Almondsbury '85/ Almondsbury Picksons.
Previous Ground: Almondsbury Rec. (until 1986).   **Programme:** 20 pages 25p
Nickname: Almonds. **Clubhouse:** 7 days, all sports, refreshments, function room, entertainment, skittles.
Hons: FA Vase R-up 78-79 (SF 77-78), Glos Co. Lg(4) 76-78 79-81 (R-up 75-76 81-82), GFA Chal. Tphy 78-79 (R-up 80-81), Avon Prem. Comb. 74-75, Glos Snr Amtr Cup 87-88, Hellenic Lg 83-84 (R-up 82-83, Lg Cup(2) 83-85).

BANBURY UNITED

Chairman: J Breslin   **Vice Chairman:** N/A   **President:** N/A.
Secretary: D K Jesson, 'Wychwood House', 3 Winchester Close, Banbury OX16 8FB (0295 257262).
Manager: Wallie Hastie   **Asst Manager:** Ian Bowyer   **Coach:** Phil Houghton.
Physio: John Source   **Commercial Mgr:** John Gardner   **Press Officer:** Barry Worsley.
Ground: The Stadium, off Station Rd, Banbury, Oxon (0295 263354).
Directions: M40 jct 11, follow signs for Banbury then BR station, turn right down narrow lane before entering station forecourt; eastern end of town.
Seats: 40   **Cover:** 800   **Capacity:** 6,500   **Floodlights:** Yes   **Founded:** 1933
Colours: White/blue/blue   **Change colours:** Blue/white/red   **Reformed:** 1965
Previous Name: Banbury Spencer   **Club Sponsors:** Cherwell Windows.   **Nickname:** Puritans.
Prev. Lges: Banbury Jnr 33-34/ Oxon Snr 34-35/ Birmingham Comb. 35-54/ W. Mids 54-66/ Southern 66-90.
Record Attendance: 7,160 v Oxford City, FA Cup 3rd Qualifying Round, 30/10/48.
Best FA Cup season: 1st Rd replay 73-74 (Also 1st Rd 47-48 61-62 72-73).
Best F.A. Trophy year: 3rd Rd 70-71 73-74.
Midweek matches: Tuesday.
Clubhouse: Match days & week-ends. Mid-week on hire. Hot food available during aftermatches.
Record transfer fee paid: £2,000 for Phil Emsden (Oxford Utd, Jan 1980)
Record transfer fee received: £20,000 Kevin Wilson (Derby, December 1979)
Programme: 24 pages 50p   **Editor:** Barry Worsley (0295 255536)
Club Shop: Yes. Programmes, mugs, ties, sweaters, badges. Contact Barry Worsley (0295 255536).
Players progressing to Football League: Ollie Kearns (Reading), Kevin Wilson (Derby), Terry Muckleberg (Oxford).
Record win: 12-0 v R.N.A.S. Culham, Oxon Snr Cup 45-46.
Record defeat: 2-11 v West Bromwich Albion 'A', Birmingham Comb. 38-39.
Top Scorer 92-93: Jody McKay, 17.   **Capt. & P.o.Y. 92-93:** Martin Singleton
Club record scorer: Brian Pike (1935-48), Tony Jacques (65-76) - both 222.
Club record appearances: Dave Matthews.
Honours: Oxon Snr Cup 78-79 87-88 (R-up 35-36 48-49 82-83 86-87 88-89 92-93), Birmingham Comb. R-up 47-48, Oxon Prof. Cup 52-53(jt) 70-71(jt) 72-73 77-78 79-80(jt), Hellenic Lg Cup R-up 91-92, Birmingham Snr Cup R-up 48-49 59-60 (SF 46-47), Oxon Snr Lg 34-35 39-40 47-48(res), Banbury Jnr Lg 33-34, Oxon Charity Cup 34-35 (R-up 39-40), Banbury Charity Cup 34-35, Banbury Gold Cross Cup R-up 34-35, Tillotson Cup 46-47 (R-up 45-46), Oxon Hosp. Cup 46-47 (R-up 45-46), Oxon Benev. Cup R-up 77-78 80-81 82-83, Daventry Charity Cup 88-89 89-90, Smiths Mem. Cup 68-69 69-70 (R-up 66-67 67-68), Hitchin Centenary Cup 68-69 (R-up 67-68), Leamington Jnr Cup 50-51 51-52, Leamington & Dist. Lg(res) 51-52, Leamington Charity Cup 51-52, Warks Comb. R-up 57-58 60-61 (Presidents Cup R-up 60-61), Midland Floodlit Cup 67-68, Prem. Midweek F'lit Lg R-up 73-74, Shaw & Kilburn F'lit Lg 77-78, Northants Snr Yth Lg Cup 91-92, Wallspan Comb. 85-86.

BICESTER TOWN

Secretary/Press Officer: Phil Allen, 38 Bassett Avenue, Bicester OX6 7TZ (0869 252125).
Commercial Manager: Secretary   **Manager:** Kevin Leach.
Coach: Steve Stillman   **Physio:** Sean Barker.
Ground: Sports Ground, Oxford Rd, Bicester (0869 241936)
Directions: From Oxford; past Tescos on outskirts of Bicester - ground on right. From Aylesbury; turn left at first island on outskirts of Bicester onto bypass, right at next island, pass Tescos & ground on right.
Seats: 250   **Cover:** 550   **Capacity:**   **Floodlights:** No   **Founded:** 1876
Colours: Red & white stripes/black/red   **Change:** Yellow/black/yellow.
Previous Leagues: Oxon Senior
Previous Name: Slade Banbury Road (pre-1923).   **Programme Editors:** A J Pickett/A Lyne.
Clubhouse: One bar   **Nickname:** Foxhunters.
Record Gate: 850 v Oxford United.
Hons: Hellenic Lg 60-1 77-78 (Lg Cup 90-91 (R-up 92-93), Div 1 76-77).

Bicester Town F.C. - Hellenic League Premier Division Cup runners-up 1992-93. Back Row (L/R): Kevin Leach (Manager), Sean Barker (Physio), Stuart Carroll, Dave Wallcraft, Shaun Adams, Matthew Cresswell, Marc Edwards, Jason Allen, Steve Sillman (Coach). Front: Mark Donohue, Phil Starrett, Mark Butler, Alan Frost, Jimmy Hamilton, Martin Swanson, Martin Keys. Photo - Steve Daniels.

CINDERFORD TOWN

Chairman: A Saunders   **Vice Chairman/Press Officer:** A Peacey   **President:** S Watkins.
Secretary: C Warren, 9c Tusculum Way, Mitcheldean, Glos GL17 0HZ (0594 543065).
Manager: Tim Harris   **Coach:** Denzil Brizland   **Physio:** Keith Marfell.
Ground: The Causeway, Hilldene, Cinderford, Glos (0594 22039).
Directions: From Gloucester take A40 to Ross-on-Wye, then A48 - Chepstow. In 10 miles turn right at Elton garage onto A4151 signed Cinderford, thru Littledean, up steep hill, right at crossroads, second left into Latimer Rd. Ground 5 mins walk from town centre.
Seats: 250   **Cover:** 1,000   **Capacity:** 3,500   **Floodlights:** Yes   **Founded:** 1922.
Club colours: White (red trim)   **Change colours:** Gold & black   **Nickname:** Town.
Record Attendance: 4,850 v Minehead, Western League, 1955-56.
Previous Leagues: Western 46-59/ Glos Northern Snr 60-62/ Warwickshire Combination 63-64/ West Midlands 65-69/ Gloucestershire County 70-73 85-89/ Midland Comb. 74-84.
Programme: 28 pages, with entry   **Editors:** Chris Warren/ Graham Bevan.
Club Shop: Souvenirs: Club badges (£2), ties, mugs etc. Programme exchanges welcome - contact secretary.
Midweek home matchday: Wednesday   **Reserve's League:** Glos. Northern Snr.
Clubhouse: Open every day. 2 bars, kitchen, 2 skittle alleys, darts, dancehall, committee room.
Captain 92-93: Warren Evans   **Top Scorer 92-93:** Colin Peacey   **P.O.Y. 92-93:** Russell Bowles.
Hons: Hellenic Lg Div 1 90-91, Glos Northern Snr Lg Div 1 38-39 60-61 (R-up(6) 35-37 61-63 66-67 80-81), Nth Glos Lg Div 1 38-39 60-61, Glos Snr Amtr Cup (Nth)(6) 49-50 54-56 68-69 70-71 76-77 (R-up 34-35 57-58 80-81), Western Lg Div 2 56-57, Warwickshire Comb. 63-64, W Mids Lg Prem Div Cup 68-69, Glos Jnr Cup (Nth) 80-81, Midland Comb. 81-82, Glos Co. Lg R-up 69-70 71-72 73-74, Glos F.A. Tphy R-up 92-93.

CIRENCESTER TOWN

President: Alec Hibberd   **Chairman:** Robin Thompson
Secretary: Brian Davis, 97 Golden Farm Rd, Cirencester, Glos GL7 1DG (0285 654274).
Ground: The Stadium, Smithsfield, Chesterton Lane, Cirencester (0285 645783).
Directions: Follow By-pass towards Bristol. The ground is signposted on the left approx quarter of a mile from town. 3 miles from Kemble (BR).
Seats: None   **Cover:** 200   **Capacity:** 1,500   **Floodlights:** Yes   **Founded:** 1870
Colours: Red & black/black/red   **Change colours:** All blue.
Record Attendance: 1,200 in 1968 FA Amateur Cup.   **Clubhouse details:** Open 5 nights
Hons: GFA Senior Amtr Cup 79-80, GFA Challenge Trophy R-up 91-92, Hellenic Lg R-up 91-92 (Div 1 73-74 (R-up 90-91), Div 1 Cup 90-91).

FAIRFORD TOWN

President: B W Wall   **Chairman:** M B Tanner
Secretary: M J Cook, "Bow Wow" Down Ampney, Cirencester GL7 1EW (0793 751240).
Ground: Cinder Lane, Fairford, Cirencester (0285 712071).
Manager: Paul Richardson   **Asst Manager:** Gerry Kelly.
Physio: T Williams   **Commercial Manager:** E Howard.
Directions: Entering Fairford on A417 from Lechlade turn left down Cinder Lane 150yds after 40mph sign. From Cirencester on same road, follow thru village and turn right down Cinder Lane 400yds after Railway Inn. Buses from Swindon, Lechlade and Cirencester.
Seats: None   **Cover:** 150   **Capacity:** 2,000   **Floodlights:** Yes   **Founded:** 1891
Colours: Red/white/red   **Change colours:** White/black/white   **Nickname:** Town.
Previous Leagues: Cirencester & District (pre-1946)/ Swindon & District 46-70.
Previous Grounds: None   **Record Gate:** 1,500 v Swindon Town, friendly 18/7/92.
Programme: 20 pages with admission   **Programme Editor:** Chairman   **Club Shop:** No.
Club Sponsors: Jewson   **Midweek home matchday:** Wednesday   **Record win:** 9-0
Clubhouse: Open each evening, weekend lunches & before and after all games   **Record defeat:** 0-9.
Captain 92-93: Bob Simpson   **Top Scorer 92-93:** Derek Labbett
P.O.Y. 92-93: Richard Hadgkiss   **Club record scorer:** Pat Toomey.
Hons: Glos Challenge Trophy 79-80 (R-up 82-83), Hellenic Lg R-up 78-79 79-80 90-91 (Premier Div Cup 78-79, Div 1 71-72, Div 1 Cup 71-72), Glos Jnr Cup 62-63, Swindon & Dist Lg 64-65 68-69.

HEADINGTON AMATEURS

President: John Dunne   **Chairman:** Donald Light   **Vice Chairman:** Paul Sammons.
Secretary: S P Giles, 60 Glebelands, Headington, Oxford OX3 7EN (0865 60810).
Manager: Jimmy Light   **Asst Manager:** Bruce McCrae
Physio: Chris Gillick   **Press Officer:** Sarah McCrae.
Ground: Barton Rec., Barton Village Road, Barton, Oxon (0865 60489).
Directions: From Green Rd r'bout, Headington, (on A40) take Barton/Islip exit (1st exit coming from Witney, last coming from London), turn left into North Way, follow road for half mile - ground at bottom of hill on left.
Seats: None   **Cover:** None   **Floodlights:** No   **Founded:** 1949.   **Nickname:** A's.
Colours: All red   **Change:** All white   **Midweek home matchday:** Wednesday   **Record win:** 5-0
Previous Leagues: Oxford City Junior 49-66/ Oxford Senior 67-88.   **Record defeat:** 1-6.
Programme: 8 pages, £1 with entry   **Editor:** Stan Hawkswood (0865 65546)   **Club Shop:** No.
Sponsors: Blanchford & Co Ltd   **Previous Ground:** Romanway, Cowley (pre-1990).
Clubhouse: Open Tues & Thurs 6-11pm, Sat matchdays 4.45-11pm. Rolls, chips, burgers, hot dogs, sweets etc.
Captain 92-93: Kent Drackett   **Top Scorer 92-93:** Ian Macaskill   **P.O.Y. 92-93:** Colin McMahon.
Club record scorer: Tony Penge   **Club record appearances:** Michael Tighe.
Hons: Oxon Snr Lg(4) 72-74 75-77 (R-up 71-72 74-75 77-78 81-82 84-85), Div 1 68-69, Pres. Cup(2) 72-74 (R-up 71-72 77-78 84-85)), Oxon Charity Cup 75-76 (I'mediate Cup 88-89), Hellenic Lg Div 1 R-up 87-88 (Res. Sect. 92-93).

KINTBURY RANGERS

President: P Adamson   **Chairman:** P Adamson
Secretary: A K Plank, 26 Kennet Road, Kintbury, Newbury RG15 0XW (0488 58460).
Ground: Recreation Ground, Inkpen Road, Kintbury (0488 57001).
Directions: Turn off A4 (signed Kintbury) between Newbury/Hungerford. 2nd left after level crossing into Inkpen Road, entrance 200yds on right by Jubilee Centre. Half mile from Kintbury (BR).
Seats: None   **Cover:** No   **Capacity:** 1,000   **Floodlights:** Yes   **Founded:** 1890
Cols: Amber/black   **Change colours:** White/blue   **Nickname:** Rangers   **Reformed:** 1943.
Prog. Ed.: N Matthews (0488 84117)   **Previous Leagues:** Newbury District/ Nth Berks.
Record Gate: 400 v Newport AFC, 1990.   **Clubhouse:** Open every night except Wednesday
Hons: Nth Berks Lg 77-78 81-82, Hellenic Lg Div 1 R-up 87-88, Berks & Bucks I'mediate Cup 60-61 (R-up 87-88).

MILTON UNITED

President: G Cannon   **Chairman:** J Cannon
Secretary: Maldwyn James, 45 Whitehorns Way, Drayton, Abingdon OX14 4LH (0235 531789).
Ground: The Sportsfield, High Street, Milton, Abingdon, Oxon (0235) 832999   **Founded:** 1926
Directions: Use A34 bypass approx 10 miles north of M4 jct.13 & 10 miles south of Oxford. Leave A34 at Milton Hill roundabout and follow signs to Milton Park Est. After roundabout follow road over railway bridge, take 1st left, ground immediately on left.
Colours: Claret & sky/sky/sky   **Change colours:** All white or all sky.
Hons: Hellenic Lg 90-91 (Div 1 89-90), Nth Berks Lg(4) 85-86 87-89 (R-up 84-85 86-87, Lg Cup(3) 84-86 88-89, Div 2 80-81, Charity Shield(4) 84-86 87-89 (R-up 82-83), Nth Berks War Mem. Cup(3) 83-85 87-88, Berks & Bucks I'mediate Cup 90-91.

MORETON TOWN

President: Lord Dulverton   **Chairman:** C Miles
Secretary: Aubrey Honour, 28 Evenlode Gdns, Moreton-in-the-Marsh, Glos GL56 0JF (0608 51392
Ground: London Road, Moreton-in-the-Marsh (0608 50861).
Directions: On main Oxford - Worcester road. Half mile from Moreton (BR).
Seats: None   **Cover:** 400   **Capacity:** 3,000   **Floodlights:** Yes   **Founded:** 1908.
Colours: White/blue/white   **Change colours:** Blue/white/blue   **Programme:** Yes
Nickname: Lilywhites   **Previous Leagues:** Cheltenham/ Mid Cotswold
Record Gate: 1,100 v Newport, 1963.   **Clubhouse:** Open every night except Monday
Hons: Biggart Cup 69-70, Hellenic Lg 73-74 75-76 82-83 (R-up 74-75 75-76 81-82 83-84 84-85 92-93, Premier Division Cup 92-93), Beighton Cup.

NORTH LEIGH

President: Mrs C Smith   **Chairman:** Mr B Norton   **Vice Chairman:** Mr P King
Secretary: Mr P J Dix, 8 Windmill Close, North Leigh, Nr Witney, Oxon OX8 6RP (0993 881199).
Manager/Coach: Mr P Townsend   **Asst Manager:** Mr P Lewis
Physio: Mr R Keen   **Press Officer:** Barry Norton (0993 881777).
Ground: Eynsham Hall Park Sports Ground, North Leigh, nr Witney, Oxon (0993 881427).
Directions: Ground is situated off A4095 Witney to Woodstock road 3 miles east of Witney. Entrance to ground is 300yds east of Main Park Entrance.
Seats: None   **Cover:** No   **Capacity:** 2,000   **Floodlights:** Due   **Founded:** 1908
Colours: Sky/navy   **Change colours:** All orange   **Nickname:** None.
Previous Grounds: None   **Previous Leagues:** Witney & District 08-89.
Programme: 20 pages, £1 with entry   **Editor:** Mr D Hodgins (0993 882566)   **Club Shop:** No.
Club Sponsors: Various   **Clubhouse:** Bar open matches. Snacks available.
Captain 92-93: D Groves   **Top Scorer 92-93:** P Coles   **P.O.Y. 92-93:** S King
Club record scorer: P Coles   **Club record appearances:** P King.
Hons: Hellenic Lg Div 1 R-up 92-93, Oxon Jnr Shield 56-57 83-84, Oxon Charity Cup 84-85 88-89, Witney & Dist. Lg(13) 50-57 84-90 (Lg Cup(10) 47-48 51-52 53-55 56-57 81-82 85-89).

RAYNERS LANE

Chairman: Dave Blewitt   **President/Commercial Mgr:** Tom Lynn (081 868 4671).
Secretary: Tony Pratt, 4 Stirling Close, Cowley, Uxbridge, Middx UB8 2BA (0895 233853).
Manager/Coach/Press Officer: Don Durkin (0753 889502)   **Asst Mgr:** Richard Hedge.
Ground: Tithe Farm Social Club, 51 Rayners Lane, South Harrow, Middx (081 866 9659).
Directions: Right from Rayners Lane Station, 1st left (Rayners Lane), grnd on right. By road: off A40 at Polish War Memorial junction (1st after Northolt aerodrome), left into A4180 (West End Rd), right into Station Approach, right into Victoria Rd at lights, over r'bout, 2nd left after next lights (Rayners Lane) - grnd half mile on left.
Seats: 32   **Cover:** 50   **Capacity:** 1,000   **Floodlights:** No   **Founded:** 1933
Colours: Yellow/green   **Change colours:** Red/black   **Nickname:** The Lane
Sponsors: A & J Bull   **Previous Lges:** Parthenon/ Spartan/ Middx.
Programme: 28 pages   **Editor:** Tom Lynn (081 8684671)   **Club Shop:** No.
Record Attendance: 550 v Wealdstone, Middx Senior Cup, 1983.
Clubhouse: 2 bars, open all day matchdays. Also tea bar.
Midweek home matchday: Tuesday   **Reserve team's League:** Middx County Lge.
Captain 92-93: Gerry Hynes   **Top Scorer 92-93:** Danny Mills
P.O.Y. 92-93: Darrell Clements   **Club record appearances:** Paul Abell.
Hons: Hellenic Lg 82-83 (Div 1 Cup 1980-81), Middx Lg 71-72, Middx Premier Cup 83-84 (R-up 72-73), Harrow Wembley & Dist. Lg 39-40 40-41 44-45 (Lg Cup 41-42 43-44 44-45), Parthenon Lg 50-51 (R-up 52-53, Lg Cup 48-49 52-53 56-57), Middx Summer Cup 1991, West Middx Midweek Lg 36-37.

SHORTWOOD UNITED

President: Hugh Robinson   **Chairman:** Peter Webb   **Vice C'man:** Chris Rivers, Stan Grant
Secretary/Press Officer: Mark Webb, 1 The Bungalow, Shortwood, Nailsworth, Stroud, Glos (0453 833204).
Manager: Steven Doughty   **Asst Manager/Coach:** Roger Smith
Physio: Adrian Brown   **Commercial Manager:** Keith Sheppard.
Ground: "Meadow Bank", Shortwood, Nailsworth, Gloucestershire (0453 833936).
Directions: In Nailsworth turn into Spring Hill then first left. Continue past shop and and keep left past "Britannia" (signposted Shortwood) - continue to end for ground. 4 miles from Stroud (BR).
Seats: 50   **Cover:** 150   **Capacity:** 5,000   **Floodlights:** Yes   **Founded:** 1900
Colours: Red/blue/red   **Change:** All blue or Blue/white/blue.   **Nickname:** The Wood.
Prev. Grnd: Table Land, Wallow Green   **Prev. Lges:** Stroud/ Glos Northern Snr/ Glos Co.
Record Attendance: 1,000 v Forest Green Rovers, FA Vase 5th Rd 81-82.   **Club Shop:** No.
Programme: 18 pages, 30p   **Programme Editor:** Keith Sheppard   **Record win:** 11-0
Sponsors: Richard Lacey Insurance   **Midweek home matchday:** Wednesday   **Record defeat:** 0-9
Reserves' Lge: Glos Northern Snr   **Rec. transfer fee received:** Paul Tester (Cheltenham, 80-81).
Clubhouse: Mon-Sat 7-11pm, Sun noon-12 & 7-10.30pm. Crisps etc in bar, hot food kitchen on matchdays.
Top Scorer 92-93: Lee Davis   **Captain & P.O.Y. 92-93:** Nick Ackland
Club record scorer: Peter Grant   **Club record appearances:** Peter Grant.
Hons: Glos Co. Lg 81-82 (R-up 80-81), Glos Tphy 83-84 91-92 (R-up 79-80), Hellenic Lg 84-85 91-92 (R-up 85-86 89-90, Div 1 R-up 83-84, Div 1 Cup 83-84), Hungerford Merit Cup, Glos Snr Amtr Cup 85-86 (R-up 79-80), Stroud Charity Cup 91-92 92-93, Stroud Lg 27-28 (Div 2 26-27 64-65(res), Div 3 25-26 49-50(res) 62-63(res)), Glos Northern Snr Lg R-up 67-68 91-92(res)(Div 2 62-63 80-81(res) 90-91(res)), Arthur Shipway Cup 78-79 79-80.

SWINDON SUPERMARINE

Secretary: Eric Stott, 43 Stanier Street, Swindon, Wilts SN1 5QU (0793 521301).
Ground: Highworth Road, South Marston, Swindon (0973) 824828
Directions: On A361 Swindon/Highworth road, adjoining Marston Industrial Estate. 6 miles from Swindon (BR) -
buses in direction of Highworth, Fairford & Lechdale. If lost ask for Vickers Sports Ground.
Seats: 75   **Cover:** 120   **Capacity:** 1,000   **Floodlights:** Yes   **Founded:** 1992.
Colours: White/blue/blue   **Change colours:** All red   **Programme:** Yes
Previous Names: Supermarine (prev. Vickers Armstrong 46-81), Swindon Athletic (prev. Penhill Yth Centre 70-84/
Penhill 84-84-89) amalgamated in 1992.
Previous Leagues: Supermarine: Wilts, *Swindon Athletic: Wilts/ Swindon & District.*
Previous Ground: Supermarine: Vickers Airfield (until mid-1960s), *Swindon Ath.: Merton 70-84/ 'Southbrook',*
Pinehurst Road 84-92.
Hons: Supermarine: Wilts Snr Cup 85-86 (R-up 74-75 84-85), Hellenic Div 1 R-Up 82-83 (Res Section West R-up
84-85 (Challenge Cup 83-84), Wilts Comb Snr 75-76, Swindon & District Lg Div 3 55-56, Dr Elliott Cup(5),
Faringdon Thursday Memorial Cup(3). *Swindon Ath.: Wilts Snr Cup 82-83 86-87 89-90 (R-up 83-84 85-86 90-91),*
Hellenic Lg Div 1 85-86 86-87, Wilts Co. Lg 82-83 83-84).

TUFFLEY ROVERS

President: A E Wathen   **Chairman:** T Newport   **Vice Chairman:** R Craddock
Secretary: D M Williams, 10 Byron Avenue, Gloucester GL2 6AF (0452 305776).
Manager: A Ireland   **Asst Manager:** J Common
Ground: Glevum Park, Lower Tuffley Lane, Gloucester (0452 504905).
Directions: Follow Gloucester city ring-rd to r'bout signed M5 South & Bristol, take 4th exit signed Hempsted &
city centre, after 200yds take 2nd right (McDonalds on corner) into Lower Tuffley Lane, ground 400yds on left.
Seats: None   **Cover:** No   **Capacity:**   **Floodlights:** No   **Founded:** 1929
Colours: Claret & blue   **Change colours:** White   **Nickname:** None
Previous Grounds: Stroud Rd, Gloucester/ Randwick Park, Tuffley.
Previous Leagues: Stroud/ Glos Northern Senior/ Glos County (pre-1991).
Programme: 10 pages with admission   **Club Shop:** No.
Club Sponsors: Port Security   **Reserve team's League:** Stroud.
Clubhouse: 800 yds from ground. Open before & after matches, and normal pub hours at other times. Snacks.
Captain 92-93: S Blythe   **Top Scorer 92-93:** Wayne Organ   **P.O.Y. 92-93:** R Harding
Hons: Hellenic Lg Div 1 92-93 (Div 1 Cup 92-93), Glos Co. Lge 90-91, Glos Snr Amtr Cup 87-88, Stroud Lg 72-73,
Glos Northern Snr Lg 87-88 (Div 2 79-80).

WANTAGE TOWN

President: **Chairman:** Ernie Smart.
Secretary: Terry Bolton, 15 Broadmarsh Close, Grove, Wantage, Oxon (02357 4223).
Ground: Alfredian Park, Wantage, Oxon (023 57) 4781
Directions: Take Hungerford Road from Wantage, ground signposted on right oppsite recreation ground.
Seats: 50   **Cover:** 300   **Capacity:** 1,500   **Floodlights:** No   **Founded:** 1892
Colours: Green & white/white/green & white   **Change colours:** Blue/white/blue
Previous Leagues: Swindon & District.   **Record Attendance:** 1,800
Prog. Editor: Eric Pride (02357) 66608   **Clubhouse:** Bar open evenings, Tues, Wed, Thurs, Fri, Sat
Hons: Hellenic Lg 80-81 (R-up 81-82, Div 1 R-up 87-88 91-92, Div 1 Cup R-up 91-92), Oxon Snr Cup 82-83.

WOLLEN SPORTS

Secretary: Terry Wollen, 4 Belle Vue Road, Swindon SN1 3HQ (0793 531818).
Ground: The Barn, Blackworth, Highworth, Wilts
Directions: Leaving Highworth heading north on A361. Ground on right 300yds past Blackworth roundabout.
Colours: Green & white/green/green   **Change colours:** All blue   **Floodlights:** No
Hons: Hellenic Lg 92-93 (Div 1 91-92, Div 1 Cup R-up 91-92), Wilts Snr Cup R-up 92-93.

DIVISION ONE CLUBS 1992-93

ARDLEY UNITED

Secretary: R Dick, 63 Halse Road, Brackley, Northants (0280 701179).
Ground: Playing Fields, Ardley.   **Colours:** All red   **Change colours:** White/navy/navy
Prev. Lge: Oxon Snr (pre-1993)   **Hons:** Oxon Snr Lg R-up 92-93 (Pres. Cup R-up 90-91 91-92).

BISHOPS CLEEVE

President: D Billingham   **Chairman:** J Davies
Secretary: Phil Tustain, 7 Dale Walk, Bishops Cleeve, Glos GL52 4PR (0242 674968).
Ground: Stoke Rd, Bishops Cleeve (084267 6752).   **Directions:** 3 miles north of Cheltenham on
A435. 3rd left in village into Stoke Rd - ground on right. 4 miles from Cheltenham (BR); served by Cheltenham to
Tewkesbury buses.
Seats: None   **Cover:** 50   **Capacity:** 1,500   **Floodlights:** No   **Founded:** 1892.
Colours: Green/silver/silver   **Change colours:** Green/black/yellow.
Prev. Lges: Cheltenham, Nth Glos   **Prev. Grnds:** The Skiller (pre-1913), Village Field (pre-1950)
Record Gate: 1,000 v Cardiff City, clubhouse opening.
Clubhouse: Full facilities, bar, dance area **Honours:** Hellenic Lg Cup R-up 90-91.

CARTERTON TOWN

President: G Fox   **Chairman:** R C Gullis
Secretary: B A Hathaway, 4 Minty Close, Carterton OX8 3LL (0993 842578).
Manager: Graham Hurn   **Press Officer:** K Rose (0993 841105).
Ground: Kilkenny Lane (0993 842410)   **Directions:** At end of Swinbrook Rd which is west of town centre
Seats: No   **Cover:** No   **Capacity:**   **Floodlights:** No   **Founded:** 1922
Colours: Yellow & blue/blue/yellow   **Change colours:** All blue   **Reformed:** 1946
Previous Leagues: Witney & District   **Clubhouse:** Recently refurbished. Lounge & licensed bar facilities.
Hons: Oxon Junior Shield 85-86, Oxon Snr Cup R-up 90-91, Witney & Dist. Lg 65-66 (Div 1 84-85 76-77), Hellenic
Lg Div 1 89-90 (Reserve Div 1989-90).

Kintbury Rangers F.C. 1992-93. Photo - Gavin Ellis-Neville.

Rayners Lane F.C., pictured before their F.A. Cup tie at Ashford Town (Middx). Photo - Eric Marsh.

Clanfield '85 F.C. 1992-93.

CHELTENHAM SARACENS

Chairman: J Utteridge   **Manager:** G Bryan.
Secretary: R Attwood, 179 Arle Road, Cheltenham GL51 8LJ (0242 515855).
Asst Manager: C Elsworthy   **Press Officer:** T G Coates (0242 520499).
Ground: Petersfield Park, Tewkesbury Road, Cheltenham (0242 589134).
Directions: 1 mile from Cheltenham centre on A4019 Tewksbury Road (next to B & Q) - 1st left over railway bridge, 1st left and follow service road.
Seats: None   **Cover:** 100   **Capacity:** 2,000   **Floodlights:** No   **Founded:** 1964.
Colours: All blue   **Change colours:** All red   **Club Shop:** No   **Nickname:** Saras.
Prog.: 20 pages, 50p (Ed: Secretary)   **Previous League:** Cheltenham 1964-86.   **Prev. Grnds:** None
Hons: Glos Snr Cup R-up 91-92.   **Clubhouse:** At 16-20 Swindon Road, Cheltenham.
Captain 92-93: John Castleton   **Top Scorer 92-93:** Colin Sweatman   **92-93 P.o.Y.:** Neil Buckland.

CIRENCESTER UNITED

President: A Day   **Chairman:** J Austin   **Vice Chairman:** B Meredith
Secretary/Press Officer: G Varley, 95 Valley Rd, Cirencester, Glos GL7 2JW (0285 657836).
Manager: G Mitchell   **Asst Mgr:** B Muir   **Coach:** A Smith   **Physio:** B Dorey
Ground: Four Acres P.F., Chesterton Lane (0285 651726).
Directions: Dual carriageway towards Bristol, under footbridge, first left after Cirencester Town F.C., ground 200yds on left hand side.
Seats: None   **Cover:** No   **Programme:** Yes   **Floodlights:** No   **Founded:** 1970
Colours: White/red/red   **Change colours:** Green & yellow   **Nickname:** Herd.
Previous Grounds: None   **Previous Name:** The Herd (pre-1990)
Previous Leagues: Cirencester & District (4 years)/ Cheltenham (8 years).
Programme: 16 pages, 50p   **Editor:** N Warriner (0285 656187)   **Club Shop:** No.
Record transfer fee paid: Pkt peanuts   **Received:** F.A.   **Sponsors:** D G Sunner (Builders)
Clubhouse: Training nights & matchdays. Rolls & sundries available.
Captain 92-93: A Smith   **Top Scorer 92-93:** R Barry   **P.o.Y. 92-93:** R Hill
Club record scorer: M Day   **Club record appearances:** A Smith.
Hons: Glos Snr Amtr Cup R-up 86-87 89-90, Cirencester Lg 72-73 74-75 (Div 2(3) 71-73 74-75, Lg Cup 74-75, Res. Cup 74-75), Cheltenham Lg 76-77 83-84 (Div 2 75-76, Lg Cup 83-84 (R-up 86-87), Snr Charity Cup 86-87), Stroud Charity Cup 86-87 (Section A 82-83 83-84), Arthur Shipway Cup 86-87 (R-up 87-88 92-93), Fairford Hospital Cup R-up(4) 83-85 90-91 92-93.

CLANFIELD

President: B Wallis   **Chairman:** B Court
Secretary: J Osborne, 70 Lancut Road, Witney, Oxon OX8 5AQ (0993 771631).
Manager: G Lock   **Asst Manager/Physio:** C Harding
Ground: Radcot Road, Clanfield, Oxon (0367 81314)
Directions: On A4095 8 miles west of Witney & 4 miles east of Faringdon on south side of Clanfield. Buses from Witney - contact Thames Transit for details.
Seats: No   **Cover:** 300   **Capacity:** 2,000   **Floodlights:** No   **Founded:** 1890
Colours: All red   **Change colours:** Blue/white/blue   **Nickname:** Robins   **Renamed:** 1985
Prev. Grnds: None   **Prev. Lges:** Nth Berks/ Witney & Dist.   **Clubhouse:** Every evening & Sat/Sun lunch
Programme: 8 pages, with admission   **Editor:** Secretary   **Club Shop:** No.
Captain 92-93: D Edsworth   **Top Scorer 92-93:** R Chester   **P.o.Y. 92-93:** P Woolford
Hons: Oxon Jnr Shield 32-33, Oxon I'mediate Cup 67-68, Witney & Dist. Lg 66-67 (Div 1 65-66, Div 2 64-65), Hellenic Lg Div 1 69-70 (Premier Div Cup 72-73, Div 1 Cup 69-70 85-86), Jim Newman Mem. Tphy 83-84 87-88, Faringdon Thursday Memorial Cup 69-70 71-72.

DIDCOT TOWN

President: Bryan Gough   **Chairman:** Jim Charman   **Manager:** Larry Hill
Secretary: J A Gardner, 8 Green Close, Didcot OX11 8TE (0235 813884).
Ground: 58 Station Road, Didcot (0235 813212).   **Clubhouse:** Every evenings and Sunday lunchtimes.
Directions: Midway down Station Rd, Didcot, on right quarter mile from Railway Station towards town centre.
Seats: None   **Cover:** 200   **Capacity:** 5,000   **Floodlights:** No   **Founded:** 1907
Colours: Red/white/red   **Change colours:** All blue
Prev. Lges: Hellenic 53-57/ Metropolitan 57-63.   **Nickname:** Railwaymen.
Record Attendance: 2,000 v Wycombe Wanderers, Berks & Bucks Senior Cup 1953.
Programme: 50p   **Programme Editor:** Ian Miller.
Honours: Hellenic Lg 53-54 (Lg Cup 1965-66 66-67, Div 1 76-77, Div 1 Cup 76-77).

EASINGTON SPORTS

Chairman: Terry Horley   **Manager:** R Teidman
Secretary: R Cogbill, 30 Addison Road, Banbury, Oxon OX16 9DH (0295 251374).
Ground: Addison Road, Easington Estate, Banbury, Oxon (0295 51374).
Directions: From Oxford A423. After passing under flyover on the outskirts take first turning left into Grange Road then third right into Addison Rd. Ground at top on left. One and a half miles from Banbury (BR).
Seats: 50   **Cover:** 150   **Capacity:** 1,000   **Floodlights:** No   **Founded:** 1946
Colours: Red & white stripes/red/red   **Change colours:** Yellow & black stripes/black/black
Programme: Free with admission.   **Previous Ground:** Bodicote.
Rec. Gate: 300 v Witney, Oxon Snr Cup 1956   **Prev. Lges:** Banbury Jnr/ Oxon Snr/ Warks Comb.
Clubhouse: Changing rooms, showers, bar facilities and food.
Honours: Oxon Snr Cup R-up, Oxon Intermediate League & Cup, Oxon Snr Lg.

HALLEN

Chairman: Mr Roy Toye   **Manager:** Terry Hale.
Secretary: C Jones, 67 Meadowland Rd, Henbury, Bristol BS10 7FW (0272 508572).
Ground: Hallen Playing Fields, Moorhouse Lane, Hallen, Nr Bristol (0272 504610).
Directions: M5 jct 17, A4018 to Henbury r'bout, right, right again at junction, next right to Station Road, left into Avonmouth Road at r'bout. One mile to Hallen, ground first left, then right into lane to ground.
Seats: No   **Cover:** No   **Clubhouse:** Yes   **Programme:** No   **Founded:** 1949
Colours: All blue   **Change Colours:** Green & white stripes/green/green
Previous Names: Lawrence Weston Athletic (80's), Lawrence Weston Hallen (pre-1991).
Prev. Grnd: Kings Weston (early 1980's)   **Previous League:** Glos County (pre-1993)   **Record Gate:** 250
Hons: Glos County Lg 92-93, Glos Snr Trophy 92-93.

HIGHWORTH TOWN

President: Alan Vockins   **Chairman:** Darren Robbins   **Vice Chairman:** Paul Haines.
Secretary: Fraser Haines, 'Journeys End', Lechlade Rd, Highworth, Swindon SN6 7HG (0793 763846).
Directions: Enter on A361 from Swindon, past Simpsons Garage, straight over island, next sharp left into Green by Vet's Surgery - ground & car park 60yds on left next to Sports Hall.
Seats: No   **Cover:** 60   **Capacity:** 1,000   **Floodlights:** No (due 93-94)
Colours: Red & white stripes   **Change colours:** All blue   **Club Shop:** No.
Programme: 16 pages, 60p   **Editor:** George Ranson (Shrivenham 782808).
Prev. Lges: Wilts/Swindon & Dist.   **Club Sponsors:** Smart Movers & BOC Storeshield.
Midweek home matchday: Wednesday   **Club record scorer:** Kevin Higgs.   **Founded:** 1893
Record win: 12-0   **Record defeat:** 2-8   **Nickname:** Worthians.   **Record Gate:** 500.
Clubhouse: Sat 12-2.30 & 4.30-11pm. Mon, Wed & Fri 7-11pm. Rolls & Hot food.
Captain 92-93: Steve Knights   **Top Scorer 92-93:** Ross Jefferies, 22   **P.O.Y. 92-93:** Shaun Proudlove.
Hons: Wilts Snr Cup 63-64 72-73 (R-up 88-89), Hellenic Div 1 Cup 88-89, Arthur Shipway Cup 88-89, Swindon & District Lg 63-64 64-65 65-66 68-69.

KIDLINGTON

President: Colin Rosser   **Chairman:** A F Grose   **Manager:** Ken Fagan
Secretary: A Canning, 6 Meadow View, Kidlington, Oxford OX5 1HQ (08675 7726).
Commercial Manager: J Nicholl   **Ground:** Yarnton Rd, Kidlington, Oxford (08675 5628).
Directions: From Kidlington r'bout (junction of A4260 & A34) A423 north to Kidlington; after 1st lights take 2nd left (Yarnton Road), ground is 200yds on the left.
Colours: Yellow/blue/yellow   **Change colours:** All green   **Floodlights:** No
Programme: 20 pages, 20p   **Programme Editor:** M A Canning   **Founded:** 1920
Previous League: Oxon Snr 47-54.   **Clubhouse:** Two bars open after matches
Honours: Oxon Snr Lg 53-54 (R-up 47-48), Hellenic Lg Cup 74-75 (R-up 68-69 73-74 74-75, Div 1 R-up 63-64 78-79), Oxon Intermediate Cup 52-53 84-85 (R-up 68-69 73-74 74-75), FA Vase 5th last sixteen 76-77.

LAMBOURN SPORTS

President: N L Fraser   **Chairman:** A E Cripps   **Manager:** J Willoughby
Secretary: C G Bettison, 13 Mill Lane, Lambourn, Berks RG16 7YP (0488 72320).
Ground: Bockhampton Rd, Lambourn, Berks (0488 71335).
Directions: From Lambourn Church take Newbury St, then 1st right into Station Rd, left at T junction into Bockhampton Rd, ground on left.
Seats: No   **Cover:** 150   **Capacity:** 2,000   **Floodlights:** No   **Founded:** 1889
Colours: Red & white stripes/red/red   **Change colours:** All blue   **Programme:** 12 pages
Previous Leagues: Newbury & Dist. 11-51/ Swindon & Dist. 51-61/ Hellenic 61-72/ Nth Berks 72-77.
Clubhouse: Bars, lounge, dancehall, billard room, kitchen, open 7 nights, Saturdays from 4pm
Hons: Berks & Bucks Snr Cup 61-62 79-80, Hellenic Div 1 81-82 (R-up 61-62, Div 1 Cup 61-62 79-80).

LETCOMBE SPORTS

Chairman: Mr D Stock   **Manager:** Jeremy Charles.
Secretary: Mr D Williams, 8 Larkdown, Wantage OX12 8HE (02357 4130).
Ground: Bassett Road, Letcombe Regis, Wantage, Oxon (02357 68685).
Directions: Follow road thru Letcombe Regis; ground on right on far side of village.
Seats: No   **Cover:** No   **Programme:** Yes   **Founded:** 1960.
Colours: White/navy.   **Sponsors:** W McKnight/ B Rowe.
Previous Lges: North Berks / Chiltonian (pre-1993)   **Clubhouse:** On ground.
Hons: Chiltonian Lg Div 1 90-91   **Local Press:** Oxford Mail/ Wantage Herald.

PEGASUS JUNIORS

President: P S Hill   **Chairman:** R W Pasley
Secretary: R J Perks, 40 Foley Street, Hereford HR1 2SQ (0432 272524).
Ground: Essex Arms Sports Ground, Widemarsh Street, Hereford (0432 268705).
Directions: 200 yds behind Hereford Utd FC (Edgar Street) - across car park. 1 mile from Barrs Court (BR).
Seats: 20   **Cover:** 50   **Capacity:** 1,500   **Floodlights:** No   **Founded:** 1955
Colours: Red/white/red   **Change colours:** All white
Previous leagues: Hereford/Worcester
Programme: 20p   **Programme Editor:** D.Llewellyn   **Clubhouse:** 48 Stowens Street.
Hons: Herefordshire Snr Amtr Cup 71-72, Herefordshire Co. Chal. Cup(5) 81-83 84-85 87-88 89-90, Worcs Snr Urn 85-86, Hellenic Lg Div 1 84-85.

PURTON

President: Graham Price   **Chairman:** Alan Eastwood   **Vice Chairman:** N Jones.
Secretary: N Webb, 5 Glevum Close, Purton, Swindon, Wilts SN5 9HA (0793 770242).
Manager: S Paish.
Ground: The Red House, Purton (0793 770262 - Saturday afternoons only).
Directions: Purton is on B4041 Wootton Bassett to Cricklade Road. Ground near village hall.
Seats: **Capacity**   **Cover:**   **Floodlights:** No   **Founded:** 1923
Colours: Red/white/red   **Change colours:** Blue & black.
Programme: 40 pagesp   **Programme Editor:** Alan Eastwood (0793 694036).
Clubhouse: Open after matches   **Sponsors:** Courtoulds.
Captain 92-93: I Jones   **Top Scorer 92-93:** J Barker
P.O.Y. 92-93: J Barker   **Club Record Scorer:** M Collier.
Hons: Wilts Lg 48-49 85-86 (Div 2 83-84, Div 3 86-87), Wilts Snr Cup(6) 38-39 48-49 50-51 54-55 87-89, Wilts Yth Cup 77-78 85-86 88-89, Fairford Hosp. Cup(2) 87-89.

WALLINGFORD TOWN

President: B Baxter   **Chairman:** A M Brannan   **Vice Chairman:** A Miles.
Secretary: R Nobes, 41 Alnatt Ave., Wallingford, Oxon OX10 8PJ (0491 836619).
Manager: L Hill   **Physio:** Jimmy Coster.
Ground: Wallingford Sports Trust, Hithercroft Rd, Wallingford, Oxon (0491 35044).
Directions: From town centre - south on A329 out of 1-way system, 100yds right into St Johns Road after r'bout at Green Tree pub, fork left at Plough pub into Hithercroft Rd, ground 200yds on right before new r'bout on new ring-rd. From Didcot - turn right at new r'bout on ring-rd, ground on left at next r'bout. 2 miles from Cholsey (BR). Buses from Reading and Oxford to town centre.
Seats: No   **Cover:** 500   **Capacity:** 1,500   **Floodlights:** No   **Founded:** 1922
Club colours: Red & black hoops/black/black   **Change colours:** Gold
Programme: Free with admission   **Editor:** A M Brannan (0491 835751)   **Club Shop:** No.
Nickname: The Town   **Previous Ground:** The Bull Croft 1922-78.
Previous Lge: Reading & Dist. (pre-1953) **Rec. Gate:** 1,000 v Wycombe, Berks & Bucks S.C. 1982
Players progressing to Football League: John Dreyer (Oxford United 1985).
Sponsors: Rich's Cafe American   **Midweek home matchday:** Wednesday
Record win: 15-1 v Lambourn (A), 1960s **Record defeat:** 1-7 on several occasions.
Record transfer fee paid received: £2,000 from Oxford on signing John Dreyer in 1976 - not a transfer.
Clubhouse: Weekdays 7.30-11pm, Sat noon-2 & 4-11pm, Sun noon-2 & 7-10.30pm. Rolls available Saturday.
Captain 92-93: J Brannan   **Top Scorer 92-93:** Steve Wood 28   **P.o.Y. 92-93:** A Hill
Record Scorer (since 1960): A Brannan   **Hons:** Hellenic Lg 68-69 (Premier Division Cup 58-59).

Wallingford Town F.C. 1992-93. Back Row (L/R): A Hill, F Stephens, M Bonner, T Mason, N Rourke, N Willett, H McPharlane, R Williams, G Stroud, J Winter, J Brannan, S Wood, L Hill (Manager). Front: J Coster (Physio), R McLean, M Smith, B Baxter (Sponsor), A Brannan (Chairman), A Mason, V Davey, P Noble.

WOOTTON BASSETT TOWN

Chairman: Alan Blyth
Sec./Press Officer: Mr R Carter, 14 Blackthorn Close, Wootton Bassett, Swindon Wilts SN4 7JE (0793 851386).
Manager: Micky Woolford   **Asst Manager/Coach:** Kev Moloney.
Ground: Gerard Buxton Sports Ground, Rylands Way, Wootton Bassett, Swindon (0793 853880).
Directions: M4 jnct 16 to Wootton Bassett (A3102), left at 2nd r'bout (Prince of Wales pub on right), 2nd left into Longleaze (just after Mobil garage) and Rylands Way is 3rd right by schools, ground 100yds on right. Coming from Calne/Devizes proceed thru town centre and turn right into Longleaze after Shell petrol station on right - Rylands Ave. is 3rd left. Coming from Malmesbury take last exit off r'bout by Prince of Wales pub and Longleaze is 2nd left.
Seats: None   **Cover:** 350   **Capacity:** 4,000   **Floodlights:** Due   **Founded:** 1882
Colours: Blue & white hoops   **Change colours:** Yellow/green.   **Nickname:** None.
Programme: 12 pages, free   **Programme Editor:** T.B.A.   **Club Shop:** No.
Previous Grounds: None   **Record Gate:** 2,505 v Swindon T., friendly 20/7/91.
Sponsors: Cathy Moore Recruitment   **Previous Leagues:** Wilts (pre-1988).   **Record win:** 11-2
Midweek home matchday: Tue/Wed   **Reserve team's League:** Wiltshire.   **Record defeat:** 0-9
Clubhouse: Open every matchdays, usual opening hours. Usual type of bar food available together with filled rolls. Tea & coffee available over bar. Matchday refreshments - teas, coffees, soups with light snacks.
Captain 92-93: Kevin Moloney   **Top Scorer 92-93:** Scott Vincent   **P.o.Y. 92-93:** Alan Wilson
Record scorer: Brian (Toby) Ewing   **Record appearances:** Steve Thomas.
Hons: Hellenic Lg Div 1 Cup 89-90, Wilts Lg 87-88 (Div 2 84-85, Subsidiary Cup 78-79), Wilts Snr Cup R-up 02-03 03-04 87-88, Ghia Snr 83-84, Ghia Jnr Cup R-up 88-89, FA Amateur Cup QF 26-27.

YARNTON

Chairman: M C Warner   **Vice Chairman:** A Oliver   **President:** TBA
Secretary: B G Harris, 28 Orpwood Way, Abingdon OX14 5PX (0235 526621).
Manager: A Bunting   **Asst Manager:** K Fisher   **Press Off.:** A Stiff
Ground: Little Marsh, Green Lane, Yarnton, Oxon (0865 842037).
Directions: North of Oxford on A44 - head for Woodstock/Evesham. Ground situated behind The Grapes pub. Entrance on right before roundabout. Oxford-Woodstock buses stop near ground, Oxford-Kidlington stop 30mins walk from ground.
Seats: None   **Cover:** None   **Capacity:** Unknown **Floodlights:** No   **Founded:** 1947
Colours: Blue   **Change colours:** White.   **Club Shop:** No.
Previous Grounds: None   **Previous Lges:** Witney & Dist. 47-80/ Oxon Snr 80-91.
Programme: 12 pages, £1 with admission **Record Gate:** 150 v Kidlington.   **Clubhouse:** No.
Midweek home matchday: Tuesday   **Sponsors:** Woodstock Felt Roofing & Red Lion, Yarnton
Captain 92-93: S Cooper   **Top Scorer 92-93:** D Henderson   **P.o.Y. 92-93:** D Macer
Hons: Oxford Jnr Shield 76-77, Witney & Dist. Lg Div 2 72-73 (Supplementary Cup 65-66), Oxon Snr Lg Div 1 80-81 (Ben Turner Cup 90-91), Oxon Jnr Chal. Cup 56-57 72-73, Fred Ford Mem. Cup 76-77, Burford Spts Cup 76-77.

OXFORDSHIRE
'BANBURY SPORTS' SENIOR LEAGUE

President: Mr A Search,
Chairman: Mr R A Brock,
Hon. Secretary: Mr K Rogers,
65 Bagley Close, Kennington, Oxford OX1 5LT (0865 739173)

The oustanding feature of the 1992-93 season was the success of Garsington F.C. They were Premier Division champions and also winners of the Presidents Cup and the Oxfordshire F.A. Charity Cup. In addition, their reserve team were finalists in the Clarendon Cup. Ardley United finished the season as runners-up in the Premier Division and as result have been promoted to the Hellenic League (Garsington not wishing to go up). Long Crendon have been relgated to Division One whilst Launton Sports and Pressed Steel Fisher, who finished as champions and runners-up in Division One, have been promoted. Chipping Norton Town have been relgated from the Hellenic League and will compete in the Premier Division.

Gerald Hayes, Hon. Fixtures Secretary

PREM. DIVISION	P	W	D	L	F	A	PTS
Garsington	26	17	5	4	51	21	56
Ardley United	26	17	4	5	56	38	55
Worcester Coll OB	26	14	8	4	67	39	50
Blackbird Leys	26	14	4	8	60	48	46
Oakley United	26	13	6	7	63	47	45
Watlington	26	12	3	11	56	48	39
Eynsham	26	10	3	13	55	50	33
Old Woodstock	26	9	5	11	44	48	33
Quarry Nomads	26	9	6	11	52	71	33
Oxford Univ. Press	26	9	4	13	42	56	31
Woodstock Town	26	9	3	14	39	45	30
A P Sports	26	6	9	11	52	55	27
Bletchington	26	6	7	13	37	52	25
Long Crendon	26	2	2	22	29	85	8

Division One	P	W	D	L	F	A	PTS
Launton Sports	26	19	5	2	64	25	62
Pressed Steel Fisher	26	19	3	4	92	27	60
John Radcliffe	26	17	4	5	73	33	55
Kennington Utd	26	16	4	6	78	35	52
Garsington Res.	26	12	8	6	52	36	44
Marston Saints	26	11	9	6	60	49	42
Charlton United	26	12	4	10	51	53	40
Quarry Nomads Res	26	10	3	13	49	65	33
Ardley Utd Res	26	8	6	12	46	61	30
Bicester Civil Serv.	26	7	4	14	41	68	26
Marlborough	26	6	6	14	35	58	24
Eynsham Res	26	5	7	14	36	74	22
Old Woodstock Res	26	2	7	17	39	69	*10
Salesians	26	1	3	22	21	106	&9

* - 3pts deducted & - 3pts awarded

Division Two	P	W	D	L	F	A	PTS
Kennington Res	28	21	2	5	84	43	65
Worcester COB Res	28	19	5	4	75	27	62
Woodstock T. Res	28	18	5	5	90	39	59
AP Spts & Soc. Res	28	16	5	7	73	40	53
Long Crendon Res	28	16	5	7	60	42	53
Launton Spts Res	28	16	4	8	87	49	52
Bletchington Res	28	14	6	8	83	49	48
Marlborough Res	28	13	5	10	58	51	44
Watlington Res	28	12	3	13	78	61	39
Oxford U.P. Res	28	10	2	16	49	74	32
Oakley Utd Res	28	9	4	15	65	75	31
Bicester C.S. Res	28	5	4	19	59	129	19
Salesians Res	28	4	5	19	32	75	17
Charlton Utd Res	28	3	5	20	38	115	14
Marston Saints Res	28	4	0	24	40	102	12

PREMIER DIVISION RESULTS 1992-93

HOME TEAM	1	2	3	4	5	6	7	8	9	10	11	12	13	14
1. A P Sports	*	0-1	4-4	6-0	1-4	2-2	0-2	2-2	1-3	7-1	4-4	1-1	0-2	3-3
2. Ardley United	3-0	*	3-1	3-1	3-1	0-3	3-1	3-2	1-0	4-2	5-1	1-1	0-3	2-2
3. Blackbird Leys	1-0	1-2	*	0-2	3-2	1-0	4-1	2-2	3-1	1-0	6-7	1-0	5-1	4-2
4. Bletchingdon	1-1	1-1	0-1	*	2-2	0-3	4-0	1-3	3-0	1-2	3-3	1-4	1-1	1-0
5. Eynsham	1-4	0-4	1-2	0-2	*	0-1	4-0	1-3	5-0	0-1	4-3	3-2	3-2	3-4
6. Garsington	2-0	6-1	2-1	3-2	2-1	*	3-1	2-0	0-1	1-0	2-0	2-0	1-2	3-3
7. Long Crendon	0-3	0-2	1-1	2-5	1-3	1-1	*	1-3	2-4	3-2	1-3	1-5	2-4	1-7
8. Oakley United	4-2	3-1	6-3	2-2	4-2	2-2	3-1	*	4-1	2-3	5-0	2-3	3-2	0-3
9. Old Woodstock	2-3	0-2	1-3	2-2	0-0	0-0	3-0	0-1	*	4-2	4-1	2-4	4-2	0-1
10. Oxford University Press	1-1	2-4	3-3	3-1	1-3	0-3	2-0	2-3	2-2	*	2-2	2-1	1-0	0-2
11. Quarry Nomads	2-4	1-2	3-1	2-1	1-1	0-2	5-4	1-1	1-1	4-1	*	2-1	0-5	3-2
12. Watlington	4-2	4-2	1-2	3-0	1-5	1-2	2-0	3-1	3-6	3-1	5-2	*	1-4	1-1
13. Woodstock Town	1-1	1-2	0-4	2-0	0-4	0-2	2-1	2-0	1-2	0-2	0-1	0-1	*	1-1
14. Worcester College OB	4-0	1-1	3-2	3-0	3-2	2-1	7-2	2-2	1-1	4-1	1-3	2-1	3-1	*

DIVISION ONE RESULTS 1992-93

HOME TEAM	1	2	3	4	5	6	7	8	9	10	11	12	13	14
1. Ardley Utd Reserves	*	0-3	1-2	2-1	1-8	3-3	1-3	3-4	8-0	1-1	2-2	1-5	2-0	4-2
2. Bicester Civil Service	1-3	*	1-4	1-1	2-1	1-4	1-6	0-1	2-1	3-0	3-2	0-5	0-1	3-5
3. Charlton United	3-2	1-1	*	6-0	0-3	2-1	0-5	2-2	0-1	3-5	1-0	1-4	3-2	3-1
4. Eynsham Reserves	2-0	2-2	2-4	*	2-5	2-3	0-8	2-2	1-1	1-1	2-0	3-7	1-2	3-0
5. Garsington Reserves	1-1	4-0	2-2	2-2	*	0-0	1-1	0-4	1-0	3-2	1-1	2-4	0-3	3-1
6. John Radcliffe	8-1	4-0	1-0	4-1	1-2	*	2-5	2-1	5-0	3-3	2-0	0-1	8-2	3-1
7. Kennington United	4-0	2-3	4-1	2-1	0-0	1-2	*	2-2	2-0	1-2	3-0	1-0	7-1	6-0
8. Launton Sports	1-0	4-0	2-3	9-0	2-1	4-0	4-0	*	2-1	3-3	5-0	3-1	2-1	8-0
9. Marlborough	0-1	3-2	2-3	3-2	1-2	0-0	0-2	0-2	*	2-1	3-3	2-8	2-3	6-0
10. Marston Saints	3-0	1-1	3-1	6-0	1-1	0-4	3-1	3-4	2-2	*	1-1	3-3	3-2	1-0
11. Old Woodstock Res	1-1	1-7	0-5	0-3	0-4	1-4	4-4	0-1	3-3	0-1	*	2-4	0-3	11-0
12. Press Steel Fisher	1-2	6-0	5-0	4-1	4-0	1-2	3-2	1-1	2-0	6-0	2-0	*	1-1	4-0
13. Quarry Nomads Res.	2-2	5-3	2-0	0-1	0-2	0-1	4-5	0-3	1-1	1-6	3-2	0-6	*	4-2
14. Salesians	0-4	1-1	1-1	0-0	1-3	1-6	0-1	0-10	0-1	2-5	1-5	0-4	2-6	*

DIVISION TWO RESULTS 1992-93

HOME TEAM	1	2	3	4	5	6	7	8	9	10	11	12	13	14	15
1. AP Sports & Soc. Res	*	7-2	1-3	6-2	1-1	0-1	0-2	2-1	3-0	6-1	3-2	9-1	1-0	2-1	0-2
2. Bicester Civil S. Res	2-3	*	3-4	2-2	0-5	1-3	2-8	2-7	6-2	6-3	2-4	3-2	2-4	1-7	0-2
3. Bletchingdon Res	0-0	2-2	*	8-1	1-0	3-2	1-4	1-1	10-1	3-3	10-1	3-0	2-4	2-1	0-1
4. Charlton United Res	0-5	0-0	1-4	*	2-5	1-6	2-2	2-1	0-2	2-2	0-5	2-1	5-4	1-3	0-3
5. Kennington Utd Res	5-1	6-3	4-3	2-1	*	4-2	6-2	2-1	5-2	0-2	4-0	3-0	1-1	3-2	3-0
6. Launton Sports Res	4-0	3-3	1-1	8-2	3-4	*	0-1	3-3	1-0	6-3	3-0	7-1	2-0	2-2	2-4
7. Long Crendon Res	0-0	5-1	2-4	5-3	2-0	0-5	*	1-2	2-1	1-0	3-0	2-1	3-2	2-2	1-1
8. Marlborough Res	1-1	5-3	2-1	5-1	2-6	5-4	3-0	*	3-1	0-1	1-1	2-0	0-4	1-5	0-1
9. Marston Saints Res	3-4	0-3	2-6	8-1	2-4	0-5	0-2	0-1	*	2-4	3-2	1-3	1-5	1-3	1-4
10. Oakley Utd Res	3-2	12-2	3-1	5-2	1-2	2-3	0-5	4-2	1-2	*	4-2	1-2	2-2	2-4	0-4
11. Oxford U.P. Res	0-6	5-1	2-3	3-0	1-3	2-1	1-2	0-1	2-1	3-0	*	0-0	4-1	3-1	0-8
12. Salesians	1-1	1-4	0-3	2-2	4-1	2-4	1-2	1-2	4-0	1-1	1-3	*	0-9	1-1	0-1
13. Watlington Res	1-5	13-3	1-0	6-0	0-1	1-4	1-1	0-5	4-2	6-5	2-1	2-1	*	0-1	1-2
14. Woodstock T. Res	1-2	7-0	3-1	7-1	3-2	4-1	2-0	3-1	4-1	3-0	6-1	6-1	4-3	*	2-2
15. Worcester COB Res	0-2	7-0	3-3	3-2	1-2	0-1	1-0	1-1	11-1	1-0	4-1	1-0	3-1	2-2	*

PRESIDENTS CUP 1992-93

First Round

Oakley United v AFC Cowley	4-1		Ardley United v Garsington	1-2
Bicester Civil Service v Blackbird Leys	2-4		A.P. Sports (bye)	
Quarry Nomads v Pressed Steel Fisher	2-5		Worcester College Old Boys v Launton Sports	1-3
Oxford University Press v Bletchingdon	2-1		Watlington v Woodstock Town	2-4
Salesians v Eynsham	0-5		Kennington United v Long Crendon	4-2
Marston Saints v Charlton United	2-5		Old Woodstock (w/o) Northway United (scr.)	
Marlborough v John Radcliffe	1-3			

Second Round

Oxford University Press (bye)			Charlton United v A.P. Sports	1-3
Old Woodstock v Blackbird Leys	6-7(aet)		Eynsham v Oakley United	3-2
Woodstock Town v Pressed Steel Fisher	5-2		Launton Spts v Kennington	2-2(aet),0-1(aet)
Garsington (bye)			John Radcliffe (bye)	

Quarter Finals

Garsington v John Radcliffe	3-1		Blackbird Leys ASC v Oxford University Press	2-3
Woodstock Town v A.P. Sports	3-2(aet)		Eynsham v Kennington United	1-4(aet)

Semi-Finals

Woodstock Town v Garsington	1-2		Kennington Utd v Oxford U.P.	2-2,4-1(aet)

Final: Garsington 3, Kennington United 1 (aet)

BEN TURNER CUP (for Presidents Cup First Round losers)

Second Round

Marlborough v Long Crendon	1-4		Quarry Nomads v Marston Saints	6-2
Bletchingdon v Worcester COB	3-3(aet),0-1			

Quarter Finals

Watlington v Salesians	3-1		Worcester College Old Boys v Quarry Nomads	2-1
Ardley United v Long Crendon	5-0		Bicester Civil Service (bye)	

Semi-Finals

Worcester College Old Boys v Watlington	5-0		Ardley v Bicester Civil Service	4-1

Final: Worcester College Old Boys 3, Ardley United 0

CLARENDON CUP 1992-93

First Round

Quarry Nomads Res v Eynsham Res	4-1		Woodstock T. Res v Old Woodstock Res	4-1
Worcester Col. OB Res v Ardley Utd Res	0-2		Charlton Utd Res v Marston Saints Res	3-4
Bicester Civil S. Res v Oakley Utd Res	1-2		A P Sports Res v Long Crendon Res	1-7
Watlington Res v Kennington Utd Res	2-4		Launton Spts Res v Garsington Res	1-4
Salesians Res v Bletchingdon Res	1-7		Oxford U.P. Reserves v Marlborough Res	0-3

Second Round

Marston Saints Res v Marlborough Res	0-1		Kennington Utd Res v Long Crendon Res	5-2
All other clubs - byes				

Quarter Finals

Woodstock T. Res v Oakley Utd Reserves	6-1		Marlborough Res v Quarry Nomads Reserves	2-5
Bletchingdon Reserves v Kennington Utd Res	3-1		Garsington Reserves v Ardley United Res	5-0

Semi-Finals

Garsington Reserves v Woodstock Town Res	2-0		Quarry Nomads Res v Bletchingdon Reserves	1-2

Final: Bletchingdon Reserves 1, Garsington Reserves 1

IVOR GUBBINS CUP (First Round losers in Clarendon Cup)

First Round

Launton Sports Res v Oxford U.P. Res	1-3	Charlton United Res v Salesians Reserves 3-2

Quarter Finals

Old Woodstock Res v Eynsham Reserves	3-2	Bicester Civil Service Res v A P Sports Res 0-11
Watlington Res v Charlton Utd Reserves	3-0	Oxford U.P. Res v Worcester COB Res 0-0*(aet)*,0-2

Semi-Finals

Worcester College OB Res v A P Sports Res 2-0		Watlington Res v Old Woodstock Res 2-7

Final: Worcester College Old Boys Reserves 1, Old Woodstock Reserves 0

PREMIER DIVISION CLUBS 1993-94

A.P. SPORTS & SOCIAL
Secretary: S Maycock, 3 The Camellias, Banbury, Oxon OX16 7YT (0295 275124).
Ground: Croughton, Nr Banbury.
Colours: Blue/black/blue   **Reserve's colours:** All yellow.

BLACKBIRD LEYS A.S.C.
Secretary: M O'Donnell, 53 Fernhill Rd, Cowley, Oxford (0865 772391).
Ground: Pegasus Road, Blackbird Leys, Oxford.
Colours: Mauve/black/black   **Change colours:** Black & red/black/black.

BLETCHINGDON
Secretary: J Clack, 111 Woodstock Rd, Yarnton, Oxford (08675 71228).
Ground: Oxford Road, Bletchingdon.
Colours: Sky & claret/claret/blue (Res: yellow & green/green/yellow)   **Change colours:** All red.

CHIPPING NORTON TOWN
Secretary: R J Tanner, 3 Cotswold Terrace, Chipping Norton, Oxon OX7 5DU (0608 641490).
Ground: Hailey Rd (0608 642562).
Colours: Black & white stripes/white/white   **Change colours:** Red/blue/white.

EYNSHAM
Secretary: G Bailey, 8 Stratford Drive, Eynsham, Oxford OX8 1QJ (0865 882829).
Ground: Eynsham P.F., Oxford Road, Eynsham, Oxford.
Colours: White/black/black.   **Reserves' colours:** Yellow/black/yellow.

GARSINGTON
Secretary: C Moss, 8 Birch Rd, Garsington, Oxford (086736 704).
Ground: Off Denton Lane, Garsington (086736 720).
Colours: All green.   **Change colours:** White/black/black

LAUNTON SPORTS
Secretary: M Ramage, 3 Sherwood Close, Launton, Bicester, Oxon (0869 242036).
Ground: Launton Playing Field, Launton, Bicester, Oxon.
Colours: Red/black/black   **Change colours:** Grey/black/black.

OAKLEY UNITED
Secretary: A J Walker, 6 Brookside, Oakley, Aylesbury, Bucks HP18 9PN (0844 238355).
Ground: Recreation Ground, Oxford Road, Oakley, Aylesbury, Bucks.
Colours: All white (Res: Orange/black/red)   **Change colours:** blue.

OLD WOODSTOCK
Secretary: T Halls, 20 Oxford Rd, Farmoor, Oxford OX2 9NN (0865 863871).
Ground: Marlborough School, Shipton Rd, Woodstock, Oxon.
Colours: Blue & white/red/red (Res: Blue & white/green/green)   **Change colours:** Red/black/red.

OXFORD UNIVERSITY PRESS
Secretary: I Weston, 63 Jordan Hill, Banbury Rd, Oxford OX2 8EU (0865 510500).
Ground: Oxford University Press Sports Ground, Jordan Hill, Banbury Rd, Oxford (0865 562421).
Colours: All royal (Res: Yellow/red/red)   **Change colours:** Reverse.

PRESSED STEEL FISHER
Secretary: Mrs J A Measor, 1 Vicarage Close, Chalgrove, Oxon OX9 7RD (0865 890793).
Ground: Roman Way, Cowley.
Colours: Sky/blue/blue   **Change colours:** Red/black/black.

QUARRY NOMADS
Secretary: K Dolton, 58 Pitts Rd, Headington, Oxford (0865 65332).
Ground: Margarets Rd, Headington, Oxford.
Colours: Black & white/black/white   **Change colours:** All red

WATLINGTON
Secretary: S Muir, 9 Shirburn Str., Watlington, Oxon (0491 612644).
Ground: Shirburn Road, Watlington, Oxon. (B4009).
Colours: Red & black/black/black (Res: blue & white/blue/blue)   **Change:** All yellow.

WOODSTOCK TOWN
Secretary: R Peake, 86 New Rd, Woodstock, Oxon (0993 811816).   **Ground:** New Road, Woodstock.
Colours: All red (Res: Red & black/red/red)   **Change colours:** All white.

WORCESTER COLLEGE OLD BOYS
Secretary: G Heppell, 1 Bampton Close, Littlemore, Oxford OX4 5NN (0865 779433).
Ground: Roman Way, Cowley.
Colours: Sky/navy/navy   **Change colours:** Yellow/black/black.

DIVISION ONE CLUBS 1993-94

BICESTER CIVIL SERVICE
Secretary: I Moore, 50 Wear Rd, Bicester, Oxon (0869 248765).
Ground: Rodney House, London Road, Bicester, Oxon.
Colours: Red & white/blue/blue (Res: all blue)   **Change colours:** White/blue/red.

CHARLTON UNITED
Secretary: A W Smith, 1 Manor Farm Buildings, Church Lane, Charlton-on-Otmoor, Oxon OX2 2UA (086733 642).
Ground: Charlton P.F.
Colours: Blue & white/white/blue   **Change colours:** All red.

CHIPPING NORTON TOWN RES., EYNSHAM RES., GARSINGTON RES. *(page 743)*

JOHN RADCLIFFE
Secretary: A Glass, Unit 6, Fitzharris Trading Est., Wootton Rd, Abingdon, Oxon (0865 247573).
Ground: John Radcliffe Hospital Grounds.
Colours: All blue   **Change colours:** Black & white/black/black.

KENNINGTON UNITED
Secretary: Mr A Lawson, 1 Hound Close, Abingdon, Oxon OX14 2LU (0235 559864).
Ground: Playfield Rd, Kennington, Oxford.
Colours: Green & yellow/green/yellow   **Change colours:** All sky.

LONG CRENDON
Secretary: R Gower, 26 Friars Furlong Rd, Long Crendon, Aylesbury (0844 208642).
Ground: Chearsley Rd, Long Crendon, Aylesbury, Bucks.
Colours: Green & white/black/black (Res: Red & white/black/black)   **Change:** Blue & white/blue/white.

MARLBOROUGH
Sec: S Hutton, 122 Herschel Cres., Littlemore, Oxford (0865 715047)
Ground: Orchard Way, Littlemore, Oxford
Colours: Blue/white/blue (Res: Red/black/Chdnge cols: Yellow & blue/blue/blue.

MARSTON SAINTS
Secretary: Miss E Davonport, 32 Elms Drive, Old Marston, Oxford OX3 0NJ (0865 249575).
Grnd: Boults Lane, Old Marston, Oxford   **Colours:** All red   **Reserves' cols:** Yellow/blue/blue

QUARRY NOMADS RES. *(page 743)*

SALESIANS
Secretary: Mr C Nelson, 21 Trinity Street, Oxford (0865 250169).
Ground: Westminster College, Westminster Way, Oxford.
Colours: Red & blue/blue/blue   **Change colours:** All yellow.

WHEATLEY UNITED
Secretary: K Creed, 2 Fernhill Close, Tiddington, Oxon OX9 2NA (0844 338832).
Colours: All blue   **Ground:** Holton Sports Field, Wheatley.

WOODSTOCK TOWN RES., WORCESTER COLLEGE OLD BOYS RES. *(page 743)*

Division Two 1993-94: A P Sports Res., Bicester Civil Service Res., Bletchingdon Res., Charlton Utd Res., John Radcliffe Res., Kennington Utd Res., Launton Sports Res., Long Crendon Res., Marlborough Res., Marston Saints Res., Oakley Utd Res., Old Woodstock Res., Oxford University Press Res., Salesians Res., Watlington Res.

SWINDON & DISTRICT LEAGUE
(Established 1891)

PREM. DIV.	P	W	D	L	F	A	PTS
The Monkey Club	22	19	2	1	88	24	40
Genesis	22	14	5	3	78	40	33
South Marston	22	15	1	6	86	44	31
Walcot	22	13	3	6	67	39	29
Raychem S.S.C.	22	13	1	8	61	46	27
Greatfield Utd	22	10	6	6	53	39	26
Bishopstone T.H.	22	8	3	11	54	68	19
Lower Stratton	22	8	2	12	48	72	18
C.S. Magpies	22	5	5	12	44	65	15
Coleview United	22	5	3	14	36	63	13
Blyskawica	22	2	3	17	32	83	7
Bakers 'R'	22	1	4	17	28	92	6

DIV. ONE	P	W	D	L	F	A	PTS
Ivy Leaf	24	24	0	0	152	16	48
C.F.C.	24	15	3	6	61	38	33
Nat Semiconductor	24	13	5	6	73	40	31
Pinehurst Res.	24	11	7	6	53	34	29
Sundstrand	24	12	2	10	57	46	26
Raychem SSC Res.	24	11	3	10	56	58	25
Supermarine	24	9	5	9	51	50	23
Sanford Res.	24	9	5	10	51	65	23
Haydon Wick	24	10	2	12	51	61	22
Lower Stratton Res.	24	8	5	11	42	58	21
Monkey Club Res.	24	4	4	16	44	98	12
Bakers 'R' Res.	24	4	3	17	26	83	11
Wroughton Res.	24	1	4	18	26	96	6

DIV. TWO	P	W	D	L	F	A	PTS
Old Nick	22	19	3	0	92	16	41
Salamandre	22	17	2	3	94	28	36
Highworth Ath.	22	16	3	3	82	23	35
W H Smith	22	9	7	6	82	53	25
Jacobs Ladder	22	10	3	9	62	46	23
A.C. Wanderers	22	10	0	12	55	59	20
Spectrum XI	22	8	2	12	62	65	18
Phoenix Flyers	22	6	6	10	58	65	18
Farepak	22	7	2	13	65	87	16
Dunbar Wills Res.	22	6	1	15	40	106	13
Ivy Leaf Res.	22	5	3	14	37	67	13
Prince of Wales	22	2	2	18	21	135	6

(Division Three & Youth Division opposite)

DIV. THREE	P	W	D	L	F	A	PTS
Pinehurst Comm.	23	20	0	3	139	40	40
Jacobs Ladder Res.	24	17	1	6	101	46	35
Suffolk Arms	24	13	6	5	71	39	32
Morris Str. WMC	24	14	2	8	76	55	30
Cricklade T. Res.	24	13	3	8	89	56	29
Rodbourne Man'gton	24	11	4	9	82	74	26
Lydiard Sports	24	11	2	11	73	66	24
A.F.C. Zimmer	24	10	3	11	46	80	23
Pheonix F. Res.	24	8	5	11	61	71	21
Top Cue	24	6	4	14	38	68	16
Dormers United	24	7	1	16	40	102	15
Supermarine Res.	23	4	4	15	38	78	12
Park Youth Centre	24	2	3	19	40	119	7

YOUTH DIV.	P	W	D	L	F	A	PTS
Devizes	10	9	1	0	88	11	19
Purton	10	7	1	2	39	37	15
Stround Town Yths	10	6	2	2	51	21	14
Sussex Squ. Strikers	10	2	1	7	26	57	5
Toothill	10	2	1	7	20	64	5
Westbourne Park	10	0	2	8	16	50	2

LORD JERSEY F.A. (Est. 1887)

The Lord Jersey Association has been in existence for over 100 years, the first Jersey Cup being in 1887-88 when Middleton Stoney beat Deddington 4-2. The Association is named after Lord Jersey whose seat and estate is in the area covered by the Association.

League football did not appear to start until around the time of the Second World War. At first, there was only one division, but in 52-53 there were three. The Association peaked in 1983 when a 4th Division was added. To be correct, the divisions are called Jersey Shields and the whole set-up is never referred to as a league.

The area covered is from the Chilterns in the east to the Cotswolds in the West and Oxford in the south. Rules state that clubs should refrain spectators from entering the field of play, i.e. most pitches are roped. Most clubs have social facilities.

In the past, Brill United have progressed to the Chiltonian League plus at least six of the current Oxon Senior League clubs have played in the Lord Jersey. At the end of the season numerous Cup are played, all with evening kick-offs except the Jersey Cup which is played on Easter Monday or May Bank Holiday Monday. A programme is issued for each final.

Details supplied by Andy Molden.

Division One	P	W	D	L	F	A	PTS
K.E.A. United	18	20	0	3	69	20	48
Bardwell	18	10	5	3	68	32	35
Heyford Athletic	18	11	1	6	53	36	34
Middle Barton	18	10	2	6	47	27	32
Hethe	18	9	4	5	34	27	31
Team Unipart	18	9	2	7	37	35	29
Fritwell	18	8	1	9	34	37	25
Arncott	18	4	0	14	22	58	12
Kirklington	18	2	3	13	22	64	9
Red Lion Marauders	18	1	1	16	30	80	4

Division Two	P	W	D	L	F	A	PTS
Piddington	20	17	1	2	81	18	52
K.E.A. Utd Res.	20	14	3	3	96	29	45
Merton	20	14	2	4	64	28	44
Lynx	20	12	4	4	57	25	40
Forest Hill	20	10	2	8	49	35	32
Wootton	20	8	1	11	37	44	25
A.F.C. Weston	20	7	2	11	48	75	23
Souldern	20	6	2	12	26	56	20
Viking Spts Utd	20	4	3	13	27	56	15
Middle Barton Res.	20	4	1	15	18	68	13
Red Lion M. Res.	20	3	1	16	20	89	10

Division Three	P	W	D	L	F	A	PTS
Hethe Res.	22	15	2	5	84	44	47
Bardwell Res.	22	14	4	4	75	30	46
Fritwell Res.	22	14	3	5	83	31	45
Heyford A. Res.	22	12	4	6	77	49	40
Kirklington Res.	22	12	4	6	59	48	40
Merton Res.	22	10	3	9	54	63	33
Steeple Aston	22	9	2	11	48	66	29
Heyford United	22	7	7	8	48	39	28
Crusaders	22	7	3	12	47	61	24
Arncott Res.	22	6	2	14	53	75	20
Wootton Res.	22	4	1	17	34	124	13
Team Unipart Res.	22	3	3	16	46	78	12

DIVISION ONE CLUBS 1993-94
(Tel. codes 0869 unless stated)

ARNCOTT
Ground: Arncott Rec.   Sec: D Cox (249095)

BARDWELL
G: Pingle Field, Bicester   S: A Simpson (246785)

FRITWELL
G: Fewcott Rd PF   S: P Griffin (0280 701604)

HETHE
G: Hardwick Rd PF   S: W Mansfield (277219)

HEYFORD ATHLETIC
G: Lower Heyford PF   S: A Jupp (320151)

K.E.A. UNITED
G: Ashdene Rd, Bicester   Mrs H Horner (244186)

MERTON
G: Merton PF   S: W Ensor (242817)

MIDDLE BARTON
G: Worton Rd   S: Ms J Reed (47388)

PIDDINGTON
G: Widnell Lane   S: R Bayliss (0844 237101)

TEAM UNIPART
Cuttleslowe Pk, Oxf.   R Vircavs (0865 716650)

DIVISION TWO CLUBS 1993-94
(Tel. codes 0869 unless stated)

BARDWELL RESERVES (as above)

FOREST HILL
G: Stanton Rd   S: P Cooper (0867 72837)

HETHE RESERVES (as above)

K.E.A. UTD RESERVES (as above)

KIRKLINGTON
G: Kirklington Spts Field   S: M Mowat (50525)

LYNX
Sandy Lane, Cowley   S Hands (0865 244365)

RED LION MARAUDERS
G: Church Lane, Islip   S: D Cowan (0867 571695)

SOULDERN
G: Souldern PF   S: M Lillis (346715)

VIKING SPORTS UNITED
G: Cuttleslowe Pk, Oxf.   S: C Mott (243143)

(A.F.C.) WESTON
Weston-on-the-Green Rec.   Mrs O'Brien (50884)

WOOTTON
G: Castle Rd PF   S: L Bourne (0865 742361)

DIVISION THREE CLUBS 1993-94
(Tel. codes 0869 unless stated)

ARNCOTT RESERVES (as above)

CRUSADERS
Skimmingdish Lane, Bicester   B Monk (243174)

FRITWELL RESERVES (as above)

HEYFORD ATHLETIC RESERVES (as above)

HEYFORD UNITED
Somerton Rd, Upper Heyf.   I Lough-Scott (232788)

KIRKLINGTON RESERVES (as above)

MERTON RESERVES (as above)

MIDDLE BARTON RESERVES (as above)

RED LION MARAUDERS RESERVES (as above)

STEEPLE ASTON
G: Robinsons Close   S: A Peckham (47756)

TEAM UNIPART RESERVES (as above)

WOOTTON RESERVES (as above)

WITNEY & DISTRICT LEAGUE

Chadlington eventually secured the title despite poor end of season form. They finished five points ahead of former champions West Witney despite losing three of their last four fixtures. Brize Norton and Carterton Eagles finished third and fourth respectively to qualify for next season's Oxfordshire Charity Cup. Charlbury Town fought back from 1-2 down to beat Ducklington in a thrilling Senior Cup final at Clanfield, while in the Supplementary Cup, Ascott United beat Chipping Norton Reserves 2-1 in the final replay to add that trophy to their Division Four title. The Fred Ford Memorial Cup was won by Chadlington, the Jack Busby Memorial Trophy by Spartan Rangers Reserves, and the Junior Challenge Cup by Chadlington Reserves. In Division One, Hailey stole the title from season-long league leaders Bampton Town on goal difference.

Premier Division	P	W	D	L	F	A	PTS
Chadlington	20	15	1	4	67	23	31
West Witney	20	12	2	6	42	21	26
Brize Norton	20	12	2	6	54	40	26
Carterton Eagles	20	10	4	6	37	34	24
Hanborough	20	9	4	7	38	37	22
Charlbury Town	20	9	3	8	36	33	21
Spartan Rangers	20	8	3	9	39	38	19
Ducklington	20	8	3	9	34	39	19
Enstone Sports	20	7	4	9	30	38	18
Tackley	20	4	4	12	35	50	12
Stonesfield	20	0	2	18	10	68	2

Division One	P	W	D	L	F	A	PTS
Hailey	20	17	1	2	57	20	35
Bampton Town	20	16	3	1	64	31	35
Kingham All Blacks	20	9	3	8	50	26	21
Minster Lovell	20	8	4	8	36	35	20
Hanborough Res.	20	8	2	10	44	53	18
Alvescot	20	7	3	10	43	39	17
West Witney Res.	20	7	3	10	37	43	17
F.C. Mills	20	7	3	10	28	41	17
Milton	20	7	2	11	35	52	16
Swinbrook	20	5	3	12	39	78	13
Spartan Rgrs Res.	20	5	1	14	33	48	11

Division Two	P	W	D	L	F	A	PTS
Witney Royals	18	14	1	3	71	34	29
Aston	18	12	4	2	66	22	28
North Leigh 'A'	18	12	3	3	56	21	27
Chadlington Res.	18	11	2	5	55	44	24
Bladon	18	5	4	9	31	46	14
Crusaders	18	6	2	10	41	56	14
Carterton T. 'A'	18	5	4	9	34	52	14
Ducklington Res.	18	6	2	10	35	60	14
F.C. Mills Res.	18	4	2	12	30	51	10
Cassington	18	2	2	14	26	59	6

Division Three	P	W	D	L	F	A	PTS
Chipping Norton U.	22	18	1	3	88	34	37
Allandale	22	17	2	3	89	28	36
Charlbury T. Res	22	14	3	5	81	42	31
West Witney 'A'	22	12	2	8	64	55	26
Stonesfield Res.	22	8	6	8	32	40	24
Adlestrop	22	10	3	9	51	43	23
Brize Norton Res.	22	7	7	8	57	54	21
Enstone Res.	22	8	2	12	46	73	18
Fieldtown	22	7	3	12	60	72	17
North Kidlington	22	6	3	13	51	79	15
Alvescot Res.	22	3	5	14	28	47	11
Milton Res.	22	2	3	17	14	94	7

Division Four	P	W	D	L	F	A	PTS
Ascott United	22	21	0	1	142	23	42
Carterton United	22	18	3	1	110	31	39
Hailey Res.	22	9	8	5	54	37	26
Spartan Rgrs 'A'	22	11	4	7	55	52	26
F.C. Mills 'A'	22	9	3	10	58	60	21
Cassington Res.	22	9	2	11	57	65	20
Kingham A.B. Res.	22	6	7	9	64	64	19
Carterton T. 'B'	22	6	7	9	44	55	19
Chipping N. Utd Res.	22	6	7	9	57	72	19
Charlbury T. 'A'	22	6	5	11	31	74	17
Witney Royals Res.	22	3	4	15	33	97	10
Hanborough 'A'	22	2	2	18	24	99	6

Division Five	P	W	D	L	F	A	PTS
Freeland	22	16	3	3	100	31	35
Stanton Harcourt	22	14	5	3	71	28	33
Newland	22	13	6	3	67	38	32
Swinbrook Res.	22	13	4	5	66	39	30
Aston Res.	22	12	3	7	48	32	27
Fieldtown Res.	22	9	5	8	55	40	23
Bampton T. Res.	22	8	6	8	42	41	22
Minster Lovell Res.	22	7	3	12	42	56	17
Tackley Res.	22	6	5	11	41	85	17
Carterton U. Res.	22	6	4	12	52	71	16
Bladon Res.	22	1	4	17	30	88	6
Alvescot 'A'	22	2	3	17	14	94	7

OXFORD CITY JUNIOR LEAGUE (Est. 1891)

Premier Division	P	W	D	L	F	A	PTS
Crown & Thistle	16	11	2	3	44	26	24
Wheatley United	16	10	3	3	62	25	23
Barton Youth	16	9	2	5	34	25	20
North Oxford	16	6	4	6	32	28	16
East Oxford	16	6	4	6	27	27	16
Port Mahon	16	6	4	6	39	45	16
Marston	16	5	2	9	37	56	12
The Fox	16	3	5	8	29	46	11
Beckley Sports	16	2	2	12	21	48	6

Premier Cup winners: Wheatley
Premier Cup R-up: Barton Youth

Division One	P	W	D	L	F	A	PTS
White Eagles	14	13	0	1	77	12	26
Oxgas Sports	14	10	0	4	55	28	20
Prince of Wales	14	7	3	4	55	32	17
Great Hoseley	14	7	2	5	40	42	16
Tetsworth	14	6	2	6	39	27	14
Great Milton	14	5	1	8	38	44	11
Red Lion (Wolvercote)	14	1	2	11	25	89	4
Nth Oxford Res.	14	1	2	11	17	72	4

C.J.L. Cup winners: Barton Youth
C.J.L. Cup R-up: White Eagles
Couling Cup winners: Barton Youth
Couling Cup R-up: Wheatley
Inter-Lge (with Lord Jersey FA): KEA Utd
Inter-Lge Cup R-up: Prince of Wales

OXFORDSHIRE YOUTH LEAGUE

Under-17	P	W	D	L	F	A	PTS
Abingdon Town	12	10	1	1	40	9	21
Oxford City	12	8	3	1	32	9	19
Didcot Town	12	8	1	3	32	14	17
Wantage Town	12	5	1	6	23	32	11
Riverside	12	4	2	6	20	26	10
South Courtney	12	2	0	10	15	37	4
Southfield	12	1	0	11	14	49	2

Under-18	P	W	D	L	F	A	PTS
Milton United	10	8	1	1	52	9	17
Abingdon United	10	7	1	2	30	18	15
Witney Town	10	5	2	3	31	19	12
Carterton Town	10	4	0	6	16	23	8
Chinnor	10	2	1	7	11	37	5
Bicester Town	10	1	1	8	17	51	3

GLOUCESTERSHIRE COUNTY LEAGUE

Chairman: Mr A C Barratt.
Vice-Chairman: J D Hart.
Treasurer: P T McPherson.
Hon. Secretary: Mr D J Herbert,
8 Fernhurst Road, St George,
Bristol BS5 7TQ (0272 517696).

	P	W	D	L	F	A	PTS
Hallen	34	26	2	6	91	35	80
Old Georgians	34	24	5	5	77	37	77
Ellwood	34	21	4	9	93	50	67
D.R.G. (F.P.)	34	20	3	11	74	42	63
Wotton Rovers	34	16	9	9	61	56	57
Harrow Hill	34	16	6	12	67	54	54
Patchway Town	34	14	11	9	59	43	53
Cadbury Heath	34	15	6	13	52	51	51
Henbury Old Boys	34	13	11	10	52	49	50
Pucklechurch Spts	34	14	4	16	46	56	46
St Philips M.A.S.	34	12	7	15	53	51	43
St Marks C.A.	34	12	6	16	43	52	42
Campden Town	34	10	10	14	39	55	40
Winterbourne Utd	34	10	7	17	47	70	37
Dowty Dynamoes	34	8	8	18	49	63	32
Smiths Athletic	34	8	8	18	42	62	32
Stapleton	34	6	5	23	42	87	23
Hambrook	34	2	6	26	19	93	12

HALLEN FINAL CELEBRATIONS!

Hallen lifted the G.F.A. Challenge Trophy with a 4-1 win over Cinderford Town from the Premier Division of the Spectre Hellenic League which completed a double after lifting the League championship. When Old Georgians went to Hallen in the league and won 3-2 the title was between the two sides. At that stage Old Georgians, with six games left, were seven points clear of Hallen who had seven games, but they managed to pick up only eleven points whilst their rivals amassed 21 and never looked back to become worthy champions.

At the other end of the table, Hambrook were relegated. They recorded their first League win at the 26th attempt - a 1-0 win over local rivals Pucklechurch on 20th March, but could not avoid the drop. This left Dowty Dynamos, Smiths Athletic and Stapleton battling to stay out of the remaining relegation spot, and it was the latter who lost out with matches running out and dropping several silly points. However, they have been reprieved by the fact that Hallen were accepted into the Spectre Hellenic League.

D J Herbert, Hon. Secretary.

COUNTY LEAGUE RESULTS 1992-93

HOME TEAM		1	2	3	4	5	6	7	8	9	10	11	12	13	14	15	16	17	18
1.	CADBURY HEATH	*	3-0	3-0	2-1	0-3	0-4	1-0	1-2	1-1	1-2	0-1	2-0	1-0	2-1	2-1	4-2	0-1	3-4
2.	CAMPDEN TOWN	0-1	*	1-0	1-2	0-4	0-3	3-2	3-2	0-2	1-3	1-1	0-0	2-1	0-3	2-0	4-2	1-1	0-2
3.	DOWTY DYNAMOS	4-3	0-0	*	1-2	1-3	0-1	4-1	1-2	2-2	2-3	1-1	2-3	0-4	2-2	2-1	4-2	3-1	4-2
4.	D.R.G. (F.P.)	0-0	3-0	1-0	*	1-4	1-3	4-0	4-3	3-2	1-0	4-0	2-0	2-1	1-3	0-2	4-0	1-2	2-3
5.	ELLWOOD	1-3	2-1	2-2	1-3	*	2-0	6-0	5-5	1-2	1-2	5-1	3-1	3-1	4-1	3-1	4-2	2-1	3-4
6.	HALLEN	3-1	5-2	5-2	0-0	1-2	*	7-0	3-0	5-1	2-3	4-3	5-2	1-2	1-0	4-3	4-1	4-1	3-1
7.	HAMBROOK	3-2	2-4	1-4	0-7	0-1	0-3	*	0-1	1-1	0-1	1-2	1-0	1-5	0-0	0-0	0-0	1-1	0-4
8.	HARROW HILL	3-2	2-0	1-1	3-5	3-2	0-2	5-1	*	3-2	1-3	1-0	2-1	0-3	1-0	3-1	4-0	4-1	1-1
9.	HENBURY O.B.	5-0	1-1	1-0	0-0	0-5	1-3	3-1	1-0	*	1-0	1-1	1-0	1-1	1-1	1-3	1-0	3-0	2-4
10.	OLD GEORGIANS	1-1	2-0	3-0	1-0	5-3	1-2	2-1	1-1	2-2	*	1-1	3-0	2-2	2-1	3-1	4-2	5-3	3-1
11.	PATCHWAY TOWN	0-2	0-0	1-0	1-0	2-0	3-0	4-0	1-1	0-0	0-1	*	4-1	1-4	2-0	7-0	6-2	1-0	4-0
12.	PUCKLECHURCH	0-0	0-2	2-0	3-1	2-2	0-1	4-1	1-0	1-2	1-5	2-0	*	3-0	0-1	1-0	4-3	3-1	2-0
13.	ST MARKS C.A.	1-0	0-0	0-0	1-6	1-2	2-0	0-7	2-1	2-0	3-1	1-2	*	2-2	0-0	1-2	0-2	0-2	
14.	ST PHILIPS M.A.S.	1-2	3-4	0-0	2-3	0-5	1-0	3-0	2-1	5-2	0-2	2-2	1-2	1-0	*	2-1	5-0	2-2	1-2
15.	SMITHS ATHLETIC	1-2	1-1	3-2	1-0	2-2	0-3	3-1	2-1	0-0	0-1	1-3	1-1	0-2	0-2	*	3-2	4-1	1-1
16.	STAPLETON	2-2	1-1	1-0	0-1	0-2	1-0	3-1	1-4	0-3	2-2	1-2	1-1	3-1	2-1	*	0-1	1-2	
17.	WINTERBOURNE UTD	1-3	1-1	2-0	1-5	2-1	0-4	4-0	1-4	2-2	1-5	1-1	3-1	0-1	0-1	3-2	5-1	*	1-1
18.	WOTTON ROVERS	2-2	1-3	3-2	0-4	0-2	1-1	1-1	0-0	1-0	0-2	2-2	3-1	2-0	4-3	2-2	2-0	3-0	*

Leading Scorers: S Price (Hallen) 25, M Brown (Ellwood) 19, C Brain (Harrow Hill) 18, G Cox (Henbury) 18, A Kerr (Ellwood (5 for Hallen)) 17, I Shephard (Wotton) 17, S Beacham (Hallen) 16, A Gorton (St Marks) 16, K Horseman (Patchway) 16, S Britton (D.R.G.) 15, P Bartley (Old Georgians) 14, G Bell (Hallen) 14, S Bignell (Old Georgians) 14.

Sporting Shield *(following marks are awarded to clubs by their opponents for 1992-93):*
Harrow Hill 116, Smiths Athletic 111, Campden Town 110, D.R.G. (F.P.) 109, Pucklechurch Sports 108, Old Georgians 106, Cadbury Heath 105, Henbury O.B. 104, Wotton Rovers 104, Dowty Dynamo 102, Stapleton 100, Hallen 99, Hambrook, 98, St Marks C.A. 98, St Philips M.A.S. 98, Ellwood 96, Winterbourne 92, Patchway Town 85 *(Maximum: 170).*

GLOUCESTERSHIRE COUNTY LEAGUE CLUBS 1993-94
CADBURY HEATH

Secretary: K Major, 135 Fishponds Rd, Eastville, Bristol BS5 6PR (0272 444410).
Ground: 'Springfield', Cadbury Heath Rd, Warmley, Bristol (0272 675730).
Directions: A420 from Bristol through Kingswood, across new r'bout, right into Tower Rd North, past school, right into Cadbury Heath Rd, ground immediately on right down alley.
Colours: Red/black/black (red tops). **Change Colours:** Yellow/black/black (red tops).
Hons: Glos Co. Lg 70-71 71-72 72-73 73-74 (R-up 74-75 90-91 91-92), Glos Amtr Cup Sth(3), FA Vase QF.

CAMPDEN TOWN

Secretary: D J Benfield, 14 Harvard Avenue, Honeybourne, Evesham, Worcs WR11 5XU (0386 831935).
Ground: Recreation Ground, Catbrook, Chipping Campden, Glos. (0386 840124).
Directions: In Chipping Camden village, just east of Broadway, Worcs.
Colours: Amber/black/amber   **Change Colours:** All red.

D.R.G.

Secretary: J A Jacobs, 80 The Meadows, Hanham, Bristol BS15 3PB (0272 611845).
Ground: 'Shortwood', Carsons Road, Mangotsfield, Bristol (0272 560390).
Directions: M4 jct 19 onto M32, off at jct 1 onto A4174 follow signs for Downend then Mangotsfield. Continue through town, road becomes Carsons Road, ground on right after factory.
Seats: None   **Cover:** No   **Capacity:** 1,000   **Clubhouse:** Yes   **Founded:** 1962
Colours: Maroon & blue stripes/maroon/maroon   **Change Colours:** Yellow/maroon/maroon
Previous Name: R.W.P. (pre-1986)   **Previous Ground:** St Johns Lane 62-66.   **Clubhouse:** Yes.
Record Gate: 500 v Pucklechurch Sports, Bristol Combination 1/4/86.

DOWTY DYNAMOS

President: C J M Walker   **Chairman:** J Brayshaw   **Manager:** Alan Gough
Secretary: C J Brown, 25 Courtenay Street, Cheltenham, Glos GL50 4LR (0242 511117).
Ground: Dowty Arle Court Sports Ground, Hatherley Lane, Cheltenham (0242 525515).
Directions: In Cheltenham follow signs for GCHQ. Ground adjacent.   **Clubhouse:** Yes
Colours: Royal & white/royal/blue & white   **Change Colours:** Red/blue/blue
Programme: 20 pages, 25p   **Prev. Name:** Alstone Dynamos 47-79   **Founded:** 1947
Hons: Glos Nthn Snr Lg 90-91, Cheltenham Lg R-up 88-89 (Div 2 76-77 79-80), Winchcombe Cup 89-90 (R-up 90-91).

ELLWOOD

Secretary: R J Cole, 64 Allaston Rd, Lydney, Glos. GL15 5ST (0594 844395).
Ground: Bromley Rd, Ellwood, Coleford, Glos (0594 832927).
Colours: All royal blue   **Change Colours:** Red/royal blue/royal blue

ENDSLEIGH

Secretary: N Toplis, 136 Stratton Heights, Cirencester, Glos GL7 2RL (0285 643104).
Ground: Cheltenham Town F.C. *(see page 487)*
Colours: Blue/blue/white   **Change colours:** Yellow/blue/white.
Previous Ground: The Folley, Swindon Road, Cheltenham (pre-1993)
Prev. Lge: Glos Northern Snr (pre'93)   **Hons:** Glos Northern Snr Lg 92-93 (Div 1 91-92).

HARROW HILL

Secretary: R C Beckett, 'Sunny View', Bridge Rd, Harrow Hill, Drybrook, Glos GL17 9ST (0594 543390).
Ground: Larksfield Rd, Harrow Hill, Drybrook, Glos (0954 543873).
Directions: A40 from Gloucester for for seven miles, left onto A4136 and continue for eight miles to Harrow Hill, right into Trinity Road near Church, right into Larkfield Road after half a mile, ground on right.
Seats: No   **Cover:** Yes   **Capacity:** 2,000   **Clubhouse:** Yes   **Founded:** 1932
Colours: Blue/claret/sky   **Change Colours:** Yellow/claret/blue.
Record Gate: 500-600, local cup, 1960s.
Best FA Vase season: 1st Rd 88-89   **Hons:** Glos Northern Snr Lg(4) 63-65 71-72 81-82.

HENBURY OLD BOYS

Secretary: C B Barron, 126 Charlton Rd, Westbury-on-Trym, Bristol BS10 6NL (0272 504002).
Ground: Arnall Drive Playing Fields, Henbury, Bristol (0272 590475).   **Directions:** M5 jct 17, down Cribbs Causeway, into Station Road, left into Henbury Rd, ground on left.
Founded: 1962
Colours: Amber & black/black/black   **Change Colours:** Blue/black/black.
Hons: Avon Combination 82-83 (Lg Cup 83-84), Glos Snr Amtr Cup South, Fry Club Cup 92-93.

OLD GEORGIANS

Secretary: I Stiddard, 18 Clare Rd, Kingswood, Bristol BS15 1PJ (0272 672879).
Ground: St George's School PF, Johnsons Lane, Whitehall, Bristol (0272 516888).
Directions: M32 jct 2, left, left, right at lights, right behind Kings Head. Buses 6 or 7 from central Bristol. One mile from Stapleton Road (BR).
Seats: None   **Cover:** No   **Capacity:** 1,500   **Clubhouse:** Yes   **Founded:** 1905.
Colours: Sky (navy sleeves)/navy/navy   **Change Colours:** Red/navy/red
Record Gate: 770 v Stansted, FA Vase QF 4/3/84.   **Manager:** Brian Tufton.
Hons: Glos Co. Lg 82-83 84-85 (R-up 83-84 92-93), Glos Challenge Tphy, Glos Snr Amtr Cup Sth, FA Vase QF 83-84.

PATCHWAY TOWN

Secretary: R Stewart, 22 Arlingham Way, Patchway, Bristol, BS12 5NQ (0272 792983).
Ground: 'Scott Park', Coniston Rd, Patchway, Bristol (0272 691203)
Directions: M5 jct 16, A38 towards Bristol, right into Coniston Road, ground signposted Scott Park.
Colours: Black & white stripes/black/black   **Change Colours:** All royal blue
Hons: Glos County Lg 91-92

PUCKLECHURCH SPORTS

Secretary: R B Savage, 54 Shortwood Rd, Pucklechurch, Bristol BS17 3RN (0272 373972).
Ground: Pucklechurch Recreation Ground, Pucklechurch, Abson (0275 822102).
Directions: M32 jct 1 follow A4174 through Downend to Mangotsfield, left signposted Pucklechurch, continue to village, turn right, ground on left.
Seats: No   **Cover:** None   **Clubhouse:** Yes   **Prog:** 32 pages,40p   **Editor:** M Dowse.
Colours: Green/white/green   **Change Colours:** All white.
Hons: Avon Comb. 77-78 78-79 87-88 (Div 2 66-67, Lg Cup 77-78 78-79 87-88), Glos Jnr Cup 65-66 82-83, Bristol & District Lg 72-73.

ST. MARKS C.A.

Secretary: W Pember, 11 Linworth Rd, Bishops Cleeve, Cheltenham, Glos GL52 4PF (0242 673800).
Ground: As Dowty Dynamos (above)
Colours: Royal blue/royal blue/red   **Change Colours:** Red with white hoop/royal blue/red
Hons: Glos Northern Snr Lg 74-75 78-79 83-84.

ST. PHILIPS MARSH ADULT SCHOOL

Secretary: T R Green, 35 Braienkridge Rd, Brislington, Bristol BS4 3SW (0272 770530).
Ground: John Harvey Sports Ground, Norton Lane, Whitchurch, Bristol (0272 837271).
Directions: A37 south from Bristol, through Whitchurch, right into Norton Lane just after humped back bridge. Ground first right.
Seats: No   **Cover:** No   **Clubhouse:** Yes   **Programme:** Yes   **Founded:**
Colours: White/black/black   **Change Colours:** Red & white/red/red.

SMITHS ATHLETIC

Secretary: P H Jurd, 11 Shawgreen Lane, Prestbury, Cheltenham, Glos GL52 3BS (0242 529188).
Ground: The Newlands, Evesham Rd, Bishops Cleeve, Cheltenham (0242 672752).
Colours: All royal blue   **Change Colours:** All red.
Hons: Glos Northern Snr Lg 91-92   **Previous League:** Glos Northern Snr (until 1992).

STAPLETON

Secretary: J Catley, 123 Old Gloucester Rd, Hambrook, Bristol (0272 569110).
Ground & Directions: Frenchay Park Playing Field, Frenchay, Bristol. M32 jct 1, A4174, follow signs to Frenchay Hospital - ground opposite. Or M32 jct 2, follow signs for Frenchay through Stapleton, ground on left.
Seats: No   **Cover:** No   **Clubhouse:** Yes   **Programme:** Yes   **Founded:** 1932.
Colours: All burgundy   **Change Colours:** White/white/purple.

TOTTERDOWN ATHLETIC

Secretary: Mrs G V Salter, 65 Novers Park Drive, Knowle, Bristol BS4 1RH (0272 632720).
Ground: Bristol & West Indian Cricket Ground, Gordon PF, Gordon Rd, Whitehall, Bristol.
Directions: Opposite Old Georgians F.C. - see opposite.
Colours: Yellow/blue/blue   **Change Colours:** All red.
Prev. Lge: Bristol & Suburban (pre'93)   **Hons:** Bristol & Suburban Lg R-up 92-93.

WINTERBOURNE UNITED

Secretary: J Lloyd, 31 Park Avenue, Winterbourne, Bristol BS17 1NH (0454 775841).
Ground: Parkside Ave. Rec., Winterbourne, Bristol. - Behind school, just beyond shops in Winterbourne.
Seats: No   **Cover:** Yes   **Clubhouse:** Yes   **Previous Lge:** Avon Comb. (until 1992)
Colours: White/red/red   **Change Colours:** Blue & white stripes/blue/blue

WOTTON ROVERS

Secretary: M P Excell, 94 Bearlands, Wotton-under-Edge, Glos. GL12 7SB (0453 845178).
Ground: Synwell Playing Field, Synwell Lane, Wotton-under-Edge (0453 842929).
Directions: From Wotton war memorial down hill and follow Synwell Lane. Ground on left.
Seats: None   **Cover:** No   **Capacity:** 2,000   **Clubhouse:** Yes   **Founded:** 1959.
Colours: All royal blue   **Change Colours:** White/white/red
Record Gate: 2,000   **Programme:** 20 pages, 50p
Previous Names: Synwell Rovers (pre-1959)/ Wotton-under-Edge FC.

ENDSLEIGH CHELTENHAM LEAGUE

Division One	P	W	D	L	F	A	PTS
Bourton Rovers	24	18	3	3	67	29	39
Northleach	24	17	2	5	84	40	36
Crescent United	24	14	7	3	64	25	33
Smiths Ath. Res.	24	14	3	7	58	34	31
The Court	24	13	4	7	71	48	30
Woodmancote	24	10	4	10	57	41	24
St Marks CA Res.	24	10	4	10	39	35	24
Eagle Star	24	10	3	11	41	56	23
Andover Sford	24	10	2	12	52	48	22
Chelt. Civil Serv.	24	5	6	13	42	65	16
D. Electrics	24	4	5	15	31	63	13
Bishops Cleeve Res	24	3	7	14	38	71	13
Winchcombe	24	2	2	20	21	110	6

Divison Two	P	W	D	L	F	A	PTS
RAF Inns'th	22	16	3	3	82	26	35
Smith Ath. 'A'	22	16	3	3	65	29	35
Endsleigh Res.	22	15	3	4	66	30	33
Cl P'folio	22	11	8	3	65	37	30
Siddington	22	9	7	6	60	42	25
Campden T. Res.	22	8	5	9	49	46	21
Bredon	22	7	7	8	44	47	21
Cheltenham Rov.	22	7	4	11	39	52	18
St.Marks C.A. 'A'	22	6	6	10	48	70	18
Prestbury Res.	22	5	3	14	28	52	13
Newtown Wdrs	22	2	4	16	28	87	8
Woodcote Res.	22	3	1	18	27	83	7
Charlton Kings	0	0	0	0	0	0	0

Division Three	P	W	D	L	F	A	PTS
Warden Hill	20	14	6	0	81	17	34
Kings	20	15	1	4	62	24	31
Broadwell Res.	20	14	3	3	74	39	31
Hoppers	20	10	4	6	90	45	24
Dowty Dyn. Res.	20	10	3	7	49	43	23
Eagle Star res	20	6	6	8	48	53	18
D. Ashchurch	20	7	2	11	38	50	16
D. Staverton	20	6	3	11	46	67	15
Northchurch Res.	20	4	4	12	31	72	12
Beeches	20	4	1	15	44	81	9
Bourton Res.	20	3	1	16	32	104	7

Division Four	P	W	D	L	F	A	PTS
Brockworth Res.	24	21	3	0	144	21	45
Endsleigh 'A'	24	16	5	3	67	29	37
Whitbread	24	15	3	6	78	47	33
Chelt. C.S. Res.	24	13	6	5	70	39	32
Winchcombe Res.	24	10	4	10	51	55	24
Spirax Saracens	24	10	3	11	48	45	23
Bredon Res.	24	9	3	12	58	66	21
Chelt. Saracens 'A'	24	9	3	12	50	62	21
Prior Old Boys	24	7	5	12	48	69	19
Siddington Res.	24	5	10	9	42	45	18
Gas Green	24	8	2	14	48	58	18
St.Marks C.A. 'C'	24	6	5	13	49	75	17
Rowanfield	24	1	0	23	15	157	2

Division Five	P	W	D	L	F	A	PTS
Dowty Sport	24	17	4	3	88	41	38
Andoversford Res.	24	17	3	4	81	23	37
Bassalona	24	16	4	4	69	41	36
Shipton O.	24	13	7	4	64	45	33
Smiths Athletic 'C'	24	12	3	9	61	35	27
Broadhill Res.	24	10	4	10	45	50	24
Kings Res.	24	8	5	11	57	67	21
Great Rissington	24	10	1	13	55	66	21
Prestbury Res.	24	8	3	13	38	50	19
Beeches Res.	24	8	2	14	48	71	18
Eagle Star 'A'	24	4	7	13	27	50	15
D. Staverton Res.	24	6	3	15	45	73	15
Gas Green Res.	24	3	2	19	26	92	8

Division Six	P	W	D	L	F	A	PTS
Falcons	24	20	3	1	80	10	40
Barn'st'wth	24	17	2	5	71	32	36
Boddington	24	14	6	4	79	24	34
Bishops Cleeve 'A'	24	14	4	6	74	32	32
Caradon M'A	24	14	3	7	76	36	31
Chelt. Civil Serv.'A'	24	11	2	11	64	57	24
Chelt. Saracens 'C'	24	10	2	12	58	78	22
Cl. Portfolio Res.	24	7	7	10	61	43	21
Spa. Gla'tor	24	6	6	12	50	72	18
Row'f'ld Res.	24	9	2	13	52	65	17
Newtown Res.	24	7	4	13	35	72	16
Charlton Kings Res.	24	2	4	18	33	97	8
Gas Green 'A'	24	1	3	20	26	141	5

GLOUCESTERSHIRE
NORTHERN SENIOR LEAGUE

President: H J Morgan.

Vice-President: A D Bushell.

Chairman: R Davis.

Vice-Chairman: E J George.

Hon. Secretary: W N Pember, 11 Linworth Rd,
Bishops Cleeve, Cheltenham GL52 4PF (673800).

Endsleigh, in only their second year of membership of the League, took the title by a comfortable five points. The Cheltenham based club also won the G.F.A. Senior Cup defeating Division Two champions Brockworth in the final with the game's only goal. Runners-up Broadwell earned their highest placing since 1976-77 when they finished second in Division Two. Dursley Town in third place led the table for a long period but fell away during March. However, the club celebrated its centenary during the season. The top scorer in Division One was Peter Turnbull of Endsleigh with 26.

Elected into Division Two as champions of the Cheltenham League, Brockworth lost their first two games, then went undefeated for the remainder of the season, and their goals tally earned them the League Merit Shield. Two Forest of Dean clubs fought out the runners-up slot, Viney St Swithins producing some good results in the last two weeks of the season to beat Worrall Hill on goal difference. The leading scorer in Division Two was Pete Williams with 26 for champions Brockworth.

In the final of the Forest Green Rovers Supporters Cup, Brockworth outplayed Division One side Longford to win 5-0, the latter fading badly after a good start to the season. The final, played at Forest Green Rovers F.C., produced some good football for a sizeable crowd.

The League Sportsmanship awards were won by Longford (Divsion One) and I.C.I. Fibres (Division Two). The Touchline Flags Linesman award also went to Longford.

W N Pember, League Secretary.

Division One	P	W	D	L	F	A	PTS
Endsleigh	30	24	3	3	103	28	51
Broadwell Amtrs	30	20	6	4	60	29	46
Dursley Town	30	19	6	5	53	26	44
Hardwicke	30	18	7	5	67	33	43
Frampton United	30	20	2	8	72	45	42
Kings Stanley	30	14	4	12	48	46	32
Sharpness	30	14	3	13	60	57	31
Longford	30	11	7	12	63	58	29
Lydbrook Athletic	30	11	7	12	45	58	29
Shortwood Utd Res.	30	11	3	16	62	61	25
Berkeley Town	30	8	8	14	41	60	24
Hilldene Ath.	30	8	7	15	27	50	23
Cam Bulldogs	30	7	7	16	39	55	21
Coleford United	30	5	7	18	31	73	17
Longlevens	30	4	6	20	38	73	14
Brimscombe/Thrupp	30	2	5	23	21	78	9

Division Two	P	W	D	L	F	A	PTS
Brockworth	30	25	3	2	117	28	53
Viney St Swithins	30	17	8	5	78	36	42
Worrall Hill	30	20	2	8	71	47	42
Stonehouse F'way	30	19	3	8	76	46	41
Bibury	30	18	2	10	75	51	38
Lydney Town	30	14	8	8	71	42	36
Newent Town	30	11	6	13	48	67	28
Taverners	30	9	9	12	46	42	27
Cinderford T. Res *	30	10	7	13	47	59	25
ICI Fibres	30	10	5	15	38	64	25
Vikings *	30	11	4	15	58	89	24
Nuclear Electric	30	8	7	15	41	52	23
Gala/Wilton	30	8	5	17	44	78	21
Charfield	30	7	6	17	43	63	20
Yorkley	30	6	6	18	37	73	18
Whitecroft	30	4	5	21	37	87	13

* - 2pts deducted.

Broadwell Amateurs - Division One runners-up 1992-93. Back Row (L/R): M Hale (Chairman), G Matthews, M Blandford, D Baldwin, G Reddan, P Brooks, R Gordon, G Barnes (Secretary), S Edwards (Manager). Front: D Frowen, P Ennis, C Stephens, A Coles (Captain), D McDonald, S Merry, G Hurcombe. Photo - James Wright.

FOREST GREEN ROVERS SUPPORTERS CLUB TROPHY

First Round

Cam Bulldogs v Taveners	0-1	Longford v Nuclear Electric	5-3
Broadwell Amateurs v Coleford	2-0	Bibury v ICI Fibres	1-1*(Bibury on pens)*
Lydney Town v Endsleigh	4-2	Yorkley v Newent Town	2-6
Viney St Swithins v Dursley Town	1-0	Longlevens v Sharpness	2-2*(Sharpness on pens)*
Hilldene Athletic v Vikings	1-0	Hardwicke v Berkeley Town	2-1
Whitecroft v Cinderford Town Reserves	0-3	Gala Wilton v Shortwood United Reserves	4-2
Frampton United v Worrall Hill	3-2	Charfield v Stonehouse Freeway	0-5
Brockworth v Kings Stanley	7-2	Brimscombe & Thrupp v Lydbrook Athletic	0-1

Second Round

Newent Town v Bibury	1-5	Broadwell Amateurs v Cinderford Town Reserves	6-0
Lydbrook Athletic v Brockworth	4-5	Taveners v Hilldene Athletic	1-3
Viney St Swithins v Gala Wilton	3-1	Hardwicke v Lydney Town	2-4
Frampton United v Sharpness	3-0	Longford v Stonehouse Freeway	1-0

Quarter-Finals

Frampton United v Viney St Swithins	3-0	Brockworth v Bibury	2-2*(Brockworth on pens)*
Longford v Broadwell Amateurs	4-2	Hilldene Athletic v Lydney Town	0-2

Semi-Finals

Lydney Town v Brockworth	0-2	Longford v Frampton United	2-0

Final *(at Forest Green Rovers F.C.)*: Brockworth 5, Longford 0

FIRST DIVISION CLUBS 1993-94

BERKELEY TOWN
Secretary: Alan Dimery, 22 Jubilee Rd, Dursley, Glos GL11 4ES (Dursley 542981).
Colours: Green & yellow stripes/green   **Change colours:** All blue.
Ground: Station Rd, Berkeley.

BROADWELL AMATEURS
Secretary: G D Barnes, 61 North Rd, Broadwell, Coleford, Glos GL16 7BX (0594 832523).
Colours: Claret & blue.   **Change colours:** Yellow/blue.
Ground: The Hawthorns, Broadwell, Coleford (0594 837347).

BROCKWORTH
Secretary: Andrew Bracewell, 10 Boverton Drive, Brockworth, Glos GL3 4DB (0452 610160).
Colours: White/black   **Change colours:** Amber/black.
Ground: Mill Lane, Brockworth (0452 862556).
Hons: Glos Northern Snr Lg Div 1 92-93 (Lg Cup 92-93), Cheltenham Lg 91-92.

CAM BULLDOGS
Secretary: J R Jewitt, 58 Woodview Rd, Dursley, Glos GL11 5SE (0453 548879).
Colours: All yellow   **Change colours:** Red/green.
Ground: Cam Sports Club, Everlands, Cam (0453 546736).

COLEFORD UNITED
Secretary: T Smith, 3A Lower Palmers Flat, Coalway, Coleford, Glos GL16 7LT (0594 834791).
Colours: White/black   **Change colours:** Red/black.
Ground: King George V Playing Fields, Victoria Rd, Coleford.

DURSLEY TOWN
Secretary: P James, 8 Meadow Vale, Tilsdown, Dursley, Glos GL11 6HJ (0453 547413).
Colours: Red/black   **Change colours:** All blue.
Ground: Recreation Ground, Kingshill Road, Dursley, Glos.

FRAMPTON UNITED
Secretary: H G Tudor, 'Ad Extremum', Frampton-upon-Severn, Glos GL2 7EA (0452 740224).
Colours: Royal & white stripes   **Change colours:** All white.
Ground: Bell Field, Frampton-on-Severn

HARDWICKE
Secretary: A J King, 25 Elmsgrove Road East, Hardwicke, Glos GL2 6PY (0452 728603).
Colours: All white   **Change colours:** All yellow.
Ground: Green Lane, Hardwicke (0452 720587).

HILLDENE ATHLETIC
Secretary: Gary Sleeman, 26 Forest View, Buckshaft Rd, Cinderford, Glos GL14 3DP (0594 822950).
Colours: Sky blue.   **Change colours:** Red.
Ground: Miners Welfare Ground, Barleycorn Square, off Station Street, Cinderford.

KINGS STANLEY
Secretary: R K Bassett, 8 Guildings Way, Kings Stanley, Stonehouse, Glos GL1 3LF (0453 824012).
Colours: Maroon & royal blue.   **Change colours:** Black & white.
Ground: Marling Close, Kings Stanley (0453 828975).

LONGFORD
Secretary: T Godwin, 2 Abbotts Cottage, Sandhurst, Gloucester GL2 9NW (0452 730727).
Colours: Sky/navy.   **Change colours:** Red & white stripes.
Ground: Longford Playing Fields, Longford Lane.

LYDBROOK
Secretary: J A Price, 'Wobage', Fourth Avenue, Greytree, Ross-on-Wye HR9 7HR (0989 63788).
Colours: Black & white.   **Change colours:** Blue.
Ground: Reeds, Lower Lydbrook.

SHARPNESS
Secretary: J Thomas, 69 Oldminster Rd, Sharpness, Nr Berkeley, Glos GL13 9UR (0453 811397).
Colours: Red/white   **Change colours:** All white or all blue.
Ground: Berkeley Vale Community School.

SHORTWOOD UNITED RESERVES *(see page 735)*

VINEY ST SWITHINS

Secretary: A R Thomas, 'Ravenscoft', 28 Allaston Rd, Lydney, Glos GL15 5ST (0594 843634).
Colours: Red/black **Change colours:** Blue/white.
Ground: Viney St Swithins Sports & Social Club, Viney Hill (0594 510658).

WORRALL HILL

Secretary: B Wadley, 9 Hillside Terrace, Joys Green, Lydbrook, Glos GL17 9DY (0594 860587).
Colours: All red **Change colours:** All blue.
Ground: Worrall Hill, Lydbrook, Glos (0594 860532).

SECOND DIVISION CLUBS 1993-94

BIBURY

Secretary: P W Brown, 43 Pheasant Way, Cirencester GL7 1BJ (0285 655169).
Colours: Red/black **Change colours:** Blue/black.
Ground: Aldsworth Rd, Bibury.

BRIMSCOMBE & THRUPP

Secretary: B F Roberts, 16 Berrells Rd, Tetbury, Glos GL8 8ED (0666 502545).
Colours: White/navy **Change colours:** All navy.
Ground: The Meadow, London Rd, Brimscombe, Nr Stroud, Glos.

CHARFIELD

Secretary: P Kirby, 209 Dovecote, Yate, Bristol BS17 4PF (0454 316266).
Colours: Red/navy **Ground:** Charfield Memorial Hall (0454 260204).

CINDERFORD TOWN RESERVES *(see page 734)*

ELLWOOD RESERVES *(see page 748)*

G.A.L.A. WILTON

Secretary: T R Onions, 19 Teddington Gdns, Gloucester GL4 9RL (0452 612420).
Colours: Old gold/black **Change colours:** Yellow/blue.
Ground: Gala Club, Fairmile Gardens, Tewkesbury Rd, Gloucester (0452 524447).

I.C.I. FIBRES

Secretary: Charles Taylor, 3 Vineyards Close, Charlton Kings, Cheltenham Glos GL53 8NH (0242 237617).
Colours: Sky/blue **Change colours:** White/black.
Ground: I.C.I. Sports Ground, Green Street, Brockworth (0452 371040).

LONGLEVENS

Secretary: W G Davis, 28 Simon Road, Longlevens, Gloucester GL2 0TP (0452 422450).
Colours: Red/white **Change colours:** Yellow/white.
Ground: The Pavilion, Longford Lane, Longlevens, Gloucester (0452 308152).

LYDNEY TOWN

Secretary: R A Sansom, 17 Woodland Rise, Lydney, Glos GL15 5LH (0594 843210).
Colours: White/navy **Change colours:** Yellow/navy.
Ground: Lydney Recreation Trust Ground (0594 844523).

NEWENT TOWN

Secretary: John Jones, 1 West View, Newent, Glos GL18 1TE (0531 821465).
Colours: Orange & blue & white/blue **Change colours:** All red.
Ground: Wildsmith Meadow, Gloucester Rd, Newent, Glos (0531 821509).

NUCLEAR ELECTRIC

Secretary: P L Nurden, 52 Gambier Parry Gdns, Gloucester GL2 9RD (0452 411506).
Colours: Yellow/green **Change colours:** All red.
Ground: As I.C.I. Fibres (above).

STONEHOUSE FREEWAY

Secretary: M Smith, 2 The Cottage, The Cross, Eastington, Stonehouse, Glos GL10 3AB (0453 824214).
Colours: Black & white hoops/black **Change colours:** White/black.
Ground: Oldends Lane, Stonehouse, Glos.

TAVERNERS

Secretary: David Burton, 41 Fairmead, Cam, Dursley GL11 5JR (0453 548000).
Colours: Blue **Change colours:** White.
Ground: Recreation Ground, High Street, Hawkesbury Upton, Avon.

VIKINGS (STROUD)

Secretary: A R Brown, 1 St Lawrence Rd, Barnwood, Gloucester GL4 7QR (0452 615446).
Colours: Orange & white. **Change colours:** Claret & blue.
Ground: Birds Eye Walls Sports & Social Club, Hammonds Way, Barnwood, Gloucester.

YATE TOWN 'A' *(see page 527)*

YORKLEY

Secretary: Malcolm Waters, Bailey Hill Store, Bailey Hill, Yorkley, nr Lydney GL15 4SP (0594 562245).
Colours: Royal, scarlet & white diagonal stripes/blue **Change colours:** Green.
Ground: Yorkley Recreation Ground.

COUNTY OF AVON
PREMIER COMBINATION

(Established 1957)

Hon. Secretary: Vernon Windell,
89 St Peters Rise, Headley Park, Bristol BS13 7NA.

PREM. DIV.	P	W	D	L	F	A	PTS	DIV. ONE	P	W	D	L	F	A	PTS
Bristol St George	30	20	4	6	70	36	44	Olveston United	30	20	7	3	73	31	47
Hanham Athletic	30	18	6	6	75	26	42	Longwell Gn Spts	30	18	8	4	60	27	44
Oldland Decora	30	17	6	7	69	43	40	Staple Hill	30	18	7	5	79	36	43
Nicholas Wanderers	30	15	6	9	65	43	36	Chipping Sodbury	30	14	8	8	59	35	36
Shaftesbury Crus.	30	15	5	10	64	49	35	Hartcliffe	30	13	9	8	51	44	35
Highridge United	30	15	3	12	63	43	33	Hallen Res.	30	14	7	9	54	48	35
Thornbury Town	30	13	7	10	47	34	33	Bristol 5 Old Boys	30	12	8	10	51	43	32
Hillfield Old Boys	30	11	10	9	50	49	32	Shirehampton Res.	30	11	9	10	48	37	31
Bitton	30	12	8	10	53	58	32	Lawrence Rovers	30	13	5	12	64	55	31
Iron Acton	30	13	4	13	42	50	30	Bristol University	30	12	4	13	63	62	28
Sea Mills Park	30	11	4	15	55	58	26	Patchway T. Res.	30	8	10	12	43	44	26
Sun Life	30	10	6	14	61	67	26	Pucklechurch Res.	30	11	4	15	34	43	26
Bristol Union	30	8	9	13	43	49	25	Archway St Philips	30	7	10	13	38	53	24
Spartak Downend	30	6	7	17	43	78	19	Henbury O.B. Res.	30	7	5	18	37	76	19
Frampton Athletic	30	5	4	21	32	84	14	Hambrook Res.	30	5	2	23	32	95	12
Barr United	30	5	3	22	25	90	13	Wick Kingsway	30	4	3	23	27	84	11

Premier Division Constitution 93-94 *(Ground Addresses italicised)*:
Bitton *(Bitton Rec.)*, Bristol St George *(Butler Memorial, Whiteway Rd)*, Bristol Spartak Downend *(Whitchurch, Bristol)*, Bristol Union *(University PF, Coombe Lane)*, Hambrook *(Whiteshill Common, Moorend Lane, Hambrook)*, Hanham Athletic *(Vicarage Rd, Hanham)*, Highridge Utd, Hillfields O.B. *(Thicket Ave., Fishponds)*, Iron Acton *(Sunnyside Lane, Iron Acton)*, Longwell Green Sports *(Shellards Rd, Longwell Green)*, Nicholas Wanderers *(Dundridge PF)*, Oldland Decora *(Coronation Park, Oldland)*, Olveston Utd *(The Plain, Old Down, Tockington, Bristol)*, Sea Mills Park *(Sea Mills Rec.)*, Shaftesbury Crusade *(Landseer Ave., Lockleaze)*, Sun Life *(Sun Life Spts Ground, Cribbs Causeway)*, Thornbury Town *(Munday PF, Kington Lane, Thornbury)*.

Division One Constitution 93-94: Archway St Phillips *(Iron Mould Lane, Brislington)*, Barr United *(BAWA Ground, Southmead Rd)*, Bristol 5 O.B. *(St George School)*, Bristol University *(University PF, Coombe Lane)*, Chipping Sodbury *(The Ridings, Chipping Sodbury)*, Frampton Athletic *(Beesmoor Rd, Frampton Cotterell)*, Hallen Reserves, Hartcliffe, Henbury Old Boys Reserves, Lawrence Rovers *(Lawrence Weston PF)*, Patchway Town Reserves, Pucklechurch Spts Reserves, St Philips Marsh Adult School Reserves, Shirehampton Reserves, Staple Hill *(Blackhorse Rd, Mangotsfield)*.

Henbury Old Boys of the Gloucestershire County League pictured after winning the 1992 Fry Club Cup. Back Row (L/R): Keith Parkins, Nicky Summerhill, Ken Smith (Trainer), Bob Pritchard, Chris Hawkes, Bob Godfrey, Martin Osmond, Simon Monks, Gary Pruett, Cyril Pritchard (Manager). Front Row (L/R): Dave Sheppard, Lee Thomas, John Coote, Mervyn Egan, Geoff Cox, Bob Davies. Photo - James Wright.

BRISTOL & SUBURBAN LEAGUE

(Established 1894)

Premier Division	P	W	D	L	F	A	PTS
Yate Town Res.	32	24	3	5	103	30	51
Totterdown Ath.	32	21	9	2	86	32	51
Broad Plain House	32	21	6	5	99	46	48
Almondsbury	32	20	7	5	83	38	47
Avonmouth	32	19	3	10	68	44	41
St Aldhelms	32	16	6	10	79	52	38
Stoke Gifford Utd	32	13	9	10	70	59	35
Nat West Court	32	12	9	11	51	44	33
P & W United	32	12	9	11	61	56	33
Glenside Hosp SC	32	11	9	12	48	69	31
Filton Athletic	32	9	8	15	59	78	26
Avon Fire Brigade	32	8	9	15	40	51	25
TDR Dynamo	32	9	5	18	64	98	23
Lockleaze	32	6	9	17	34	76	21
Patchway Nth End	32	6	6	20	51	107	18
Ridings High	32	5	4	23	38	82	14
Port of Bristol	32	2	5	25	31	103	9

Premier Div. Two	P	W	D	L	F	A	PTS
Exeter United	28	22	5	1	100	35	49
Old Georgians Res.	28	20	3	5	92	37	43
Bristol Telephones	28	19	4	5	73	39	42
Southmead Athletic	28	17	4	7	91	54	38
Imperial Saints	28	13	6	9	64	53	32
Potterswood	28	10	9	9	62	62	29
Cadbury Hth Res.	28	10	7	11	53	53	27
Portway Bristol	28	9	8	11	51	51	26
Teyfant Athletic	28	9	4	15	53	67	22
Tytherington Rocks	28	8	6	14	34	50	22
Almass	28	8	4	16	45	82	20
Hartcliffe OB	28	9	2	17	39	73	20
Rolls Royce OB	28	6	6	16	42	58	18
Wanderers	28	5	7	16	44	88	17
Ashton Rangers	28	5	5	18	36	77	15

Division One	P	W	D	L	F	A	PTS
CTK Southside	30	21	7	2	104	35	49
Alveston D.S.	30	22	3	5	85	42	47
Premier Forklift	30	22	2	6	105	52	46
Fishponds OB	30	18	5	7	83	39	41
EP Somerdale Utd	30	16	8	6	92	48	40
St Aldhelms Res.	30	17	4	9	81	53	38
Avonmouth Res.	30	11	11	8	68	50	33
Avon Dynamo	30	14	4	12	63	73	32
Nat.Smelt.Co.	30	11	6	13	73	73	28
Glenside H. Res.	30	10	5	15	55	66	25
Bristol North West	30	9	5	16	72	81	23
Old Georgians 'A'	30	8	7	15	52	64	23
Imperial Utd Res.	30	10	3	17	58	75	23
Aztecs	30	6	4	20	42	81	16
Patchway N.E.Res.	30	4	1	25	41	143	9
Pt of Bristol Res.	30	3	1	26	34	133	7

Division Two	P	W	D	L	F	A	PTS
Thrissell Nomads	28	21	2	5	75	29	44
Exeter Utd Res.	28	19	6	3	72	38	44
BC Timbers	28	19	5	4	80	30	43
Broad Plain Res.	28	16	2	10	69	45	34
ICI Severnside	28	14	5	9	75	45	33
SA/Phoenix	28	13	6	9	61	50	32
Frenchay Hospital	28	12	5	11	61	55	29
Whitchurch	28	11	4	13	50	60	26
Bristol Crusaders	28	10	6	12	62	76	26
Horfield OB	28	10	5	13	52	65	25
Corinthian Sports	28	10	2	16	56	71	22
Almonds Safeway	28	8	4	16	51	84	20
Raysfield	28	8	3	17	56	96	19
Fromeside	28	4	6	18	35	64	14
Melbury United	28	2	5	21	34	81	9

Division Three	P	W	D	L	F	A	PTS
Totterdown A. Res.	32	24	5	3	120	33	53
Clifton Rangers	32	22	6	4	106	38	50
Bristol St Andrews	32	21	5	6	107	58	47
Oldbury O.S.	32	18	7	7	90	60	43
Nat W. Court Res.	32	17	4	11	109	60	38
Portway Bris. Res.	32	15	6	11	92	67	36
Stockwood Gn Res.	32	15	6	11	84	71	36
Stoke Gifford Utd	32	12	5	15	70	73	29
P & W United Res.	32	8	13	11	57	60	29
Fishponds OB Res.	32	11	7	14	46	63	29
Tytherington Res.	32	10	7	15	59	99	27
Parson Street OB	32	8	9	15	59	74	25
Bristol Tele. Res.	32	10	5	17	43	76	25
Deveys	32	9	6	17	66	79	24
Good Viewing Spts	32	9	4	19	84	92	22
Sefton Park	32	6	6	20	42	140	18
AFC Universal	32	5	3	24	42	133	13

Division Four	P	W	D	L	F	A	PTS
London Life	30	24	3	3	118	34	51
Old Georgians 'B'	30	23	4	3	103	34	50
Lockleaze Sports	30	21	4	5	110	29	46
Avonmouth 'A'	30	17	7	6	74	45	41
Almondsbury Res.	30	17	7	6	75	46	41
Imperial Sts Res.	30	15	4	11	71	55	34
Bris. Corinthians	30	14	5	11	82	86	33
Frenchay H. Res.	30	10	8	12	54	60	28
St Annes Town	30	11	5	14	63	69	27
Nat.Smelt.Co. Res.	30	8	7	15	53	55	23
Sthmead Res. (-2pts)	30	7	9	14	54	73	21
Hengrove Ath BC	30	8	5	17	52	89	21
Avon Dynamo Res.	30	7	7	16	40	80	21
Brandon Sports	30	6	3	21	38	83	15
Patchway N.E. 'A'	30	5	4	21	35	107	14
Wanderers Res.	30	4	4	22	23	100	12

Division Five	P	W	D	L	F	A	PTS
New Allies	28	21	5	2	109	30	47
Exeter United 'A'	28	16	8	4	78	39	40
Ridings High Res.	28	14	7	7	63	53	35
Horfield OB Res.	28	17	0	11	79	51	34
Hartcliffe OB Res.	28	16	1	11	83	60	33
Broad Plain H. 'A'	28	12	3	13	70	59	27
EP Somerdale Res.	28	10	6	12	71	79	26
Filton Ath. Res.	28	10	6	12	53	70	26
Bris. St And. Res.	28	11	3	14	62	72	25
Whitchurch Res.	28	11	3	14	68	81	25
Glenside Hosp 'A'	28	10	5	13	44	68	25
Bris. Crusaders Res.	28	9	5	14	46	65	23
Nat W. Court 'A'	28	10	1	17	56	65	21
Hewlett Packard	28	5	9	14	65	88	19
Nat.Smelt.Co. 'A'	28	5	4	19	43	110	14

Division Six	P	W	D	L	F	A	PTS
CTK Southside Res.	30	28	2	0	196	22	58
ICI Severnside Res.	30	24	1	5	106	47	49
Almondsbury 'A'	30	17	5	8	108	62	39
Clifton Rgrs Res.	30	16	6	8	76	57	38
Alveston D.S. Res.	30	17	3	10	72	54	37
Patchway N.E. 'B'	30	16	4	10	94	65	36
Avon Fire Brig. Res.	30	13	9	8	67	54	35
Thrissell Res.	30	13	5	12	72	82	31
Lockleaze Spts Res.	30	12	4	14	62	75	28
Corinthian Spts Res.	30	12	3	15	62	96	27
Fishponds OB 'A'	30	9	4	17	48	97	22
London Life Res.	30	8	5	17	50	85	21
Port of Bris. 'A'	30	6	6	18	41	89	18
SA/Phoenix Res.	30	6	4	20	58	84	16
Wanderers 'A'	30	6	3	21	35	96	15
Parson St OB Res.	30	3	4	23	43	125	10

BRISTOL & DISTRICT LEAGUE (Est. 1892)

Senior Division	P	W	D	L	F	A	PTS
St Philips MAS Res.	28	21	3	4	104	31	45
Winterbourne U. Res.	28	19	5	4	85	30	43
Haynes Roofing	28	18	6	4	93	25	42
Soundwell Vict.	28	14	6	8	64	42	34
Highridge Utd Res.	28	13	8	7	57	40	34
Made For Ever	28	14	5	9	57	52	33
Hartcliffe C.C.	28	11	8	9	66	62	30
Sth Bristol Central	28	12	5	11	50	55	29
DRG (FP) Res.	28	9	8	11	51	52	26
Greyfriars Ath.	28	9	8	11	45	58	26
St. Pancras	28	9	5	14	42	45	23
Iron Action Res.	28	9	4	15	39	71	22
Frampton Ath. Res.	28	5	6	17	36	75	16
Hillfields Park	28	6	2	20	39	106	14
Eden Grove	28	1	1	26	24	108	3

Division One	P	W	D	L	F	A	PTS
BAWA Aces	28	17	7	4	74	45	41
Tormarton	28	17	6	5	84	30	40
Seymour United	28	18	4	6	76	51	40
Fishponds Ath.	28	17	6	5	59	35	40
Imperial Courage	28	16	4	8	82	40	36
Hanham Ath. Res.	28	13	8	7	66	34	34
I.M.L. Spts (-2pts)	28	12	5	11	53	50	27
St Stephens	28	11	5	12	51	52	27
Totterdown Utd	28	8	10	10	41	48	26
Stapleton Res.	28	7	7	14	47	75	21
Parnalls	28	7	6	15	46	68	20
Kingsgrove Utd	28	7	5	16	45	83	19
AEK Rangers	28	7	3	18	48	72	17
Westbury Victoria	28	5	5	18	41	83	15
Rangeworthy	28	7	1	20	45	92	15

Division Two	P	W	D	L	F	A	PTS
Roman Glass	28	19	5	4	76	27	43
Crosscourt United	28	17	6	5	65	31	40
Oldland Dec. Res.	28	16	2	10	60	48	34
Westerleigh Sports	28	14	4	10	57	41	32
Dunridge Rovers	28	15	2	11	63	55	32
Stan Butt Sports	28	12	7	9	69	70	31
Lawrence Rvrs Res.	28	12	7	9	45	48	31
Hillfields OB Res.	28	12	4	12	57	55	28
Knowle United	28	12	2	14	49	50	26
Breakways C&D	28	7	11	10	59	64	25
Nich Wands Res.	28	8	7	13	46	48	23
Kingswood Carry'st	28	9	4	15	59	77	22
Henbury OB 'A'	28	7	5	16	45	67	19
Shaftesbury C. Res.	28	5	7	16	38	70	17
Victoria Court	28	4	9	15	41	78	17

Division Three	P	W	D	L	F	A	PTS
Staple Hill Res.	30	23	3	4	92	32	49
Olveston Utd Res.	30	21	4	5	90	35	46
Bitton Res.	30	18	7	5	89	23	43
Ace Kitchens	30	20	1	9	91	54	41
Cleevewood	30	16	7	7	90	54	41
Sea Mills Park Res.	30	14	8	8	81	45	36
Bristol Union Res.	30	13	8	9	82	50	34
Barton Hill Rgrs	30	13	8	9	52	42	34
University Res.	30	13	5	13	79	43	30
Rotunda	30	9	8	13	48	55	26
Sun Life Res.	30	6	11	13	46	58	23
Made for Ever Res.	30	9	4	17	37	58	22
Nich Wanderers 'A'	30	8	5	17	38	81	21
Wick Kingsway Res.	30	7	5	18	35	67	19
Frampton Ath. 'A'	30	7	1	22	46	76	15
Eden Grove Res.	30	1	0	29	16	239	2

Division Four	P	W	D	L	F	A	PTS
Chipping Sod. Res.	28	23	2	3	118	35	48
S.B.C. Res.	28	23	1	4	102	48	47
Longwell Green Res.	28	18	4	6	82	33	40
Hilton Rangers	28	17	4	7	73	37	38
Frys 'A'	28	13	5	10	58	50	31
Pucklechurch 'A'	28	12	4	12	58	58	28
Soundwell V. Res.	28	12	4	12	59	64	28
Highridge U. 'A'	28	11	3	14	59	54	25
Old Sudbury	28	9	7	12	55	75	24
Oldland Dec 'A'	28	10	4	14	53	62	24
Long Ashton Res.	28	10	3	15	77	78	23
Rangeworthy Res.	28	8	7	13	49	83	23
DRG (FP) 'A'	28	6	8	14	38	59	20
Bristol Albion	28	5	4	19	30	86	14
Avon St George	28	2	2	24	28	116	6

Division Five	P	W	D	L	F	A	PTS
Hartcliffe Res.	28	26	2	0	106	38	54
Sandringham Spts*	28	20	2	6	96	49	40
Archway St P. Res.	28	18	2	8	81	46	38
LA Sports	28	17	0	11	89	59	34
Greyfriars Ath Res.	28	17	0	11	85	58	34
Bendix Specials	28	14	5	9	69	48	33
Bitton 'A'	28	15	2	11	59	54	32
Rail Bristol	28	13	3	12	55	62	29
AEK Rangers Res.	28	12	4	12	77	62	28
Totterdown A. Res.	28	11	5	12	49	59	27
St Pancras Res.	28	11	3	14	56	75	25
Dundridge R. Res.	28	5	5	18	41	81	15
BAWA Aces Res.	28	6	3	19	41	88	15
Bristol 5 OB Res.	28	3	2	23	26	77	8
Wick Kingsway 'A'	28	2	2	24	28	102	6

* - 2pts deducted.

Division Six	P	W	D	L	F	A	PTS
Hanham Ath 'A'	30	23	5	2	133	37	51
St. Nicholas	30	24	3	3	125	32	51
Westerleigh Res.	30	18	9	3	90	37	45
Winterbourne 'A'	30	17	6	7	77	50	40
Frys 'B'	30	16	3	11	97	54	35
Hilfields OB 'A'	30	11	10	9	82	56	32
Parnalls Res.	30	13	5	12	73	68	31
University 'A'	30	12	5	13	74	79	29
Sea Mills Park 'A'	30	9	9	12	62	75	27
Sun Life 'A'	30	12	2	16	58	79	26
Shireway Sports	30	10	6	14	67	92	26
Fishponds A. Res.	30	9	6	15	52	61	24
St. Stephens Res.	30	10	4	16	52	73	24
Breakaways Res.	30	6	2	22	51	108	14
Westbury Vict. Res.	30	6	1	23	59	179	13
Bendix Spec. Res.	30	4	4	22	29	101	12

BRISTOL DOWNS LEAGUE

DIV. ONE	P	W	D	L	F	A	PTS
The Mont	26	21	3	2	72	14	45
Sneyd Park	26	20	3	3	82	27	43
Clifton St Vincents	26	19	4	3	95	42	42
Old Cothamians	26	18	3	5	90	26	39
Clifton Rockets	26	16	3	7	76	32	35
DDAS	26	15	2	9	62	44	32
Retainers	26	8	6	12	46	65	22
KGC Panels	26	8	4	14	34	61	20
Europa Saints	26	9	1	16	42	52	19
Torpedo	26	7	5	14	54	71	19
West Town United	26	8	3	15	35	61	19
Ceramic Palace	26	6	4	16	28	62	16
Tebby	26	3	5	18	27	80	11
Stowells C.P.	26	0	2	24	12	118	2

DIV. TWO	P	W	D	L	F	A	PTS
Sneyd Park Res,	26	23	3	1	100	21	48
DDAS Res.	26	16	8	2	64	34	40
O. Cothamians Res.	26	16	4	6	68	34	36
Pump House	26	17	2	7	61	37	36
St Judes	26	13	5	8	65	38	31
Clifton St V. Res.	26	11	6	9	57	56	28
Conham Rangers	26	9	6	11	51	52	24
Portland O.B.	26	9	5	12	56	78	23
Europa Saints Res.	26	7	8	11	47	50	22
Clifton Rockets Res.	26	9	3	14	51	60	21
K.E. Warmley	26	7	2	17	43	69	16
Hager	26	5	5	16	55	112	15
Luccombe Garage	26	6	1	19	29	69	13
Broad Plain	26	4	3	19	49	86	11

DIV. THREE	P	W	D	L	F	A	PTS
Royal Mail Drivers	26	20	3	3	81	28	43
Sneyd Park 'A'	26	18	3	5	73	31	39
Southmead United	26	17	4	5	86	44	38
F.D.L. Sports	26	13	7	6	64	32	33
Glenvic Sports	26	12	6	8	63	46	30
Retainers Res.	26	13	4	9	59	58	30
Severnside	26	12	5	9	66	54	29
Torpedo Res.	26	12	4	10	57	46	28
Courage Olympic	26	9	5	12	49	62	23
The Mont Res.	26	8	6	12	66	70	22
Clifton St V. 'A'	26	8	4	14	45	66	20
Old Cothamians 'A'	26	7	4	15	46	63	18
C & C Tyres	26	2	2	22	17	115	6
Conham Rgrs Res.	26	1	3	22	22	79	5

DIV. FOUR	P	W	D	L	F	A	PTS
Davison Printers	28	23	2	3	95	29	48
Sneyd Park 'B'	28	20	2	6	95	49	42
Springer Athletic	28	17	6	5	96	42	40
Bristol Leisurewear	28	13	9	6	68	47	35
Cotswool Old Boys	28	11	11	6	79	55	33
Broad P. Res. (-2pts)	28	13	7	8	79	58	31
DDAS 'A'	28	8	9	11	65	63	25
St Judes Res.	28	11	3	14	84	98	25
St Andrews	28	9	6	13	68	66	24
Pump House Res.	28	9	4	15	65	81	22
West Town U. Res.	28	10	2	16	61	86	22
Clifton St V. 'B'	28	9	4	15	48	92	22
Bristol Deaf	28	8	5	15	47	82	21
KGC Panels Res.	28	7	6	15	45	64	20

'CRISTIE' STROUD & DISTRICT LEAGUE

DIV. ONE	P	W	D	L	F	A	PTS
Yate Town 'A'	30	20	5	5	88	48	45
Whiteshill Utd	30	17	5	8	80	39	39
Tuffley Rvrs Res.	30	16	7	8	63	41	39
Upton St Leonards	30	16	5	9	83	66	37
Ebley	30	16	3	11	71	49	35
Randwick	30	15	5	10	68	49	35
Tetbury Town	30	14	9	8	67	56	35
Whitminster	30	13	7	10	54	50	33
Wotton Rvrs Res.	30	13	7	10	56	56	33
Uley	30	11	8	11	62	57	30
Thornbury T. Res.	30	10	9	11	50	46	29
Eastcombe	30	11	6	13	49	57	28
Slimbridge	30	9	8	13	64	71	26
Brimscombe & T. Res	30	8	6	16	40	70	22
Minchinhampton	30	5	2	23	41	97	12
Cam Bulldogs Res	30	1	2	27	21	105	4

DIV. TWO	P	W	D	L	F	A	PTS
Longlevens Res,	28	20	5	3	69	36	45
Coaley Rovers	28	19	6	3	80	38	44
Kings Stanley Res.	28	16	7	5	73	35	39
AC Horton (1972)	28	18	3	7	82	55	39
Uplands United	28	15	3	10	69	53	33
Leonard Stanley	28	13	5	10	69	51	31
Dursley T. Res.	28	12	4	12	63	48	28
Alkerton Rangers	28	11	5	12	64	71	27
Oakridge	28	5	12	11	38	55	22
Whiteshill Utd Res.	28	8	6	14	47	67	22
Frampton Utd Res.	28	9	4	15	42	62	22
Kingswood	28	8	5	15	35	45	21
Tibberton Utd	28	9	3	16	41	71	21
Berkeley T. Res.	28	4	7	17	34	73	*11
Glos Civil Service	28	4	3	21	42	85	11

* - 1pt deducted. Paganhill withdrew without playing

DIV. THREE	P	W	D	L	F	A	PTS
Hillesley Utd	30	20	6	4	97	32	46
Longford Res.	30	21	4	5	91	40	46
Laurentian Life	30	19	5	6	77	46	43
Ramblers	30	17	6	7	90	66	40
Nuclear Elec. Res.	30	17	5	8	80	47	39
Hardwicke Res.	30	18	3	9	65	44	39
Glevum United	30	16	6	8	90	59	38
Shurdington Utd	30	11	8	11	55	64	30
Woodchester	30	10	7	13	55	76	27
Tuffley Rovers 'A'	30	8	8	14	42	50	24
Charfield Res.	30	7	8	15	43	75	22
Stonehouse F. Res.	30	7	7	16	53	68	21
Shipton Moyne	30	8	5	17	64	91	21
Cashes Green	30	7	4	19	40	76	18
ICI Fibres Res.	30	6	2	22	32	79	14
Wotton Rvrs 'A'	30	3	6	21	38	91	12

DIV. FOUR	P	W	D	L	F	A	PTS
Horsley Utd Res.	28	21	3	7	84	38	45
Uley Res.	28	19	5	4	79	35	43
Taverners Res.	28	19	3	6	78	34	41
Slimbridge Res.	28	14	7	7	80	48	35
Chalford	28	15	4	9	66	58	34
Longlevens 'A'	28	12	8	8	50	53	32
United Mills	28	11	7	10	50	49	29
Randwick Res.	28	9	7	12	52	72	25
Whitminster Res.	28	10	4	14	53	59	24
Bensons	28	10	3	15	40	61	23
Dursley T. 'A'	28	9	4	15	51	57	22
Coaley Rovers Res.	28	8	3	17	49	71	19
Minchinhampton. Res	28	6	7	15	48	73	19
Price Walker	28	7	3	18	32	60	17
Tetbury T. Res. (-1pt)	28	1	10	17	33	77	11

DIV. FIVE	P	W	D	L	F	A	PTS
Vikings Res.	30	26	3	1	120	39	55
Thornbury T. 'A'	30	23	3	4	104	32	49
Nympsfield	30	20	6	4	77	35	46
N.S.S.C.	30	18	3	9	95	43	39
Kingswood Res.	30	15	8	7	62	49	38
Slimbridge 'A' (-2pts)	30	13	5	12	74	63	29
Ebley Res.	30	12	5	13	66	66	29
Oakridge Res.	30	10	7	13	53	53	27
Reeves United	30	11	5	14	48	59	27
Eastcombe Res.	30	11	5	14	68	82	27
Laurentian L. Res.	30	12	3	15	65	85	27
Upton St Leo. Res.	30	10	6	14	60	66	26
Uley 'A'	30	8	3	19	48	101	19
Wickwar United	30	5	4	21	35	86	14
Berkeley T. 'A'	30	4	5	21	39	90	13
Glos C.S. Res.	30	4	5	21	31	94	13

(continued opposite)

DIV. SIX	P	W	D	L	F	A	PTS
Arlingham	28	24	1	3	120	46	49
Ramblers Res.	28	21	4	3	110	33	46
Parkside United	28	19	2	7	93	41	40
Horsley Utd Res.	28	17	3	8	87	62	37
Shurdington R. Res.	28	15	3	10	50	47	33
L.D.S.	28	13	3	12	66	53	29
Uplands Utd Res.	28	11	3	14	63	73	25
Leonard Stanley Res.	28	10	4	14	47	65	24
Stonehouse F. 'A'	28	9	6	13	58	80	24
Eagle Star 'B'	28	11	1	16	48	55	23
Alkerton Res. (-2pts)	28	9	4	15	54	68	20
Kings 'A' (-1pt)	28	10	1	17	55	89	20
Woodchester Res.	28	7	3	18	45	89	17
Winchester Wdrs	28	7	2	19	51	101	16
F.C. Westrip	28	5	4	19	36	82	14

Paganhill Res. withdrew without playing

DIV. SEVEN	P	W	D	L	F	A	PTS
Old Barnwoodians	24	19	1	4	97	30	39
North Nibley	24	17	2	5	79	41	36
Sherston T. Res.	24	15	6	3	73	41	36
Glevum Utd Res.	24	13	5	6	70	53	31
Dursley T. 'B'	24	12	2	10	67	54	26
N.S.S.C. Res.	24	10	3	11	66	63	23
Cashes Green Res.	24	10	3	11	53	52	23
Pressboard	24	8	7	9	49	52	23
Shipton Moyne Res.	24	6	7	11	41	57	*17
Bensons Res.	24	6	3	15	56	80	15
Newcomers	24	3	1	18	27	63	11
Hillview Rgrs	24	3	1	20	29	109	7

* - 2pts deducted
Cam Bulldogs 'A' withdrew without playing
Newport Towers withdrew without making fixtures

TAUNTON & DISTRICT LEAGUE

DIVISION ONE	P	W	D	L	F	A	PTS
Bishops Lydeard	22	16	3	3	96	40	35
Priorswood Utd	22	16	3	3	89	34	35
British Cellophone	22	14	4	4	79	37	32
Sydenham Rang.	22	13	2	7	58	34	28
Wyvern	22	10	8	4	65	46	28
Middlezoy Rov.	22	11	6	5	55	39	28
Westonzoyland	22	9	4	9	41	43	22
Nether Stowey	22	5	4	13	36	76	14
Wembldon United	22	5	4	13	40	98	14
Hulan United	22	3	4	15	38	61	10
Spaxton	22	4	2	16	39	83	10
Alcombe Rovers	22	3	2	17	46	91	8

DIVISION TWO	P	W	D	L	F	A	PTS
Priorswood Res.	22	14	6	2	67	32	34
Highbridge Town	22	15	3	4	69	35	33
Victoria Inn	22	13	4	5	58	34	30
Knight Rangers	22	11	3	8	61	44	25
Hinkley Point	22	9	5	8	68	67	23
Norton Fitzwarren	22	9	3	10	63	65	21
Dulverton Town	22	7	5	10	42	50	19
Watchet T. Res.	22	6	6	10	36	51	18
Bishops Lyd. Res.	22	6	5	11	45	70	17
Club Rangers	22	6	4	12	32	42	16
Porlock	22	4	7	11	36	61	15
Middlezoy R. Res.	22	4	5	13	35	61	13

DIVISION THREE	P	W	D	L	F	A	PTS
British Cel. Res.	22	17	3	2	92	25	37
British Rail	22	13	3	6	71	50	29
Rockwell Green	22	11	4	7	57	50	26
Marketeers	22	11	3	8	53	60	25
Redgate	22	10	3	9	72	70	23
Williton	22	10	3	9	44	48	23
Staplegrove	22	10	2	10	51	42	22
Avimo Eagles	22	8	6	8	42	34	22
Taverners	22	7	3	12	45	58	17
Bridgwater T. 'A'	22	6	4	12	43	83	16
Crown Dynamos	22	5	5	12	44	61	15
Wyvern Res.	22	3	3	16	31	64	9

DIVISION FOUR	P	W	D	L	F	A	PTS
Parkway Rangers	22	20	1	1	96	33	41
Alcombe Rvrs Res.	22	14	2	6	71	41	30
Highbridge Res.	22	12	3	7	61	38	27
Tone Vale Hospital	22	11	3	8	55	48	25
Dunster Rangers	22	10	3	9	79	59	23
Civil Service	22	10	3	9	74	66	23
North Petherton	22	10	3	9	50	56	23
Quantock Pride (-2pts)	22	9	5	8	69	68	21
Williton Wandrs	22	8	3	11	46	77	19
Hemyock	22	5	6	11	41	62	16
Staplegrove Res.	22	3	2	17	40	89	8
Exmoor Rangers	22	2	2	18	58	103	6

DIVISION FIVE	P	W	D	L	F	A	PTS
Wembdon Crickets	22	17	2	3	70	30	36
British Rail Res.	22	15	2	5	67	44	32
Shepherds Wedn.	22	14	2	6	64	37	30
British Cel. Colts	22	13	3	6	71	48	29
Blackbrook Res.	22	12	4	6	70	42	28
Haygrove	22	10	5	7	53	46	25
Porlock Res.	22	8	3	11	50	42	19
Norton Fitz.Res.	22	8	3	11	50	53	19
Stogursey G'hounds	22	7	3	12	50	56	17
Linden	22	5	4	13	42	64	14
Spaxton Res.	22	3	2	17	39	98	8
Nether Stowey Res.	22	2	3	17	25	91	7

'T.N.T. EXPRESS' BATH & DISTRICT LEAGUE

DIVISION ONE	P	W	D	L	F	A	PTS
Corinthian Spts	24	18	3	3	82	20	39
Civil Service	24	15	6	3	76	31	36
Freshford	24	17	1	6	62	39	35
Oval Sports	24	12	6	6	40	36	30
Westwood Utd	24	11	4	9	42	39	26
Larkhall Ath. 'A'	24	10	6	8	39	42	26
Bath University	24	9	7	8	57	45	25
Whiteway C.A.	24	6	10	8	52	53	22
Oldfield Sports	24	6	5	13	47	64	17
Aces	24	6	5	13	40	62	17
Rudloe	24	5	4	14	26	52	14
Green Pk Rgrs	24	5	3	16	22	57	13
Brains S.A.	24	6	0	18	34	75	12

DIVISION TWO	P	W	D	L	F	A	PTS
Odd Down 'A'	26	17	5	4	89	33	39
Keynsham Gas	26	17	5	4	92	45	39
Keynsham C.C. Res.	26	14	5	7	92	60	33
Crown & Anchor	26	14	4	8	63	59	32
Colerne	26	14	3	9	89	62	31
Avalon	26	11	9	6	46	38	31
Weston Wdrs	26	14	3	9	65	62	31
Marshfield	26	7	9	10	50	58	23
Claverton Acad.	26	9	4	13	69	63	22
Rose & Crown	26	5	10	11	49	80	20
Bath Univ. Res.	26	6	6	13	46	80	18
Bath W. Fruit	26	7	2	16	50	93	16
Whiteway C.A. Res.	26	6	3	17	55	126	15
Stothert & Pitt	26	3	6	17	41	76	12

(continued overleaf)

BATH DIV. 3	P	W	D	L	F	A	PTS
Blue Bowl Hanham	24	21	2	1	134	18	44
Westgate	24	18	4	1	117	21	40
Cor. Spts Res.	24	16	3	5	67	59	35
Old Crown	24	11	5	8	67	59	27
Aces Res.	24	8	5	11	57	70	21
Bath Univ. 'A'	24	7	7	9	57	73	21
Alexandra Park	24	8	4	12	65	81	20
Oldfield Spts Res.	24	8	3	13	50	95	19
Civil Service Res.	24	6	6	12	48	58	18
Keynsham Gas Res.	24	7	3	14	36	66	17
Westwood Utd Res.	24	6	5	13	46	88	17
Southdown Park	24	7	3	14	48	88	17
Twerton St M.	24	4	5	15	42	90	13

DIVISION FOUR	P	W	D	L	F	A	PTS
L. West End (-2pts)	24	23	0	1	123	16	44
Beaston Lions	24	22	0	2	86	36	44
Odd Down 'B'	24	14	3	7	63	45	31
D.A.S. Rovers	24	13	2	9	74	51	28
Oval Sports Res.	24	12	2	10	69	69	26
Weston Wdrs Res.	24	10	5	9	68	70	25
Saltford Res.	24	10	3	11	50	72	23
Combe Park Rgrs	24	8	3	13	39	56	19
Newton Park Col.	24	6	6	12	51	70	18
Brains S.A. Res.	24	7	2	15	58	70	16
Stothert & Pitt Res.	24	6	2	16	46	101	14
Rose & Crown Res.	24	4	4	16	36	89	12
Newton & Cor.	24	4	3	17	49	76	11

WESTON-SUPER-MARE & DISTRICT LEAGUE

DIVISION ONE	P	W	D	L	F	A	PTS
East Worle	22	17	3	2	71	21	37
Wedmore	22	11	7	4	58	40	29
Portishead 'A'	22	11	5	6	49	37	27
Cleeve West Town	22	11	5	6	48	37	27
Bourneville Rovers	22	9	5	8	56	38	23
RAF Locking	22	8	6	8	35	40	22
Draycott	22	8	5	9	47	52	21
Milton Crusaders	22	5	8	9	46	61	18
Blackford	22	7	4	11	43	68	18
Wrington-Redhill Res.	22	6	5	11	37	41	17
Nailsea Manor Park	22	4	5	13	33	61	13
Clevedon Utd 'A'	22	2	8	12	31	58	12

DIVISION TWO	P	W	D	L	F	A	PTS
Hutton	22	17	3	2	67	22	37
Burnham Utd.Res.	22	17	2	3	77	27	36
Worlebury Southside	22	12	6	4	56	41	30
Winscombe Res.	22	13	2	7	67	39	28
UKC Sports	22	10	2	10	57	59	22
St Geo. (E-in-G) Res.	22	8	4	10	43	51	20
Berrow	22	8	2	12	36	61	18
Kenn Valley	22	6	5	11	32	45	17
Langford Rovers	22	6	5	11	32	54	17
Banwell Res.	22	7	2	13	44	66	16
Congresbury Res.	22	6	1	15	26	52	13
Backwell Utd.Colts	22	4	2	16	53	73	10

DIVISION THREE	P	W	D	L	F	A	PTS
Kewstoke	22	16	4	2	87	28	36
Yatton Athletic Res.	22	16	2	4	82	41	34
Portishead 'B'	22	14	2	6	60	24	30
Cheddar Res.	22	12	6	4	64	32	30
South Park Rgrs	22	11	2	9	58	52	24
King Alfred SC	22	9	5	8	52	59	23
Churchill '70 Res.	22	7	5	10	49	50	19
St Geo. (E-in-G) 'A'	22	8	2	12	36	56	18
Kenn Valley Res.	22	5	7	10	38	50	17
Weston St Johns 'A'	22	5	4	13	41	61	14
Nailsea Utd 'A'	22	5	2	15	38	75	12
Wrington Redhill 'A'	22	3	1	18	29	106	7

DIVISION FOUR	P	W	D	L	F	A	PTS
East Worle Res.	20	17	0	3	69	26	34
Cleeve W.T. Res.	20	13	4	3	59	28	30
West Huntspill Ham.	20	13	1	6	71	44	27
Nailsea Utd 'B'	20	11	2	7	61	37	24
Shipham	20	8	5	7	47	48	21
Ashcombe Park Rgrs	20	8	4	8	53	43	20
Hutton Res.	20	6	5	9	53	39	17
Yatton Athletic 'A'	20	8	1	11	37	44	17
Winscombe Colts	20	7	2	11	46	61	16
Blagdon	20	4	1	15	27	66	9
Congresbury 'A'	20	2	1	17	19	106	5

DIVISION FIVE	P	W	D	L	F	A	PTS
Selkirk United	24	19	4	1	132	26	42
Clevedon Utd.Colts	24	16	8	0	84	26	40
Portishead W.M.C.	24	15	2	7	84	43	32
Weston St.Johns 'B'	24	12	3	9	72	45	27
Farleigh Sports Res.	24	11	5	8	65	50	27
Worle Res.	24	11	3	10	52	47	25
UKC Sports Res.	24	11	0	13	64	101	22
Wrington-Redhill Colts	24	8	5	11	46	55	21
JC Sports	24	7	6	11	55	74	20
Blackford Res.	24	7	4	13	55	88	18
Draycott Res.	24	6	3	15	44	91	15
Burnham Utd Colts	24	5	4	15	41	86	14
Wedmore Res.	24	4	1	19	31	93	9

DIVISION SIX	P	W	D	L	F	A	PTS
Bournville R. Res.	24	17	4	3	73	34	38
Spartans Weston	24	14	7	3	64	30	35
Milton Crus. Res.	24	16	0	8	71	37	32
Kewstoke Res.	24	13	4	7	72	53	30
Milton Baptist Dyn.	24	11	7	6	71	54	29
Cheddar Colts	24	12	4	8	70	41	28
Portishead WMC Res.	24	8	8	8	67	63	24
Worlebury S'side Res.	24	8	7	9	46	42	23
Yatton Athletic 'B'	24	8	7	9	46	56	23
Selkirk Utd. Res.	24	6	7	11	58	62	19
Berrow Res.	24	6	4	14	40	74	16
King Alfred SC Res	24	5	2	17	54	102	12
Severn Royals	24	0	3	21	32	116	3

Devizes Town - Great Mills Lge. Back (L/R): Tony Hanley (Physio), Paul Comer, Andy Davies, Nathan Sheridan, Jeff Roberts, Rob Fry, Kevin Whitbread, Jamie Rowe, David Lloyds, Paul McKay (Coach), Andy Stevens (Mgr). Front: Chris Dodd (Sec.), Martin Allen, Dave Holden, Mark Godley, Glyn Merritt, Mark Strickland. Photo - James Wright.

WESTERN LEAGUE

President: E K Brown
Chairman: S G Priddle
Vice Chairman: R J Webber
Treasurer: Mr Joan Ellis

Hon. Secretary: M E Washer, 16 Heathfield Rd, Nailsea, Bristol BS19 1EB (0275 851314)

A FANTASTIC CENTENARY SEASON

If centenary years are meant to be the sort of occasions when one celebrates past history and looks forward to the future, then this season certainly fulfilled both requirements. A memorable Centenary Weekend and Dinner in Bristol on the actual date in September was remembered by everyone who attended from the top echelons of Football, across the spectrum of County Football, and representatives of the press and radio media.

One wondered how the season could produce anything to match, for Clevedon were already stamping their authority on the championship, and in racing parlance, no futher bets were being taken. We had all overlooked the steady progress of Tiverton who, along with Clevedon, progressed steadily in the F.A. Vase. As the season grew in length, so the Vase field decreased and with bated breath we waited to see if both teams could reach the final. Alas it was not to be, as Clevedon eventually succumbed in the sandy bog called Canvey Island in the Fifth Round. By extreme irony, the Semis brought together Canvey and Tiverton, and Tivvy managed a well earned and hard battled trip to Wembley. This was indeed icing on a very good cake, and despite the Vase final being on the same weekend as the League's Convention weekend at Dawlish, hasty arrangements were made to see how we could get both quarts into the pint point. After all, everybody in the West was off to Wembley, and thus we arranged the Les Phillips Cup final at Dawlish to be replaced by the Combination Cup final, and chartered an aeroplane from Exeter to Luton and a mini-coach from Luton to Wembley.

The Les Phillips final was contested between Clevedon Town and Tiverton Town, and was, I believe, the first one between the champions and runners-up of the League. After the disappointment of Wembley, I think no-one begrudged Tiverton their triumph on the eve of the F.A. Cup final, although the margin of 5-1 certainly surprised us all.

The end of season saw us lose the Reserve sides of Plymouth Argyle and Torquay United, and the inevitable promotion of Clevedon Town to the Beazer Homes League. Three clubs were promoted from Division One; Odd Down the champions, runners-up Calne Town after many near misses, and also third placed Crediton United whose progress has been rapid in their short membership with us. At the bottom of the League we unfortunately bid farewell to Melksham who are replaced under the Pyramid system by Wiltshire League champions Pewsey Vale.

All in all a most memorable season, and as someone said at the Convention, it is going to take something pretty momentous in the next 99 years to beat this. Unfortunately, we won't be around to verify it, - unless - well we all dream don't we?

Maurice Washer, League Secretary

The Clevedon side that took the club to the 1992-93 Premier Division championship. Back Row (L/R): Jamie Ward, John Durham, Stuart Minall, Mark Stevens, Brendan Dowd, Ian Willmott, Gary Marshall. Front: Damon Palfrey, Wayne Morris, Nicky Brooks, Dave Ewens, Andy Perrett. Mascot: Master Perrett. Photo - James Wright.

PREMIER DIV.	P	W	D	L	F	A	PTS
Clevedon Town	38	34	4	0	137	23	106
Tiverton Town	38	28	8	2	134	30	92
Saltash United	38	22	8	8	98	51	74
Taunton Town	38	22	8	8	62	37	74
Mangotsfield United	38	20	8	10	89	47	68
Torrington	38	17	10	11	69	44	61
Westbury United	38	18	7	13	50	45	61
Paulton Rovers	38	15	10	13	76	51	55
Torquay Utd Res.	38	16	7	15	58	62	55
Plymouth A. Res.	38	15	9	14	72	64	54
Exmouth Town	38	14	9	15	47	59	51
Elmore	38	14	5	19	54	71	47
Bristol Manor Farm	38	10	13	15	49	59	43
Bideford	38	11	8	19	59	66	41
Frome Town	38	9	12	17	57	75	39
Chippenham Town	38	8	14	16	65	86	38
Minehead	38	10	8	20	59	88	38
Liskeard Athletic	38	8	9	21	61	87	33
Chard Town	38	6	3	29	37	119	21
Dawlish Town	38	2	2	34	17	186	8

DIV. ONE	P	W	D	L	F	A	PTS
Odd Down	40	27	10	3	87	26	91
Calne Town	40	23	12	5	97	47	81
Crediton United	40	23	11	6	79	43	80
Brislington	40	22	8	10	77	41	74
Warminster Town	40	22	7	11	70	50	73
Clyst Rovers	40	18	13	9	75	48	67
Keynsham Town	40	19	10	11	66	50	67
Backwell United	40	16	14	10	68	52	62
Barnstaple Town	40	15	10	15	62	58	55
Bridport	40	14	13	13	67	66	55
Heavitree United	40	14	9	17	64	69	51
Devizes Town	40	15	6	19	61	84	51
Bishop Sutton	40	14	8	18	55	55	50
Welton Rovers	40	12	11	17	69	65	47
Wellington	40	11	14	15	53	65	47
Glastonbury	40	13	5	22	52	70	44
Larkhall Athletic	40	11	5	24	59	81	38
Ilfracombe Town	40	8	9	23	47	94	33
Ottery St Mary	40	9	5	26	53	116	32
Radstock Town	40	7	10	23	38	60	31
Melksham Town	40	6	12	22	39	98	30

COMBINATION	P	W	D	L	F	A	PTS
Barnstaple Res.	26	21	1	4	95	26	64
Taunton Town Res.	26	20	2	4	94	26	62
Ottery S.M. Res.	26	13	5	8	46	36	44
Wellington Res.	26	14	2	10	59	57	44
Elmore Res.	26	12	5	9	56	54	41
Clyst Rovers Res.	26	11	6	9	62	40	39
Crediton Utd Res.	26	11	5	10	51	48	38
Torrington Res.	26	10	6	10	52	50	36
Exmouth T. Res.	26	10	5	11	48	47	35
Heavitree Utd Res.	26	9	7	10	56	54	34
Tiverton T. Res.	26	8	5	13	50	68	29
Chard Town Res.	26	4	8	14	39	70	20
Minehead Res.	26	5	2	19	42	104	17
Dawlish Town Res.	26	4	1	21	28	98	13

LES PHILLIPS CUP 1992-93

First Round

Wellington v Liskeard Athletic	0-3	Torrington v Ottery St Mary	5-1
Ilfracombe Town v Saltash United	0-4	Dawlish Town v Torquay United Reserves	1-5
Westbury United v Keynsham Town	2-0	Warminster Town v Backwell United	3-0
Paulton Rovers v Brislington	0-2	Calne Town v Devizes Town	2-3
Welton Rovers v Glastonbury	2-0	Mangotsfield United v Radstock Town	3-0

Second Round

Taunton Town v Heavitree United	3-0	Minehead v Exmouth Town	0-1
Torrington v Elmore	2-0	Bideford v Crediton United	1-0
Saltash United v Chard Town	6-0	Barnstaple Town v Tiverton Town	0-1
Torquay United Reserves v Liskeard Ath.	2-3	Clyst Rovers v Plymouth Argyle Reserves	3-1
Larkhall Athletic v Frome Town	1-3	Devizes Town v Mangotsfield United	0-1
Chippenham Town v Clevedon Town	2-5	Melksham Town v Bridport	1-2
Bishop Sutton v Westbury United	0-1	Warminster Town v Bristol Manor Farm	4-0
Brislington (w/o) Clandown (scr.)			

Third Round

Exmouth Town v Tiverton Town	2-3	Brislington v Clevedon Town	0-2
Devizes Town v Bideford	2-1	Bridport v Frome Town	2-0
Mangotsfield United v Saltash United	2-4	Westbury United v Warminster Town	3-1
Taunton Town v Clyst Rovers	0-1	Liskeard Athletic v Torrington	1-2

Quarter Finals

Torrington v Bridport	5-4	Clyst Rovers v Clevedon Town	0-2
Devizes Town v Saltash United	1-6	Westbury United v Taunton Town	1-3

Semi-Finals

Clevedon Town v Torrington	2-1	Tiverton Town v Saltash United	2-1

Final (at Taunton Town FC, Fri 14th May): Tiverton Town 5, Clevedon Town 1 (att: 1,476)

COMBINATION KNOCK-OUT CUP

First Round

Clyst Rovers Res v Ottery St M. Reserves	2-4	Taunton Town Res v Tiverton Town Reserves	2-3
Elmore Reserves v Wellington Reserves	4-3	Torrington Reserves v Barnstaple Town Reserves	1-6
Dawlish Town Reserves v Crediton Utd Res	1-10	Exmouth Town Reserves v Chard Town Reserves	8-1

Quarter Finals

Exmouth Town Res v Crediton Town Res	4-2	Ottery St Mary Reserves v Elmore Reserves	3-2
Tiverton Town Reserves v Barnstaple T. Res	3-8	Heavitree United Reserves v Minehead Reserves	3-8

Semi-Finals

Minehead Reserves v Barnstaple Town Res	1-10	Exmouth Town Res v Ottery St Mary Reserves	7-3

Final (at Clyst Rovers F.C., Sat 1st May): Taunton Town Reserves 4, Chard Town Reserves 0

PREMIER DIVISION RESULT CHART 1992-93

HOME TEAM	1	2	3	4	5	6	7	8	9	10	11	12	13	14	15	16	17	18	19	20
1. Bideford	*	2-1	5-1	1-1	0-1	7-0	2-0	0-0	2-2	2-3	2-2	2-2	4-2	1-0	0-4	2-3	0-3	5-2	3-2	0-1
2. Bristol MF	2-0	*	3-0	2-2	0-2	3-0	2-0	2-1	0-1	1-2	0-1	6-3	1-0	2-2	3-3	1-1	1-1	0-3	1-5	1-1
3. Chard Town	1-2	3-0	*	2-2	1-5	2-1	1-0	2-3	1-3	0-6	1-4	3-0	0-3	0-0	1-4	0-2	0-3	1-2	0-2	0-0
4. Chippenham	1-2	1-0	4-2	*	0-5	9-0	3-4	3-0	2-2	2-2	1-3	3-3	2-4	1-0	2-2	0-4	2-2	3-3	0-3	0-1
5. Clevedon	4-0	2-0	4-0	7-2	*	18-0	6-0	4-1	3-2	5-1	1-1	1-0	3-1	4-0	4-1	2-0	0-0	1-0	5-1	3-0
6. Dawlish	2-2	0-2	2-6	0-3	0-8	*	0-2	0-2	0-3	0-0	0-14	2-0	1-3	0-4	0-5	3-1	0-8	0-5	0-5	1-2
7. Elmore	2-1	0-0	2-0	2-3	0-3	5-0	*	3-0	2-1	3-2	1-3	3-2	1-3	3-4	1-2	0-1	4-3	0-1	0-2	2-0
8. Exmouth	3-2	1-1	2-1	0-0	1-2	2-0	2-0	*	3-2	2-0	2-0	1-0	0-0	1-1	1-1	3-0	0-5	1-1	1-4	0-0
9. Frome Town	2-1	2-2	0-1	0-0	1-4	5-1	1-1	1-4	*	0-1	2-1	5-1	0-0	3-3	2-3	0-2	1-3	4-3	1-1	0-1
10. Liskeard	2-2	1-2	4-1	1-4	1-3	4-0	3-2	2-2	2-2	*	1-5	2-2	0-2	0-2	3-5	1-1	1-4	3-1	1-1	3-3
11. Mangotsfield	3-1	2-2	8-1	2-2	1-3	4-0	1-2	2-1	1-0	1-0	*	4-4	0-2	2-0	2-1	0-0	1-1	5-1	2-2	3-2
12. Minehead	1-0	2-0	5-0	0-0	1-3	3-1	0-1	3-1	0-0	4-2	5-3	*	0-10	3-1	0-2	0-1	1-3	1-1	2-0	1-3
13. Paulton	2-0	1-2	3-0	2-2	2-3	7-0	1-1	0-1	2-0	3-2	0-2	2-0	*	2-3	1-3	0-0	4-2	1-2	1-1	0-1
14. Plymouth A.	2-0	0-0	5-0	4-1	1-2	7-1	1-1	3-0	7-4	3-1	1-3	4-2	4-4	*	1-5	0-1	1-0	0-3	3-2	0-2
15. Saltash U.	1-1	2-2	8-2	3-1	0-1	8-1	4-2	4-3	7-1	3-2	0-1	4-0	2-0	0-1	*	1-1	0-0	1-0	2-2	2-0
16. Taunton T.	1-0	1-0	4-1	3-1	2-6	6-0	3-0	1-0	1-1	4-0	1-0	3-1	0-0	1-4	2-1	*	1-2	0-1	3-1	1-1
17. Tiverton T.	2-1	4-1	9-1	3-1	1-1	9-0	5-1	7-1	6-0	4-1	1-0	6-0	4-1	3-0	4-1	2-0	*	6-1	2-0	6-0
18. Torquay U.	0-4	2-1	3-0	3-1	1-1	2-0	1-1	0-1	1-0	3-0	1-0	1-4	2-2	3-2	1-3	2-3	0-6	*	0-0	1-2
19. Torrington	4-0	1-1	4-0	5-0	0-4	6-0	3-1	1-0	0-1	2-1	2-0	2-2	0-3	0-0	2-0	0-1	0-0	2-0	*	1-0
20. Westbury	1-0	4-1	2-1	4-0	0-3	4-0	0-1	1-0	2-2	1-0	0-2	2-1	2-2	2-0	0-1	0-2	2-3	0-1	3-0	*

DIVISION ONE RESULT CHART 1992-93

HOME TEAM	1	2	3	4	5	6	7	8	9	10	11	12	13	14	15	16	17	18	19	20	21
1. Backwell	*	0-0	1-3	1-0	3-1	0-1	1-1	4-2	1-2	3-0	1-1	3-0	0-2	0-2	3-2	0-3	7-0	3-0	1-3	2-2	1-1
2. Barnstaple	0-0	*	0-0	1-0	3-2	0-1	2-1	1-3	1-3	1-3	0-2	4-0	2-1	2-2	5-0	0-4	2-1	2-1	2-3	1-0	2-3
3. Bridport	2-3	4-1	*	2-2	1-1	2-6	0-2	1-0	1-2	5-2	2-2	1-0	2-1	5-2	4-1	0-0	2-0	0-3	0-1	1-1	2-4
4. Bishop Sut.	0-1	3-2	0-1	*	1-1	1-4	1-3	0-1	1-1	4-1	2-1	1-2	1-3	2-1	3-0	0-1	2-0	3-2	1-2	0-1	2-2
5. Brislington	3-1	3-0	0-1	1-0	*	2-1	0-0	1-0	5-0	2-1	3-0	1-1	1-5	2-1	7-0	1-1	5-0	2-1	0-1	0-0	1-2
6. Calne Town	1-1	4-2	3-0	1-1	2-1	*	1-1	2-2	4-2	2-1	5-0	7-1	1-4	1-0	2-0	1-1	2-2	1-3	3-0	1-1	2-0
7. Clyst Rvrs	1-2	1-1	1-2	4-2	3-2	3-5	*	1-2	3-1	1-1	0-1	4-0	2-0	0-0	0-0	0-2	5-2	2-2	3-0	3-0	4-2
8. Crediton	3-3	2-0	4-0	1-0	2-2	2-2	1-1	*	3-1	4-3	1-0	3-1	1-2	2-1	1-1	2-2	4-1	1-0	3-1	2-0	2-2
9. Devizes	0-2	1-0	3-1	1-3	1-1	2-2	0-0	0-4	*	1-1	1-2	4-3	1-4	2-0	2-1	1-4	3-1	0-1	0-2	2-3	2-0
10. Glastonbury	2-0	0-1	2-0	1-0	0-1	0-2	1-1	0-1	3-3	*	1-2	1-5	2-3	3-2	5-1	1-2	1-3	2-1	0-1	2-0	1-2
11. Heavitree	0-2	3-3	3-1	1-1	1-4	2-2	0-6	0-2	4-0	5-0	*	6-0	1-2	1-1	2-2	0-1	3-0	1-3	1-2	1-2	1-0
12. Ilfracombe	2-2	0-0	2-2	1-3	0-1	0-1	2-2	1-2	0-1	1-3	2-4	*	0-0	1-2	1-1	0-2	1-3	1-0	0-4	1-0	2-2
13. Keynsham	2-2	1-1	0-2	3-0	2-1	1-1	1-2	0-0	1-0	0-0	1-2	4-0	*	0-3	4-2	1-0	3-1	0-0	0-1	2-0	3-3
14. Larkhall	0-0	0-2	0-5	1-3	0-1	1-3	1-3	0-2	6-4	0-1	1-4	4-1	4-0	*	1-2	1-4	2-4	2-0	2-1	0-2	3-2
15. Melksham	2-2	0-4	1-1	0-3	3-1	0-5	0-2	0-3	3-1	2-1	1-1	1-3	0-3	0-7	*	0-4	3-0	1-2	1-5	0-0	1-1
16. Odd Down	1-1	2-1	2-2	1-1	1-0	3-0	4-1	3-0	4-1	2-1	2-0	8-0	3-1	1-2	2-0	*	7-2	2-0	0-0	1-0	1-0
17. Ottery S.M.	0-6	2-3	2-2	1-2	1-4	2-4	1-3	0-4	0-1	1-0	1-2	1-1	0-1	2-1	2-2	2-1	*	3-2	0-6	2-0	0-9
18. Radstock	1-1	1-1	3-2	0-0	0-2	0-5	2-0	2-2	1-3	0-1	1-2	0-1	1-2	0-0	1-1	1-2	0-1	*	1-2	1-2	0-1
19. Warminster	1-2	0-3	2-2	1-4	1-2	0-0	1-2	2-1	2-4	5-0	3-2	4-1	0-0	3-2	1-0	1-1	2-1	1-1	*	1-2	1-1
20. Wellington	3-0	1-1	2-2	2-1	1-4	2-5	1-1	1-1	2-3	1-3	2-1	1-4	4-2	4-1	2-2	1-1	2-2	0-0	1-2	*	1-1
21. Welton R.	1-2	3-1	1-1	1-2	0-2	0-2	1-2	1-3	4-1	0-2	1-1	3-4	3-0	2-2	1-2	0-1	4-3	2-0	0-1	3-1	*

Odd Down - Division One champions 1992-93. Back Row (L/R): Joe Matano, Jamie Walter, Terry Mancini, Steve Langley, Lee Burns, Matthew Pike, Steve Retford, Steve Fuller. Front: Simon Charity, Kevin Dyer, Sean Booker, Duncan Fear, Tommy Gilbert. Photo - James Wright.

END OF SEASON STATISTICS
ATTENDANCES

PREMIER DIVISION

Club	Total	Ave.	200+ gates
Bideford	2824	149	1
Bristol Mnr F.	1292	68	1
Chard Town	1362	72	
Chippenham	1858	98	
Clevedon T.	8006	421	18
Dawlish T.	1435	75	1
Elmore	2735	144	2
Exmouth	2297	121	2
Frome Town	1942	102	
Liskeard	2277	120	3
Mangotsfield	3425	180	5
Minehead	1795	94	1
Paulton Rovers	2870	151	3
Plymouth Argyle	4596	242	12
Saltash United	2785	146	4
Taunton Town	5265	277	19
Tiverton Town	6952	366	17
Torquay United	4153	218	11
Torrington	2035	107	2
Westbury United	2239	123	1
Total (380 recorded)	**62233**	**168**	**103**

FIRST DIVISION

Club	Total	Ave.	200+ gates
Backwell United	1343	67	
Barnstaple	2177	109	
Bishop Sutton	2000	100	2
Bridport	2774	139	
Brislington	1573	78	
Calne Town	2323	116	3
Clyst Rovers	1218	61	
Crediton United	2522	126	1
Devizes Town	1343	67	
Glastonbury	1157	58	
Heavitree United	958	48	
Ilfracombe Town	1853	98	1
Keynsham Town	1330	66	1
Larkhall Athletic	1041	52	
Melksham	1659	83	
Odd Down	1466	73	2
Ottery St Mary	1113	56	
Radstock Town	1026	51	
Warminster Town	3340	167	6
Wellington	1489	74	
Welton Rovers	1801	90	
Total (420 recorded)	**35036**	**84**	**16**

Top Scorers (League only)

A Perrett (Clevedon) 41
K Smith (Tiverton) 37
J Durham (Clevedon) 34
D Mitchell (Mangotsfield) 32
P Everett (Tiverton) 27
I Southcott (Liskeard) 25

Top Scorers

P Horwat (Calne Town) 32
G Lewis (Warminster Town) 29
N Gauntlett (Crediton United) 26

Highest Attendances

1295 - Clevedon Town v Tiverton Town *(17/4/93)*
1120 - Tiverton Town v Elmore *(9/4/93)*
1015 - Mangotsfield United v Clevedon Town *(9/4/93)* - game abandoned at half-time.
925 - Elmore v Tiverton Town *(28/13/92)*
628 - Clevedon Town v Mangotsfield United *(28/12/92)*
547 - Clevedon Town v Plymouth Argyle Reserves *(6/11/92)*
510 - Tiverton Town v Chippenham Town *(4/4/93)*
484 - Plymouth Argyle Reserves v Saltash United *(29/9/92)*
484 - Clevedon Town v Taunton Town *(20/2/93)*
448 - Clevedon Town v Dawlish Town *(24/4/93)*
440 - Torrington v Bideford *(28/12/92)*

No. of players registered: 2,061 (91-92: 2,054 90-91: 2,040 89-90: 1,944 88-89: 1,727).
Transfers Actioned: 241 (91-92: 232 90-91: 194 89-90: 241 88-89: 206).

The Tiverton Town side whose exploits, particularly in the F.A. Vase, had the fans flocking to Ladysmead. Back Row (L/R): Keith Symonds (Physio), Kevin Smith, Steve Hynds, Phil Everett, Jason Smith (now Coventry City), Ian Nott, Mark Saunders, Steve Daly, Mark Short, Martyn Rogers (Manager). Front: Matthew Scott, Neil Saunders, Hedley Steele (Captain), Lee Annunziata, Peter Rogers. Mascots: Andrew Pardoe & Darren Goff. Photo - Paul Dennis.

GREAT MILLS WESTERN LEAGUE PREMIER DIVISION TEN YEAR RECORD

	83/4	84/5	85/6	86/7	87/8	88/9	89/0	90/1	91/2	92/3
Barnstaple Town	3	13	17	11	12	9	18	20	–	–
Bideford	6	2	3	6	10	16	16	12	4	14
Bristol City Res	–	3	9	3	7	–	–	–	–	–
Bristol Manor Farm	8	6	11	5	8	6	12	14	16	13
Chard Town	–	11	21	22	–	15	15	16	18	19
Chippenham Town	16	7	5	9	20	12	13	17	14	16
Clandown	17	14	14	20	22	–	–	–	–	–
Clevedon Town	7	17	10	12	13	11	10	11	2	1
Dawlish Town	14	16	8	14	15	19	14	9	13	20
Devizes Town	19	22	–	–	–	–	–	–	–	–
Elmore	–	–	–	–	–	–	–	–	9	12
Exmouth Town	1	4	1	2	6	2	5	19	17	11
Frome Town	4	18	13	19	18	17	20	13	19	15
Liskeard Athletic	5	10	2	4	1	4	2	8	12	18
Mangotsfield Utd	13	8	6	10	3	18	3	1	8	5
Melksham Town	18	9	16	18	21	–	–	–	–	–
Minehead	10	12	12	21	19	21	–	–	11	17
Ottery St Mary	–	–	–	–	–	–	–	18	21	–
Paulton Rovers	–	5	19	16	14	8	11	10	10	8
Plymouth Argyle Res	9	15	20	7	4	5	7	3	6	10
Radstock Town	–	–	–	17	16	14	19	21	–	–
Saltash United	2	1	4	1	2	1	8	6	5	3
Shepton Mallet Town	11	21	22	–	–	–	–	–	–	–
Swanage Town & Herston	–	–	–	–	11	10	9	–	–	–
Taunton Town	12	20	7	8	9	3	1	7	7	4
Tiverton Town	–	–	–	–	–	–	4	4	3	2
Torquay United Reserves	–	–	–	–	–	–	–	–	–	9
Torrington	–	–	15	15	17	20	17	2	15	6
Wellington	20	–	–	–	–	–	–	–	–	–
Welton Rovers	–	–	–	–	–	13	21	15	20	–
Westbury United	–	–	–	–	–	–	–	–	–	7
Weston-super-Mare	15	19	18	13	5	7	6	5	1	–
No. of Clubs	20	22	22	22	22	21	21	21	21	20

GREAT MILLS WESTERN LEAGUE DIVISION ONE TEN YEAR RECORD

	83/4	84/5	85/6	86/7	87/8	88/9	89/0	90/1	91/2	92/3
Backwell United	6	7	6	9	10	9	2	16	12	8
Barnstaple Town	–	–	–	–	–	–	–	–	17	9
Bath City Reserves	11	13	11	3	4	15	18	12	4	–
Bishop Sutton	–	–	–	–	–	–	–	–	13	13
Bridport	RES	–	–	–	–	3	4	6	9	10
Brislington	–	–	–	–	–	–	–	–	8	4
Bristol City Res.	1	–	–	–	–	–	–	–	–	–
Calne Town	–	–	–	19	13	4	12	3	7	2
Chard Town	2	–	–	–	2	–	–	–	–	–
Clandown	–	–	–	–	–	14	13	14	18	–
Clyst Rovers	–	–	–	–	–	–	–	–	–	6
Crediton United	–	–	–	–	–	–	–	10	3	3
Devizes Town	–	–	14	6	6	5	10	8	20	12
Elmore	19	14	15	14	18	20	14	2	–	–
Glastonbury	7	12	18	22	19	19	19	21	14	16
Heavitree United	16	11	10	21	16	11	11	20	22	11
Ilfracombe Town	–	21	19	20	15	8	3	9	10	18
Keynsham Town	5	8	16	13	7	10	8	13	6	7
Larkhall Athletic	14	10	5	7	5	1	6	19	15	17
Melksham Town	–	–	–	–	–	12	9	15	21	21
Minehead	–	–	–	–	–	–	20	1	–	–
Odd Down	13	22	21	12	14	6	5	4	11	1
Ottery St Mary	18	9	7	11	9	13	1	–	–	19
Paulton Rovers	3	–	–	–	–	–	–	–	–	–
Portway-Bristol	9	1	1	2	–	–	–	–	–	–
Radstock Town	15	6	2	–	–	–	–	–	16	20
Swanage Town & Herston	4	4	8	1	–	–	–	–	–	–
Tiverton Town	21	17	13	16	3	2	–	–	–	–
Torquay Utd Res.	–	–	–	–	–	–	–	7	2	–
Torrington	–	2	–	–	–	–	–	–	–	–
Warminster Town	12	19	22	10	11	18	15	18	5	5
Wellington Town	–	5	12	18	12	7	17	11	19	15
Welton Rovers	8	16	17	8	1	–	–	–	–	14
Westbury United	–	20	20	15	8	16	7	5	1	–
Weymouth Reserves	20	18	9	17	–	–	–	–	–	–
Wimborne Town	10	3	4	5	–	–	–	–	–	–
Yeovil Town Reserves	17	15	3	4	17	17	16	17	–	–
No. of Clubs	21	22	22	22	19	20	20	21	22	21

BIDEFORD

President: Ernie Hopkins   **Chairman:** J McElwee   **Manager:** P Buckingham
Secretary: David Jewell, 75 Stukley Rd, Bideford, N Devon EX39 3EH (0237 479180).
Ground: Sports Ground, Kingsley Road, Bideford (0237 274974).
Directions: A361 for Bideford - ground on right as you enter the town.
Seats: New stand   **Cover:** 1,000   **Capacity:** 6,000   **Floodlights:** Yes   **Founded:** 1946
Colours: Red/red & white/red   **Change colours:** All blue.
Previous Name: Bideford Town   **Previous Lges:** Western 49-72/ Southern 72-75
Prev. Ground: Hansom Ground (1 season)   **Record Gate:** 6,000 v Gloucester, FA Cup 4th Qual. 1960
Programme: 16 pages, 20p   **Programme Editor:** John Hopkins
Midweek Matchday: Wednesday.   **Clubhouse:** Open lunchtimes and evenings
Hons: Western Lg 63-64 70-71 71-72 81-82 82-83 (Div I 51-52, Lg Cup 71-72 84-85, Alan Young Cup 64-65 69-70, Merit Cup 68-69), Devon Snr Cup 79-80, Devon St Lukes Cup 81-82 83-84, FA Cup 1st Rd 64-65(replay) 73-74 77-78 81-82.

BRISTOL MANOR FARM

President: Fred Wardle   **Chairman:** Laurie West   **Vice Chairman:** Brian Barlett.
Secretary: Iain Anderson, 195 Mount Hill Rd., Hanham, Bristol BS15 2SU (0272 616426.
Manager: Chris Rex   **Asst Manager:** Graham Stacey   **Physio:** Steve Coles.
Ground: The Creek, Portway, Sea Mills, Bristol (0272 683571).
Directions: M5 jct 18 (Avonmouth Bridge), follow A4 for Bristol - U-turn on dual carriageway by Bristol & West sports ground and return for half mile on A4 - ground entrance is down narrow lane on left (hidden entrance). Near to Sea Mills station (BR Temple Meads-Severn Beach line).
Seats: 84   **Cover:** 350   **Capacity:** 2,000   **Floodlights:** Yes   **Year Formed:** 1964
Colours: Red/black/white   **Change colours:** White/red   **Nickname:** The Farm
Prev. Name: Manor Farm O.B. 1964-68   **Prev. Lges:** Bristol Suburban 64-69/ Somerset Snr 69-77.
Previous Grounds: None   **Record Attendance:** 500 v Portway, Western Lg 1974.
Programme: Yes   **Programme Editor:** Steve Price   **Club Shop:** No.
Club Sponsors: Wardle Fencing.   **Reserve team's League:** Somerset Senior.
Clubhouse: Lounge bar, entertainments, skittle alley, bar meals. Open every night and lunchtime Sat & Sun.
Record win: 8-2, away to Frome, 2/9/84   **Record defeat:** 1-8, away to Exmouth, 5/5/86.
Record transfer fee paid: Nil   **Received:** £3,000 for Nicky Dent (Yeovil Town, 1989).
Captain & P.o.Y. 92-93: Peter Hall   **Top Scorer 92-93:** Danny Slee
Club record scorer: Chris Rex, 222   **Club record appearances:** Paul Williams, 797.
Hons: Western Lg Div 1 82-83, Glos Tphy 87-88, Glos Amtr Cup 89-90, Somerset Snr Lg Div 1 (Lg Cup, Div 2).

CALNE TOWN

President: The Mayor of Calne   **Chairman:** Mr David Syms   **Vice Chairman:** Mr Laurie Drake.
Secretary: Mr Andy Brewer, 9 Fitzmaurice Square, Calne, Wilts SN11 8NL (0249 815744).
Manager: Graham Fell   **Coach:** Clive Maguire   **Physio:** Dave Heath.
Press Officer: Secretary   **Commercial Manager:** David Staples.
Ground: Bremhill View, Lickhill Rd., North End, Calne (0249 816716).
Directions: From Bristol to Chippenham, on entering town keep left all the way taking slip road to North End, off main Swindon Road.
Seats: 78   **Cover:** 250   **Capacity:** 2,500   **Floodlights:** Yes   **Founded:** 1887.
Colours: White/black/white   **Change colours:** Yellow/blue/yellow   **Nickname:** Lilywhites
Midweek Matches: Wednesday   **Sponsors:** Gilomatics/ Wessex Alliance   **Club Shop:** No.
Programme: 24 pages, 40p   **Programme Editor:** Mr Laurie Drake (0249 814471).
Previous League: Wilts Co. (pre-1986)   **Record Gate:** 1,100 v Swindon, Friendly 25/7/1987.
Prev. Names: Calne Town (est. 1886)/ Harris Utd - clubs merged/ Calne & Harris Utd - 1920-67.
Reserves' League: Wilts Co. Lge   **Prev. Ground:** Anchor Road Rec. 1887-1967.
Record win: 10-0 v Heavitree United   **Record defeat:** 1-5 v Minehead.
Clubhouse: Mon-Fri 7-11pm, Sat-Sun 12-11pm. Filled rolls, hot food, tea, coffee, sweets etc.
Club record scorer: Robbie Lardner   **Club record appearances:** Gary Swallow, 259.
Captain 92-93: Clive Maguire   **Top Scorer 92-93:** Peter Horwat, 32   **P.O.Y. 92-93:** Gary Bartlett.
Hons: Western Lg Div 1 R-up 92-93, Wilts Snr Cup 12-13 34-35 84-85 (R-up 1893-94 94-95 1911-12 49-50), Wilts Lg 33-34 ('Ghia' Cup 80-81 85-86, Div 2 79-80, Div 3 85-86, Div 4 81-82).

Calne Town - Division One runners-up 1992-93.

CHIPPENHAM TOWN

President: G W Terrell　　　**Chairman:** D S Webb　　　**Manager:** Geoff Evans.
Secretary: Arthur Wimble, 31 Southmead, Chippenham, Wilts SN14 0RT (0249 655461).
Commercial Manager: R G Terrell　　　**Physio:** P Christopher.
Ground: Hardenhuish Park, Bristol Road, Chippenham (0249 650400).
Directions: M4 jct 17, A429 into Chippenham, follow signs for Trowbridge/Bath until r'bout, left onto A420 into town, ground 200yds on left. 5 mins walk from railway station on main A420 Bristol Road.
No. of seats: 100　　　**Covered Accom:** 300　　　**Capacity:** 4,000
Floodlights: Yes　　　**Year Formed:** 1873　　　**Midweek matches:** Wednesday
Club colours: All blue　　　**Change colours:** Old gold/black/old gold.
Previous Leagues: Hellenic, Wiltshire Senior, Wiltshire Premier.
Previous Grounds: Westmead, Lowden, Little George Lane, Malmesbury Rd
Record Gate: 4,800 v Chippenham Utd, Western Lg
Programme: 32 pages, 20p　　　**Programme Editor:** Sandie Webb
Clubhouse: On ground above Stand with bar, skittles etc.
Hons: FA Cup 1st Rd 51-52, Western Lg 51-52 (Div 2 52-53(Res) 80-81), Wilts Shield, Wilts Snr Cup, Wilts Snr League.
Local Newspapers: Chippenham News, Wilts Gazette

CREDITON UNITED

Chairman: D J Blanchflower　　　**Manager:** T Atkins
Secretary: Brian Maunder, 39 Geneva Close, Exeter, Devon EX2 4NH (0392 411592).
Ground: Lord's Meadow Sports Centre, Crediton (0363 24671).
Directions: A337 to Crediton from Exeter, right onto A3072 (signposted Tiverton) at White Hart Hotel, turn right into Commercial Rd for Lord's Meadow Ind. Est.- Sports Centre car park 250 metres on left.
No. of seats: 150　　　**Covered Accom:** 150　　　**Capacity:** 2,000　　　**Floodlights:** No
Club colours: Blue/black/black　　　**Change colours:** Amber/white/blue.
Midweek Matches: Wednesday
Previous Leagues: Devon & Exeter　　　　　　**Hons:** Devon County Cup & Devon Snr Cup S-Final

ELMORE

Chairman: A J Cockram　　　**Vice Chairman:** A Davey　　　**President:** W Jones
Secretary: Mrs A Freeman, C/O the Club (See Below).
Manager: Ken Freeman　　　**Asst Manager:** S Downs　　　**Coach:** M Mitchell.
Physio: A Morgan　　　**Commercial Manager:** K Sharland (0884 242842).
Ground: Horsdon Park, Tiverton, Devon EX16 4DE (0884 252341).
Directions: M5 Jct 27, A373 towards Tiverton, leave at 1st sign for Tiverton & Business Park, ground 500yds on right.
Seats: 200　　　**Cover:** 300　　　**Capacity:** 3,000　　　**Floodlights:** Yes　　　**Founded:** 1947
Midweek matches: Tuesday　　　**Club Sponsors:** Ken White Signs.
Colours: Green & white　　　**Change colours:** Yellow & black　　　**Nickname:** Eagles.
Previous Leagues: Devon & Exeter 47-74/ South Western 74-78.
Previous Grounds: None　　　**Record Gate:** 1,271 v Tiverton, Western Lg 27/12/92.
Programme: 12 pages, 30p　　　**Editor:** Mrs Freeman (0884 242842)
Club Shop: Yes, selling clothing, kit, programmes, memorabilia. Contact Mr K Sharland (0884 242842).
Record win: 17-0　　　**Record defeat:** 2-7
Clubhouse: 11am-11pm Mon-Sat, 12-3 & 7-10.30pm Sat. Full canteen service - hot & cold meals & snacks.
Captain 92-93: A Skinner　　　**Top Scorer 92-93:** M Seatherton　　　**P.O.Y. 92-93:** R Smeath
Club record scorer: M Seatherton　　　**Club record appearances:** P Webber.
Hons: East Devon Snr Cup 72-73 75-76, Western Lg Cup 90-91 (Div 1 R-up 90-91, Prem Div Merit Cup R-up 91-92, Div 1 Merit Cup 86-87 89-90 90-91), Devon St Lukes Cup R-up 90-91, Devon Snr Cup 87-88, Devon Intermediate Cup 60-61, Football Express Cup 60-61, Devon & Exeter Lg Div 2A 73-74 86-87(res)(Div 1A 76-77(res)), Devon Yth Cup 77-78.

EXMOUTH TOWN

President: Mr Brian Bradley　　　**Chairman:** Mr P Marshall　　　**Vice Chairman:** Mr John Disball
Secretary: Mr D J Richardson, 44 Whitchurch Ave., Exeter EX2 5NT (0392 430985).
Manager: John Bryan　　　**Assistant Manager:** Paul Dixon.
Physio: Mr S Bull　　　**Commercial Manager:** Mr J Trail.
Ground: Southern Road, Exmouth (0395 279085 (Office)).
Directions: On right side of main Exeter to Exmouth road (A376). Half mile from Exmouth (BR) station.
Seats: 100　　　**Cover:** 250　　　**Capacity:** 2,500　　　**Floodlights:** Yes　　　**Year Formed:** 1933
Colours: Royal & white　　　**Change colours:** Yellow & white.
Nickname: 'Town' or 'Blues'　　　**Previous Lge:** Devon & Exeter 1933-73.
Programme: 36 pages, 30p　　　**Editor:** Phil Hiscox (0392 494967)
Midweek home matchday: Tuesday　　　**Sponsors:** Bristol & West Property Services.
Previous Grounds: Maer Cricket Field 33-38 48-64; Raleigh Park, Withycombe 38-39
Club Shop: Yes. Selection of non-League programmes (up to 20,000 in stock) and other club souvenirs.
Record Gate: 2,395 v Liverpool XI, friendly in 1987.
Record win: 8-1 v Bristol Manor F., 1986　　　**Record defeat:** 1-9 v Frome Town, 1976.
Clubhouse: Open every night and weekend lunchtimes. Snacks available.
Captain 92-93: Keith Pitman　　　**Top Scorer 92-93:** Bobby Dawson　　　**P.O.Y. 92-93:** Mike Napper
Club Record Scorer: Mel Pym, 117　　　**Club Record Appearances:** Steve Hynds, 242 (in Western Lg)
Hons: FA Vase SF 84-85; Western Lg 83-84 85-86 (R-up 86-87 88-89; Lg Cup 88-89; Div 1 R-up 81-82; Sportmanship Tphy 86-87 92-93); Devon Premier Cup 70-71 79-80; Devon St Lukes Cup 84-85 88-89 89-90; Devon Snr Cup 50-51; East Devon Snr Cup 50-51 82-83; Harry Wood Mem. Cup 81-82; Exmouth Chal. Cup 64-65 65-66 66-67 68-69 70-71 71-72 73-74

FROME TOWN

President: Mr C W Norton   **Chairman:** Mr G Norris   **Vice Chairman:** Mr A Castle
Secretary: Mrs S J Merrill, 56 Nightingale Ave., Frome, Somerset BA11 2VW (0373 473820).
Manager: Phil Morris   **Asst Manager:** T Bull   **Press Officer:** Steve Jupp.
Ground: Badgers hill, Berkeley Road, Frome (0373 464087).
Directions: Locate "Vine Tree Inn", Bath Road; ground 100 yds from Inn (1 mile from town centre and Frome BR station).
Seats: 250   **Cover:** 800   **Capacity:** 5,000   **Floodlights:** Yes   **Founded:** 1904
Colours: All red   **Change colours:** White/black/black   **Nickname:** Robins.
Previous Grounds: None   **Previous League:** Wilts Premier   **Club Shop:** No.
Programme: 30 pages, 50p   **Programme Editor:** Secretary
Sponsors: Woodman Furniture
Midweek home matchday: Tuesday   **Reserve team's League:** Somerset Senior.
Clubhouse: Evenings & weekends. Cold food only.
Captain 92-93: Tom Crowley   **Top Scorer 92-93:** Dean Elliott   **P.o.Y. 92-93:** Steve Wright
Hons: Western Lg 78-79 (Div 2 19-20, Div 2 R-up 54-55, Lg Cup 79-80 82-83, Merit Cup 82-83, Alan Young Cup 79-80, Subsidiary Cup 59-60), FA Cup 1st Rd 54-55, Somerset Premier Cup 66-67 68-69 82-83, Wilts Premier Lg 62-63, Western Co's F'lit Cup 83-84, Somerset Snr Cup 32-33 33-34 50-51, Somerset Snr Lg 06-07 08-09 10-11 (Div 1(res) 90-91, Div 3(res) 85-86, Lg Cup(res) 91-92).

LISKEARD ATHLETIC

President: TBA   **Chairman:** David Hick   **Vice Chairman:** Dave Rawlings
Secretary: Adrian Wilton, Martina, Dawes Close, Dobwalls, Liskeard, Cornwall PL14 6JD (0579 20980).
Manager: Jimmy Hargreaves   **Asst Manager/Coach:** Alan Gillett.
Commercial Manager: Alan Mayne (0579 343593).
Ground: Lux Park, Liskeard, Cornwall (0579 42665).
Directions: Take Tavistock Road (A390) from town centre, after 1/2 mile turn left on St Cleer Road (following signs to Lux Park Sports Complex) and the ground is 200 yards on left. Half mile from Liskeard BR station.
Seats: 100   **Cover:** 300   **Capacity:** 2,000   **Floodlights:** Yes   **Year Formed:** 1889
Club colours: All blue   **Change colours:** All green   **Nickname:** Blues.
Previous Leagues: East Cornwall Premier, Plymouth & District, South Western 66-79.
Midweek matchday: Tuesday   **Players progressing to Football Lge:** Bradley Swiggs.
Programme: 10 pages, 30p   **Editor:** Commercial Manager.   **Club Shop:** No.
Record win: 8-1   **Record defeat:** 1-6   **Record transfer fee received:** £1,000.
Sponsors: Jollys soft drinks/ Robin Wotton Electrical/ Gilbert Outfitters.
Clubhouse details: (0579 342665) Normal licensing hours. Hot & cold food available.
Captain 92-93: Neil Williams   **Top Scorer & P.o.Y. 92-93:** Ian Southcott.
Club record scorer: Not known   **Club record appearances:** Brian Bunney, 500+.
Hons: South Western Lg 76-77 78-79 (R-up 75-76 77-78; Lg Cup 76-77 78-79) Western Lg 87-88 (R-up 85-86 89-90, Merit Cup 80-81); Cornwall Snr Cup 04-05 83-84 84-85 85-86 88-89 89-90 (R-up 70-71 75-76 76-77 78-79); Cornwall Charity Cup 21-22 79-80, Cornwall Jnr Cup 05-06 13-14 26-27; SW Pratten Cup 78-79; E Cornwall Prem RAOB Cup 67-68, Plymouth & Dist. Lg 60-61 (Div 1 59-60 (R-up 54-55 73-74), Div 2 76-77(Res), Victory Cup 60-61, Charity Cup 59-60), E Cornwall Prem. Lg (Reserves) 84-85 92-93 (Lg Cup 88-89).

MANGOTSFIELD UNITED

President: Mr A J Hill   **Chairman:** Mr R Davis   **Vice Chairman:** Mr P Selway
Secretary: Mr R Gray, 105 Chiltern Close, Warmley, Bristol BS15 5UW (0272 616523).
Manager: R Jones   **Physio:** J Cummings   **Press Officer:** Secretary
Ground: Cossham Street, Mangotsfield, Bristol BS17 3EW (0272 560119).
Directions: M4 jct 19, M32 jct 1; A4174 marked Downend, through lights, over double mini-r'bout to Mangotsfield, left by village church onto B4465 signposted Pucklechurch, ground quarter mile on right. From central Bristol take A432 thru Fishponds, Staple Hill, to Mangotsfield and turn right by village church onto B4465. From Bath/Keynsham take A4175, right at island at Willsbridge onto A431, then rejoin A4175 at next island (Cherry Garden Hill) to Bridge Yate, straight over double mini-r'bout and take 1st left, right into Carsons Rd after 1 mile and follow to Mangotsfield village & turn right by church onto B4465.
Seats: 300   **Cover:** 800   **Capacity:** 2,500   **Floodlights:** Yes   **Founded:** 1950
Colours: Maroon & sky   **Change colours:** All white   **Nickname:** The Field
Players to progress to Football League: G.Megson, S.White, G.Penrice, P.Purnell, N.Tanner, M.Hooper.
Previous Leagues: Bristol & District 50-67/ Avon Premier Combination 67-72.
Record Gate: 2,386 v Bath City, FA Cup 77-78
Programme: 32 pages, 50p.   **Programme Editor:** Bob Smale (0272 401926).
Club Shop: Yes. Contact Ron Loftus (0272 756510), David Smale (0272 662246) or Bob Smale.
Clubhouse: Open 11am-11pm. Snacks - hot food on matchdays. Lounge bar for official functions etc.
Sponsors: Apron Roofing Supplies
Midweek home matchday: Tuesday   **Reserve team's League:** Somerset Senior.
Captain 92-93: Denis McCoy   **Top Scorer & P.o.Y. 92-93:** Dave Mitchell
Hons: Western Lg 90-91 (Lg Cup 73-74 (R-up 86-87) Div 1 R-up 82-83); Somerset Prem. Cup 87-88 (R-up 88-89); Glos Snr Cup 68-69 75-76; Glos FA Trophy 84-85 86-87 90-91; Hungerford Invitation Cup 74-75; Rothmans National Cup R-up 77-78, Hanham Invitation Charity Cup 84-85 85-86, Somerset Snr Lg(Reserves) Div 2 75-76 (Div 3 74-75), Somerset Comb. Cup 74-75, Glos Yth Shield 81-82 84-85 (R-up 82-83), Somerset Floodlit Yth Lg 81-82 82-83 83-84 84-85 87-88, Somerset Yth Shield 76-77.

MINEHEAD

President: A C Copp   **Chairman:** David Gaydon   **Manager:** Craig Laird.
Secretary: Thomas Smith, Marley's, Martlett Road, Minehead TA24 5QE (0643 703698).
Ground: The Recreation Ground, Irnham Road, Minehead, Somerset (0643 704989).
Directions: Entering town from east on A39 turn right into King Edward Road at Police station, first left into Alexandra Rd and follow signs to car park; ground entrance within. Regular buses to Minehead from Taunton, the nearest railhead.
No. of seats: 250   **Covered Accom:** 700   **Capacity:** 3,500   **Floodlights:** Yes
Club colours: All blue   **Change colours:** All yellow   **Year Formed:** 1889
Programme: 24 pages, 20p   **Editor:** Secretary.   **Midweek Matches:** Wednesday
Prev. Lges: Southern Snr, Southern 72-83.   **Record Gate:** 3,600 v Exeter, FA Cup 2nd Rd, 17/12/77.
Hons: Southern Lg R-up 76-77 (Div 1 Sth 75-76, Merit Cup 75-76), Western Lg R-up 66-67 71-72 (Div 1 90-91, Alan Young Cup 67-68 (jt with Glastonbury), Somerset Premier Cup 60-61 73-74 76-77.

ODD DOWN

President: **Chairman:** Dave Loxton   **Vice Chairman:**
Secretary: Mike Mancini, 36 Caledonian Rd., East Twerton, Bath BA3 2RD (0225 423293).
Manager: Paul Gover.
Ground: Combe Hay Lane, Odd Down, Bath (0225 832491).
Directions: On main Bath/Exeter road - leaving Bath turn left into Combe Hay Lane opposite Lamplighters Pub. 40 mins walk from Bath (BR).
Seats: 50   **Cover:** 100   **Capacity:** 1,000   **Floodlights:** Yes.   **Founded:** 1901
Colours: White/black/black   **Change colours:** Green/white/green
Previous Leagues: Wilts Premier, Bath & District, Somerset Senior
Midweek Matches: Wednesday
Hons: Western Lg Div 1 92-93, Somerset Snr Cup 91-92.

PAULTON ROVERS

President: Mr T Pow   **Chairman:** Mr D Bissex   **Vice Chairman:** Mr D Carter
Secretary: Mr J E Pool, 111 Charlton Park, Midsomer Norton, Avon BA3 4BP (0761 415190).
Manager: Steve Gay   **Physio:** John Pool.
Press Officer: W Pope   **Commercial Manager:** K Simmons.
Ground: Athletic Ground, Winterfield Road, Paulton (0761 412907).
Directions: Leave A39 at Farrington Gurney (approx 15 miles south of Bristol), follow A362 marked Radstock for two miles, left at junction B3355 to Paulton, ground on right.
Seats: 138   **Cover:** 200   **Capacity:** 5,000   **Floodlights:** Yes   **Founded:** 1881
Colours: White/maroon/maroon   **Change colours:** All yellow   **Nickname:** Rovers.
Midweek matches: Tuesday   **Previous Leagues:** Wilts Premier/ Somerset Snr.
Previous Grounds: Chapel Field/ Cricket Ground/ Recreation Ground 1946-48.
Record Gate: 2,000 v Crewe, FA Cup, 1906-07
Programme: 20 pages   **Programme Editor:** Keith Simmons
Club Shop: Old programmes available - contact secretary.
Clubhouse: 3 bars, lounge, skittle alley, dance hall. Capacity 300. Catering facilities.
Club Sponsors: Truro Plaza/ Design Windows/ Berkley Coaches.
Midweek home matchday: Tuesday   **Reserve team's League:** Somerset Snr.
Captain 92-93: Greg Taylor   **Top Scorer & P.o.Y. 92-93:** Graham Colbourne.
Hons: Western Lg Div 1, Somerset Snr Cup 00-01 02-03 03-04 07-08 08-09 09-10 34-35 67-68 68-69 71-72 72-73 74-75, Somerset Snr Lg.
Local Newspapers: Bath Evening Chronicle, Bristol Evening Post, Western Daily Post.

SALTASH UNITED

President: P Skinnard   **Chairman:** M Howard   **Manager:** Chris Harrison
Secretary: C D Phillips, 85 Lakeview Close, Tamerton Foliot, Plymouth PL5 4LT (0752 705845).
Ground: Kimberley Stadium, Callington Road, Saltash, Cornwall (0752 845746).
Directions: First left after crossing Tamar Bridge, through town centre, at top of town fork right at mimi r'bout, ground 400 yds ahead on left.
No. of seats: 250   **Covered Accom:** 250   **Capacity:** 3,000
Floodlights: Yes   **Year Formed:** 1947   **Nickname:** The Ashes
Club colours: All red   **Change colours:** Black & white stripes/black/black
Previous Leagues: Cornwall Snr/ South Western 51-59 62-76/ East Cornwall Premier 59-62.
Programme: 20 pages, 30p   **Programme Editor:** T.B.A.
Clubhouse: Club attached to stand and caters for dancing and club activities.
Hons: Cornwall Snr Lg 49-50 50-51, Western Lg 84-85 86-87 88-89 (R-up 83-84 87-88, Lg Cup 86-87 87-88 (R-up 88-89), Div 1 76-77, Merit Cup 79-80 87-88), Sth Western Lg 53-54 75-76 (R-up 52-53 73-74 74-75, Lg Cup 51-52 69-70 73-74), Cornwall Snr Cup 50-51 74-75 81-82 87-88 90-91.
Local Newspapers: Western Evening Haerald, The Cornish Times.   **Midweek Matches:** Wednesday

TAUNTON TOWN

Chairman: T F Harris   **Vice Chairman:** A J Rutland.
Secretary: Mrs Debie Cridland, C/O the club (see below) (0823 324546).
Manager: Terry Rowles   **Asst Manager:** David Jenkins.
Ground: Wordsworth Drive, Taunton, Somerset TA1 2HG (0823 278191).
Directions: Leave M5 Jct 25, follow signs to town centre, at 2nd set of lights turn left into Wordsworth Drive; ground on left. 25 mins walk from Taunton (BR); turn left out of station and follow road right through town centre bearing left into East Reach. Follow road down and turn right into Wordsworth Drive shortly after Victoria pub.
Seats: 250   **Cover:** 1,000   **Capacity:** 4,000   **Floodlights:** Yes   **Year Formed:** 1947
Midweek matches: Monday   **Club Sponsors:** Stella Artois.   **Nickname:** Peacocks
Club colours: Sky blue & claret/claret/sky blue
Change colours: Yellow/blue/yellow.   **Record Gate:** 2,960 v Torquay, Western Lg. 1958
Record win: 11-1 v Ottery St Mary (A), Western League Premier Division 91-92.
Record defeat: 0-8 v Cheltenham Town (A), F.A. Cup 2nd Qualifying Rd, 28/9/91.
Newsline: 0891 122 901   **Previous Lges:** Western 54-77/ Southern 77-83.
Programme: 28 pages, 50p   **Editor:** Secretary   **Club Shop:** No.
Clubhouse: Social club to accommodate 300, full bar facilities, separate bar & hall for private functions.
Captain 92-93:   **Top Scorer 92-93:** Phil Hunt.
Hons: Western Lg 68-69 89-90 (Alan Young Cup 73-74 75-76(jt with Falmouth), Charity Chall. Cup 49-50 50-51), Somerset Snr Lg 52-53, Somerset Prem. Cup R-up 82-83 89-90 92-93, FA Cup 1st Rd 81-82 (lost 1-2 at Swindon).

TIVERTON TOWN

President: Dan McCauley   **Chairman:** Gordon Anderson   **Vice Chairman:** Mike Mogford
Secretary: Alan Disney, 56 Melbourne St., Tiverton, Devon EX16 5LB (0884 253829).
Manager: Martyn Rogers   **Asst Manager:** John Owen
Physio: Keith Symmonds   **Press Officer:** Sid Chorley.
Ground: Ladysmead, Bolham Road, Tiverton, Devon EX16 8SG (0884 252397).
Directions: M5 Jct 27, west towards Tiverton on A373, continue to end of dual carriageway and turn left at r'about; ground entrance 300yds on right alongside BP petrol station.
Seats: 300   **Cover:** 700   **Capacity:** 3,000   **Floodlights:** Yes   **Year Formed:** 1920
Colours: Amber/amber/black   **Change:** All white (black facings)   **Nickname:** Tivvy.
Programme: 24 pages, 50p   **Programme Editor:** James Wade (0823 278878)
Club Shop: Programmes, metal badges, scarves, hats etc available. Contact James Wade (0823 278878).
Previous League: Devon & Exeter   **Previous ground:** The Elms, Blundell Road 1920-39
Clubhouse: Lunctimes, evenings. All day Sat during the season. 3 bars. Food (burgers, hot dogs, chips etc).
Players progressing to Football League: Jason Smith (Coventry City, 1993).
Midweek matches: Wednesday   **Record Gate:** 2,602 v Canvey Island, FA Vase SF 20/3/93.
Captain 92-93: Hedley Steele   **Top Scorer & P.o.Y. 92-93:** Kevin Smith (57 Lge & Cup gls)
Hons: FA Vase R-up 92-93, FA Cup 1st Rnd 90-91 (lost 2-6 at Aldershot) 91-92 (lost 0-5 at Barnet); Western Lg R-up 92-93 (Lg Cup 92-93, Amateur Trophy 77-78 78-79, Div 1 R-up 88-89); Devon St Lukes Cup 90-91 91-92 92-93; Devon & Exeter Lg 51-52 66-67 70-71 84-85; Devon Snr Cup 55-56 65-66; East Devon Snr Cup 35-36 37-38 52-53 55-56 60-61 62-63 66-67; North Devon Charity Cup 72-73 86-87

Tiverton's Player-of-the-Year and top-scorer Kevin Smith unleashes a powerful shot during the F.A. Vase Semi-Final first leg at home to Canvey Island. Photo - Paul Dennis.

TORRINGTON

President: Frank Morris   **Chairman:** TBA
Sec./Press Officer: Robert T Dymond, Back Flat, 12 South Street, Torrington, Devon EX38 8HE (0805 23569).
Manager: John Hore   **Asst Manager:** Nigel Menhenick   **Physio:** Owen Cooke.
Ground: Vicarage Field, School Lane, Great Torrington (0805 22853).
Directions: (From North, Barnstaple, Exeter, South Molton) In town centre turn left by parish church, turn right at swimming pool, ground behind swimming pool. Good parking. Red Bus from Bideford and Barnstaple (nearest BR station). Bus stop 300yds from ground.
Seats: None   **Cover:** 2,000   **Capacity:** 4,000   **Floodlights:** Yes   **Year Formed:** 1908
Midweek Matches: Wednesday   **Club Sponsors:** Bideford Tool   **Club Shop:** No.
Cols: Green & white hoops/white/white   **Change colours:** Blue & white stripes/navy/blue.
Programme: 32 pages, 30p   **Programme Editor:** Secretary & Rachel Hutchings.
Previous Grounds: None   **Nickname:** Torrie or Supergreens   **Record win:** 18-0.
Previous Leagues: North Devon/ Devon & Exeter/ South Western 77-84.
Clubhouse: Weekdays 7-11pm, Sat 11am-11pm, Sun 12-3 & 7-10.30pm. Two bars. Light snacks available. New kitchen and offices being built to open 1993-94.
Local Newspapers: North Devon Journal, Bideford Gazette
Record transfer fee paid: Nil   **Received:** £3,000 for Dave Walter (Yeovil Town).
Captain 92-93: Mike Gilbert   **Top Scorer 92-93:** Martin Nicholls 30 (24 in league).
P.o.Y. 92-93: Andy Stevens
Club record scorer: Trevor Watkins, 254   **Club record appearances:** Nigel Reed, 450+.
Hons: Western Lg R-up 90-91 (Lg Cup R-up 91-92, Div 1 R-up 84-85, Merit Cup 91-92), South Western Lg R-up 80-81 82-83 (Lg Cup 80-81), Devon Cup, Devon & Exeter Lg & Cup double, various local cup wins inc. Torridge Cup 92-93.

WESTBURY UNITED

Chairman: Philip Alford   **Vice Chairman:** Bert Back   **President:** George Nicholls.
Secretary: Ernie Barber, 7 Farleigh Close, Westbury, Wilts. BA13 3TF (0373 822117).
Manager: Ian Harris   **Asst Manager:** Ted Miluk   **Physio:** Andy Goodenough
Press Officer: Paul Lusty   **Commercial Manager:** Tom Lawrence.
Ground: Meadow Lane, Westbury (0373 823409).
Directions: In town centre, A350, follow signs for BR station, Meadow Lane on right (club signposted). Ten mins walk from railway station (on main London-South West + South Coast-Bristol lines).
Seats: 150   **Cover:** 150   **Capacity:** 3,500   **Floodlights:** Yes   **Year Formed:** 1921
Colours: Green/black/white   **Change colours:** Red/white/red
Midweek Matches: Wednesday   **Prev. Leagues:** Wilts Comb./ Wilts Co. (pre-1984)
Nickname: White Horsemen   **Previous Ground:** Redland Lane (pre-1935).
Programme: 16 pages, 30p   **Programme Editor:** Eli Manasseh (0373 826754).
Club Shop: Yes. Shirts, scarves, hats, badges and various programmes.
Sponsors: Wheelers Electrical   **Reserve Team's league:** Trowbridge District.
Record Gate: 4,000 v Llanelli, F.A. Cup 1st Rd 1937 (match was on Littlewoods coupon!).
Clubhouse: Evenings 7-11pm, Fri, Sat & Sun lunctimes 12-3pm.
Captain 92-93: Pete Fielding   **Top Scorer 92-93:** Adie McHugh   **P.O.Y. 92-93:** Steve Perrin.
Honours: Western Lg Div 1 91-92, Wilts Senior Cup 31-32 32-33 47-48 51-52, Wilts Combination, Wilts Lg 34-35 37-38 38-39 49-50 50-51 55-56, Wilts Premier Shield R-up 92-93.

DIVISION ONE CLUBS 1993-94

BACKWELL UNITED

President: W Roberts   **Chairman:** Chris Strong
Secretary: W C Coggins, 34 Westfield Road, Backwell, Bristol BS19 3ND (0275 463424).
Manager: Adrian Britton   **Coach:** Gerry Sweeney.
Ground: Recreation Ground, Backwell, Avon (0275 462612).
Directions: Near centre of Backwell on main A370 Bristol to Weston-super-Mare road. 15 mins walk from Nailsea & Backwell (BR); turn right out of station, right at traffic lights, ground quarter mile on right.
No. of seats: None   **Covered Accom:** 150   **Capacity:** 1,000   **Floodlights:** No
Club colours: All red   **Change colours:** All sky   **Year Formed:** 1911
Programme: 16 pages, 20p.   **Programme Editor:** Mike Stone   **Midweek Matches:** Tuesday
Previous Leagues: Bristol Surburban (Pre 1970); Somerset Senior 70-83
Record attendance: 400 v Robinsons, Somerset Lg, 1982
Club Honours: Somerset Snr Lg 77-78 79-80 80-81 81-82 82-83 (Lg Cup 82-83 (R-up 79-80) Div 1 72-73); Somerset Snr Cup 81-82; SW Co.'s Sutton Transformer Cup 81-82

BARNSTAPLE TOWN

President: Wilf Harris   **Chairman:** Vic Hamilton-Philip   **Vice Chairman:** Peter Woodhams.
Secretary: Gordon Lavercombe, 1 Haldene Terrace, Yeo Vale, Barnstaple, Devon EX32 7AQ (0271 79481).
Manager: Bryan Hill   **Physio:** Dr Amir Arslenagic   **Comm. Mgr:** Nigel Gross.
Ground: Mill Road, Barnstaple, North Devon (0271 743469).
Directions: A361 towards Ilfracombe (from M5 Jct 26), in Barnstaple follow A361 Ilfracombe signs, second left after crossing small bridge is Mill Road.
Seats: 250   **Cover:** 1,000   **Capacity:** 5,000   **Floodlights:** Yes   **Year Formed:** 1906
Colours: Red & white   **Change colours:** White & blue   **Nickname:** Barum.
Sponsors: N T Shapland & Petter   **Prev. Lges:** Nth Devon, Devon & Exeter, S. Western
Prev. Grounds: Town Wharf (Pre 1920's); Highfield Rd, Newport (until 1935), Pilton Pk, Rock Pk.
Previous Name: Barnstaple Ship Yard   **Rec. Gate:** 6,200 v Bournemouth, FA Cup 1st Rd, 1954
Programme: 16 pages, 30p   **Programme Editor:** Nigel Gross (0271 46605).
Midweek Matches: Tuesday   **Local Press:** N. Devon Journal Herald   **Club Shop:** No.
Record transfer fee paid: £4,000 for Joe Scott (Hungerford Town, 1980).
Record transfer fee received: £6,000 for Ian Doyle (Bristol City).
Clubhouse: Full license. Bar snacks.   **Club record appearances:** Trevor Burnell
Captain 92-93: Mark Richards   **Top Scorer 92-93:** Dave Slade   **P.O.Y. 92-93:** Ian Baker.
Hon: Western Lg 52-53 79-80 (R-up 80-81 81-82, Div 1 49-50, Merit Cup 74-75 83-84 84-85, Combination 92-93), FA Cup 1st Rd replay 51-52, Devon Professional Cup 62-63 64-65 67-68 69-70 71-72 72-73 74-75 76-77 77-78 78-79 79-80 80-81, Devon Lg, Devon St Lukes Cup 87-88, Devon Snr Cup 92-93, Devon Youth Cup 48-49 51-52.

BISHOP SUTTON

Chairman/Press Off.: Alex Thomas   **Vice Chairman:** Roy Penney   **President:** Bob Redding.
Secretary: Lester Hammond, Cornerways, Church Lane, Bishop Sutton B18 4XA (0275 332673).
Manager: Martin Finn   **Physio:** Roy Penney   **Comm. Mgr:** G Williams.
Ground: Lake View, Wick Road, Bishop Sutton (0272 333097).
Directions: On A368 at rear of Butchers Arms pub – Ground signposted on left entering village from the West.
Seats: None   **Cover:** 200   **Capacity:** 1,500   **Floodlights:** No   **Founded:** 1977.
Cols: All blue   **Change colours:** All red.   **Sponsors:** Harlequin Motor Centre.
Midweek Matches: Tuesday   **Previous Ground:** Adjacent cricket field   **Nickname:** Bishops.
Prev. Leagues: Weston & Dist. Yth/ Bristol & Avon/ Somerset Snr (pre 1991)   **Club Shop:** No.
Programme: 10 pages, £1 with entry   **Reserve team's League:** Somerset Senior.
Record win: 15-0 v Glastonbury Res.   **Record Gate:** 400 v Bristol City, friendly.
Clubhouse: Open matchdays. Rolls, pies and usual pub food available.
Captain 92-93: Lee Weaver   **Top Scorer 92-93:** Andy Bateman   **P.O.Y. 92-93:** Glen Jones
Hons: Somerset Snr Lg R-up 89-90 (Div 1 83-84 (R-up 81-82), Div 2 82-83), Bristol & Avon Lg 80-81 (Div 2 79-80), Somerset Jnr Cup 80-81, Weston Yth Lg 77-78, Chew Valley KO Cup 83-84, Mid-Somerset Lg(Res) R-up 82-83 (Div 3 81-82).

BRIDPORT

President: Mrs L Parker   **Chairman:** D Fowler   **Manager:** Geoff Joy
Secretary: Keith Morgan, 95 Orchard Crescent, Bridport DT6 5HA (0308 25113).
Ground: The Beehive, St Mary's Field, Bridport, Dorset (0308 23834).
Directions: Take West Bay road from town centre, turn right immediately before Palmers Brewery.
Seats: 200   **Capacity:** 2,000   **Floodlights:** Yes   **Founded:** 1887
Cols: Red & black/black/red & black   **Change:** Blue & white/white/blue & white   **Nickname:** Bees
Midweek Matches: Wednesday   **Programme Editor:** P S Ennals
Previous Grounds: Pymore (pre 1930s); Crown Field (pre 1953)
Previous Leagues: Perry Street/ Western 61-84/ Dorset Combination 84-88.
Record Attendance: 1,150 v Exeter City, 1981; 3,000 v Chelsea, at Crown, 1950
Hons: Western Lg Cup 70-71 72-73 77-78 (R-up 76-77, Merit Cup 69-70 71-72 73-74); FA Vase 5th Rd 88-89; Dorset Comb.(3) 85-88 (Lg Cup 86-87 87-88); Dorset Snr Cup(8) 63-64 69-71 75-76 78-81 87-88; Dorset Snr Amtr Cup(6) 48-50 54-55 56-57 70-72; W. Dorset Chal. Bowl 07-08; Perry Str. Lg 22-23; Mark Frowde Cup 76-77 88-89

BRISLINGTON

President: Dick Ollis   **Chairman:** Paul Bishop   **Manager:** Jamie Patch
Secretary: F G Durbin, 52 Arlington Road, St Annes, Bristol BS4 4AJ (0272 777169).
Ground: Ironmould Lane, Brislington (0272 778531).
Directions: Four miles out of Bristol on main A4 to Bath – turn left up lane opposite Garden Centre
Seats: None   **Cover:** Yes   **Floodlights:** No   **Hons:** Somerset Snr Cup 92-93.
Previous ground: Council pitch   **Programme Editor:** Bob Perrott
Colours: Red/black/red   **Change colours:** All blue

CHARD TOWN

President: John Smith   **Chairman:** Brian Beer   **Vice Chairman:** Roy Goodland.
Secretary: Colin Dunford, 27 Manor Gardens, Ilchester, Yeovil, Somerset BA22 8LE (0935 841217).
Manager: Bob Russell   **Ground:** Town Ground, Zembard Lane, Chard (04606 61402).
Directions: 150 yards from the town centre, off Combe Street. 8 miles from Crewkerne BR station.
Seats: None   **Cover:** 200   **Capacity:** 1,500   **Floodlights:** Yes   **Founded:** 1920
Club colours: All maroon   **Change colours:** All sky   **Nickname:** Robins.
Prev. Lges: Somerset Snr 20-24 48-75/ Perry Street 25-48.
Programme: 50p   **Programme Editor:** Secretary.
Midweek matches: Wednesday   **Clubhouse:** Matchdays & most evenings. Snacks served
Captain & P.o.Y. 92-93: Craig Rice   **Top Scorer 92-93:** Richard Hill.
Hons: Som. Snr Lg 49-50 53-54 59-60 67-68 69-70 (Lg Cup 61-62 71-72 76-77); Western Lg Div 1 R-up 83-84 87-88 (Merit Cup 82-83, Comb. Cup(Res) 91-92 (R-up 92-93)); Som. Snr Cup 52-53 66-67; S W Co's Cup 88-89

CLYST ROVERS

President: Mr P W Brown   **Chairman:** Malcolm Hale   **Vice Chairman:** Colin Dadson
Secretary: John Edwards, Lamorna, Pinn Lane, Pinhoe, Exeter EX1 3RF (0392 68633).
Manager: Sammy Kingdom   **Asst Manager:** Mike Follett   **Physio:** Bill Wreford.
Press Officer: Sammy Kingdom   **Commercial Manager:** Mr Bob Hookway (0884 259975).
Ground: Waterslade Park, Clyst Honiton, Devon (0884 259152).
Directions: A30 following signs for Exeter Airport. Coming from Exeter take 1st right after airport turning (ground signposted) up narrow 200yds past Duke of York Pub.
Seats: 130   **Cover:** 300   **Capacity:** 3,000   **Floodlights:** Yes   **Founded:** 1926.
Colours: Blue & white   **Change colours:** Red & black   **Reformed:** 1951.
Midweek Matches: Wednesday   **Previous Grounds:** Fair Oak 1926-44.
Previous Leagues: Exeter & District 26-44 51-66/ Exeter & District Sunday 67-82/ South Western 81-92.
Programme: 32 pages, 30p   **Editor:** Ray Dack (0392 215075)   **Nickname:** Rovers.
Club Shop: Yes - new for 1993-94. Programmes, souvenirs etc.
Sponsors: Vantage Pharmacy, Paignton   **Record Gate:** 768 v Tiverton, Devon St Lukes final 11/5/93.
Record win: 6-0 v Heavitree United, 1993.
Record defeat: 0-12 v Torpoint Athletic, South Western League, October 1990.
Clubhouse: Open one and a half hours before kick off and after game. Excellent food available.
Captain 92-93: Gary Lewis   **Top Scorer 92-93:** Dean Roberts 29   **P.o.Y. 92-93:** Kevin Daniels.
Hons: Devon St Lukes Cup R-up 92-93, Western Lg Cup SF 92-93.

DAWLISH TOWN

President: M Swift   **Chairman:** Bob Webster   **Manager:** Rod Hawker
Secretary: Graham Jones, 133 Kingsdown Cres., Dawlish, Devon EX7 0HB (0626 866004).
Ground: Playing Fields, Exeter Road, Dawlish (0626 863110).
Directions: Approx 1 mile from centre of town, off main Exeter road (A379).
Seats: 200   **Cover:** 200   **Capacity:** 2,000   **Floodlights:** Yes   **Founded:** 1889
Cols: Green & white/white/green & white   **Change colours:** Blue & white/blue/blue & white.
Previous League: Devon & Exeter.   **Previous Ground:** Barley Bank 1875-1900
Record defeat: 0-18 v Clevedon (A), Western League Premier Division 92-93.
Record Gate: 1,500 v Heavitree Utd, Devon Prem. Cup Q-Final
Programme: 34 pages, 30p   **Programme Editor:** Gerry Turner
Midweek home matchday: Tuesday   **Clubhouse:** Open nightly, situated in car park opposite ground.
Hons: Western Lg Cup 80-81 83-84, Devon Premier Cup 69-70 72-73 80-81, Devon Snr Cup 57-58 67-68, Devon St Lukes Cup 82-83, FA Vase Quarter Finals 86-87.

DEVIZES TOWN

Chairman: B Taylor   **Manager:** A Stevens
Secretary: Chris Dodd, 69 Broadleas Park, Devizes, Wilts SN10 5JG (0380 726205).
Ground: Nursteed Road, Devizes. (0380 722817).
Directions: Off Nursteed Road (A342 signposted Andover); leaving town ground on right opposite Eastleigh Rd.
Seats: 370   **Cover:** 400   **Capacity:** 2,500   **Floodlights:** Yes   **Founded:** 1883
Cols: Red & white stripes/black/black   **Change colours:** Green & white/white/white
Previous Ground: London Rd (pre 1946)   **Previous Name:** Southbroom (until early 1900s)
Previous Leagues: Wilts Comb./ Wilts Premier.
Hons: Wilts Snr Cup 07-08 49-50 56-57 57-58 58-59 60-61 61-62 62-63 65-66 67-68 70-71 71-72 73-74 78-79.

GLASTONBURY

President: Mr L R Reed   **Chairman:** Keith Harmon   **Manager:** S White.
Secretary: David McCartney, 3 Pound Close, Glastonbury BA6 9LG (0458 831701).
Ground: Abbey Moor Stadium, Godney Road, Glastonbury, Somerset (0458 831460).
Directions: At bottom of town centre take Northload Street, first right after crossing bridge, ground immediately on right.
No. of seats: Nil   **Covered Accom:** 200   **Capacity:** 1,500   **Floodlights:** Yes
Colours: Old gold/black/old gold   **Change colours:** White/white/orange   **Year Formed:** 1890
Previous Leagues: Bristol & District, Bristol Suburban   **Midweek Matches:** Wednesday
Previous Ground: Abbey Park (Pre-1982).
Hons: Western Lg 48-49 50-51 69-70 (R-up 47-48 51-52, Lg Cup 65-66, Alan Young Cup 67-68 (jt with Minehead) 70-71); Somerset Professional Cup 37-38 48-49; Somerset Snr Cup 35-36; Somerset Charity Cup 32-33; Somerset Jnr Cup 12-13 13-14; Somerset Lg 49-50 50-51

HEAVITREE UNITED

President: Mr E Drew   **Chairman:** Mr B Conoway   **Vice Chairman:** Mr K Carpenter
Secretary: Mr A S Kitson, 13 Tuckfield Close, Wonford, Exeter EX2 5LR (0392 72027).
Manager/Coach: Bill Ring   **Asst Manager:** D Bray   **Physio:** R Channing.
Ground: Wingfield Park, East Wonford Hill, Exeter, Devon (0392 73020).
Directions: Leave M5 at Exeter Granada Services, follow signs for City Centre/ Heavitree for approx. 3 miles and ground is situated on left at top of East Wonford Hill.
Seats: 150   **Cover:** 150   **Capacity:** 500   **Floodlights:** No   **Founded:** 1885.
Colours: All royal (yellow trim)   **Change colours:** White & black stripes   **Nickname:** Heavies.
Programme: 20 pages, 20p   **Editor:** Dave Jeffery (0392 73020)   **Club Shop:** No.
Prev. Ground: Heavitree Park (pre-1950)   **Previous Lges:** Exeter & Dist./ Devon & Exeter.
Club Sponsors: Refuge Assurance   **Record Gate:** 350 v Exeter City, friendly 1989.
Midweek home matchday: Tuesday
Record win: 6-0 v Ilfracombe Town   **Record defeat:** 0-13 v Larkhall Athletic.
Clubhouse: 12am-12pm daily. Wide range of matchday hot food.
Captain 92-93: Steve Channing   **Top Scorer 92-93:** Mark Heaver   **P.o.Y. 92-93:** M Woodman
Club record scorer: John Laskey   **Club record appearances:** Alan Kingdom.
Hons: Exeter & Dist Lg 46-47 51-52 (Snr Div 2 56-57 59-60 60-61 67-68), Devon & Exeter Lg 70-71 76-77, Devon Snr Cup 46-47 60-61 70-71, E Devon Snr Cup 46-47 70-71 76-77, Wheaton Tphy 87-88.

Heavitree United F.C. 1992-93. Back Row (L/R): Andy Langabeer (Sponsor), Rob Palethorpe (Sponsor), Ray Channing (Physio), Marcus Woodman, Simon Harris, Dean Clark, Ian Percival, Paul Manning, Bill Ring (Manager), Denis Gray (Asst Manager). Front: Terry Wheatley, Paul Knight, Darren Clifford, Steve Channing, John Laskey, Martin Green, Andy Phillips, Neal Cane.

ILFRACOMBE TOWN

President: Stan Biddick   **Chairman:** Reg Gibbs.
Secretary: Tony Alcock, 2 Worth Road, Ilfracombe, North Devon EX34 9JA (0271 862686).
Manager: Dave Sheehan   **Asst Manager:** Alan Ray.
Coach: Mark Creek   **Physio:** Paul Jaggers.
Ground: Marlborough Road, Ilfracombe, Devon (0271 865939).
Directions: A361 to Ilfracombe, 1st right in town after lights, follow road to top, ground on left.
Seats: None   **Cover:** 450   **Capacity:** 4,500   **Floodlights:** Yes   **Founded:** 1902
Colours: Blue & white   **Change colours:** T.B.A.   **Nickname:** Bluebirds
Record attendance: 3,000 v Bristol City, Ground opening, 2/10/24
Previous Names: Ilfracombe F.C.02-09/ Ilfracombe Utd 09-14/ Ilfracombe Comrades 14-20.
Previous Grounds: Shaftesbury Field/ Brimlands/ Killacleave (all pre-1924).
Previous Leagues: North Devon 04-14 20-22 60-84/ East Devon Premier 22-31/ Exeter & District 32-39 46-49/ Western 49-59/ South Western League (Reserves) 53-54.
Programme: 12 pages, 30p   **Club Sponsors:** T.B.A.   **Club Shop:** No.
Midweek home matchday: Tuesday   **Reserve team's League:** North Devon.
Record win: 10-0 v Chipping Sodbury, 51-52.
Record defeat: 0-8 v Odd Down (A), Western League Division One, 92-93.
Clubhouse: Every night 7-11pm and weekend lunchtimes. Hot & cold meals on matchdays.
Captain & P.o.Y. 92-93: Mark Creek   **Top Scorer 92-93:** Alec Anning 17.
Club record scorer: Paul Jenkins   **Club record appearances:** Bobby Hancock 363.
Hons: East Devon Premier Lg 25-26 28-29 29-30, North Devon Senior Lg, North Devon Premier Lg 66-67 70-71 81-82 82-83, Western Lg Div 2 R-up 52-53.

Ilfracombe Town. Back (L/R): Tony Reed, Stuart Westcott, Gary Bennett, John Schiller, Kevin Nicholls, Mark Affleck, Alec Anning. Front: Keith Harcombe, Mark Creek, Brett Andrews, Rob Townsend, Richard Schiller. Photo - James Wright.

KEYNSHAM TOWN

President: K Dowling   **Chairman:** A Weaver   **Vive Chairman:** C Smith
Secretary: Adrian Summers, 8 Wells Close, Whitchurch, Bristol BS14 0PD (0275 835761).
Manager: John Ellener   **Physio:** A Weaver
Press Officer: D Brassington   **Commercial Manager:** L Dowling
Ground: Crown Field, Bristol Road, Keynsham (0272 865876).
Directions: A4 from Bristol to Bath, ground on left before entering village opposite Crown Inn. Bus service every 30 mins from Bristol passes ground. 10 mins walk from Keynsham BR station.
Seats: 120   **Cover:** 500   **Capacity:** 2,000   **Floodlights:** Yes   **Founded:** 1895
Colours: Amber   **Change colours:** White   **Nickname:** K's.
Previous Grounds: The Hams 1886-1910; Gaston 1910-25; Park Road 25-30; Charlton Rd 30-39.
Record Gate: 3,000 v Chelsea, floodlight opening 88-89. Competitive: 2,160 v Saltash, Amateur Cup, Oct 1952.
Previous Leagues: Bristol District, Bristol Comb., Bristol Premier, Somerset Snr.
Programme: 32 pages, 25p   **Editor:** Brian Pratt (0275 835219)   **Club Shop:** No.
Club Sponsors: Phone City   **Clubhouse:** Evenings & before & after games. Sunday lunch. Snacks.
Midweek home matchday: Tuesday   **Reserve team's League:** Somerset Senior.
Captain 92-93: Steve Clarke   **Top Scorer & P.O.Y. 92-93:** Roger Coke.
Hons: Somerset Lg Div 1 77-78; Somerset Snr Cup 51-52 57-58; GFA Jnr Cup 25-26, Somerset & Avon (South) Premier Cup 79-80, FA Cup 4th Qualifying Rd.

LARKHALL ATHLETIC

President: A J Rhymes   **Chairman:** A J Grace   **Manager:** Gerald Rich
Secretary: Mervyn Liles, 9 Eastbourne Ave., Claremont Rd., Bath BA1 6EW (0225 319427).
Ground: "Plain Ham", Charlcombe Lane, Larkhall, Bath (0225 334952).
Directions: A4 from Bath, 1 mile from city centre turn left into St Saviours Rd. In Larkhall square fork left, and right at junction, road bears into Charlcombe Lane. Ground on right as lane narrows.
Seats: None   **Cover:** 50   **Capacity:** 1,000   **Floodlights:** No   **Founded:** 1914
Colours: All royal blue   **Change colours:** All red
Previous League: Somerset Snr   **Midweek Matches:** Tuesday
Hons: Som. Snr Cup 75-76, Som. Snr Lg, Western Lg Div 1 88-89 (Div 1 Merit Cup(4) 83-86 87-88(jt with Yeovil Res).

Larkhall Athletic. Back (L/R): Tom Saunders, Stewart Bradley, Leigh Portch, Geoff Howell, Chris Ansty, Ian Laslett, Paul Rankin. Front: Richard Wych, Richard Parker, Bruce Fanning, Paul Miles, Steve Brown. Photo - James Wright.

OTTERY ST MARY

President: H F Pinney   **Chairman:** D Priest   **Manager:** T.B.A.
Secretary: Brian Barnden, 37 Eastlands, Hemyock, Cullompton, Devon EX15 3QP (0823 680981).
Ground: Washbrook Meadows, Butts Road, Ottery St Mary, Devon (0404 813539).
Directions: From main town square, turn left following road around church, 2nd right into Butts Rd. Or, B3177 to Ottery from A30 Honiton by-pass - ground on left past Otter workshops.
No. of seats: 120   **Covered Accom:** 120   **Capacity:** 2,000
Floodlights: Yes   **Year Formed:** 1911   **Nickname:** The Otters
Colours: Yellow (blue trim)/royal/royal   **Change colours:** All white.
Previous Leagues: Devon & Exeter Premier, South Western 74-76.
Record Gate: 2,500 v Nottingham Forest, 1985
Programme: 36 pages, 20p.   **Programme Editor:** Ray Dack
Clubhouse details: On ground.
Hons: E Devon Snr Cup, Devon & Exeter Lg, Western Lg Div 1 89-90
Midweek Matches: Wednesday

PEWSEY VALE

President: **Chairman:** M Britten   **Manager:** K Franklin.
Secretary: Mrs Barbara Flippance, 17 Slater Rd, Pewsey SN9 5EE (0672 63665).
Ground: Recreation Ground, Ball Rd, Pewsey (0672 62990).
Directions: On entering Pewsey from A345, at the Market Place proceed to end of High Street and turn right into Ball Rd, entrance to ground on right opposite pub. BR to Pewsey station.
Seats: **Cover:** Yes   **Capacity:**   **Floodlights:** No   **Year Formed:**
Colours: White/blue/white   **Change colours:** Red/black/red.
Previous League: Wiltshire County (pre-1993).
Previous Name: Pewsey Y.M. (until late 1940s).
Midweek home matchday: Wednesday   **Hons:** Wiltshire County League 92-93.

RADSTOCK TOWN

President: Mr D Seymour   **Chairman:** Mr R A Rendall   **Vice Chairman:** Mr D Gregory
Secretary: Mr Ron Rendall, 32 Huish Court, Writhlington, Radstock, Avon BA3 3LR (0761 435573).
Manager: Mike Garland   **Asst Manager:** Nigel Bryant.
Ground: Southfield, Frome Hill, Radstock (0761 435004).
Directions: From Radstock centre take A362 for Frome, up hill and turn right before Fromeway Inn and right again into ground car park. Rail to Bath BR station, then bus.
Seats: 150   **Cover:** 150   **Capacity:** 2,000   **Floodlights:** Yes   **Year Formed:** 1895
Cols: Red & black quarters/black/red   **Change colours:** Blue & white halves/blue/blue
Midweek Matches: Wednesday   **Record Gate:** 2,000 v Yeovil, FA Cup, 1937
Previous Grounds: None   **Previous Leagues:** Somerset Senior/ Wilts County.
Programme: 16 pages, 20p   **Programme Editor:** James Mitchard
Club Shop: Starting soon. Contact secretary.
Clubhouse details: Two bars, skittle alley and darts. Open Fri-Sat 7-11pm (2-11pm Sat during season), Sun noon-3 & 7-10.30pm. Matchday tea hut sells hot & cold snacks & drinks.
Nickname: Rads   **Reserve team's League:** None.
Captain 92-93: D Mullings   **P.O.Y. 92-93:** C Curtis (Players' choice: D Mullings).
Hons: Somerset Snr Lg 27-28 28-29 76-77 78-79 (Div 1 72-73), Somerset Snr Cup(13 - a record) 1895-96 1905-06 27-28 29-30 31-32 36-37 38-39 59-60 63-64 65-66 73-74 82-83 84-85), Western Lg Div 1 R-up 85-86.

WARMINSTER TOWN

President: Tony Coward   **Chairman:** Bob Peaty   **Vice Chairman:** Colin Ball.
Secretary: Dave Carpenter, Cley View, 46 Upper Marsh Rd, Warminster, Wilts (0985 212198).
Manager: Peter Russell.
Ground: Weymouth Street, Warminster, Wilts BA12 0985 217828).
Directions: Take A350 for Weymouth from lights at centre of town - ground on left at brow of hill.
Seats: 80   **Cover:** 150   **Capacity:** 2,000   **Floodlights:** No   **Founded:** 1878
Cols: Red & black hoops/black/black   **Change:** All sky   **Nickname:** Red & blacks
Previous Grounds: None   **Previous League:** Wiltshire
Record Gate: 1,500 for Ladies International, England v Wales, mid-1970s.
Programme: 24 pages, 30p   **Editor:** Chris Finch (0985 217326)   **Club Shop:** No.
Sponsors: Lyons Seafoods   **Clubhouse:** Open nightly (skittles) + matchdays.
Midweek home matchday: Wednesday   **Reserve team's League:** Wiltshire.
Captain & P.O.Y. 92-93: Paul Newman   **Top Scorer 92-93:** Gary Lewis, 34 League & Cup.
Hons: Wilts Snr Cup 1900-01 02-03 10-11 (R-up 09-10 26-27 32-33 53-54); Wilts Prem. Lg 56-57; Wilts Jnr Cup R-up 21-22 27-28 55-56 58-59; Central Wilts Lg 08-09

WELLINGTON

President: Alan Shire   **Chairman:** Selwyn Aspin
Manager: Marino Griffiths
Secretary: Tony Brown, 6 Courtland Rd, Wellington, Somerset TA21 8ND (0823 662920).
Ground: Wellington Playing Field, North Street, Wellington, Somerset (0823 664810).
Directions: At town centre traffic lights turn into North St., then first left by Fire Station into the public car park that adjoins the ground.
Seats: None   **Cover:** 200   **Capacity:** 3,000   **Floodlights:** Yes   **Founded:** 1892
Colours: Coral (purple & white trim)/purple/purple
Change colours: Blue & claret stripes/blue/blue
Previous Leagues: Taunton Saturday, Somerset Senior   **Midweek Matches:** Tuesday
Hons: Somerset Snr Lg Div 1 R-up, Rowbarton & Seward Cup.

WELTON ROVERS

Chairman: Roy James
Secretary: Geoff Baker, 6 Longfellow Road, Westfield, Radstock, Bath (0761 413742).
Manager: Alan O'Leary   **Asst Manager:** John Goss.
Physio: Bob Stokes   **Press Officer:** John Churchill.
Ground: West Clewes, North Road, Midsomer Norton, Somerset (0761 412097).
Directions: A367 Bath to Radstock – right at lights at foot of hill onto A362, ground on right.
Seats: 300   **Cover:** 300   **Capacity:** 2,400   **Floodlights:** Yes   **Year Formed:** 1887
Colours: Green & white/white/white   **Change colours:** Royal blue.   **Nickname:** Rovers.
Previous Grounds: None   **Previous Leagues:** None   **Club Shop:** No.
Record Gate: 2,000 v Bromley, FA Amateur Cup 1963
Programme: 12 pages, 25p   **Programme Editor:** S Paget
Club Sponsors: J J Saunders
Midweek home matchday: Monday   **Reserve team's League:** Somerset Senior.
Clubhouse: 7.30-11pm daily, Sat matchdays 1.30-2.45pm, Sun noon-2pm.
Captain 92-93: Chris Dzioba   **Top Scorer & P.o.Y. 92-93:** Trevor O'Neill 20 goals.
Club record scorer: Ian Henderson, 51
Hons: Western Lg 11-12 64-65 65-66 66-67 73-74 (Div 1 59-60 87-88; Amateur Cup 56-57 57-58 58-59 59-60; Alan Young Cup 65-66 66-67 67-68(joint)); Somerset Snr Cup 06-07 11-12 12-13 13-14 19-20 24-25 25-26 60-61 61-62 62-63, Somerset I'mediate Cup 77-78, Somerset Jnr Cup 06-07(joint) 24-25 30-31, WBC Clares City of Wells Cup 78-79.

YEOVIL & DISTRICT LEAGUE

PREM. DIV.	P	W	D	L	F	A	PTS
Henstridge	22	18	1	3	79	30	37
Heron	22	13	4	5	68	32	30
Somerton	22	12	6	4	55	38	*28
Wincanton Town	22	12	3	7	56	40	27
Bishop's Caundle	22	9	6	7	57	40	24
Martock United	22	8	8	6	43	46	24
Milborne Port	22	7	7	8	49	45	21
Ilchester	22	7	5	10	40	45	19
Langport Town	22	7	3	11	36	48	17
Bradford Abbas	22	6	4	12	35	70	16
St Crispin	22	2	6	14	25	61	10
Baltonsborough	22	3	3	16	30	78	9

* - 4pts deducted

DIV. ONE	P	W	D	L	F	A	PTS
Stoke	22	17	2	3	76	27	36
Long Sutton Res.	22	13	5	4	56	32	31
Westland Spts Res.	22	13	3	6	74	32	29
Ash Rovers	22	10	9	3	52	37	29
Tintinhull	22	13	2	7	65	44	28
Masons Arms	22	7	8	7	51	53	22
Sherborne T. Res.	22	7	7	8	38	49	21
Milborne Port Res.	22	5	6	11	39	46	16
Chilthorne	22	4	7	11	41	51	15
Westland Association	22	5	4	12	43	71	14
Henstridge Res.	22	4	6	12	36	70	14
Templecombe	22	3	3	16	27	85	9

DIV. TWO	P	W	D	L	F	A	PTS
Bruton Town	22	19	1	2	87	20	39
Trinity	22	18	2	2	90	22	38
Normalair	22	13	2	7	59	53	28
Keindon Mandeville	22	12	3	7	62	47	27
Castle Cary Res.	22	11	4	7	56	30	26
Corinthians	22	11	2	9	52	40	24
Somerton Res.	22	8	1	13	45	62	17
Wincanton T. Res.	22	7	3	12	42	77	17
St Crispin Res.	22	5	4	13	28	55	14
Ilchester Res.	22	5	3	14	29	58	13
Martock Utd Res.	22	5	3	14	27	67	13
Baltonsborough Res.	22	3	2	17	28	74	8

DIV. THREE	P	W	D	L	F	A	PTS
A.F.C. Camel	22	16	2	4	53	30	34
Odcombe	22	14	4	4	65	51	32
Street Res.	22	13	3	6	61	32	29
Ansford Rovers	22	13	4	5	72	36	*28
Long Sutton Colts	22	12	4	6	58	42	28
Yetminster	22	8	5	9	56	57	21
Barwick & Stoford	22	7	6	9	51	48	20
Tintinhull Res.	22	8	4	10	61	60	20
Langport T. Res.	22	6	5	11	52	68	17
Stoke Res.	22	7	2	13	50	54	16
Spartans	22	5	5	12	31	49	15
Keinton M. Res.	22	1	1	20	25	108	3

* 2pts deducted

DIV. FOUR	P	W	D	L	F	A	PTS
Charlton Athletic	18	13	3	3	65	25	29
Milborne Port 'A'	18	13	1	4	60	24	27
Kingsbury	18	13	0	5	52	27	26
Pen Mill	18	8	3	7	33	35	19
Yeovil Saints	18	6	5	7	35	34	17
Bradford Res.	18	6	4	8	39	31	16
Normalair Res.	18	5	4	9	43	66	14
Templecombe Res.	18	4	3	11	22	52	11
Yetminster Res.	18	4	3	11	20	50	11
Charlton United	18	4	2	12	18	52	10

DIV. FIVE	P	W	D	L	F	A	PTS
Bishop's Caun. Res.	20	17	3	0	93	24	37
Chilthorne Res.	20	11	3	6	54	35	25
Yeovil Rangers	20	11	2	7	58	47	24
Pen Mill Res.	20	9	4	7	62	48	22
Wessex	20	10	1	9	45	54	21
Corinthians Res.	20	8	4	8	53	47	20
Greyhound	20	8	4	8	49	46	20
Montacute	20	7	4	9	56	62	18
Barn Lane Athletic	20	8	0	12	34	74	16
Barwick Res.	20	5	2	13	55	68	12
Odcombe Res.	20	1	3	16	22	76	5

COLBORNE TROPHIES
SOMERSET SENIOR LEAGUE

Hon. Secretary: C R Rose,
Sutley House, Pilton, Shepton Mallet BA4 4BL.

TITLE GOES TO LONG SUTTON

From its formation in 1890 until 1949 the League consisted of just one division, and in 1946 had a mere eight clubs of which only four remain in membership; the mid-Somerset trio of Glastonbury, Street and Wells City, along with Odd Down. Somerton Amateurs were champions that year. Now their are sixty clubs (72 teams) in four divisions - few Senior Leagues have expanded at such a rate.

Member clubs have always been a 'loyal bunch' as I can only recall the dismissal of about two clubs since the last war. Just recently they extended this loyalty to the two unfortunates seeking re-election - Nailsea Town and their neighbours Nailsea United Reserves - with a confortable majority.

The League's popularity still exists as the two Nailsea clubs had to fight off the opposition of thirteen candidates at the consitution meeting. But, if the expansion of the 'Pyramid' gets the go-ahead, clubs will only enter the League on merit providing they have the necessary facilities.

But that's in the future - what about the season just completed?

There have been some remarkable feats during the season with promotion and relegation decided, in some cases, only in the final week. The League was sponsored for the first time, and probably it was a good idea not to have to select a 'Team of the Year'. But, combined with their Cup exploits, two immediately spring to mind - Long Sutton and Saltford.

Long Sutton have a remarkable record since being steered into the League in 1982 by their long-serving secretary Bob Sams. It took them only three years to gain Premier Division status amassing 267 goals en route. They finished fourth in their first year, were runners-up in their second, and have never dropped below eigth. They have never lacked the ability to score goals - in their very first season they scored 106 in the League, and in 1992-93 they again scored 106 on their way to becoming League Champions for the first time. However, in the League Cup final (Premier and First Division) they lost on penalties to Shirehampton after extra-time, and in the County Senior Cup they were beaten, ironcally, by Saltford 0-1 in the Semi-Final.

Saltford enjoyed undoubtedly their most successful season since joining the senior ranks in 1975. It could hardly have been a better time for Chris Wheeler to become secretary as the club won Division Two and reached two cup finals, winning one. They reached the County Senior Cup final for the first time, losing to Great Mills League Brislington only 0-1, but had better fortune in the League Cup defeating Farleigh Sports 4-2, and this at a time when the 'Sports' had had a late burst scoring 37 goals in their final nine games.

The Bristol Channel coastline, and in particular Clevedon, has been a successful area. Clevedon Town Reserves won the First Division as their senior side won promotion to the Beazer Homes League, all celebrated on their new stadium named after the Hand brothers who did so much for the club over many years. Although finishing second, Portishead Reserves cannot go up because their first team are already in the Premier - Westlands of Weston take their place along with Burnham United. Wells City, who experienced relegation in 1992, finished fifth drawing no fewer than fourteen matches. Watchet Town, after promotion the previous year, go down, as do Cheddar and Mendip Wells.

The latest two clubs to join the League went if different directions. Blackbrook, after an average start in new surroundings, fought back well after a prolonged inactive spell to finish in the top half of Division Two, but Nailsea Town, who did so well in their first year, gradually slipped into the Division Three re-election area.

Neighbours Temple Cloud and Clutton are relegated to Division Three where there was an exciting battle for promotion. Once again, Glastonbury Reserves missed out by four points after heading the division for some three months, and in the end the successful clubs were Keynsham Cricketers, Churchill Club and Paulton Rovers Reserves.

As in all sports, there has to be 'winners' and 'losers' and a little bit of luck. Perhaps those who missed out on the luck will get their turn in season 1993-94.

L J C Heal, League Life-Member

FINAL LEAGUE TABLES 1992-93

PREM. DIV.	P	W	D	L	F	A	PTS
Long Sutton	34	24	8	2	106	41	80
Clevedon United	34	23	5	6	85	38	74
Bridgwater T. '84	34	15	9	10	67	53	54
Shepton Mallet T.	34	16	6	12	72	61	54
Portishead	34	15	7	12	60	53	52
Fry Club	34	14	9	11	64	58	51
Shirehampton	34	13	10	11	60	47	49
Brislington Res.	34	14	6	14	54	54	48
Mangotsfield Res.	34	15	4	15	60	61	*47
Imperial United	34	12	10	12	55	44	46
Weston-s-Mare Res.	34	14	4	16	67	61	46
Avon & Som. Pol.	34	11	10	13	58	66	43
Bristol M.F. Res.	34	10	9	15	59	59	39
Castle Cary	34	10	9	15	65	71	39
Peasedown Athletic	34	11	5	18	62	78	38
Longwell Gr. Abbot.	34	10	6	18	51	99	36
Weston St Johns	34	10	3	21	51	86	33
Frome Town Res.	34	7	4	23	44	110	25

* - points deducted

DIV. ONE	P	W	D	L	F	A	PTS
Clevedon T. Res.	34	24	7	3	85	30	*78
Portishead Res.	34	24	5	5	86	35	77
Burnham United	34	19	7	8	78	49	64
Westland United	34	18	6	10	77	56	60
Wells City	34	13	14	7	70	45	53
Keynsham T. Res.	34	15	6	12	55	62	51
Bishop Sutton Res.	34	15	6	13	59	47	*50
Stockwood Green	34	14	7	13	66	66	49
Hengrove Athletic	34	14	5	14	61	69	47
Larkhall Ath. Res.	34	12	7	15	64	65	43
Dundry Athletic	34	12	8	14	53	64	*43
Congresbury	34	11	6	17	51	64	39
Nailsea United	34	10	8	16	51	62	38
Winscombe	34	8	13	13	50	60	*35
Ilminster Town	34	10	5	19	38	66	35
Cheddar	34	10	3	21	51	87	33
Watchet Town	34	7	7	20	38	70	28
Mendip Wells	34	6	6	22	30	66	24

* - points deducted

DIV. TWO	P	W	D	L	F	A	PTS
Saltford	34	22	2	10	64	35	68
Robinsons	34	18	11	5	68	32	65
Bridgwater T. Res.	34	18	6	10	70	58	60
Imperial Bristol	34	17	8	9	62	37	59
Odd Down Res.	34	16	10	8	67	39	58
St George E.in G.	34	17	6	11	72	56	57
Blackbrook	34	15	8	11	69	62	53
Long Ashton	34	14	9	11	72	59	51
Timsbury Athletic	34	14	9	11	44	40	51
Backwell Utd Res.	34	13	9	12	56	41	48
Wrington-Redhill	34	11	10	13	44	50	43
Welton Rovers Res.	34	10	11	13	52	67	41
Tunley Athletic	34	11	5	18	48	67	38
Weston St J. Res.	34	11	5	18	38	76	38
Clevedon Utd Res.	34	9	10	15	50	63	37
Clutton	34	6	10	18	45	72	28
Fry Club Res.	34	6	8	20	41	71	*25
Temple Cloud	34	6	7	21	42	79	25

* - points deducted

DIV. THREE	P	W	D	L	F	A	PTS
Keynsham C.C.	34	27	3	4	108	26	*83
Churchill Club '70	34	23	6	5	115	46	75
Paulton Rvrs Res.	34	23	5	6	85	37	74
Glastonbury Res.	34	22	4	8	72	41	70
Farleigh Sports	34	18	1	15	92	64	54
Clandown	34	16	6	12	70	59	54
Banwell	34	15	9	10	64	56	54
Westland U. Res.	34	14	10	10	70	52	52
Worle	34	14	5	15	42	53	47
Imperial Bris. Res.	34	11	7	16	54	65	*39
Yatton Athletic	34	10	7	17	49	60	37
Wells City Res.	34	11	3	20	45	63	36
Shepton Mal. Res.	34	11	3	20	48	107	36
Robinsons Res.	34	8	9	17	41	74	33
Hengrove Ath. Res.	34	9	5	20	49	79	32
Street	34	8	7	19	51	78	31
Nailsea Town	34	8	7	19	49	85	*30
Nailsea Utd Res.	34	8	3	23	40	101	27

* - points deducted

SOMERSET SENIOR LEAGUE DIVISION ONE RESULT CHART 1992-93

HOME TEAM	1	2	3	4	5	6	7	8	9	10	11	12	13	14	15	16	17	18
Burnham United	*	0-2	1-0	0-1	5-1	0-0	5-4	3-1	2-0	6-1	3-1	1-1	2-4	2-1	2-1	1-1	0-3	1-1
Bishop Sutton Reserves	1-3	*	1-0	2-5	3-4	0-1	1-1	2-1	1-3	0-0	1-1	5-0	1-2	1-2	4-0	2-2	1-0	2-1
Cheddar	1-4	0-1	*	0-1	4-3	1-5	3-1	3-2	2-3	2-2	5-0	0-3	1-2	3-0	1-3	2-9	1-3	2-2
Clevedon Town Reserves	1-1	4-0	7-0	*	6-1	3-2	5-2	2-0	0-2	2-1	2-1	4-1	1-1	3-0	6-1	3-1	2-1	2-0
Congresbury	1-4	0-1	5-1	0-2	*	1-2	0-0	2-1	0-0	2-1	1-0	1-1	2-4	0-0	3-1	1-2	1-2	1-1
Dundry Athletic	2-1	0-1	1-1	0-3	2-5	*	6-3	2-2	2-1	1-2	0-1	1-0	1-3	6-3	1-3	0-1	4-2	1-1
Hengrove Athletic	1-2	2-1	4-1	0-2	3-1	1-2	*	2-1	2-2	4-5	1-3	3-4	2-3	2-2	0-0	2-1	1-1	
Ilminster Town	2-0	1-7	0-1	1-1	1-0	1-2	1-3	*	0-1	3-0	1-0	0-2	0-2	2-1	3-0	1-4	0-0	1-0
Keynsham Town Reserves	1-2	2-1	1-4	2-2	1-3	1-1	3-0	6-3	*	2-2	2-1	2-1	1-2	1-5	3-0	3-2	3-7	2-0
Larkhall Athletic Reserves	1-5	0-1	1-0	1-2	5-1	1-3	1-2	4-2	2-3	*	5-0	1-1	2-0	2-1	4-0	1-2	1-2	2-2
Mendip AFC Wells	0-5	2-0	2-1	0-1	1-2	1-1	0-1	1-2	1-3	1-3	*	0-2	4-1	1-3	0-0	0-0	0-0	2-1
Nailsea United	2-3	0-2	3-1	0-0	3-0	0-1	0-1	1-2	3-0	0-1	2-1	*	2-1	4-1	5-2	0-4	0-3	2-2
Portishead Reserves	3-1	3-1	4-2	2-0	2-0	7-0	3-1	4-1	4-0	1-1	4-0	4-0	*	5-2	1-1	3-0	4-2	2-0
Stockwood Green	1-2	2-1	3-0	2-2	0-4	4-2	3-1	0-0	1-2	4-1	2-0	2-2	1-0	*	2-0	2-7	6-2	1-1
Watchet Town	4-0	0-5	2-3	1-1	1-0	0-0	1-2	4-0	0-2	2-3	2-1	1-2	0-2	2-2	*	1-3	1-2	0-3
Wells City	1-1	3-3	0-1	0-2	2-2	2-0	3-0	0-0	4-0	1-1	0-0	3-3	2-1	1-1	1-1	*	3-4	4-1
Westland United	3-3	0-2	6-1	2-1	1-3	1-1	1-3	1-2	2-0	3-0	6-2	6-3	1-1	3-2	1-0	1-1	*	1-3
Winscombe	1-7	2-2	2-3	2-6	1-0	2-0	1-2	5-0	0-0	3-2	3-2	2-2	0-0	1-2	1-0	1-1	1-3	*

SOMERSET SENIOR LEAGUE DIVISION TWO RESULT CHART 1992-93

HOME TEAM	1	2	3	4	5	6	7	8	9	10	11	12	13	14	15	16	17	18
Backwell United Reserves	*	4-0	6-1	2-2	1-1	1-0	0-2	1-1	1-2	2-2	3-0	1-1	2-0	5-0	0-1	1-2	1-1	2-3
Bridgwater Reserves	2-1	*	1-3	2-0	5-3	2-1	0-0	2-5	4-0	3-2	0-2	2-0	2-1	2-2	2-1	4-0	4-1	5-1
Blackbrook	1-2	3-2	*	7-4	5-3	3-1	2-3	1-1	1-1	0-0	2-1	4-3	4-0	2-1	3-3	1-1	5-0	5-0
Clevedon United Reserves	1-0	4-2	1-1	*	1-1	3-1	1-2	0-6	1-2	0-0	2-0	2-2	2-3	0-0	2-0	2-0	3-0	0-0
Clutton	0-1	3-2	1-4	2-1	*	2-0	1-4	2-3	0-3	0-2	0-5	0-2	1-2	1-1	3-1	1-4	2-3	4-0
Fry's Reserves	0-5	0-1	4-1	4-3	1-5	*	3-0	0-2	0-1	0-1	0-4	1-1	3-0	0-1	1-1	2-2	1-1	5-1
Imperial Bristol	3-1	1-0	3-1	3-1	0-0	2-1	*	2-3	2-2	0-2	1-1	0-1	2-1	0-1	4-1	4-1	5-2	0-1
Long Ashton	2-2	1-2	4-1	2-3	3-3	4-1	0-3	*	1-1	1-1	2-3	2-2	1-0	2-1	0-0	2-3	2-0	
Odd Down Reserves	2-0	5-1	4-0	1-1	1-1	0-0	2-1	3-0	*	1-1	0-3	4-1	1-1	2-3	2-1	1-1	1-1	1-2
Robinsons	0-1	1-4	3-0	2-2	3-1	1-1	3-1	2-2	0-0	*	0-1	2-1	4-2	1-0	3-1	5-1	6-0	5-0
Saltford	2-1	1-3	3-1	2-1	3-0	1-0	1-0	0-2	0-3	1-4	*	6-1	2-1	3-1	1-0	0-1	5-0	
St.George	3-0	5-2	0-2	7-2	4-0	2-1	1-1	2-4	3-1	1-2	1-2	*	5-1	0-0	2-1	2-1	5-4	1-2
Temple Cloud	2-3	1-2	0-0	1-2	1-1	2-2	1-3	3-5	0-3	1-3	0-1	1-3	*	2-2	1-5	1-5	2-0	3-2
Timsbury Athletic	3-0	0-1	4-1	2-1	1-1	2-0	1-3	1-0	2-5	3-2	1-0	0-2	1-1	*	1-0	0-1	1-1	1-0
Tunley Athletic	1-0	1-1	1-1	2-2	1-1	0-3	7-5	0-6	0-3	1-4	1-2	2-0	0-3		*	1-0	3-1	0-1
Wrington/Redhill	1-1	1-1	0-1	1-0	3-1	2-2	2-2	0-2	2-0	0-0	0-1	0-2	1-0	2-3		*	2-3	1-1
Welton Rovers Reserves	1-2	2-2	0-2	2-0	1-1	8-2	0-0	3-2	2-1	0-0	0-0	1-3	4-1	2-2	1-3	1-2	*	1-0
Weston St.Johns Reserves	1-4	2-2	1-0	1-0	0-0	5-1	0-5	2-0	2-5	1-2	0-4	3-2	0-2	0-3	1-2	4-2	1-1	*

SOMERSET SENIOR LEAGUE DIVISION THREE RESULT CHART 1992-93

HOME TEAM	1	2	3	4	5	6	7	8	9	10	11	12	13	14	15	16	17	18
Banwell	*	4-2	1-1	2-1	2-0	2-0	2-3	0-4	3-1	4-0	1-3	2-2	0-0	8-0	0-2	1-1	1-0	1-1
Clandown	4-0	*	3-3	3-0	2-3	4-2	2-0	2-1	5-0	4-0	1-4	2-0	2-0	3-1	4-2	1-0	1-1	0-1
Churchill	2-2	4-1	*	5-2	3-1	4-1	2-0	2-1	7-0	2-0	4-6	2-3	8-1	9-0	4-1	1-1	4-1	4-2
Farleigh Sports	2-2	1-0	1-2	*	1-4	4-2	6-1	0-3	2-3	6-0	2-4	9-0	5-2	2-4	3-0	5-1	3-1	2-1
Glastonbury Reserves	3-0	4-0	0-0	3-7	*	5-1	3-2	0-0	2-0	2-2	0-1	3-0	4-2	4-1	0-1	1-0	2-0	1-0
Hengrove Athletic Reserves	1-4	1-4	0-3	1-3	2-3	*	2-2	1-2	2-0	5-1	3-3	1-0	1-4	3-1	2-5	0-2	2-1	3-0
Imperial Reserves	0-3	1-2	2-2	0-2	1-4	0-1	*	0-2	4-2	2-0	1-3	6-1	2-2	2-0	0-2	1-4	1-2	2-1
Keynsham CR.	6-0	3-2	2-0	4-0	2-1	4-1	5-1	*	2-2	6-0	3-1	3-1	6-0	4-0	3-0	1-1	4-0	7-2
Nailsea Town	0-2	2-2	1-4	4-4	0-1	4-1	0-1	3-2	*	2-1	2-2	1-1	3-1	3-5	0-0	2-2	1-5	1-2
Nailsea United Reserves	0-0	2-0	0-6	1-3	2-1	5-0	2-4	0-6	4-0	*	0-1	3-1	1-2	1-2	0-1	1-1	110-1	2-2
Paulton Rovers Reserves	1-2	3-0	3-0	2-1	3-2	0-0	4-0	0-1	4-0	4-0	*	1-0	5-0	5-0	3-0	7-2	2-1	1-1
Robinsons Reserves	2-3	4-2	0-2	1-1	1-1	1-1	2-0	0-5	2-1	4-5	1-1	*	1-2	1-3	2-0	0-5	4-0	1-0
Street	0-2	1-1	1-2	3-0	1-2	0-3	1-5	0-2	4-1	4-1	1-3	1-1	*	5-1	1-1	0-1	1-2	3-0
Shepton Mallet Reserves	3-2	3-2	0-7	2-4	1-3	2-1	1-7	0-4	2-5	4-0	2-3	3-3	1-1	*	1-3	0-6	3-1	1-3
Worle	2-3	3-1	2-4	2-1	0-1	0-2	0-1	4-2	3-0	0-2	0-2	1-0	2-1	1-1	*	1-1	1-0	3-2
Westland United Reserves	4-0	0-5	4-2	0-3	0-	1-1	0-0	1-2	0-3	7-2	2-0	0-0	3-2	1-0	2-1	*	1-2	1-0
Wells City Reserves	3-0	1-1	0-4	0-6	3-4	2-0	1-1	2-4	0-1	1-2	3-1	0-1	3-1	4-1	0-1	1-1	*	0-1
Yatton Athletic	2-1	0-1	3-5	1-0	0-2	3-2	1-1	0-2	2-1	3-1	2-3	4-0	2-2	0-1	4-0	2-2	1-3	*

PREMIER DIVISION CLUBS 1993-94

AVON & SOMERSET CONSTABULARY
Ground: Police Sports Ground, Napier Mills Rd, Kingsweston, Bristol.   **Secretary:** A Taylor (0272 864703)
Directions: M5 jct 18, B4054 towards Shirehampton, left at crossroads up Kingsweston Lane, ground on right opposite Kingsweston House School. Half mile from Shirehampton (BR).

BRIDGWATER TOWN '84
Ground: Fairfax Park, Fairfax Road, Bridgwater.   **Secretary:** Miss Wright (0278 421189)
Directions: M5 jct 23, follow signs to Glastonbury (A39), turn right for Bridgwater (A39), turn left for Bridgwater College (Parkway), ground half mile on right; enter through college. One mile from Bridgwater (BR).

BRISLINGTON RESERVES (see page 770)

BRISTOL MANOR FARM RESERVES (see page 764)

BURNHAM UNITED
Ground: Burnham Road Playing Field, Casis Close, Burnham-on-Sea.   **Secretary:** S Brooks (0278 785928)
Directions: M5 jct 22, ground close to Burnham town centre. Highbridge (BR), Bus 21 from Taunton.

CASTLE CARY
Ground: Donald Pither Memorial Field, Ansford Rd, Castle Cary.   **Secretary:** R Blacker (0749 342846)
Directions: In village, one mile from Castle Cary station (main line from London Paddington).

CLEVEDON TOWN RESERVES (see page 510)

CLEVEDON UNITED
Ground: Coleridge Vale P.F., Coleridge Vale Road, Clevedon.   **Secretary:** M Henley (0272 879096)
Directions: M5 jct 20, follow sea front signs, ground in middle of housing estate on left hand side.

FRY CLUB
Ground: Cadbury Schweppes, Somerdale, Keynsham, Bristol (0272 861235)   **Sec:** M Harris (0272 867938)
Directions: On A4175, outside Keynsham BR station in Somerdale factory complex.

IMPERIAL UNITED
Ground: Imperial Athletic Club, West Town Lane, Knowle, Bristol.   **Secretary:** D Brown (0272 716977)
Directions: A37 south of Bristol, left into West Town Lane (signed Stockwood and Brislington), ground opposite next mini r'bout. Buses 54 and 57 from Bristol Temple Meads (BR).

LONG SUTTON
Ground: Recreation Ground, Long Sutton.   **Secretary:** R Sams (0458 241395)
Directions: Ground entrance on south side of A372 about three miles east of Langport. Bus 54, Taunton-Yeovil.

MANGOTSFIELD UNITED RESERVES (see page 766)

PEASEDOWN ATHLETIC
Ground: Miners Welfare, Church Road.   **Secretary:** R Clark (0761 34006)
Directions: On A367 Bath-Radstock road just south of Peasedown St John, close to Red Post Inn.

PORTISHEAD
Ground: Bristol Road Playing Fields, Portishead.   **Secretary:** N Trenchard (0272 849976)
Directions: M5 jct 19, A369 towards Portishead, left at r'bout, ground on left after right hand bend.

SHEPTON MALLET TOWN
Ground: Playing Fields, West Shepton, Old Wells Rd, Shepton Mallet (07490 344609).
Secretary: R Willmott (0749 342992)
Directions: Into town centre and follow signs for Eye Hospital. Ground behind.

SHIREHAMPTON
Ground: Recreation Ground, Penpole Lane, Shirehampton, Bristol.   **Secretary:** D Campbell (0272 827720)
Directions: M5 jct 18, B4054 into Lower High Street, left into Penpole Lane. Ground half mile on left. Half mile from Shirehampton (BR).

WESTLAND UNITED
Ground: Winterstoke Road, Weston-super-Mare.   **Secretary:** J Astridge (0934 515314)
Directions: As Weston-super-Mare FC (see page 526) then continue up Winterstoke Road to Westlands Helicopter complex; ground on right.

WESTON-SUPER-MARE RESERVES (see page 526)

DIVISION ONE CLUBS 1993-94

BISHOP SUTTON RESERVES (see page 769)

BRIDGWATER TOWN '84 RESERVES (see above)

CONGRESBURY
Ground: Broadstone Playing Fields, Stonewell Lane, Congresbury (0934 832150)
Secretary: C Sherwin (0934 876083)
Directions: A38 south from Bristol, take B3133 for Congresbury at Lower Langford. Entering Congresbury turn left immediately before Post Office, bear right, ground at end of narrow lane.

DUNDRY ATHLETIC
Ground: Crabtree Lane, Dundry.   **Secretary:** S Saunders (0272 830085)
Directions: A38 south from Bristol (signed Airport), left for Dundry half mile after motel, ground unmissable in village.

FROME TOWN RESERVES (see page 766)

HENGROVE ATHLETIC
Ground: Norton Lane, Whitchurch, Bristol (0272 832894).   **Secretary:** G Close (0272 835700)
Directions: A37 south from Bristol, through Whitchurch, right into Norton Lane just after humped-back bridge, ground half mile on left.

ILMINSTER TOWN

Ground: Recreation Ground, Ilminster.　　　　　**Secretary:** C Williams (0460 54577)
Directions: In town centre turn into Ditton Street, turn right at petrol station, ground on left.

KEYNSHAM TOWN RESERVES (see page 772)

LARKHALL ATHLETIC RESERVES (see page 772)

LONGWELL GREEN ABBOTONIANS

Ground: Community Association, Shellards Rd, Longwell Green.　　**Secretary:** R Threader (0272 670306)
Directions: From Bristol; A4175 Keynsham to Willsbridge, left up steep hill (Willsbridge Hill), across r'bout, right fork into Shellards Road, ground on right behind Community Centre.

NAILSEA UNITED

Ground: St Marys Grove, Old Church, Nailsea (0275 856892)　　**Secretary:** J Hobbs (0275 855432)
Directions: M5 jct 20, B3130 through Tickenham to Nailsea High Street. Bear right, ground on south side of town clearly signposted Grove Sports Centre. One mile from Nailsea & Backwell (BR).

PORTISHEAD RESERVES (see previous page)

ROBINSONS

Ground: D.R.G. Athletic Club, St Johns Lane, Bedminster, Bristol.　　**Secretary:** D Palmer (0272 649251)
Directions: From Bristol Temple Meads follow Wells road (A37), right at lights by Y.M.C.A., across two mini r'bouts, ground 400 yards on left behing Engineers Arms. Ten minutes walk from Bedminster (BR).

SALTFORD

Ground: Norman Road, Saltford.　　　　　**Secretary:** C A Wheeler (0272 324670)
Directions: A4 Bristol to Bath. Turn off into Norman Road in Saltford.

STOCKWOOD GREEN

Ground: Old Knowle Cricket Club, Stockwood Lane.　　**Secretary:** R Llewellyn (0272 833460)
Directions: As Imperial (previous page) but continue up Sturminster Road. At top of hill turn right, then left into Stockwood Lane. Ground on sharp bend on right.

WELLS CITY

Ground: The Athletic Grnd, Rowdens Rd, off Glastonbury Rd, Wells　**Secretary:** R Cowell (0749 676260)
Directions: Rowdens Road is a right turn off the A39 entering Wells from Glastonbury (the south).

WESTON ST JOHN

Ground: Coleridge Road, Bourneville, Weston-super-Mare.　　**Secretary:** R Flaskett (0934 515260)
Directions: As for Weston-super-Mare FC (see page 526) then proceed up Winterstoke Road, right into Byron Road, left into Coleridge Road, ground on left.

WINSCOMBE

Ground: Recreation Ground, The Lynch, Winscombe.　　**Secretary:** R Liddiard (0934 843396)
Directions: A38 south from Bristol, turn right for Winscombe at Sidcot,' left at sharp bend, ground at end.

DIVISION TWO CLUBS 1993-94

BACKWELL UNITED RESERVES (see page 769)

BLACKBROOK

Grnd: Blackbrook Pavillion, Blackbrook Way, Taunton (0823 333435)　　**Sec:** R A Smith (0823 278579)
Directions: M5 jct 25 and head for Taunton centre, left at 1st lights (Creech Castle Hotel junction), left at sharp right-hand bend into Ilminster and follow signs to Sports Centre.

CHEDDAR

Ground: Bowdens Park, Wells Road, Cheddar.　　**Secretary:** M Higginbottom (0934 744102)
Directions: Ground on south side of A371 on eastern fringe of Cheddar.

CHURCHILL CLUB '70

Ground: Recreation Field, Ladymead Lane, Churchill.　　**Secretary:** B W Bullock (0934 834310).
Directions: A38 south from Bristol to Churchill traffic lights; ground on right.

CLEVEDON UNITED RESERVES (see previous page)

IMPERIAL BRISTOL

Ground & Directions: As Imperial United (previous page)　　**Secretary:** M Jones (0272 713743)

KEYNSHAM CRICKETERS

Ground: Manor Road Playing Field, Keynsham, Bristol.　　**Secretary:** W Howis (0272 869334)
Directions: A4175 into Keynsham, straight over 1st mini-r'bout, left at 2nd, down Bath Hill, over double mini-r'bout and next r'bout into Wells Way, left fork into Manor Road, ground on right.

LONG ASHTON

Ground: Recreation Ground, Keedwell Hill, Long Ashton.　　**Secretary:** P Thorne (0275 852300)
Directions: M5 jct 19, A369 towards Bristol, at r'bout follow B3128 to Long Ashton, left into village, ground right up Keedwell Hill.

MENDIP WELLS

Ground: Old Frome Road, Wells.　　　　**Secretary:** N Church (0749 674347)
Directions: From Wells city centre follow signs to Mendip Hospital. Ground on right immediately after golf course.

ODD DOWN RESERVES (see page 767)

PAULTON ROVERS RESERVES (see page 767)

ST GEORGE EASTON-IN-GORDANO

Ground: Court Hay, Easton-in-Gordano.　　**Secretary:** Mrs Jones (0275 372875)
Directions: M5 jct 19, A369 towards Bristol into Easton-in-Gordano village, left into St Georges Hill which joins Priory Road, ground on left.

TIMSBURY ATHLETIC

Ground: Recreation Field, North Road, Timsbury.　　**Secretary:** M Sage (0761 71290)
Directions: As for Tunley (following page) but continue into Timsbury. Ground at crossroads by Cricket Club.

TUNLEY ATHLETIC

Ground: Recreation Field, Tunley. **Secretary:** Mrs Fear (0761 70749)
Directions: A367 Bath-Radstock road, turn right onto B3155, through Tunley, ground on right.

WATCHET TOWN

Ground: The Memorial Ground, Doniford Road (0984 31041). **Secretary:** M Clausen (0984 31773)
Directions: On coast road, east of town.

WELTON RVRS RESERVES (see page 774)

WESTON ST JOHN RESERVES (see previous page)

WRINGTON-REDHILL

Ground: Recreation Ground, Silver Street, Wrington. **Secretary:** B Bull (0934 862027)
Directions: A38 south from Bristol, right towards Wrington at foot of steep hill after airport, ground in Wrington village.

DIVISION THREE CLUBS 1993-94

BANWELL

Ground: Riverside Ground, Riverside, Banwell. **Secretary:** C Gibbons (0934 512903).
Directions: A38 south from Bristol, right onto A368 at Churchill, into Banwell village, right, right again after pub into narrow lane.

CLANDOWN

Ground: Thynne Field, Clandown, Radstock (0761 419805) **Secretary:** C Herron (0761 432814).
Directions: Half mile out of Radstock off A367 towards Bath - turn left at top of steep hill.

CLUTTON

Ground: Warwick Fields, Upper Bristol Road, Clutton **Secretary:** S Elias (0761 453503)
Directions: Ground behind Warwick Arms on right of A37 south from Bristol.

FARLEIGH SPORTS

Ground: Farleigh Hospital, Flax Bourton **Secretary:** L Cox (0272 642186).
Directions: A370 Bristol to Flax Bourton then follow signs to Farleigh Hospital.

FRY CLUB RESERVES (see previous page)

GLASTONBURY RESERVES (see page 771)

HENGROVE ATHLETIC RESERVES (see previous page)

IMPERIAL BRISTOL RESERVES (see previous page)

NAILSEA TOWN

Ground: Fryth Way, Causeway View, Nailsea **Secretary:** C Garraway (0454 201499)

NAILSEA UTD RESERVES (see previous page)

ROBINSONS RESERVES (see previous page)

SHEPTON MALLET RESERVES (see Premier Div.)

STREET

Ground: Tannery Field, Middlebrooks, Street. **Secretary:** L Clark (0458 45869)
Directions: Near Millfields School.

TEMPLE CLOUD

Ground: Camley Playing Fields, Temple Inn Lane, Temple Cloud. **Secretary:** D Flower (0275 831432)
Directions: A37 south from Bristol, left into Temple Lane at Temple Inn, ground on right.

WELLS CITY RESERVES

WESTLANDS SPORTS RESERVES (see Premier Division)

WORLE

Ground: Recreation Ground, Station Road, Worle. **Secretary:** D Brine (0934 625585)
Directions: A370 from Bristol to Worle, ground on right at junction with Station Road.

YATTON ATHLETIC

Ground: 'Hangstone', Stowey Road, Yatton. **Secretary:** A Coombes (0934 833997)

PERRY STREET LEAGUE

PREM. DIV.	P	W	D	L	F	A	PTS
Merriott Rovers	22	18	1	3	79	17	55
Combe St Nicholas	22	17	2	3	82	18	53
Crewkerne	22	17	1	4	95	29	52
South Petherton	22	14	2	6	64	30	44
Lyme Regis	22	10	4	8	53	48	34
Norton	22	10	2	10	53	42	32
Axminster Town	22	8	7	7	41	34	31
Drimpton	22	6	5	11	47	73	23
Ilminster Spartak	22	6	3	13	36	63	21
Ilminster Town Res.	22	4	7	11	41	73	19
Perry Street	22	2	3	11	32	99	9
Misterton	22	1	1	20	20	117	4

DIV. ONE	P	W	D	L	F	A	PTS
Hinton	24	17	2	5	69	33	53
Combe St Nich. Res.	24	16	4	4	78	30	52
Shepton Beauchamp	24	15	5	4	69	30	50
Winsham	24	13	4	7	75	50	43
Forton	24	13	3	8	55	34	42
Crewkerne Res.	24	11	4	9	64	34	37
Beaminster Res.	24	10	7	7	45	40	37
Thorncombe	24	11	3	10	58	54	36
Chard W.M.C.	24	8	6	10	44	48	30
Merriott Rvrs Res.	24	7	4	13	39	55	25
Pymore	24	6	5	13	31	50	23
Netherbury	24	3	1	20	28	92	7
Axmouth Town	24	1	2	21	20	125	5

DIV. TWO	P	W	D	L	F	A	PTS
Halstock	24	18	2	4	77	39	56
Chard Youth Club	24	16	5	3	60	41	53
Axminster T. Res.	24	14	5	5	75	24	47
Lyme Regis Res.	24	14	5	5	66	39	47
Crewkerne 'A'	24	13	4	7	60	53	43
Barrington	24	11	3	10	67	51	36
Farway	24	9	7	8	58	37	34
Sth Petherton Res.	24	9	4	11	64	53	31
Millwey Rise	24	9	4	11	51	57	31
Norton Res.	24	8	4	12	52	60	28
Chard United	24	4	3	17	39	73	15
Hawkchurch	24	4	2	18	43	90	14
Misterton Res.	24	3	0	21	25	120	9

DIV. THREE	P	W	D	L	F	A	PTS
Powermatic	22	17	5	0	70	21	56
Seavington	22	17	4	1	82	35	55
Shepton B. Res.	22	15	0	7	55	31	45
Drimpton Res.	22	13	4	5	75	40	43
Charmouth	22	13	2	7	62	38	41
Uplyme	22	11	0	11	60	46	33
Axminster T. 'A'	22	10	3	9	37	33	33
Netherbury Res.	22	4	6	12	41	58	18
Dowlish	22	5	3	14	31	62	18
Pymore Res.	22	3	5	14	30	83	14
Crewkerne 'B'	22	4	1	17	42	84	13
Millwey Rise Res.	22	3	1	18	25	79	10

DIV. FIVE	P	W	D	L	F	A	PTS
Combe St Nich. 'A'	22	16	3	3	77	35	51
Farway Res.	22	13	2	7	50	43	41
Hinton Res.	22	13	1	8	67	50	40
Forton Res.	22	11	6	5	72	46	39
Cotley	22	11	4	7	59	46	37
Chard W.M.C. Res.	22	10	6	6	52	37	36
Winsham Res.	22	9	4	9	44	33	31
Charmouth Res.	22	9	4	9	63	62	31
Barrington Res.	22	9	3	10	36	53	30
Thorncombe Res.	22	6	3	13	35	56	21
Perry Street Res.	22	2	3	17	44	82	9
Colyton	22	2	3	17	25	81	9

Street F.C. - of the Somerset Senior League. Back Row (L/R): R Townsend, M Lewis, J Pickersgill, S Hill, N Merish, J Keirle, C Hamlett. Front: P Keirle, W Bradshaw, P Carmichael, T Hamlett. Photo - James Wright.

WESTWARD DEVELOPMENTS
DEVON COUNTY LEAGUE

Chairman: Brian Williams.
Vice-Chairman: William Smale.
Chairman: Barry Widdicombe.
Hon. Secretary: Roger Lowe, Panorama,
Lamerton, Tavistock, Devon PL19 8SD (0822 613516).

The first season of the newly-formed Devon County League was officially opened by the Chairman of the Football Association, Sir Bert Millichip, on August 22nd at Willand Rovers. The generous three year sponsorship provided by Westwards Developments (Totnes) Ltd has assured the League of a good financial basis.

The League champions, Buckfastleigh Rangers, led the race from the start and next season are hoping to repeat this performance and so be able to take advantage of the Pyramid system to be promoted to the Great Mills Western League.

Newton Abbot also enjoyed a good season being runners-up in the league and winners of the League's 'Bass' knockout cup, with Willand Rovers being the losing finalists.

All founder-member clubs have enjoyed their first season in the new County League, competing against new opponents and subsequently making new football friends. The 'Sporting Trophy' went to Newton St Cyres.

Clubs are striving hard to improve their ground facilities which will raise the standard of the League and ensure its future.

Roger Lowe, League Secretary.

FINAL TABLE	P	W	D	L	F	A	PTS
Buckfastleigh Rgrs	30	25	4	1	86	21	79
Newton Abbot	30	21	5	4	91	31	68
N.T. Paignton	30	20	5	5	81	38	65
Weston Mill O.V.	30	16	6	8	57	46	54
Newton St Cyres	30	15	7	8	61	44	52
Stoke Gabriel	30	15	7	8	62	47	52
Alphington	30	13	8	9	50	37	47
Elburton Villa	30	12	6	12	62	49	42
Willand Rovers	30	11	5	14	67	70	38
Teignmouth	30	9	8	13	52	60	35
Plymstock United	30	10	5	15	47	61	35
Chagford	30	8	4	18	38	82	28
Cullompton Rgrs	30	7	4	19	33	64	25
Topsham Town	30	6	6	18	46	75	24
Ivybridge Town	30	3	6	21	34	84	15
E.A.F. Plymouth	30	3	6	21	36	94	15

SPORTING COMPETITION

Newton St Cyres	8.39
Willand Rovers	8.05
Stoke Gabriel	8.03
Elburton Villa	7.90
Newton Abbot	7.85
Plymstock Utd	7.81
N.T. Paignton	7.80
West Mill O.V.	7.74
Cullompton Rgrs	7.67
Topsham Town	7.53
Chagford	7.41
Teignmouth	7.38
Alphington	7.30
Ivybridge Town	7.16
Buckfastleigh	6.96
E.A.F. Plymouth	6.12

(based on marks out of 10, awarded by referees)

LEAGUE 'BASS' CUP FINAL:
Newton Abbot 5, Willand Rovers 0

TOP SCORERS (LGE & BASS CUP):
G Ross (Newton Abbot) 28
C Acton (Willand Rovers) 27
G Perry (Buckfastleigh) 24
S Barber (Newton St Cyres) 22
P Moats (N.T. Paignton) 20

CLUB DIRECTORY 1993-94

ALPHINGTON

Secretary: Mr A J Smith, 7 Cordery Rd, St Thomas, Exeter EX2 9DH (0392 438571).
Ground: The Chronicles, Church Road, Alphington (0392 79556)
Cover: Yes   **Clubhouse:** Yes   **Floodlights:** No   **Programme:** Yes
Previous League: Devon & Exeter.

BUCKFASTLEIGH RANGERS

Secretary: Mrs J Voisey, 61 Oaklands Park, Buckfastleigh TQ11 0AP (0364 42446).
Ground: Ducks Pond Playing Fields, Buckfastleigh, Devon
Directions: On east side of 3380, just off main A38, to south of Buckfastleigh village centre.
Cover: No   **Clubhouse:** Yes   **Floodlights:** Yes.
Previous League: South Devon.
Captain 92-93: John Impey   **Top Scorer 92-93:** G Perry, 24.
Hons: Devon County Lg 92-93.

CHAGFORD

Secretary: Mrs M Cosford, West Corndon Farm, Chagford TQ13 8EE (0647 432442).
Ground: Padley Common, Chagford.
Previous League: South Devon.

CULLOMPTON RANGERS

Chairman: M Scott   **Vice Chairman:** D Clode   **President:** L Bourne
Secretary: K Norman, 78 Langlands Rd, Cullompton (0884 33539).
Manager: B Kerslake   **Asst Manager/Coach:** Rob Broomfield.
Ground: Speeds Meadow, Duke Street, Cullompton, Devon.
Directions: M5 jct 28, head for town centre, turn left, through thru town centre for 1 mile, left into Meadow Lane, past sports centre, right at T-junction, left after 100yds and follow signs.
Seats: None   **Cover:** 100   **Capacity:**   **Floodlights:** No   **Founded:** 1943
Colours: Red & black   **Change colours:** Royal blue   **Nickname:** Rangers
Previous League: Devon & Exeter 43-92   **Previous Grounds:** Station Drive/ Court Drive/ Exeter Rd.
Programme: 10 pages, £1 with entry   **Programme Editor:** Secretary   **Club Shop:** No.
Club Sponsors: Manor House Hotel   **Reserve team's League:** Devon & Exeter.
Clubhouse: Licensed bar open nightly at 8pm, after matches and Sunday lunctimes. Basket meals. Half-time tea.
Captain 92-93: Rob Broomfield   **Top Scorer 92-93:** S Rowland   **P.O.Y. 92-93:** D Greening.
Hons: Devon & Exeter Lg 61-62 63-64 (Snr Div 59-60 78-79, Jnr Div 3 49-50 59-60(res)), East Devon Snr Cup 83-84, Devon Premier Cup R-up 84-85, Axminster Hosp. Cup 92-93, Golesworthy & Grange Cup 92-93.

Cullompton Rangers F.C. 1992-93. Back Row (L/R): Ricky Holmes, Rob Bloomfield (Captain), Mike Partridge, Steve Rowland, Adrian King, James Wheatcroft, David Greening. Front: Roland Broomfield, Albie Cruse, Nick Parsons, Peter Wilcox, Daren Pengelly, Ray Pratt. Photo - James Wright.

ELBURTON VILLA

Secretary: Mr S Matthews, 64 Wembury Rd, Elburton, Plymouth PL9 8HF (0752   492109).
Ground: Haye Road, Elburton, Plymouth.
Cover: **Floodlights:** No   **Clubhouse:** No   **Tea Bar:** Yes   **Programme:** Yes.
Previous League: Plymouth & Dist.

IVYBRIDGE TOWN

Secretary: Mr B Flood, 18 St Austin Close, Ivybridge PL21 9BZ (0752 894536)
Manager: Brian Howard   **Asst Manager:** Garth Goodwin.
Ground: Erme Playing Fields, Ivybridge (0752 892584).   **Previous League:** Plymouth & Dist.
Directions: Coming from Plymouth on A38 take Ivybridge turn, double back over A38 and take 1st left - ground entrance quarter mile on right after Industrial Estate.
Cover: No   **Floodlights:** No   **Clubhouse:** Yes   **Tea Bar:** Yes   **Programme:** No

1992-93. Back Row (L/R): Garth Goodwin (Asst Manager), Steven Treeby, Mike Hopkins, Darren ...s, Andy Frost, James Lynch, Brian Howard (Manager). Front: John Dawe, Neil Treeby, Leigh ...anni, Dave Young, Wayne Seldon. Photo - James Wright.

NEWTON ABBOT

President: Mr S Riddler   **Chairman:** Mr R Flaherty   **Vice Chairman:** Mr J Hazlewood
Secretary: Mr R Perkins, 21 Prospect Terrace, Newton Abbot, Devon (0626 61596).
Managers: D Kendal/I Sanderson   **Ground:** The Playing Fields, Coach Rd, Newton Abbot (0626 335011).
Directions: Half mile off the Torquay Road leading to Newton Abbot centre, past Ford Park tennis courts.
Seats: None   **Cover:** No   **Capacity:**   **Floodlights:** No   **Founded:** 1964
Colours: White/black/black   **Change colours:** Yellow or Red   **Nickname:** None.
Previous Names: Newton Dynamos/ Newton Abbot Dynamos.
Previous Grounds: Centrax Sports Field (for 24 years).
Previous Leagues: South Devon Minor 64-66/ South Devon 66-77 89-92/ South Western 77-89.
Programme: 24 pages, £1 with entry   **Programme Editor:** J Hazlewood   **Club Shop:** No.
Club Sponsors: M Hoare
Midweek home matchday: Wednesday   **Reserve team's League:** South Devon.
Clubhouse: Open Fri evenings & weekend lunchtimes & evening. Variety of food available.
Captain 92-93: A Pike   **Top Scorer 92-93:** G Ross, 30
Hons: Devon Co. Lg R-up 92-93 (Lg Cup 92-93), Herald Cup 72-73 74-75 75-76 (R-up 73-74), Devon Prem. Cup R-up 82-83 87-88 (Snr Cup R-up 90-91, I'mediate Cup R-up 74-75), Sth Devon Lg R-up 72-73 (Div 1 87-88 (R-up 71-72), Div 2 70-71 85-86 (R-up 69-70), Div 3 84-85, Div 4 75-76 80-81, Div 5 R-up 78-79 91-92, Div 6 R-up 78-79 91-92, Div 7 89-90, Jnr Div 2 68-69, Jnr Div 3 67-68, Charity Shield R-up 73-74 75-76 76-77, Les Bishop Cup 74-75 75-76 80-81 (R-up 68-69), Ronald Cup 69-70 81-82 82-83, Greenaway Cup 79-80 (R-up 71-72), Clive Olney Cup 88-89 (R-up 89-90), Torbay Comb. Div 2 76-77, Tyrone Power Cup R-up 75-76, Dahl Cup 75-76 (R-up 64-65), W Treeby Cup 92-93(res), Sth Western Lg Sporting Tphy 86-87.

NEWTON ST CYRES

Chairman: Kelvyn Baker   **Vice Chairman:** David Holman   **President:** John Harris
Secretary: Roger Dymond, 12 New Estate, Newton St Cyres, Devon (0392 851719).
Manager: Kevin Skinner   **Physio:** Ray Wright
Ground: The Recreation Ground, Station Rd, Newton St Cyres, Devon (0392 851546).
Directions: A377 from Exeter towards Crediton, on reaching Newton Cyres proceed to village centre, and turn right (signposted BR station) - ground half mile on right. Trains to Exeter Central station or buses from Exeter coach station.
Seats: None   **Cover:** None   **Capacity:** 550   **Floodlights:** No   **Founded:** 1956
Colours: Red & white   **Change colours:** Blue & white   **Nickname:** Saints
Previous Grounds: None   **Previous Leagues:** Devon & Exeter 56-92.
Programme: 6-8 pages, 50p   **Programme Editor:** T.B.A.   **Club Shop:** No.
Sponsors: De Paula Spts/ Quickes   **Reserve team's League:** Devon & Exeter.
Clubhouse: Mon-Fri 8-11pm, Sat 4.30-11pm, Sun noon-2 & 7-11pm. Food available after Saturday matches - burgers, chips, pasties etc.
Captain 92-93: Karl Pitman   **Top Scorer & P.O.Y. 92-93:** Sean Barber
Club record scorer: Dave Newbery   **Club record appearances:** Kelvyn Baker.
Hons: Devon Premier Cup 88-89 (Snr Cup 74-75, I'mediate Cup 72-73), Devon & Exeter Lg 88-89 (Lg Cup 88-89), East Devon Snr Cup 88-89 89-90 90-91 92-93.

NORTHERN TELECOM PAIGNTON

Chairman/Press Officer: J Sargent (0803 854551)   **Vice Chairman:** J O'Connor
Secretary: Miss J Adams, 51 Laura Grove, Paignton (0803 558696).
Manager: E Kelly   **Asst Manager:** D Newton   **Coach:** W Young
Physio: P Gabriel   **Commercial Manager:** John Foster (0803 521878)
Ground: Long Road, Paignton (0803 57062).
Directions: From Newton Abbot follow signs to Brixham, right into Long Rd at N/T factory - pitch 100yds on right.
Seats: None   **Cover:** None   **Capacity:** 2,000   **Floodlights:** No   **Founded:** 1968
Colours: Red & black   **Change colours:** All blue   **Nickname:** None
Previous Name: S.T.C. Paignton 68-92   **Previous League:** South Devon 68-92.   **Prev. Grounds:** None
Programme: £1 with admission   **Editor:** John Foster (0803 521878)   **Club Shop:** No.
Club Sponsors: Bass   **Record Gate:** v Southampton, 1992 - new changing rooms opening.
Clubhouse: Yes. Wide range of food.   **Reserve team's League:** South Devon
Captain 92-93: Dave Stocker   **Top Scorer 92-93:** Paul Moats
P.O.Y. 92-93: W Young   **Club record appearances:** Steve Carpenter.
Hons: Herald Cup 87-88 89-90 (R-up 91-92), Sth Devon Lg Div 1 R-up 78-79 (Div 2 75-76, Div 3 74-75 88-89(res), Div 4 73-74), Devon Premier Cup R-up 89-90, Beli Cup 87-88 88-89, Devon Yth Cup 89-90.

PLYMOUTH PARKWAY

Chairman: G Baggott
Secretary: S Cadmore, 25 Dudley Gdns, Plymouth, Devon PL6 5PE (0752 782661).
Manager: K Pond   **Asst Manager:** G Baggott   **Physio:** V Easterbrook
Ground: Parkway Sports Club, Tamar Vale, Ernesettle Lane, Ernesettle, Plymouth   (0752 363080).
Directions: Take Ernesettle exit off A38 & follow signs to Ernesettle Industrial Estate - ground on right halfway down steep hill.
Seats: None   **Cover:** 50   **Capacity:**   **Floodlights:** Due   **Founded:** 1987
Colours: Yellow/royal   **Change colours:** Tangerine/black   **Nickname:** Parkies
Previous Name: E.A.F. Plymouth 87-93.   **Previous Lge:** Plymouth & Dist. 87-92   **Prev. Grounds:** None
Programme: 4 pages, 30p   **Programme Editor:** Secretary   **Club Shop:** No.
Sponsors: Parkway Sports Club   **Reserve team's League:** Plymouth & District.
Record win: 22-0   **Record defeat:** 0-8
Clubhouse: Open 11am-3 & 7-11pm, and all day Saturdays. Hot food & drinks available.
Captain 92-93: A Barlow   **Top Scorer 92-93:** M Goldstone
P.O.Y. 92-93: G Stevens   **Club record appearances:** Paul Mapstone ('keeper) 153.
Hons: Plymouth & Dist. Lg Div 2 90-91 (Div 4 Cup 88-89 (R-up 91-92(res)), Div 3 Cup R-up 89-90 84).

PLYMSTOCK UNITED

Chairman: J Cain   **Vice Chairman:** J Challen   **President:** R Burroughs
Secretary: A Demuth, 35 Treveneague Gdns, Manadon, Plymouth PL2 3SX (0752 782807).
Manager: Tim Halford   **Asst Manager:** Des Hill
Commercial Mgr: Allen Stone   **Press Officer:** John George (0752 335011).
Ground: Deans Cross, Plymstock, Plymouth, Devon (0752 406776).
Directions: Local bus service to Plymstock Broadway.
Seats: None   **Cover:** No   **Floodlights:** No   **Club Shop:** No.   **Founded:** 1946
Colours: Red/white   **Change colours:** Gold/black   **Nickname:** Reds.
Previous Grounds: None   **Previous Leagues:** Plymouth & District (pre-1992).
Programme: 20 pages, 50p - voted best in League   **Editor:** John George (0752 335011)
Sponsors: J G Business Machines   **Clubhouse:** Normal bar hours. Hot food to order.
Midweek home matchday: Tues/Thurs   **Reserve team's League:** Plymouth & Dist.
Record win: 15-0 v Bere Alston   **Rec. defeat:** 4-7 v Newton St Cyres, Devon Prem. Cup 89-90
Captain 92-93: Tony Cawse   **Top Scorer 92-93:** Matt Jarvis   **P.o.Y. 92-93:** T.B.A
Club record scorer: Unknown   **Club record appearances:** A Demuth 350 approx, 1980-92.
Hons: Plymouth & Dist Lg 66-67 74-75 84-85 (R-up 75-76 76-77 90-91), Devon Snr Cup R-up 87-88, Victory Cup 67-68 74-75 78-79 86-87 (R-up 62-63 69-70 71-72 76-77 77-78 83-84).

STOKE GABRIEL

Secretary: Mr B Prowse, 269 Teignmouth Rd, St Marychurch, Torquay TQ1 4RT (0803 327930).
Ground: G J Churchward Mem. Grnd, Broadley Lane, Stoke Gabriel
Previous League: Sth Devon.

TEIGNMOUTH

Chairman: Mr A Leggatt   **Manager:** Mr I Cornish   **Physio:** Mr M Wilson
Secretary: Mr P Crawford, 6 Higher Brimley, Teignmouth, TQ14 8JS (0626 772108).
Ground: Coombe Valley, Lower Combe Lane, Teignmouth, Devon (0626 772688).
Directions: Situated at very end of Fourth Ave., below Lovells Homes Estate. Coming from Newton Abbot direction; thru lights at Shaldon Bridge, 1st left into Mill Lane, 1st right after 100yds into Fourth Ave., 2nd right, car park on left. Rail to Teignmouth (BR).
Seats: None   **Cover:** 1,500   **Club Shop:** No   **Floodlights:** No   **Founded:** 1946
Colours: White/black/black   **Change colours:** Red & black hoops   **Nickname:** Teigns
Previous Grounds: None   **Previous Leagues:** Sth Devon 46-82 89-92/ Sth Western 82-89.
Sponsors: Coggins Developments   **Programme:** Not for 5 years. Hope to restary 93-94
Reserve team's League: South Devon.   **Clubhouse:** Mon-Fri 5-11pm, Sat noon-11, Sun noon-3 & 7-10.30
Record win: 5-1 v Topsham (H)   **Rec. defeat:** 2-6 v Willand (A) - both in Devon Lg 92-93.
Captain 92-93: Ian Gallacher   **Top Scorer 92-93:** Patrick Twitchin
P.o.Y. 92-93: Peter Harris   **Club record appearances:** Joe Dunn 520.
Hons: Torbay Herald Cup 58-59 79-80 81-82, Sth Western Lg Cup R-up 85-86, Sth Devon Lg Div 1 85-86(res).

TOPSHAM TOWN

Secretary: Mr D G Marks, 66 Gloucester Rd, Exeter EX4 2EE (0392 58896).
Ground: Coronation Field, Exeter Road, Topsham (0392 873678).
Cover: Yes   **Seats:** No   **Clubhouse:** Yes   **Floodlights:** No   **Programme:** Yes
Colours: Royal blue/white
Previous League: Devon & Exeter.

WESTON MILL OAK VILLA

Secretary: Mr R Carpenter, 11b St Eval Place, Ernsettle, Plymouth PL5 2RN (0752 364037).
Ground: W.M.O.V. Sports Ground, Ferndale Rd, Weston Mill, Plymouth.
Cover: No   **Floodlights:** No   **Clubhouse:** Yes   **Tea Bar:** Yes   **Programme:** Yes
Colours: Green/black/green.
Previous Name: Oak Villa   **Previous League:** Sth Western 87-89/ Plymouth & Dist.
Previous Ground: Tamar Spts & Social Club, Ernesettle (whilst in South Western League).

Weston Mill Oak Villa, pictured before their staggering 6-5 home win against luckless E.A.F. Plymouth on Boxing Day morning. Photo - James Wright.

Wooden-spoonists E.A.F (Ex-Air Flyers) Plymouth, who will see if a change of name brings them a change of fortune in 1993-94 - they are now known as Plymouth Parkway. Back Row (L/R): R Fice, A McBeth, M Jones, S Burford, K Weston (Captain), Martin Oliver, I Smith, D Rowe. Front: Mike Oliver, S Bressland, V Howe (Manager), A Barlow, D Taylor. Photo - James Wright.

WILLAND ROVERS

Chairman: M Mares   **Vice Chairman:** R Jones   **President:** J Spearing
Secretary/Press Officer: A L Jarrett, 2 College Court, Uffculme, Cullompton EX15 3EQ (0884 841210).
Manager: Mike Howe   **Coach:** Mike Mitchell
Ground: Silver Street, Willand, nr Cullompton, Devon (0884 33885).
Directions: Ground situated on east side of B3181, halfway between M5 jcts 27 & 28. 2 miles from Tiverton Parkway BR station. Regular buses from Exeter via Cullompton.
Seats: 200   **Cover:** 200   **Capacity:** 1,000   **Floodlights:** No   **Founded:** 1946
Colours: White/black/black   **Change colours:** All blue   **Nickname:** Rovers
Previous Grounds: None   **Previous Lges:** Tiverton & Dist. 46-58/ Devon & Exeter 58-92.
Programme: 8 pages, with admission   **Programme Editor:** Secretary   **Club Shop:** No.
Club Sponsors: Verbeer Manor   **Record Gate:** 500 v Newton Abbot, League, 22/8/92.
Midweek home matchday: **Reserve team's League:** North Devon.
Clubhouse: Open Sat 11am-2pm & 4.30-11pm, weekday evenings & Sun lunchtime. Food available.
Record scorer: Adrian Gladstone-Smith   **Club record appearances:** Mike Mitchell.
Captain 92-93: Steve Hayman   **Top Scorer 92-93:** Chris Acton   **P.o.Y. 92-93:** Darren Cork
Hons: Devon Snr Cup 85-86 (I'mediate Cup 66-67), Devon Co. Lg Cup R-up 92-93, Exeter & Dist. Lg Snr Div 1 70-71 (Jnr Div 1 67-68, Jnr Div 2 64-65, Jnr Div 3 65-66, Premier Lg Cup 79-80), East Devon Snr Cup 72-73 91-92.

Willand Rovers pictured with Football Association Chairman Sir Bert Millichip at their home fixture against Newton Abbot on August 22nd - the official launch of the new County League.

BIDEFORD TOOL
NORTH DEVON LEAGUE
President: Mr A S Beer.
Chairman: Mr W Smale.
Vice Chairman: Mr G Shapland.
Hon. Secretary: H W Bartlett, 20 Granville Avenue,
Yeo Vale, Barnstaple EX32 7AH (43415).

Premier Division	P	W	D	L	F	A	PTS
Bradworthy	34	27	3	4	131	37	57
Appledore Res.	34	26	3	5	93	31	55
Combe Martin	34	25	3	6	105	47	53
Fremington	34	21	6	7	118	49	48
Braunton	34	17	5	12	68	53	39
Bideford 'A'	34	15	7	12	82	66	37
Dolton	34	12	12	10	65	67	36
Chittlehampton	34	14	5	15	63	61	33
Holsworthy Res.	34	13	7	14	79	88	33
Morwenstow	34	12	7	15	77	91	31
Ilfracombe 'A'	34	11	8	15	70	74	30
Putford	34	12	6	16	65	73	30
Parkhead	34	13	4	17	74	95	30
Shamwickshire Rvrs	34	9	6	19	73	111	24
Chivenor	34	10	4	20	60	115	24
Barnstaple AAC	34	9	5	20	54	106	23
Lynton	34	6	5	23	59	128	17
South Molton	34	5	2	27	72	116	12

Wooden spoonists South Molton won five matches all season, yet those victories were by margins of 9-1 (twice), 8-0, 6-0 & 3-0.

PREMIER DIV. (BRAYFORD) CUP First Round
South Molton 0, Bradworthy 1
Lyton 1, Holsworthy Res. 1
Second Round
Ilfracombe Town 'A' 1, Bideford 'A' 2
Parkhead 4, Braunton 5
Appledore Res. 5, Dolton 0
Chivenor 0, Bradworthy 3
Lynton 1, Fremington 3
Combe Marton 3, Chittlehampton 2
Barnstaple A.A.C. 3, Putford 1
Morwenstow 4, Shamwickshire 2
Quarter Finals
Bideford 'A' 1, Braunton 2
Appledore Res. 2, Bradworthy 1
Fremington 1, Combe Martin 0
Barnstaple A.A.C. 6, Morwenstow 2
Semi Finals
Braunton 1, Appledore Res. 0
Fremington 3, Barnstaple A.A.C. 0
Final (8/5/93 at Barnstaple Town)
Fremington 4, Braunton 1

Senior Division	P	W	D	L	F	A	PTS
Willand	28	23	3	2	134	39	49
Topsham	28	20	2	6	83	38	42
Hearts of Oak	28	16	6	6	96	51	38
Admiral Vernon	28	14	9	5	92	45	37
Shebbear	28	15	7	6	79	50	37
Bradworthy	28	15	4	9	54	51	34
Fremington Res.	28	10	8	10	65	56	28
Hartland	28	13	1	14	59	66	27
Braunton Res.	28	11	1	16	72	82	23
Sporting VSW	28	7	6	15	54	71	20
Cmbe Martin Res.	28	9	2	17	51	90	20
Northam Lions	28	7	4	17	54	83	18
North Molton	28	6	5	17	59	115	17
Dolton Res.	28	6	4	18	51	102	16
Barnstaple T. Colts	28	6	2	20	49	113	14

SENIOR DIV. (COMBE MARTIN) CUP 1st Round
Combe Martin Res. 2, Hartland 1
Admiral Vernon 4, Dolton Res. 1
Fremington Res. 0, Barnstaple Colts 2
Hearts of Oak 3, Shebbear 2
North Molton 3, Willand 4
Braunton W/O Pyworthy
Topsham 3, Northam Lions 2
Sporting VSW 3, Bradworthy Res. 0
Quarter Finals
Combe Martin 2, Admiral Vernon 3
Barnstaple Colts 1, Hearts of Oak 6

Willand 2, Braunton Res. 1
Topsham 1, Sporting VSW 0
Semi Finals
Admiral Vernon 4, Hearts of Oak 0
Willand 8, Topsham 3
Final (1/5/93 at Combe Martin)
Willand 2, Admiral Vernon 1

Intermediate Div 1	P	W	D	L	F	A	PTS
Bratton Fleming	22	15	4	3	77	38	34
Wrey Arms	22	16	2	4	61	23	34
Appledore 'A'	22	14	3	5	70	32	31
Torrington 'A'	22	14	2	6	71	50	30
Parkhead Res.	22	9	6	7	64	51	24
Hts of Oak Res.	22	12	0	10	70	61	24
Clovelly	22	11	1	10	68	58	23
Sth Molton Res	22	7	5	10	66	74	19
Ilfracombe 'B'	22	8	1	13	55	60	17
Combe Martin 'A'	22	4	6	12	38	63	14
Northam Lions Res.	22	3	2	17	25	104	8
Shamwickshire Res.	22	2	2	18	33	84	6

Bratton Fleming won the title by the smallest margin in living memory - one goal. They needed to win their final game by three goals to pip Wrey Arms, and just made it, 4-1, the fourth goal being an own-goal in the final minutes.

INT. DIV. 1 (ARLINGTON) CUP 1st Round
Shamwickshire Res. 2, N. Lions Res. 1
Heart of Oak Res. 0, Wrey Arms 1
Sth Molton Res. 5, Ilfracombe T. 'B' 2
Appledore 'A' W/O Sporting VSW Res.
Bratton Fleming 6, Torrington 'A' 1
Quarter Finals
Combe Martin 'A' 2, Shamwickshire Res. 1
Wrey Arms 2, South Molton Res.1
Appledore 'A' 4, Bratton Fleming 2
Clovelly 2, Parkhead Res. 1
Semi Finals
Combe Martin 'A' 1, Wrey Arms 3
Appledore 'A' 2, Clovelly 3
Final (29/4/93 at Bideford F.C.)
Clovelly 3, Wrey Arms 2

Intermediate Div 2	P	W	D	L	F	A	PTS
Mortehoe	22	21	0	1	95	27	42
Shaplands	22	20	0	2	110	23	40
Swimbridge	22	20	0	2	79	44	29
Merton	22	9	7	6	55	28	25
B. Brewer	22	8	6	8	38	51	22
Chivenor Res.	22	9	3	10	55	62	21
E.D.L.	22	8	2	12	53	59	18
Hartland Res.	22	8	2	12	37	65	18
Chit'hampton Res.	22	3	10	9	37	56	16
Lynton Res.	22	6	3	13	43	79	15
Nth Molton Res.	22	3	4	15	30	76	10
Braunton 'A'	22	4	0	18	44	106	8

Mortehoe won 21 straight games, only to lose the last the last match to Shaplands who had tailed them doggedly all season, only losing two games themselves. Shaplands took revenge in the Divisional Cup final.

INT. DIV. 2 (NORTH DEVON) CUP First Round
E.D.L. 1, Merton 3
Chivenor Res. 0, Shaplands 4
Swimbridge 4, Braunton 'A' 1
Mortehoe 5, Chittlehampton Res. 0
Quarter Finals
Northam Lions Res. 0, Merton 3
Swimbridge 2, Shaplands 1 *(after 1-1)*
Mortehoe 4, Hartland Res. 2
B. Brewer 2, Lynton Res. 3
(continued overleaf)

Semi Finals
Merton 1, Shaplands 2
Mortehoe 13, Lynton Res. 0
Final (24/4/93 at Ilfracombe Town)
Shaplands 3, Mortehoe 2

Intermediate Div 3	P	W	D	L	F	A	PTS
Westward Ho!	26	22	4	0	111	23	48
Ad. Vernon Res.	26	18	4	4	106	59	40
Georgeham	26	15	6	5	83	47	36
Wrey Arms Res.	26	17	1	8	95	50	35
St Mary's	26	15	3	8	75	66	33
B'staple AAC Res.	26	14	3	9	67	37	31
Goodleigh	26	14	2	10	103	65	30
B'ple Riverside	26	9	4	13	70	112	22
Putford Res.	26	8	5	13	66	77	21
Landkey	26	7	3	16	61	64	17
Shaplands Res.	26	6	4	16	47	87	16
B. Fleming Res.	26	5	4	17	40	104	14
Shebbear Res.	26	4	3	19	42	112	11
Woolsery	26	3	4	19	50	113	10

INT. DIV. 3 (APPLEDORE SHIPBUILDERS) CUP

First Round
B. Fleming Res. 1, Ad. Vernon Res. 10
Wrey Arms Res. 3, Shaplands Res. 0
Westward Ho! 2, B'staple AAC Res. 1
Shebbear Res. 1, St Mary's 2
Barnstaple Riverside 4, Goodleigh 1
Woolsery 0, Putford Res. 2 (after 3-3)
Quarter Finals
Georgeham 1, Admiral Vernon Res. 2
Wrey Arms Res. 1, Westward Ho! 2
St Mary's 7, Barnstaple Riverside 3
Putford Res. 3, Landkey 1
Semi Finals
Admiral Vernon Res. 2, Westward Ho! 3
Putford Res. 2, St Mary's 3 (after 5-5)
Final (21/4/93 at Appledore F.C.)
Westward Ho! 4, St Mary's 0

PREMIER DIVISION RESULT CHART 1992/93

HOME TEAM	1	2	3	4	5	6	7	8	9	10	11	12	13	14	15	16	17	18
1. Appledore Res.	*	2-2	3-0	2-1	3-2	1-0	1-2	2-0	2-0	3-0	1-1	5-1	2-0	6-1	4-0	4-0	7-1	2-0
2. Barnstaple A.A.C.	1-0	*	2-2	2-7	0-1	2-3	4-1	1-5	3-0	2-3	2-2	0-7	5-3	3-3	0-2	2-1	2-2	3-1
3. Bideford 'A'	1-0	4-2	*	1-3	2-3	3-0	4-1	1-5	0-0	3-5	3-1	4-1	3-0	5-1	4-5	1-2	1-1	8-2
4. Bradworthy	1-1	5-0	2-1	*	2-1	0-2	13-0	2-1	4-2	3-2	6-1	5-1	4-1	2-1	4-0	6-0	7-0	8-1
5. Braunton	2-3	4-0	1-1	1-5	*	3-3	7-0	3-0	2-1	0-3	W-L	2-3	W-L	1-2	3-2	0-0	3-0	3-0
6. Chittlehampton	0-3	2-0	6-2	0-3	0-1	*	4-2	2-3	1-2	2-2	0-1	1-1	1-2	1-0	5-2	2-1	3-1	2-0
7. Chivenor	1-3	2-4	0-2	1-3	1-2	1-0	*	2-3	2-3	2-5	2-2	2-0	4-1	1-7	0-3	4-0	3-1	3-3
8. Combe Martin	1-2	6-2	3-2	4-2	3-2	3-2	4-1	*	2-2	2-1	3-4	3-0	7-1	1-1	8-0	2-1	7-1	7-1
9. Dolton	0-2	1-0	2-4	2-2	3-1	1-1	2-3	4-1	*	2-2	2-2	2-1	4-2	3-1	2-2	2-2	1-1	3-0
10. Fremington	4-1	1-5	1-1	1-0	9-1	4-0	1-1	8-2	*	6-0	11-0	6-2	7-1	2-1	3-4	8-1	2-1	
11. Holsworthy Res.	0-4	1-2	1-3	2-4	1-2	1-0	7-1	1-2	3-3	1-2	*	1-1	6-4	5-2	3-3	1-3	5-2	5-3
12. Ilfracombe Town 'A'	0-2	5-0	3-1	0-1	1-1	1-0	3-3	0-1	0-0	4-2	5-1	*	2-2	2-7	2-3	2-1	8-2	5-3
13. Lynton	0-4	6-0	3-2	1-5	2-3	0-1	2-2	1-2	1-1	1-0	3-3	0-7	*	2-2	7-2	6-0	1-6	1-0
14. Morwenstow	4-5	4-1	0-2	0-7	3-2	1-1	2-1	0-1	1-4	0-4	5-2	0-0	8-2	*	3-3	1-0	3-1	4-0
15. Parkhead	0-2	6-1	2-2	1-0	4-3	2-6	2-3	0-3	3-0	3-0	2-3	3-2	7-4	2-0	*	1-3	1-1	6-3
16. Putford	1-5	2-4	0-2	3-5	2-2	2-0	3-4	0-3	2-3	1-1	2-3	2-0	6-1	4-4	2-1	*	1-1	6-1
17. Shamwickshire	4-2	2-1	2-2	0-3	2-4	3-6	2-4	1-4	3-1	2-5	2-3	1-0	10-2	9-2	6-0	0-2	*	2-1
18. South Molton	0-4	6-0	3-5	1-5	0-3	2-5	9-1	1-4	3-5	0-2	3-4	2-2	9-1	1-3	3-0	1-2	8-0	*

SENIOR DIV.

	1	2	3	4	5	6	7	8	9	10	11	12	13	14	15
1. Admiral Vernon	*	2-2	3-3	9-0	5-1	2-2	7-1	3-2	6-1	5-0	2-1	4-1	2-3	1-1	1-3
2. Barnstaple T. Colts	3-2	*	0-1	4-3	2-2	2-4	2-4	0-5	5-2	4-3	1-7	5-4	2-5	5-4	1-12
3. Bradworthy Res.	2-1	W-L	*	2-1	2-1	3-4	1-2	2-2	1-0	4-1	1-5	6-2	3-2	4-2	1-6
4. Braunton Res.	3-3	8-0	3-1	*	8-1	3-2	5-2	1-7	5-0	4-5	1-4	2-3	1-3	1-2	0-3
5. Dolton Res.	1-6	7-1	1-0	0-2	*	5-1	1-2	2-11	2-5	1-0	1-5	0-3	3-5	1-1	3-7
6. Fremington Res.	3-3	4-1	1-2	6-0	0-1	*	2-1	1-2	7-1	3-3	4-2	4-1	0-2	3-2	0-3
7. Hartland	1-4	W-L	0-1	0-3	5-1	0-3	*	0-1	6-4	6-2	1-1	2-0	0-3	4-1	3-2
8. Hearts of Oak	0-2	4-1	1-1	5-4	6-4	1-1	1-2	*	2-2	4-1	3-1	3-2	5-1	4-0	3-5
9. North Molton	0-1	7-2	4-5	1-5	3-3	4-4	2-11	0-7	*	2-1	2-8	2-3	4-2	4-3	0-4
10. Northam Lions	2-2	W-L	3-1	2-3	0-1	2-2	2-1	6-4	7-2	*	2-3	3-3	1-3	1-2	2-6
11. Shebbear	2-2	2-0	1-2	1-2	3-2	2-0	3-2	0-3	2-1	1-0	*	6-2	2-4	0-6	4-1
12. Sporting V.S.W.	2-4	4-3	1-1	4-2	2-2	1-1	1-0	1-1	2-2	0-4	0-1	*	2-4	4-0	3-4
13. Topsham	3-2	7-1	2-0	8-0	5-0	1-0	5-4	1-4	2-2	3-0	1-0	W-L	*	3-1	0-1
14. West Down (CM)	1-7	3-1	1-4	4-2	6-3	3-0	1-2	4-2	1-2	5-1	1-6	W-L	0-5	*	1-7
15. Willand	1-1	6-1	1-0	W-L	6-1	3-3	7-1	3-3	8-0	8-0	8-0	5-3	2-1	9-1	*

INT. DIV. 1

	1	2	3	4	5	6	7	8	9	10	11	12
1. Appledore 'A'	*	3-2	5-1	10-0	3-0	6-1	4-0	3-0	3-1	2-2	5-1	1-2
2. Bratton Fleming	3-1	*	2-1	3-2	11-0	4-2	5-0	4-1	3-1	3-3	1-5	7-3
3. Clovelly	5-0	1-4	*	2-3	5-1	2-1	7-3	3-4	6-1	6-2	4-3	1-3
4. Combe Martin 'A'	1-1	1-3	2-3	*	1-2	2-2	4-1	1-6	4-4	2-5	0-0	0-4
5. Hearts of Oak Res.	1-3	2-3	12-3	5-1	*	2-4	6-2	6-3	3-1	8-3	1-3	0-2
6. Ilfracombe Town 'B'	3-2	4-2	1-2	0-2	4-0	*	6-1	0-2	5-0	5-2	2-7	1-3
7. Northam Lions Res.	1-7	1-6	2-2	3-2	0-5	1-0	*	0-8	1-0	2-3	3-4	0-8
8. Parkhead Res.	2-2	2-2	1-0	2-2	2-3	4-3	2-2	*	6-0	3-3	4-4	0-2
9. Shamwickshire Res.	0-5	1-4	1-8	1-4	4-3	2-4	8-1	3-6	*	2-2	L-W	0-3
10. South Molton Res.	1-2	1-1	3-1	2-1	1-3	6-5	8-0	4-5	8-2	*	3-5	1-4
11. Torrington 'A'	5-1	3-4	2-4	3-2	1-3	4-1	3-1	3-1	3-1	8-3	*	3-2
12. Wrey Arms	0-1	0-0	2-1	1-1	1-4	4-1	6-0	1-0	2-0	4-0	4-1	*

INT. DIV. 2

	1	2	3	4	5	6	7	8	9	10	11	12	13
1. Braunton 'A'	*	7-0	3-1	2-3	2-8	1-6	3-4	4-1	L-W	0-3	10-1	1-9	1-6
2. B. Brewer	6-0	*	2-2	1-1	1-0	2-0	7-4	1-1	1-6	1-1	5-0	1-4	0-4
3. Chittlehampton Res.	6-3	0-0	*	3-2	4-4	0-1	0-3	2-2	3-9	1-1	*	1-2	2-6
4. Chivenor Res.'	5-4	2-0	1-1	*	1-2	5-0	3-2	3-1	2-3	8-2	11-3	2-9	3-4
5. E.D.L.	2-5	2-3	3-1	3-1	*	3-1	7-3	1-5	1-2	3-0	3-1	0-2	1-4
6. Hartland Res.	4-3	3-1	2-4	2-4	3-2	*	4-3	1-1	0-3	2-2	3-1	0-1	1-6
7. Lynton Res.	6-2	0-2	0-0	1-1	2-1	2-3	*	0-1	1-4	6-0	*	1-11	1-6
8. Merton	15-0	1-1	1-1	7-1	4-0	3-0	0-2	*	0-1	3-0	5-0	3-2	1-1
9. Mortehoe	W-L	5-2	4-1	5-2	3-2	7-0	12-0	3-1	*	3-0	5-2	4-3	5-2
10. North Molton Res.	3-2	1-3	1-1	4-2	1-2	3-4	2-3	0-1	2-9	*	5-1	1-5	2-9
11. Northam Lions 'A'	*	0-7	3-5	*	3-4	*	2-5	L-W	0-9	2-3	*	*	2-2
12. Shaplands	8-0	5-0	4-1	4-0	8-3	7-0	5-0	3-2	3-2	6-0	*	*	4-1
13. Swimbridge	10-1	2-3	2-2	2-3	3-2	3-0	4-0	1-1	1-5	2-1	6-1	0-5	*

N.B. Northam Lions withdrew. Playing record expunged and shown here for interest only.

INT. DIV. 3	1	2	3	4	5	6	7	8	9	10	11	12	13	14
1. Admiral Vernon Res.	*	4-1	7-1	6-2	4-0	5-4	6-3	4-3	2-3	1-2	7-0	1-2	6-4	1-6
2. Barnstaple A.A.C. Res.	2-2	*	5-0	2-1	2-3	3-0	1-3	7-2	3-0	1-0	7-0	0-3	5-3	3-0
3. Barnstaple Riverside	2-5	3-1	*	3-3	4-12	3-6	3-2	7-3	3-2	3-3	6-4	0-5	3-2	3-7
4. Bratton Fleming Res.	1-6	1-1	3-5	*	2-8	2-1	2-1	0-3	3-5	6-3	2-1	1-11	2-2	1-3
5. Georgeham	4-5	1-2	1-1	3-0	*	3-3	3-0	2-2	4-3	3-2	1-2	2-2	6-2	1-0
6. Goodleigh	5-8	1-2	7-1	6-1	1-3	*	4-2	1-2	8-2	10-1	10-1	2-5	3-0	2-1
7. Landkey	2-4	2-1	8-1	3-0	1-5	1-2	*	1-1	8-0	2-3	6-0	0-3	2-2	2-4
8. Putford Res.	1-1	1-5	4-2	3-0	1-1	3-4	2-2	*	4-5	10-2	5-1	1-4	3-4	1-4
9. St Mary's	2-2	2-1	5-1	6-0	2-3	2-1	1-0	3-1	*	6-1	3-2	3-3	5-1	2-4
10. Shapland Res.	0-4	1-7	0-3	3-0	0-0	2-2	2-5	4-1	2-4	*	7-3	0-3	1-1	2-4
11. Shebbear Res.	3-5	1-1	3-3	2-3	1-6	1-3	W-L	2-4	1-1	1-3	*	1-5	7-2	1-6
12. Westward Ho!	1-1	2-1	6-1	11-1	3-1	3-2	4-2	3-0	5-0	W-L	10-0	*	10-0	1-1
13. Woolsery	3-4	0-3	2-6	1-1	2-3	3-9	4-2	3-4	1-5	3-2	0-3	2-5	*	3-7
14. Wrey Arms Res.	2-5	1-0	6-2	5-2	0-4	5-6	6-1	5-1	2-3	4-1	6-1	0-1	6-0	*

ELLIOTT & SAUNDERS
DEVON & EXETER LEAGUE

PREM. DIV.	P	W	D	L	F	A	PTS
Exeter City 'A'	26	20	2	4	98	24	62
Budleigh Salterton	26	18	4	4	76	37	58
Exeter Civil Serv.	26	17	5	4	76	25	56
Clyst Valley	26	15	5	6	64	43	50
Chelston	26	15	4	7	82	38	49
Buckland Athletic	26	11	6	9	63	58	39
St Martins	26	11	5	10	68	54	38
Okehampton Argyle	26	10	8	8	46	48	38
Lapford	26	10	2	14	55	59	32
Beer Albion	26	9	4	13	38	55	31
Exmouth Amateurs	26	7	8	11	36	44	29
Honiton Town	26	5	2	19	25	65	17
Sidmouth Town	26	4	3	19	22	84	15
Offwell & W'worthy	26	0	2	24	24	139	2

SENIOR CLUB DIRECTORY

BEER ALBION
Ground: Furzebrake, Stovar Long Lane, Beer (0297 24324)   **Secretary:** R Hoare (0297 22146).

BUCKLAND ATHLETIC
Ground: Recreation Ground, off Coach Rd, Newton Abbot   **Secretary:** Mrs Holmes (0626 69345)

BUDLEIGH SALTERTON
Ground: Greenway Lane, Budleigh Salterton   **Secretary:** N Pannell (0395 445877).

CHELSTON
Ground: Armada Park, Nut Bush Lane, Chelston, Torquay   **Secretary:** D Birkinshaw (0803 613445).

CLYST VALLEY
Ground: Exmouth Rd, Clyst St Mary   **Secretary:** J Luscombe (0392 56631)

EXETER CITY 'A'
Ground: Cat & Fiddle, Sidmouth Rd, Clyst St Mary (0395 32784)   **Secretary:** M Radford (0392 424950).

EXETER CIVIL SERVICE
Ground: Foxhayes, Exwick (0392 73976)   **Secretary:** Miss Masters (0392 411882).

EXMOUTH AMATEURS
Ground: Imperial Recreation Ground, Exmouth.   **Secretary:** N Adair (0395 268776).

HONITON TOWN
Ground: Mountbatten Park, Ottery Moor Lane, Honiton (0404 42503)   **Secretary:** Mrs Barrass (0404 43445).

LAPFORD
Ground: Edgerly Lane, Edgerly Cross, Lapford (0363 83128)   **Secretary:** J Burrows (0363 83358).

OFFWELL & WIDWORTHY
Ground: Offwell Recreation Ground   **Secretary:** Mrs Fowler (0404 83652).

ST MARTINS EXMINSTER
Ground: Adjoins Exminster Cricket Club   **Secretary:** Mrs Brown (0392 832067)

SIDMOUTH TOWN
Ground: Manstone Rec., Manstone Lane, Sidmouth   **Secretary:** N Anthony (0395 577782).

SENIOR DIV. 1

	P	W	D	L	F	A	PTS
University of Exeter	28	24	3	1	122	36	75
Exeter St Thomas	28	21	5	2	106	28	68
Feniton	28	17	6	5	100	57	57
Budleigh S. Res.	28	15	5	8	69	58	50
Culm United	28	15	3	10	97	58	48
East Budleigh	28	14	6	8	76	50	48
Westexe Rovers	28	12	4	12	67	67	40
London & Manch.	28	11	7	10	80	85	40
Sidbury United	28	12	3	13	80	62	39
Dawlish Town 'A'	28	8	5	15	34	69	29
Lympstone	28	7	7	14	48	59	*25
Morchard Bishop	28	6	6	16	57	89	24
Rockbeare Rockets	28	6	5	17	46	91	23
Newtown	28	5	5	18	43	89	20
Ottery St M. Res.	28	0	4	24	25	152	4

SENIOR DIV. 2

	P	W	D	L	F	A	PTS
Cheriton Fitzpaine	28	25	1	2	128	29	76
Wonford	28	17	5	6	84	49	56
Pinhoe	28	17	7	4	90	46	*55
Bickleigh	28	14	8	6	88	57	50
Hatherleigh Town	28	12	6	10	63	45	42
Univ. of Exeter Res.	28	11	6	11	74	73	39
Exeter St T. Res.	28	10	6	12	49	65	36
Woodbury Salterton	28	9	8	11	60	76	35
Village Inn	28	10	5	13	67	98	35
Dunkeswell Rovers	28	10	4	14	57	50	34
Littleham	28	10	7	11	61	65	*34
Exmouth Atrs Res.	28	9	6	13	58	61	33
Chulmleigh	28	8	4	16	52	77	28
North Tawton	28	4	10	14	41	67	22
Honiton T. Res.	28	1	3	24	36	150	6

SENIOR DIV. 3

	P	W	D	L	F	A	PTS
Tedburn St Mary	30	24	3	3	124	45	75
Queens Head	30	21	3	6	110	43	66
Bampton	30	20	4	6	95	61	64
Exeter C.S. Res.	30	15	9	6	94	55	54
Colyton	30	14	8	8	75	56	50
Witherbridge	30	12	7	11	77	65	43
Northlew	30	13	3	14	61	69	42
Dawlish Town 'B'	30	12	5	13	62	67	41
Halwill	30	10	6	14	45	55	36
Sidmouth T. Res.	30	10	6	14	50	61	36
Lympstone Res.	30	10	3	17	54	65	*32
Kentisbeare	30	8	7	15	73	89	31
Bradninch	30	8	7	15	59	101	31
Univ. of Exeter 'A'	30	9	3	18	59	93	30
St Mark's	30	9	3	18	56	99	30
Culmstock	30	3	7	20	38	108	*13

INTER DIV. 1

	P	W	D	L	F	A	PTS
Dawlish Villa	28	22	4	2	92	27	70
Bow A.A.C.	28	19	2	7	71	37	59
Seaton Town	28	17	6	5	70	33	57
Broadclyst	28	16	6	6	72	45	54
Pinhoe Res.	28	12	8	8	69	57	44
Westexe Rvrs Res.	28	11	7	10	49	53	40
Follygate	28	12	3	13	79	74	39
Winkleigh	28	10	7	11	61	67	37
London & M. Res.	28	10	7	11	54	57	37
Sidbury Utd Res.	28	12	0	16	49	75	36
Tipton St John	28	9	6	13	66	69	33
South Zeal Utd	28	9	2	17	52	66	29
Silverton	28	9	2	17	59	92	29
East Budleigh Res.	28	5	4	19	37	91	19
Newtown Res.	28	3	4	21	30	87	13

INTER DIV. 2

	P	W	D	L	F	A	PTS
Alphington Res.	22	16	4	2	80	26	52
Buckland Ath. Res.	22	15	3	4	78	34	48
Newton St C. Res.	22	14	2	6	79	40	44
Cullompton R. Res.	22	13	4	5	58	32	43
Newton Poppleford	22	13	2	7	71	49	41
Okehampton Res.	22	11	8	3	48	28	41
Crediton Utd 'A'	22	10	4	8	65	51	34
Woodbury	22	8	1	13	55	67	25
Culm United Res.	22	6	3	13	49	55	21
Queens Head Res.	22	6	3	13	43	54	21
Morchard Bish. Res.	22	1	2	19	34	90	5
Offwell & W. Res.	22	0	2	20	25	159	2

INTER DIV. 3

	P	W	D	L	F	A	PTS
St Martin's Res.	28	21	3	4	121	40	66
King's Arms	28	19	3	6	98	54	60
Dunkeswell R. Res.	28	17	6	5	81	35	57
Wonford Res.	28	17	5	6	114	66	56
Awliscombe	28	17	1	10	61	59	52
Feniton Res.	28	17	3	8	82	54	*51
Payhembury	28	12	6	10	92	71	42
Tedburn S.M. Res.	28	11	2	15	66	84	35
White Horse	28	11	2	15	73	104	*34
Sandford	28	11	0	17	78	90	33
Crescent	28	10	2	16	73	81	32
Clyst Valley Res.	28	8	7	13	62	66	31
Medical Sickness	28	8	2	18	53	107	26
Rockbeare R. Res.	28	4	6	18	42	87	18
St Mark's Res.	28	1	4	23	43	141	7

INTER DIV. 4

	P	W	D	L	F	A	PTS
Thorventon	28	23	3	2	121	37	72
Crediton Utd 'B'	28	17	4	7	89	47	55
Univ. of Exeter 'B'	28	15	4	9	93	63	49
Colyton Res.	28	14	6	8	66	36	48
Cheriton F. Res.	28	15	4	9	74	62	*48
Y.M.C.A.	28	12	5	11	68	74	41
Beer Albion Res.	28	12	5	11	64	79	41
Bickleigh Res.	28	11	7	10	72	52	40
Upottery	28	10	6	12	63	69	36
Dawlish Villa Res.	28	10	4	14	39	58	34
Winkleigh Res.	28	9	4	15	57	70	31
Hatherleigh T. Res.	28	9	2	17	41	89	29
Bampton Res.	28	7	5	16	48	79	26
Newton St C. 'A'	28	7	3	18	57	104	24
Bratton Clovelly	28	6	4	18	57	90	22

INTER DIV. 5

	P	W	D	L	F	A	PTS
Bradninch Res.	28	21	4	3	137	39	67
Crescent Res.	28	20	4	4	100	45	64
Lapford Res.	28	18	2	8	129	59	56
Seaton Town Res.	28	15	6	7	91	57	51
Witheridge Res.	28	15	5	8	67	47	50
N. Poppleford Res.	28	15	0	13	79	74	45
Halwill Res.	28	12	7	9	53	53	43
Sampford Peverell	28	12	6	10	80	79	42
North Tawton Res.	28	13	2	13	60	71	41
Kentisbeare Res.	28	11	5	12	51	68	38
Okehampton 'A'	28	7	6	15	63	62	27
Tipton St J. Res.	28	7	5	16	56	93	26
Culmstock Res.	28	7	3	18	42	99	24
Awliscombe Res.	28	4	5	19	39	85	17
Silverton Res.	28	2	2	24	29	145	8

* - point(s) deducted

ARKINS & ASHTON
PLYMOUTH & DISTRICT LEAGUE

PREM. DIVISION

	P	W	D	L	F	A	PTS
Prince Rock	26	23	3	0	118	18	49
Falstaff Wanderers	26	17	3	6	78	46	37
Tavistock Res.	26	16	4	6	69	35	36
Marjons	26	12	6	8	68	51	30
Dynamo Villa	26	12	5	9	49	44	29
Woodland Fort	26	12	4	10	59	51	28
Torpoint Ath. Res.	26	9	5	12	49	47	23
Civil Service	26	10	3	13	56	66	23
Old Suttonians	26	9	5	12	62	88	23
Hooe St John	26	8	5	13	52	71	21
Millbrook Res.	26	6	8	12	48	65	20
Plymstock Utd Res.	26	8	2	16	38	62	18
Satellite Sports	26	7	3	16	53	87	17
Ivybridge United	26	3	4	19	39	99	10

MOD-DEC WINDOWS SOUTH DEVON LEAGUE

President: M W Benney, Esq.

Chairman: E O Benney.

Hon. Secretary: W G L Parker,

23 Higher Coombe Drive, Teignmouth (7745277)

The season had its difficulties due to the bad weather in January and certain clubs having success in various cup competitions. The Premier Division was won by Newton Abbot Spurs with Upton Athletic as runners-up. Combined '89 in Division Four went all through the season without losing a league match, and, in addition to their championship, they won the Devon Intermediate Cup.

The Torbay Herald Cup final had an attendance of nearly 2,000 and was played between Upton Vale and Dartmouth Y.M.R.C. These were two new names for the final, and Upton Vale ran out winners.

The winners of the various divisional cups were: **Belli Cup** - Winners: Upton Athletic, R-up: Newton Abbot Spurs, **Dartmouth Cup** - Winners: Newton Abbot Spurs Reserves, R-up: Paignton Town, **Lidstone Cup** - Winners: Brixham Utd, R-up Newton Rangers Reserves, **Ronald Cup** - Winners: Keignsteign Athletic Reserves, R-up: Chudleigh Athletic, **Bill Treeby Cup** - Winners: Newton Abbot Reserves9, R-up: Broadhempston Utd, **Les Bishop Cup** - Winners: Combined '89, R-up: Torquay Christians in Sport, **Ivor Andrews Cup:** Winners: Newton Villa, R-up: Totnes Town Reserves.

W G L Parker, Hon. Secretary

Premier Division	P	W	D	L	F	A	PTS
Newton A. Spurs	30	23	2	5	76	24	48
Upton Athletic	30	20	6	4	55	19	46
Upton Vale	30	16	5	9	52	42	37
Newton Rangers	30	14	7	9	56	50	35
Dartmouth YMRC	30	11	10	9	56	49	32
Kingsteignton A.	30	13	5	12	49	55	31
Watts Blake Bearne	30	13	4	13	48	48	30
Newton Town	30	12	5	13	45	62	29
Stoke Gabriel Res.	30	10	8	12	48	51	28
Brixham Villa	30	11	6	13	40	46	28
Dartmouth United	30	11	5	14	54	63	27
Waldon	30	9	8	13	61	60	26
Hele Rovers	30	9	7	14	40	50	25
Dartington Utd	30	7	6	17	42	60	20
Galmpton United	30	7	6	17	43	67	20
Newton '66	30	6	6	18	49	68	18

Division One	P	W	D	L	F	A	PTS
Bovey Tracey	26	22	3	1	87	22	47
Newton Spurs Res.	26	20	4	2	78	19	44
Teign Village	26	20	2	4	79	39	42
Windsor United	26	18	4	4	113	39	40
Paignton Town	26	14	3	9	73	51	31
South Brent	26	13	3	10	62	51	29
Victoria Rangers	26	10	4	12	48	67	24
Kingswerswell	26	8	6	12	49	56	22
Ipplepen Athletic	26	8	3	15	46	58	19
Upton Ath. Res.	26	8	3	15	45	76	19
Chelston Res.	26	5	6	15	36	66	16
Liverton United	26	6	2	18	37	83	14
Beesands Rovers	26	5	3	18	41	77	13
St Marychurch/Gr.	26	1	2	23	31	121	4

Division Two	P	W	D	L	F	A	PTS
Brixham United	26	23	1	2	83	26	47
Brixham Town	26	18	17	4	5	99	41	38
Buckfastleigh Res.	26	18	2	6	96	43	38
Loddiswell	26	16	4	6	93	44	36
Newton Rangers	26	13	6	7	71	50	32
N.T. Paignton Res.	26	13	5	8	89	51	31
Totnes Town	26	12	6	8	63	46	30
B'combe Corries	26	11	4	11	50	62	26
Foxhole United	26	9	4	13	59	63	22
Moretonhampstead	26	8	2	16	47	80	18
Harbertonford	26	6	3	17	53	85	15
Galmpton Utd Res	26	5	5	16	23	68	15
Kingskerswell Res.	26	3	5	18	36	81	11
Dittisham United	26	2	1	23	30	152	5

Division Three	P	W	D	L	F	A	PTS
Kingsteignton Res.	26	17	4	5	73	29	38
Dartington U. Res.	26	17	4	5	70	35	38
Chudleigh Athletic	26	16	4	6	63	38	36
Ashburton	26	15	5	6	67	45	35
Brixham Villa Res.	26	14	4	8	73	49	32
Newton 66 Res.	26	9	10	7	43	39	28
Churston Ferrers	26	13	1	12	58	51	27
Paignton Villa	26	11	3	12	71	76	25
Dartmouth Utd Res.	26	8	7	11	52	66	23
Ilsington Res	26	8	5	13	54	65	21
Bishopsteignton	26	7	5	14	59	61	19
D'mouth YMRC Res.	26	6	6	14	40	72	18
Centrax	26	5	4	17	39	74	14
Newton United	26	3	4	19	25	86	10

Division Four	P	W	D	L	F	A	PTS
Combined '89	26	25	1	0	155	26	51
T'quay Chr.in Spt	26	21	4	1	107	24	46
Babbacombe Rgrs	26	16	4	6	103	55	36
Newton Town	26	14	4	8	64	62	32
Staverton	26	15	1	10	92	61	31
Channings Wood	26	13	4	9	77	67	30
Paignton Utd	26	11	5	10	53	49	27
N.T. P'ton Saints	26	11	2	13	72	64	24
Windsor Utd Res.	26	9	4	13	77	75	22
Watts Blake B. Res.	26	7	6	13	64	76	20
Thurlestone & S.M.	26	7	4	15	48	89	18
Kellaton United	26	6	5	15	48	72	17
Liverton Utd Res.	26	3	1	22	38	160	7
Meadowbrook Ath.	26	1	1	24	24	142	3

Division Five	P	W	D	L	F	A	PTS
Buckfastleigh 'A'	26	21	3	2	86	37	45
Teignmouth Res.	26	21	2	3	103	30	44
Newton Abbot Res.	26	20	3	3	82	29	43
Broadhempston Utd	26	18	2	6	105	36	38
Ipplepen Ath. Res.	26	15	1	10	55	57	31
Hele Rovers Res.	26	12	6	8	62	41	30
Waldon Res.	26	10	3	13	65	75	23
Victoria Rgrs Res.	26	9	5	12	46	63	23
Torbays Gents	26	8	5	13	59	63	21
South Brent Res.	26	8	5	13	64	76	21
Bovey Tracey Res.	26	7	3	16	48	89	17
Foxhole Utd Res.	26	5	6	15	36	84	16
Ashburton Res.	26	3	1	22	43	84	7
B'combe C. Res.	26	1	3	22	32	122	5

Division Six	P	W	D	L	F	A	PTS
Chagford Reserves	26	19	6	1	75	26	44
Newton Villa Res.	26	19	5	2	90	27	43
Brixham Utd Res.	26	18	4	4	78	33	40
East Allington U.	26	17	5	4	66	27	39
Totnes Town Res.	26	12	7	7	48	26	31
Bradley Villa	26	13	4	9	60	45	30
B'combe Rgrs Res.	26	11	3	12	62	79	25
Paignton Villa Res.	26	9	6	11	64	74	24
Teign Village Res.	26	8	3	15	52	52	19
Bishopsteignton Res.	26	7	5	14	48	68	19
Harbertonford Res.	26	7	3	16	43	65	17
Dartington Hall	30	5	1	20	34	77	11
Beesands Rvrs Res.	26	4	3	19	29	84	11
Dittisham Utd Res.	26	4	3	19	39	105	11

Division Seven	P	W	D	L	F	A	PTS
Combined '89 Res.	26	21	3	2	101	43	45
Abbotskerswell	26	21	1	4	99	32	43
Watcombe United	26	19	3	4	86	36	41
Loddiswell Res.	26	18	4	4	93	40	40
Chudleigh Ath. Res.	26	17	3	6	103	49	37
Brixham T. Res.	26	13	3	10	80	65	29
Sth Brent Extras	26	11	4	11	56	64	26
M'hampstead Res	26	9	4	13	57	86	22
Newton Utd Res.	26	5	6	15	39	66	16
Paignton Utd Res	26	6	3	17	46	103	15
Thurlestone Res.	26	6	2	18	52	93	14
Staverton Res.	26	5	3	18	51	81	13
Riviera	26	5	3	18	55	99	13
Centrax Res.	26	4	2	20	41	102	10

PREMIER DIVISION CLUBS 1993-94

BOVEY TRACEY
Secretary: Mr Allen Cowell, 22 South View, Bovey Tracey TQ13 9AQ (0626 834564).
Ground: Bovey Tracey Rec/ Mill Marsh Park   **Colours:** Green & red

BRIXHAM VILLA
Secretary: J W L Harris, 47 Great Rea Rd, Brixham TQ5 9SW (0803 856671).
Ground: St Mary's Park, Brixham   **Colours:** Royal & white.

DARTINGTON UNITED
Secretary: Charles Stephens, Pelekas, 2 The Bridge Path, Cherry Cross, Totnes TQ9 5ES (0803 864832).
Ground: Dorothy Elmhirst Mem. Ground, Dartington   **Colours:** Royal/red/royal.

DARTMOUTH UNITED
Secretary: Miss D Vince, 141 Townstal Rd, Dartmouth TQ6 9HY (0803 833791).
Ground: Longcross   **Colours:** White & black/black.

DARTMOUTH Y.M.R.C.
Secretary: W Rothwell, 22 Townstal Rd, Dartmouth TQ6 9HY (0803 834355).
Ground: Coronation Park, Dartmouth   **Colours:** All red.

HELE ROVERS
Secretary: P Addis, 38 Chatsworth Rd, Torquay TQ1 3BL (0803 211281).
Ground: Barton Downs.   **Colours:** Grey & black/black.

KINGSTEIGNTON
Secretary: Mr J R Bibbings, 26 Meadow View, Wear Farm, Bishopsteignton TQ14 9PX (0626 770734).
Ground: Broadpark, Broadway Rd, Kingsteignton   **Colours:** Red/white/red.

NEWTON ABBOT SPURS
Secretary: Mark Hayman, Newsagents, Dolpin Square, Bovey Tracey TQ13 9AL (0626 832505).
Ground: Recreational Trust Centre, Marsh Rd, Newton Abbot   **Colours:** All blue.

NEWTON RANGERS
Secretary: Mrs Jill Setherton, 5 Yellows Close, Bradley Valley TQ12 1YF (0626 335823).
Ground: Forches Cross   **Colours:** All blue.

NEWTON TOWN
Secretary: Mrs G Slatter, 23 Randolph Court, The Churchills, Newton Abbot TQ12 1QY (0626 66852).
Ground: Denbury PF   **Colours:** Yellow/red.

STOKE GABRIEL RESERVES *(see page 784)*

TEIGN VILLAGE
Secretary: G J Beer, 59 Teign Village, Bovey Tracey, Devon TQ13 9QJ (0626 852605).
Ground: Teign Village Sports Field   **Colours:** Scarlet/black.

UPTON ATHLETIC
Secretary: Mr Allan J Bastow, 63 Western Rd, St Marychurch, Torquay TQ1 4RJ (0803 327134).
Ground: Cricketfield Rd   **Colours:** All red.

UPTON VALE
Secretary: J McPherson, 9 Stanbury Rd, Shiphay, Torquay (0803 663760).
Ground: Cricketfield Rd   **Colours:** Navy/white/red.

WALDON
Secretary: Stewart Ball, Kingfisher Lodge, Castle Rd, Torquay TQ1 3BA (0803 295891).
Grnd: Windmill Hill, top Audley Ave., Torquay   **Cols:** Sky & maroon stripes (white sleeves)/white/sky.

WATTS BLAKE BEARNE
Secretary: Colin D Freestone, 11 Jubilee Rd, Newton Abbot, Devon TQ12 1LB (0626 65886).
Ground: Abbrook Farm, Kingsteignton   **Colours:** Yellow & blue/blue/blue.

DIVISION ONE 1993-94

BRIXHAM TOWN
Secretary: Paul Collier, 15 Holwell Rd, Brixham TQ5 9NE (0803 882280).
Ground: Furzeham Green, Brixham   **Colours:** Blue.

BRIXHAM UNITED
Secretary: Mark Buley, 6 Rea Barn Rd, Brixham TQ5 9DU (0803 858872).
Ground: Wall Park, Wall Park Rd, Brixham   **Colours:** Blue & white/blue.

CHELSTON
Secretary: D Birkinshaw, 80 Marldon Rd, Torquay TQ2 7EH (0803 613445).
Ground: Armada Park, Nutbush Lane, Torquay   **Cols:** Grey & black lattice/black/black

GALMPTON UNITED

Secretary: W E Treeby, 3 Greenway Park, Galmpton, nr Brixham TQ5 0NA (0803 842329).
Ground: Galmpton & Churston War Mem. PF   **Colours:** Green & white.

IPPLEPEN UNITED

Secretary: Dave Crimp, 41 Pembroke Rd, Paignton TQ3 3UR (0803 553186).
Ground: Ipplepen Village PF   **Colours:** Red/black/red.

KINGSKERSWELL

Secretary: John Wilson, 'Fluder Patch', Fluder Hill, Kingskerswell TQ12 5JD (0803 873546).
Ground: The Playing Field, Kingskerswell   **Colours:** Orange & black/black/black.

LIVERTON UNITED

Secretary: Don Pady, 3 Priory Ave., Kingskerswell TQ12 5AQ (0803 873015).
Ground: Halford, Liverton   **Colours:** Sky & black.

NEWTON ABBOT '66

Secretary: Mr Jerry Allen, 39 Hilton Rd, Newton Abbot TQ12 1BJ (0626 66241).
Ground: Osborne Park   **Colours:** Sky/navy/sky.

PAIGNTON TOWN

Secretary: David G D Faux, 24 Collingwood Rd, Paignton TQ4 5PG (0803 522940).
Ground: Clennon Valley   **Colours:** Yellow & black/black/black.

SOUTH BRENT

Secretary: Keith Trent, 34 Deer Park, Ivybridge PL21 0HY (0752 698352).
Ground: Palstone Park   **Colours:** Orange/black.

VICTORIA RANGERS

Secretary: Mrs J Stone, 13 Barnfield Close, Galmpton, Brixham TQ5 0LY (0803 843160).
Ground: Northern Telecom (top pitch), Long Rd, Paignton   **Colours:** White & grey/black/black & white.

WINDSOR UNITED

Secretary: Michael A Smith, 11 Down View Rd, Denbury, Newton Abbot TQ12 4LH (0803 813258).
Ground: Stoodley Knowle, Torquay   **Colours:** Black & white stripes/black.

Plus the Reserve sides of: Newton Abbot Spurs, Upton Athletic *(playing at Barton Downs)*

DIVISION TWO 1993-94

BABBACOMBE CORINTHIANS

Secretary: Tony Bowden, 14 Peasland Rd, Watcombe Park, Torquay TQ2 8NY (0803 312176).
Ground: Stoodley Knowle (pitch one)   **Colours:** Red & black

BEESANDS ROVERS

Secretary: Joe Johnston, 'Valseph', The Green, Beesands, Nr Kingsbridge TQ7 2EJ (0548 580650).
Ground: Beesands Cellars   **Colours:** Black & amber/black.

FOXHOLE UNITED

Secretary: E J B Rolfe, 38 Ramshill Rd, Paignton TQ3 3PP (0803 550741).
Ground: Belfield Park, Belfield Rd, Brixham   **Colours:** Ice blue/maroon.

HARBERTONFORD

Secretary: S Jane, 1 Mill Meadow, Harbertonford TQ9 7SZ (0803 732479).
Ground: The Hams, Harbertonford   **Colours:** Yellow/green/green.

LODDISWELL

Secretary: Andy Guard, 8 Alvington Terrace, Kingsbridge TQ7 1HD (0548 853615).
Ground: Loddiswell PF   **Colours:** Green/black/black

MORETONHAMPSTEAD

Secretary: Miss J Shears, 7 Bowring Mead, Moretonhampstead TQ13 8NP (0647 40244).
Ground: Wadley Brook, Moretonhampstead   **Colours:** Amber & black.

ST MARYCHURCH & TORQUAY GRAMMARIANS

Secretary: Mr Trevor Douglas, 53 Shrewsbury Ave., Barton, Torquay TQ2 8AE (0803 329410).
Ground: Torquay Boys Grammar School   **Colours:** White & blue/blue.

TOTNES TOWN

Secretary: Graham Brown, 47 Higher Cadewell Lane, Torquay TQ2 7EX (0803 613397).
Ground: Borough Park, Totnes   **Colours:** Red & white/red/red.

Plus the Reserve sides of: Buckfastleigh Rangers *(see page 781)*, Dartington United, Galmpton United, Kingsteignton, Newton Rangers, Northern Telecom Paignton *(see page 783)*.

DIVISION THREE 1993-94

ASHBURTON

Secretary: A P C Daw, 76 East Str., Ashburton TQ13 7AX (0364 529938).
Ground: Chuley Rd, Ashburton   **Colours:** Red & white/red/red.

BISHOPSTEIGNTON UNITED

Secretary: Mr D Laughton, 5 Buckeridge Rd, Teignmouth TQ14 8NU (0626 776992).
Ground: Humber Park, Bishopsteignton   **Colours:** All blue.

CHUDLEIGH ATHLETIC

Secretary: G Doble, 33 New Exeter Str., Chudleigh TQ13 0DA (0626 852981).
Ground: Kate Brook, Chudleigh   **Colours:** Claret & blue/white/blue.

CHURSTON FERRERS

Secretary: Philip Worrall, 8 Burton Villa Close, Brixham TQ5 9JB (0803 853408).
Ground: Brixham Community College   **Colours:** White/navy.

COMBINED '89

Secretary: William Robinson, 32 Warren Rd, Torquay TQ2 5TL (0803 298805).
Ground: King George V PF, Torquay   **Colours:** White & blue stripes.

DITTISHAM UNITED
Secretary: Mr A Allen, 6 Galmpton Glade, Galmpton, Brixham TQ5 0LU (0803 842949).
Ground: The Meadow **Cols:** Green/black.

ILSINGTON VILLA
Secretary: Mr K Leaman, 'Little Beverley', Old Town Hill, Ilsington, Newton Abbot TQ13 9RF.
Ground: Alston Cross, nr Ashburton **Colours:** Blue/white/blue.

PAIGNTON VILLA
Secretary: Mr John Sinclair, 15 New Park Rd, Paignton TQ3 3UU (0803 665551).
Ground: Whiterock, Paignton **Colours:** Sky & claret.

TORQUAY CHRISTIANS IN SPORT
Secretary: F C Stapleton, 14 Brunel Ave., Watcombe, Torquay, Devon TQ2 8NW (0803 314222).
Ground: King George V PF, Watcombe, Torquay **Colours:** Red & white.

Plus the Reserves sides of: Brixham Villa, Dartmouth United, Dartmouth Y.M.R.C., Kingskerswell, Newton Abbot '66.

DIVISION FOUR 1993-94

BABBACOMBE RANGERS
Secretary: Mrs Cuss, 1 Avon Rd, Shiphay, Torquay TQ2 7LB (0803 613161).
Ground: Stoodly Knowle **Colours:** Yellow & black/yellow/black.

CENTRAX
Secretary: Mrs N J Morris, 57 Windsor Ave., Newton Abbot TQ12 4DN (0626 69890).
Ground: Centrax Sports Field, Newton Abbot **Colours:** Blue & black/blue/black

CHANNINGS WOOD
Secretary: W Walker, 9 Haywain Close, Edginswell, Torquay TQ2 7SG (0803 615238).
Ground: HM Prison, Channings Wood, Denbury, Newton Abbot **Colours:** Orange/blue.

KELLATON UNITED
Secretary: Mr B D Thuel, 18 Higher Park, East Prawle, Kingsbridge TQ7 2DB (0548 51297).
Ground: East Prawle **Colours:** Blue & maroon stripes/maroon

NEWTON UNITED
Secretary: S Down, 14 Prospect Terrace, Newton Abbot TQ12 2LL (0626 64256).
Ground: Bakers Park, Newton Abbot **Colours:** Purple & white stripes/purple/purple.

NORTHERN TELECOM PAIGNTON SAINTS
Secretary: Mrs D L Edwards, 10 Summerlands Close Summercombe, Brixham TQ5 0EA (0803 857324).
Ground: Long Rd, Paignton **Colours:** Blue & black stripes/black/black.

PAIGNTON UNITED
Secretary: Chris Pine, 99 Occombe Valley Rd, Paignton TQ3 1QT (0803 555900).
Ground: White Rock, Paignton **Colours:** Sky & white stripes/navy/navy.

STAVERTON & LANDSCOVE
Secretary: Miss K J Mitchelmore, Whiteways Farm, Staverton, nr Totnes TQ9 6AL (0803 826658).
Ground: Staverton Rec. **Colours:** Red/white.

THURLESTONE & SOUTH MILTON
Secretary: Mrs E Seccombe, 2 Upton Barton Cottages, South Milton, Kingsbridge TQ7 3JF (0548 560700).
Ground: Opposite Thurlestone Village Hall **Colours:** Blue.

Plus the Reserve sides of: Buckfastleigh Rangers ('A' side), Newton Town, Teignmouth *(see page 784)*, Watts Blake Bearne, Windsor United *(playing at Steps Cross, Torquay)*

DIVISION FIVE 1993-94

BROADHEMPSTON UNITED
Secretary: Mr John Bailey, Apple Cott, Dean Prior, Buckfastleigh TQ11 0LY (0364 423344).
Ground: Headlands, Broadhempston **Colours:** Sky & navy/navy/navy.

MEADOWBROOK ATHLETIC
Secretary: T N Parsons, 4 Huxhams Close, Dartington, nr Totnes TQ9 6NT (0803 762262).
Ground: Dartington **Colours:** Green & white stripes/black.

NEWTON VILLA
Secretary: Mr M G Branch, 139 East Street, Newton Abbot TQ12 2LQ (0626 51964).
Ground: Decoy Park **Colours:** Red & blue stripes/red/red.

TORBAY GENTLEMEN
Secretary: D Bowles, 3 Aycliffe Gdns, Cherry Park, Plympton, Plymouth PL7 3YN (0752 330569).
Ground: Easterfield Lane **Colours:** Red & black stripes/black/black.

Plus the Reserves sides of: Bovey Tracey, Chagford *(see page 781)*, Foxhole United, Hele Rovers, Ipplepen Athletic, Liverton United, Newton Abbot *(see page 783)*, South Brent, Victoria Rangers, Waldon.

DIVISION SIX 1993-94

ABBOTSKERSWELL
Secretary: Nick Bain, c/o 18 Barnfield Terrace, Abbotskerswell, TQ12 5PD (0626 62688).
Ground: Bakers Park, Abbotskerswell **Colours:** Orange & black.

BRADLEY VILLA
Secretary: Kevin Robins, 90 Barton Drive, Newton Abbot TQ12 1YU (0626 335308).
Ground: Decoy Lake, Newton Abbot **Colours:** Silver grey & black.

DARTINGTON HALL
Secretary: Ron Prout Jnr, 11 Newmans Cres., Dartington, Totnes TQ9 6HJ (0803 864005).
Ground: Foxhole, Dartington Hall   **Colours:** Red & blue stripes/blue/blue.

EAST ALLINGTON UNITED
Secretary: Mrs G C Weekes, 5 Vineyard Terrace, East Allington, Totnes TQ9 7QZ (0548 52411).
Ground: Rectory Rd, East Allington, Totnes   **Colours:** Green & yellow/green/green.

Plus the Reserves sides of: Ashburton, Babbacombe Corinthians, Babbacombe Rangers, Bishopsteignton, Brixham United, Combined '89, Harbertonford, Paignton Villa, Teign Village, Totnes Town.

DIVISION SEVEN 1993-94

RIVIERA SPURS
Secretary: Tony Hele, 43 Second Ave., Daison, Torquay, TQ1 4JD (0803 324132).
Ground: Windmill Hill pitch 2, Torquay   **Colours:** Blue (white sleeves)/white/red.

WATCOMBE UNITED
Secretary: Mrs L M Hooper, 28 Crownhill Park, Torquay TQ2 5LW (0803 201125).
Ground: King George V PF, Watcombe, Torquay   **Colours:** Navy & sky.

Plus the Reserve sides of: Beesands R., Brixham T., Chudleigh Ath., Dittisham United, Loddiswell, Moretonhampstead, Newton Utd, Paignton Utd, South Brent *('A' side)*, Slaverton & Landscove, Thurlestone & Sth Milton.

FALMOUTH & HELSTON LEAGUE

DIV. ONE	P	W	D	L	F	A	PTS
Penryn Ath. Res.	24	16	6	2	76	29	38
Falmouth Athletic	24	17	3	4	93	34	37
Troon	24	16	3	5	91	35	35
Wendron	24	14	7	3	70	45	35
Mawnan	24	15	3	6	84	38	33
Helston Ath. Res.	24	11	2	11	56	52	24
Hayle	24	10	4	10	50	49	24
Truro City 'A'	24	11	2	11	52	52	24
Constantine	24	10	3	11	49	64	23
Perranwell Res.	24	6	1	14	32	77	16
Duchy	24	3	4	17	44	93	10
Perranporth	24	1	5	18	24	90	7
St Day	24	1	2	21	34	102	4

Cup Winners/ Runners-up
Percy Stephens Cup: Falmouth A./ Penryn Res.
Lockhart Cup: Wendron/ Mawnan
Barker Bowl: Lizard Argyle/ Truro G.W.R.S.A.

DIV. TWO	P	W	D	L	F	A	PTS
Penryn Ath. 'A'	28	24	3	1	104	29	51
Falmouth Ath. Res.	28	22	3	3	122	35	47
Goonhilly	28	19	6	3	101	45	44
Truro G.W.R.S.A.	28	19	4	5	100	29	42
Hayle Res.	28	12	7	9	74	56	31
Ruan Minor	28	13	5	10	62	56	31
Lizard Argyle	28	11	8	9	54	34	30
Mawgan United	28	10	7	11	56	53	27
Helston Ath. 'A'	28	11	3	14	62	68	25
Mawnan Res.	28	8	6	14	79	82	22
Wendron Res. (+2pts)	28	7	5	16	40	72	21
Con'tine Res. (-2pts)	28	8	5	15	58	69	19
Lanner	28	4	4	20	47	118	12
Cury	28	2	3	23	35	118	7
Mabe	28	1	3	24	13	156	5

League Cup: Penryn Res./ Truro G.W.R.S.A.
Wheatly Cobb Cup: Hayle Res./ Ruan Minor

ONE & ALL SPORTS MINING
DIVISION LEAGUE (WEST CORNWALL)

DIV. ONE	P	W	D	L	F	A	PTS
Trelander	32	25	6	1	148	28	56
Chacewater	32	21	10	1	113	27	52
RNAS Culdrose Res.	32	20	7	3	101	47	47
Carharrack	32	18	10	4	113	41	46
Halsetown	32	18	6	8	78	40	42
Holman S.C.	32	18	5	9	71	50	41
Goonhavern	32	18	5	9	71	50	41
Gulval	32	12	10	10	72	64	34
St Newlyn East	32	13	7	12	72	73	33
Camborne Town	32	13	6	13	63	64	32
Illogan RBL Res.	32	9	9	14	67	73	27
St Ives T. Res.	32	9	8	15	48	58	26
Raymond Rovers	32	8	5	19	56	101	21
St Agnes Res.	32	7	5	20	49	92	19
Trispen	32	4	6	22	46	97	14
'A' Div. Police	32	3	2	27	45	164	8
Threemilestone SC	32	3	2	27	35	182	8

DIV. TWO	P	W	D	L	F	A	PTS
Chacewater Res.	26	21	2	3	100	40	44
Troon Res.	26	20	2	4	97	33	42
Gweek Park Rgrs	26	18	3	5	93	29	39
Rosudgeon-Kennegy	26	18	1	7	96	35	37
Holman SC Res.	26	17	2	7	76	50	36
Camborne Rovers	26	11	3	12	81	69	25
Camb. Sch. of Mines	26	9	4	13	51	79	22
Truro G.W.R. Res.	26	9	3	14	74	80	21
Frogpool-Cusgarne	26	8	5	13	53	67	21
St Ives T. 'A'	26	9	2	15	46	65	20
Trispen Res.	26	9	2	15	49	87	20
Newlyn East Res.	26	9	1	16	66	119	19
St Erth	26	4	5	17	56	92	13
St Day Res.	26	1	3	22	26	119	5

DIV. THREE	P	W	D	L	F	A	PTS
Trelawney	24	21	3	0	132	28	45
Castle United	24	18	3	3	92	25	39
Gulval Res.	24	14	3	7	69	43	31
Cubert	24	11	6	7	78	56	28
Carharrack Res.	24	11	5	8	64	60	27
Duchy Res.	24	12	2	10	71	64	26
Goonhavern Res.	24	10	3	11	51	49	23
Marazion B. 'A'	24	10	3	11	48	58	23
Long Rock 'A'	24	9	2	13	71	95	20
Perranporth Res.	24	9	1	14	45	79	19
Frogpool-Cus. Res.	24	4	5	15	34	84	13
Rosudgeon-K. Res.	24	5	1	18	38	86	11
Camborne T. 'A'	24	3	1	20	38	104	7

JEWSON SOUTH WESTERN LEAGUE

President: Mr A Jewells.

Chairman: Mr T H Scott.

Hon. Secretary: Mr Melvyn Goodenough, Rose Cottage, Horrelsford, Milton Damerel, Holsworthy EX22 7DH
(0409 261402)

Truro City completed the 'double' in 1992-93 taking the League championship for the first time for 23 years, and the League Cup by defeating Falmouth Town in the final - this was their first League Cup success since 1966-67 when they shared the trophy with St Blazey. Bodmin Town clinched the runners-up spot on the final day of the season with a 3-0 win at Falmouth Town.

Newcomers Mullion enjoyed a successful season finishing in ninth place. Devon & Cornwall Police won the Devon Premier Cup, and Launceston reached the final of the Cornwall Senior Cup where they were narrowly defeated by Saltash United of the Great Mills Western League.

Leslie Pearce from St Austell was the top marked referee, Porthleven took the League's Sporting Trophy, and newcomers Mullion were awarded the 'Best Kept Ground' trophy. For the coming season the bottom clubs, St Austell and Torpoint Athletic, are re-elected whilst Okehampton Argyle, from the Devon & Exeter League, have successfully applied to join.

M Goodenough, Hon. Secretary.

FINAL TABLE	P	W	D	L	F	A	PTS
Truro City	32	23	3	6	72	28	49
Bodmin Town	32	20	6	6	84	46	46
Newquay	32	20	5	7	76	39	45
Launceston	32	17	10	5	81	41	44
St Blazey	32	14	9	9	71	65	37
Falmouth Town	32	15	6	11	77	51	36
Holsworthy	32	12	8	12	49	54	30
Tavistock	32	11	7	14	53	77	30
Mullion	32	9	10	13	51	61	28
Appledore	32	10	8	14	56	73	28
Penzance	32	10	6	16	65	69	26
D. & C. Police	32	12	5	15	61	69	*26
Porthleven	32	9	7	16	69	82	25
Wadebridge Town	32	8	9	15	49	87	25
Millbrook	32	8	8	16	50	69	24
Torpoint Athletic	32	8	7	17	44	68	23
St Austell	32	7	4	21	61	89	18

* - 3pts points deducted

LEAGUE CUP 1992-93

Preliminary Round
Porthleven 2, Tavistock 0

First Round
Devon & Cornwall Police 1, Truro City 2
Falmouth Town 3, Bodmin Town 1
Mullion 4, Millbrook 1
Penzance 2, Porthleven 0
St Austell 3, Appledore/B.A.A.C. 1
St Blazey 1, Launceston 2
Torpoint Athletic 1, Newquay 4
Wadebridge Town 1, Holsworthy 2

Quarter-Finals
St Austell 1, Falmouth Town 2
Truro City 1, Launceston 0
Mullion 1, Penzance 2
Newquay 1, Holsworthy 1
rep: Holsworthy 0, Newquay 1

Semi-Finals
Newquay 0, Falmouth Town 1 *(at St Austell)*
Truro City 2, Penzance 1 *(at Falmouth)*

Final *(at Porthleven)*: Truro City 4, Falmouth Town 1

Leading Scorers:
A Waddell (Bodmin Town) 35, B Swiggs (Launceston) 31, S O'Brien (Penzance) 25, D Downing (Appledore) 23, S Wherry (Truro City) 20.

RESULT CHART 1992-93

HOME TEAM	1	2	3	4	5	6	7	8	9	10	11	12	13	14	15	16	17
1. Appledore	*	0-2	2-2	0-4	3-1	0-0	0-4	1-2	2-4	4-1	0-0	2-1	4-5	3-3	6-1	1-2	3-3
2. Bodmin	0-2	*	3-5	2-1	2-0	6-3	3-0	2-2	4-0	5-1	3-1	1-0	4-2	2-1	6-1	2-0	2-3
3. DC Police	1-3	1-3	*	3-3	1-4	2-3	3-1	3-0	1-0	4-2	2-3	4-1	1-2	3-2	1-0	1-2	2-2
4. Falmouth	10-1	0-3	5-2	*	2-0	2-7	4-1	0-1	3-3	2-2	1-0	6-3	1-2	5-0	3-2	0-2	7-0
5. Holsworthy	2-0	3-2	1-0	0-4	*	1-2	1-1	2-1	1-1	3-2	2-2	1-6	2-3	3-1	1-0	1-1	1-2
6. Launceston	0-1	1-1	2-3	1-0	3-0	*	3-3	1-0	2-1	1-2	1-1	9-2	1-1	7-1	8-2	3-1	7-2
7. Millbrook	1-5	2-4	1-1	0-1	1-0	2-1	*	4-2	0-2	2-3	3-1	5-2	1-1	2-2	2-2	1-2	3-1
8. Mullion	4-1	1-3	3-1	2-3	1-1	1-1	5-2	*	1-5	1-1	1-1	3-3	0-2	1-2	2-2	0-2	1-1
9. Newquay	3-0	1-1	2-1	1-0	1-0	2-2	4-0	3-0	*	4-2	5-3	3-2	3-4	3-1	7-0	0-1	2-1
10. Penzance	0-1	1-1	1-1	1-3	2-2	1-2	2-3	3-2	0-1	*	1-1	1-0	4-2	8-1	2-3	1-2	5-2
11. Porthleven	5-1	3-1	5-1	4-3	2-4	1-2	2-2	1-3	2-4	0-5	*	7-2	3-6	4-2	1-5	2-4	0-0
12. St Austell	1-1	1-5	2-1	1-1	2-4	0-1	2-1	5-0	5-4			*	2-3	6-2	1-1	1-2	1-2
13. St Blazey	3-2	4-4	2-3	1-1	2-2	1-1	0-0	3-1	1-5	3-1	2-1	5-1	*	4-1	1-3	1-1	2-3
14. Tavistock	1-1	2-0	3-1	2-0	0-1	1-2	1-0	3-3	1-1	4-2	0-4	3-1	3-2	*	3-0	0-2	3-1
15. Torpoint	1-5	1-1	0-1	0-1	0-0	0-0	5-1	0-1	0-1	2-1	2-3	4-1	0-0	2-2	*	0-2	2-0
16. Truro City	5-0	2-3	4-0	3-0	1-0	0-0	2-0	0-1	2-1	1-2	5-0	3-2	3-0	2-3	2-0	*	5-2
17. Wadebridge	1-1	1-3	2-5	1-1	3-5	0-4	2-1	2-2	1-0	1-5	4-2	1-1	3-1	1-1	1-3	0-6	*

APPLEDORE-BIDEFORD A.A.C.

Manager: Jeff Snell   **Asst Manager:** Cliff Cann   **Coach:** Ian Mansford.
Secretary: Eddie Nichols, 14 Alexandra Terrace, Bideford EX39 2PL (0237 475993).
Ground: Marshford (0237 277099)   **Floodlights:** No   **Stand:** Yes.
Directions: Before Appledore, on right of A386 approaching town.
Colours: Yellow & blue/blue/yellow   **Change colours:** All blue.
Top Scorer 92-93: D Downing.   **Record defeat:** 1-10 v Falmouth (A), S.W.L. 92-93.

BODMIN TOWN

Chairman: Mr A J Gynn   **Vice Chairman:** Mr C Hooper   **President:** Mr R Flowerdew
Secretary: Martin Mullis, 24 Jubilee Terrace, Bodmin PL31 2QE (0208 776685).
Manager: Ricky Cardew   **Physio:** Jim Brewer   **Comm. Mgr:** Mrs Sheila Chapman
Ground: Priory Park (0208 78165) - Just off town centre in large park complex, at rear of town car park.
Capacity: **Cover:** Grandstand   **Seats:** Yes   **Floodlights:** Yes   **Founded:** 1889
Colours: Amber & black/black   **Change colours:** All sky
Programme: 20 pages, 30p   **Programme Editor:** Secretary   **Club Shop:** No.
Sponsors: Gynn Construction   **Nickname:** Black & Ambers
Midweek home matchday: Wednesday   **Reserve team's League:** East Cornwall Premier.
Record win: 14-1 v Bugle (H), South Western Lg Cup 88-89.
Clubhouse: Mon-Thurs 6-11pm, Fri-Say noon-11pm, Sun noon-3 & 7-10.30pm. Bar snacks available most times.
Captain 92-93: Paul Mildon   **Top Scorer 92-93:** Andy Waddell   **P.o.Y. 92-93:** Gerry Westlake
Honours: South Western Lg 90-91 (R-up 92-93 Lg Cup R-up 77-78 88-89).

DEVON & CORNWALL POLICE

Chairman: Vacant   **Vice Chairman:** Vacant   **President:** Mr J Evans.
Secretary: Steve Bennett, C/O Police Station, Budshill Way, Crownhill, Plymouth PL6 5HT (0752 691227).
Manager: Jon Hillson.   **Asst Manager:** Peter May   **Physio:** Dave Cook
Press Officer: Sam Balsdon   **Commercial Manager:** Alan Eva.
Ground: Mill Bay Park, Plymouth   **Clubhouse:** No. Matchdays tea bar sells light snacks.
Directions: Ground in West Hoe Road, on The Hoe, Plymouth, behind the 'Pavilions' leisure centre complex in Union Street. Less than a mile from both main bus and railway stations.
Seats: No   **Cover:** No   **Capacity:** 2,000   **Floodlights:** No   **Founded:** 1967.
Colours: All blue   **Change colours:** All yellow   **Nickname:** None.
Programme: 28 pages, with admission   **Programme Editor:** Sam Balsdon   **Club Shop:** No.
Previous Leagues: None   **Previous Grounds:** Various prior to 1991-92.
Sponsors: Intercounty Transport, Launceston
Midweek home matchday: Tuesday   **Reserve team:** None.
Record win: 10-0 v Peel Centre   **Record defeat:** 3-8 v Porthleven (A), Lge 91-92.
Club record scorer: Gerry Nardiello   **Club record appearances:** Wayne Arthur.
Captain 92-93: Steve Spear   **Top Scorer 92-93:** Dave Street   **P.o.Y. 92-93:** Simon Tremaine
Hons: Devon Premier Cup 92-93, South Western Lg Cup R-up 91-92, South West Co's Police Cup(4) 87-88 90-92, Falfield Police Cup(12) 69-72 73-75 76-77 78-79 80-81 85-86 87-89 91-92, Wirral Programme Award for South Western Lg 91-92 92-93.

FALMOUTH TOWN

Chairman: Malcolm Newland   **Vice Chairman:** Paul Ashburn   **President:** Seb Coe.
Secretary: Dave Donohue, 115 Longfield, Falmouth TR11 4SR (0326 316642).
Manager: Trevor Mewton   **Ground:** Bickland Park, Bickland Vale, Falmouth, Cornwall (0326 75156).
Directions: On west edge of town - follow signs for Treginiggie Industrial Estate. One and a half miles from Penmere Halt (BR) on Falmouth-Truro branch line.
Seats: 300   **Cover:** 1,000   **Capacity:** 8,000   **Floodlights:** Yes   **Founded:** 1946.
Colours: Amber/black/amber   **Change colours:** All white.   **Club Shop:** No.
Previous Ground: Ashfield   **Record Gate:** 8,000 v Oxford Utd, FA Cup 1966
Nickname: Town   **Record win:** 10-1 v Appledore (H), S.W.L. 92-93.
Programme: 16 pages, 30p   **Editor:** Keith Rashleigh (0326 317162)   **Sponsors:** Stralfors
Midweek home matchday: Tues/Wed   **Reserve team's League:** Jollys Cornwall Comb.
Clubhouse: Mon-Fri 7-11pm, Sat 12-11pm, Sun 12-3 & 7-10.30pm. Meals available.
Captain 92-93: George Torrance   **Top Scorer 92-93:** Alan Lenton   **P.o.Y. 92-93:** Tommy Matthews
Hons: FA Vase QF 86-87, FA Cup 1st Rd 62-63 67-68 69-70, Cornish Snr Cup(10) 61-62 64-66 67-68 70-71 73-74 75-79 (R-up(7) 66-67 72-73 81-83 89-92), Western Lg(4) 74-78 (Lg Cup 74-75, Alan Young Cup 74-75 75-76 77-78(joint)), South Western Lg(12) 61-62 65-66 67-68 70-74 85-87 88-90 91-92 (R-up 58-59 64-65 69-70 87-88, Lg Cup(9) 57-59 61-63 67-68 70-71 85-86 90-92 (R-up(5) 59-60 71-72 86-88 92-93)), Cornwall Charity Cup 59-60, Cornwall Comb.(res) 83-84 (Supplementary Cup R-up 90-91).

HOLSWORTHY

Manager: Terry Andrews.   **Assistant Manager:** Peter England.
Secretary: Ray Latty, 13 Victoria Square, Holsworthy, Devon EX22 6AA (0409 253529).
Ground: Upcott Field (0409 254295)   **Nickname:** Magpies **Cover:** Yes   **Floodlights:** No.
Programme: 8 pages, £1 with entry   **Editor:** Terry Irewin.
Colours: Black & white/black/black   **Change colours:** Gold/white/gold.   **Nickname:** Magpies
Record defeat: 1-9 v St Blazey (A), S.W.L. 88-89   **Hons:** Devon Snr Cup 53-54 (Prem. Cup 71-72 76-77)

LAUNCESTON

Chairman: D Redstone   **Vice Chairman:** D Heard   **President:** D Viggers.
Secretary: Chris Martin, 3 Tavistock Road, Launceston, Cornwall PL15 9HA (0566 776175).
Manager: Roger Fice   **General Manager:** Keith Ellacott.
Physio: D James   **Ground:** Pennygillam, Launceston (0566 773279)
Directions: Follow signs to Pennygillam Industrial Est., just off main A30 - ground 400yds on left.
Programme: Yes   **Seats:** 150   **Cover:** 150   **Floodlights:** Yes   **Nickname:** Clarets
Cols: Claret & blue **Change:** Sky   **Midweek matchday:** Tues/Wed   **Club Shop:** No.
Sponsors: D Viggers Coal   **Reserve team's League:** Plymouth & Dist.
Clubhouse: Open after every game. Bar meals.
Captain 92-93: G Battams   **Top Scorer 92-93:** Bradley Swiggs   **P.o.Y. 92-93:** D Jones/ G McMillan
Hons: S. Western Lg R-up 84-85, Cornish Snr Cup 1899-1900 00-01 82-83 (R-up 92-93, Charity Cup R-up 88-89).

MILLBROOK

President: Mrs E Weekes **Chairman:** Mr J Weekes **Vice Chairman:** Mr K Townsend.
Secretary: Murray Hyslop, 14 St Andrews Street, Millbrook, Cornwall PL10 1BE (0752 823271).
Manager: Mr J Bennett **Asst Manager:** Mr S Matthews **Press Officer:** Mr W Linney.
Ground: Mill Park, Millbrook, Cornwall (0752 822113)
Directions: From Torpoint Ferry - 3 miles to Antony on A374, fork left, after 1 mile turn left again and follow B3247 to Millbrook (3 miles), take road marked 'Town Centre Southdown', right at mini-r'bout after quarter mile, ground clearly visible. From Tamar Bridge - follow signs for Torpoint, 2 miles after Polbathic take right turning marked Millbrook, 5 miles to Millbrook then proceed as above.
Capacity: **Seats:** None **Cover:** 200 **Floodlights:** Yes **Founded:** 1973.
Colours: Black & white **Change colours:** Red/black/black **Nickname:** The Brook
Prev. Ground: Insworke Pk (14yrs) **Prev. Lges:** Plymouth Comb.(8yrs)/ Plymouth & Dist.(6yrs).
Programme: 20 pages, 10p **Editor:** Mr J Weekes (0752 822637) **Club Shop:** No.
Club Sponsors: Plymouth Boat Cruises Ltd.
Midweek home matchday: Tuesday **Reserve team's League:** Plymouth & District.
Clubhouse: Weekdays 7-11pm, Sat 11am-11pm, Sun noon-3 & 7.30-10.30. Hot food (chips, burgers etc) available during and after matchdays.
Top Scorer 92-93: Richard Avery **P.O.Y. 92-93:** Rob Gregory.
Club record scorer: Unknown **Club record appearances:** John Horne 215.
Hons: South Western Lg R-up 81-82, Cornwall Snr Cup R-up 83-84 (Charity Cup 84-85, Jnr Cup 75-76), Plymouth & District Lg 80-81 (Div 1 R-up 76-77).

MULLION

President: Eric Meagor **Chairman:** Derek Wilkes **Vice Chairman:** Paul Hull.
Secretary: Stewart Colin Westwood, 4 St Mellans Terrace, Mullion, Helston, Cornwall TR12 7EH (0326 240991).
Manager: Clive Biddick **Coach:** Geoff Freeman **Comm. Mgr:** Peter Butler.
Press Officer: Secretary **Physios:** Norman Carey/ Mick Letford.
Ground: Clifden Parc, Mullion (0326 240676)
Directions: Leave Helston on A3083 signed Lizard, at Mullion Holiday Park turn right onto B3296 signed Mullion Cove, thru Mullion 1-way system and continue on B3296, take 1st right after cricket field (on left), right again after 100yds - ground 50yds on left. Helston-Lizard bus passes ground.
Capacity: 2,000 **Seats:** None **Cover:** 100 **Floodlights:** No **Founded:** 1902.
Colours: Red & white **Change colours:** All white. **Nickname:** Gulls.
Previous Leagues: Helston & Dist. 02-18/ Cornwall County 18-48/ Cornwall Snr 48-56/ Falmouth & Helston 56-69/ Cornwall Comb. 69-92.
Previous Grounds: Garro Lane/ The Commons
Club Sponsors: Compass Forest Products Ltd/ West Bromwich Building Society.
Record Gate: 1,550 v Helston, Cornwall County League, 33-34.
Prog.: 30 pages **Editor:** Secretary **Club Shop:** Yes - contact Beau Meagor (0326 240044).
Midweek home matchday: Tuesday **Reserve team's League:** Cornwall Combination.
Record win: 16-0 v Tideford (A), Cornwall Snr Cup 86-87.
Clubhouse: Normal licensing hours. Darts, pool. Hot & cold snacks and meals after matches.
Captain 92-93: Alan Carey **Top Scorer 92-93:** James Eddy
P.O.Y. 92-93: Stuart Wilkes **Club record scorer:** Andrew Harry.
Hons: Cornwall Comb.(3) 85-86 90-92 (R-up(4) 80-83 86-87, Lg Cup(2) 90-92 (R-up 88-89), Suppl. Cup 85-86), Evely Cup 90-91 91-92.

Mullion F.C., who had a happy first season in the Jewson South Western League.

NEWQUAY

Manager: Ray Nicholls **Secretary:** Brian Biggin, 8 Mitchell Ave., Newquay TR7 1BN (0637 875623).
Ground: Mount Wise (0637 872935) **Nickname:** Peppermints.
Directions: From Newquay (BR) follow 1-way system for 2 miles - ground signed on left just before Windsor Hotel.
Seats: 250 **Cover:** 500 **Capacity:** 4,000 **Floodlights:** Yes **Founded:** 1890.
Colours: Red & white/white/white **Change colours:** Sky/navy/sky.
Prev. Names: Newquay 1890-1903/ N'quay One & All 03-12/ N'quay Utd 20-27/ N'quay Rovers 27-37.
Previous Leagues: West Cornwall/ Plymouth & District 21-27/ Cornish Senior 31-51.
Hons: FA Vase 3rd Rd 90-91, Cornish Snr Cup 34-35 52-53 54-55 56-57 91-92 (R-up(9) 05-07 08-09 25-26 33-34 35-36 57-58 69-70 84-85), S. Western Lg(7) 58-60 77-78 79-80 81-82 83-84 87-88 (R-up 57-58 85-86, Lg Cup 55-56 88-89 (R-up(4) 56-58 79-81), Cornish Charity Cup(13) 06-07 08-09 53-56 57-59 62-63 69-70 74-75 76-78 88-89 (R-up(9) 07-08 20-21 56-57 60-61 73-74 75-76 81-82 84-86), W. Cornwall Lg 06-07 (R-up(2) 07-09), Cornish Snr Lg Herald Cup 34-35 (R-up(7) 33-34 35-36 49-51 55-57 58-59).

OKEHAMPTON ARGYLE

Chairman: Mr J Domaile **President:** Mr G Muddaford
Secretary: Colin Beer, 76 North Street, Okehampton, Devon (0837 52989).
Manager: Ollie Burton **Commercial Manager:** Don Hatherley.
Ground: Simmons Park, Okehampton, Devon.
Directions: From town centre follow signs to Swimming Pool - ground behind at top end of park.
Seats: None **Cover:** Yes **Programme:** Yes **Floodlights:** No **Founded:** 1929
Colours: All blue **Change colours:** All red **Nickname:** Argyle.
Previous Grounds: None **Prev. Lge:** Devon & Exeter (pre-1993) **Club Shop:** No
Club Sponsors: Okehampton Times **Record Gate:** 800 (approx.)
Reserves' League: North Devon **Clubhouse:** Under construction.
Captain 92-93: T Watkins **Top Scorer & P.o.Y. 92-93:** A Windser **Hons:** Devon Jnr Cup 47-48.

PENZANCE

President: Len Stanbury **Chairman:** Jim Dann
Secretary: Brian Harris, Hillview Cottage, Canonstown, Hayle TR27 6ND (0736 740062).
Manager: Roger Toms **Coach:** T.B.A. **Trainer:** Ken Prowse.
Ground: Penlee Park (0736 61964) **Floodlights:** Yes **Seats:** Yes **Founded:** 1888.
Directions: Seafront road past harbour, after amusement arcade turn right at r'bout (Alexander Rd), ground second right. Fifteen minutes walk from Penzance (BR); directions as above.
Colours: Black & white/black/black **Change colours:** All blue **Nickname:** Magpies.
Clubhouse: Yes **Reserve team's league:** Cornwall Comb.
Captain 92-93: Mark Damerell **Top Scorer 92-93:** S O'Brien.
Players progressing to Football League: Gerry Gazzard (Brentford), Tony Kellow (Exeter).
Hons: Cornish Snr Cup 1892-93 95-96 97-98 98-99 1903-04 07-08 47-48 60-61 72-73 80-81 (R-up 1896-97 99-1900 00-01 04-05 48-49 49-50 54-55 56-57 74-75), South Western Lg 55-56 56-57 74-75 (Lg Cup R-up 60-61), Cornwall Charity Cup 47-48 48-49 (R-up 21-22 63-64), Cornwall Snr Lg Div 2 57-58 (Div 2 Cup 53-54 54-55), Cornwall Comb. R-up 65-66 (Lg Cup 69-70 (R-up 81-82)), Cornwall Jnr Cup (West) 03-04 04-05 05-06 07-08 09-10.

Penzance F.C. 1992-93, who had their highest league finish for a decade and even topped the table in October. Back Row (L/R): R Toms (Manager), N Kellow, L Bushby, S McDonnell, M Honey, J McCallum, T Keneally, M Damerell, B Jewell (First Aid). Front: K Rule, N Phillips, P Scrace, M Davies, S O'Brien. Photo - Richard Brock.

PORTHLEVEN

President: Mr W O Allen **Chairman:** Mr W Tearney **Vice Chairman:** Mr L Williams
Secretary: Keith Downing, 27 Gibson Way, Porthleven, Helston TR13 9AN (0326 561160).
Manager: Charlie Coombes **Coach:** Paul Christie **Comm. Mgr:** Mr V James.
Ground: Gala Parc, Mill Lane, Porthleven (0208 574754).
Directions: Arriving from Penzance on A394, B3304 into Porthleven, ground on left immediately before town. Coming from Helston on B3304 ground on right as you exit town. Buses from Helston and Penzance.
Capacity: **Seats:** None **Cover:** Yes **Floodlights:** No. **Programme:** 20p
Colours: Amber/black **Change colours:** All blue **Nickname:** Fishermen
Previous Leagues: West Penwith/ Cornwall Snr/ South Western 66-77/ Cornwall Combination 77-89.
Reserves' Lge: Cornwall Comb. **Previous Grounds:** Treza Downs/ Sunset Farm.
Clubhouse: Mon-Fri 7-11pm, Sat 11am-8pm, Sun 11am-3 & 7-10.30pm. Full food menu.
P.o.Y. 92-93: P Coombes **Captain & Top Scorer 92-93:** John Burrows
Hons: Sth Western Lg R-up 72-73, Cornwall Comb.(6) 59-60 63-64 65-67 78-79 88-89 (Lg Cup(6) 62-63 64-66 83-85 86-87, Suppl. Cup 88-89 91-92(res)), Cornwall Charity Cup 70-71, Cornwall Snr Cup R-up 68-69, George Evely Cup 64-65 65-66 83-84 86-87, West Penwith Lg, Penzance Hosp. Cup, Penzance Charity Cup.

ST AUSTELL

Chairman: Reg Pope **Asst Chairman:** Derek Silk
Secretary: Peter Beard, 24 Alexandra Rd, St Austell, Cornwall PL25 4QP (0726 64138).
Manager: Glyn Avery **Asst Manager:** Colin Bunney **Physio:** N McKenna
Ground: Poltair Park (0726 77099). **Directions:** 5 mins walk north of St Austell (BR).
Seats: 200 **Cover:** 300 **Capacity:** 8,000 **Floodlights:** No **Founded:** 1890.
Colours: White/black/black **Change colours:** Blue/black/blue.
Previous Leagues: Rocky Park (1890s) **Record Gate:** 15,000 v Penzance, Senior Cup 1949.
Hons: South Western Lg 68-69 (R-up(4) 63-64 65-66 71-73, Lg Cup 64-65 71-73 87-88 (R-up 52-53 68-69 70-71 89-90)), Cornish Snr Cup(11) 11-14 33-34 38-39 45-47 63-64 68-69 71-72.

ST BLAZEY

Vice Chairman: Mr P Clemow.   **President:** Mr O Rowe   **Chairman:** Mr H Cooke
Secretary/Press Officer: Mike Newcombe, 29 Par Green, Par, Cornwall PL24 2AF (0726 818334).
Manager: David Pearce   **Coach:** David Pearce   **Physio:** Richy Brown
Ground: Blaise Park, Station Road, St Blazey (0726 814110).
Directions: A390 Liskeard-St Austell road, turn into Station Road at lights in St Blazey village; ground 100 yards on left. One and a half miles from Par (BR).
Seats: 200   **Cover:** 700   **Capacity:** 3,500   **Floodlights:** Yes   **Founded:** 1896.
Colours: Green/black   **Change colours:** All white   **Nickname:** Saints
Previous Grounds: None.
Previous Leagues: Bodmin & Dist. 07-14 20-26/ St Austell & Dist. 14-20/ Cornwall County 27-29/ Cornwall Snr 31-33 46-51/ Plymouth & Dist. 29-31 37-39.
Programme: 16 pages, 25p   **Programme Editor:** Secretary   **Club Shop:** No.
Sponsors: Smith & Treffry Ltd   **Record Gate:** 6,500 v St Austell, Cornwall Snr Cup 48-49.
Midweek home matchday: Tuesday   **Reserve team's League:** East Cornwall Premier.
Record win: 15-0 v Tavistock (H) and v Nanpean Rovers (A).
Record defeat: 0-14 v Wadebridge Town (A)
Clubhouse: Weekdays 11am-3pm & 7-11pm, Sat 11am-11.45pm, Sun noon-2.30 & 7.11pm. Bar snacks.
Captain & P.o.Y. 92-93: K Cook   **Top Scorer 92-93:** G Harrison
Club record scorer: B Tallamy   **Club record appearances:** W Isbell.
Hons: South Western Lg(6) 54-55 57-58 62-64 80-81 82-83 (R-up(9) 51-52 55-57 61-62 84-85 86-87 88-91, Lg Cup 53-54 56-57 66-67(joint) 81-82 86-87 (R-up 61-62 63-64 82-83 84-85 90-91)), Cornish Snr Cup 35-36 49-50 53-54 55-56 57-58 59-60 62-63 86-87, Cornish Charity Cup 35-36 56-57 83-84, Cornwall Snr Lg Cup (Herald Cup) 35-36 48-49.

TAVISTOCK

President: Mr G Worth   **Chairman:** Mr R A Fenner   **Vice Chairman:** Mr D R D Pethick
Secretary: Philip Lowe, 1 Bainbridge Court, Colebrook, Plympton, PL7 4HH (0752 335273).
Manager: Steve Metters   **Asst Manager:** T.B.A.   **Coach:** Alan Gillett.
Physio: Les Mewton   **Press Officer:** Chairman.
Ground: Langsford Park, Crowndale Rd, Tavistock (0822 614447)
Directions: A386 from Plymouth, left after Ford garage into Crowndale Rd, ground half mile on left.
Capacity: 2,000   **Seats:** 200   **Cover:** 200   **Floodlights:** Yes   **Founded:** 1888.
Colours: Black & red/black/red   **Change colours:** Blue & white or yellow & white
Prev. Lge: Plymouth & Dist. 06-52   **Previous Grounds:** Green Lane/ Sandy Park (pre-1940).
Programme: 32 pages, with entry   **Programme Editor:** Secretary   **Club Shop:** No.
Sponsors: Dave Carter Spts, Plymouth   **Record Gate:** 5,000 v Calstock, Bedford Cup final 1952.
Midweek home matchday: Tuesday   **Reserve team's League:** Plymouth & District.
Nickname: 'Tavy' or 'Lambs'   **Record win:** 10-0 v Penzance (A), South Western Lg 91-92.
Record transfer fee paid: Nil   **Received:** £1,000 for Neil Langman (Plymouth, Sept '53).
Players progressing to Football League: Peter Langman (Plymouth, 1951), Neil Langman (Plymouth, 1953).
Clubhouse: Open all day Saturday and evenings 6.30-10.30 or 11pm. Hot & cold food. Darts, pool, Sky T.V.
Captain 92-93: Darren Babb   **Top Scorer 92-93:** Jeff Babb
P.O.Y. 92-93: Tony Pratt   **Club record appearances:** A Pethick 1,000+.
Hons: Devon Snr Cup 1889-90 1968-69 77-78 81-82, South Western Lg Cup 68-69 (R-up 76-77 83-84), Bedford Cup on numerous occasions.

TORPOINT ATHLETIC

Manager: Phil Cardew
Secretary: Vic Grimwood, 43 Henerdon Heights, Plympton PL7 3EY (0752 81344).
Ground: Mill Field (0752 812889)
Directions: Bear left from Torpoint ferry, ground down hill on left after half a mile.
Clubhouse: Yes   **Programme:** Yes   **Seats:** Yes   **Cover:** Yes   **Floodlights:** No
Colours: Gold & black stripes/black/black   **Change colours:** All white.
Previous Grounds: Plymouth & District League.
Hons: South Western Lg 64-65 66-67 (Lg Cup R-up 65-66), Cornish Snr Cup 1896-97 1905-06 06-07 08-09 09-10 19-20 28-29 32-33.

TRURO CITY

Manager: Steve Massey
Secretary: Ray Rowe, 5 Alverton Gardens, Truro, Cornwall TR1 1JA (0872 70684).
Ground: Treyew Road, Truro, Cornwall (0872 78853)   **Seats:** Yes   **Floodlights:** Yes.
Directions: On A39 by-pass south of city. 10 mins walk from BR station; up hill and left at junction.
Colours: Red & black/black/black   **Change colours:** Yellow/red/red.
Top Scorer 92-93: Steve Wherry 20   **Reserve Team's League:** Cornish Combination.
Hons: South Western Lg 60-61 69-70 92-93 (R-up 54-55 62-63 66-67 67-68 70-71, Lg Cup 59-60 66-67(joint) 92-93 (R-up 54-55 58-59 67-68)), Cornish Snr Cup 1894-95 1901-02 02-03 10-11 23-24 26-27 27-28 37-38 58-59 66-67 69-70, Cornish Charity Cup 19-20 28-29 29-30 30-31 49-50 64-65 80-81, Cornish Snr Lg 31-32 32-33, Cornwall Comb. Supplementary Cup 92-93(res).

WADEBRIDGE TOWN

Manager: Steve Cudmore.
Secretary: Barry Cudmore, 3 Marine Terrace, Wadebridge, Cornwall PL27 7AJ (0208 813826).
Ground: Bodieve Park (0208 812537)   **Seats:** Yes   **Cover:** Ample   **Floodlights:** No
Directions: At junction of A39 and B3314 to east of Wadebridge.   **Nickname:** Bridgers.
Colours: Red/red/white   **Change colours:** All blue.
Reserve Team's League: East Cornwall Premier.
Hons: South Western Lg R-up 68-69 78-79 79-80 (Lg Cup 74-75 75-76 77-78 79-80 84-85 (R-up 62-63 69-70 81-82, Cornish Snr Cup 79-80, Cornish Charity Cup 26-27 33-34 51-52 63-64 72-73 75-76 81-82 84-85.

	83/4	84/5	85/6	86/7	87/8	88/9	89/0	90/1	91/2	92/3
Appledore/Bideford AAC	8	7	14	14	12	18	11	9	7	10
Bodmin Town	20	18	4	5	4	3	3	1	5	2
Bugle	4	1	5	12	20	15	5	8	3	–
Clyst Rovers	16	11	11	10	19	14	8	14	6	–
Devon & Cornwall Police	–	–	–	–	–	–	–	–	16	12
Falmouth Town	–	6	1	1	2	2	1	3	1	6
Holsworthy	15	19	20	18	17	17	17	16	11	7
Launceston	2	15	19	17	13	5	7	15	15	4
Millbrook	3	5	3	3	5	10	6	11	14	15
Mullion	–	–	–	–	–	–	–	–	–	9
Newquay	1	3	2	8	1	4	4	4	2	3
Newton Abbot	6	10	10	9	11	13	–	–	–	–
Oak Villa	–	–	–	–	16	11	–	–	–	–
Penryn Athletic	–	–	15	–	–	–	–	–	–	–
Penzance	18	17	17	19	15	16	15	17	18	11
Plymouth Civil Service	11	13	–	–	–	–	–	–	–	–
Plymouth Command	19	–	–	–	–	–	–	–	–	–
Portleven	–	–	–	–	–	–	16	13	8	13
St Austell	5	16	8	6	6	12	13	5	13	17
St Blazey	7	2	9	2	3	2	2	2	9	5
Tavistock	14	12	16	16	18	9	9	12	17	8
Teignmouth	17	14	18	13	10	–	–	–	–	–
Torpoint Athletic	10	9	12	15	14	8	14	6	10	16
Torquay United Res	–	–	13	7	9	–	–	–	–	–
Torrington	12	–	–	–	–	–	–	–	–	–
Truro City	13	8	6	11	8	6	10	7	4	1
Wadebridge Town	9	4	7	4	7	7	12	10	12	14
No. of Clubs	**20**	**19**	**20**	**19**	**20**	**18**	**17**	**17**	**18**	**17**

CORNISH GUARDIAN
EAST CORNWALL PREMIER LEAGUE

	P	W	D	L	F	A	PTS
Liskeard Ath. Res.	34	23	9	2	89	30	55
Nanpean Rovers	34	20	10	4	87	47	50
Roche	34	22	5	7	114	43	49
St Dennis	34	21	6	7	83	48	48
Bude	34	20	6	8	81	54	46
Sticker	34	18	8	8	83	54	44
Bugle	34	20	2	12	89	66	42
Saltash Utd Res.	34	16	9	9	70	48	41
St Blazey Res.	34	14	8	12	84	65	36
Camelford	34	13	8	13	59	53	34
Bodmin Town Res.	34	12	8	14	83	79	32
Padstow United	34	11	9	14	65	62	31
St Breward	34	9	7	18	56	68	25
Callington Town	34	9	6	19	57	76	24
Riviera Coasters	34	8	2	24	45	104	18
Foxhole Stars	34	5	5	24	41	99	15
Wadebridge T. Res.	34	6	2	26	51	120	14
Tintagel	34	2	4	28	16	136	8

LEAGUE CUP Prel. Round
Callington v Liskeard Res.	1-1,0-5
St Breward v Camelford	1-1,2-3
Padstow Utd v Saltash Utd Res.	1-2

First Round
Bodmin Town Res. v Bude	3-0
Bugle v Riviera Coasters	5-0
Foxhole Stars v Camelford	3-2
Nanpean Rvrs v Wadebridge T. Res.	1-0
Roche v Liskeard Ath. Res.	0-0,1-1,1-0
Saltash Res. v Tintagel	0-0,3-0
St Dennis v Sticker	1-1,2-3
St Blazey Res.	bye

Quarter Finals
Bugle v Foxhole Stars	6-2
Bodmin Town Res. v Roche	1-1,2-3
St Blazey Res. v Nanpean Rovers	3-4
Saltash Utd Reserves v Sticker	

Semi Finals
Nanpean Rovers v Sticker	4-2
Roche v Bugle	1-0

Final: Nanpean Rovers 2, Roche 1 (*at St Blazey*)

BUDE
Ground: Broadclose (behind school off Broadclose Hill)   **Secretary:** Miss Brotherton (0288 355855)
Directions: Behind Helston bypass, on right coming from Falmouth.
Clubhouse: Yes   **Cover:** No   **Colours:** Royal Blue

BUGLE
Ground: Molinnis (0726 851123)   **Secretary:** J Hornbuckle (0209 214695)
Ground: Turn off A391 St Austell-Bodmin road into Molinnis (right turn just after Bugle centre if coming from St Austell). 5 mins walk from Bugle BR station (Par-Newquay line) - head towards village and turn left into Molinnis.
Cover: Yes   **Seats:** Yes   **Clubhouse:** Shut   **Floodlights:** No
Colours: White & black   **Previous League:** South Western 1955-92.
Hons: South Western Lg 84-85 (Lg Cup 83-84), Cornish Snr Cup 51-52.

CALLINGTON TOWN
Ground: Callington Community School   **Secretary:** K Hoare (0566 776349)
Directions: Callington school is on right hand side of A388 travelling north of town towards St Austell. Inside school ground keep left for club's pitch.
Clubhouse: No   **Programme:** No   **Cover:** No   **Colours:** Blue.
Hons: League Cup R-up 90-91.   **Previous League:** Plymouth & Dist. Lg (pre-1990).

CAMELFORD
Ground: Tregoodwell, Roughtor Rd, Camelford   **Secretary:** R Cook (0840 213722)
Directions: Heading north east out of Camelford on A39 turn right into Roughtor Rd, ground on left.
Clubhouse: No   **Programme:** No   **Cover:** No   **Colours:** White & black.

FOXHOLE STARS

Ground: Goverseth PF, Goverseth Rd **Secretary:** M Jenkins (0726 66003)
Directions: South on B3279 from Nanpean, right down narrow lane just before row of houses entering Foxhole.
Clubhouse: No (use local W.M.C.) **Cover:** No **Colours:** Black & white
Hons: Lg Cup 90-91

NANPEAN ROVERS

Ground: Victoria Park **Secretary:** A Craddock (0726 823543)
Directions: Ground entrance on left as you travel north through village centre on B3279.
Clubhouse: Yes **Programme:** Yes **Cover:** Yes **Seats:** No.
Colours: Amber and Black **Previous League:** South Western.

PADSTOW UNITED

Ground: Jury Park, Wadebridge Rd, Padstow **Secretary:** Mrs Harris (0841 532349)
Ground Directions: On right hand side of A389 about one mile before Padstow.
Clubhouse: No **Programme:** No **Cover:** No **Colours:** Green.
Hons: Supplementary Cup 88-89.

RIVIERA COASTERS

Ground: St Austell FC (page 798) **Secretary:** G Rowett (0726 64476) **Colours:** Green

ROCHE

Ground: Trezaise Rd, Roche **Secretary:** B Strongman (0726 890838)
Ground Directions: On right hand side of B3274 as you enter Roche from St Austell direction.
Clubhouse: Yes **Programme:** No **Cover:** No **Colours:** Red **Hons:** Lg Cup R-up 92-93, Supplementary Cup runners-up 88-89.

ST BREWARD

Ground: Brake Park, St Breward **Secretary:** Mrs Kay (0208 850030)
Colours: Red & black stripes **Cover:** Yes **Clubhouse:** No.

ST DENNIS

Ground: Boscawen Park, St Dennis **Secretary:** P Searle (0726 63280)
Directions: Coming north on B3279 turn left in St Dennis village centre by Boscawen Hotel.
Clubhouse: Yes **Cover:** No **Colours:** Amber & black
Hons: East Cornwall Lg 87-88 (Lg Cup R-up 88-89).

STICKER

Ground: Ennis Farm, St Stephen Rd, Sticker **Secretary:** G Phillips (0726 61299)
Directions: Travelling west from St Austell on A390, turn right (signed St Stephens) in Sticker village. Ground on right opposite farm.
Clubhouse: No **Cover:** Yes

TINTAGEL

Ground: Memmorial PF, off Bossinney Rd, Tintagel **Secretary:** R Gabriel (0840 770244)
Clubhouse: Yes **Cover:** Yes

The League also contains the Reserve sides of: Bodmin Town (page 796), Liskeard Athletic (page 766), St Blazey (page 799), Saltash United (page 767), and Wadebridge Town (page 799).

JOLLY'S CORNWALL COMBINATION

	P	W	D	L	F	A	PTS
Penryn Athletic	36	25	8	3	98	33	58
Perranwell	36	24	5	7	88	33	53
RNAS Culdrose	36	23	6	7	98	42	52
Falmouth T. Res.	36	21	7	8	81	45	49
Pendeen Rovers	36	19	6	11	75	49	44
St Ives Town	36	17	10	9	47	32	44
Helston Athletic	36	17	7	12	78	54	41
Truro City Res.	36	16	8	12	64	43	40
Mullion Res.	36	15	8	13	58	45	38
St Agnes	36	14	9	13	38	41	37
Mousehole	36	11	9	16	38	51	31
Newquay Res.	36	12	7	17	54	60	29
Ludgvan	36	12	6	18	67	82	29
St Just	36	10	9	17	44	70	29
Penzance Res.	36	10	8	18	46	60	28
Porthleven Res.	36	10	7	18	50	87	27
Illogan RBL	36	7	6	23	37	92	20
Marazion Blues	36	4	11	21	25	76	19
RAF St Mawgan	36	3	6	27	24	116	12

COMBINATION CUP 1992-93

Preliminary Round
St Ives Town v Marazion Blues   4-2
Ludgvan v Pendeen Rovers   1-2
Penzance Reserves v Truro C. Res.   2-1

First Round
Mousehole v Helston Athletic   0-0,0-1
Mullion Res. v Newquay Reserves   1-1,0-2
Pendeen Rovers v RAF St Mawgan   4-1
Penryn Ath. v Illogan RBL   2-2,1-2
Perranwell v St Just   4-0
Penzance Res. v St Agnes   1-3
RNAS Culdrose v Porthleven Res.   2-1
St Ives Town v Falmouth T. Res.   1-2

Quarter Finals:
Newquay Res v Penryn Athletic   1-4
Perranwell v Pendeen Rovers   3-1
RNAS Culdrose v Falmouth T. Res.   1-0
St Agnes v Helston Athletic   1-1,4-0

Semi Finals
Perranwell v Penryn Athletic   3-2   RNAS Culdrose v St Agnes   1-0

Final *(at Falmouth Town FC)*: Perranwell 3, RNAS Culdrose 0

Supplementary Cup Final *(at Penryn Athletic FC)*: Truro City Reserves 1, St Just 0

HELSTON ATHLETIC

Ground: Kellaway Parc, Clodgy Lane (0326 573742) **Secretary:** L Roberts (0326 573419)
Ground Directions: On A394 Helston bypass, on right coming from Falmouth.
Clubhouse: Yes **Programme:** No **Cover:** Yes; clubhouse overhang **Colours:** Royal Blue
Hons: Cornish Senior Cup 36-37, Champ 64-65 87-88 **Reserves:** Falmouth-Helston Lg.

ILLOGAN R.B.L.

Ground: Oxland Park (0209 216488) **Secretary:** S Cooper (0209 842322)
Ground Directions: Turn right for Illogan off Camborne to Redruth road. Ground on right down Richards Lane.
Clubhouse: Yes **Programme:** No **Cover:** Stand **Colours:**
Hons: Champs 70-71 71-72 73-74, Runners-up 69-70 72-73 **Reserves:** W C'wall Mining Lg.

LUDGVAN

Ground: Fairfield (0736 740774) **Secretary:** M Brownfield (0736 740603)
Ground Directions: Turn right off A30 for Ludgvan Leaze (after Crowlas). Ground on right.
Clubhouse: Village Hall **Programme:** Yes **Cover:** Yes **Colours:** Yellow and green
Formed: 1960 **Reserves:** West Penwith League
Hons: League Cup 82-83, Eveley Cup 1983, Penzance & Dist Charity Cup 89-90, West Cornwall Hosp Cup 89-90

MARAZION BLUES

Ground: Trevenner (0736 740774) **Secretary:** B Richards (0736 69327)
Ground Directions: Through Marazion village and turn up Shop Hill opposite Fire Engine Pub.
Clubhouse: Community Centre **Programme:** No **Cover:** Yes **Colours:** All Blue
Floodlights: Installed during 1990-91 **Reserves:** West Penwith Lg.

MOUSEHOLE

Ground: Trungle Park, Paul **Secretary:** R Walker (0736 68850)
Ground Directions: In Paul village, 1 mile inland from Mousehole. **Formed:** 1922-23
Clubhouse: Yes **Programme:** Yes **Cover:** Yes **Colours:** Green & white hoops **Nickname:** Seagulls
Hons: Runners-up 85-86, League Cup 75-76, Evely Cup 1976 **Reserves:** West Penwith Lg.

PENDEEN ROVERS

Ground: Borlaise Park (0736 788274) **Secretary:** D Trezise (0736 788274)
Ground Directions: B3306 St Ives to St Just road. Ground immediately on left down road to Pendeen Lighthouse.
Clubhouse: Yes **Programme:** Yes **Cover:** Yes **Colours:** Amber and Black **Reserves:** West Penwith Lg.

PENRYN ATHLETIC

Ground: Kernick, Kernick Rd (0326 75182) **Secretary:** M Young (0326 74098)
Ground Directions: Turn off A394 at sign for Kernick Industrial estate. Ground on right on road into town.
Clubhouse: Yes **Programme:** No **Cover:** Yes **Cols:** Red & Black stripes **Reserves:** Falmouth-Helston Lg.
Previous League: South Western 85-86.
Hons: Champs 80-81 81-82 82-83 84-85 86-87 89-90 92-93 (R-up 83-84 88-89), League Cup 87-88 88-89 (R-up 90-91), Evely Cup 88-89.

PERRANWELL

Ground: Perran-Ar-Worthal PF **Secretary:** R McLean (0326 317662)
Ground Directions: On Falmouth to Truro branch-line, or by road 1 mile off A39 (turn right at Perranawortha!).
Clubhouse: No **Cover:** Yes **Colours:** Royal Blue
Hons: Champs 76-77, R-up 75-76 92-93, Lg Cup 92-93 **Reserves:** Falmouth-Helston Lg.

R.A.F. ST MAWGAN

Ground: St Eval **Secretary:** K Edmunds (0637 831007)
Ground Directions: Follow signs for St Eval from St Columb Major. Ground in village on the right.
Clubhouse No **Programme:** No **Cover:** No **Nickname:** The Airmen **Colours:** Blue and white quarters
Hons: Supplementary Cup runners-up 88-89.

R.N.A.S. CULDROSE

Ground: Sports Field (0326 574121 ext 7167) **Secretary:** R Glennie (0326 574121 ext 2265)
Ground Directions: On A3083 Helston to Lizard Road, on right just before turning to St Keverne.
Hons: Lg Cup R-up 92-93 **Reserves:** Falmouth-Helston Lg.

ST AGNES

Ground: Enys Park, West Polperro (0872 553673) **Secretary:** J Stenning (0872 552657)
Ground Directions: On cliffs to the north of the village.
Clubhouse: Yes **Programme:** Yes **Nickname:** Aggie **Colours:** White/Black **Reserves:** Falmouth-Helston Lg.

ST IVES TOWN

Ground: Lelant Saltings **Secretary:**
Ground Directions: Adjacent to Lelant Saltings BR station (St Erth-St Ives line) or fifteen mins walk from St Erth main line station. By road, turn off A30 for St Ives onto A3074, right at 1st island and left into 'Merlins' theme park - ground car park at end.
Clubhouse: No **Cover:** Yes **Colours:** Blue **Reserves:** Mining Div Lg. **Prev. Lge:** Mining Div Lg.

ST JUST

Ground: Lafrowda Park **Secretary:** P Greenfell (0736 787205)
Ground Dirctions: In village take Cape Cornwall Road. First left, left again and ground at end of terrace.
Clubhouse: Yes **Cover:** Yes **Nickname:** The Tinners **Reserves:** West Penwith Lg. **Programme:** Yes
Hons: Champs 61-62, Runners-up 62-63 63-64 73-74 74-75 76-77, Supplementary Cup R-up 92-93.

See also the Jewson South Western League section for details of Falmouth Town, Newquay, Penzance, Porthleven and Truro City who all field their Reserve sides in the Jollys Combination.

WINCHESTER & DISTRICT LEAGUE

DIV. ONE	P	W	D	L	F	A	PTS	DIV. TWO	P	W	D	L	F	A	PTS
Tabby Cat	18	13	4	1	92	26	30	Micheldever	16	14	1	1	76	19	29
Upham	18	12	5	1	87	29	29	Twyford Res.	13	13	2	1	60	12	28
Rising Sun	18	13	2	3	78	36	28	Hyde United	16	10	0	6	58	37	20
Twyford	18	11	3	4	81	31	25	Tabby Cat Res.	13	8	3	5	47	40	19
Littleton	18	10	0	8	61	46	20	Highcliffe Corinth.	16	6	2	8	36	53	14
Winch. City Res.	18	8	1	9	54	42	17	Alresford T. Res.	16	5	3	8	27	40	13
New Queens Hd	18	7	0	11	70	74	14	Winch. Castle Res.	16	3	3	10	29	42	9
Crusaders	18	3	3	12	28	109	9	Worthies Sports	16	4	1	11	34	57	9
Sparsholt	18	1	3	14	26	79	5	County Glass	16	1	1	14	14	81	3
Cheriton Sports	18	1	1	16	19	124	3								

JEWSON WESSEX LEAGUE

President: Jack Barter
Chairman: Alf Peckham **Vice-Chairman:** Cyril Hurlock
Hon. Secretary/Treasurer: Norman Cook, 5 Holmsley Court,
Bartley Meadows, Totton, Southampton SO4 2JF (0703 865464)

LINNETS EDGE OUT MAGPIES

The number of clubs competing in the first division increased to twenty-one, Gosport Borough being relegated from the Beazer Homes League and Whitchurch United promoted from the Hampshire League, in this, the seventh season of the League. The first division championship was once again not decided until the final Saturday of the season. AFC Lymington had already completed their fixtures, but had to wait and see if Wimborne Town could retain the title by beating Bournemouth Poppies by eleven goals. The task was too much for the Magpies as they were held to a 1-1 draw and therefore the Linnets were announced champions by two clear points. The Linnets are renowned for not starting too well and just before Christmas they were lying in twelfth position, whereas the Magpies seemed to be storming their way to another title as they were ten points clear and unbeaten at the turn of the year. However fortunes changed and the Linnets were unbeaten in their last twenty-nine matches, dropping just ten points, while the Magpies started to slide and dropped twenty-one points in their last twenty-two outings. The Linnets also boasted the League's joint top goalscorer in Andy Crawford with twenty-five goals, a feat equalled by Lee Mooney of Thatcham Town. Jason Lovell of Wimborne Town was third with twenty-three goals.

Bemerton Heath Harlequins enjoyed their best season by far, finishing third seven points behind Wimborne Town. During February the Harlequins were in with a good chance of taking the title themselves but a massive fixture backlog during the last three months eventually took its toll. They did take some consolation by winning the Wiltshire Senior Cup, beating Wollen Sports of the Hellenic League by 3-1 in the final played at Swindon Town FC. Thatcham Town also suffered from a heavy fixture programme in the last three months and after being up with the leaders for most of the campaign, they fell away during the last month, dropping thirteen points in their last ten games, and had to settle for fourth spot. Gosport Borough were rarely out of the top five but dropped points fairly regularly throughout the season, so should be satisfied with their first season at the lower level. Ryde Sports finished in excellent form to pull themselves up into sixth position, while Bournemouth started and finished with some style but suffered a traumatic period in mid-season after losing their manager, Peter Moore to Bashley FC. However they did well to take seventh place. Fleet Town finished in eighth spot, their highest placing since joining the League, but they could well have finished in the top six, had they not lost their final three matches. In August Fleet Town opened their fine new stand. Eastleigh were also seeking their best season in the League and it seemed as they might achieve this at Christmas as they were lying in sixth position, but they fell away in the second

AFC Lymington, Jewson Wessex League Champions 1992-93. Back Row: Peter Cox, Derek Holloway, Martin Coffin, Wayne Shaw, Lee Rankin, Andy Scullard, Tony Hamilton, Kevin Green. Front Row: Russ Perret, Jason Hervey, Dave Jenman, Glen Limburn, Darren Pitter, Greg Llewellyn, Lee Russell. Photo - Barry Rickman.

half of the season to finish ninth. Cliff Huxford's Brockenhurst team did very well to finish in the top ten and Horndean had an excellent season by their standards to finish midway in the League. Aerostructures again finished in a mid table position but Christchurch could have had their best season for some while if their away form had been a little better. Swanage Town & Herston had a very disappointing season by their own standards and it could have been even worse but for a good finish. Whitchurch United found the going very tough at the higher level in their first season following their promotion from the Hampshire League but can build on their fifteenth position next time. AFC Totton promised a great deal in mid-season but lacked the consistency in the final stages. Portsmouth RN attained forty points for the first time and so enjoyed a little more success than usual, but B.A.T. had another poor campaign. Sholing Sports still have to sort out the problems surrounding their ground for next season and the uncertainty must have affected the results on the pitch. East Cowes Vics played their home games up to Christmas at Ryde Sports as their newly laid pitch had not settled and were rarely out of the bottom three all season. Romsey Town suffered a disastrous season going to the bottom of the table in mid-December and staying there for the remainder of the season. In their last thirty-three matches they gained just a single point.

Gosport Borough won the Jewson Wessex League Cup thanks to an extra-time goal from skipper Dave Fear in an entertaining and keenly fought contest before a good crowd at Eastleigh FC. The evening was marred by the sending-off of Fleet Town's Micky Haverman and also by a break-in into Fleet Town's dressing-room during the match, which resulted in the majority of the players' personal belongings, including clothing, being stolen.

A new award was introduced this season, a Manager of the Month Award, sponsored by Millbrook Furnishing Industries, for which we extend our thanks, and in particular to Mr. Ted Croll for his continued interest and support. AFC Lymington's tremendous record throughout the season reflected the fact that their manager Trevor Williams won this award on no fewer than four occasions.

The other winners were Des McMahon of Thatcham Town (twice), Steve Slade of Bemerton Heath Harlequins and Roger Sherwood of Gosport Borough. Bournemouth were voted as winners of the "Best Programme" award. Their programme editor, Mr. Ray Murphy, who has taken over the position of secretary at Bashley FC, will be missed.

So much was expected of Wimborne Town in their defence of the F.A. Vase, but once again it was proved how unpredictable our game can be, when they failed to come through their first tie. Our congratulations go to all clubs who flew the Wessex flag in the F.A. Competitions, notably Bemerton Heath Harlequins for reaching the third round of the F.A. Vase and AFC Lymington, Brockenhurst and Bemerton Heath Harlequins in reaching the third qualifying round of the F.A. Cup.

Norman Cook, Hon. Secretary.

FIRST DIVISION	P	W	D	L	F	A	PTS
AFC Lymington	40	30	7	3	111	27	97
Wimborne Town	40	30	5	5	101	27	95
Bemerton H.H.	40	27	7	6	77	33	88
Thatcham Town	40	24	10	6	104	45	82
Gosport Boro'	40	20	12	8	83	48	72
Ryde Sports	40	21	4	15	79	61	67
Bournemouth	40	18	11	11	83	58	65
Fleet Town	40	17	10	13	79	51	61
Eastleigh	40	17	9	14	68	54	60
Brockenhurst	40	17	7	16	60	56	58
Horndean	40	15	9	16	63	66	54
Aerostructures	40	13	14	13	55	57	53
Christchurch	40	14	7	19	60	73	49
Swanage T & H.	40	11	11	18	65	78	44
Whitchurch United	40	12	6	22	57	80	42
AFC Totton	40	12	6	22	56	82	42
Portsmouth R.N.	40	10	10	20	52	83	40
B.A.T.Sports	40	9	9	22	59	83	36
Sholing Sports	40	7	10	23	46	94	31
East Cowes V.	40	8	4	28	52	106	28
Romsey Town	40	3	2	35	20	168	11

COMBINATION	P	W	D	L	F	A	Pts
AFC Lymington	38	31	3	4	121	26	96
Waterlooville(-3pts)	38	27	1	10	97	50	79
Bashley	38	20	11	7	92	49	71
Gosport Boro'	38	21	8	9	101	68	71
Havant Town	38	20	9	9	97	49	69
Newport	38	19	10	9	91	61	67
Wimborne Town	38	19	8	11	94	57	65
Bournemouth	38	18	5	15	87	91	59
Eastleigh	38	15	9	14	77	78	54
AFC Totton	38	14	9	15	70	71	51
Christchurch (-1pt)	38	14	9	15	68	67	50
B.A.T.	38	14	5	19	55	71	47
Aerostructures	38	13	4	21	58	84	43
Bemerton H.H.	38	10	12	16	72	77	42
Horndean	38	11	8	19	55	73	41
Petersfield Utd	38	10	10	18	49	82	40
Brockenhurst	38	8	10	20	47	80	34
Sholing Sports	38	9	7	22	39	77	34
Whitchurch Utd	38	8	8	22	49	92	32
Romsey Town	38	3	6	29	29	146	15

The above teams are all Reserve sides.

FIRST DIVISION LEADING GOALSCORERS

25 A.Crawford (AFC Lymington)
   L.Mooney (Thatcham Town)
23 J.Lovell (Wimborne Town)
20 T.Killick (Wimborne Town)
   D.Pitter (AFC Lymington)
19 S.Docherty (Bournemouth)
18 D.Adams (Brockenhurst)
   M.Haverman (Fleet Town)
   D.Miles (Bournemouth)
17 L.Dixon (Ryde Sports)
   M.Frampton (Fleet Town)
16 M.Savage (Bemerton Heath Harliquins)

COMBINATION LEADING GOALSCORERS

22 D.Ross (Bournemouth)
19 P.Russell (Havant Town)
18 A.Bundy (Bemerton Heath Harlequins)
   I.Ford (Gosport Borough)
17 L.Russell (AFC Lymington)
16 S.Logan (Eastleigh)
   P.Sales (Bashley)
   R.Semark (Havant Town)

DIVISION ONE RESULT CHART 1992-93

HOME TEAM	1	2	3	4	5	6	7	8	9	10	11	12	13	14	15	16	17	18	19	20	21
1. AFC Lymington	*	3-1	3-1	1-1	3-2	0-0	1-1	6-1	8-0	3-1	2-1	2-1	1-1	3-2	11-1	3-1	2-0	1-0	0-0	1-0	3-1
2. AFC Totton	0-4	*	1-1	0-2	1-2	2-1	3-2	0-3	3-0	1-2	1-2	3-3	3-2	3-1	8-0	0-1	3-0	2-0	1-4	2-0	0-3
3. Aerostructures	0-2	3-0	*	1-1	4-2	3-0	1-2	0-0	4-0	0-0	1-4	0-1	1-1	1-1	3-1	1-5	3-2	0-0	2-0	1-0	1-1
4. B.A.T.	0-2	4-1	3-1	*	0-4	2-3	1-1	1-1	2-1	1-2	1-5	0-0	0-3	4-1	5-1	0-3	7-1	1-4	0-4	1-2	1-5
5. Bemerton	0-2	2-0	3-0	1-1	*	1-0	2-0	3-2	1-0	1-0	3-0	1-0	4-1	2-1	0-1	3-0	4-0	5-3	4-1	1-1	1-1
6. Bournemouth	2-1	2-0	1-1	2-1	2-1	*	2-3	3-2	6-0	4-2	0-3	2-5	0-1	7-1	3-0	2-2	3-0	2-2	1-1	1-0	0-1
7. Brockenhurst	0-1	1-1	3-1	3-1	0-0	0-1	*	4-1	4-0	2-1	1-3	1-3	0-0	2-0	4-0	1-3	2-0	1-0	2-3	1-2	1-3
8. Christchurch	0-4	2-1	3-0	2-1	1-2	3-1	1-1	*	3-1	0-3	2-0	0-1	0-0	2-1	4-0	1-5	2-1	0-0	1-3	3-2	1-3
9. E. Cowes	3-4	3-1	1-2	2-3	1-1	1-6	0-2	2-5	*	0-1	3-3	2-5	0-1	1-4	5-0	2-1	3-3	1-2	1-3	4-1	0-3
10. Eastleigh	1-0	1-0	2-3	4-1	0-1	1-1	3-3	3-2	1-2	*	0-1	1-1	4-0	0-0	10-0	0-1	2-2	2-1	1-5	5-2	0-2
11. Fleet Town	0-0	2-3	1-1	3-3	0-0	1-2	0-2	3-0	3-0	0-0	*	1-1	5-1	3-0	7-0	4-1	1-3	3-0	0-4	4-0	1-2
12. Gosport	1-1	6-1	2-0	3-0	0-1	1-1	0-1	1-1	3-2	1-1	3-1	*	4-1	3-0	0-1	2-1	5-3	2-0	1-0	3-0	0-0
13. Horndean	1-4	1-2	0-0	1-0	0-3	1-1	4-0	3-0	3-2	1-2	0-2	0-1	*	3-2	2-0	3-2	2-3	5-2	4-3	1-2	1-2
14. Pompey RN	1-5	1-1	0-1	0-1	1-1	1-2	6-2	1-1	2-1	1-3	1-1	2-0	2-1	*	4-0	0-2	2-1	3-3	1-6	1-3	0-4
15. Romsey	0-9	0-2	0-5	1-3	1-3	2-5	1-3	2-1	0-1	1-2	0-4	0-8	1-5	1-2	*	1-3	1-1	0-5	0-9	0-4	0-8
16. Ryde Spts	1-4	5-1	0-3	2-1	1-2	3-2	3-0	2-0	1-1	0-2	2-1	4-1	2-3	1-1	2-0	*	1-0	1-1	1-2	4-3	3-1
17. Sholing	0-3	1-1	2-3	1-1	0-4	2-2	1-2	1-3	1-3	2-0	1-3	2-2	0-0	0-1	1-1	0-5	*	3-2	1-1	2-2	0-1
18. Swanage	0-3	7-1	2-1	1-1	0-2	5-3	0-2	0-3	3-1	2-2	1-1	3-3	1-1	4-1	1-0	1-0	1-2	*	0-3	3-2	1-3
19. Thatcham	0-1	1-1	2-2	2-1	2-1	0-0	1-0	5-3	3-0	4-1	2-2	2-2	2-2	2-1	4-1	3-1	5-0	4-2	*	4-0	1-2
20. Whitchurch	0-4	2-0	0-0	2-2	0-1	1-6	1-0	1-0	1-2	2-1	1-0	2-3	1-3	1-1	5-1	2-3	1-2	6-1	1-1	*	1-3
21. Wimborne	1-0	1-1	5-0	5-2	1-2	1-1	1-0	2-0	3-0	0-1	3-0	4-1	2-0	3-0	6-0	3-0	5-0	1-1	0-2	4-0	*

WESSEX LEAGUE COMBINATION RESULT CHART

HOME TEAM	1	2	3	4	5	6	7	8	9	10	11	12	13	14	15	16	17	18	19	20
1. AFC Lym. Rs	*	3-0	1-1	3-0	3-3	5-0	8-0	2-0	4-0	2-1	7-1	1-1	1-0	0-1	2-1	7-0	0-1	3-1	7-1	3-0
2. AFC Tot. Rs	3-2	*	5-1	2-1	1-2	2-0	0-2	5-0	1-1	1-6	1-4	1-0	5-1	2-2	2-2	5-0	3-2	3-1	2-1	1-3
3. Aerostr. Rs	1-6	1-2	*	0-4	1-0	3-1	2-3	2-3	5-1	0-3	1-0	2-1	3-2	1-3	1-2	1-2	2-3			
4. BAT Rs	1-5	3-1	1-2	*	0-2	0-2	0-9	2-1	1-3	0-3	0-3	4-3	2-2	1-3	3-0	5-1	3-1	1-3	1-0	1-2
5. Bashley Rs	0-2	2-2	3-0	3-3	*	1-1	8-2	1-1	5-4	8-1	2-3	1-1	5-1	4-0	3-3	3-1	1-0	5-2	5-0	0-2
6. Bemerton Rs	1-2	1-1	4-0	0-0	1-2	*	3-8	1-1	1-1	2-7	1-1	0-1	2-1	4-4	3-3	4-0	4-1	2-4	2-0	1-4
7. B'mouth Rs	0-1	0-2	2-1	0-3	1-0	1-1	*	4-1	3-2	3-4	1-7	2-1	1-0	1-1	3-1	2-0	1-2	0-3	3-3	1-2
8. B'hurst Rs	0-4	3-2	1-2	0-3	2-3	1-1	1-3	*	0-3	2-3	1-2	0-5	2-2	2-3	1-0	1-1	2-0	0-1	3-3	1-7
9. C'church Rs	0-1	2-0	1-3	3-1	2-0	1-1	1-3	1-0	*	2-4	3-1	4-2	1-1	1-1	3-1	4-1	4-0	1-3	2-1	3-3
10. Eastleigh Rs	0-4	1-1	2-0	1-3	2-2	1-0	1-1	2-2	3-4	*	2-4	1-4	5-1	1-1	1-3	0-0	2-1	0-3	1-1	0-1
11. Gosport Rs	1-0	1-1	1-1	1-1	0-2	4-2	4-1	0-3	1-1	1-3	*	5-5	3-2	2-2	2-1	5-0	6-3	3-2	3-0	2-1
12. Havant Rs	1-3	4-0	2-1	1-0	2-0	3-1	11-0	1-1	4-0	3-2	2-1	*	2-0	3-0	4-0	6-0	4-1	0-1	0-0	1-1
13. Horndean Rs	2-3	4-2	1-3	1-0	1-3	0-3	3-5	1-0	2-1	2-3	3-3	1-3	*	2-0	0-1	0-0	3-0	1-1	2-2	1-3
14. Newport Rs	0-4	3-2	4-1	2-0	3-3	3-1	5-1	3-0	2-0	3-1	2-1	1-1	3-3	*	6-0	4-1	8-0	2-3	5-0	2-0
15. P'sfield Rs	1-6	0-0	1-3	0-1	0-0	2-2	2-0	1-3	3-1	3-2	0-5	2-2	0-1	3-1	*	3-2	0-0	2-0	2-3	1-2
16. Romsey Rs	1-5	2-1	0-2	0-4	0-12	0-14	1-4	2-1	1-3	0-4	2-1	0-2	0-6	1-1	*	0-4	1-4	1-1	1-3	
17. Sholing Rs	0-3	1-3	4-1	1-2	0-2	0-4	2-3	1-0	0-0	0-0	4-1	2-0	1-1	1-1	5-1	*	0-1	0-0	0-3	
18. W'ville Rs	1-3	3-1	2-1	1-0	1-2	5-2	3-0	5-0	4-1	3-0	5-1	3-2	4-2	4-0	0-1	4-2	4-0	*	5-0	1-3
19. W'church Rs	1-4	1-0	3-5	0-2	0-2	4-0	0-1	1-1	3-1	1-3	2-6	0-5	1-0	1-4	1-3	6-2	0-1	2-1	*	3-4
20. Wimborne Rs	0-1	5-6	1-1	2-3	0-0	2-2	1-2	1-1	3-3	3-2	3-3	0-2	6-0	10-0	5-0	1-2	2-3	2-1	*	

WESSEX LEAGUE CUP 1992-93

First Round

Aerostructures v Swanage	2-8
B.A.T. v East Cowes Victoria Athletic	5-2
Eastleigh v Thatcham Town	2-5
Ryde Sports v A.F.C. Totton	0-2
Whitchurch United	7-2

Second Round

Portsmouth RN v AFC Totton	4-5
B.A.T. v Swanage Town & Herston	5-2
Bemerton v Fleet Town	3-3(4-5 pens)
Bournemouth v Thatcham Town	3-7
Brockenhurst v Horndean	4-2
Sholing Sports v Romsey Town	6-3
Whitchurch United v Gosport Borough	0-2
Wimborne Town v AFC Lymington	5-4

Quarter-Finals

Fleet v Thatcham	3-3(Fleet on pens)
Gosport Borough v B.A.T.	3-1
Sholing Sports v Brockenhurst	1-3
Wimborne Town v AFC Totton	3-4

Semi Finals

Fleet Town v A.F.C. Totton	8-1
Gosport Borough v Brockenhurst	5-0

Final

Gosport Borough v Fleet Town	1-0(aet)

WESSEX COMBINATION CUP 1992-93

First Round

AFC Lymington Res v Aerostructes Res	5-3
A.F.C. Totton Res v Gosport B. Res	1-4
Bemerton Hth Res v Eatleigh Res	2-1
Waterlooville Res v Horndean Res	1-4

Second Round

Whitchurch Res v Bashley Res	0-1
Horndean Res v Newport Res	2-4
Petersfield Res v Christchurch Res	4-3
Wimborne Res v Sholing Spts Res	1-0
Bemerton Hth Res v AFC Lymington Res	1-0
Bournemouth Res v B.A.T. Res	3-0
Havant Town Res v Brockenhurst Res	11-1
Romsey Town Res v Gosport Boro. Res	1-4

Quarter-Finals

Petersfield Res v Bashley Res	1-0
Wimborne Res v B'mouth Res	4-2(W. expelled)
Bemerton Res v Gosport Borough Res	0-1
Havant Town Res v Newport Res	3-1

Semi-Finals

Gosport B. Res v Petersfield Res	3-0
Havant Town Res v Bournemouth Res	3-1

Final

Havant Town Res v Gosport Borough Res	2-0

WESSEX LEAGUE FIRST DIVISION RECORD (SINCE FORMATION)

	86/7	87/8	88/9	89/0	90/1	91/2	92/3
Aerostructures Spts & Soc.	-	13	10	12	16	9	12
A.F.C. Lymington	-	-	5	5	9	2	1
A.F.C. Totton	3	8	14	6	14	17	16
Bashley	1	1	1	-	-	-	-
B.A.T.	-	-	-	3	8	16	18
Bemerton Heath Harlequins	-	-	-	8	18	8	3
Bournemouth	15	10	12	10	3	6	7
Brockenhurst	17	18	16	17	7	12	10
Christchurst	-	5	13	15	15	13	13
East Cowes Victoria Athletic	-	9	8	13	13	14	20
Eastleigh	8	12	9	14	12	10	9
Fleet Town	-	-	-	18	10	11	8
Folland Sports (see Aerostructures)							
Gosport Borough	-	-	-	-	-	-	5
Havant Town	5	2	2	11	1	-	-
Horndean	14	14	11	16	20	18	11
Lymington Town	10	19	-	-	-	-	-
Newport Isle of Wight	4	4	3	2	-	-	-
Portals Athletic	12	-	-	-	-	-	-
Portsmouth Royal Navy	13	16	17	19	17	19	17
Romsey Town	16	3	7	1	4	4	21
Road Sea Southampton	2	-	-	-	-	-	-
Ryde Sports	-	-	-	-	11	7	6
Sholing Sports	9	7	15	9	19	15	19
Steyning Town	11	17	-	-	-	-	-
Swanage Town & Herston	-	-	-	-	2	5	14
Thatcham Town	6	11	4	7	6	3	4
Wellworthy Athletic	7	15	-	-	-	-	-
Whitchurch United	-	-	-	-	-	-	15
Wimborne Town	-	6	6	4	5	1	2

AEROSTRUCTURES SPORTS & SOCIAL CLUB

Chairman: S. Charles   **Manager:** Paul Whitfield/Sean Mallon   **Gen. Mgr:** Nigel Kent
Secretary: James Clay, 'Tequila', Bridge Rd, Bursledon, Southampton SO3 8AH (0703 403698).
Ground: Folland Park, Kings Avenue, Hamble (0703 452173).
Directions: M27 junction 8, then B3397 to Hamble. One and a half miles from Hamble (BR); turn right out of station, proceed for one mile then turn right into Queens Avenue. Ground 50 yards on right.
Midweek Matches: Tues (1st team), Wed (Res)   **Previous Name:** Folland Sports (pre-1990).
Colours: White/white/red   **Change colours:** Maroon/black/white.   **Floodlights:** Yes
Best FA Vase season: Extra-Preliminary Round 90-91 91-92
Clubhouse: 300 capacity social club. Tennis, bowls, hockey.
Honours: Hants Lg Div 3 80-81 (Div 4 79-80), Hants Intermediate Cup 79-90, Southampton Snr Cup(4).

ANDOVER

Chairman: K Cunningham-Brown   **President:** R Coleman
Secretary: Ms Elsy Ardolino, The Coach House, The Holt, Tangley, Andover, Hants SP11 0RY (0264 70656).
Manager: Mike Burford   **Physio:** Terry Carr.
Ground: Portway Stadium, West Portway Industrial Estate, Andover SP10 3LF (0264 333052).
Directions: On western outskirts - follow any sign to Portway Industrial estate. Approx 2 miles from station.
Capacity: 3,000   **Cover:** 250   **Seats:** 250   **Floodlights:** Yes   **Founded:** 1883.
Programme: 20 pages, 50p   **Club Shop:** No.   **Metal Badges:** Yes.
Colours: Red & black shirts/black/red   **Change colours:** Tangarine/white/tangarine
Sponsors: Hospital Saving Association.
Previous Leagues: Salisbury & District/ Hants 1896-98 99-1901 02-62/ Southern 1898-99 1971-93/ Western 1962-71.
Previous Name: Andover Town   **Previous Ground:** The Walled Meadow (until 1989).
Midweek home matchday: Tuesday   **Reserve Team's League:** None (2 youth sides).
Record Gate: 1,100 v Leicester, ground opening. *(3,484 v Gillingham at Walled Meadow, previous ground).*
Best F.A. Cup season: 1st Rd 62-63 (lost 0-1 to Gillingham).
Record Fees - Paid: £8,000 for Roger Emms (Newbury).
        Received: £6,000 for Jeremy Stagg (Bashley).
Players progressing to Football League: Keith Wilson (Southampton 1959), Nigel Spackman (B'mouth 1980), Colin Court (Reading 1981), A Kingston (Southampton), P Brown (Southampton, Walsall), Emeka Nwajiobi (Luton).
Clubhouse: As a pub, but available for private functions.
Club Record Scorer: T Randall 73   **Club Record Appearances:** P Pollard 469
Honours: FA Tphy 3rd Qualifying Rd 69-70 70-71, Western Lg R-up 69-70 70-71, Hants Lg 13-14 24-25 33-34 44-45 48-49 50-51 61-62 (R-up 42-43, Northern Div 13-14, Div 2 R-up 37-38, Combination (reserves) 87-88), Salisbury & Dist Lg 1894-95 95-96 96-97 99-1900 03-04 07-08 12-13, Hants Senior Cup 48-49 50-51 55-56 64-65, Russell Cotes Cup 23-24 31-32 37-38 44-45 52-53 58-59 60-61 61-62, Pickfords Cup 50-51, Hants Intermediate Cup 59-60 60-61, Hants Junior Cup 19-20 (R-up 1893-94 1910-11 12-13), May Lg 1899-00 00-01 01-02 07-08 08-09.

B.A.T. SPORTS

Chairman: Mr D Batt   **Sec:** D Saich, 32 Salcombe Cres., Totton, Southampton SO4 3FP (0703 860797).
Ground: B.A.T. Sports Ground, Southern Gdns, off Ringwood Road, Totton (0703 862143).
Directions: Into centre of Totton, proceed up Ringwood Rd past small r'bout, 2nd left into Southern Gardens. Half mile from Totton (BR), bus X2 (Southampton-Bournemouth).
Seats: 12-15   **Cover:** 50   **Capacity:** 3,000   **Floodlights:** Yes   **Founded:** 1925
Midweek Matches: Tuesday   **Colours:** Blue & white halves/blue/white   **Change:** All red.
Programme: 8-10 pages, 30p   **Best FA Vase year:** Extra-Preliminary Rd 91-92
Clubhouse: Normal licensing hrs, all day for members' sports facilities. Darts, pool, juke box. Hot & cold snacks.

BEMERTON HEATH HARLEQUINS

Chairman: George Parker   **President:** Peter Say.
Secretary: D J Heather, 31 Hollows Close, Salisbury, Wilts SP2 8JU (0722 32600).
Manager: Steve Slade   **Physio:** Andy Nash   **Coach:** Gary Cross
Ground: Western Way, Bemerton Heath, Salisbury, Wilts (0722 331925).
Directions: Turn off A36 Salisbury-Bristol Rd at Skew Bridge (right turn if coming out of Salisbury), 1st left into Pembroke Rd for half mile, 2nd left along Western Way - ground quarter mile at end. 40 mins walk from Salisbury (BR) station. Bus 351 or 352 from city centre stops at junction of Pembroke Rd/ Western Way.
Clubhouse: Yes   **Cover:** 350   **Floodlights:** Yes   **Founded:** May 1989
Previous Names: Bemerton Athletic, Moon FC & Bemerton Boys; all merged in 1989.
Previous Leagues: B'ton Ath.: Salis. & Wilts Comb., Moon: Salis. & Andover Sunday, B'ton Boys: Mid Wilts.
Cols: Black & white **Change colours:** Amber/white/white   **Nickname:** Quins   **Prog.:** 32 pages, 50p
Midweek Matches: Tuesday   **Record Gate:** 480 v Bognor, FA Cup 2nd Qual Rd 1992.
Captain 92-93: Darren Lush   **Top Scorer 92-93:** Roger Maynard.
P.O.Y. 92-93: Darren Lush   **Club record appearances:** Keith Richardson.
Hons: Wilts Snr Cup 92-93. Wilts Lg(3) as Bemerton Athletic

BOURNEMOUTH

Chairman: B Roche   **Vice Chairman:** J B Wood   **President:** D Nippard
Secretary: W G Johnston, 25 Edward Rd, Bournemouth BH11 8SX (0202 5711767).
Manager: Tommy Taylor   **Physio:** M Moylen   **Press Officer:** B Sklan.
Ground: Victoria Park, Winton, Bournemouth, Dorset (0202 515123).
Directions: Any bus to Wimborne Road, Winton. 2 miles from Bournemouth Central (BR).
Seats: 250   **Cover:** 250   **Capacity:** 3,000   **Floodlights:** Yes   **Founded:** 1875.
Colours: All red   **Change colours:** All yellow   **Nickname:** Poppies.
Programme: 58 pages, 50p   **Editor:** Ray Murphy (0202 517607)   **Club Shop:** No.
Sponsors: A1 Windscreens   **Midweek Matches:** Tuesday   **Prev. Lge:** Hants.
Previous Ground: Dene Park 1888-90   **Local Newspaper:** Evening Echo.   **Rec. Gate:** Unknown
Previous Names: Bournemouth Rovers 1875-88/ Bournemouth Dene Park 1888-90.
Clubhouse: Open daily 7-11pm. Sandwiches & hot snacks (burgers, chips etc).
Captain 92-93: Tony Gibney   **Top Scorer 92-93:** Sean Docherty
P.O.Y. 92-93: Charlie Miles   **Club record scorer:** B Head
Hons: Hants Lg 13-13 21-22, B'mouth Snr Cup 66-67 89-90, Texaco F'lit Cup R-up 91-92, Hant I'mediate Cup 49-50 69-70, Hants Yth Cup 54-55 57-58 67-68.

BROCKENHURST

Chairman: Mr B Mellor
Secretary: Mr D Chandler, 300 Salisbury Road, Totton, Southampton SO4 3LZ (0703 862957)
Ground: Grigg Lane, Brockenhurst, Hants (0590 23544).
Directions: 400 yds from Brockenhurst station, just off main shopping area.
Seats: 200   **Cover:** 300   **Capacity:** 2,000   **Floodlights:** Yes   **Founded:** 1898
Midweek Matches: Tues (Wed reserves)   **Clubhouse:** Every evening plus Tues, Sat & Sun lunchtimes.
Colours: Blue & white stripes/white/blue   **Change colours:** All red.
Programme: 12 pages, 20p, **Editor:** C Fisher   **Prev. League:** Hants 24-26 47-86
Hons: Hants I'mediate Cup 61-62, B'mouth Snr Cup 60-61, Hants Lg 75-76 (R-up 73-74 79-80, Div 2 70-71 (R-up 60-61), Div 3 59-60), F.A. Amateur Cup 2nd Rd 73-74.

Bockenhurst F.C. 1992-93. Photo - Gavin Ellis-Neville.

CHRISTCHURCH

Chairman: Gerald Page   **Vice Chairman:** Cliff Taylor   **President:** Duncan Hillyer
Secretary: Mrs D Page, 89 Parkway Drive, Bournemouth BH8 9JS (0202 304996).
Manager: Alan Bryant   **Asst Manager:** Steve Hudspith.
Physio: Brian Finch   **Press Officer:** Dennis James.
Ground: Christchurch Sporting Club, Hurn Bridge, Avon Causeway, Christchurch (0202 473792).
Directions: A338 from Ringwood, turn off signed Hurn Airport on left. Before Airport use mini roundabout & take exit signed to Sopley and ground is immediately on the right. 3 miles from Christchurch (BR).
Seats: 15   **Cover:** 50   **Capacity:** 2,000   **Floodlights:** Yes   **Founded:** 1885
Midweek Matches: Wednesday   **Previous League:** Hampshire.
Previous Ground: Barrack Rd Recreation Ground (until 1984).
Colours: All royal blue (white trim)   **Change colours:** All yellow   **Nickname:** Priory
Programme: 16 pages, 25p   **Programme Editor:** John Whiting/Pete Gardner.
Clubhouse: Normal pub hours. Cooked food at lunchtimes.
Captain 92-93: Steve Joyce   **Top Scorer 92-93:** Richard Glenister.
P.o.Y. 92-93: Martin Beardsley   **Club record appearances:** John Haynes.
Honours: Hants Jnr Cup 1892-93 1911-12 20-21, Hants Int. Cup 86-87, Pickford Cup 1991, Hants Lg Div 2 37-38 47-48 85-86 (Div 3 56-57), B'mouth Snr Cup(5) 56-57 59-60 67-70.

DOWNTON

Secretary: R Hillman (0725 20815)
Ground: Brian Whitehead Sports Ground, Wick Lane, Downton (0725 22162).
Directions: Travelling south from Salisbury on A338 turn right into Wick Lane opposite turn for Downton village centre - ground quarter mile on left.   **Previous League:** Hants (pre-1993).

EAST COWES VICTORIA ATHLETIC

Chairman: M Diaz   **President:** A Woolford.
Secretary: L Bray, 57 Grange Rd, East Cowes, I.O.W. PO32 6DY (0983 200276).
Ground: Beatrice Avenue Ground, East Cowes, I.O.W. (0938 297165).
Manager: G O'Rourke   **Asst Manager:** R Smith.
Directions: From the ferry: 1 mile from town centre on lower main road to Newport or Ryde, near Whippingham Church adjacent to Osborne Middle School.
Seats: 200   **Cover:** 400   **Capacity:** 4,000   **Floodlights:** Yes   **Founded:** 1968.
Midweek Matches: Wednesday   **Sponsors:** I.O.W. Group '90   **Club Shop:** No.
Previous Names: East Cowes Victoria (founded 1888) merged with East Cowes Athletic in 1968.
Previous Leagues: (E.C. Vics): I.O.W. 1898-19 21-22 25-26 27-47/ Hants 47-87.
Colours: Red & white stripes/black/white   **Change colours:** Blue.   **Nickname:** Vics.
Programme: 12 pages, 25p   **Programme Editor:** Andrew James
Record Gate: 200 v Poole Town, 1954   **Clubhouse:** Yes. Matchday crisps and confectionary.
Midweek home matchday: Wednesday   **Reserve team's League:** Isle of Wight Lge.
Captain 92-93: Stuart Ellsbury   **P.o.Y. 92-93:** Richard Durham.
Honours: (as East Cowes Vics pre-'68): Wessex Lg Cup 87-88, I.O.W. Gold Cup, I.O.W. Lg 1898-99, I.O.W. Chal. Cup 1900-01, I.O.W. Mem. Cup 19-20, Hants Lg Div 1(2) (Div 3 West 47-48).

EASTLEIGH

Chairman: Mr A G Froud   **President:** TBA
Secretary: D H Brooks, 50 Forest Hills Drive, Townhill Park, Southampton SO2 3HY (0703 557147).
Manager: Don Gowans   **Asst Manager:** Mark Barber   **Physio:** Derek Browning.
Press Officer: Mrs D Gowans   **Commercial Manager:** John Pothecary (0962 713685).
Ground: 'Ten Acres', Stoneham Lane, North Stoneham, Eastleigh SO5 3HT (0703 613361).
Directions: M27 to Jct 5, to r'bout - exit marked Stoneham Lane, ground on left but carry on to r'bout and come back down Stoneham Lane, turning right opposite Concord Club. Ground 400 yds on left. Three quarters of a mile from Southampton Parkway (BR). Bus 48 (Southampton-Winchester) to Stoneham Church stop.
Seats: 150   **Cover:** 210   **Capacity:** 4,300   **Floodlights:** Yes   **Founded:** 1946.
Midweek home matches: Tuesday   **Prev. Lges:** Southampton Jnr & Snr 46-59/ Hants 50-86.
Colours: All royal blue   **Change colours:** Yellow & emerald   **Nickname:** None.
Programme: 32 pages with admission   **Programme Editor:** John Pothecary   **Club Shop:** No.
Record Gate: 2,500 v Southampton, floodlight opener 30/9/75.
Club Sponsors: Various   **Previous Names:** Swaythling Ath. 46-73/ Swaythling 73-80
Previous Grounds: Southampton Common 46-47/ Walnut Avenue, Swaythling 47-75.
Clubhouse: Licence 11am-11pm Mon-Sat plus Sundays. Extensive facilities for weddings, parties, skittles and seminars. All catering undertaken.
Record win: 12-1 v Hythe & Dibden, home 11/12/48   **Record defeat:** 0-11 v Austin Spts, away 1/1/47.
Captain 92-93: Mark Harrison   **Top Scorer 92-93:** Simon Logan, 21   **P.o.Y. 92-93:** Jason Scannell.
Club record scorer: Johnny Williams, 177 **Club record appearances:** Ian Knight, 611.
Hons: FA Vase 4th Rd 90-91, Wessex Lg Cup R-up 91-92, Hants Lg Div 2 69-70 (R-up 54-55 60-61 62-63 64-65(Res), Div 3(W) 50-51 53-54 70-71(Res), Comb.(Res) 86-87)), Hants Midweek F'lit Cup 78-79, Soton Snr Lg(W) 49-50 (R-up 51-52(Res), Div 1 56-57(Res) 57-58(Res)), Russell Cotes R-up 76-77 80-81 89-90, Hants I'mediate Cup 50-51 56-57(Res) 74-75(Res)(R-up 73-74(Res)), Soton Snr Cup(Res) 74-75 78-79 87-88 (R-up(8) 55-56 57-59 60-61 66-67 71-72 80-81 87-88), Soton Jnr Lg Div 2 47-48(Res), Reg Mathieson Tphy(Res) 74-75 78-79 87-88.

FLEET TOWN

Chairman: A Cherry   **Vice Chairman:** A Worthington   **President:** L Hocking
Secretary: Mr S D Lunt, 156 Kings Road, Fleet, Hants GU13 9DT (0252 615303).
Ground: Calthorpe Park, Crookham Road, Fleet, Hants (0252 623804).
Directions: From Fleet town centre at crossroads, Crookham 200 yds right turn.
Seats: 200   **Cover:** 400   **Capacity:**   **Floodlights:** Yes   **Founded:** 1890.
Midweek Matches: Wednesday   **Club Sponsors:** Hart Leisure.   **Nickname:** Blues
Colours: Navy & sky stripes/navy/navy   **Change colours:** White & red/red/white & red.
Programme: 20 pages   **Club Shop:** No   **Clubhouse:** Yes
Reserves' League: Suburban   **Previous Lges:** Hants/ Athenian/ Combined Co's
Record win: 7-0   **Record transfer paid:** £1,500 to Farnborough, 1991.
Captain 92-93: John Hamm   **Top Scorer 92-93/ Club Record Scorer:** Mark Frampton
P.o.Y. 92-93: Paul Dear   **Club record appearances:** Paul Dear.
Hons: Wessex Lg Cup R-up 92-93, Hants Lg Div 2 R-up 61-62 (Div 1 R-up 60-61), Aldershot Snr Cup 92-93, Hants Yth Lg Div 3 92-93.

GOSPORT BOROUGH

Chairman: I T Hay   **President:** W J Adams.
Secretary: B V Cosgrave, 2 Cavanna Close, Rowner, Gosport PO13 0PE (0329 285087).
Manager: Roger Sherwood   **Asst Manager:** Paul Smith   **Coach:** Alan Williams
Physio: Barry Williamson   **Commercial Director:** Roger Barrett
Ground: Privett Park, Privett Road, Gosport, Hants (0705 583986).
Directions: M27 junct 11, then A32 Fareham to Gosport, at Brockhurst r-about (after about 3 miles) right into Military Road passing thru H.M.S. Sultan, left into Privett Road at next r-about, ground 300 yds on left signed 'Privett Park Enclosure'. 2 miles from Portsmouth Harbour (BR) or Fareham (BR).
Capacity: 5,000   **Cover:** 650   **Seats:** 620   **Floodlights:** Yes   **Founded:** 1944.
Prog.: 20 pages, 50p **Editor:** Ian Hay (0329 283852)   **Club Shop:** No   **Metal Badges:** Yes
Colours: Yellow/blue/blue   **Change colours:** Blue/white/red.   **Sponsors:** Eurokit
Midweek matchday: Wednesday   **Prev. Lges:** Portsmouth 44-45/ Hants 45-78/ Southern 78-92
Previous Name: Gosport Borough Athletic **Record Gate:** 4,770 v Pegasus, FA Amtr Cup 1951.
Nickname: The Boro'   **Previous Grounds:** None.
Best F.A. Cup season: 4th Qualifying Rd 80-81 (lost to Windsor & Eton).
Record Fees - Paid: £6,000 for Sandy Baird (Basingstoke Town, 1990)
           Received: £30,000+ for Gareth Williams (Aston Villa, 1987).
Record win: 14-0 v Cunliffe-Owen, Hampshire Lg Div 1 45-46.
Record defeat: 0-9 twice; v Newport, Hants Lg Div 1 47-48. v Gloucester (A), Southern Lg Prem Div 89-90.
Players progressing to Football League: Peter Harris (P'smouth, N'castle & Scotland), B Sherwood, D Dimmer, S Berry, Ron Blackman (Reading 1947), Richard Pearson (P'smouth 1949), Albert Mundy & Mike Barnard (P'smouth 1951), Peter Smith (G'ham 1954), Alan Grant (Brighton 1956), Brian Gibbs (B'mouth 1957), Gary Juryeff (P'smouth), Robert Carroll (Brentford 1986), Gareth Williams (A Villa 1988).
Clubhouse: (0705 525460). Open matchdays from 1.30pm Saturday, 6.30pm Wednesday. Refreshment hut sells hot food and drinks.
Record Scorer: Richie Coulbert 192   **Record Appearances:** Tony Mahoney 764.
92-93 Captain: Dave Fear   **92-93 P.o.Y.:** John Diaper   **92-93 Top scorer:** Kevin Maddock
Local Newspapers: Portsmouth Evening News, Southampton Evening Echo.
Honours: FA Trophy 1st Rd 88-89, FA Amateur Cup 3rd Rd 47-48 66-67, FA Vase 6th Rd replay 77-78, Wessex Lg Cup 92-93, Southern Lg Div 1 South R-up 84-85, Hants Lg 45-46 76-77 77-78 (Div 3 (Reserves) 70-71 75-76), Portsmouth Lg R-up 44-45, Hants Senior Cup 87-88, Hants Intermediate Cup 70-71, Portsmouth Senior Cup 61-62 69-70 70-71, South West Counties Pratten Challenge Cup 77-78.

HORNDEAN

Chairman: Mr J Knight   **President:** Ron Coldrick
Vice Chairman: John Knight   **Treasurer:** Rosmarie Crouch.
Secretary: Mrs Gladys Berry, 74 Five Heads Road, Horndean PO8 9NZ (0705 591698).
Ground: Five Heads Park, Five Heads Road, Horndean (0705 591363).
Directions: 8 miles north of Portsmouth, just off A3. Five Heads Road is a turning off main road. 2 miles from Rowlands Castle (BR).
Seats: 50   **Cover:** 200   **Capacity:** 3,200   **Floodlights:** Yes   **Founded:** 1887
Midweek Matches: Wednesday
Previous Ground: Horndean Rec. 1887-1969.
Colours: Red/black/red   **Change colours:** Green & white/green/green.
Programme: 16 pages, with admission   **Programme Editor:** Derek Usher
Record Gate: 1,560 v Waterlooville, Victory Cup April 1971.
Best FA Cup season: 1st Qualifying Round replay 1982-83.
Best FA Vase season: 1sr Round 85-86 88-89.
Clubhouse: Open every evening plus Sat & Sun lunctimes
Honours: Hants Div 2 79-80 (Div 3 75-76, Div 4 74-75), Portsmouth Senior Cup 75-76 79-80 (R-up 86-87, Portsmouth Lg 69-70 70-71 71-72, Wessex Lg Cup R-up 86-87, Portsmouth Jnr Cup 64-65.

(A.F.C.) LYMINGTON

Chairman: John Mills   **Vice Chairman:** Ian Snook   **President:** Howard Wilkinson
Manager: Trevor Williams   **Coach:**   **Asst Mgr:** Derek Binns.
Commercial Manager/ Press Officer: John Mills (0590 682830).
Secretary: John Osey, 9 Samphire Close, Lymington Meadows, Lymington, Hants SO41 9LR (0590 676995).
Ground: Lymington Sports Ground, Southampton Road, Lymington (0590 671305).
Directions: M27 jct 1, follow signs (A337) to Lymington via Lyndhurst and Brockenhurst, ground on left (signposted) 250yds after 2nd set of lights on entering town. 1 mile from Lymington Town BR station.
Seats: 200   **Cover:** 200   **Capacity:** 3,000   **Floodlights:** Yes   **Founded:** 1988
Midweek Matches: Monday   **Record Gate:** 1,098 v Southampton, stand opening 1989.
Colours: Red & black hoops/black/red   **Change colours:** Yellow/green/green.   **Nickname:** Linnets
Club Shop: Yes, selling scarves, ties, enamel badges, car stickers, programmes (League & non-League). Contact Stephen Jones (0590 676040).
Previous Name: Lymington Town (until 1988 when the club merged with Wellworthy Athletic).
Previous Ground: Ampress Ground (Wellworthy Athletic), until 1988 merger.
Previous Lges: Lymington Town: Hants/ Wessex. Wellworthy: Bournemouth/ Hants/ Wessex.
Best FA Vase season: 3rd Qualifying Rd 92-93 (lost 0-1 at home to Cheltenham Town).
Record win: 11-1 v Romsey Town (H), Wessex League 92-93.
Record defeat: 0-8 v Basingstoke Town, 1990.
Clubhouse: Sat 2-7pm and training and match nights. Rolls, hot pies.
Programme: 36 pages, 40p   **Programme Editor:** John Mills (0590 682830).
Club Sponsors: Hardleys Timber & Building Merchants.
Club Record Scorer: David Perrett 96   **Club Record Appearances:** Glen Limburn 261 (out of poss. 263)
Captain 92-93: Glen Limburn   **P.o.Y. 92-93:** Simon Jackson
Top Scorers 92-93: Andy Crawford 37, Darren Pitter 28.
Honours: Wessex Lg 92-93 (R-up 91-92, Lg Cup 88-89, Comb.(res) 92-93), Hants Senior Cup R-up 89-90, Texaco Cup 91-92, Bournemouth Senior Cup 92-93, Russell Cotes Cup R-up 91-92 92-93, Pickford Cup R-up 92-93. As Lymington Town: Russell Cotes Cup 35-36, Bournemouth Senior Cup 83-84 (R-up 69-71 84-85), Hants Lg Div 3 67-68 (Div 2 R-up 83-84), Pickford Cup 52-53. As Wellworthy Athletic: Bournemouth Senior Cup 87-88 (R-up 53-54), Hants Intermediate Cup 56-57 84-85, Pickford Cup 84-85, Bournemouth Lg 84-85, Hants Lg Div 3 R-up 85-86.

PETERSFIELD TOWN

Secretary: M Nicholl, 49 Durford Rd, Petersfield, Hants GU31 4ER (0730 261735).
Manager: Shaun McCartney   **Asst Manager:**
Ground: Love Lane, Petersfield, Hants (0730 262177).
Directions: On A3 circulatory system. 10 mins walk from Petersfield BR station heading towards London.
Seats: 135   **Cover:** 385   **Capacity:** 4,000   **Floodlights:** Yes   **Reformed:** 1993
Midweek Matches: Tuesday   **Previous Leagues:** None
Colours: T.B.A.   **Change colours:** T.B.A.   **Club Shop:** No.
Programme: T.B.A.   **Clubhouse:** Yes.
Record Gate: 1,300 - Petersfield United F.C. v Portsmouth, friendly, 1985.
Hons: None.   **Best F.A. Cup season:** Not entered to date.

PORTSMOUTH ROYAL NAVY

Chairman: Mr J Molloy
Secretary: Mr G Howells, 20 Redlands Lane, Fareham, Hants PO14 1EY (0329 221146).
Manager: Mr R Smith   **Asst Manager:** Mr P Spinks.
Ground: RN Stadium, Burnaby Road, (West) Portsmouth (0705) 822351 Ext. 24235).
Directions: From Portsmouth Harbour (BR), drive towards Southsea along The Hard Pass under the rail bridge, road is now St George Rd, and ground is on the left.
Seats: 500   **Cover:** 500   **Capacity:** 1,500   **Floodlights:** Yes   **Founded:** 1962
Midweek Matches: Monday   **Previous Ground:** Victory Stadium 1962-87.
Colours: All royal blue   **Change colours:** All red   **Club Shop:** No.
Programme: 28 pages, free with entry   **Previous League:** Hampshire.
Clubhouse: Bar open 1 hr before k.o. and for 2 hrs after game. Matchday and by arrangement only.
Captain 92-93: Steve Stone   **Top Scorer 92-93:** Paul Spinks   **P.o.Y. 92-93:** David Barclay
Hons: Basingstoke Lg Div 2, Hants Lg Div 2 67-68 77-78 80-81.

RYDE SPORTS

President: John Keynes   **Chairman:** Mr S Rann
Secretary: Raymond Fleming, Glenmead, Chilton Lane, Brighstone, Isle of Wight PO30 4DR (0983 740113).
Manager: Graham Daish   **Asst Manager:** Len Cade.
Ground: Smallbrook Stadium, Ashey Rd, Ryde (0983 812906).   **Previous Ground:** Partlands (pre-1990).
Directions: From the Pier Head follow directions to the Royal Isle of Wight Hospital, carry on past the hospital turning left at the Partlands Hotel - ground is one mile along Ashey Road. Not served by public transport.
Seats: 450   **Cover:** 1,500   **Capacity:** 5,000   **Floodlights:** Yes   **Founded:** 1888.
Midweek Matches: Wednesday   **Previous League:** Hants.
Colours: Red/white/red   **Change colours:** White/blue/blue.   **Metal Badges:** Yes.
Programme: 32 pages, 50p.   **Programme Editor:** Secretary   **Nickname:** The Reds.
Travel Sponsors: Hovertravel   **Club Sponsors:** Colemans Carpet Superstore.
Best FA Vase season: Prel. Rd 90-91   **Best FA Cup season:** 3rd Rd Proper 35-36.
Record Gates: 3,100 v Aston Villa 17/12/90. 2,400 v Sheffield Wednesday 26/3/90.
Players progressing to Football League: Roy Shiner (Sheff Wed), Keiron Baker & Kevin Allen (Bournemouth).
(Also Wally Hammond played for Ryde before achieving fame in cricket).
Clubhouse: Open everyday. Large bar, restaurant, fitness centre, gym, treatment room.   **Club shop:** Yes.
Honours: FA Air Cup 47-48 (2-4 v Clevedon) 48-49 (1-2 v Cheshunt), Hants Lg 1899-00 25-26 89-90 (Div 2 88-89, Div 3 64-65), Hants Snr Cup(8) 1899-00 03-04 25-26 34-39, IOW Gold Cup(7) 26-27 46-47 48-49 55-56 61-64, IOW Snr Challenge Cup 1898-99, IOW Gold Cup(7) 26-27 46-47 48-49 55-56 61-64, IOW Challenge Cup 27-28 80-81, P'mouth Snr Cup 1899-00 00-01 05-06 19-20 53-54 66-67 89-90, IOW Charity Cup(7) 18-22 44-47, Ryde & Dist Cup 89-90, Westwood Cup 84-85, IOW Lg 20-21 (Div 2 80-81).

SHOLING SPORTS

President: Mr George Dunn   **Chairman:** Mr B P Sivier.
Secretary: Mr B F Nash, 74 The Grove, Sholing, Southampton SO2 9LU (0703 445444).
Manager: Steve Clarke   **Asst Manager:** Ian Knight   **Coach:** Bill Moore.
Ground: Birch Lawn, 137 North East Road, Sholing, Southampton (0703 449381).
Directions: M27 Jct 8, A3024 then 6th turning on left - ground on right. One and a half miles from Sholing (BR).
Seats: 150   **Cover:** 300   **Capacity:** 1,500   **Floodlights:** Yes   **Founded:** 1901.
Midweek Matches: Wed (Tues Res)   **Clubhouse:** Daily, normal licensing hours.
Colours: Black & white/black/black & white   **Change:** Red & black/white/red.
Programme: 12 pages, with admission   **Programme Editor:** Ward Puddle
Best FA Vase season: QF   **Record Gate:** 1,200 v Gosport, Hants Snr Cup 1983.
Honours: Russell Cotes Cup 71-72 82-83 84-85, Hants Snr Cup 22-23 73-74 82-83, Hants Lg 73-74 82-83 83-84 (East Div 62-63 69-70), S'hampton Snr Cup(6) 19-22 38-39 61-62 79-80, S'hampton Snr Lg(4) 19-21 37-39, S'hampton Jnr Lg(4) 33-34 38-39 59-61, S'hampton Jnr Cup 59-60, Hants Int. Cup 37-38.

SWANAGE TOWN & HERSTON

Chairman: Mr P McLeod   **Vice Chairman:** Mr L Marsh   **President:** Mayor of Swanage
Secretary: Mrs H Ibbs, 8 Steppes, Langton Matravers, Swanage, Dorset BH19 3EY (0929 423570).
Manager: Mr A McManus   **Coach:** Mr B Benjafield
Physio: Mr P Stockley   **Press Officer:** Mr C Smith (0929 426362).
Ground: Days Park, off De Moulham Road, Swanage, Dorset (0929 424633).
Directions: A351 to Swanage, turn left onto sea front, 2nd left into Seaward Rd, 1st right into De Moulham Rd, through north beach car park into ground. Bus no. 21 from Poole stops in Seaward Rd 200yds from ground.
Seats: 150   **Cover:** 150   **Capacity:** 2,000   **Floodlights:** Yes   **Founded:** 1898.
Midweek Matches: Tuesday   **Previous Lge:** Dorset Comb./ Western 84-91.
Colours: White/black/black.   **Change colours:** Blue/yellow/blue.   **Club Shop:** No.
Programme: Yes   **Editor:** Mr D Ibbs (0929 423570)   **Previous Grounds:** None.
Previous Name: Swanage FC (merged with Herston in late 1960s)
Nickname: The Swans   **Reserve team's League:** Dorset Combination.
Clubhouse: Open match days & special functions organised by local organisations. Hot snacks + usual pub cold snacks available.
Captain 92-93: Andy McManus   **Top Scorer 92-93:** Alan Fooks   **P.o.Y. 92-93:** Phil Turner
Club record scorer: Alan Fooks   **Club record appearances:** Alan Fooks.
Hons: Western Lg Div 1 88-89, Wessex Lg R-up 90-91, Dorset Snr Cup 89-90, Mark Frowde Cup 89-90.

Gosport Borough F.C. 1992-93. Back Row (L/R): Roger Sherwood (Manager), John Diaper, Dave Wood, Gary Payne, Adam Gage, Dave Fear, Simon Preston, Kevin White, Ian Rew, Paul Smith (Asst Manager) George Bramble (Physio). Front: Stuart Hoare, Nicky Goater, Alan Williams, Kevin Maddock, Nigel Long. Photo - Colin Stevens.

Portsmouth Royal Navy F.C. 1992-93.

Swanage Town & Herston F.C. 1992-93. Photo - Colin Stevens.

THATCHAM TOWN

Chairman: Mr A E Hyde   **President:** Dave Quaintance
Secretary: Eric Bailey, 201 Kersey Cres., Newbury, Berks RG13 1SW (0635 42396).
Manager: Des McMahon   **Press Off:** Phil Liles (0635 66018)   **Coach:** Dave Cox
Ground: Waterside Park, Crookham Rd, Thatcham, Berks (0635 862016/873912).
Directions: 2 mins walk from from Thatcham BR station.
Seats: 300   **Cover:** 300   **Capacity:** 3,000   **Floodlights:** Yes   **Founded:** 1896
Midweek Matches: Tuesday   **Best FA Vase season:** QF 88-89
Colours: Blue & white stripes/blue/blue   **Change colours:** White/white/red
Programme: 28 pages, 40p   **Programme Editor:** Dave Ware
Previous Ground: Station Road 51-52/ Lancaster Close 52-92.
Record Gate: 600 v Fulham, floodlight opening (at Lancaster Close).
Clubhouse: Open every evening & weekend lunchtimes.   **Honours:** Wessex Lg Cup 90-91 91-92.

(A.F.C.) TOTTON

Chairman: Mr P Maton   **Vice Chairman:** Mr P Maiden   **President:** Mr D Maton.
Secretary: Mrs S Benfield, 35 Fishers Rd, Totton, Southampton SO4 4HW (0703 865421).
Manager: Mr G Chant   **Asst Manager/Coach:** Mr E Harper.
Commercial Mgr: Mr E Ffister   **Press Officer:** Mr P Chilcott (0703 860453).
Ground: Testwood Park, Testwood Place, Totton, Southampton (0703 868981).
Directions: 5 mins walk from Totton station. Turn off r'bout in Totton centre into Library Rd, then 1st left & 2nd rd.
Seats: 200   **Cover:** 250   **Capacity:** 2,500   **Floodlights:** Yes   **Founded:** 1886
Record Gate: 600 v Windsor & Eton, F.A. Cup 4th Qualifying Rd 82-83.
Sponsors: Burger Rack   **Midweek Matches:** Wednesday
Colours: Blue & white/blue/blue   **Change colours:** Red/white/red   **Nickname:** Stags.
Club Shop: No   **Programme:** 30 pages with admission
Previous Name: Totton FC (until merger with Totton Athletic in 1979).
Previous League: Hants 1886-1986   **Previous Grounds:** Downs–Park/ Mayfield Park.
Clubhouse: Open for matches and training sessions. Burgers, sandwiches, tea, coffee, biscuits etc available.
Captain 92-93: Various   **Top Scorer 92-93:** Derek Hitchcock 19   **P.O.Y. 92-93:** Gary Rose.
Hons: Hants Lg(2)

WHITCHURCH UNITED

Chairman: Mr C Varndell.
Secretary: Mr N Spencer, 54 Winchester Rd, Whitchurch, Hants RG28 7HP (0256 896895).
Ground: Long Meadow, Winchester Road, Whitchurch (0256 892394).
Directions: From Whitchurch (BR) station; turn left after Railway Inn, follow road to end, turn right into main road, arriving in town turn left along Winchester Road. Ground three quarters of a mile on left.
Seats: 200   **Cover:** Yes   **Capacity:**   **Floodlights:** Yes   **Founded:**
Midweek Matches: Wednesday (Monday for Reserves).
Colours: Red & black/black/white   **Change colours:** Blue & white/white/blue.
Programme: 28 pages   **Previous Leagues:** Hants (pre-1992).
Clubhouse: Hot food on matchdays. Sports hall incorporating squash courts and indoor bowling green

WIMBORNE TOWN

Chairman: Mr B Maidment   **Vice Chairman:** Mr P Goulding   **President:** Sir Michael Hanham, Bart
Secretary: Mr K Holloway, 1 Laburnum Close, Ferndown, Dorset BH22 9TX (0202 892795).
Manager: Nick Bridle   **Asst Manager:** Kevin Mulkern.
Physio: S Edwards   **Press Officer:** S Churchill.
Ground: Cuthbury, Cowgrove Road, Wimborne, Dorset BH21 4EL (0202 884821).
Directions: Wimborne to Blandford Road, behind Victoria Hospital.
Seats: None   **Cover:** 400   **Capacity:** 3,250   **Floodlights:** Yes   **Founded:** 1878
Midweek Matches: Tuesday   **Club Sponsors:** Ryan Homes.   **Nickname:** Magpies
Record Gate: 3,250 v Bamber Bridge, FA Vase Semi Final 2nd Leg, 28/3/92.
Cols: Black & white stripes/black/black   **Change colours:** Green & white/white/gree & white.
Programme: 36 pages, 50p   **Programme Editor:** Secretary
Club Shop: Yes, selling programmes, hats, scarves, t-shirts, replica kit, pens, metal badges.
Best FA Vase season: Winners   **Best FA Cup season:** 1st Rd Proper 82-83.
Previous Leagues: Dorset/ Western 81-86.
Record win (in Wessex Lg): 8-0 v Eastleigh 91-92 & v Romsey Town 92-93.
Record defeat (in Wessex Lg): 2-6 v Thatcham Town 91-92.
Record transfer fee paid: £5,500 for J P Lovell (Bashley, 1992).
Record transfer fee received: £6,000 for J P Lovell (Bashley, 1989).
Clubhouse: Evenings 7-11pm, Sat noon-11pm, Sun noon-3 & 7-10.30pm. Bar. Skittle alley.
Captain 92-93: S Richardson   **Top Scorer 92-93:** J P Lovell, 32
P.O.Y. 92-93: Andy Taplin.   **Club Record Scorer:** G Manson 50, 1980-81.
Honours: FA Vase 91-92, Wessex Lg 91-92 (R-up 92-93, Lg Cup R-up 90-91), Hants Snr Cup SF 89-90, Dorset Lg Div 1(2) 80-81 81-82 (R-up 38-39 72-73, Div 2 31-32 34-35 36-37 (R-up 35-36), Lg Cup R-up(4) 72-74 80-82), Dorset Snr Cup(4) 80-82 85-86 91-92, Mark Frowde Cup 92-93, Dorset Snr Amateur Cup 36-37 63-64, Dorset Jnr Cup 31-32 36-37 (R-up 13-14 34-35), Dorset Minor Cup 12-13, Dorset Jnr Amateur Cup(4) 34-36 38-39.

COMBINATION DIVISION CONSTITUTION 1993-94

Aerostructures Reserves
AFC Lymington Reserves
AFC Totton Reserves
Bashley Reserves
B.A.T. Reserves
Bemerton Hth Harl. Reserves
Bournemouth Reserves

Brockenhurst Reserves
Christchurch Reserves
Downton Reserves
Eastleigh Reserves
Gosport Borough Reserves
Havant Town Reserves
Horndean Reserves

Newport I.O.W. Reserves
Petersfield Town Res.
Sholing Sports Reserves
Waterlooville Reserves
Whitchurch Utd Reserves
Wimborne Town Reserves

HAYWARD BOURNEMOUTH LEAGUE

DIV. ONE	P	W	D	L	F	A	PTS
Westover Motors	24	21	2	1	82	16	65
B'mouth Civil S.	24	19	3	2	73	26	60
Lansdowne	24	13	8	3	91	40	47
Stour Vale	24	15	2	7	53	41	47
Parley Spts Res.	24	10	7	7	43	36	37
Downton Res.	24	10	1	13	47	45	31
B'mouth Electric	24	9	2	13	49	73	29
Ferndown Town Spts	24	7	7	10	42	56	28
New Milton Res.	24	7	5	12	47	54	26
Hamworthy Eng. Res.	24	7	5	12	40	74	26
Queens Park Ath.	24	5	6	13	34	59	21
Redlynch/Woodfalls	24	4	3	17	28	60	15
B'mouth Spts Res.	24	2	3	19	28	77	9

DIV. TWO	P	W	D	L	F	A	PTS
Solar Services	22	20	2	0	93	20	62
Trinidad	22	15	3	4	63	28	48
Sway	22	14	4	4	66	34	46
Abbey Life	22	12	6	4	61	36	42
AFC Lymington 'A'	22	12	3	7	82	37	39
Burton	22	8	3	11	55	78	27
Bisterne Utd	22	6	6	10	26	49	24
B'mouth C.S. Res.	22	7	2	13	54	67	23
Westover Mtrs Res.	22	7	2	13	43	65	23
Parkview	22	6	3	13	34	55	21
Ringwood T. Res.	22	5	5	12	33	55	20
B'mouth Elec. Res.	22	0	1	21	27	113	1

DIV. THREE	P	W	D	L	F	A	PTS
Panthers	24	17	3	4	106	52	54
New Milton 'A'	24	15	5	4	70	37	50
Southbourne	24	15	3	6	61	36	48
Tudor Paving	24	15	1	8	77	45	46
Verwood T. Res.	24	12	5	7	67	49	41
Christchurch 'A'	24	9	7	8	60	59	33
Bransgore	24	9	6	9	42	46	33
West Moors	24	10	1	13	67	69	31
Highcliffe	24	8	4	12	51	49	28
Chase Manhattan	24	8	4	12	48	55	28
Sundial Windows	24	8	2	14	59	73	26
Somerford Sports	24	5	3	16	37	84	18
Burton Res.	24	3	0	21	33	124	9

DIV. FOUR	P	W	D	L	F	A	PTS
P & G Bluebird	24	16	4	4	83	36	52
Dorset Kings	24	16	3	5	80	37	51
B'mouth Spts 'A'	24	12	6	6	71	47	42
Stour Vale Res.	24	13	2	9	51	41	41
Hinton United	24	11	6	7	61	39	39
Alderholt	24	11	6	7	63	46	39
Milford	24	10	4	10	45	59	34
Fordingbridge Turks	24	8	5	11	41	55	29
Wilverley	24	7	6	11	46	59	27
Sway Res.	24	6	6	12	34	54	24
Hordle Spurs	24	5	4	15	32	64	19
Queens Pk Ath. Res.	24	5	4	15	36	73	19
Bisterne Res. (-6pts)	24	7	2	15	47	80	17

DIV. FIVE	P	W	D	L	F	A	PTS
A.E.C.C.	22	17	3	2	78	29	54
Pennington St Marks	22	14	3	5	71	43	45
Portcastrian	22	13	3	6	72	29	42
Bisterne Utd 'A'	22	12	3	7	75	59	39
Ashton United	22	11	2	9	65	43	35
Parkview Res.	22	8	8	6	42	39	32
Landowne 'A'	22	8	5	9	49	48	29
Westover Mtrs 'A'	22	9	2	11	44	49	29
Highcliffe Res.	22	6	5	11	37	74	23
Meyrick	22	5	5	12	42	72	20
Ringwood T. 'A'	22	5	2	15	39	66	17
Somerford Spts Res.	22	3	1	18	26	89	10

DIV. SIX	P	W	D	L	F	A	PTS
Burley (-3pts)	24	23	1	0	117	43	67
Trinidad Res.	24	16	4	4	81	31	52
New Milton 'B'	24	15	5	4	83	45	50
Littledown	24	15	3	6	83	47	48
Pennington SM Res.	24	13	1	10	63	68	40
Bisterne Utd 'B'	24	11	4	9	78	69	37
Abbey Life Res.	24	10	3	11	67	69	33
Alderholt Res.	24	8	3	13	51	67	27
Colourcare	24	7	5	12	48	56	26
Redlynch & W. Res.	24	7	2	15	42	67	23
Dean Spartans	24	6	3	15	45	68	21
Magna Spurs	24	4	2	18	36	110	14
Griffin	24	3	0	21	31	85	9

Wimborne Town with the pre-season Mark Frowde Cup, won by beating Weymouth 2-0 at the Wessex Stadium with goals from Robbie Sweetlove and Tommy Killick. Photo - Mr I Martin.

DORSET COMBINATION (Founded 1957)

President: A P Humphries, Esq.
Vice Presidents: T Coll, T W Scorah, D Walters
Chairman: E Maidment, Esq.

Hon. Secretary: G A Theobald, Esq.,
41 South Road, Corfe Mullen, Wimborne BH21 3HZ (0202 697994).
Press Officer: T W Scorah (0202 699650).

	P	W	D	L	F	A	PTS
Westland Sports	38	28	6	4	118	28	90
Sherborne Town	38	24	7	7	109	45	79
Hamworthy Eng.	38	22	9	7	81	37	75
Hamworthy United	38	23	4	11	112	74	*70
Bournemouth Spts	38	21	3	14	72	59	66
Flight Refuelling	38	17	10	11	84	61	*60
Portland United	38	19	6	13	68	62	*60
Dorchester T. Res.	38	17	7	14	79	57	58
Shaftesbury	38	17	6	15	84	71	57
Parley Sports	38	14	15	9	64	56	57
Poole Town Res.	38	16	8	14	68	58	56
Swanage T.H. Res.	38	15	9	14	67	61	54
Sturminster Newton	38	14	9	15	68	59	51
Blandford United	38	13	12	13	55	50	51
Holt United	38	13	5	20	61	91	44
Gillingham Town	38	13	3	22	55	78	42
Weymouth Res.	38	11	7	20	51	83	40
Wareham Rangers	38	7	3	28	58	121	*23
Bridport Res.	38	5	6	27	36	113	21
Cranborne	38	2	3	33	37	162	9

* - pts deducted

LEADING SCORERS 1992-93

Danny Alford (Shaftesbury)	48
Mike Satterley (Hamworthy United)	40
Martin Shepherd (Westland Sports)	34
John Inglis (Sherborne Town)	33
Colin Burton (Westland Sports)	26
Steve Mullcock (Hamworthy Engineering)	24
Steve Manuel (Hamworthy United)	22
Ray Cody (Dorchester (inc 6 for Portland))	20
Andy Walters (Dorchester Town Reserves)	20
Paul Spence (Bournemouth Sports)	19
Darren Pritchett (Hamworthy Engineering)	18
Simon Freak (Blandford United)	17
John Lewis (Portland United)	17
Andy Cherrett (Bournemouth Sports)	15

WESTLAND SPORTS WIN AT A CANTER

The chase for the League Championship was a one-horse race for virtually the whole season, with Westland Sports moving to the top in mid-September and remaining there to collect their first title since joining the League in 1981. In contrast, the runners-up spot was not decided until the last games of the season, with both Hamworthy Engineering and Sherborne Town going into their respective last matches with a chance of securing second place. Eventually this honour went to Sherborne, with Hamworthy Engineering, who were elected from the Bournemouth League, finishing third in their debut season.

At the other end Cranborne once again found life difficult, finishing bottom for the second time since joining the League four years ago and conceding 162 goals in 38 matches. Along with Bridport Reserves, they were forced to seek re-election.

The Combination Cup final, played at Bridport, saw Westland defeat Portland United 4-2 to complete the second part of a League and Cup double.

Sherborne Town became the first winners of the Trevor Williams Fair Play Cup, closely followed by Weymouth Reserves and Sturminster Newton. The Fair Play competition was inaugurated at the start of the season to perpetuate the name of Trevor Williams, a Life Vice-President of the League, and also to foster better discipline.

The Representative team, under the management of Blandford United's Mike Royal, retained the Ramsbury Trophy beating the Wiltshire County League 1-0 in their annual fixture, the match being held at Shaftesbury F.C.

The Combination sees only one change for 1993-94 with Weymouth Sports (formerly Weymouth Taxi Co.), from Division One of the Dorset League, replacing Cranborne who failed to gain re-election at the A.G.M. It was third time lucky for Weymouth Sports who been unsuccessful in two previous applications to join the League.

Geoff Theobald, Secretary.

COMBINATION LEAGUE CUP 1992-93

First Round

Bridport Reserves v Bournemouth Sports	0-4	Dorchester Town Res. v Gillingham Town	6-2
Shaftesbury v Portland United	0-2	Swanage Town & Herston v Cranborne	7-0

Second Round

Blandford United v Bournemouth Sports	2-1	Dorchester Town Reserves v Wareham Rangers	7-0
Flight Refuelling v Holt United	1-1,1-0	Hamworthy United v Sherborne Town	3-2
Parley Sports v Hamworthy Engineering	1-2	Portland United v Poole Town Reserves	4-0
Swanage T. & H. Res. v Weymouth Res.	3-1	Sturminster Newton United v Westland Sports	2-4

Quarter Finals

Portland United v Flight Refuelling	4-0	Hamworthy Engineering v Dorchester T. Res.	0-3
Swanage T. & H. Res. v Hamworthy Utd	3-0	Westland Spts v Blandford United	2-2,6-0

Semi Finals

Dorchester Reserves v Portland U.	2-2,3-4(aet)	Westland Sports v Swanage Town & Herston	3-0

Final (at Bridport F.C.): Westland Sports 4, Portland United 2

Parley Sports (light shirts) in a spin as they lose 1-6 at already crowned champions Westlands Sports. Photo - Tim Lancaster.

Hamworthy Engineering F.C., who had a magnificent first season in the Combination. Back Row (L/R): Jack Bellows (Physio), Steve Barrington (Temporary Manager), Stephan Matherson, Mark Tappin, Paul Stevens, Steve Mulcock, Gary Rider, Dave Mabey, Keith Hatchard, Ray Willis (Trainer). Front: Gary Moores, Robbie Downes, Dave Webber, Darren Pritchett, Andy Elms, Geoff Eaton. Photo - James Wright.

Portland United pictured before the League Cup final at Bridport. It was their fifth Combination Cup final - and their fifth defeat! Photo - Tim Lancaster.

RESULT CHART 1992-93

HOME TEAM	1	2	3	4	5	6	7	8	9	10	11	12	13	14	15	16	17	18	19	20
1. Blandford	*	1-4	3-0	3-0	1-1	2-2	2-1	0-1	4-1	1-2	1-1	1-3	1-1	2-0	3-1	0-1	3-1	0-3	0-1	3-1
2. B'mouth SC	2-1	*	5-0	7-1	0-3	2-1	1-1	0-2	2-3	1-0	0-0	3-1	2-1	5-1	4-3	2-1	4-2	3-1	0-2	3-1
3. Bridport Res	2-2	1-3	*	2-1	1-2	1-4	1-0	1-5	0-6	0-3	1-5	2-4	3-2	2-1	1-3	1-1	1-1	1-3	0-4	0-1
4. Cranborne	0-4	1-2	2-0	*	1-9	0-4	0-3	0-0	0-1	2-8	3-3	1-2	0-3	0-1	0-5	1-4	2-10	4-1	0-3	0-6
5. Dorch. Res	0-0	0-1	1-1	5-0	*	3-1	0-2	1-2	2-5	3-1	2-1	2-0	1-2	3-2	1-1	1-1	0-2	6-0	1-4	2-1
6. Flight Ref.	1-1	1-3	2-3	8-0	4-2	*	2-1	3-2	2-2	2-7	2-2	0-0	1-0	3-2	2-1	3-1	1-1	4-1	1-2	2-2
7. Gillingham	1-1	2-1	4-0	2-1	1-6	0-4	*	1-2	2-4	3-1	2-4	3-1	0-3	4-3	1-2	0-2	3-0	2-1	1-0	4-1
8. Ham. Eng.	0-0	3-0	1-0	7-0	2-1	2-3	2-0	*	2-2	5-0	2-0	1-1	1-0	1-0	2-0	2-1	1-1	1-0	3-4	2-1
9. Ham. United	2-1	2-1	5-1	5-1	2-1	0-4	4-1	2-1	*	8-0	5-1	1-2	2-3	2-5	1-6	3-2	1-2	3-2	1-3	6-1
10. Holt Utd	0-4	2-1	0-2	2-2	0-1	1-6	3-2	3-3	0-2	*	0-1	2-1	4-3	0-2	1-2	0-1	0-2	5-3	6-1	1-2
11. Parley Spts	1-1	0-0	2-0	3-1	1-1	0-2	2-0	0-0	2-1	2-3	*	1-2	3-1	2-4	2-2	3-2	1-0	2-2	0-0	4-2
12. Poole Res.	1-3	5-2	4-1	3-0	3-2	2-0	2-1	1-1	0-3	0-1	0-3	*	7-2	0-1	2-2	1-1	0-0	2-1	1-4	1-0
13. Portland	5-1	2-0	3-3	2-1	3-2	3-1	1-2	0-5	2-3	5-1	2-1	3-2	*	1-0	2-0	1-1	0-0	2-1	1-1	1-1
14. Shaftesbury	1-1	0-1	2-2	7-3	1-3	2-2	2-1	4-1	5-5	1-1	0-0	5-2	1-0	*	2-1	1-7	7-1	4-1	4-2	4-1
15. Sherborne	3-0	2-0	7-1	6-2	0-0	2-1	3-0	4-2	7-2	7-1	2-2	1-0	3-2	*	2-0	2-0	4-2	2-0	9-0	
16. Stur. Newton	0-1	1-3	3-0	7-0	3-1	0-0	2-1	1-7	2-4	1-1	2-0	1-2	2-1	1-3	*	2-2	6-0	0-1	2-2	
17. Swanage Rs.	2-0	3-0	3-1	7-0	2-4	1-1	4-1	2-0	0-0	1-2	2-4	0-3	1-2	2-1	0-4	3-0	*	2-1	1-4	1-1
18. Wareham	2-3	5-1	5-1	8-7	0-4	1-3	1-1	0-10	2-5	1-0	0-2	1-8	0-1	0-2	1-1	1-3	0-3	*	1-3	3-2
19. Westand	0-0	2-0	6-0	9-0	4-0	4-0	6-1	0-1	3-0	1-1	6-1	0-0	5-0	4-1	1-1	3-0	3-0	9-3	*	6-1
20. Weym. Res.	2-0	3-2	2-1	1-0	1-2	2-1	3-1	0-2	0-5	0-0	1-1	1-1	1-2	0-2	3-2	2-3	1-2	1-0	0-2	*

Highest Aggregate: Wareham Rgrs 8, Cranborne 7   **Biggest Win:** Wareham Rgrs 0, Hamworthy Eng. 10
Most goal scored in a League match by an individual: 6 - Mike Satterley for Hamworthy Utd v Weymouth Reserves.

3 goals or more in one game: Danny Alford (Shaftesbury) 7 times, Mike Satterley (Hamworthy U.) 5, Steve Mullcock (Hamworthy E.) 4, Martin Shepherd (Westland) 3, Mark Watson (Hamworthy U.) 3, Colin Burton (Westland) 2, John Inglis (Sherborne) 2. All once: Steve Norman & Simon Booth (Holt), Andrew Croft & Bruce Jones (Swanage), Darren Pritchett & Richard Hooley (Hamworthy E.), Dean Jack & Gary Judd (Sturminster N.), Gary Maidment (Cranborne), Steve Manuel (Hamworthy U.), Steve Randall & Adrian Mosley (Flight Ref.), Colin Sayers & Chris Osmond (Westland), Paul Selby (Wareham), Paul Spence (B'mouth Spts), Adrian Trimby (Poole), Dave Whalley (Dorchester).

Combination Cup Leading Scorers: Colin Burton (Westland) 6, John Lewis (Portland) 6, Martin Shepherd (Westland) 6, Andy Walters (Dorchester) 6, Darran Whyton (Portland) 6, Robin Dickson (Swanage) 3, Mark Lawley (Portland) 3, Colin Sayers (Westland) 3, Colin Stanger (Dorchester) 3.

Sherborne Town - Dorset Combination runners-up 1992-93. Photo - Tim Lancaster.

Hamworthy United F.C. 1992-93. Back Row (L/R): S Manuel, S Parker, A Hoare, P Cook, D Russell, R French, L Robertson. Front: M Worssell, M Satterley, T Firth, S Griffee, T Pidgley, M Watson. Photo - James Wright.

DORSET COMBINATION CLUBS 1993-94

BLANDFORD UNITED

Chairman: G Pike
Secretary: David A Thomas, 45 Badbury Drive, Blandford Forum, Dorset DT11 7UJ (0258 456570).
Ground: Recreation Ground, Park Lane, Blandford Forum, Dorset. (HQ Tel: 0258 456374).
Colours: Royal/white/royal   **Change colours:** All red
Cover: No   **Programme:** Yes   **Clubhouse:** No
92-93 Top Scorers: Simon Freak 17, Kevin Manson 6, Richard Knight 6, Steve Webb 6.

BOURNEMOUTH SPORTS CLUB

Chairman: T Bloor.
Secretary: Albert Langworthy, Nesika Illahee, Castle View Drive, Wareham Rd, Lychett Matravers BH16 6DX (0202 625565).
Ground: Chapel Gate, East Parley, Christchurch, Dorset BH23 6BD (0202 581933).
Colours: Gold/black/black   **Change colours:** All sky
Cover: No   **Programme:** Yes   **Clubhouse:** Yes
92-93 Top Scorers: Paul Spence 19, Andy Cherrett 15.

BRIDPORT RESERVES

92-93 Top Scorers: Nick Edwards 6, Ellis Hoole 5 *(See page 770 for other info.)*

DORCHESTER TOWN RESERVES

92-93 Top Scorers: Andy Walters 20, Ray Cody 14 *(See page 490 for other info.)*

FLIGHT REFUELLING

Chairman: B White.
Secretary: Harry W Doyle, 27 Fairview Cres., Broadstone, Poole BH18 9AP (0202 698393).
Ground: Merley Park, Merley, Wimborne, Dorset (0202 885773).
Colours: Sky/navy/navy   **Change colours:** All yellow
Cover: No   **Programme:** Yes   **Clubhouse:** Yes
92-93 Top Scorers: Steve Raines 14, Adrian Mosley 13.

GILLINGHAM TOWN

Chairman: E Murphy.
Secretary: David J Ayles, 37 Sylvan Way, Bay Road, Gillingham SP8 4EQ (0747 822065).
Ground: Hardings Lane, Gillingham (0747 823673).
Cols: Tangerine & black/black/black   **Change colours:** Blue/navy/blue
Cover: Yes   **Programme:** Yes   **Clubhouse:** Yes
92-93 Top Scorers: Chris Chambers 8, Sean Bartlett 7, Tim Benjafield 7.

HAMWORTHY ENGINEERING

Chairman: M Robson.
Secretary: Ray Willis, 52 Heckford Rd, Poole BH15 2LY (0202 677063).
Ground: Hamworthy Rec. Club, Magna Rd, Canford Magna, Wimborne, Dorset BH21 3AE (0202 881922).
Colours: All green   **Change colours:** White & blue stripes/navy/navy
Cover: No   **Programme:** No   **Clubhouse:** Yes
92-93 Top Scorers: Steve Mullcock 24, Darren Pritchett 18.

HAMWORTHY UNITED

Chairman: M Squire
Secretary: Roy Mitchener, 68 St Mary's Rd, Poole, Dorset BH15 2LL (0202 676128).
Ground: The County Ground, Blandford Close, Hamworthy, Poole, Dorset (0202 674974).
Colours: Maroon & sky/sky/maroon   **Change colours:** Green & black stripes/black/black
Cover: Yes   **Floodlights:** Yes   **Programme:** Yes   **Clubhouse:** Yes
92-93 Top Scorers: Mike Satterley 40, Steve Manuel 22.

HOLT UNITED

Chairman: H Richardson.
Secretary: Mark Willis, 63 Victoria Close, Corfe Mullen, Wimborne, Dorset BH21 3TX (0202 605089).
Ground: Petersham Lane, Gaunts Common, Holt, Wimborne, Dorset (0258 840379).
Colours: Red & white/white/red   **Change colours:** Yellow/green/yellow
Cover: No   **Programme:** No   **Clubhouse:** Yes
92-93 Top Scorers: Steve Norman 10, Andre Linford 8.

PARLEY SPORTS

Chairman: O Williams.   **Secretary:** Mrs Yvonne Hallam, 106 New Rd, Parley, Bournemouth.
Ground: Parley Sports Club, Christchurch, West Parley, Bournemouth, Dorset (0202 573345).
Colours: Yellow/blue/yellow   **Change colours:** Blue/yellow/blue
Cover: No   **Programme:** No   **Clubhouse:** Yes
92-93 Top Scorers: Graham Dark 10, Freddie Warren 10, Jimmy Fry 7.

POOLE TOWN RESERVES

Colours: Red & white stripes/white/red & white.   **Change colours:** All blue.
92-93 Top Scorers: Shane Loder 10, Adrian Trimby 9 *(See page 545 for other info.)*

PORTLAND UNITED

Chairman: R Carlyle.
Secretary: David M Camp, 23 Four Acres, Weston, Portland DT5 2LG (0305 821816).
Ground: Grove Corner, Portland (0305 823690).
Colours: Blue/blue/red   **Change colours:** Red & white/white/blue.
Cover: Yes   **Programme:** Yes   **Clubhouse:** Yes
92-93 Top Scorers: John Lewis 17, Mark Lawley 12.

SHAFTESBURY

Chairman: P Humphries.
Secretary: Miss Alison Charlton, 33 St Rumbolds Rd, Shaftesbury SP7 8NE (0747 54584).
Ground: Cockrams, Coppice Street, Shaftesbury (0747 53990).
Colours: Red/black/red   **Change colours:** All green
Cover: Yes   **Floodlights:** Yes   **Programme:** No   **Clubhouse:** Yes
92-93 Top Scorers: Danny Alford 48, Malcolm Burt 5, William Stevens 5.

SHERBORNE TOWN

Chairman: I Shipper.
Secretary: Roger V Woolmington, 23 Harbour Rd, Sherborne DT9 4AL (0935 813048).
Ground: Raleigh Grove, The Terrace Playing Fields, Sherborne (0935 816110).
Colours: Black & white stripes/black/black   **Change colours:** All tangerine
Cover: Yes   **Programme:** Yes   **Clubhouse:** Yes
92-93 Top Scorers: John Inglis 33, David Mann 14.

STURMINSTER NEWTON

Chairman: R Clarke.
Secretary: David Walters, 44 Filbridge Rise, Sturminster Newton, Dorset DT10 1BP (0258 472381).
Ground: Ricketts Lane, Sturminster Newton, Dorset. (HQ (RBL) Tel: 0258 472437).
Colours: Red/black/black   **Change colours:** All blue
Cover: Yes   **Programme:** Yes   **Clubhouse:** No
92-93 Top Scorers: Kevin Trew 15, Dean Jack 8.

SWANAGE TOWN & HERSTON RESERVES

92-93 Top Scorers: Bruce Jones 11, Andrew Croft 10   *(See page 810 for other info.)*

WAREHAM RANGERS

Secretary: Mrs Carol White, 9 Bere Road, Wareham, Dorset BH20 4DB (0929 551765).
Ground: Wareham Recreation Ground, Worgret Rd, Wareham, Dorset.
Colours: Amber & black/black/black   **Change colours:** All royal blue
Cover: No   **Programme:** Yes   **Clubhouse:** No
92-93 Top Scorers: Andy Griffiths 14, Mark Tubbs 10.

WESTLAND SPORTS

Secretary: Alan Fisher, 103 Tintagel Road, Yeovil BA21 3RD (0935 26456).
Ground: Westland Sports Ground, Westbourne Grove, Yeovil (0935 703811).
Colours: Jade/black/jade   **Change colours:** Yellow/white/yellow.
Cover: No   **Programme:** Yes   **Clubhouse:** No
92-93 Top Scorers: Martin Shepherd 34, Colin Burton 26.

WEYMOUTH RESERVES

92-93 Top Scorers: Paul Hammond 8, Martin Harvey 7   *(See page 550 for other info.)*

WEYMOUTH SPORTS

Secretary: Bob Clewett, 18 Hawthorn Close, Dorchester, Dorset DT1 2PQ (0305 266470).
Ground: Weymouth College, Cranford Ave., Weymouth, Dorset (0305 208859/208860).
Cols: Yellow & black stripes/black/black & yellow   **Change:** Black & jade stripes/black/black & jade
Prev. Lge: Dorset (champs 1993)   **Previous Name:** Weymouth Taxi Co. (pre-1993).

DORSET COUNTY LEAGUE

	P	W	D	L	F	A	PTS
Weymouth Taxi Co.	28	19	5	4	82	20	43
Stourpaine	28	19	5	4	84	33	43
Weston United	28	16	6	6	78	39	38
Chideock	28	16	5	7	74	46	38
Allendale	28	15	5	8	79	49	35
Littlemoor Sports	28	14	6	8	55	51	34
Hamworthy Utd Res.	28	14	5	9	63	49	33
Moreton	28	12	3	13	62	61	27
Dorchester YMCA	28	10	6	12	58	60	26
Flight Ref. Res.	28	11	3	14	38	59	25
Broadmayne Res.	28	9	6	13	64	75	24
Blandford U. Res.	28	10	2	16	52	76	22
Okeford United	28	6	4	18	46	81	16
Bere Regis	28	5	5	18	35	76	15
Portland Wdrs	28	1	0	27	38	137	2

ANDOVER & DISTRICT LEAGUE

PREM. DIV.	P	W	D	L	F	A	PTS
Broughton Res.	16	13	1	2	45	13	40
Stockbridge Res.	16	10	2	4	62	38	32
New Street Res.	16	8	5	3	47	26	29
A.B.C. United	16	9	2	5	47	28	29
G.B.E. Legg	16	7	1	8	60	53	22
Longparish	16	6	3	7	27	33	21
St Mary Bourne Res.	16	6	2	8	33	48	20
East Woodhay	16	3	1	12	21	55	10
Wallop	16	1	1	14	30	78	4

DIV. ONE	P	W	D	L	F	A	PTS
Enham	22	19	1	2	120	33	58
Inkpen	22	16	3	3	85	30	51
I.T.P.S.	22	14	1	7	81	57	43
Locomotors	22	13	3	6	89	62	42
Blaizers	22	12	1	9	67	39	37
Wallop Res.	22	10	4	8	76	56	34
Kings Somborne Res.	22	9	5	8	63	63	32
Stannah	22	10	1	11	65	66	31
Ducal	22	6	2	14	47	66	20
Longparish Res.	22	5	1	16	43	70	16
Folly Inn	22	2	1	19	34	129	7
G.B.E. Legg Res.	22	2	1	19	44	143	7

WILTSHIRE FOOTBALL LEAGUE

President: D.S.Paget
Chairman: D.C.Kilford   **Vice-Chairman:** C.W.Cousins
Hon. General Secretary: P.J. Ackrill, 3 Dallas Avenue,
Swindon, Wiltshire

PEWSEY VALE AWAIT PROMOTION

Meetings have been held with the Joint Liaison Committees of the Pyramid system involving the Great Mills Western League and The Spectre Hellenic League. At the time of going to print with this report, Pewsey Vale Football Club remain extremely anxious as to the outcome of their application to join the Great Mills Western League as champions of division one.

Pewsey Vale have worked wonders at their ground. A year ago the club requested an inspection by the Management Committee in order to ascertain the amount of alterations needed to meet the standards for entry into the Great Mills Western League. Within a year the dressing-rooms have been re-vamped, the pitch enclosed with steel tubing, brick built dug-outs erected, hard standing and covered accommodation for spectators. The Management Committee sincerely hope their application will be successful, as this may lead the way for other member clubs to follow suit and improve their ground and facilities, to the standard required for promotion under the Pyramid system.

The inclement weather prior to Christmas resulted in only three games being played in the Floodlight Cup competition by the end of January, so it was decided to abondone the competition for this season. This action was taken reluctantly and to avoid placing extra pressure on clubs durng the latter end of the season, to play games.

The representative fixture was played against the Dorset Combination League at Shaftesbury and after an entertaining game, the League team lost 1-0. Considering that Team Manager Kevin Cranmer had to replace seven players from the original squad that was selected, the performance was an outstanding feat. The Management Committee wish to record its thanks to clubs who provided replacement players at the very last moment, this kind of co-operation is always appreciated.

P.J.Ackrill (Secretary)

DIVISION ONE	P	W	D	L	F	A	PTS
Pewsey Vale	30	22	5	3	88	20	71
Shrewton Utd	30	19	5	6	76	42	62
Biddestone	30	18	6	6	74	41	60
Amesbury T.	30	19	3	8	73	42	60
Ferndale A.	30	16	5	9	65	42	53
Walcot A.	30	14	6	10	55	48	48
Sanford	30	14	5	11	59	47	47
Pinehurst	30	12	5	13	53	62	41
Aldbourne P.	30	9	9	12	52	55	36
Chiseldon*	30	9	7	14	41	69	31
Devizes T.R.	30	8	6	16	59	70	30
Burmah Castrol	30	7	9	14	47	62	30
Calne Town R.	30	7	9	14	32	52	30
Dorcan	30	8	6	16	42	78	30
Wroughton	30	5	10	15	31	59	25
Broham	30	3	4	23	31	89	13

* - 1pt deducted.

DIVISION THREE	P	W	D	L	F	A	PTS
Salisbury M.	30	21	6	3	103	30	69
Box Rovers	30	20	5	5	75	35	65
Aldbourne P.Res	30	20	4	6	82	47	64
Nat.Semiconductor	30	17	5	8	60	36	56
Pewsey V.Res	30	16	5	9	78	32	53
Pinehurst Res	30	16	1	13	57	40	49
Sanford Res	30	15	3	12	63	50	48
W'ton Bassett Spt	30	14	3	13	57	54	45
Blunsden Utd	30	13	2	15	52	81	41
Marlborough T.R	30	11	5	14	66	78	38
Corsham T.Res	30	11	5	14	57	72	38
Ferndale Ath.R.	30	11	3	16	55	77	36
Burmah Castrol R	30	8	2	20	40	71	26
Ramsbury	30	6	4	20	30	102	22
Minety	30	5	6	19	53	99	21
Wroughton Res	30	5	3	22	47	80	18

DIVISION TWO	P	W	D	L	F	A	PTS
Marlborough T.	24	18	4	2	67	26	58
Corsham T.	24	16	2	6	60	23	50
Tisbury Utd	24	15	4	5	63	32	49
Malmesbury V.	24	13	6	5	52	33	45
W'ton Bassett T.R	24	13	2	9	45	43	41
Bradford T.	24	10	6	8	48	31	36
Plessey Semics	24	10	5	9	42	39	35
Purton Res.	24	10	5	9	47	48	35
Warminster T.R.*	24	6	6	12	54	66	23
Melksham T.R.	24	5	6	13	29	64	21
Stratton Ath.	24	5	4	15	29	60	19
Dunbar Wills	24	5	3	16	42	67	18
Chippenham T.R.	24	3	1	20	29	75	10

* - 1pt deducted.

DIVISION FOUR	P	W	D	L	F	A	PTS
Dorcan Reserves	26	19	2	5	81	36	59
Plessey Semics R	26	18	3	5	71	36	57
West Swindon	26	16	5	5	85	40	53
Down Ampney	26	14	5	7	76	52	47
Walcot Ath.Res	26	14	4	8	72	51	46
Grove*	26	15	1	10	82	49	45
Tidworth United	26	11	3	12	78	56	36
Biddestone Res	26	10	5	11	63	64	35
AFC Cricklade	26	9	4	13	50	54	31
Bromham Res	26	8	4	14	47	66	28
Sherston Town	26	8	2	16	36	70	26
Dunbar Wills R.	26	8	1	17	41	91	25
Cricklade Town	26	7	3	16	33	70	24
Chiseldon Res	26	3	2	21	26	106	11

* - 1pt deducted.

'ADDKEY' LEAGUE SENIOR CUP 1992-93

First Round

Amesbury Town v Chiseldon	3-2	Ferndale Athletic v Biddestone	3-2
Corsham Town v Walcot Athletic	1-2	Calne Town Reserves v Bromham	3-0
Burmah Castrol v Devizes Town Reserves	1-2	Melksham Town Reserves v Avebury Park	0-4
Warminster T. Reserves v Dunbar Wills	3-0	Wroughton v Shrewton United	0-6
Pinehurst *(w/o)* Westbury Utd Reserves *(scr)*		Tisbury U. Res. *(disq)* Malmesbury Victoria *(w/o)*	
Purton Reserves *(w/o)* West Swindon *(scr)*		Wootton Bassett Reserves v Aldbourne Park	2-4
Sanford v Bradford Town	2-1	Chippenham Town Reserves v Dorcan	1-3
Stratton R.E. v Marlborough	0-1	Plessey Semics v Pewsey Vale	0-5

Second Round

Amesbury Town v Ferndale Athletic	4-2	Walcot Athletic v Calne Town Reserves	3-0
Devizes Town Reserves v Avebury Park	1-3	Warminster Town Reserves v Shrewton United	1-2
Pinehurst v Malmesbury Victoria	1-0	Purton Reserves v Aldbourne Park	1-5
Sanford v Dorcan	4-0	Marlborough v Pewsey Vale	3-6

Quarter-Finals

Amesbury Town v Walcot Athletic	1-0	Avebury Park v Shrewton United	0-2
Pinehurst v Aldbourne Park	1-0	Sanford v Pewsey Vale	0-1

Semi-Finals

Amesbury Town v Shrewton United	2-0	Pinehurst v Pewsey Vale	0-2

Final: Amesbury Town 2, Pewsey Vale 1 *(aet)*

'FOUNTAINS TROPHIES' LEAGUE JUNIOR CUP

First Round

Aldbourne Pk Res. v Biddestone Res.	5-3	West Swindon *(w/o)* Dunbar Wills Res. *(scr)*	
Salisbury Manor v Wroughton Res.	7-0	Box Rovers v Grove	2-4
National Semi v Plessey Semics Reserves	2-3	Chiseldon Reserves v AFC Cricklade	1-2
Bromham Reserves v Cricklade Town	3-0	Corsham Town Res. v Pewsey Vale Res.	2-3
Tidworth United v Blunsdon United	6-1	Wootton Bassett Sports *(bye)*	
Ramsbury v Sherston Town	4-2	Burmah Castrol Reserves v Avebury Park Res.	3-2
Pinehurst Reserves v Minety	2-0	Down Ampney v Walcot Athletic Reserves	2-0
Sanford Reserves v Marlborough Reserves	2-1	Ferndale Athletic v Dorcan Reserves	0-1

Second Round

Aldbourne Park Res. v West Swindon	4-3	Salisbury Manor v Grove	1-4
Plessey Semics Reserves v AFC Cricklade	1-2	Bromham Reserves v Pewsey Vale Reserves	1-7
Tidworth United v Wootton Bassett Sports	3-1	Ramsbury v Burmah Castrol Reserves	6-3
Pinehurst Reserves v Down Ampney	3-2	Sanford Reserves v Dorcan Reserves	1-3

Quarter-Finals

Aldbourne Park Reserves v Grove	2-1	AFC Cricklade v Pewsey Vale Res.	3-3,0-2
Tidworth United v Ramsbury	5-3	Pinehurst United Reserves v Dorcan Reserves	1-3

Semi-Finals

Aldbourne Park Reserves v Pewsey Vale Res. 3-0		Tidworth United v Dorcan Reserves	0-3

Final: Aldbourne Park Reserves 3, Dorcan Reserves 2

DIVISION ONE CLUBS 1993-94

ALDBOURNE PARK
Secretary: Ms S Archer, 27 Claridge Close, Aldbourne, Swindon SN8 2BS (0672 40758).
Ground: Farm Lane, Aldbourne. **Colours:** Sky/navy *(Res: yellow/green)*

AMESBURY TOWN
Secretary: Mrs N Chalmers, 43 Coltsfoot Close, Amesbury SP4 7NP (0980 624101).
Ground: Amesbury Rec (0980 623489) **Colours:** Blue/white/blue.

BIDDESTONE
Secretary: Mrs B Short, 1 Hartham Lane, Biddestone, Chippenham SN14 7EA (0249 714724).
Ground: Cuttle Lane, Biddestone **Colours:** Red & blue stripes/blue/blue *(Res: all red)*

BURMAH CASTROL
Secretary: Mr I G Watters, 15 Lucerne Close, Middleleaze, Swindon SN5 9GQ (0793 887628).
Ground: Burmah House, Pipers Way, Swindon (via Broome Manor Golf Club)(0793 523142).
Colours: Red & black hoops/red/red *(Res: all green).*

CHISELDON
Secretary: Mr S Morgan, 58 Station Rd, Chiseldon, Swondon SN4 0PW (0793 740125).
Ground: Chiseldon Rec. **Colours:** Red/blue *(Change & Res: white/blue)*

CORSHAM TOWN
Secretary: Mrs P Kilmurray, 21 Tellcroft Close, Corsham SN13 9JH (0249 714918).
Ground: Lacock Rd (0249 715609) **Colours:** Red & white/red *(Res: White & black/black)*

FERNDALE ATHLETIC
Secretary: Mr M Baker, 38 Farriers Close, Swindon SN1 2QT (0793 431259).
Ground: County Ground Extension (Swindon Town F.C.)(0793 523088).
Colours: Gold/black/gold *(Red & white/white/red)*

MARLBOROUGH TOWN
Secretary: Mr D W G Cripps, 62 Five Stiles Rd, Marlborough SN8 4BE (0672 512741).
Ground: Elcot Lane (0672 513340) **Colours:** Royal & red stripes *(Res: all maroon).*

MELKSHAM TOWN
Secretary: Mr P R Macey, 30 Wellington Square, Bowerhill, Melksham SN12 6QX (0225 706876).
Ground: The Conigre, Melksham (0225 702843). Just off main square at back of town car park.
Colours: Old gold/black/black.

PINEHURST
Secretary: Mr N J Merrett, 72 York Rd, Swindon SN1 2JU (0793 539472).
Ground: Pinehurst School Field, Beech Ave., Swindon.
Colours: White/blue/blue *(Res: Black & grey stripes/black/black).*

SANFORD

Secretary: Mr A L Pike, 41 Gays Place, Upper Stratton, Swindon SN2 6LN (0793 826082).
Ground: G.W.R. Sports Club, Swindon (0793 523019) **Colours:** Red & black/black/red

SHREWTON UNITED

Secretary: Mrs M Withers, Fleming Farm, Shrewton, nr Salisbury SP3 4ER (0980 620065).
Ground: Shrewton Rec. **Colours:** Maroon/blue.

TISBURY UNITED

Secretary: Mr F L Hopgood, Hill-Tops, 1 Cuffs Lane, Tisbury SP3 6LG (0747 870246).
Ground: Station Rd Rec, Tisbury (0747 871314) **Colours:** Red/black/black

WALCOT ATHLETIC

Secretary: Mr J McIlherron, 25 Kingswood Ave., Park North, Swindon SN3 2RB (0793 486855).
Ground: Southbrook Rec, Pinehurst Rd, Swindon (0793 611171).
Colours: Red/blue/blue *(Res: Green/grey/green).*

Plus the Reserve sides of: *Calne Town (page 764), Devizes Town (page 770).*

DIVISION TWO CLUBS 1993-94

BRADFORD TOWN

Secretary: Miss K Stevens, 12 Magnon Rd, Bradford-on-Avon BA15 1PT (0225 865526).
Ground: St Laurence Sch., Ashley Rd entrance, Bradford-on-A. **Colours:** All yellow.

BROMHAM

Secretary: Mr G Riggs, Oliver Cromwell, 71 St Ediths Marsh, Bromham, nr Chippenham SN15 2JF (0380 850293).
Ground: Jubilee PF, New Rd, Bromham (0380 850671) **Cols:** White/black *(Res: royal/white)*

DORCAN

Secretary: Mr S Sell, 8 Ashbury Ave., Nythe, Swindon SN3 3LY (0793 527186).
Grnd: Oakfield Sch., Marlowe Ave., Swindon (0793 535043) **Colours:** Sky/navy/white.

DUNBAR WILLS

Secretary: Mr A M Pickett, 78 Southbrook Street Extension, Swindon SN2 1HG (0793 523980).
Grnd: King Edwards Place, Foxhill, nr Swindon (0793 791282) **Cols:** Tangerine/black/black.

MALMESBURY VICTORIA

Secretary: Mrs M Picter, 14 White Lion Park, Malmesbury SN16 0QW (0666 822623).
Grnd: Flying Monk Ground, Gloucester Rd, Malmesbury (0666 822141) **Cols:** White & black stripes/black.

PLESSEY SEMICS

Secretary: Mr C Bennett, 15 Mellow Ground, Haydon Wick, Swindon SN2 3QJ (0793 726715).
Ground: Plessey Spts Ground, Ermin Street, Stratton, Swindon **Colours:** All blue.

STRATTON ATHLETIC

Secretary: Mrs R Marsh, 65 Rowton Way, Freshbrook, Swindon SN5 8PW (0793 870826).
Ground: Burderop Park, Wroughton **Colours:** All red.

WROUGHTON

Secretary: Mr C G Swatton, 23 Lydiard Park, Hook Str.,, Wootton Bassett SN4 8EF (0793 855194).
Grnd: Weir Field, Wroughton **Colours:** White & blue.

Plus the Reserve sides of: *Chippenham Town (page 765), Pewsey Vale (page 773), Purton (page 739), Warminster Town (page 773), Wootton Bassett Town (page 740).*

DIVISION THREE CLUBS 1993-94

BLUNSDON UNITED

Secretary: Mr K Hobbs, 31 Burnet Close, Woodhall Park, Swindon SN2 2RT (0793 728059).
Ground: Sutton Park Rec., Blunsdon **Colours:** White/blue/white.

BOX ROVERS

Secretary: Mr P Goulding, 20 Sunderland Close, Melksham SN12 6TZ (0225 704988).
Ground: Box Recreation Ground **Colours:** All blue.

NATIONAL SEMICONDUCTOR

Secretary: Mr S Herlihy, 16 Winwick Rd, Freshbrook, Swindon SN5 8NF (0793 481706).
Ground: Maunsall Way, Wroughton **Colours:** Royal/white.

SALISBURY MANOR

Secretary: P Burden (0793 852584) **Ground:** Salisbury City F.C. *(see page 546).*

WEST SWINDON

Secretary: Mr A Morton, 21 Borage Close, Haydon Wick, Swindon SN2 2TF (0793 723568).
Ground: Greendown School, West Swindon **Colours:** Blue & white.

WOOTTON BASSETT SPORTS

Secretary: Mr M Smedley, 31 Tennyson Rd, Wootton Bassett SN4 8HL (0793 852584).
Ground: Wootton Bassett Comprehansive School **Cols:** White (blue sleeves)/blue/blue

Plus the Reserve sides of: *Aldbourne Park, Burmah Castrol, Corsham Town, Dorcan, Ferndale Ath., Marlborough Town, Melksham Town, Pinehurst, Plessey Semics, Sanford.*

DIVISION FOUR CLUBS 1993-94

ASHTON KEYNES

Secretary: Mr J Pointing, 66 Melmore Gdns, Cirencester GL7 1NS (0285 655126).
Ground: Rixon Gate, Ashton Keynes **Colours:** Blue/white/blue.

CHIPPENHAM BOROUGH

Secretary: Mr R Harvey, 21 Fairfoot Close, Chippenham SN14 0PJ (0249 656012).
Ground: West Mead Lane, Chippenham **Colours:** Blue & black stripes/black/black

CRICKLADE TOWN
Secretary: Mr W J Locke, 11 Drew Str., Rodbourne, Swindon SN2 2HP (0793 520634).
Grnd: Cricklade Leisure Centre, Stones Lane, Cricklade (0793 750011) **Cols:** Green & white/green/green.

DOWN AMPNEY
Secretary: Mr D F Lawrence, 5 Limes Place, Latton, nr Cricklade, Swindon SN6 6DR (0793 751525).
Ground: Broadleaze, Down Ampney   **Colours:** All blue.

GROVE
Secretary: Mr D Coe, 305 Queens Drive, Swindon SN3 1AU (0793 539108).
Ground: As Walcot Ath. *(page 821)*   **Colours:** Blue & black stripes/black/black.

HIGHWORTH ATHLETIC
Secretary: Mr P D Hayward, 12 Brookfield, Highworth, Swindon SN6 7HY (0793 763012).
Ground: Barra Close Rec, Highworth   **Colours:** Blue & black/black/black.

MINETY
Secretary: Mr G W Chinnock, 'Jumar', Upper Minety, Malmesbury SN16 9PR (0666 860361).
Ground: Silver Street PF, Minety (0666 860802).   **Colours:** Amber/black.

RAMSBURY
Secretary: Mr R G Mills, 14 Swans Close, Ramsbury, Marlborough, Wilts SN8 2PH (0672 20468).
Ground: Hilldrop Lane Rec, Ramsbury, Marlborough   **Colours:** Blue (white trim)

RAYCHEM SPORTS & SOCIAL
Secretary: Mr R J Wheatley, 18 Shapwick Close, Nythe, Swindon SN3 3RQ (0793 527500).
Ground: Crosslink Centre, Ermin Str., Swindon (0793 831511) **Colours:** Black & white stripes/black.

SHERSTON TOWN
Secretary: Miss J Price, The Angel Inn, Sherston, Malmesbury SN16 0PY (0666 840238).
Ground: Knockdown Rd, Sherston, Malmesbury   **Colous:** All red.

TIDWORTH UNITED
Secretary: Mr J Murdoch, 711 Ordnance Rd, Tidworth, Hants SP9 7QB (0980 46840).
Ground: Arcot Road, Tidworth, Hants   **Colours:** All royal blue.

Plus the Reserve sides of: *Biddestone, Bromham, Chiseldon, Dunbar Wills, Walcot Ath., Wroughton.*

BASINGSTOKE & DISTRICT LEAGUE

PREM. DIV.	P	W	D	L	F	A	PTS
Hook	20	18	1	1	64	14	55
Basing Rovers	20	15	0	5	81	53	45
Tadley	20	13	4	3	88	31	43
Sherborne St Johns	20	13	1	6	69	33	40
Burghclere	20	10	0	10	53	47	30
Wootton St Lawrence	20	9	2	9	50	44	29
Oakley Athletic	20	7	4	9	42	54	25
Kingsclere	20	6	3	11	44	63	21
B & T Winkle	20	6	3	11	43	67	21
Sherfield	20	2	0	18	30	99	6
Bramley United	20	1	2	17	28	87	5

DIV. TWO	P	W	D	L	F	A	PTS
Alpha Windows	22	17	3	2	83	26	54
Gordons Contract S.	22	14	3	5	80	29	45
Priestley	22	12	5	5	68	36	41
Burghclere Res.	22	11	4	7	58	43	37
Overton Utd 'A'	22	12	0	10	72	52	36
Hart Rovers	22	10	6	6	62	47	36
Impression Res.	22	11	2	9	74	44	35
Sherborne Res.	22	11	2	9	62	59	35
Ropley	22	6	3	13	51	83	21
Hatch Warren	22	4	5	13	44	112	17
Mercantile Group	22	3	2	17	27	88	11
Unipath	22	1	5	16	36	98	8

DIV. ONE	P	W	D	L	F	A	PTS
Long Sutton	22	17	4	1	93	24	55
Impression	22	17	3	2	111	25	54
Tadley Res.	22	15	3	4	67	40	48
Hook Res.	22	15	1	6	81	38	46
Wootton Res.	22	11	4	7	49	44	37
Popinjay	22	9	4	9	51	62	31
Lightning Print	22	7	6	9	46	59	27
AFC Aldermaston 'A'	22	7	4	11	50	50	25
FC Winklebury	22	5	5	12	52	81	20
Sun Life Canada	22	5	3	14	42	75	18
B'stoke Labour C.	22	2	2	18	48	97	8
Headley	22	1	3	18	28	123	6

DIV. THREE	P	W	D	L	F	A	PTS
Tadley 'A'	22	15	3	4	77	29	48
Hillborne	22	13	8	1	75	32	47
Kingsclere Res.	22	13	5	4	75	35	44
J Davy	22	11	5	6	75	35	38
Silchester	22	10	7	5	60	45	37
Southern Gas	22	10	5	7	67	48	35
Burghfield C.S.	22	11	2	9	66	55	35
Fox Newfound	22	9	1	11	47	56	28
Herriard Spts	22	7	5	10	46	61	26
Cromwell Inn	22	6	1	15	50	70	19
Bramley Utd Res.	22	4	3	15	31	63	14
Uptown	22	0	1	21	15	155	1

NORTH HAMPSHIRE LEAGUE

PREM. DIV.	P	W	D	L	F	A	PTS
Ludgershall Spts	20	16	3	1	79	26	51
Overton Utd Res.	20	13	4	3	56	31	43
AFC Ald'maston Res.	20	11	4	5	41	31	*37
Malshanger Res.	20	10	3	7	45	40	33
St Mary Bourne	20	9	4	7	50	43	31
RAPC Worthy Down	20	8	3	9	39	50	27
Winch. Castle Res.	20	6	5	9	38	55	23
Alresford T. Res.	20	5	5	10	52	44	20
AFC Charlton	20	4	5	11	39	61	17
Kings Somborne	20	5	2	13	37	68	17
Worthies Sports	20	3	2	15	40	67	11

* - 3pts awarded

SUPP. LGE CUP	P	W	D	L	F	A	PTS
Ludgershall Spts	6	4	2	0	21	9	14
AFC Aldermaston Res.	6	3	0	3	14	11	9
AFC Charlton	6	2	0	4	9	14	6
Alresford T. Res.	6	1	2	3	9	19	5

Leading Scorers:
I Winstone (Ludgershall Spts) 22, C Smith (AFC Aldermaston) 21, S Coombes (Ludershall Spts) 18, J Costello (RAPC Worthy Down) 14, C Lawes (Alresford Town Res.) 14, D Pidduck (Alresford Town Res.) 12, B Spanswick (Ludgershall Spts) 12, J Barnes (Kings Somborne) 10, J Edwards & G Gibbons (Overton Res.) 10, R Lane (Alresford Res.) 10, M Nolan (Malshanger Res.) 10, G Smith (AFC Charlton Res.) 10.

C.H.B.
HAMPSHIRE LEAGUE

Chairman: Mr Norman White.

Hon. Secretary: Mr John Moody,
13 Tadfield Cres., Romsey SO51 8AN
(0794 514073)

PIRELLI WIN LAST TITLE UNDER COUNTY'S ADMINISTRATION

The closing of the 1992-93 season was a sad occasion following the decision of the Hampshire F.A. Council by 27 votes to 25 to take the League's administration away from the County office. I was personally very sorry that this decision was taken for I am sure that the benefits of it remaining far outweigh the reasons given for change. However, we were very grateful for the excellent sponsorship from the C.H.B. Group, and it is pleasing to report that they will be continuing with us next season.

Our thanks is also recorded to David Creedon of Trophyman for once again sponsoring the League Cup, and our congratulations this year go to Cowes Sports who beat New Street 2-0 in a quite electric final at Fareham.

In Division One a number of clubs were fancied for the championship which eventually went to Pirelli General who had two points more than Bishops Waltham. Division Two winners were Portsmouth Civil Service after winning Division Three the previous year, and they rounded off an excellent season by retaining the Hampshire Intermediate Cup. Hedge End won Division Three and will be looking forward to their promotion.

The Ground Grading Committee have made a number of visits during the season, and it is pleasing to see standards improving. Special mention must be made of the superb facilities at New Milton and New Street, and also of the floodlighting and work completed at Cowes Sports.

The League Committee once again met local association representatives, and following discusions agreed to accept five new clubs for 1993-94; Bishopstoke Social, Hamble Club & Athletic, Hilsea Club, Portsmouth Civil Service Reserves and Ludgershall Sports. Downton are promoted to the Jewson Wessex League, whilst Romsey Town, relegated under the Pyramid system, make the opposite journey. Clubs withdrawing from the League are Laverstock & Ford, who return to the Salisbury League after just one season, Netley Athletic Victoria, Midanbury and Lansdowne. Meanwhile, Nutfield United have renamed themselves Nursling.

John Moody, League Secretary.

DIV. ONE	P	W	D	L	F	A	PTS
Pirelli General	32	23	5	4	71	26	74
Bishops Waltham	32	22	6	4	101	40	72
Downton	32	20	7	5	72	33	67
Fleetlands	32	19	5	8	58	44	62
Cowes Sports	32	18	6	8	79	49	60
Blackfield & Langley	32	16	9	7	63	40	57
Overton United	32	15	6	11	56	46	51
New Milton	32	14	7	11	55	49	49
Colden Common	32	13	6	13	63	51	45
Bass Alton Town	32	13	5	14	68	57	44
Winchester City	32	10	6	16	47	69	36
Malshanger	32	9	7	16	32	48	34
A.C. Delco	32	8	9	15	33	51	33
Locksheath	32	6	7	19	48	78	25
Aresford Town	32	6	7	19	40	73	25
Awbridge	32	6	5	21	39	82	23
Midanbury	32	1	3	28	30	119	6

DIV. TWO	P	W	D	L	F	A	PTS
P'mouth Civil S.	34	28	2	4	93	30	86
New Street	34	26	3	5	77	29	81
Verwood Town	34	21	5	8	80	41	68
Paulsgrove	34	17	9	8	79	56	60
Netley Central	34	14	8	12	64	52	50
Broughton	34	13	10	11	57	54	49
Fleet Spurs	34	14	5	15	62	53	47
Nutfield United	34	11	14	9	53	47	47
Hayling United	34	12	10	12	45	57	46
Liss Athletic	34	11	10	13	65	51	43
Basing Rovers	34	11	7	16	47	80	40
Otterbourne	34	10	9	15	51	52	39
Ringwood Town	34	9	8	17	39	58	35
Braishfield	34	10	5	19	39	61	35
West Wight	34	8	11	15	37	63	35
Brading Town	34	7	12	15	46	61	33
AFC Aldermaston	34	7	6	21	38	73	26
Netley Ath. Vict.	34	6	8	20	38	92	26

DIV. THREE	P	W	D	L	F	A	PTS
Hedge End	30	21	4	5	88	30	67
Stockbridge	30	20	4	6	87	50	64
Vosper Thornycroft	30	19	4	7	76	41	61
Drayton Park	30	18	3	9	66	51	57
Ecchinswell	30	13	10	7	55	34	49
Esso (Fawley)	30	12	11	7	55	34	47
Lansdowne	30	14	8	8	60	59	*47
Fleetlands Res.	30	13	5	12	57	50	44
Swanmore	30	11	7	12	59	52	40
Winchester Castle	30	9	7	14	48	75	&33
Netley Cent. Res.	30	7	11	12	39	56	32
Compton	30	7	10	13	66	75	31
Laverstock & Ford	30	8	7	15	40	58	31
Bass Alton Res.	30	4	11	15	39	67	23
Covies	30	4	5	21	31	81	17
Winch. City Res.	30	1	11	18	26	80	14

* - 3pts deducted
& - 1pt deducted

DIVISION ONE RESULT CHART 1992-93

HOME TEAM	1	2	3	4	5	6	7	8	9	10	11	12	13	14	15	16	17
1. A.C. Delco	*	2-1	2-1	0-1	0-2	1-1	4-5	1-1	2-4	1-1	1-0	0-1	3-0	0-0	0-1	0-1	1-3
2. Alresford Town	1-1	*	4-4	1-1	1-6	1-1	1-3	2-3	0-0	0-3	0-2	2-3	4-2	4-1	2-1	2-1	3-2
3. Awbridge	4-1	2-1	*	0-3	1-4	1-2	1-0	1-3	0-4	0-1	1-1	1-2	3-2	0-3	0-0	2-3	0-4
4. Bass Alton Town	0-1	4-0	5-2	*	0-2	1-1	2-1	3-3	2-3	2-4	5-3	0-0	7-2	2-3	5-0	1-3	8-4
5. Bishops Waltham T.	4-1	3-0	2-0	5-1	*	3-4	1-1	6-4	0-1	1-1	6-2	3-0	2-0	4-1	1-0	2-3	1-1
6. Blackfield & Langley	0-0	3-0	3-0	2-1	1-1	*	2-0	2-1	4-1	5-2	1-4	1-0	7-0	1-1	1-2	0-3	3-2
7. Colden Common	2-2	2-1	6-3	6-1	0-3	1-1	*	2-3	2-0	1-2	5-2	0-0	4-1	0-1	0-1	2-1	1-0
8. Cowes Sports	3-0	3-3	8-1	3-2	2-4	2-0	3-2	*	1-3	1-3	4-2	1-0	2-2	3-1	1-0	2-3	3-0
9. Downton	1-0	3-1	1-0	0-1	1-1	1-1	6-1	4-3	*	2-1	3-0	2-0	2-1	5-2	5-0	1-2	3-0
10. Fleetlands	2-0	2-0	3-0	1-0	1-4	2-1	1-1	0-2	3-2	*	2-1	0-1	3-2	0-3	3-1	1-0	2-2
11. Locksheath	1-1	5-0	2-1	0-4	3-3	1-3	0-5	0-5	0-2	1-1	*	0-1	8-2	0-2	0-1	2-2	1-0
12. Malshanger	0-1	1-0	2-3	0-1	1-6	1-3	2-2	0-1	1-3	0-3	2-2	*	6-1	0-1	0-0	1-1	4-0
13. Midanbury	1-2	1-1	2-3	0-1	1-9	0-3	1-5	0-1	0-5	0-3	4-3	0-0	*	0-7	2-4	0-1	0-4
14. New Milton	2-2	2-1	3-1	2-2	2-4	0-2	1-0	0-0	1-1	0-2	1-1	2-1	3-0	*	1-0	1-3	6-0
15. Overton United	4-0	2-3	3-1	3-1	2-4	2-1	3-2	1-1	1-1	5-2	2-0	1-2	6-1	5-1	*	1-1	3-1
16. Pirelli General	0-1	3-0	1-1	3-1	2-0	3-1	1-0	1-0	1-1	3-0	6-0	5-0	4-1	5-1	2-0	*	2-0
17. Winchester City	3-2	1-0	1-1	1-0	1-5	2-2	0-1	0-6	1-1	2-4	2-1	2-0	3-1	2-0	1-1	1-3	*

DIVISION ONE CLUBS 1993-94

A.C. DELCO
Secretary: Adrian Gray, 1 The Badgers, Netley Abbey, Southampton SO3 5PT (0703 455026).
Ground: A.C. Delco Spts Ground, Stoneham Lane, Eastleigh (0703 613334).
Colours: Sky & white stripes/black/sky   **Change:** Red & black stripes/black/red & black

ALRESFORD TOWN
Secretary: Ross Debenham, 11 Lindley Gdns, Alresford, Hants SO24 9PU (0962 734420).
Ground: Arlebury Park, Alresford, Hants (0962 735100).
Colours: White/black/black   **Change:** Blue/navy/navy

BASS ALTON TOWN
Secretary: A J M Hillman, 19a Beechwood Rd, Alton, Hants GU34 1RL (0420 87103).
Ground: Bass Spts Ground, Anstey Rd, Alton (0420 82465).
Colours: Black & white/black/black   **Change:** Green & white & red & blue

BISHOPS WALTHAM TOWN
Secretary: Kay Parris, 46 Oaklands Way, Titchfield Common, Fareham, Hants PO14 4LF (0489 589564).
Ground: Hoe Road Spts Ground, Bishops Waltham (0489 891841).
Colours: Blue/blue/white   **Change:** Yellow/black/black

BLACKFIELD & LANGLEY
Secretary: K Bevis, 57 Whitefield Rd, Holbury, Southampton, Hants SO4 1HW (0703 891854).
Ground: Gang Warily Rec., Newlands Rd, Blackfield, Southampton, Hants (0703 893603).
Colours: Green/white/green   **Change:** Yellow/blue/yellow

COLDEN COMMON
Secretary: Mr B Cleave, 30 The Ridings, Bishopstoke, Eastleigh SO5 6PR (0703 602374).
Ground: Colden Common Recreation Ground, Main Road, Colden Common (0962 712365).
Colours: Red & white stripes/black/red   **Change:** All yellow

COWES SPORTS
Secretary: Mr W G Murray, 53 Park Rd, Cowes, Isle of Wight PO31 7LY (0983 294445).
Ground: Westwood Park, Park Rd, Cowes, Isle of Wight (0983 293793).
Colours: Blue & white stripes/black/blue   **Change:** All red

FLEETLANDS
Secretary: Mr Paul Coulter, 19 The Yews, Horndean, Waterlooville PO8 0BH (0705 599409).
Ground: Lederle Lane, Gosport, Hants (0329 239723).
Colours: Red & black/white/white   **Change:** All blue

LOCKSHEATH
Secretary: R H Setchfield, 58 Pimpernel Close, Priory Park, Locksheath SO3 6TN (0489 583229).
Ground: Locksheath Rec, Warsash Rd, Titchfield Common, Eastleigh (0489 581021).
Colours: Red/black/red   **Change:** All white

MALSHANGER
Secretary: Fred Norris, 9 Goddards Firs, Oakley, Basingstoke, Hants RG23 7JL (0256 781697).
Ground: Malshanger Spts Field, Malshanger, Basingstoke (0256 780285).
Colours: White/white/purple   **Change:** Orange & blue or white/black or blue/orange or blue

NETLEY CENTRAL SPORTS
Secretary: Mrs M A Ellis, 20 Bembridge, Netley Abbey, Southampton SO3 5PN (0703 453744).
Ground: Netley Rec, Station Rd, Netley Abbey, Southampton (0703 452267).
Colours: Blue & white/blue/blue   **Change:** Red & white/black/red

NEW MILTON TOWN
Secretary: Mr J A Wyatt, 12 Pinewood Rd, Hordle, Lymington, Hants SO41 0GP (0425 611670).
Ground: Fawcetts Spts Ground, Christchurch Rd, New Milton, Hants BH25 6QF (0425 628191).
Colours: Yellow & blue/blue/blue   **Change:** All maroon
Previous Name: New Milton FC (pre-1993)   **Previous Ground:** Adjacent pitch (pre-1992)

NEW STREET
Secretary: Mrs Waterman (0264 362751)
Ground: Foxcolte Park, Charlton Down.

OVERTON UNITED
Secretary: R Taylor, 18 Waltham Rd, Overton, Hants RG25 3NJ (0256 770835).
Ground: Recreation Centre, Bridge Street, Overton (0256 770561).
Colours: Blue & white stripes/white/blue   **Change:** All yellow

Alresford Town attack during their 1-1 draw at home to Blackfield & Langley. Photo - Jon Holloway.

Bass Alton Town F.C. 1992-93. Photo - Eric Marsh.

Cowes Sports F.C. - League Cup winners 1992-93. Photo - Eric Marsh.

PAULSGROVE

Secretary: V Collins, 33 Portobello Grove, Portchester, Fareham PO16 8HX (0705 611508).
Ground: The Grove Club, Marsden Rd, Paulsgrove (0705 324102).
Colours: Red & black stripes/black/red   **Change:** Sky & maroon/skyk/maroon

PIRELLI GENERAL

Secretary: R W Hawkins, Pirelli General Spts & Social Club, The Pavilion, Dew Lane, Eastleigh, Hants SO5 5YE (0703 612721).
Ground: Jubilee Spts Ground, Chestnut Ave., Eastleigh (0703 612721).
Colours: Blue/white/red   **Change:** Yellow/black/yellow

PORTSMOUTH CIVIL SERVICE

Secretary: P Shires, 242 Grafton Street, Mile End, Portsmouth PO2 7LH (0705 645813).
Ground: Portsmouth Civil Service Spts Ground, Copnor Rd, Portsmouth (0705 662538).
Colours: Yellow/blue/blue   **Change:** Red/white/red

ROMSEY TOWN

Secretary: Mr Bill Clouder, 15 Malmesbury Rd, Romsey, Hants SO51 8FS (0794 518556).
Ground: The By-Pass Ground, South Front, Romsey, Hants (0794 512003).
Colours: White/black/black & white   **Change:** All red

VERWOOD TOWN

Secretary: Mrs J A Fry, 19a Noon Hill Rd, Verwood, Dorset BH31 7DB (0202 822826).
Ground: Potterne Park, Potterne Way, Verwood, Dorset.
Colours: Red & white/red/red   **Change:** White & blue/blue/red

WINCHESTER CITY

Secretary: Geoffrey Cox, 9 Burnetts Gdns, Horton Heath, Eastleigh, Hants SO5 7BY (0703 693021).
Ground: Hillier Way, Abbotts Barton, Winchester (0962 863553).
Colours: Red & white/black/red   **Change:** All blue

DIVISION TWO CLUBS 1993-94

AWBRIDGE

Secretary: Miss Z C Wilson, 29 Borley Rd, Romsey, Hants SO51 8AG (0794 518969).
Ground: The Village Hall Field, Cross Roads, Awbridge, nr Romsey, Hants.
Colours: Red & black/black/black   **Change:** Blue/white/white

BASING ROVERS

Secretary: Mr C J Dale, 13 Howard View, Basingstoke, Hants RG22 6LF (0256 26604).
Ground: Old Basing Rec, The Street, Old Basing (0256 844254).
Colours: All red   **Change:** Yellow/black/black

BRADING TOWN

Secretary: James R Lee, 'The Stables', 42 High Str., Brading, Isle of Wight (0983 407560).
Ground: Vicarage Lane, Brading, Isle of Wight (0983 405217).
Colours: Maroon & white stripes/white/white   **Change:** White (red trim)/black/red

BRAISHFIELD

Secretary: Mr W A Reid, 15 Addison Close, Romsey, Hants SO51 (0794 517991).
Ground: Braishfield Recreation Ground, Braishfield, Hants.
Colours: Yellow & emerald stripes/emerald/yellow & emerald.   **Change:** Old gold/black/black

BROUGHTON

Secretary: A R Hammerton, 19 Plough Gdns, Broughton, Stockbridge, Hants SO20 8AF (0794 301495).
Ground: The Sports Field, Buckholt Rd, Broughton, Stockbridge, Hants.
Colours: Blue & white stripes/white/white (blue tops)   **Change:** Green/black/green

DRAYTON PARK

Secretary: Mr R W Chandler, 46 Stratford House, Sackville Str., Southsea, Portsmouth PO5 4EX (0705 812569).
Ground: Drayton Park, Lower Drayton Lane, Drayton, Portsmouth, Hants.
Colours: Red & black stripes/black/red   **Change:** Tangerine/white/tangerine.

ECCHINSWELL

Secretary: Mr R Francis, 12 Willowmead Close, Wash Common, Newbury, Berks RG14 6RW (0635 48139).
Ground: Ecchinswell Rec, Ecchinswell, nr Newbury.
Colours: All red   **Change:** Green & white/black/green.

FLEET SPURS

Secretary: Miss C Fitzpatrick, 11 Regent Str., Fleet, Hants GU13 9NR (0252 629954).
Ground: Peter Driver Spts Ground, Bourley Rd, Church Crookham, Hants.
Colours: Red & black stripes/black/red   **Change:** Blue/white/white.

HAYLING UNITED

Secretary: Mrs S Westfield, 12 Wheatlands Ave., Hayling Island, Hants PO11 9SG (0705 463305).
Ground: Hayling Park, Hayling Island, Hants.
Colours: Red & white hoops/white/black   **Change:** All red

HEDGE END

Secretary: M J Oliver, 25 Blossom Close, Botley, Southampton, Hants SO3 2FR (0489 786308).
Ground: Norman Rodaway Playing Fields, Hedge End, Southampton.
Colours: Black & white stripes/black/black   **Change:** All blue

LISS ATHLETIC

Secretary: Alan Ridding, Imberdown, Woodlands Lane, Liss, Hants GU33 7EZ (0730 894007).
Ground: Newman Collard PF, Hill Brow Rd, Liss, Hants (0730 894022).
Colours: All blue   **Change:** All yellow

NURSLING

Secretary: P E Hurst, 2 Horns Drove, Rownhams, Southampton, Hants SO1 8AH (0703 734061).
Ground: Nursling Recreation Ground, Nursling Str., Nursling, Southampton, Hants.
Colours: Maroon & blue/blue/blue   **Change:** Yellow/red/red.
Previous Name: Nutfield F.C. (pre-1993).

Drayton Park F.C., who earned promotion in their first season in the League. Photo - Eric Marsh.

Ecchinswell F.C., also promoted from Division Three for 1993-94. Photo - Eric Marsh.

Covies F.C., who play on Farnborough Town's original ground.

OTTERBOURNE

Secretary: R J Broom, 249 Passfield Rd, Eastleigh, Hants SO5 5DE (0703 323992).
Ground: Oakwood Park, off Oakwood Ave., Otterbourne (0962 714681).
Colours: Blue & white stripes/blue/blue   **Change:** Yellow/black/black.

RINGWOOD TOWN

Secretary: N Crewe, 278 Windham Rd, Bournemouth, Dorset BH1 4QU (0202 398975).
Ground: Long Lane, Ringwood, Hants (0425 473448).
Cols: Red & white stripes/black/red & white   **Change:** Blue/black/blue

STOCKBRIDGE

Secretary: Miss Noreen Durrant, 122 Buriton Rd, Harestock, Winchester, Hants SO22 6JG (0962 883772).
Ground: The Recreation Ground, High Street, Stockbridge, Hants.
Colours: All red   **Change:** All blue

VOSPER THORNYCROFT

Secretary: Sean Jordan, 7 St Lawrence Close, Hedge End, Southampton SO3 4TJ (0489 790163).
Ground: Vospers Spts Ground, Portsmouth Rd, Sholing, Southampton (0489 403829).
Colours: Blue & black halves/black/blue   **Change:** Yellow/red//red

WEST WIGHT

Secretary: Gerry Beale, 75 Sandcroft Ave., Ryde, Isle of Wight PO33 2TU (0983 565956).
Ground: Camp Rd, Freshwater, Isle of Wight (0983 754780).
Colours: White (royal trim)/royal/royal   **Change:** All yellow

DIVISION THREE CLUBS 1993-94

A.F.C. ALDERMASTON

Secretary: Mr Gareth Dew, 58 Portway, Baughurst, Hants RG26 5PE (0734 811271).
Ground: Recreation Society, Aldermaston (0734 814111 ex4544).

BISHOPSTOKE SOCIAL

Secretary: Kevin John Bennett, 56 Chatsworth Rd, Boyatt Wood, Eastleigh, Hants SO5 4PE (0703 642123).
Ground: Chicken Hall Lane, Bishopstoke, Eastleigh, Hants (0860 452620).
Colours: All blue   **Change:** Red/black/red & black

COMPTON

Secretary: M Allerton, 28 Keats Close, Olivers Battery, Winchester SO22 4HR (0962 869574).
Ground: Shepherds Lane, Compton Down, nr Winchester (0962 712083).
Colours: All red   **Change:** Grey/maroon/white

COVIES

Secretary: Mr John Marchment, 223 Sandy Lane, Cove, Farnborough, Hants GU14 9LA (0252 545764).
Ground: Queens Road Recreation Ground, North Camp, Farnborough, Hants.
Colours: Yellow/green/green   **Change:** All red

ESSO (FAWLEY)

Secretary: Mr A Haws, 40 Hollybank Rd, Hythe, Southampton, Hants SO4 5FQ (0703 843402).
Ground: Esso Recreation Club, Long Lane, Holbury, Southampton, Hants.
Colours: White/blue/red   **Change:** Green (yellow pinstripe)/green/green

HAMBLE CLUB

Secretary: Mr S E Riddle, 44 Kinsbourne Way, Thornhill, Southampton SO2 6HB (0703 463953).
Ground: Mount Pleasant PF, Hamble Lane, Hanble, Southampton, Hants (0703 452327).
Colours: All red   **Change:** Blue & white stripes/blue/blue.

HILSEA CLUB

Secretary: Mr Terry Harwood, 147 Manners Rd, Southsea, Hants PO4 0BD (0705 839776).
Ground: Portsmouth Sailing Centre, Eastern Rd, Portsmouth PO3 5LY (0705 663873).
Colours: Yellow/blue/white   **Change:** Maroon/blue/white.

LUDGERSHALL SPORTS CLUB

Secretary: Mr B Roberts, 9 Martin Way, Harewood Park, Andover, Hants SP10 5PF (0264 338311).
Ground: Astor Cres., Ludgershall (0264 790338).
Colours: Blue & black/black/black   **Previous Lge:** Nth Hants (champs + Lge Cup winners 92-93)

SWANMORE

Secretary: Mr F H Wiltshire, 16 Sycamore Rd, Waltham, Southampton, Hants SO3 1ED (0489 893726).
Ground: New Road Recreation Ground, New Road, Swanmore, Hants.
Colours: White/navy/white   **Change:** Yellow/navy/yellow.

WINCHESTER CASTLE

Secretary: A J Rutter, 31 Whistler Close, Basingstoke, Hants RG21 3HN (0256 50922).
Ground: Hants County Council Spts Ground, Petersfield Rd (A31) (Chilcomb), Winchester. Hants.
Colours: Red/navy/red   **Change:** All white

This Division also contains the Reserve sides of: Bass Alton Town, Fleetlands, Netley Central Sports, Portsmouth Civil Service and Winchester City.

SOUTHAMPTON SENIOR LEAGUE

PREM. DIV.	P	W	D	L	F	A	PTS
Fair Oak	26	18	5	3	68	20	41
Bishopstoke Social	26	18	4	4	80	27	40
Hamble Club	26	19	2	5	77	38	40
Queens Keep	26	16	4	6	57	23	36
West End	26	15	2	9	57	40	32
A.C. Delco Res.	26	12	6	8	37	38	30
Colden Cmn Res.	26	12	3	11	51	43	27
Pirelli Gen. Res.	26	9	5	12	37	51	23
Hythe & Dibden	26	7	7	12	31	49	21
Old Tauntonians	26	6	7	13	45	55	19
Millbrook & Maybush	26	6	4	16	38	57	16
Cadnam United	26	5	5	16	36	60	15
B.T.C. (So'ton)	26	4	6	16	37	91	14
Brendon	26	3	4	19	21	80	10

SENIOR 1	P	W	D	L	F	A	PTS
Ordnance Survey	26	17	5	4	68	30	39
Durley	26	17	3	6	66	38	37
Otterbourne Res.	26	14	4	8	61	40	32
C.H.B. Aztecs	26	14	3	9	72	39	31
Salisbury Green	26	11	9	6	43	32	31
Bishopstoke S. Res.	26	11	8	7	47	45	30
Chamberlayne Spts	26	11	7	8	72	47	29
North Baddesley	26	12	4	10	41	37	28
Bis. Waltham Res.	26	9	4	13	64	50	22
Netley R.B.L.	26	8	6	12	45	48	22
Netley Ath. V. Res.	26	9	3	14	54	72	21
Ampfield	26	8	4	14	41	55	20
Midanbury Res.	26	8	2	16	52	68	18
Michelmersh/Timsbury	26	1	2	23	18	143	4

SENIOR 2	P	W	D	L	F	A	PTS
Vosper T'croft Res.	26	17	5	4	64	32	39
Hamble Club Res.	26	16	4	6	47	27	36
Esso (Fawley) Res.	26	15	5	6	69	42	35
East Boldre	26	13	8	5	65	43	34
Hythe A.S.	26	9	11	6	55	44	29
West End Res.	26	12	3	11	47	38	27
Braishfield Res.	26	10	6	10	56	57	26
Lordswood Utd	26	9	5	12	57	52	23
Old Taunt. Res.	26	9	5	12	48	62	23
Locksheath Res.	26	9	4	13	71	74	22
M.M.I. Sports	26	6	9	11	38	50	21
Warsash	26	7	5	14	41	68	19
Awbridge Res.	26	6	4	16	40	72	16
Hythe & Dib. Res.	26	3	8	15	37	74	14

JUNIOR 1	P	W	D	L	F	A	PTS
Horntree Sports	22	17	4	1	90	28	38
Swift Sporting	22	15	5	2	90	44	35
Testside Maybush	22	12	5	5	52	32	29
Lyndhurst	22	11	5	6	79	49	27
Blackfield & L. Res.	22	11	4	7	54	32	26
Sholing Select	22	11	3	8	60	41	25
Ordnance S. Res.	22	8	6	8	54	39	22
Nutfield Res.	22	6	4	12	45	72	16
Totton United	22	6	4	12	48	83	16
So'ton University	22	6	1	15	56	109	13
Old Issonians	22	4	3	15	32	87	11
Albion Sports	22	1	4	17	31	75	6

JUNIOR 2	P	W	D	L	F	A	PTS
A.F.C. Solent	22	17	3	2	83	23	37
B & Q	22	17	2	3	83	23	36
Hedge End Res.	22	17	2	3	76	36	36
Queens Keep Res.	22	10	5	7	55	38	25
Ford Sports	22	11	1	10	64	44	23
Eastleigh Spartans	22	8	6	8	53	45	22
Compton Res.	22	8	6	8	39	44	22
Woodhouse Services	22	9	3	10	45	37	21
Eastleigh Comrades	22	8	2	12	40	60	18
Otterbourne 'A'	22	5	3	14	36	63	13
Brendon Res.	22	2	5	15	32	64	9
B.T.C. So'ton Res.	22	1	0	21	15	131	2

JUNIOR 3	P	W	D	L	F	A	PTS
Swanmore Res.	22	13	5	4	56	18	31
A & G Eastleigh	22	14	2	6	65	33	30
Bishopstoke S. 'A'	22	9	10	3	52	28	28
A.F.C. Dynamo	22	12	3	7	51	43	27
Chartwell Green	22	9	8	5	39	27	26
Bitterne Sports	22	10	3	9	36	33	23
Pirelli General 'A'	22	8	5	9	39	53	21
Winsor Sports	22	7	6	9	34	41	20
Vosper T'croft 'A'	22	8	1	13	50	58	17
Mottisfont	22	7	3	12	28	49	17
Swift Sporting 'B'	22	6	4	12	40	55	16
S.U.S.A.	22	2	4	16	21	73	8

JUNIOR 4	P	W	D	L	F	A	PTS
Four Star Spts	22	20	1	1	94	23	41
A.F.C. Masons	22	15	3	4	73	38	33
Brookwood	22	15	2	5	76	58	32
Lordswood Utd Res.	22	15	1	6	80	45	31
Durley Res.	22	11	5	6	66	45	27
Langley Manor	22	9	4	9	75	59	22
Inmar Electrical	22	10	2	10	58	47	22
A.F.C. Marchwood	22	9	2	11	49	62	20
A.F.C. Aldermoor	22	6	1	15	42	72	13
Nth Baddesley Res.	22	5	1	16	50	93	11
Burridge Sports	22	3	2	17	39	78	8
Michelmersh/T. Res	22	2	0	20	24	106	4

JUNIOR 5	P	W	D	L	F	A	PTS
S.D.E.S.	20	16	4	0	108	13	36
B.T.M. Sports	20	15	3	2	75	25	33
C.H.B. Aztecs Res.	20	11	5	4	58	39	27
Millbrook Furnishing	20	11	1	8	65	51	23
A & G E'leigh Res.	20	8	4	8	40	49	20
E'leigh Spartans Res.	20	9	2	9	37	49	20
West End Sports	20	6	5	9	40	55	17
Spartans	20	6	2	12	32	56	14
Pearce	20	4	4	12	22	56	12
Compton 'A'	20	4	2	14	30	61	10
Brendon 'A'	20	3	2	15	34	87	8

JUNIOR 6	P	W	D	L	F	A	PTS
Wildern	20	11	7	2	59	22	29
Testwood United	20	12	3	5	63	39	27
Eastleigh Ensigns	20	11	3	6	63	42	25
Cory Sports	20	9	7	4	51	33	25
Woodmill Athletic	20	8	5	7	52	45	21
Mottisfont Res.	20	6	8	6	36	39	20
Ordnance Survey 'A'	20	8	4	8	48	55	20
Queens Keep 'A'	20	6	5	9	34	49	17
A.S.S.C. Res.	20	5	4	11	40	63	14
Harlandic	20	5	3	12	30	46	13
Romsey Rovers	20	3	3	14	37	80	9

JUNIOR 7	P	W	D	L	F	A	PTS
Testside Mayb. Res.	24	14	4	4	90	36	32
Chamberlayne Res.	22	15	1	6	80	33	31
A.F.C. Clock	22	12	6	4	56	37	30
Fair Oak Res.	22	13	3	6	43	27	29
Snows B'ness Forms	22	9	6	7	33	29	24
East Boldre Res.	22	9	5	8	62	51	23
Hythe & Dibden 'A'	22	10	1	11	40	52	21
Custom Covers	22	8	4	10	35	40	20
Ford Sports Res.	22	5	5	12	24	44	15
Itchen Saints	22	5	5	12	37	65	15
Welcome Athletic	22	5	5	12	44	77	15
Lyndhurst Res.	22	4	1	17	26	79	9

JUNIOR 8	P	W	D	L	F	A	PTS
Wellow Res.	22	19	2	1	98	20	40
Ampfield Res.	22	15	2	5	74	34	32
Solent Youth	22	14	3	5	87	45	31
A.F.C. Holbury	22	11	3	8	77	57	25
Four Star Res.	22	11	3	8	57	65	25
Owlesbury	22	10	3	9	68	60	23
Gleneagles	22	10	2	10	59	57	22
Totton Select	22	9	3	10	61	75	21
Anchor Electric	22	8	2	12	69	74	18
A.F.C. Southside	22	8	2	12	56	68	18
Inter Northam	22	4	1	11	47	79	9
Alma	22	0	0	22	19	138	0

JUNIOR 9	P	W	D	L	F	A	PTS
Townhill Park	22	21	0	1	135	29	42
Mill Hill	22	19	0	3	139	41	38
B & Q Res.	22	14	3	5	87	37	31
Pearce Res.	22	13	3	6	87	46	29
Sporting B & Q	22	12	1	9	54	55	25
Inmar Elec. Res.	22	9	3	10	64	55	21
Itchn Saints Res.	22	10	1	11	62	72	21
Swift Sporting 'A'	22	8	2	12	66	79	18
Warren United	22	7	0	15	57	119	14
Brookwood Res.	22	6	0	16	42	87	12
Snows B.F. Res.	22	4	1	17	35	85	9
Michelmersh & T. 'A'	22	2	0	20	24	147	4

'SPORTIQUE' PORTSMOUTH NORTH END LEAGUE

DIV. ONE	P	W	D	L	F	A	PTS
Dunham Bush	18	16	2	0	113	29	34
Grant Thornton	18	14	2	2	65	23	30
Belle Vue	18	10	3	5	91	35	23
Sparta '81	18	10	2	6	63	59	22
Anmore	18	9	0	9	60	39	16
Phoenix	18	7	1	10	46	58	15
Viviers U.K.	18	6	1	11	35	60	13
Kingston Arrows	18	4	3	11	47	74	11
St Helena Utd	18	3	4	11	33	64	10
Cosmos '87	18	1	2	15	27	138	4

DIV. TWO	P	W	D	L	F	A	PTS
Invincible	22	16	2	4	98	55	34
P.R.S.C.	22	12	6	4	76	52	30
A.E.S.	22	12	5	5	82	51	29
Britax Wingard	22	10	6	6	76	47	26
Old Portmuthians	22	11	4	7	64	61	26
S.C.D.	22	9	6	7	63	59	24
Shearer	22	10	3	9	69	56	23
Portsmouth Nalgo	22	8	5	9	63	66	21
Keys '92	22	6	7	9	51	66	19
Oakville	22	7	4	11	43	62	18
Swan Sports	22	4	2	16	41	54	10
P.S.G.	22	1	2	19	26	117	4

DIV. THREE	P	W	D	L	F	A	PTS
Gunwharf	16	13	1	2	96	27	27
Somerstown '90	16	12	1	3	90	36	25
Portsmouth Nomads	16	12	1	3	64	29	25
Ashbys	16	9	0	7	69	48	18
Hilsea Club Res.	16	9	0	7	67	67	18
South Coast	16	5	2	9	46	65	12
Wilcon Homes	16	4	2	10	45	66	10
Marriotts Of.	16	4	0	12	35	106	8
Oakville Res.	16	0	1	15	19	87	1

DIV. FOUR	P	W	D	L	F	A	PTS
Anmore Res.	18	15	0	3	79	28	30
Spice Island	18	12	2	4	53	31	26
Spithead Spitfires	18	9	5	4	53	26	23
Southsea Commoners	18	9	3	6	55	41	21
Southside	18	9	1	8	74	50	19
Old Portmuthians	18	9	1	8	50	47	19
British Star	18	8	1	9	51	61	17
Sparta '81	18	3	6	9	29	54	12
Copnor	18	3	1	14	24	53	7
Nautech	18	2	2	14	22	105	6

'SPORTIQUE' PORTSMOUTH & DISTRICT LEAGUE

PREM. DIV.	P	W	D	L	F	A	PTS
Jubilee United	16	13	1	2	80	27	27
P'mouth C.S. Res.	16	11	1	4	48	36	23
Hilsea Club	16	10	2	4	41	22	22
Ventora	16	7	4	5	50	39	18
Wicor Mill	16	7	1	8	48	58	15
Sportique	16	5	3	8	27	36	13
Paulsgrove Res.	16	5	2	9	38	33	12
Portchester Utd	16	5	1	10	25	46	11
Car 'R' Us	16	1	1	14	15	84	3

93-94 Constitution: Clanfield, George & Dragon, Havant Rangers, Jubilee United, Mayflower, Paulsgrove Rovers, Portchester, Portchester United, Ventora, Wicor Mill.

SENIOR DIV.	P	W	D	L	F	A	PTS
Clanfield	20	13	4	3	68	24	30
George & Dragon	20	12	3	5	57	34	27
Portchester	20	10	3	7	54	45	23
Havant Rangers	20	9	2	9	50	60	20
Castleville	20	5	4	11	41	60	14
Carberry	20	3	1	16	37	84	7

N.B. Three clubs withdrew during the season, so the remaining clubs played each other four times.
93-94: Division discontinued.

JUNIOR 1	P	W	D	L	F	A	PTS
Mayflower	18	15	3	0	68	18	33
George & D. Res.	18	10	2	6	53	33	22
Hayling Utd Res.	18	7	5	6	58	40	19
Hilsea Club Res.	18	6	4	8	50	44	16
Drayton Park Res.	18	6	3	9	39	37	15
Sportsmans	18	5	3	10	33	63	13
Sparta '81	18	3	2	13	23	87	8

N.B. Two clubs withdrew during the season, so the remaining clubs played each other three times.
93-94: Carberry, Clanfield Res., Drayton Park Res., George & Dragon Res., Hayling Utd, Hilsea Club Res., Mayflower, R.T.C.. (To play each other 3 times - 21 fixtures).

JUNIOR 2	P	W	D	L	F	A	PTS
Clanfield	16	11	2	3	39	24	24
R.T.C.	16	10	2	4	45	24	22
I.B.M. Portsmouth	16	8	5	3	36	21	21
Wicor Mill Res.	16	9	2	5	52	34	20
Fleur-de-Lys	16	8	3	5	39	27	19
A.F.C. Bedhampton	16	8	0	8	35	40	16
Portchester Res.	16	3	4	9	21	47	10
New Roebuck	16	3	1	12	28	45	7
Havant Rgrs Res.	16	1	3	12	21	53	5

93-94: A.F.C. Bedhampton, Fawcett Inn, Fleur-de-Lys, Harbour Light Res., Havant Rgrs Res., I.B.M. South Hants (formerly I.B.M. Portsmouth), Portchester Res., Sportsmans, Wicor Mill (To play each other 3 times - 24 fixtures).

HAMPSHIRE LOCAL ASSOCIATION CUP FINALS 1992-93

ALDERSHOT SENIOR CUP: *(won by Royal Engineers)*
BOURNEMOUTH SENIOR CUP *(at A.F.C. Bournemouth, Wed 12th May):* A.F.C. Lymington Reserves 1, Westover Motors 0
ISLE OF WIGHT SENIOR (GOLD) CUP *(at Cowes Sports, Thurs 6th May):* Newport I.O.W. 3, Shanklin 0
NORTH HANTS SENIOR CUP *(Sat 1st May, at Portals Sports Ground):* New Street 3, Stockbridge 2
NORTH HANT MAY (JUNIOR 'A') CUP *(Sat 24th April, at Basingstoke Town):* Hook 2, Kingsclere 1
NORTH HANTS JUNIOR 'B' CUP *(Sat 24th April, at Whitchurch United):* Priestley 2, Twyford Reserves 1
PORTSMOUTH SENIOR CUP *(Tues 4th & Mon 10th May, both at Havant Town):* Waterlooville Reserves 1;0 Drayton Park 1;0 *(Waterlooville Reserves won 5-4 on penalties)*
SOUTHAMPTON SENIOR CUP *(Wed 21st April, at Southampton F.C.):* Blackfield & Langley 5, B.A.T. Sports Reserves 1
SOUTHAMPTON JUNIOR 'A' CUP *(Mon 12th April, at A.C. Delco):* Ordnance Survey Reserves 7, Lyndhurst 2
SOUTHAMPTON JUNIOR 'B' CUP *(Mon 3rd May, at Aerostructures F.C.):* S.D.E.S. 1, Wildern 0

NORTHERN PREMIER LEAGUE

President: N.White, Esq.
Chairman: K.Marsden, Esq.
Vice-Chairman: K.F.Brown Esq.
Secretary/Treasure: R.D.Bayley, Esq.
22 Woburn Drive, Hale, Altrincham, Cheshire WA15 8LZ
(061 980 7007 - Fax: 061 980 7007)

Southport, Winsford United and Bridlington Town were the names that dominated the 1992/93 campaign. It said much for the sheer consistency of Southport that no other club in the League's history has amassed so many points as did Winsford without finishing champions.

Not many pundits (apart from Winsford followers) would seriously dispute that the title found its rightful home at Haig Avenue for, in between losing their first and last games of the season, the "Sandgrounders" tasted defeat on only two other occasions during their assult on the championship. Their strength was the ability to attack in numbers and defend in depth, with Stevie Haw's prolific goal-scoring being only one part of the jig-saw that Brian Kettle and his assistant Steve Joel pieced together. The defence was almost water-tight, whilst several players managed double figures in the goalscoring stakes. Nevertheless, not many people took Southport's application for membership of the GM Vauxhall very seriously, given the fact they needed to spend some £150,000 to bring their ground up to the standard required for membership. If Brian Kettle's side provided heroics on the field to capture the premier division title, then chairman, Charlie Clapham and his board of directors contributed a miracle off it, by having a superb stadium awaiting the ground inspection. A magnificent achievement both on and off the field of play for which Southport are to be truly congratulated.

Southport may well have been worthy champions, but there was no doubting who were the cup kings as Winsford reached no fewer than four cup finals, winning all of them! They took the Northern Premier League cup, on penalties, after first division underdogs, Warrington Town, fluffed a spot-kick with only minutes of extra-time remaining, beat Southport in the NPL President's Cup, and then inflicted defeat upon Conference outfit, Northwich Victoria in the Mid-Cheshire Cup final. In their 70th game of the campaign Mike McKenzie's boys made the Cheshire FA's decision to play the final of their Senior Cup at Wincham Park, home of their opponents, Witton Albion, an irrelevance as Winsford positively outplayed the Conference side to capture their fourth Cup.

Winsford's opponents in the League's cup final, Warrington Town, incidentally, created a record by becoming the first club from outside the top flight to contest the final. They also had a good run in the FA Trophy where they reached the last eight before their dream of becoming the first club to appear in both an FA Vase and FA Trophy evaporated following the sale of leading scorer Liam Watson and influential midfielder Neil Whalley for fees totaling £85,000.

In the first division, geoligical problems possibly decided the championship. North Shields failed to make the starting line-up following going into liquidation, when their ground was also found to have serious underground faults. After just three games of the season, Bridlington Town installed former North Shields boss, Colin Richardson, as manager and never looked back. As well as wrapping up the title a long way from the finishing line, Town also captured the FA Vase as well as reaching the first divison cup final, where they were somewhat surprisingly beaten by Guiseley who must have been in some turmoil foolowing the resignation of manager, Gordon Raynor, only days before the crucial second leg decider.

If the title was decided early, the runners-up spot certainly was not, with Guiseley, Warrington Town, and Ashton United all taking it in turn during April to wear the mantle of favourites. Whilst all three were busy watching each other, one-time rank outsiders Knowsley Unietd, came up on the outside to take their chance on the final day of the season.

The relegation stakes saw founder-memebrs, Goole Town, lose their ever present premier division status after well over 1,000 appearances, whilst Mossley also failed to avoid the drop after more than 900 games in the top division. At the bottom of the first division, Rossendale United set all sorts of unwanted records and depart fro the North West Counties League. Their forlorn campaign was, perhaps, summed up when they received one final kick in the teeth from Lancaster City who beat them with goals in the last minute of the season!

In addition to first division sides Warrington Town and Bridlington Town making their mark on the national stage as mentioned earlier, premier outfits, Accrington Stanley, Marine and Southport all combined to produce an excellent advertisement for Northern Premier League football by reaching the second round proper of the FA Cup with the "Mariners" eventually being the last non-League side in the country left in the competition. This was a just reward for Roly Howard's team who so comprehensively defeated Football League side Halifax Town in the first round proper that the scoreline could, without any exaggeration, have been seven rather than the four they settled for. For nostalgia, however, the media loved Accrington's run and TV cameras were present at the Crown Ground as early as the second qualifying round game with Bradford Park Avenue. A nice touch here was the free inclusion in the match magazine of an exact replica of the programme from the last time the two clubs had met in the Football League in the early 1960s. A crowd of almost 11,000 saw Accrington depart the competition at Ewood Park where Crewe Alexandra inflicted a painful defat. But even that showed the strength of the NPL game - the Crewe squad contained no fewer than seven players signed from NPL clubs!   **R.D. Bayley (Secretary)**

NORTHERN PREMIER LEAGUE CHALLENGE CUP 1992-93

Preliminary Round

Curzon Ashton v Eastwood Town	5-2	Radcliffe Borough v Shepshed Albion	2-1

First Round

Alfreton Town v Ashton United	2-3	Bridlington Town v Guiseley	2-1
Rossendale United v Gretna	1-1,0-3	Harrogate Town (w/o) North Shields (scr)	
Knowsley United v Great Harwood Town	2-1	Lancaster City v Farsley Celtic	1-2
Netherfield v Congleton Town	2-0	Radcliffe Borough v Caernarfon Town	2-3
Workington v Curzon Ashton	1-0	Worksop Town v Warrington Town	1-3

Second Round

Bridlington Town v Knowsley United	0-1	Caernarfon Town v Ashton United	3-2
Whitley Bay v Chorley	2-2,3-1	Colwyn Bay v Harrogate Town	6-0
Farsley Celtic v Winsford United	1-2	Accrington Stanley v Gainsborough Trinity	1-1,0-1
Goole Town v Barrow	1-3	Gretna v Frickley Athletic	3-2
Hyde United v Droylsden	3-2	Marine v Morecambe	1-0
Matlock Town v Horwich R.M.I.	3-1	Mossley v Emley	1-6
Netherfield v Leek Town	2-0	Southport v Buxton	4-1
Warrington Town v Bishop Auckland	1-0	Fleetwood Town v Workington	2-2,0-1

Third Round

Emley v Colwyn Bay	1-1,2-3	Gainsborough Trinity v Barrow	2-1
Knowsley United v Gretna	1-2	Marine v Caernarfon Town	1-0
Matlock Town v Netherfield	2-2,3-0	Whitley Bay v Warrington Town	1-3
Winsford United v Hyde United	4-0	Workington v Southport	2-1

Quarter Finals

Gainsborough Trinity v Workington	2-4	Marine v Gretna	1-1,2-3(aet)
Matlock Town v Warrington Town	1-2	Winsford United v Colwyn Bay	3-0

Semi-Finals (Two Legs)

Warrington Town v Gretna	3-2,1-1	Workington v Winsford United	0-1,0-1

Final (at Manchester City FC, Tues 27th April): Winsford United 1, Warrington Town (Winsford United won 6-5 on penalties after extra-time)

NORTHERN PREMIER LEAGUE PRESIDENT'S CUP 1992-93

First Round

Buxton v Netherfield	3-1	Caernarfon Town v Morecambe	1-3
Emley v Worksop Town	1-2	Guiseley v Accrington Stanley	0-4
Hyde United v Colwyn Bay	0-1	Knowsley United v Southport	1-4
Warrington Town v Marine	2-3	Winsford United v Leek Town	2-1

Quarter Finals

Accrington Stanley v Southport	3-5	Buxton v Morecambe	0-3
Marine v Worksop Town	3-0	Winsford United v Colwyn Bay	5-3

Semi-Finals (Two Legs)

Marine v Winsford United	1-1,1-3	Southport v Morecambe	2-0,0-1

Final: Winsford Utd 2, Southport 0;   Southport 4, Winsford 3 (Winsford won 5-4 on aggregate)

NORTHERN PREMIER LEAGUE FIRST DIVISION CUP 1992-93

First Round

Shepshed Albion v Ashton United	1-1,1-2	Briidlington Town v Curzon Ashton	2-1
Caernarfon Town v Netherfield	2-1	Congleton Town v Knowsley United	1-2
Great Harwood Town v Gretna	2-0	Lancaster City v Eastwood Town	1-0

Second Round

Ashton United v Rossendale United	3-1	Bridlington Town v Alfreton Town	3-2
Caernarfon Town v Farsley Celtic	0-1	Great Harwood Town (w/o) North Shields (scr)	
Guiseley v Warrington Town	1-0	Lancaster City v Knowsley United	2-1
Worksop Town v Radclifffe Borough	1-1,0-1	Workington v Harrogate Town	0-2

Quarter Finals

Ashton United v Bridlington Town	0-3	Guiseley v Harrogate Town	1-1,4-0
Great Harwood Town v Radcliffe Borough	1-1,3-1	Farsley Celtic v Lancaster City	4-4,2-3

Semi-Finals (Two Legs)

Lancaster City v Guiseley	1-5,1-1	Bridlington Town v Great Harwood Town	2-2,3-0

Final: Guiseley 1, Bridlington Town 1;   Bridlington Town 2, Guiseley 3 (Guiseley won 3-2 on aggregate)

H.F.S. LOANS LEAGUE ATTENDANCES 1992-93

PREMIER DIVISION ATTENDANCE CHART 1992-93

HOME TEAM	1	2	3	4	5	6	7	8	9	10	11	12	13	14	15	16	17	18	19	20	21	22
1. Accrington	*	801	513	471	459	392	407	1049	703	671	513	545	508	604	465	458	495	1288	463	641	288	467
2. Barrow	1558	*	1165	1278	1094	1126	1534	1502	1711	1080	1127	848	941	1006	971	1510	1047	1194	1421	1510	1252	1193
3. B Auckland	313	297	*	238	261	217	273	241	241	249	271	380	215	221	302	221	213	332	240	426	401	302
4. Buxton	325	393	325	*	351	343	273	374	291	351	236	227	243	323	810	280	497	348	320	327	311	412
5. Chorley	376	330	101	183	*	150	224	200	214	276	155	176	328	210	144	247	212	418	195	501	187	287
6. Colwyn Bay	140	298	215	128	187	*	150	186	118	92	110	102	131	149	188	186	120	253	126	350	136	551
7. Droylsden	323	404	148	216	351	347	*	301	149	225	161	153	203	247	263	156	209	166	342	593	186	311
8. Emley	369	290	377	249	254	283	216	*	229	512	546	372	250	196	365	389	497	311	447	504	346	342
9. Fleetwood	266	498	206	72	159	242	115	124	*	136	133	117	146	181	168	150	199	430	103	334	113	185
10. Frickley	257	225	209	286	222	231	178	325	200	*	278	274	148	191	265	234	178	174	170	393	104	223
11. G Trinity	398	481	401	446	283	326	349	407	313	419	*	494	338	334	348	474	479	351	410	520	380	454
12. Goole	211	305	212	183	188	210	243	302	190	305	235	*	188	260	222	185	223	190	190	298	220	210
13. Horwich	255	303	186	174	410	173	183	225	208	196	189	173	*	172	210	201	186	265	158	339	189	207
14. Hyde	444	414	284	403	334	280	440	349	278	307	253	251		*	242	343	305	307	812	576	261	652
15. Leek	525	516	359	565	408	360	407	319	402	366	253	369	346	414	*	470	457	544	368	732	324	660
16. Marine	355	611	349	362	681	418	331	335	311	325	334	306	344	384	481	*	323	602	345	1611	326	533
17. Matlock	377	516	365	476	274	256	308	347	297	425	397	269	288	356	570	372	*	304	370	367	341	360
18. Morecambe	680	1075	369	350	450	350	409	292	525	350	320	367	362	356	407	440	388	*	395	680	529	395
19. Mossley	401	455	215	300	343	238	644	395	219	187	308	244	208	509	202	279	270	401	*	567	225	350
20. Southport	1328	1723	678	752	526	765	1185	419	1207	2230	1007	382	883	534	1157	2078	913	904	544	*	1128	1177
21. Whitley Bay	173	359	453	267	203	227	315	219	207	308	109	180	156	253	188	131	238	201	149	205	*	235
22. Winsford	380	420	450	390	304	401	457	546	556	486	280	403	242	412	406	460	429	541	526	801	401	*

FIRST DIVISION ATTENDANCE CHART 1992-93

HOME TEAM	1	2	3	4	5	6	7	8	9	10	11	12	13	14	15	16	17	18	19	20	21
1. Alfreton	*	167	173	110	78	128	181	126	106	123	80	101	81	135	101	94	106	142	120	111	228
2. Ashton Utd	282	*	327	215	229	721	255	278	170	288	347	314	227	154	225	246	207	263	274	356	243
3. Bridlington	173	270	*	209	238	188	275	205	195	202	703	256	191	170	322	201	181	221	299	231	260
4. Caernarfon	59	270	117	*	93	211	61	72	77	67	170	86	88	85	61	66	88	80	120	68	115
5. Congleton	118	242	173	128	*	88	132	238	142	135	124	117	124	111	156	138	171	129	206	136	202
6. Curzon Ash.	124	398	138	146	137	*	117	180	102	137	164	129	96	129	146	109	162	106	138	138	149
7. Eastwood T.	293	95	180	126	94	142	*	136	92	113	153	123	115	142	93	91	132	220	97	166	233
8. Farsley	142	137	239	116	121	129	121	*	122	151	517	221	172	118	137	98	184	123	139	167	168
9. Gt Harwood	132	264	212	178	78	185	111	187	*	190	140	248	98	195	128	428	165	186	100	278	208
10. Gretna	80	92	240	156	150	101	130	147	97	*	196	110	154	251	140	90	205	120	104	246	80
11. Guiseley	616	535	703	418	502	492	521	525	595	539	*	512	497	514	582	495	444	553	581	362	357
12. Harrogate	175	301	273	226	216	185	172	281	246	202	605	*	184	236	206	208	221	158	192	252	275
13. Knowsley	84	91	182	116	110	131	72	121	64	106	185	156	*	92	74	127	107	74	180	73	88
14. Lancaster	105	121	136	94	51	102	138	127	204	147	58	66		*	107	84	106	82	96	149	188
15. Netherfield	85	177	153	165	132	132	136	124	152	171	237	135	204	278	*	122	211	147	177	322	121
16. Radcliffe	86	183	92	94	91	104	88	86	147	150	161	102	54	111	101	*	135	92	130	82	128
17. Rossendale	272	161	182	144	125	136	121	135	412	196	236	127	111	187	181	103	*	103	189	230	141
18. Shepshed	185	115	285	159	129	252	228	119	201	197	237	235	134	197	153	140	182	*	125	168	174
19. Warrington	191	201	227	202	191	287	244	206	275	168	213	174	378	166	172	208	239	233	*	253	182
20. Workington	124	232	319	227	134	252	230	136	189	209	187	207	177	202	170	168	134	130	168	*	246
21. Worksop	315	313	371	219	201	292	508	335	301	276	313	241	427	405	332	321	321	360	321	366	*

'MAIL ON SUNDAY' MANAGER OF THE MONTH AWARDS

Month	Premier Player	Premier Manager	Div. 1 Player	Div. 1 Manager
Sept.	D Sutton (Leek)	B Kettle (Southport)	J Dunn (Warrington)	S Waywell (Curzon)
Oct.	R Payne (Chorley)	B Kettle (Southport)	P Smith (Gt Harwood)	C Richardson (Brid'ton)
Nov.	B Ross (Marine)	N Baker (Leek)	M Roderick (Shepshed)	G Raynor (Guiseley)
Dec.	N Bramald (Emley)	R Howard (Marine)	D Nicely (Congleton)	A Tinsley (Fleetwood)
Jan.	P Chadwick (Hyde)	M McKenzie (Winsf.)	M Jackson (Netherfld)	D Brownbill (Warr'ton)
Feb.	A Hoskin (Accrington)	B Kettle (Southport)	C Shaw (Ashton Utd)	A Cook (Workington)
Mar.	J Brady (Barrow)	G Simpson (Gainsb.)	K Evans (Curzon)	T Spencer (Worksop)
Apr.	D Sheridan (Winsford)	M McKenzie (Winsf.)	J Priestley (Gretna)	A Whittaker (Netherfield)

FIVE GOALS IN A GAME:
Bob Clarke for Emley at Mossley (League Cup, 8/12/92)
Phil Chadwick for Hyde United at Emley (23/1/93)
Ian Cain for Morecambe at Goole Town (24/4/93)
Gary Waller for Worksop Town at Congleton Town (12/4/93)

Premier Division

	P	W	D	L	F	A	Pts
Southport	42	29	9	4	103	31	96
Winsford United	42	27	9	6	91	43	90
Morecambe	42	25	11	6	93	51	86
Marine	42	26	8	8	83	47	86
Leek Town	42	21	11	10	86	51	74
Accrington Stanley	42	20	13	9	79	45	73
Frickley Athletic	42	21	6	15	62	52	69
Barrow	42	18	11	13	71	55	65
Hyde United	42	17	13	12	87	71	64
Bishop Auckland	42	17	11	14	63	52	62
Gainsborough Trinity	42	17	8	17	63	66	59
Colwyn Bay	42	16	6	20	80	79	54
Horwich	42	14	10	18	72	79	52
Buxton	42	13	10	19	60	75	49
Matlock Town *	42	13	11	18	56	79	47
Emley	42	13	6	23	62	91	45
Whitley Bay	42	11	8	23	57	96	41
Chorley	42	10	10	22	52	93	40
Fleetwood Town	42	10	7	25	50	77	37
Droylsden	42	10	7	25	47	84	37
Mossley	42	7	8	27	53	95	29
Goole Town	42	6	9	27	47	105	27

* - 3pts deducted.

Top Scorers

John Coleman (Morecambe)	33
Steve Haw (Southport)	32
Paul Beck (Accrington Stanley)	26
Chris Camden (Peter Donnelly)	26
Andy Graham (Hyde United)	26
Brain Ross (Marine)	25

THE PREMIER DIVISION RESULT CHART 1992-93

HOME TEAM	1	2	3	4	5	6	7	8	9	10	11	12	13	14	15	16	17	18	19	20	21	22
1. A.Stanley	*	2-0	0-0	2-2	3-1	3-1	4-1	6-1	1-0	1-1	0-1	3-0	2-1	1-1	2-0	1-1	2-0	1-1	2-2	2-2	2-0	1-3
2. Barrow	2-0	*	4-3	3-2	2-1	5-0	3-0	0-1	2-0	1-2	2-2	4-1	1-1	2-1	1-2	3-1	1-0	0-3	2-2	0-2	0-1	0-0
3. Bishop Auck.	0-0	2-1	*	0-0	5-0	1-1	2-0	2-1	0-1	0-3	2-2	1-1	1-0	3-0	1-0	1-0	0-1	2-2	4-0	1-3	3-2	2-2
4. Buxton	0-1	0-4	0-3	*	2-3	1-0	1-2	3-0	0-3	2-0	2-3	2-1	2-2	2-1	2-1	1-5	1-1	4-1	6-1	0-2	0-0	2-3
5. Chorley	0-1	1-1	0-0	1-1	*	4-2	2-0	1-3	2-1	1-2	1-0	1-5	2-2	3-3	2-1	0-6	1-1	1-2	4-2	1-6	1-4	0-4
6. Colwyn Bay	1-0	2-3	1-2	7-3	1-0	*	3-0	2-1	3-1	0-1	3-0	4-2	4-2	2-4	2-3	2-2	3-1	0-1	2-1	2-4	4-4	2-3
7. Droylsden	3-3	1-3	1-1	0-0	2-2	1-1	*	1-2	1-1	2-1	0-2	1-0	1-3	1-0	0-1	1-3	2-0	0-1	1-4	2-5	1-2	0-4
8. Emley	0-3	1-1	2-3	1-1	2-1	1-1	1-3	*	4-3	2-0	0-2	1-2	5-3	1-5	5-5	4-1	2-2	1-2	2-0	0-4	2-1	1-2
9. Fleetwood T.	0-2	2-2	0-1	0-2	1-1	1-2	1-6	3-1	*	1-1	1-2	3-1	1-1	1-2	3-0	3-1	2-3	1-2	3-2	1-2	2-2	1-2
10. Frickley Ath.	3-2	2-1	3-0	2-0	2-1	1-0	0-1	3-1	2-1	*	4-0	3-0	2-1	1-1	1-2	0-0	1-0	2-0	2-1	2-5	3-0	1-2
11. Gainsboro' T.	0-2	1-0	1-1	1-2	1-1	2-1	2-1	1-0	1-0	0-1	*	3-0	2-2	2-0	1-4	0-1	2-4	2-3	1-1	1-1	7-1	3-1
12. Goole Town	0-5	1-0	1-0	0-2	0-2	3-1	1-2	0-0	0-0	1-3	1-4	*	1-2	1-1	0-1	2-3	0-4	2-8	1-1	0-5	5-1	2-4
13. Horwich RMI	2-2	0-2	2-1	3-0	2-1	0-2	2-1	1-3	2-1	3-1	2-0	3-1	*	3-5	1-1	0-3	2-4	0-1	5-2	1-1	3-3	2-0
14. Hyde Utd	2-6	2-2	3-1	2-2	4-0	3-1	2-1	1-0	3-1	0-0	7-2	3-3	4-1	*	2-4	1-2	2-0	2-2	4-2	1-1	2-1	3-3
15. Leek Town	3-1	2-2	2-3	5-1	3-0	1-4	2-1	2-0	4-1	4-0	1-2	6-1	0-0	3-3	*	0-1	6-0	0-0	3-3	1-0	3-0	0-0
16. Marine	2-0	2-2	2-0	1-3	1-0	2-1	2-1	2-0	2-0	2-0	2-1	6-3	3-0	3-1	1-1	*	2-2	0-3	1-0	2-1	3-1	2-0
17. Matlock Town	1-2	0-1	1-5	1-0	3-1	1-1	2-2	2-1	0-1	2-1	2-1	3-3	3-2	0-1	1-2	1-0	*	0-6	0-3	1-5	1-2	3-3
18. Morecambe	2-0	3-1	2-1	2-1	2-0	3-1	2-0	7-4	4-2	3-0	3-4	1-1	3-2	3-3	1-1	1-1	2-2	*	3-1	0-2	4-2	0-0
19. Mossley	0-5	1-2	3-1	2-3	1-4	1-4	0-1	1-2	2-0	1-2	2-1	0-0	1-4	1-2	0-4	0-3	0-0	1-0	*	0-2	5-0	2-4
20. Southport	2-2	3-0	1-0	2-1	7-1	2-0	3-0	1-2	5-0	2-1	0-0	3-0	3-2	1-0	0-0	0-0	3-0	1-1	3-0	*	1-0	0-1
21. Whitley Bay	1-1	1-1	1-4	2-0	2-2	2-4	5-0	2-0	0-1	3-2	3-0	2-0	0-1	1-0	0-2	1-5	2-3	0-3	1-1	1-5	*	0-3
22. Winsford Utd	2-0	1-4	2-0	1-1	0-1	3-2	5-2	5-1	2-0	1-1	1-0	3-0	3-1	1-0	2-0	5-1	0-0	2-0	1-0	1-2	6-0	*

ACCRINGTON STANLEY

Accrington Stanley F.C. 1992-93. Back Row (L/R): Paul Burns, Ian Urmson, Tony Keyes (Coach), John Hughes, Charlie Cooper, John Armfield, Bernie Hughes, Steve Allcock, Jim McCluskie, Jimmy Collins, Steve Lampkin, Wayne Goodison, Alan Crane (Physio). Front: Mike Lutkevitch, Paul Beck, Phil Staley (Manager), Eddie Johnston, Terry Williams, Ashley Hoskin.

Chairman: John S Alty
President: J C Prescott.
Secretary: Philip Terry, 8 Princess Street, Colne, Lancs BB8 9AN (0286 866768).
Manager: Phil Staley
Physio: Alan Crane
Coach: Tony Keyes.
Press Officer: John S Alty (061 339 2487)
Commercial Advisor: J Butterfield
Ground: Crown Ground, off Livingstone Road, Accrington (0254 383235).
Directions: Arriving on A680 from Clayton-le-Moors Livingstone Road is on left 50 yds past Crown Hotel. From M62/M66, through town centre on A680 - Livingstone Road 500 yds on right after Victoria Hospital. One and a half miles from Accrington (BR).
Capacity: 2,420 **Cover:** 1,650 **Seats:** 200 **Floodlights:** Yes **Metal Badges:** Yes
Club Shop: Yes, selling replica kits, sweaters, t-shirts, ties, scarves etc. Contact Jim Shaw (0254 383235).
Colours: Red/white/red **Change colours:** All sky
Previous Leagues: Lancs Combination 70-78/ Cheshire County 78-82/ North West Counties 82-87.
Midweek home matchday: Wednesday **Reserve Team:** None.
Sponsors: Hollands Pies, Baxenden.
Record Attendance: 2,096 v Fleetwood Town, FA Cup 4th Qualifying Rd 27/10/90 *(10,081 v Crewe Alexandra, F.A. Cup Second Round Proper 5/12/92 - played at Ewood Park, Blackburn).*
Best F.A. Cup season: Second Rd Proper 92-93 (lost 1-6 at home to Crewe Alexandra).
League clubs defeated in F.A. Cup: None.
Record win: 9-0 v Ashton Town, Lancashire Combination 75-76.
Record defeat: 1-9 v Runcorn (A), F.A. Cup 2nd Qualifying Rd replay 85-86.
Record Fees - Paid: £2,250 for Bernie Hughes (Droylsen 90-91).
Received: £10,000 for Martin Clark (Crewe A. 92-93).
Players progressing to Football League: David Hargreaves (Blackburn Rovers 1977), Ian Blackstone (York City).
Clubhouse: Open two nights and matchdays. Private functions. Well stocked tea bar in ground.
Club Record Scorer: David Hargreaves 318
Club Record Appearances: David Hargreaves 310.
92-93 Captain & P.O.Y.: Eddie Johnston
92-93 Top scorer: Paul Beck 21.
Local Press: Accrington Observer (0254 871444), Lancashire Evening Telegraph (0254 63588).
Local Radio Stations: Radio Lancashire, Red Rose Radio.
Newsline: 0898 122 921.
Honours: North West Counties Lg R-up 86-87, Cheshire County Lg Div 2 80-81 (R-up 79-80), Lancs Combination 73-74 77-78 (R-up 71-72 75-76, Lg Cup 71-72 72-73 73-74 76-77), George Watson Trophy 71-72 73-74 74-75, John Duckworth Trophy 85-86, Lancs Junior Cup (now ATS Trophy) R-up 85-86, FA Trophy 1st Rd 72-73 78-79 92-93, Lancs under-18 Yth Cup 89-90.

PROGRAMME DETAILS:
Pages: 32 Price: £1
Editor: Secretary

Barrow F.C. 1992-93. Back Row (L/R): Bert Friars (Asst Trainer), Neil Doherty, David Eaves, Andy Rooney (Captain), Darren Oldroyd, David Smith, Darren Hoyland, David Addenbrook, Mick Cloudsdale (Trainer). Front: Harry Wiggins, Kevin Formley, Darren Heesom, John Brady, Shaun McIlwane, Tony Edwards. Photo - Ged Rule.

Chairman: J Barker   **President:** W A McCullough.
Secretary: C H Whiteside, c/o The Club (below).
Manager: Richard Dinnis   **Asst Manager:** Les Rigby
Physio: Mick Cloudsdale   **Press Officer:** Phil Yelland (031 445 1010)
Ground: Holker Street Ground, Wilkie Rd, Barrow-in-Furness, Cumbria LA14 5UH (0229 820346/823839).
Commercial Office: 102 Scott Str., Barrow-in-Furness (0229 823061 - Manager Mrs Linda Barker).
Directions: M6 to junction 36, A590 to first r-bout on outskirts of Barrow (Park Road (from Autumn 1993 A590 will lead directly into Park Rd)), soingposted industrial route, after about 2 miles turn left into Wilkie Rd - ground on right.
Capacity: 6,500   **Cover:** 1,200   **Seats:** 1,200   **Floodlights:** Yes   **Metal Badges:** Yes
Club Shop: Yes - on popular side of ground.
Colours: White/royal/royal   **Change colours:** Red & black halves/black/black.
Previous Leagues: Lancs Combination 01-21/ Football League 21-72 / Northern Premier 72-79 83-84 86-89/ GMV Conference 79-83 84-86 89-92.
Previous Grounds: The Strawberry & Little Park, Roose.
Midweek home matchday: Tuesday   **Reserve Team's League:** Northern Comb.
Record Attendance: 16,840 v Swansea Town, FA Cup Third Round 1954. For non-league game: 6,002 v Enfield, F.A. Trophy Semi-Final, April 1988.
Best F.A. Cup season: Third Round Proper on nine occasions including once as a non-league club (90-91, lost 0-1 at Bolton Wanderers).
Record win: 12-0 v Cleator, F.A. Cup 1920.
Record defeat: 1-10 v Hartlepools United, Football League Division Four 1959.
Record Fees - Paid: Undisclosed
              Received: £40,000 for Kenny Lowe (Barnet, January 1991).
Players progressing to Football League: Ian McDonald, Neil McDonald, John Laisby, Barry Diamond, Frank Gamble, Barry Knowles, Glen Skivington, Paul Byron, Levi Edwards, Kenny Lowe, Mark Dobie, Tony Rigby.
Clubhouse: Barrow Sports & Leisure centre next to ground (0229 823839). Snack bars around ground.
Club Record Goalscorer: Colin Cowperthwaite 282 (Dec '77-Dec '92)
Club Record Appearances: Colin Cowperthwaite 704
92-93 Captain: Andy Rooney.
92-93 P.o.Y.: John Brady
92-93 Top scorer: John Brady, 22 Lge + 3 Cup.
Sponsors: Cape Contracts.
Local Press: North West Evening Mail (0229 821835), Barrow & West Cumberland Advertiser (0229 832032).
Local Radio Stations: BBC Radio Furness, BBC Radio Cumbria, Red Rose, Bay Radio.
Newsline: 0898 888 620.
Honours: FA Trophy 89-90 (SF 87-88), Northern Premier Lg 83-84 88-89 (Lg Cup R-up 87-88, Lg Shield 84-85), Bord Lord Trophy R-up 90-91, Cumbrian Cup 82-83 83-84 (R-up 84-85), Lancs Floodlit Cup R-up 86-87, Lancs Snr Cup 54-55 (R-up 51-52 65-66 66-67 69-70), Lancs Chal. Trophy 48-49(reserves) 80-81 (R-up 81-82 84-85), Lancs Comb. 20-21 (R-up 13-14, Div 2 R-up 04-05 10-11).

PROGRAMME DETAILS:
Pages: 32 Price: £1
Editor: Secretary

BISHOP AUCKLAND

The Bishop Auckland defence struggle to contain Barrow top-scorer John Brady (left) during the Premier Divisio fixture at Kingsway. Photo - Ged Rule.

Chairman: C Townsend   **Vice Chairman:** S Newcomb **President:** W B Botcherby
Secretary: N Postma, 18 Wynyard Grove, Bishop Auckland DL14 8RF (0388 608330).
Manager: Harry Dunn   **Asst Mgr:** Tony Boylan   **Coach:** Tony Boylan
Press Officer: Secretary   **Physio:** J Moore.
Ground: Kingsway, Bishop Auckland, County Durham (0388 603686).
Directions: A1 to Scotch Corner then follow signs to Bishop Auckland. Ground in town centre (rear of Newgate Str). Half mile from station.
Capacity: 5,000   **Cover:** 2,000   **Seats:** 600   **Shop:** Yes   **Metal Badges:** £3.00
Colours: Sky & Navy blue   **Change colours:** Red & white.   **Sponsors:** T.B.A.
Previous Leagues: N East Counties 1889-90/ Northern Alliance 1890-91/ Northern 1893-1988.
Midweek home matchday: Wednesday   **Reserve Team:** None.
Record Attendance: 17,000 v Coventry, FA Cup 2nd Rd 6/12/52.
Record win: 13-0   **Record defeat:** 1-7.
Best FA Cup season: 4th Rd 54-55 (lost 1-3 at home to York City).
League clubs beaten in FA Cup: Crystal Palace, Ipswich 54-55, Tranmere 56-57.
Record Fees - Paid: £2,000   **Received:** £6,000 for Andy Toman.
Players progressing to Football League: Bob Paisley (Liverpool), Fred Richardson & Seamus O'Connell (Chelsea 1946 & 54), Robert Hardisty & Ken Williamson (Darlimgton 1946 & 52), William Shergold (Newport 1947), Norman Smith (Fulham 1948), Ron Steel & Ken Murray (Darlington 1950), Arthur Adey (Doncaster 1950), Frank Palmer & Alan Stalker (Gateshead 1951 & 58), Arthur Sewell (Bradford City 1954), Gordon Barker (Southend 1954), Jack Major (Hull 1955), Harry Sharratt (Oldham 1956), Frank McKenna (Leeds 1956), John Barnwell (Arsenal 1956), Derek Lewis (Accrington Stanley 1957), Corbett Cresswell (Carlisle 1958), Warren Bradley (Man Utd), Laurie Brown (Northampton), Paul Baker (Southampton), Micky Gooding (Rotherham), Keith Nobbs & Andy Toman (Hartlepool), Peter Hinds (Dundee Utd).
Clubhouse: Open every lunchtime and evening noon-4 & 7-11pm, and Saturday matchdays noon-4 & 5-6 & 7-11pm. Large bar, pool, juke box. Also snack bar within grounds sells hot & cold pies & drinks.
Club Record Appearances: Bob Hardisty
92-93 Captain: L Boyle
92-93 P.o.Y.: L Boyle
92-93 Top scorer: Gary Hyde.
Local Newspapers: Northern Echo, Evening Gazette, N'castle Journal.
Local Radio Stations: Radio Cleveland, Radio Tees.
Honours: FA Amateur Cup(10) 1895-96, 1899-1900 13-14 20-22 34-35 38-39 54-56 57-58 (R-up(8) 01-02 05-06 10-11 14-15 45-46 49-51 53-54), FA Trophy 4th Rd 78-79 88-89, Northern Lg(19) 1898-99 1900-02 08-10 11-12 20-21 30-31 38-39 46-47 49-52 53-56 66-67 84-86 (R-up(16) 03-04 05-06 14-15 19-20 21-23 36-38 39-40 47-49 52-53 60-61 72-73 78-79 86-87, Lg Cup(7) 49-51 53-55 59-60 66-67 75-76), D'ham Chall Cup 1891-92 98-99 1930-31 38-39 51-52 55-56 61-62 66-67 84-85 85-86 87-88, HFS Loans Lg Div 1 R-up 88-89. Plus tournaments in Isle of Man, Spain, Portugal etc.

PROGRAMME DETAILS:
Pages: 28 **Price:** 50p
Editor: N Postma
(0388 608330)

BOSTON UNITED

Boston United F.C. 1992-93. Back Row (L/R): Ernie Moss (Asst Manager), Ian Bennyworth (now Gainsborough Trinity), Steve Chambers, Mark Hallam (now Hednesford Town), Steve Lister (now Matlock Town), Paul Bastock, Trevor Slack, Robbie Curtis, Drew Coverdale, Darren Smith, Glen Maddison (Kit Asst). Front: Richard Toone, Steve Stoutt, Les McJannet (now Matlock Town), Martin Hardy, Peter Morris (Manager), Neil Grayson, John Graham, David Cork (now Worksop Town). Photo courtesy of A & K Markham.

Chairman: Mr A E Bell   **Vice Chairman:** Mr Pat Malkinson **President:** Mr S Burgess.
Secretary: John Blackwell, 14-16 Spain Place, Boston, Lincs PE26 6HN (0205 364406(club office)).
Manager: Peter Morris   **Coach:** Ernie Moss.
Coach: Tony Keyes.   **Press Officer:** The Club Offices
Commercial Manager: Secretary.
Ground: York Street, Boston, Lincs (0205 364406-office, 365524/5-matchday no., 354063-fax).
Directions: A1 to A17 Sleaford-Boston, over rail crossing, bear right at Eagle pub to lights over haven Bridge, thru lights opposite B & Q, right into York Street. Ground just off town centre.
Capacity: 8,771   **Cover:** 8,771   **Seats:** 1,826   **Floodlights:** Yes   **Metal Badges:** Yes
Club Shop: Yes, but at club office (as secretary's address, above) not ground.
Colours: Amber/black/amber   **Change colours:** All blue.
Previous Leagues: Midland 21-58 62-64/ Southern 58-61/ Central Alliance 61-62/ United Counties 65-66/ West Midlands (Regional) 66-68/ Northern Premier 68-79/ Alliance Premier (Conference) 79-93.
Previous Grounds: None.   **Previous Names:** Boston Town/ Boston Swifts.
Midweek home matchday: Wednesday   **Reserve Team:** None.
Sponsors: Batemans Brewery.
Record Attendance: 10,086 v Corby Town, floodlight inauguration 1955.
Best F.A. Cup season: Third Rd Proper replay 73-74 (lost 1-6 at home to Derby County after 0-0 draw).
League clubs defeated in F.A. Cup: Derby 55-56, Southport 70-71, Hartlepool 71-72, Crewe 82-83.
Record win: 14-0 v Spilsby Town, Grace Swan Cup.
Record Fees - Paid: £14,000 for Micky Nuttell (Wycombe Wanderers).
                      Received: £25,000 for Gary Jones (Southend United, 1993).
Players progressing to Football League: Jim Smith (Colchester), Steve Thompson (Lincoln), Brendon Phillips (Mansfield), Gordon Simmonite (Blackpool), Simon Garner (Blackburn), John Froggatt & Bobby Svarc (Colchester), David Gilbert (Northampton), Tim Dalton (Bradford City), Gary Jones (Southend).
Clubhouse: (0205 362967) Open every day except Tuesday. Live entertainment Saturday, pool, darts, dominoes, Sunday football teams.
Club Record Scorer: Jimmy Rayner 55, 66-67.
Club Record Appearances: Billy Howells, 500+.
92-93 Captain: Martin Hardy.
P.o.Y. 92-93: Paul Bastock.
92-93 Top scorer: Gary Jones.
Newsline: 0898 121 539.
Honours: F.A. Trophy R-up 84-85, Northern Premier Lg 72-73 73-74 76-77 77-78 (R-up 71-72, Lg Cup 73-74 75-76 (R-up 77-78), Challenge Shield 73-74 74-75 76-77 77-78), Lincs Snr Cup 34-35 36-36 37-38 45-46 49-50 54-55 55-56 76-77 78-79 85-86 87-88 88-89, East Anglian Cup 60-61, Central Alliance 61-62 (Lg Cup 61-62), Utd Counties Lg 65-66 (Lg Cup 65-66), West Midlands (Regional) 66-67 67-68, Eastern Professional Floodlit Cup 71-72 (R-up 76-77), Non-League Champion of Champions Cup 72-73 73-74 76-77 77-78, Midland Lg R-up 55-56, Lincs Lg(reserves) R-up 81-82 82-83.

PROGRAMME DETAILS:
Pages: 44 **Price:** £1
Editor: Secretary

BRIDLINGTON TOWN

Alan Radford (centre), Bridlington Town's Wembley goalscorer in the F.A. Vase final on 8th May, shares his moment of glory with Lee Harvey (left) and Alan Tyrell. Photo - Graham Cotterill.

Chairman: Charles Dunn **Vice Chairman:** Barry Garton.
Secretary: Alan Proudlock, 49 Star Hill Rd, Driffield, Nth Humbs YO25 7EY (0377 241821).
Manager: Colin Richardson **Asst Manager:** George Cook.
Physio: George Halley **Press Officer:** Tony Harrison
Ground: *Queensgate, Bridlington YO16 5LN (0262 670391). N.B. For 1993-94, the club will be playing all home games at Doncaster Rovers F.C.*
Directions: *A166 to Bridlington, through first lights, over island signed town centre, left at second set of lights, Queensgate ground on right. To Belle Vue, Doncaster - From north, A1(M), A638 to Doncaster centre then follow signs towards Bawtry (A638), at r'bout take 3rd exit into Bawtry Rd, ground on right. From west, A635 to Doncaster centre then as above. From east; M18, A630 signed Doncaster, at r'bout turn left into Bawtry Rd - ground on right. From South - M1, M18, A6128 signed Doncaster (A6182) at r'bout after 2 miles follow signs for Scunthorpe & Racecourse, right into Bawtry Rd (A638) at r-bout just before racecourse, ground on right.*
N.B. - all ground details below apply to Queensgate
Capacity: 3,000 **Cover:** 740 **Seats:** 740 **Floodlights:** Yes **Club Shop:** Yes
Colours: All red **Change colours:** All white
Sponsors: East Riding Sacks Ltd.
Previous Leagues: Driffield & District Minor/ Driffield & District/ East Riding Amateur/ Yorkshire 24-39 59-82/ Northern Counties East 82-90.
Previous Name: Bridlington Central United (until 1959).
Midweek home matchday: T.B.A.
Reserve Team's League: Northern Co's (East) Reserve Div.
Record Attendance: 2,102 v Scarborough, FA Cup 1st Qualifying Rd 8/9/62.
Best F.A. Cup season: 1st Rd 60-61 (lost 2-3 at Bishop Auckland) 91-92 (1-2 at home to York City).
League clubs defeated in F.A. Cup: None.
Players progressing to Football League: Mick Head (Hull 1953), Phillip Stubbins (Mansfield), Gary Brattan (Cambridge Utd), David Bowman (Scarborough 1983), Andy Shaw (York 1988), Clive Freeman (Swansea), David Wilkes (Carlisle), Darren France (Hull), Linton Brown (Halifax and Hull), Ian Taylor (Carlisle), Neil Grayson (York), Mick Norbury Cambridge Utd (1991).
Clubhouse: (0262 606879). Open everyday. Pool, darts, games machines. Hot and cold food.
92-93 Captain: Steve Brentano **92-93 P.o.Y.:** Ged Parkinson.
92-93 Top scorer: Graeme Jones 30.
Local Newspapers: Hull Daily Mail, Bridlington Free Press, Scarborough Evening News.
Local Radio Stations: Humberside - Viking.
Honours: FA Vase 92-93 (R-up 89-90), Northern Premier Lg Div 1 92-93 (Div 1 Cup R-up 92-93), Northern Counties East Lg 89-90 (Lg Cup 88-89 (R-up 89-90)), Yorkshire Lg R-up 65-66 (Lg Cup 59-60 60-61 65-66, Div 2 74-75), East Riding Senior Cup 30-31 52-53 56-57 60-61 64-65 66-67 69-70 71-72 88-89 92-93 (R-up 85-86 86-87 87-88 89-90).

BUXTON

Buxton goalkeeper Jimmy O'Donnell brings down Barrow's Neil Dohertyy. He was sent off, and 'Doc' got up to score from the spot and condemn Buxton to a 0-1 home defeat. Photo - Ged Rule, courtesy of the North West Evening Mail.

Chairman: G S Worth   **Vice Chairman:** S Dakin.
Secretary/Press Officer: D Belfield, 20 Hereford Road, Buxton SK17 9PG (0298 26033).
Manager: Ernie Oliver   **Asst Manager:** G Mallander   **Physio:** K Perrins
Ground: The Silverlands, Buxton, Derbyshire (0298 24733).
Directions: Within 200 yards of Buxton Market Place, opposite County Police HQ. Half mile from Buxton (BR).
Capacity: 4,000   **Cover:** 2,500   **Seats:** 490   **Floodlights:** Yes   **Club Shop:** No
Colours: All white (blue trim).   **Change colours:** All yellow (blue trim).
Sponsors: Josiah Tetley.
Previous Leagues: The Combination 1891-99/ North Derbyshire/ E Cheshire/ Manchester 1907-32/ Cheshire County 32-73.
Midweek home matchday: Tuesday
Record Attendance: 6,000 v Barrow, FA Cup 1st rd 51-52.
Best F.A. Cup season: 3rd Rd 51-52. Also 2nd Rd 58-59, 1st Rd 62-63.
League clubs defeated in F.A. Cup: Aldershot 51-52.
Best F.A. Trophy season: Quarter Finals 70-71 71-72.
Record Fees - Paid: £5,000 for Gary Walker (Hyde United, 1989)
    Received: £16,500 for Ally Pickering (Rotherham, 1989).
Players progressing to Football League: Peter Robinson (Notts Co 1950), John Higgins (Bolton 1950), Maurice Brooks (Stockport 1951), Ray Parker (Bradford City 1951), Fred Marlow (Grimsby 1951), Ian Greaves (Man Utd 1953), John Brindley (Chesterfield 1953), Les Ferriday (Walsall 1954), John Good (Tranmere 1955), Jimmy Anders (Bradford PA 1956), William Haydock (Man City 1959), Anthony Parkes (Blackburn 1970), Andy Proudlove (Sheffield Wednesday 1975), Graham Collier (York City 1978), Harry Charlton (Darlington 1979), Ally Pickering (Rotherham 1990).
Clubhouse: (0298 23197). Open nightly + Sunday lunchtimes. Tetleys beers, no hot food.
Club Record Goalscorer: Dave Herbert
Club Record Appearances: Mick Davis.
92-93 Captain: Les Hunter
92-93 P.o.Y.: Gary Walker
92-93 Top scorer: Stuart Lowe 22.
Local Newspapers: Buxton Advertiser (0298 22118/22119), Matlock Mercury (Matlock 2432/3).
Local Radio Stations: Radio Derby.
Honours: Northern Premier Lg Cup 90-91 (Presidents Cup R-up 81-82), Cheshire County 72-73 (R-up 46-47 62-63, Lg Cup 56-57 57-58 68-69), Manchester Lg 31-32 5-60(reserves)(R-up 04-05 28-29 29-30 30-31, Lg Cup 25-26 26-27), Derbyshire Senior Cup 38-39 44-45 45-46 56-57 59-60 71-72.

PROGRAMME DETAILS:
Pages: 36 **Price:** 60p
Editor: Tony Tomlinson
(0484 718907)

CHORLEY

Two Chorley defenders cannot prevent Gerry Hatto of visiting Frickley Athletic getting in a shot. Frickley won this Premier Division fixture, on 2nd January, 2-1 and went top of the League. Photo - Colin Stevens.

Chairman: D Murgatroyd　　**Vice Chairman:** M Bolton　　**President:** Dr P J Wren.
Secretary/Press Officer: Alan Robinson, 55 Janice Drive, Fulwood, Preston, Lancs PR2 4TY (0772 719266).
Manager: Glen Buckley　　**Physio::** Dr Philip Earl
Commercial Manager: G Haydock.
Ground: Victory Park, Duke Street, Chorley, Lancs (0257 263406).
Directions: M61 jct 6, A6 to Chorley, going past Yarrow Bridge Hotel on Bolton Rd turn left at 1st lights into Pilling Lane, 1st right into Ashley Str., ground 2nd left. From M6; jct 27, follow signs to Chorley, left at lights, continue for two and a half miles on A49, right onto B5251, on entering Chorley turn right into Duke Street 200yds after Plough Hotel. Quarter mile from Chorley (BR).
Capacity: 9,000　　**Cover:** 4,000　　**Seats:** 900　　**Floodlights:** Yes　　**Club Shop:** No
Colours: White & black stripes/black/black　　**Change colours:** Red/white/red.
Previous Leagues: Lancs Alliance 1890-94/ Lancs 94-1903/ Lancs Comb. 03-68 69-70/ Northern Premier 68-69 70-72 82-88/ Cheshire County 72-82/ GMV Conference 88-90.
Previous Grounds: Dole Lane 1883-1901/ Rangletts Park 01-05/ St George's Park 05-20.
Midweek home matchday: Tuesday　　**Reserve Team's League:** Alliance League.
Sponsors: None.　　**Record Gate:** 9,679 v Darwen, 1931-32.
Best F.A. Cup year: 2nd Rd 86-87 (lost in replay at Preston), 90-91 (lost at Shrewsbury).
League clubs defeated in F.A. Cup: Accrington 46-47/ Wolves 86-87/ Bury 90-91.
Record Fees - Paid: £900 for Geoff Twentyman (Formby)
　　　　　　Received: £22,500 for Paul Mariner (Plymouth Argyle, 1973).
Players progressing to Football League: Charles Ashcroft (Liverpool 1946), William Healey (Arsenal 1949), Stan Howard (Huddersfield 1952), Derek Hogg (Leicester 1952), William Norcross (Southport 1959), Micky Walsh (Blackpool 1971), Paul Mariner (Plymouth 1973), Graham Barrow (Wigan 1976), Steve Galliers (Wimbledon 1977), Kevin Tully (Bury 1980), Geoff Twentyman (Preston 1983), Gary Buckley (Bury 1984), Chris Hunter (Preston 1984).
Clubhouse: (0257 275662). Open every evening. Entertainment at weekends.
Snacks available.
Club Record Goalscorer: Peter Watson.
92-93 Captain: Paul Cuddy
92-93 P.o.Y.: Peter McCrae.
92-93 Top scorer: Peter McCrae.
Local Newspapers: Lancs Evening Post, Chorley Guardian (0257 264911).
Local Radio Stations: Radio Lancs, Red Rose.
Honours: Northern Premier Lg 87-88, Cheshire Co. Lg 75-76 76-77 81-82, Lancs Comb. 19-20 22-23 27-28 28-29 32-33 33-34 45-46 59-60 60-61 63-64 (R-up 21-22 26-27 48-49 62-63 64-65 65-66, Lg Cup 24-25 58-59 62-63), Lancs Lg 1896-97 98-99, Lancs Alliance 2892-93 (R-up 93-94), Lancs Jnr Cup 1893-94 1908-09 23-24 39-40 45-46 57-58 58-59 60-61 63-64 64-65 75-76 79-80 81-82 82-83, FA Tphy QF (replay) 76-77.

PROGRAMME DETAILS:
Pages: 18 **Price:** 70p
Editor: S Seymour

Formed: 1885

COLWYN BAY

'Bay' or 'Seagulls'

Colwyn Bay F.C. 1992-93. Back Row (L/R): Steph Rush (Asst Manager), Darren Tinson, Trevor Ball, Phil Evans, Graham Roberts, Timmy Williams, Mark Challinor, Tommy Lloyd, Steve Jones. Front: Lee Harvey, Les Armour, Paul Nelson, Peter Donelly, Steve Morgan, Mark Woods, Darren Martin, Johnny Carmichael (Physio). Photo - Ifor Clwyd.

Chairman: Mr G Owens   **Vice Chairman:** Mr J A Humphreys **President:** Mr I G Grant.
Secretary/Press Officer: Mr A J Banks, 15 Smith Avenue, Old Colwyn, Clwyd LL29 8BE (0492 516941).
Manager: Bryn Jones   **Asst Mgr:** Steph Rush
Physio: John Carmichael.
Ground & Directions: As Ellesmere Port Town F.C. (See Bass North West Counties League section).
Capacity, Seats etc: As Ellesmere Port Town F.C. (See Bass North West Counties League).
Metal Badges: Yes
Club Shop: Yes - postal applications only - contact secretary.
Colours: Sky/maroon/sky   **Change colours:** Red/white/red.   **Sponsors:** T.B.A.
Previous Grounds: Eiras Park 1930-82/ Llanelian Road 82-92/ Northwich Victoria F.C. 92-93.
Previous Leagues: Nth Wales Coast 01-21 33-35/ Welsh National 21-30/ Nth Wales Comb. 30-31/ Welsh Lg (Nth) 45-84/ North West Counties 84-91.
Midweek home matchday: Tuesday   **Reserve Team:** None.
Record Attendance: 5,000 (at Eiras Park) v Borough United, 1964.
Best F.A. Cup season: First Round Proper 87-88.
League clubs defeated in F.A. Cup: None.
Clubhouse: Open before and after matches. Usual club food (pies etc).
92-93 Captain: Dave Brett
92-93 P.O.Y.: Steve Jones
92-93 Top scorer: Peter Donelly.
Local Newspapers: North Wales Weekly News, North Wales Pioneer.
Honours: Northern Premier Lg Div 1 91-92 (Div 1 Cup 91-92), North West Counties Lg R-up 90-91 (Div 3 R-up 83-84, Lg Cup 88-89, Floodlit Cup 90-91), Welsh Cup SF 91-92, Welsh National Lg R-up 27-28 29-30, Nth Wales Comb. 30-31, Welsh Lg Nth 64-65 82-83 83-84 (R-up 35-36 45-46 63-64, Lg Cup 27-28), Alves Cup 63-64, Cookson Cup 73-74 79-80 80-81 81-82 83-84, Barritt Cup 79-80 81-82 83-84, Nth Wales Coast Chal. Cup 30-31 31-32 81-82 82-83 83-84, Nth Wales Coast Jnr Cup 1898-99.

'THE NON-LEAGUE PLAYERS'
1993-94 EDITION

AVAILABLE DURING THE SEASON, WILL FEATURE DETAILS OF COLWYN BAY'S PLAYERS, AND INDEED THE PLAYERS OF ALL CLUBS IN THE TOP FOUR PYRAMID LEAGUES. FOR MORE DETAILS ON THIS PUBLICATION SEE THE ADVERT NEAR THE FRONT OF THIS DIRECTORY.

PROGRAMME DETAILS:
Pages: 28 Price: 60p
Editor: M Richardson
(0492 878953)

DROYLSDEN

Droylsden concede the first goal, to Tony Rigby, during their defeat at Barrow. Photo - Ged Rule.

Chairman: David Pace
Secretary: Gordon Hargreaves, 44 Morar Road, Dukinfield SK16 4BB (061 344 2075).
Manager: Stan Allan   **Asst Manager:** Jim Coffey.
Ground: The Butchers Arms Ground, Market Street, Droylsden, Manchester (061 370 1426).
Directions: 4 miles east of Manchester via A662 Ashton New Road, behind Butchers Arms Hotel.
Capacity: 3,500   **Cover:** 2,000   **Seats:** 500   **Shop:** Yes   **Metal Badges:** Yes.
Colours: All red   **Change colours:** All yellow
Previous Leagues: Manchester/ Lancs Com 36-39 50-68/ Cheshire County 39-50 68-82/ NW Counties 82-87.
Midweek home matchday: Tuesday   **Reserve Team:** None.
Sponsors: Alpha Court Windows.
Record Attendance: 4,250 v Grimsby, FA Cup 1st rd 1976.
Best F.A. Cup season: 2nd Rd 78-79.
League clubs defeated in F.A. Cup: Rochdale 78-79.
Record transfer fees received: £11,000 for Tony Naylor (Crewe).
Record win: 13-2 v Lucas Sports Club.
Players progressing to Football League: Albert Butterworth & F Letchford (Blackpool 1931), William Davies & Maurice Randall (Crewe 1947), William Mellor (Accrington 1950), Geoff Tonge (Bury 1960), David Campbell (WBA 1962), Kevin Randall (Bury 1965), Peter Litchfield (Preston 1979), Tony Naylor (Crewe 1990).
Clubhouse: Pub hours except atchdays. Pool and darts.
Club Record Scorer: E Gillibrand 78 (1931-32)
92-93 Captain: John Burns
92-93 P.o.Y.: C Booth
92-93 Top scorer: Steve Bunter.
Local Newspapers: Droysden Reporter (061 303 1910), Advertiser.
Local Radio Stations: BBC Manchester.
Honours: Northern Prem Lg Div 1 R-up 89-90 (Div 1 Cup 87-88), NW Counties Lg Div 2 86-87, Cheshire County Lg R-up 39-40 45-46 (Lg Cup 77-78 (R-up 76-77)), Lancs Comb Div 2 R-up 55-56 58-59 62-63, Manchester Lg 30-31 32-33 (Lg Cup 23-24 33-34), Manchester Premier Cup 80-81 (R-up 83-84 90-91), Manchester Senior Cup 72-73 75-76 78-79 (R-up 72-73 75-76 78-79), Manchester Intermediate Cup 59-60 64-65 69-70, Manchester Challenge Shield 46-47.

PROGRAMME DETAILS:
Pages: 20 Price: 50p
Editor: John Schofield

Formed: 1903

EMLEY

Emley F.C. 1992-93. Back Row (L/R): Daryl Brook (Coach), Charlie Bradshaw, Martin Baker, Richard Crossley, Robert Wraight, Neil Griffiths, Simon Jones, Andrew Kettlewell, Stephen Dyson (Coach), Stephen Codd (Player-Manager). Front: Peter Matthews (Chairman), Richard Hopley, Nicky Bramald, Jamie Shipman, Philip Hutchinson, Lee Burrows, Dean Pritchard. Photo courtesy of the Huddersfield Daily Examiner.

Chairman: Peter Matthews　　**Vice Chairman:** Roy Shirley　　**President:** Peter Maude
Secretary: Gordon Adamson, 219 Rowley Lane, Lepton, Huddersfield HD8 0EH (0484 602720).
Manager: Steve Codd　　**Coach:** Daryl Brook/ Stephen Dyson.
Physio: Daryl Brook.
Ground: Emley Welfare Sports Ground, Emley, Huddersfield (0924 848398).
Directions: Follow Huddersfield signs from M1 junction 38, left onto A636 at r'bout, then right after about three quarters of a mile for Emley. From M62 jct 23 to Huddersfield ring-road, follow Wakefield signs for 5 miles, thru Lepton, past White Horse pub on left and turn right at top of next hill - just under 3 miles to Emley. Floodlights unmissable in small village. Seven miles from Huddersfield (BR) station - buses to Emley Cross.
Capacity: 3,000　　**Cover:** 800　　**Seats:** 250　　**Floodlights:** Yes　　**Metal Badges:** Yes.
Club Shop: Yes. On ground, stocks all Emley souvenirs and sportswear, programmes and magazines. Contact Mrs Linda Sykes through club number.
Colours: Sky/maroon/sky　　**Change colours:** All white.
Sponsors: Perrys Rover Dealers, Huddersfield.
Previous Leagues: Huddersfield/ Yorkshire 69-82/ Northern Counties East 82-89.
Midweek home matchday: Monday　　**Reserve Team's League:** Northern Co's Reserve Div.
Record Attendance: 5,134 v Barking, FA Amateur Cup Third Round Proper 1/2/69. *9,035 v Bolton Wanderers, FA Cup First Round Proper 17/11/92; matched staged at Huddersfield Town FC.*
Best F.A. Cup season: First Round Proper 91-92 (lost 0-3 at home to Bolton Wanderers).
Record Fees Received: £10,000 for John Francis (Sheffield United, 1988).
Players progressing to Football League: Alan Sweeney (Hartlepool United 1979), Graham Cooper (Huddersfield Town 1984), John Francis (Sheffield United 1988), Shaun Smith (Crewe Alexandra 1992).
Clubhouse: (0924 848398). Members' social club open five nights a week and Saturday & Sunday. Bingo, discos, occasional caberet.
Club Record Goalscorer: Mick Pamment 305
Club Record Appearances: Ray Dennis 711.
92-93 Captain: Martin Baker
92-93 P.o.Y.: Robert Wraight.
92-93 Top scorer: Bob Clarke.
Local Newspapers: Huddersfield Examiner (0484 430000), Huddersfield & District Chronicle.
Local Radio Stations: Radio Leeds, Radio Sheffield.
Honours: FA Vase R-up 87-88 (SF 86-87), FA Trophy 4th Rd 90-91, FA Amateur Cup 3rd Rd replay 69-70, Northern Premier Lg Div 1 R-up 90-91, Northern Counties East Lg(2) 87-89 (R-up 85-86, Reserve Div 82-83 83-84 84-85 87-88, Reserve Div Cup 82-83 85-86), Yorkshire Lg 75-76 77-78 79-80 81-82 (R-up(5) 72-74 76-77 78-79 80-81, Lg Cup 69-70 78-79 81-82, Div 2 R-up 69-70, Reserve Div 79-80 81-82, Reserve Div Cup 81-82), Sheffield & Hallamshire Senior Cup 75-76 79-80 80-81 83-84 88-89 90-91 91-92, Huddersfield Challenge Cup 82-83 83-84 85-86, Huddersfield Lg(4) 65-69.

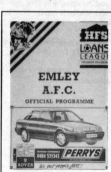

Midfield action from Fleetwood Town's F.A. Cup win at Accrington Stanley two years ago.

Chairman: Paul Murfin.
Secretary: T.B.A.
Manager: Steven Edwards   **Asst Manger:** T.B.A.
Commercial Manager: Anne Bibby.
Ground: Highbury Stadium, Park Avenue, Fleetwood, Lancs (0253 856096).
Directions: M55 jct 3, A585 to Fleetwood, just before town centre there is a fire station on left where road crosses tram tracks - turn back past fire station and then turn right - ground straight ahead on Park Avenue. Nearest rail station is seven miles distant at Poulton-le-Fyle. Tram stop - Nansen Rd, 400yds.
Capacity: 9,500   **Cover:** 700   **Seats:** 200   **Floodlights:** Yes   **Club Shop:** Yes.
Colours: Red & white/white/red   **Change colours:** White/black/black.
Previous Leagues: Cheshire County 78-82/ North West Counties 82-87.
Previous Grounds: None *(predecessors Fleetwood F.C. played at Euston Ground 1937-38).*
Midweek home matchday: Wednesday   **Reserve Team:** None.
Sponsors: Archbell Greenwood Structural Engineers.
Record Attendance: 3,000 v Exmouth Town, F.A. Vase Semi Final 2nd Leg 84-85. *Ground Record: 6,000 - Fleetwood F.C. v Rochdale, F.A. Cup First Round Proper 65-66.*
Best F.A. Cup season: First Rd Proper 80-81 (0-4 at Blackpool), 90-91 (1-4 at Atherstone United).
League clubs defeated in F.A. Cup: None.
Record Fees - Paid: £5,000 for Rob Wakenshaw (Southport).
         Received: £25,000 for Steve Macauley (Crewe Alexandra).
Players progressing to Football League: Paul Sanderson (Manchester City), Phil Clarkson & Steve Macauley (Crewe Alexandra 1991), Andy Lyons (Crewe Alexandra 1992). *Frank Swift (Manchester City) from predecessors Fleetwood F.C.*
Clubhouse: Open normal licensing hours.
Club Record Scorer: David Barnes 101.
Club Record Appearances: Stuart Robinson 388.
92-93 Captain:
92-93 Top scorer:
Local Press: West Lancashire Evening Gazette, Fleetwood Weekly News.
Local Radio Stations: Radio Lancashire, Red Rose Radio.
Honours: F.A. Vase R-up 84-85, Northern Premier Lg Div 1 87-88 (Presidents Cup 89-90 (R-up 90-91), Lg Cup R-up 88-89), North West Counties Lg Div 2 83-84, F.A. Trophy 1st Rd 88-89 90-91.

PROGRAMME DETAILS:
Pages: 24 **Price:** 50p
Editor: S Presnail

FRICKLEY ATHLETIC

The Blues

Gerry Hatto torments the Chorley defence as Frickley Athletic win 2-1 at Duke Street on 2nd January to go top of the Premier Division. Photo - Colin Stevens.

Chairman: Mike Twiby   **President:** M High.
Secretary: Bob Bates, 2 Lincoln Crescent, South Elmsall, Pontefract WF9 2TJ (0977 644575).
Manager: Ronnie Glavin   **Physio:** T McCroakam   **Coach:** A Miller.
Financial Secretary: D Fisher.
Ground: Westfield Lane, South Elmsall, Pontefract (0977 642460/644453).
Directions: Follow signs for South Elmsall from A1 and A638. Left at Superdrug warehouse, right at T junction and immediately left up Westfield Lane (signposted Frickley Colliery). Left into Oxford Road (opposite Westfield Hotel) - ground at bottom on right. Two miles from South Elmsall (BR).
Capacity: 6,000   **Cover:** 2,500   **Seats:** 800   **Floodlights:** Yes   **Club Shop:** Yes.
Colours: All blue   **Change colours:** Yellow & black.
Previous Leagues: Sheffield/ Yorkshire 22-24/ Midland Counties 24-33 34-60 70-76/ Cheshire County 60-70/ Northern Premier 76-80/ GMV Conference (Alliance Premier) 80-87.
Midweek home matchday: Tuesday   **Sponsors:** Ramset Construction.
Record Attendance: 6,500 v Rotherham United, F.A. Cup First Round 1971.
Previous Name: Frickley Colliery Athletic.
Best F.A. Cup season: 3rd Rd 1985-86 (lost 1-3 at home to Rotherham). 2nd Rd 84-85 (0-1 at Darlington). 1st Rd 36-37 57-58 63-64 71-72 73-74 83-84 86-87 88-89.
League clubs defeated in F.A. Cup: Hartlepool United 85-86.
Record Fees - Paid: £1,800
                Received: £12,500 for Paul Shirtliff (Boston Utd).
Players progressing to Football League: Dennis Smith & Jack Brownsword (Hull 1946), Stan Scrimshaw (Halifax 1947), William Callaghan (Aldershot 1949), Leo Dickens 1950), John Ashley & Graham Caulfield (York 1950 & 67), Ron Barritt (Leeds 1951), John Pickup (Bradford PA 1955), Tom Hymers & Arthur Ashmore & Stewart Gray (Doncaster 1958 & 66 & 78), Colin Roberts (Bradford City 1959), Derek Downing (Middlesbrough 1965), Graham Reed & Russell Wilcox (Northampton 1985 & 86), Will Foley (Swansea 1986), Gary Brook (Newport 1987).
Clubhouse: Harlequin Club outside ground. TV, pool, other facilities.
Club Record Scorer: K Whiteley
Local Newspapers: S Yorks Times (0977 642214), Hemsworth & S Elmsall Express (0977 640107).
Local Radio Stations: Radio Sheffield, Radio Hallam, Radio Leeds.
Honours: Alliance Premier Lg R-up 85-86, Midland Counties Lg R-up 72-73 (Lg Cup 75-76), Yorkshire Lg R-up 23-24, Sheffield & Hallamshire Senior Cup 27-28 56-57 60-61 62-63 66-67 78-79 85-86 87-88 89-90, Sheffield Association Lg 20-21 (R-up 11-12), FA Trophy 4th Rd 84-85.

PROGRAMME DETAILS:
Pages: 40 Price: T.B.A.
Editor: D Fisher

The Gainsborough Trinity's 'Northolme' ground.

Chairman: John Davis **Vice Chairman:** P F C Lobley **President:** Ken Marsden
Secretary: Frank Nicholson, 9 North Street, Morton, Gainsborough, Lincs DN21 3AS (0427 615239).
Manager: Gary Simpson. **Asst Manager:** P Barker **Coach:** C Gaffney.
Physio: E Beaumont **Commercial Manager:** B Martin.
Ground: The Northolme, North Street, Gainsborough, Lincs (0427 613295).
Directions: Ground situated in town centre, 250 yds from the Post Office and magistrates court. Two miles from Lea Road (BR).
Capacity: 7,500 **Cover:** 5,000 **Seats:** 238 **Floodlights:** Yes **Club Shop:** Yes.
Colours: Royal blue (white trim)/white/blue & white **Change colours:** White/black/black.
Previous Leagues: Mids Counties 1889-96 1912-60 61-68/ Football League 1896-1912/ Central Alliance 60-61.
Club Sponsors: National Power West Burton.
Midweek home matchday: Tuesday **Record Gate:** 9,760 v Scunthorpe Utd, Midland Lge 1948.
Best F.A. Cup season: 3rd Rd 1886-87. 1st Rd on 33 occasions; 1885-86 97-98 1905-14 27-34 35-36 37-39 45-47 48-49 50-54 59-60 66-67 83-84.
League clubs defeated in F.A. Cup: Rotherham United 1894-95/ Stockport County 1913-14/ Crewe 28-29 31-32/ Port Vale 37-38/ Gateshead 38-39/ Mansfield Town 45-46.
Record Fees - Paid: £3,000 for Stuart Lowe (Buxton 89-90)
Received: £20,000 for Tony James.
Record win: 7-1 v Whitley Bay **Record defeat:** 2-7 v Hyde United.
Players progressing to Football League: A Morton & S Foxall & J Cockcroft (West Ham), Arthur Hall (Chesterfield 1947), Jack Haigh (Liverpool 1949), Norman Curtis (Sheffield Wednesday 1950), Des Thompson & Steve Richards (York 1951 & 86), Terry Farmer & Barry Webster & John Woodall (Rotherham 1952 & 56 & 74), Maurice Robinson & Roy Brown (Doncaster 1952 & 53), John Burnett & Robert Ham (Grimsby 1958 & 64), Robert Pashley & Mike Woldworth (Scunthorpe 1959 & 76), Simon Jones (Rochdale 1963), William Purton (Bradford City 1975), Keith Ripley (Huddersfield 1978), Stewart Evans (Sheffield United 1980), Tony James & Ian Bowling & John Scofield (Lincoln 1988), David Redfearn (Stockport).
Clubhouse: Executive 'Club on the Park' (0427 615625) open nightly and Saturday matchday lunctimes. Full license and restaurant facilities.
Club Record Scorer: Monty Brown.
Club Record Appearances: Monty Brown.
Local Newspapers: Gainsborough News, Lincolnshire Echo.
Local Radio Stations: BBC Radio Lincs.
92-93 Captain: R Losan.
92-93 Top Scorer: C Bishop 12.
92-93 P.o.Y.: D Fox.
Hons: Northern Premier Lg Cup 81-82 (R-up 71-72), Midland Co's Lg 1890-91 1927-28 48-49 66-67 (R-up 1891-92 95-96 1913-14 28-29), Lincs Snr Cup(15) 1889-90 92-93 94-95 97-98 1903-05 06-07 10-11 46-49 50-51 57-59 63-64, FA Tphy 2nd Rd 2nd rep. 86-87.

PROGRAMME DETAILS:
Pages: 24 **Price:** 50p
Editor: K Croft
(0427 615625)

HORWICH R.M.I.

Horwich R.M.I.'s ground viewed front its North East corner. Photo - C C G Blackwell.

Chairman: Garry Culshaw   **President:** G H Fisher, Esq.
Secretary: Brian Hart, 'Meadow View', 7 Rectory Gdns, Daisy Hill, Westhoughton, Bolton BL5 2RG (0942 818669).
Manager: Mick Holgate   **Asst Manager:** T.B.A.   **Coach:** T.B.A.
Press Officer: P O'Berg
Ground: Grundy Hill, Ramsbottom Road, Horwich, Bolton BL6 5NH (0204 696908).
Directions: M61 junction 6, follow Horwich signs at r-about, bear left then right, just before zebra crossing, into Victoria Road, ground alongside road on left. 3 miles from Blackrod (BR). Buses - 126 from Preston, 517 from Wigan, 575 from Bolton.
Capacity: 5,000   **Cover:** 3 sides   **Seats:** 500   **Floodlights:** Yes   **Club Shop:** Yes
Colours: Blue & white stripes/blue/blue
Change colours: Maroon & white/maroon/maroon.
Sponsors: Dunhall Financial Services, Horwich.
Previous Leagues: Lancs Alliance 1891-97/ Lancs 1897-1900/ Lancs Combination 17-18 19-39 46-68/ Cheshire County 68-82/ North West Counties 82-83.
Midweek home matchday: Wednesday
Reserve Team's League: Northern Football Combination.
Record Attendance: 4,500.
Best F.A. Cup season: 1st Rd 28-29 82-83.
League clubs defeated in F.A. Cup: None.
Record Fee Received: £2,000 for Tony Caldwell (Bolton).
Players progressing to Football League: Harold Lea & David Holland & Jim Cunliffe (Stockport 1958 & 59 & 60), Frank Wignall (Everton 1958), Gary Cooper (Rochdale 1973), Tony Caldwell (Bolton 1983), Raymond Redshaw (Wigan 1984), Tony Ellis (Oldham 1986).
Clubhouse: Open every evening.
Local Newspapers: Bolton Evening News (Bolton 22345).
Local Radio Stations: Radio Lancs, Red Rose Radio.
Honours: FA Trophy QF 90-91, Premier Inter League (GMAC) Cup 87-88, Cheshire County Lg 78-79 (Challenge Shield 78-79), Lancs Combination 57-58 (R-up 29-30 55-56 66-67), Lg Cup 28-29 53-54 56-57 65-66, Div 2 R-up 48-49 50-51), West Lancs Lg 10-11 11-12, Lancs Junior Cup 24-25 29-30 (R-up 53-54 57-58 62-63 82-83), Lancs Floodlit Trophy 84-85 (R-up 83-84), Lancs FA Cup 84-85.

PROGRAMME DETAILS:
Pages: 28 **Price:** 50p
Editor: Garry Culshaw

Formed: 1919

HYDE UNITED

The Tigers

Hyde United 1992-93. Back Row (L/R): Stuart Taylor, Andy Graham, David Nolan, John O'Neill, Mike Housley, John McGrath, Alan Nicholas, Brendan Hudson, Paul Daughtrey. Front: Gary Henshaw, Russ Hooton, Ian Callaghan, Darren Thornton, Phil Chadwick. Mascot: Natalie Slater.

Chairman: S C Hartley   **Vice Chairman:** A Slater   **President:** D Gale.
Secretary: Alan Slater, 83 King Edward Road, Hyde, Cheshire SK14 5JJ (061 368 3687).
Manager: Ged Coyne   **Asst Manager:** Tommy Martin
Physio: C I Wych.   **Coach:** Tony Sutton/Jimmy Walker
Press Officer: Secretary   **Commercial Manager:** TBA
Ground: Tameside Stadium, Ewen Fields, Walker Lane, Hyde SK14 5PL (061 368 1031).
Directions: On entering Hyde follow signs for Tameside Leisure Park - in Walker Lane take second car park entrance near Leisure Pool and follow road around to the stadium. Quarter of a mile from Newton (BR).
Capacity: 4,000   **Cover:** 2,000   **Seats:** 400   **Floodlights:** Yes   **Metal Badges:** Yes
Colours: Red/white/black   **Change colours:** Sky/blue/blue.
Club Shop: Yes. Replica shirts, scarves, sports shirts, baseball caps, bronx hats, badges. Contact either Alan Slater (061 368 3687) or Brian Slater (061 303 8891).
Previous Leagues: Lancashire & Cheshire 19-21/ Manchester 21-30/ Cheshire County 30-68 70-82/ Northern Premier 68-70. *Predecessors, Hyde FC: Lancs Lg 1889-90/ Lancs Combination 1906-17.*
Midweek home matchday: Monday   **Record Attendance:** 9,500 v Nelson, FA Cup 1952.
Best F.A. Cup season: 1st Rd 54-55 (v Workington), 83-84 (v Burnley). *Hyde FC: 1st Rd 1887-88.*
Record Fee Paid: £8,000 for Jim McCluskie (Mossley, 1989).
Record Fee Received: £17,500 for Simon Rudge (Runcorn, 1989).
Record Defeat: (as Hyde F.C.) 0-26 v Preston North End, F.A. Cup.
Players progressing to Football League: Charles McClelland & John Webber & Patrick Barry (B'burn 1946 & 47 & 48), L Battrick (Manc. City 1968), Jack Hilton (Wrexham 1950), David Teece (Hull 1952), Ray Calderbank & William Bell & Neil Colbourne (R'dale 1953 & 74 & 80), Jeff Johnson (Stockport 1976), David Constantine & Donald Graham (Bury 1979), George Oghani (Bolton 1983), Kevin Glendon (Burnley 1983), Peter Coyne (Swindon 1984).
Club Sponsors: Tameside Bottled Gas.
Clubhouse: (061 368 1621). Open most nights, full facilities, 150 seats.   **Stewards:** Lil & Doug.
Club Record Scorer: P O'Brien 247   **Club Record Appearances:** S Johnson 623.
92-93 Captain: R Hooton   **92-93 Top scorer:** P Chadwick/ A Graham, both 20.
92-93 Players' P.O.Y.: P Chadwick   **92-93 Supporters' P.O.Y.:** A Graham.
Local Newspapers (+Tel.Nos.): North Cheshire Herald & Hyde Reporter (061 368 3595).
Local Radio Stations: GMR, Piccadilly.
Honours: FA Trophy SF 88-89, Premier Inter-Lge Cup R-up(2) 88-90, Northern Premier Lg R-up(2) 87-89 (Lg Cup 85-86 88-89 (R-up 83-84), Challenge Shield R-up 86-87 90-91), Cheshire County Lg(3) 54-56 81-82 (Lg Cup 33-34 52-53 54-55 72-73 81-82, Lg Challenge Shield(2) 80-82 Manchester Lg(5) 20-23 28-29 29-30 (Lg (Gilgryst) Cup(4) 27-29 49-50 70-71), Cheshire Senior Cup 45-46 62-63 69-70 80-81 89-90, Manchester Senior Cup 74-75 (Int Cup 55-56 56-57(jt), Junior Cup 21-22 68-69), Lancs & Cheshire Floodlit Cup(2) 54-56, Ashton Challenge Cup(6) 30-34 39-40 47-48, Hyde Challenge Cup(2) 27-29, Reporter Cup(3) 72-74 75-76, Gavin Nicholson Mem Trophy 79-80, Lancs Floodlit Trophy(2) 86-88, Edward Case Cup(4) 56-8 59-60 80-81.

SCORELINE
Hyde United
Football Club

PROGRAMME DETAILS:
Pages: 36 Price: 70p
Editor: R Stanley

KNOWSLEY UNITED

Knowsley United F.C. - Northern Premier League Division One runners-up 1992-93. Back Row (L/R): Keith Vincent, Ray Birch, Tommy King, Andy Johnston, Steve Jackson, Dave Pennell, Dave Siddell. Front: Dave O'Brien, Peter Edwards, Peter Orr, Joe Barton (Captain), Brian Kilsman, Archie Lloyd. Photo - James Wright.

Chairman: Mr P G Orr. **President:** The Mayor of Knowsley.
Secretary J Williams, 3 Brownmoor Park, Crosby, Liverpool L23 0TL (051 928 8359).
Manager: P J Orr **Coach:** R Willingham **Physio:** L Blasberry
Press Off.: Sec. + Ken O'Brien **Commercial Manager:** D Johnstone.
Ground: Alt Park, Endmoor Road, Huyton, Merseyside L36 3LV (051 480 2529).
Directions: Come off M62 at junction 6 onto M57. Leave at junction 2 (Prescot), onto Liverpool Rd at r'bout, 3rd right at 3rd set of lights into Seth Powell Way. From Jct 3 (Huyton), go straight across r-about onto Huyton link road (Seth Powell Way) and turn right at lights. From Liverpool; East Prescot Rd-Liverpool Rd (6 miles) - turn left into Seth Powell Way. Buses 10, 10a, 8, 210 to Page Moss. Nearest station is Huyton 2 miles away - bus from station to Page Moss.
Capacity: 9,000 **Cover:** 3,500 **Seats:** 350 **Floodlights:** Yes **Club Shop:** Due
Colours: Red & black hoops. **Change colours:** Yellow & black hoops.
Sponsors: Rogersons (Builders).
Previous Name: Kirkby Town (pre-1988) **Previous Leagues:** North West Counties 84-91.
Previous Grounds: Simonswood Lane, Kirkby 84-86/ Kirkby Sports Centre 86-88.
Midweek matchday: Tuesday **Reserve Team's League:** Liverpool Co. Comb.
Women's Team League: F.A. National League, Premier Division.
Record Attendance: 900 v Everton, Liverpool Senior Cup, 1984.
Best F.A. Cup season: 4th Qualifying Round 91-92 (lost 0-1 at Telford United).
Record win: 10-1 v Flixton **Record defeat:** 1-7 v Colwyn Bay.
Record Fee Paid Received: Undisclosed for Mike Marsh (Liverpool).
Players progressing to Football League: Phil Daily (Wigan), Mike Marsh (Liverpool), Rodney McDonald (Walsall), Steve Farrelly (Chester City).
Clubhouse: Lounge, 2 Function Suites, Sponsors Box, Directors Room.
Clubhouse open normal licensing hours - filled rolls available. Refreshment bar in ground sells pies, rolls, chips, tea, coffee oxo etc.
Club Record Goalscorer: Jimmy Bell, 50.
92-93 Captain: Joe Barton.
92-93 P.O.Y.: Dave O'Brien.
92-93 Top scorer: Dave Siddell, 27.
Local Press: Liverpool Daily Post/Liverpool Echo (051 227 2000), Knowsley Challenger (051 548 0710).
Local Radio Stations: Radio Merseyside (051 708 5500), Radio City.
Hons: FA Vase 5th Rd 90-91 91-92, Northern Premier Lg Div 1 R-up 92-93, North West Counties Lg 90-91 (R-up 88-89 89-90, Div 2 85-86, Div 3 84-85, Raab Karcher Cup 89-90, Champions v Cup Winners Trophy 89-90).

Knowsley United F.C.

Welcome to Alt Park

MAIN SPONSOR
Rogersons

PROGRAMME DETAILS:
Pages: 32 **Price:** 70p
Editor: Dave Cookson
(0772 749 768)

LEEK TOWN

Frenetic action in the Leek Town goalmouth as the home side defend against Runcorn. Photo - Rob Ruddock.

Chairman: Godrey Heath   **President:** T.B.A.
Secretary: Michael Rowley, 62 London Rd, Chesterton, Newcastle, Staffs ST5 7DY (0782 562890).
Manager: Neil Baker   **Asst Manager:** Trevor Mullet
Coach: Steve Norris   **Commercial Manager:** Neil Biddulph
Physio: Jim Robinson/ Martin Parr.   **Press Officer:** Mike Cope
Ground: Harrison Park, Macclesfield Road, Leek ST13 8LD (09538 399278. Fax 0538 399826).
Directions: Opposite chemical works on A53 Macclesfield road half a mile north west of Leek.
Capacity: 3,500   **Cover:** 3,000   **Seats:** 400   **Floodlights:** Yes   **Metal Badges:** Yes
Club Shop: Yes - contact manager Neil Biddulph.
Colours: Blue/white/blue   **Change colours:** Red/yellow/red   **Sponsors:** TBA.
Previous Leagues: Staffs County/ Manchester 51-54 57-73/ West Mids (B'ham) 54-56/ Cheshire County 73-82/ North West Counties 82-87.
Previous Names: Abbey Green Rovers/ Leek Lowe Hamil.
Midweek home matchday: Tuesday
Record Attendance: 3,512 v Macclesfield Town, F.A. Cup Second Qualifying Round 73-74.
Best F.A. Cup season: 2nd Rd replay 90-91 (lost 0-4 at Chester after 1-1 draw).
League clubs defeated in F.A. Cup: Scarborough 90-91.
Record Fees - Paid: £2,000 for Simon Snow (Sutton Town)
                Received: £2,500 Tony Griffiths (Telford).
Players progressing to Football League: Geoff Crosby (Stockport 1952), Bill Summerscales & Mark Bright & Martyn Smith (Port Vale 1970 & 81 & 84), Paul Edwards (Crewe 1989).
Clubhouse: (0538 383734). Open nightly + weekend lunchtimes.
Club Record Goalscorer: Alan Vickers
Club Record Appearances: Gary Pearce 447.
Local Newspapers: Leek Post & Times (0538 399599), Evening Sentinel (0782 289800).
Local Radio Stations: Radio Stoke, Signal Radio.
Newsline: 0898 664 353.
Honours: F.A. Trophy R-up 89-90 (QF 85-86), Northern Premier Lg Div 1 89-90 (Div 1 Cup R-up 88-89, Lg Shield 90-91), North West Co's Lg Cup 84-85 (Charity Shield 84-85), Cheshire County 74-75 (Challenge Shield 74-75), Manchester Lg 51-52 71-72 72-73 (Lg Cup 72-73), Staffs Snr Cup R-up 54-55 81-82 (Jnr Cup 51-52 70-71 (R-up 47-48 48-49 49-50)), Staffs Co. Lg 50-51 69-70 70-71 73-74 (R-up 47-48 49-50, Lg Cup 70-71 73-74), Leek Post Charity Shield 46-47, Leek Cup 47-48 52-53 70-71 71-72 (R-up 46-47), May Bank Cup 47-48 50-51 71-72, Hanley Cup 48-49 70-71 (R-up 49-5), Mid Cheshire Lg Div 2 87-88 (Div 2 Cup 87-88).

PROGRAMME DETAILS:
Pages: 36 Price: 70p
Editor: Mike Cope

MARINE

The Marine defence suffers at the hands of Emley's Graham Cooper (centre). The Mariners were sunk 1-4 in this Premier Division fixture in Yorkshire on 17th October. Photo - Barry Lockwood.

Chairman: Tom Culshaw **President:** D Hargreaves.
Secretary: John Wildman, 4 Ashbourne Avenue, Blundellsands, Liverpool L23 8TX (051 924 5248).
Manager: Roly Howard **Asst Manager/Coach:** Roger Patience
Physio: John Bradshaw **Press Officer:** David Wotherspoon
Ground: Rossett Park, College Road, Crosby, Liverpool (051 924 1743).
Directions: College Road is off main Liverpool-Southport road (A565) in Crosby. Ground ten minutes walk from Crosby & Blundell Sands (Mersey Rail). Bus No. 92.
Capacity: 2,500 **Cover:** 1,900 **Seats:** 400 **Floodlights:** Yes **Metal Badges:** Yes.
Club Shop: Yes, selling replica kit, baseball caps, polo shirts, scarves, mugs, pens/pencils, bookmarks, car stickers, combs, tax disc holders.
Colours: White/black/black **Change:** Yellow/green/green
Sponsors: Boddingtons & Higsons.
Previous Leagues: Liverpool Zingari/ Liverpool County Combination/ Lancs Combination 35-39 46-69/ Cheshire County 69-79.
Previous Name: Waterloo Melville 1894-1903
Previous Ground: Waterloo Park 1894-1903.
Midweek home matchday: Tuesday **Record Gate:** 4,000 v Nigeria, Friendly 1949.
Best FA Cup year: 3rd Rd 92-93 (lost 1-3 at Crewe Alexandra). Also 2nd Rd rep. (v Hartlepool) 75-76. Also 1st Rd 32-33 45-46 46-47 47-48 74-75 89-90.
League clubs defeated in F.A. Cup: Barnsley 75-76, Halifax Town 92-93.
Record Fee Received: £12,250 for Ian Nolan (Tranmere Rovers, 1991).
Players progressing to Football League: James Veacock & Anthony Sharrock & Steve Brooks (Southport 1947 & 73 & 77), Sam Parker (Accrington 1948), Harry Conner (Stoke 1953), Alf Jones (Leeds 1960), Gary Williams (Preston 1972), John Lacy (Fulham & Spurs), Paul Beesly (Sheffield Utd), Mark Kearney (Everton 1981), Alan Finlay (Shrewsbury 1981), Paul Cook (Norwich), Paul Edwards (Crewe & Coventry), Ian Nolan (Tranmere).
Clubhouse: Open daily. Concert Hall (250 seats). Members Lounge (100 seats). **Club Record Goalscorer:** Paul Meachin 200
Club Record Appearances: Peter Smith 952
92-93 Captain: Jon Gautrey
92-93 Top Scorer: Chris Camden 34, Brian Ross 33.
Local Newspapers: Crosby Herald, Liverpool Echo, Daily Post (051 227 2000).
Local Radio Stations: BBC, Radio Merseyside, Radio City.
Hons: FA Amtr Cup R-up 31-32 (SF 46-47), FA Trophy SF 83-84 91-92, Northern Prem Lg R-up 85-86 91-92 (Lg Cup 84-85 91-92 (R-up 80-81 85-86), Presidents Cup R-up 83-84 86-87), Cheshire Co. Lg 73-74 75-76 77-78 (R-up 72-73), Lancs Comb. R-up 46-47 (Lg Cup 46-47 63-64 68-69), Liverpool Comb. 27-28 30-31 33-34 34-35 (Lg Cup 30-31), Lancs Tphy 87-88 90-91, Lancs Jnr Cup 78-79, Lancs Amtr Cup 21-22 25-26 30-31 31-32 32-33, Liverpool Snr Cup 78-79 84-85 87-88 89-90, Liverpool Non-Lge Cup 68-69 75-76 76-77, Liverpool Chal. Cup 42-43 44-45 71-72.

PROGRAMME DETAILS:
Pages: 24 Price: 50p
Editor: David Wotherspoon

MATLOCK TOWN

Matlock Town goalkeeper Richard Harrison punches clear from under the nose of Morecambe forward Steve Holden. However, the Gladiators still crashed to a 0-6 home defeat on 27th March. Photo - Andrew Mollitt.

Chairman: Donald T Carr
Secretary: K F Brown, 'Barncroft', 1 Malvern Gardens, Matlock DE4 3JH (0629 584231).
Manager: Ron Reid   **Physio:** G Buckner
Press Officer: G M Tomlinson (0629 3763)
Commercial Manager: Mrs S Tomlinson.
Ground: Causeway Lane, Matlock, Derbyshire (0629 55362/583866).
Directions: On A615, 500 yds from town centre and Matlock (BR).
Capacity: 7,500   **Cover:** 2,000   **Seats:** 240   **Floodlights:** Yes   **Club Shop:** Yes
Colours: Royal blue/white/royal blue   **Change colours:** All yellow.
Sponsors: Zanussi/ Westons of Wirksworth.
Previous Ground: Hall Leys (last century).
Previous Leagues: Midland Counties 1894-96 1961-69/ Matlock & District/ Derbys Senior/ Central Alliance 24-25 47-61/ Central Combination 34-35/ Chesterfield & District 46-47.
Midweek home matchday: Tuesday
Record Attendance: 5,123 v Burton Albion, FA Trophy 1975.
Best F.A. Cup season: 3rd Rd 76-77. Also 1st Rd 1885-86 86-87 86-87 87-88 1959-60 74-75 75-76 89-90.
League clubs defeated in F.A. Cup: Mansfield Town 76-77.
Record Fees - Paid: £300 for Mick Chambers (Grantham)
           Received: £10,000 for Ian Helliwell (York).
Players progressing to Football League: Keith Haines (Leeds 1959), Wayne Biggins (Burnley 1984), Darren Bradshaw (Chesterfield 1987), Les McJannet (Scarborough 1987), Ian Helliwell (York 1987).
Clubhouse: Gladiators Social Club, on ground, open six nights per week.
Local Newspapers: Matlock Mercury, Derbyshire Times.
Local Radio Stations: Radio Derby.
Honours: FA Trophy 74-75, Northern Premier Lg R-up 83-84 (Lg Cup 77-78, Shield 78-79), Midland Counties Lg 61-62 68-69, Central Alliance (North) 59-60 60-61 (R-up 61-62 62-63, Div 1 Cup R-up 61-62, Div 2 59-60, Div 2 Cup 59-60 60-61), Derbyshire Senior Cup 74-75 76-77 77-78 80-81 83-84 84-85 91-92 (R-up 60-61 72-73 73-74 75-76 80-81 81-82 82-83 89-90), Derbyshire Divisional Cup (North) 61-62 (R-up 62-63), Evans Halshaw Floodlit Cup 88-89, Anglo-Italian Non-League Cup 1979.

PROGRAMME DETAILS:
Pages: 36 **Price:** 70p
Editor: D Phillips

MORECAMBE

Morecambe F.C. 1992-93, with the Northern League Presidents Cup, won the previous Spring. Back Row (L/R): R Danson, P Gibson, O Parillon, G Dullagan, M Allison, P Byrom, P Tomlinson, P Borrowdale, D Edge. Front: R Ventry, A Russell, I Cain, P Lodge (Asst Manager), B Griffiths (Manager), I Brown, J McMahon, S Horrocks.

Chairman: Eddie Weldrake **Vice Chairman:** Fred O'Brien.
Secretary: Dermot Cooke, 40 Empress Str., Accrington, Lancs BB5 1SG (0254 386040).
Manager: Bryan Griffiths **Asst Mgr:** John Davidson **Physio:** David Edge
Press Officer: Neil Marsden (0524 833358).
Chief Executive: Niegel Webster.
Ground: Christie Park, Lancaster Road, Morecambe LA4 4TJ (0524 411797/832230).
Directions: Ground on main town centre road, on left arriving from Lancaster. Two miles from Morecambe Promenade (BR).
Capacity: 3,500 **Seats:** 1,000 **Floodlights:** Yes **Club Shop:** Yes **Metal Badges:** Yes
Colours: Red & black stripes/white/black & red
Change colours: White (blue collars)/black/white
Newsline: 0898 446 826. **Sponsors:** Asics.
Previous Ground: Woodhill Lane 1920. **Previous Leagues:** Lancs Combination 20-68.
Midweek home matchday: Tuesday **Record Gate:** 9,383 v Weymouth, FA Cup 3rd Rd 13/1/62.
Best FA Cup year: 3rd Rd 61-62. 1st Rd(13) 36-37 56-57 58-59 61-63 66-67 68-69 74-77 78-80 85-86 91-92.
League clubs defeated in F.A. Cup: Chester 61-62.
Record Fees - Paid: £7,500 to Fleetwood for Ian Cain, 1988
Received: £6,000 from Colne Dynamoes for Barrie Stimpson.
Players progressing to Football League: Fred Blondel & Malcolm Darling (Bury 1946 & 78), Herbert Harrison (Accrington 1947), Gordon Milne (Preston 1956), Ray Charnley (Blackpool 1957), Geoff Slack (Stockport 1958), Ron Mitchell (Leeds 1958), Derek Armstrong (Carlisle 1961), Alan Taylor (Rochdale 1973), John Coates (Southport via Burscough & Skelmersdale 1975), Keith Galley (Southport 1975), Brian Thompson (West Ham 1977), David Eyres (Blackpool), Kenny Lowe (Barnet via Barrow), Steve Gardner (Bradford City), Dave Lancaster (Chesterfield).
Clubhouse: The Shrimps Club. Open every evening.
Club Record Scorer: Keith Borrowdale 289
Club Record Appearances: Steve Done 579.
92-93 Captain: Andy Grimshaw
92-93 P.o.Y.: John Coleman
92-93 Top scorer: John Coleman, 45.
Local Newspapers: Morecambe Visitor (0524 414531).
Local Radio: Radio Lancs, Red Rose Radio.
Hons: F.A. Trophy 73-74, Northern Premier Lg Presidents Cup 91-92, Lancs Combination(5) 24-25 61-63 66-68 (R-up 25-26, Lg Cup 26-27 45-46 64-65 66-68), Lancs Jnr Cup (now ATS Tphy)(7) 25-27 61-63 68-69 85-87, Lancs Snr Cup 67-68, Lancs Lg Div 2 83-84.

PROGRAMME DETAILS:
Pages: 36 Price: 60p
Editor: P Oldrieve

WHITLEY BAY

The main stand at Whitley Bay's Hillheads Park ground. Photo - James Wright.

Chairman: G Wallace   **Vice Chairman:** J Gray   **President:** C E Fuller MBE
Secretary: Rob Harding, 22 Cambridge Avenue, Whitley Bay NE26 1BB (091 251 5179).
Manager: Bobby Graham   **Asst Manager:** P Dixon   **Coach:** S Black
Physio: Dave Ashton   **Press Officer:** P Dixon
Commercial Manager: W Dixon.
Ground: Hillheads Park, Hillheads Road, Whitley Bay, Tyne & Wear (091 2513680).
Directions: 1 mile walk from bus station - leave St Pauls Church southward, turn right at r-about, ground 3rd left at rear of ice rink. Whitley Bay or Monkseaton metro stations, both 1 mile.
Capacity: 4,500   **Cover:** 650   **Seats:** 450   **Floodlights:** Yes   **Metal Badges:** Yes
Club Shop: Yes, selling programmes, club scarves, baseball hats, bobble hats, badges, mugs, t-shirts, car stickers, ties, pens, key rings.
Colours: Blue & white stripes/blue/blue   **Change colours:** All yellow
Record Fee (Paid & Received): £500
Previous Leagues: Tyneside 09-10 Northern Alliance 50-55/ North Eastern 55-58/ Northern 58-88.
Previous Name: Whitley Bay Athletic 1950-58.
Midweek home matchday: Wednesday   **Record Gate:** 7,301 v Hendon, FA Amateur Cup 1965.
Record win: 12-0 v Shildon 1961   **Record defeat:** 1-8 v Bishop Auckland 1979.
Best F.A. Cup season: 3rd Rd 89-90 (lost 0-1 at Rochdale). 2nd Rd 90-91 (lost 0-1 at home to Barrow).
League clubs defeated in F.A. Cup: Scarborough, Preston North End 89-90.
Players progressing to Football League: William Dodd (Burnley 1956), William Younger (Nottm Forest 1957), Ron Brown (Blackpool 1965), John Ritchie (Port Vale 1965), John Brodie & Aiden McCaffery (Carlisle 1967 & 88), Mike Spelman (Wolves 1969), Tony Harrison (Southport 1977), Mark Miller (Gillingham 1981), Garry Haire (Bradford City 1983 Stewart Ferebee (Darlington 1987).
Clubhouse: Open every night 7-11pm & weekends 11am-3pm additionally. Bar and concert room. Lounge, darts, pool, 5-a-side courts.
Club Record Goalscorer: Billy Wright 307
Club Record Appearances: Bill Chater 640.
92-93 Captain: Tony Burgess
92-93 P.o.Y.: Andy Cowans
92-93 Top scorer: Ian Chandler 18.
Local Newspapers: The News, Guardian, Herald & Post.
Local Radio: Radio Newcastle, Metro.
Honours: FA Amateur Cup SF 65-66 68-69, FA Trophy 3rd Rd 86-87, Northern Premier Lg Div 1 90-91 (Div 1 Cup 88-89 90-91), Northern Lg 64-65 65-66 (R-up 59-60 66-67 68-69 69-70), Lg Cup 64-65 70-71 (R-up 67-68)), Northern Alliance 52-53 53-54 (Lg Cup 52-53 53-54), Northumberland Senior Cup 52-53 60-61 63-64 64-65 67-68 68-69 69-70 70-71 72-73 86-87 (R-up 53-54 54-55 55-56 65-66 76-77 85-86 90-91).

PROGRAMME DETAILS:
Pages: 24 **Price:** 60p
Editor: Len Bone

WINSFORD UNITED

Winsford United prior to the Cheshire Senior Cup final against Witton Albion at Wincham Park. A surprise 3-0 victory gave the Blues one of their astounding four cup successes. Photo - Keith Clayton.

Chairman: Chris Clarke   **President:** J Deans.
Secretary: Gerry Fuller, c/o Winsford Utd F.C. (see below) (0606 862008).
Manager: Graham Heathcote   **Asst Manager:** T.B.A.
Ground: Barton Stadium, Wharton, Winsford, Cheshire CW7 3EU (0606 593021).
Directions: From north; M6 junction 19, A556 towards Northwich to Davenham, then A5018 to Winsford. From south; M6 junction 18, A54 through Middlewich to Winsford. Ground quarter mile off main road in Wharton area of town. 1 mile from Winsford (BR).
Capacity: 6,000   **Cover:** 5,000   **Seats:** 250   **Floodlights:** Yes   **Club Shop:** No.
Colours: Royal/white/royal   **Change colours:** Maroon/white/white.
Sponsors: Dickson Motors Ltd, Winsford (Ford).
Previous Name: Over Wanderers (prior to 1914).
Previous Leagues: The Combination 02-04/ Cheshire County 19-40 47-82/ North West Counties 82-87.
Midweek home matchday: Wednesday   **Record Attendance:** 7,000 v Witton Albion 1947.
Best F.A. Cup season: 2nd Rd 1887-88. Also 1st Rd 1975-76 1991-92.
League clubs defeated in F.A. Cup: None.
Record Fees - Paid: Nil
         Received: £6,000 for Neville Southall from Bury.
Players progressing to Football League: William Foulkes (Chester 1948), Cliff Marsh (Leeds 1948), Bennett Nicol (Rochdale 1949), Eric Johnson (Coventry 1952), Walter Hughes (Liverpool 1954), Reg Lewis (Luton 1954), William Heggie (Accrington 1955), Joe Richardson (Birmingham City 1959), John Abbott (Crewe Alexandra 961), Robert Walters (Shrewsbury 1962), Phil Mullington (Rochdale 1978), Neville Southall (Bury 1980), Mark Came (Bolton Wanderers 1984), Dave Bamber (Blackpool), Bob Sutton (West Ham United), J Richardson (Sheffield United), Stanley Wood (West Bromwich Albion), R Pearce (Luton Town).
Clubhouse: Mon-Sat 8-11pm, Sun 8-10.30pm
Club Record Goalscorer: Graham Smith 66
Club Record Apps: Edward Harrop 400.
92-93 Captain: Cec Edey
92-93 P.o.Y.:
92-93 Top scorer: Bevon Blackwood.
Local Newspapers: Winsford Chronicle, Winsford Guardian.
Local Radio Stations: Signal, Piccadilly.
Honours: Northern Premier Lg R-up 92-93 (Div 1 R-up 91-92, Lg Cup 92-93, Presidents Cup 92-93, Div 1 Cup SF 89-90), Cheshire County Lg 20-21 76-77 (R-up 74-75 79-80, Lg Cup 49-50 55-56 59-60 76-77 78-79 79-80 80-81 (R-up 36-37 68-69 77-78)), Cheshire Senior Cup 58-59 79-80 92-93, Mid-Cheshire Snr Cup 90-91 92-93 (R-up 88-89), Cheshire Amateur Cup 00-01 02-03, Lancs Comb/Cheshire County Inter-Lg Cup 62-63, FA Trophy QF 77-78.

PROGRAMME DETAILS:
Pages: 20 Price: 50p
Editor: Andrew Maylor

Northern Premier League Premier Division Ten Year Records

	83/4	84/5	85/6	86/7	87/8	88/9	89/0	90/1	91/2	92/3
Accrington Stanley	–	–	–	–	–	–	–	–	8	6
Bangor City	–	10	13	2	7	4	10	18	20	–
Barrow	1	–	–	15	5	1	–	–	–	–
Bishop Auckland	–	–	–	–	–	–	11	7	11	10
Burton Albion	5	6	5	12	–	–	–	–	–	–
Buxton	21	22	19	13	16	15	16	8	5	14
Caernarfon Town	–	–	17	3	3	12	21	–	–	–
Chorley	14	19	20	9	1	–	–	14	21	18
Colne Dynamoes	–	–	–	–	–	–	1	–	–	–
Colwyn Bay	–	–	–	–	–	–	–	–	–	12
Droylsden	–	–	–	–	–	–	–	13	15	20
Emley	–	–	–	–	–	–	–	–	6	16
Fleetwood Town	–	–	–	–	–	7	8	4	10	19
Frickley Athletic	–	–	–	–	10	9	13	10	14	7
Gainsborough Trinity	9	11	4	20	20	17	12	20	18	11
Gateshead	–	–	1	–	18	21	2	–	–	–
Goole Town	18	16	22	16	12	6	19	12	12	22
Grantham Town	4	21	–	–	–	–	–	–	–	–
Horwich R.M.I.	8	9	16	22	13	20	14	16	13	13
Hyde United	11	4	10	11	2	2	4	11	9	9
Leek Town	–	–	–	–	–	–	–	9	4	5
Macclesfield Town	6	2	9	1	–	–	–	–	–	–
Marine	12	5	2	4	9	5	9	6	2	4
Matlock Town	2	13	21	7	19	13	6	17	19	15
Morecambe	19	18	3	6	4	16	15	3	3	3
Mossley	22	15	12	10	17	10	18	15	16	21
Oswestry Town	20	14	18	17	21	–	–	–	–	–
Rhyl	7	17	14	18	8	8	22	–	–	–
Shepshed Albion	–	–	–	–	–	18	20	21	22	–
South Liverpool	3	20	15	5	15	11	5	19	–	–
Southport	16	12	6	8	14	14	7	5	7	1
Stafford Rangers	10	1	–	–	–	–	–	–	–	–
Stalybridge Celtic	–	–	–	–	–	19	17	2	1	–
Whitley Bay	–	–	–	–	–	–	–	–	17	17
Winsford United	–	–	–	–	–	–	–	–	–	2
Witton Albion	13	3	11	14	11	3	3	1	–	–
Workington	15	8	8	21	22	–	–	–	–	–
Worksop Town	17	7	7	19	6	22	–	–	–	–
No. of Clubs	**22**	**22**	**22**	**22**	**22**	**22**	**22**	**21**	**22**	**22**

The look on the face of Emley goalkeeper Wraight's face says it all - he has just been beaten by a header from Andy Rooney giving Barrow their goal in their first ever league visit to Emley. Photo - Ged Rule.

Division One

	P	W	D	L	F	A	Pts
Bridlington Town	40	25	11	4	84	35	86
Knowsley United	40	23	7	10	86	48	76
Ashton United	40	22	8	10	81	54	74
Guisley	40	20	10	101	90	64	70
Warrington Town	40	19	10	11	85	57	67
Gretna	40	17	12	11	64	47	63
Curzon Ashton	40	16	15	9	69	63	63
Great Harwood Town	40	17	9	14	66	57	60
Alfreton Town	40	15	9	16	80	80	54
Harrogate Town	40	14	12	14	77	81	54
Worksop Town	40	15	9	16	66	70	54
Radcliffe Borough	40	13	14	13	66	69	53
Workington	40	13	13	14	51	61	52
Eastwood Town	40	13	11	16	49	52	50
Netherfield	40	11	14	15	68	63	47
Caernarfon Town	40	13	8	19	66	74	47
Farsley Celtic	40	12	8	20	64	77	44
Lancaster City	40	10	12	18	49	76	42
Shepshed Albion	40	9	12	19	46	66	39
Congleton Town	40	10	7	23	58	95	37
Rossendale United	40	5	5	30	50	126	20

Top Scorers

Andy Whittaker (Netherfield)	27
Peter Coyne (Radcliffe Borough)	26
Chris Shaw (Ashton United)	23
Steve French (Harrogate Town)	22
Graeme Jones ((Bridlington Town)	21
Gary Waller (Worksop Town)	21

THE FIRST DIVISION RESULT CHART 1992-93

HOME TEAM	1	2	3	4	5	6	7	8	9	10	11	12	13	14	15	16	17	18	19	20	21
1. Alreton T.	*	1-2	2-3	1-0	4-1	0-1	1-2	1-3	4-0	2-3	3-5	3-2	2-1	3-2	3-3	2-2	5-3	2-1	0-3	1-1	6-2
2. Ashton Utd	6-2	*	1-1	2-0	1-2	5-1	1-4	3-1	0-0	1-1	5-2	2-1	3-0	4-0	3-0	2-1	2-0	1-1	2-1	2-1	1-0
3. Bridlington T.	1-4	6-2	*	0-0	5-1	1-0	2-0	1-1	3-0	1-0	2-1	3-0	2-0	0-0	2-1	4-0	6-3	5-0	1-1	0-0	1-0
4. Caernarfon T.	2-3	1-3	2-2	*	3-2	3-1	1-1	3-4	2-4	1-4	1-0	2-4	1-3	4-2	1-5	0-0	3-0	1-1	4-1	0-1	0-2
5. Congleton T.	3-2	1-0	3-3	0-2	*	0-3	0-0	2-1	1-2	0-1	1-1	3-3	1-2	1-2	0-4	1-2	6-1	1-2	2-1	0-3	1-3
6. Curzon Ashton	1-1	2-2	2-1	0-2	2-2	*	3-3	1-1	3-2	0-4	4-3	4-1	1-1	3-0	1-4	0-1	4-1	1-0	3-3	2-1	2-1
7. Eastwood T.	2-1	1-2	0-0	2-2	0-2	1-2	*	2-0	0-2	1-1	1-3	5-3	1-3	0-2	1-0	1-1	1-3	0-0	4-0	0-1	0-0
8. Farsley C.	2-3	1-1	0-2	0-4	3-2	0-1	0-1	*	1-0	3-0	0-3	0-1	1-3	3-0	1-1	1-3	7-1	2-2	1-1	1-2	2-2
9. G.Harwood T.	2-1	2-1	1-2	1-1	4-0	1-1	0-1	7-0	*	3-2	2-2	2-2	1-3	2-1	0-3	1-0	2-0	5-2	3-2	2-2	4-2
10. Gretna	2-3	3-0	1-3	4-2	5-1	0-0	2-2	3-2	2-1	*	0-1	3-2	1-5	1-2	2-1	3-3	3-0	2-1	2-0	0-0	3-0
11. Guiseley	1-1	4-1	2-2	3-1	5-1	3-3	2-1	3-2	2-0	0-0	*	2-3	1-2	5-0	4-2	1-1	3-2	1-1	3-2	4-3	3-1
12. Harrogate T.	2-2	1-1	1-5	3-0	2-1	1-5	3-3	1-6	1-1	2-0	3-2	*	1-1	2-0	1-0	2-3	3-0	1-0	2-2	1-1	1-1
13. Knowsley U.	0-1	3-2	3-1	3-1	5-0	5-0	0-1	2-0	0-0	0-1	4-2	3-0	*	1-2	3-2	0-1	2-0	2-2	4-3	4-1	1-0
14. Lancaster C.	1-1	1-2	2-1	0-3	1-1	0-0	1-0	1-2	0-1	0-0	1-3	1-1	1-1	*	3-3	1-5	2-0	1-1	2-2	1-3	0-1
15. Netherfield	1-1	1-2	1-1	1-1	1-1	2-2	3-0	0-1	2-0	1-4	1-1	1-1	1-2	3-3	*	6-1	3-2	0-0	0-1	1-2	1-1
16. Radcliffe B.	3-1	0-2	0-3	1-3	1-3	1-1	1-2	4-2	5-2	0-0	0-1	4-2	1-1	2-1	3-0	*	1-1	3-0	1-1	1-1	3-3
17. Rossendale U	1-1	1-7	0-1	1-4	1-4	1-1	0-2	3-2	0-4	1-0	1-1	1-6	3-8	2-4	1-2	4-3	*	1-2	2-7	2-2	0-1
18. Shepshed Abl.	1-2	3-1	0-1	3-1	0-1	1-2	0-2	1-1	1-0	0-0	0-2	3-0	0-2	2-3	0-3	2-2	2-0	*	0-3	1-1	1-0
19. Warrington T.	4-2	0-0	0-1	3-1	6-1	3-3	3-0	3-1	1-0	0-0	3-2	4-3	3-0	0-2	2-0	4-1	5-0	*	2-1	1-1	
20. Workington	2-1	3-2	0-1	2-1	2-1	1-0	1-0	1-3	0-0	0-1	0-0	2-3	1-5	1-3	1-1	1-1	2-2	0-2	1-7	1-2	*	0-0
21. Worksop T.	3-1	0-1	0-4	1-2	6-4	0-3	0-3	2-3	1-1	2-1	1-0	0-3	1-1	6-2	5-2	4-2	5-4	4-2	1-0	3-0	*

ALFRETON TOWN

Formed: 1959

The Reds

Alfreton Town F.C. 1992-93. Back Row (L/R): P Mitchell (Co-Manager), P Catlin, K Edwards, J Mayberry, P Darby, L Colton, M Earnshaw, S Copeland, D Hague (Co-Manager). Front: M Walsh, J Rocca, N Greaves, L Walshaw, T Atkinson, C Hutchinson.

Chairman: Sean Egan   **Vice Chairman:** David Bearder.
Secretary: Roger Taylor, 9 Priory Rd, Alfreton, Derbyshire DE55 7JT (0773 835121).
Manager: Danny Hague   **Press Officer:** Chris Tacey (0773 511012).
Commercial Manager: Linden Davison.
Ground: Town Ground, North Street, Alfreton, Derbyshire(0773 830277).
Directions: M1 junction 28 and follow A38 towards Derby for 1 mile, left onto B600, right at main road to town centre and after half a mile turn left down North Street - ground on right. Half mile from Alfreton & Mansfield Parkway (BR) station. Buses 242 & 243 from both Derby and Mansfield.
Capacity: 5,000   **Cover:** 1,000   **Seats:** 172   **Floodlights:** Yes   **Metal Badges:** Yes
Club Shop: Yes, selling programmes (English & Scottish Lge + non-Lge), club badges, pens, key rings, ties, sewn-on badges. Contact Mr Brian Thorpe, 13 Oakland Str., Alfreton, Derbyshire (0773 836251).
Colours: Red & white/red/red   **Change colours:** Grey & white/black/white.
Previous Leagues: Central Alliance *(before reformation 21-25)* 59-61/ Midland (Counties) *25-27* 61-82/ Northern Counties (East) 82-87.
Midweek home matchday: Wednesday   **Reserve Team's League:** East Mids Regional Alliance.
Sponsors: M I M Electrical Services
Record Attendance: 5,023 v Matlock Town, Central Alliance 1960.
Best F.A. Cup season: 1st Rd 3rd replay 69-70. Also 1st Rd 73-74.
League clubs defeated in F.A. Cup: Lincoln 24-25, but none since club's reformation in 1959.
Record win: 15-0 v Loughborough   **Record defeat:** 2-9 v Worksop 1961, 0-8 v Bridlington 1992.
Record Fees - Paid: £1,000 for R Mountain (Matlock)
                Received: £1,500 for T Henson (Chesterfield), for Matt Walsh (Leek Town).
Players progressing to Football League: Martin Wright (Chesterfield 1968), Alan Woodward (Grimsby 1970), Alan Taylor (Chelsea 1972), Andy Kowalski (Chesterfield 1973), Tony Henson (Chesterfield 1981), Ricky Greenhough (Chester City 1985), Philip Greaves (Chesterfield 1986), Keith Smith (Exeter 1989).
Clubhouse: Clubhouse on ground for members. Hot & cold food & drinks available on ground. Supporters Clubs just outside ground open 11am-4pm matchdays and 7-11pm at night.
Record Goalscorer: J Harrison 303.
Record Appearances: J Harrison 560.
92-93 Captain: A Kirk.
92-93 P.o.Y.: Jon Rocca/ John McFadzean.
Local Newspapers: Derbyshire Times, Derby Evening Telegraph, Nottingham Evening, Ripley/Heanor News, Mansfield Chad.
Local Radio Stations: Radio Derby.
Honours: FA Trophy 3rd Qualifying Rd replay 83-84 85-86, Northern Counties (East) Lg 84-85 (Lg Cup 84-85), Midland (Counties) Lg 69-70 73-74 76-77 (R-up 71-72 80-81 81-82, Lg Cup 71-72 72-73 73-74), Derbyshire Senior Cup 60-61 69-70 72-73 73-74 81-82 (R-up 92-93), Derbyshire Divisional Cup (North) 64-65, Evans Halshaw Floodlit Cup 87-88. *Before reformation in 1959: Central Alliance 23-24 (Lg Cup 22-23).*

PROGRAMME DETAILS:
Pages: 36 **Price:** 50p
Editor: Chris Tacey
(0773 511012)

ASHTON UNITED

Ashton United, pictured in their impressive new stand.

Chairman: John Milne   **Vice Chairman:** Mrs A Cummings   **President:** Sid Sykes.
Secretary: Ernest Jones, 2 Anderton Grove, Hurst Cross, Ashton-under-Lyme OL6 9EF (061 339 9987).
Manager: Kevin Keelan   **Asst Manager:** Steve Waywell
Press Officer: Sara Routledge   **Commercial Manager:** Ray Lee
Ground: Surrey Street, Hurst Cross, Ashton-u-Lyne OL6 8DY (061 339 4158. Fax-061 652 6413).
Directions: M62 jct 20, A627(M) to Oldham, keep in righthand 2 lanes, leave at Ashton sign after 2 miles passing Belgrade Hotel, take A627 at next island, keep in left lane and take slip road signed Ashton-under-Lyme, at island follow Stalybridge/Park Road sign, go straight ahead for 3 miles to ground at Hurst Cross. BR to Charles Street (Ashton), or Stalybridge. Buses 331, 332, 337, 408 (Ashton-Stalybridge) all pass ground.
Seats: 250   **Cover:** 750   **Capacity:** 4,500   **Floodlights:** Yes
Club Shop: Yes - contact Mr K Lee (061 330 9800).
Colours: Red/black/black   **Change colours:** Yellow/black/black.
Record Attendance: 11,000 v Halifax Town, FA Cup First Round 1952.
Midweek matches: Monday.
Club Sponsors: Coral Travel.
Previous Name: Hurst 1878-1947   **Previous Ground:** Rose Hill 1878-1912.
Previous Leagues: Manchester/ Lancs Combination 12-23 48-64 66-68/ Midland 64-66, Cheshire Co. 23-48 68-82/ North West Counties 82-92.
Record Transfer Fees - Paid: £1,000 for Peter McDonnell (Knowsley United, 1992).
                     Received: £15,000 for Karl Marginson (Rotherham United).
Best FA Cup season: 1st Rd replay 52-53 (lost 1-2 at Halifax after 1-1 draw). Also 1st Rd 55-56 (lost 1-6 at Southport).
Players progressing to Football League: Alan Ball (Blackpool, Everton, Arsenal & England), John Mahoney (Stoke City & Wales), Barney Daniels (Manchester City), Rodney Jones (Rotherham United), Alf Arrowsmith (Liverpool), Nelson Stiffle (Crystal Palace & Bournemouth).
Clubhouse: Open 11am-11pm. Refreshment bar open matchdays.
92-93 Captain: Ricky Blackman
92-93 Top Scorer: Chris Shaw, 16.
92-93 P.o.Y.: Chris Shaw
Club Record Appearances: Micky Boyle, 462.
Hons: Manchester Snr Cup 1884-85 13-14 75-76 77-78, Manchester Lg 11-12, Lancs Comb. Div 2 60-61 (Lg Cup 62-63), Manchester Prem. Cup 79-80 82-83 92-93, North West Counties Lg 91-92 (Challenge Cup 91-92, Div 2 87-88, Floodlit Lg 90-91, Challenge Shield 92-93), Manchester Challenge Shield 35-36 38-39 49-50 53-54 (R-up 34-35 39-40), Manchester Intermediate Cup 58-59 62-63 65-66 (R-up 60-61 64-65), Manchester Jnr Cup(4) 1893-94 10-12 32-33.

PROGRAMME DETAILS:
Pages: 40 **Price:** 60p
Editor: Carol Wright

BAMBER BRIDGE

Bamber Bridge - runners-up in the Bass North West Counties League, and upgraded to the Northern Premier League because champions Atherton L.R. did not seek promotion themselves.

President: Harold Hargreaves **Chairman:** D Allan **Vice Chairman:** H Milburn.
Secretary/Press Officer: D G Spencer, 11 Tennyson Place, Walton-le-Dale, Preston, Lancs PR5 4TT (0772 34355).
Manager: Tony Greenwood **Coach:** T.B.A. **Asst Manager:** T.B.A.
Physio: A Jones **Commercial Manager:** D Dundersdale.
Ground: Irongate, Brownedge Road, Bamber Bridge, Preston, Lancs (0772 627387).
Directions: M6 Junct 29, A6 (Bamber Bridge Bypass) towards Walton-le-Dale, to r'bout, A6 London Road to next r'bout, 3rd exit signed Bamber Bridge (Brownedge Road) and first right. Ground 100 yds at end of road on left. Just over a mile from Bamber Bridge (BR).
Seats: 150 **Cover:** 650 **Capacity:** 2,500 **Floodlights:** Yes **Metal badges:** Yes.
Club Shop: Yes - a Supporters Club caravan on ground. Sells hats, cups, scarves, key rings, badges etc plus large selection of programmes. Contact Kevin Walker (0772 30685).
Colours: White/black/white. **Change colours:** All yellow. **Sponsors:** T.B.A.
Midweek Matches: Tuesday **Reserve Team's League:** North West Alliance.
Previous Leagues: Preston & District 52-90/ North West Counties 90-93.
Previous Ground: King George V Ground, Higher Walton 1952-86.
Record Gate: 2,241 v Preston North End 1988. Competitive: 2,020 v Wimborne Town, F.A. Vase Semi Final 1st leg 21/3/92.
Best F.A. Vase season: Semi Finalists 91-92 (lost 0-2 on aggregate to Wimborne Town).
Best F.A. Cup season: Second Qualifying Round 92-93 (lost 0-4 at home to Spennymoor United).
Clubhouse: On ground, open all day Saturday matchdays, every evening except Monday and Sunday lunchtimes. Refreshment cabin on ground serves hot & cold drinks, pies, sandwiches crisps etc during matches.
92-93 Captain: Jez Baldwin
92-93 P.o.Y.: Dave Leaver
92-93 Top scorer: Stuart Farnell 43.
Hons: FA Vase SF 91-92, North West Co's Lg R-up 92-93 (Div 2 91-92, F'lit Cup R-up 91-92), Preston & Dist Lg(4) 80-81 85-87 89-90 (R-up 78-79 82-83 84-85), Guildhall Cup 78-79 80-81 84-85 89-90 (R-up 77-78 79-80 87-88), Lancs Amtr Shield 81-82 (R-up 80-81 89-90), Lancastrian Brigade Cup 76-77 89-90 90-91.

PROGRAMME DETAILS:
Pages: T.B.A. **Price:** 50p
Editor: Rob Gillies
(0772 52795)

CAERNARFON TOWN

Caernarfon Town's Paul Allen wards off the challenge of Gretna livewire David Thompson. Caernarfon were beaten 2-4 in this away fixture on 5th September, surely the first time a Welsh team have played a Scottish team in an English league. Photo - Alan Watson.

President: Jack F Thomas.
Chairman: Dr Emrys Price-Jones   **Vice-Chairman:** Eilian Angel/ Geriant Lloyd-Owen.
Football Secretary: J E Watkins, 20 South Penrallt, Caernarfon, Gwynedd LL55 1NS (0286 674045).
Manager: Roy Soule   **Physio:** Ian Humphreys
Commercial Manager: Jimmy Edwards   **Press Officer:** Dr Emrys Price-Jones (0286 830631).
Ground & Directions: As Curzon Ashton FC (see page 864).
Capacity, Seats etc: As Curzon Ashton (page 864).   **Metal Badges:** Yes
Club Shop: Not at Curzon Ashton, but shop still runs at the club's true home ground; The Oval, Caernarfon. Sells old programmes, scarves, badges etc when in stock.
Colours: Yellow & green halves/green/green   **Change colours:** Red/white/red
Previous Leagues: North Wales Coast 06-21/ Welsh National 26-30/ North Wales Combination 32-33/ Welsh Lg (North) 37-76 77-80/ Lancs Combination 80-82/ North West Counties 82-85.
Previous Ground: The Oval, Marcus Street, Caernarfon (ground vacated at end of 1991-92 season due to conflict with F.A. of Wales over the League of Wales).
Previous Name: Caernarfon Athletic.   **Reserve Team:** None.
Midweek home matchday: T.B.A.   **Club Sponsors:** T.B.A.
Record Attendance: 6,002 v Bournemouth, FA Cup 2nd Rd 1929.
Best F.A. Cup season: 3rd Rd replay 86-87 (lost 0-1 at Barnsley). Also 2nd Rd 29-30.
League clubs defeated in F.A. Cup: Darlington 29-30/ Stockport County, York City 86-87.
Record win: 16-2 v Holyhead, Cookson Cup 11/3/39.
Record defeat: 0-18 v Colwyn Bay (A), North Wales Coast League 14/3/08.
Record Transfer Fee Received: £2,500.
Players progressing to Football League: Ernie Walley (Spurs), Gwyn Jones (Wolves 1955), Wyn Davies & Haydn Jones (Wrexham 1960 & 64), Tom Walley (Arsenal 1964), Paul Crooks (Stoke 1986), David Martindale & Steve Craven & David Higgins (Tranmere 1987).
Clubhouse: *(at The Oval, Marcus Street, Caernarfon)* 2 snooker tables, darts, fruit machines and entertainment, pool.
Club Record Goalscorer: Walter Jones 255 (1906-26)
Club Record Appearances: Walter Jones 306.
92-93 Captain: Dave Barnett
92-93 P.O.Y.: Dave Barnett
92-93 Top scorer: Tony Livens 21.
Local Newspapers: Caernarfon Herald, Liverpool Daily Post.
Local Radio Stations: Radio Cymru/Wales.
Honours: FA Tphy 1st Rd replay 87-88, North West Co's Lg R-up 84-85 (Div 2 R-up 82-83), Lancs Comb 81-82 (Lg Cup 80-81), Welsh Lg (North)(4) 46-47 65-66 77-79 (R-up(4) 56-58 72-73 79-80), Alves Cup(4) 38-39 74-75 77-79, Cookson 56-57 77-78, North Wales Combination 32-33, Welsh National Lg 26-27 29-30 (R-up 28-29), North Wales Coast Lg 11-12.

CLWB PÊL-DROED TREF

CAERNARFON

TOWN FOOTBALL CLUB

SADWRN · SATURDAY
MAI 2 MAY
1992

HFS LOANS LEAGUE
FIRST DIVISION

CAERNARFON TOWN
v
NETHERFIELD

HFS LOANS LEAGUE

Rhaglen/Programme 50c.p.

PROGRAMME DETAILS:
Pages: 44 Price: 50p
Editor: Dr Emrys Price-Jones

Formed: 1901 # CONGLETON TOWN Humbugs/Bears

Congleton Town's Mick Biddle shoots at goal during an F.A. Cup tie at Witton Albion. Photo - Duncan Cook.

Chairman: Cliff Salt
Secretary: John Vernon Pullen, 70 Belgrave Avenue, Congleton, Cheshire CW12 1HT (0260 77128).
Manager: William Wright   **Physio:** B Harper
Press Officer: Chris Phillips (0260 271713)
Ground: Booth Street Ground, Crescent Road, Congleton, Cheshire (0260 274460).
Directions: On approach to Congleton via Clayton bypass take second right after fire station, into Booth Street. Two miles from Congleton (BR).
Capacity: 5,000   **Cover:** 1,200   **Seats:** 250   **Floodlights:** Yes   **Club Shop:** Yes
Colours: White & black stripes/black/black & white   **Change colours:** All red
Previous Leagues: Crewe & Dist/ North Staffs/ Macclesfield/ Cheshire 20-39 46-65 78-82/ Mid Cheshire 68-78/ North West Counties 82-87.
Previous Name: Congleton Hornets *(prior to current club's formation in 1901).*
Reserve Team: Congleton Town Hornets - Sportscene International (Staffs Senior) League.
Midweek home matchday: Wednesday
Record Attendance: 7,000 v Macclesfield, League 53-54.
Best F.A. Cup season: 1st Rd 89-90 (lost 0-2 at Crewe).
League clubs defeated in F.A. Cup: None.
Record Fees - Paid: None   **Received:** £5,000 for D Frost (Leeds).
Players progressing to Football League: Ron Broad (Crewe 1955), Jack Mycock (Shrewsbury 1958), Steve Davies (Port Vale 1987), L Hamlet (Leeds), Jimmy Quinn (West Ham, N Ireland), Ian Brightwell (Man City).
Clubhouse: Open every day.
Club Record Goalscorer: Mick Biddle (150+)
Club Record Appearances: Ray Clack (600+)
Local Newspapers: Congleton Chronicle (0260 273737), Staffs Evening Sentinel (0782 289800).
Local Radio Stations: Radio Stoke, Signal.
Honours: North West Counties Lg R-up 85-86, Cheshire County Lg R-up 20-21 21-22 (Div 2 81-82), Mid Cheshire Lg 73-74 75-76 77-78 (R-up 69-70 71-72 76-77, Lg Cup 71-72), Cheshire Senior Cup 20-21 37-38, FA Trophy 3rd Qualifying Rd 89-90 90-91, F.A. Vase 4th Rd 76-77 80-81.

PROGRAMME DETAILS:
Pages: 32 Price: 50p
Editor: P Warren

CURZON ASHTON

Curzon Ashton's Ian Redman (right) puts a lot of effort into his aerial challenge of Gary Messenger during the goalless draw at Gretna on 6th March. Photo - Alan Watson.

Chairman: Harry Twamley   **Vice Chairman:** Peter Booth   **President:** Peter Mayo.
Secretary: Alun Jones, 36 Forrest Road, Denton, Manchester M34 1RL (061 336 8004).
Manager: David 'Taffy' Jones   **Assistant Manager:** Peter Tilley.
Physio: Dave Pover   **Press Officer:** David Murray (061 7757509)
Ground: National Park, Katherine Street, Ashton-under-Lyne OL7 6DA (061 330 6033).
Directions: Behind Ashton police station off Manchester Rd (A635), Ashton-under-Lyme., one and a half miles from Ashton-under-Lyme (BR).
Capacity: 5,000   **Cover:** 450   **Seats:** 350   **Floodlights:** Yes
Club Shop: Due to be opened during 1993-94 season - contact club number.
Colours: All royal blue   **Change colours:** Yellow/black/black.
Sponsors: Byford Computer Services/ P M Communications.
Previous Lges: Manchester Amtr/ Manchester (until 1978)/ Cheshire Co. 78-82/ North West Co's 82-87.
Midweek home matchday: Monday   **Record Gate:** 1,826 v Stamford, FA Vase SF 1980.
Best F.A. Cup season: Third Qualifying Round replay 89-90 (lost 1-3 at Mossley after 1-1 draw).
Record win: 6-1 v Radcliffe Borough   **Record defeat:** 1-5 v Knowsley United.
Record Transfer Fees - Paid: £1,000 for Garry Stewart (Witton Albion, 1993).
                               Received: £1,500 for Steve Wigley (Nottm Forest, 1981).
Players progressing to Football League: Gordon Taylor (Bolton Wanderers 1962), Steve Wigley (Nottm Forest 1981), Malcolm O'Connor (Rochdale 1983), Eric Nixon (Manchester City 1983).
Clubhouse: Open every night. Food on matchdays. Function room for private hire. Also, five-aside astro pitch available for hire every day.
Club Record Goalscorer: Alan Sykes
Club Record Appearances: Alan Sykes 620.
92-93 Captain & P.o.Y.: Kenny Clements
92-93 Top scorer: Keith Evans.
Local Newspapers: Ashton Reporter, Ashton Advertiser.
Local Radio Stations: Manchester Radio, Piccadilly.
Honours: FA Vase SF 79-80, Cheshire County Lg Div 2 R-up 78-79 (Reserve Div 81-82), Manchester Lg 77-78 (R-up 74-75 75-76, Lg Cup 77-78 (R-up 74-75 75-76), Murray Shield R-up 75-76, Reserve Div 74-75 75-76 76-77 77-78), Manchester Amateur Lg 63-64 65-66 (R-up 64-65 79-80(Res) 80-81(Res)), Manchester Premier Cup 81-82 83-84 85-86 86-87 89-90, Manchester Intermediate Cup 71-72 72-73 73-74 (R-up 70-71), Manchester Amateur Cup R-up 63-64, Ashton Challenge Cup 64-65 67-68, Philips F'lit Cup R-ups 77-78, FA Trophy 2nd Qualifying Rd 82-83 84-85, North West Counties Reserve Div 82-83 84-85 (R-up 83-84, Lg Cup 84-85 (R-up 83-84 85-86)), Northern Combination Supplementy Cup 87-88 88-89, South East Lancs Lg Shield R-up 84-85.

PROGRAMME DETAILS:
Pages: 16 **Price:** 50p
Editor: Ian Seymour

EASTWOOD TOWN

Eastwood Town 1992-93.

Chairman: George Belshaw   **Vice Chairman:** Richard James   **President:** John Holmes.
Secretary/Press Officer: Paddy Farrell, 7 Primrose Rise, Newthorpe, Notts NG16 2BB (0773 715500).
Manager: Bryan Chambers   **Reserves' Mgr:** Paul McFarland   **Physio:** Derek Myatt.
Ground: Coronation Park, Eastwood, Notts (0773 715823).
Directions: From North - M1 junction 27 then follow Heanor signs via Brinsley to lights in Eastwood. Turn left then first right after Fire Station - ground entrance on Chenton Street. From South - M1 jct 26, A610 to Ripley, leave at 1st exit (B6010), follow to Eastwoos, left at lights, first left at 'Man in Space' - ground entrance on Chenton Street. Nearest rail station is Langley Mill. Buses every 10 mins (R11, R12 or R13) from Victoria Centre, Nottingham. Journey time 40 mins.
Capacity: 5,090   **Cover:** 790   **Seats:** 200   **Floodlights:** Yes   **Metal Badges:** Yes
Club Shop: Due to open this season, selling programmes and badges etc. Contact Gordon Bradford (0773 765622).
Colours: Black & white stripes/black/black   **Change colours:** All yellow or all white.
Previous Leagues: Notts Alliance 53-61/ Central Alliance 61-67/ East Midlands 67-71/ Midland Counties 71-82/ Northern Counties (East) 82-87.
Previous Names: None - predecessors Eastwood Collieries disbanded in 1953.
Previous Ground: Also Coronation Park 1953-65 - previous pitch now town bowling green.
Midweek home matchday: Tuesday **Record Attendance:** 2,723 v Enfield, FA Amateur Cup, February 1965.
Best F.A. Cup season: Final Qualifying Rd replay 75-76 (lost 0-1 at Wycombe Wanderers).
Record win: 26-0   **Record defeat:** 1-7.
Record Fees - Paid: £500 for Jamie Kay, Gainsborough Trinity 90-91.
     Received: £20,000 for Richard Liburd (Middlesbrough 92-93).
Players progressing to Football League: John Butlet (Notts County 1957), Tony Woodcock, Paul Richardson, Alan Buckley, Steve Buckley, Richard Liburd (Middlesbrough 92-93).
Clubhouse: Large social club open daily - normal licensing hours (Sat 11am-11pm, midweek matches 6.30-11pm). Hot & cold food available.
Steward: Mrs Margaret Haskey (0773 715823)
Club Record Goalscorer: Martin Wright
Club Record Appearances: Arthur Rowley, over 800 1st team games, but not a single booking, 1955-76.
92-93 Captain: Stuart Wiggins
92-93 P.O.Y.: Mark Place
92-93 Top scorer: Mark Richardson
Sponsors: Melfin (UK) Ltd.
Local Newspapers: Eastwood Advertiser (0773 713563), Nottingham Evening Post (0602 482000), Derby Telegraph (0332 291111).
Local Radio Stations: Radio Nottingham, Radio Trent.
Honours: Northern Counties (East) Lg R-up 82-83 84-85, Midland Counties Lg 75-76 (R-up 74-75 77-78, Lg Cup 77-78 79-80), Central Alliance 63-64 (R-up 64-65), Notts Alliance 56-57 (R-up 53-54 54-55 55-56 57-58 58-59 59-60, Lg Cup 55-56), East Midlands Lg R-up 68-69, Notts Senior Cup 75-76 77-78 78-79 79-80 82-83 83-84 88-89 89-90 91-92 (R-up 57-58 63-64 65-66), Evans Halshaw Floodlit Cup R-up 89-90, Notts Intermediate Cup 86-87, Ripley Hospital Charity Cup(6) 76-81, FA Trophy 1st Rd 78-79, FA Amateur Cup 3rd Rd replay 67-68.

PROGRAMME DETAILS:
Pages: 24 **Price:** TBA
Editor: TBA

FARSLEY CELTIC

Farsley Celtic F.C. 92-93. Back Row (L/R): Kevin Taylor, Phil Sharpe, Martin Pattison, Wayne Baker, Floyd Peltier, David Hanson, Darren Edmonds, Tommy Graham (Coach/Commercial Manager). Front: Steve Nicholson, Mark Hamilton, Richard Hepworth, Robert Sharp (Mascot), Jeremy Smith, Nigel Smith, Richard Harrison. Photo - James Wright.

Chairman: John E Palmer **Vice Chairman:** Paul Glover.
Secretary: Brian Whitehead, 29 Wellington Rd, Bradford BD2 3AT (0274 638832).
Manager: Denis Metcalf **Coach/Commercial Manager:** Tommy Graham.
Physio: Tony Gregg **Press Officer:** Tong Beckton (0532 564206)
Ground: Throstle Nest, Newlands, Farsley, Pudsey, Leeds LS28 5BE (0532 561517).
Directions: From North East: A1 south to Wetherby, A58 to Leeds, at 1st island (approx 8 miles) take 3rd exit (A6120 ring-rd), follow Bradford signs to 12th r'bout (approx 12 miles) - 1st exit (B6157 Stanningley). From M62 jct 26, M606 (Bradford) to r'bout, 4th exit (A6177) passing Rooley pub on left, continue on Rooley Lane - Sticker Lane passing Morrisons store on left to lights (approx 3 miles) - right onto A647 (Leeds) to 2nd r'bout, 2nd exit (B6157 Stanningley). Continue 800yds passing Police & Fire Stations on left. Turn left down New Street at Tradex warehouse before turning right into Newlands. Ground at bottom of road. 1 mile from New Pudsey (BR). Buses 17, 72 and 508 from Leeds.
Capacity: 5,000 **Cover:** 1,250 **Seats:** 430 **Floodlights:** Yes **Metal Badges:** Yes.
Club Shop: Yes. League and non-league programmes and magazines. Club badges, scarves, ties, sweaters, training suits, polo and T-shirts. Various souvenirs and photographs. Contact Brian Faulkner (0532 550749) at 27 Rycroft Court, Leeds LS13 4PE.
Colours: Sky & navy stripes/navy/navy **Change colours:** White/white/navy.
Previous Grounds: Red Lane, Farsley/ Calverley Lane, Farsley (prior to 1948).
Prev. Lges: West Riding County Amateur/ Leeds Red Triangle/ Yorkshire 49-82/ Northern Counties (East) 82-87.
Midweek home matchday: Wednesday **Reserve Team's League:** Northern Counties (E) Reserve Div.
Record Attendance: 11,000 (at Elland Road) v Tranmere Rovers, FA Cup 1st Rd 1974.
Best F.A. Cup season: 1st Rd 74-75 (see above). Lost 0-2.
League clubs defeated in F.A. Cup: None.
Players progressing to Football League: Barry Smith (Leeds 1951), Paul Madeley (Leeds 1962), William Roberts (Rochdale 1988).
Clubhouse: Lounge, games room and committee room open every evening and Friday and weekend lunchtimes. New multi-purpose Leisure Centre available evenings and afternoons.
Steward: Stuart Shaw.
92-93 Captain: Kevin Taylor
92-93 P.o.Y.: Kevin Taylor
92-93 Top scorer: Keith Sanderson
Local Newspapers: Yorkshire Evening Post, Telegraph & Argus, Pudsey Times.
Local Radio Stations: Radio Leeds, Radio Aire, Radio Pennine.
Honours: FA Vase QF 87-88, FA Amateur Cup 3rd Rd 34-35, West Riding County Cup 57-58 59-60 66-67 70-71 83-84 87-88, Yorkshire Lg 59-60 68-69 (R-up 57-58 58-59 70-71 71-72, Div 2 51-52, Lg Cup 62-63 63-64 66-67).

PROGRAMME DETAILS:
Pages: 22 **Price:** 50p
Editor: Raymond Maule
(0274 662428)

GOOLE TOWN

Barrow's Neil Doherty powers a fine header just over the Goole Town bar during the Premier Division fixture at Holker Street. Photo - Ged Rule.

Chairman: Christopher J Raywood **President:**
Vice President: E Shaw **Vice Chairman:** D O'Hearne.
Secretary/Press Officer: Graeme Wilson, 12 Thorntree Close, Goole, North Humbs DN14 6LN (0405 763316).
Manager: Tim Hotte **Asst Manager:** T.B.A. **Physio:** Colin Naylor
Coach: Richard Dawson **Commercial Mgr:** Mr T Burdass (0302 831650).
Ground: The Victoria Pleasure Ground, Carter Street, Goole (0405 762794 - matchdays).
Directions: M62 junction 36, then A614. On entering Goole turn left at second set of lights - Carter Street is the sixth right. 400 yds from Goole Town (BR).
Capacity: 4,500 **Cover:** 4,000 **Seats:** 200 **Floodlights:** Yes **Shop:** Yes
Colours: Blue & red stripes/blue/red **Change colours:** All green.
Previous Leagues: Yorkshire 24-48/ Midland Counties 48-60 61-68/ Central Alliance 60-61.
Midweek home matchday: Tuesday **Record Fee Received:** £10,000 for Tony Galvin (Spurs).
Record Attendance: 8,700 v Scunthorpe United, Midland Counties Lg 1950.
Best F.A. Cup season: 3rd Rd 1956-57 (lost at Nottm Forest). Also 1st Rd on eight other occasions; 14-15 49-50 51-52 55-56 57-58 67-69 76-78 84-85.
League Clubs defeated in F.A. Cup: Workington 56-57.
Players progressing to Football League: Eric Binns (Burnley 1949), Arthur Hall & Les Bloadley & John Kaye & Steve Shutt (Scunthorpe 1951 & 52 & 60 & 85), William Linacre & Malcolm Thompson & David Stewart (Hartlepool 1953 & 68 & 83), Bernard Shaw (Lincoln 1953), Eric Cousans (Walsall 1954), Brian Handley (Aston Villa 1957), Gordon Robbins (Crewe Alexandra 1958), Alan Darby (Doncaster 1959), Mitchell Dournie (Bradford City 1959), Arthur Taylor (Hull 1962), Stan Marshall (Middlesbrough 1963), John Woodall (York 1967), Ian Pearson (Plymouth 1974), Tony Galvin (Spurs 1978), Brian Ferguson (Southend 1983), Chris Maples (Chesterfield 1986), I Sampson (Sunderland), J Smith (Wigan).
Club Record Scorer: Brian Howard
Club Record Appearances: Jimmy Kelly 475.
Local Newspapers: Goole Times (763391), Hull Mail (762647), Goole Courier (763073).
Local Radio Stations: BBC Radio Radio Humberside, Viking FM.
Honours: Northern Premier Lg Cup 87-88, Yorkshire Lg 27-28 36-37 47-48 (Lg Cup 33-34 48-49), West Riding County Cup 38-39 50-51 51-52 56-57 68-69 69-70 75-76 76-77 77-78 86-87 88-89 91-92, West Riding Snr Cup(1), FA Trophy 3rd Rd 74-75.

HFS LOANS LEAGUE
GOOLE TOWN A.F.C.
v
BANGOR CITY
SATURDAY 12th OCTOBER

f:HfS LOANS LEAGUE

VICTORIA PLEASURE GROUNDS, GOOLE
SEASON 1991/92

PROGRAMME DETAILS:
Pages: 16 Price: 50p
Editor: G Wilson, A Lawson

GREAT HARWOOD TOWN Robins

Great Harwood Town's 'Showground' which has always been the venue of senior football in the town having been previously the home of the now defunct Great Harwood F.C. who also played in the Northern Premier League. Photo - C C G Blackwell.

Chairman: C R Hickey
Secretary: G Snowden, 54 Queens Road, Accrington, Lancs (0254 395266).
Manager: Eric Whalley   **Asst Manager:** D Sargeant.
Commercial Manager: J Dobson.
Ground: The Showground, Wood Street, Great Harwood, Lancs (0254 883913).
Directions: M66 from Manchester to Haslingden exit, A680 through Baxenden, Accrington to Clayton-le-Moors, left at the Hyndburn Bridge Hotel into Hyndburn Road and right into Wood Street to ground. Or M6 jct 31, Clitheroe/Skipton road to Trafalgar Hotel, A677 to Blackburn, left at Moat House Hotel and follow ring-road to M65 junction, A678 to Rishton, left at lights (B6536) to Gt Harwood, right at Town Gate into Queen Str., follow signs for Lomax Square, left into Park Rd, right into Balfour Street to ground. 3 miles from Rishton (BR), 6 miles from Blackburn (BR). Various buses from Heyes Lane & Park Road to Blackburn & Accrington.
Seats: 200   **Cover:** 700   **Capacity:** 2,500   **Floodlights:** Yes   **Club Shop:** No
Reserve Team: None   **Record Gate:** 5,397 v Manchester Utd 1980
Colours: All red   **Change colours:** All blue.
Midweek Matches: Wednesday   **Club Sponsors:** None at present.
Previous Name: Great Harwood Wellington.
Previous Leagues: West Lancashire/ Lancs Combination 79-82/ North West Counties 82-92.
Previous Ground: Park adjacent to the Showground until demise of Great Harwood F.C. in 1978.
Best FA Cup season: 1st Qualifying Round replay 92-93 (lost 1-2 at home to Atherton L.R. after 1-1 draw).
Best FA Vase season: Quarter Finals 90-91.
Clubhouse: Yes - The Sportsman just outside ground. Normal licensing hours. Full bar facilities. Squash courts and gym. Hot & cold snacks and drinks on matchdays from tea bar within ground.
92-93 Captain: Martin Eatough.
92-93 Top Scorer: Peter Smith
Hons: North West Counties Lg R-up 91-92 (Div 2 90-91, Lamot Pils Tphy 89-90 (R-up 90-91), Tennents Floodlit Trophy 91-92), Lancs ATS Challenge Trophy 91-92 (R-up 90-91).

PROGRAMME DETAILS:
Pages: 20 **Price:** 50p
Editor: Barry Marsden

Gretna F.C. 1992-93.

Chairman: Ian B Dalgleish   **Vice Chairman:** Jack Gass   **President:** Thomas Kerr.
Secretary: Keith Rhodes, 8 Graitney, Gretna, Carlisle, Cumbria CA6 5AR (0461 37447).
Coach: John Halpin.   **Manager:** Michael McCartney   **Asst Mgr/Physio:** William Bentley
Press Officer: Secretary   **Commercial Manager:** Fred Sheckley (0461 38011).
Ground: Raydale Park, Domminion Rd., Gretna, Carlisle (0461 37602).
Directions: 8 miles north of Carlisle on A74. Buses leave Carlisle on the half hour.
Seats: 385   **Cover:** 800   **Capacity:** 3,000   **Floodlights:** Yes
Club Shop: Yes, selling pennants, programmes, sweaters, scarves, hats, magazines, balls, T-shirts, badges. Contact Mr Fred Sheckley (0461 38011).
Club colours: Black & white hoops/black/black & white
Change colours: All yellow.   **Midweek Matches:** Tuesday
Record Gate: 2,307 v Rochdale, F.A. Cup First Round Proper, 16/11/92.
Previous Leagues: Dumfriesshire Amateur 47-47/ Carlisle & District 47-51/ Cumberland 51-52/ Northern 83-92.
Midweek matchday: Tuesday   **Previous Ground:** Station Park 1946-47.
Club Sponsors: Gables Hotel.
Record win: 13-0   **Record defeat:** 1-5.
Best season in F.A. Cup: 1st Round Proper 1991-92 (lost 1-3 in replay at Rochdale).
Players progressing to Football League: John Hamilton (Hartlepool United 1982), Russell Black & Don Peattie (Sheffield United) 1984.
Clubhouse: Bar, lounge, TV room, concert room. Cooked meals available. Open every day. Late bar at weekends.
Club record scorer: Denis Smith   **Club record appearances:** William Cross.
Captain 92-93: Alan Carruthers   **Top Scorer 92-93:** John Halpin   **P.o.Y. 92-93:** Les Armstrong.
Local Newspapers: Cumberland News
Honours: Northern Lg 90-91 91-92 (Lg Cup 90-91), Cumberland Senior Cup (8), F.A. Trophy 3rd Rd 90-91, J.R. Cleator Cup 89-90 90-91 91-92, Craven Cup 91-92, Carlisle & Dist. Lg (28)(Charity Shield(25), Lg Cup(20), Benevolent Cup(15)).

PROGRAMME DETAILS:
Pages: 26 **Price:** 50p
Editor: Fred Sheckley
(0461 38011)

GUISELEY

Guiseley's Neil Buckley inflicts a committed tackle on David Thompson (hoops) as his side achieve a 1-0 win at Gretna on 22nd August. Photo - Alan Watson.

Chairman: Gary Douglas **President:** David Brotherton.
Secretary/Press Officer: Philip Rogerson, 8 Viewlands Cres., Chevin End, Menston, Ilkley, West Yorkshire LS29 6BH (0943 879236).
Manager: Ray McHale **Asst Manager:** Garry Watson.
Physio: John Rhodes **Commercial Manager:** Ray McHale.
Ground: Nethermoor, Otley Road, Guiseley, Leeds LS20 8BT (0943 873223).
Directions: Via M1 to M62 junction 28, follow Leeds road to Leeds ring-road to junction of A65 at Horsforth. At r-about turn left onto A65 through Rawdon to Guiseley centre. Ground quarter of a mile past traffic lights, on the right, entrance on A65 opposite Silver Cross factory. Additional car parking available off Ings Crescent. Five mins walk from Guiseley (BR/Metro) station.
Capacity: 3,000 **Cover:** 800 **Seats:** 427 **Floodlights:** Yes **Metal Badges:** Yes
Club Shop: Yes, selling programmes, various items of clothing, key rings, badges, mugs etc. Phone either club office no. (above) or clubhouse (below).
Colours: All white **Change colours:** All yellow.
Sponsors: Abbey Hire.
Previous Grounds: None.
Previous Leagues: West Riding Co. Amtr/ West Yorks/ Yorkshire 68-82/ Northern Co's (East) 82-91.
Midweek home matchday: Monday **Reserves' League:** Northern Co's (East) Reserve Div.
Record Attendance: 2,486 v Bridlington Town, FA Vase Semi Final 1st Leg 89-90.
Best F.A. Cup season: First Round Proper 1991-92 (lost 0-1 at Chester City).
League clubs defeated in F.A. Cup: None to date.
Players progressing to Football League: Keith Walwyn (York City), Frank Harrison (Halifax Town), Dean Walling (Carlisle United), Richard Annan (Crewe Alexandra).
Clubhouse: (0943 872872) Open before and after all games (closes 11pm). Snack bar within ground open before and during matches.
92-93 Captain: Colin Horgarth
92-93 P.o.Y.: Calvin Allen.
92-93 Top scorer: Linton Brown/ R Whellans (Reserves: Patrick Flaherty 29).
Local Newspapers: Yorkshire Evening Post, Bradford Telegraph & Argus, Airedale & Wharfdale Observer, Wharfe Valley Times.
Honours: FA Vase 90-91 (R-up 91-92, SF 89-90), Northern Premier Lg Div 1 Cup 92-93, Northern Counties (East) Lg 90-91 (Lg Cup 90-91), West Riding County Cup(4), Yorkshire Lg R-up 79-80 81-82 (Lg Cup 79-80).

'THE NON-LEAGUE PLAYERS'
1993-94 EDITION

AVAILABLE DURING THE SEASON, WILL FEATURE DETAILS OF GUISELEY'S PLAYERS, AND INDEED THE PLAYERS OF ALL CLUBS IN THE TOP FOUR PYRAMID LEAGUES. FOR MORE DETAILS ON THIS PUBLICATION SEE THE ADVERT NEAR THE FRONT OF THIS DIRECTORY.

PROGRAMME DETAILS:
Pages: 20 **Price:** 60p
Editor: Phil Rogerson
(0943 879236)

HARROGATE TOWN

Harrogate Town F.C. 1992-93. Back Row (L/R): David Whitehead (Physio), Mick Doig (Coach), Steve Learoyd, Marc Philpott, Lee Dutton, Mark Fenton (Goalkeeper), Paul Williamson, Geoff Barker, Brian Duffy, Alan Smith (General Manager). Front: Mark Clifton, Alan Higgins, Chris Annan, Steve French, Kenny Dennis, John Gallagher. Mascots: Joanne Welford, Paul Smith.

Chairman: George Dunnington   **President:** C Margolis.
Secretary: Roy Dalby, 123a Dene Park, Harrogate, HG1 4JX (0423 567973).
Manager: John Deacey   **Asst Manager:** T.B.A.   **Coach:** David Harvey
Ground: Whetherby Road, Harrogate. (0423 883671 (880675-press)).
Directions: From Leeds turn right at traffic lights (Appleyard's) into Hookstone Road, continue to Woodlands Hotel (traffic lights) turn left into Wetherby Road, ground on the right. From Harrogate (BR), turn left and left again, cross road (Odeon Cinema), proceed for about 400yds to main road, cross over to The Stray (open land) using footpath which leads to Wetherby Rd, ground 200yds on left.
Capacity: 3,800   **Cover:** 600   **Seats:** 450   **Floodlights:** Yes   **Metal Badges:** Yes
Club Shop: Yes, selling scarves, ties, pens shirts and other common souvenirs.
Colours: Amber/black/amber   **Change colours:** All blue.
Previous Names: Harrogate FC 26-34/ Harrogate Hotspurs 36-50.
Previous Ground: Starbeck Lane 1919-20.
Previous Leagues: Yorkshire 20-21 22-31 51-82/ Midland 21-22/ Northern 31-32/ Harrogate & District 36-46/ West Yorkshire 46-51/ Northern Counties (East) 82-87.
Midweek home matchday: Tuesday   **Reserve Team's Lge:** Northern Co's (East) Reserve Div.
Club Sponsors: Crystal Motors.
Record Attendance: 3,208 v Starbeck LNER (now Harrogate R.A.), Whitworth Cup final 1948.
Best F.A. Cup season: 3rd Qualifying Rd 87-88 (lost 0-2 at Bishop Auckland after a 1-1 draw).
League clubs defeated in F.A. Cup: None.
Record win: 9-1 v Winsford   **Received:** 0-7; v Hyde Utd & v Lancaster City.
Players progressing to Football League: Stewart (York City 1979), Tim Hotte (Halifax Town 1985), Andy Watson (Halifax Town 1988).
Clubhouse: On ground, open Tuesday, Thursday and every other Wednesday in addition to every matchday. Sandwiches available.
92-93 Captain: Paul Williamson
92-93 P.o.Y.: Lee Dutton
92-93 Top scorer: Steve French 26.
Local Newspapers: Yorkshire Post, Harrogate Herald Advertiser.
Local Radio Stations: Radio Leeds, Radio York, local hospital radio.
Honours: FA Vase 4th Rd 89-90, Northern Premier Lg Div 1 Cup 89-90, Northern Counties (East) Div 1 (Nth) R-up 84-85 (Reserve Div 85-86, Reserve Div Cup 86-87), Yorkshire Lg Div 1 26-27 (Div 2 81-82, Div 3 R-up 71-72 80-81), West Riding County Cup 62-63 72-73 85-86, West Riding Challenge Cup 24-25 26-27.

PROGRAMME DETAILS:
Pages: 48 **Price:** 50p
Editor: Ken Welford
(0423 889186)

CITY OF LANCASTER

Lancaster City's Ian Noteman is denied by the combined efforts of Ashton United defender Karl Marginson and goalkeeper Chris Holmes, and his side slip to a 1-2 home defeat on 26th September. Photo - Alan Watson.

Chairman: John Bagguley   **Vice Chairman:** K Lancaster.   **President:** M Woodhouse.
Secretary: Barry Newsham, 104 Willow Lane, Forest Park, Lancaster LA1 5QF (0524 35774).
Manager: Alan Tinsley   **Coach:** George Norrie   **Physio:** Brian Maudsley
Commercial Mgr: Mike Hoyle.   **Press Officer:** Secretary or John Bagguley (0850 824000).
Ground: Giant Axe, West Road, Lancaster (0524 382238).
Directions: M6 junction 33 (from south) or 34 (from north), follow signs to Lancaster centre then to railway station, follow road down hill - ground on right. Quarter mile from Lancaster (BR), 5 mins walk from bus station.
Capacity: 5,000   **Cover:** 1,000   **Seats:** 350   **Floodlights:** Yes   **Metal Badges:** Yes
Club Shop: Yes - contact D Henig at club.
Colours: Blue/white/blue   **Change colours:** All yellow
Sponsors: Reebok UK.   •
Previous Leagues: Lancs Combination 05-10 11-15 19-70/ Northern Premier 70-82/ North West Counties 82-87.
Reserve Team's League: North Western Alliance.
Previous Names: Lancaster Town   **Previous Ground:** Quay Meadow 05-06 (clubs 1st 2 games only!)
Midweek home matchday: Wednesday   **Record Attendance:** 7,500 v Carlisle, FA Cup 1936.
Best F.A. Cup season: 2nd Rd 46-47 (0-4 v Gateshead) 72-73 (1-2 v Notts County). Also 1st Rd on 8 other occasions; 28-29 29-30 30-31 31-32 33-34 37-38 38-39 47-48.
League Clubs defeated in F.A. Cup: Barrow, Stockport County 21-22.
Record win: 7-0 v Eastwood Hanley.
Players progressing to Football League: John McNamee (Workington 1975), Brendan O'Callaghan (Stoke City), Ian Stevens (Stockport County 1986), Glenn Johnstone (Preston North End), Martin Clark (Crewe Alexandra), Gus Wilson (Crewe Alexandra).
Clubhouse: Open matchdays.
Club Record Appearances: Edgar J Parkinson.
92-93 Captain: Dave Woodburn.
92-93 P.o.Y.: Brian Curwen.
92-93 Top scorer: Martin Horsfield.
Local Newspapers: Lancaster Guardian, Morcambe Visitor, Lancaster Evening Post.
Local Radio Stations: Lancaster Radio, Red Rose.
Honours: Northern Premier Lg Cup R-up 79-80 (Div 1 Cup R-up 90-91), Lancs Combination 21-22 29-30 34-35 35-36 (R-up 19-20 22-23 27-28 51-52, Lg Cup 21-22, Div 2 R-up 14-15), Lancs Junior Cup (ATS Challenge Trophy) 27-28 28-29 30-31 33-34 51-52 74-75 (R-up 06-07 08-09 19-20 26-27), FA Vase 2nd Rd 86-87 90-91, FA Trophy 3rd Rd 74-75 75-76, Lancs Yth (under 18) Cup 87-88 88-89 (R-up 86-87 89-90).

PROGRAMME DETAILS:
Pages: 32 **Price:** 50p
Editor: D Henig
(c/o the club)

Formed: 1903

MOSSLEY

Lillywhites

The Mossley (white shirts) defence close down Hyde United's Dave Nolan in the New Year's Day derby on Hyde's synthetic pitch. Mossley lost 2-4 and were ultimately relegated. Photo - Colin Stevens.

Chairman: Roger Finn **President:** J Anderson.
Secretary: Les Fitton, 25 Rushmere, 18th Fairway, Ashton-under-Lyme OL6 9EB (061 330 2182).
Manager: Steve Taylor **Asst Manager:** Geoff Lutley. **Physio:** Tony Sutton
Commercial Manager: Chris Brophy (061 330 6186).
Ground: Seel Park, Market Street, Mossley, Ashton-under-Lyme (0457 832369).
Directions: Off M62; from west via Oldham, Lees and Grotton; from east via Saddleworth. From M1 or Sheffield via Stalybridge then Mossley. Half mile from Mossley (BR), buses 153 from Manchester, 343 from Oldham or 350 from Ashton.
Capacity: 4,500 **Cover:** 1,500 **Seats:** 200 **Floodlights:** Yes **Club Shop:** Yes
Colours: White/black/black **Change colours:** Yellow/blue/yellow.
Previous Leagues: Ashton/ South East Lancs/ Lancs Combination 18-19/ Cheshire County 19-72.
Previous Names: Park Villa 03-04/ Mossley Juniors 04-09.
Previous Ground: Luzley.
Midweek home matchday: Tuesday **Record Attendance:** 7,000 v Stalybridge, 1950.
Best F.A. Cup season: 2nd Rd replay 49-50. Also 2nd Rd 80-81, 1st Rd 69-70 77-78 78-79 79-80 81-82 83-84.
League clubs defeated in F.A. Cup: Crewe Alexandra, 80-81.
Record Fees - Paid: £2,300 **Received:** £25,000 for Eamon O'Keefe (Everton, 1979).
Players progressing to Football League: John Wright (Blackpool 1946), Tom Bell & Albert Wadsworth (Oldham 1946 & 49), Albert Lomas (Rochdale 1950), Arthur Tyrer (Leeds 1946), Eric Williams (Halifax 1951), John Willis (A Villa 1958), Mike Eckershall (Torquay 1959), Alan Roberts (Bradford PA 1969), Gary Pierce (Huddersfield 1971), Eamon O'Keefe (Everton 1979), David Young (Wigan 1983).
Clubhouse: Open nights and matchdays.
Local Newspapers: Oldham Evening Chronicle, Saddleworth & Mossley Reporter.
Local Radio Stations: Radio Manchester, Piccadilly.
Honours: FA Trophy R-up 79-80, Northern Premier Lg 78-79 79-80 (R-up 80-81 81-82 82-83, Lg Cup 78-79 88-89 (R-up 75-76 81-82), Challenge Shield 88-89 (R-up 78-79 79-80 80-81 81-82)), Cheshire County Lg R-up 19-20 69-70 (Lg Cup 20-21 60-61), Manchester Premier Cup 88-89 90-91, Manchester Intermediate Cup 60-61 66-67 67-68 (R-up 58-59 63-64 70-71 78-79), Manchester Challenge Shield 14-15 33-34 37-38 48-49 (R-up 36-37 38-39 50-51), Reporter Floodlit Cup 74-75 88-89, North West Floodlit Cup R-up 76-77.

PROGRAMME DETAILS:
Pages: 28 **Price:** 50p
Editor: Julian Thomas

NETHERFIELD

Netherfield's Andy Whittaker, who with 27 goals was the top-scorer in the Northern Premier League First Division, takes on the Bridlington defence at Parkside on 9th January. Photo courtesy of the Westmorland Gazette.

Chairman: David Willan   **President:** Ty Power.
Secretary/Press Officer: Peter Savage, 46 Hayclose Road, Kendal (0539 726488).
Manager: Tony Hesketh   **Asst Manager:** Keith Galley
Physio: M Winn   **Commercial Manager:** Angela Athersmith
Ground: Parkside Road, Kendal, Cumbria (0539 722469).
Directions: M6 junction 36, follow Skipton sign for 200 yds, left at r-bout, straight into Kendal and follow signs for Netherfield shoe factory, turn into Parkside Road opposite factory main offices - ground 400 yds. One and a half miles from Oxenholme (BR) station - bus service to shoe factory.
Capacity: 4,800   **Cover:** 1,000   **Seats:** 250   **Floodlights:** Yes   **Club Shop:** No.
Colours: White/black/red   **Change colours:** Yellow/green/yellow.   **Sponsors:** 'K' shoes
Previous Leagues: Westmorland/ North Lancs/ Lancs Combination 45-68/ Northern Premier 68-83/ North West Counties 83-87.
Midweek home matchday: Tuesday   **Reserve Team's League:** Westmorland Lg.
Record Attendance: 5,184 v Grimsby Town, FA Cup 1st Rd 1955.
Record win: 11-0 v Great Harwood 22/3/47.
Record defeat: 0-10 v Stalybridge Celtic 1/9/84.
Record transfer fee paid: Undisclosed for Tom Brownlee (Bradford City, 1966).
Record transfer fee received: £7,000 for Andy Milner (Manchester City, 1989).
Best F.A. Cup season: 2nd Rd replay 63-64 (lost 1-4 at Chesterfield after 1-1 draw). Also 2nd Rd 49-50, 1st Rd 45-46 48-49 52-53 54-55 55-56 64-65.
Players progressing to Football League: John Laidlaw (Carlisle 1946), Louis Cardwell (Crewe 1947), Herbert Keen (Barrow 1953), Alec Aston (Preston 1955), Horace Langstreth (Torquay 1956), John Simpson (Lincoln 1957), Dennis Rogers (Accrington 1959), Tom Brownlee (Bradford City 1965), Peter McDonnell (Bury 1973), Keith Silken (Workington 1973), Roger Wicks (Darlington 1981), Andy Milner (Man City).
Clubhouse: The Park, open all matchdays. Pies & pasties available.
Club Record Goalscorer: Tom Brownlee
92-93 Captain: Wayne Maddock/ Chris Ward
92-93 P.o.Y.: Les Breakell
92-93 Top scorers: Andy Whittaker 27.
Local Newspapers: Westmorland Gazette (0539 720555), Lancaster Evening Post.
Local Radio Stations: Radio Cumbria, Red Rose.
Hons: FA Vase 3rd Rd 89-90, FA Tphy 2nd Rd 80-81, Lancs Comb. 48-49 64-65 (R-up 45-46 53-54 61-62 63-64, Lg Cup 55-56 60-61), Westmorland Snr Cup(12) 24-25 31-33 35-36 46-48 63-64 65-66 71-72 86-87 89-89 90-91.

PROGRAMME DETAILS:
Pages: 40 Price: 60p
Editor: Secretary

RADCLIFFE BOROUGH

Radcliffe Borough goalkeeper Dave Ryan stands no chance as he is beaten by a header from Waterloo Dock's Carl Finley. This equaliser set up a remarkable 3-1 win for the visiting Liverpool County Combination side in the F.A. Vase First Round on 31st October. Photo - Rob Ruddock.

Chairman: Ian Wood   **Vice Chairman:** Bernard Manning Jnr   **President:** A A Swarbrick.
Secretary: Graham E Fielding, 93 Callender Street, Ramsbottom, Bury, Lancs BL0 9DU (0706 825299).
Manager: Ken Bridge   **Asst Manager/Coach:** Jimmy Golder   **Physio:** Ivor Jones
Press Officer: M Collins   **Commercial Manager:** F Lomax.
Ground: Stainton Park, Pilkington Road, Radcliffe, Lancs M26 0PE (061 725 9197).
Directions: M62 junction 17 - follow signs for Whitefield and Bury then A665 to Radcliffe. Through town centre, turn right into Unsworth Street (opposite Turf Hotel), ground half mile on left, Colshaw Close Easy. Half a mile from Radcliffe (BR).
Capacity: 3,000   **Cover:** 1,000   **Seats:** 350   **Floodlights:** Yes   **Club Shop:** No.
Colours: All blue   **Change colours:** All red.
Sponsors: Comet Copiers.
Previous Ground: Bright Street 1949-70.
Previous Leagues: South East Lancs/ Manchester 53-63/ Lancs Combination 63-71/ Cheshire County 71-82/ North West Counties 82-87.
Midweek home matchday: Tuesday   **Reserve Team:** None.
Record Attendance: 1,468 v Caernarvon Town, North West Counties League 1983.
Best F.A. Cup season: Second Qualifying Rounds replay 75-76 (lost 1-4 at Rossendale United after 2-2 draw).
Record Fees - Paid: £5,000 for Gary Walker (Buxton, 1990)
                Received: £5,000 for Kevin Hulme (Bury, 1989).
Players progressing to Football League: Jim Hayman (Bury 1950), Ian Wood (Oldham Athletic 1965), Robert Hutchinson (Rochdale 1974), Gary Hawarth (Rochdale 1984), Kevin Hulme (Bury 1989).
Clubhouse: (061 723 4181). 'The Footballers' - public house on ground. No food available.
Club Record Goalscorer: Gary Haworth
Club Record Appearances: Chris Lilley.
92-93 Captain: Simon Whittle.
92-93 P.O.Y.: Peter Coyne
92-93 Top scorer: Peter Coyne.
Local Newspapers: Radcliffe Times, Bolton Evening News, Manchester Evening News.
Local Radio Stations: Greater Manchester Radio (GMR), Piccadilly.
Honours: North West Counties Lg 84-85 (Div 2 82-83), Lancs Combination Lg Cup 69-70), Manchester Lg R-up 55-56 (Lg Cup 58-59(joint)), FA Trophy 1st Rd 72-73.

PROGRAMME DETAILS:
Pages: 28 **Price:** 50p
Editor: Mervyn Collins

SPENNYMOOR UNITED The Moors

Spennymoor United's Andy Shaw steers the ball past Sheffield goalkeeper Darren Lomas for the Moor's fifth and final goal in a Northern Counties (East) League Premier Division fixture on 24th April. Photo - Andrew Mollitt.

Chairman: Mr J B Hindmarsh   **Vice Chairman:** Mr J Norman   **President:** Mr T Beaumont
Secretary: Mr J Nutt, 41 Warwick Close, Grange Estate, Spennymoor, County Durham DL15 6UU (0388 812179).
Manager: Matty Pearson   **Asst Manager:** Dave Barton   **Physio:** John Lumley
Commercial Mgr: Des Beamson   **Press Officer:** Mr J B Hindmarsh (0388 815168).
Ground: Brewery Field, Durham Road, Spennymoor, County Durham DL16 6JN (0388 811934).
Directions: From South; A1(M), A167, A688, straight on at mini-r'bout, 3rd exit at next large r'bout (St Andrews church opposite), pass Asda on left, straight on at junction, pass Salvin Arms (Durham Rd), ground 200 yds on left. From A167 North - leave at Croxdale (N.E.S.S. factory), right at cemetary on left - this is Durham Rd - ground half mile on right. Nearest rail station is Durham - buses from there.
Seats: 300   **Cover:** 1,500   **Capacity:** 7,500   **Floodlights:** Yes
Club Shop: Planned to open during 1993-94 season.
Club colours: Black & white stripes/black/black   **Change colours:** All red
Midweek home matches: Wednesday   **Sponsors:** Home: Rothmans (Spennymoor). Away: Welland Medical
Reserve Team: None   **Previous Ground:** Wood Vue 1901-1904.
Previous Leagues: Mid Durham 01-05/ Northern 05-08 60-90/ North Eastern 08-37 38-58/ Wearside 37-38/ Midland Counties 58-60/ Northern Counties (East) 90-93.
Record Gate: 7,202 v Bishop Auckland, Durham County Challenge Cup 30/3/57.
Local Press: Northern Echo/ The Journal.
Best FA Cup season: 3rd Rd 36-37 (lost 1-7 at West Bromwich Albion).
Best FA Trophy season: Semi Final 77-78.
Record win: 19-0 v Eden Colliery, North Eastern Lge 6/2/37.
Record defeat: 0-16 v Sunderland 'A', Durham Snr Cup 4/1/02 (Half-time: 0-10).
Players progressing to Football League: Jack Oaks, Tommy Dawson, Bert Johnson (all Charlton Athletic).
Record Transfer Fee Received: £20,000 for Michael Heathcote (Sunderland, 1988).
Clubhouse: (0388 814100) Open nightly 7-11pm, Sat noon-11pm, Sun noon-2 & 7-10.30pm. Bar snacks available. Private functions. Well stocked tea bar in ground.
Club Record Scorer: Dougie Humble 200+
Club Record Appearances: Ken Banks 800+
92-93 Captain & P.o.Y.: Brian Healy
92-93 Top scorer: Keith Gorman.
Hons: Northern Lg(6) 67-68 71-72 73-74 76-79 (R-up(3) 74-75 79-81, Lg Cup(5) 65-66 67-68 79-81 86-87, Turney Wylde Cup 80-81, J R Cleator Cup 80-81 86-87), Northern Counties (East) Lg 92-93 (Lg Cup 92-93), Durham Challenge Cup 29-30 44-45 45-46 53-54 62-63 67-68 72-73 73-74 74-75 75-76 82-83; Durham Benevolent Bowl 26-27 29-30 31-32 47-48 58-59 60-61, North Eastern Lg(4) 09-10 44-46 56-57 (Lg Cup 28-29).

PROGRAMME DETAILS:
Pages: 32 Price: 50p
Editor: Peter Mains
(091 378 0135)

WARRINGTON TOWN

The Warrington Town side that contested the second most important match in the club's history - the Vauxhall F.A. Trophy Quarter-Final at Sutton United on 13th March. Photo - Eric Marsh.

Chairman: R Hennessey   **Vice Chairman:** C Henshall   **President:** R Smith.
Secretary: Graham Ost, 120 Warrington Rd, Penketh, Warrington, Cheshire WA5 2JZ (0925 722540).
Manager: Derek Brownbill   **Asst Manager:** Alan Blair
Coach: Dennis Smith   **Press Officer:** Colin Serjent
Commercial Manager: Joan Gleave.
Ground: Cantilever Park, Common Lane, off Loushers Lane, Latchford, Warrington WA4 2RS (0925 31932).
Directions: M6 junction 20, then A50 towards Warrington. After 2 miles turn left immediately after swing bridge into Station Road, ground 600yds on left. From town centre travel 1 mile south on A49, left at lights into Loushers Lane, ground quarter mile on right. 2 miles from Warrington Bank Quay (BR).
Capacity: 2,500   **Cover:** 500   **Seats:** 200   **Floodlights:** Yes   **Club Shop:** No.
Colours: Yellow/blue/yellow   **Change colours:** Red/white
Sponsors: Whitbread Plc.
Previous Name: Stockton Heath 1949-62.
Best F.A. Cup season: 3rd Qualifying Rd 88-89 (lost 1-2 at home to Leek Town).
Best F.A. Vase season: Finalists 86-87 (lost 2-3 to St Helens Town).
Best F.A. Trophy season: Quarter-Finalists 92-93 (lost 1-2 at Sutton United).
Previous Leagues: Warrington & Dist. 49-52/ Mid-Cheshire 52-78/ Cheshire Co. 78-82/ North West Co's 82-90.
Midweek home matchday: Wednesday   **Reserve Team's League:** Northern Combination.
Record Attendance: 3,000 v Halesowen Town, FA Vase Semi Final 1st leg 85-86.
Players progressing to Football League: Sam Morris (Chester 1951), John Green (Tranmere 1958), Roger Hunt (Liverpool 1959), John Richards (Wolves), John Bramhall (Tranmere 1976), Mark Leonard (Everton, Stockport, Bradford City).
Clubhouse: Weekdays 1pm-11pm, Sat. noon-11pm, Sun. 12-3pm, 7pm-10.30pm.
Club Record Goalscorer: L Arnold 60
Local Newspapers: Warrington Guardian (0925 33033), Warrington Mercury, Manchester Evening News, Liverpool Post & Echo.
Local Radio Stations: Radio Merseyside, Radio Manchester (GMR).
Honours: FA Vase R-up 86-87 (SF 85-86), FA Trophy QF 92-93, North West Counties Lg 89-90 (Lg Cup 85-86 87-88 88-89 (R-up 89-90), Div 2 R-up 86-87, Div 3 R-up 82-83, Reserve Div West 89-90), Mid Cheshire Lg 60-61 (R-up 57-58, Lg Cup 54-55 55-56) 11-12 72-73, Altrincham Amateur Cup 54-55.

PROGRAMME DETAILS:
Pages: 36 **Price:** 50p
Editor: Garry Clarke

WORKINGTON

Workington 1992-93. Back Row (L/R): Nigel Dustin, Paul Barwise, Lee Bowen, Paul Campbell, John Holliday, Lee Copeland, Keith Glover, Malcolm Rice, Billy Gilmour, Dale Brotherton, Alan Cook (Manager). Front: Jackie Hather, Danny Wheatley, Chris Collins, Peter Crellan (Mascot), Graham Flynn, Paul Doolan, Graham Caton, Kevin Logue. Photo - Cumbrian Newspapers Ltd.

Chairman: J J Donald   **President:** E Fisher.
Secretary: Tom Robson, 12 Derwent Bank, Seaton, Workington CA14 1EE (0900 605208).
Manager: Alan Cook   **Asst Manager:** Billy Gilmour
Press Officer: Steve Durham (0946 61380)   **Physio:** Reg Carther.
Ground: Borough Park, Workington, Cumbria CA14 2DT (0900 602871).
Directions: A66 into town, right at 'T' junction, follow A596 for three quarters of a mile - ground is then visible and signposted. Ground is to north of town centre quarter of a mile from Workington (BR) station and half mile from bus station in town centre.
Capacity: 2,500   **Cover:** 800   **Seats:** 200   **Floodlights:** Yes   **Metal Badges:** Yes
Club Shop: Yes - contact Martin Wingfield (0900 818346).
Colours: Red/white/red   **Change colours:** Sky/black/sky.   **Sponsors:** T.B.A.
Reserve Team's League: County Youth.
Previous Leagues: Cumberland Association 1890-94/ Cumberland Snr 94-1901 03-04/ Lancs Lge 1901-03/ Lancs Combination 04-10/ North Eastern 10-11 21-51/ Football League 51-77.
Midweek home matchday: Tuesday   **Previous Ground:** Lonsdale Park 1884-1937.
Record Attendance: 21,000 v Manchester United, F.A. Cup 3rd Rd 1958.
Best F.A. Cup season: 4th Rd, 1933-34. Competition Proper on 53 other occasions.
Record win: 17-1 (pre-1900)
Record loss: 0-9 v Chorley (A), Northern Premier Lge Premier Division, 10/11/87.
Record Fees - Paid: £6,000 for Ken Chisholm (Sunderland, 1956).
             Received: £33,000 for Ian McDonald (Liverpool, 1974).
Players progressing to Football League: Numerous, the best known being John Burridge.
Clubhouse: Open matchdays and for private functions. Food on matchdays restricted menu.
Club Record Goalscorer: Billy Charlton 193
Club Record Apps: Bobby Brown 419.
92-93 Captain: Graham Flynn
92-93 P.o.Y.: Graham Flynn
92-93 Top scorer: Paul Campbell 12.
Local Newspapers: Evening News & Star, Times & Star (John Walsh 0900 601234).
Local Radio Stations: BBC Radio Cumbria (0228 31661).
Honours: Football League Cup QF 63-64 64-65, Football Lg: 5th Div 3 65-66, 3rd Div 4 63-64, Northern Premier Presidents Cup 83-84, North Eastern Lg R-up 38-39 (Lg Cup 34-35 36-37 (R-up 37-38)), Cumberland County Cup 1886-87 87-88 88-89 89-90 90-91 95-96 96-97 97-98 98-99 1906-07 07-08 09-10 24-25 34-35 36-37 37-38 49-50 53-54 67-68 85-86 (R-up 1885-86 91-92 1899-1900 00-01 02-03 08-09 11-12 23-24 26-27 29-30 46-47 68-69 78-79), FA Trophy 1st Rd replay 77-78.

PROGRAMME DETAILS:
Pages: 20 **Price:** 50p
Editor: Steve Durham
(0946 61380)

WORKSOP TOWN

Worksop Town F.C. 1992-93 pictured in front of the clubhouse at their new Sandy Lane ground. Back Row (L/R): Ian Clark, Paul Mainwaring, Darren Brookes, Paul Norton, David Moss (now Doncaster Rovers), Paul Barnett, Dave Cunnington. Front: Adrian Shaw, Kenny Clark, Neil Pickering, Linden Whitehead, Gary Thorpe, Lee Howard.

Chairman: Mel Bradley **Vice Chairman:** W E Peace.
Secretary: W E Peace, 72 Woodburn Drive, Chapeltown, Sheffield S30 4YT (0742 468160).
Manager: Tommy Spencer **Asst Manager:** John Stokes **Physio:** Tommy Watson.
Press Officer: Mel Bradley **Commercial Manager:** Christine Scott.
Ground: Babbage Way, off Sandy Lane, Worksop, Notts.
Directions: M1 jct 31 (from north) jct 30 (from south), follow Worksop signs, join A57 and follow signs for Sandy Lane Industrial Estate - ground on left. 5 mins walk from station.
Capacity: 1,500 **Cover:** 660 **Seats:** 360 **Floodlights:** Yes. **Metal Badges:** Yes.
Club Shop: The Tigershop selling badges, scarves, magazines, programmes. 30 page catalogue from Steve Jarvis, 10 Wood End Drive, Ravenshead, Notts NG15 9EJ.
Colours: Amber/black **Change colours:** Blue/white.
Previous Grounds: Netherton Road/ Bridge Meadow/ Central Avenue (prior to 1989)/ The Northolme (Gainsborough Trinity F.C.) (shared) 89-92.
Previous Leagues: Midland (Counties) 1896-98 1900-30 49-60 61-68 69-74/ Sheffield Association 1898-99 1931-33/ Central Combination 33-35/ Yorkshire 35-39/ Central Alliance 47-49 60-61/ Northern Premier 68-69.
Midweek home matchday: Monday **Sponsors:** Eyres of Worksop
Reserve Team's League: Doncaster Senior (Youth Team: Notts Youth League).
Record Attendance: 1,503 v Sheffield United, friendly. *At Central Avenue: 8,171 v Chesterfield, FA Cup 1925.*
Record win: 20-0 v Staveley, 1/9/1894 **Record defeat:** 1-11 v Hull City Reserves, 55-56.
Best FA Cup year: 3rd Rd 55-56 (lost 0-1 at Swindon). 2nd Rd 25-26. 1st Rd 07-08 21-22 22-23 26-27 61-62 78-79.
League Clubs defeated in F.A. Cup: Rotherham Town 1893-94/ Grimsby Town 94-95/ Nelson 1921-22/ Chesterfield 22-23/ Coventry City 25-26.
Record Fees - Paid: None. **Received:** £10,000 for Martin Hardy (Boston U. 1987).
Players progressing to Football League: Jack Brown (Sheff Wed & England), Gordon Dale (Chesterfield 1948), Alan Daley (Doncaster 1950), Kevin Wood (Grimsby 1951), Harry Jarvis (Notts County 1951), Brian Taylor (Leeds 1951), Stan Rhodes & Dennis Gratton & Alan Hodgkinson & John Harrison (Sheffield United 1951 & 52 & 53 67), Stanley Lloyd & Peter Marshall (Scunthorpe 1954), Albert Rhodes (QPR 1954), Robert Moore (Rotherham 1955), Harold Mosby (Crewe 1956), Les Moore (Derby 1957), Herbert Bowery (Nottm Forest 1975), Tony Moore (Rochdale 1984), Steve Adams (Scarborough 1987).
Clubhouse: Tigers Club. Normal licensing hours. Pool, quiz nights, disco etc.
Club Record Goalscorer: Kenny Clark, 115.
Club Record appearances: Dave Cunnington, 315.
92-93 Captain: Neil Pickering
92-93 P.O.Y.: David Cunnington.
92-93 Top scorer: Gary Waller.
Local Press: Worksop Guardian (500500), Worksop Star (486335), Nottingham Football Post (0602 475221).
Local Radio Stations: Radio Sheffield, Radio Hallam, Radio Lincoln.
Hons: Northern Prem. Lg Presidents Cup 85-86, Midland Co's Lg 21-22 65-66 72-73 (R-up 62-63 66-67 73-74), Sheffield Association Lg 1898-99, Sheffield & Hallamshire Snr Cup 23-24 52-53 54-55 65-66 69-70 72-73 81-82 84-85, Mansfield Charity Cup, F.A. Trophy 2nd Rd replay 73-74.

Worksop Town Football Club

PROGRAMME DETAILS:
Pages: 28-32 **Price:** 50p
Editor: Mel Bradley
(0909 500491/500500)

Northern Premier League Division One Seven Year Records

	87/8	88/9	89/0	90/1	91/2	92/3
Accrington Stanley	4	6	3	4	–	–
Alfreton Town	11	20	18	22	20	9
Ashton United	–	–	–	–	–	3
Bishop Auckland	–	2	–	–	–	–
Bridlington Town	–	–	–	9	6	1
Caernarfon Town	–	–	–	14	5	16
Colne Dynamoes	–	1	–	–	–	–
Colwyn Bay	–	–	–	–	1	–
Congleton Town	9	10	6	11	17	20
Curzon Ashton	18	13	8	10	11	7
Droylsden	6	4	2	–	–	–
Eastwood Hanley	7	8	21	–	–	–
Eastwood Town	17	12	11	6	15	14
Emley	–	–	5	2	–	–
Farsley Celtic	5	14	12	21	12	17
Fleetwood Town	1	–	–	–	–	–
Gretna	–	–	–	–	–	6
Great Harwood Town	–	–	–	–	–	8
Guiseley	–	–	–	–	4	4
Harrogate Town	10	8	9	19	10	10
Irlam Town	13	15	15	17	21	–
Knowsley United	–	–	–	–	8	2
(City of) Lancaster	16	7	10	8	16	18
Leek Town	3	3	1	–	–	–
Netherfield	19	21	20	12	9	15
Newtown	–	9	14	13	14	–
Penrith	14	16	22	–	–	–
Radcliffe Borough	12	17	17	16	13	12
Rhyl	–	–	–	5	18	–
Rossendale United	–	–	13	15	19	21
Shepshed Albion	–	–	–	–	–	19
Stalybridge Celtic	2	–	–	–	–	–
Sutton Town	15	22	–	–	–	–
Warrington Town	–	–	–	7	7	5
Whitley Bay	–	5	4	1	–	–
Winsford United	8	19	7	18	2	–
Workington	–	11	16	20	22	13
Worksop Town	–	–	19	3	3	11
No. of Clubs	**19**	**22**	**22**	**22**	**22**	**21**

Workington goalkeeper Lee Copeland gratefully cluthches a cross, but the Reds lost 0-1 at home to the powerful Bridlington Town side on 14th March. Photo - Alan Watson.

THE CARLING
N.W. COUNTIES LEAGUE

President: Canon J.R.Smith, M.A.
Chairman: J.E.Hincliffe   **Treasure:** K.H.Dean
Hon. Secretary: M.Darby, 87 Hillary Road, Hyde, Cheshire SK14 4EB

Having acepted seven new clubs into division two in the summer of '92, which in turn enabled no fewer than eight clubs to be promoted into the top section. A very open league title was expected - in reality it was scarcely anything other than a two-horse race.

Bamber Bridge, second division champions and FA Vase semi-finalists in the spring, were expected of be one of the leading lights and they didn't disappoint, setting a cracking pace that others simply found too hot to handle. But by Christmas their impressive form was on the wain and in January they were beaten for the first time in 21 league starts. By now Atherton LR were growing in stature and both dark houses Chadderton and Prescot were in touch. The leadership finally changed hands in February with 'LR' in unstoppable mood. In all they put together an incredible 15-match winning league sequence. Others maintained a good rate behind but the Atherton club were moving further ahead and out of sight. Only a dramatic change in fortunes would now deny the Crilly Park club the championship, but it was Bamber Bridge who found the run-in difficult leaving LR 23 points clear on the back of an amazing 39-game unbeaten run. Indeed 'Brig' almost lost the runners-up spot to Chadderton right at the death - A last minute Penrith equaliser denied 'Chaddy' victory in their last game and the certainty of overhauling them.

At the bottom of division one it was also clear cut. Blackpool Mechanics had the dubious distinction of having more managerial changes than league successes and Skelmersdale United never fully recovered from a dreadful start....but the latter were saved from relegation due to events in a more interesting division two.

The strong element of unknowns in this section made it difficult to predict. Early on newcomers Stantondale from Liverpool were in top gear, former West Lancs League club Burnley Bank Hall were brilliant on their travels, and reformed Ellesmere Port Town were always in the top six, but ultimately it came down to unfashionable clubs Oldham Town and Maghull, who always had plenty in hand, and Bootle, who put a tremendous run together in the closing weeks. They won 12 of their last 15 games, remaining unbeaten in the last 11, but they ran out of matches as they headed the table entering May. Oldham suffered some serious setbacks in the run-in and finished up having to win their last match to overhaul Bootle....and that was at Maghull, who were always in control of their own destiny. The Merseysiders won that game and took the title a few days later, thanks in part to one unbeaten league sequence of 18 games.

On the Domestic Cup front, division one clubs ruled the roost for once. Burscough went one better by lifting the Bass Challenge Cup, defeating Nantwich in a good Gigg Lane final, having been runners-up 12 months earlier. Newcastle Town outmaneouvre Chadderton to claim the Tennents Floodlit Trophy at Springfield Park while Stantondale did likewise in the Lamot Pils Trophy to deny Maghull a possible league and cup double.

County and national-wise it was a disappointing season. The odd HFS scalp was claimed in the early stages of the FA Cup, but after a good opening to the FA Vase, all came to grief by Round Three having had eight clubs in the Second Round. Cup specialists Burscough were our one leading light in the County competitions, defeating Everton Reserves en route to the Liverpool Senior Cup Final but they found all-conquering Southport just a touch to clever in the Goodison Park climax.

Alan Bartlam (Press Officer).

Atherton L.R. 1992/93 - Bass North West Counties Division One Champions.

DIV. ONE	P	W	D	L	F	A	PTS
Atherton L.R.	42	33	7	2	75	25	106
Bamber Bridge	42	24	11	7	81	37	83
Chadderton	42	24	11	7	99	64	83
Prescot A.F.C.	42	20	12	10	68	44	72
Newcastle Town	42	20	8	14	70	57	68
Bradford Park Ave.	42	19	8	15	54	43	65
Clitheroe	42	17	8	17	61	40	59
St Helens Town	42	16	11	15	79	62	59
Salford City	42	15	13	14	58	61	58
Burscough	42	16	10	16	58	68	57
Flixton	42	14	15	13	50	42	57
Blackpool Rovers	42	16	9	17	66	64	57
Nantwich Town	42	14	15	13	60	60	57
Penrith	42	15	11	16	62	67	56
Bacup Borough	42	14	13	15	66	59	55
Glossop North End	42	16	9	17	70	67	*54
Darwen	42	14	10	18	54	61	52
Eastwood Hanley	42	14	10	18	45	57	52
Maine Road	42	12	9	21	55	63	45
Kidsgrove Athletic	42	9	8	25	53	94	35
Skelmersdale Utd	42	7	10	25	45	84	31
Blackpool Mech.	42	2	4	36	27	137	10

* - 3 points deducted

RES. DIV. SOUTH	P	W	D	L	F	A	PTS
Flixton Res.	18	14	3	1	69	19	45
Nth Trafford Res.	18	11	3	4	49	23	36
Chadderton Res.	18	10	4	4	64	30	34
Salford City Res.	18	10	3	5	34	29	33
Maghull Res.	18	7	6	5	39	32	27
Kidsgrove Ath. Res.	18	7	2	9	38	39	23
Maine Road Res.	18	4	7	7	34	44	19
Glossop N.E. Res.	18	4	3	11	30	45	15
Castleton Gab. Res.	18	3	2	13	46	63	11
Irlam Town Res.	18	3	1	14	19	98	10

DIV. TWO	P	W	D	L	F	A	PTS
Maghull	34	21	9	4	77	26	72
Bootle	34	20	8	6	89	49	68
Oldham Town	34	20	6	8	79	47	66
Ellesmere Port T.	34	16	9	9	65	46	57
Stantondale	34	16	9	9	59	49	57
Castleton Gabriels	34	15	10	9	61	48	55
North Trafford	34	14	9	11	67	63	51
Formby	34	14	9	11	49	49	51
Atherton Collieries	34	14	7	13	63	67	49
Burnley Bank Hall	34	14	4	16	87	77	46
Westhoughton T.	34	14	3	17	65	75	*42
Cheadle Town	34	12	7	15	44	48	*40
Squires Gate	34	11	5	18	56	73	38
K. Chell	34	10	8	16	52	72	38
Holker Old Boys	34	8	13	13	57	60	37
Ashton Town	34	8	8	18	51	74	32
Nelson	34	7	7	20	47	82	28
Irlam Town	34	4	5	25	47	110	17

* - 3 points deducted

RES. DIV. NORTH	P	W	D	L	F	A	PTS
Bamber Bridge Res.	18	13	4	1	51	10	43
Atherton L.R. Res.	18	13	2	3	56	20	41
Darwen Res.	18	8	6	4	36	32	30
Burnley Bk H. Res.	18	8	3	7	24	37	27
Westhoughton Res.	18	6	6	6	24	30	24
Atherton Coll. Res.	18	5	5	8	31	34	20
Holker O.B. Res.	18	4	7	7	22	26	19
Ashton Town	18	5	3	10	30	38	18
Blackpool M. Res.	18	4	5	9	21	44	17
Squires Gate Res.	18	1	5	12	27	51	8

RESERVE DIVISIONS CHAMPIONSHIP DECIDER:
Bamber Bridge 1, Flixton 3 (24/4/93)

'BASS' MONTHLY AWARDS

Month	Div. 1 Player	Div. 1 Manager	Div. 2 Player	Div. 2 Manager
Sept.		B Massie (Bamber B)		A McCumiskey (Maghull)
Oct.		D Morris (Atherton LR)		D Porter (Holker OB)
Nov.	R Johnson (Eastwd)	M Holgate (St Helens)		H Hazard (Oldham Town)
Dec.	A Moloney (Flixton)	R Perkins (Burscough)	D Sutton (Ashton Town)	D McArdle (Ellesmere Pt)
Jan.	I Walsh (Skel'dale)	A Bradshaw (Clitheroe)	R Burrows (Ellesmere Pt)	R Grundy/
			G Manning (N Trafford)	T Lawson (Stantondale)
Feb.	I Monk (Clitheroe)	C Jackson (Nantwich)	A Shawcross (West'ghton)	D McArdle (Ellesmere)
Mar.	J Parrett (Bacup)	B Massie (Bamber B)	S O'Neil (Bootle)	T Fagan (Bootle)
Apr.	D Underwood (C'roe)	D Morris (Atherton LR)	A Strange (Castleton)	P Hennerty (Formby)

Division One 'Manager of the Year': Dave Morris (Atherton L.R.)
Division One 'Player of the Year': Ian Monk (Clitheroe)
Division Two 'Manager of the Year': Arthur McCumiskey (Maghull)
Division Three 'Player of the Year': Mick Gilmore

Maghull skipper Billy Roberts lifts the Division Two championship trophy before his side's 5-1 thrashing of Atherton Collieries on F.A. Cup final morning.

'BASS' CHALLENGE CUP 1992-93

First Round

Atherton Collieries v Maghull	1-3
Irlam Town v Burnley Bank Hall	2-0
Nelson v Ellesmere Port Town	1-8
Oldham Town v Ashton Town	2-3
Holker Old Boys v Castleton Gabriels	1-0
K Chell v Cheadle Town	2-0
North Trafford v Stantondale	1-3
Squires Gate v Westhoughton Town	0-0,2-6

Second Round

Ashton Town v Stantondale	2-3
Bamber Bridge v Penrith	3-3,2-1
Bootle v Nantwich Town	1-5
Chadderton v St Helens Town	1-1,4-3
Ellesmere Port Town v Bacup Borough	3-0
Glossop North End v Newcastle Town	1-0
Prescot v Kidsgrove Athletic	4-0
Skelmersdale United v Maghull	2-2,3-4(aet)
Atherton Laburnum Rovers v Flixton	4-2
Blackpool Rovers v Holker Old Boys	2-2,5-1
Braford Park Avenue v Maine Road	2-2,1-0
Clitheroe v Eastwood Hanley	3-1
Formby v Burscough	0-4
Irlam Town v Blackpool Mechanics	1-4
Salford City v Darwen	1-2
Westhoughton Town v K Chell	5-1

Third Round

Bamber Bridge v Blackpool Mechanics	6-2
Burscough v Clitheroe	6-2
Glossop North End v Bradford Park Avenue	4-1
Stantondale v Prescot	1-3
Blackpool Rovers v Darwen	1-1,0-3
Ellesmore Port Town v Nantwich Town	0-3
Maghull v Chadderton	1-4
Westhoughton Town v Atherton L.R.	0-0,0-2

Quarter-Finals

Burscough v Bamber Bridge	4-1
Nantwich Town v Chadderton	1-0
Glossop North End v Atherton Laburnum Rvrs	2-0
Prescot v Darwen	5-0

Semi-Finals (Two Legs)

Burscough v Prescot	1-0,2-2
Nantwich Town v Glossop North End	3-1,2-1

Final *(at Bury F.C.)*: Burscough 2, Nantwich Town 1

Burscough in exuberant mood after their victory over Nantwich at Gigg Lane.

'TENNENTS' FLOODLIT TROPHY

GROUP A.	P	W	D	L	F	A	PTS
Skelmersdale Utd	6	4	0	2	17	8	12
Ellesmere Port T.	6	4	0	2	13	7	12
Flixton	6	3	0	3	7	8	9
Atherton L.R.	6	1	0	5	2	16	3

RESULTS		1	2	3	4
1.	Atherton Laburnum Rovers	*	0-2	1-0	1-3
2.	Ellesmere Port Town	3-0	*	2-0	4-1
3.	Flixton	1-0	3-2	*	0-2
4.	Skelmersdale United	7-0	3-0	1-3	*

GROUP C.	P	W	D	L	F	A	PTS
Clitheroe	6	5	1	0	14	2	16
Salford City	6	2	1	3	5	7	7
Bacup Borough	6	2	1	3	5	9	7
Darwen	6	1	1	4	3	9	4

RESULTS		1	2	3	4
1.	Bacup Borough	*	0-2	3-1	2-0
2.	Clitheroe	4-0	*	1-0	4-1
3.	Darwen	0-0	1-3	*	1-0
4.	Salford City	2-0	0-0	2-0	*

GROUP B.	P	W	D	L	F	A	PTS
Bamber Bridge	6	5	0	1	19	7	15
Penrith	6	4	0	2	15	9	12
Blackpool Rovers	6	2	1	3	10	9	7
Blackpool Mech.	6	0	1	5	5	24	1

RESULTS		1	2	3	4
1.	Bamber Bridge	*	7-0	3-2	4-2
2.	Blackpool Mechanics	0-2	*	1-1	1-6
3.	Blackpool Rovers	0-2	5-2	*	0-1
4.	Penrith	3-1	3-1	0-2	*

GROUP D.	P	W	D	L	F	A	PTS
Nantwich Town	6	4	1	1	8	3	13
Newcastle Town	6	3	3	0	14	7	12
Kidsgrove Athletic	6	1	2	3	7	12	5
Eastwood Hanley	6	0	2	4	5	12	2

RESULTS		1	2	3	4
1.	Eastwood Hanley	*	0-3	0-2	3-3
2.	Kidsgrove Athletic	1-1	*	1-2	1-1
3.	Nantwich Town	1-0	2-0	*	0-1
4.	Newcastle Town	2-1	6-1	1-1	*

(continued from page 883)

GROUP E.	P	W	D	L	F	A	PTS
Chadderton	6	5	0	1	12	4	15
Bradford Park Ave.	6	4	1	1	13	11	13
Maine Road	6	1	1	4	8	10	4
Glossop North End	6	0	2	4	7	15	2

RESULTS		1	2	3	4
1.	Bradford Park Avenue	*	0-4	4-2	2-1
2.	Chadderton	1-3	*	1-0	3-0
3.	Glossop North End	2-2	1-2	*	1-1
4.	Maine Road	1-2	0-1	5-1	*

GROUP F.	P	W	D	L	F	A	PTS
Prescot A.F.C.	6	4	1	1	13	4	13
Burscough	6	2	3	1	8	9	9
Bootle	6	1	3	2	9	11	6
St Helens Town	6	1	1	4	5	11	4

RESULTS		1	2	3	4
1.	Bootle	*	1-1	2-4	1-1
2.	Burscough	2-2	*	0-4	3-1
3.	Prescot	1-2	0-0	*	1-0
4.	St Helens Town	2-1	1-2	0-3	*

Quarter Finals

Bamber Bridge 2, Prescot A.F.C. 0

Newcastle Town 1, Skelmersdale United 0

Nantwich Town 3, Clitheroe 1

Chadderton 3, Bradford Park Avenue 0

Semi Finals

Nantwich Town 1, Chadderton 3

Newcastle Town 2, Bamber Bridge 1

Final *(at Wigan Athletic F.C)*: Chadderton 0, Newcastle Town 2

Newcastle Town celebrate their success in the Tennents Floodlit Trophy final.

'LAMOT PILS' CHALLENGE TROPHY 1992-93

Preliminary Round

K Chell v Ellesmere Port Town	1-2	Squires Gate v Nelson	2-1

First Round

Ashton Town v Atherton Collieries	1-2	Burnley Bank Hall v North Trafford	4-2
Cheadle Town v Ellesmere Port Town	1-2	Formby v Maghull	1-1,0-2
Holker Old Boys v Squires Gate	2-0	Oldham Town v Castleton Gabriels	2-2,4-1
Stantondale v Irlam Town	3-1	Westhoughton Town v Bootle *(at Bootle)*	1-5

Quarter-Finals

Bootle v Maghull	0-3	Atherton C. v Burnley B.H.	3-3,3-3(aet 4-1 pens)
Ellesmere Port Town v Holker Old Boys	2-1	Oldham Town v Stantondale	0-2

Semi-Finals (Two Legs)

Ellesmere Port Town v Maghull	0-5,2-1	Stantondale v Atherton Collieries	5-2,2-4(aet)

Final *(at Burscough F.C.)*: Stantondale 2, Maghull 1

Stantondale rejoice in winning a trophy in their first season in the North West Counties League.

DIVISION ONE RESULT CHART

HOME TEAM	1	2	3	4	5	6	7	8	9	10	11	12	13	14	15	16	17	18	19	20	21	22
1. Atherton LR	*	1-0	2-0	2-0	3-1	2-0	1-0	2-1	1-1	0-0	1-0	1-0	1-0	3-1	2-0	1-0	4-0	4-3	4-0	2-0	1-0	1-0
2. Bacup Bor.	2-5	*	1-1	5-0	4-2	0-0	1-0	1-2	1-1	2-3	1-3	1-0	2-0	1-1	1-1	2-2	1-2	2-2	1-2	2-2	1-1	3-1
3. Bamber Bdge	3-1	1-2	*	6-0	1-1	1-1	1-0	7-1	0-1	2-1	1-0	2-1	3-0	2-0	2-0	1-1	5-1	4-1	0-0	2-2	1-0	1-0
4. B'pool Mech.	0-3	0-4	0-5	*	0-1	0-2	0-4	2-4	0-3	1-5	1-2	0-3	3-0	2-3	0-2	2-4	0-7	1-4	1-5	0-3	0-4	2-3
5. B'pool Rvrs	1-2	1-0	1-0	4-0	*	2-0	6-2	1-2	2-0	1-3	4-1	3-3	2-0	3-0	2-1	1-2	1-0	1-2	0-3	0-3	1-1	1-0
6. B'ford PA	1-2	1-3	0-2	2-1	2-1	*	1-2	1-2	1-0	1-0	1-2	2-2	1-0	2-0	2-0	0-1	1-0	2-1	2-1	3-0	2-0	
7. Burscough	0-0	4-1	0-2	3-3	2-2	2-2	*	1-3	2-1	1-0	0-0	4-1	3-2	0-2	0-1	2-1	1-0	0-0	0-0	3-2	1-3	1-0
8. Chadderton	1-2	3-1	2-2	6-0	3-1	3-2	2-2	*	2-3	2-2	4-2	1-1	4-1	3-1	2-1	3-0	1-0	0-0	2-0	4-0	4-2	6-4
9. Clitheroe	0-1	5-1	2-3	2-0	0-0	1-0	1-0	0-0	*	3-1	5-0	2-1	0-1	3-1	0-1	3-0	0-1	4-2	0-1	0-2	5-0	2-0
10. Darwen	0-1	1-4	0-1	2-1	1-0	2-1	2-3	1-1	1-1	*	0-1	0-1	0-3	3-1	0-2	2-1	2-0	5-1	1-2	1-1	1-1	0-0
11. E. Hanley	0-2	2-2	1-3	0-0	1-0	0-2	0-1	0-3	1-0	0-1	*	0-1	2-1	0-1	2-0	1-1	5-0	2-3	0-3	1-0	2-2	2-0
12. Flixton	0-0	0-1	1-2	2-0	1-1	2-0	2-1	2-2	0-0	4-1	0-1	*	0-2	3-0	0-0	4-0	1-1	1-1	1-1	3-3	1-0	1-1
13. Glossop	2-4	1-0	1-1	5-0	2-0	1-2	1-2	3-1	1-0	0-1	2-0	0-0	*	7-2	2-1	2-2	3-1	1-2	1-1	3-5	0-3	2-0
14. Kidsgrove	0-0	0-1	1-3	2-3	3-3	0-0	1-4	3-2	3-1	3-0	1-3	0-1	0-4	*	2-2	1-2	3-1	1-4	1-4	0-1	2-2	2-2
15. Maine Rd	2-2	0-2	3-1	3-0	1-2	0-2	1-2	2-2	1-0	0-0	1-1	1-2	3-3	4-1	*	1-2	1-3	2-0	1-2	0-3	3-0	2-2
16. Nantwich	1-3	1-1	2-2	1-0	1-2	1-1	6-0	1-0	1-0	2-3	1-1	4-1	2-2	1-1	2-1	*	3-4	2-1	2-2	2-1	0-0	2-0
17. Newcastle	0-2	0-0	0-1	6-0	2-2	2-1	3-1	2-2	2-0	2-0	1-2	0-3	2-2	3-1	2-1	2-2	*	1-0	2-1	2-2	5-0	3-1
18. Penrith	2-2	0-5	3-0	2-1	3-0	0-6	4-2	1-1	1-2	1-1	1-1	0-0	2-3	3-0	2-1	1-0	0-1	*	1-1	0-1	0-2	2-0
19. Prescot	0-1	1-0	0-0	0-0	3-3	2-0	0-0	2-3	1-1	2-0	1-0	2-0	1-1	4-0	1-3	0-1	1-0	1-2	*	4-1	4-1	4-2
20. St Helens	2-0	1-1	2-1	7-0	1-3	0-0	4-0	1-3	1-1	5-1	2-2	0-1	5-1	2-4	1-2	0-0	0-2	3-2	3-0	*	3-3	1-0
21. Salford	1-2	2-1	0-0	4-1	2-1	2-2	2-2	2-3	1-0	2-2	2-0	1-0	0-1	1-0	3-2	2-0	1-1	0-0	1-3	1-0	*	3-0
22. Skelmersdale	0-1	1-1	0-5	2-2	3-2	0-1	3-0	2-3	1-6	0-4	1-1	1-1	2-1	2-4	3-1	1-1	0-0	1-3	1-2	3-2	2-0	*

North West Counties Division One 10-Year Record

	83/4	84/5	85/6	86/7	87/8	88/9	89/0	90/1	91/2	92/3
Accrington Stanley	7	15	11	2	-	-	-	-	-	-
Ashton United	19	-	-	-	-	17	9	3	1	-
Atherton Laburnum Rovers	-	-	-	-	17	14	14	18	11	1
Bacup Borough	-	-	-	-	-	-	-	14	14	15
Bamber Bridge	-	-	-	-	-	-	-	-	-	2
Blackpool Mechanics	-	-	-	-	-	-	-	-	-	22
Blackpool Rovers	-	-	-	-	-	-	-	-	4	12
Bootle	16	14	15	5	13	9	11	13	18	-
Bradford Park Avenue	-	-	-	-	-	-	-	-	17	6
Burscough	4	3	9	12	10	10	17	-	-	10
Caernarfon Town	14	2	-	-	-	-	-	-	-	-
Chadderton	-	-	-	-	-	-	18	-	-	3
Clitheroe	-	-	1	3	3	12	5	15	9	7
Colne Dynamoes	-	-	-	-	1	-	-	-	-	-
Colwyn Bay	-	-	-	-	4	4	3	2	-	-
Congleton Town	9	10	2	11	-	-	-	-	-	-
Curzon Ashton	5	6	8	19	-	-	-	-	-	-
Darwen	20	-	-	-	7	5	6	16	10	17
Eastwood Hanley	-	5	3	14	-	-	-	4	3	18
Ellesmere Port & Neston	-	-	-	-	6	11	-	-	-	-
Fleetwood Town	-	8	5	8	-	-	-	-	-	-
Flixton	-	-	-	-	-	7	12	7	8	11
Formby	13	17	20	-	14	18	-	-	-	-
Glossop (North End)	15	16	18	20	18	-	-	-	-	16
Great Harwood Town	-	-	-	-	-	-	-	-	2	-
Irlam Town	-	-	6	18	-	-	-	-	-	-
Kidsgrove Athletic	-	-	-	-	-	-	-	-	-	20
Kirkby Town (See Knowsley United)										
Knowsley United	-	-	-	4	9	2	2	1	-	-
Lancaster City	6	19	-	-	-	-	-	-	-	-
Leek Town	11	9	7	16	-	-	-	-	-	-
Leyland Motors	17	11	12	13	11	8	13	12	-	-
Maine Road	-	-	-	-	-	-	-	9	16	19
Nantwich Town	-	-	-	-	-	-	7	11	12	13
Netherfield	18	18	17	17	-	-	-	-	-	-
Newcastle Town	-	-	-	-	-	-	-	-	-	5
Penrith	2	20	16	9	-	-	-	17	6	14
Prescot A.F.C.	10	13	19	-	12	15	10	6	5	4
Prescot Cables (see Prescot A.F.C.)										
Radcliffe Borough	3	1	14	15	-	-	-	-	-	-
Rossendale United	-	-	-	10	2	1	-	-	-	-
St Helens Town	8	12	10	6	5	3	8	8	15	8
Salford (City)	-	-	-	-	15	16	16	19	-	9
Skelmersdale United	-	-	-	-	16	13	15	10	7	21
Stalybridge Celtic	1	4	4	1	-	-	-	-	-	-
Vauxhall G.M.	-	-	-	-	-	-	4	5	13	-
Warrington Town	-	-	-	-	8	6	1	-	-	-
Winsford United	12	7	13	7	-	-	-	-	-	-
No. of clubs competing	20	20	20	20	18	18	18	19	18	22

DIVISION TWO RESULT CHART 1992-93

HOME TEAM		1	2	3	4	5	6	7	8	9	10	11	12	13	14	15	16	17	18
1.	Ashton Town	*	1-3	1-1	3-4	2-3	2-1	1-2	3-1	0-0	5-1	1-4	0-2	4-1	1-2	2-3	1-3	1-1	0-4
2.	Atherton Col.	3-3	*	1-4	4-1	0-2	1-0	2-1	0-2	2-2	5-2	2-0	1-5	5-1	2-3	3-5	4-2	2-1	2-1
3.	Bootle	5-0	3-3	*	3-3	5-3	4-0	2-1	2-1	1-0	9-3	3-1	3-1	5-1	0-3	2-1	4-2	3-1	4-2
4.	Burnley B.H.	1-2	3-2	1-1	*	3-3	3-1	1-3	0-1	3-5	6-0	0-2	1-2	4-6	0-1	1-2	2-3	1-3	3-2
5.	Castleton	3-3	1-0	1-2	4-7	*	0-0	2-0	0-1	1-3	0-1	3-2	0-2	3-0	1-1	2-1	1-1	1-1	0-1
6.	Cheadle Town	2-0	1-1	0-3	0-4	2-3	*	3-1	1-1	0-1	1-0	4-1	3-0	5-0	1-2	0-2	3-0	3-2	1-4
7.	Ellesmere Pt T.	1-1	3-1	1-0	0-5	1-1	1-1	*	3-1	0-0	3-0	6-1	1-1	2-1	1-3	1-1	3-1	2-1	1-2
8.	Formby	2-1	6-2	0-0	1-0	0-2	1-1	1-3	*	0-0	3-2	2-1	0-0	2-3	3-2	1-1	4-2	1-2	1-0
9.	Holker O.B.	1-4	0-0	2-1	1-4	0-1	3-1	2-2	3-0	*	7-3	1-1	1-4	1-1	1-1	1-1	2-3	1-2	0-1
10.	Irlam Town	0-0	3-3	2-3	0-3	1-4	0-1	1-4	2-3	1-4	*	3-3	1-5	4-2	3-0	2-4	1-4	1-2	1-2
11.	K Chell	0-2	1-0	1-0	4-3	2-3	1-2	0-3	5-3	1-1	1-1	*	0-3	2-3	0-0	3-7	4-1	2-2	2-2
12.	Maghull	4-0	3-0	0-2	4-0	1-1	0-0	3-3	1-1	3-2	5-0	4-0	*	3-0	2-1	2-1	1-0	2-3	4-0
13.	Nelson	1-3	1-1	1-5	3-4	0-2	1-2	1-1	0-2	2-2	1-2	0-2	0-0	*	1-1	1-2	3-2	0-1	3-2
14.	Nth Trafford	4-0	2-3	0-0	1-5	2-2	1-0	3-1	2-1	7-4	4-1	3-3	0-1	2-4	*	1-6	1-3	3-1	3-2
15.	Oldham Town	3-1	0-1	2-1	1-2	0-0	2-1	0-0	2-2	2-1	0-1	0-5	1-1	1-3	3-5	*	1-2	5-0	4-0
16.	Squires Gate	3-1	0-2	3-3	1-1	0-5	0-2	0-3	3-0	2-1	5-1	1-0	0-5	1-1	1-1	3-5	*	1-2	4-2
17.	Stantondale	2-2	0-2	4-0	3-3	1-2	2-1	0-0	0-3	1-1	3-2	1-1	0-1	1-1	0-2	1-0	1-0	*	4-2
18.	Westhoughton T.	2-2	0-2	4-2	7-6	1-2	3-2	1-3	1-2	2-1	5-2	3-0	0-0	0-2	3-2	2-4	1-0	1-6	*

10-Year Record

	83/4	84/5	85/6	86/7	87/8	88/9	89/0	90/1	91/2	92/3
Ashton Town	-	-	-	-	10	17	10	15	17	16
Ashton United	-	4	14	3	1	-	-	-	-	-
Atherton Collieries	-	-	-	-	8	11	8	18	13	9
Atherton L.R.	9	10	11	17	-	-	-	-	-	-
Bacup Borough	-	-	-	-	22	9	2	-	-	-
Bamber Bridge	-	-	-	-	-	-	-	4	1	-
Blackpool Mechanics	-	-	-	12	15	16	3	5	3	-
Blackpool Wren Rovers	10	6	3	4	3	4	4	2	-	-
Bootle	-	-	-	-	-	-	-	-	-	2
Bradford Park Avenue	-	-	-	-	-	-	-	3	-	-
Burnley Bank Hall	-	-	-	-	-	-	-	-	-	10
Burscough	-	-	-	-	-	-	-	9	4	-
Castleton Gabriels	-	-	-	-	-	-	-	11	8	6
Chadderton	8	8	6	7	13	3	-	12	11	-
Cheadle Town	-	-	-	-	12	14	6	7	9	12
Clitheroe	-	1	-	-	-	-	-	-	-	-
Colne Dynamoes	6	9	7	8	-	-	-	-	-	-
Colwyn Bay	-	-	5	5	-	-	-	-	-	-
Darwen	-	16	15	6	-	-	-	-	-	-
Droylsden	5	5	10	1	-	-	-	-	-	-
Eastwood Hanley	2	-	-	-	-	-	-	-	-	-
Ellesmere Port & Neston	7	18	13	10	-	-	-	-	-	-
Ellesmere Port Town	-	-	-	-	-	-	-	-	-	4
Fleetwood Town	1	-	-	-	-	-	-	-	-	-
Flixton	-	-	-	-	2	-	-	-	-	-
Ford Motors	12	12	17	-	17	-	-	-	-	-
Formby	-	-	-	11	-	-	17	5	8	-
Glossop	-	-	-	-	-	13	14	8	6	-
Great Harwood Town	16	7	8	15	14	7	5	1	-	-
Holker Old Boys	-	-	-	-	-	-	-	-	15	15
Irlam Town	3	2	-	-	-	-	-	-	-	18
K Chell	-	-	-	-	-	-	-	-	-	14
Kidsgrove Athletic	-	-	-	-	-	-	-	14	10	-
Kirkby Town/ Knowsley Utd	-	-	1	-	-	-	-	-	-	-
Lancaster City	-	-	12	13	-	-	-	-	-	-
Lytham	14	-	-	-	-	-	-	-	-	-
Maghull	-	-	-	-	6	8	7	13	16	1
Maine Road	-	-	-	-	5	2	1	-	-	-
Nantwich Town	18	11	18	-	21	5	-	-	-	-
Nelson	-	-	-	-	16	-	-	-	-	17
Newcastle Town	-	-	-	-	4	6	13	6	2	-
Newton	-	-	-	-	20	18	16	-	-	-
North Trafford	-	-	-	-	-	-	-	-	-	7
Oldham Town	-	-	-	16	11	15	9	16	12	3
Padiham	-	17	-	-	19	12	11	-	-	-
Prescot B.I.	13	-	-	-	-	-	-	-	-	-
Prescot Cables	-	-	-	14	-	-	-	-	-	-
Rossendale United	15	14	2	-	-	-	-	-	-	-
Salford City	17	15	16	18	-	-	-	-	7	-
Skelmersdale United	11	13	9	9	-	-	-	-	-	-
Squires Gate	-	-	-	-	-	-	-	-	14	13
Stantondale	-	-	-	-	-	-	-	-	-	5
Vauxhall G.M.	-	-	-	-	7	1	-	-	-	-
Warrington Town	4	3	4	2	-	-	-	-	-	-
Daisy Hill/ Westhoughton Town	-	-	-	-	18	10	15	10	18	11
Whitworth Valley	-	-	-	-	9	-	-	-	-	-
No. of clubs competing	18	18	18	18	22	18	16	18	18	18

DIVISION ONE CLUBS 1993-94

ATHERTON LABURNUM ROVERS

President: P Eckersley **Chairman:** T.B.A.
Secretary: Brian Seddon, 18 First Ave., Atherton M29 0HX (0942 870872).
Manager: Dave Morris **Vice Chairman/Treasuer:** A Grundy
Ground: Crilly Park, Spa Road, Atherton, Greater Manchester (0942 883950).
Directions: M61 to Jct 5, follow signs for Westhoughton, left onto A6, right onto A579 (Newbrook Rd/Bolton Rd) over the railway bridge, right into Upton Rd passing Atherton Central Station, left into Springfield Rd and left again into Hillside Rd into Spa Rd and ground.
Seats: 300 **Cover:** 600 **Capacity:** 2,000 **Floodlights:** Yes **Founded:** 1954
Record Gate: 1,500 v Bolton Wanderers, friendly 22/7/92.
Colours: Yellow/sky/sky **Change colours:**
Previous leagues: Bolton Comb., Cheshire Co. 80-82.
Previous Name: Laburnam Rvrs 54-79 **Previous Grounds:** Laburnam Rd 54-56, Hagfold 56-66
Programme: 48 pages **Programme Editor:** John Bullen **Club Shop:** No
Midweek Matches: Tuesday **Clubhouse:** Open normal licensing hours.
Local Press: Bolton Evening News. **Hons:** N.W. Co's Lg 992-93 (Champions Cup 92-93)

Atherton's Bob Holgate and Bob Pizelis win this race to the ball in their side's pre-season friendly against Bolton Wanderers. Bruce Rioch's first team squad beat the Rovers 4-0, but the North West Counties League side, destined to have a fabulous season, had the consolation of their highest ever attendance. Photo - Colin Stevens.

BACUP BOROUGH

President: W Shufflebottom **Chairman:** W Heywood **Vice Chairman:** D Whatmough
Secretary: F Manning, 14 Osborne Terrace, Stacksteads, Bacup OL13 8JZ (0706 873664).
Manager: Ian Rishton **Coach:** Mick Higgins **Commercial Mgr:** G Bracewell
Ground: West View, Cowtoot Lane, Blackthorn, Bacup, Lancashire (0706 878655).
Directions: From M62, M66 onto A681 through Rawtenstall to Bacup centre, left onto A671 towards Burnley, after approx 300 yds right (immed. before the Irwell Inn) climbing Cooper Street, right into Blackthorn Lane then first left into Cowtoot Lane to ground.
Seats: 500 **Cover:** 1,000 **Capacity:** 3,000 **Floodlights:** Yes **Founded:** 1875
Colours: Black & white stripes/black/black **Change colours:** All red
Previous league: Lancs Comb. 03-82. **Midweek Matches:** Tuesday.
Previous Name: Bacup FC. **Previous Grounds:** None
Programme: 12 pages, 30p **Editor:** D Whatmough (0706 875041) **Club Shop:** Not yet
Club Sponsors: Hoover Ltd **Record Gate:** 4,980 v Nelson 1947 **Nickname:** The Boro
Clubhouse: Open matchdays and private functions (for which buffets can be provided). Pies and sandwiches on matchdays.
Captain 92-93: John Parkinson **P.o.Y. 92-93:** John Parrett **Club record scorer:** Jimmy Clarke
Hons: Lancs Jnr Cup 10-11 (R-up 22-23 74-75), Lancs Comb. 46-47 (Lg Cup R-up 46-47 80-81, NW Co's Lg Div 2 R-up 89-90.

BLACKPOOL ROVERS

Chairman: J Nolan **Manager:** John Dodd.
Secretary: P Kimberley, 34 Priory Gate, South Shore, Blackpool, Lancs FY4 2QE (0253 49853).
Ground: Bruce Park, School Road, Marton, Blackpool, Lancs (0253 60570).
Directions: M6 to M55, leave at Jct 4, left onto A583, sharp right at 1st lights (Whitehill Rd)., follow signs for Airport. Ground approx 1.5 miles on right. 6 miles from Blackpool North (BR).
Seats: 250 **Cover:** 750 **Capacity:** 1,000 **Floodlights:** Yes **Founded:** 1931
Record Gate: 800 v Manchester City, floodlight opener October 1991.
Colours: All red **Change colours:** All blue
Programme: 20 pages, 20p **Programme Editor:** P Kimberley **Club shop:** No
Clubhouse: Open matchdays only **Midweek matches:** Tuesday.
Previous Name: Wren Rovers **Prev. Lges:** Blackpool Amtr, West Lancs, Lancs Comb. 72-82.
Hons: W Lancs Lg 69-70 70-71 (Lg Cup(2)), Lancs FA Shield 69-70 70-71, Lancs Comb. 78-79 80-81 (R-up 77-78, Lg Cup 78-79, Bridge Shield 76-77).

BOOTLE

Chairman: John McComish   **Manager:** Tommy Fagan
Secretary/Press Officer: Paul Carr, 58 Orchard Hey, Old Roan, Bootle, Merseyside L30·8RY (051 526 9228).
Ground: Bucks Park, Northern Perimeter Road, Netherton, Bootle, Merseyside L30 7PT (051 526 1851).
Directions: At end of M57 & M58 follow signs to Bootle/All Docks. Ground on right so turn right at next lights by Police station after bend. Entrance 150 yds on right. 300 yds from Old Roan statiom. Bus 55 (150yds from ground), 302 341 345 350 (350yds).
Seats: 400   **Cover:** 1,400   **Capacity:** 5,000   **Floodlights:** Yes   **Founded:** 1953
Record Gate: 750 v Carshalton Athletic, FA Trophy 2nd Rd 31/1/81.
Colours: All blue   **Change colours:** All yellow   **Nickname:** Bucks
Previous Grounds: Edinburgh Park 1953-73, Orrell Mount 1973-78.
Previous leagues: Liverpool Shipping, Liverpool County Comb., Lancs Comb. 74-78, Cheshire Co. 78-82.
Previous Name: Langton 1953-73   **Club Shop:** Hope to be open for start of 93-94 season.
Programme: 24 pages, 30p   **Programme Editor:** Secretary   **Clubhouse:** Yes
Midweek home matchday: Tuesday   **Reserve team's League:** Liverpool Co. Combination
Record win: 9-1 v Glossop 8/2/86   **Record defeat:** 1-8 v Accrington S. 19/2/83.
Capt. & P.o.Y. 92-93: Billy Loughlin   **Top Scorer 92-93:** Steve O'Neill (21 in 24 games)
Local Newspapers: Bootle Times   **Club record appearances:** Peter McCumiskey (almost 400).
Hons: North West Co's League Div 2 R-up 92-93, Liverpool Challenge Cup 64-65 75-76 78-79, Liverpool Amtr Cup 65-66 67-68 73-74, Lancs Amtr Cup 69-70, Liverpool County Combination 64-65 65-66 67-68 68-69 69-70 70-71 71-72 72-73 73-74, George Mahon Cup 66-67 67-68 68-69 69-70 72-73 73-74, Lancs Combination 75-76 76-77 (League Cup 75-76), Cheshire County League Div 2 76-77 (League Cup 76-77).

BRADFORD PARK AVENUE

Chairman: R Robinson   **President:** C Atkinson.
Secretary: A Sutcliffe, 2 Glenlee Rd, Bradford, West Yorks BD7 2QA (0274 576460).
Manager: Jim MacKay   **Asst Manager:** D Richmond.
Physio: D Stordy   **Press Officer:** T R Clapham.
Ground: Batley Rugby Taverners Club, Mount Pleasant, Batley WF17 7NL (0924 470062).
Directions: M62 Jct 27, onto M62 towards Huddersfield, follow signs to Batley R.L.F.C.
Seats: 500   **Cover:** 500   **Capacity:** 5,000   **Floodlights:** Yes   **Reformed:** 1988
Midweek Matches: Tuesday   **Record Gate:** 1,740 v Leeds Utd, pre-season 1989
Colours: White/green/white   **Change colours:** Amber/black/red   **Nickname:** Avenue
Programme: 32 pages, 60p   **Club Shop:** Yes - contact G Sawyer (0274 607780).
Clubhouse: Run by rugby club, open matchdays. Tea bar, snacks.
Previous Leagues: West Riding County Amtr 88-89, Central Mids 89-90.
Prev. Grounds: Manningham Mills, Bradford 88-89/ Bramley R.L.F.C., McLaren Field, Bramley, Leeds 89-93.
Record win: 6-0 v Penrith (A) 92-93   **Record defeat:** 0-6 v Gainsborough Town (A) 89-90.
Club record scorer: Darren Wardman   **Club record appearances:** Rohan Eli
Captain 92-93: Gary Stanley   **Top Scorer 92-93:** Rohan Eli   **P.o.Y. 92-93:** Graham Jones/Gary Cox
Hons: West Riding Snr Cup 90-91   **Best FA Cup year:** 2nd Qual. Rd 92-93 (0-2 at Accrington)

BURSCOUGH

President: John Mawdsley   **Chairman:** Frank Parr   **Vice Chairman:** Stuart Heaps
Secretary: Stan Strickland, 109 Redgate, Ormskirk, Lancs L39 3NW (0695 574722).
Manager: Russell Perkins   **Assistant Manager:** Bob Howard
Physio: Bob Cottam   **Press Officer/Commercial Mgr:** Mark Parr (0704 896243).
Ground: Victoria Park, Mart Lane, Burscough, Ormskirk, Lancs (0704 893237).
Directions: M6 Jct 27, follow signs thru Parbold A5209, right into Junction Lane (signed Burscough & Martin Mere) to lights, right onto A59 from Ormskirk to Burscough Village, 2nd left over canal bridge into Mart Lane to ground. Half a mile from Burscough Bridge BR station (Wigan-Southport line). Further from Burscough Junction (Ormskirk-Preston line).
Seats: 220   **Cover:** 500   **Capacity:** 3,000   **Floodlights:** Yes   **Founded:** 1946
Colours: Green/white/white   **Change colours:** All white   **Nickname:** Linnets
Programme: 24 pages, 40p   **Editor:** Mark Parr (0704 896243)   **Club Shop:** No
Midweek Matches: Tuesday   **Best FA Cup season:** 1st Rd(4) 59-60 77-78 79-81
Previous Grounds: None   **Record Gate:** 3,500 v Crewe Alexandra, FA 1st Rd 1959
Previous Leagues: Liverpool County Comb. 46-53, Lancs Comb. 53-70, Cheshire Co. 70-82.
Club Sponsors: Blueline Taxis   **Reserve team:** None.
Record win: 10-0 v Cromptons Recreation, Lancashire Combination 1947.
Record defeat: 1-8 v Morecambe (H), F.A. Cup Third Qualifying Round 1961.
Record transfer fee paid: Undisclosed for Arthur Green (Burton Albion, 1948).
Record transfer fee received: £1,250 for Louis Bimpson (Liverpool, 1953).
Clubhouse: 'Barons Club' (privately owned, access from outside ground). Mon-Thurs 7-11pm, Fri 4-11pm, Sat 1-11pm, Sun noon-3 & 7-10.30pm. No food. John Smiths & Websters beers.
Captain 92-93: Tony Quinn   **Top Scorer 92-93:** Kevin Still
P.o.Y. 92-93: Ian Owen   **Club record scorer:** Wesley Bridge, 73 in one season.
Hons: Cheshire County League R-up 70-71 (League Cup 74-75 (R-up 73-74)), Liverpool Snr Non-League Cup 71-72, Lancs Combination 55-56 69-70, Lancs Jnr Cup 47-48 49-50 66-67, Nth West Co's League 82-83 (League Cup 92-93 (R-up 91-92), Challenge Shield 82-83), George Mahon Cup 47-48, Liverpool County Combination 49-50 (Div 2 53-54), Liverpool Challenge Cup 47-48 51-52, Liverpool Snr Cup R-up 92-93, Bill Tyrer Memorial Trophy 1990.

Bootle, whose brilliant end of season form took them into second place in Division Two. Photo - Colin Stevens.

Bradford Park Avenue attack during their 'home' tie away to Burscough in the F.A. Cup. Photo - Ian Kelly.

Burscough F.C. proudly display the League Cup won on April 22nd 1993. The trophy is 100 years old being the original Lancashire Combination Trophy. Back Row (L/R): Roy Baldwin, Gordon Castle, Bill Fairclough (Committee), Brendan Doyle, Tommy Knox, Ian Owen, Sean Togher, Alan Robinson, Steve Perkins, Gary Martindale, Brian Fairclough, Stuart Heaps (Vice-Chairman), Stan Strickland (Secretary). Front: Andy Doyle, Martin Lowe, Tony Quinn (Captain), Russ Perkins (Manager), Chris Carr (Blueline Taxis - Main Sponsor), Frank Parr (Chairman), Bobby Howard, Colin Stafford, Kevin Still.

CHADDERTON

President: Derek Glynn   **Chairman:** Harry Mayall   **Vice Chairman:** Keith Chadwick
Secretary: David Ball, 9 Roxbury Avenue, Salem, Oldham, Lancs OL4 5JE (061 678 9624).
Manager: Peter Evans   **Asst Managers:** Steve Willcock/ Mick McKay
Coach: Keith Tierney   **Physio:** Roy Houghton   **Press Officer:** Bob Barber
Ground: Andrew Street, Chadderton, Oldham, Lancs (061 624 9733).
Directions: M62 Jct 20, A627(M) to Oldham. Motorway then becomes dual carriageway. Turn left at first major traffic lights A669 (Middleton Road), then first left opposite 'Harlequin' P.H. into Burnley Street - Andrew Street 2nd left. 1 mile from Oldham Werneth (BR), buses 458 & 459 (Oldham-Manchester) stop at the Harlequin.
Seats: 200   **Cover:** 700   **Capacity:** 2,500   **Floodlights:** Yes   **Founded:** 1947
Best Gates: 1,500 v Guinness Exports 1969 & 1,257 v Oldham Athletic, pre-season friendly 1991.
Colours: Red & white/white/red   **Change colours:** All yellow   **Nickname:** Chaddy
Programme: 28-32 pages   **Programme Editor:** Secretary
Club Shop: No, but ties, mugs, pens, coasters, key rings, car stickers etc are on sale in clubhouse. Contact Dave Greaves (061 624 9733).
Midweek Matches: Wednesday   **Clubhouse:** Matchdays only. Hot & cold snack during & after games
Players progressing to Football League: David Platt (Crewe, Aston Villa, Bari, Juventus, Sampdoria).
Previous Leagues: Oldham Amateur, Manchester Amateur, Manchester 64-80, Lancs Comb. 80-82
Previous Grounds: None   **Club Sponsors:** Failsworth Foam Ltd.
Captain 92-93: Wayne Jones   **P.O.Y. 92-93:** Wayne Jones (club), Carlton Dove (supporters')
Top Scorer 92-93: Dave Kershaw 41   **Club Record Appearances:** Billy Elwell 750+ (1964-90).
Hons: Oldham Amateur Lg Cup 54-55, Manchester Amateur Lg 62-63 (North Div 55-56), Manchester Prem Cup R-up 82-83 (Challenge Tphy 71-72 (R-up 72-73)), Manchester Lg Div 1 66-67 (Div 2 64-65, Gilgryst Cup. 69-70, Murray Shield 65-66), Lancs Comb. Cup R-up 81-82, Alfred Pettit & Hulme Celtic Cup 61-62, Nth West Co's Floodlit Tphy R-up 92-93 (Reserve Div 85-86 (R-up 90-91), Reserve Cup 91-92 (R-up 90-91)), Manchester Yth Cup 59-60 (R-up 60-61).

CLITHEROE

Chairman: C Murphy   **President:** Jer Aspinall
Secretary: C Wilson, 4 Moss Street, Clitheroe, Lancs BB7 1DP (0200 24370).
Manager: Alan Bradshaw.   **Ground:** Shawbridge, Clitheroe, Lancs (0200 23344).
Directions: M6 jct 31, A59 to Clitheroe (17 miles), pass 'Visit Historic Clitheroe' sign, left into Pendle Rd for 1 mile, ground behind 'The Bridge Inn' on the right. 11 miles from BLackburn (BR).
Seats: 200   **Cover:** 750   **Capacity:** 4,000   **Floodlights:** Yes   **Founded:** 1877
Record Gate: 1,600 v Atherstone Utd, FA Vase 82-83.   **Club Shop:** No
Colours: Blue with white pin stripe/blue/blue   **Change colours:** All red
Previous Leagues: Blackburn & Dist./Lancs Comb. 03-04 05-10 25-82.
Clubhouse: Matchday only.   **Previous Name:** Clitheroe Central 1877-1914.
Programme: 4 pages, 20p   **Programme Editor:** Ian Rimmer   **Hons:** Lancs Comb. 79-80 (Lg Cup 34-35), Lancs Challenge Tphy 1892-93 1984-85, NW Co's Lg 85-86 (Div 2 84-85, Div 3 83-84).
Local Newspapers: Clitheroe Advertiser, Citizen, Lancs Evening Tele.   **Midweek Matches:** Tuesday

DARWEN

President: E Devlin   **Chairman:** M Elsworth
Secretary: Lynn Atkinson, 58 Harwood Str., Darwen, Lancs BB3 1PD (0254 761755).
Manager: Ian McGarry   **Commercial Mgr:** Mick Rathbone.
Ground: Anchor Ground, Anchor Road, Darwen, Lancs (0254 705627).
Directions: A666 Blackburn/Bolton road, 1 mile north of Darwen town centre, turn right at Anchor Hotel, ground 100 yds on left. One and a half miles from Darwen (BR), bus 51 to Anchor Hotel.
Seats: 250   **Cover:** 2,000   **Capacity:** 4,000   **Floodlights:** Yes   **Founded:** 1875
Record Gate: 9,000 v Luton, FA Cup 1909   **Previous Ground:** Barclay Bank.
Colours: Red & white/white/red   **Change colours:** All blue
Prev. Lges: Football Alliance 1889-91, Football Lg 91-99, Lancs Lg 99-03, Lancs Comb. 03-75, Ches. Co. 75-82.
Programme: 20 pages, 20p   **Programme Editor:** N Walsh   **Club Shop:** No
Clubhouse: Matchday only.   **Best FA Cup season:** Semi Finals
Hons: NW Co's Lg 82-83, Lancs Lg 01-02, Lancs Comb. 30-31 31-32 72-73 74-75 (Lg Cup 29-30 30-31 74-75, Lancs Jnr Cup 72-73, George Watson Tphy 72-73, Lancs FA Yth Cup 74-75, Lancs F'lit Tphy 89-90.
Local Newspapers: Darwen Advertiser, Lancs Eve. Tele.   **Midweek Matches:** Wednesday

EASTWOOD HANLEY

Chairman: Philip Poole   **Vice Chairman:** Geoff Eccleston   **President:** Gerald Littlehales
Secretary: John L Reid, 2 Northam Rd, Sneyd Green, Stoke-on-Trent, Staffs ST1 6DA (0782 279062).
Manager: Jimmy Wallace   **Asst Mgr/Coach:** Michael Bates   **Physio:** Graham Plant
Commercial Mgr: Richard Marsh   **Press Officer:** Geoff Eccleston (0782 47187).
Ground: Berryhill Fields, Trentmill Rd, Hanley, Stoke-on-Trent, Staffs (0782 274238).
Directions: M6 Jct 16, A500 to 2nd r'bout (about 10 miles), turn left (under bridge), left again onto A52 (signed Leek), cross A50 after 1 mile, after a further quarter mile turn right into Trentmill Rd (Ray Booth Cars). From south; M6 jct 15, follow A500 past Stoke City F.C., then follow as above from r'bout. One mile from Stoke-on-Trent (BR).
Seats: 250   **Cover:** 1,500   **Capacity:** 3,500   **Floodlights:** Yes   **Founded:** 1946
Record Gate: 5,000 v Stoke City (Brooks Bros Testimonial) 1978
Colours: All blue   **Change:** Yellow/black/yellow   **Nickname:** Blues.
Previous Leagues: Mid-Cheshire, Manchester, West Midlands (Regional) 68-78, Cheshire County 78-82, North West Counties Lg 82-87, Northern Premier 87-90.
Programme: 32 pages, 35p   **Editor:** Geoff Eccleston (0782 47187)   **Club Shop:** No
Previous Names: Eastwood (Hanley added to contrast with Town), Trent Rovers (incorporated in 1982).
Players progressing to League: Melia Alecksic (Spurs), Maurice Doyle (QPR).
Clubhouse: Open matchdays. Refreshment bar open matchdays.
Midweek home matchday: Tuesday   **Reserve team:** None.
Record win: 11-2 v Manchester University (A), Manchester League Cup.
Record defeat: 1-9 v Alvechurch, West Midlands (Regional) League, 1964.
Record transfer fee paid: Nil   **Received:** £1,300 for Steve Norris (Leek Town).
Top Scorer 92-93: Philip Hulme 25   **Captain & P.O.Y. 92-93:** Michael Bates
Record scorer: A Tunstall 84 (63-64)   **Record appearances:** Mick Astley, 1968-78.
Hons: Manc. Lg Gilgryst Cup 67-68, Staffs Snr Cup 85-86, Staffs FA Vase 81-82.
Local Newspapers: Evening Sentinel, S-o-T Herald & Post.

Chadderton F.C. pictured at Springfield Park, Wigan, before the final of the Tennents Floodlit Trophy.

Peter Muncey (right) of Eastwood Hanley just beats Kurt Whipp to the ball as the Potteries side record a 1-0 home win in a league fixture on 15th August. Photo - Colin Stevens.

Eastwood Hanley F.C. 1992-93. Photo - Colin Stevens.

FLIXTON

Vice-Chairman: Mr J Mitchell. **President:** Councillor F H Eadie **Chairman:** Mr A Carter
Secretary: T S Entwistle, 14 Woodhouse Rd, Davyhulme, Urmston, Manchester M31 2DJ (061 747 9937).
Manager: Brian Griffin **Asst Manager:** Alan Heathcote **Coach:** David Higgs
Press Off.: Trevor Entwistle **Commercial Manager:** David Trow.
Ground: Valley Road, Flixton, Manchester M31 2RQ (061 748 2903).
Directions: M63 Jct 3, B5214 (signed Urmston), follow Trafford General Hosp. signs, at 4th r'bout take 3rd exit (Woodbridge Rd), ground at top. One and a quarter miles from Flixton BR station (trains from Manchester Oxford Rd) - turn right out of station onto Flixton Rd, left after quarter mile into Woodsend Rd, at r'bout after quarter mile take 2nd exit into Woodbridge Rd - ground at top. Take any bus from Manchester Picadilly bus station to Flixton and alight at Flixton Red Lion.
Seats: 200 **Cover:** 600 **Capacity:** 2,000 **Floodlights:** Yes **Founded:** 1960.
Record Gate: 1,145 v Manchester Utd 1989-90, Inauguration of Floodlights
Colours: Blue & white stripes/white/blue **Change colours:** All yellow **Nickname:** Flixs
Previous leagues: South Manchester & Wythenshawe 60-63/ Lancs & Cheshire 63-73/ Manchester 73-86.
Programme: 36 pages, 50p **Editor:** Graham Foxall (061 746 9726) **Club Shop:** Not yet
Best FA Cup season: 1st Qualifying Round replay 91-92 (lost 1-2 at Mossley after 1-1 draw).
Best FA Vase season: 3rd Rd 91-92
Midweek Matches: Tuesday **Reserves' League:** North Western Alliance.
Record win: 7-1 v Daisy Hill 86-87 **Record defeat:** 1-10 v Knowsley Utd 90-91.
Clubhouse: Open daily 1-3 & 7.30-11pm. Sandwiches available most evenings.
Club Record Scorer: Gary McDonald **Club Record Appearances:** John Mitchell/ Stan Matthews.
Capt. 92-93: Aidan Moloney **P.o.Y. 92-93:** John Eaton **Top Scorer 92-93:** Gary McDonald, Andy Green 10
Hons: NW Co's Lg Div 2 R-up 87-88 (Div 3 R-up 86-87, Div 3 Cup SF 86-87, Res. Chal. Cup 87-88 90-91 (R-up 88-89 89-90 91-92 92-93), Res. Div East 89-90, Res. Div Sth 92-93), Manc. Lg R-up 78-79 81-82 85-86 (Div 1 77-78, Div 2(res) 82-83 85-86, Open Tphy 80-81), Lancs Amtr Cup 79-80 (R-up 80-81), Manc. Chal. Tphy 83-84 (R-up(2) 84-86), Manc. Prem. Cup R-up 86-87 91-92, Manc. Amtr Cup R-up 88-89.

GLOSSOP NORTH END

Chairman: P Heginbotham **President:** C T Boak
Secretary: P Hammond, 15 Longmoor Road, Simmondley, Glossop, Derbys SK13 9NH (0457 863852).
Manager: Gordon Rayner **Physio:** Mr Harvey.
Commercial Manager: Mike Perkin. **Press Officer:** Secretary.
Ground: Arthur Goldthorpe Stadium, Surrey Street, Glossop, Derbys (0457 855469).
Directions: A57 (Manchester-Sheffield) to Glossop town centre, turn into Shrewsbury Street, follow to top of the hill, left at T-junction for ground. 700 yds from Glossop (BR). Buses 236 & 237 from Manchester.
Seats: 209 **Cover:** 509 **Capacity:** 2,374 **Floodlights:** Yes **Founded:** 1886
Cols: Blue & white stripes/blue/red **Change colours:** All gold. **Nickname:** Hillmen.
Prog.: 32 pages, 30p, **Editor:** Mr P Heginbotham (061 439 3932). **Club Shop:** Yes, progs + souvenirs.
Midweek Matches: Tuesday **Sponsor:** Davis Blank Furniss Solicitors.
Clubhouse: Licensed bar. Hot & cold drinks and pies etc on matchdays.
Record Attendance: 10,736 v Preston North End, FA Cup 1913/14
Record transfer fee paid: £3,000 for Andy Gorton (Lincoln City, 1989).
Record transfer fee received: £3,000 for Andy Gorton (Oldham Athletic, 1990).
Previous Names: Glossop North End 1886-1898/ Glossop FC 1898-1992.
Prev. Lges: Midland 1896-98/ Football Lge 1898-1915/ Manch. 15-56 66-78/ Lancs Comb. 56-66/ Cheshire Co. 78-82.
Captain 92-93: Pete Jamieson **Top Scorer 92-93:** Keith Ingham **P.o.Y. 92-93:** Steve Orrell.
Hons: Nth West Co's Lg Lamot Pils Trophy 90-91, Manchester Lg 27-28 (Gilgryst Cup 22-23 29-30 34-35 74-75), Football Lg Div 2 R-up 1898-99, FA Amateur Cup QF 08-09.

KIDSGROVE ATHLETIC

Chairman: D Stringer **Manager:** Phil Yeomans.
Secretary: Mr C Smith, 4a Ravenscliffe Rd, Kidsgrove, Stoke-on-Trent, Staffs ST7 4ET (0782 786493).
Ground: Clough Hall, Hollinwood Road, Kidsgrove, Stoke-on-Trent, Staffs (0782 782412).
Directions: M6 Jct 16, A500 towards Stoke, 2nd junction onto A34 towards Manchester, turn right at 1st set of lights into Cedar Ave., 2nd right into Lower Ash Rd., and 3rd left into Hollinwood Road to ground.
Seats: Yes **Cover:** Yes **Capacity:** **Floodlights:** Yes **Year Formed:** 1952
Colours: All sky **Record Gate:** 538 **Clubhouse:** Yes **Midweek Home Matches:** Wednesday
Prev. Leagues: Staffs Co./ Mid Cheshire (pre-1991). **Hons:** Mid Cheshire Lg 70-71 78-79 86-87 87-88 (R-up 68-69 85-86, Lg Cup 67-68 69-70 85-86 (R-up 84-85 86-87)), Staffs Co. FA Vase 78-79 88-89, Sentinel Cup 66-67 76-77 84-85 (R-up 58-59 78-79 79-80 83-84), Leek Cup 84-85, Hanley Cup 65-66.

MAINE ROAD

Chairman: Mr R Meredith **President:** Mr F G Thompson.
Secretary: Mr K Hunter, 157 Aston Ave., Fallowfield, Manchester M14 7HN (061 226 9937).
Manager: Mr D Barber **Coach:** Mr R Meredith **Press Officer:** Mr P Randall
Ground: Manch. Co. FA Grnd, Brantingham Rd., Chorlton-cum-Hardy, Manchester M21 1TG (061 862 9619).
Directions: M63 Jct 7, A56 towards City Centre, right onto A5145, onto A6010 to Chorlton, through lights (ignore pedestrian lights), left at next lights, left into Withington Rd, left into Branthingham Rd, ground 400 yds on left. Manchester A-Z ref. 59-4E/4F. 2 miles from Stretford (Metrolink(tram)), 3 miles from Piccadilly and Victoria (BR). Buses 85, 102, 103, 168, 188, 276, 277.
Seats: 200 **Cover:** 700 **Capacity:** 2,000 **Floodlights:** Yes **Founded:** 1955
Colours: All blue **Change:** All yellow **Nickname:** Blues **Midweek home matchday:** Tuesday
Prev. Name: City Supporters Rusholme **Rec. Gate:** 875 v Altrincham, FA Cup 2nd Qual. Rd 29/9/90.
Prev. Grnds: Hough End PF 55-73/ Ward Street 63-73/75/ Tootal Spts Ground 75-79/ Leesfield 79-80.
Previous Leagues: Rusholme Sunday 55-66/ Manchester Amtr Sunday 66-72/ Manchester 72-87.
Programme: 48 pages, 50p **Editor:** Mr R Price (061 442 7269) **Souvenir Shop:** None
Best FA Vase year: 2nd Rd 89-90 91-92 **Best FA Cup year:** 2nd Qual. 2nd replay 92-93.
Rec. win: 15-0 v Little Hulton 2/9/86 **Record defeat:** 6-10 v Old Altrinchamians 22/9/79.
Clubhouse: Before/during/after games. Refreshment bar sells hot & cold drinks, pies, crisps, confectionary.
P.o.Y. 92-93: Paul Varden **Captain & Top Scorer 92-93:** Mike Dunphy
Record scorer: John Wright 140 **Record appearances:** Robin Gibson 382.
Hons: Manc. Prem. Lg(4) 82-86 (R-up 86-87, Div 1 73-74, Div 2 72-73, Gilgryst Cup(2) 82-84 (R-up(2) 85-87), Murray Shield(2) 72-74), Manc. Prem. Cup 87-88 (Chal. Cup(4) 82-83 84-87, I'mediate Cup(2) 75-77, Amtr Cup 72-73), NW Co's Lg Div 2 89-90 (R-up 88-89).

NANTWICH TOWN

President: E J Davies   **Chairman:** A Pye
Secretary: Mr Albert Pye, 5 Gresty Buildings, Nantwich, Cheshire, Cheshire CW5 5PX (0270 629867).
Manager: Clive Jackson.   **Asst Manager:** John Brydon.
Coach: John Brydon   **Physio:** Keith Leigh.
Ground: Jackson Avenue, off London Road, Nantwich, Cheshire (0270 624098).
Directions: M6 Jct 16, A500 for Nantwich (about 8 miles), continue on A52 over railway crossing (London Rd), first right into Jackson Avenue. From Chester take A51. 3 miles from Crewe (BR).
Seats: 150   **Cover:** 550   **Capacity:** 1,500   **Floodlights:** Yes   **Founded:** 1894
Record Gate: 2,750 v Altrincham, Cheshire Senior Cup 66-67.
Colours: Green   **Change colours:** All yellow.   **Club Sponsors:** Railway Hotel.
Nickname: The Dabbers   **Midweek matchday:** Wednesday.
Programme: 18 pages, 50p   **Programme Editor:** Che Kerrin (0270 624098).
Reserves' League: Crewe & Dist.   **Club Shop:** Yes (contact Che Kerrin at above no.).
Record transfer fee paid: N/A   **Record fee received:** £2,500 (P Mayman, Northwich).
Clubhouse: Every night except Sunday 8pm-11pm. Hot pies available.
Previous Leagues: Shropshire & Dist./ The Combination 1892-94 1901-10/ Lancs Comb. 12-15/ Cheshire Combination 19-38/ Manchester/ Mid-Cheshire/ Cheshire County 68-82.
Previous Name: Nantwich FC (pre 1973) **Club Record Scorer:** Gerry Duffy, 42 in 61-62.
Captain 92-93: John Diskin   **Top Scorer 92-93:** J Giblin, 16.
Hons: Cheshire Co. Lg 80-81 (R-up 00-01), Ches. Snr Cup 32-33 75-76 (R-up 1898-99 13-14 29-30), Ches. Jnr Cup 1895-96 (R-up 1890-91 96-97), Manc. Lg R-up 66-67 (Gilgryst Cup R-up 67-68), Crewe & Dist Cup 97-98 98-99 01-02 61-62 (R-up 1889-90 90-91 04-05 51-52 60-61), The Combination R-up 02-03, Crewe Amtr Comb. 46-47, Shropshire & Dist Lg R-up 1891-92, Mid Ches. Lg 63-64 (R-up 61-62 64-65, Lg Cup 61-62 63-64 (R-up 64-65)), Ches. Amtr Cup 63-64 (R-up 61-62), Ches. Jnr Cup 1895-96 (R-up 90-91 96-97), Mid Ches. Cup 48-49.

NEWCASTLE TOWN

Chairman: Mr J W Walker   **President:** Mr K H Walshaw.
Secretary: John F Cotton, 293 Weston Road, Weston Coyney, Stoke-on-Trent, Staffs ST3 6HA (0782 333445).
Ground: 'Lyme Valley Parkway Stadium', Lilleshall Road, Clayton, Newcastle-under-Lyne, Staffs (0782 662351).
Directions: M6 jct 15, A500 for Stoke, left at r'bout A519 for Newcastle, right at 2nd r'bout into Stafford Ave., 1st left into Tittensor Road to ground. 3 miles from Stoke-on-Trent (BR).
Seats: 300   **Cover:** 1,000   **Capacity:** 4,000   **Floodlights:** Yes   **Founded:** 1986
Midweek Matches: Tuesday   **Club Sponsors:** Henleys Ford
Previous Names: Parkway Hanley (founded 1964, later Clayton Park/ Parkway Clayton)/ Newcastle Town (founded 1980) - clubs merged in 1986.
Record Attendance: 3,586 v Stoke City, friendly August 1991. *Competitive:* 577 v Gresley Rovers, F.A. Vase 4th Rd 18/1/92. Parkway Clayton: 2,620 v Stoke City, 1964.
Colours: Royal/white/royal   **Change colours:** All yellow   **Nickname:** Castle.
Programme: 40 pages, 50p   **Editor:** Peter Tindall (0260 28093)
Club Shop: Due to open during 1993-94 season. Non-League programmes already on sale - contact secretary.
Previous Lges: Hanley & Dist. Sunday/ North Staffs Sunday/ Potteries & Dist. Sunday/ Newcastle/ Staffs Co./ Mid Cheshire.
Previous Grounds: Hanley Park 64-79/ Northwood Lane, Clayton 79-85.
Record win: 7-0 v Blackpool Mechanics, 8-1 v Holker Old Boys.
Record defeat: 0-5 v Eastwood Hanley (A).
Clubhouse: On ground, open Saturday matchdays noon-7.30pm and midweek 5-11pm. Hot and cold food always available.
Captain 92-93: Neil Pesteridge   **Top Scorer 92-93:** Neal Beardmore 21   **P.o.Y. 92-93:** Darren Chetwyn
Club record scorer: Shaun Wade 54   **Club record appearances:** Philip Butler 185.
Hons: Nth West Co's Lg Div 2 R-up 91-92 (Floodlit Tphy 92-93, Lamot Pils Tphy 91-92), FA Vase 5th Rd 91-92, Mid Cheshire Lg 85-86 (R-up 86-87, Div 2 82-83 90-91(res), Lg Cup 84-85), Newcastle Mayor's Charity Cup 89-90, Staffs FA Vase 92-93(res), Midland Sunday Cup 85-86 86-87 (R-up 84-85 87-88), Potteries & Dist Sunday Lg 84-85 85-86 (Lg Cup 84-85 85-86), Staffs Sunday Cup 79-80 (R-up 86-87), Leek Cup 87-88, Sentinel Sunday Cup 84-85, Sentinel u-18 Shield 86-87, Staffs Yth u-18 Cup 88-89 92-93 (R-up 86-87, u-16 86-87), Wirral programme award (for NWCL) 88-89 91-92 (Div 2 87-88 88-89 90-91 91-92).

Newcastle Town F.C. 1992-93. Back Row (L/R): Dave Buckley (Coach), Phil Smith (Asst Manager), Colin Lee, Trevor Brissett, Simon Pope, Paul Stanway, Mark Gibbs, Kenny Lawton, Mark Wooldridge, Dean Challinor, Paul Goodstadt, John Smith. Front: Dave Ritchie, Dean Gillick, Neal Beardmore, Michael Mack (Henleys Ford - Main Sponsor), Neil Pestridge (Captain), Glyn Chamberlain, Chris Hagan.

PENRITH

Chairman: D Johnson   **Vive Chairman/Press Officer:** M Robson
Secretary: W Brogden, 47 Folly Lane, Penrith, Cumbria CA11 8BU (0768 62551).
Manager: Mike Herring   **Physio:** B Kendall.
Ground: Southend Road Ground, Penrith, Cumbria (0768 663318).
Directions: M6 Jct 40, onto dual carriageway to Appleby & Scotch Corner, turn off at next r'bout approx half a mile into Penrith, follow A6 into town, take 1st left for ground. Three quarters of a mile from Penrith (BR).
Seats: 200   **Cover:** 1,000   **Capacity:** 4,000   **Floodlights:** Yes   **Founded:** 1894
Colours: Blue/white/blue   **Change colours:** All red   **Nickname:** Blues.
Previous leagues: Carlisle & Dist., Northern 48-82, NW Co's 82-87, Northern Prem. 87-90
Programme: 24 pages, 30p   **Editor:** Mr J Bell (0768 63898)   **Club Shop:** No
Players progressing to Football League: K Sawyers, G Fell, G Mossop (all Carlisle).
Best FA Cup season: 2nd Rd 81-82   **League Clubs beaten in FA Cup:** Chester 81-82.
Midweek Matches: Wednesday   **Record Gate:** 4,000 v West Auckland, 1961.
Record transfer fee paid: £750 for A Carruthers (Netherfield)
Record transfer fee received: £1,000 for B Brown (Queen of the South)
Previous Grounds: None.
Reserve team: None   **Sponsors:** Titteringtons Holidays
Record win: 13-2 v Parton Utd   **Record defeat:** 0-13 v Bishop Auckland.
Clubhouse: Open Thurs-Fri 9.30pm-2am, Sat 2-6pm & 9.30pm-2an, Wed match nights 6.30-10.30pm.
Club record scorer: C Short   **Club record appearances:** Ray Thornton.
Captain 92-93: Tony Monoghan   **Top Scorer 92-93:** Tony Fyfe   **P.o.Y. 92-93:** Paul Renwick.
Local Press: Cumberland & Westmorland Herald, Cumberland News.
Hons: Northern Lg R-up 61-62, NW Co's Lg R-up 83-84, Cumberland Snr Cup 60-61 61-62 62-63 63-64 64-65 65-66 70-71 72-73 74-75 80-81.

PRESCOT A.F.C.

President: Mr B F Taylor   **Chairman:** Mr G Glover
Secretary: Mr G H Hayward, 38 Central Ave., Prescot, Merseyside L34 1NB (051 430 6762).
Manager: Joe Gibiliru   **Asst Manager:** Lee Madin
Commercial Manager: John Richards (0744 57613).
Ground: 'Sandra Park', Hope Street, Prescot, Knowsley, Merseyside (051 430 0507).
Directions: M62 Jct 7, A57 to Prescot town centre (3 miles), right into Hope Street. Three quarters of a mile from Prescot (BR). Buses 10, 10A, 10C from Liverpool & Wigan.
Seats: 400   **Cover:** 2,000   **Capacity:** 8,000   **Floodlights:** Yes   **Founded:** 1884
Record Gate: 8,122 v Ashton National, 1932   **Metal Badges:** Yes.
Colours: Gold/black/black   **Change colours:** All red   **Nickname:** Tigers.
Previous Names: Prescot Athletic/ Prescot Cables 46-65 80-90/ Prescot Town 65-80.
Previous Leagues: Liverpool Co. Comb./ Lancs Comb. 1897-98 18-20 27-33 36-67/ Ches. Co. 33-36 78-82/ Lancs Lg 01-02/ Mid Cheshire 67-78.
Programme: 30 pages, 40p   **Programme Editor:** S Richards   **Club Shop:** No
Midweek Matches: Tuesday   **Best FA Cup season:** 2nd Rd 57-58 59-60
Clubhouse: Refreshment bar, open matchdays/evenings for hot & cold refreshments.
Hons: Ches. Co. 35-57 (Lg Cup 47-48), Ches. Co. Lg 78-79, Mid Ches. Lg 76-77, L'pool Non-League Cup(4) 51-53 58-59 60-61, L'pool Chal. Cup(6) 27-30 48-49 61-62 77-78, Lancs Int. Cup 1895-96, George Mahon Cup 23-24 25-27 36-37, Lord Wavertree Cup 65-66.

ROSSENDALE UNITED

Chairman: Tony Saunders   **President:** Clifford Barcoft.
Secretary: Hughie Cairney, 9 Cloister Drive, Darwen, Lancs BB3 3JX (0254 773642).
Manager: Geoff Lutley   **Physio:** Sid Parkinson
Press Off.: John Dunn (0706 228907)
Ground: Dark Lane, Newchurch, Rawtenstall, Rossendale, Lancs (0706 215119).
Directions: M66, then A682 to Rawstenstall, keep left around r'bout past library until Bishop Blaize pub, right into Newchurch Road (past market), after a mile turn right into Staghills Road - through estate to ground (half mile). Buses 32 or 33 from Rawtenstall (to Todmorden, Edgenride or Burnley) stop at ground.
Capacity: 4,000   **Cover:** 1,000   **Seats:** 400   **Floodlights:** Yes   **Founded:** 1898
Club Shop: Yes, selling programmes, magazines, metal badges, souvenirs. Contact Ian Turtle (0706 227027).
Colours: Blue & white/white/blue   **Change colours:** Yellow (blue sleeves)/blue/yellow
Previous Leagues: North East Lancs Comb./ Lancs Comb. 1898-99 1901-70/ Central Lancs 1899-1901/ Cheshire County 70-82/ North West Counties 82-89/ Northern Premier 89-93.
Previous Grounds: None   **Nickname:** 'Dale' or 'Stags'.
Midweek home matchday: Monday   **Record Attendance:** 3,400 v Shrewsbury, FA Cup 75-76.
Programme: 36 pages, 50p   **Editors:** John Dunn (0706 228907), Anthony Brown (221081).
Best F.A. Cup season: 2nd Rd 71-72 (1-4 v Bolton at Bury FC). Also 1st Rd 75-76 (0-1 at home to Shrewsbury Town).
Record win: 10-0 v Wigan Rovers, Lancs Combination 69-70.
Record defeat: 0-14 v Morecambe, Lancs Comination 67-68.
Record Fees - Paid: £3,000 for Jimmy Clarke (Buxton, 1992).
          Received: £1,500 for Dave O'Neill (Huddersfield Town), 1974).
layers progressing to Football League: Tommy Lawton, Geoff Smith (Bradford City 1952), Edmund Hartley & William O'Loughton (Oldham 1956 & 60), Colin Blunt (Burnley 1964), Fred Eyre (Bradford PA 1969), Dave O'Neill (Huddersfield), Carl Parker (Rochdale 1992).
Clubhouse: Evenings & matchdays. Hot snacks. Snooker room. Pool, darts, satellite TV, concert room.
Club Record Goalscorer: Bob Scott   **Club Record Appearances:** Johnny Clarke 770, 1947-65.
92-93 Captain: Mickey Fuller   **92-93 P.o.Y.:** Mickey Fuller (club), Steve Walker (players')
92-93 Top scorer: Jimmy Clarke 11   **Local Radio Stations:** Red Rose, Radio Lancashire.
Local Newspapers: Rossendale Free, Lancs Evening Telegraph, Rossendale Herald & Post, Rossendale Mail.
Honours: North West Counties Lg 88-89 (R-up 87-88, Div 2 R-up 85-86), Lancs Comb 26-27 (R-up 54-55, Lg Cup 28-29, Div 2 56-57), Cheshire County Lg 70-71 (R-up 71-72 73-74, Lg Cup 73-74), Lancs Junior Cup (ATS Challenge Tphy) 11-12 72-73 (R-up 27-28), Central Lancs Lg 1900, Lancs Floodlit Cup 70-71 71-72 73-74, FA Vase 5th Rd 86-87 88-89, FA Tphy 2nd Rd 81-82.

Rossendale United F.C. 1992-93. Back Row (L/R): Ian Rishton (Caretaker Manager), Chris Grimshaw, Craig Dewhurst, Andy Cawking, Mark Pye, Gary Rishton, Ged Walsh, Dave Feeney, Billy Greenan (Coach). Front: Jimmy Clarke, Barry Diamond, Dave Leigh, Simon Westwell, Ian Pilkington, Ray Davis.

ST HELENS TOWN

President: A Kelsall　　　　　**Chairman/Press Officer:** J Barrett
Secretary: W J Noctor, 95 Sutton Park Drive, Marshalls Cross, St Helens WA9 3TR (0744 816182).
Manager: Mick Holgate　　　　**Asst Manager:** James McBride.
Ground: Town Ground, Houghton Road, Sutton, St Helens, Merseyside (0744 812721).
Directions: M62 Jct 7, A57 towards Warrington, left at lights onto A568 towards St Helens for 2 miles to r'bout, take A570 for just under a mile, right at lights into Robins Lane, straight on to Station Rd, at crossroads with station on right straight straight across into Leonard Street, right at t-junction, ground on right. New link road at M62 opening late 1993. Buses 121, 122, 5D, 41, 6 to St Helens Junction.
Seats: 200　　　**Cover:** 550　　　**Capacity:** 4,400　　**Floodlights:** Yes　　**Founded:** 1901
Colours: Blue/white/blue　　　　**Change colours:** All yellow　　　**Reformed:** 1946
Record Gate: 4,000 v Manchester City, Bert Trautmann transfer match, April 1950.
Previous Leagues: Lancs Comb. 03-14 49-75/ Liverpool County Combination 49-74/ Cheshire County 74-82.
Programme: 24 pages, 40p　　　**Editor:** John McKiernan (0744 815726)　　**Nickname:** 'Town'
Club Shop: Yes, selling badges, scarves, pennants, non-League and League publications - contact secretary.
Midweek Matches: Wednesday　　　　**Local Newspapers:** Reporter, Star, Leader,Echo.
Previous Grounds: Park Road 01-23/ City Road 52-53.
Reserve team's League: St Helens Combination.
Record win: 10-4 v Everton 'B' 1952　　**Record loss:** 1-8 v Liverpool Res., L'pool Snr Cup 1950.
Clubhouse: Weekdays 8-11pm, Saturday matchdays 2-6.30pm.
Captain 92-93: Glenn Walker　　　**Top Scorer 92-93:** Steve Pennington 22
P.O.Y. 92-93: Stuart Phoenix　　　**Club record appearances:** Alan Wellens.
Hons: FA Vase 86-87, George Mahon Cup 49-50, Lancs Comb. 71-72 (Div 2 50-51, Lg Cup R-up 70-71), Liverpool Snr Cup R-up 76-77, Lancs Jnr Cup R-up 66-67, Bass Charrington Cup 72-73, St Helens Comb. Hosp. Cup Winners & R-up.

St Helens Town F.C. 1992-93. Back Row (L/R): Mark Eales (Physio), Peter Smith (Assistant Manager), Tyrone Grimes, Lee Dyer, Paul Blasbery, Ian Skidmore, Glenn Walker, Paul Musker, Steve Hart, Jimmy McBride, Mick Holgate (Manager). Front: Jamie Fahey, Martin Lowe, Gary Lowe, Darren Rigby, Steve Pennington, Steve King, Stuart Phoenix, Derek McClatchey. Photo - Richard Brock.

SALFORD CITY

Chairman: Harold Brearley   **Manager:** Billy Garton.   **Asst Manager:** Sid White.
Secretary: Mr Frank McCauley, 22 Beverley Road, Pendlebury, Swinton, Manchester M27 1HY (061 7360021).
Press Officer: Ged Carter   **Commercial Manager:** Mike Hilditch.
Ground: Moor Lane, Kersal, Salford, Manchester (061 792 6287).
Directions: M62 jct 17, A56 Bury New Road to Manchester, continue thro' 4 sets of lights, right into Moor Lane, 1st left into Neville Road to ground. 4 miles from Manchester Victoria (BR). Buses 96, 139, 94, 95 to Moor Lane.
Seats: 260   **Cover:** 600   **Capacity:** 8,000   **Floodlights:** Yes   **Founded:** 1940
Midweek Matches: Tuesday   **Record Attendance:** 3,000 v Whickham FA Vase 1981
Colours: Tangerine/black/black   **Change colours:** Blue & white stripes/blue/blue.
Prev. Names: Salford Central 40-63/ Salford Amateurs 1963 until merger with Anson Villa/ Salford FC.
Previous Ground: Crescent, Salford   **Previous Leagues:** Manchester 63-80/ Cheshire Co. 80-82.
Programme: 24 pages, 50p   **Programme Editor:** Secretary   **Nickname:** Ammies.
Clubhouse: Open matchdays only. Hot snacks.
Captain 92-93: Mark Molyneaux   **Top Scorer 92-93:** Ged Kimmins   **P.O.Y. 92-93:** Darren Quick.
Hons: Lancashire Amateur Cup 72-73 74-75 76-77, Manchester Senior Cup(4) 73-77, Manchester Challenge Cup(3) 73-76, Manchester Lg(4) 74-77 78-79 (Div 1 68-69, Open Tphy 75-76, Murray Shield 68-69), Manchester I'mediate Cup. *As Anson Villa: Manchester Lg Div 2 62-63 (Open Tphy 77-78(res)).*

SKELMERSDALE UNITED

Chairman: D Tomlinson   **Vice Chairman:** T Garner.
Secretary/Press Officer: Ken Hilton, 58 Higgins Lane, Burscough, Ormskirk, Lancs L40 7SD (0704 894504).
Manager: Jimmy Williams   **Asst Manager/Physio:** Kevin Melling.
Coach: Peter Smith   **Commercial Manager:** Ralph Martin.
Ground: White Moss Park, White Moss Road, Skelmersdale, Lancs (0695 22123).
Directions: M58 Jct 3, at 2nd r'bout take 3rd exit towards Skelmersdale, continue for approx 1 mile, ground on the right. 4 miles from Ormskirk (BR).
Seats: 250   **Cover:** 1,000   **Capacity:** 10,000   **Floodlights:** Yes   **Founded:** 1882
Record Gate: 7,500 v Slough FA Amateur Cup 1967
Colours: Blue/white/white.   **Change colours:** All yellow   **Nickname:** Skemmers
Previous Leagues: Liverpool County Combination, Lancashire Combination 1891-93 03-07 21-24 55-68 76-78, Cheshire County 68-71 78-82, Northern Premier 71-76.
Previous Ground: Sandy Lane 1882-1958.
Programme: 20 pages, 50p   **Programme Editor:** Team effort   **Club Shop:** No
Club Sponsors: Tamcos Training   **Reserve team:** None.
Record transfer fee received: £10,000 for Russell Payne (Liverpool, 1990).
Clubhouse: None, but matchday food bar sells hot drinks, soup, hot pies & pasties etc.
Best FA Cup year: 1st Rd 67-68 (0-2 at Scunthorpe), 68-69 (0-2 at Chesterfield), 71-72 (0-4 at Tranmere).
Midweek Matches: Tuesday   **Local Press:** Ormskirk & Skelmersdale Advertiser.
Captain 92-93: Peter Smith   **Top Scorer 92-93:** Phil McNally.
Hons: FA Amateur Cup 70-71 (R-up 66-67), Ches. Co. Lg(2) 68-70 (Jubilee Cup 69-70), Liverpool Co. Combination 10-11 13-14 14-15 19-20 38-39 39-40 45-46 50-51 51-52 53-54, Lancashire Combination Div 2 55-56, Liverpool Challenge Cup 11-12 13-14 19-20 20-21 38-39 39-40 45-46 46-47, Lancashire Amateur Shield 07-08, George Mahon 24-25 34-35 39-40 51-52 54-55, Lancashire F'lit Cup 69-70, Lancashire Jnr Cup(3) 14-15 69-71, Ashworth Cup 70-71, Barassi Anglo-Italian Cup 70-71, Liverpool Non-League Cup(2) 73-75, North West Co's Lg Cup R-up 82-83 (Reserve Cup 83-84).

Prescot A.F.C. 1992-93, pictured with their 'Tiger' mascot. Photo courtesy of the Liverpool Star.

DIVISION TWO CLUBS 1993-94

ASHTON TOWN

President: W Pomfrett   **Chairman:** G Messer
Secretary: C G Ashcroft, 8 Mason Close, Ashton-in-Makerfield, Wigan WN4 8SD (0942 717565).
Ground: Edge Green Street, Ashton-in-Makerfield, Wigan WN4 8SY (0942 719168).
Directions: M6 Jct 23, A49 to Ashton-in-M. Right at lights onto A58 towards Bolton. After 3/4 mile turn right at 'Rams Head' P.H. into Golbourne Rd. After 200 yds right into Edge Green Str. Ground at end.
Record Gate: 600 v Accrington Stanley 76-77   **Floodlights:** No   **Founded:** 1965
Colours: Red with white pin stripe/red/red   **Change colours:** All sky blue
Best FA Vase season: Prelim. Rd 84-85
Previous Leagues: Warrington, Lancs Comb. 03-11 71-78, Ches. Co. 78-82.
Midweek Matches: Tuesday   **Hons:** Warrington Lg Guardian Cup.

ATHERTON COLLIERIES

Chairman: A P Delooze   **Vice Chairman:** W Shaw   **President:** J Fielding
Secretary: A P Delooze, 40 Winmarleigh Gdns, Pennington, Leigh (0942 679255/886600).
Manager: Alan Lord/ Steve Walton   **Asst Manager:** I Lamb
Physio: Trevor Ball   **Training Co-ordinator:** Julie Haslam
Press Officer: Chris Casey   **Commercial Manager:** Mark Billington.
Ground: Alder House, Alder Street, Atherton, Gt Manchester (0942 884649).
Directions: M61 Jct 5, follow sign for Westhoughton, left onto A6, right onto A579 (Newbrook Rd/Bolton Rd) into Atherton. *(From M61 jct 4, left, right onto A6 after 80yds, left down Newbrook Rd at 1st lights).* At lights next to Atherton town hall turn left into High Str., 2nd left into Alder St. to ground. Quarter mile from Atherton Central (BR).
Seats: 60   **Cover:** 800   **Capacity:** 2,500   **Floodlights:** Yes   **Founded:** 1916
Record Gate: 3,300 Lancs Comb. 1920's   **Nickname:** Colls
Colours: Black & white stripes/black/black.   **Change colours:** All yellow.
Midweek Matches: Tuesday   **Club Sponsors:** I G Heatons   **Club Shop:** No.
Programme: 35 pages, 50p   **Programme Editor:** Barry Taylor (0542 888700/886600)·
Previous Leagues: Bolton Comb. 20-50 52-71, Lancs Comb. 50-52 71-78, Cheshire Co. 78-82.
Clubhouse: Evenings & matchdays. Matchday food: pie & peas, hamburgers, sandwiches, tea & coffe.
Captain 92-93: Steve Wallace   **P.o.V.:** Keith Schofield   **Top Scorer 92-93:** John Dobson.
Hons: NW Co's. Lg Div 3 86-87, Bridge Shield 85-86, Lancs Jnr Shield 19-20 22-23 41-42 45-46 56-57 64-65.

BLACKPOOL MECHANICS

Chairman: Thomas Baldwin   **Vice Chairman:** John Sanderson   **President:** Peter Sutton
Sec./Press Off./Physio: William Singleton, 'Circular Quay', 36 Colwyn Ave., Blackpool FY4 4EU (0253 768105).
Manager: Bobby Thomson (ex-Hibs, Middlesbrough, Blackpool)   **Asst Manager:** Joe Hulme.
Coach: Stephen Parkinson   **Commercial Manager:** Jim Taylor.
Ground: Back Common Edge Rd, Blackpool, Lancs (0253 761721).
Directions: M6 to M55, follow Airport signs. Left at r'bout along A583 (Preston New Rd) to lights, right into Whitehill Rd, becomes School Road, to lights. Straight over main road & follow signs for Blackpool Mechanics F.C. to ground. Rail to Blackpool North - then bus 11c from Talbot Road bus station (next to rail station) and alight at Shovels Hotel, Common Edge Rd.
Seats: 250   **Cover:** 1,700   **Capacity:** 2,000   **Floodlights:** Yes   **Founded:** 1947
Club colours: All green   **Change colours:** All blue   **Nickname:** Mechs
Programme: 10 pages, 50p   **Editor:** Steve Goss (0253 43946)   **Metal Badges:** Yes
Midweek home matchday: Tuesday   **Club Sponsors:** Yates Wine Lodge, Talbot Rd, Blackpool.
Club Shop: Yes, Managed by Steve Goss (142 Clifton Drive, South Shore, Blackpool (0253 43946). Ties, sweaters, old programmes, metal badges.
Prev. Ground: Stanley Pk 47-49   **Record Gate:** 1,200 v Morecambe, Lancs Comb, August 1968
Previous Leagues: Blackpool & Fylde Combination, West Lancs, Lancs Comb. 62-68.
Clubhouse: Match days, training nights. Dancehall. Matchday food: pie & peas, hot dogs, hamburgers, hot pot.
Captain, Top Scorer & P.o.V. 92-93: Darren Atkinson.
Hons: Lancs Comb. 74-75 (Bridge Shield 72-73, George Watson Tphy 75-76), NW Co's. Lg Div 3 85-86, W Lancs Lg 60-61 62-63 (R-up 59-60), Fylde & Dist Lg 53-54 56-57 (R-up(3) 54-56 57-58, Div 2 50-51, Lg Cup 52-53 57-58 (R-up 55-56 58-59)), Bannister Cup 52-53 56-57 (R-up(3) 55-56 57-59), Evening KO Cup 61-62, B'pool & Dist Amtr Lg Brackwell Cup R-up(2) 57-59, Lancs Jnr Shield 57-58 60-61 (R-up 54-55), Richardson Cup(2) 60-62, B'pool Co-op Medal 54-55 60-61. Nederlands Cuttrale Sportsbond Festival: Den Haag Cup R-up 53-54, Dordrecht R-up 55-56, Rotterdam R-up 59-60.

CASTLETON GABRIELS

Chairman: T E Butterworth   **Vice Chairman:** R Butterworth.
Secretary: David Lord, 34 Fairway, Castleton, Rochdale OL11 3BU (0706 522719).
Manager: Paul Jones   **Assistant Manager:** Gary Thompson.
Coach: P Jones/P Howard/J McIlwraith   **Press Officer:** David Entwistle (0706 523972)
Ground: Butterworth Park, Chadwick Lane, off Heywood Rd., Castleton, Rochdale (0706 527103).
Directions: M62 Jct 20, A6272M to r'bout. Left towards Castleton (A664 Edinburgh Way) to next r'bout, keeping Tesco Superstore to the left, take 1st exit to next r'bout, take 2nd exit into Manchester Rd (A664), after just under mile turn right at 'Top House' P.H. into Heywood Rd., to end & ground on right.
Seats: 100   **Cover:** 300   **Capacity:** 1,500   **Floodlights:** No   **Founded:** 1924
Colours: Blue/navy blue/blue.   **Change colours:** Red/white/red.   **Nickname:** Gabs.
Prev. Name: St Gabriels (pre-1960s)   **Previous Ground:** Park pitches/ Springfield Pk 1960s-81.
Previous Leagues: Rochdale Sunday Schools 24-84/ Manchester 84-89.
Record Gate: 640 v Rochdale, pre-season friendly 1991. Competitive: 450 v Bamber Bridge 86-87, Lancs Shield
Programme: 28 pages, 50p   **Editor:** David Entwistle (0706 523972)   **Club Shop:** No.
Record win: 6-0 v Westhoughton Town (A), North West Counties League Division Two 23/11/91.
Record defeat: 0-5 v Formby (A), Lamot Pils Trophy 4/1/92.
Clubhouse: Open seven nights a night and all day Saturday. Pie & peas and sandwiches available matchdays (pie & peas only at Reserve matches).
Top Scorer 92-93: Steve Johnson 10   **Captain & P.o.Y. 92-93:** Gary Broadbent
Midweek home matchday: Tuesday   **Club record scorer:** Tom KcKenna 16, season 1991-92.
Hons: Manc. Lg 86-87 (Murray Shield 86-87), Nth West Co's Lg Cup SF 91-92.

CHEADLE TOWN

President: Freddie Pye   **Chairman:** C Davies   **Manager:** TBA.
Secretary: Susan Burton, 2 Lavington Ave., Cheadle, Cheshire SK8 2HH (061 491 2190).
Ground: Park Road, Cheadle, Cheshire SK8 2AN (061 428 2510).
Directions: M63 Jct 11 to r'bout, A560 (Stockport Road) towards Cheadle, 1st left after lights into Park Rd to ground. 1 mile from Gatley (BR), buses from Stockport & Altrincham.
Seats: 300   **Cover:** 300   **Capacity:** 2,500   **Floodlights:** No   **Founded:** 1961
Record Gate: 550 v Stockport County, 1988   **Midweek Matches:** Wednesday
Colours: All White   **Change colours:** Green & black stripes/black/black.
Programme: 20 pages, 25p   **Programme Editor:** Chris Davies   **Club Shop:** No
Clubhouse: Normal weekday hours plus lunch on Sunday and from 2.15pm on Sat.
Previous Grounds: Hyde United 5yrs, Glossop 3yrs
Previous Name: Grasmere Rovers 1961-83   **Previous Leagues:** Manc. (pre 1987).
Hons: Manchester Lg Div 1 79-80 (R-up 80-81 81-82), Manchester Amtr Cup 79-80, Manchester Challenge Cup R-up(3) 79-82, Derbys Cup 80-81 (R-up 81-82).

ELLESMERE PORT TOWN '92

Chairman: Mr T Andrews   **Vice Chairman:** Mr P Furlong   **President:** Mr J Rigg.
Secretary: C Andrews, 14 Alder Drive, Great Sutton, South Wirral L66 2UG (051 356 8154).
Manager: Frank O'Brien   **Asst Manager:** T.B.A.
Physio: Billy Whitfield   **Press Officer:** Fred Price   **Ground:** Ellesmere Port Stadium, Thornton Rd, Ellesmere Port, South Wirral (051 357 1594).
Directions: M56, M53 (Ellesmere Port, Birkenhead) then junction 10, A5117 signed Queensferry, then B5132 signed Ellesmere Port centre. After about a mile turn right following Thornton Rd Ind. Estate and Stadium signs onto Wolverham Rd, carry on down Wolverham Rd across r'bout to bottom, right into Thornton Rd, stadium quarter mile on left.
Seats: 300   **Cover:** 499   **Capacity:** 1,550   **Floodlights:** Yes   **Founded:** 1992
Programme: 32 pages, 50p   **Editor:** Paul Nicholson (0928 791039)   **Nickname:** Port/Town
Cols: Claret & blue/white/white   **Change colours:** Gold/black/black
Club Shop: Yes, selling enamel badges, scarves, programmes etc. Contact Paul Nicholson (0928 791039).
Previous Grounds: None   **Previous Leagues:** None
Record Gate: 585 v Chester City, friendly 4/8/92
Midweek home matchday: Tuesday   **Reserve team:** None.
Record win: 8-1 v Nelson (A), North West Counties League Challenge Cup 1st Rd 92-93.
Record defeat: 0-5; v Burnley Bank Hall (H), North West Countiess Lg Div 2 92-93, v Maghull (H) North West Counties Lg Lamots Pils Tphy SF 1st leg 92-93.
Captain 92-93: Nicky Brookman   **Top Scorer 92-93:** Stewart Manders 40.
Record scorer: Stewart Manders 40   **Record appearances:** Rob Burrows 47.
Hons: Lamot Pils Trophy SF 92-93.

FORMBY

Chairman: Chris Welsh
Secretary: B G Prescott, 5 Abbotts Way, Formby, Merseyside L37 6DR (0704 879857).
Manager: Peter Hennerty   **Assistant Manager:** Mike Scott.
Coach: Billy Buck   **Physio:** Keith Johnson
Commercial Manager/ Press Officer: Paul Lawler (0704 878409).
Ground: Brows Lane, Formby, Merseyside (07048 72603).
Directions: A565 Liverpool-Southport, turn for Formby at lights opposite Di-it-All DIY into Altcar Rd, fork left at junction to r'bout (opposite Blundell Arms Hotel), take 2nd exit then sharp left into Duke Street, 1st right into Elbow Lane, ground entrance 50yds on left. Half a mile from Formby (BR), buses from Formby & Southport stations.
Seats: 200   **Cover:** 500   **Capacity:** 2,000   **Floodlights:** No   **Founded:** 1919
Midweek Matches: Wednesday.   **Record Gate:** 2,500 v Oldham, FA Cup 1st Rd 24/11/73
Colours: Yellow/blue/yellow   **Change:** White/black/black   **Nickname:** Squirrels
Programme: 25 pages, 30p   **Editor:** Paul Lawler (0704 878409)
Club Shop: Yes, stocking programmes, enamel badges and other souvenirs. Contact Paul Lawler (0704 878409).
Best FA Cup season: 1st Rd 73-74 (lost 0-2 at home to Oldham Athletic).
Club Sponsors: Under negociation.
Previous Leagues: Liverpool Co. Comb. 19-68/ Lancs Comb. 68-71, Ches. Co. 71-72.
Reserve team: None
Record win: 11-1 v Earle (H) 18/10/52
Record defeat: 0-10 v Irlam Town (H) 18/1/86.
Record transfer fee paid: Unknown   **Received:** £1,000 for Geoff Twentyman (Chorley).
Clubhouse: Social club and offices sadly destroyed in fire in September 1990, and as yet unreplaced. However, matchday refreshment bar stocks hot food & drinks.
Top Scorer 92-93: Leon Norris 11   **Captain & P.O.Y. 92-93:** Paul Byrne
Hons: Liverpool Co. Comb. 48-49 (R-up 51-52 52-53 64-65, George Mahon Cup 64-65 67-68 (R-up 55-56 56-57), Liverpool Senior Cup 77-78 (R-up 84-85, Challenge Cup 52-53 63-64 67-68 (R-up 64-65), Amtr Cup(3) 29-30 47-49), Lancs Amtr Cup 34-35.

HASLINGDEN

Secretary: F G Rule, 13 Knoul Meadow, Helmshore, Rossendale BB4 4LW (0706 226450).
Ground: Ewood Bridge, Manchester Rd, Haslingden, Lancs (0706 217814).
Directions: From South: M66 Blackburn/Clitheroe exit, left at r'bout past Woolpack Hotel, sharp left at bottom of hill - ground 100yds on right. From North; M6 Jct 31, A59 to Blackburn, take ring-road at Moat House Hotel and follow signs to M65, leave M65 at jct 8 and follow signs for Bury, follow dual-c'way for about 5 miles and leave at Todmorden exit, right at lights, straight across r'bout by Woolpack Hotel, then follow as above.
Seats: **Cover:**   **Capacity:**   **Floodlights:** Yes   **Founded:** 1969
Colours: Tangerine/black/tangerine   **Change colours:**   **Nickname:**
Midweek Matches: Tuesdays   **Previous Leagues:** West Lancashire (pre-1993)
Hons: West Lancs Lg Div 2 80-81 (R-up 92-93, Presidents Cup 71-72 80-81 92-93).

Simon O'Brien finds a gap between Irlam Town players Arthur Byrne (3), Steve Canfield (keeper) and Dave Feeney, to slot home Atherton Collieries' second in a 5-2 home win on 31st August. Photo - Alex Miste.

Richie Laughton notches Ellesmere Port's first in a 3-1 win at Burnley Bank Hall in February. Photo - Rob Ruddock.

Castelton Gabriels F.C. 1992-93. Photo - Colin Stevens.

HOLKER OLD BOYS

Chairman: Ron Moffatt   **Vice Chairman:** Ray Sharp.
Secretary: Allan Wilson, 56 Fairfield Lane, Barrow-in-Furness, Cumbria LA13 9AL (0229 822983).
Mgr: James Capstick/Des Johnson   **Coach:** Jimmy Ballantyne.
Commercial Manager: Christine Ballantyne.
Ground: Rakesmoor Lane, Howcoat, Barrow-in-Furness, Cumbria (0229 828176).
Directions: M6 Jct 36, A590 to Barrow-in-Furness, on entering Barrow, continue across r'bout, 2nd right (Dalton Lane) to top of road, right into Rakesmoor Lane, ground on right.
Seats: 40   **Cover:** 150   **Capacity:** 2,500   **Floodlights:** Yes   **Founded:** 1936
Cols: Green/white/green or white   **Change colours:** Blue/red   **Nickname:** Cobs.
Midweek Matches: Wednesdays   **Club Sponsors::** Riflemans Garage.
Previous Leagues: North Western/ Furness Premier/ West Lancs 70-91.
Previous Grounds: None.
Programme: 20 pages, 30p   **Rec. Gate:** 400 v Emlyn Hughes All Stars **Club Shop:** No.
Record win: 12-0   **Record defeat:** 1-8 v Newcastle T. (H) 91-92.
Clubhouse: Weekdays 8-11pm, Sat noon-11pm, Sunday normal licensing hours.
Top Scorer 92-93: Lee O'Keeffe   **Captain & P.o.Y. 92-93:** James Capstick
Club record scorer: Dave Conlin   **Hons:** W Lancs Lg 86-87, Lancs Co. FA Shield 88-89 90-91.

IRLAM TOWN

Chairman: K A Marsh   **Vice Chairman:** E Keiller.
Secretary: Kenneth A Marsh, 69 Silver Str., Irlam, Manchester M30 (061 775 7742).
Manager: Stuart Parker   **Press Officer:** D W Murray
Ground: Silver Street, Irlam (061 775 5599).
Directions: M6 jct 21 then east on A57 - Silver Street is opposite the Sports pub after five and a half miles. Or, M63 jct 2 and west on A57 for two and a half miles - turn right after Nags Head (PH). 1 mile from Irlam (BR).
Capacity: 3,000   **Cover:** 500   **Seats:** 250   **Floodlights:** Yes   **Club Shop:** No
Colours: All gold   **Change colours:** Red & black.   **Floodlights:** Yes
Programme: 28 pages, 50p   **Programme Editor:** D W Murray
Prev. Lges: Manc. (until 1978)/ Cheshire Co. 78-82/ Nth West Co's 82-87/ Northern Prem. 87-92.
Midweek matchday: Tuesday   **Record Gate:** 2,000 v Man Utd, f'light opening 1986.
Record Fees - Paid: **Received:** £8,000.
Players progressing to Football League: Tony Caldwell (Bolton Wanderers), Tony Jarvis (Oldham Athletic 1986), Graham Leishman (Mansfield Town 1988).
Clubhouse: Lounge, vault, kitchen, dressing rooms, committee.
Local Newspapers: Advertiser, Manchester Evening News.
Local Radio: Piccadilly, Key 103.   **Sponsors:** P M Communications, M L Electro Optics.
Hons: FA Vase 5th Rd 81-82, FA Amateur Cup 1st Rd 70-71, North West Counties Div 2 R-up 84-85, Manchester Lg 73-74 (R-up 76-77, Gilgryst Cup 73-74), Manchester Premier Cup 84-85 (R-up 78-79 81-82 87-88). *Reserves: Manchester Amateur Cup 81-82, North West Counties Lg Reserve Div 83-84 (Lg Cup 82-83 85-86), Northern Combination 88-89 (Lg Cup 87-88 88-89 89-90).*

K. CHELL

Secretary: Reg Barnsley, 42 Scotia Road, Burslem, Stoke-on-Trent ST6 4EP (0782 896315).
Ground: Kay's Sports & Social Club, Uplands Avenue, Chell, Tunstall, Stoke-on-Trent (0789 837607).
Directions: M6 jct 15, A500, A50 to Tunstall, follow signs to Chatley, Whitfield Mining Museum and Congleton (A527) - at top of hill island after 1.5 miles take small lane on left (Uplands Avenue) - ground at top (if in trouble ask for Chell Cricket Ground). Regular bus service from Stoke-on-Trent.
Seats: 200   **Cover:** Yes   **Floodlights:** Yes   **Founded:** 1991   **Programme:** 16 pages
Colours: Blue & black/black/black   **Change colours:** All red
Clubhouse: 2 tiered - converted cricket pavilion.
Previous League: West Midlands (Regional) 1991-92.

MAGHULL

Chairman: L Jacques   **Vice Chairman:** G Fisher   **President:** M Latham.
Secretary: D Sherlock, 14 Alexander Drive, Lydiate, Merseyside L31 2NJ (051 526 2306).
Manager: Arthur McCumiskey   **Asst Manager:** T Kidman.
Coach: T Barry   **Press Officer:** A Boyd (051 526 4715).
Ground: Old Hall Field, Hall Lane, Maghull, Merseyside (051 526 7320).
Directions: M57 or M58 to end (Switch End), A59 towards Preston (Northway) to lights at Hall Lane, turn right following signs for Maghull Station. Ground 400 yds on the left. Half mile from Maghull (BR).
Seats: None   **Cover:** 75   **Capacity:** 500   **Floodlights:** No   **Founded:** 1921
Club colours: All royal   **Change colours:** Red/black/black
Programme: 14 pages, 50p   **Programme Editor:** Press Officer   **Club Shop:** No.
Midweek Matches: Tuesday   **Record Gate:** 500 v Marine, L'pool Chal. Cup 1982/83
Previous Ground: Pimbley Recreation Ground 1921-59.
Previous Leagues: I Zingara/ Liverpool Co. Comb./ Lancs Comb. 72-78/ Cheshire Co. 78-82.
Clubhouse: Fully licenced bar open matchdays and training nights. Hot & cold food available.
Captain 92-93: Billy Roberts   **Top Scorer 92-93:** Graham Hughes.
Club record scorer: Unknown   **Club record appearances:** Bobby Price.
Hons: Liverpool Co. Amtr Cup 34-35 62-63, Liverpool Co. Chal. Cup 79-80 85-86, Lancs FA Amtr Cup 48-49 57-58, Lancs Comb. Cup 77-78, Liverpool Co. Comb. 66-67, North West Co's Lg Div 2 92-93.

NELSON

Secretary: C King (0282 616394)
Ground: Victoria Park, Lomesway, Nelson, Lancs (0282 63820).
Colours: Blue & white.
Previous Leagues: Lancashire 1889-98 1900-01/ Football League 1898-1900/ Lancashire Combination 01-16 46-82/ Nth West Counties 82-88/ West Lancashire 88-92.
Hons: Lancs Lg 1895-96 (R-up 97-98), Lancs Comb. 1949-50 51-52 (R-up 47-48 50-51 60-61, Lg Cip 49-50 50-51 59-60, Bridge Shield 75-76, George Watson Tphy 78-79, Div 2 R-up(res) 47-48 51-52), Lancs Jnr Cup 07-08 54-55, FA Cup 2nd Rd Proper 30-31(replay) 50-51 (1st Rd 32-33 51-52 53-54).

Holker Old Boys F.C. 1992-93. Photo courtesy of the North West Evening Mail.

Stantondale 1, Irlam Town 1 - 15/8/92. The Irlam Town defence lies prone as Mark Wilson (centre) scores Stantondale's first goal in the North West Counties League. Photo - Rob Ruddock.

Maghull F.C., Division Two champions 1992-93.

NORTH TRAFFORD

Chairman: Ackerley   **Vice Chairman:** D Brown   **President:** K Illingworth.
Secretary: David Brown, 5 The Avenue, Sale, Cheshire M33 4PB (061 976 2560).
Manager: David Law   **Asst Mgr:** Wilhelm Johannessen   **Coach:** John Ferguson.
Physio: Roy Davies   **Comm. Mgr/Press Off.:** David Law (061 748 5376).
Ground: Shawe View, Shawe Rd, off Chassen Road, Flixton, Urmston, Manchester M31.
Directions: M63 jct 4, B5158 towards Urmston, 1st exit at island, right into Moorside Rd at next lights, 2nd exit at next island, left at next lights and then 3rd right into Chassen Rd, 2nd right into Shawe Rd, ground on left.
Capacity: 2,000   **Seats:** 72   **Cover:** 272   **Floodlights:** No   **Founded:** 1990
Colours: All white   **Change Colours:** All red.   **Nickname:** The North
Previous Grounds: None   **Previous League:** Mid-Cheshire 90-92.
Programme: 24 pages, 50p   **Editor:** David Law (061 748 5376)   **Club Shop:** No.
Sponsors: Illingworth Developments   **Record Gate:** 208 v Northwich Vics, friendly Aug 92.
Midweek home matchday: Tuesday   **Captain 92-93:** Kevan Hawkins   **Clubhouse:** No.

OLDHAM TOWN

Chairman: K Hughes   **Manager:** Harold Hazard.
Secretary: Peter Wilson, 33 Park Cres., Chadderton, Oldham, Lancs OL9 (061 624 9602).
Ground: Nordens Road, off Middleton Road, Chadderton, Oldham, Lancs (061 624 0914).
Directions: M62 Jct 20, A627(M) Broadway to lights, right into Middleton Rd A669, right at Shell garage (on right) after 1 mile, next right up hill Chadderton Park Rd, 1st right into York Rd before crest of hill, at bottom follow road onto dirt track to ground. 2 miles from Werneth Oldham (BR). Buses 59, 181, 182, 184.
Seats: 50   **Cover:** 200   **Capacity:** 500   **Floodlights:** No   **Founded:** 1964
Record Gate: 250 v Mossley, Manchester Premier Cup 1987/88
Colours: Blue/white/blue.   **Midweek Matches:** Wednesday
Programme: 16 pages, 25p   **Programme Editor:** M Kirfoot.
Previous Ground: National Park   **Clubhouse:** Open evenings and matchdays.
Prev. Names: Dew Construction/ Oldham Dew.   **Prev. Lges:** Manch. Amtr/ Lancashire Comb. 81-82.

SQUIRES GATE

Chairman: W Carr   **Vice President:** Brian Addison.   **Manager:** Mark Spedding.
Secretary: John Maguire, 2 Squires Court, Cairn Grove, Blackpool, Lancs FY4.
Ground: School Road, Marton, Blackpool, Lancs (0253 798584).
Directions: M6 to M55 jct 4, left onto A583, right at 1st lights (Whitehall Rd) follow signs for airport. Ground approx. one and a half miles on right.
Seats: 2 rows   **Cover:** One side   **Capacity:**   **Floodlights:** No   **Formed:** 1948
Colours: All royal   **Midweek Matches:** Tuesday   **Prog.:** 20 pages   **Clubhouse:** Yes
Prev. Lges: W. Lancs (pre-1991)   **Hons:** W. Lancs Lg Div 2 80-81 (Richardson Cup 86-87).

STANTONDALE

Chairman: K Wood   **Manager:** R Grundy/T Lawson
Secretary: Ken Baker, 10 Haymans Gree, Maghull, Merseyside L31 6DA (051 526 4041).
Ground: Leisure Time Club, Orrell Lane, Bootle, Merseyside L20 (051 525 2115).
Directions: M57 to M58 to end at Switch Island, follow signs to Bootle and Docks (A5063) Dunnings Bridge Rd to r'bout, left into Netherton Way, take lefthand lane at lights into Orrell Lane, ground on left next to M.F.I.
Colours: Green/silver/white   **Midweek home matchdays:** Tuesday   **Floodlights:** No
Previous League: Liverpool County Combination (pre-1992).   **Founded:** 1986.
Hons: Liverpool County Comb. 90-91 (Div 2 87-88), Liverpool Jnr Cup 90-91, Liverpool Challenge Cup 91-92, McEwans Lager Cup 91-92.

WESTHOUGHTON TOWN

Chairman: D Haworth   **Manager:** Steve Walton/ Alan Cord.
Secretary: Mrs Haworth, 50 Parkway, Westhoughton, Bolton, Lancs (0942 840730).
Ground: New Sirs, St James Street, Westhoughton, Bolton, Lancs (0942 818544).
Directions: M61 Jct 5, A58 (Snydale Way/Park Road) for 1.5 miles, left into Leigh Road (B5235) for 1 mile, right fork to Daisy Hill. Straight forward between Church and School into St James Street. Ground 250 yds on the left. Half mile from Daisy Hill (BR).
Seats: 200   **Cover:** 450   **Capacity:** 2,000   **Floodlights:** No   **Founded:** 1952
Colours: Red & white stripes/black/red & black.   **Change colours:** All royal blue.
Programme: 8 pages, 20p.   **Programme Editor:** Barry Young
Previous Name: Daisy Hill   **Midweek Matches:** Tuesday (Reserve Wednesday)
Previous Grounds: Various   **Clubhouse:** Open normal licensing hours.
Record Attendance: 2,000 v Horwich R.M.I, Westhoughton Charity Cup final May 1980.
Previous Leagues: Westhoughton/ Bolton Comb./ Lancs Combination. 78-82.
Hons: Bolton Comb. 62-63 72-73 75-76 77-78 (Lg Cup(4) 59-60 61-62 71-73), Lancs Shield 61-62 71-72 86-87.

RESERVE DIVISION CUP 92-93

GROUP A.	P	W	D	L	F	A	PTS
Ashton Town Res.	8	3	3	2	17	13	12
Kidgsgrove A. Res.	8	3	3	2	7	8	12
Salford City Res.	8	2	5	1	14	5	11
Atherton Coll. Res.	8	3	2	3	19	23	11
Glossop N.E. Res.	8	1	3	4	10	18	6

GROUP B.	P	W	D	L	F	A	PTS
Atherton L.R. Res.	8	5	2	1	28	8	17
Flixton Res.	8	4	2	2	23	12	14
Westhoughton Res.	8	3	3	2	33	11	12
Maghull Res.	8	3	3	2	26	13	12
Irlam Town Res.	8	0	0	8	4	70	0

GROUP C.	P	W	D	L	F	A	PTS
Bamber Brid. Res.	6	6	0	0	17	6	18
Chadderton Res.	6	3	0	3	12	9	9
Nth Trafford Res.	6	3	0	3	7	9	9
Holker O.B. Res.	6	0	0	6	2	16	0

N.B. Burnley Bank Hall withdrew - record expunged

GROUP D.	P	W	D	L	F	A	PTS
Darwen Res.	8	6	2	0	24	6	20
Maine Road Res.	8	4	2	2	16	11	14
Squires Gate Res.	8	3	2	3	9	12	11
Castleton G. Res.	8	2	2	4	16	21	8
Blackpool M. Res.	8	1	0	7	9	24	3

Quarter Finals
Aston Town Res. 5, Maine Road Res. 3
Atherton L.R. Res. 1, Chadderton Res. 2
Bamber Bridge Res. 7, Kidsgrove Athletic Res. 3
Darwen Res. 0, Flixton Res. 1

Semi Finals
Aston Town Res. 1, Bamber Bridge Res. 2
Chadderton Res. 1, Flixton Res. 1
replay: Flixton Res. 2, Chadderton Res. 0

Final
Bamber Bridge Res. 4, Flixton Res. 1

North Trafford F.C., North West Counties League newcomers in 1992-93. Photo - Colin Stevens.

Oldham Town 2, Ellesmere Town 1 - 7/11/92. The home sides (hoops) put on the pressure. Photo - Colin Stevens.

Westhoughton Town F.C. 1992-93. Photo - John L Newton.

LANCASHIRE & CHESHIRE AMATEUR LEAGUE

DIVISION ONE	P	W	D	L	F	A	PTS
Disley Amateurs	24	18	3	3	52	25	39
O.Ashtonians	24	17	3	4	71	24	37
Pendle	24	13	5	6	59	41	31
Bedians	24	13	5	6	63	48	31
Cheadle Heath N.	24	10	9	5	52	43	29
Old Standians	24	8	7	9	50	49	23
Heaton Mersey	24	8	5	11	48	52	21
Heywood OB	24	8	5	11	42	56	21
Mellor	24	7	5	12	32	50	19
West Didsbury	24	7	4	13	39	61	18
Vymura Hyde	24	6	5	13	43	54	17
Hazel Grove	24	6	4	14	40	60	16
O.Stretfordians	24	4	2	18	41	69	10

DIVISION TWO	P	W	D	L	F	A	PTS
Cheadle Hulme	22	15	5	2	56	30	35
Oldham College	22	10	10	2	62	34	30
Bradford Parish	22	11	5	6	56	41	27
Aldermere	22	10	6	6	46	31	26
Fletcher Bolton	22	7	8	7	51	45	22
South Manchester	22	8	6	8	45	43	22
Romiley	22	8	6	8	48	52	22
O.Stopfordians	22	7	6	9	49	49	20
Hooley Bridge C.	22	6	8	8	44	52	20
O.Stoconians	22	6	7	9	45	45	19
Oldham Albion	22	6	4	12	33	52	16
West Flixton	22	1	3	18	15	76	5

DIVISION C	P	W	D	L	F	A	PTS
Oldham College	22	18	2	2	84	31	38
Romiley	22	16	3	3	73	30	35
Oldham Victoria	22	12	5	5	63	50	29
Oldham Teachers	22	13	2	7	72	51	28
Metro	22	11	2	9	65	49	24
Urmston	22	10	4	8	59	58	24
Gatley	22	8	3	11	54	57	19
O.Stretfordians	22	7	4	11	60	55	18
Moston B.HSOB	22	6	2	14	29	64	14
Old Stopfordians	22	5	3	14	53	75	13
Excise	22	3	6	13	27	65	12
Heaton Mersey	22	2	6	14	32	88	10

DIVISION THREE	P	W	D	L	F	A	PTS
Urmston	22	17	3	2	93	25	37
Gatley	22	16	3	3	56	27	35
Metro	22	12	4	6	64	41	28
Stand Athletic	22	12	2	8	55	47	26
East Chorlton	22	12	1	9	44	49	25
Oldham Victoria	22	11	2	9	61	51	24
Manchester YMCA	22	9	3	10	48	46	21
Clarksfield St.Ed.	22	7	4	11	54	69	18
Parrswood Cel.	22	7	3	12	40	55	17
Excise	22	4	5	13	27	54	13
Oldham Teachers	22	6	1	15	47	77	13
Moston B.HSOB	22	3	1	18	22	70	7

DIVISION D	P	W	D	L	F	A	PTS
O.Ashtonians A	20	15	3	2	78	27	33
Bedians A	20	16	1	3	88	45	33
Calrksfield St.Eds	20	13	1	6	75	43	27
Mellor A	20	9	3	8	45	51	21
O.Standians A	20	9	3	8	55	62	21
Cheadle Hulme	20	9	2	9	48	55	20
Parrswood C.	20	7	3	10	41	63	17
O.Stoconians A	20	5	5	10	41	53	15
Vymura Hyde A	20	5	3	12	47	67	13
Hazel Grove	20	4	3	13	33	60	11
West Didsbury	20	4	1	15	47	72	9

DIVISION A	P	W	D	L	F	A	PTS
Hooley Bridge C.	24	14	6	4	69	41	34
Bedians	24	13	8	3	67	44	34
Cheadle Hulme	24	13	5	6	71	40	31
S.Manchester	24	13	5	6	58	45	31
Pendle	24	10	8	6	67	56	28
Cheadle H.Nomads	24	10	4	10	52	47	24
Vymura Hyde	24	10	3	11	58	66	23
Old Standians	24	6	9	9	56	63	21
West Didsbury	24	7	6	11	48	63	20
Old Ashtonians	24	6	7	11	59	64	19
Mellor	24	7	5	12	49	61	19
Hazel Grove	24	6	3	15	30	54	15
Parrswood C.	24	5	3	16	38	78	13

DIVISION E	P	W	D	L	F	A	PTS
Cheadle Heath N.	22	19	1	2	88	31	39
Hooley Bridge C.	22	19	0	3	99	33	38
Oldham Alb. A	22	13	1	8	64	48	27
Aldermere A	22	10	4	8	44	49	24
Heywood OB A	22	8	5	9	49	53	21
Oldham Teachers A	22	7	6	9	47	52	20
Moston B.HSOB A	22	9	2	11	43	56	20
S.Manchester	22	9	1	12	49	46	19
O.Stretfordians	22	4	10	8	44	63	18
Romiley	22	6	4	12	47	68	16
Manchester YMCA	22	4	5	13	48	73	13
Disley	22	3	3	16	31	81	9

DIVISION B	P	W	D	L	F	A	PTS
Old Stoconians	22	15	4	3	61	29	34
Disley	22	13	2	7	72	40	28
Heywood OB	22	11	6	5	62	32	28
Bradford Parish	22	9	8	5	66	45	26
Stand Athletic	22	11	4	7	59	42	26
Manchester YMCA	22	12	2	8	65	67	26
Oldham Albion	22	9	7	6	51	37	25
Fletcher Bolton	22	9	4	9	58	49	22
Clarksfield St.Eds.	22	8	3	11	64	62	19
Aldermere	22	6	5	11	53	55	17
East Chorlton	22	4	0	18	31	106	8
West Flixton	22	2	1	19	24	102	5

DIVISION F	P	W	D	L	F	A	PTS
Bedians B	20	16	1	3	85	40	33
Vymura Hyde B	20	14	0	6	71	35	28
Heywood OB B	20	12	3	5	60	46	27
O.Ashtonians B	20	12	2	6	63	47	26
Aldermere B	20	10	2	8	66	50	22
O.Standians B	20	9	3	8	67	67	21
O.Stoconians B	20	7	6	7	58	45	20
Mellor B	20	7	1	12	58	66	15
Oldham Alb. B	20	5	4	11	58	74	14
Oldham Teachers B	20	2	6	12	45	83	10
Moston B.HSOB B	20	1	2	17	27	105	4

SOUTHPORT & DISTRICT AMATEUR LEAGUE

DIVISION ONE	P	W	D	L	F	A	PTS
Shake Vaults*	21	18	2	1	72	20	40
Heathfield Ath.**	20	11	5	4	57	31	31
Formby Dons**	20	11	4	5	60	28	30
Birkdale United	22	12	6	4	59	41	30
High Park	22	10	3	9	61	50	23
Crossens	22	8	6	8	48	44	22
Formby J.S.C.O.B.	22	8	5	9	58	49	21
Leisure Sports*	21	7	2	12	49	61	18
Blowick	22	5	6	11	46	62	16
Forest Rangers	22	2	2	18	27	96	6
St.Pauls	22	1	0	21	12	106	2

* - Awarded 2pts
** - Awarded 4pts

DIVISION TWO	P	W	D	L	F	A	PTS
Formby Dons Res*	19	16	0	3	61	18	34
Southport YMCA*	19	11	5	3	56	30	29
Heathfield Ath.Res*	18	13	0	5	58	32	28
Southbank	20	10	5	5	64	23	25
Ormskirk West End*	18	7	5	6	54	39	21
Blowick Res	20	9	3	8	58	49	21
Crossens Res**	18	5	2	11	43	37	16
Shake Vaults Res*	20	4	6	10	57	50	16
Formby Jscob Res	20	5	5	10	39	44	15
Forest Rang's Res	20	1	3	16	29	89	5

* - Awarded 2pts
** - Awarded 4pts

CARLSBERG-TETLEY
WEST CHESHIRE LEAGUE

President: K Halsall
Treasurer: R Prescott

Hon. Secretary: L Bullock, 8 Cambridge Rd,
Bromborough, Wirral L62 7JA (051 334 3545)

CHRISTLETON AND CAMMELL LAIRD SHARE HONOURS

The First Division title was won by Chester side Christleton whose only previous success had come in 1969-70. They took hold of top spot early in the campaign, and despite being relentlessly pursued by a number of clubs, finally finished four points clear of runners-up Merseyside Police. Their strength lay in a defence which conceded only three goals at home, and just nineteen in total, all season.

It was all the more surprising then that in the Pyke Cup final against previous champions Cammell Laird they were three down in half an hour only to show their character by taking a 4-3 lead in extra-time. But, in one of the best finals for years, the shipbuilders bounced back to gain a 5-4 victory.

Lairds also showed themselves as top dogs in Cheshire at this level as they collected the Cheshire Building Society Amateur Cup by defeating Capenhurst in the final. All four semi-finalists were Tetley Walker West Cheshire League clubs. To complete a fine hat-trick for the club, Cammell Laird's reserve side became Second Division champions by finishing two points ahead of Poulton Victoria Reserves, while the West Cheshire Bowl was lifted by Blacon Youth Club who beat Runcorn-based Mond Rangers.

Capenhurst's disappointment at being beaten in the Cheshire Amateur Cup was eased by their success in the Wirral Senior Cup final against league rivals Mersey Royal. The Wirral Amateur Cup final was another all-West Cheshire League affair with Poulton Victoria getting the better of West Kirkby. Other league members to gain cup honours were Merseyside Police in the Lancashire Amateur Cup, Christleton in the Chester Senior Cup and Mond Rangers in the Runcorn Senior Cup, whilst Heswall were Cheshire's representatives when lifting the Northern Counties Cup.

As the season drew to a close, the League representative side collected the Benevolent Bowl when goals from Mike Smith (Cammell Laird) and Gareth Drury (Vauxhall Motors) produced a 2-0 win over the Green Insulation Mid-Cheshire League.

Once again the League executives actively encouraged referees throughout the season to apply the laws of the game concerning foul and abusive language with players being immediately dismissed from the field of play for its use.

The League are grateful for the continuing support of its sponsor who have undergone a slight name change - in future the League will be known as the Carlsberg-Tetley West Cheshire Association Football League.

Ray Concliffe, Hon. Publicity Officer

Cammell Laird F.C. - Pyke Cup winners 1992-93. Back Row (L/R): Ian Cooke, Steve Parnell, Mike Connor (Captain), Mike Smith, Ian Banford, Alan Greatbanks, Ian Kerr, Steve Rule, Jamie Carpenter, John Power, Ian Doran. Front: Dave Galloway, Nick Dillon, Robbie Glanvill, Jimmy Kelly, Steve Kelly. Trophies: Pyke Cup, Cheshire Amateur Cup.

DIVISION ONE	P	W	D	L	F	A	PTS
Christleton	30	22	6	2	65	19	50
Merseyside Police	30	21	4	5	84	35	46
Vauxhall Motors	30	18	5	7	76	40	41
Bromborough Pool	30	17	6	7	65	43	40
Heswall	30	17	4	9	73	37	38
Poulton Victoria	30	14	9	7	55	39	37
Cammell Laird	30	14	8	8	71	39	36
Capenhurst	30	13	5	12	58	55	31
Ashville	30	12	6	12	68	57	30
Mersey Royal	30	12	5	13	39	50	29
Stork	30	9	7	14	35	61	25
Shell	30	8	4	18	46	95	20
Gen. Chemicals	30	6	4	20	34	63	16
Upton Ath. Assn	30	5	5	20	41	73	15
Newton	30	5	5	20	31	75	15
Moreton	30	2	7	21	27	87	11

DIVISION TWO	P	W	D	L	F	A	PTS
Cammell Laird Res.	34	21	9	4	91	45	51
Poulton Vic. Res.	34	22	5	7	96	42	49
Mond Rangers	34	21	6	7	89	43	48
Christleton Res.	34	20	7	7	76	38	47
West Kirby	34	20	6	8	69	37	46
Blacon Youth Club	34	18	6	10	85	67	42
Vauxhall M. Res.	34	14	11	9	61	58	39
Stork Res.	34	14	8	12	70	63	36
Manor Athletic	34	12	10	12	74	68	34
Bromboro. P. Res.	34	13	8	13	72	75	34
Ashville Res.	34	12	8	14	55	63	32
St Werburghs	34	13	5	16	74	79	31
Heswall Res.	34	8	12	14	55	64	28
Mersey Ryl Res.	34	6	10	18	43	70	22
Mersey Pol. Res.	34	7	8	19	58	97	22
Willaston	34	6	7	21	40	92	19
Shell Res.	34	6	5	23	47	109	17
Rivacre Rossfield	34	4	7	23	55	100	15

DIVISION ONE RESULT CHART 1992-93

HOME TEAM	1	2	3	4	5	6	7	8	9	10	11	12	13	14	15	16
1. Ashville	*	1-4	2-2	2-0	1-2	6-1	3-2	0-1	0-0	1-0	4-1	2-0	5-3	4-0	6-1	2-2
2. Bromborough Pool	3-2	*	3-0	1-1	0-1	2-1	3-2	0-1	3-1	3-1	4-1	2-2	5-2	0-1	4-1	1-1
3. Cammell Laird	3-5	5-0	*	1-1	3-0	2-0	0-0	2-2	2-3	4-1	6-0	1-1	5-0	2-2	4-1	2-0
4. Capenhurst	1-0	2-2	2-4	*	0-3	2-0	1-2	6-0	1-2	3-1	0-1	3-1	0-3	6-0	6-2	3-1
5. Christleton	3-0	2-0	1-0	5-0	*	1-0	2-0	2-0	3-1	4-0	7-0	0-0	4-1	1-0	1-0	1-1
6. General Chemicals	4-3	0-2	2-0	1-2	1-2	*	2-4	2-2	1-2	1-1	1-0	0-1	0-1	1-0	3-2	1-3
7. Heswall	2-0	2-0	1-0	5-1	0-0	4-1	*	0-1	1-6	4-0	2-0	0-2	6-0	0-1	2-2	2-1
8. Mersey Royal	1-3	2-3	0-2	0-3	1-3	2-1	4-0	*	0-4	1-1	4-1	1-1	3-2	0-0	1-0	0-5
9. Merseyside Police	3-0	1-1	2-1	5-2	2-2	5-1	0-4	4-0	*	2-0	1-0	3-0	5-1	6-2	3-0	2-1
10. Moreton	1-5	1-1	0-3	0-1	0-1	1-1	0-4	1-5	0-7	*	1-1	2-2	3-2	3-0	1-4	1-3
11. Newton	1-1	1-2	0-2	0-2	1-4	1-1	2-3	0-3	0-6	4-1	*	2-1	2-4	1-2	2-2	2-4
12. Poulton Victoria	3-2	2-4	0-2	1-1	1-0	2-0	0-0	2-0	2-1	6-4	3-1	*	4-2	5-0	2-1	2-2
13. Shell	5-3	0-5	1-5	3-3	2-5	1-3	1-10	1-0	0-3	0-0	1-1	0-2	*	4-1	1-0	0-7
14. Stork	2-2	2-3	3-3	3-0	2-3	3-1	1-5	1-0	0-0	3-0	0-3	0-0	2-2	*	1-0	1-2
15. Upton Athletic Association	2-2	0-2	4-4	5-2	1-1	4-2	0-4	0-3	2-3	3-1	2-0	1-6	0-2	0-1	*	1-2
16. Vauxhall Motors	4-1	4-2	2-1	1-3	1-1	2-1	3-2	0-1	5-1	8-1	1-2	2-1	3-1	4-1	1-0	*

DIVISION TWO RESULT CHART 1992-93

HOME TEAM	1	2	3	4	5	6	7	8	9	10	11	12	13	14	15	16	17	18
1. Ashville Reserves	*	1-4	3-0	1-3	0-2	3-1	3-1	1-1	2-1	1-1	2-1	1-0	3-0	2-2	2-1	2-3	0-1	4-2
2. Blacon Youth Club	3-0	*	4-2	4-4	2-2	4-0	0-4	2-2	5-0	1-1	1-0	4-2	2-1	4-3	4-4	2-0	0-1	5-0
3. Bromborough Pool Reserves	2-2	3-2	*	1-5	1-1	1-3	2-1	2-1	6-1	0-8	3-5	2-0	3-2	2-2	3-2	1-1	0-0	1-2
4. Cammell Laird Reserves	1-1	7-0	0-3	*	2-2	1-1	0-0	4-0	4-1	4-2	4-3	7-2	6-1	6-0	1-1	1-1	3-0	2-0
5. Christleton Reserves	2-0	0-1	1-2	5-0	*	2-0	3-1	2-0	2-1	1-1	0-0	5-1	3-1	3-0	5-1	2-1	0-3	4-0
6. Heswall Reserves	2-2	2-4	2-4	3-0	0-1	*	3-1	0-3	4-1	2-1	2-1	2-2	0-2	1-1	1-1	0-0	1-1	1-1
7. Manor Athletic	1-1	7-3	1-0	2-4	3-3	3-2	*	2-2	4-0	1-2	2-1	2-2	2-3	5-3	3-2	2-0	2-0	4-1
8. Mersey Royal Reserves	4-1	0-5	1-1	0-2	0-2	1-0	0-0	*	3-3	0-0	1-2	5-6	1-1	6-2	0-1	0-1	0-6	0-2
9. Merseyside Police Reserves	3-0	1-1	4-4	0-4	2-5	4-3	4-3	3-1	*	1-2	0-2	2-0	2-4	1-3	1-1	1-1	3-3	3-2
10. Mond Rangers	4-1	6-1	2-1	5-0	4-2	4-0	2-2	2-0	5-2	*	2-3	2-1	6-0	3-0	7-0	2-1	1-2	3-2
11. Poulton Victoria Reserves	4-2	3-1	2-2	0-1	2-0	2-0	5-2	3-3	2-2	4-1	*	3-1	5-1	3-0	2-1	1-0	4-0	9-0
12. Rivacre Rossfield	0-4	0-2	2-4	1-3	0-2	1-2	3-3	2-2	3-2	1-3	2-5	*	2-5	3-3	3-3	7-2	1-2	2-1
13. St Werburghs	1-2	2-4	3-2	1-2	4-3	2-2	1-1	4-1	2-4	0-1	0-4	6-1	*	4-1	2-1	3-3	0-2	4-2
14. Shell Reserves	2-0	0-4	1-4	0-2	1-1	0-8	2-1	0-2	3-2	0-1	1-7	2-1	0-7	*	2-4	2-4	0-3	2-4
15. Stork Reserves	2-2	2-3	4-1	1-3	3-2	4-1	4-0	3-0	6-2	1-3	0-1	3-1	0-3	2-1	*	4-2	2-1	0-0
16. Vauxhall Motors Reserves	2-1	3-2	4-3	2-2	0-3	3-3	3-2	2-0	2-0	4-0	3-3	1-1	2-1	4-1	0-0	*	3-1	1-0
17. West Kirby	4-1	2-1	2-0	1-1	1-2	1-1	2-2	2-3	4-0	3-1	2-0	3-1	4-1	3-1	0-2	3-0	*	3-0
18. Willaston	2-1	2-0	1-6	0-2	0-3	2-2	2-4	1-0	1-1	1-1	0-4	2-0	2-2	2-6	1-4	2-2	0-3	*

Upton Athletic Association F.C. 1992-93. Photo - Colin Stevens.

WEST CHESHIRE LEAGUE CLUBS 1993-94

(Div. 1 Constitution Unchanged. Div. 2: Capenhurst Reserves replace St Werburghs).

ASHVILLE

Chairman: Kenny Baker
Secretary: Eddie Parker, 26 Mere Heath, Moreton, Wirral L46 3SH (051 678 0745).
Ground & Directions: Villa Park Cross Lane, Wallasey Village, Wallasey (051 638 2127). Cross Lane is off Leasowe Road, entrance behind Wallesey Rugby Club. Merseyrail to Wallesey Village - cross road to Mosslands Drive, School Lane on right, ground under bridge.
Colours: White/black/black.　　　　　　　　　　　　　　　　　　　　　　　　**Founded:** 1949

BLACON YOUTH CLUB

Chairman: Peter Barnes
Secretary: Colin Lawson, 54 Adelaide Road, Blacon, Chester CH1 5SZ (0244 375508).
Ground & Directions: Cairns Crescent Playing Fields, Blacon, Chester. Parkgate Road to the Ben Whitehouse Garage, approach new island, 3rd exit into Blacon, along Blacon Avenue to Parade Shops (RHS), left opposite, 1st right, Western Avenue 2nd right, Melbourne Road, 1st right, Cairns Crescent. Buses 1,2,2a,2e to Blacon from Chester bus station.
Colours: Black & white stripes/black/black　　　　　　　　　　　　　　　　　**Founded:** 1964

BROMBOROUGH POOL

Chairman: Arthur Margerison
Secretary: Alan Pringle, 3 Willow Grove, Moreton, Wirral L46 0TU (051 677 0065).
Ground & Directions: The Green, South View Road, Bromborough Pool (051 645 3476). A41 from Ellesmere Port and Chester to Bromborough. Into Dock Road at Port Sunlight Works, past Fire Station, left into Pool Village, 1st right down Village Green - pavilion on far left of green. Buses C1,C3,C4 from Chester - alight at Bromborough Pool Lane. 41 MPTE from Birkenhead.
Cols: All blue (white pinstripe)　　　　**Sponsors:** Ocean Software　　　　**Founded:** 1884

CAMMELL LAIRD

Chairman: Arthur Parker
Secretary: Ray Steele, 46 Croft Avenue, Bromborough, Wirral L62 2BR (051 334 8998).
Ground & Directions: Kirklands, St Peters Road, Rock Ferry, Birkenhead (051 645 5991). A41 New Chester Road to Rock Ferry - turn down Proctor Road - ground behind Crosville Bus Station.
Colours: All blue　　　　　　　　　　**Sponsors:** MET ARC　　　　　　　　**Founded:** 1900

CAPENHURST

Chairman: Dave Kilfoyle
Secretary: Roger Knight, 8 Wenlock Gardens, Great Sutton, South Wirral L66 2QZ (051 355 5736).
Ground & Directions: Capenhurst Sports Ground, Capenhurst Lane, Capenhurst (051 339 4101). A41 Birkenhead/Chester road to Capenhurst lights, down Capenhurst Lane, over railway, past BNLF factory, ground on right. Crosville bus C41 to Capenhurst lights on A41. Train to Capenhurst (Wirral Line).
Founded: 1952　　**Colours:** Claret & sky　　**Sponsors:** BNF/Urenco Capenhurst Atlantic Communcations

CHRISTLETON

Chairman: Ron Mayers
Secretary: Kenneth Price, 35 Canadian Avenue, Hoole, Chester CH2 3HQ (0244 313513).
Ground & Directions: Little Heath, Christleton (0244 332153). Turn off A51 Chester/Northwich road at sign to Littleton and Christleton - follow road to pond on the left and turn left. Bus from Chester to Christleton.
Colours: Red/black/red　　　**Covered:** Yes　　　　　　　　　　　　**Founded:** 1966
Sponsors: Kidsons Impey Chester Motor Auctions.

GENERAL CHEMICALS

Chairman: Michael Jaques
Secretary: Roy Nickson, 44 York Street, Runcorn, Cheshire WA7 5BA (0928 576632).
Ground & Directions: ICI (Weston) Club, Sandy Lane, Weston Point, Runcorn. M56 to Runcorn Expressway - take Castner Kellner turn off. 1 mile from Runcorn (BR). Bus to Weston Point.
Previous Name: Castner Kellner　　**Covered Accomdation:** 100　　　　**Floodlights:** Y
Colours: Navy & white stripes　　　**Sponsors:** O'Hares Electrical　　　**Founded:** 1958

HESWALL

Chairman: Ernie Wakelam
Secretary: Jake Horan, 13 Reedville, Bebington, Wirral L63 2HS (051 644 0459).
Ground & Directions: Gayton Park, Brimstage Road, Heswall, Wirral (051 342 7523). From Birkenhead; Barnston Road, left into Brimstage Road, then first right. From Chester; Chester High Road to Gayton r-bout, Brimstage Rd then 1st right. From West Kirkby; Telegraph, left at Gayton r-bout then 1st right. 1 mile from Heswall Hills (BR).
Colours: Yellow/blue/yellow　　**Rec. Gate:** 1,000 v Sheff. Wed. 7/8/87　　**Founded:** 1891

MANOR ATHLETIC

Chairman: Tony Bell
Secretary: Stewart Galtress, 3 Centurion Close, Meols, Wirral L47 7BZ (051 632 3211).
Ground & Directions: Unilever Sports Ground, Bromborough. A41 Chester New Road to Candy (Kelvinator) factory, left (from Birkenhead) into Old Hall Road, 1st right. Buses to Green Lane, Bromborough.
Colours: White/black/red　　　　　**Sponsors:** Vavoline Oil Company　　　**Founded:** 1968

MERSEY ROYAL

Chairman: Tony Nelson　　　　　　　　　**Secretary:** Billy Morris, 28 Charlwood Close, 3rd Avenue, Manor Green, Beechwood, Birkenhead L43 9XF (051 678 7161).
Ground & Directions: As Manor Athletic (above).
Colours: Red & white/red/red　　　**Sponsors:** Hanks Construction　　　　**Founded:** 1946
Prevvious Ground: Valley Road, Bidston, Birkenhead (pre-1992).

MERSEYSIDE POLICE

Chairman: Pat Carraghan.
Secretary: Eddie McGrath, 36 Gaywood Court, St Nicholas Rd, Blundellsands L23 6XN.
Ground & Directions: Fairfield Sports Ground, Prescot Road, Liverpool L7 0JD (051 228 2352). From city travel via Kensington towards Old Swan, into Prescot Road - ground on corner with Fairfield Street. One and a half miles from Limestreet (BR).
Colours: Maroon/maroon/sky　　　**Sponsors:** Davies & Co, surveyors　　　**Founded:** 1885
Record Attendance: 1,500 v Kent Police, National Police Final 22/5/73.

MOND RANGERS

Chairman: Roy Roberts
Secretary: John Worthington, 5 Bellingham Drive, Runcorn WA7 4XN (0928 567477).
Ground & Directions: Ground-share at General Chemicals FC (see preceding page).
Colours: Sky/blue/blue.   **Club Sponsors:** Comid Engineering   **Founded:** 1967

MORETON

Chairman: Ray Navarro
Secretary: Tony Heffernan, 30 Appleton Drive, Upton, Wirral L49 1SJ (051 678 5973).
Ground & Directions: 73 Upton Road, Moreton, Wirral (051 677 3235). M53 jct 2, follow signs to Moreton - ground quarter mile on right. MPTE bus 3 passes ground.
Colours: Red/navy/navy   **Sponsors:** Fluid Power Services   **Founded:** 1900

NEWTON

Chairman: Fred Sherlock
Secretary: Alan Dabner, 41 St David Road, Claughton, Birkenhead L43 8SW (051 652 5648).
Ground & Directions: Millcroft, Frankby Road, Greasby, Wirral (051 677 8382). M53 to West Kirby, left at lights, right at lights at Upton Cross, ground 3 miles on left in Frankby Road. MPTE bus 96 from Birkenhead Woodside passes ground, MPTE 78 terminus 3 mins walk.
Colours: Yellow/blue/white   **Sponsors:** Cory Bros Shipping   **Founded:** 1933

POULTON VICTORIA

Chairman: Tom Quinn
Secretary: H Deery, 15 Dorset Drive, Irby, Wirral L61 8SX (051 648 2903).
Ground & Directions: Victoria Park, Rankin Street, Wallesey (051 638 3559). Wallesey Docks signs off M53, right into Limelin Lane by Vics Club, Rankin Street 6th left. Buses 10 & 11 to Gorsey Lane from Birkenhead. 20 mins from Birkenhead North (BR).
Colours: All royal blue   **Club Sponsors:** Windsors (Wallesey)   **Founded:** 1935
Previous Ground: Wallace Park 1935-72

RIVACRE ROSSFIELD

Chairman: Dorian Harvey
Secretary: K R Hornby, 310 Chester Road, Whitby, Ellesmere Port L66 2NY (051 356 1695).
Ground & Directions: Rivacre Sports & Social Club, Rivacre Road, Overpool, Ellesmere Port (051 355 2574). From lights at junction of Rossmore and Overpool Roads (cemetery gates), proceed down Rivacre Road - club on right. Crosville buses C3 & C4 to Overpool Cemetery.
Colours: Tangerine/black/black   **Club Sponsors:** Rivacre Social Club   **Founded:** 1954

SHELL

Chairman: Roy Jones
Secretary: Joseph Davies, 35 Glencoe Road, Great Sutton, South Wirral L66 4NA (051 339 0652).
Ground & Directions: Chester Road, Whitby, Ellesmere Port (051 355 2704/2364). A5117 turn right at 3rd island coming from M53 jct 10 (4th coming from jct 10); club on right. All buses to Ellesmere Port (BR), or C3 from Chester.
Colours: Red/blue/blue   **Sponsors:** Portions Control Ltd   **Founded:** 1924

STORK

Chairman: Keith Formston.
Secretary: Steve Carter, 7 Elm Rd, Bebington, Wirral L63 8PF (051 645 6697).
Ground & Directions: Unilever Sports Ground Bromborough (see Manor Athletic - page 907).
Colours: All green   **Sponsors:** The Village Leisure Hotel   **Founded:** 1920

UPTON ATHLETIC ASSOCIATION

Chairman: Peter Upton
Secretary: Barry Gaulton, St Marks Crescent, Whitby, Ellesmere Port L66 2XD (051 339 1504).
Ground & Directions: Cheshire County Council Sports & Social Club, Plas Newton Lane, Chester CH2 1PR (0244 318167). At end of M53, right, right at A41 r'bout (signed Zoo), 1st right into Mannings Lane, ground 100yds on left.
Colours: All blue   **Founded:** 1964

VAUXHALL MOTORS

Chairman: Tony Woodley
Secretary: Steve McInerney, 12 Merton Rd, Gt Sutton, South Wirral L66 2SW (051 356 0941).
Ground & Directions: Vauxhall Sports Ground, Rivacre Road, Ellesmere Port (051 327 2115). Turn into Hooton Green off A41 at Hooton crossroa, left at 'T' junction, right at next 'T' junction, ground 100 yds on right.
Colours: Sky/navy/sky   **Club Sponsors:** James Edwards   **Founded:** 1963
Floodlights: Y

WEST KIRBY

Chairman: Ken Raine.
Secretary: Mrs Carole Paisey, 80a Banks Road, West Kirby L48 0RE (051 625 6936).
Ground & Directions: Marine Park, Greenbank Road, West Kirby (051 625 7734). From Concourse, West Kirby, along Orrysdale Road and Anglesey Road into Greenbank Road.
Colours: White/blue/blue   **Club Sponsors:** Don Walker Insurance   **Founded:** 1895

WILLASTON

Chairman: Martin Collins
Secretary: Harvey Rushton, 31 Moss Close, Willaston, South Wirral L62 2XQ (051 327 7419).
Ground & Directions: Recreation Ground, Neston Road, Willaston, South Wirral. Off A41 at Hooton crossroads, along Hooton Road and through Willaston; ground on right behing Primary School.
Colours: All white   **Founded:** 1962

WEST CHESHIRE LEAGUE, AND OTHER LOCAL CUPS 1992-93

PYKE CUP
First Round
Cammell Laird v Heswall	4-2	Newton v Christleton	0-1
Moreton v Shell	1-2	Vauxhall Motors v Merseyside Police	2-3
Mersey Royal v Capenhurst	0-2	General Chemicals v Ashville	2-3
Poulton Victoria v Stork	5-1 (aet)	Upton Athletic Assn v Bromborough Pool	2-0

Quarter Finals
Cammell Laird v Merseyside Police	3-1	Upton Athletic Assn v Poulton Victoria	0-3 (aet)
Ashville v Christleton	0-1	Capenhurst v Shell	2-1

Semi-Finals
Christleton v Capenhurst	2-1	Cammell Laird v Poulton Victoria	2-0

Final: Cammell Laird 5, Christleton 4 *(aet)*

CASTELMAINE XXXX COMPETITION
Semi-Finals (Divisional Winners)
Manor Athletic v Christleton	2-3	Willaston v Ashville	6-5

Final: Willaston 5, Christleton 4

BILL WEIGHT MEMORIAL TROPHY
Semi-Finals
Cammell Laird v Poulton Victoria Reserves	3-2	Shell v Mond Rangers	2-3

Final: Cammell Laird 3, Mond Rangers 0

WIRRAL SENIOR CUP
First Round
Ashville v Vauxhall Motors	0-1	Mersey Royal v Willaston	1-0
Newton v Poulton Victoria	1-3	Shell v Cammell Laird	0-7
Stork v Capenhurst	0-1		

Quarter Finals
Bromborough Pool v Poulton Victoria	0-3	Mersey Royal v Heswall	2-0
Moreton v Capenhurst	0-3	Vauxhall Motors v Cammell Laird	4-1

Semi-Finals
Vauxhall Motors v Capenhurst	0-1	Mersey Royal v Poulton Victoria	2-1

Final: Capenhurst 2, Mersey Royal 1

WEST CHESHIRE LEAGUE BOWL
First Round
Vauxhall Motors v Christleton	1-0	Stork v Poulton Victoria	5-5,3-5

Second Round
Rivacre Rossfield v Merseyside Police	3-5	West Kirby v Mersey Royal	3-2
Blacon Youth Club v Shell	5-0	Vauxhall Motors v Ashville	3-1
Mond Rangers v St Werberghs	3-0	Heswall v Poulton Victoria	3-1
Bromborough Pool v Manor Athletic	0-6	Cammell Laird v Willaston	8-1

Quarter Finals
Heswall v Blacon Youth Club	2-3	Merseyside Police v Vauxhall Motors	3-3,1-4
Mond Rangers v Cammell Laird	3-2	Manor Athletic v West Kirby	0-1

Semi-Finals
Mond Rangers v Vauxhall Motors	4-3	Blacon Youth Club v West Kirby	1-1,2-1

Final: Blacon Youth Club 2, Mond Rangers 0

WIRRAL AMATEUR CUP
Second Round
West Kirby v Bebington Hawks	3-1	Rivacre Rossfield *(w/o)* Ellesmere Pt T. *(scr)*	
Capenhurst v Stork	3-5	Poulton Victoria v Newton	2-0
Heswall v Cammell Laird	1-5	Mersey Royal v Vauxhall Motors	0-2
Bromborough Pool v Ashville	1-2		

Quarter Finals
West Kirby v Rivacre Rossfield	2-0	Stork v Mersey Ferries	6-3
6auxhall Motors v Ashville	3-2	Poulton Victoria v Cammell Laird	3-0

Semi-Finals
Vauxhall Motors v West Kirby	1-2	Poulton Victoria v Stork	7-2

Final: Poulton Victoria 4, West Kirby 0

CHESTER SENIOR CUP
Final: Christleton 2, Team Blacon 0

LANCASHIRE AMATEUR CUP
Final: Merseyside Police 1, Wythenshawe Amateurs 0

CHESTER CHALLENGE CUP
Final: Manweb beat Christleton Reserves on penalties.

GREEN INSULATION
MID-CHESHIRE LEAGUE

President: W Salt, Esq.
Chairman: R Atherton, Esq.
Vice Chairman: J A Walton, Esq.
Treasurer: T B Riley, Esq.
Hon. Secretary: E B Davies,
34 Ryebank Road, Firswood, Manchester M16 0FP (061 881 5732).

IMPRESSIVE GROVE UNITED RETAIN TITLE

Winnington Park turned out to be the surprise team in a season that again went to the last week before a champion emerged. After very nearly being relegated at the end of the 1991-92 season, only being saved by the resignation of North Trafford who left to join the North West Counties League, Winnington Park's fortunes changed dramatically and after leading the First Division for most of the season they finished in a creditable runners-up spot.

The championship went to Grove United who, after faltering with injuries and being side-tracked by their entry into the F.A. Vase in which they were a credit to the League, finished with a good run to clinch the title for the second time in two years. Earlier contenders had included Linotype, Knutsford, Wilmslow and Barnton, whilst Chorlton Town's second half of the season saw them give the leaders a run for their money.

Malpas ran out easy winners of Division Two, but needed to win their games in hand to do so; this was due to good runs in cup competitions. It looks as though one or two sides in the First Division are in for a shock next season. Middlewich Athletic were easy runners-up and they too will be promoted.

The League Cup finals were a little disappointing, but all finalists are to be congratulated on their achievements. Knutsford, 1-0 winners over Winnington Park, took the Division One Cup played on Warrington Town's ground, whilst the Division Two Cup was settled by a 2-1 score in favour of Rylands Reserves over Knutsford Reserves at Winnington Park.

Following the resignation of Newcastle Town Reserves, only one team is relegated from Division One this being the unfortunate Bramhall Reserves who now have to leave the League. Two newcomers are Lostock Gralam from the Crewe League, who used to be one of the leading clubs in this league, and Grove United Reserves who return after one year in the Stockport League.

The West Cheshire League were again winners of the annual inter-League challenge match, but the Mid-Cheshire side played well and the 2-0 scoreline flattered the victors as both teams provided a truly fine game.

E B Davies, Hon. Secretary

LEAGUE TABLES 1992-93

DIVISION ONE	P	W	D	L	F	A	PTS
Grove United	30	22	4	4	87	28	70
Winnington Park	30	19	5	6	67	32	62
Chorlton Town	30	18	4	8	68	49	58
Barnton	30	15	9	6	57	49	54
Knutsford	30	16	5	9	59	45	53
The Beeches	30	15	5	10	62	44	50
Linotype	30	14	6	10	57	51	48
Wilmslow Albion	30	11	6	13	51	65	39
Hanley Town	30	10	6	14	39	43	36
Whitchurch Alport	30	10	4	16	46	59	34
Rylands	30	9	6	15	41	57	33
Broadheath Cen.	30	9	6	15	55	72	33
Poynton	30	9	5	16	47	61	32
Garswood United	30	7	5	18	48	69	26
Bramhall	30	7	4	19	42	69	25
Newcastle T. Res.	30	6	6	18	28	61	24

DIVISION TWO	P	W	D	L	F	A	PTS
Malpas	34	28	5	1	116	35	89
Middlewich Ath.	34	24	5	4	90	49	77
Pilkington	34	20	7	7	83	51	67
Littlemoor	34	18	4	12	88	63	58
Bollington Ath.	34	16	5	13	71	65	53
I.C.I. Pharms.	34	16	4	14	80	67	52
The Beeches	34	14	10	10	71	64	52
Warrington T.Res	34	11	12	11	63	58	45
Alsager	34	12	7	15	59	59	43
Knutsford Res.	34	11	9	13	45	53	42
Rylands Res.	34	11	6	17	56	77	39
Linotype Res.	34	9	12	13	50	61	39
Chorlton T. Res.	34	11	6	17	65	77	39
Poynton Res	34	9	9	16	52	66	36
Garswood Utd Res.	34	8	12	14	41	63	36
Styal	34	7	10	17	52	67	31
Bramhall Res.	34	8	5	21	41	100	29
Wilmslow A. Res.	34	4	7	23	53	104	19

DIVISION ONE RESULT CHART 1992-93

HOME TEAM	1	2	3	4	5	6	7	8	9	10	11	12	13	14	15	16
1. Barnton	*	1-0	2-0	1-0	2-1	0-4	0-0	1-2	0-1	6-2	2-0	2-2	3-3	2-1	2-2	0-0
2. Bramhall	0-2	*	5-3	1-1	2-1	0-1	3-5	1-4	0-1	2-0	0-1	0-4	1-3	1-1	2-1	0-4
3. Broadheath	3-3	5-2	*	2-2	1-3	2-4	2-1	0-6	2-2	0-0	2-0	0-2	3-0	1-4	7-1	0-1
4. Chorlton Town	1-2	0-3	3-2	*	4-2	0-7	0-0	3-3	0-1	1-0	3-2	4-2	2-1	5-2	4-0	3-2
5. Garswood United	2-3	2-3	2-1	2-3	*	1-4	3-3	1-	1-3	6-3	1-1	4-2	0-0	2-0	3-2	2-4
6. Grove United	6-0	1-1	3-1	3-2	6-2	*	6-0	1-3	2-2	3-1	6-0	3-1	3-0	2-1	4-1	1-0
7. Hanley Town	2-0	2-0	1-1	1-2	2-1	4-0	*	2-3	2-0	1-0	0-1	2-0	2-3	0-0	1-3	0-1
8. Knutsford	3-5	2-0	6-1	0-2	0-0	0-2	2-1	*	3-3	1-0	1-2	0-0	3-2	0-1	1-3	2-2
9. Linotype	2-4	3-1	0-0	2-4	3-2	1-4	1-0	1-3	*	0-0	2-3	4-2	4-3	3-4	7-1	0-1
10. Newcastle Town Reserves	1-2	4-3	3-1	1-5	3-0	0-3	2-2	1-0	0-0	*	1-3	0-0	2-1	1-0	1-1	0-1
11. Poynton	2-2	2-4	2-3	1-5	0-0	0-3	0-2	1-2	0-1	3-1	*	5-0	3-3	9-0	0-6	1-3
12. Rylands	1-1	3-1	2-4	1-3	1-0	0-2	1-0	0-2	1-3	1-0	1-1	*	2-1	1-3	1-1	4-0
13. The Beeches	3-1	3-1	2-3	2-1	2-0	1-0	0-1	6-0	4-3	6-0	2-1	2-0	*	2-1	1-0	1-1
14. Whitchurch Alport	2-2	4-1	4-1	1-4	4-1	0-2	2-0	0-1	1-2	2-0	3-1	1-3	0-4	*	2-2	0-2
15. Wilmslow Albion	1-2	2-2	1-3	0-1	1-2	2-1	3-0	3-3	3-1	3-2	1-0	3-1	-1	2-1	*	0-4
16. Winnington Park	3-4	3-2	5-1	2-1	1-1	2-2	2-1	3-0	0-1	4-1	1-2	4-1	2-0	2-1	7-1	*

DIVISION TWO RESULT CHART 1992-93

HOME TEAM	1	2	3	4	5	6	7	8	9	10	11	12	13	14	15	16	17	18
1. Alsager	*	0-1	7-3	5-2	1-1	1-3	0-0	1-2	0-1	2-5	3-5	2-0	2-0	2-3	1-1	1-3	4-0	0-3
2. Bramhall Reserves	1-1	*	0-5	1-3	1-3	2-0	1-0	1-1	1-0	0-5	2-3	1-0	1-1	1-4	2-6	1-3	1-4	1-6
3. Bollington Athletic	2-0	1-1	*	1-2	1-0	2-1	1-2	4-2	2-2	0-3	2-3	1-2	1-0	4-0	4-2	6-1	4-3	1-0
4. Cholton Town Reserves	0-0	3-3	0-1	*	3-2	0-2	1-3	2-1	1-5	2-5	1-3	0-2	1-1	3-4	4-3	2-2	3-3	3-2
5. Garswood United Reserves	2-0	1-0	1-1	0-6	*	3-2	1-0	0-2	2-6	1-2	1-1	1-1	2-1	1-1	0-0	3-3	0-3	2-0
6. ICI Pharmaceuticals	2-6	6-1	1-2	1-0	3-1	*	5-2	1-1	4-2	3-6	2-3	1-1	2-0	3-0	3-3	1-0	2-2	5-1
7. Knutsford Reserves	0-2	5-1	2-3	2-0	2-0	1-2	*	2-1	1-0	1-1	1-3	0-3	1-0	2-2	0-0	1-2	0-0	2-0
8. Linotype Reserves	1-0	5-4	2-3	3-1	1-1	4-2	0-0	*	1-2	1-3	1-1	0-2	0-0	2-0	1-0	2-4	0-3	3-3
9. Littlemoor	1-3	5-2	5-3	2-1	2-0	4-0	0-2	2-1	*	2-5	2-2	0-3	1-1	5-2	1-2	1-0	1-2	11-0
10. Malpas	1-0	6-0	3-1	4-1	1-1	4-1	4-0	5-1	3-1	*	5-0	3-1	2-1	3-1	5-1	0-2	2-2	9-0
11. Middlewich Athletic	4-0	3-1	3-0	3-1	8-3	5-3	1-0	1-0	3-2	0-2	*	0-0	5-0	1-3	3-1	3-0	1-0	4-1
12. Pilkington	2-2	2-0	3-2	5-2	4-2	2-1	3-1	1-1	6-2	3-4	4-1	*	2-0	4-2	4-0	2-1	3-2	1-1
13. Poynton Reserves	3-5	1-2	2-2	3-1	2-1	2-1	4-4	2-2	2-3	1-5	0-1	4-3	*	2-1	2-1	0-1	1-3	2-2
14. Rylands Reserves	0-1	4-2	1-2	1-1	0-0	0-4	3-4	2-2	1-1	0-5	1-5	0-3	0-3	*	3-0	3-1	3-2	3-1
15. Styal	1-2	0-1	2-2	2-3	2-0	4-1	5-0	2-2	1-5	0-1	0-1	2-2	0-2	1-0	*	2-3	1-0	2-4
16. The Beeches Reserves	6-3	6-1	3-1	2-7	2-2	1-1	1-1	1-2	1-3	2-2	1-2	4-3	4-4	3-1	0-0	*	1-1	5-1
17. Warrington Town Reserves	0-0	6-1	2-0	0-2	1-1	0-4	0-0	3-0	4-6	1-3	3-3	2-2	3-2	1-3	1-1	1-1	*	3-1
18. Wilmslow Albion Reserves	0-2	1-2	4-3	0-3	0-2	1-3	3-3	2-2	1-2	2-2	3-5	2-4	1-3	2-4	1-4	0-1	1-2	*

DIVISION ONE CUP 1992-93

First Round

Winnington Park v Grove United	1-1,1-0	Broadheath Central v Knutsford	1-1,0-1
Newcastle Town Reserves v Linotype	2-4	Chorlton Town v The Beeches	2-2,1-3
Garswood United v Barnton	1-3	Hanley T. v Whitchurch A.	0-1 *(Whitchurch expelled)*
Poynton v Wilmslow Albion	0-1	Bramhall v Rylands	4-3

Second Round

Knutsford v Wilmslow Albion	1-0	Linotype v Bramhall	0-1
The Beeches v Barnton	3-0	Hanley Town v Winnington Park	0-2

Semi-Finals (two legged)

Knutsford v The Beeches	1-0,0-0	Winnington Park v Bramhall	5-1,1-3

Final *(at Warrington Town F.C.)*: Knutsford 1, Winnington Park 0

DIVISION TWO CUP 1992-93

Preliminary Round

The Beeches Reserves v Malpas	4-1	Middlewich Athletic v Linotype Reserves	3-2

First Round

Bollington Athletic v Wilmslow A. Res.	3-1	Styal v Chorlton Town Reserves	1-2
Littlemoor v Pilkington	3-0	Rylands Reserves v Poynton Reserves	3-2

Second Round

Bollington Athletic v Alsager	2-2,2-0	Middlewich v Rylands Res.	2-0 *(Middlewich expelled)*
Chorlton Res. v Knutsford Res.	2-2,1-2		

Semi Finals (two legged)

Bollington Ath. v Knutsford Res.	1-4,1-1	Littlemoor v Rylands Reserves	1-2,2-3

Final *(at Winnington Park F.C.)*: Rylands Reserves 2, Knutsford Reserves 1 *(aet)*

DIVISION ONE CLUBS 1993-94

BARNTON
Chairman: William Perrin **Manager:** Mike Alcock/ Steve Moore.
Secretary: Peter Stanley, 10 Westfield Grove, Barnton, Nr Northwich, Cheshire CW8 4QB (0606 782305).
Ground: Townfield, Townfield Lane, Barnton.
Directions: Turn off A553 (Northwich-Runcorn) at Beech Tree Inn in Barnton village into Beech Lane. Right at T-junction with Townfield Lane - ground 200yds on left.
Colours: Black & white stripes/black/black. **Change Colours:** Amber/black/amber.

(THE) BEECHES
Chairman: Gordon Rigby **Manager:** D Corrigan.
Secretary: David Corrigan, 7 Burrows Avenue, Haydock, St Helens WA11 0DE (0744 572273).
Ground: Beechams Social Club, Sutton Rd, St Helens (0744 25906).
Directions: Approach from Widnes on A570, right at lights after St Helens Hospital into Sutton Rd, right at next lights, ground 200yds on left.
Colours: All blue **Change Colours:** Claret & blue/claret/claret

BROADHEATH CENTRAL
Chairman: J Tighe **Manager:** Michael Merry.
Secretary: David Murphy, 10 Green Drive, Timperley, Altrincham WA15 6JW (061 980 1925).
Ground: Viaduct Rd, Broadheath, Altrincham. **Directions:** One and a half miles north of Altrincham on A56 Manchester Road; turn right immediately after B & Q and Halfords. A-Z ref. 2D 79.
Colours: Black & red stripes/black/black **Change Colours:** All blue.

CHORLTON TOWN
Chairman: Ronald Anderson **Manager:** I R Jarratt
Secretary: Jim Calderbank, 9 Trafford Drive, Timperley, Altrincham WA15 6ET (061 969 1156).
Ground: Longford Stadium, Longford Park.
Directions: A-Z ref. P58 4C. From M63 take A56 Chester Road towards Manchester, right into Edge Lane shortly after passing under M63, left into Ryebank Rd after a few hundred yds, ground 400yds on left.
Cols: Black & red stripes/white/white (Blue & black stripes/black/black:Res) **Change Colours:** All white.

GARSWOOD UNITED
Chairman: D Finnegan **Manager:** A Aspinall.
Secretary: John Richards, 359 Elephant Lane, Chatto Heath, St Helens WA9 5HF (0744 851569).
Ground: Simms Lane Ends, Garswood Road, Garswood, Nr Wigan (0744 892258).
Directions: A580 towards Liverpool, right into Liverpool Rd (A58), left into Garswood Rd (signposted Garswood), follow round, left at triangle, upto crossroads, straight ahead, entrance 100yds on left.
Colours: Blue & white stripes/blue/blue **Change Colours:** All red.

GROVE UNITED

Chairman: J J Murphy **Manager:** S Crowther.
Secretary: Mark Boothby, 68 Deneside Cres., Hazel Grove, Cheshire SK7 4NU (061 456 7610).
Ground: Half Moon Lane, Alfreton Rd, Offerto/ Lisburne Lane, Stockport.
Directions: Lisburne Lane is a continuation of Cherry Tree Lane off the A6 or Dialstone Lane. M56 jct 13, 4th exit at r'bout A626, at 2nd lights after one and a half miles turn right at Golden Hind pub.
Colours: Red/black/black **Change Colours:** All blue.

HANLEY TOWN

Chairman: D Bould **Manager:** T.B.A.
Secretary: Mrs Alma Rhodes, 89 Greasley Rd, Abbey Hulton, Stoke-on-Trent (0782 543020).
Ground: Abbey Lane, Abbey Hulton, Hanley, Stoke-on-Trent (0782 267234).
Directions: M6 jct 16, A500 (5th exit), left under bridge, 6th right, go to bottom, left to lights (2 miles), turn right and through next lights, 2nd left is Fellbroke Lane, ground quarter mile on left (after houses).
Colours: Navy/navy/white **Change Colours:** Red/red/white.

KNUTSFORD

Chairman: Richard Walker **Manager:** Kenneth Harrison
Secretary: Michael Binnie, The Bungalow, 145 Manchester Rd, Wilmslow SK9 2JN (0625 537909).
Ground: Manchester Road, Knutsford.
Directions: Situated on Knutsford to Altrincham & Warrington road.
Colours: Red/white (All blue:Res) **Change Colours:** All blue (White or red:Res)

LINOTYPE

Chairman: G Smith **Manager:** K Gardner
Secretary: Graham Fothergill, 11 St Marys Rd, Sale, Cheshire M33 1SB (061 969 4999).
Ground: British Airways Club, Clay Lane, Timperley, Altrincham (061 980 7354).
Directions: Clay Lane off Thorley Lane. Off A560 Altrincham-Stockport road (Timperley, Altrincham). corner.
Colours: White/black/red **Change Colours:** Red & black/black/black.

MALPAS

Chairman: Peter Downey **Manager:** Bernard Lloyd.
Secretary: Bernard Lloyd, 15 Springfield Avenue, Malpas, Cheshire SY14 8QD (0948 860812).
Ground: Malpas & District Sports Club, Oxheys, Wrexham Rd, Malpas, Cheshire (0948 860662).
Directions: On arrival in Malpas, up Church Str., carry on into Wrexham Rd, right into ground which is signposted.
Colours: Red/blue/red **Change Colours:** All blue.

MIDDLEWICH ATHLETIC

Chairman: B Fletcher **Manager:** P McAleer.
Secretary: Brian Longley, 16 Northway, Holmes Chapel CW4 7EF (0477 373310).
Ground: Seddon Street, Middlewich, Cheshire.
Directions: St Michaels Way to Webb Street, Seddon Street on left.
Colours: Red/white/red **Change Colours:** All blue.

POYNTON

Chairman: J Malam **Manager:** C Nicholson (I Cook: Reserves).
Secretary: Paul Burch, 24 Brooklands Avenue, Poynton, Cheshire SK12 1HZ (0625 871205).
Ground: London Road North, Poynton (0625 875765).
Directions: On main A523 between Macclesfield and Hazel Grove, approx 300yds from Poynton village centre traffic lights.
Colours: Red/black/black **Change Colours:** White & blue/blue/blue.

RYLANDS

Chairman: Fredrick Bibby **Manager:** T Selby.
Secretary: Ian Finchett, 31 Elizabeth Drive, Padgate, Warrington WA1 4JQ (0925 816911).
Ground: Gorsey Lane, Warrington (0925 35700).
Directions: M6 jct 21, A57 to Warrington, through two sets of lights, right at the Chevvies Rock'n Roll Cafe, carry straight on, ground on right.
Colours: Maroon & grey/maroon/grey **Change Colours:** All yellow.

WHITCHURCH ALPORT

Chairman: J Jackson **Manager:** P Wainwright.
Secretary: Andrew Mitchell, 8 Mill Cottages, Grindley Brook, Whitchurch, Salop SY13 4QH (0948 6150).
Ground: Yockings Park, Whitchurch, Shropshire.
Directions: To lights on A41 main through road, left up Talbot Street to Ready Mix concrete plant; ground 200yds further on left.
Colours: Red & white stripes/black/black **Change:** Yellow/green/yellow.

WILMSLOW ALBION

Chairman: Geoff Thornton **Manager:** Rob O'Connor (Winnie Montrose: Reserves).
Secretary: John Smith, 3 Holly Farm House, Isherwood Rd, Carrington, Urmston M31 4BH.
Ground: Oakwood Farm, Styal Rd, Styal, Wilmslow (0625 535823).
Directions: M56 jct 6, A538 towards Wilmslow, 1st left for Styal (Altrincham Rd) after Airport tunnel, and procced to T-junction passing Styal FC and Ship Inn - ground 2nd left opposite Quarry Bank Mill. A-Z ref 982A.
Colours: Yellow/blue/yellow **Change Colours:** All blue.

WINNINGTON PARK

Chairman: D Rathbone **Manager:** Philip Lea.
Secretary: Raymond Burrows, 43 Greenback Lane, Northwich CW8 1JP (0606 77195).
Ground: Moss Farm, Northwich (0606 79987) **Previous Name:** I.C.I. Alkali.
Directions: A559 towards Chester, 1 mile outside Northwich turn left into Moss Rd which leads to Moss Farm.
Colours: Blue & white hoops/blue/blue **Change Colours:** White/navy/white.

DIVISION TWO CLUBS 1993-94

ALSAGER
Chairman: Kevin Dean **Manager:** P Clegg.
Secretary: John Dykes, 7 Dairylands Rd, Church Lawton, Stoke-on-Trent ST7 3FU (0270 877722).
Ground: The Town Ground, Wood Park, Alsager.
Directions: M6 jct 16, A500 towards Stoke, turn left for Alsager after half mile, follow lane to lights, in village centre turn right into Lawton Rd, 3rd left Moorhouse Avenue, 2nd right Woodland Court, ground entrance on righthand corner.
Colours: Black & white/black/black **Change Colours:** Blue/black/black.

(THE) BEECHES RESERVES *(see page 911)*

BOLLINGTON ATHLETIC
Chairman: A Deery **Manager:** Michael McKernan.
Secretary: Anthony Holmes, 79 Parkgate Rd, Macclesfield, Cheshire SK11 7SZ (0625 615044).
Ground: Recreation Ground, Bollington.
Directions: Turn off A523 (Macclesfield-Stockport) at 1st sign for Bollington. Follow for one and a half miles to Dog & Partridge, left into Adlington Rd, ground 100yds on right.
Colours: Jade & silver/silver **Change Colours:** Tangerine/black.

BRAMHALL
Chairman: M Cruse **Manager:** Mark Weaver.
Secretary: Bernard Johnson, 25 Bean Leach Rd, Hazel Grove SK7 4LD (061 456 2542).
Ground: Lumb Lane, Bramhall.
Directions: Centre of Bramhall take Lumb Lane (pizza shop on corner), grnd 300yds on right behind village club.
Colours: Red/black/black **Change Colours:** Yellow/blue/blue (All blue:Res)

CHORLTON TOWN RESERVES *(see page 911)*

GARSWOOD UNITED RESERVES *(see page 911)*

GROVE UNITED RESERVES *(see page 912)*

LINOTYPE RESERVES *(see page 912)*

KNUTSFORD RESERVES *(see page 912)*

LITTLEMOOR
Chairman: Frank Morris **Manager:** Frank Sanders.
Secretary: Stanley McQuarrie, 46 Bramhall Lane, Stockport SK2 6HZ (061 429 66394).
Ground: Ward Street, St Marys Way, Stockport.
Directions: M63 jct 13 onto St Marys Way - ground 4th on left 1 mile on right. A-Z ref 74 4C.
Colours: Black & white stripes/black/black **Change:** Blue/white/blue.

LOSTOCK GRALAM
Chairman: D Washburn **Manager:** G Knop.
Secretary: Andy Hough, 44 Shelley Ave., Wincham, Northwich, Cheshire CW9 6PH (0565 733383).
Ground: Slow & Easy Hotel, Manchester Rd, Lostock Gralam, Northwich.
Directions: M6, A556 signed Chester, right at island after 4 miles onto Manchester Rd, Slow & Easy Hotel 1 mile on right - ground behind.
Cols: Sky & white stripes/white/blue **Prev. Lges:** Mid-Cheshire/ Crewe & Dist. (R-up 92-93)

PILKINGTON RECREATION
Chairman: G Barlow **Manager:** J Dawson.
Secretary: Dave Johnson, 4 Darent Rd, Haydock, Merseyside WA11 0HH (0744 34734).
Ground: Ruskin Drive, St Helens (0744 22893).
Directions: M6 jct 23, A580, left at 3rd lights, continue to Hope Anchor pub, right into Bishop Rd, continue to halt sign, follow road around to Ruskin Rd (2nd left). Ground in Ruskin Rd.
Colours: Green & yellow/green/green **Change Cols:** Maroon & grey/maroon/maroon & grey.

POYNTON RESERVES *(see page 912)*

RYLANDS RESERVES *(see page 912)*

STYAL
Chairman: Ben Hurren **Manager:** D Wyatt.
Secretary: Alan Jones, 1 Oak Brow Cottages, Altrincham Rd, Styal, Wilmslow SK9 4JE (0625 530270).
Ground: Altrincham Road, Styal (0625 529303).
Directions: From M56 take A538 towards Wilmslow, 1st left after tunnel, before the Valley Lodge Hotel, ground two miles up on left.
Colours: Amber & yellow/red/white **Change Colours:** All blue.

WARRINGTON TOWN RESERVES *(see page 877)*

WILMSLOW ALBION RESERVES *(see page 912)*

(A.F.C.) ZENECA
Chairman: David Black **Manager:** Glyn H Ingham.
Secretary: Neal Roberts, 18 Chatsworth Ave., Macclesfield, Cheshire SK11 7DB (0625 617718).
Ground: I.C.I. Cals Social Centre, Alderley Park (0625 512902).
Directions: From A537 (Knutsford-Macclesfield) turn left at Monks Heath traffic lights (jct with A34). 1st right after 200yds in Matthews Garden Centre, immediate right, then left and follow road to Sports Centre.
Colours: All royal blue **Change Colours:** Red & black/black/red.
Previous Name: I.C.I. Pharmaceuticals (pre-1993).

Wilmslow Albion, who had a much improved season in the Mid-Cheshire League in 92-93. Photo - Colin Stevens.

Ricky Griffiths (right), of Mid-Cheshire League champions Grove United, tussles with a Nantwich player during the 1-1 F.A. Vase draw in October. Grove pulled off a major coup by winning the away replay 4-1. Photo - Colin Stevens.

Burnley Bank Hall F.C., who sadly have had to withdraw from the North West Counties League after just one season. Vandalism to their ground means it no longer means the league's requirements. Photo - John L Newton.

JOHN SMITH'S BITTER
WEST LANCASHIRE LEAGUE

President: H Johnstone, Esq.
Chairman: D Procter, Esq.
Hon. Secretary: W Carr, Esq., 60 Selby Avenue, Blackpool.

The First Division League and Cup double was achieved by Vickers Sports Club from Barrow-in-Furness for only the eleventh time since the formation of the League in 1905, and but for fellow leaguers Leyland D.A.F. who beat them 2-1 in the final of the prestigious Lancashire 'Adidas' Challenge Shield, Vickers would have completed a grand slam previously only achieved by Blackpool Mechanics in 1960. Runners-up were Feniscowles from Blackburn who came from mid-table with an excellent end-of-season dash gaining 28 points from the last 30.

Leyland D.A.F. won the Second Division by the narrowest of margins from Haslingden. Both teams had jockeyed for the top position all season and with only one game to play they were on level points. Haslingden gained a four-goal advantage in their last game, but in a cliff-hanger final match for Leyland they beat promotion contenders Blackrod Town 5-0 to finish champions. Haslingden's disappointment was softened by beating Leyland 4-3 in an excellent Presidents Cup final at Turf Moor, Burnley, so that although both team came close to the Second Division Cup and League double by the narrowest of margins, an exciting season ended with honours even and both teams going up along with Kirkham & Wesham whose final run bettered a challenge from at least five other promotion contenders.

Leyland D.A.F. also won the Lancashire 'Adidas' Challenge Shield from an entry of 207 teams representing all areas of the county. The League provided three of the semi-finalists (as against all four the previous year). Ten West Lancashire League teams have appeared in the final in the past eight years, and six have won this prestigious trophy.

Turton were losing finalists in the Richardson Cup, and runners-up of the Reserve Division. Their last chance of silverware came in the Subsidiary Cup, but their experienced squad took three excellent final games before they got the better of a youthful and skilled Fleetwood Hethketh from Southport.

The very competitive Reserve Division also produced close finishes with Freckleton needing to at least draw their last home game against the youthful second placed B.A.C. Preston, Houston Cup winners, and again experience won the day. The Cup and League double was also a possibility in the Reserve Division South East group, but the eventual champions Eagley, who had been chased throughout the season by Turton, lost in a dramatic cup final to B.A.C. Preston.

Three new clubs have been accepted for 1993-94; Fulwood Amateurs, Charnock Richard, and Lancashire Constabulary who replace Wigan Rovers, who failed to gain re-election, Longridge United (resigned) and Haslingden who have been accepted into the North West Counties League.

Derrick Procter, Chairman.

Premier Division 1992-93

	P	W	D	L	F	A	PTS
Vickers S.C.	34	25	4	5	102	36	79
Feniscowles	34	22	7	5	72	39	73
B.A.C. Preston	34	21	6	7	95	37	69
Eagley	34	20	8	6	91	58	68
Poulton Town	34	19	9	6	70	47	66
Turton	34	20	5	9	84	59	65
Wigan College	34	16	4	14	88	57	52
Freckleton	34	14	8	12	66	70	50
Burnley United	34	14	8	12	66	66	*47
Vernon Carus	34	14	3	17	57	69	*42
Lytham St Annes	34	11	7	16	61	68	40
Springfields	34	11	6	17	49	90	39
Glaxo	34	11	4	19	71	80	37
Dalton United	34	10	7	17	58	77	37
Thornton Inter.	34	8	9	17	70	76	33
Colne British Legion	34	8	7	19	62	71	31
Norcross & Warbeck	34	8	8	23	38	106	17
Blackpool Rangers	34	1	6	27	33	127	9

* - Points adjusted

Richardson Cup Winners: Vickers Sports Club
Richardson Cup Runners-up: Turton

Division Two

	P	W	D	L	F	A	PTS
Leyland D.A.F.	34	25	7	2	102	30	82
Haslingden	34	26	4	4	113	42	82
Kirkham & Wesham	34	16	12	6	56	38	60
Tempest United	34	17	5	12	74	61	56
Lansil	34	15	9	10	75	57	54
Blackrod Town	34	16	8	10	82	57	*53
B.A.E. Canberra	34	16	8	10	70	52	*53
Multipart	34	15	8	11	72	58	53
Wyre Villa	34	13	9	12	80	65	48
Fleetwood Hesketh	34	12	9	13	52	67	45
Blackpool Rvrs Res.	34	12	6	16	60	73	42
Barrow Wanderers	34	11	8	15	70	78	41
Hesketh Bank	34	11	5	18	59	77	38
Longridge United	34	11	4	19	73	111	37
Carnforth Rangers	34	8	10	16	35	62	34
Padiham	34	9	5	20	47	83	32
B.A.E. Warton	34	5	6	23	54	107	21
Wigan Rovers	34	4	5	25	39	95	17

* - Points adjusted

Presidents Cup Winners: Haslingden
Presidents Cup Runners-up: Leyland D.A.F.

Reserve Section North/West

	P	W	D	L	F	A	PTS
Freckleton Res.	22	15	3	4	51	27	48
BAC Preston Res.	22	13	5	4	50	23	44
Kirkham & Wes. Res.	22	11	3	8	44	34	36
Blackpool Rgrs Res	22	10	4	8	35	41	34
Norcross & W. Res.	22	10	3	9	42	47	33
Vickers SC Res	22	10	2	10	61	49	32
Wyre Villa Res	22	9	3	10	54	55	30
Lytham St A. Res	22	8	5	9	43	37	29
Springfield Res.	22	9	5	8	52	50	*29
Lansil Res.	22	8	5	9	44	43	*26
Thornton I. Res.	22	6	1	15	42	58	19
B.A.E. Warton Res.	22	2	3	17	17	71	9

* - Points awarded

Reserve Section South/East

	P	W	D	L	F	A	PTS
Eagley Res.	22	18	2	2	83	30	56
Turton Res.	22	17	1	4	55	21	52
Poulton Town Res.	22	11	2	9	53	54	37
Burnley Utd Res.	22	11	3	8	52	42	36
Feniscowles Res.	22	11	2	9	58	48	35
Fleetwood H. Res.	22	8	3	11	55	57	27
Tempest Utd Res.	22	7	5	10	39	50	26
Padiham Res.	22	7	5	10	26	43	26
Blackrod T. Res.	22	7	3	12	55	58	24
Haslingden Res.	22	10	3	9	48	43	*21
Multipart Res.	22	5	4	13	49	74	19
Hesketh Bank Res.	22	1	4	17	27	80	7

* - Points adjusted

Houston Cup Winners: B.A.C. Preston Res.
Houston Cup Runners-up: Eagley Res.

DIVISION ONE CLUBS 1993-94

BRITISH AIRCRAFT CORPORATION PRESTON
Ground: Riverside Spts Grnd, Sth Meadow Lane, Preston (0772 51009) **Sec:** Mr F Heaton (0772 724751).

BURNLEY UNITED
Ground Barden Lane Spts Grnd, Burnley.   **Sec:** Mr R Greenwood (0282 34739).

COLNE BRITISH LEGION
Ground Holt House (top of Harrison Drive), Colne (0282 862335)   **Sec:** Mr W Alexander (0282 866638).

DALTON UNITED
Ground Railway Meadow, Beckside Rd, Dalton-in-Furness (0229 62799)   **Sec:** Mr D Lacey (0229 64202).

EAGLEY
Ground Eagley Sports Complex, Dunscar Bridge, Bolton (0204 54191)   **Sec:** Mr M Hackin (0204 595863).

FENISCOWLES
Ground Livsey Branch Road, Feniscowles, Blackburn (0254 208210)   **Sec:** Mr A Akeroyd (0254 706931).

FRECKLETON
G: Hodgson Mem. Grnd, Bush Lane, Freckleton, Nr Preston (0772 67139)   Mrs L O'Reilly (0772 634773).

GLAXCO SPORTS CLUB
G: Glaxco S.C., Nth Lonsdale Rd, Ulverston (0229 52804/52300)   **Sec:** Mr M Simpson (0229 54981).

KIRKHAM & WESHAM
Ground Coronation Rd Recreation Ground, Kirkham   **Sec:** Mr R Davey (0772 685049).

LEYLAND D.A.F.
Ground Thurston Road, Leyland, Lancs (0772 422400)   **Sec:** Mr J Hickson (0772 431066)

LYTHAM ST ANNES
G: Lytham Cricket & Sports Club, Church Rd, Lytham St A. (0253 734137)   Mr P Shearer (0253 738676).

POULTON TOWN
Ground Cottam Hall PF, Blackpool Old Rd, Poulton-le-Fylde   **Sec:** Mr M Sponder (0253 890284).

SPRINGFIELDS
G: S.S.R.A. Spts Grnd, Dodney Drive, Lea, Preston (0772 726131)   **Sec:** Mr T Threlfall (0772 718959).

THORNTON INTERNATIONAL
Prev. Name: I.C.I. Thornton   **G:** Gamble Road, Thornton Clevellys   **Sec:** Mr J F Wright (0253 868430).

TURTON
Ground Moorfield, Edgworth.   **Sec:** Mr L Donlan (0204 593387).

VERNON CARUS
Ground Factory Lane, Penwortham (0772 744006)   **Sec:** Mr T Beswick (0772 745007).

VICKERS SPORTS CLUB
Ground Hawcoat Lane, Barrow-in-Furness (0229 825296)   **Sec:** Mrs M Else (0229 834766).

WIGAN COLLEGE
Ground Christopher Park, Standish (0942 41140)   **Sec:** Mr R T Hale (0257 462424).

DIVISION TWO CLUBS 1993-94

BRITISH AEROSPACE CANBERRA
Ground British Aerospace Samlesbury   **Sec:** Mr S P Halse (0254 777050).

BRITISH AEROSPACE WARTON
G: British Aerospace Spts Grnd, Bank Lane, Warton (0772 632134)   **Sec:** Mr S Broomfield (0772 632392).

BARROW WANDERERS
Ground Lesh Lane, off Abbey Rd, Barrow-in-F. (0229 825224)   **Sec:** Mr M Poole (0229 839148).

BLACKPOOL RANGERS
Ground Fleetwood Road, Bispham (0253 853308)   **Sec:** T.B.A.

BLACKPOOL (WREN) ROVERS RESERVES (See Bass Nth West Co's Lge)

BLACKROD TOWN
G: Blackrod Community Centre, Vicarage Rd, Blackrod (0204 692614)   **Sec:** Mr D Almond (0942 818663).

CARNFORTH RANGERS
Ground Close to town centre   **Sec:** Mr K Webster (0524 735322).

CHARNOCK RICHARD
G: Charter Lane, off Chorley Lane, Charnock Richard (0257 79948)   **Sec:** Mr J B Stringer (0257 792474).

FLEETWOOD HESKETH
Ground Fylde Road, Southport (0704 27968)   **Sec:** Mr B Charnock (0704 895588).

FULWOOD AMATEURS
Ground Close to M6 jct 32 on M6 and A6-M55 junction   **Sec:** Mr A Wilson (0772 798256).

HESKETH BANK
Ground Hesketh Spts Field, Station Road, Hesketh Bank   **Sec:** Mr C Taylor (0772 815844).

LANSIL
Ground Lansil Sports Ground, Caton Rd, Lancaster   **Sec:** Mr M E Miller (0524 33962).

LANCASHIRE CONSTABULARY
G: Police HQ, Saunders Lane, off A59 at Hutton, nr Preston   **Sec:** Mr B Woodburn (0772 652867).

MULTIPART
Ground St Georges Park, Duke Street, Chorley (0257 270103)   **Sec:** Mr D Jolly (0257 270518).

NORCROSS & WARBRECK
Ground: Norcross Lane, Cleveleys, nr Blackpool (0253 852415)   Sec: Mr B Roberts (0253 825179).
PADIHAM
Ground: Well Street, off Church Street, Padiham (0282 73742)   Secretary: Mr D Howarth (0282 22983).
TEMPEST UNITED
Ground: Tempest Rd, Chow Moor Village, Westhoughton (0942 811938) Sec: Mrs L Laird (0942 812772).
WYRE HILL
Ground: Stalmine Village, nr Knott End   Secretary: Mr G Bradley (0253 810637).

EAST LANCASHIRE LEAGUE

President: Mr H Waddington.
Chairman: Mr R A Little.   **Vice Chairman:** Mr K Dean.
Hon. Secretary: Mr I Bulcock, 52 Cottontree Lane, Colne BB8 7BH (0282 866844).

Div. One	P	W	D	L	F	A	PTS
Foxhill	30	21	3	6	94	42	45
Barnoldswick Utd	30	18	6	6	81	45	42
Whalley	30	19	3	8	78	47	41
Johnsons	30	15	5	10	66	58	35
Clitheroe Res.	30	15	6	9	87	45	*30
Gt Harwood Utd	30	17	6	7	86	43	x33
Rock Rovers	30	15	3	12	61	56	33
Sabden	30	11	10	9	79	54	32
Rimington	30	12	8	10	66	47	32
Helmshore Utd	30	12	7	11	70	58	31
Colne United	30	13	5	12	80	72	31
Ribchester	30	11	6	13	53	74	28
Trawden Celtic	30	8	5	17	56	82	21
Clifton Athletic	30	3	8	19	41	78	14
Oswaldwistle Town	30	4	6	20	41	103	14
Colne R.B.L. Res.	30	1	3	16	29	163	5

* - 2 points deducted.   x - 6 points deducted.

Div. Two	P	W	D	L	F	A	PTS
Mill Hill St P.	28	25	3	0	116	13	53
Worsthorne Utd	28	20	5	3	109	39	45
Crosshills	28	19	1	8	108	48	*37
Read United	28	15	6	7	78	33	x35
Foxhill Res.	28	12	9	7	73	58	33
Chatburn	28	11	6	11	84	65	28
Colne Utd Res.	28	12	3	13	59	67	27
Rock Rvrs Res.	28	11	5	12	60	79	27
Nelson Res.	28	11	2	15	57	68	24
Nelson G.S.O.B.	28	10	3	15	43	73	23
Pendle Foret 'A'	28	8	5	15	42	70	21
Barnoldswick Res.	28	9	2	17	57	78	20
Whalley Res.	28	8	3	17	55	80	x18
Sabden Res.	28	6	2	20	36	105	14
Pendle Foret 'B'	28	5	1	22	24	113	11

* - 1 point deducted.   x - 2 points deducted.

DIVISION ONE RESULT CHART 1992/93

HOME TEAM		1	2	3	4	5	6	7	8	9	10	11	12	13	14	15	16
1.	Barnoldswick United	*	1-0	3-1	3-0	2-2	1-3	3-1	1-1	1-3	6-0	8-0	1-1	5-1	5-3	2-0	4-2
2.	Clifton Athletic	1-1	*	0-6	8-0	5-1	1-3	2-2	4-0	2-2	2-3	1-2	0-2	0-1	0-2	1-1	0-4
3.	Clitheroe Res.	1-1	7-2	*	6-1	4-0	3-1	1-1	2-1	1-2	3-1	1-1	4-1	2-3	2-2	4-0	1-2
4.	Colne Brit. Legion Res.	1-3	2-1	1-8	*	2-5	0-6	0-10	1-5	1-7	1-1	0-4	3-3	0-7	0-4	0-4	1-4
5.	Colne United	0-0	6-0	6-1	*	0-4	3-4	5-3	3-4	5-1	4-3	1-5	2-3	1-1	1-3	3-2
6.	Foxhill	1-5	2-0	0-4	8-1	8-1	*	3-1	3-1	3-1	3-0	2-0	4-2	2-3	3-1	6-2	1-0
7.	Gt Harwood Utd	1-2	8-1	1-0	4-0	2-1	1-1	*	2-0	2-1	5-1	7-0	2-0	0-2	2-0	3-1	1-3
8.	Helmshore United	7-1	1-0	3-0	5-0	2-5	0-0	3-1	*	1-1	7-3	2-0	1-1	2-3	2-4	4-1	0-1
9.	Johnsons S.C.	0-3	1-1	1-2	3-2	0-4	2-7	0-0	4-0	*	5-1	0-0	3-5	4-1	3-0	2-1	1-0
10.	Oswaldwistle Town	1-6	4-1	1-5	3-7	3-3	1-4	0-5	0-3	*	4-3	1-1	3-3	0-2	1-2	1-3
11.	Ribchester	0-2	4-1	4-3	2-1	1-1	2-6	2-2	3-2	4-1	1-1	*	1-2	2-1	1-4	3-2	1-1
12.	Rimington	2-1	1-1	2-2	13-1	3-1	0-1	4-2	5-2	1-2	2-0	3-0	*	1-1	1-0	2-2	1-2
13.	Rock Rovers	1-2	1-1	2-1	7-0	1-2	0-2	1-3	2-3	2-4	4-0	1-4	1-0	*	2-1	2-1	0-1
14.	Sabden	6-1	5-1	3-3	10-4	3-3	4-1	3-3	0-0	6-2	1-4	4-2	3-0	2-3	*	3-3	2-2
15.	Trawden Celtic	4-3	3-3	1-4	3-0	1-5	0-5	4-7	2-4	1-2	2-1	2-3	2-1	1-2	1-1	*	3-2
16.	Whalley	1-3	2-1	4-3	10-2	0-2	3-2	0-4	3-3	3-2	5-0	5-0	2-1	4-0	2-1	5-3	*

DIV. TWO		1	2	3	4	5	6	7	8	9	10	11	12	13	14	15
1.	Barnoldswick Utd Res.	*	0-5	4-3	0-2	1-2	1-6	2-1	4-1	0-2	9-1	1-3	1-0	3-1	2-2	1-8
2.	Chatburn	3-2	*	7-1	0-3	7-2	0-1	4-1	2-2	4-4	8-0	0-2	6-1	5-3	5-5	2-3
3.	Colne United Res.	2-0	2-2	*	3-2	1-2	1-2	4-2	1-2	1-0	4-0	1-0	1-2	5-0	4-2	0-9
4.	Crosshills	4-1	5-2	2-1	*	3-2	1-2	1-2	5-1	5-2	11-0	4-2	1-3	7-1	5-0	1-1
5.	Foxhill Res.	8-2	2-1	2-2	5-3	*	1-1	2-4	1-1	1-1	2-3	1-1	4-4	3-0	6-3	2-3
6.	Mill Hill St Peters	4-0	4-0	8-0	5-2	4-0	*	7-0	5-0	6-0	4-2	5-0	12-0	7-2	3-0	3-1
7.	Nelson Res.	2-0	2-3	2-0	2-7	4-0	0-4	*	3-4	1-2	5-2	1-4	0-1	0-2	3-1	1-3
8.	Nelson G.S.O.B.	2-3	0-0	0-2	0-5	0-3	0-7	0-3	*	3-1	5-1	1-3	3-2	0-1	3-0	3-5
9.	Pendle Forest 'A'	3-1	3-2	4-6	1-6	1-3	0-2	4-1	1-2	*	1-2	1-1	0-4	3-0	2-1	0-3
10.	Pendle Forest 'B'	3-2	1-4	0-3	0-4	0-8	0-0	0-3	0-1	4-0	*	0-3	0-2	1-2	0-5	1-7
11.	Read United	1-1	4-3	3-2	1-5	0-2	0-5	2-2	5-1	1-1	7-0	*	6-2	2-0	7-2	4-2
12.	Rock Rovers Res.	1-4	2-2	2-2	2-1	3-3	1-3	1-5	3-4	4-0	4-1	1-7	*	2-3	3-2	3-3
13.	Sabden Res.	1-10	3-5	3-2	1-6	1-1	1-3	2-2	1-3	1-3	0-1	1-5	1-4	*	0-1	3-6
14.	Whalley Res.	3-2	3-2	0-2	3-4	2-3	0-3	3-4	2-0	4-1	3-1	3-3	1-3	1-2	*	2-1
15.	Worsthorne United	4-0	4-0	5-3	5-3	2-2	0-0	3-1	4-1	1-1	4-0	5-1	3-0	8-0	6-1	*

PRESIDENTS CUP 1992-93

First Round

Great Harwood United v Colne United	2-3	Clitheroe Res. v Nelson Grammar School Old Boys 10-2
Johnsons S.C. v Helmshore United	1-3	Chatburn v Rimington 1-1(aet),3-1
Rock Rovers v Nelson Reserves	5-0	Ribchester United v Oswaldwistle Town 2-1
Crosshills v Read United	4-2	Westhorne United v Whalley 2-1

Second Round

Ribchester United v Trawden Celtic	4-2	Clitheroe Reserves v Clifton Athletic 4-1(aet)
Foxhill v Colne United	5-1	Pendle Forest 'A' v Mill Hill St Peter 1-6
Chatburn v Worsthorne United	2-5	Nelson Reserves v Barnoldswick United 2-5(aet)
Sabden v Crosshills	3-3(aet),2-1	Colne Royal British Legion Res. v Helmshore Utd 0-7

(continued overleaf)

(continued from page 917) **Quarter-Finals**

Clitheroe Reserves v Sabden	3-1	Foxhill v Barnoldswick United	3-1*(aet)*
Mill Hill St Peters v Ribchester United	3-0	Worsthorne United v Helmshore United	4-4*(aet)*

Semi-Finals

Clitheroe Reserves v Foxhill	3-1	Mill Hill St Peters v Helmshore Utd	1-0

Final: Clitheroe Reserves 0, Mill Hill St Peters 0 *(Clitheroe Reserves won 4-3 on penalties)*

B.E.P. DIVISION TWO CUP 1992-93 First Round

Chatburn v Nelson Grammar School O.B.	4-2	Colne United Reserves v Whalley Reserves	2-1
Foxhill Reserves v Sabden Reserves	2-0	Barnoldswick Utd Reserves v Worsthorne United	0-5
Read United v Crosshills	2-4*(aet)*	Mill Hill St Peters v Pendle Forest 'A'	4-0
Rock Rovers Reserves v Nelson Reserves	3-0		

Quarter-Finals

Crosshills v Chatburn	8-0	Colne United Reserves v Worsthorne United	0-5
Foxhill Reserves v Pendle Forest 'B'	3-1	Mill Hill St Peters v Rock Rovers Reserves	6-0

Semi-Finals

Foxhill Reserves v Crosshills	2-4*(aet)*	Mill Hill St Peters v Worsthorne United	3-3*(aet)*,1-0

Final: Crosshills 2, Mill Hill St Peters 0

CLUB DIRECTORY

BARNOLDSWICK UNITED
Secretary: Mr D Bowditch, 10 Roundell Rd, Barnoldswick, Lancs BB8 6EB (0282 817278).
Ground: West Close, Victory Park, Barnoldswick.
Colours: All blue   **Reserves colours:** Red & white.

BURNLEY BANK HALL
Secretary: Mrs J Moore, 5 Haverholt Close, Colne, Lancs (0282 868857).
Ground: Colne Road, Burnley, Lancs (0282 26695).
Colours: Blue & white   **Change colours:** All white   **Founded:** 1964
Record win: 16-2 v Tower (Heywood)   **Record defeat:** 2-8 v Feniscowles.
Metal Badges: Yes, £2,50   **Prev. Lges:** Lancs Amtr/ W Lancs/ N.W. Co's 92-93.
Record Gate: 1,200 v Burnley (friendly)   **Club Record Scorer + Appearance Maker:** Keith Blackburn

CHATBURN
Secretary: Mr T Dewhurst, 'Stoneleigh', Longworth Rd, Billington, Blackburn (0254 822808).
Ground: Chatburn Playing Field.
Colours: Maroon/blue/maroon.   **Change colours:** White & black/black/black.

CLIFTON ATHLETIC
Secretary: Mr L Cooke, 12 Calgarry Ave., Lammack, Blackburn, Lancs BB1 7DS (0254 670761).
Ground: Griffin Ground, Mill Hill, Blackburn.
Colours: Black & white/black.   **Change colours:** Yellow & blue/yellow/yellow.

CLITHEROE RESERVES (See Bass North West Counties League section)

COLNE BRITISH LEGION RESERVES
Secretary: Mr W Alexander, 101 Keighley Rd, Colne, Lancs BB8 0QG (0282 866638).
Ground: Holt House, Colne *(former Colne Dynamoes ground)* (0282 862335. British Legion club: 863313).
Colours: All yellow.   **Change Colours:** Blue & white/blue/blue.

COLNE UNITED
Secretary: Mr S Bannister, 13 Duke Str., Winewall, Colne, Lancs BB8 8AD (0282 871617).
Ground: Sough Park, Kelbrook, Earby, Colne.
Colours: All blue   **Change colours:** Red & white/blue/blue

CROSSHILLS
Secretary: Mr A Knox, 33 Ash Grove, Sutton-in-Craven, Keighley, West Yorks (0535 632088).
Ground: Sutton Fields, Sutton-in-Craven, Keighley, West Yorkshire.
Colours: All red   **Change colours:** Blue/black/red.

FOXHILL
Secretary: Mr A Dempsey, Heron Way, Oswaldtwistle, Accrington BB5 3AP (0254 394675).
Ground: Heys Playing Field, Heron Way, Oswaldtwistle, Accrington.
Colours: Green & yellow   **Change colours:** All blue.

GREAT HARWOOD UNITED
Secretary: Mr W Holden, 21 Delph Mount, Great Harwood, Lancs BB6 7QF (0254 884758).
Ground: Lyndon House, Great Harwood.
Colours: Red & black/black/black   **Change colours:** Blue/black.

HELMSHORE UNITED
Secretary: Mr I Walkden, 13 Piccadilly Str., Haslingden, Rossendale BB4 5LU (0706 226753).
Ground: Marl Pitts, Newchurch Rd, Rawtenstall.
Colours: Red & blue/red/red.   **Change colours:** Blue & white/blue.

JOHNSONS S.C.
Secretary: Mr C Hayhurst, 182 New Line, Bacup, Lancs OL13 9RU (0706 878323).
Ground: Bacup Borough F.C. (see Bass North West Counties League section).
Colours: All blue   **Change colours:** Grey/black/blue.

MILL HILL ST PETERS
Secretary: Mr P Walsh, 187 St Aidans Avenue, Blackburn BB2 4EA (0254 260424).
Ground: Mill Hill, Blackburn.
Colours: All green   **Change colours:** Claret & blue/maroon/blue.

NELSON RESERVES (See Bass North West Counties League section)

NELSON GRAMMAR SCHOOL OLD BOYS
Secretary: Mr J Crabtree, 46 Borrowdale Rd, Reedley, Burnley BB10 2SG (0282 692211).
Ground: Surrey Rd, Nelson   **Colours:** Red/black   **Change:** Silver/black.

OSWALDTWISTLE TOWN
Ground: Mount Carmel School, Willows Lane, Accrington.
Secretary: T.B.A.   **Colours:** All blue   **Change colours:** All yellow.

PENDLE FOREST
Secretary: Mr L Townsend, 5 Rake Top Ave., Higham, Burnley BB12 9BB (0282 73904).
Ground: Old Laund Booth, Fence (off Padiham-Nelson by-pass).
Colours: All blue   **Change colours:** All green.

READ UNITED
Secretary: Mr D Hacking, 39 Whalley Rd, Read. **Ground:** Rear of Read Cricket Club, Whalley Rd, Read.
Colours: Yellow/green/black   **Change colours:** Green/black.

RIBCHESTER
Secretary: Mr A Walmsley, 47 Mardale Rd, Longridge, Preston, Lancs PR3 3EU (0772 784362).
Ground: Ribchester Playing Field (opposite car park).
Colours: Yellow/black   **Change colours:** All blue.

RIMINGTON
Secretary: Mr L Whittaker, 2 Dorset Drive, Clitheroe, Lancs BB7 2BQ (0200 29112).
Ground: Coulthurst Memorial Field, Back Lane, Rimington (behind Black Bull).
Colours: Tangerine/black   **Change colours:** Yellow/black.

ROCK ROVERS
Secretary: Mr R Davies, 2 Lancaster Str., Colne, Lancs BB8 9AZ (0282 864203).
Ground: As Colne R.B.L. (above).   **Colours:** Blue/blue/yellow   **Change:** All red.

SABDEN
Secretary: Mr T Bromley, 89 Whalley Rd, Sabden, Blackburn BB6 9EA (0282 76554).
Ground: Nutter Barn Field, Sabden, Blackburn.
Colours: Red & blue/blue/blue   **Change colours:** Red & black/black/red.

TRAWDEN CELTIC
Secretary: Mr M Timberlake, 191 Cotton Tree Lane, Colne, Lancs BB8 7BN (0282 868143).
Ground: Trawden Recreation Ground, Rock Lane, Trawden.
Colours: Black & white/black/red   **Change colours:** Red & blue/blue/blue.

WHALLEY
Secretary: Mrs A Bury, 59 Lord Str., Oswaldtwistle, Accrington, Lancs BB5 3EF (0254 235443).
Ground: Queen Elizabeth Playing Field, Mitton Rd, Whalley.
Change colours: Red & white/white/red.   **Colours:** Blue & white/white/red

WORSTHORNE UNITED
Secretary: Mr K Stopforth, 43 Heckenhurst Ave., Worsthorne, Burnley BB10 1JN (0282 29092).
Ground: Worsthorne, Lennox Rd.
Colours: Yellow & green/green/yellow   **Change colours:** Blue/black/black.

MANCHESTER LEAGUE

President: A Booth.
Vice Presidents: G S Sinclair, W P D Haig.
Hon. Secretary: F Fitzpatrick, 102 Victoria Rd, Stretford M32 0AD (061 865 2726).

Premier Div.	P	W	D	L	F	A	PTS
Wythenshawe Amtrs	34	24	4	6	82	37	76
Woodley Sports	34	21	4	9	92	57	67
East Manchester	34	19	10	5	67	37	67
Dukinfield Town	34	19	7	8	62	41	64
Abbey Hey	34	17	9	8	66	42	60
Springhead	34	15	9	10	97	69	54
Little Hulton	34	15	6	13	80	85	51
Prestwich Heys	34	13	9	12	54	52	48
Mitchell Shackleton	34	12	10	12	61	50	46
Highfield Utd	34	13	5	16	50	57	44
Ramsbotton United	34	14	1	19	56	78	43
Stockport Georgians	34	12	5	17	55	72	41
B.T.C.L.	34	12	5	17	61	81	41
Whitworth Valley	34	11	6	17	67	80	39
Gtr Manchester Police	34	9	8	17	45	57	35
Wythenshawe Town	34	9	7	18	59	77	34
Silcoms Woodside	34	6	8	20	50	84	26
I.C.I. Blackley	34	5	7	22	43	91	22

Div. One	P	W	D	L	F	A	PTS
Atherton Town	32	23	4	5	96	39	73
Monton Amateurs	32	20	8	4	75	45	68
Old Altrinchameians	32	16	11	5	64	34	59
Avro	32	17	8	7	64	39	59
Breighmet United	32	15	7	10	85	50	52
Manchester Royal	32	15	6	11	68	48	51
Gorton Town	32	14	8	10	71	44	50
New Mills	32	14	7	11	72	52	49
Whalley Range	32	14	5	13	58	56	47
Pennington	32	13	8	11	58	57	47
Scared Heart	32	14	4	14	59	57	46
Winton United	32	9	6	17	66	78	33
Hollinwood	32	8	7	17	60	75	31
Milton	32	8	6	18	51	64	30
Crompton	32	8	5	19	57	83	29
Ashton Athletic	32	5	9	18	32	83	24
British Vita	32	3	3	26	27	159	12

Div. Two	P	W	D	L	F	A	PTS
Abbey Hey Res.	30	23	5	2	90	39	74
Wythenshawe A. Res.	30	21	4	5	70	30	67
Springhead Res.	30	20	2	8	98	47	62
E. Manchester Res.	30	15	9	6	69	36	54
Stockport Geo. Res.	30	14	7	9	50	43	49
Mitchell S'ton Res.	30	14	5	11	45	50	47
Dukinfield T. Res.	30	12	8	10	77	61	44
Highfield Utd Res.	30	11	10	9	57	57	43
I.C.I. Blackley Res.	30	11	3	16	62	89	36
Whalley Range Res.	30	11	2	17	63	88	35
Ramsbottom Utd Res.	30	8	10	12	51	59	34
Monton Amtrs Res.	30	9	4	17	70	78	31
W'shawe Town Res.	30	7	7	16	56	68	28
Prestwich H. Res.	30	7	6	17	51	104	27
O. Altrinch. Res.	30	6	6	18	47	79	24
B.T.C.L. Res.	30	5	4	21	45	73	19

Div. Three	P	W	D	L	F	A	PTS
Manch. Royal Res.	30	21	4	5	99	35	67
Hollinwood Res.	30	20	5	5	110	48	65
Woodley Spts Res.	30	20	2	8	88	50	62
Avro Res.	30	18	7	5	74	38	61
Atherton T. Res.	30	18	3	9	74	48	57
Winton Utd Res.	30	16	5	9	82	60	53
Whitworth V. Res.	30	14	8	8	74	48	50
New Mills Res.	30	16	0	14	62	56	48
Milton Res.	30	11	5	14	52	62	38
Gorton Town Res.	30	10	5	15	54	72	35
Breighmet Utd Res.	30	10	5	15	50	75	35
Pennington Res.	30	10	4	16	52	70	34
Sacred Heart Res.	30	8	9	13	45	64	33
Crompton Res.	30	5	3	22	40	81	18
British Vita Res.	30	5	2	21	45	132	17
G.M. Police Res.	30	3	2	25	22	84	11

Murray Trophy Winners: Breighmet United
Murray Trophy Runners-up: Old Altrinchameians
Open Trophy Winners: Abbey Hey Reserves
Open Trophy Runners-up: Springhead Reserves

Gilgryst Cup Winners: Woodley Sports
Gilgryst Cup Runners-up: Mitchell Shackleton

MANCHESTER LGE PREMIER DIVISION CLUBS 1993-94

ABBEY HEY
Secretary: A Vaughan, 94 Parsonage Rd, Heaton Moor, Stockport SK4 4JL (061 442 0036).
Colours: Green & white/white/green   **Ground:** Goredale Avenue, Gorton (061 231 7147).
Directions: A57 towards Hyde, right into Woodland Avenue approx one & a half miles past Belle Vue junction, right again into Ryder Brow Rd, 1st left after bridge into Goredale Ave.

ATHERTON TOWN
Secretary: G Butler, 43 Hope Fold Ave., Atherton, Lancs M29 0BW (0942 870326).
Colours: All royal   **Ground:** Howe Bridge Spts Centre, Howe Bridge, Atherton (0942 870403).
Directions: A579 Atherton to Leigh road - Sports Centre on left approx one & a half miles from Atherton.

B.T.C.L.
Secretary: P Sinclair, 4 Printon Ave., Blackley, Manchester M9 3JH (061 740 3342).
Colours: Blue/white/blue   **Ground:** G.M.T., White House, Middleton Rd, Crumpsall.
Directions: From Manchester via Cheetham Hill Rd to Half Way House hotel, right into Middleton Rd, ground entrance three quarters of a mile on left just before railway bridge.

DUKINFIELD TOWN
Secretary: L Walton, 280 Yew Tree Lane, Dukinfield, Cheshire SK16 5DN (061 338 6108).
Colours: Yellow/blue/yellow   **Ground:** Blocksages Birch Lane, Dukinfield.
Directions: To Ashton along by-pass, right at 2nd island into Dewsnap Lane, left into Birch Lane, ground 100yds on lefy behind public baths and Colliers garage.

EAST MANCHESTER
Secretary: D Wilkinson, 76 Sandy Lane, Dukinfield, Cheshire SK16 5NL (061 330 4450).
Colours: Sky/navy/blue   **Ground:** G.M.T. Tranport Ground, Mount Rd, Gorton (061 224 1176).
Directions: A57 from Manchester or Hyde to Belle Vue junction, turn into Mount Rd, ground 1 mile on left after Mellands Field.

GREATER MANCHESTER POLICE
Secretary: P Davidson, 2 Oakwood, Sale M33 5RH (061 962 2327).
Colours: Green & white/white/green   **Ground:** Hough End Police Club (061 856 1798).
Directions: Princess Parkway from central Manchester, right at Mauldeth Rd West, ground entrance half mile on left.

HIGHFIELD UNITED
Secretary: J Flynn, 58 Springside Rd, Bury BL9 5JQ (061 764 9986).
Colours: Red/white/red   **Ground:** Bridge Hall Lane, Bury (061 797 2282).
Directions: A58 from Bury centre towards Heywood, at M66 junction pass under motorway and Bridge Hall Lane is first left - ground 200yds on left.

LITTLE HULTON UNITED
Secretary: Mrs E Blood, 4 Cloudstock Grove, Little Hulton, Worsley M28 6DR (061 790 8925).
Colours: All royal   **Change colours:** Sky & white stripes/white/white.
Ground: Avon Close, off Worsley Avenue, Little Hulton.
Directions: A6 from Manchester, two miles after Walkden turn left towards Tyldesley into Armitage Lane, left at Welcome pub after half mile into Madamswood Lane, 2nd right into Worsley Ave., 2nd right is Avon Close. Or, M61 jct 4, A6 towards Manchester, right into Armitage Lane and follow as above.

MITCHELL SHACKLETON
Secretary: C L Flynn, 3 Adelaide Str., Swinton, Manchester M27 3JW (061 794 7953).
Colours: Green & white hoops/white/green   **Change colours:** All maroon.
Ground: Salteye Park, Peel Green, Eccles (061 788 8373).
Directions: Leave M63 at Peel Green r'bout (jct 2), take A57 Liverpool Road towards Irlam, ground entrance half mile on left behind Kara Cafew opposite Barton airport. Or, follow A57 from Manchester via Salford & Eccles, then follow Irlam signs.

MONTON AMATEURS
Secretary: T Lee, 28 Wheatley Rd, Swinton, Manchester M27 3RW (061 793 8033).
Colours: All royal   **Ground:** As Mitchell Shackleton (above).

PRESTWICH HEYS
Secretary: M Johnston, 23 Fairways, Horwich, Bolton BL6 5QA (0204 692086).
Colours: Red & white stripes/black/red   **Ground:** Sandgate Rd, Prestwich (061 773 8888).
Directions: Follow Old Bury Rd (A665) from Manchester to Prestwich, right into Heywood Rd, 3rd left into Mount Rd/Sandgate Rd - ground on right.

RAMSBOTTOM UNITED
Secretary: H Williams, 35 Nuttall Lane, Ramsbottom BL10 9JX (0706 823029).
Colours: Blue & white/blue & white/blue   **Ground:** Ramsbottom Cricket Club (0706 822799).
Directions: M66 jct 1, A56 towards Ramsbottom, left down Bury New Rd after 1 mile, left again immediately after River Bridge.

SPRINGHEAD
Secretary: K Gibson, 1 Little Oak Close, Lees, Oldham OL4 3LW (061 627 3760).
Colours: Red/white/red   **Ground:** St John Str., Lees, Oldham (061 627 0260).
Directions: From Oldham (Mumps r'bout) follow A669 towards Lees for approx one & a half miles, left at St John Str., grounds 500yds on right.

STOCKPORT GEORGIANS
Secretary: M Kennedy, 45 Shakespeare Rd, Bredbury, Stockport SK6 2HS (061 494 5210).
Colours: Blue & white/blue/white   **Ground:** Cromley Rd, Woodsmoor (061 483 6581).
Directions: Follow Stockport-Hazel Grove Rd (A6), right into Woodsmoor Lane at Davenport Theatre, 1st left into Moorland Rd, left at Flowery Field for Cromley Rd.

WHITWORTH VALLEY
Secretary: A Riley, 31 John Street, Whitworth, Rochdale OL12 8BT (0706 852619).
Colours: All royal   **Ground:** Rawstron Str., Whitworth (0706 853030).
Directions: Bacup road (A671) from Rochdale, after just over 2 miles turn left at Whitworth centre into Tonge Lane then 3rd right left into Crown Park Way.

WOODLEY SPORTS

Secretary: D Dawson, 19 Woodstock Rd, Woodley, Stockport SK6 1QP (061 236 9177).
Colours: Orange/white/orange   **Ground:** Lambeth Grove, off Mill Lane, Woodley (061 494 6429).
Directions: A560 from Stockport towards Woodley, left into Mill Str./Mill Lane at St Marks Church, Woodley, then 2nd right into Lambeth Grove.

WYTHENSHAWE AMATEURS

Secretary: S R Hall, 14 Southpark Rd, Gatley, Cheadle, Cheshire SK8 4AN (061 428 6074).
Colours: Blue & white stripes/blue/blue   **Ground:** Longley Lane, Northenden (061 998 7268).
Directions: Princess Parkway from Manchester to Post House hotel, via Palatine Rd & Moor End Rd to Longley Lane - ground entrance opposite Overwood Rd.

WYTHENSHAWE TOWN

Secretary: P Whiles, 29 Lorna Rd, Cheadle Hulme SK8 5BJ (061 485 7380).
Colours: All royal   **Ground:** Ericstan Park, Timpson Rd, Baguley, Manchester (061 998 5076).
Directions: Princess Parkway from Manchester, right into Altrincham Rd (A560), left into Southmoor Rd and 1st right into Timpson Rd - ground at end.

MANCHESTER LGE DIVISION ONE CLUBS 1993-94

ASHTON ATHLETIC

Secretary: S Halliwell, 20 Kings Rd, Golborne, Warrington WA3 3PJ (0942 270778).
Colours: All green   **Ground:** Brocstedes Park, Brocstedes Rd, North Ashton, Wigan (0942 716360).
Directions: A580 or M6 to Haydock Island, A49 to Ashton (Bryn Cross), left at lights onto Downall Green Rd, over M6, 2nd right, 2nd right is Brocstedes Rd.

AVRO

Secretary: D Kindon, 77 Hampton Rd, Failsworth, Manchester M35 9JA (061 688 8278).
Colours: All blue   **Ground:** British Aerospace Sports Club, Broadway, Failsworth (061 681 3083).
Directions: A62 Manchester to Oldham road, left at Broadway (A663), ground entrance 200yds on left.

BREIGHTMET UNITED

Secretary: P G Lee, 37 Meadow Close, Little Lever, Bolton BL3 1LJ (0204 792280).
Colours: White/black/red   **Ground:** Moss Park, Back Bury Rd, Breightmet, Bolton (0204 33930).
Directions: From Manchester follow A56 Bury road, at Whitefield take A665 towards Radcliffe, at Radcliffe proceed to Bolton Rd/Countess Lane and Radcliffe Moor Rd to A58 junction, left towards Bolton - ground half mile situated behind Coopers Egg Packing station.

BRITISH VITA

Secretary: A Palkimas, 115 Boothroyden Rd, Higher Blackley, Manchester M9 3SD (061 653 0908).
Cols: Black & white stripes/black/black   **Ground:** British Vita Works, Don Str., Middleton (061 643 1133).
Directions: A699 from Middleton or Oldham, turn down Don Str. at British Vita Works - pitches at bottom on right.

CROMPTON

Secretary: Mr B Jackson, 9 Balmoral Close, Milnrow OL16 3EL (0706 50768).
Colours: Blue & white/blue/blue   **Ground:** Crompton Cricket Club, Glebe Str., Shaw (0706 847421).
Directions: From Manchester via Oldham road (A62) and Broadway/Shaw Rd (A663) to 'Big Lamp' r'bout near Shaw, by-pass Shaw centre, left into Salt Str., right into Glebe Street.

HOLLINWOOD

Secretary: K Evans, 20 Meadow Rise, High Crompton, Shaw, Oldham OL2 7QG (0706 840987).
Colours: All blue   **Ground:** Lime Lane, Hollinwood (061 681 3385).
Directions: Oldham Road (A62) from Manchester to Roxy Cinema, right into Hollins Rd, 1st right into Albert Street, left at junction with Roman Road, 1st right into Lime Lane for quarter mile.

I.C.I. BLACKLEY

Secretary: D McKay, 10 Lorraine Close, Hopwood, Heywood OL10 2JR (0706 368931).
Colours: White & blue hoops/white/white   **Ground:** Hazelbottom Rd, Lower Crumpsall (061 205 5412).
Directions: A665 Cheetham Hill Rd froom Manchester, right into Queens Rd (A6010), left into Smedley Rd after half mile, fork right into Hazelbottom Rd, ground entrance 400yds on left.

MANCHESTER ROYAL

Secretary: S Law, 529 Parrswood Rd., Didsbury, Manchester M20 0SQ (061 445 9426).
Colours: Red (black trim)/black/red (black trim)   **Ground:** Barnes Hospital, Cheadle.
Directions: From Manchester, hospital entrance is on the left of Kingsway just after M63 jct 10. Keep left within hospital grounds, pitch is adjacent to motorway.

MILTON

Secretary: D Hopkinson, 32 Willbutts Lane, Rochdale OL11 5AY (0706 526600).
Colours: Green & yellow stripes/black/yellow
Ground: Athletic Stadium, Springfield Park, off Bolton Rd, Rochdale.
Directions: From Manchester via Middleton (A664) to Hollins, A6046 towards Heywood then A58 towards Rochdale - Park on left after one and a half miles. Or, M62 jct 20 then follow Heywood signs (A58) - Park on right after one and a half miles.

NEW MILLS

Secretary: A Bowers, 5 Digland Villas, New Mills SK12 4HS (0663 744932).
Colours: Amber/black/black   **Ground:** Church Lanw, New Mills (0663 747435).
Directions: A6 to Swan Hotel, left into Albion Rd, continue to Church Rd, left into Church Lane.

OLD ALTRINCHAMIANS

Secretary: K Ingham, 27 Oakleigh Ave., Timperley, Altrincham, Cheshire WA15 6QT (061 962 6496).
Colours: Black & white stripes/black/black   **Ground:** Crossford Bridge P.F., Meadows Rd, Sale.
Directions: From Manchester via Stretford (A56), under M63, left at lights into Dane Rd, 1st left into Meadows Rd, ground entrance at end.

PENNINGTON

Secretary: K J Mullineaux, 271 Devonshire Rd, Atherton, Manchester M29 9QB (0942 879769).
Colours: Royal & white stripes/white/blue　　**Ground:** Jubilee Park, Leigh Rd, Atherton (0942 894703).
Directions: From Manchester follow East Lancs Rd towards Liverpool, right at Greyhound hotel towards Leigh, in Leigh take Atherton Rd (A579), ground on left after about one & a half miles before G.M.T. offices.

SACRED HEART

Secretary: K D Devlin, 61 Buersil Ave., Balderstone, Rochdale, Lancs OL16 4TR (0706 313309).
Colours: Red/red/red & black　　**Ground:** Fox Park, Belfield Mill Lane, Rochdale.
Directions: M62 jct 21, follow Rochdale signs, right at 2nd lights into Albert Royds Street, ground half mile on right.

SILCOMS WOODSIDE

Secretary: T Hutchinson, 64 Tarbet Drive, Breight, Bolton BL2 6LT (0204 29502).
Colours: Blue & white hoops/blue/blue & white　　**Ground:** Snow Hill, Darcy Lever, Bolton.
Directions: M62/M63 to M61 then A666 to Bolton south, 2nd right into Castle Street and then via Radcliffe Rd - ground one and a half miles on right past Farmers Arms Hotel at Darcy Lever. Entrance in Ormond Str.

STAND ATHLETIC (New entrant 1993-94)

WHALLEY RANGE

Secretary: R Lapsley, 8 Withnell Rd, Burnage, Manchester M191GHN (061 432 6158).
Colours: Black & red stripes/black/black (red tops)　　**Ground:** King's Rd, Chorlton (061 881 2618).
Directions: Princess Parkway from Manchester, right at Wilbraham Rd, left at Withington Rd South, King's Rd is 1st right, ground entrance opposite Daventry Rd.

WINTON UNITED

Secretary: G Luxton, Wayoh Fold Farmhouse, Blackburn Rd, Entwistle, Bolton BL7 0PZ (0204 853588).
Colours: Royal & white/royal/royal　　**Ground:** Granary Lane, Worsley (061 794 1249).
Directions: Eccles New Rd (A57) from Manchester, proceed via Eccles centre towards Irlam, right at Patricroft Bridge into Worsley Rd/Barton Rd (B5211) - ground 2 miles on left, entrance to Granary Lane just before Bridgwater Hotel.

ST HELENS COMBINATION

'STAR' PREM. DIV.	P	W	D	L	F	A	PTS
Hen & Chickens	18	14	3	1	66	26	45
Prescot Celtic	18	11	3	4	49	33	36
Prescot 'A'	18	11	2	5	51	38	35
Globe	18	10	1	7	51	39	31
Prescot B.I.C.C.	18	7	5	6	54	45	26
St Helens T. 'A'	18	7	5	6	47	43	26
Blackbrook	18	4	5	9	27	42	17
York	18	4	3	11	32	47	15
Rainford Nth End	18	3	4	11	22	54	13
Pilkington Res.	18	3	1	14	20	52	10

DIV. ONE	P	W	D	L	F	A	PTS
Fingerpost Qu. Arms	20	17	2	1	83	14	53
Clock Face Coly.	20	14	3	3	68	39	45
Railway	20	10	2	8	48	37	32
Hosp. Spts & Social	20	9	5	6	59	50	32
E. Sutton Labour	20	8	6	6	53	44	30
Rifle	20	9	3	8	42	42	30
Prescot BICC Res.	20	9	2	9	50	57	29
Globe Res.	20	6	3	11	35	44	21
Earlestown '91	20	6	3	11	43	65	21
Carborundum	20	5	3	12	40	71	18
Sidac Social	20	0	2	18	32	90	2

DIV. TWO	P	W	D	L	F	A	PTS
Ravehead Royals	22	16	3	3	73	29	51
Hammer	22	13	5	4	80	40	44
Fridaymen	22	13	4	5	57	40	43
YMCA Carr Mill	22	11	7	4	71	38	40
Roundhouse	22	12	3	7	63	47	39
Church Tavern	22	8	5	9	41	51	29
Millhouse	22	8	4	10	63	68	28
York Res.	22	8	4	10	49	62	28
Wheatsheaf	22	8	1	13	55	42	25
Athletico Parr	22	7	3	12	41	57	24
Pilkington 'A'	22	5	4	13	48	70	19
Sutton Cricket C.	22	1	1	20	30	127	4

DIV. THREE	P	W	D	L	F	A	PTS
Guild Hall	26	21	1	4	108	52	*62
Old Ecclestonians	26	20	4	2	85	36	*62
Brown Cow	26	19	4	3	90	50	61
Manor Smithy	26	15	7	4	83	48	52
Blackbrook Res.	26	13	5	8	70	56	44
Old Windletonians	26	12	5	9	67	56	41
Bull (Newton-le-W.)	26	10	7	9	69	56	37
Primrose Vaults	26	11	3	12	65	65	36
Wargrave	26	8	3	15	60	80	27
Rainford N.E. Res.	26	8	1	17	41	78	25
West Bank	26	7	2	17	51	111	23
Wheatsheaf Res.	26	6	1	19	54	80	19

* - 2 points deducted

CREWE & DISTRICT LEAGUE

'Norpak & Normid' Premier Division	P	W	D	L	F	A	PTS
Nantwich T. Res.	20	15	2	3	76	30	32
Lostock Gralam	20	15	1	4	81	31	31
Prince of Wales	20	15	3	2	58	23	*31
Crewe Rolls Royce	20	11	1	8	67	56	23
Meadow Vale	20	10	2	8	41	44	22
Gresty Road	20	9	1	10	42	54	19
Malpas Reserves	20	7	4	9	48	49	18
Alsager	20	6	1	13	36	51	*11
Hays Chemicals	20	3	4	13	22	49	10
Congleton Athletic	20	3	2	15	31	63	8
Alsager College	20	4	3	13	30	82	x3

* - 2 points deducted
x - 8 points deducted

'Norpak & Normid' Division One	P	W	D	L	F	A	PTS
Whitebarn	16	14	1	1	77	12	29
B.O.C. Tanshield	16	11	1	4	56	30	23
Winnington Ave. Y.C.	16	9	2	5	73	26	20
Sandbach	16	9	2	5	32	30	20
Rolls Royce Res.	16	8	1	7	50	38	17
Bunbury	16	7	1	8	44	44	15
Crewe Villa	16	5	3	8	36	35	13
Malpas 'A'	16	3	1	12	24	64	7
Wickstead	16	0	0	16	9	122	0

HALLMARK LIVERPOOL COUNTY COMBINATION

DIV. ONE	P	W	D	L	F	A	PTS
St Dominics	30	24	4	2	111	41	76
Lucas Sports	30	22	5	3	100	45	71
Crawfords U.B.	30	20	5	5	82	34	65
Ayone	30	18	7	5	71	44	61
Waterloo Dock	30	18	4	8	80	38	58
Electric Supply	30	15	9	6	85	38	54
Yorks Cop. Tubes	30	14	4	12	77	63	46
Ford Motors	30	11	8	11	60	67	41
Earle	30	9	8	13	67	76	35
Crystal Villa	30	8	6	16	51	72	30
Littlewoods Ath.	30	6	9	15	57	93	27
Speke	30	6	8	16	56	82	26
B.R.N.E.S.C.	30	7	4	19	64	102	25
Mossley Hill	30	5	6	19	48	86	21
Eldonians	30	6	3	21	47	96	21
Bootle Reserves	30	3	6	21	44	123	15

DIV. TWO	P	W	D	L	F	A	PTS
Beesix	26	16	6	4	94	47	54
Ches. Lines S. L'pool	26	17	4	5	75	36	*52
Stockbridge	26	15	5	6	72	43	50
Royal Seaforth	26	15	2	9	50	49	47
B.R.N.E.S.C. Res.	26	14	4	8	76	51	*43
Plessey G.P.T.	26	12	4	10	59	56	40
Knowsley Utd Res.	26	12	5	9	64	61	*38
Halewood Town	26	9	8	9	43	49	35
Electric Supply Res.	26	8	9	9	46	46	33
Mersey Dks & H. Co.	26	8	8	10	53	51	*29
Camadale	26	7	7	12	51	67	28
Speke Reserves	26	4	4	18	44	76	16
Mossley Hill Res.	26	4	4	18	32	75	16
Merseybus	26	3	6	17	41	93	15

* - 3 points deducted

PETER COYNE (GEO MAHON) CUP:
Winners: Lucas Sports
Runners-up: Yorkshire Copper Tubes

MERSEY CERAMICS (LORD WAVERTREE) CUP:
Winners: Halewood Town
Runners-up: Knowsley United Reserves

McEWANS LAGER (FRED MICKLESFIELD) CUP:
Winners: Ayone
Runners-up: Speke

A brilliant save by Mossley Hill's Dave Fitzgibbon denies Joe Rice (on ground) as Cheshire Lines South Liverpool record a 4-2 home win in this Division Two fixture on 10th October. Photo - Rob Ruddock.

Waterloo Dock F.C., whose fine F.A. Vase run did the Combination proud. Photo - Colin Stevens.

ALEX STEWART ASSAYERS
LIVERPOOL I ZINGARI LEAGUE

PREM. DIVISION	P	W	D	L	F	A	PTS
Aigburth P.H.	26	18	7	1	77	39	43
Selwyn	26	17	5	4	70	30	39
R.E.M.Y.C.A. Utd	26	17	5	4	63	28	39
Liver Vaults	26	15	3	8	72	51	33
Quarry Bank OB	26	13	7	6	60	49	33
East Villa	26	13	6	7	78	52	32
Old Xaverians	26	10	3	13	49	64	23
Stoneycroft	26	7	7	12	53	67	21
Warbreck	26	7	5	14	56	68	19
Roma	26	8	3	15	54	87	19
Liverpool Nalgo	26	7	3	16	48	70	17
Collegiate OB	26	8	1	17	44	71	17
Netherley R.B.L.	26	7	2	17	59	83	16
Aintree Villa	26	3	6	17	39	74	12

1993-93 Constitution: Aigburth P.H., Collegiate Old Boys, East Villa, Leyfield, Liver Vaults, Liverpool Nalgo, Old Xaverians, Quarry Bank Old Boys, R.E.M.Y.C.A. Old Boys, Roma, Selwyn, Stoneycroft, Unity B.C.O.B., Warbreck.

DIVISION ONE	P	W	D	L	F	A	PTS
Leyfield	26	18	3	5	79	40	39
Unity B.C.O.B.	26	15	6	5	79	49	36
St Aloysius	26	15	6	5	70	45	36
De La Salle OB	26	16	2	8	65	40	34
St Mary's C.O.B.	26	13	3	10	60	50	29
Dove and Olive	26	10	6	10	58	59	26
Old Bootleians	26	10	5	11	57	73	25
Edge Hill B.C.O.B.	26	8	8	10	46	49	24
Essemmay O.B.	26	6	10	10	65	68	22
Shrewsbury House OB	26	8	6	12	64	74	22
Alsop OB	26	7	7	12	46	72	21
Sefton & District	26	6	7	13	38	67	19
Walton Village	26	7	3	16	63	75	17
Dista	26	6	2	18	40	69	14

1993-93 Constitution: Aintree Villa, Alsop Old Boys, Blacklow Brow, De la Salle Old Boys, Dove & Olive, Edge Hill B.C.O.B., Essemay O.B., Jabisco, Old Bootleians, Sefton & District, Shrewsbury House Old Boys, St Aloyius, St Mary's College Old Boys, Walton Village

DIVISION TWO	P	W	D	L	F	A	PTS
Jabisco *	26	21	1	4	114	51	43
Blacklow Brow	26	20	2	4	75	35	42
Maghull Town *	26	16	6	4	62	41	38
Sacre Coeur F.P.	26	14	5	7	69	47	33
N.E.L.T.C. #	26	13	6	7	78	56	30
Hillfoot Hey OB *#	26	14	2	10	71	60	28
Liobians	26	12	3	11	48	41	27
Southport Trinity#	26	10	7	9	61	59	27
Old Holts	26	13	1	12	60	59	27
Waterloo G.S.O.B.	26	8	4	14	55	62	20
Bluecoat OB	26	7	5	14	76	70	19
Riversdale College	26	6	1	19	60	83	13
Rockville (Wallasey)	26	6	1	19	47	108	13
B.T. Liverpool	26	0	0	26	23	129	0

* - 2pts deducted.
\# - 2pts awarded.

1993-93 Constitution: Bluecoat Old Boys, Dista, Hillfoot Hey Old Boys, Lee Jones OLd Boys, Liobians, Maghull Town, N.E.L.T.C., Oaks Institute, Old Holts, Riversdale College, Rockville (Wallesey), Sacre Coeur F.P., Southport Trinity, Waterloo Grammar School Old Boys.

CHALLENGE CUP FINAL (at Lucas Sports)
Jabisco 2, R.E.M.Y.C.A. United 2 *(aet)*
Jabisco 1, R.E.M.Y.C.A. United 1 *(aet, Jabisco won 8-7 on penalties)*

CHALLENGE CUP FINAL (at Lucas Sports)
St Aloyius 2, Edge Hill B.C.O.B. 0

HUGH LATIMER SPORTSMANSHIP TROPHY: Hillfoot Hey Old Boys

REFEREE OF THE YEAR: S Coffey.

It was great to see the name South Liverpool back on the football map in 1992-93. 'South' merged with relegated Liverpool County Combination side Cheshire Lines and, playing as Cheshire Lines South Liverpool, won promotion back to Division One. Back Row (L/R): Mike Ryman (Manager), Keith Jones, Darren Mason, Paul Morris, Paul Jones, Tony Pownall, Alan Johnston, Karl Marsh. Front: Martin Ryman, Joe Rice, Mick Rice, Tommy Murphy, Eugene Lam. Photo - Rob Ruddock.

NORTHERN COUNTIES (EAST) LEAGUE

President: H F Catt.
Chairman: C Morris.
Treasurer: G A Freeman.
Publicity Officer: K Motley (0423 508984)

Hon. Secretary: B Wood, 6 Restmore Ave.,
Guiseley, Leeds LS20 9DG (0943 874558)

SPENNYMOOR ACHIEVE OBJECTIVE

For the second consecutive season, the Premier Division title went to a North Eastern side who had switched from the Northern League during that competition's isolation from the Pyramid. However, unlike North Shields twelve months earlier, Spennymoor United were taken to the wire and in the end their winning margin over second placed Pickering Town was only goal difference. Spennymoor now accede to the Northern Premier League, thus achieving the goal that had taken them out of the Northern League three years ago.

The 'double' was again won in 1993-94, but again Spennymoor had to work harder than North Shields to achieve it. They were forced to come from behind at home in the semi-finals against a spirited Stocksbridge Park Steels side, and the final was an equally tight affair against Thackley. The Moors were unable, however, to emulate their Tyneside rivals 'treble' of 1991-92; they were defeated by Brigg Town in the semi-finals of the Presidents Cup which was ultimately won by Maltby Miners Welfare.

The honours in Division One went to the new arrivals from the Websters Central Midlands League; Lincoln United and Hucknall Town. They are promoted, and Arnold Town and Louth United will try to follow in their footsteps in 1993-94.

Spennymoor winger Gary Cowell gets in a cross as the champions-elect thrash Sheffield 5-0. Photo - Andrew Mollitt.

PREM. DIV.	P	W	D	L	F	A	PTS
Spennymoor United	38	26	7	5	102	33	85
Pickering Town	38	27	4	7	90	48	85
Nth Ferriby Utd	38	23	7	8	90	40	76
Maltby M.W.	38	21	11	6	69	40	74
Thackley	38	20	7	11	62	39	67
Brigg Town	38	16	14	8	55	39	62
Denaby United	38	15	11	12	71	63	56
Ossett Albion	38	16	7	15	68	60	55
Eccleshill Utd	38	16	6	16	65	65	54
Winterton Rgrs	38	14	7	17	61	72	49
Ashfield United	38	12	11	15	69	88	47
Ossett Town	38	13	7	18	69	71	46
Belper Town	38	11	12	15	56	62	45
Liversedge	38	12	8	18	56	77	44
Sheffield	38	12	6	20	55	70	42
Stocksbridge PS	38	10	11	17	54	70	41
Pontefract Coll.	38	11	8	19	62	88	41
Glasshoughton W.	38	9	9	20	46	77	36
Armthorpe Welfare	38	8	8	22	49	81	32
Harrogate R.A.	38	3	9	26	49	115	18

DIV. ONE	P	W	D	L	F	A	PTS
Lincoln United	26	17	5	4	62	31	56
Hucknall Town	26	15	6	5	54	32	51
Hallam	26	15	5	6	50	23	50
Yorks Amateur	26	14	3	9	42	29	45
R.E.S. Parkgate	26	12	9	5	39	38	45
Tadcaster Albion	26	12	5	9	51	43	41
Rossington Main	26	9	7	10	33	31	34
Hall Road Rangers	26	9	6	11	48	43	33
Garforth Town	26	8	8	10	34	38	32
Worsbrough Bridge	26	7	8	11	33	48	29
Hatfield Main	26	6	6	14	40	63	24
Immingham Town	26	5	8	13	38	51	23
Brodsworth M.W.	26	6	4	16	41	65	22
Selby Town	26	5	4	17	34	64	19

Bradley Rangers failed to complete fixtures, therefore record expunged.

PREMIER DIVISION RESULT CHART 1992-93

HOME TEAM	1	2	3	4	5	6	7	8	9	10	11	12	13	14	15	16	17	18	19	20
1. Armthorpe	*	1-3	1-2	2-0	0-1	0-2	4-0	3-1	1-0	1-4	0-2	2-3	0-6	1-3	2-3	3-1	0-1	1-3	0-2	1-3
2. Ashfield U.	2-0	*	2-0	1-1	2-2	2-1	3-4	2-2	3-1	3-3	1-3	0-7	1-0	5-1	3-3	1-2	1-2	2-2	0-1	2-4
3. Belper Town	1-1	1-1	*	1-3	0-3	2-1	1-1	3-1	3-1	1-3	0-2	2-2	3-1	0-1	1-4	1-0	2-3	1-1	1-1	2-2
4. Brigg T.	5-2	1-1	1-2	*	1-0	2-1	2-1	3-0	5-0	0-0	1-2	0-0	1-1	1-2	1-0	4-1	2-1	2-1	0-0	1-2
5. Denaby	2-2	3-0	2-1	1-1	*	2-2	0-2	1-2	4-2	2-3	0-3	0-4	3-1	0-1	1-1	4-4	3-1	1-0	1-1	3-2
6. Eccleshill	1-0	3-1	4-0	1-1	1-2	*	3-1	2-3	2-2	0-1	1-3	1-0	1-2	1-0	6-3	1-2	1-1	1-1	0-3	3-0
7. Glass'ton	1-2	0-4	0-0	1-1	1-4	2-3	*	3-2	2-3	0-1	1-3	1-1	0-1	1-1	4-3	2-0	1-3	0-3	1-0	2-0
8. H'gate R.A.	0-1	0-3	2-9	1-2	3-4	2-3	3-3	*	1-2	0-2	2-2	6-2	1-3	0-4	3-3	1-1	0-5	3-3	0-2	1-3
9. Liversedge	2-2	4-1	2-1	1-3	1-3	2-1	2-0	1-1	*	1-3	0-2	3-1	3-1	1-4	2-2	2-0	2-0	0-2	1-2	2-3
10. Maltby	6-0	2-3	1-1	0-1	1-1	1-1	1-0	0-0	2-2	*	2-4	1-0	5-0	0-4	2-1	1-0	0-0	2-1	2-1	2-0
11. Nth Ferriby	2-1	1-1	1-1	4-0	2-0	5-1	3-0	3-0	3-4	0-0	*	1-3	3-0	6-1	3-0	1-3	2-3	1-1	4-0	0-0
12. Ossett A.	1-3	5-6	2-2	2-1	2-1	0-1	0-0	2-1	4-0	1-1	2-1	*	1-2	1-2	0-0	3-1	3-2	2-1	0-2	3-1
13. Ossett T.	1-1	6-1	2-2	1-2	1-1	1-3	3-3	10-1	2-4	1-2	2-1	1-2	*	1-3	3-2	1-2	1-1	2-1	2-0	3-2
14. Pickering	3-1	5-0	3-0	1-1	2-0	4-1	3-1	7-1	3-0	1-2	1-1	2-1	2-1	*	2-1	2-3	2-0	3-1	2-4	2-1
15. Pontefract	2-2	0-4	2-1	0-0	0-5	4-2	1-2	3-1	2-2	2-1	1-6	2-1	3-1	0-2	*	2-3	0-6	0-1	2-3	0-4
16. Sheffield	0-0	2-2	1-0	1-3	2-3	2-3	0-0	3-1	3-0	1-2	2-1	1-3	1-2	1-2	0-2	*	0-0	5-1	1-3	1-2
17. Spennymoor	3-3	7-0	3-1	0-0	2-2	3-0	5-0	4-1	1-0	6-2	2-1	5-2	3-0	5-0	3-0	5-0	*	3-0	3-1	0-0
18. Stocksbridge	2-2	1-1	1-3	1-1	3-2	3-1	1-3	0-3	1-3	0-2	1-2	3-3	0-3	1-4	0-1			*	3-1	0-4
19. Thackley	4-1	2-0	0-1	2-0	3-1	1-2	5-2	2-0	0-0	0-0	1-3	2-0	0-0	1-4	4-1	3-0	0-1	0-0	*	3-0
20. Winterton	3-2	5-1	0-3	1-1	3-3	1-3	2-0	1-1	1-1	0-5	1-2	2-0	3-2	0-2	1-2	2-1	0-6	2-4	0-2	*

DIVISION ONE RESULT CHART 1992-93

HOME TEAM	1	2	3	4	5	6	7	8	9	10	11	12	13	14
1. Brodsworth Miners Welfare	*	1-3	1-4	1-0	1-5	2-0	2-4	2-3	0-2	1-1	2-3	2-4	4-1	0-1
2. Garforth Town	1-1	*	0-0	0-0	0-1	2-1	2-3	0-2	0-0	0-0	4-2	3-0	2-1	2-1
3. Hallam	2-5	2-0	*	1-0	7-0	1-2	3-0	1-1	0-1	3-0	4-0	2-0	0-1	3-2
4. Hall Road Rangers	6-1	2-1	1-2	*	4-2	1-2	3-2	0-0	2-0	3-0	4-0	1-1	0-2	2-1
5. Hatfield Main	2-3	2-0	3-2	1-1	*	3-5	2-2	1-1	2-2	1-4	1-0	2-2	1-2	1-5
6. Hucknall Town	4-2	2-1	0-0	2-1	3-1	*	1-0	1-2	2-2	1-0	2-0	1-0	5-0	1-1
7. Immingham Town	2-2	0-4	1-3	4-4	3-0	1-4	*	3-1	1-1	2-2	1-2	0-2	3-3	0-1
8. Lincoln United	2-1	7-1	2-0	5-3	7-2	3-1	2-1	*	2-2	0-3	3-2	4-1	6-0	1-0
9. R.E.S. Parkgate	1-0	4-3	1-1	3-1	0-3	2-2	3-1	0-0	*	1-0	2-2	4-3	0-2	2-0
10. Rossington Main	2-3	1-1	1-1	1-3	2-1	1-2	0-0	0-1	0-1	*	3-1	3-1	1-0	2-1
11. Selby Town	4-3	1-2	0-1	4-4	2-1	0-5	1-0	2-3	0-1	0-2	*	0-0	2-2	2-4
12. Tadcaster Albion	6-0	3-1	0-3	3-1	3-1	2-2	0-2	2-1	6-2	1-1	4-2	*	1-0	0-2
13. Worsborough Bridge M.W.	1-1	1-1	1-3	2-1	1-1	1-1	1-1	1-3	0-2	0-2	4-1	2-3	*	3-2
14. Yorkshire Amateur	1-0	0-0	0-1	2-0	1-0	3-2	2-1	1-0	5-0	2-1	2-1	1-3	1-1	*

'G & W' ENGINEERING LEAGUE CUP 1992-93

First Round

Garforth Town v Bradley Rangers	3-1
Worsborough Bridge M.W. v Hatfield Main	4-1
Immingham Town v Hallam	0-0,3-4

Second Round

Ashfield United v Ossett Town	3-5
Garforth Town v Stockbridge Pk Steels	0-4
Hall Road Rgrs v Maltby Miners Welfare	0-3
Lincoln United v Harrogate Railway Ath.	7-0
Pickering Town v Liversedge	0-1
Selby Town v Spennymoor United	1-6
Tadcaster Albion v R.E.S. Parkgate	1-1,4-3
Worsborough Bridge v Armthorpe Welfare	3-1
Brigg Town v Denaby United	2-3
Brodsworth Miners Welfare v Glasshoughton Welf.	0-1
Hucknall Town v Ossett Albion	2-0
North Ferriby United v Belper Town	1-0
Rossington Main v Eccleshill United	6-0
Sheffield v Winterton Rangers	4-2
Thackley v Hallam	1-0
Yorkshire Amateur v Pontefract Collieries	4-2

Third Round

Denaby United v Ossett Town	2-1
Spennymoor United v Glasshoughton Welfare	5-1
Thackley v Sheffield	0-0,4-2
Yorkshire Amateur v Liversedge	0-2
Maltby Miners Welfare v Hucknall Town	2-1
Tadcaster Albion v Lincoln United	1-4
Worsborough Bridge M.W. v Rossington Main	1-1,1-0
North Ferriby United v Stocksbridge Pk Steels	1-2

Fourth Round

Liversedge v Denaby United	3-4
Stocksbridge Park Steels v Lincoln United	2-1
Spennymoor United v Maltby Miners Welfare	4-1
Worsborough Bridge Miners Welfare v Thackley	0-2

Semi-Finals

Thackley v Denaby United	2-0
Spennymoor United v Stocksbridge Park Steels	2-1

Final (at Ossett Albion F.C., Tues 4th May): Spennymoor United 2, Thackley 1

PRESIDENT'S CUP 1992-93

First Round

Armthorpe Welfare v Sheffield	2-0
Hatfield Main v Belper Town	1-2
Liversedge v Yorshire Amateur	3-2
North Ferriby United v Ossett Town	3-0
Rossington Main v Hucknall Town	1-0
Stocksbridge Park Steels v Glasshoughton W.	1-0
Brigg Town v Denaby United	2-0
Immingham Town v Ashfield United	1-8
Maltby Miners Welfare v Winterton Rangers	3-0
Pontefract Collieries v Pickering Town	1-0
Spennymoor United v Harrogate Railway Athletic	5-0

Second Round

Brigg Town v Ashfield United	3-0
Lincoln United v Belper Town	4-0
Pontefract Collieries v Liversedge	5-3
Rossington Main v Maltby Miners Welfare	3-3,0-1
Eccleshill United v North Ferriby United	4-1
Ossett Albion v Thackley	1-1,3-1
R.E.S. Parkgate v Armthorpe Welfare	1-3
Spennymoor United v Stocksbridge Park Steels	4-0

Third Round

Brigg Town v Ossett Albion	3-3,4-1
Maltby Miners Welfare v Eccleshill Utd	1-0
Lincoln United v Spennymoor United	1-2
Pontefract Collieries v Armthorpe Welfare	3-0

(continued opposite)

(continued from opposite)
Semi-Finals
Spennymoor United v Brigg Town   1-2   Maltby Miners Welfare v Pontefract Collieries   3-1
Final (at Lincoln United F.C.): Maltby Miners Welfare 3, Brigg Town 0

Northern Counties (East) Premier Division Ten Year Record

	83/4	84/5	85/6	86/7	87/8	88/9	89/0	90/1	91/2	92/3
Alfreton Town	4	4	6	1	–	–	–	–	–	–
Appleby Frodingham	14	16	18	–	–	–	–	–	–	–
Armthorpe Welfare	–	–	13	12	2	11	7	9	13	19
Arnold	2	7	1	–	–	–	–	–	–	–
Ashfield United	13	12	7	5	–	–	8	12	2	11
Belper Town	11	1	9	15	16	10	12	13	11	13
Bentley Victoria	18	15	14	14	–	–	–	–	–	–
Boston	12	17	17	19	–	–	–	–	–	–
Bridlington Town	–	–	–	10	4	3	1	–	–	–
Bridlington Trinity	16	9	19	17	13	16	4	–	–	–
Brigg Town	–	–	–	18	15	14	10	5	8	6
Denaby United	–	6	11	6	3	6	3	15	3	7
Eastwood Town	5	2	5	13	–	–	–	–	–	–
Eccleshill United	–	–	–	–	–	–	–	–	17	9
Emley	3	8	2	4	1	1	–	–	–	–
Farsley Celtic	–	–	8	2	–	–	–	–	–	–
Glasshoughton Welfare	–	–	–	–	–	–	–	–	19	18
Grimethorpe Miners Welfare	–	–	–	–	9	15	17	–	–	–
Guisborough Town	8	5	–	–	–	–	–	–	–	–
Guiseley	7	3	3	16	7	5	11	1	–	–
Hallam	–	–	–	–	10	12	14	–	–	–
Harrogate Railway Athletic	–	–	–	–	12	8	5	7	18	20
Harrogate Town	–	–	–	9	–	–	–	–	–	–
Hatfield Main	–	–	–	–	11	2	2	–	–	–
Heanor Town	17	18	15	–	–	–	–	–	–	–
Ilkeston Town	6	13	20	–	–	–	–	–	–	–
Liversedge	–	–	–	–	–	–	–	–	14	14
Long Eaton United	–	–	4	11	14	13	–	–	–	–
Maltby Miners Welfare	–	–	–	–	–	–	–	6	7	4
Mexborough Town	15	19	–	–	–	–	–	–	–	–
North Ferriby United	–	–	–	3	6	4	6	4	4	3
North Shields	–	–	–	–	–	–	2	2	1	–
Ossett Albion	–	–	–	–	17	17	16	14	10	8
Ossett Town	–	–	–	–	–	–	–	8	12	12
Pickering Town	–	–	–	–	–	–	–	–	–	2
Pontefract Collieries	–	14	12	8	8	7	13	16	16	17
Sheffield	–	–	–	–	–	–	9	–	6	15
Spalding United	1	11	16	–	–	–	–	–	–	–
Spennymoor United	–	–	–	–	–	–	–	3	5	1
Stocsbridge Park Steels	–	–	–	–	–	–	–	–	–	16
Sutton Town					(see Ashfield United)					
Thackley	9	10	10	7	5	9	15	11	9	5
Winterton Rangers	10	–	–	–	–	–	–	10	15	10
No. of Clubs	**18**	**19**	**20**	**19**	**17**	**17**	**18**	**16**	**19**	**20**

Pickering Town F.C., who did brilliantly to finish in second spot in their first season in the Premier Division. Back Row (L/R): Andrew Thornton, Robert Pickering, Andrew Barnett, Gavin Howell, Tony Bryden, Paul Bowes, Steven Drake. Front: Ged Ledden, Mark Aitken, Peter Collier, Nicky Cass, Mark Ash. Photo - Colin Stevens.

Northern Counties (East) Division One Ten Year Record

(Includes Division One Central (C), Division One North (N), Division One South (S))

	83/4	84/5	85/6	86/7	87/8	88/9	89/0	90/1	91/2	92/3
Armthorpe Welfare	–	1C	–	–	–	–	–	–	–	–
Arnold Kingswell	12S	8S	–	–	–	–	–	–	–	–
Blidworth Welfare	–	15S	–	–	–	–	–	–	–	–
Borrowash Victoria	1S	2S	7	–	–	–	–	–	–	–
Bradley Rangers	4N	3N	10	5	5	15	–	–	3	w/d
Bridlington Town	11N	5N	6	–	–	–	–	–	–	–
Brigg Town	–	2C	12	–	–	–	–	–	–	–
Brodsworth Miners Welfare	–	–	–	–	–	–	–	–	15	13
Collingham & Linton	–	16N	–	–	–	8	10	–	–	–
Denaby United	2S	–	–	–	–	–	–	–	–	–
Dronfield United				(see Norton Woodseats)						
Eccleshill United	–	–	–	–	7	7	7	5	–	–
Farsley Celtic	3N	1N	–	–	–	–	–	–	–	–
Frecheville Community	11S	16S	–	–	10	13	11	–	–	–
Fryston Colliery Welfare	–	16C	–	–	–	–	–	–	–	–
Garforth Town	6N	9N	–	11	14	6	6	6	11	9
Glasshoughton Welfare	–	–	–	–	–	–	–	11	–	–
Graham Street Prims	–	14S	–	–	–	–	–	–	–	–
Grimethorpe Miners Welfare	–	10C	–	12	–	–	–	–	–	–
Hallam	9S	9S	–	6	–	–	–	2	5	3
Hall Road Rangers	–	14N	–	–	–	–	–	–	6	8
Harrogate Railway Athletic	–	4N	14	4	–	–	–	–	–	–
Harrogate Town	7N	2N	3	–	–	–	–	–	–	–
Harworth Colliery Institute	14S	5S	8	–	–	–	–	–	–	–
Hatfield Main	12N	5C	11	3	–	–	–	8	16	11
Hucknall Town	–	–	–	–	–	–	–	–	–	2
Immingham Town	–	–	–	–	9	9	9	–	9	12
Kimberley Town	–	16S	–	–	–	–	–	–	–	–
Kiveton Park	–	12S	–	14	11	10	8	–	–	–
Lincoln United	5S	11S	–	–	–	–	–	–	–	1
Liversedge	13N	8N	–	–	–	–	2	3	–	–
Long Eaton United	10S	1S	–	–	–	–	–	–	–	–
Maltby Miners Welfare	6S	11C	–	9	3	4	5	–	–	–
Mexborough Town	–	–	13	16	15	11	15	13	–	–
North Ferriby United	9N	7N	1	–	–	–	–	–	–	–
Norton Woodseats	13S	–	–	–	–	–	–	–	–	–
Oakham United	–	13S	–	–	–	–	–	–	–	–
Ossett Albion	5N	4C	5	1	–	–	–	–	–	–
Ossett Town	14N	8C	–	–	–	–	3	–	–	–
Phoenix Park	–	12N	–	–	–	–	–	–	–	–
Pickering Town	–	11N	–	–	–	5	14	4	2	–
Pilkington Recreation	–	6C	16	10	13	16	–	–	–	–
Pontefract Collieries	1N	–	–	–	–	–	–	–	–	–
R.E.S. Parkgate	7S	9C	–	15	4	12	12	9	8	5
Retford Rail	–	4S	–	–	–	–	–	–	–	–
Rossington Main	–	–	–	–	–	–	–	–	7	7
Rowntree Mackintosh	2N	6N	4	2	2	2	1	–	–	–
Scarborough Reserves	8N	–	–	–	–	–	–	–	–	–
Selby Town	–	13N	–	–	–	–	–	7	13	14
Sheffield	4S	8S	2	17	8	1	–	1	–	–
Staveley Works	8S	7S	–	7	12	–	–	–	–	–
Stocksbridge Park Steels	–	–	–	–	–	–	–	–	1	–
Stocksbridge Works	–	14C	–	–	–	–	–	–	–	–
Tadcaster Albion	–	17N	–	–	–	–	–	–	12	6
Thorne Colliery	–	7C	–	–	–	–	–	–	–	–
Wombwell Town	–	15C	–	–	–	–	–	–	–	–
Woolley Miners Welfare	3S	3C	9	13	6	3	4	–	–	–
Worsborough Bridge M.W. & Ath.	–	13C	–	–	–	–	–	–	10	10
York Railway Institute	10N	10N	–	8	1	14	13	10	14	–
Yorkshire Amateurs	–	15N	–	–	–	–	–	–	4	4
Yorkshire Main	–	12C	–	–	–	–	–	12	–	–
No. of Clubs	**14N** **14S**	**17N** **16S** **16C**	**16**	**18**	**16**	**16**	**15**	**13**	**16**	**14**

PREMIER DIVISION CLUBS 1993-94

ARMTHORPE WELFARE

Chairman: Alan Bell   **Vice Chairman:** James Houston
Secretary: Eric Cottam, 'Roydean', Whiphill Lane, Armthorpe, Doncaster DN3 3JP (0302 832514).
Manager: Carl Leighton   **Asst Manager:** John McKeown   **Coach:** Steve Taylor.
Physio: Joey Johnson   **Comm. Manager:** Peter Camm   **Press Officer:** Sharon Morgan.
Ground: Welfare Ground, Church Str., Armthorpe (0302 833674-Welfare, 0302 831247-Club No.).
Directions: From north: Turn left at main r'bout in centre of Doncaster, straight across next r/about on to Wheatley Hall Rd. Right at Mines Rescue Station, go to top of hill on to Armthorpe Rd. From south: M18 jct 4, on to A630, left at r'bout then proceed to next r'bout and turn right. Ground 400yds on left behind Plough Inn. Two and a half miles from Doncaster (BR). Buses A2, A3 & 181 pass ground.
Formed: 1926   **Disbanded:** 1974   **Reformed:** 1976
Seats: 200   **Cover:** 400   **Capacity:** 2,500   **Floodlights:** Yes   **Nickname:** Wellie.
Midweek matches: Tuesday   **Record Att.:** 2,000 v Doncaster R., Charity match 85-86
Colours: White/navy/white   **Change colours:** Navy/white/navy   **Club Shop:** No.
Programme: 24 pages   **Editor:** Miss Sharon Morgan (0302 834475).
Previous League: Doncaster Senior   **Club Sponsors:** Houston Transport.
Local Paper: Doncaster Evening Star   **Clubhouse:** No. Wheatsheaf Hotel used after matches.
Record win: 7-0   **Record defeat:** 1-7
Captain 92-93: Steve Taylor   **Top Scorer 92-93:** Simon Johnson   **P.o.Y. 92-93:** Mark Brogan
Club record scorer: Martin Johnson   **Club record appearances:** Gary Leighton.
Club honours: Northern Co's East Lg R-up 87-88 (Lg Cup R-up 91-92, Div 1 R-up 83-84, East Central Div 1 84-85); Doncaster & Dist. Lg 82-83 (Div 1 81-82, Div 2 79-80, Div 3 78-79; Lg Cup 79-80 80-81 81-82 82-83; Challenge Cup 82-83); West Riding Chall. Cup 81-82 82-83; Goole & Thorne Dist. Cup 82-83

ASHFIELD UNITED

President: Frank Haynes M.P.   **Chairman:** Roy Gregory   **Treasurer:** Gillian Gregory
Secretary: William Roper, 82 Columbia St., Huthwaite, Sutton-in-Ashfield, Notts NG17 2JA (0623 554657).
Manager: Gary Saxby   **Asst Manager:** Rod Arnold   **Coach:** Mick Vinter
Commercial Manager: Andrew Turner (0773 710309).
Ground: Lowmoor Road, Kirkby-in-Ashfield, Notts (0623 752181).
Directions: From M1 jct. 38 at 5th lights turn right onto B6021 (s.p. Kirkby-in-Ashfield). After half mile turn right immediately after crossing railway lines. Ground is on left approx 1 mile (before Lowmoor Inn and opposite Texas)
Seats: 200   **Cover:** 500   **Capacity:** 8,000   **Floodlights:** Yes   **Founded:** 1885.
Club Shop: Yes (contact Leighton Morris).
Prev. Name: Sutton Town 1885-1992   **Midweek matches:** Wednesday   **Nickname:** Snipes
Club colours: Blue/claret/blue   **Change colours:** White/black
Programme: 36 pages, 30p   **Programme Editor:** Gordon Foster (0623 794281).
Previous leagues: Notts & District, Notts & Derbys, Midland Comb., Derbys Senior, Central Comb., Notts Alliance, Central Alliance, Midland League, NE Counties, Northern Premier.
Previous Grounds: Dog & Duck 1885-97/ New Cross 98-1919/ Avenue Ground 19-39/ Skegby MW 49-51/ Prestic. Rd 51-77.
Record attendance: 1,562 v Leeds, floodlight opening, 1980. *At Priestic Rd: 6,000 v Peterborough Utd, 1958. At The Avenue: 8,000 v Reading, FA Cup 1933.*
Local newspapers: Notts Free Press, Sutton & Kirkby News
Club honours: Notts Snr Cup 08-09 12-13 13-14 23-24 55-56 57-58 59-60 61-62 62-63 63-64 67-68 69-70 71-72 72-73 73-74 74-75 76-77; Notts & Dist Lg 05-06 06-07; Derby Snr Lg 30-31 31-32 32-33; Central Alliance 50-51; Northern Co. East Lg R-up 91-92 (Lg Cup 85-86); Mansfield Charity Cup 1892-93 05-06 23-24; Sutton Charity Cup 29-30 30-31 31-32; Byron Cup 30-31 31-32; FA Cup 2nd Rnd 1933-34

BELPER TOWN

President: Alan Benfield   **Chairman:** Phil Varney   **Manager:** Steve Powell
Secretary: P E Wainwright, 11 Stanton Ave, Belper, Derbys DE56 1EE (0773 825675).
Asst Manager: Mick Williamson   **Press Officer:** D R Laughlin/S Wilton
Ground: Christ Church Meadow, Bridge Street, Belper (0773 825549).
Directions: From M1 North, Jnct. 28 onto A38 towards Derby, turn off at A610 (s.p. Ripley/Nottingham), then 4 exit at roundabout towards Ambergate. At junction with A6 (Hurt Arms Hotel) left to Belper. Ground on right past traffic lights. 400 yards from Belper (BR).
Seats: 200   **Cover:** 1,500   **Capacity:** 6,000   **Floodlights:** Yes   **Year formed:** 1883
Club colours: Gold/black/gold   **Change colours:** Sky & white   **Nickname:** Nailers
Midweek matches: Tuesday   **Programme:** 16 pages, 30p, **Editor:** David Laughlin.
Rec. Gate: 3,600 v Ilkeston, 1951   **Prev. Lges:** Central Alliance 57-61/ Midland Co's 61-82
Clubhouse details: Bar (Tetley and Castlemaine). Hot & cold food.
Prev. Ground: Acorn Ground (pre-1951)   **Local newspapers:** Derby Evening Telegraph, Belper News
Club honours: Midland Counties Lg 79-80, Central Alliance League 1958-59, N. Counties East League 1984-85, Derbys Snr Cup 58-59 60-61 62-63 79-80, FA Cup 1st Round Proper 1887-88 (4th Qual. Rnd 1964-65).

BRIGG TOWN

President: B Robins   **Chairman:** H Williams   **Manager:** Ralph Clayton
Secretary: R B Taylor, 'Highfield House', Barton Rd, Wrawby, Brigg, South Humbs DN20 8SH (0652 652284).
Coach: John Kaye   **Commercial Manager:** H Williams
Ground: The Hawthorns, Hawthorn Avenue, Brigg (0652 652767).
Directions: From M180 Scunthorpe East, A18 through Brigg leaving on Wrawby Rd, left into East Parade/Woodbine Ave, follow houses on right into Hawthorn Ave. One mile from Brigg (BR).
Seats: 250   **Cover:** 2 Stands   **Capacity:** 4,000   **Floodlights:** Yes   **Year formed:** 1864
Colours: Black & white stripes/black/black   **Change colours:** Orange shirts
Programme: 16 pages   **Programme Editor:** Secretary   **Nickname:** Zebras
Previous Leagues: Lindsey/ Lincs 48-76/ Midland Counties 76-82
Previous Grounds: Manor House Convent, Station Rd (pre 1939); Brocklesby Ox 1939-59
Clubhouse: Licensed club open matchdays   **Rec. Gate:** 2,000 v Boston U. 1953 (at Brocklesby Ox).
Honours: Northern Co's East Lg Presidents Cup R-up 91-92 92-93, Lincs Lg 49-50 53-54 73-74 75-76 (Div I 68-69 69-70 70-71 71-72, Lg Cup 49-50 65-66 68-69 69-70 72-73); Mids Co's Lg 77-78 (Lg Cup 77-78), Lincs 'A' Snr Cup 75-76 76-77, Lincs 'B' Snr Cup 54-55 56-57 66-67 68-69 84-85.

ECCLESHILL UNITED

President: Vacant   **Chairman:** Keith Firth
Secretary: Lewis N Dixon, 61 Mount St., Eccleshill, Bradford BD2 2JN (0274 638053).
Physio: Gordon McGlynn   **Press Officer:** Bill Rawlings (0274 635753).
Ground: Plumpton Park, Kingsway, Wrose, Bradford BD2 1PN (0274 615739).
Directions: M62 jct 26 onto M606, right on Bradford Ring Road A6177, left onto A650 for Bradford at 2nd r'bout. A650 Bradford Inner Ring Road onto Canal Rd, branch right opposite Woodheads Builders Merchants into Kings Rd, fork right after 30mph sign to junction with Wrose Rd, across junction - continuation of Kings Rd, 1st left onto Kingsway - ground 200 yds on roght. 2 miles from Bradford (BR). Buses 686 or 687 for Wrose.
Seats: 225   **Cover:** 225   **Capacity:** 2,225   **Floodlights:** Yes   **Year Reformed:** 1948
Nickname: Eagles   **Midweek matches:** Wednesday
Colours: Royal & white stripes   **Change colours:** Yellow
Programme: 24-28 pages, 30p   **Programme Editor:** Bill Rawlings (0274 635753).
Previous Ground: Myers Lane   **Record Gate:** 600 v Bradford City 90-91.
Record win: 7-1 v Yorkshire Main (H), Northern Counties (East) League Division Two 86-87.
Record defeat: 0-6 v Rossington Main (A), Northern Counties League Cup 2nd Rd 92-93, & v Great Harwood Town (A), F.A. Cup Preliminary Rd 91-92.
Previous Leagues: Bradford Amateur/ West Riding County Amateur.
Previous Names: Phoenix Park, Eccleshill F.C.; clubs merged in 1985.
Club Shop: Pennants, enamel badges, programmes available from Bill Rawlings at club.
Clubhouse: Open evenings 7.30-11pm (Sat noon-11pm) and noon-3pm Sundays. Bar, lounge, games room, kitchen (hot & cold snacks), committee room
Captain 92-93: Barry Gallacher   **Top Scorer 92-93:** Paul Viner 14, Les Corbally 13.
P.O.Y. 92-93: Dave Bramill   **Club record scorer:** Paul Viner.
Local newspapers: Bradford Telegraph & Argus, Bradford Star Free Press.
Club honours: Northern Counties East Div 2 R-up 86-87 (Reserve Div 86-87 89-90 (R-up 87-88)); Bradford Amtr Lg Cup 61-62; Bradford & Dist. Snr Cup 84-85; Bradford & Dist. FA Snr Cup 85-86; West Riding County Amateur Lg 76-77

DENABY UNITED

President: Alan Wilson   **Chairman:** Frank Martin   **Manager:** John Reed.
Secretary: Mrs B Norton, 2 Castle Grove Terrace, Low Rd, Conisborough DN12 3EA (0709 864042).
Asst. Manager: John Kirk   **Coach:** Daral Pugh.
Ground: Tickhill Square, Denaby Main, Doncaster (0709 864042).
Directions: From Conisbrough take first left in Denaby along Wadworth St. From Mexborough take first right after Reresby Arms, left on to Bolton St. then left on to Wheatley Street. Rail to Conisbrough.
Seats: 250   **Cover:** 350   **Capacity:** 6,000   **Floodlights:** Yes   **Year formed:** 1895
Clubhouse: None.   **Midweek matches:** Tuesday or Wednesday
Club colours: Red/white/red   **Change colours:** Yellow/green/yellow
Programme: 32 pages 20p   **Programme Editor:** Barrie Dalby (0709 851283)
Previous Leagues: Midland 20-60 61-65/ Central Alliance 60-61/ Yorks 65-82.
Record attendance: 3,801 v Oldham Athletic, FA Cup 1st Rnd Proper 15/11/58
Local newspapers: South Yorks Times, Doncaster Free Press.
Honours: Yorks Lg R-up 67-68 (Div 2 R-up 66-67, Div 3 R-up 81-82, Lg Cup 71-72); Northern Counties East Div 1 South R-up 83-84; Midland Lg R-up 07-08; Sheffield & Hallamshire Snr Cup 05-06 09-10 32-33, 35-36, 86-87

GLASSHOUGHTON WELFARE

President: R Rooker   **Chairman:** Mr G Day
Secretary: E Jones, 'Marrica', Westfields Ave., Cutsyke, Castleford W10 5JJ (0977 556257).
Manager: Mr Wayne Day   **Asst Manager/Coach:** Mr M Ripley.
Ground: Glasshoughton Welfare, Leeds Rd, Glasshoughton, Castleford (0977 518981).
Directions: M62 junct. 31 or 32 towards Castleford. From exit 32 the road comes into Glasshoughton. From exit 31 turn right at 2nd roundabout at Whitwood Tech. College. Ground is on left in Leeds Road. Car park on ground. 1 mile from Castleford (BR).
Club colours: All blue   **Change colours:** All yellow
Seats: None   **Covered:** 250   **Capacity:** 2,000   **Floodlights:** Yes   **Founded:** 1964
Record Att.: 300 v Bradford C - F'light opening 1990
Previous Name: Anson Sports 1964-76   **Previous Ground:** Saville Park 1964-76
Previous League: West Yorkshire   **Clubhouse:** Bar & refreshment facilities.
Programme: 20 pages, 20p   **Programme Editor:** Mr G Day.

HUCKNALL TOWN

President: Andy Stewart   **Chairman:** Robert Spray
Secretary: Brian Scothern, 95 Brookfield Avenue, Hucknall, Notts NG15 6FF (0602 634208).
Manager: Edward Mullane   **Asst Mgr:** John H Coleman   **Coach:** Mick Vinter
Ground: Watnall Road, Hucknall, Notts (0602 641292).
Directions: M1 jct 27, A608 to lights, right onto A611 to town centre, left at lights in market place, down High Street, right into Watnall Rd at lights - follow to island and entrance on right after. From M1 jct 26 follow Nottm signs to lights on island, left onto A610, right at Three Ponds Pub onto B600 towards Watnall, 200 yds past Queens Head turn right signed Hucknall, follow over motorway and past Rolls Royce - ground on left. 7 miles from Nottingham (BR) - bus 344.
Capacity: 2,000   **Seats:** 100   **Cover:** 1,100   **Floodlights:** No   **Founded:** 1946.
Colours: Yellow/black/yellow   **Change colours:** White/red/red
Midweek home matches: Tuesday
Programme: 50p   **Programme Editor:** Robert Spray
Prev. Ground: Wigham Park 46-54   **Clubhouse:** Every night and weekend lunchtimes
Previous Name: Hucknall Colliery Welfare (until closure of pit in 1988).
Previous League: Notts Alliance/ Central Midlands (pre-1992).
Record Gate: 1,300 v Arnold Town, Central Mids Lg 26/12/89.
Local Newspapers: Hucknall & Bulwell Dispatch/ Nottm Evening Post/ Nottm Football Post.
Hons: Northern Counties (East) Lg Div 1 R-up 92-93, Central Mids Lg(2) 89-91 (R-up 91-92, Lg Cup(3) 89-92), Notts All.(4) 76-78 87-89 (Lg Cup 78-79, Div 1 72-73, Div 2 70-71, Intermediate Cup 72-73); Notts Snr Cup 84-85 90-91 (R-up 83-84 85-86 87-88 89-90); FA Vase QF 85-86.

Eccleshill United F.C. 1992-93. Photo - Colin Stevens.

Denaby United F.C. 1992-93. Back Row (L/R): J Hardie (Sponsor), J Duffy, J Longstaff, S Lanaghan, D Kaye, G Margetts, P Cooke, I Curry, A Cracknell, G Kay, T Hulley (Sponsor). Front: G Mozley, D Lawrence, J Dovan (Mascot), D Pugh, G Peart. Photo - Ian Maxwell.

Glasshoughton Welfare F.C. 1992-93. Photo - Colin Stevens.

Hucknall Town - Division One runners-up 1992-93. Back Row (L/R): Paul Tomlinson, Paul Hancock, Ian Hannagh, Chris Burton, Marc Smoczyk, Tim Preece, Dave Wainwright, Steve Borucki. Front: Lee Farmery, Jason Simpson, Anthony Thompson, Phil Towle, John Chamberlain, Paul Smalley, Wayne Scott.

LINCOLN UNITED

President: A Simpson   **Chairman:** K Roe   **Vice Chairman:** P Morley
Secretary/Press Officer: Keith Weaver, 22 Grainsby Close, Lincoln LN6 7QF (0522 531832).
Manager: Gary Goddard   **Asst Manager:** Gerard Creane   **Coach:** John Wilkinson.
Physio: Anthony Adams   **Commercial Manager:** Roy Parnham.
Ground: Ashby Avenue, Hartsholme, Lincoln (0522 690674).
Directions: From Newark A46 onto Lincoln relief road (A446), right at 2nd r'bout for Birchwood (Skellingthorpe Rd), go for 1 mile passing lake and Country Park, 1st right 10yds after 30mph sign into Ashby Ave., ground entrance 200 yds, opposite Old Peoples home. From north proceed along A57 via Saxilby until reaching A46 Lincoln Relief Road - continue on this and turn left at r'bout signed Birchwood then as above. 3 miles from Lincoln Central (BR).
Capacity: 1,750   **Seats:** 150   **Covered:** 250   **Founded:** 1938   **Floodlights:** Yes
Colours: All white   **Change Colours:** All yellow   **Nickname:** United
Programme: 40 pages, 50p   **Editor:** John Wilkinson (0522 788880)
Club Shop: No, but old programmes on sale on matchdays - contact secretary.
Clubhouse: Open every day normal licensing hours. Matchday snack bar - hot & cold food & drinks.
Prev. Lges: Lincs 45-48 60-67/ Lincoln 48-60/ Yorks 67-82/ Northern Co's East 82-86/ Central Mids 82-92.
Prev. Grounds: Skew Bridge (1940's)/ Co-op Spts Ground (til mid-60's)/ Hartsholme Cricket Grnd (til '82).
Previous Name: Lincoln Amateurs (until an ex-professional signed in 1954).
Record Gate: 1,200 v Crook Town, FA Amateur Cup 1st Rd Proper, 1968.
Best FA Cup season: First Round Proper 91-92 (lost 0-7 at Huddersfield Town).
Club Sponsors: Hykeham Forum Supplies/ City Tyre Experts.
Midweek home matchday: Tuesday   **Reserve team's League:** Lincolnshire.
Record win: 10-0 v Winterton   **Record defeat:** 0-7 v Heanor Town, 1989.
Record transfer fee paid: £250 for Dean Dye (Sutton Town, July 1990) - only player ever bought.
Record transfer fee received: £3,000 for Dean Dye (Charlton Athletic, July 1991).
Captain 92-93: Paul Ward   **Top Scorer 92-93:** Tony Simmons, 30 in all competitions.
Record scorer: Terry Nelson 175   **Record appearances:** Brian Davies 436.
Local Newspapers: Lincolnshire Echo, Lincoln Standard.
Hons: Northern Co's (E) Lg Div 1 92-93 (Div 1 Sth 82-83, Div 2 85-86); Yorks Lg 70-71 73-74 (Lg Cup 70-71), Lincs Lg 63-64, Lincs Snr 'A' Cup 72-73 85-86 (R-up 91-92), 'B' Cup 63-64 70-71), Central Mids Lg 91-92 (Wakefield Cup 90-91), Evans Halshaw Floodlit Cup R-up 92-93, Lincs I'mediate Cup(7) 67-73 80-81.

A Lincoln United forward goes down under a challenge from a Bradley Rangers defender, but no penalty was awarded. Lincoln recorded a 3-1 away in this November game and went on to win the title and a second consecutive promotion. Meanwhile, Bradley failed to complete their fixtures and have dropped out of the League. Photo - Barry Lockwood.

LIVERSEDGE

Chairman: Bob Gawthorpe   **Manager:** Colin Penrose   **Asst Mgr:** Stuart Harrison
Secretary/Press Officer: Michael Balmforth, 5 Victoria Rd., Gomersal, Cleckheaton BD19 4RG (0274 862123).
Ground: Clayborn Ground, Quaker Lane, Hightown Rd, Cleckheaton, West Yorks (0274 862108).
Directions: M62 jct 26, A638 into Cleckheaton, right at lights on corner of Memorial Park through next lights & under
railway bridge, 1st left (Hightown Rd) and Quaker Lane is approx quarter mile on left which leads to ground. From M1
jct 40, A638 thru Dewsbury and Heckmondwike to Cleckheaton, right at Memorial Park lights then as above. Buses 218
& 220 (Leeds-Huddersfield) and 227 (Leeds-Brighouse) pass top of Quaker Lane.

Seats: None	**Cover:** 250	**Capacity:** 2,000 **Floodlights:** Yes	**Founded:** 1910
Colours: Blue & white		**Change colours:** yellow & black	**Nickname:** Sedge
Programme: 28 pages, 30p		**Programme Editor:** Secretary	**Club Shop:** No
Midweek Matches: Tuesday		**Club Sponsors:** Various	

Previous Leagues: Spen Valley/ West Riding County Amateur 22-72/ Yorkshire 72-82.
Previous Ground: Primrose Lane, Hightown.**Clubhouse:** Matchdays, Tues, Thursday. Pool, TV. Pies + crisps
Players progressing to Football League: Garry Briggs (Oxford), Martin Hirst (Bristol City).
Captain 92-93: Paul Smith   **P.o.Y. 92-93:** John Hendrick   **Top Scorer 92-93:** Paul Murphy
Local Press: Yorkshire Evening Post, Telegraph & Argus, Cleckheaton Reporter, Spenbrough Guardian.
Hons: West Riding Co. Chal. Cup 48-49 51-52 69-70; West Riding County Cup 89-90; North Counties East Lg Div 1 R-up 89-90 (Div 2 R-up 88-89); West Riding Co. Amtr Lg(6) 23-24 25-27 64-66 68-69 (Lg Cup 57-58 64-65).

MALTBY MINERS WELFARE

President: Sir Jack Laydon   **Chairman:** H Henson   **Vice Chairman:** A Turner.
Secretary: Mr S P Mallinder, 109 Sycamore Avenue, Bramley, Rotherham, Sth Yorks S66 0PA (0709 549958).
Manager: Gary Walker   **Asst Mgr:** Malcolm Walker   **Physio:** T Morris
Commercial Mgr: A Marshall   **Press Officer:** N Dunhill (0709 815676).
Ground: Muglet Lane, Maltby (0709 812462 (match days)).
Directions: Exit M18 at junct with A631. Two miles into Maltby, right at crossroads at Queens Hotel corner on to B6427.
Ground 3/4 mile on left. Bus 101 from Rotherham stops at ground. Bus 287 from Sheffield to Queens Hotel, then follow
as above.

Seats: 150e	**Cover:** 300	**Capacity:** 2,000 **Floodlights:** Yes	**Reformed:** 1972
Sponsors: Jack Green Sports		**Midweek home matchday:** Tuesday	**Clubhouse:** No
Record Gate: 1,500 v Sheffield Wed., friendly June 91-92. Competitive: 940 v Thackley, Yorks Lg Cup 77-78.			
Colours: White/black/white		**Change colours:** Yellow/blue/yellow	**Nickname:** Miners
Programme: 12 pages, 50p		**Editor:** Nick Dunhill (0709 815676)	**Club Shop:** No
Previous name: Maltby Main		**Previous leagues:** Sheffield Co. Snr/ Yorks 73-82.	
Reserve team: None		**Record win:** 6-0	**Record defeat:** 2-5

Top Scorer 92-93: Robert Haddrell   **Captain & P.o.Y. 92-93:** Mick Stewart
Hons: Sheffield & Hallamshire Snr Cup 77-78, Northern Counties East Lg Presidents Cup 92-93 (SF 90-91),
Mexborough Montague Cup 76-77 80-81 90-91, Yorks Lg R-up 77-78, Sheffield Wharncliffe Cup 80-81.

NORTH FERRIBY UNITED

President: Brian Thacker   **Chairman:** Jeff Frank   **Vice Chairman:** Roy Wallis
Secretary: Stephen Tather, 16 Peasholme, Heads Lane, Hessle, E Yorks HU13 0NY (0482 642046).
Manager: Peter Daniel   **Asst Mgr:** Dave Robinson   **Press Officer:** Roy Wallis
Ground: Grange Lane, Church Road, North Ferriby HU14 3AA (0482 634601).
Directions: Main Leeds-Hull road A63 or M62, North Ferriby is 8 miles west of Hull. Into North Ferriby, thru village past
the Duke of Cumberland Hotel, right down Church Rd, ground half mile on left. One mile from North Ferriby (BR).

Seats: 200	**Cover:** 500	**Capacity:** 5,000 **Floodlights:** Yes	**Founded:** 1934.
Colours: Green/white		**Change colours:** Maroon/sky	**Nickname:** United
Midweek home matches: Tuesday		**Sponsors:** Beaver Developments	**Club Shop:** No
Programme: 28 pages, 25p		**Programme Editor:** Jeff Frank	

Previous leagues: East Riding Church/ East Riding Amateur/ Yorks 69-82.
Record attendance: 1,800 v Tamworth, FA Vase Semi-Final, 1989
Record transfer fee received: £2,000 for Dean Winatt (Hull City, 1991-92).
Clubhouse details: Bar, lounge, TV, pool – open every night
Local newspapers: Hull Daily Mail
Captain 92-93: R Woomble   **P.o.Y. 92-93:** N Young   **Top Scorer 92-93:** S McKenzie
Hons: FA Vase SF 88-89 (QF 89-90, 5th Rd 87-88); Yorkshire Lg R-up 75-76 (Lg Cup 74-75, Div 2 70-71), Northern Co's
East Div 1 85-86 (Lg Cup R-up) 90-91, Presidents Cup 90-91, Div 1 (North), R-up 82-83, Reserve Div R-up 90-91); East
Riding Snr Cup 70-71 76-77 77-78 78-79 90-91; East Riding Church Lg 37-38.

OSSETT ALBION

President: Miss Helen Worth   **Chairman:** N A Wigglesworth
Secretary: David Chambers, 109 South Parade, Ossett, West Yorks WF5 0EB (0924 276004).
Manager: Jimmy Allen   **Assistant Managers:** Chris Mear/ Peter Hulme.
Coach: Brian Crowther   **Physio:** Stuart Gayside/John Hirst
Ground: Dimple Wells, Ossett (0924 273618-club, 0924 280450-ground (matchday only)).
Directions: M1 jct 40. Take Wakefield road, right at Post House Hotel down Queens Drive. At end right then second left
down Southdale Rd. At end right, then first left down Dimple Wells (cars only). Coaches take second left following the
road for 200yds bearing left twice. Four miles from both Wakefield and Dewsbury BR stations. Buses 116 and 117.

Seats: 200	**Cover:** 350	**Capacity:** 3,000 **Floodlights:** Yes	**Founded:** 1944
Nickname: Albion		**Midweek matches:** Tuesday	
Colours: Old gold/black/black		**Change colours:** Blue/white/blue	
Programme: 44 pages		**Programme Editor:** N Wigglesworth (0924 275630).	

Previous Lges: Heavy Woollen Area/ Yorks 57-82
Record Gate: 1,200 v Leeds Utd, 1986
Clubhouse: Full bar facilities open 7 days and catering
Sponsors: Gledhill of Ossett   **Local newspapers:** Wakefield Express
Hons: Yorks Lg 74-75 (R-up 59-60 61-62, Lg Cup 75-76, 76-77, Div 2 78-79, 80-81 (R-up 58-59)); Northern Co. East Div
1 86-87 (Lg Cup 83-84); West Yorks Lg 53-54 55-56 (Div 2 52-53, Lg Cup 52-53); West Riding County Cup 64-65 65-66
67-68; Wheatley Cup 56-57 58-59

OSSETT TOWN

President: John Carter   **Chairman:** Graham Firth   **Vice Chairman:** G Froggett
Secretary: F Lloyd, 27 Park Close, Mapplewell, Barnsley S75 6BY (0226 382415).
Manager: Alastair Millar   **Coach:** Derek Parker   **Physio:** Karen Wood
Press Officer: B Saul   **Commercial Manager:** D Coxhill.
Ground: Ingfield, Prospect Road, Ossett, Wakefield (0924 272960).
Directions: M1 jct 40, A638 (signed Dewsbury) to Ossett town centre, left at lights opposite bus station on ring road, ground on left. Three miles from Wakefield (BR).
Seats: 360   **Cover:** 650   **Capacity:** 4,000   **Floodlights:** Yes   **Founded:** 1936
Colours: All red   **Change colours:** All blue   **Midweek matches:** Tuesday
Programme: 20 pages, 50p   **Programme Editor:** Bruce Saul
Club Shop: Yes, selling programmes, sweaters, badges, baseball hats.
Sponsors: Action Stations   **Record Gate:** 2,600 v Manchester Utd, friendly 1988
Clubhouse details: Bar, pool, darts. Open 7 nights & lunchtimes per week. Sandwiches & pies.
Local Press: Dewsbury Reporter   **Previous Leagues:** Leeds/ Yorkshire 45-82.
Prev. Ground: Fern House, Ossett   **Record fee received:** £1,350 for D Blackburn (Swansea T. 1957).
Captain 92-93: D Bursztyn   **P.O.Y. 92-93:** S Worsfold   **Top Scorer 92-93:** Paul Elsworth
Hons: West Riding County Cup 81-82, Northern Co's Lg Cup 89-90 (Reserve Div 88-89, Reserve Cup 87-88 88-89).

PICKERING TOWN

President: S P Boak   **Chairman:** M T Jones   **Vice Chairman:** A Dunning
Secretary/Press Officer: K W Sales, 4 Northway, Pickering, North Yorks YO18 8NN (0751 73348).
Manager: Nigel Tate   **Assistant Manager/Physio:** Michael Hudson
Coach: Shaun McGinty   **Commercial Manager:** B Wood.
Ground: Recreation Club, Mill Lane (off Malton Rd), Pickering, North Yorkshire (0751 73317).
Directions: A169 from Malton, 1st left past Police Station and B.P. garage into Mill Lane, ground 300yds on right.
Seats: 100   **Cover:** 500   **Capacity:** 2,000   **Floodlights:** Yes   **Founded:** 1888
Midweek matches: Tuesday   **Club Sponsors:** Flamingoland   **Nickname:** Pikes
Programme: 32 pages, 50p   **Programme Editor:** Secretary.   **Club Shop:** Not yet
Colours: Royal/white/royal   **Change colours:** Yellow/blue.
Reserves' Lge: York & Dist.   **Record Gate:** 1,412 v Notts County, friendly, August 1991.
Previous leagues: Beckett/ York & District/ Scarborough & District/ Yorkshire 72-82.
Clubhouse: Open 1.30pm for Saturday games, 6pm for midweek games. Various beers. Food available from Football Club Kitchen at half-time and after games.
Players progressing to Football League: Chris & Craig Short (both Scarborough & Notts County).
Local Press: Pickering Gazette & Herald, Yorkshire Evening Press, Mercury, Scarborough Evening News.
Captain 92-93: Mark Ash   **P.O.Y. 92-93:** Tony Bryden   **Top Scorer 92-93:** Peter Collier
Hons: Northern Co's East Lg R-up 92-93 (Div 2 1987-88, Div 1 R-up 91-92), Yorks Lg Div 3 73-74, Nth Riding County Cup 90-91.

PONTEFRACT COLLIERIES

President: R Blatherwick   **Chairman:** Anthony Dunwell, JP   **Vice Chairman:** D Walker
Secretary: Sid Mason, 16 Harefield Rd, Pontefract, West Yorks WF8 2HX (0977 707756).
Manager: Ged Elliott   **Asst Mgr:** Frank McLaughlin   **Coach:** Roland Lanes.
Physio: Julios Voros   **Press Officer:** Barry Bennett (0977 682593).
Ground: Skinner Lane, Pontefract, West Yorkshire (0977 702180).
Directions: M62 jct 32 towards Pontefract. Left at traffic lights opposite Racecourse entrance (travelling through Pontefract follow Racecourse/Leeds signs to traffic lights and turn right) - ground past Territorial Army unit. 1 mile from Monkhill (BR). All Leeds and Castleford buses stop near ground.
Seats: 100   **Cover:** 400   **Capacity:** 2,000   **Floodlights:** Yes   **Founded:** 1958
Midweek home matches: Tuesday   **Club Sponsors:** Various   **Nickname:** Colls
Colours: All blue   **Change colours:** All yellow   **Club Shop:** No
Programme: 8 pages, 30p   **Programme Editor:** Barry Bennett (0977 682593).
Previous leagues: West Yorkshire 58-79/ Yorkshire 79-82.
Record attendance: 1,000 v Hull City - floodlight opening 1985.
Clubhouse: Fully licensed. Hot & cold snacks. Open one and a half hours before any game, and after games with hours to suit demand.
Local Press: Pontefract & Castleford Express
Club Record Scorer: Martin Brock   **Club Record Appearances:** John Brown
Captain 92-93: Karl Slater   **P.O.Y. 92-93:** Darrell Bowman   **Top Scorer 92-93:** Martin Brock
Hons: Northern Co's East Lg Div 1 83-84 (Div 2 R-up 82-83, Floodlit Comp 87-88 88-89); Yorks Lg Div 3 81-82; West Riding Co. Cup R-up 87-88 90-91; Embleton Cup 82-83 86-87; Castleford FA Cup 82-83 86-87; West Yorks Lg.

SHEFFIELD

Chairman: Alan Methey   **Vice Chairman:** Paul Wilder.
Secretary: Stephen Hall, 24 Crofton Ave., Sheffield S6 1WF (0742 344553).
Manager: Kenny 'Jock' Johnson   **Coach:** Andy Jackson
Ground: Sheffield International Stadium (Don Valley), Worksop Rd, Sheffield S9.
Directions: From north: M1 jct 34, straight on at traffic island (directly underneath motorway), at next island take 6th exit following City Centre signs, Stadium approx 1 mile on left. From south: M1 jct 33 City Link. Take 2nd exit from dual carriageway signposted A57, right at bottom of slip road to lights at bottom of hill, right at lights, at Morrisons supermarket turn left, follow road to stadium on right. Rotherham buses from city centre pass ground.
Seats: 25,000   **Cover:** 13,000   **Capacity:** 25,000   **Floodlights:** Yes   **Founded:** 1856.
Colours: Red/black/black   **Change colours:** All blue.   **Nickname:** Club.
Programme: Average 10 pages, 30p   **Editor:** B Willis (0742 392423).   **Club Shop:** No.
Previous league: Yorks 49-82   **Club Sponsors:** Penegrove Country Club, Agenda.
Prev. grounds: Abbeydale Park, Dore (pre-'89)/ Sheffield Amat. Spts Club, Hillsborough Park Stadium 89-91.
Clubhouse: No.   **Record Gate:** 2,000 v Barton Rovers, FA Vase SF 76-77.
Midweek home matchday: Monday   **Reserve team's League:** None.
Capt. 92-93: Neil Brown   **Top Scorer 92-93:** Mark Walshaw   **P.O.Y. 92-93:** Jimmy Flynn, Gavan Walker
Hons: FA Amtr Cup 03-04, FA Vase R-up 76-77, Northern Co's East Lg Div 88-89 90-91, Yorks Div 2 76-77.

Ossett Town F.C. 1992-93.

Ossett Town's Dean Trott fires a shot as his side lose 1-2 at home to Sheffield. Photo - Barry Lockwood.

Pontefract Collieries F.C. 1992-93. Back Row (L/R): Roland Lanes (Coach), Frank McLaughlin (Asst Manager), Andy Hayward, Karl Slater, Mick Price, Gary Deakin, Darrel Bowman, David Watts, Phil Belch, Ged Elliott (Manager). Front: Paul Corbett (Captain), Martin Brock, Chris Sambrook, Steve Whitelam, Lincoln Woods, Craig Siddall. Mascots: Ian Deakin, Sarah Slater. Photo - Richard Brock.

STOCKSBRIDGE PARK STEELS

President: C D Sedgwick   **Chairman:** A Bethel
Secretary: Michael Grimmer, 48 Hole House Lane, Stocksbrige, Sheffield S30 5BP (0742 886470).
Manager: Mick Horne   **Asst Manager:**
Ground: Bracken Moor Lane, Stocksbridge, Sheffield (0742 882045).
Directions: From Sheffield on main Manchester road A616 (9 miles) from M1 jnt 36 – on arriving at Stocksbridge turn left into Nanny Hill under the Clock Tower and continue up the hill for about 500 yds.
Colours: Royal blue/yellow   **Change colours:** All yellow
Seats: 700   **Cover:** 800   **Capacity:** 3,500   **Floodlights:** Yes   **Nickname:** Steels
Metal badges: Yes (£1.75)   **Midweek matches:** Wednesday
Programme: 44 pages, 50p   **Editor:** David Webster (Sheffield 337457)
Record Gate: 2,000 v Sheffield Wednesday, Floodlight opening 90-91.
Previous Names: Stocksbridge Works, Oxley Park; clubs merged in 1986.
Previous Leagues: Sheffield Amateur/ Sheffield Association/ Yorkshire 49-82.
Local newpapers: Sheffield Trader, Green'un, The Star
Clubhouse: Open seven days (lunchtime & evenings)
Hons: Northern Co's East Lg Div 1 91-92 (Lg Cup SF 92-93, Presidents Cup SF 91-92), Sheffield & Hallamshire Snr Cup 51-52, Yorks Lg 51-52 54-55 55-56 56-57 57-58 61-62 62-63 (R-up 60-61, Div 2 50-51 64-65, Div 3 70-71 74-75 (R-up 78-79), Lg Cup 61-62).

THACKLEY

President: Maurice Selby   **Chairman:** Vacant   **Manager/Coach:** Warren Rayner
Secretary: Stewart Willingham, 3 Kirklands Close, Baildon, Shipley, West Yorks BD17 6HN (0274 598589).
Asst Manager: Jan Kudelinitzky   **Physio:** Maurice Atkinson/ John Waller.
Treasurer: Paul Clark   **Press Officer:** Jamie Scott (0274 611520).
Ground: Dennyfield, Ainsbury Avenue, Thackley, Bradford (0274 615571).
Directions: On main Leeds/Keighley A657 road, turn off at Thackley corner which is 2 miles from Shipley traffic lights and 1 mile from Greengates lights. Ainsbury Avenue bears to the right 200yds down the hill. Ground is 200yds along Ainsbury Avenue on the right. 3 miles from Bradford Interchange (BR), one and a half miles from Shipley (BR). Buses to Thackley corner (400 yds).
Seats: 100   **Cover:** 300   **Capacity:** 3,000   **Floodlights:** Yes   **Founded:** 1930.
Colours: Red & white/white/red   **Change colours:** All white
Midweek matches: Tuesday
Programme: 28 pages, 30p   **Programme Editor:** Secretary
Club Shop: Yes. Programmes, souvenirs. Metal badges available - £2.50 + s.a.e. Contact Jamie Scott (0274 61152).
Previous leagues: Bradford Amateur, W. Riding County Amateur, W. Yorks, Yorks 67-82.
Record Att.: 1,500 v Leeds Utd 1983   **Previous name:** Thackley Wesleyians 1930-39.
Sponsors: Aprodite Shipping.   **Best FA Vase year:** 5th Rd 80-81 (0-2 v Whickham).
Players progressing to Football League: Tony Brown (Leeds, Doncaster, Scunthorpe, Rochdale), Ian Ormondroyd (Bradford City, Aston Villa, Derby, Leicester).
Clubhouse details: Hot & cold snacks on matchdays. Open Tues-Sunday evenings, matchdays and weekend lunchtimes. Boardroom, committee room, dancefloor, darts, pool, gaming machines.
Local Press: Bradford Telegraph & Argus, Bradford Str, Aire Valley Target.
Hons: Yorks Lg Div 2 73-74, West Yorks Lg 66-67, West Riding Co. Amtr Lg 57-58 58-59 59-60, West Riding Co. Cup 73-74 74-75, West Riding Co. Chal. Cup 63-64 66-67, Bradford & Dist. Snr Cup(10) 38-39 49-50 55-56 57-60 65-67 78-79 87-88.

WINTERTON RANGERS

President: J W Hiles   **Chairman:** D Waterfall   **Vice Chairman:** A Smith
Secretary/Press Officer: G Spencer, 2 Dale Park Ave., Winterton, Scunthorpe, Sth Humbs DN15 9UY (0724 732039).
Manager: Mick Wild   **Asst Manager/Coach:** Kev Rooney
Ground: West Street, Winterton, Scunthorpe, South Humberside (0724 732628).
Directions: From Scunthorpe take A1077 Barton-on-Humber road for 5 miles. On entering Winterton take second right (Eastgate), third left (Northlands Road) and first right (West Street). Ground 200yds on left
Seats: 200   **Covered:** 200   **Capacity:** 3,000   **Floodlights:** Yes   **Founded:** 1930
Colours: White/navy/white   **Change colours:** All red   **Nickname:** Rangers
Midweek home matches: Wednesday   **Sponsors:** Ledgerwood Motors   **Club Shop:** No.
Programme: 28-36 pages, 50p   **Programme Editor:** M Fowler (0724 732628).
Previous Grounds: Watery Lane 1930-48.   **Best FA Vase year:** QF 76-77
Best FA Cup year: 4th Qualifying Rd replay 76-77 (lost 2-3 at Droylsden after 3-3 draw).
Previous League: Scunthorpe & Dist. 45-65/ Lincs 65-70/ Yorkshire 70-82.
Record attendance: 1,200 v Sheffield Utd – Official opening of floodlights, October 1978.
Record transfer fee received: £5,000 for Henry Smith (Leeds United, 1979).
Clubhouse: Open matchdays & evenings Mon-Sat, hot & cold food available on matchdays. Pool and snooker rooms.
Local Press: Scunthorpe Evening Telegraph
Players progressing to Football League: Henry Smith (Leeds, Hearts), Keith Walwyn (Chesterfield, York, Carlisle), Rick Greenhough (Chester, York)
Captain 92-93: Pat Clarke   **P.o.Y. 92-93:** Andy Carrick   **Top Scorer 92-93:** Andy Sugden
Hons: Lincs Jnr Cup 47-48 61-62; Lincs Snr 'B' Cup 69-70; Yorks Lg 71-72 76-77 78-79 (Lg Cup 80-81); Northern Co's East Lg Div 2 89-90; S'thorpe Lg & Cup many times; Philips National F'light 6-aside 76-77.

Ossett Albion F.C. 1992-93.

Pickering's Mark Aitken wins an aerial battle with Kent Noble of Eccleshill. Photo - Colin Stevens.

Thackley F.C. 1992-93. Back Row (L/R): J Waller (Physio), A Taylor, M Wood, A Lamb, J Wilcox, J Hawkes, M Wright, S Taylor, W Fletcher. Front: P Hutchinson, M Nevison, A Grace, W Rayner (Manager), J Kudginitzky (Asst Manager), S Howley, C Wells, S Warburton.

DIVISION ONE CLUBS 1993-94

ARNOLD TOWN

President: Alan Croome   **Chairman:** David Law.
Secretary: Stan Barlow, 95 Plains Rd, Nottm NG3 5QD (0602 529068).
Manager: Ray O'Brien   **Asst Mgr:** Peter Moody.
Ground: King George V Playing Fields, Gedling Rd, Arnold, Nottm (0602 263660).
Directions: From Nth M1 jct 26, B6004 (Stockhill Lane) 3 miles to A60 (White Hart pub on left), right at A60, immediate left (St Albans Rd), thru lights by Sainsburys, left at rear of Sainsburys, ground on right adjacent to market. From A1(M)/A614/A60 to lights (White Hart on right), 1st left thru lights, St Albans Rd then as above. From Nottm ring-road left into A60, right into Nottingham Rd after quarter mile to lights at Sainsburys, right then as above. Four miles from Nottingham Midland BR station. Buses 53, 55, 59 pass ground, buses 25, 26, 40 56, 57, 58 within 100yds.
Capacity: 3,500   **Seats:** 150   **Cover:** 950   **Floodlights:** Yes   **Founded:** 1989
Midweek matches: Tuesday   **Sponsors:** Mapperley Sports   **Nickname:** Eagles
Cols: Yellow & blue/blue/yellow   **Change Colours:** White (blue trim)
Programme: 12-16 pages, 50p   **Editor:** Diane Burrows (0602 266669)   **Club Shop:** No.
Prev. Names: Arnold F.C. (founded 1928 as Arnold St Marys) merged with Arnold Kingswell (founded 1962) 1989.
Previous Grounds: Calverton Road Rec. 28-57/ Church Lane 57-62. *Kingswell: Nottingham Rd 62-89.*
Previous Leagues: Central Midlands 89-93. *Arnold FC: Notts Alliance (pre-war)/ Central Alliance 55-63/ Midland 63-82/ Northern Co's East 82-87. Kingswell: East Midlands (pre'76)/Midland 76-82/ Northern Co's East 82-86/ Central Midlands 86-89.*
Record Gate: 3,390; Arnold F.C. v Bristol Rovers, FA Cup 1st Rd, December 1967.
Reserves' Lge: Central Midlands   **Clubhouse:** Matchdays & training night. Hot food on matchdays.
Record win: 7-0 v Glapwell, Central Midlands League
Record defeat: 0-5 v Lincoln United, F.A. Vase replay.
Record transfer fee paid: Nil   **Rec'd** (Arnold FC): £2,000 for Devon White (Lincoln C., 1985).
Captain 92-93: Mark Goodwin   **Top Scorer 92-93:** Peter Fletcher 30 (18 League)
Players' P.O.Y. 92-93: Mark Goodwin   **Manager's/Supporters' P.O.Y.:** Peter Fletcher.
Record scorer: Richard Johnson 70   **Record appearances:** Richard Johnson 140.
Hons: Central Mids Lg 92-93 (R-up 88-89, Lg Cup 87-88 (R-up 90-91), Floodlit Cup 89-90); Northern Co's East Lg 85-86; Notts Snr Cup 60-61 64-65 65-66 68-69 70-71 92-93; FA Cup 1st Rd 66-67 76-77; FA Tphy 2nd Rd 71-72; Midland Co's Lg R-up 70-71 (Lg Cup 74-75). *Arnold Kingswell: Midland Co's Lg Div 1 79-80 (R-up 75-76 78-79 81-82).*

BRODSWORTH WELFARE

Chairman: Mr J Yorke   **Press Officer:** Mr J Mounsey
Secretary: W Galloway, 28 Lutterworth Drive, Adwick-le-Street, Doncaster DN6 7DF (0302 724345).
Manager: N Brandon   **Asst Manager:** P Cooke   **Physio:** J Bedford.
Ground: Welfare Ground, Woodlands, Nr. Doncaster (0302 728380).
Directions: Adjacent to the old Great North Rd (A638), 3 miles north of Doncaster at Woodlands. Ground entrance approx 30 yds into Welfare Rd. Left turn into Car Park. Regular bus service from North Bridge Bus Station, Doncaster.
Seats: No   **Cover:** 250   **Capacity:** 3,000   **Floodlights:** No   **Founded:** 1912
Colours: TBA   **Change colours:** TBA   **Club Shop:** No   **Nickname:** Brody
Previous Name: Brodsworth Main   **Previous Leagues:** Doncaster Snr/ Sheffield/ Yorks.
Midweek home matchday: Tuesday   **Programme:** 8 pages, compiled by committee.
Record fee paid: Nil   **Record fee received:** From Wolves for Barry Stobart, 1960.
Clubhouse: No. Matchday drinks and snacks at Foresters Arms Hotel, off Doncaster Rd in Woodlands.
Captain 92-93: Phil Thomas   **Top scorer 92-93:** Gary Cygan, 18 goals.
Hons: Yorks Lg 24-25, Donc. & Dist. Lg 84-85 (Lg Cup 85-86, Div 2 78-79, Div 2 78-79), Sheffield Jnr Cup 83-84, Mexborough Montagu Cup 91-92 92-93.

GARFORTH TOWN

President: Norman Hebbron   **Chairman:** Stephen Hayle.
Secretary: Paul Bracewell, 24 Coupland Rd, Garforth, Leeds LS25 1AD (0532 863314).
Manager/Coach: Paul Dooley   **Asst Manager:** Fred Bennett   **Physio:** Ken Mills
Commercial Mgr: Mike Fullerton   **Press Officer:** Kevin Strangeway (0532 866500).
Ground: Brierlands Lane, Aberford Road, Garforth, Leeds (0532 864083).
Directions: From South/East/North, A642 from A1 to Garforth, ground one and a half miles on left over brow of hill. From South West, M62 jct 30, A642 to Garforth (A63 to Garforth from Leeds), thru Garforth on A642, ground on right 1 mile on from lights just past junior school and Indian restaurant. Buses 18 & 83 from Leeds, alight at East Garforth Post Office - ground 500yds on right walking away from Garforth. By rail to Garforth (Leeds-York) line - cross over bridge to Safeways side and ground just under 1 mile down road.
Seats: None   **Cover:** 100   **Capacity:** 2,000   **Floodlights:** No   **Founded:** 1965
Cols: Red (navy stripe)/navy/red   **Change colours:** Green & white stripes/green/green
Prog.: 28 glossy pages, 50p   **Editor:** Kevin Strangeway (0532 866500)
Nickname: The Miners
Club Shop: Open before & during matches selling non-League and Football League programmes.
Previous leagues: Leeds Sunday Combination/ West Yorks/ Yorks 78-82.
Previous names: Miners Arms 64-78, Garforth Miners 78-79
Clubhouse: Open matchdays & training nights.
Midweek home matches: Tuesday   **Record attendance:** 817 v Leeds, friendly 1987
Club Sponsors: Clarks of Wakefield
Record win: 7-0 v Immingham Town (H), Northern Counties (East) League Division One 1991-92.
Record defeat: 1-7 v Lincoln United (A), Northern Counties (East) League Division One 1992-93.
Club record scorer: Vinnie Archer   **Club record appearances:** Philip Matthews (1982-93).
Capt. 92-93: Martin Tetley   **P.O.Y. 92-93:** Tim Hope   **Top Scorer 92-93:** Brian Tonge 21 (18 for Reserves)
Hons: FA Vase QF 85-86; Northern Co's East Lg Div 2 R-up 85-86; Yorks Lg Div 3 R-up 79-80, Barkston Ash Snr Cup 80-81 84-85 85-86 86-87 92-93.

HALL ROAD RANGERS

President: E Richardson   **Chairman:** Joe Urbanowicz   **Vice Chairman:** Terry Neylon
Secretary: E Richardson, 35 Hall Road, Hull, Nth Humbs HU6 8QW (0482 43781).
Manager: Pete Smith   **Asst Manager:** Dave Stead   **Coach:** Pat Heard
Ground: Dene Park, Dene Close, Beverley Rd, Dunswell, Nr Hull (0482 850101).
Directions: Hull-Beverley road (A1079 and A1174). Dunswell is first village from the Hull boundary. Entrance to ground on A1174 is 20 yds past large r/about and opposite Dunswell Village road sign. Four & a half miles from Hull (BR).
Seats: 50   **Cover:** 750   **Capacity:** 1,200   **Floodlights:** No   **Founded:** 1959.
Colours: Blue & white hoops/blue/blue   **Change colours:** All green
Previous ground: Hull Co-Op (until 1968)
Record Gate: 350 v Hull City XI, August '91.
Programme: 12 pages, 25p   **Programme Editor:** Mrs Sue Smith (0482 437402)
Club Shop: Yes, selling pennants, scarves, hats, shirts, mugs.
Midweek Matches: Wednesday   **Nickname:** Rangers.
Clubhouse: Open all week for drinks and snacks. Bar snacks. Snooker, pool, darts.
Local Press: Hull Daily Mail   **Previous Leagues:** East Riding/ Yorks 68-82.
Captain 92-93: Paul Osbourne   **Top Scorer 92-93:** Roy Jackson, Mark Rookyard.
Record Scorer: G James   **Record Appearances:** G James.
Hons: Northern Co's East Lg Div 2 90-91, Yorks Lg Div 3 72-73 79-80, East Riding Snr Cup 72-73.

Hall Road Rangers F.C. 1992-93

Garforth Town F.C. 1992-93. Back Row (L/R): Ken Mills (Physio), Peter Bush (Manager), Andy Jackson, Phil Matthews, John Batty, Glen Brazier, Tim Hope, Brian Tonge, Keith Matthews, Micky Adams, Fred Bennett (Assistant Manager). Front: Steve Templeton, Colin Payne, Kevin Crombie, Martin Tetley, Stuart Wilson, Mark Hamilton. Photo - Colin Stevens.

HARROGATE RAILWAY ATHLETIC

President: J Robinson   **Chairman:** C Robinson
Secretary: W D Oldfield, 80 Stonefall Ave., Harrogate, Nth Yorks HG2 7NP (0423 888941).
Manager: G Shepherd   **Coach:** P Williamson   **Physio:** J Tope
Press Officer/Programme Ed.: C Dinsdale (0423 521815)   **Commercial Mgr:** C W Robinson (0423 880022).
Ground: Station View, Starbeck, Harrogate (0423 885539).
Directions: A59 Harrogate to Knaresborough road. After approx 1.5 miles turn left just before railway level crossing. Ground is 150 yds up the lane. Adjacent to Starbeck (BR). Served by any Harrogate to Knareborough bus.
Seats: None   **Cover:** 600   **Capacity:** 3,000   **Floodlights:** Yes   **Founded:** 1935
Club colours: All red   **Change:** White & blue hoops   **Nickname:** The Rail
Midweek home matchday: Wednesday   **Rec. Gate:** 1,400; 1962 FA Amtr Cup   **Sponsors:** T.B.A.
Club Shop: Yes, selling programmes, pennants, badges etc. Contact K Dinsdale (0423 521815).
Previous leagues: West Yorkshire/ Harrogate District/ Yorkshire 55-73 80-82.
Clubhouse: Games, TV room, lounge, open normal public house hours every day. Hot food.
Top Scorer 92-93: R Turnbull 20   **Captain & P.o.Y. 92-93:** L Swales.
Hons: Northern Co's (East) Lg Cup 86-87   **Local Newspaper:** Pontefract & Castleford Express.

Harrogate Railway Athletic F.C. Photo - Richard Brock.

HALLAM

Chairman: A Scanlan   **Vice Chairman:** A Cooper   **President:** T Stones.
Secretary: G L Holland, 34 Standon Cres., Sheffield S9 1PP (0742 421899).
Manager: G Kenny   **Physio:** J Beachell   **Press Off.:** M Radford
Ground: Sandygate, Sandygate Road, Crosspool, Sheffield S10 (0742 309484).
Directions: A57 Sheffield to Glossop Rd, left at Crosspool shopping area signed 'Lodge Moor' on to Sandygate Rd. Ground half mile on left opposite Plough Inn. 51 bus from Crucible Theatre.
Seats: None   **Cover:** 200   **Capacity:** 2,000   **Floodlights:** Yes   **Year formed:** 1860
Nickname: Countrymen   **Club Sponsors:** H.I.S. & Umbro Int. Ltd.
Colours: Blue/white/blue   **Change colours:** All red
Programme: 8 pages with entry   **Editor:** Mark Radford (0742 434529).   **Club Shop:** No.
Midweek Matches: Wednesday   **Previous leagues:** Yorks 52-82.
Record Gate: 2,000 v Hendon, FA Amtr Cup 3rd Rd 1959. (13,855 v Dulwich at Hillsborough, FA Amtr Cup 1955).
Clubhouse: Licensed bar and meals in Plough Inn opposite. Hot & cold snacks in ground for matches.
Record win: 7-0 v Hatfield Main (H) 92-93, & v Kiveton Park (H) 69-70.
Rec. loss: 0-7 v Hatfield Main (A) 88-89   **Local Press:** Star, Green'Un, Sheffield Telegraph.
Captain 92-93: Steve Sidebottom   **Top Scorer 92-93:** Peter Cotton 20   **P.o.Y. 92-93:** Mick Fletcher
Club record scorer: A Stainrod 46   **Club record appearances:** P Ellis 500+.
Hons: NCEL Div 1 R-up 90-91, Yorks Lg Div 2 60-61 (R-up 56-57), Sheff/Hallamshire Snr Cup 50-51 61-62 64-65 67-68.

Hallam F.C. 1992-93.

HATFIELD MAIN

President: A Jones   **Chairman:** A Jones   **Vice Chairman:** B Keenan
Secretary: Mr Bruce Hatton, 92 Ingram Rd, Dunscroft, Doncaster, Sth Yorks DN7 4JE (0302 841648).
Manager: John Reed   **Asst Manager:** John Kirk   **Coach:** Darryl Pugh.
Physio: Tommy Kirk.
Ground: Dunscroft Welfare Ground, Dunscroft, Doncaster, Sth Yorks (0302 841326).
Directions: From Doncaster (A18) Scunthorpe Rd to Dunsville, left at Flarepath Hotel down Broadway. Ground half mile on right. Half mile from Stamforth & Hatfield (BR). Buses every fifteen minutes from Doncaster.

Seats: None **Cover:** 400	**Capacity:** 4,000 **Floodlights:** Yes	**Founded:** 1936.
Programme: 12 pages, 25p	**Editor:** Paul Bennett (0302 841196)	**Club Shop:** No.
Colours: Red & white/red/red	**Change colours:** Yellow/blue/yellow.	**Nickname:** The Main
Previous League: Yorkshire 55-82.	**Clubhouse:** Full licensing hrs. Hot & cold snacks.	
Hons: West Riding Co. Cup.	**Record Gate:** 750 v B. Auckland, FA Amtr Cup	
Midweek home matchday: Tuesday	**Reserve team's League:** Doncaster Senior.	
Captain 92-93: Lal Dutt	**Top Scorer 92-93:** Danny Lawrence.	
P.o.Y. 92-93: Alan Bell	**Club record appearances:** Lal Dutt.	

IMMINGHAM TOWN

President: Steve Davies   **Chairman:** Alan Morrish   **General Mgr:** John Spreckley
Secretary: T Paul, 28 Anglian Way, Market Rasen, Lincs LN9 3RP (0673 843654).
Manager: Micky Duffy   **Physio:** Steve Howard
Ground: Woodlands Avenue, Immingham (0469 75724).
Directions: M180 & A180 – 1st exit to Immingham. Straight on at r/about, through lights and right a 2nd r/about. Entrance on right between ATS Tyres and Lectec Services. 3 miles from Habrough (BR). Buses from Grimsby.
Colours: Maroon & sky blue stripes/maroon/maroon   **Change:** White with black pinstripe/black/black

Seats: None **Cover:** 100	**Capacity:** 2,500 **Floodlights:** Yes **Founded:** 1969.	
Prev. Lges: Grimsby/ Lincs	**Record attendance:** 1,200 v Grimsby Town, 8/8/89.	
Programme: 32 pages, 40p	**Programme Editor:** Rob Hart.	

Hons: Northern Co's East Lg Div 2 R-up 86-87, Lincs Snr 'B' Cup 73-74 80-81 (R-up 81-82 83-84), Lincs Lg Cup 71-72 86-87 (Chal. Cup 83-84 84-85, Div 2 Cup R-up 76-77), Grimsby Lg 70-71, Lincs Cup 70-71, War Mem. Cup R-up 71-72, Lambert Cup 72-73 74-75, Tom Fox Cup 83-84, Bill Allinson Cup R-up 86-87, Grimsby Suppl. Cup 86-87.

LOUTH UNITED

President: Mr C Hounsram   **Chairman:** Mr P Smith.
Secretary/Press Officer: Mr P Smith, 84 Scartho Road, Grimsby, South Humberside DN33 2BG (0472 879356).
Manager: Peter Lea   **Asst Manager:** Martin Teanby   **Coach:** Brian Casey
Club Manager: Jim Bloomer   **Commercial Manager:** George Baglin
Ground: Park Avenue, Louth, Lincs (0507 607351).
Directions: A16 To Louth Market Place, exit via Eastgate/Eastfield Rd, to 1st junction, past Fire Station.

Capacity: 4,000 **Seats:** None	**Cover:** 400 **Founded:** 1947	**Floodlights:** Yes
Midweek matches: Tuesday	**Club Sponsors:** R.G.B. Packaging, Grimsby.	
Programme: 12 pages, 50p	**Editor:** Mr A Jordan (0507 607570)	**Club Shop:** No
Colours: All royal blue	**Change Colours:** T.B.A.	**Sponsors:** T.B.A.
Reserves' League: Lincolnshire	**Record Gate:** 3,200 v Derby Co., friendly, October 1990.	
Previous Grounds: None	**Previous Names:** Merger of Louth Nats & Louth Town.	

Record transfer fee paid: £10,000 for Martyn Chalk (Derby County, 1990).
Previous Leagues: Lincs 47-75 82-88/ Midland Co's Lg 76-82/ Central Midlands 88-93.
Players progressing to Football League: Terry Donovan (Grimsby), Paul Bartlett (Derby), Brian Klug (Ipswich), Glen Cockerill (Lincoln, Watford, Southampton), Peter Rawcliffe (Grimsby), Peter Green (Grimsby), Martyn Chalk (Derby).
Clubhouse: Weekdays 6.30-11.45pm, Sat noon-11.45pm. Full bar facilities. Snacks: filled rolls, crisps, nuts etc.
Top Scorer 92-93: Allan Cooper 29   **Captain & P.o.Y. 92-93:** Steve Newby.
Record Scorer: Peter Rawcliffe 39   **Record Apperances:** Gary Smith 476.
Hons: Lincs Lg 72-73 86-87 85-86 (Div 1 57-58 66-67 67-68, Lg Challenge Cup 73-74 86-87, Lg Charity Cup 55-56 56-57 67-68, Lg Supplementary Cup 85-86), Central Mids Lg Cup R-up 92-93 (F'lit Cup R-up 91-92), Lincs Snr 'A' Cup 77-78 (Snr'B' Cup 91-92).

R.E.S. PARKGATE

President: T L Dabbs   **Chairman:** A T Dudill   **Vice Chairman:** R Goodwin
Secretary: Bruce Bickerdike, 2 Cardew Close, Rawmarsh, Rotherham S62 6LB (0709 522305 (tel & fax)).
Manager: A J Senior   **Asst Manager:** Paul Greaves   **Physio:** P Sheffield.
Press Officer: Bruce Bickerdike (0709 522305).
Ground: Roundwood Sports Complex, Green Lane, Rawmarsh, Rotherham (0709 523471).
Directions: From Rotherham A633 to Rawmarsh. From Doncaster A630 to Conisbrough, then A6023 through Swinton to Rawmarsh. Ground at Green Lane – right from Rotherham, left from Conisbrough at the Crown Inn. Ground 800yds on right

Seats: 300 **Cover:** 300	**Capacity:** 1,000 **Floodlights:** Yes **Founded:** 1969	
Colours: White/black/white	**Change colours:** All sky.	

Nickname: The Gate or The Steelmen.

Midweek matches: Tuesday	**Club Sponsors:** Rotherham Engineering Steels.
Programme: 20 pages, 50p	**Editor:** Bruce Bickerdike (0709 522305) **Club Shop:** No.
Previous Grounds: None	**Previous Name:** B.S.C. Parkgate (until mid-eighties).

Record attendance: v Worksop 1982
Previous leagues: Rotherham Association/ Whitbread County Senior/ Yorkshire 74-82
Clubhouse: Licensed bar, 2 lounges, including dance floor. Open until 10.30pm Mon-Thurs & Sun, 11pm Fr-Sat. Meals available lunchtime Wed-Sat.
Local Newspapers: Star/ Green'Un/ Rotherham Advertiser/ Sth Yorks Times/ Dearne Valley Weekender.
P.o.Y. 92-93: Ian Garnham   **Captain 92-93:** Colin Seaman (brother of Arsenal's David).

ROSSINGTON MAIN

President: K Melvin **Chairman:** Mr S Tagg **Commercial Mgr:** G Shaw
Secretary: Mr Malcolm Day, 3 Coronation Way, Rossington, Doncaster DN11 0RL (0302 863516).
Manager/Coach: Mr D Carlin **Asst Mgr/Coach:** Mr S Downing
Ground: Welfare Ground, Oxford St, Rossington, Doncaster (0302 865524).
Directions: Enter Rossington and go over the railway crossings. Pass the Welfare Club on right, Oxford Street is next right - ground is at bottom. 8 miles from Doncaster (BR).
Seats: 200 **Cover:** 500 **Capacity:** 1,200 **Floodlights:** Yes **Founded:** 1925
Colours: All blue **Change colours:** All white. **Midweek matches:** Tuesday
Programme: 32 pages, 50p **Programme Editor:** Mr S Tagg.
Prev. Lges: Yorks / Central Mids. **Record attendance:** 1,200 v Doncaster Rovers (date unknown).
Clubhouse: Rossington Miners Welfare **Local Newspapers:** Village Life - own newspaper.
Club honours: Central Mids Lg Prem. Div 84-85 (Prem. Div Cup 84-85, Div 1 Cup 83-84).

SELBY TOWN

President: R Coultish **Chairman:** J Vause **General Mgr:** B Wilkes
Secretary: T Mitchell, 22 The Mount, Selby, North Yorks YO8 9BH (0757 708035).
Asst. Manager: J Storey **Coach:** B Walker.
Ground: Flaxley Road Ground, Richard Street, Selby, North Yorkshire YO8 0BN.
Directions: From Leeds, left at main traffic lights in Selby down Scott Rd. then 1st left into Richard St. From Doncaster go straight across main traffic lights into Scott Road then 1st left. From York right at main traffic lights into Scott Rd, and 1st left. 1 mile from Selby (BR).
Seats: 100 **Cover:** 750 **Capacity:** 5,000 **Floodlights:** Yes **Founded:** 1911
Club colours: All white **Change colours:** All red.
Programme: 12 pages, 30p **Programme Editor:** M Fairweather (0757 705376).
Nickname: The Robins **Main Sponsors:** Irwin & Co Builders
Prev. League: Yorkshire (1920-82) **Prev. ground:** Bowling Green, James St. 1920-51
Past players to progress to Football League: Numerous
Best FA Cup performance: Second Round Proper 1954-55
Best FA Vase performance: Preliminary Round 1989-90
Record attendance: 7,000 v Bradford Park Avenue (FA Cup 1st Rnd 1953-54)
Clubhouse: Bar at ground open first and second team matchdays
Midweek Matches: Wednesday **Local Newspaper:** Selby Times.
Club honours: Yorkshire Lg 32-33 34-35 35-36 52-53 53-54 (R-up 24-25 25-26 27-28 28-29 30-31 31-32 50-51 55-56, Div 3 R-up 74-75, Lg Cup 37-38 53-54 54-55 62-63); Northern Co. East Div 2 R-up 89-90; West Riding Snr Cup 37-38; West Riding Co Cup 27-28 48-49; West Riding Chall. Cup 34-35 35-36

TADCASTER ALBION

Chairman: M Burnett **President:** Lord Edward Stourton. **Manager:** S Alford
Secretary/Chairman/Treasurer: M Burnett, 52 Hollin Hill, Leeds LS28 2PP.
Ground: The Park, Ings Lane, Tadcaster. 0937 832844
Directions: From West Riding and South Yorks, turn right off A659 at John Smith's Brewery Clock. From East Riding turn left off A659 after passing over river bridge and pelican crossing (New Street).
Cols: Red (white trim)/white/red **Change colours:** White/black/black
Programme: 20 pages. **Programme Editor:** L West.

WORSBROUGH BRIDGE M.W. & ATHLETIC

Chairman: Mr J Wright **Press Officer:** Mr A Wright (0226 243418).
Secretary: D Smith, 18 Shield Avenue, Worsbrough Bridge, Barnsley, S. Yorks S70 5BQ (0226 243418).
Manager: K Paddon **Asst Manager:**
Ground: Park Road, Worsbrough Bridge, Barnsley (0226 284452).
Directions: On the A61 Barnsley-Sheffield road two miles south of Barnsley, 2 miles from M1 jnt 36 opposite Blackburns Bridge. Two and a half miles from Barnsley (BR). Yorkshire Traction run buses every 10 mins thru Worsbrough Bridge.
Seats: 175 **Cover:** 175 **Capacity:** 2,000 **Floodlights:** Due **Founded:** 1921
Colours: All red **Change colours:** Yellow/blue **Reformed:** 1947
Record attendance: 2,300 v Blyth Spartans, FA Amateur Cup 1971
Previous Leagues: Barnsley 52-61/ County Snr 62-70/ Yorks 71-82. **Prog:** 20 pages, 20p
Hons: Northern Co's East Lg Div 1 R-up 90-91 (Div 3 R-up 85-86), Sheffield Snr Cup R-up 72-73, County Snr Lg 65-66 69-70 (R-up 62-63, Lg Cup 65-66), Barnsley Lg 52-53 58-59 59-60 (Lg Cup 56-57 58-59 (R-up 53-54)), Beckett Cup 57-58.

YORKSHIRE AMATEUR

President: Rayner Barker **Chairman:** William Ellis
Secretary: Brian Whaley, 50 Moseley Wood Walk, Leeds LS16 7HG (0532 679806).
Manager: Malcolm White **Asst Mgr:** Steve Jeffery **Coach:** Brian Richardson
Physio: Terry Davies **Commercial Manager:** Ian White (0532 666732).
Ground: Bracken Edge, Sycamore Avenue, Leeds LS8 4DZ (0532 624093).
Directions: From South M1 to Leeds, then A58 Wetherby Road to Fforde Green Hotel, left at lights and proceed to Sycamore Ave. (on right). From East A1 to Boot & Shoe Inn then to Shaftesbury Hotel, turn right into Harehills Lane, then to Sycamore Avenue. Two and a half miles from Leeds (BR). Buses 2, 3 & 20 from Briggate to Harehills Ave.
Seats: None **Cover:** 160 **Capacity:** 1,550 **Floodlights:** Yes **Founded:** 1919.
Colours: White/blue/red **Change colours:** All red **Nickname:** Ammers.
Midweek Matches: Tuesday **Previous ground:** Elland Road 1919-20
Sponsors: Bridge Electrical **Record Gate:** 4,000 v Wimbledon, FA Amateur Cup 1932.
Programme: 8 pages, 30p **Programme Editor:** Ian White (0532 666732)
Club Shop: Yes, selling sweat shirts, ties, badges, caps, scarves. Contact W Ellis (0405 839990).
Previous League: Yorks 20-24 30-82.
Clubhouse: Bar, tea bar, games room, lounge. Every night 8.30-11pm, Sat matchdays noon-11pm, Sun lunchtime noon-3pm.
Local Newspapers: Yorkshire Post/ Yorkshire Evening Post/ North Leeds Advertiser.
Top Scorer 92-93: Gary Jackson **Captain & P.o.Y. 92-93:** Brian Hill.
Hons: FA Amtr Cup SF 31-32, West Riding Co. Cup(3), Yorks Lg 31-32 (Div 2 58-59 (R-up 52-53 71-72), Div 3 77-78, Lg Cup 32-33), Leeds & Dist. Snr Cup.

Northern Counties (East) Divisions Two & Three Ten Year Record

(Includes Division Two North (N), Division Two South (S)

	83/4	84/5	85/6	86/7	87/8	88/9	89/0	90/1	91/2	92/3
Armthorpe Welfare	2N	N/A	–	–	–	–	–	–	N/A	N/A
Arnold Kingswell	–	N/A	12/2	–	–	–	–	–	N/A	N/A
Blidworth Welfare	9S	N/A	–	–	–	–	–	–	N/A	N/A
Bradley Rangers	–	N/A	–	–	–	–	3/2	4/2	N/A	N/A
Brigg Town	4S	N/A	–	–	–	–	–	–	N/A	N/A
Brodsworth Miners Welfare	–	N/A	–	–	–	12/2	9/2	12/2	N/A	N/A
Brook Sports	14N	N/A	–	–	–	–	–	–	N/A	N/A
Collingham	11N	N/A	–	1/3	5/2	2/2	–	–	N/A	N/A
Dronfield United	–	N/A	–	–	–	6/2	13/2	11/2	N/A	N/A
Eccleshill United	–	N/A	3/3	2/2	–	–	–	–	N/A	N/A
Frecheville Community	–	N/A	11/2	1/2	–	–	–	–	N/A	N/A
Fryston Colliery Welfare	7/N	N/A	12/3	18/2	13/2	14/2	4/2	8/2	N/A	N/A
Garforth Town	–	N/A	2/2	–	–	–	–	–	N/A	N/A
Glasshoughton Welfare	–	N/A	4/3	12/2	12/2	5/2	6/2	–	N/A	N/A
Graham Street Prims	3S	N/A	8/3	–	–	–	–	–	N/A	N/A
Grimethorpe Miners Welfare	9N	N/A	7/2	–	–	–	–	–	N/A	N/A
Hallam	–	N/A	5/2	–	–	–	–	–	N/A	N/A
Hall Road Rangers	10N	N/A	6/3	4/2	11/2	7/2	12/2	1/2	N/A	N/A
Harrogate Railway Athletic	1N	N/A	–	–	–	–	–	–	N/A	N/A
Immingham Town	–	N/A	–	3/2	–	–	–	9/2	N/A	N/A
Kimberley Town	2S	N/A	14/3	–	–	–	–	–	N/A	N/A
Kiveton Park	10S	N/A	8/2	–	–	–	–	10/2	N/A	N/A
Lincoln United	–	N/A	1/2	–	–	–	–	–	N/A	N/A
Liversedge	–	N/A	10/2	11/2	6/2	2/2	–	–	N/A	N/A
Maltby Miners Welfare	–	N/A	6/2	–	–	–	–	–	N/A	N/A
Oakham United	5S	N/A	7/3	–	–	–	–	–	N/A	N/A
Ossett Town	–	N/A	14/2	10/2	4/2	1/2	–	–	N/A	N/A
Phoenix Park	5N	N/A	–	–	–	–	–	–	N/A	N/A
Pickering Town	6N	N/A	15/2	14/2	1/2	–	–	–	N/A	N/A
Pilkington Recreation	12N	N/A	–	–	–	–	14/2	13/2	N/A	N/A
R.E.S. Parkgate	–	N/A	9/2	–	–	–	–	–	N/A	N/A
Retford Rail	12S	N/A	–	–	–	–	–	–	N/A	N/A
Retford Town	1S	N/A	–	–	–	–	–	–	N/A	N/A
Rowntree Mackintosh	–	N/A	–	–	–	–	–	3/2	N/A	N/A
Selby Town	4N	N/A	11/3	8/2	10/2	3/2	2/2	–	N/A	N/A
Staveley Works	–	N/A	4/2	–	–	–	–	–	N/A	N/A
Stocksbridge Works	11S	N/A	10/3	–	–	–	–	–	N/A	N/A
Stocksbridge Park Steels	–	N/A	–	7/2	8/2	9/2	7/2	7/2	N/A	N/A
Sutton Trinity	13S	N/A	–	–	–	–	–	–	N/A	N/A
Tadcaster Albion	13N	N/A	9/3	13/2	15/2	10/2	10/2	6/2	N/A	N/A
Thorn Colliery	8N	N/A	16/2	–	–	–	–	–	N/A	N/A
Winterton Rangers	–	N/A	–	16/2	9/2	11/2	1/2	–	N/A	N/A
Wombwell Town	8S	N/A	13/3	17/2	14/2	–	–	–	N/A	N/A
Worsborough Bridge Miners W.	7S	N/A	2/3	6/2	5/2	4/2	11/2	2/2	N/A	N/A
York Railway Institute	–	N/A	3/2	–	–	–	–	–	N/A	N/A
Yorksire Amateur	3N	N/A	5/3	9/2	3/2	13/2	8/2	5/2	N/A	N/A
Yorkshire Main	6S	N/A	13/2	15/2	7/2	8/2	5/2	–	N/A	N/A
No. of Clubs	14N		16/2	18/2	15/2	14/2	14/2	13/2		
	13S		14/3							

R.E.S. Parkgate F.C. 1992-93. Photo - Colin Stevens.

943

'BASS' DERBYSHIRE SENIOR LEAGUE

Bass Prem. Div.	P	W	D	L	F	A	PTS
Little Eaton	22	16	3	3	45	15	35
Ockbrook	22	15	2	5	63	30	32
Stanley Common	22	13	2	7	47	47	28
Allenton Athletic	22	12	4	6	43	35	28
Melbourne Dynamoes	22	10	3	9	49	38	23
Santos	22	10	2	10	64	54	22
Castle Donnington T.	22	9	3	10	50	39	21
Allestree	22	9	1	12	45	52	19
Park Tavern	22	6	6	10	27	34	18
Malt Shovel	22	6	4	12	29	57	16
Mickleover Sports	22	6	1	15	30	53	13
Aston	22	3	3	16	25	63	9

Carling Black L. D1	P	W	D	L	F	A	PTS
Grenville Athletic	22	19	0	3	73	25	38
Alfreton Athletic	22	16	2	4	64	24	34
Tutbury Hawthorn	22	15	2	3	69	40	32
Belper St Johns	22	10	6	6	50	39	26
Smalley Villa	22	9	5	8	37	40	23
Qualcast	22	8	5	9	59	47	21
Hemington	22	9	2	11	40	47	20
Darley Kestrels	22	6	5	11	38	53	17
Sudbury Park	22	6	5	11	49	65	17
Findern	22	4	5	13	41	63	13
Ashbourne Town	22	5	3	14	35	74	13
Concorde United	22	5	4	15	42	80	10

Worthington D2	P	W	D	L	F	A	PTS
Sermatech	22	15	6	1	80	27	36
Alvaston & B'ton OB	22	15	5	2	56	20	35
AC Rolls Royce	22	12	4	6	58	27	28
Little Eaton Res.	22	12	4	6	67	38	28
Spa Inn	22	11	4	7	59	41	26
Punjab United	22	9	3	10	40	42	21
Belper Thorntons	22	9	2	11	48	52	20
Allestree Res.	22	7	6	9	51	60	20
Shipley	22	7	3	12	47	86	17
Bargate Rovers	22	5	4	13	32	66	14
Commercial Inn	22	4	2	16	32	78	10
Mickleover Spts Res.	22	2	5	15	26	59	9

Lamots Pils D3	P	W	D	L	F	A	PTS
Ambergate	24	19	2	3	107	38	40
Belper St J. Res.	24	15	6	3	75	41	36
Qualcast Res.	24	16	3	5	88	43	35
Aston Res.	24	15	5	4	76	34	35
Melbourne D. Res.	24	13	2	9	87	43	28
Christians	24	12	1	11	51	62	25
Derventio	24	9	6	9	55	57	24
Alvaston & Boulton	24	9	3	12	55	63	21
St Marys	24	7	5	12	50	79	19
Scholl	24	7	4	13	54	77	18
South Wingfield	24	8	1	15	34	74	17
Castle Don. T. Res.	24	5	3	16	46	73	13

CHESTERFIELD LEAGUE

DIV. ONE	P	W	D	L	F	A	PTS
Welbeck Colliery	22	15	4	3	51	22	34
Mosborough Trinity	22	13	6	4	81	28	31
Bridge Broad Oaks	22	12	6	4	55	34	30
Killamarsh Jnrs Ath.	22	14	4	4	72	28	*29
Markham Colliery	22	13	1	8	61	32	27
Holymoorside	22	9	5	8	48	44	23
Unstone Athletic	22	10	3	9	53	52	&22
Industry Inn	22	8	3	11	50	63	19
Spinning Wheel	22	6	4	12	34	48	16
New Whitt Ath.	22	5	3	14	25	77	13
Castle Arms	22	4	3	15	38	66	11
Hasland New Inn	22	1	3	18	23	97	&4

* - 3pts deducted. & - 1pt deducted

DIV. TWO	P	W	D	L	F	A	PTS
SOS Plant Hire	18	13	2	3	69	46	28
Renishaw Jnrs	18	12	3	3	74	22	27
Millers	18	10	3	5	47	35	23
Poolsbrook SW	18	10	2	6	59	40	22
Rose & Crown	18	10	1	7	68	61	21
Birdholme United	18	8	1	9	53	52	17
Shirebrook Rangers	18	5	5	8	42	55	15
Creswell Old Boys	18	4	3	11	44	67	11
Shirebrook Northern	18	2	13	35	64	8	
Sterling Tubes	18	3	2	13	23	72	8

DIV. THREE	P	W	D	L	F	A	PTS
Harwood Installations	18	15	3	0	93	16	33
Shirebrook	18	11	5	2	66	26	28
Duckmanton M.W.	18	11	4	3	64	30	26
John Smedleys	18	9	3	6	55	39	21
Sheepbridge Spts	18	9	2	7	57	41	20
The Pod	18	7	4	7	46	32	18
Barlow K.R	18	7	2	9	31	28	16
Anglo Fuels	18	3	1	14	42	82	7
Creswell OB Res.	18	1	2	15	19	78	4
Hardy & Hansons	18	3	1	14	28	129	*4

* - 3pts deducted

HOPE VALLEY LEAGUE

PREM. DIV.	P	W	D	L	F	A	PTS
Dove Holes	26	26	0	0	123	20	78
Bradwell	26	18	2	6	69	38	56
Whaley Bridge	26	15	5	6	82	30	50
Chinley	26	15	3	8	74	31	48
Peak Dale United	26	14	2	10	68	58	44
Brampton	26	13	4	9	72	49	43
Tideswell United	26	13	3	10	55	43	42
Dronfield Woodhouse	26	12	5	9	49	45	41
Bamford	26	6	9	9	47	51	33
Chapel Town	26	7	6	13	47	64	27
Totley Sports	26	7	4	15	56	78	25
Hayfield	26	7	2	16	41	59	23
Dronfield Contact 77	26	1	3	21	36	99	6
Holmesfield Rgrs	26	0	2	24	24	168	2

A. DIVISION	P	W	D	L	F	A	PTS
Stoney Middleton	26	19	4	3	78	38	61
Cote Heath	26	17	6	3	76	44	57
Youlgrave Utd	26	15	5	6	80	30	50
Peak Dale Utd Res.	26	15	4	7	72	38	49
Dove Holes Res.	26	12	7	6	53	49	43
Bakewell	26	12	5	8	49	32	41
Chinley Res.	26	10	5	10	48	44	35
Buxworth	26	10	4	11	59	61	34
Bradwell Res.	26	9	4	12	59	63	31
Hathersage	26	9	4	12	58	70	31
Holmesfield Phoenix	26	7	5	14	60	90	26
Chapel Town Res.	26	7	3	14	50	82	24
Totley Spts Res.	26	4	3	19	41	76	15
Bakewell Wheatsheaf	26	2	1	23	25	109	7

B. DIVISION	P	W	D	L	F	A	PTS
Calver	26	19	4	2	97	27	61
Blue Circle	26	17	6	3	72	31	57
Winster St John	26	15	6	5	73	36	51
Whaley Bridge Res.	26	15	3	6	86	49	48
Baslow	26	14	4	8	103	53	48
Hayfield Res.	26	13	1	12	57	49	40
Youlgrave Utd Res.	26	10	5	11	38	47	35
Grindleford	26	9	6	11	60	59	33
Buxworth Res.	26	9	4	13	54	68	31
Bamford Res.	26	9	3	14	60	85	30
Edale	26	8	5	13	42	73	29
Tideswell Res.	26	7	4	15	57	72	25
Hathersage Res.	26	8	4	15	44	84	22
Stoney Middleton Res.	26	2	1	23	23	123	7

JOHN SMITH'S BITTER CENTRAL MIDLANDS LEAGUE

President: L Nowicki
Chairman: F.A.Harwood
Hon. Secretary: Mr A.E.Goodacre,
6 Maddison Avenue, Chadesden, Derby DE2 6HZ
Public Relations Officer: Stan Wilton, 'Haven Holme', 57 Main Road,
Smalley, Ilkeston, Derbyshire, DE7 6DS.

Season 1992/93 will undoubtedly be remembered as the one in which the league made considerable progress. After years of finding its chosen route forward consistently blocked, minds and attitudes were freshly programmed towards the Northern Pyramid and establishment firmly anchored. The league were pleased to push two more clubs up the promotion ladder to the Northern Counties East League - Louth United and champions Arnold Town.

The destination of the Supreme Division title was the closest in the history of the league, going right to the last day of the season. Arnold Town had looked worthy champions for a long while until stage fright set in over Easter allowing Heanor Town to draw level on points. But alas, Heanor's free scoring attack left themsleves a little to much to do in their final game at Kimberley Town, and although they out in a barnstorming finish to win 4-2, Arnold's 3-0 success on the same day at Glapwell was enough to see them lift the crown. Heanor's reward was to parade the division's two top goalscorers in Graham Millington and Alan Park.

The premier division became a one-horse race from the sixth week of the season. It was not a case of who could stop Sandiacre Town from winning the championship, as who could beat them. In the end no-one could and they stretched their unbeaten run to 34 games to lift the title by 15 points. Just to prove that it was no fluke they became the first premier division side to win the league cup, defeating Louth United 4-1 at Notts County's Meadow Lane ground before over 600 spectators, to complete a magnificent double.

Sheffield Aurora lifted the Wakefield Floodlit Cup with a 2-0 success over Gedling Town in a close game played at Hucknall Town.

In addition to the promotions of Arnold Town and Louth United, Wombwell Town left the league due to financial problems and Mickleover Royal British Legion were relegated over ground restrictions. However, the saddest part was the close season deaths of two of our most likeable and sociable clubs, Kilburn Miners Welfare and Mexborough Town. New clubs in membership next season will be Staveley Miners Welfare, Mickleover Sports, Kingston and Thorne Colliery.

At the league's annual general meeting, the clubs honoured chairman Frank Harwood and treasurer Tony Baugh with life memberships. A well-deserved honour to two excellent ambassadors of the game who, between them, have clocked up almost thirty years service to the league.

A number of our clubs have suffered unforseen close season problems, some of which have been encoutered because of the pit closures. Many have been steadfastly overcome, a number thanks to the generosity of nearby colleries and voluntary help from their former employees. It has been both heart-warming and encouraging, and I would hope that, through football, some will be helped into finding new employment.

Kiveton Park, Long Eaton United, Rossington and Sandiacre Town have been promoted to the supreme division. I hope and believe it will give the league new impetus.

Stan Wilton (Public Relations Officer)

Steve Hare scores for Arnold Town as his side clinch the league title with a 3-0 away victory over Glapwell in the last game of the season. Photo: Colin Stevens.

SUPREME DIV.	P	W	D	L	F	A	PTS
Arnold Town	30	22	4	4	76	32	70
Heanor Town	30	22	4	4	80	42	70
Blidworth Welfare	30	18	7	5	45	22	61
Harworth Colliery I.	30	18	2	10	60	42	56
Priory (Eastwood)	30	12	11	7	47	35	47
Mickleover R.B.L.	30	14	4	12	51	48	46
Gedling Town	30	14	3	13	64	55	45
Shirebrook Colliery	30	13	4	13	78	65	43
Louth United	30	11	7	12	60	46	40
Glapwell	30	11	5	14	53	60	38
Borrowash Victoria	30	11	5	14	59	71	38
Kimberley Town	30	8	8	14	43	57	32
Sheffield Aurora	30	8	6	16	48	69	30
Nettleham United	30	7	7	16	53	76	28
Oakham United	30	4	5	21	26	64	17
Wombwell Town	30	4	4	22	28	87	16

Top Scorers: Graham Millington (Heanor) 32, Alan Park (Heanor) 24, Brendan Yates (Shirebrook) 22, David Waller (Glapwell) 19, Peter Fletcher (Arnold) 18, David Taylor (Arnold) 18, Mark Daly (Gedling) 16, Neil Farrow (Harworth) 16, Lee Aulton (Harworth) 15, Brett Marshall (Kimberley (4 for Oakham)) 15, Keith Maxwell (Shirebrook) 15.

RESERVE PREM.	P	W	D	L	F	A	PTS
Arnold T. Res.	28	20	6	2	77	27	66
Shirebrook Res.	28	19	5	4	78	34	62
Hucknall T. Res.	28	15	8	6	57	30	53
Oakham Utd Res.	28	14	6	8	61	38	48
Borrowash Res.	28	10	10	8	48	50	40
Wombwell T. Res.	28	12	4	12	47	51	40
Mickleover Res.	28	11	5	12	56	44	38
Priory E'wood Res.	28	9	7	12	48	52	34
Biwater Res.	28	8	9	11	45	62	33
Norton W'seats Res.	28	7	11	10	48	59	32
Kimberley T. Res.	28	8	7	13	48	55	31
Bidworth W. Res.	28	8	6	14	47	56	30
Bulwell Utd Res.	28	7	5	16	50	74	26
Rossington Res.	28	7	4	17	34	69	25
Derby R. Res.	28	7	3	18	45	88	24

Top Scorers: Stephen Hill (Shirebrook) 26, Tim Mutimer (Oakham) 22, Steven Bull (Arnold) 18, Jamie Brownlee (Arnold) 17, Darren Telford (Blidworth) 17, David Martin (Biwater) 16.

PREM. DIVISION	P	W	D	L	F	A	PTS
Sandiacre Town	36	31	4	1	127	24	97
Rossington	36	25	7	4	91	49	82
Kiveton Park	36	20	4	12	80	49	64
Norton Woodseats	36	20	2	14	79	68	62
Long Eaton United	36	19	4	13	80	58	61
Derby C.&W.(R'kitts)	36	16	11	9	65	46	59
S.Normanton Ath.	36	16	10	10	62	58	58
Derby Rolls R.	36	15	6	15	60	62	51
Askern Miners Wel.	36	13	9	14	79	71	48
Stanton Ilkeston	36	14	4	18	61	64	46
Kilburn Miners Wel.	36	13	7	16	63	82	46
Mexborough T.Ath.	36	13	6	17	61	58	45
Biwater	36	12	7	17	63	70	43
Newhall United	36	13	4	19	69	88	43
Radford	36	12	4	20	63	106	40
Blackwell Miners W.	36	9	7	20	41	84	34
Bulwell United	36	7	10	19	63	91	31
Nuthall	36	8	7	21	42	79	31
Shardlow St James	36	6	7	23	40	82	25

Top Scorers: David King (Sandiacre) 38, Glyn Stacey (Sandiacre) 31, Gary Weston (Long Eaton) 31, Tony Hattersley (Askern) 26, Robert Palmer (Kiveton Park) 25, Robert Nelson (Rossington) 24, Barry Davies (Mexborough) 22, Mark Robinson (Sandiacre) 21, Amjad Kham (Radford) 20, Lee Storey (Rossington) 20, Stephen Wells (Long Eaton) 20, Gary O'Brien (Norton Woodseats) 18, Kevin Joyce (Newhall) 17, Lee Bradley (Newhall) 16, Richard Farrell (Bulwell) 16, Andrew Fitzmaurice (Kiveton Park) 15, Leslie Harris (Kiveton Park) 15, Nick Tobin (Biwater) 15.

RES. DIV. ONE	P	W	D	L	F	A	PTS
Glapwell Res.	18	15	0	3	67	20	45
Derby C & W Res.	18	11	3	4	48	27	36
Stanton Ilk. Res.	18	10	2	6	41	32	32
Arnold Town 'A'	18	8	6	4	40	20	30
Long Eaton U. Res.	18	8	3	7	42	43	27
Harworth CI Res.	18	7	3	8	43	42	24
Radford Res.	18	6	4	8	30	42	22
Shardlow St J. Res.	18	5	3	10	27	35	18
Nuthall Res.	18	4	5	9	28	47	17
Derby Rolls R. 'A'	18	1	1	16	18	76	4

Top Scorers: Terry Griffin (Harworth) 27, Paul Smith (Stanton) 13, Stuart Coke (Arnold 'A') 10, Howard Malcolm (Nuthall) 10.

SUPREME DIV. RESULTS	1	2	3	4	5	6	7	8	9	10	11	12	13	14	15	16
1. Arnold Town	*	2-1	4-2	1-4	3-0	1-5	3-1	4-1	3-0	2-0	5-2	3-0	2-0	5-0	2-1	5-0
2. Blidworth Welfare	1-1	*	4-0	1-0	2-1	1-0	2-0	2-1	2-2	1-3	2-1	2-0	0-0	2-0	2-1	4-1
3. Borrowash Victoria	3-2	1-1	*	0-0	1-3	3-3	1-2	3-3	4-2	2-5	0-2	1-0	2-4	2-2	5-1	2-0
4. Gedling Town	1-4	2-1	1-2	*	1-4	3-1	2-3	3-0	2-0	0-3	5-2	3-0	5-1	1-3	4-2	5-2
5. Glapwell	0-3	1-3	3-1	2-0	*	0-3	4-5	2-0	1-3	2-1	1-1	1-4	1-2	3-2	4-0	
6. Harworth C.I.	0-3	1-2	2-1	2-1	2-1	*	1-2	1-0	0-4	1-0	0-2	3-0	0-0	6-1	1-2	4-2
7. Heanor Town	0-0	1-0	6-3	4-3	3-2	1-0	*	2-3	2-1	2-1	7-1	4-1	2-0	1-2	4-2	3-1
8. Kimberley Town	0-0	0-0	3-5	0-1	1-1	2-3	2-4	*	1-0	2-1	1-1	3-2	1-1	3-4	3-0	2-1
9. Louth United	2-4	1-2	4-0	4-0	1-1	0-3	1-1	4-1	*	0-0	2-3	4-2	1-1	3-1	2-2	5-0
10. Mickleover R.B.L.	0-1	0-0	3-1	1-5	3-0	1-4	0-3	1-1	3-2	*	0-6	1-0	0-1	1-1	2-5	5-0
11. Nettleham	2-2	0-1	2-3	1-2	2-5	1-2	1-1	2-2	1-3	1-4	*	2-2	0-0	1-4	2-6	2-1
12. Oakham United	0-1	0-2	0-2	2-2	1-1	3-4	1-4	2-1	1-3	0-1	1-2	*	0-2	2-0	1-4	0-2
13. Priory (Eastwood)	1-0	0-0	1-3	0-3	3-3	0-1	1-1	1-0	2-0	2-3	3-2	4-0	*	6-3	0-1	1-1
14. Sheffield Aurora	1-2	0-2	4-0	2-5	4-1	1-2	0-1	1-3	1-1	2-3	0-5	1-2	0-0	*	2-3	2-1
15. Shirebrook Colliery	2-5	1-2	3-2	3-3	2-3	1-2	2-4	5-2	1-3	1-0	8-1	1-1	3-1	2-2	*	5-1
16. Wombwell Town	2-3	1-0	1-4	1-0	3-0	0-4	1-6	0-1	0-5	1-3	2-2	0-1	1-1	2-2	0-6	*

PREMIER DIV. RESULTS	1	2	3	4	5	6	7	8	9	10	11	12	13	14	15	16	17	18	19
1. Askern Welfare	*	8-4	2-1	1-0	2-0	3-0	3-5	2-0	5-0	1-1	4-1	2-4	3-3	1-1	2-2	0-0	0-0	2-0	0-2
2. Biwater	1-2	*	0-2	3-2	3-2	0-1	0-0	2-1	1-2	2-1	1-3	3-0	0-1	2-3	1-3	2-1	1-1	2-1	
3. Blackwell Miners W.	2-1	1-1	*	1-0	2-2	4-2	1-3	0-3	1-1	1-1	0-2	0-3	0-1	2-3	0-4	0-3	3-2	1-1	0-3
4. Bulwell United	2-4	0-5	1-1	*	1-4	0-2	6-2	2-2	3-5	2-7	5-1	3-3	1-1	2-5	3-5	0-3	1-1	1-1	1-3
5. Derby Carriage & W.	3-1	1-1	2-0	2-0	*	1-0	1-2	1-0	3-0	0-2	0-3	1-1	2-2	9-2	0-0	1-1	1-0	3-0	3-1
6. Derby Rolls Royce	2-4	3-2	5-2	2-1	1-1	*	5-2	0-2	2-0	1-1	3-2	0-2	2-0	4-0	1-2	1-2	2-2	2-2	3-1
7. Kilburn Miners Welfare	5-4	3-3	4-1	1-1	1-3	1-2	*	2-1	0-1	2-0	2-1	1-7	2-1	2-2	2-3	0-4	2-0	3-5	2-0
8. Kiveton Park	1-1	3-1	4-0	4-1	3-0	4-0	4-1	*	2-1	3-0	4-1	4-3	1-0	5-2	1-3	1-2	3-0	1-0	1-2
9. Long Eaton United	4-1	4-0	1-1	3-5	5-3	4-1	1-0	1-2	*	3-1	3-1	2-1	1-1	4-1	0-1	0-3	4-0	1-2	7-0
10. Mexborough Town	3-1	1-3	4-2	1-0	0-0	1-0	1-2	1-1	2-1	*	6-0	1-2	0-2	9-0	2-5	1-6	1-1	1-3	1-0
11. Newhall United	6-2	3-2	1-5	1-3	3-3	0-0	0-2	2-3	1-0	*	2-3	4-2	7-3	1-3	2-1	3-1	4-0	1-6	
12. Norton Woodseats	0-5	3-1	7-0	2-3	1-3	0-2	3-1	0-4	2-1	1-0	3-0	*	4-1	5-2	1-2	0-5	5-0	1-2	0-3
13. Nuthall	2-0	0-3	3-0	3-2	0-3	2-2	0-2	2-1	0-5	1-2	1-0	0-1	*	1-3	0-4	1-3	2-2	0-4	1-2
14. Radford	4-2	2-0	0-1	1-1	0-1	1-2	3-2	2-4	4-2	2-3	1-1	1-4	3-2	*	2-4	0-4	2-0	3-5	2-1
15. Rossington	3-2	3-2	2-1	0-1	2-2	3-1	2-2	1-3	2-1	2-0	6-3	5-1	3-2	2-1	*	2-4	4-1	2-0	1-1
16. Sandiacre Town	2-0	6-2	7-0	7-2	3-1	4-0	1-1	4-2	4-1	3-1	4-1	6-1	8-0	3-0	*	4-0	2-0	0-0	
17. Shardlow St James	4-3	0-2	3-4	1-5	0-1	0-2	4-1	3-0	1-2	1-4	1-3	0-1	1-1	3-2	0-0	0-3	*	1-4	1-3
18. South Normanton Ath.	1-1	1-1	1-0	0-0	3-2	2-2	2-4	0-0	2-3	5-0	0-2	2-0	2-2	1-7	0-2	*	3-1		
19. Stanton Ilkeston	2-4	1-4	3-0	3-1	0-0	4-2	3-0	2-2	0-4	1-2	4-0	0-1	4-1	1-2	0-2	2-3	2-3	*	

RESERVE PREM. RESULTS	1	2	3	4	5	6	7	8	9	10	11	12	13	14	15
1. Arnold Town Reserves	*	5-1	0-0	4-1	2-1	4-0	2-2	0-0	4-2	3-0	0-3	3-1	3-0	2-1	3-1
2. Biwater Reserves	0-0	*	3-1	2-2	3-3	3-4	0-4	2-0	1-3	3-3	0-2	2-1	0-4	0-4	5-2
3. Blidworth Welfare Res	0-1	2-2	*	2-3	0-5	4-0	1-5	0-1	4-1	0-2	3-3	0-2	1-0	2-5	1-2
4. Borrowash V. Res	1-1	0-2	2-0	*	4-2	1-1	3-1	1-1	0-2	2-0	1-0	1-1	1-1	0-3	3-1
5. Bulwell United Res	4-5	1-2	3-2	2-2	*	3-2	2-0	2-2	2-2	1-3	1-5	3-1	0-3	0-3	3-1
6. Derby Rolls Royce	0-5	8-2	0-10	4-6	0-1	*	2-3	5-3	1-0	1-2	1-0	0-4	4-2	0-4	1-2
7. Hucknall Town Res.	2-2	1-0	1-2	2-0	2-0	2-0	*	3-2	1-0	1-1	0-1	2-1	9-0	1-2	2-2
8. Kimberley Town Res.	3-2	0-1	2-3	3-2	9-4	1-2	0-0	*	2-1	5-1	0-2	4-1	2-1	1-3	2-3
9. Mickleover R.B.L. Res	0-2	1-1	4-0	4-0	5-0	4-0	1-3	1-1	*	2-1	6-1	2-3	2-0	0-2	0-2
10. Norton Woodseats Res.	2-5	2-2	1-1	2-2	2-2	4-4	2-3	1-1	4-4	*	1-4	1-1	3-0	2-1	4-0
11. Oakham Utd Reserves	0-2	3-3	3-3	1-2	3-2	2-0	1-1	4-1	4-0	0-1	*	3-4	3-0	1-1	5-1
12. Priory (Eastwood) Res.	0-4	2-1	0-1	3-3	3-0	6-1	0-2	4-1	1-2	1-1	1-1	*	1-1	1-6	3-1
13. Rossington Reserves	0-2	1-2	1-2	3-3	1-3	3-2	1-1	3-1	0-4	4-2	0-1	1-0	*	1-6	3-2
14. Shirebrook Coll. Res.	2-9	2-1	1-1	0-2	2-0	6-1	1-1	3-0	2-2	3-0	2-1	2-2	7-0	*	2-1
15. Wombwell Town Res.	0-2	1-1	3-1	2-0	4-0	1-1	1-2	0-0	2-1	3-0	1-4	3-0	2-0	1-3	*

RESERVE DIV.1 RESULTS	1	2	3	4	5	6	7	8	9	10
1. Arnold Town 'A'	*	0-0	5-2	2-1	0-0	5-1	2-0	2-3	0-0	4-2
2. Derby C & W Res.	2-1	*	5-1	1-5	6-0	2-4	4-3	3-1	4-0	1-2
3. Derby Rolls Royce 'A'	0-6	0-6	*	1-4	5-2	2-1	3-0	3-1	2-4	1-2
4. Glapwell Reserves	1-4	0-1	4-0	*	5-2	2-1	3-0	3-1	6-2	8-2
5. Harworth Res.	2-3	1-3	10-1	2-4	*	5-2	5-1	6-3	0-1	1-1
6. Long Eaton U. Res.	1-1	2-2	4-3	2-5	1-2	*	3-1	4-1	3-0	4-2
7. Nuthall Reserves	2-2	0-3	3-1	0-3	0-0	3-3	*	3-2	2-3	0-4
8. Radford Reserves	2-1	0-0	1-1	0-6	1-3	3-2	1-1	*	0-3	2-1
9. Shardlow SJ Res	0-0	2-3	6-0	0-1	4-1	0-3	2-3	0-2	*	0-2
10. Stanton Ilkeston Res	1-0	5-2	2-0	0-3	2-3	5-0	4-1	2-2	2-0	*

LEAGUE CUP 1992-93

Preliminary Round

Mexborough Town v Sandiacre Town	3-5
Radford v Nuthall	1-2
Kilburn Miners Welfare v Newhall Utd	1-1,1-7
Shardlow St James v Bulwell United	1-2

First Round

Arnold Town v Heanor Town	1-1,2-0
Blidworth Welfare v Nettleham	0-5
Derby Rolls Royce v Mickleover R.B.L.	0-3
Harworth Colliery I. v Shirebrook Colliery	2-1
Kiveton Park v Norton Woodseats	2-2,0-1
Newhall United v Rossington	3-1
Priory (Eastwood) v Askern Welfare	6-1
South Normanton Athletic v Biwater	1-0
Blackwell Miners Welfare v Derby Carriage & W.	3-1
Bulwell United v Wombwell Town	2-3
Gedling Town v Borrowash Victoria	0-4
Kimberley Town v Oakham United	2-2,1-3
Long Eaton United v Sandiacre Town	0-2
Nuthall v Louth United	2-2,0-6
Sheffield Aurora v Stanton Ilkeston	2-2,3-4
Glapwell (w/o) Fryston Colliery Welfare (scr)	

Second Round

Borrowash Victoria v Newhall United	4-1
Glapwell v Blackwell Miners Welfare	4-1
Sandiacre Town v Priory (Eastwood)	2-0
Wombwell Town v Louth United	0-2
Arnold Town v Mickleover Royal British Legion	2-3
Oakham United v South Normanton Ath.	0-0,1-6
Stanton Ilkeston v Harworth Colliery Inst.	3-2

Quarter Finals

Glapwell v South Normanton Athletic	2-0
Norton Woodseats v Borrowash Victoria	0-5
Mickleover Royal British Legion v Sandiacre Town	1-3
Stanton Ilkeston v Louth United	1-3

Semi-Finals

Louth v Glapwell (at Blidworth)	2-0
Sandiacre v Borrowash (at Heanor Town)	3-1

Final (at Notts County F.C.): Sandiacre Town 4, Louth United 1

Sandiacre Town, League Cup winners and Premier Division champions 1992-93. Photo - David Whyatt.

WAKEFIELD FLOODLIT CUP 1992-93

GROUP A.	P	W	D	L	F	A	PTS
Louth United	6	5	0	1	12	7	15
Nettleham	6	3	2	1	11	8	11
Harworth Coll. I.	6	1	1	4	10	15	4
Wombwell Town	6	0	3	3	8	11	3

RESULTS		1	2	3	4
1.	Harworth Colliery Inst.	*	2-3	0-1	2-2
2.	Louth United	3-1	*	2-1	1-0
3.	Nettleham	3-1	3-2	*	2-2
4.	Wombwell Town	3-4	1-1	1-1	*

GROUP C.	P	W	D	L	F	A	PTS
Gedling Town	6	4	0	2	15	10	12
Arnold Town	6	3	1	2	10	9	10
Kimberley Town	6	2	1	3	10	14	7
Blidworth Welfare	6	1	2	3	6	8	5

RESULTS		1	2	3	4
1.	Arnold Town	*	0-0	1-3	4-0
2.	Blidworth Welfare	3-0	*	1-3	1-1
3.	Gedling Town	1-2	2-1	*	2-3
4.	Kimberley Town	2-3	2-4	2-0	*

GROUP B.	P	W	D	L	F	A	PTS
Sheffield Aurora	6	5	0	1	16	11	15
Glapwell	6	2	3	1	11	10	9
Oakham United	6	2	2	2	11	10	8
Shirebrook Colliery	6	0	1	5	6	13	1

RESULTS		1	2	3	4
1.	Glapwell	*	1-1	4-2	1-1
2.	Oakham United	2-2	*	0-2	1-0
3.	Sheffield Aurora	3-1	4-3	*	4-3
4.	Shirebrook Colliery	1-2	1-4	0-1	*

GROUP D.	P	W	D	L	F	A	PTS
Mickleover R.B.L.	6	5	1	0	16	6	6
Borrowash Victoria	6	2	0	4	11	10	6
Priory (Eastwood)	6	1	3	2	10	10	6
Heanor Town	6	1	2	3	6	17	5

RESULTS		1	2	3	4
1.	Borrowash Victoria	*	1-2	0-1	0-2
2.	Heanor Town	0-5	*	0-4	3-3
3.	Mickleover R.B.L.	3-2	4-1	*	3-3
4.	Priory (Eastwood)	2-3	0-0	0-1	*

Semi-Final: Gedling 2, Mickleover 1 *(at Kimberley)*

Semi-Final: Sheffield Aurora 3, Louth 0 *(at Blidworth)*

Final: Gedling 2, Sheffield Aurora 0 *(at Hucknall)*

KEN MARSLAND TROPHY 1992-93

GROUP A.	P	W	D	L	F	A	PTS
Harworth Cl Res.	8	7	0	1	34	11	21
Arnold Town 'A'	8	7	0	1	27	8	21
Shardlow SJ Res.	8	3	0	5	8	17	9
Nuthall Res.	8	1	1	6	7	20	4
Derby R.R. Res.	8	1	1	6	9	29	4

RESULTS		1	2	3	4	5
1.	Arnold Town 'A'	*	7-1	1-3	3-2	1-0
2.	Derby Rolls Royce 'A'	3-6	*	3-6	2-0	2-4
3.	Harworth Cl Res.	2-3	5-0	*	8-2	6-0
4.	Nuthall Reserves	0-2	0-0	2-3	*	0-1
5.	Shardlow SJ Res.	0-5	3-1	0-1	0-1	*

GROUP C.	P	W	D	L	F	A	PTS
Stanton Ilk. Res.	8	6	0	2	19	11	18
Glapwell Res.	8	5	2	1	20	12	17
Derby C & W Res.	8	3	1	4	22	17	10
Radford Res.	8	3	0	5	11	19	9
Long Eaton Res.	8	1	1	4	12	25	4

RESULTS		1	2	3	4	5
1.	Derby C & W Res.	*	1-1	7-2	3-2	1-3
2.	Glapwell Reserves	2-1	*	4-1	1-0	3-2
3.	Long Eaton Res.	4-3	2-2	*	1-2	1-4
4.	Radford Reserves	0-5	2-5	2-1	*	2-1
5.	Stanton Ilk. Res.	3-1	3-2	1-0	2-1	*

Final:
Harworth Reserves 4, Stanton I. Res 0 *(at Kimberley)*

RESERVE CHALLENGE CUP 1992-93

First Round

Biwater Reserves v Hucknall Town Res.	1-3
Bulwell Utd Res. v Oakham Res.	5-5,0-1
Glapwell Res. v Shirebrook C. Res.	2-2,2-4
Nuthall Res. v Mickleover RBL Res.	0-3
Stanton Ilkeston Res. v Blidworth Res.	1-3
Borrowash Vic. Res. v Arnold Town Res.	1-1,1-3(aet)
Derby R.R. Reserves v Harworth Cl Res	7-1
Long Eaton Utd Res v Derby C & W Res.	1-3
Radford Reserves v Derby R.R. 'A'	6-0

Second Round

Arnold Town 'A' v Hucknall Town Reserves	1-4
Derby C & W Res v Wombwell Town Res.	2-2,1-3
Norton Woodseats Res v Derby R.R. Res.	4-2
Rossington Res. v Radford Reserves	2-3
Arnold Town Reserves v Blidworth Wel. Res	3-1
Mickleover RBL Res v Kimberley Town Res.	2-1
Priory Eastwood Res v Oakham United Res	3-3,1-3
Shardlow St J. Res v Shirebrook Coll. Res	0-1

Quarter-Finals

Hucknall Town Res v Wombwell Town Res	4-0
Norton Woodseats Res. v Shirebrook C. Res	3-2
Oakham United Res. v Arnold Town Reserves	1-2
Radford Reserves v Mickleover RBL Res	1-1,0-5

Semi-Finals

Hucknall Res v Mickleover Res *(at Borrowash)*	0-1
Arnold Res v N. Woodseats Res *(at Glapwell)*	2-3

Final *(at Kimberley Town F.C.):* Norton Woodseats Reserves 2, Mickleover R.B.L. Reserves 1

NEWSLETTER

THE LEAGUE PRODUCES A FORTNIGHTLY NEWSLETTER CONTAINING THE LATEST INFORMATION FROM MEMBER CLUBS, UP-TO-DATE LEAGUE TABLES, FORTHCOMING FIXTURES AND LEADING GOALSCORERS. THE SUBSCRIPTION LIST IS OPEN TO SUPPORTERS AND GROUNDHOPPERS AND COSTS £7.00 FOR SEASON. CHEQUES SHOULD BE MADE PAYABLE TO THE CENTRAL MIDLANDS LEAGUE AND SENT, TOGETHER WITH THE FULL POSTAL ADDRESS, TO THE LEAGUE'S PUBLIC RELATIONS OFFICER, MR S WILTON, 'HAVEN HOLME', 57 MAIN ROAD, SMALLEY, ILKESTON, DERBYSHIRE DE7 6DS.

SUPREME DIVISION SEVEN YEAR RECORDS

	86/7	87/8	88/9	89/0	90/1	91/2	92/3
Arnold Town	9	10	2	3	4	8	1
Blidworth Welfare	–	–	–	–	17	7	3
Borrowash Victoria	5	7	8	11	12	13	11
Boston	–	12	1	7	9	–	–
Bradford Park Avenue	–	–	–	16	–	–	–
Crookes				(see Sheffield Aurora)			
Gedling Town	–	–	–	–	–	–	7
Gainsborough Town	8	4	3	10	13	–	–
Glapwell	–	–	–	–	–	18	10
Grimsby Borough	–	14	17	20	–	–	–
Harworth Colliery Institute	2	1	5	4	6	4	4
Heanor Town	4	5	4	2	2	11	2
Hinckley	12	17	–	–	–	–	–
Hinckley Town	1	2	–	–	–	–	–
Hucknall Town	–	–	–	1	1	2	–
Ilkeston Town	10	3	7	6	–	–	–
Kimberley Town	11	15	14	18	–	–	12
Lincoln United	3	8	12	3	1	–	–
Long Eaton United	–	–	–	5	–	–	–
Louth United	–	9	11	12	10	3	9
Melton Town	–	–	15	15	15	16	–
Mickleover R.B.L.	–	–	–	–	–	6	6
Nettleham	–	–	–	–	5	10	14
Oakham United	6	11	6	13	11	12	15
Priory (Eastwood)	–	–	–	14	14	9	5
Rossington Main	13	13	16	19	8	–	–
Sheffield Aurora	7	6	10	8	7	5	13
Shirebrook Colliery	–	–	–	–	–	14	8
Stanton Ilkeston	–	16	13	17	–	17	–
Staveley Works	–	–	9	–	–	–	–
Wombwell Town	–	–	–	–	16	15	16
No. of Clubs	13	17	17	20	17	18	16

SUPREME DIVISION CLUBS 1993-94

BLIDWORTH WELFARE

President: Ray Hilton　　**Chairman**: Julian Sperry　　**Vice Chairman**: Dave Wilkinson
Secretary: Bill Deakin, 220 Brick Kiln Lane, Mansfield, Notts NG19 6LR (0623 29033).
Manager: Andy Brown　　**Asst Manager**: John Miller　　**Coach**: Shaun Hird.
Physio: Paul Deakin　　**Press Officer**: Pete Craggs, 21 Pecks Hill, Mansfield.
Ground: Welfare Ground, Mansfield Rd, Blidworth, Mansfield (0623 798724).
Directions: On B6020, Rainworth side of Blidworth. Served by Mansfield-Nottingham buses.
Capacity: 6,000　　**Seats**: 200　　**Cover**: 700　　**Floodlights**: Yes　　**Reformed**: 1982.
Programme: 38 pages, 50p　　**Editor**: Pete Craggs　　**Club Shop**: No.
Colours: All blue　　**Change colours**: All yellow　　**Nickname**: Hawks
Midweek home matchdays: Wednesday　　**Record Gate**: 400 v Shirebrook Colliery 1989-90.
Previous Grounds: None.　　**Previous Leagues**: Northern Co's (East) 82-86.
Record win: 6-0 v Harworth Colliery Institute (H), League Cup 91-92.
Record defeat: 0-11 v Sheffield Aurora (A), Central Midlands League 90-91.
Clubhouse: New club ('Welfare Social Club') just built - to open 93-94, normal matchday hours.
Club record scorer: Andy Locker　　**Club record appearances**: Dave Colley.
Captain 92-93: Simon Kazsiba　　**P.o.Y. 92-93**: Russ Jackson.
Top Scorers 92-93: Ian Dudley 9, Tony Nicholson 8, Peter Vernon 8.　　**Hons**: None.

Blidworth Welfare. Back Row (L/R): John Miller (Asst Manager), Andy Brown (Manager), John Clayton, Peter Vernon, Russ Jackson, Mark Stacey, Shane Dudley, Steve Giles, Jimmy Garner, Alan Crewe, Bill Deakin. Front: Darren Telford, Ian Dudley, Simon Kazsiba (Captain), Paul Clamp, Shaun Ceney, Richard Marriott, Dave Colley.

BORROWASH VICTORIA

Chairman: Ian Anderson   **Vice Chairman:** Peter Erwin.
Sec./Press Officer: Ian Collins, 30 Margreave Road, Chaddesden, Derby DE2 6JD (0332 678016).
Manager/Coach: Peter McGurk   **Physio:** Ray Bonser.   **Commercial Mgr:** Les Bullimore.
Ground: Asterdale Club, Borrowash Road, Spondon, Derby (0332 668656).
Directions: M1 jct 25, A52 towards Derby, 3rd left off by-pass into Borrowash Rd, ground 400 yds on left. 2 mins from Spondon (BR). Nottingham to Derby buses pass nearby.

Capacity: 5,000	**Seats:** No	**Covered:** 500 **Floodlights:** Yes **Founded:** 1911

Capacity: 5,000   **Seats:** No   **Covered:** 500   **Floodlights:** Yes   **Founded:** 1911
Midweek matches: Tuesday   **Prev. Grnd:** Dean Drive, B'wash 11-84   **Reformed:** 1963.
Colours: Red/white/black   **Change Colours:** All yellow   **Nickname:** Vics.
Programme: 16 pages, 50p   **Editor:** Secretary.
Club Shop: No, but club ties, pens, pencils and key rings are available - contact secretary.
Record Gate: 2,000 v Nottingham Forest, floodlight opening 22/10/85.
Prev. Lges: Derby Sunday School & Welfare 52-57/ Derby Comb./ Midland 79-82/ Northern Co's East.
Club Sponsors: T/T Print.   **Clubhouse:** Normal pub hours. Hot & cold food.
Record win: 11-1   **Record defeat:** 3-8
Capt. & P.o.Y. 92-93: Mark Townsend   **Top Scorers 92-93:** Paul Galloway & Steve McCabe, 11.
Club record scorer: Paul Acklam   **Club record appearances:** Neil Kellogg.
Hons: Northern Co's East Lg Div 1 Sth 83-84 (R-up 84-85, Div 2 Sth R-up 82-83), Derby Comb. 77-78 (R-up(10) 65-66 68-74 75-77 78-79, Lg Cup 68-69 75-76 (R-up 63-64 66-67), Midland Co's Lg Div 80-81 (Div 1 Cup 80-81), Derbys Snr Cup R-up 90-91, Derbys Div. Cup 73-74 (R-up 70-71 72-73), B E Webbe Cup R-up 88-89, FA Cup 3rd Qual. Rd 91-92.

GEDLING TOWN

Chairman: R A Ash   **President:** P M Robinson.
Secretary/Press Officer: Robert Huckerby, 30 Vernon Ave., Carlton, Nottingham NG4 3FX (0602 617942).
Manager: Dave Sands/ Cameron Holroyd   **Physio:** Pete Tyas
Doctor: Alan Scott   **Commercial Manager:** Dave Sands.
Ground: 'Riverside Ground', rear Ferry Boat Inn, Stoke Inn, Stoke Biddulph, Gedling, Nottm (0602 770258).
Directions: From Notts County F.C., A612 towards Southwell for 2 miles to Burton Joyce, Station Rd, then Stoke Lane. Ground rear of Ferry Boat Inn.
Capacity: 2,000   **Seats:** None   **Cover:** 500   **Floodlights:** Yes   **Founded:** 1989.
Colours: Red/black/red   **Change colours:** Yellow/blue/yellow   **Nickname:** None.
Previous Grounds: None   **Previous Leagues:** Notts Amateur.
Programme: 32 pages, 50p   **Programme Editor:** Secretary   **Club Shop:** No.
Midweek home matchday: Wednesday   **Sponsors:** Barrett Homes/ P R Scaffolding Ltd.
Record Gate: 250 v Arnold Town, Wakefield Floodlit Trophy 1992-93.
Record win: 5-0   **Clubhouse:** Matchdays only. Hot & cold food. Licensed bar.
Record scorer: Darren Terry   **Record appearances:** G Watson.
P.O.Y. 92-93: Mark Daley   **Captain 92-93:** G Watson
Top Scorer 92-93: Mark Daly 16, Michael Bradley 13.
Hons: Central Mids Lg Div 1 90-91 (Premier Div R-up 91-92, Wakefield Floodlit Trophy 92-93), Notts Amtr Lg 89-90 (Snr Cup R-up 89-90).

GLAPWELL

Secretary: Steven Brown, 2 Carter Lane West, Shirebrook, Mansfield NG20 8NA (0623 743661).
Manager: Roger Caton   **Ground:** Hall Corner, Park Ave., Glapwell, Chesterfield, Derbyshire (0623 812213).
Directions: A617 towards Mansfield from M1 jct 29, left at Young Vanish Inn after 2 miles, ground 100yds on right. From Mansfield on A617, right at Glapwell crossroads after 5 miles, ground 100 yds on right.
Colours: Black & white stripes/black/black   **Change colours:** Red/black/black.
Floodlights: Yes   **Midweek home matches:** Wednesday
Programme: 16 pages, 30p   **Programme Editor:** Brian Caton.
Top Scorers 92-93: David Waller 19, Peter Morgan 6, Steven Harris 6.

HARWORTH COLLIERY INSTITUTE

Chairman: Paul Wilson   **Vice Chairman:** Steve Owen   **President:** Bert Fielding.
Secretary: Tom Brogan, 30 Lindsey Road, Harworth, Doncaster, Sth Yorks DN11 8QH (0302 750132).
Manager: Allan Needham   **Physio:** Harry Farnsworth.
Press Officer: Mark Hickling   **Commercial Manager:** Allan Needham.
Ground: Recreation Ground, Scrooby Rd, Bircotes, Doncaster (0302 750614).
Directions: From Blyth take A614 for approx 2 miles, turn left at top of hill.
Capacity: 2,000   **Seats:** None   **Cover:** 750   **Founded:** 1931   **Floodlights:** Yes
Midweek matches: Wednesday   **Programme:** 16 pages, 30p (Editor: Steve Owen).
Colours: All red   **Change Colours:** White & blue.   **Nickname:** Reds.
Clubhouse: Matchdays & Sunday lunchtimes. Darts, pool, food
Record Gate: 350 v Congleton, 1989.   **Prev. Lges:** Yorks 46-50 77-82/ Northern Co's East
Cap. 92-93: Bob Needham **Top Scorer 92-93:** Neil Farrow 16, Lee Aulton 15   **P.o.Y. 92-93:** Lee Aulton
Hons: Wharncliffe Cup, Webbe Cup 86-87 87-88, Central Mids Lg 87-88 (R-up 86-87, F'lit Cup 91-92), Sheffield & Hallamshire Snr Cup SF 87-88

HEANOR TOWN

Secretary: Keith Costello, 45 Stainsby Avenue, Heanor, Derbyshire DE75 7EL (0773 719446).
Manager: Bill Brindley   **Ground:** The Town Ground, Mayfield Avenue, Heanor (0773 713742/715815).
Directions: North: M1 (J27), A608. South: M1 (J26), A610-A608
Capacity: 3,500   **Seats:** 200   **Cover:** 800   **Floodlights:** Yes
Programme: 20 pages, 30p   **Programme Editor:** Secretary   **Clubhouse:** Yes
Midweek matches: Wednesday   **Record Gate:** 6,411 v Carlisle, FA Cup 1958.
Colours: White/black/blue   **Change Colours:** All red
Previous Name: Heanor Athletic   **Top Scorers 92-93:** Graham Millington 32, Alan Park 24.
Previous League: Midland Co's 1894-97 98-1900 26-28 61-72 74-82/ Central Alliance 21-25 47-61/ West Mids (Regional) 72-74/ Northern Co's Lg East 82-86.
Hons: Central Mids Lg Cup R-up 86-87 92-93 (B E Webbe Removals Cup 88-89), West Mids Reg. Lg R-up 72-73; Midland Co's Lg R-up 65-66 67-68; Derbys Snr Cup(9) 1892-94 1946-47 65-69 70-71 78-79; FA Cup 1st Rd 58-59 63-64.

Borrowash Victoria F.C. 1992-93.

Gedling Town F.C. 1992-93. Back Row (L/R): Cameron Holroyd (Manager), Andy Elliott, John Sowter, Karl Steggles, Darren Abbott, Chris Hankbury, Richard Cutts, Dave Sands (Manager). Front: Shane Guyatt, Graham Harrodd, Frank Guddemi, Gary Watson (Captain), Jimmy Johnson, Mark Daley, Martin Knight, Miss Huckerby (Guest).

Heanor Town F.C., Supreme Division runners-up 1992-93. Photo - Gavin Ellis-Neville.

KIMBERLEY TOWN

Chairman: Russell Penney **Vice Chairman:** George Giddins **President:** Reg Izzard.
Secretary: Horace Hibbert, 62 Eastwood Road, Kimberley, Nottingham NG16 2HZ (0602 383382).
Manager: Graham Walker **Asst Manager:** Brian Harrison.
Press Officer: Gary Jayes **Commercial Manager:** Carl Parkin.
Ground: Stag Ground, Nottingham Road, Kimberley (0602 382788).
Directions: Through Nuthall from M1 jct 26 to Kimberley, ground signposted 150 yds after Stag Inn. 6 miles from Nottingham (BR). Trent Buses R11, R12, R13, 357 & 358 all stop outside ground.
Seats: None **Cover:** 150 **Capacity:** 2,500 **Floodlights:** Yes **Founded:** 1948
Colours: Royal/black/royal **Change colours:** White/black/white **Nickname:** Stags.
Previous Grounds: None **Previous Name:** Kimberley YMCA, 1948-56.
Sponsors: Electric Video Entertainments **Record Gate:** 1,122 v Eastwood, Mids Lg April 76.
Previous Leagues: Notts Amateur 48-55/ Central Alliance 55-66/ East Midlands 66-71/ Midland Counties 71-80/ Northern Counties (East) 80-86.
Programme: 20 pages, 20p
Midweek home matchday: Tuesday **Editor:** Neil Hibbert (0602 383382) **Club Shop:** No.
Record win: 8-1 **Clubhouse:** Matchdays and evenings, snacks available.
Record transfer fee paid: Nil **Record defeat:** 1-9 v Bridlington Trinity, 4/5/81.
Captain & P.o.Y.92-93: Allan Caurah **Received:** £2,000 for Andy Hill (Derby, Sept '81).
Club record scorer: Graham Cutts **Top Scorers:** Brett Marshall 15 (4 for Oakham), Darren Taylor 6
Club record appearances: Dennis Froggatt.
Hons: Notts Amateur Lg Div 1 54-55, Central Alliance Div 2 R-up 57-58).

KIVETON PARK

Secretary/Prog. Editor: John Holden, 184 Wales Road, Kiveton Park, Sheffield S31 8RE (0909 779508).
Manager: Brian Mellon **Ground:** Hard Lane, Kiveton Park, Sheffield (0836 690873).
Directions: Follow Worksop signs from M1 exit 31, left down Goosecar Lane after a quarter mile, over crossroads and ground is 200 yds on the right before rail bridge.
Capacity: 2,000 **Seats:** 200 **Floodlights:** Due 93-94. **Founded:** Early 1900s
Colours: Claret/sky/claret **Change colours:** Black & white stripes/black/black
Programme: 24 pages, 50. **Midweek home matchday:** Tuesday
Hons: Yorks Lg Div 2 77-78 **Prev. Lges:** Yorks 63-82/ Northern Co's East 82-91.
Top Scorers 92-93: Robert Palmer 25, Andy Fitzmaurice 15, Les Harris 15.

LONG EATON UNITED

Chairman: J C Fairley **Vice Chairman:** M Reynolds.
Secretary/Press Officer: G W Whitehead, 16 Holly Ave., Breaston, Derby DE72 3BG (0332 872849).
Manager: J Fairley Jnr/ B Webster **Coach:** J Fairley Jnr.
Physio: J Hopkins **Commercial Manager:** A Spray.
Ground: Grange Park, Station Road, Long Eaton, Nottingham (0602 735700).
Directions: From Nottingham, A52 to r'bout by 'Bardills Garden Centre', left onto B6003 to t-junction & lights, right into Station Rd, ground opposite Speedway Stadium. From M1 jct 25, A52 signed Nottingham, right onto B6003 at 1st r'bout then as above. 2 miles from Long Eaton (BR).
Seats: None **Cover:** 500 **Capacity:** 5,000 **Floodlights:** No **Founded:** 1956
Colours: All blue **Change:** Yellow/green/black. **Nickname:** Blues.
Previous Name: Long Eaton Town. **Record Gate:** 2,000 - 1973 FA Cup.
Previous Leagues: Central Alliance 59-61/ Midland Co's 61-82/ Northern Co's East 82-89.
Programme: 16-20 pages, 30p **Previous Grounds:** None. **Club Shop:** No.
Midweek home matchday: Tuesday **Sponsors:** M C Builders/ Railway Inn, Long Eaton.
Record transfer fee received: £5,000 for Anton Lambert (Scunthorpe), £3,000 for Garry Birtles (Nottm Forest).
Clubhouse: Open matchdays one hour either side of kick-off. Hot & cold drinks, confectionery, sausage rolls, burgers etc.
Captain 92-93: Steve Simmonds **Top Scorer 92-93:** Gary Weston 32, Stephen Wells 20.
Club Record Scorer: Gary Weston 32, Graham Walker 32.
Hons: Derbys Snr Cup 64-65 75-76, Midland Co's Lg R-up 76-77, Central Alliance Div South 58-59, Northern Co's (East) Div 1 South 84-85.

NETTLEHAM

Secretary: John Wilson, 21 Chaucer Drive, Lincoln LN2 4LN (0522 530566).
Manager: Paul Tittcomb **Ground:** Mulsanne Park, Field Close, Nettleham (0522 750007).
Directions: A46 approx. 3 miles north of Lincoln, right at Brown Cow Pub, proceed past Church 2nd turning on right.
Colours: All blue **Colours:** Red (white trim)/red/red **Floodlights:** Yes.
Midweek home matches: Tuesday **Programme:** 48 pages, 50p (Editor: Colin Benton).
Top Scorer 92-93: Gary Wells 12, James Rainey 7, Robin Smith 7.
Hons: Central Mids Lg Premier Division Cup R-up 87-88, Village Tphy, Nursing Cup, Kelly Read Cup, Blankney Hunt Cup, Lincoln & Dist. Amtr Cup R-up, Joe Miller Tphy(2).

OAKHAM UNITED

Manager: Steve Giles.
Secretary: Gary Leivers, 84 Mansfield Rd, Skegby, Sutton-in-Ashfield, Notts NG16 3EN (0623 517038).
Ground: Mansfield Hosiery Mills, Mansfield Rd, Sutton-in-Ashfield, Notts (0623 552376).
Directions: From M1 junction 28, A38 for Mansfield, ground half mile past Sutton on left. A617 from Mansfield towards M1. 3 miles from Alfreton/Mansfield Parkway (BR).
Capacity: 2,000 **Seats:** None **Cover:** 350 **Founded:** 1969 **Floodlights:** Yes
Midweek matches: Tuesday **Previous Lges:** Midland Co's/ Northern Co's East
Clubhouse: Every evening and weekend lunchtimes. Darts, pool, meals and hot snacks on matchdays.
Colours: White/navy/white **Change Colours:** Yellow/green/yellow
Programme: 28 pages, 30p **Programme Editor:** Bill Newson
Record Gate: 500 v Sutton Town, Midland Counties League 79-80.
Top Scorers 92-93: Wayne Bennett 8, Giulio Acierno 4.
Hons: Midland Co's Div 1 Lg Cup 79-80 (Div 1 R-up 79-80)

The Kimberley 'keeper is beaten by this Alan Park lob in the home tie against Heanor Town.

Priory (Eastwood) F.C. Photo - Gavin Ellis-Neville.

Graham Shaw of Priory (Eastwood) expertly tackles Graham Millington, but his side still lose 0-2 at title-chasing Heanor Town. Photo - Gavin Ellis-Neville.

PRIORY (EASTWOOD)

Secretary: Steve Wadsley, 3 Wainfleet Close, Ilkeston, Derbyshire DE7 9HR (0602 300422).
Manager: Kevin Smith
Ground: Birnam Park, off Eastwood By-Pass, Eastwood, Nottingham (0836 749883).
Directions: M1 junction 26 to Langley Mill, ground on left

Capacity: 2,000 **Seats:** 200	**Cover:** 200	**Founded:** 1967	**Floodlights:** Yes
Midweek matches: Tuesday	**Prog.:** 20 pages, 30p (Ed.: Reg Forde)		**Clubhouse:** No.
Colours: Red/black/black	**Change Colours:** Yellow/white/white		

Previous League: Notts Amtr/ Central Alliance/ East Mids Regional Alliance.
Club honours: Central Mids Lg Prem. Div 88-89 (Div 1 R-up 87-88), East Mids Regional Alliance Div 1, Notts Intermediate Cup 90-91(reserves).

ROSSINGTON

Chairman: Mr K Spencer
Sec./Press Off.: Ian Wilson, The Wickets, 3 Hollin Close, Rossington, Doncaster DN11 0XX (0302 867221).
Joint Managers: Mr I Wilson, Mr G Mountford. **Physio:** G Murden.
Ground: Welfare Ground, West End Lane, Rossington, Doncaster (0302 868272).
Directions: From south: M18 jct 1, A631 to Bawtry via Maltby/Tickhill, 1 mile out of Tickhill take B6463 to Rossington. From north: A638 out of Doncaster towards Bawtry, 4 miles from Racecourse to Rossington. In Rossington take road to colliery, over level crossing, ground on right after Sports Centre. 6 miles from Doncaster (BR) - buses run every 15 mins from Southern Bus Station (journey time 25 mins) - ground 5 mins walk from terminus.

Seats: None **Cover:** 200 **Capacity:** Unknown **Floodlights:** No **Founded:** 1990
Colours: Red/black/navy **Change colours:** White/black/sky **Club Shop:** No.
Previous Ground: Station FC: Tornedale School Field 73-85 (still used by Sunday & Youth sides).
Previous Leagues: Station FC: Bentley 73-79/ Donc. Snr 80-85. Haslam Sports: Local Sunday football.
Previous Names: Station Hotel 73-82/ Station 82-89. Merged with Haslam Sports/ Rossington Haslam 89-90.
Programme: 40+ pages, 50p **Programme Editor:** Secretary **Club Shop:** No.
Sponsors: Rossington Hall Investments **Record Gate:** 234 v Emley, Sheffield Snr Cup 12/12/92.
Nickname: The Locals **Midweek home matchday:** Wednesday
Record win: 14-1 (Sheff. Jnr Shield) **Record defeat:** 1-6 (Doncaster Senior Lge).
Clubhouse: Evenings & matchdays. Sandwiches, rolls, satellite TV, pool
Captain 92-93: J Whittle **Top Scorer 92-93:** Robert Nelson
Players' P.O.Y. 92-93: Lee Storey **Manager's P.O.Y. 92-93:** Nigel Feirn.
Club record scorer: Tommy Henderson **Club record appearances:** Tommy Henderson.
Hons: Central Mids Lg Div 1 87-88 (Prem Div R-up 92-93, Div 1 Cup R-up 86-87 87-88, Res. Div 1 Cup 87-88, Res. Div 2 Champs Cup R-up 86-87), Doncaster Snr Lg Div 2 R-up 85-86 (Div 1 Cup 87-88), Sheffield & Hallamshire Jnr Shield 83-84, Bentley Lg 77-78 78-79 (Lg Shield 74-75 78-79).

SANDIACRE TOWN

President: Albert Nelson **Chairman:** Les Fountain.
Secretary: Mel Williams, 38 Pasture Road, Stapleford NG9 8GL (0602 392415).
Manager: M O'Kane/ M Burrows **Coach:** B Bates/M Rose
Physio: L Fountain/ J Watson. **Press Officer:** A Walker. **Commercial Manager:** J Thornhill.
Ground: St Giles Park, Stanton Road, Sandiacre, Nottingham NG10 5EP (0602 392880).
Directions: M1 jct 25, follow signs to Saniacre passing Post House Hotel on right, straight over crossroads into Rushy Lane and towards Stanton, 1st right after 1000yds into Stanton Rd, ground at bottom after another 1000yds. Trent buses from Nottingham to Derby alighting at Sandiare Market Place - from traffic lights go along Canal Street (canal on your right) eventually past Comet (on right) then left into Church Street, follow to Stanton and ground is 200yds on right (total distance half mile).

Seats: None **Cover:** None **Capacity:** **Floodlights:** Due **Founded:** 1978
Cols: Red (white sleeves)/red/red **Change:** Blue (white sleeves)/sky/sky **Reformed:** 1991
Previous Grounds: None **Previous Leagues:** Midlands Regional Alliance.
Programme: 32 pages, 50p **Programme Editor:** Secretary **Club Shop:** No.
Sponsors: Nelson Tools (Nottm) **Midweek home matchday:** Tuesday **Nickname:** Saints.
Record win: 12-0 v Ilkeston Reserves **Record defeat:** 0-4 v Eastwood Town Reserves.
Clubhouse: Members club open 8-11pm daily, Sunday lunchtimes, and from 4.40pm Saturday matchdays. Cobs, crisps etc - mobile cafe provides hot food (burgers, hot dogs, peas) and hot & cold drinks on matchdays.
Record scorer: Mark Robinson 56 **Record appearances:** Mark Robinson 62.
Captain 92-93: Ged Le Blond **Top Scorer 92-93:** Dave King 48 **P.O.Y. 92-93:** Mark Robinson
Hons: Central Mids Lg Premier Div 92-93 (Lg Cup 92-93), Midlands Regional Alliance 91-92.

SHEFFIELD AURORA

President: P W F Wilson **Chairman:** G A Harper.
Secretary: D Brown, 139 Whitehill Rd, Brinsworth, Rotherham, Sth Yorks S60 5JQ (0709 363878).
Manager: John Eastwood **Coach:** S Berresford **Physio:** A Atkinson.
Press Officer: G B Stirling **Commercial Manager:** P Cresswell.
Ground: Aurora Sports & Social Club, Bawtry Rd, Brinsworth, Rotherham S60 5ND (0709 372613).
Directions: M1 jct 34 (Meadowhall), exit island onto A631 Bawtry Rd, ground 1 mile on right. Buses from Sheffield; 24 to Maltby or 19 to Brinsworth.

Capacity: 2,000 **Seats:** None **Cover:** 300 **Floodlights:** Yes **Founded:** 1964.
Colours: White/blue **Change Colours:** All red **Nickname:** Aurora
Previous Grounds: None **Previous Lges:** Matchard/ Whitbread Co. Senior.
Previous Name: Crookes **Rec. Gate:** 650 v Worksop, Sheffield Snr Cup 90-91
Programme: 10 pages, 50p **Programme Editor:** P Cresswell **Club Shop:** No.
Club Sponsors: Aurora Plc **Midweek home matchday:** Tuesday or Friday.
Record win: 11-0 v Blidworth (H), Central Mids Lg 90-91 **Record defeat:** 1-6
Clubhouse: Normal licensing hours. Snacks and buffets available.
Club record scorer: S Marshall **Club record appearances:** John Eastwood.
Captain 92-93: S Berresford **P.O.Y. 92-93:** Andy Cutts.
Top Scorer 92-93: Anthony Walker 13, Sean Needham 6, David Jacques 6.
Hons: Centrals Midlands Lg Wakefield Floodlit Cup 90-91, Sheffield & Hallamshire Snr Cup R-up 85-86, Hatchard Lg Div 1 83-83, Whitbread Co. Snr Lg 83-84 (Lg Cup 85-86).

SHIREBROOK TOWN

Secretary: Steve Wall, 26 Carter Lane West, Shirebrook, Mansfield, Notts NG20 8NA (0623 747638).
Manager: Paul Elrick/ Neil McAllister.   **Ground:** BRSA Ground, Langwith Rd, Mansfield (0623 742535).
Directions: M1 jct 29, A617 to Mansfield, 2.5 miles, B6407 Shirebrook, through town to Langwith Rd. Bus 81 from Chesterfield or 23 from Mansfield.
Capacity: 2,000   **Seats:** 120   **Cover:** 200   **Floodlights:** Yes   **Founded:** 1985
Cols: Red & black stripes/black/red   **Change Colours:** White/white/black
Prev. Name: Shirebrook Colliery 85-93   **Programme:** 28 pages, 30p (Editor: Secretary).
Midweek home matches: Tuesday   **Clubhouse:** Normal licensing hours.

STAVELEY MINERS WELFARE

Secretary: John Wilmot, 12 Winster Rd, Staveley, Chesterfield, Derbyshire S43 3NJ (0246 340636).
Ground: Inkersall, Staveley, Derbyshire (0246 471441).
Colours: Blue & black stripes/black/black   **Floodlights:** Yes
Midweek home matches: Wednesday   **Previous League:** Whitbread County Snr (pre-1993)
Programme: 12 pages, 30p   **Programme Editor:** Secretary.

Rossington F.C., Premier Division runners-up 1992-93. Back Row (L/R): Joey Whittle, Brendan McGrane, Darren Swift, Steve Lodge, Michael Brammall, Kevin Simpson, Chris Simpson. Front: Ian Wilson (Manager), Robert Nelson, Lee Storey, Gordon Henderson, David Clark, Nigel Feirn, Colin Holvey, Gary Mountford (Player-Manager).

Glapwell F.C. pictured before entertaining Arnold Town on Saturday 5th May. Glapwell could not stop Arnold clinching the title but, with some promising young players coming through their ranks, they enjoyed a much better season than in 1991-92 when they finished bottom. Photo - Colin Stevens.

PREMIER DIVISION CLUBS 1993-94

ASKERN MINERS WELFARE

Secretary: Miss Lynn Sudworth, 12 Marlborough Rd, Askern, Doncaster DN6 0LN (0302 712814).
Ground: Doncaster Road, Askern, Doncaster (0302 700957).
Floodlights: No   **Colours:** White (black stripes)/white/black
Midweek home matches: Tuesday or Thursday
Programme: 20 pages, 50p   **Programme Editor:** Ron Poundall.
Top Scorers: Tony Hattersley 26, Mark Illman 12.

BIWATER

President: B W S Nuttall, MBE JP   **Chairman:** P Owen   **Vice Chairman/Asst Mgr:** A Bramley
Secretary: Alan Kilcline, 4 Deerpark Crescent, Wingerworth, Chesterfield S42 6XF (0246 276707).
Manager/Coach: Phil Tingay   **Physio:** D Stoppard
Press Officer: D Jones   **Commercial Manager:** R Haney.
Ground: John's Street, off Market Street, Clay Cross.   **Directions:** A61 Chesterfield-Derby road, turn onto A6175 (signed M1) in Clay Cross Centre, then north into Brassington Street and follow to ground.
Seats: None   **Cover:** 150   **Capacity:**   **Floodlights:** No   **Reformed:** 1952
Colours: Red/white/red   **Change colours:** Blue/black/black.   **Nickname:** The Works
Previous Grounds: None   **Previous Name:** Clay Cross Works 1952-1988.
Prev. Lges: Ripley & Dist./ Chesterfield & Dist./ Sutton & Skegby/ Matlock & Dist./ East Mids/ Derbys Snr.
Programme: 50p   **Programme Editor:** P Owen   **Club Shop:** No.
Club Sponsors: Biwaters Plc   **Record Gate:** 364 v Matlock, Derbyshire Snr Cup.
Midweek matchday: Mon or Wed   **Clubhouse:** Open matchdays only.
Club record scorer: G Simpson   **Club record appearances:** Bobby Wilks 350.
Captain 92-93: R Fox   **P.O.Y. 92-93:** P Gould.
Top Scorer 92-93: Nick Tobin 15, David Bradley 14.
Hons: F.A. Vase QF, Central Midlands Lg Premier Div 79-80 (Div 1 83-84, Div 1 Cup 88-89 (R-up 89-90), Reserve Div 1 88-89 (R-up 91-92)). *Plus virtually every major honour in above Leagues.*

BLACKWELL MINERS WELFARE

Secretary: Julian Riley, 22 Glinton Ave., Blackwell, Alfreton, Derbys DE55 5HD (0773 862411).
Ground & Directions: Welfare Ground, Primrose Hill, Blackwell, Derbyshire DE55 5JE. (0773 811295). A38 towards Mansfield from M1 jct 38, left onto B6406 after half a mile, left after a mile, ground on left.
Cols: Red & white stripes/red/red   **Change colours:** All silver grey.   **Floodlights:** No.
Midweek home matchdays: Wednesday   **Programme:** 28 pages, 50p (Editor: Secretary).
Top Scorers 92-93: Mark Dowdall 9, Julian Riley 7.

DERBY CARRIAGE & WAGON (RECKITTS)

Chairman: Lee Astle   **Joint Managers:** Stewart Woodings, Mark Webster.
Secretary: Mrs P Webster, 20 Strathmore, Alvaston, Derby (0332 753059).
Coach: M Bentley   **Physio:** M Ward.
Ground: Carriage & Wagon Welfare, Longbridge Lane, off Ascot Drive, Derby (0332 571376).
Directions: M1 jct 25, A52 towards Derby, A5111 Raynesway (ring-road) for about 3 miles, right at 1st island (A6 - city centre), left at 2nd island into Ascot Drive, Longbridge Lane 1st right after filling station, ground at bottom.
Seats: None   **Cover:** None   **Capacity:** 600   **Floodlights:** No   **Founded:** 1935
Colours: Yellow & black   **Change colours:** Blue & yellow   **Nickname:** Wagon
Sponsors: Reckitt & Colman   **Previous Grounds:** None.
Previous Leagues: Derby Amtr/ Derby Comb./ Derbys Snr/ Central Alliance/ East Mids Regional.
Programme: 32 pages, 30p   **Editor:** Mick Allen (0332 702198)   **Club Shop:** No.
Midweek home games: Mon or Wed   **Clubhouse:** Normal hours. Hot pies etc available.
Captain 92-93: Lee Astle   **Top Scorer 92-93:** Jon Gormley 13, Gary Ward 11
P.O.Y. 92-93: Wayne Thompson
Hons: Central Alliance 77-78, East Mids Regional Lg R-up 83-84 (Div 1 81-82), Central Mids Lg Premier Div R-up 85-86 (Premier Div Cup R-up 85-86, Div 1 Cup 89-90 (R-up 90-91), Prem Div Sportsmanship Cup 85-86), Derby Floodlit Cup R-up 85-86, Derby Divisional Cup (Sth) R-up 83-84.

DERBY ROLLS ROYCE

Secretary: Michael Lomax, 47 Cleveland Avenue, Caddesden, Derby DE2 6SB (0332 664183).
Manager: D Tice   **Ground:** Rolls Royce Rec. Society, Moor Lane, Derby (0332 249167).
Directions: Derby ringroad, Osmaston Park Road, Moor Lane; ground adjacent to Swimming Baths.
Cols: Blue & white stripes/blue/blue   **Change:** Black & white stripes/black/black
Floodlights: No   **Midweek home matchday:** Wedneshay
Programme: 8-12 pages, 50p   **Programme Editor:** Paul McCracken.
Top Scorers 92-93: Peter Boyce 7, Anthony Burns 7.

KINGSTON

Secretary: Derek Smith, 17a Borough Road, South Cade, Brough, North Humberside HU15 2BU (0430 422494).
Ground: Kingston School, Brough, Hull, North Humberside.
Cols: All claret   **Previous Leagues:** None   **Founded:** 1993   **Floodlights:** No
Midweek home matchday: Wednesday   **Programme:** 12 pages, 30 (Editor: Secretary)

MICKLEOVER ROYAL BRITISH LEGION

President: A N Waplington   **Chairman:** N L Appleby
Secretary: Ray Taylor, 15 Inglwood Avenue, Mickleover, Derby DE3 5RT (0332 515047).
Manager: Tony Shaw   **Assistant Manager:** Richard Walshe.
Ground: Ypres Lodge, Western Rd, Mickleover (0332 513548).
Colours: Red/black/red   **Midweek home matchday:** Tuesday   **Founded:** 1945
Previous Leagues: Derbys Sunday/ East Mids/ Derby Premier.   **Floodlights:** No.
Previous Grounds: Ypres Lodge 45-91/ Gresley Rovers FC 91-92/ Belper Town FC 92-93.
Programme: 28 pages, 30p   **Top Scorers 92-93:** Stephen Brown 11, Lee Thomas 6.
Hons: Centrals Mids Lg Premier Div 89-90 90-91 (R-up 88-89), Lg Cup 88-89 89-90), East Mids Lg 80-81, Derbys Divisional Cup South 80-81.

MICKLEOVER SPORTS

Secretary: Derek Hewitt, 1 Milton Close, Mickleover, Derbyshire DE3 5QN (0332 515295).
Ground: Mickleover Sports Ground, Station Rd, Mickleover, Derby (0332 521167).
Midweek matchdays: Tuesday   **Colours:** Red & black stripes/black/red.
Programme: 28 pages   **Programme Editor:** Tony Shaw   **Floodlights:** No.

NEWHALL UNITED

Chairman: Sid Gutteridge
Secretary: David Wain, 26 Willow Drive, Newhall, Swadlincote, Derbys DE11 0NW (0283 225188).
Manager: TBA   **Physio:** Melvyn Mole & Bob Evans.
Ground: Hewfields Ground, St Johns Drive, Newhall, Swadlincote (0283 551029).
Directions: Turn off A50 (Burton to Ashby-de-la-Zouch) down into Newhall at Chesterfield Arms, to bottom and turn right into Main Street. Left at Lamb Inn into Oversetts Rd, 2nd right into John Street, left into St Johns Drive, ground on left.
Seats: 80   **Cover:** 400   **Capacity:** 2,000   **Floodlights:** Due 93-94.
Cols: Blue & white hoops/blue/white   **Change colours:** All white.   **Nickname:** Blues
Programme: 24 pages, 25p   **Programme Editor:** Nigel Tilley (0283 211207)
Club Sponsors: British Coal (Opencast)   **Record Gate:** 2,000 v Burton Albion, FA Cup.
Midweek home matchday: Wednesday   **Previous Leagues:** Central Alliance/ E Mids Regional.
Clubhouse: Brand new. Brick built out of proceeds of landsale.   **Club Shop:** No.
Captain 92-93: Kevin Joyce   **P.O.Y. 92-93:** Neil Jenkins (players') Neil Hall (Mgr's)
Top Scorers 92-93: Kevin Joyce 17, Lee Bradley 16.
Club record scorer: John Wain, 506   **Club record appearances:** John Wain, 347.
Hons: Derbys Prem. Lg 73-74 78-79 (Lg Cup 72-73), Bass Vase 73-74, Mavis Marsland Bowl R-up 91-92.

NORTON WOODSEATS

Secretary: Kevin Murphy, 11 Victoria Str., Dronfield, Sheffield S18 6PL (0246 411523).
Manager: Brian Thackeray/ Kevin Murphy.
Ground & Directions: Coach & Horses Ground, Stubley Hollow, Sheffield Road, Dronfield (0246 413269-matchdays). Turn for Dronfield off A61 Chesterfield/Sheffield road, ground on way out of Dronfield opposite Coach & Horse pub.
Colours: Blue/whiteblue   **Change:** Yellow/blue/yellow.   **Floodlights:** Due
Midweek home matchday: Tuesday   **Prev. Names:** Norton Woodseats Amtr/ Dronfield Utd.
Previous Leagues: Yorks 49-82/ Northern Co's East 82-91.
Programme: 20 pages, 50p   **Programme Editor:** David Taylor (0742 649754).

NUTHALL

President: Bill Smith   **Chairman:** A Farmer   **Vice Chairman:** R Naylor.
Secretary: Tony Benniston, 117 Broad Lane, Brinsley, Nottm NG16 5BU (0773 712350).
Manager/Coach: G Webster   **Asst Mgr:** M Cook   **Physio:** A Gunn.
Press Officer: K Robinson   **Commercial Manager:** J Heading.
Ground & Directions: Basil Russell Playing Fields, Maple Drive, Nuthall, Nottingham (0602 384765). M1 jct 26/ A610 southbound left southbound, right northbound.
Seats: None   **Cover:** 50   **Floodlights:** No   **Founded:** 1976   **Nickname:** Larks
Colours: Sky/navy/sky   **Change colours:** All yellow.
Previous Grounds: None   **Previous Leagues:** East Midlands Regional.
Programme: 30 pages, 50p   **Editor:** Mr P Taylor (0602 507071)   **Club Shop:** No.
Clubhouse: Open matchdays. Food & drinks from one hour prior to kick-off.
Club record scorer: J Paxton   **Club record appearances:** L Wild.
Captain 92-93: S Whylky   **P.O.Y. 92-93:** P Doleman.
Top Scorer 92-93: Steve Carruthers 8, Glynn Hague 7.
Hons: Central Mids Lg Snr Div 84-85 (Premier Div Cup R-up 84-85, Div 1 Cup SF 89-90), East Mids Regional Lg 82-83 83-84 (R-up 79-80 80-81, Div 1 R-up 78-79, Lg Cup 81-82 (R-up 79-80 83-84)), Notts Intermediate Cup 79-80 (Snr Cup SF 84-85, Jnr Cup R-up 78-79 (SF 79-80), Minor Cup 82-83), Central Alliance Div 1 R-up 79-80.

RADFORD

Secretary: Chris Daykin, 22 Balmoral Grove, Hucknall, Nottm.
Manager: Brian Mantle   **Ground:** Radford Road, Radford, Nottm (0602 423250).
Directions: A610 Alfreton Road, left just into Bobbersmill Road, ground at top on right.
Cols: Claret & blue/blue/blue   **Change:** White/black/black   **Floodlights:** No
Midweek home matchdays: Tuesday   **Programme:** 16 pages, 30p (Editor: Secretary).
Previous name: Radford Olympic.   **Hons:** Derbys Prem. Lg Div 1 R-up 84-85.
Top Scorers 92-93: Amjad Khan 20, Michael Wilson 11.

SHARDLOW ST JAMES

President: D Irving   **Chairman:** W Shaw.
Secretary: S R Symcox, 22 West End Drive, Shardlow, Derby DE7 2GY (0332 792733).
Manager: Graham Proudler   **Asst Manager:** J Beard   **Physio:** D Spencer.
Ground: The Wharf, Shardlow, Derby.
Directions: A6 Derby/Leicester, 6 miles out of Derby at Shardlow take next left after Shardlow church (on right), ground 100yds on left.
Colours: Sky/navy/sk   **Club Sponsor:** Mr D Irving.   **Nickname:** Saints
Previous Lges: Derby Amtr/ Derby Welfare/ Derby Snr/ Derby Premier/ Central Mids/ Midland Regional Alliance.
Previous Grounds: Coronation Field, Shardlow/ Willn Lane, Shardlow.
Programme: 20 pages, 50p   **Programme Editor:** Kevin Tristam   **Club Shop:** No.
Nickname: Saints   **Clubhouse:** No   **Floodlights:** No.
Club record scorer: W Shaw   **Club record appearances:** Rob Green.
Capt. 92-93: C Hill   **Top Scorer 92-93:** Martin Curley 11, Mark Foote 7   **P.O.Y. 92-93:** M Keogh
Hons: Central Mids Lg Div 1 R-up 84-85 (Div 1 Cup R-up 84-85), Mids Regional Alliance 90-91 (Lg Cup 90-91, Div 1 89-90, Jnr Cup 89-90), Derbyshire Divisional Cup (Sth) R-up 90-91, Derbyshire Premier Lg Premier Div Cup 78-79 (Snr Div Cup 73-74, Reserve Div R-up 80-81, Reserve Div Cup 79-80), Derby & District Comb. Div 2 70-71 (Div 5 68-69 (R-up 67-68), Div 3 Cup 69-70, Div 5 Cup 68-69).

SOUTH NORMANTON ATHLETIC

Chairman: Terry Ball   **President:** Monsieur A Thibaudeau. **Manager:** Trevor Wasp.
Secretary: Peter Kane, 3 Mansfield Road, South Normanton, Derby DE55 2ER (0773 580637).
Asst Mgr: Chris Lee   **Coach:** Jim McGowan.   **Physio:** Terry Hodson.
Ground & Directions: South Normanton Miners Welfare, Lees Lane, South Normanton, Derby (0773 581491, club-811396). B6109 from from M1 exit 28, right after 1 mile at Texaco garage, left at The Clock pub, ground at bottom of Lees Lane.
Colours: Yellow/blue/yellow   **Midweek home matchdays:** Tuesday   **Floodlights:** No
Programme: 60-72 pages, 50p   **Programme Editor:** Kevin Miles   **Cover:** Yes.
Hons: Alfreton & Dist. Sunday Lg 86-87 (Div 2 83-84, Div 3 R-up 80-81, Suppl. Shield 84-85, W L Screen Bowl 86-87), Mansfield Sunday Lg Prem. Div Cup 88-89 (Div 1 R-up 87-88).

STANTON (ILKESTON)

Secretary: Mrs Pat Barksby, 2 Witham Close, Tapton, Chesterfield S41 0UH (0246 558129).
Manager: Martin Cooper.   **Ground & Directions:** Hallam Fields Sports Ground, Stanton Club, Hallam Fields, Nr Ilkeston, Derbys (0602 323244). From South, M1 (J25) to Nottm, 1st r-about turn left. From North, M1 (J26), Ilkeston, through to to Hallam Fields.
Capacity: 2,000   **Seats:** None   **Cover:** 300   **Floodlights:** No   **Founded:** 1921.
Cols: Blue & white stripes/blue/blue   **Change Colours:** Yellow/black/blue
Programme: 28 pages, 50p   **Programme Editor:** Graham Barksby.
Previous Leagues: Central Alliance 55-58/ Derbyshire Premier/ East Mids Regional Alliance.
Previous Name: Stanton Works.   **Midweek home matchday:** Tuesday
Hons: Central Mids Lg Prem. Div 85-86 86-87 (Prem. Div Cup 85-86).

THORNE COLLIERY

Secretary: Glyn Jones, Democratic Club & Institute, Southfield Rd, Thorne, Doncaster DN8 5NS (0405 816329).
Ground: Miners Welfare Ground, Southfield Rd, Thorne, Doncaster.
Cols: Blue & white stripes/blue/blue   **Prev. Lge:** Doncaster Snr (pre-1993)   **Floodlights:** No.
Programme Editor: Secretary   **Midweek home matchday:** Wednesday

NETZ MIDLAND REGIONAL ALLIANCE

MATLOCK UNITED'S LATE RUN SECURES TITLE

Season 1992-93 was a remarkable one for the Netz Midlands Regional Alliance as it was a very competitive one. Matlock United finally won the title, but going into the Quarter-Finals of the League Challenge Cup, which they lost 0-1 to Belper Town Reserves, they were more concerned about relegation than championships. However, following that defeat they embarked on a run which saw them win fifteen out of seventeen matches, and one of the two defeats was in the Derbyshire North Divisional Cup final. To show the strength of the League, Normanton Athletic finished as runners-up in the Premier Division and won the Derbyshire South Divisional Cup beating third placed Mackworth United in the final. Fourth placed Belper Town Reserves won the Belper Nursing Cup after losing out to local rivals Belper United in the Challenge Cup final which was played in front of a crowd of 400. Actually, crowds were up throughout the League with Ilkeston Town Reserves regurlarly playing in front of 200 plus, and the Belper teams frequently topping the ton figure.

Pinxton, after missing out on promotion last season, made no mistake this time, an eleven point cushion meaning the title was won long before the end of the season. There was, however, a real dogfight for the runners-up spot. Slack & Parr eventually took it through a last match win while results elsewhere went in their favour. Both Mackworth United Reserves and Royal Crown '86 slipped up when a win would have put them second. Royal Crown '86 did have the consolation of winning the Junior Cup, but for the team, Kirk Hallam Castle, they beat in the final, it was a disappointing end to the season; they led the division for a long time before losing form and finishing with nothing.

When a team scores 141 goals and loses only once, you would think that they would be runaway champions. Well, Slack & Parr Reserves won Division Two, but it was not confirmed until the penultimate match of the season such was the challenge of runners-up Brailsford Reserves and third-placed Belper United Reserves. The latter missed out on promotion, and indeed the latter part of the season was an anti-climax as they had led their own first team in the semi-final of the Challenge Cup. A late equaliser followed by a last minute winner virtually signalled the end of their season as a winning force.

Mention of Belper United leads nicely onto the goalkeeping situation they and Belper Town experienced at the end of the season. When the Town found themselves without a custodian in the Northern Counties (East) League, United's Neil Sparham stepped in to fill the gap. Fortunately, United had kept his registration because when all their other keepers were injured, Neil returned to play in the Challenge Cup final, against - Belper Town Reserves.

Looking ahead to 1993-94, Ashfield United Reserves join the Premier Division with Brailsford 'A' and Petersham United coming into Division Two. Leaving the League are Ruddington Village, Selston, and Royal Crown '86.

David Robinson

PREM. DIVISION	P	W	D	L	F	A	PTS
Matlock United	30	20	2	8	72	43	62
Normanton Athletic	30	18	6	6	76	34	60
Mackworth Utd	30	18	4	8	80	39	58
Belper Town Res.	30	17	4	9	84	55	55
Belper United	30	15	7	8	82	51	52
Butterley Brick	30	14	5	11	53	54	47
Ripley Town	30	14	5	11	47	48	47
Brailsford	30	13	7	10	56	48	46
Ilkeston Town Res.	30	11	11	8	60	45	44
Alfreton Town Res.	30	11	3	16	56	66	36
Rowsley '86	30	9	7	14	53	73	34
Riddings St James	30	8	9	13	43	69	33
Selston	30	8	5	17	56	78	29
Eastwood Town Res	30	9	2	19	62	87	29
Ruddington Village	30	7	4	19	45	90	25
Holbrook Miners W.	30	4	7	19	30	75	19

DIVISION ONE	P	W	D	L	F	A	PTS
Pinxton	26	19	3	4	73	38	60
Slack & Parr	26	14	7	5	72	38	49
Mackworth Utd Res.	26	15	3	8	71	49	48
Royal Crown '86	26	15	3	8	65	50	48
Swanwick P'rich Rd	26	13	6	7	74	50	45
Kirk Hallam Castle	26	12	8	6	56	35	44
Littleover Ivanhoe	26	12	5	9	58	47	41
Gotham United	26	9	4	13	46	53	31
Draycott	26	8	5	13	60	73	29
Matlock United Res.	26	6	9	11	37	65	27
Holbrook St Michaels	26	8	2	16	56	59	26
Ripley Town Res.	26	7	5	14	51	68	26
West Hallam	26	5	5	16	29	64	20
New Eastwood	26	6	1	19	34	93	19

DIVISION TWO	P	W	D	L	F	A	PTS
Stock & Parr Res.	26	23	2	1	141	15	71
Brailsford Res.	26	21	3	2	95	30	66
Belper United Res.	26	21	1	4	115	32	64
Draycott Res.	26	13	6	7	69	47	45
Swanwick P. Rd Res.	26	13	4	9	67	47	43
Derby Arms	26	13	3	10	78	47	42
Ripley Town 'A'	26	11	5	10	70	50	38
Holbrook MW Res.	26	12	2	12	66	52	38
Rolls Royce & Assoc.	26	11	4	11	56	51	37
Ilkeston Mitre	26	5	5	16	40	98	20
Riddings S.J. Res.	26	5	4	17	40	119	19
Holbrook S.M. Res.	26	5	3	18	48	121	18
Colmanhay	26	4	1	21	32	133	13
New Eastwood Res.	26	1	5	20	27	102	8

Premier Division Constitution 93-94 (*Ground Addresses italicised*):
Alfreton Town Reserves (see page 859), Ashfield United Reserves (see page 929), Belper Town Reserves (see page 929), Belper United (*Whitemoor Hall, Whitemoor Lane, Belper*), Brailsford (*Osmaston Polo Ground, Osmaston, nr Ashbourne*), Butterley Brick (*Waingroves Brickworks, Peasehill Rd, Ripley*), Eastwood Town Reserves (see page 865), Holbrook Miners Welfare (*Shaw Lane, Holbrook, Derby (0332 880259)*), Ilkeston Town Reserves (see page 681), Mackworth United (*Mackworth Tertiary College, Prince Charles Ave., Mackworth, Derby*), Matlock United (*Cavendish Rd PF, Matlock*), Normanton Athletic (*Alvaston Park, Meadow Lane, Alvaston, Derby (0332 571221)*), Ridding St James (*The Park, West Str., Riddings, Derbyshire (Leabrook 607907)*), Ripley Town (*Derbyshire Police HQ, Coach Rd, Nottingham Rd, Ripley) Tockington, Bristol*), Rowsley '86 (*Rowsley Rec*), Slack & Parr (*Long Lane, Kegworth, Derby (0509 674206)*).

Division One Constitution 93-94: Brailsford Reserves, Draycott (*Gertrude Rd, Draycott, Derby*), Gotham United (*Memorial PF, Nottingham Rd, Derby*), Holbrook St Michaels (*Holbrook Park, Mellors Lane, Holbrook, Derbyshire*), Kirk Hallam Castle (*East Mids Electricity Spts Ground, High Lane East, West Hallam, Derbys (0602 329982)*), Littleover Ivanhoe (*King George V PF, off Carlisle Ave., Littleover, Derby (0332 766076)*), Mackworth Utd Reserves, Matlock Utd Reserves, New Eastwood (*Hall Park Sch., Mansfield Rd, Eastwood, Notts*), Ripley Town Reserves, Selston (*Selston Parish Hall, Mansfield Rd, Selston, Notts (0773 810411)*), Slack & Parr Reserves, Swanwick Pentrich Road (*Highfield Rd, Swanwick, Derbyshire*), West Hallam (*Beech Lane Rec, West Hallam*).

Division Two Constitution 93-94: Belper Utd Reserves, Brailsford 'A', Cotmanhay (*Pavilion Rd, Cotmanhay, Ilkeston*), Derby Arms, Draycott Reserves, Holbrook Miners Welfare Reserves, Holbrook St Michaels Reserves, Ilkeston Mitre, New Eastwood Reserves, Petersham United, Ridding St James Reserves, Ripley Town 'A', Rolls Royce & Associates (*Breaston Park, off Longmoor Lane, Breaston, Derbys*), Swanwick Pentrich Road Reserves.

LINCOLNSHIRE LEAGUE

	P	W	D	L	F	A	PTS
Humberside United	36	30	4	2	113	28	*92
Hykeham Town	36	29	1	6	100	38	88
Appleby Frod. Ath.	36	22	5	9	103	49	+68
Immingham B.W.	36	17	11	8	79	51	&64
Lincoln Utd Colts	36	19	5	12	82	61	63
Bottesford Town	36	17	8	11	83	62	60
Wyberton	36	17	5	14	88	68	56
Skegness Town	36	15	5	16	84	89	50
Sleaford Town	36	12	9	15	57	57	45
Ruston Sports	36	13	6	17	60	64	45
Louth United Res.	36	12	9	15	66	77	45
Boston Res.	36	12	9	15	59	75	45
Spilsby Town	36	12	8	16	56	75	44
Grimsby Ross Amtr	36	12	5	18	64	88	x44
Louth Old Boys	36	11	8	17	51	68	41
Nettleham Res.	36	11	5	20	59	87	38
Lincoln Athletic	36	10	6	20	52	87	36
Mablethorpe Ath.	36	8	6	22	56	101	30
Eaton Hall College	36	3	6	27	36	112	15

* - 2pts deducted
+ - 3pts deducted
& - 2pts awarded
x - 3pts awarded

Constitution 93-94 (*Ground Addresses italicised*):
Appleby Frodingham (*Brumby Hall, Ashby Rd, Scunthorpe (0724 843024)*), Boston Reserves (see page 658), Boston United Reserves (see page 838), Bottesford Town (*Ontario Rd, Bottesford, Scunthorpe (0724 871883)*), Grimsby Amateurs (formerly Grimsby Ross Amateurs)(*Ross Spts, Weelsby Rd, Grimsby (0472 356952)*), Hykeham Town (*Memorial PF, North Hykeham*), Hykeham United (formerly Lincoln Athletic)(*Fen Lane, North Hykeham*), Immingham Blossom Way Sports (*Blossom Way, Immingham (0469 572612)*), Immingham Town Reserves (see page 941), Limestone Rangers, Lincoln Moorlands (*Moorlands Spts Ground, Newark Rd, Lincoln (0522 520184)*), Lincoln United Colts (see page 922), Louth Old Boys (*London Rd, Louth (0507 603928)*), Louth United Amateurs (formerly Louth Utd Reserves - see page 941), Retford B.R.S.A. (formerly Eaton Hall College)(*British Rail Ground, Retford*), Ruston Sports (*R.M.S.C. Club, Newark Rd, Lincoln (0522 680057)*), Skegness Town (*Burgh Rd, Skegness (0754 4385)*), Sleaford Town (*Boston Rd, Sleaford (0529 306959)*), Spilsby Town (*Ancaster Ave., Spilsby*), Wyberton (*Causeway, Wyberton (0205 353526)*).

NOTTS FOOTBALL ALLIANCE

President: R.J.Leafe
Chairman: A.Wright
General Secretary: E.R.Rudd,
18 Whitegate Vale, Clifton Estate, Nottingham.
Treasurer: R.Hepworth

LAST GAME WINNERS

All three league championships, were won on their last match of the season. In the Senior Division, Clipstone Miners Welfare clinched the title by beating Pelican at home by 3-0. Clipstone Miners Welfare also reached the final of the League Senior Cup where they went down to GPT by 4-0.

GPT had another great season in winning the League Senior Cup and finishing runners-up in the league, one point behind Clipstone Miners Welfare. Radcliffe Olympic and John Player, the bottom two, are relegated to Division One with Sneinton and Wollaton being promoted to the Senior Division.

In Division One, Sneinton and Wollaton were leading the table for most of the season. Sneinton, requiring one point in their last game, made a 0-0 draw with Southwell City to win the Championship by one point. Credit must go to Wollaton. By gaining promotion from Division Two in their first season, they have now completed a double by gaining promotion to the Senior Division for the 1993/94 season. Rainworth Miners Welfare Reserves and Clifton All Whites have been relegated to Division Two.

Division Two again was decided on the last game of the season. Linby C W led the table from the beginning of the season, but Ollerton Bevercotes in their last few matches took the Championship to finish four points clear.

With the Division Two being a team short the two bottom clubs, Carlton Athletic Reserves and Basford United Reserves were removed from the competition, and replaced by Boots Athletic Reserves, Pelican Reserves, and Welbeck CW.

The Nottinghamshire Senior Cup was won by Arnold Town who beat Rainworth Miners Welfare by 3-1. Praise must go to Rainworth Miners Welfare on reaching the Notts Senior Cup Final.

The Nottinghamshire Intermediate Cup Final was an all-Notts Football Alliance affair with Hucknall Rolls Royce Welfare Reserves beating Radcliffe Olympic by 4-3.

This year it has been a very tight and successful season, the League discipline cases have been very low, although the Nottinghamshire Football Association disipline has increased.

E.R.Rudd (Secretary).

SENIOR DIVISION	P	W	D	L	F	A	PTS
Clipstone MW	30	19	6	5	73	31	63
GPT FC	30	18	8	4	80	35	62
Worthington S.	30	18	4	8	54	39	58
Dunkirk FC	30	17	2	11	82	62	53
Rainworth MW	30	15	8	7	48	37	53
Boots Athletic	30	14	5	11	67	47	47
Hucknall R.R.Welf	30	14	5	11	63	52	47
Notts Police	30	12	7	11	47	41	43
Pelican FC	30	13	4	13	46	53	43
Ruddington FC	30	9	8	13	43	60	35
Greenwood M'dows	30	9	7	14	33	51	34
Thoresby CW	30	7	11	12	49	53	32
Bulwell FV	30	7	10	13	27	50	31
Cotgrave MW	30	7	5	18	47	77	26
Radcliffe Olympic	30	7	3	20	47	75	24
John Player FC	30	6	3	21	44	87	21

DIVISION ONE	P	W	D	L	F	A	PTS
Sneinton FC	30	23	4	3	73	34	73
Wollaton FC	30	22	6	2	97	33	72
Keyworth United	30	18	5	7	68	35	59
Basford United	30	17	5	8	59	32	56
Gedling CW	30	16	6	8	91	45	54
Worthington S.R.	30	14	7	9	74	65	49
Southwell City	30	14	6	10	47	35	48
Hucknall RR.W.R.	30	11	5	14	51	58	38
City Sher Hospital	30	10	8	12	59	76	38
Awsworth Villa	30	10	6	14	66	65	36
Carlton Athletic	30	9	5	16	52	64	32
Clipstone MW Res	30	8	7	15	43	61	31
Bilsthorpe CW	30	7	5	18	47	69	26
Stapleford Villa	30	7	5	18	37	67	26
Rainworth MW Res	30	5	5	20	38	96	20
Clifton A W	30	4	5	21	40	97	17

DIVISION TWO	P	W	D	L	F	A	PTS
Ollerton B/Cotes	32	22	8	2	79	26	74
Linby CW	32	21	7	4	88	28	70
Abacus	32	20	5	7	81	45	65
Retford United	32	20	6	7	82	49	65
GPT Res	32	19	5	8	100	68	62
Teversal Grange	32	15	12	5	81	50	57
Attenborough FC	32	15	7	10	69	36	52
Calverton CW	32	13	5	14	56	66	44
John Player Res	32	12	4	16	71	72	40
Bestwood MW	32	11	5	16	71	64	38
Fairham FC	32	10	7	15	49	57	37
Dunkirk FC Res	32	10	7	15	59	68	37
Greenwood M. R.	32	10	2	20	51	102	32
British Rail Newark	32	7	8	17	58	99	29
Ruddington FC Res	32	7	7	18	48	95	28
Basford United R.	32	6	3	23	51	114	21
Carlton Ath.R.	32	3	5	24	30	85	14

NOTTS ALLIANCE SENIOR DIVISION RESULT CHART 1992-93

HOME TEAM	1	2	3	4	5	6	7	8	9	10	11	12	13	14	15	16
1. Boots Athletic	*	3-0	1-1	6-0	2-4	1-4	6-0	5-2	1-4	0-0	0-2	2-2	1-2	0-2	5-1	2-3
2. Bulwell Forest Villa	1-2	*	0-0	1-0	0-3	1-0	0-0	2-1	2-2	1-1	1-4	1-0	1-5	2-0	2-2	0-3
3. Clipstone Miners Welfare	2-1	7-0	*	6-3	3-1	7-2	1-3	3-1	0-0	1-0	3-0	4-0	2-0	3-1	1-0	4-1
4. Cotgrave Colliery Welfare	0-1	2-2	1-4	*	5-6	1-5	2-2	1-2	2-0	1-1	0-1	0-7	0-1	5-2	1-0	2-2
5. Dunkirk	2-3	5-3	2-1	1-3	*	2-2	2-1	5-2	5-0	2-0	5-0	1-1	2-1	4-2	1-2	1-3
6. G.P.T. (Plessey)	3-1	1-1	1-1	6-1	2-0	*	3-0	2-3	0-1	2-2	2-2	5-2	0-0	2-1	0-0	3-1
7. Greenwood Meadows	1-2	1-0	0-2	1-0	4-5	0-1	*	0-3	5-0	0-3	1-0	0-0	0-0	0-0	2-2	1-0
8. Hucknall Rolls Royce Welfare	2-3	3-1	0-1	3-1	2-0	1-3	1-2	*	4-1	2-0	2-1	5-3	1-1	0-1	3-3	4-0
9. John Player	0-5	1-2	4-7	2-4	0-2	0-5	4-1	1-3	*	3-2	2-0	1-2	1-3	2-3	1-2	1-2
10. Nottinghamshire Police	2-1	1-1	3-0	0-2	2-7	1-4	4-0	1-0	3-0	*	3-1	2-1	0-1	5-1	2-1	2-1
11. Pelican	3-3	1-0	1-0	3-2	4-3	2-4	1-0	0-3	2-4	3-0	*	3-0	1-3	2-2	3-1	0-1
12. Radcliffe Olympic	0-2	0-2	0-3	0-2	3-5	2-3	0-2	2-4	8-4	2-1	3-1	*	3-1	1-3	2-8	0-1
13. Rainworth Miners Welfare	1-1	0-0	3-0	2-1	5-1	0-6	4-1	2-2	4-2	2-1	1-3	1-1	*	0-2	2-0	0-3
14. Ruddington	2-2	1-0	0-2	2-2	1-2	0-5	3-3	2-2	2-0	2-1	1-0	3-1	1-2	*	0-4	1-4
15. Thoresby Colliery Welfare	2-1	0-0	2-2	5-3	3-2	1-1	2-4	1-1	0-0	0-3	3-3	1-0	3-3	1-3	*	0-1
16. Worthington Simpson	0-3	2-0	1-1	3-1	2-1	2-3	2-0	3-2	5-3	0-0	0-2	4-1	0-0	2-1	2-0	*

NOTTS ALLIANCE DIVISION ONE RESULT CHART 1992-93

HOME TEAM	1	2	3	4	5	6	7	8	9	10	11	12	13	14	15	16
1. Awsworth Villa	*	1-1	2-1	2-4	1-2	2-3	5-1	3-0	3-2	4-5	4-2	1-2	3-0	2-1	1-2	2-2
2. Basford United	2-1	*	2-1	1-3	3-0	4-1	1-0	2-0	1-0	0-1	7-0	2-5	4-1	0-1	1-1	1-2
3. Bilsthorpe Colliery Welfare	3-1	3-5	*	2-1	4-6	7-0	1-1	1-5	2-0	1-3	2-2	0-3	0-1	3-1	2-5	0-3
4. Carlton Athletic	3-5	1-2	3-2	*	3-1	1-1	1-0	1-2	1-1	0-1	4-2	2-3	3-0	0-1	0-2	2-2
5. City & Sherwood Hospital	1-6	1-3	1-4	2-2	*	3-2	1-0	0-2	7-1	0-5	4-1	1-1	3-3	4-2	1-2	1-1
6. Clifton All Whites	1-1	2-4	0-0	3-1	1-3	*	4-2	0-8	1-2	2-2	2-2	0-2	1-3	2-4	2-3	1-6
7. Clipstone Miners Welfare Reserves	1-1	1-1	2-0	3-1	2-3	2-1	*	1-3	1-1	2-1	5-2	0-2	2-1	3-1	1-2	0-3
8. Gedling Colliery Welfare	2-2	0-1	3-1	3-2	5-0	5-0	5-5	*	3-0	4-2	7-1	1-2	1-1	3-1	2-2	2-4
9. Hucknall Rolls Royce Reserves	3-0	0-1	3-2	5-3	2-2	4-3	1-2	1-1	*	2-0	4-2	0-1	0-1	0-0	5-3	0-3
10. Keyworth United	4-1	3-0	1-1	3-1	2-2	0-5	1	2-1	4-1	*	9-0	0-1	0-1	1-0	4-1	2-2
11. Rainworth Miners Welfare Reserves	2-3	2-2	0-1	0-0	4-0	1-0	2-0	0-7	3-6	1-1	*	0-2	0-2	4-1	0-1	1-5
12. Sneinton	2-2	2-1	3-1	3-4	4-3	6-2	4-1	2-2	4-1	1-0	3-1	*	2-1	1-2	3-2	1-2
13. Southwell City	2-0	1-2	2-0	0-2	2-3	2-0	1-1	4-1	1-0	0-1	3-0	0-0	*	3-1	1-3	3-0
14. Stapleford Villa	2-1	2-3	1-1	4-1	0-0	2-3	0-0	0-2	0-3	1-2	2-3	0-2	0-4	*	2-1	3-3
15. Worthington Simpson Reserves	6-5	1-1	5-0	4-1	1-1	7-2	4-1	2-1	1-1	3-0	2-4	0-0	3-3	6-1	*	2-2
16. Wollaton	3-1	4-0	4-1	4-1	7-3	5-0	2-1	2-0	2-0	4-0	5-0	2-4	1-0	6-1	6-0	*

NOTTS ALLIANCE DIVISION TWO RESULT CHART 1992-93

HOME TEAM	1	2	3	4	5	6	7	8	9	10	11	12	13	14	15	16	17
1. Abacus	*	1-2	9-0	1-1	2-0	2-1	5-0	2-1	0-1	1-0	6-1	2-2	1-1	0-2	5-2	2-1	3-1
2. Attenborough	0-1	*	9-3	0-0	5-0	1-1	2-0	2-2	1-0	3-1	8-1	3-0	1-2	0-2	1-1	1-2	0-3
3. Basford United Reserves	5-0	0-5	*	1-3	3-2	3-0	1-2	4-3	0-0	2-5	1-2	2-5	0-2	1-4	1-4	2-3	1-1
4. Bestwood Miners Welfare	1-2	1-0	8-1	*	3-3	3-4	1-2	1-3	5-2	4-4	0-1	4-1	2-2	1-2	1-3	6-1	3-4
5. Bristish Rail Newark	4-2	1-4	6-3	1-2	*	2-1	1-3	1-0	1-1	2-2	6-4	0-3	2-2	0-5	1-3	2-2	1-4
6. Carlton Athletic Reserves	1-3	1-2	0-2	1-2	1-1	*	0-2	3-0	1-1	0-1	2-4	0-6	1-2	0-3	0-3	3-3	0-1
7. Calverton Colliery Welfare	1-2	1-1	7-3	2-3	0-2	5-1	*	1-0	5-2	1-2	3-2	3-3	0-0	0-3	1-0	5-0	2-2
8. Dunkirk Reserves	0-3	0-0	3-3	0-3	4-4	4-1	2-0	*	1-1	7-2	3-4	2-6	2-5	0-4	3-1	3-0	1-2
9. Fairham	1-0	0-4	4-0	2-1	2-2	1-0	1-0	3-4	*	2-4	2-3	4-2	0-3	0-1	1-2	5-0	0-1
10. G.P.T. Reserves	1-6	1-0	5-3	1-0	9-0	4-0	5-1	1-1	3-0	*	3-2	7-2	2-6	2-4	2-2	5-0	1-3
11. Greenwood Meadows Reserves	1-5	1-1	3-0	1-4	2-5	3-0	2-4	0-2	0-3	0-7	*	0-3	0-7	1-5	1-2	4-0	0-4
12. John Player Reserves	2-5	1-0	1-2	2-1	2-0	2-0	7-1	1-2	1-3	2-4	2-3	*	0-3	1-3	6-2	0-2	1-4
13. Linby Colliery Welfare	2-2	1-2	0-0	4-1	8-2	4-0	2-0	3-0	3-0	2-3	1-1	4-0	*	1-2	2-0	2-0	1-1
14. Ollerton & Bevercotes Miners W.	0-1	3-2	4-1	1-0	3-1	3-1	4-0	4-0	1-1	4-4	4-0	2-2	2-0	*	0-1	1-1	0-0
15. Retford United	7-1	1-3	3-2	3-1	6-1	8-0	2-2	2-1	3-1	5-1	2-0	1-1	0-5	0-0	*	2-1	1-1
16. Ruddington Reserves	1-3	3-2	1-0	4-3	3-2	3-5	0-2	0-4	3-3	1-5	3-4	1-3	0-3	2-2	2-6	*	3-3
17. Teversal Grange	3-3	1-4	8-1	4-2	5-2	2-2	5-0	1-1	2-1	2-3	4-0	2-2	1-3	2-2	2-4	2-2	*

NOTTS ALLIANCE SENIOR CUP 1992-93

First Round

G.P.T. v Cotgrave Colliery Welfare	3-0	City & Sherwood Hospital v Thoresby C.W.	1-2
Rainworth Miners Welfare v Sneinton	2-0(aet)	John Players v Pelican	1-2
Worthington Simpson v Carlton Athletic	2-0	Bulwell Forest Villa v Ruddington	0-2
Notts Police v Keyworth United	0-1	Hucknall Rolls Royce Welfare v Southwell City	6-3
Gedling Miners Welfare v Stapleford Villa	1-3	Clifton All Whites v Bilsthorpe Colliery Welfare	0-4
Basford United v Greenwood Meadows	0-2	Clipstone Welfare v Dunkirk	2-1

Second Round

G.P.T. v Boots Athletic	2-1	Thoresby Colliery Welfare v Radcliffe Olympic	4-2
Pelican v Rainworth Miners Welfare	4-6	Wollaton v Worthington Simpson	2-1
Hucknall R.R. Welfare v Ruddington	1-2	Awsworth Villa v Keyworth United	0-2
Stapleford Villa v Bilstphorpe C. Welfare	2-1	Clipstone Welfare v Greenwood Meadows	1-1(aet),1-0

Quarter Finals

Thoresby Colliery Welfare v G.P.T.	0-8	Rainworth Miners Welfare v Wollaton	1-1(aet),4-3
Ruddington v Keyworth United	3-2	Stapleford Villa v Clipstone Welfare	1-3

Semi-Finals

G.P.T. Plessey v Wollaton	5-2	Ruddington v Clipstone Welfare	1-2

Final: G.P.T. 4, Clipstone Welfare 0

NOTTS ALLIANCE INTERMEDIATE CUP 1992-93

First Round

Fairham v Greenwood Meadow Reserves	2-1	Ruddington Reserves v Linby Colliery Welfare	1-0
Abacus v Rainworth Miners Welfare Reserves	5-1	Clipstone Welfare Reserves v G.P.T. Reserves	1-4
Teversal Grange v Dunkirk Reserves	3-1(aet)		

(continued overleaf)

(continued from page 961) **Second Round**

Worthington Simpson Reserves v Fairham	3-1	
British Rail v Abacus	1-7	
Teversal Grange v Bestwood Miners Welfare	2-4	
Carlton Athletic Reserves v Ollerton & B.	0-7	

Ruddington Reserves v Hucknall R.R. Reserves	2-1
G.P.T. Reserves v John Player Reserves	2-3
Retford United v Basford United Reserves	0-2*(aet)*
Calverton Welfare v Attenborough	1-3

Quarter Finals

Worthington Simpson Res. v Ruddington Res.	1-0	John Player Reserves v Abacus	2-1
Bestwood M.W. v Basford Utd Reserves	7-3	Attenborough v Ollerton & Bevercotes M.W.	2-0

Semi-Finals

Worthington S. Res. v John Players Res.	4-1*(aet)*	Bestwood Miners Welfare v Attenborough	0-1

Final: Worthington Simpson Reserves 3, Attenborough 1 *(after 1-1 draw)*

LEAGUE TOP-SCORERS 1992-93

Senior Div.	**Div. One**	**Div. Two**
Mark Gore (Worthington) 28	Richard Smyth (Wollaton) 29	Andy Powell (Retford) 32

'MANAGER OF THE SEASON' AWARDS 1992-93

Senior Div.	**Div. One**	**Div. Two**
John Slater (Clipstone)	Glen Birkin (Sneinton)	A Owen (Ollerton & Bevercotes)

SENIOR DIVISION CLUBS 1993-94

BOOTS ATHLETIC
Secretary: Ian Whitehead, 55 Longmoor Lane, Breaston, Derbys DE1 3RB (0331 74203).
Ground: Lady Bay, West Bridgford, Nottingham (0602 822392). **Colours:** Blue & white/black
Hons: Notts Alliance Div 1 91-92 (Lg Cup 91-92), Notts I'mediate Cup R-up 91-92.

BULWELL FOREST VILLA
Secretary: W Matthews, 322 St Albans Road, Bulwell, Nottm (0602 278010).
Ground: Haywood Clinic, Beckhampton Road, Bestwood Estate, Nottingham.
Colours: Yellow & blue/blue **Hons:** Notts Alliance Div 1 R-up 91-92

CLIPSTONE WELFARE
Secretary: Barry Clarke, 40 Church Road, Clipstone, Mansfield, NG21 9DG (0623 640829).
Ground & Directions: Clipstone Lido Ground (0632 655674). B6030 from Mansfield, on left entering Clipstone.
Colours: Black & red stripes/black/red
Hons: Notts Snr Cup 85-86, Notts Alliance 72-73 73-74 74-75 92-93 (Lg Cup 72-73 73-74 74-75 (R-up 92-93)), Notts I'mediate Cup 55-56.

COTGRAVE COLLIERY WELFARE
Secretary: David Southern, 185 Ringleas, Cotgrave, Nottm NG12 3PQ (0602 894940).
Ground: Cotgrave Miners Welfare. **Colours:** Yellow/Blue

DUNKIRK
Secretary: Mr John G Peck, 5 Thistledown Rd, Clifton, Nottm NG11 9DP (0602 842147).
Ground & Directions: The Ron Steel Sports Ground, Trentside Farm, Clifton Bridge, Nottingham (0602 850803). Ring Road - Clifton Bridge (North End), Industrial Estate, Lenton Lane.
Colours: Red/Black
Hons: Notts Alliance Div 1 84-85 (Div 2 82-83, Lg Cup R-up 84-85), Notts I'mediate Cup 83-84.

GREENWOOD MEADOWS
Secretary: Barry Hall, 34 Sullivan Close, Marmion Estate, Nottm NG3 2HX (0602 582459).
Ground: Lenton Lane, Clifton Bridge, Nottingham. **Colours:** Grey & white/black

G.P.T.
Secretary: Roger Marshall, Sports Office, G.P.T., Beeston, Nottm (0602 433669).
Colours: All sky **Ground:** Trent Vale Rd, Beeston, Nottm (0602 258320)
Hons: Notts Alliance 66-67 91-92 (R-up 92-93, Lg Cup 92-93).

HUCKNALL ROLLS ROYCE WELFARE
Secretary: Peter Williams, 38 Tiverton Close, Hucknall, Nottm NG15 6JT (0602 635724).
Ground: Sports and Social Club, Entrance Watnall Road (0602 630134).
Colours: Yellow/burgundy/burgundy **Hons:** Notts I'mediate Cup 92-93

NOTTINGHAMSHIRE POLICE
Secretary: Mr Bob Fawcett, 21 Bird Close, Kingshaven, Mansfield, Notts NG18 4AZ (0632 636911).
Ground & Directions: Force Training School, Epperstone Manor, Notts. On A60 Mansfield Road, on right from City Centre (2 miles).
Colours: White/Black
Hons: Notts Snr R-up 91-92, Notts All. Div 1 & Lge Snr Cup R-up 85-86, PAAN Nat. K-O Comp 63- 64.

PELICAN
Secretary: Paul Asher, 14 Thaxted Close, Bilborough, Nottm NG8 4NG (0602 288625).
Ground: John Pearson Spts Ground, Lenton Lane, Nottm (0602 868255) **Colours:** All Blue.
Hons: Notts Alliance Lg Cup 90-91 (R-up 91-92).

RAINWORTH MINERS WELFARE
Secretary: Alan Wright, 10 Faraday Road, Mansfield NG18 4ES (0632 24379).
Ground & Directions: Kirklington Road, Rainworth. On A617 Mansfield - Newark Road.
Colours: All White
Hons: Notts Alliance 77-78 78-79 79-80 80-81 81-82 82-83 (Lg Cup 81-82), Notts Snr Cup 80-81 81-82 (R-up 82-83 92-93), FA Vase R-up 82-82, Thorn EMI F'lit Cup R-up 82-83 83-84 84-85.

RUDDINGTON
Secretary: John Fisk, 3 Savages Road, Ruddington, Nottm NG11 6EW (0602 842552).
Ground & Directions: The Elms Park Ground, Loughborough Road, Ruddington (0602 844976). On A60 Nottm to Loughborough, 5 miles out of Nottingham.
Colours: Red & black/blue **Honours:** Notts Comb. Lg 79-80 (Lg Cup 70-71 76-77 80-81).

SNEINTON
Secretary: Paul Shelton, 28 Freda Close, Gedling, Nottm NG4 4GP (0602 877527).
Ground: Stoke Lane, Gedling, Nottingham. **Colours:** Blue & black stripes/black/black.
Hons: Notts Alliance Div 1 92-93, Notts Intermediate Cup 91-92.

THORESBY COLLIERY WELFARE
Secretary: Brian Wathall, 29 First Ave., Edwinstowe, Nr Mansfield NG21 9NZ (0632 823885).
Ground: Thoresby Colliery, Fourth Avenue, Edwinstowe, Nr Mansfield. **Colours:** Blue/navy

WOLLATON
Secretary: Glyn Brewer, 15 Renfrew Drive, Wollaton, Nottm NG8 2FX (0602 281471).
Ground: Wollaton Sports Club, Wollaton Village, Nottm (0602 289748).
Colours: Maroon/sky/maroon **Hons:** Notts All. Div 1 R-up 92-93 (Div 2 91-92 (I'mediate Cup R-up 91-92)).

WORTHINGTON SIMPSONS
Secretary: Anthony Hopkinson, 109 Hawton Lane, Balderton, Newark, Notts NG24 3EH (0636 79883).
Ground & Directions: Lowfields, off Hawton Lane, New Baldeton, Newark, Notts (0636 702672). From Newark,
A6065 to Newark Hospital, right into Bowbridge Road, cont. 1 mile, left by timber yard, over bridge then right. From
A1 (By-pass) A6065 Newark to lights. Ahead then left into Hawton Lane.
Colours: Maroon/blue **Hons:** Notts Alliance Lg Cup (Intermediate Cup(res) 92-93).

NOTTS ALLIANCE DIVISION ONE CLUBS 1993-94
AWSWORTH VILLA
Secretary: Keith Slaney, 24 Attewell Road, Awsworth, Nottm NG16 2SY (0602 302514).
Ground: Attewell Road, Awsworth. **Colours:** All Blue

BASFORD UNITED
Secretary: Paul Dobson, 26 Chevin Gardens, Top Valley, Nottm NG5 9ES (0602 274790).
Ground & Directions: Greenwich Ave., Sports Ground, Bagnall Road, Basford, Nottm (0602 423918). M1 (J26)
follow signs 'A610 Nottingham' then 'B6004 Arnold' into Mill Street.
Colours: Yellow/black **Hons:** Notts Snr Cup 46-47 87-88, Notts Alliance Div 1 R-up 71-72 84-85.

BILSTHORPE COLLIERY WELFARE
Secretary: Mr Les Lee, 42 Chapel Lane, Ravenshead, Mansfield NG15 9DA (0623 794442).
Ground: Bilsthorpe C.W. Ground, Eakring Road, Bilsthorpe. **Colours:** All white.

CARLTON ATHLETIC
Secretary: Mr Roy Loach, 47 Fraser Rd, Carlton, Nottingham NG4 1NP (0602 872072).
Ground: Carlton Hill, Recreation Ground, Carlton (0602 615689). **Colours:** White/black

CITY & SHERWOOD HOSPITALS
Secretary: Mr Peter Donohoe, 2 Campden Green, Clifton Est., Nottm NG11 8BN (0602 844034).
Ground: C.O.D. Military Ground, Chilwell (0602 254811). **Colours:** All Royal Blue

CLIPSTONE WELFARE RESERVES *(As preceding page except colours are all white)*

GEDLING COLLIERY WELFARE
Secretary: Mrs Maureen Chambers, 8 Fraser Road, Carlton, Nottm NG4 1NJ (0602 612994).
Ground: Gedling Colliery Welfare, Plains Road, Mapperley (0602 266300) **Colours:** Yellow/blue

HUCKNALL ROLLS ROYCE WELFARE RESERVES *(see preceding page)*

JOHN PLAYERS
Secretary: Ron Walton, 27 St Margarets Ave., Aspley Lane, Nottm NG8 5GD (0602 292027).
Ground & Directions: Aspley Lane, Nottm (0602 294244). Corner of Nottingham ring road B690 turn towards City
Centre.
Colours: Green & gold/green/green.
Hons: Notts Alliance 21-22 22-23 23-24 24-25 25-26 26-27 67-68 68-69 69-70 85-86 89-90.

KEYWORTH UNITED
Secretary: Maurice G Simpson, 25 Waddington Drive, Wilford Hill, West Bridgford, Nottm NG2 7GT (0602 232921).
Ground: Platt Lane, Keyworth (0607 75998). **Colours:** Green/Black

LINBY COLLIERY MINERS WELFARE
Secretary: D G Dickens, 4 Old Mill Close, Bestwood, Nottingham, NG6 8TA (0602 276598).
Ground: Church Lane, Linby **Colours:** Red/White
Hons: Notts Alliance Div 2 R-up 92-93.

OLLERTON & BEVERCOTES MINERS WELFARE
Secretary: Mr Jack Graham, 7 Petersmith Drive, New Ollerton, Newark NG22 9SD (0623 863127).
Ground: Walesby Lane, New Ollerton. **Colours:** Amber/black
Honours: Notts Alliance Div 2 92-93.

RADCLIFFE OLYMPIC
Secretary: C Johnson, 2 The Firs, Holme Pierrepont, Radcliffe-on-Trent NG12 2LT (0602 333791).
Ground: Wharf Lane, Radcliffe-on-Trent. **Colours:** White/red.

SOUTHWELL CITY
Secretary: P K Johnson, 63 The Ropewalk, Southwell, Notts NG25 0AL (0636 814386).
Ground: War Memorial Ground, Southwell (0636 4386) **Colours:** Black pin stripes/Black

STAPLEFORD VILLA
Secretary: Mr Clyde Davis, 25 Grace. Drive, Aspley, Nottm NG8 5AG (0602 290529).
Ground: Bramcote Park, Ilkeston Rd Entrance. **Colours:** White/Blue

WORTHINGTON SIMPSONS RESERVES
Colours: Maroon/sky *(Other details as above)*

NOTTS ALLIANCE DIVISION TWO CLUBS 1993-94

ABACUS
Secretary: Mr Stephen Bingley, 6 Brisbane Close, Mansfield Woodhouse NG19 8QZ (0623 23072).
Ground: Sherwood Colliery Sports Ground, Debdale Lane, Mansfield Woodhouse, Notts.
Colours: Black & white stripes.

ATTENBOROUGH
Secretary: Terry Allen, 3 Firth Close, Arnold, Nottingham NG5 8RU (0602 200698).
Ground & Directions: The Village Green, The Strand, Attenborough, Beeston, Nottingham. Midway between Beeston & Long Eaton on A6005 - adjacent to Nature Reserve (via Attenborough Lane).
Colours: All blue   **Change cols:** White/black/black.   **Previous Lge:** Central Mids (pre-1992)

BESTWOOD MINERS WELFARE
Secretary: Mrs Alana Jackson, 9 Derwent Drive, Hucknall, Nottm NG15 6DS (0602 630189).
Ground: Bestwood Workshops, Park Rd, Bestwood (0602 273711).   **Colours:** White/blue.

BOOTS ATHLETIC RESERVES *(As page 962)*

BRITISH RAIL (NEWARK)
Secretary: Mr J Todd, 15 Lamb Close, Newark, Notts (0636 72709).
Ground: Devan Park, Newark, Notts.   **Colours:** All blue.

CALVERTON COLLIERY WELFARE
Secretary: Brian Hillary, 20 Gorse Close, Calverton, Nottm NG14 6QB (0602 653906).
Ground: Calverton Colliery   **Colours:** White/blue/blue.

CLIFTON ALL WHITES
Secretary: Keith Elliott, 61 Greencroft, Clifton Est., Nottm NG11 8GT (0602 215401).
Ground & Directions: Green Lane, Clifton Est., Nottm (0602 844903). Off A6005 Nottingham - Long Eaton Road.
Colours: All white   **Hons:** Notts Alliance Div 1

DUNKIRK RESERVES *(As page 962)*

FAIRHAM
Secretary: Graham Deakin, 18 Vernon Avenue, Wilford, Nottm NG11 7AE (0602 816984).
Ground: Rigley Sports Ground, Cotgrave Colliery, Cotgrave.   **Cols:** Blue & white hoops/white

G.P.T. RES., GREENWOOD MEADOWS RES., JOHN PLAYER RES., PELICAN RES., RAINWORTH MINERS WELFARE RESERVES *(As Senior & First Division details)*

RETFORD UNITED
Secretary: Jeff Lamb, 18 Northumbria Drive, Retford, Notts, DN22 7PR (0602 705833).
Ground: Oaklands Lane (Off London Road), Retford, (enter via Caledonian Road).
Colours: Black & white stripes/black

RUDDINGTON RESERVES *(colours: Blue & claret/white - as page 962)*

TEVERSAL GRANGE
Secretary: Kevin Newton, 8 Vere Ave., Sutton in Ashfield, Notts NG17 2ES (0623 511402).
Ground: Carnarvon Street, Sutton in Ashfield.   **Colours:** Red & black hoops/red/red.

WELBECK COLLIERY
Secretary: Mr Ron Turner, 1 Newcastle Str., Warsop, Mansfield, Notts NG20 0NQ (0623 846244).
Ground: Welbeck Colliery Pit (0623 842611).   **Colours:** Yellow/blue/yellow
Previous League: Chesterfield & District (champions 1992-93).

Calverton Colliery Welfare F.C., pictured before their 2-3 home defeat at the hands of Bestwood Miners Welfare on 24th March. Photo - John Hanson.

WHITBREAD COUNTY SENIOR LEAGUE

League Secretary: R.A.Bowler, 1 Holbein Close, Dronfield Woodhouse, Sheffield S18 6QH
Publicity Officer: John Hamer, 3 Ians Way, Ashgate, Chesterfield S40 4PY

Frecheville CA, who had formerly competed in the Northern Counties East League proved that they are capable of performing at a higher standard once again when they clinched the Premier League title and completed the double by lifting the Whitbread Trophy.

Frecheville, who withdrew from the pyramid after being faced with the ever increasing costs of stringent ground grading requirements, had retained the nucleus of their experienced side along with manager Glyn Robotham and together this provided the base for their success. The previous season the Sheffield based side had taken the first division title but after three defeats in their opening four fixtures in the top flight further silverware looked a remote possibility.

But Robotham's introduction of some exciting young talent from the steel city proved a master stroke which saw his side put together an impressive thirteen game unbeaten run, of which twelve were won, to soar up the table and lift the honours.

The first half of the campaign was dominated by Hallam Reserves and Parramore Sports who up to Christmas had just a single defeat between them. But into 1993 and both suffered sharp decline. Hallam's form dipped alarmingly as they managed just one point from a possible eighteen after the turn of the year, and slid down to eleventh spot.

Mexborough Main Street, consistently a top six side in recent seasons, must have thought it was their year when after taking the initiative led the pack for ten weeks, but eventually had to settle for third spot.

The League's most successful club in recent years, Ash House, were mounting a strong challenge but were knocked back with successive defeats against Phoenix and Main Street, before recovering to secure runners-up place. While Goldthorpe Colliery climbed up to second spot after a run of twelve wins in fourteen games but after looking a good bet for the double, reaching the Trophy Final, their injury-hit side slumped and they ended in fourth place.

At the other end of the table, Oughtibridge looked totally out of their depth failing to win a League game until their penultimate fixture after their fate was sealed in early April.

Despite some battling performances, ABM's abysmal home record in which they were unable to win any games on their own soil, saw them relegated. ABM won 3-0 at the previous year's champions Phoenix and beat high flying Goldthorpe 2-1.

But there is a reprieve for third from bottom RES Parkgate Reserves who retain their top flight status after the withdrawl of White Rose Throstles.

High Green Villa's remarkable run of success continued when they surged to the first division title with a nine point advantage over their nearest rivals. Villa, who lost just once in a marvellous campaign, have made it a hat-trick of championships since joining the league three years ago. Also promoted were Brunsmeer Athletic, the only side to beat Villa, and high scoring Treeton Welfare.

Staveley MW, who swept to the second division title with an eight point advantage and cracked in over 100 goals, announced that they would be leaving the County Senior after only two seasons for the Central Midlands League. Staveley, who made rapid strides improving their facilities last season including with the erection of floodlights and proposals for covered standing, were confidently expecting to join the Supreme Division.

Throstles Ridgeway gave the champions a great battle but after losing their April showdown with Staveley 1-0 had to settle for runners-up. They, along with third placed Stockbridge Park Steels Reserves, move up to the first division.

John Hamer (Publicity Officer).

Frechville C.A. - the only team to achieve the Premier Division Championship and Whitbread Trophy double.

PREM. DIVISION	P	W	D	L	F	A	PTS
Frencheville C.A.	26	18	4	4	66	23	58
Ash House	26	17	3	6	54	23	54
Mexborough M.S.	26	16	5	5	52	32	53
Goldthorpe Coll.	26	16	2	8	68	40	50
White Rose Thr'tls	26	15	3	8	64	38	48
Parramore Sports	26	10	8	8	36	31	38
Hallam	26	10	7	9	48	45	37
Phoenix	26	10	5	11	31	46	35
Denaby & C'by MW	26	9	6	11	57	50	33
Worsbrough B.	26	8	4	14	34	48	28
Wath Saracens Ath.	26	8	3	15	36	51	27
R.E.S. Parkgate	26	8	3	15	33	64	27
A.B.M.	26	5	5	16	42	73	20
Oughtibr W.M.S.C.	26	1	4	21	26	83	7

DIVISION ONE	P	W	D	L	F	A	PTS
High Green Villa	26	22	3	1	83	13	69
Brunsmeer Ath.	26	18	6	2	59	19	60
Treeton Welfare	26	17	4	5	91	46	55
Penistone Church	26	16	3	7	90	56	51
British Gas*	26	12	7	7	68	48	42
Thurcroft I'hoe*	26	11	5	10	67	45	37
Caribbean Sports	26	10	5	11	44	54	35
Yorkshire Main	26	9	4	13	51	74	31
Wath St.James	26	8	6	12	44	60	30
Woodsetts Welfare	26	8	2	16	50	80	26
Rawm & R'roft WMC	26	7	4	15	43	55	25
Industry	26	8	1	17	38	83	25
Swinton Athletic	26	4	4	18	29	70	16
Ecclesfield R.R.	26	3	4	19	25	79	13

* 1pt deducted for breach of rule.

DIVISION TWO	P	W	D	L	F	A	PTS
Staveley M.W.	28	23	4	1	106	22	73
Throstles Ridgeway	28	20	5	3	66	26	65
Stocksbridge P.S.	28	17	6	5	75	43	57
Sheffield Gas	28	14	4	10	56	35	46
Sheffield Oakhouse	28	14	4	10	68	56	46
Clifton Rovers	28	11	9	8	58	54	42
Sheff. Centralians	28	10	10	8	35	33	40
Kiveton Park	28	11	4	13	41	42	37
Sheff. Bankers *	28	9	5	14	53	58	31
Penistone Ch. Res	28	8	5	15	43	59	29
Rossington M'n Utd	28	6	11	11	40	60	29
Sheffield Post Off.	28	7	5	16	46	72	26
Brit Steel St'less	28	7	3	18	53	72	24
Old Edwardians	28	6	6	16	35	63	24
Abbeydale	28	6	1	21	38	118	19

* - 1pt deducted for breach of rule.

PREMIER DIVISION RESULT CHART 1992-93

HOME TEAM	1	2	3	4	5	6	7	8	9	10	11	12	13	14
1. A.B.M.	*	0-1	1-2	1-2	2-8	0-2	2-3	2-2	1-3	2-5	2-5	3-3	1-4	2-2
2. Ash House	5-1	*	3-0	0-2	1-2	1-0	1-1	2-0	1-0	1-0	1-0	4-1	2-1	3-0
3. Denaby & Cadeby Miners Welfare	3-4	2-2	*	1-3	1-5	3-3	5-0	3-1	3-1	1-3	1-1	6-0	1-3	2-2
4. Frechville Community Association	4-1	0-2	2-0	*	1-2	3-0	2-4	3-1	0-2	0-0	3-1	3-0	4-1	7-0
5. Goldthorpe Colliery	1-2	0-6	1-0	2-3	*	3-4	3-1	4-1	1-1	2-2	5-0	0-1	2-0	2-3
6. Hallam Reserves	2-2	3-3	4-2	0-6	3-1	*	1-0	5-1	1-1	1-3	6-1	0-0	1-1	1-0
7. Mexborough Main Street	3-1	2-1	4-4	1-1	0-4	2-1	*	1-1	3-0	3-0	4-1	1-1	2-0	1-0
8. Oughtibridge W.M.S.C.	4-5	0-5	2-5	1-4	0-2	3-2	0-3	*	1-3	0-2	0-1	1-4	0-7	1-3
9. Parramore Sports	1-1	1-1	0-0	0-0	1-2	0-2	2-1	0-0	*	3-1	1-3	3-1	2-1	2-2
10. Phoenix	0-3	1-3	0-3	1-1	0-3	2-2	0-3	2-1	0-4	*	1-1	1-0	1-3	1-0
11. R.E.S. Parkgate Reserves	0-2	0-2	0-6	1-4	2-5	2-1	0-1	3-3	1-3	1-0	*	3-1	1-4	1-0
12. Wath Saracens Athletic	4-1	0-1	1-3	0-2	0-2	2-0	0-4	5-0	2-0	1-2	4-1	*	1-3	3-2
13. White Rose Throstles	3-0	5-2	3-0	0-2	2-4	3-2	1-2	3-1	2-2	4-0	3-0	2-1	*	3-3
14. Worsborough Bridge M.W. Reserves	1-0	0-2	1-0	1-4	3-2	0-1	0-2	4-1	1-0	1-2	1-3	1-3	3-0	1-2	*

COUNTY SENIOR LEAGUE DIVISION ONE RESULT CHART 1992-93

HOME TEAM	1	2	3	4	5	6	7	8	9	10	11	12	13	14
1. British Gas	*	0-1	6-2	0-0	1-3	3-1	3-1	2-1	5-0	3-2	2-3	5-1	4-1	4-1
2. Brunsmeer Athletic	3-0	*	2-3	3-0	0-2	3-1	2-1	2-0	3-1	1-1	5-1	2-0	6-1	2-1
3. Caribbean Sports	0-0	1-1	*	7-0	0-4	0-3	0-1	3-1	4-0	2-2	1-3	4-0	2-1	1-0
4. Ecclesfield Red Rose	0-2	2-2	1-2	*	0-1	0-3	1-5	3-3	2-0	2-2	1-3	0-1	0-3	2-3
5. High Green Villa	1-1	0-3	3-0	5-0	*	1-0	4-0	2-0	5-0	2-0	1-1	2-0	8-1	2-0
6. Industry	0-4	0-5	0-1	1-3	0-8	*	2-4	2-0	3-2	1-2	0-5	0-2	0-6	7-5
7. Penistone Church	5-2	1-2	5-0	6-3	3-7	4-4	*	1-1	0-2	3-2	3-2	3-3	9-3	8-1
8. Rawmarsh & Ravenscroft W.M.C.	1-3	0-2	3-3	2-0	1-2	1-4	2-4	*	4-4	3-1	5-0	1-2	4-0	1-3
9. Swinton Athletic	3-3	0-2	0-1	1-0	1-8	0-1	1-5	1-2	*	3-0	0-0	0-5	2-2	1-2
10. Thurcroft Ivanhoe	4-2	0-0	5-2	10-10-1	6-0	0-1	3-0	4-1	*	3-5	5-1	3-2	2-1	
11. Treeton Welfare	1-1	2-3	5-2	9-0	0-2	10-14-2	3-0	5-2	2-1	*	2-2	7-1	7-1	
12. Wath St. James	3-3	1-1	5-2	0-2	1-1	2-4	1-6	3-1	0-2	2-0	3-5	*	1-0	1-3
13. Woodsetts Welfare	4-4	0-3	3-1	2-1	0-4	3-0	2-4	0-2	2-1	1-6	2-3	3-1	*	3-4
14. Yorkshire Main	6-5	0-0	0-0	3-1	0-4	3-0	2-5	2-4	2-1	3-3	2-3	3-3	0-4	*

COUNTY SENIOR LEAGUE DIVISION TWO RESULT CHART 1992-93

HOME TEAM	1	2	3	4	5	6	7	8	9	10	11	12	13	14	15
1. Abbeydale	*	2-0	2-7	0-1	3-3	3-1	2-0	2-0	1-4	1-4	1-5	3-6	0-4	0-5	0-3
2. British Steel Stainless	4-6	*	5-0	2-3	2-5	2-2	0-2	4-0	4-2	1-4	2-4	4-3	0-1	2-5	0-3
3. Clifton Rovers	6-0	3-3	*	2-0	4-2	1-1	3-1	2-5	0-0	0-1	2-0	5-3	1-4	1-6	0-1
4. Kiveton Park Reserves	3-0	1-2	1-1	*	3-2	2-1	2-4	2-1	0-1	2-1	0-1	4-2	0-2	1-3	1-2
5. Old Edwardians	1-3	4-3	0-0	0-5	*	2-3	1-1	1-0	0-3	0-3	0-1	0-1	1-3	1-1	1-1
6. Penistone Church Reserves	5-3	4-2	1-5	1-3	1-2	*	2-0	2-0	0-1	1-1	4-0	6-2	2-1	0-2	1-2
7. Rossington Main United	5-2	0-2	2-2	1-0	0-1	1-1	*	3-3	0-0	1-1	3-3	1-1	1-1	2-2	0-3
8. Sheffield Bankers	4-0	3-2	2-3	1-1	2-1	5-1	7-3	*	1-1	3-3	0-4	4-2	1-4	1-2	1-3
9. Sheffield Centralians	2-0	2-0	0-1	0-0	2-0	4-0	0-0	0-2	*	1-0	0-0	1-3	2-2	1-1	1-4
10. Sheffield Gas	10-12-0	0-1	1-0	1-2	1-0	2-0	2-1	0-1	*	3-1	4-0	0-5	1-1	1-2	
11. Sheffield Oakhouse	6-1	2-3	2-2	1-5	2-0	4-1	8-1	2-1	1-1	1-4	*	5-3	2-4	4-1	4-0
12. Sheffield Post Office	2-0	1-1	2-1	1-1	2-2	2-0	0-2	2-2	4-1	1-3	0-1	*	0-4	1-2	0-2
13. Staveley Miners Welfare	7-1	2-0	6-1	3-0	8-1	3-0	5-2	2-0	0-0	3-0	6-3	5-0	*	7-3	1-1
14. Stocksbridge Park Steels	6-0	2-1	3-3	5-0	2-1	3-0	4-1	1-3	6-3	3-2	3-1	2-1	0-2	*	1-3
15. Throstles Ridgeway	4-1	4-2	1-1	1-0	3-1	2-2	2-3	3-0	3-1	2-1	5-0	6-1	0-1	0-0	*

WHITBREAD TROPHY

Third Round

Frecheville CA v Sheffield Bankers	3-1
Stocksbridge PS v Swinton Athletic	11-0
White Rose Throstles v Sheffield Gas	2-3
Oughtobridge WMSC v Phoenix	0-1
Parramore Sports v Brunsmeer Athletic	0-4
Staveley MW v Mexborough M.S.	4-0, 1-1
Hallam v Sheffield Oakhouse	8-1
Goldthorpe Colliery v Treeton Welfare	3-0

Quarter-Finals

Frecheville CA v Stocksbridge PS	5-2
Sheffield Gas v Phoenix	1-2
Brunsmeer Athletic v Staveley MW	0-1
Goldthorpe Collier v Hallam	4-3

Semi-Finals
(both played at Rossington Main)

Frecheville CA v Phoenix	3-0
Staveley MW v Goldthrope Colliery	2-3, 1-1

Final
(played at Bracken Moor Stocksbridge PS FC)
Frecheville CA 5-4 Goldthorpe Colliery

Frecheville lifted the Whitbread Trophy after one of the most dramatic finals since the competition began. The Sheffielders clinched a thrilling 5-4 extra-time triumph over fellow Premier Division rivals Goldthorpe Colliery following a nerve-jangling clash at Stocksbridge Parks Steel Bracken Moor in which the advantage switched from one side to the other throughout the frenetic last hurdle tie.

Frecheville's hero was striker Mark Thompson, plucked from local football, to star in the County Senior's showpiece with a strike just two minutes from the end of extra time to snatch a last gasp victory. It was agony for Goldthorpe as Thompson netted with last defender Towning and keeper Tongue lying prostrate in the goal mouth after an accidental collision between the pair, while earlier unlucky Colliery had led on no fewer than three occasions and missed from the spot with two minutes of normal time remaining.

The Dearne Valley men went ahead after 18 minutes when Dave Salkeld's low shot went inside the far post only for Frecheville to respond immediateley through pacy left winger Richard Taylor. The Silkstone Road outfit took a 2-1 lead on the half-hour after Tongue dropped a corner and Waring pounced to net from close range, but on the stroke of half-time the colliers saw Dave Kelly smash home a glorious 25 yarder to level.

The excitement continued into the second period when leading scorer Shaun Hartley ran onto a long ball down the middle swept past his marker and clipped the ball home for Goldthorpe to regain the advantage, only for Waring to make it 3-3 with a beautifully struck free-kick from 20 yards.

After Garry Hough had seen his controversial spot kick saved, the match moved into the additional half hour and there was a memorable introduction for 18 year old substitute Shaun Young as he thumped in a cracker of a goal for Goldthorpe to go in front for a third time. But as the final moved into the second period, the lush turf of one of South Yorkshire's best playing surfaces was taking its toll on Goldthorpe's tired players and Spencer Noble was allowed far too much room on the right and as Tongue advanced the midfielder slid the ball past him to make it four apiece, before Thompson added the final twist to an enthralling contest to give Frecheville the silverware.

Goldthorpe Colliery - Whitbread Trophy runners-up.

PREMIER DIVISION CLUBS 1993-94

ASH HOUSE
Secretary: T Cottam, 41 Pleasant Rd, Sheffield S12 2BD (0742 390897).
Ground: Sheffield Transport, Meadowhead, Sheffield.
Directions: Sheffield A61 Chesterfield road, 4 miles to r'bout, right off Greenhill Main Road on left.

BRUNSMEER ATHLETIC
Secretary: S J Oldfield, 64 Mount View Rd, Sheffield S8 8PH (0742 586357).
Ground: Dore Sports Ground, Townhead Rd, Dore.
Directions: A621, right into Dore Rd after 5 miles, left; The Meadway.

DENABY & CADEBY MINERS WELFARE
Secretary: A Randall, 37 Craganour Place, Denaby Main, Doncaster DN12 4AS (0709 860963).
Ground & Directions: Denaby United FC (see Northern Counties East League section).

FRECHEVILLE C.A.
Secretary: R Green, 15 Birley Moor Close, Sheffield S12 3BQ (0742 633836).
Ground: Silkstone Road, Frecheville, Sheffield.
Directions: From city A616 for 4 miles on Newark Road, left opposite shopping precinct into Silkstone Road.

GOLDTHORPE COLLIERY
Secretary: D Taverner, 50 East Avenue, Wombwell, Barnsley S73 8QQ (0226 757304).
Ground: Dearne C.M.W., Furlong Road, Goldthorpe.
Directions: From Rotherham A633 to Wath, left at r'bout to Goldthorpe. At Angel turn left under bridge; ground 600 yards on left.

HIGH GREEN VILLA
Secretary: T Staples, 41 Woodburn Drive, Chapeltown S30 4YT (0742 468560).
Ground: High Green Playing Fields, Bottomley Close.
Directions: A61 north for 5 miles, right at Howbrook crossroads into Greengate Lane.

MEXBOROUGH MAIN STREET
Secretary: A A Hough, 4 Cranswick Way, Conisborough, Doncaster DN12 3AY (0709 866479).
Ground & Directions: As Mexborough Town (see Websters Central Midlands League section).

PARRAMORES SPORTS
Secretary: R Blagden, 85 Youlgrave Drive, Sheffield S12 4SF (0742 640026).
Ground: Armroyd Lane, Elsecar, Barnsley.
Directions: From junction 36, M1 take Barnsley road to second r'bout, right to Chapeltown, left under bridge, second right Armroyd Lane ground on right.

PHOENIX
Secretary: D M Taylor, 22 Wilding Way, Kimberworth, Rotherham S61 1PQ (0709 555451).
Ground: Phoenix Sports Ground, Pavilion Lane, Bawtry Road, Brinsworth, Rotherham.
Directions: M1 jct 34, A631 to Rotherham - turn left after British Oxygen.

TREETON WELFARE
Secretary: P A Neville, 70 Hurtley Brook Ave., Sheffield S50 0HL (0742 450158).
Ground: Washfield Lane, Treeton.
Directions: Exit Sheffield Parkway to Catcliffe, then Treeton, right at Station Hotel, left in Arundel Avenue.

WATH SARACENS
Secretary: P Henry, 11 Elm Way, Wath-upon-Dearne, Rotherham S63 7PF (0709 874200).
Ground: Wath Sports Centre, Moor Road, Wath-upon-Dearne.
Directions: Rotherham, A633 through Rawmarsh, left at r'bout, left at next r'bout, Moor Road 400 yds on right.

THE DIVISION ALSO CONTAINS THE RESERVE SIDES OF: HALLAM *(see page 940)*, R.E.S. PARKGATE *(see page 941)*, WORSBOROUGH BRIDGE MINERS WELFARE ATHLETIC *(see page 942)*.

DONCASTER & DISTRICT SENIOR LEAGUE

PREM. DIVISION	P	W	D	L	F	A	PTS
Thorne Colliery	28	22	3	3	95	22	69
Northgate WMC	28	19	6	3	82	36	63
Carcroft V. WMC	28	20	3	5	58	33	63
Hemsworth MW	28	14	8	6	75	37	50
Kinsley Boys	28	13	10	5	75	38	49
Sth Kirkby Colliery	28	14	4	10	81	57	46
Hemsworth Town	28	14	4	10	51	41	46
Fishlake	28	11	7	10	42	42	40
Goole Town Res.	28	12	3	13	58	60	39
Hemsworth St.Pat.	28	9	4	15	56	71	31
Frickley Ath. Res.	28	7	4	17	50	67	25
Ings Lane	28	8	1	19	55	92	25
Askern Welfare	28	5	7	16	39	88	22
Yorkshire Main	28	3	4	21	30	85	13
Edlington WMC	28	2	6	20	38	116	12

DIVISION ONE	P	W	D	L	F	A	PTS
Peglers	26	18	6	2	59	29	60
Plant Works	26	17	3	6	58	33	54
Highfields MW	26	15	5	6	48	38	50
Skellow Grange	26	11	6	9	59	40	39
White Hart United	26	11	5	10	67	51	38
Scawsby United	26	11	5	10	65	57	38
Tickhill Town	26	12	2	12	54	63	38
Sutton Rovers	26	9	9	8	61	51	36
Lodge	26	11	2	13	58	62	35
Edlington British L.	26	10	3	13	44	51	33
Scawthorpe Social	26	8	8	10	47	44	32
Hemsworth MW Res.	26	7	3	16	38	72	24
Bentley Colliery	26	5	5	16	47	63	20
Cantley Hawthorn	26	4	4	18	37	88	16

DIVISION TWO	P	W	D	L	F	A	PTS
Hatfield Main Res.	30	25	4	1	135	40	79
Brookside WMC	30	23	1	6	129	52	70
Tally Ho	30	22	3	5	92	30	69
Ackworth United	30	19	3	8	108	52	60
Sth Elmsall Cheq.	30	17	5	8	110	63	56
Hemsworth K'head	29	14	7	8	73	53	49
S. Kirkby C. Res.	30	12	5	13	80	87	41
Hemsworth T. Res.	30	12	2	16	49	64	38
Cantley Hawthorn	30	10	5	15	68	86	35
Rossington Main J.	29	10	4	15	65	88	34
White Hart U. Res.	30	9	7	14	56	93	34
R.F.S.	30	9	4	17	52	84	31
Doncaster K'head	30	8	4	18	54	100	28
Kinsley Boys Res.	30	6	5	19	66	89	23
Hemsworth S.P. Res	30	6	3	21	64	122	21
Sutton Rvrs Res.	30	3	6	21	51	149	15

WEST YORKSHIRE LEAGUE

President: W.Keyworth

Chairman: J.Hill
Secretary: Kevin Parkinson,
9 Lake Lock Drive, Stanley, Wakefield WF3 4HN

PREMIER DIVISION

The Premier had a couple of early set backs with the withdrawl of Holbeck and Nostell. This meant only 18 League games and no margin for a couple of early season defeats! The season started well for Champions Carlton, who beat Beeston, Robin Hood and drew with Horsforth in their first three games without conceding a goal, to be the early pacesetters. Horsforth soon got into their stride and with Carlton they were the early leaders. They kept exchanging top spot until January, then a bad spell in heavy going saw Carlton's experienced team founder against younger opponents from Wakefield and Beeston. Those two defeats, 5-3 and 4-0 respectively, were to be the two defeats which eventually ruined their title hopes. Horsforth continued to pick up points but a drop off of form around February saw their hopes fade too. Whitkirk, who had been amongst the favourites for a tilt at the title, had early season injuries and manager Steve Higo was never able to field the same team, twice, although they did have the result of the season with their defeat of Horsforth 8-3. Wakefield's expected title challenge never got going, although they did take points off the top three teams. Robin Hood had picked up the former Holbeck manager, Mally Jones and several players. He managed to lead them to the premier league cup final, their first for several seasons. Their league form showed a lack of goals, only 20 scored in 18 games, but the defence was sound only conceding the same amount. Swillington had a big turn over of players over the season, with several having NCE experience but again a settled side was the problem and following their expulsion from the Barkston Ash Cup their season faded.

The struggle at the bottom developed into a dog fight between Featherstone, Sherburn and East End Park. Sherburn had a new manager and a new young team, who often found several of them called up to represent the County under 18s. This culminated in a string of late season matches and the Rose never got out of the bottom three. Featherstone found themselves using over thirty players for one team and again injuries hampered their chances, but they did continue to play football throughout and have to be commended for their efforts. Likewise at the Park, Les Farrar and Kenny Briggs found the pull of Elland Road often left them with several recognised players missing. The title ended up at Beeston, who having lost two of their first three games went unbeaten for the rest of the season, conceding only 11 goals on the way. They also took the League Cup defeating the Hood 3-0 and reached the Invitation Shield final.

DIVISION ONE

The first division also suffered from late withdrawls and in fact only nine teams finished the season. Rothwell Athletic made the transition from Division Two look easy as they became the early pacemakers with GN Khalsa. Only Horbury looked capable of giving the top two a run and they were in contention right up to April. Great Preston had a strange season; after Christmas they only won one game in the League but managed to reach two Cup Finals! Probably the surprise team in the Division was Barwick, Barry Kellosoff's men only had three points from seven games on the 7th December, but apart from a League Cup defeat, they never lost another League match. They ended up in their highest position for several years. The two teams to disappoint this time were the two West Leeds teams, Armley Athletic and neighbours Upper Armley. Both ended mid-table and will be looking for improvement next time round, especially Upper Armley, who had done the double in this Division the season before. Snydale and Carlton Reserves ended in the bottom two and although they reached two Cup semi-finals the Carlton management duo of Nelson and Kitchen's position was hindered by the lack of experienced players in important positions. GN showed a new measure of consistencey not seen before. No doubt the return of Mally Connor from Bridlington Town before the turn helped their cause as they went on to a League and Cup double. The winner for the League title against Great Preston came in the 94th minute! They beat the same opposition in the League Cup 4-1 and then went on to pip Beeston in the Invitation Shield 3-2 to round off a tremndous season.

DIVISION TWO

The Division Two race as expected was a two-horse race between the promoted clubs, Bramley and Belle Isle WMC. The much fancied Bramley side with their array of ex-Farsley Celtic players, lost their one and only league game early in the season to Whitkirk Reserves and this eventually cost them the league. Belle Isle drew five games and Bramley three to leave them level on points after 20 games. The South Leeds club had the better goal difference and this saw them home. They also reached the League Cup Final but met their match in Seacroft WMC who ran out winners 5-2. If the East Leeds club had put the Cup team out each week they would no doubt have been in contention for League too. Whitkirk and Beeston Reserves were both in contention early on, but first team calls probably hampered both teams. They did meet in the Leeds District Cup however, and the final was a treat for the nuetral observer as the 'Kirk ran out winners 4-3 before a crowd of 500 at East End Park. Oddyssey again showed good form at home, but on their travels failed to make an impact. Upper Armley Reserves, who won this division a couple of seasons ago, found themselves fighting relegation and just avoided the drop when they got a point from their last game of the season. This left Monk Fryston, Lofthouse Foods and Leeds City to battle it out. Fryston scraped through on goal difference and with a fine ground all they need do is find some good young players to help them up the table. Leeds City's Roy Dixon had an uphill struggle from day one and they were unable to avoid the drop into Division three. Lofthouse who came bottom resigned ay the end of the season and their position was academic at the final analysis.

Terry Rowe

PREM.

	P	W	D	L	F	A	PTS
Beeston St Anth.	18	13	3	2	52	11	29
Carlton Athletic	18	12	4	2	36	17	28
Horsforth S.M.	18	9	5	4	39	28	23
Wakefield	18	8	4	6	35	28	20
Whitkirk Wanderers	18	7	5	6	36	34	19
Robin Hood Ath.	18	8	3	7	20	20	19
Sherburn W.R.	18	6	1	11	30	44	13
Swillington M.W.	18	3	5	10	22	41	11
E. End Pk W.M.C.	18	4	2	12	32	49	10
Featherstone Coll.	18	3	2	13	19	51	8

DIV. ONE

	P	W	D	L	F	A	PTS
G.N. Khalsa	16	12	2	2	46	24	26
Rothwell Athletic	16	12	1	3	42	23	25
Horbury Town	16	7	4	5	32	23	18
Barwick	16	6	4	6	47	38	16
Armley Athletic	16	5	5	6	32	31	15
Upper Armley O.B.	16	5	4	7	31	38	14
Great Preston	16	2	8	6	28	31	12
Snydale Rd Ath.	16	4	3	9	32	45	11
Carlton Ath. Res.	16	3	1	12	29	66	7

DIV. THREE

	P	W	D	L	F	A	PTS
Nostell M.W.	20	17	3	0	71	24	37
Calverley Utd	20	13	3	4	75	43	29
Wakefield Res.	20	12	3	5	60	28	27
B.B.A.	20	11	4	5	40	34	26
Dewsbury M. Ath.	20	7	5	8	39	42	19
Pontefract Town	20	7	4	9	41	41	18
Willowfield Celtic	20	7	3	10	31	46	17
Woodhouse M.M.	20	7	2	11	36	39	16
Woodhouse Hill	20	6	1	13	43	68	13
Swillington M.W.	20	4	2	14	35	72	10
Gt Preston Res.	20	3	2	15	18	52	8

DIV. TWO

	P	W	D	L	F	A	PTS
Belle Isle WMC	20	15	5	0	72	25	35
Bramley	20	15	3	1	65	23	35
Whitkirk W. Res.	20	11	2	7	56	42	24
Rothwell Town	20	11	1	8	54	22	23
Beeston S.A. Res.	20	9	4	7	41	36	22
Seacroft WMC	20	7	3	10	38	43	17
Oddyssey	20	6	4	10	41	50	16
U. Armley O.B. Res.	20	5	3	12	25	62	13
Monk Fryston Utd	20	5	2	13	30	47	12
Leeds City	20	5	2	13	33	55	12
Lofthouse Foods	20	5	1	14	26	55	11

DIV. FOUR

	P	W	D	L	F	A	PTS
Mount St Mary's	20	15	3	2	77	17	33
Belle I. WMC Res.	20	13	5	2	49	23	31
Rothwell Ath. Res.	20	14	2	4	53	23	30
Frank Ford	20	13	1	6	45	36	27
Horbury T. Res.	20	7	5	8	40	38	19
Robin Hood Ath.	20	5	6	9	27	37	16
Yorks Copper Wks	20	6	3	11	33	47	15
Sherburn W.R. Res.	20	5	5	10	41	61	15
Barwick	20	3	6	11	40	65	12
Pontefract T. Res.	20	5	1	14	27	51	11
Woodlesford	20	4	3	13	20	54	11

PREMIER DIVISION RESULT CHART

	1	2	3	4	5	6	7	8	9	10
1. Beeston St. Anthony's	*	1-2	4-2	4-1	5-0	1-0	3-0	3-0	1-1	5-1
2. Carlton Athletic	0-4	*	3-2	3-0	0-0	0-0	4-0	5-0	2-2	1-1
3. East End Park WMC	0-4	1-4	*	7-1	0-4	2-3	3-2	1-2	2-3	1-5
4. Featherstone Colliery	1-5	0-2	1-0	*	1-7	1-2	3-2	1-1	0-2	2-4
5. Horsforth St. Margarets	1-1	1-2	1-1	2-1	*	2-0	2-0	2-2	2-2	2-0
6. Robin Hood Athletic	1-0	0-1	2-2	1-0	0-2	*	0-3	0-2	1-2	0-0
7. Sherburn White Rose	1-4	0-2	4-1	1-2	3-2	1-4	*	2-3	2-0	1-1
8. Swillington Miners Welfare	1-3	0-1	1-2	2-2	1-2	0-3	2-4	*	1-3	2-2
9. Wakefield	0-0	5-3	1-3	2-1	1-4	0-1	6-1	4-1	*	0-1
10. whitkirk Wanderers	0-0	1-2	4-2	4-1	8-3	1-2	2-3	1-1	2-1	*

DIVISION ONE RESULT CHART

	1	2	3	4	5	6	7	8	9
1. Armley Athletic	*	3-2	1-2	1-1	2-3	1-1	1-4	3-3	3-0
2. Barwick	2-1	*	2-1	4-4	2-3	2-3	3-1	7-1	4-4
3. Carlton Athletic Reserves	2-6	2-6	*	1-1	2-6	1-5	1-3	6-5	4-0
4. Great Preston	2-3	2-2	6-1	*	0-1	0-0	1-2	2-2	3-1
5. G.N.Khalsa	4-1	5-3	5-3	2-1	*	2-1	2-0	0-1	2-2
6. Horbury Town	1-1	2-1	5-1	1-1	0-1	*	0-1	2-1	7-2
7. Rothwell Athletic	3-1	2-1	8-0	2-1	3-3	3-2	*	1-0	2-1
8. Snydale Road Athletic	0-3	1-3	4-1	2-2	2-7	5-1	2-4	*	1-3
9. Upper Armley Old Boys	1-1	3-3	3-1	6-1	1-0	0-1	4-3	0-2	*

DIVISION TWO RESULT CHART

	1	2	3	4	5	6	7	8	9	10	11
1. Beeston St. Anthony Reserves	*	0-1	0-3	2-4	2-3	4-3	4-2	1-1	4-0	1-0	2-1
2. Belle Isle WMC	2-2	*	0-0	2-1	2-1	4-1	2-2	5-1	1-0	5-2	5-3
3. Bramley	5-2	4-4	*	3-1	4-0	3-0	5-1	3-2	1-0	2-0	1-1
4. Leeds City	0-7	2-5	2-4	*	3-2	2-1	2-3	0-3	3-3	6-0	2-5
5. Lofthouse Foods	0-1	2-2	1-3	1-0	*	0-4	2-1	2-4	1-2	1-2	2-4
6. Monk Fryston United	2-3	0-6	0-2	1-2	2-0	*	1-1	2-4	1-0	2-1	1-2
7. Oddyssey	4-0	1-4	2-3	1-1	1-2	1-1	*	4-2	3-2	7-1	6-3
8. Rothwell Town	1-3	1-3	1-2	3-0	6-1	2-1	5-0	*	3-2	5-0	3-2
9. Seacroft WMC	1-1	2-6	2-6	3-0	2-1	2-4	3-0	5-2	*	1-1	4-1
10. Upper Armley Old Boys Reserves	1-1	1-4	1-9	2-0	0-4	3-1	2-1	3-4	3-2	*	1-1
11. Whitkirk Wanderers Reserves	2-1	0-3	3-2	4-2	4-1	5-2	5-0	3-1	1-2	6-1	*

DIVISION THREE RESULT CHART

	1	2	3	4	5	6	7	8	9	10	11
1. B.B.A.	*	5-2	3-1	2-1	2-2	1-0	2-2	1-5	0-1	1-5	0-2
2. Calverley United	2-2	*	3-1	2-2	3-3	10-3	10-3	3-0	2-0	8-1	4-1
3. Dewsbury Moor Athletic	0-3	2-1	*	2-1	1-6	1-1	7-0	1-3	1-1	3-2	2-2
4. Great Preston Reserves	1-3	0-1	3-2	*	0-2	0-0	2-0	0-4	0-2	1-3	0-2
5. Nostell Miners Welfare	6-2	5-1	4-2	4-1	*	2-1	2-1	2-1	7-0	3-1	2-0
6. Pontefract Town	0-1	2-6	1-2	4-0	3-3	*	1-2	1-0	0-1	4-1	5-2
7. Swillington Miners Welfare Reserves	0-3	2-4	1-5	5-2	2-3	2-3	*	2-3	3-5	4-2	2-1
8. Wakefield Reserves	1-1	6-4	0-0	5-0	1-2	1-4	5-0	*	6-3	5-0	0-0
9. Willowfield Celtic	1-3	1-5	3-0	1-2	0-4	2-2	1-1	1-5	*	3-0	2-0
10. Woodhouse Hill W.M.C.	0-2	2-3	4-4	2-1	3-4	2-1	8-4	1-5	4-3	*	2-6
11. Woodhouse Moor Meths	2-3	2-1	0-2	6-1	0-4	2-5	2-0	2-4	1-0	3-0	*

DIVISION FOUR RESULT CHART	1	2	3	4	5	6	7	8	9	10	11
1. Barwick Reserves	*	1-3	1-3	2-2	1-1	3-5	4-0	1-3	2-2	3-1	3-3
2. Belle Isle Reserves	1-1	*	2-1	0-0	3-3	1-0	1-1	0-2	5-1	6-0	3-1
3. Frank Ford	4-3	2-3	*	1-1	3-1	4-3	4-0	1-2	2-1	2-0	4-2
4. Horbury Town Reserves	5-2	4-1	2-3	*	1-1	2-1	2-1	3-5	2-3	1-2	0-2
5. Mount St.Mary's	3-2	2-2	5-1	4-0	*	4-0	3-0	2-0	6-1	5-0	4-0
6. Pontefract Town Reserves	0-3	2-3	1-2	0-4	2-0	*	1-3	1-4	4-2	1-0	2-3
7. Robin Hood Athletic Reserves	4-0	0-1	4-1	1-1	0-3	1-1	*	1-4	5-1	0-0	1-1
8. Rothwell Athletic Reserves	4-1	1-3	4-1	3-1	0-3	5-0	3-0	*	1-1	3-0	1-2
9. Sherburn W.R. Reserves	1-1	0-5	1-3	2-6	0-6	4-1	4-0	2-2	*	5-2	3-3
10. Woodesford	3-3	0-3	0-1	4-2	0-8	1-2	0-0	1-2	2-0	*	4-3
11. Yorkshire Copper Welfare	2-1	1-3	0-2	1-0	1-2	2-0	0-2	0-4	3-7	4-0	*

PREMIER DIVISION CUP 1992-93

First Round

Wakefield v East End Park W.M.C.	4-0	Sherburn White Rose v Beeston St Anthony's	0-6

Second Round

Horsforth St Margarets v Carlton Athletic	2-3	Swillington Miners Welfare v Wakefield	2-2,2-3
Whitkirk Wanderers v Beeston St Anthonys	1-3	Robin Hood Athletic v Featherstone Colliery	2-0

Semi-Finals

Wakefield v Beeston St Anthonys	0-1	Carlton Athletic v Rood Hood Athletic	0-0,0-1

Final: Beeston St Anthonys 3, Rood Hood Athletic 0

DIVISION ONE CUP 1992-93

First Round

Horbury Town v Upper Armley Old Boys	0-1	Barwick v Armley Athletic	2-2,3-0

Second Round

Snydale Road Athletic v Barwick	3-5	Great Preston v Upper Armley Old Boys	6-2
Rothwell Athletic v G.N. Khalsa	2-3	Carlton Athletic Reserves (bye)	

Semi-Finals

G.N. Khalsa v Barwick	1-0	Great Preston v Carlton Athletic Reserves	5-0

Final: G.N. Khalsa 4, Great Preston 1

DIVISION TWO CUP 1992-93

First Round

Whitkirk Wdrs Reserves v Bramley	0-1	Belle Isle W.M.C. v Oddyssey	4-2
Rothwell Town v Monk Fryston United	3-1		

Second Round

Seacroft W.M.C. v Lofthouse Foods	3-2	Beeston St Anthony's Reserves v Bramley	0-2
Upper Armley O.B. Res. v Belle Isle W.M.C.	2-4	Leeds City v Rothwell Town	2-3

Semi-Finals

Rothwell Town v Seacroft W.M.C.	2-3	Bramley v Belle Isle W.M.C.	1-4

Final: Seacroft W.M.C. 5, Belle Isle W.M.C. 2

DIVISION THREE CUP 1992-93

First Round

Dewsbury Moor Ath. v Gt Preston Res.	5-4	Willowfield Celtic v Woodhouse Moor Methodists	1-5
Calverley United v Nostell Miners Welfare	3-1		

Second Round

Pontefract Town v Dewsbury Moor Athletic	0-2	Woodhouse Moor Methodists v Wakefield Reserves	1-3
B.B.A. v Calverley United	1-4	Swillington M.W. Res. v Woodhouse Hill W.M.C.	5-2

Semi-Finals

Wakefield Reserves v Calverley United	0-3	Swillington M.W. Res. v Dewsbury Moor Athletic	1-2

Final: Calverley United 1, Dewsbury Moor Athletic 0 (after 2-2 draw)

DIVISION FOUR CUP 1992-93

First Round

Mount St Marys v Rothwell Ath. Reserves	2-3	Horbury Town Res. v Pontefract Town Reserves	1-2
Robin Hood Ath. Reserves v Barwick Reserves	3-1		

Second Round

Woodlesford v Belle Isle W.M.C. Res.	5-5,2-1	Sherburn White Rose Res.v Yorks Copper Works	3-2
Frank Ford v Rothwell Athletic Reserves	4-0	Pontefract Town v Robin Hood Athletic Reserves	0-3

Semi-Finals

Woodlesford Reserves v Frank Ford	1-4	Sherburn White Rose Res. v Rood Hood Ath. Res.	1-2

Final: Frank Ford 1, Rood Hood Athletic Reserves 0 (after 1-1 draw)

PREMIER DIVISION CLUBS 1993-94

BEESTON ST ANTHONY'S

Secretary: N Hutton, 22 Sefton Terrace, Beeston, Leeds LS11 7EL (0532 703151).
Ground & Directions: Beggars Hill. Beggars Hill is situated behind Pullans Builders. from Leeds - A653 Dewsbury Road, right at Tommy Wass Pub (2.5 miles from Leeds) onto Old Lane, right at 'T' junction, left into Sunnyview Gdns at Beeston Manor Elderly Persons' Home, car park and dressing rooms 50yds on right.
Colours: Green/black.   **Change colours:** Red/black.

CARLTON ATHLETIC

Secretary: R Hargreaves, 11 Newton Drive, Outwood, Wakefield WF1 3HZ (0924 826141).
Ground & Directions: Carlton Cricket Club. Via A61, Leeds/Wakefield Road, travel to Half Way House (Public House) at Robin Hood. Proceed to Rothwell down the A654, taking first right after approx. half a mile. This leads to Carlton, turn right to ground quarter mile on left. Via M62 or A642, Exit Motorway at junction 30. Travel towards Wakefield on A642 quarter mile only and then proceed towards Lofthouse along B6135. Continue for 1 mile passing under motorway to the top of the hill. Don't turn left to Lofthouse, but travel straight on with the ground in view on the right.
Colours: Yellow & blue/blue/blue.   **Change colours:** Black & white stripes/white/white.

EAST END PARK W.M.C.

Secretary: D Dickinson, 20 Ecclesburn Avenue, Leeds LS9 9BZ (0532 485553).
Ground & Directions: Skelton Road. Buses from Leeds City Centre to White Horse Hotel, York Rd. Take bridge over main road into Skelton Terrace, then 2nd left & 1st right into Skelton Rd. Ground on left.
Colours: Sky & navy squares.   **Change colours:** Maroon & navy blue.

FEATHERSTONE COLLIERY

Secretary: M Smith, 'Derwent', Thorpe Lane, Thorpe Audlin, Pontefract WF8 3FW. (0977 620709).
Ground & Directions: Cressey's Corner. In Featherstone at the junction of Featherstone Lane and Green Lane, turn into Halfpenny Lane, 1st right down to rail crossing, ground over the crossing.
Colours: Maroon & sky/sky/maroon.   **Change colours:** Blue & white stripes/white/blue.

GASCOIGNE UNITED

Secretary: M Liversidge, 169 Fairburn Drive, Garforth, Leeds LS25 2JD (0532 865623).
Ground & Directions: Great North Road. Follow A63 from Leeds passing Garforth. Turn left just before A1 to Micklefield and take first left into the ground after the railway bridge.
Colours: Blue & white hooped/blue/blue.

HORSFORTH ST MARGARETS

Secretary: R Cowling, 4 Jackman Drive, Horsforth, Leeds LS18 4HS (0532 585358).
Ground & Directions: Cragg Hill Recreation Ground. Ground is situated on the Horsforth Ring Road A6120 (Broadway) halfway between the Ringway and the Eleventh Earl Public Houses.
Colours: Red/navy/navy   **Change colours:** Sky & white stripes/sky/sky.

KNARESBOROUGH TOWN

Secretary: T Barrett, 26 Park House Green, Harrogate, North Yorkshire HG1 3HW (0423 509031).
Ground & Directions: Manse Lane. Via A1 or A58 from Leeds to Wetherby, follow signs for Knaresborough. Manse Lane is just before the Wetherby Road/York Road on the outskirts of town, half a mile from the A1.
Colours: Red & white/white/red.   **Change colours:** All white

ROBIN HOOD ATHLETIC

Secretary: A Parker, 88 Mexborough Street, Leeds LS7 3JF (0532 628227).
Ground & Directions: Coach & Horses Hotel. A61 Leeds/Wakefield Road to the Coach & Horses Public House at Robin Hood. Kettlethorpe Bus No.110 alighting at the Coach & Horses Public House.
Colours: Green/black.   **Change colours:** Red/black.

SHERBURN WHITE ROSE

Secretary: W Poskitt, 14 Deighton Avenue, Sherburn-in-Elmet, Leeds LS25 6BR (0977 684781).
Ground & Directions: Recreation Ground. Take the Tadcaster Road from Sherburn traffic lights at main crossroads. Ground is on right just before de-restriction road sign.
Colours: Red/blue/red.   **Change colours:** Blue & white hoops/blue.

SWILLINGTON MINERS WELFARE

Secretary: F Boon, 39 Neville Grove, Swillington, Leeds LS26 8QN (0532 867833).
Ground & Directions: Welfare Sports Ground. From M62 exit junction 30 (A642) and follow signs fo Garforth. On entering village the Club is on the right. Ground to the rear of the club.
Colours: All red.   **Change colours:** White/red/white.

WAKEFIELD

Secretary: A Wolfe, 28 Cliff Street, off Batley Road, Wakefield WF2 0DW (0924 364035).
Ground & Directions: Stanley Royd Hospital. M62 jct 30, A642 towards Wakefield for 2 miles. Pass Pinderfields and turn right at entrance to Stanley Royd Hospital and ground on left.
Colours: All blue.   **Change colours:** Red/navy/navy.

WHITKIRK WANDERERS

Secretary: N S Beaumont, 7 Kingsway, Whitkirk, Leeds LS5 7BU (0532 644499).
Ground & Directions: Off Selby Rd. Located off Selby Rd behind Cemetery almost opposite the Brown Cow Pub, Whitkirk, Selby Road.
Colours: All sky   **Change colours:** All blue.

DIVISION ONE CLUBS 1993-94

ARMLEY ATHLETIC

Secretary: S Walker, 19 Otley Old Road, Leeds LS16 6HB (0532 672684).
Ground & Directions: Western Flatts Park. By road turn off Armley Gyratory r'bout left to Wortley via Wellington Rd, Oldfield Lane, Greenhill Lane to Western Flatts Park.
Colours: Green & yellow stripes/green/green.   **Change:** Maroon/sky/sky.

BARWICK

Secretary: B Kollesoff, 3 Leeds Rd, Barwick-in-Elmet, Leeds LS15 4JE (0532) 812638).
Ground & Directions: Back of Village Hall. From Leeds take A64 (York Rd) to Seacroft r'bout (6 miles) and follow signs for Barwick, right on entering Barwick at New Inn, 1st left into Chapel Lane.
Colours: Maroon/sky   **Change colours:** Black & blue striped/black/black.

BELLE ISLE W.M.C.

Secretary: D Siddle, 53 Manor Farm Drive, Leeds LS10 3RE (0532 712214).
Ground & Directions: Belle Isle Primary School. A61 from Leeds, right at lights into Church Str., pass Hunslet shopping centre to Belle Isle Rd, after Belle Isle Circus (r'bout) 1st right into Windmill Rd. From Wakefield to Half Way Garage, 1st left onto Sharp Lane past Omnibus Pub., travel down Belle Isle Rd, left into Windmill Rd.
Colours: Green & white hoops/green/green.   **Change colours:** All white.

BRAMLEY

Secretary: B Davies, 43 Raynville Grange, Bramley, Leeds LS13 2QD (0532 744156).
Ground & Directions: Bramley Park. Entrance is from Moorfields, Town Street, Bramley (adjacent to Conservative Club and near to the Globe Hotel).
Colours: White/black/white.   **Change colours:** Yellow/blue/white.

G.N. PRINCE PHILLIPS

Secretary: J Bravo, 7b Grange Crescent, Leeds LS7 4ET (0831 371643)
Ground & Directions: Prince Philip Centre. From Leeds City Centre take the main road to Harrogate (A61) onto Scott Hall Rd. Scott Hall Avenue is 2nd left turn which is signposted Prince Philip Centre.
Cols: All orange   **Change colours:** All white   **Prev. Name:** G.N. Khalsa (pre-1973)

GREAT PRESTON

Secretary: V Donnelly, 51 Hollinhurst, Allerton Bywater, Castleford WF10 2HY (0532 871713).
Ground & Directions: At side of New Inn. Berry Lane is off the main Leeds/Castleford Rd thru Gt Preston.
Colours: All green.   **Change colours:** Sky/navy/sky.

HORBURY TOWN

Secretary: G Lee, 31 Nettleton Street, Ossett, West Yorks WF5 8HQ (0924 280489).
Ground & Directions: Parker Rd PF. From Wakefield to Huddersfield Road A642, 1st right off Horbury By-pass after passing under motorway, uphill towards Horbury/Ossett B6128 for 1 mile, 2nd right opposite Horbury School onto New Str., Carr Lodge Park on right. Via M1; jct 40, towards Wakefield A638 for half mile, 1st right after lights into Broadway. At the end of Broadway this meets Wakefield/Huddersfield Road A642. Turn right then as above.
Cols: Blue & black/black/black.   **Change colours:** Red & black/black/black.

ROTHWELL ATHLETIC

Secretary: T Wilkinson, 23 Whitehall Croft, Rothwell, Leeds LS26 0JD (0532 820767).
Ground & Directions: Leeds/Pontefract Road. A639 from Leeds towards Oulton. Ground on left.
Colours: Navy (blue & red flashes)/navy   **Change:** Sky/navy/navy.

ROTHWELL TOWN

Secretary: P Richardson, 55 Meadowgate Drive, Lofthouse, Wakefield WF3 3SR (0924 870720).
Ground & Directions: Royds Lane. Ground is 300 yards on left of Royds Lane, which leads off Marsh Street in Rothwell town Centre.
Colours: Maroon/blue.   **Change colours:** Red & black hoops/black.

UPPER ARMLEY OLD BOYS

Secretary: J Plowright, 29 Armley Grange View, Leeds LS12 3QP. (0532 797134).
Ground & Directions: Moorfield Rec. From Leeds take Leeds/Bradford Rd through Armley. Turn left at Kentucky Fried Chicken onto Armley Ridge Rd, club on left.
Colours: White/black/black.   **Change colours:** Red & blue stripes/blue/blue.

This Division also includes the reserves sides of: Beeston St Anthonys and Whitkirk Wdrs.

DIVISION TWO CLUBS 1993-94

B.B.A.

Secretary: J M Stead, 166 Whitechapel Rd, Cleckheaton, BD19 6HR (0274 879147).
Ground & Directions: B.B.A. Spts Centre. M62 jct 26 (Chain Bar), ground adjacent to r'bout.
Cols: Yellow & navy/navy/navy   **Change colours:** Red & black stripes/black/black.

CALVERLEY UNITED

Secretary: D Young, 15 Warehouse Row, Calverley Bridge, Rodley, Leeds LS13 1NF (0532 561452).
Ground & Directions: Victoria Park. A647 Leeds/Greengates Rd past Calverley Church - ground on left.
Colours: Red/black/white.   **Change colours:** All red.

DEWSBURY MOOR ATHLETIC

Secretary: N.Longstaff, 38 School Lane, Dewsbury Moor, Dewsbury WF13 4DU (0924 469973).
Ground & Directions: Pilgrim Park. M62 jct 28, A653 to Dewsbury, A644 for one and a half miles, right after Fire Station on to Ravensholme Rd, at T-junction turn left, dressing rooms on right.
Colours: Blue & yellow/blue   **Change colours:** Red & white/blue.

MONK FRYSTON UNITED

Secretary: P Collins, 7 York Rd, Monk Fryston, Leeds LS25 5JF (0977 685524).
Ground & Directions: Lowfield Lane, at the Selby Fork Motel. On A1 take A63 Selby Road, thru Monk Fryston village and after half-mile past Texaco Garage turn right into Lowfield Lane which is narrow and unmarked except for club sign.
Colours: Amber/black.   **Change colours:** Black & white stripes/black.

NOSTELL MINERS WELFARE

Secretary: R Winfield, 13 Edward Drive, Outwood, Wakefield WF1 2LL (0924 826408).
Ground & Directions: Nostell M.W. Leave Wakefield on A638 Doncaster Road. After approx. three and a half miles turn right opposite Crofton Arms into Crofton Village, one and a quarter miles to The Slipper pub, left and Welfare 400m away.
Colours: Red/white/red.   **Change colours:** Orange/white/orange.

ODDYSSEY

Secretary: J Barrett, 96, Scarrbottom Rd, Halifax HX2 7DZ (0422 362069).
Ground & Directions: Saville Park. Huddersfield Road out of Halifax for 1 mile, right into Dryclough Lane (before Halifax gen. Hospital) which leads into Skircoat Moor Rd, 1st right after crossroads, ground at top of Saville Park, 400yds from dressing rooms.
Cols: Green & white/black/black   **Change colours:** Sky & navy stripes/black/black.

PONTEFRACT TOWN

Secretary: PThorpe, 26 Windsor Rise, Pontefract, W.Yorkshire WF8 4PZ (0977 780359).
Ground & Directions: Pontefract Barracks PF. M62 jct 32, past racecourse to Pontefract for approx. 1 mile, right into Wakefield Rd, ground half mile on left.
Colours: Green & yellow stripes/green/green   **Change:** Sky/navy/navy.

SEACROFT W.M.C.

Secretary: B Hughes, 1 Stocks Rise, Seacroft, Leeds LS14 6HU (0532 640370)
Ground & Directions: Seacroft WMC. Bus from Leeds to Kentmere Avenue, Seacroft. Cross road to club.
Colours: Red/black/red.   **Change colours:** All light blue.

WILLOWFIELD CELTIC

Secretary: K.Bush, 84 Rolls Head Road, Norton Tower, Halifax HX2 0LH ((0422 380181).
Ground & Directions: Holmes Park. M62 jct 26, A58 to Halifax, A646 Todmorden/Burnley road for approx. three and a half miles to Luddendenfoot, left at British Furtex, over canal bridge to car park.
Colours: All white.   **Change colours:** Green & white hoops.

WOODHOUSE MOOR METHODISTS

Secretary: D Drake, 52 Moseley Wood Gdns, Leeds LS16 7HR (0532 671863).
Ground & Directions: Soliders Field. Roundhay Rd out of Leeds, left at Oakwood Clock lights, ground on left.
Colours: Navy/white   **Change colours:** Sky/white.

This Division also includes the reserves sides of: Carlton Ath., Upper Armley O.B., Wakefield.

DIVISION THREE CLUBS 1993-94

FRANK FORD

Secretary: T McIntyre, 13 Warley Rd, King Cross, Halifax HX1 3SU (0274 499821 W).
Ground & Directions: Broomfield Ave. Take main Halifax to Huddesfield Road until Halifax Hosp., up Dudwell Lane and dressing rooms are at the top. M62 jct 24, take road to Elland following Halifax signs to top of Salterhebble hill (Halifax Gen. Hosp.), left up Dudwell lane to dressing rooms at Standard of Freedom Pub.
Cols: Black & white stripes/black/black. **Change colours:** Red & black stripes/black/black.

GARFORTH W.M.C.

Secretary: A Fisher, 3 Summerhill Rd, Garforth, Leeds LS25 1AX (0532 869099)
Ground & Directions: Garnforth Community College. A63 (Selby Road) or A639/A642 from Leeds to Old George r'bout near Garforth, follow A63, left towards Garforth at top of hill, college quarter mile on right.
Colours: White/blue/black. **Change colours:** Tangerine/white/tangerine.

LEEDS CITY

Secretary: R Dixon, The Old Lodge, 151 Otley Road, Leeds LS6 3QG (0532 432100).
Ground & Directions: Bedquilts PF. Main Leeds to Otley Road, 1st right past Cemetery (St Helen's Lane), entrance to ground is on left hand side at first junction (Adel Lane).
Colours: Sky/navy/white & blue **Change colours:** White/navy blue/white.

MOUNT ST MARY'S

Secretary: E J McDermott, 10 The Close, Saxton Gdns, Leeds LS9 8HW (0532 439228).
Ground & Directions: Snake Lane. From York Road A64 follow signs for Pontefract down Pontefract Lane to the Bridgefield Pub, ground opposite. Bus No.63 from outside Bus Station or bus No.27 from Eastgate, alight at the Bridgefield Pub.
Colours: Green & white/green. **Change colours:** Blue & white/black shorts.

WOODHOUSE HILL W.M.C.

Secretary: R Cunniff, 58 Garforth Drive, Altofts, Normanton WF6 2NQ.
Ground & Directions: Woodland Sch. PF. M62 jct 31, A655 towards Normanton for one and a half miles to Woodhouse Hill WMC. Dressing rooms are at rear of ground. Park cars in club car park.
Colours: Red/black/red. **Change colours:** Green & white hoops.

YORKSHIRE COPPER WORKS

Secretary: R Lawrence, 56 Langdale Rd, Woodlesford, Leeds LS26 8XF (0532 820487).
Ground & Directions: Haigh Park Rd. A61 Leeds/Wakefield Road passing thru Hunslet to Stourton, at lights before John Waddington bear left on A639 Pontefract Rd, ground on left after half mile. Bus from Central Bus Station C Stand to Yorkshire Copper Works.
Colours: White/black/black. **Change colours:** Orange/black/orange.

This Division also includes the reserve sides of: Barwick, Belle Isle W.M.C., Horbury Town, Robin Hood Ath., Rothwell Ath., Sherburn White Rose and Whitkirk Wanderers ('A' team).

DIVISION FOUR CLUBS 1993-94

HOLBECK W.M.C.

Secretary: C Blakey, 22 Shafton Lane, Holbeck, Leeds LS11 9RE (0532 434081)
Ground & Directions: Churwell Hill. Take the exit from M62/M621 for Leeds United A.F.C., pass the football ground with the Peacock Pub on the left for half a mile, straight on at r'bout passing the Drysalters Pub on left to next r'bout, right onto Churwell Hill, ground 400yds on right.
Colours: Jade & white stripes/white/blue.

NORTH LEEDS W.M.C.

Secretary: K Pears, 2 Foundry Place, Leeds LS9 6DA (0532 403787).
Ground & Directions: Amaranth Cricket Club. Travel from Leeds A64 or via Ring Road to Crossgates. Turn down Austhorpe Rd which is adjacent to the Arndale Centre passing Vickers Tank Factory. Continue further along unmade road (Don't give up) to Farm gates. Go through gates and the ground is behind the Farm at Amaranth Cricket club.
Cols: Green & yellow/green/green **Change colours:** Black & blue stripes/black/black.

(A.F.C.) WHITECOTE

Secretary: K J Hollock, 10 Newlay Lane Place, Leeds LS13 2BB (0532 554323).
Ground & Directions: Stanningley Park - Pitch No.4. A65 from Leeds, left at Kirkstall lights then right after Clover Warehouse onto B6157 Leeds and Bradford road. Proceed to 'T' junction and turn left, then right at Sunwin Rover into Halfmile Lane. Dressing rooms on right.
Colours: Sky/navy/navy **Change colours:** Red/white/red.

YORKSHIRE SAINTS

Secretary: J Dunne, 12 Longfellow Grove, Stanley, Wakefield WF3 4PL (0924 826795).
Ground & Directions: Fearnville Recreation Ground. From Leeds City Centre, follow A58 Wetherby Road. Turn right at roundabout with Oakwood Lane. Fearnville Rec half a mile on left.
Colours: Green/white/green. **Change colours:** White/black/black.

This Division also includes the reserve sides of: Dewsbury Moor Ath., Frank Ford, Garforth W.M.C., Great Preston, Horsforth St Margarets, Pontefract Town, Seacroft W.M.C., Swillington M.W., Yorkshire Copper Works.

WEST RIDING COUNTY
AMATEUR LEAGUE

Hon. Secretary: Mr D H Humpleby,
1 The Leys, Baildon, Shipley, Bradford BD17 5PR.

PREM. DIVISION	P	W	D	L	F	A	PTS
Aberford Albion	26	18	4	4	64	38	40
Wibsey	26	16	3	7	52	32	35
Brighouse Town	26	17	0	9	53	36	34
Ferrybridge Am.	26	13	5	8	53	32	31
Field	26	13	3	10	49	42	29
Crag Road Utd	26	11	6	9	50	48	28
Tyersal	26	12	2	12	48	53	26
Marsden	26	8	9	9	39	41	25
Rawdon Old Boys	26	8	7	11	45	53	23
Halifax Irish	26	9	4	13	52	53	22
Ovenden W. Riding	26	8	6	12	37	38	22
Salts	26	8	2	16	42	59	18
Gascoigne United	26	6	4	16	37	60	16
Altofts	26	5	5	16	35	71	15

Divisional Cup winners: Field

DIVISION ONE	P	W	D	L	F	A	PTS
Campion	30	21	6	3	107	41	48
Farnley WMC	30	21	4	5	66	34	46
T.S. Harrison	30	18	7	5	87	40	43
Otley Town	30	14	8	8	74	49	36
Hall Green United	30	13	9	8	60	55	35
Lower Hopton	30	12	8	10	44	37	32
Steeton	30	13	6	11	80	75	32
Morley Town	30	12	5	13	58	64	29
Allerton Bywater	30	10	7	13	63	84	27
Brook Motors	30	9	6	15	77	78	24
Ventus/Yeadon C.	30	8	8	14	56	72	24
Bowling Celtic	30	7	8	15	51	66	22
Springfield Y.C.	30	8	5	17	66	94	21
Ardsley Celtic	30	8	5	17	46	74	21
Dudley Hill Ath	30	8	5	17	53	88	21
Littletown	30	7	5	18	44	81	19

Divisional Cup winners: Campion

DIVISION THREE	P	W	D	L	F	A	PTS
Phoenix	30	22	7	1	112	22	51
Allerton AFC	30	21	8	1	113	42	50
Wibsey 'A'	30	19	6	5	111	44	44
Tyersal Res.	30	18	5	7	93	51	41
Pudsey Liberial	30	15	7	8	89	61	37
Crag Road Utd Res.	30	13	8	9	71	78	34
Eccleshill Utd	30	13	5	12	79	63	31
Salts G.S.O.B.	30	12	7	11	53	54	31
Farnley Res.	30	12	2	16	70	82	26
Hunsworth	30	11	4	15	63	79	26
Salthorn	30	11	4	15	69	99	26
Old Modernians	30	7	4	19	64	105	18
Bailiff Bridge	30	7	3	20	47	99	17
Lucas	30	7	2	21	54	108	16
Littletown Res.	30	6	3	21	48	115	15
Haworth	30	6	2	22	61	102	14

Divisional Cup winners: Phoenix

DIVISION TWO	P	W	D	L	F	A	PTS
Brighouse T.Res	28	23	3	2	90	34	49
Westbrook Wand.	28	18	4	6	75	41	40
Bradford Rovers	28	15	4	9	80	54	34
Greetland	28	15	4	9	86	63	34
Ovenden W.R. Res	28	16	2	10	68	58	34
Eastmoor Albion	28	15	3	10	83	59	33
Green Lane AFC	28	14	4	10	73	49	32
Aberford Albion R.	28	13	4	11	63	63	30
Bowling	28	10	8	10	67	73	28
Field Res.	28	11	5	12	73	69	27
Black Horse	28	8	7	13	73	85	23
Pontefract	28	6	6	16	53	65	18
Trinity Ath.	28	7	4	17	44	73	18
Altofts Res.	28	4	5	19	4	107	13
Dynamoes	28	2	3	23	41	118	7

Divisional Cup winners: Ovenden W.R. Reserves

RESERVE DIVISION	P	W	D	L	F	A	PTS
Salts Res.	32	25	2	5	97	44	52
Wibsey Res.	32	20	8	4	101	48	48
Otley Town	32	20	6	6	95	51	46
Campion	32	20	3	9	120	80	43
Bradford Rovers	32	18	6	8	107	69	42
Rawdon Old Boys	32	17	7	8	83	45	41
Westbrook Wdrs	32	16	7	9	80	65	39
Hall Green Utd	32	15	5	12	67	72	35
Ardsley Celtic	32	14	5	13	81	81	33
Bowling Celtic	32	10	8	14	63	75	28
Steeton	32	9	9	14	69	85	27
Marsden	32	9	7	16	62	95	25
Lower Hopton	32	9	5	18	67	92	23
Bowling	32	6	7	19	71	95	19
Pontefract	32	6	6	20	48	97	18
Ventus-Yeadon C.	32	4	6	22	48	93	14
Trinity Athletic	32	3	5	24	33	104	11

Divisional Cup winners: Wibsey

PREMIER DIVISION RESULT CHART 1992-93

HOME TEAM	1	2	3	4	5	6	7	8	9	10	11	12	13	14
1. Aberford Albion	*	3-4	2-1	3-1	2-1	1-1	2-1	5-3	3-2	4-2	3-1	3-1	3-0	0-0
2. Altofts	1-1	*	1-7	3-2	1-3	1-3	2-1	2-5	0-2	4-0	1-3	1-0	1-2	0-1
3. Brighouse Town	2-0	5-1	*	2-0	2-1	4-1	4-1	3-2	0-2	1-0	2-1	2-1	3-1	0-2
4. Crag Road United	4-0	2-2	2-0	*	0-6	2-3	2-2	3-1	3-2	0-3	1-1	4-1	1-3	3-5
5. Ferrybridge Amateurs	1-0	2-0	1-3	2-2	*	1-0	3-0	2-1	0-0	6-0	2-2	3-2	1-0	2-3
6. Field	1-2	6-0	3-2	0-4	1-2	*	4-0	1-0	1-0	1-1	6-2	2-5	3-4	2-3
7. Gascoigne United	2-4	2-0	0-2	1-2	4-3	0-1	*	2-3	2-3	1-0	2-1	3-0	0-5	3-3
8. Halifax Irish	2-4	2-2	3-0	1-2	2-1	0-1	3-2	*	4-1	2-0	3-4	1-2	3-2	3-1
9. Marsden	1-3	2-1	4-0	1-1	2-2	1-1	2-2	1-1	*	1-1	0-4	1-0	1-1	1-2
16. Ovenden West Riding	1-4	1-1	0-2	1-1	1-0	0-1	3-0	2-0	2-2	*	1-2	2-0	5-0	0-1
11. Rawdon Old Boys	2-2	1-1	0-2	1-3	1-1	2-3	2-0	2-2	1-3	1-3	*	3-1	1-4	1-0
12. Salts	3-4	6-0	2-1	1-0	2-1	2-1	1-4	2-2	1-3	0-7	3-3	*	2-0	1-3
13. Tyersal	0-5	6-3	0-3	2-3	0-4	1-2	1-1	3-2	3-0	3-1	2-0	3-2	*	2-1
14. Wibsey	0-1	3-2	5-0	1-2	1-2	2-0	4-1	3-1	2-1	0-0	2-3	2-1	2-0	*

	1	2	3	4	5	6	7	8	9	10	11	12	13	14	15	16
1. Allerton Bywater	*	1-2	2-2	3-2	1-5	5-3	2-2	0-2	3-1	4-4	2-3	3-3	1-2	4-2	0-2	3-2
2. Ardsley Celtic	2-3	*	3-1	1-1	2-3	1-4	2-4	0-1	1-3	0-4	1-5	2-3	4-1	0-1	1-3	3-3
3. Bowling Celtic	1-2	1-1	*	1-3	1-7	3-1	3-1	1-2	2-0	2-3	0-1	1-3	7-0	1-1	3-1	3-0
4. Brook Motors	5-1	5-2	2-2	*	1-4	8-1	1-3	4-2	1-2	0-1	2-2	0-3	3-4	4-1	2-2	6-3
5. Campion	11-28-1		5-0	5-2	*	4-0	1-4	1-1	6-1	3-0	3-0	1-1	2-1	5-1	1-1	4-1
6. Dudley Hill Athletic	2-2	2-3	2-1	1-2	0-2	*	1-4	2-3	0-0	0-3	2-1	2-4	1-3	6-3	1-8	2-1
7. Farnley	2-0	2-2	3-1	3-0	1-3	5-1	*	2-0	1-0	2-2	2-0	1-0	1-3	1-1	2-1	4-1
8. Hall Green United	3-3	1-1	3-3	3-2	3-2	0-6	0-2	*	5-3	0-1	7-1	2-1	2-1	1-1	2-2	5-2
9. Littletown	4-1	3-0	1-5	3-3	1-2	1-1	0-4	0-2	*	2-5	0-3	1-7	2-2	2-5	1-6	4-2
10. Lower Hopton	0-1	0-1	0-0	1-1	0-1	1-1	1-2	1-1	2-1	*	1-0	4-1	2-1	0-0	2-0	1-2
11. Morley Town	2-1	0-1	4-2	6-4	1-1	1-3	1-2	2-3	1-1		*	0-2	3-2	1-1	0-3	4-2
12. Otley Town	0-2	2-2	3-3	3-1	2-3	3-0	3-0	1-1	2-1	2-0	6-2	*	2-2	2-3	3-3	1-1
13. Springfield	1-5	3-4	3-0	1-3	4-9	2-4	1-2	1-3	2-3	4-2	2-3	1-6	*	8-1	2-2	3-3
14. Steeton	7-3	3-0	2-1	6-4	5-2	7-1	2-3	4-1	4-1	2-1	3-5	1-2	5-0	*	1-2	1-5
15. T. S. Harrison	7-3	3-0	2-1	6-4	5-2	7-1	2-3	4-1	4-1	2-1	3-5	1-2	5-0	1-2	*	1-5
16. Ventus/Yeadon	1-1	1-3	1-1	6-4	2-2	2-2	1-0	2-0	1-2	0-1	3-2	3-2	2-3	2-2	1-1	*

PREMIER DIVISION CLUBS 1993-94

ABERFORD ALBION

Secretary: P A Walton, 18 Highfield Rd, Aberford, Leeds LS25 (0532 813206).
Ground & Directions: The Willows, off A1 bypass, Aberford (0532 813248) Adjacent to Sewage Works; From Leeds on A64 and join A1 southbound, left into Yorkshire Water premises 1/4 mile past Aberford turn off. All others proceed North through Aberford village and join A1 south. (NB. All vehicles must turn left on leaving ground)
Colours: Yellow/yellow/red   **Change colours:** All green.

BRIGHOUSE TOWN

Secretary: N Wilson, Lundy House, Limes Ave., Halifax HX3 0NT (0422 345057).
Ground & Directions: St Giles Road, Hove Edge, Brighouse. M62 jct 26, A58 to Hipperholme lights, left until Dusty Miller, 1st left and immediate left down Spout House Lane, past Old Pond Inn, ground quarter mile on right.
Colours: Tangerine/black/black   **Change colours:** White/navy/navy.

CAMPION

Secretary: A Shepherd, 1 Avocet Close, Bradford BD8 0RB (0274 884152).
Ground & Directions: Manningham Mills CC, Scotchman Rd, Heaton, Bradford (0274 546726). Manningham Lane out of Bradford, at corner of Manningham Park turn left up Oak Lane, right at 1st lights into Heaton Rd, left up Scotchman Rd.
Change: Red/black/red.   **Cols:** Blue & blue stripes/blue/blue

CRAG ROAD UNITED

Secretary: R Knight, 23 Easthorpe Court, Eccleshill, Bradford BD2 2PB (0274 635889).
Ground & Directions: Apperley Bridge, Greengates, Bradford. To Greengates traffic lights, 500 yards down Harrogate Road, ground on right after canal bridge.
Colours: Red/white/red   **Change colours:** All white.

FARNLEY

Secretary: P Walker, 7 Water Lane, Farnley, Leeds LS12 5LX (0532 637306).
Ground & Directions: Lawns Lane, Farnley (0532 638826). Leeds-Bradford Ring Road, A6110 to Butt Lane r'bout (by Reservoir), up Butt Lane, cross Tong Rd to Club on right, left at top of hill, and Chapel Lane is 1st right, which becomes Lawns Lane after the Church.
Cols: Blue & white hoops/blue/blue   **Change colours:** Yellow/black/black.

FERRYBRIDGE AMATEURS

Secretary: M Gilbert, 67 Manor Park Avenue, Nevison, Pontefract WF8 2PX (0977 709142).
Ground & Directions: Castleford Lane, Ferrybridge (0977 552614). M62 J32, left towards Castleford. After 1/2 mile right on B6136 towards Ferrybridge. Ground on right opposite Power Station and before a bridge.
Colours: Amber/black   **Change colours:** Blue/white.

FIELD A.F.C.

Secretary: C Clough, 8 Hospital Rd, Riddlesden, Keighley BD20 5EP (0274 603782).
Ground & Directions: Hollingwood Lane, Lidget Green, Bradford (0274 571750). Clayton bus from city centre, alight at Works Ground behind new warehouse opposite works. By car leave Bradford on Thornton Rd, 1st left into Listerhills Rd, and continue forward to left turn into Hollingwood Lane, in front of Fields Printers.
Colours: Blue/blue/white   **Change:** Green & white/green/green

HALIFAX IRISH CLUB

Secretary: R Stephenson, 10 Marldon Rd, Nothowram, Halifax HX3 7BP (0422 201594).
Ground & Directions: Natty Lane, Illingworth, Halifax (0422 360134). Keighley Rd (A629) out of Halifax for 3 miles. Fire station on left, 200yds turn right down Natty Lane. From Keighley/Thornton, Natty Lane 2nd left after 'Sportsman'.
Colours: Green/white/gold   **Change colours:** Black & white.

MARSDEN

Secretary: D Warwick, 44 Western Rd, Cowlersley, Huddersfield HD7 5TH (0484 647807).
Ground & Directions: Fall Lane, Marsden, Huddersfield (0484 844191). A62 Huddersfield Ring Road (signed Oldham/Manchester) for 7 miles out of Huddersfd to Marsden, 1st turn left after Fire Station into Fall Lane, left at r'about into car park
Colours: Black & white stripes/black   **Change colours:** All blue.

OVENDEN WEST RIDING

Secretary: S Smith, 192 Illingworth Road, Bradshaw, Halifax HX2 9XH (0422 248753).
Ground & Directions: As Halifax Irish Club (above).
Colours: Red/black/black   **Change colours:** Red & blue stripes.

RAWDON OLD BOYS

Secretary: D Saynor, 10 West Lea Grove, Yeadon, Leeds LS19 7EF (0532 506037).
Ground & Directions: Hanson Field, Rawdon. A658 from Bradford to Rawdon lights, right towards Leeds, then 100yds left (Over Lane) to Emmott Arms, left to ground. A65 from Leeds, right before Rawdon lights opposite Airedale Air Conditioning onto Layton Lane, left at top onto Town Str., right imm. before Emmott Arms.
Colours: Maroon & sky/sky/sky   **Change colours:**

SALTS

Secretary: S A Griggs, 17 Longwood Ave, Bingley BD16 2RX (0274 569090).
Ground & Directions: Salts Playing Fields, Hirst Lane, Shipley (0274 587427). From Bradford A650, from Leeds A657 to Saltaire, right at r'bout via Clarence Rd and Hirst Lane, cross canal bridge.
Colours: Yellow/blue/yellow   **Change colours:** All blue.

TYERSAL

Secretary: H Foster, 5 Norwood House, Sticker Lane, Bradford BD4 8DR (0274 666060).
Ground & Directions: Arkwright Street, off Dick Lane, Bradford 4. Leave Bradford on Leeds Road to large Phoenix Park r'bout, right onto Dick Lane. Please do not use pub car park.
Colours: White/blue/blue   **Change:** Red & white/white/red & black.

WIBSEY

Secretary: D Nolan, 21 Glendale Drive, Bradford BD6 2LT (0274 602934).
Ground & Directions: Harold Park, Low Moor. From Odsal Top, Huddersfield road to Low Moor, right into Common Rd after 1 mile (Heaton Building Soc. on corner), Park Rd 100 yds on left - do not park on main road.
Colours: Blue & white halves/white   **Change:** Red & black checks/black/red & black

FIRST DIVISION CLUBS 1993-94

ALLERTON BYWATER

Secretary: M Bednall, 49 Edward Avenue, Allerton Bywater, Castleford WF10 2HA (0532 867048).
Ground & Directions: Ninevah Lane, Leeds Rd, Allerton Bywater. M62 exit 30, A642 to Rothwell for 2 miles, left at r'bout, right at next on A642 towards Garforth for 2 miles, at Pelican Crossing right towards Allerton Bywater. Right after 2 miles at 'T' junction and Ninevah Lane is 1/10th mile on right.
Colours: Sky/navy/navy   **Change colours:** Yellow & blue/white/white

ALTOFTS

Secretary: M Bell, 67 Churchfield Croft, Altofts, Normanton WF6 2QB (0924 893507).
Ground & Directions: Altofts Sports Club, Lock Lane, Altofts (0924 892708). M62, exit 31 (Normanton), A655 towards Castleford for half mile, left at Rising Sun and follow road 1 1/2 miles into Altofts. Lock Lane 2nd right after 'The Popular', ground 300yds on right.
Colours: Red & white/black/black   **Change colours:** Blue/white.

BOWLING CELTIC

Secretary: Stewart Delaney, 557 Huddersfield Rd, Wyke, Braford BD12 (0274 605423).
Ground & Directions: Avenue Rd P.F., Bowling Park, West Bowling, Bradford. From Bradford via Manchester Road, after 1 mile left on Parkside Road, (opposite Admiral Nelson Pub) continue forward to Junction of Avenue Road. From top of M606 take 4th exit off Rooley r'bout then 1st left immediately after 'Rooley' pub, right onto Parkside Rd at t-junction, ground 500yds on left.
Colours: All green   **Change:** Blue & white halves/black/black

BROOK MOTORS

Secretary: W Kaye, 31 Northwood Park, Kirkburton, Huddersfield HD8 0PY (0484 604122).
Ground & Directions: New Mill Rd, Brockholes, near Honley, Huddersfield. Leave Huddersfield centre/ring-road on A616 Sheffield Road, at Lockwood Bar lights bear left (still on A616), 4 miles from ring-road is Brockholes, ground on right of entrance to Brook Crompton Ltd.
Change: All white or all red.   **Colours:** Blue & white stripes/white/blue

HALL GREEN UNITED

Secretary: S Marsden, 28 Church View, Crigglestone, Wakefield WF4 3PF (0924 253095).
Ground & Directions: Haslegrove Sports Ground, Criggleston (0924 254544). M1 jct 39, left to Wakefield, 1st right to Crigglestone, 1st right again to Crigglestone, past Empire Stores, 1st right after last house on right, to Haverold Lane, onto end to Painthorpe Country Club, left onto Painthorpe Lane, ground 300 yards on left
Colours: Yellow/blue/yellow   **Change colours:** Red/black/black.

LOWER HOPTON

Secretary: R Smith, 5 Bright St., Mirfield WF14 0NJ (0924 492780).
Ground & Directions: Woodend Rd, Lower Hopton, Mirfield (0924 492048). To Mirfield Town Centre, A644, turn down Newgate, under railway, over river, turn right & right again on Woodend Rd.
Colours: Red/blue/blue   **Change:** All gold.

MORLEY TOWN

Secretary: Melvyn Hudson, 20 Brayshaw Rd, East Ardsley, nr Wakefield WF3 2JJ (0924 825833).
Ground & Directions: Brookes PF, Nepshaw Lane, Morley. A650 Bradford-Wakefield Road to Angel Pub, Bruntcliffe, turn left down Bruntcliffe Lane, and the Snooker Club is half mile on left. Ground across car park.
Colours: All maroon (sky trim)   **Change colours:** All blue.

OTLEY TOWN

Secretary: G W Jones, 3 Swain Hile St., Yeadon, Leeds LS19 7HF (0532 500208).
Ground & Directions: Old Show Field, Pool Rd, Otley (0943 461025). Harrogate road out of Otley, ground on right just after Garden centre.
Colours: Tangerine/black/tangerine   **Change:** Blue & white/white/blue

SPRINGFIELD Y.C.

Secretary: A Smith, 58 Wightman St, Bradford BD3 0LD (0274 630862).
Ground & Directions: Rear of Springfield Boys Club, Idlethorpe Way, Thorpe Edge, Bradford (Bradford 611976). Idlethorpe Way is via Cavendish Road, off Bradford Road, Idle, from Five Lane Ends
Colours: All yellow   **Change colours:** Green/blue.

STEETON

Secretary: A Bates, 56 Eelholme View, Beechcliffe, Keighley BD20 6AY (0535 663397).
Ground & Directions: Summer Hill Lane, Steeton. A650 from Keighley towards Skipton, turn right at Steeton traffic lights, after 200 yards turn right opposite Steeton Hall Hotel.
Colours: Green & yellow/green/green   **Change:** Black & blue/black/black.

T. S. HARRISON

Secretary: R Fisher, 32 Berwick Ave, Heckmondwike WF16 9AE (0924 402206).
Ground & Directions: T S Harrison Sports & Social Club, Healey Lane, Batley (0924 475859). From Heckmondwike Market Place travel up High Street signed to Batley, to Junction PH, left past Craven Heifer PH, left hand fork and ground left opposite Healey Junior School.
Colours: White/black   **Change colours:** All red.

VENTUS & YEADON CELTIC
Secretary: Frank Vento, 120 Pullan Ave., Eccleshill, Bradford BD2 3RN (0274 638346).
Ground & Directions: Dam Lane, Yeadon, Leeds. Right onto Rooley Lane (A6177), across 2 r'bouts, at 3rd lights right down Harrogate Rd (A658), 4 miles to Rawdon, thru 1st lights, left at next lights on High Street, right after The Swan (500m) onto Dam Lane, ground on right.
Colours: Black & white stripes/black/black (white band)   **Change colours:** White/black.

WESTBROOK WANDERERS
Secretary: Paul Lewty, 20 Gladstone Str., Farsley, Pudsey, Leeds LS28 5HZ (0532 553451).
Ground: Horsforth School, Lea Lane East. Turn up Fink Hill from Leeds ring-road (adj. Eleventh Earl pub) signed Horsforth Centre, left after 600yds on St Margarets Ave., 1st left is Lea Lane East, school entrance 1st left.
Colours: Blue & white stripes/black/black   **Change colours:** White/black/black.

This division also contains the reserve side of: Brighouse Town.

SECOND DIVISION CLUBS 1993-94

ALLERTON
Secretary: Barry Sutcliffe, 2 Tannerbrook Close, Calayton, Bradford BD14 6NJ (0274 884179).
Ground & Directions: Rhodesway School. From top of M606 left on Mayo Ave, over roundabout, thru 4 sets of lights, follow dual c'way (Allerton Rd) round to left, 1st turning after sharp bend is Rhodesway, school on right.
Colours: Grey/blue/blue   **Change colours:** T.B.A.

ARDSLEY CELTIC
Secretary: Stuart Scott, 31 Clifton Avenue, Stanley, Wakefield, WF3 4HB (0924 870993).
Ground & Directions: White Horse, Main Str., East Ardsley. From Tingley r'bout (M62 jct 28) A650 towards Wakefield for approx. 1 1/2 miles, turn right into East Ardsley Cricket Club opposite White Horse.
Colours: Green & white/white/green   **Change:** Blue & white/white/blue.

BOWLING
Secretary: Neil Smith, 39 Lister Ave., East Bowling, Bradford BD4 7QP (0274 737895).
Ground & Directions: Fairfax Upper School, Lister Ave., Bradford. A650 Wakefield-Bradford road towards Bradford, left into Lister Ave. quarter mile on Bradford side of Dudley Hill (ring-road) flyover, school on left.
Colours: Navy & sky stripes/navy/navy   **Change:** Black & white stripes/black/black

BRADFORD ROVERS
Secretary: Lubo Simic, 47 Oaks Lane, Allerton, Bradford BD15 7RT (0274 499537).
Ground: As Campion (page 976)   **Previous Name:** Dubrovnic (pre-1992).
Colours: Blue & white stripes/blue   **Change:** Red & black stripes/white.

DUDLEY HILL ATHLETIC
Secretary: C Cook, 12 Richardson Street, Oakenshaw, Bradford BD12 7EH (0274 394524).
Ground & Directions: Hunsworth Lane, East Bierley. From Bradford up Wakefield Rd thru Dudley Hill r'bout up Tong Street to Tong Cemetery, right to South View Road, then down Hunsworth Lane, ground 100yds left.
Cols: Black & white stripes/black/white   **Change colours:** Green/black/green.

EASTMOOR ALBION
Secretary: Eric Sykes, 3 Kirkwood Grove, Tingley WF3 1PJ (0532 534296).
Ground: Eastmoor High School, Warmfield View, Wakefield (0924 364576). M62 jct 30 towards Wakefield, pass Pinderfields and Stanley Royd hospitals, left at lights and follow Queen Elizabeth Rd to Eastmoor School.
Colours: All skye   **Change:** Red & black or Black & white

GOLCAR UNITED
Secretary: Margaret Whitaker, 8 Burcott Drive, Outlane, Huddersfield HD3 3FY (0422 378901).
Ground & Directions: Longfield Rec, Golcar. Manchester Road out of Huddersfield, right to Milnsbridge, left up Scar Lane, right at British Legion to Longfield Rec.
Colours: Green/black/black   **Change colours:** Yellow/black/black

GREEN LANE
Secretary: Gerard Coriette, 10 Queens Ave., Bradford BD2 4BP (0274 641474).
Ground & Directions: Cliffe Rd, Peel Park (0274 726563). A650 to Bolton Rd, right onto Cliffe Rd, ground on left.
Colours: All blue   **Change colours:** Green & white/white

GREETLAND
Secretary: Peter Walker, 15 Sunnybank Drive, Greetland, Halifax HX4 8NB (0422 378203).
Ground & Directions: Greetland Community Centre, Rochdale Road, Greetland, Halifax (0422 370140). M62 jct 24, A629 towards Halifax, left signed Greetland after half mile, right at r'bout, after 400yds bear left following Greetland signs along Saddleworth Rd for 1 mile, right at lights by Shears Inn, right at next lights, left after 1 mile, Community Centre on right after St Thomas' Church.
Colours: White/green   **Change colours:** Green/white

LITTLETOWN
Secretary: D Knight, 2 Norwood Drive, Moor Lane, Birkenshaw, Bfd BD11 2NS (0274 874915).
Ground & Directions: Beck Lane, Heckmondwike. From Bradford, thru Cleckheaton on A638 past Spenborough Baths, forward through 'Swan' traffic lights. Approx 1/4 mile past NEGAS Service Centre turn right down Wormald Street, to end, then Cross Union Road, through tunnel turn left, ground at end of road
Colours: Maroon/sky/sky   **Change:** Red, white & blue stripes/blue/blue

PHOENIX
Secretary: M Breeze, 17 Green Ave., Silsden, Keighley BD20 9LD (0535 669940).
Ground & Directions: Utley, Keighley. Old Skipton road from Keighley, 2nd right after Roebuck Inn, ground on left.
Colours: Black & white stripes/black/black & white hoops   **Change cols:** Silver grey & green.
Previous Ground: Beckfoot Grammar Sch., Wagon Lane, Bingley (pre-1993).

SELBY R.S.S.C.
Secretary: Mark Pearce, 4 Meadow Drive, Thorpe, Willoughby, Selby, Nth Yorks YO8 9PN (0757 706406).
Ground & Directions: Denison Rd, Selby (00757 703880). M62 jct 34, A19 for 6 miles, right at 1st lights, over canal & level crossing, left at t-jct, 1st right into Abbotts Rd, right at t-jct, ground quarter mile on right..
Colours: Yellow/black/yellow   **Change colours:** White/black/red.

This division also contains the reserve sides of: Aberford Albion, Ovenden West Riding *(playing at Shroggs Park, Lee Mount)*.

THIRD DIVISION CLUBS 1993-94

BANKFOOT
Secretary: Stephen Chapman, 24 Watty Hall, Wibsey, Bradford BD6 3AP (0274 600348).
Ground & Directions: Fifth Street, Cleckheaton Rd, Low Moor. Cleckheaton Rd from Bradford to Odsal Top, left signed Dewsbury for quarter mile, gate to playing fields on right, ground lower down Cleckheaton Rd opp. Elf Garage.
Colours: White/sky   **Change colours:** Red & white/white

DYNAMOES
Secretary: Alan Brotherhead, 4 St Margarets Ave., Holmewood, Bradford BD4 9AJ (0274 823576).
Ground & Directions: Broomwood School. A650 Wakefield-Bradford road, Tong Street turn, down Dawson Lane near C D Bramalls or approach down Burnham Ave. from Bierley r'bout on ring-road.
Colours: Red & black stripes/black/red   **Change colours:** All green

HAWORTH
Secretary: Keith Lawton, 8 Perry Close, Ingrow, Keighley, West Yorks BD22 7EE (0274 600450).
Ground & Directions: Marley Stadium, Keighley. Bradford towards Keighley, at Magnet showrooms, Crossflatts, left onto new dual c'way, ground visible approaching 2nd r'bout - right at r'bout.
Colours: Black & white stripes/black   **Change colours:** Blue & red stripes/blue.

HECKMONDWIKE TOWN
Secretary: W Wright, 21 School St., Moorbottom, Cleckheaton BD19 6AF (0274 879702).
Ground & Directions: Heckmondwike Secondary School, Leeds Old Road, Heckmondwyke (0924 442907). A62 Leeds/Huddersfield Rd., at Half Way PH turn into White Lee Rd., 2nd right into Leeds Old Rd, school car park 200 yards on left
Cols: Sky & navy/navy/sky   **Change:** Orange & white/black/black   **Prev. Name:** Black Horse (pre-1993)

HUNSWORTH
Secretary: Alan Hepworth, 217 Moor Lane, Birkenshaw, Bradford BD11 2NX (0274 682693).
Ground & Directions: Birkenshaw Middle School, Bradford Road, Birkenshaw (0274 852179). On A651 Bradford-Heckmondwike road at r'bout with A58.
Cols: Blue (white & red trim) **Change:** Red & white stripes/black/black   **Prev. Name:** Savile (pre-1992)

PONTEFRACT
Secretary: Mark Scott, 6 Avenue Terrace, Halfpenny Lane, Pontefract WF8 4BE (0977 703141).
Ground & Directions: Pontefract Park (0977 702228). Next to racecourse. M62 jct 32 towards Pontefract, right at 1st lights, immediate right into park - follow road over racecourse to car park.
Colours: Royal & red stripes/royal   **Change colours:** Grey/black/black.

PUDSEY LIBERAL
Secretary: R Brook, 44 Brunswick Road, Pudsey LS28 7NA (0532 569059).
Ground & Directions: Pudsey Grangefield School (0532 577193). Travel from Thornbury Barracks along Galloway Lane towards Pudsey, fork left into Owlcotes Rd, over hill (becomes Cemetary Rd) go straigt over Richard Shaw Lane junction, 1st left, school 200yds on left.
Colours: Maroon & blue/blue/blue   **Change:** Amber & black/black/black or white

SALTHORN
Secretary: Lawrence Barraclough, 7 Richardson Ave., Wibsey, Bradford BD6 1HF (0274 603286).
Ground & Directions: Victoria Park, Oakenshaw, Bradford. From Odsal Top, Bradford, left down Cleckheaton Rd signed Dewsbury, ground 1 mile on right.
Colours: Red & white diamonds/red/red   **Change colours:** Blue & white checks/blue/blue

SALTS GRAMMAR SCHOOL OLD BOYS
Secretary: P Hellewell, "Stonelands", 28 Belmont Rise, Baildon BD17 5AW (0274 583742).
Ground & Directions: Salts Grammar School, Higher Coach Road, Baildon, Shipley. From Shipley take A6038 Otley Road, and after 1/2 mile turn left into Green Lane. Continue straight ahead for 1 mile, and after Cup & Ring PH, Salts Grammar School on right.
Colours: White (navy stripe)/navy/white   **Change:** Blue & black stripes/black.

TRINITY ATHLETIC
Secretary: James Mattocks, 97 Grafton Lane, Clayton, Bradford BD14 6PD (0274 814677).
Ground & Directions: The Dell, Cliffe Lane West, Baildon. From Shipley lights along Otley Rd, left towards Baildon at 2nd lights (Junction pub), left into Cliffe Avenue at pelican crossing after 1 mile, Cliffe West 200yds on left, ground on left.
Colours: White/blue   **Change colours:** All yellow.

This division also includes the reserve sides of: Altofts, Field, Wibsey ('A' team).

DIVISION FOUR (A) 1993-94

1. Braford Rovers Res.
2. Campion Res.
3. Crag Rd United Res.
4. Farnley Res.
5. Hall Green Res.
6. Littletown Res.
7. Otley Town Res.
8. Rawdon O.B. Res.
9. Salts Res.
10. Tyersal Res.
11. Westbrook Res.
11. Wibsey 'B'

DIVISION FOUR (B) 1993-94

1. Ardsley Celtic Res.
2. Bowling Res.
3. Bowling Celtic Res.
4. Lower Hopton Res.
5. Marsden Res.
6. Phoenix Res.
7. Pontefract Res.
8. Salts G.S.O.B. Res.
9. Steeton Res.
10. T.S. Harrison Res.
11. Trinity Ath. Res.
11. Ventus & Yeadon C. Res.

EAST RIDING COUNTY LEAGUE

President: W A Piercy.
Hon. Secretary: D Simmons, 24 Gorton Road,
Willerby, North Humberside HU10 (0482 658998).

Premier Division	P	W	D	L	F	A	PTS
Sculcoates Am.	20	13	6	1	57	25	32
Westella Shopa.	20	9	6	5	39	24	24
Leconfield	20	9	6	5	43	31	24
Haltemprice	20	8	7	5	45	41	23
Holme Rovers	20	9	4	7	31	32	22
North Cave	20	7	6	7	37	32	20
Rudston United	20	6	6	8	36	39	18
Cavalier	20	5	7	8	16	22	17
North Newbald	20	7	2	11	31	47	16
Beverley O.G.	20	5	5	10	39	48	15
Woodlands	20	2	5	13	20	53	9

Division One	P	W	D	L	F	A	PTS
Mkt Weighton	22	12	7	3	50	31	31
Howden Amateurs	22	13	3	6	69	41	29
North Cave Res.	22	11	6	5	52	37	28
Brandesburton	22	10	4	8	52	49	24
Viking Safeway	22	9	5	8	57	52	23
Westella S. Res.	22	7	8	7	47	40	22
Hodgson Grovehill	22	8	5	9	69	64	21
Holme Rovers Res.	22	7	7	8	46	62	21
N.M.G. Antiques	22	7	3	12	42	54	17
Thorngumbald	22	7	3	12	51	65	17
Anlaby Amateurs	22	6	4	12	42	65	*14
Hook Amateurs	22	5	3	14	41	67	13

* - 2 points deducted

Division Two	P	W	D	L	F	A	PTS
Anlaby United	22	18	3	1	106	26	39
Easington United	22	15	5	2	86	48	35
Sculcoates Res.	22	13	5	4	64	28	31
Bransholme Ath.	22	12	2	8	73	49	26
Skidby Millers	22	9	6	7	60	50	24
Long Riston	22	10	3	9	73	72	23
Aldbrough Utd	22	7	7	8	41	53	21
Haltemprice Res.	22	8	4	10	59	61	20
Royal Oak	22	7	2	13	43	65	16
Walton Club	22	5	1	16	47	89	11
Beverley Town	22	3	3	16	39	89	9
Barkers	22	4	1	17	37	98	9

Division Three	P	W	D	L	F	A	PTS
Black Prince Ryls	21	20	0	1	128	26	40
Holmpton United	22	14	5	3	66	38	33
Hessle O.B. Marl.	21	14	4	3	56	24	32
Beverley O.G. Res.	22	12	2	8	66	52	26
Walkington	22	8	7	7	42	46	23
Thorngumbald Res.	22	6	6	10	42	67	18
Mkt Weighton Res.	22	5	7	10	37	50	17
Tickton	22	7	3	12	36	52	17
Leven M.C.	22	5	6	11	49	62	16
Wawne	22	6	2	14	48	86	14
Leconfield Res.	22	3	7	12	47	75	13
Holme Rvrs 'A'	22	6	1	15	35	74	13

Division Four	P	W	D	L	F	A	PTS
Anlaby Am. Res.	20	17	2	1	89	28	36
Howden Am. Res.	20	17	1	2	91	32	35
Riston Bay Horse	20	11	7	2	78	39	29
Nth Newbald Res.	20	10	4	6	61	42	24
Westella S. 'A'	20	7	6	7	57	48	20
Sloop	20	5	6	9	48	65	16
Holme Rovers 'B'	20	6	3	11	43	61	15
Brandesburton Res.	20	5	3	12	40	44	13
Molescroft Rgrs	20	5	2	13	30	59	12
Mkt Weighton 'A'	20	5	2	13	34	77	12
Long Riston Res.	20	3	2	15	19	95	8

LEAGUE SENIOR CUP: WINNERS: Rudston United RUNNERS-UP: North Newbald
LEAGUE JUNIOR CUP: WINNERS: Anlaby United RUNNERS-UP: Hodgson Grovehill.
H. ROBINSON CUP: WINNERS: Black Prince Royals RUNNERS-UP: Market Weighton Utd Reserves.
H. E. DEAN CUP: WINNERS: Rudston United RUNNERS-UP: Westella Shopacheck

PREMIER DIVISION RESULT CHART 1992/93

HOME TEAM	1	2	3	4	5	6	7	8	9	10	11
1. Beverley Old Gramm.	*	2-0	2-4	4-1	2-1	2-3	2-3	2-3	0-1	1-1	1-1
2. Cavalier	1-1	*	2-3	0-0	0-2	2-1	1-0	1-0	1-2	1-2	3-0
3. Haltemprice	1-3	2-1	*	3-3	2-2	2-1	5-2	3-3	2-4	1-1	3-3
4. Holme Rovers	4-1	3-0	2-1	*	3-2	1-0	0-1	3-1	1-5	2-1	0-3
5. Leconfield	5-2	0-2	3-1	3-1	*	0-0	4-0	2-2	1-1	3-3	2-2
6. North Cave	2-2	1-1	2-2	2-1	2-4	*	2-3	2-2	1-3	3-2	2-0
7. North Newbald	2-2	3-0	3-5	2-2	0-2	0-4	*	2-0	1-2	0-4	3-1
8. Rudston United	5-2	0-0	1-3	0-1	2-1	2-1	3-0	*	3-6	2-1	1-2
9. Sculcoates Amateurs	7-2	0-0	3-0	0-0	2-4	0-0	5-3	3-3	*	2-1	8-1
10. Westella Shopacheck	3-2	0-0	0-0	2-1	4-0	1-2	3-0	2-1	1-1	*	4-1
11. Woodlands	0-4	0-0	0-2	1-2	0-2	2-6	0-3	2-2	0-2	1-3	*

DIV. ONE	1	2	3	4	5	6	7	8	9	10	11	12
1. Anlaby Amateurs	*	2-4	4-3	3-3	1-1	3-2	2-0	1-4	3-4	4-0	1-3	1-1
2. Brandesburton	3-1	*	4-3	7-4	2-1	1-3	2-3	0-0	0-3	3-3	3-2	2-2
3. Hogson Grovehill	6-1	0-3	*	10-3	5-1	4-3	0-0	2-3	5-1	4-4	4-4	3-1
4. Holme Rovers Reserves	0-0	2-6	4-3	*	4-1	2-2	1-1	1-1	1-2	7-2	1-0	1-1
5. Hook Amateurs	3-5	4-2	3-1	2-3	*	2-4	0-1	3-2	2-5	1-0	0-4	2-3
6. Howden Amateurs	3-1	3-1	7-5	3-0	11-2	*	6-4	4-0	2-1	3-2	2-3	2-3
7. Market Weighton	5-1	3-0	8-1	0-0	1-1	1-0	*	2-0	3-0	3-0	3-0	2-2
8. N.M.G. Antiques	1-4	1-2	2-3	3-0	3-1	2-1	2-2	*	2-5	4-6	3-0	3-1
9. North Cave Reserves	5-3	0-0	2-3	2-3	2-1	2-2	2-2	3-1	*	3-1	1-1	2-2
10. Thorngumbald	4-2	3-2	2-5	1-2	1-4	2-2	2-3	0-1	*	*	2-1	6-6
11. Viking Safeway	5-2	3-1	5-5	7-3	5-5	0-2	2-4	3-2	4-3	2-0	*	2-2
12. Westella Shopa. Res.	0-1	3-4	0-0	5-1	2-1	0-2	0-2	5-0	0-2	5-0	3-1	*

DIVISION TWO RESULT CHART 1992/93

HOME TEAM		1	2	3	4	5	6	7	8	9	10	11	12
1.	Albrough United	*	1-4	3-2	1-1	1-2	0-0	4-3	3-8	0-3	1-1	1-1	3-2
2.	Anlaby United	7-0	*	10-1	6-0	6-0	4-2	4-0	7-1	6-2	3-0	3-2	4-1
3.	Barkers	2-5	0-9	*	3-1	0-6	2-4	3-3	1-2	3-2	0-3	0-3	4-2
4.	Beverley Town	1-3	0-8	3-2	*	0-5	2-3	3-5	5-4	1-2	0-0	4-4	5-2
5.	Bransholme	3-2	3-1	14-0	6-1	*	1-3	3-5	2-3	1-1	2-4	3-0	5-3
6.	Easington United	5-5	4-4	4-2	6-2	4-3	*	7-2	5-2	12-0	1-0	4-4	2-1
7.	Haltemprice Reserves	3-1	2-4	1-0	4-0	0-2	4-3	*	2-3	0-0	2-6	1-1	2-3
8.	Long Riston	0-0	3-3	5-3	10-2	3-5	3-5	5-4	*	1-4	1-8	3-4	4-1
9.	Royal Oak	0-1	1-3	2-3	5-3	5-1	1-3	7-0	0-2	*	2-5	1-2	4-3
10.	Sculcoates Am. Res.	2-2	0-0	5-2	4-1	2-0	0-0	4-1	2-5	1-0	*	4-1	9-0
11.	Skidby Mill	3-1	1-4	5-1	3-2	3-4	1-3	3-3	2-2	5-2	1-3	*	8-0
12.	Walton Club	0-3	2-6	6-3	3-2	2-2	5-6	1-5	4-3	2-5	3-1	1-3	*

DIVISION THREE RESULT CHART 1992/93

HOME TEAM		1	2	3	4	5	6	7	8	9	10	11	12
1.	Beverley Old Gram. Res.	*	1-3	1-7	5-1	0-2	2-4	6-1	5-2	4-3	1-2	3-1	6-4
2.	Black Prince Royals	4-1	*	5-1	8-0	6-1	9-1	7-0	2-1	11-0	10-2	4-1	10-2
3.	Hessle Old Boys Marlboro.	3-0		*	3-2	1-1	7-1	3-2	2-2	2-0	3-0	2-4	2-2
4.	Holme Rovers 'A'	0-5	0-8	1-4	*	1-3	3-7	3-2	0-2	0-2	2-1	0-1	1-2
5.	Holmpton United	3-1	0-4	2-1	4-1	*	4-1	5-2	7-2	2-5	1-1	1-1	6-2
6.	Leconfield	3-8	1-4	0-0	3-5	2-2	*	1-1	2-2	2-2	1-2	1-2	2-3
7.	Leven M.C.	2-3	1-6	1-2	6-1	2-4	4-4	*	2-2	1-3	3-1	4-4	5-0
8.	Mkt Weighton Reserves	0-0	3-0	0-4	0-1	0-6	3-6	2-4	*	1-1	3-0	1-1	3-3
9.	Thorngumbald Reserves	4-4	3-9	0-3	1-3	1-1	2-1	0-0	1-4	*	6-3	1-1	1-6
10.	Tickton	1-2	2-4	0-2	4-1	1-4	3-1	2-2	1-0	4-1	*	0-1	1-2
11.	Walkington	1-4	3-8	0-3	2-2	0-2	2-2	2-1	2-1	0-2	1-1	*	8-1
12.	Wawne	1-4	2-6	0-1	1-7	3-5	5-1	1-3	0-3	5-3	1-4	2-4	*

DIVISION FOUR RESULT CHART 1992/93

HOME TEAM		1	2	3	4	5	6	7	8	9	10	11
1.	Anlaby Amateurs Reserves	*	6-0	4-2	4-1	2-2	8-1	3-1	4-1	6-4	5-4	3-0
2.	Brandesburton Reserves	2-3	*	7-1	2-4	1-0	1-2	2-0	1-3	2-4	5-1	2-2
3.	Holme Rovers 'B'	0-3	2-2	*	2-5	7-0	3-0	2-3	1-1	1-7	3-4	4-2
4.	Howden Amateurs Reserves	3-1	3-2	7-3	*	11-2	4-1	3-0	5-2	3-3	6-0	2-1
5.	Long Riston Reserves	1-6	3-1	0-1	0-10	*	2-6	2-3	0-7	0-6	0-4	1-10
6.	Market Weighton 'A'	0-9	1-5	2-0	4-3	1-3	*	3-2	2-7	3-6	2-4	1-1
7.	Molescroft Rangers	2-6	3-2	3-6	0-3	1-2	2-1	*	1-0	0-1	2-2	1-6
8.	North Newbald Reserves	1-3	1-0	7-2	2-4	2-0	1-1	2-1	*	2-2	6-3	6-2
9.	Riston Bay	2-2	2-1	1-1	2-3	8-0	7-0	6-0	4-4	*	5-4	2-2
10.	Sloop	0-4	3-2	1-2	1-6	1-1	4-3	2-2	2-3	3-3	*	4-4
11.	Westella Shopa. 'A'	1-7	0-0	2-0	0-5	7-0	5-0	5-3	4-3	2-3	1-1	*

PREMIER DIVISION CLUBS 1993-94

BEVERLEY OLD GRAMMARIANS
Secretary: Nick Gutteridge, 212 Goddard Ave., Hull (446548).
Ground: Grammar School, Queensgate, Beverley   **Colours:** Red & black/black.

CAVALIER CLUB
Secretary: Mike Myers, 30 Beech Close, Coltman Str., Hull HU3 2SW (0482 226758)
Ground: Pitch 2, Oak Road PF, Hull   **Colours:** Green & yellow stripes.

HALTEMPRICE
Secretary: Keith Failey, 77 Beech Rd, Ellhoughton, HU15 1JY (0482 666994)
Ground: King George V PF, Beverley Rd, Kirkella   **Colours:** Blue & white.

HOLME ROVERS
Secretary: Paul Harrison, 31 Back Lane, Holme-on-Spalding Moor, York (0430 860277)
Ground: Village Hall, High Str., Holme-on-Spalding Moor   **Colours:** T.B.A.

HOWDEN AMATEURS
Secretary: Alan Payling, 27 The Meadows, Howden DN14 7DU (0430 430782)
Grnd: Ashes Playing Field, Howden   **Colours:** Red & black.

LECONFIELD
Secretary: Andy Card, 14 Elvington Cres., Leconfield, HU17 7LD (0964 550874)
Ground: Miles Lane, Leconfield   **Colours:** Yellow/green

MARKET WEIGHTON UNITED
Secretary: John Hall, 41 Princess Rd, Market Weighton YO4 3BU (0430 873660)
Ground: Goodmanham Rd, Market Weighton   **Colours:** Green & white.

NORTH CAVE
Secretary: Cliff Robson, 6 Blanshards Lane, North Cave HU15 2LN (0430 422071)
Ground: Church Street PF, North Cave   **Colours:** Blue.

NORTH NEWBALD
Secretary: Ken Smith, 13 Church Mount, North Newbald, York YO4 3SY (0430 827438)
Grnd: South Newbald Rd PF, North Newbald   **Colours:** Yellow & red.

RUDSTON UNITED
Secretary: R W Overfield, 18 Eastgate, Rudston, Driffield YO25 0UX (0262 420397).
Ground: Burton Fleming Rd PF, Rudston   **Colours:** All blue.

SCULCOATES AMATEURS
Secretary: Tony Exton, 9 32nd Avenue, Hull HU6 9SD (0482 802600)
Ground: Pitch No.1 Oak Rd Playing Fields, Hull   **Colours:** Black & white.

WESTELLA SHOPACHECK
Secretary: Roger Wauby, 6 First Lane, Anlaby, Hull (651060) **Colours:** Black & white stripes/black
Ground: Swanland PF, West Leys Rd, Swanland (Res & 'A': As Haltemprice (page 981))

WOODLANDS
Secretary: Raymond Kinder, 46 Victoria Str., Goole DN14 5EX (0405 768826)
Ground: West Park, Airmyn Rd, Goole **Colours:** Purple & white stripes/purple.

DIVISION ONE CLUBS 1993-94

ANLABY UNITED
Secretary: Steve Smith, 12 Hawkshead Green, Malham Ave., Hull HU4 7SZ (562925).
Ground: King George V PF, Beverley Rd, Kirkella **Colours:** White & black

BEAVER
Secretary: Ian Helliwell, Orchard Farm House, 32 West End, Walkington, Hull HU17 8SX (0482 881302)
Ground: Beverley Leisure Centre, Flemingate, Beverley **Colours:** White/black.
Previous Name: N.M.G. Antiques (pre-1993).

BLACK PRINCE ROYALS
Secretary: Barry Hagues, 11 The Garth, Cottingham (875517)
Ground: Pitch 6, Dane Park, Orchard Park Estate **Colours:** Red & black.

BRANDESBURTON
Secretary: Kevin Atkinson, 35 Reedsway, Brandesburton YO25 8S (0964 543807)
Ground: Catwick Lane, Brandesburton **Colours:** Black & amber stripes.

EASINGTON UNITED
Secretary: Mrs Judith Foster, 5 Humber Lane, Patrington, Hull HU12 0PJ.
Ground: Low Farm, Easington **Colours:** White & blue

GILBERDYKE UNITED
Secretary: Paul Todd, 10 Chapel Garth, Gilberdyke, Brough, Hull HU15 2UH (0430 449557)
Ground: Gilberdyke Village Hall **Colours:** Blue & black stripes.
Previous Name: Wards Gilberdyke (pre-1993).

HODGSON
Secretary: Steve Bruce, 47 Queensmead, Beverley HU17 8PQ (0482 868633)
Ground: Beverley Leisure Centre, Flemingate, Beverley **Colours:** Yellow & blue.

THORNGUMBALD
Secretary: Arthur Brummit, 9 Bridge Bungalows, Burstwick, Hull HU12 9JS (0964 622271)
Ground: Plumtree Rd, Thorngumbald **Colours:** White & navy stripes.

VIKING SAFEWAY
Secretary: J Pheasnt, 27 Ullswater Grove, Goole DN14 6JR (0405 765456)
Ground: West Park, Western Rd, Goole **Colours:** Yellow/red.

This Division also includes the reserve sides of: Holme Rovers, North Cave, Westella Shopacheck.

DIVISION TWO CLUBS 1993-94

ALDBROUGH UNITED
Secretary: Alan Thomas, 7 Ash Grove, Headlands Park, Aldbrough, North Humbs HU11 4SQ (0964 527238)
Ground: Garton Rd Rec., Aldbrough **Colours:** Black & red stripes/black.

ANLABY AMATEURS
Secretary: Ray Harteveld, 14a Pease Court, High Street, Hull HU1 1NG (0482 589254)
Grnd: As Haltemprice (page 981) **Colours:** Yellow & blue

BRANSHOLME ATHLETIC
Secretary: Alan Clark, 187 Sutton Rd, Hull HU6 7DP (0482 802449)
Ground: Bude Rd, Bransholme **Colours:** Red & white.

HOLMPTON UNITED
Secretary: Wayne Christie, 20 Garrick Close, Pocklington YO4 2YX (0759 306796)
Ground: Welwick Rd, Patrington **Colours:** White & blue.

HOOK AMATEURS
Secretary: Kevin Young, 'Manavale', High Str., Hook, Goole DN14 5NY (0405 760322)
Ground: Church Lane, Hook **Colours:** Green & yellow.

LONG RISTON
Secretary: Harry Grimston, 14 Riseway, Long Riston, Hull HU11 5JN (0964 562053).
Ground: The Playing Field, Long Riston **Colours:** Blue & yellow.

ROYAL OAK
Secretary: Jim Calvert, c/o Royal Oak Pub, Cartwright Ave., Beverley (0482 862416)
Ground: Central Avenue, Beverley. **Colours:** Blue & white stripes

SKIDBY MILLERS
Secretary: Ron Leveridge, 121 Main Str., Skidby, Cottingham, Hull HU16 5TX (0482 847289)
Ground: Skidby PF, Manor Garth, Skidby **Colours:** Red & white.

WALTON CLUB
Secretary: S Holbrook, 60 Patterdale Rd, Spring Bank West, Hull HU5 5AR (0482 509888).
Ground: King George V PF, Beverley Rd, Kirkella **Colours:** White & blue.

This Division also includes the reserve sides of: Beverley O.G., Haltemprice, Sculcoates Amateurs.

DIVISION THREE CLUBS 1993-94

BARKERS
Secretary: Michael Shipley, 38 Eastgate, Beverley, HU17 0DT (0482 865520)
Ground: Beverley Leisure Centre, Flemingate, Beverley. **Colours:** Claret/black.

BEVERLEY TOWN
Secretary: Terry Brocklehurst, 10 Waterside Rd, Beverley HU17 0PP (0482 871336)
Ground: Beverley Leisure Centre, Flemingate, Beverley   **Colours:** Sky & claret stripes.

HORNSEA OLD BOYS
Secretary: Neil Scott, 11 Town Farm, Skipsea, Hornsea YO25 8UB (0262 468121).
Ground: Hornsea School, Hornsea   **Colours:** Red & black.

LEVEN MEMBERS' CLUB
Secretary: Michael Caygill, Elm Tree Lodge, West Str., Leven, Beverley HU17 5LE (0964 542298)
Ground: Leven PF, North Street, Leven.   **Colours:** Maroon.

RISTON BAY HORSE
Secretary: John Carlill, 1 Joiners Shop Row, Long Riston (0964 562245)
Ground: King George V PF, Cottingham   **Colours:** Claret & blue.

TICKTON
Secretary: Alan Hayton, 41 Scotts Garth Close, Tickton, Beverley HU17 9RQ (0964 542040)
Ground: Playing Fields, Main Str., Tickton, Beverley   **Colours:** White & blue

WALKINGTON
Secretary: Martin Davey, 30 West End Rd, Walkington, Beverley, HU17 8SX (0482 871020)
Ground: Beech View, Walkington, Beverley.   **Colours:** Royal blue & black.

This Division also includes the reserve sides of: Anlaby Amateurs, Holme Rovers ('A' team), Howden Amateurs, Leconfield, Market Weighton Utd, Thorngumbald.

DIVISION FOUR CLUBS 1993-94

GROVEHILL AMATEURS
Secretary: Colin Conman, 191 Holmechurch Lane, Beverley HU17 0QE (0482 864500)
Ground: Longcroft School, Burton Rd, Beverley   **Colours:** Green
Previous Name: Sloop (pre-1993).

LITTLE WEIGHTON
Secretary: Stephen Christmas, 4 The Close, Little Weighton HU20 3XA (841366).
Ground: Old Village Rd, Little Weighton   **Colours:** Blue/maroon.

MOLESCROFT RANGERS
Secretary: Roy Ritson, 20 Hargreave Close, Beverley HU17 7BG (862723)
Ground: Longcroft School, Burton Rd, Beverley   **Cols:** Blue & black stripes/black

This Division also includes the reserve sides of: Brandesburton, Holme Rovers ('B' team), Howden Amateurs ('A' team), Long Riston, Market Weighton Utd ('A' team), North Newbald, Skidby Millers, Viking Safeway, Westella Shopacheck.

CARLISLE & DISTRICT LEAGUE

FINAL TABLE	P	W	D	L	F	A	PTS
Abbeytown	24	17	5	2	71	30	39
Wigton	24	14	6	4	60	31	34
Museum	24	15	3	6	75	48	33
Gillford Pk Res.	24	15	3	6	58	52	33
Northbank	24	15	1	8	79	35	31
Longtown	24	15	0	9	68	55	30
Penrith Res.	24	10	5	9	70	62	25
Whitehaven Miners	24	12	0	12	60	50	24
Carlisle City Res.	24	8	6	10	57	42	22
Silloth	24	8	4	12	41	52	20
Hearts	24	4	0	20	36	101	8
Sporting Club	24	3	1	20	48	113	7
Wigton Harriers	24	2	2	20	33	85	6

LGE CUP FINAL: Whitehaven Mnrs 3, Abbeytown 2

CLUB DIRECTORY 1993-94

ABBEYTOWN
Secretary: G Mattinson, 17 Golf Terrace, Silloth (32316).
Ground: Abbeytown Recreation Ground   **Colours:** Red & black.

ASPATRIA
Secretary: J W Pattinson, 67 Lawson Str., Aspatria (20733)
Ground: St Mungos Park, Aspatria   **Colours:** T.B.A.

CARLISLE CITY RES., GILLFORD PARK RES. *(see Courage Northern Alliance section)*

JOINERS ARMS
Secretary: D Bell, 27 Granville Rd, Carlisle (21574)
Ground: Sheepmount   **Colours:** White.

LONGTOWN
Secretary: R Boguszynski, 27 Esk Str., Longtown (Longtown 825)
Ground: Lochinvar School   **Colours:** Blue

MUSEUM
Secretary: J Earl, 56 Crummock Str., Carlisle (28019)
Ground: Richardson Street, Carlisle.   **Colours:** Red.

NORTHBANK
Secretary: W Martin, 26 Jackson Rd, Houghton, Carlisle (31226).
Ground: Keenan Park   **Colours:** Red.

SPORTING MUSEUM
Secretary: M Pearson, 38 Hillary Grove, Carlisle (512311)
Ground: Richardson Street, Carlisle   **Colours:** Green

SILLOTH
Secretary: S Hart, 10 Skiddaw Str., Silloth (31817).
Ground: Eden Street, Silloth.   **Colours:** Blue.

WHITEHAVEN MINERS SOCIAL
Secretary: M Morton, 35 Criffel Rd, Parton, Whitehaven (695658)
Ground: Rec. Ground (Whitehaven 65421)(next to Rugby League ground)   **Colours:** Red

WIGTON
Secretary: J Hetherington, 40 South End, Wigton (42955)
Ground: Barton Laws   **Colours:** Black & white stripes

WIGTON HARRIERS
Secretary: G Johnston, 34a King Str., Wigton (45155)
Ground: Barton Laws   **Colours:** White

Action from the West Riding County Amateur League - Huddersfield side Marsden (stripes) are held to a 2-2 draw at home by Gascoigne United hoops on 31st October. Photo - Barry Lockwood.

A Blyth Spartan clears his lines against Chester-le-Street in a Northern League Division One fixture on Easter Saturday. Photo - Martin Wray.

FEDERATION BREWERY
NORTHERN LEAGUE

President: Ernest Armstrong, P.C.
Chairman: A. Clark
Hon. Secretary: A.Golightly I.P.F.A., 85 Park Road North,
Chester-le-Street, Co.Durhum DH3 3SA (091 388 2056)

Manchester United deserved to win the F.A. Prmeier League which pleased alot of fans all over the country. Whitby Town deserved to win the Northern League, which also pleased a lot of people down Yorkshire way because they'd had to wait 66 long years to do it. Unquestionably the Northern League's 104th season was yet another successful one, at least on the field of play. Though our administration remains admirable, and our cameraderie complete, our relationship with leagues nominally above us in the Pyramid is - at best - uneasy. Northern League teams did pretty well in National Competitions. Blyth Spartans reached the First Round of the F.A. Cup beaten by Southport after a thrilling "game of the season". Both Northallerton Town and Dunston Federation got to the later stages of the F.A. Trophy and F.A. Vase before losing to more experienced teams. All three County Senior Cups were won by our clubs. Newcastle Blue Star shocked a Newcastle Reserves side packed with players with first team experience in the Northumberland Senior Cup, Murton beat Bishop Auckland, nominally two leagues higher, in the Durham Challenge Cup, and Guisborough overcame Rowntrees in the North Riding Senior Cup. The North-east winter was uncharacteristically mild with little snow or frost, and it was mostly rain on flooded pitches which resulted in postponments. Happily, with the completion of seven new stets of floodlights, rearranged fixtures were readily accommodated and the season finished on time. Our congratualtions to those clubs whose efforts and initiative in obtaining new lights brightened a long winter in more ways then one.

If anything, it was high unemployment and the deep recession in the North-east which most affected Northern League clubs. The closure of collieries, shipyards, factories and many businesses in an already depressed area dealt killing blows to many sports. Some clubs struggled financially and several reached crisis point before the end of a painful season for them. Vandalism and arson attacks were targetted on clubs and the worst hit, South Bank and Washington, suffered the loss of their facilities. As one club secretary said: "We have to work like hell just to stand still." Crime seems to be the single greatest problem facing many clubs, and it is hard to find an answer. But none folded to date, in point of fact, to their credit, no N.L. club has folded in the last sixty years. (A most remarkable statistic when considering the demise of so many football clubs in other areas of England.) Nevertheless, a number of clubs, particularly the older ones, their glory-days long gone, found life most difficult. It is some of the newer clubs that have progressed well, and the strength and reputation of the League is as good as ever. Our clubs more than hold their own against clubs from supposedly higher leagues in cup competitions and former N.L. clubs have all been notably successful. Bishop Auckland, Whitley Bay, Spennymoor and North Shields (sadly now defunct) have all won quick promotion since leaving and Gretna will surely follow the trend - this bears out the quality of N.L. football.

Whitby Town FC, Northern League Champions 1992-93.

Lack of cash and maybe willing helpers meant fewer clubs running an U-19 team in our Banks Youth League with the result that the League will be opened up to other clubs in the Pyramid of Football during the coming season. The benefits of developing young players are now beginning to show in several clubs and there is no doubt that the effort is worthwhile.

Everyone enjoyed the ideal last day finish to the Northern League season. Four clubs fought out an exciting run-in to the First Division Championship which was settled only by the final day's results. Whitby Town became worthy champions over second-placed Billingham Synthonia. Dunston Federation had earlier proved themselves good winners of the Second Division by several points and Eppleton, Shildon and Billingham Town were neck and neck for the two remaining promotion places with the Town's single point at Bedlington on the last day proving insufficient. None of the League's fancied teams managed to reach the League Cup final, but Seaham Red Star and Brandon put on a rousing show at Billingham Town to draw 2-2 after extra-time. Seaham finally won 3-0 on penalties when, to everyone's amazement, Brandon missed their first three attempts. Has there ever been another 3-0 win in a penalty competition? The F.A.'s Chief Executive, Graham Kelly, a surprise guest, honoured the proceedings by presenting the cup and awards.

The Division One relegation issue became controversial because of the disputed promotion of Whitby Town. The League lodged a complaint with the Football Association and pointed out that the rules of the H.F.S. Northern Premier League specifically forbade the promotion of any Northern League club to their competition until Northern League grounds met their criteria. To our great disappointment, but perhaps not quite so much to our surprise, the H.F.S. had ruled that our clubs' grounds failed to meet their ground criteria. In the light of experience this is completely unjustified because Northern League pitches are better than most. The F.A.'s Pyramid committee threw out the complaint inexplicably stating that: "Whilst recognising that the question of relative ground grading standards was a matter requiring attention..." it accepted the present H.F.S. criteria. No decision was made regarding the promotion of Whitby Town, creating further uncertainty.

In our view, ground criteria play too important a part in the progress and development of clubs at the lower levels of the Pyramid. The Taylor Report and stringent safety standards are not applicable to grounds where the attendance averages less than a couple of hundred spectators. But it seems that the Northern League clubs are expected to pay the price simply because they did not join the Pyramid in 1980 - a free choice without conditions or penalties, confirmed by senior F.A. officials at the time; the reasons then - geography and economics - were fully justified but have altered since. Consequently, there is much ill-feeling and resentment amongst N.L. clubs at the F.A's lack of support for the League's representation made on this and several other issues. Over the last few years the N.L. has been consistently disadvantaged by F.A. decisions which have seemed illogical. Two years ago the League was obliged by the intransigence of the H.F.S. to accept level 4 of the Pyramid structure after originally being offered level 2. The anomaly of this decision is, that the N.L. First Division feeds into an H.F.S. League consisting mostly of clubs in the F.A. Vase when all clubs in the N.L. First Division compete in the F.A. Trophy - a bizarre arrangement but condoned by the F.A. This has caused much confusion. The policy of repeatedly promoting clubs to the H.F.S. League without any relegation is denuding the leagues at the base of the Pyramid. As there is a shortage of suitable clubs these leagues are constantly below strength. The N.L. advocated a reduction in the complement of 44 clubs in the H.F.S. League as the sensible and obvious solution, maintaining that fewer mid-week games involving lengthy travel would be welcomed by its clubs. We believe that it is the F.A. who should establish such principles by exercising proper control and direction. The contrasting friendly relationship which exists between the leagues in the North-East Pyramid section is an example to the rest. The Northern League has full support and a good understanding with its two feeder leagues, the Vaux Wearside and McEwans Northern Alliance. Here there is mutual trust with everyone's objective being the greater good of the game.

The League's innovative second Groundhopper 8 match Easter weekend received wonderful support and acclaim throughout the whole of Britain and even beyond, and is now regarded as the highlight of the season by those dedicated followers of our national game. They and others are equally complimentary about the League's six-weekly magazine "Northern Ventures, Northern Gains", now sold and prized nationally. This popular magazine is regarded as a bargain buy recording the affairs, humour and happenings around N.L. clubs. It highlights the League's policies and ideals and advocates and promotes all that is best for the game. Enjoyment of matches is paramount, and the League's determination to eradicate foul and abusive language both on and off the field, to eliminate dissent and to make the referee's task an easier one is well recorded.

Other good news is that after hundreds of hours of effort and negotiation by the League's officers we again have a major sponsor. The Federation Brewery will sponsor the League next season to the tune of £25,000, a tremendous confidence booster which will be of great benefit to clubs, and add spice to the competition for honours. So the Northern League season closed on a high note with its splendid end-of-season Dinner attended by many guests including directors and representatives of the new sponsors. The occasion marks the start of a new phase in the proud history of the Northern League.

Arthur Clark (League Chairman)

League Tables

DIVISION ONE	P	W	D	L	F	A	PTS
WHITBY TOWN	38	26	10	2	104	30	88
BILLINGHAM SYN.	38	25	10	3	98	41	85
GUISBOROUGH T.	38	25	9	4	91	35	84
BLYTH SPARTANS	38	26	4	8	83	35	82
SEAHAM RED S.	38	21	10	7	76	45	73
DURHAM CITY	38	21	10	7	73	51	73
STOCKTON	38	14	15	9	65	59	57
MURTON	38	14	12	12	72	65	54
CHESTER-LE-S.	38	15	8	15	82	82	53
CONSETT	38	15	7	16	54	56	52
NORTHALLERTON	38	13	14	11	54	47	*50
WEST AUCKLAND	38	12	9	17	64	76	45
NEWCASTLE B.S.	38	12	6	20	64	81	42
TOW LAW TOWN	38	11	8	19	65	73	41
BRANDON UTD	38	11	5	22	47	81	38
HEBBURN	38	8	11	19	74	94	**29
FERRYHILL	38	6	10	22	51	97	28
EASINGTON	38	6	8	24	51	94	26
PETERLEE	38	3	9	26	40	105	18
SOUTH BANK	38	3	11	24	34	95	*17

* = 3pts deducted ** = 6 pts deducted

DIVISION TWO	P	W	D	L	F	A	PTS
DUNSTON FED.	38	30	5	3	139	34	95
EPPLETON CW	38	27	7	4	116	51	88
SHILDON	38	25	6	7	93	24	81
BILLINGHAM T.	38	24	8	6	89	36	80
PRUDHOE E.E.	38	18	7	13	65	53	61
EVENWOOD TOWN	38	18	7	13	75	68	61
WHICKHAM	38	19	3	16	71	62	60
ASHINGTON	38	17	5	16	77	70	56
ALNWICK TOWN	38	16	7	15	51	61	55
RYHOPE CA	38	16	8	14	67	61	*53
DARLINGTON CB	38	14	11	13	48	53	*50
NORTON & S.A.	38	13	5	20	54	79	44
ESH WINNING	38	13	4	21	70	82	43
SHOTTON COM.	38	11	10	17	53	74	43
WASHINGTON	38	10	9	19	54	74	39
WILLINGTON	38	12	3	23	61	106	39
BEDLINGTON T.	38	11	3	24	64	86	*33
CROOK TOWN	38	9	9	20	45	78	*33
HORDEN C.W.	38	6	8	24	48	99	26
LANGLEY PARK	38	5	7	26	52	141	22

* = 3pts deducted

DIVISION ONE RESULT CHART 1992-93

HOME TEAM	1	2	3	4	5	6	7	8	9	10	11	12	13	14	15	16	17	18	19	20
1. Billingham Synthonia	*	1-0	2-0	2-2	2-0	3-1	7-3	2-1	2-2	7-2	4-1	4-1	2-1	6-1	1-1	0-0	2-1	3-0	6-3	1-1
2. Blyth	0-1	*	2-1	4-2	2-0	1-1	8-3	7-0	0-2	3-0	3-2	1-2	3-0	3-0	2-2	3-1	2-0	2-0	2-1	0-1
3. Brandon	1-2	0-3	*	3-2	0-4	0-0	1-1	2-3	2-2	0-9	1-0	0-3	6-1	0-1	2-2	7-0	1-3	3-0	1-7	
4. Chester Town	4-3	1-3	4-0	*	2-1	0-2	2-1	4-2	1-3	3-2	1-0	0-1	1-1	5-0	3-3	4-0	3-3	2-2	3-4	1-3
5. Consett	0-1	0-2	2-0	4-4	*	4-1	3-2	1-1	0-4	1-1	1-1	0-1	3-2	1-2	1-0	2-1	2-1	2-0	2-4	
6. Durham City	0-3	2-1	0-1	0-0	0-1	*	0-2	3-2	1-1	7-0	2-1	4-3	2-2	1-0	1-0	0-0	3-2	1-1	2-0	1-0
7. Easington	1-4	1-3	0-1	0-1	0-0	2-4	*	3-3	0-3	6-3	1-1	6-1	0-1	2-2	1-3	0-1	1-1	2-5	2-3	1-4
8. Ferryhill	1-5	0-1	2-4	1-0	0-2	1-1	1-1	*	2-5	4-1	1-1	3-2	1-3	2-1	1-2	1-1	1-2	2-2	0-4	1-5
9. Guisborough	2-0	1-0	1-1	5-1	2-0	1-3	3-0	6-0	*	3-1	2-2	2-1	1-	2-1	1-2	3-0	1-1	4-0	4-0	1-1
10. Hebburn	2-0	0-2	0-1	3-5	2-2	2-3	2-2	1-2	1-2	*	3-2	1-3	1-3	4-4	4-2	5-1	3-1	4-1	1-1	
11. Murton	1-1	0-3	1-0	3-2	4-0	3-1	2-1	3-1	3-3	0-4	*	2-1	3-3	1-2	2-2	4-1	3-3	0-1	1-0	3-5
12. Newcastle Blue Star	0-2	0-3	0-1	4-1	5-3	2-7	1-2	3-0	2-4	2-2	3-2	*	1-2	3-5	3-0	1-2	3-2	0-0	1-3	
13. Northallerton	0-1	0-1	4-2	6-3	1-0	0-0	2-0	1-1	0-0	2-2	0-1	1-1	*	1-0	5-1	0-0	4-2	0-2	0-2	
14. Peterlee	0-6	1-3	0-2	2-6	1-2	2-4	1-2	1-1	0-5	2-2	0-1	0-0	1-1	*	1-2	2-1	2-0	2-1	2-2	2-3
15. Seaham Red Star	2-4	3-1	2-1	3-1	1-0	1-1	2-0	1-2	3-1	0-1	5-0	1-1	2-3	5-1	*	3-1	0-0	1-0	3-1	1-1
16. South Bank	0-2	1-2	0-2	0-1	0-3	1-1	2-0	2-1	2-4	1-5	1-2	3-3	1-1	0-3	0-3	*	2-2	1-1	1-3	0-7
17. Stockton	0-0	2-0	3-0	1-2	2-0	1-2	0-1	5-4	1-0	2-1	2-2	2-1	2-0	6-2	1-1	5-1	*	1-1	1-1	1-1
18. Tow Law Town	2-2	1-2	5-1	1-2	1-1	1-2	4-0	6-4	0-0	4-2	0-3	1-2	0-1	3-1	1-3	4-2	1-2	*	4-1	0-2
19. West Auckland	2-2	1-3	3-0	1-3	0-4	2-4	4-0	1-1	1-2	6-2	2-1	1-1	2-0	3-0	1-0	1-1	3-3	3-2	*	0-2
20. Whitby Town	2-2	1-1	4-0	6-1	0-0	5-0	3-0	3-0	0-2	1-0	1-1	7-0	2-1	4-0	1-1	5-1	4-0		*	

DIVISION TWO RESULT CHART 1992-93

HOME TEAM	1	2	3	4	5	6	7	8	9	10	11	12	13	14	15	16	17	18	19	20
1. Alnwick	*	3-1	3-0	0-4	1-1	1-0	0-1	3-7	3-2	2-1	3-1	2-0	1-1	1-1	4-1	1-0	1-0	2-3	2-1	2-1
2. Ashington	3-3	*	4-0	1-2	2-1	4-0	2-5	2-1	2-3	3-4	1-0	3-1	5-1	1-0	1-1	0-2	7-3	0-2	1-2	2-1
3. Bedlington	4-2	2-2	*	3-3	3-0	1-1	0-2	3-2	4-3	6-1	6-2	1-3	1-2	2-3	1-2	0-2	1-2	0-2	0-2	1-2
4. Billingham Town	5-0	5-1	1-0	*	6-0	0-3	3-4	2-0	4-1	4-0	4-1	0-0	1-2	1-3	0-0	0-2	0-0	1-0		
5. Crook Town	4-1	1-2	2-1	3-3	*	0-2	0-4	0-0	0-4	2-0	2-2	3-4	1-1	0-2	1-3	0-6	0-1	1-1	3-2	3-0
6. Darlington CB	0-2	1-3	1-4	0-1	0-0	*	1-3	0-2	0-4	1-1	3-1	1-1	3-2	2-1	0-2	1-0	4-1	0-0	1-0	2-0
7. Dunston Federation	2-0	2-0	8-0	1-1	8-2	6-0	*	3-3	8-0	3-0	4-0	5-1	2-1	4-1	3-1	1-1	3-1	5-1	2-1	4-3
8. Eppleton CW	1-1	3-0	3-2	1-1	4-2	0-0	3-2	*	5-2	2-0	7-3	9-1	4-1	4-0	0-0	0-5	3-2	3-0	3-0	4-0
9. Esh Winning	1-0	2-3	1-2	1-2	1-5	1-4	0-3	1-5	*	0-1	1-2	9-0	4-1	2-3	2-3	0-0	2-2	1-2	1-1	4-0
10. Evenwood	1-1	2-4	3-0	2-1	0-3	1-2	1-1	1-7	3-2	*	4-1	9-0	2-1	5-0	4-4	3-2	1-1	1-0	1-0	4-5
11. Horden	1-3	2-0	0-4	1-2	3-2	0-4	2-5	0-0	2-0	0-1	*	3-1	0-1	0-0	2-4	2-2	0-2	1-1	1-1	
12. Langley Park	2-0	4-3	1-6	2-3	0-0	1-3	1-7	1-7	1-3	0-4	1-1	*	3-3	0-4	3-3	0-3	1-3	1-1	0-4	6-0
13. Norton	1-0	2-1	2-1	1-0	0-1	0-0	0-6	1-2	0-1	0-3	4-1	5-2	*	2-0	1-2	0-3	1-0	3-2	2-3	2-1
14. Prudhoe EE	5-0	2-1	4-1	2-4	1-0	0-0	1-2	4-1	2-3	0-1	3-3	1-0	5-0	*	2-0	2-2	2-1	4-1	0-2	0-3
15. Ryhope CA	0-1	2-5	0-2	0-1	5-0	1-3	1-4	1-2	4-2	1-1	4-0	4-1	2-0	0-0	*	2-3	1-2	2-3	2-4	4-1
16. Shildon	2-0	1-0	5-0	1-0	1-0	2-1	2-1	1-2	2-3	3-0	4-1	8-1	5-2	1-1	3-0	*	4-0	1-0	3-0	4-0
17. Shotton	1-0	1-1	1-0	1-3	1-0	2-2	0-0	1-2	3-0	1-1	1-7	2-2	4-3	1-0	2-0	0-2	*	3-3	2-3	3-1
18. Washington	0-1	1-1	4-0	1-2	1-2	1-0	0-4	2-3	1-1	1-4	6-3	5-0	2-5	0-2	0-1	1-1	1-1	*	0-3	1-3
19. Whickham	1-0	0-2	2-1	1-6	2-0	2-3	0-3	2-3	0-3	1-1	3-0	5-2	6-1	1-2	2-1	2-1	5-2	0-2	*	4-1
20. Willington	0-1	2-3	3-1	1-7	0-0	2-1	0-1	1-0	4-1	2-4	4-2	3-2	4-3	2-1	1-3	1-1	0-5	3-1	8-2	3-4	*

NORTHERN LEAGUE CUP 1992-93

First Round

Washington v Brandon United	0-3
Durham City v Seaham Red Star	1-4
Murton v Alnwick Town	2-1
Billingham Town v Ashington	4-0
Chester-le-Street Town v Dunston F.B.	3-2(aet)
West Auckland Town v Shotton Comrades	4-0
Ferryhill Athletic v South Bank	1-0
Esh Winning v Guisborough Town	0-6
Prudhoe East End v Blyth Spartans	1-3
Northallerton Town v Shildon	1-3
Hebburn v Evenwood Town	2-1
Bedlington Terriers v Consett	2-3
Horden Colliery Welfare v Newcastle Blue Star	1-3
Whickham v Billingham Synthonia	0-2
Stockton v Ryhope Community Ass.	2-0(ab.,)3-0
Eppleton Colliery Welfare v Peterlee Newtown	0-1

Second Round

Blyth Spartans v Seaham Red Star	0-2
Murton v Consett	3-6
Newcastle Blue Star v West Auckland	0-3
Ferryhill Athletic v Guisborough Town	1-3
Brandon United v Shildon	2-1
Hebburn v Billingham Town	3-1
Chester-le-Street Town v Billingham Synthonia	0-2
Stockton v Peterlee Newtown	2-0

(continued overleaf)

Quarter Finals *(continued from page 987)*

Brandon United v Hebburn	2-0	West Auckland v Guisborough Town		1-3
Seaham Red Star v Consett	1-0	Billingham Synthonia v Stockton		5-0

Semi-Finals

Seaham Red Star v Guisborough 1-1 *(5-3 pens)*   Brandon United v Billingham Synthonia   2-1

Final *(at Billingham Town F.C., Wed 5th May)*: Brandon 2, Seaham 2 *(aet, Seaham won 3-0 on pens)*

Northern League Division One Ten Year Record

	83/4	84/5	85/6	86/7	87/8	88/9	89/0	90/1	91/2	92/3
Alnwick Town	-	-	-	-	-	-	8	19	-	-
Ashington	17	-	-	-	-	-	-	-	-	-
Bedlington Terriers	-	-	2	20	-	-	-	-	-	-
Billingham Synthonia	7	12	19	-	3	1	1	4	5	2
Billingham Town	-	-	20	-	-	5	19	-	-	-
Bishops Auckland	5	1	1	2	6	-	-	-	-	-
Blyth Spartans	1	2	4	1	1	9	9	3	6	4
Brandon United	-	-	8	12	10	7	18	17	15	15
Chester-le-Street Town	-	8	7	16	18	19	-	-	-	9
Consett	12	15	13	13	20	-	6	5	9	10
Crook Town	14	16	9	17	17	20	-	-	-	-
Durham City	-	-	-	-	-	14	17	20	-	6
Easington Colliery	-	-	-	10	15	13	20	-	17	18
Evenwood Town	18	-	-	-	-	-	-	-	-	-
Ferryhill Athletic	16	14	18	18	14	8	13	8	16	17
Gretna	8	6	11	7	7	3	2	1	1	-
Guisborough Town	-	-	-	-	5	4	7	2	4	3
Hartlepool United Reserves	-	-	10	15	-	-	-	-	-	-
Hebburn	-	-	-	-	-	-	-	-	-	16
Horden Colliery Welfare	10	17	-	-	-	-	-	-	-	-
Langley Park	-	-	-	-	-	-	-	-	19	-
Murton	-	-	-	-	-	-	-	13	2	8
Newcastle Blue Star	-	-	-	4	2	6	4	10	13	13
Northallerton Town	-	-	-	-	-	-	-	9	8	11
North Shields	2	5	12	6	9	18	-	-	-	-
Peterlee Newtown	13	9	6	19	-	-	-	16	12	19
Ryhope Community	-	10	15	14	19	-	-	-	-	-
Seaham Red Star	-	-	-	-	-	16	10	11	11	5
Shildon	15	18	-	-	12	17	14	14	18	-
South Bank	6	3	3	8	16	15	16	12	7	20
Spennymoor United	11	11	14	3	11	11	11	-	-	-
Stockton	-	-	-	-	-	10	5	18	-	7
Tow Law Town	4	4	5	9	8	2	3	7	10	14
West Auckland Town	-	-	-	-	-	-	-	-	14	12
Whickham	-	-	-	-	-	-	15	15	20	-
Whitby Town	3	7	16	11	13	12	12	6	3	1
Whitley Bay	9	13	17	5	4	-	-	-	-	-
No. of Clubs	**18**	**18**	**20**	**20**	**20**	**20**	**20**	**20**	**20**	**20**

Division Two Record

	83/4	84/5	85/6	86/7	87/8	88/9	89/0	90/1	91/2	92/3
Alnwick Town	14	14	10	7	6	2	-	-	9	9
Ashington	-	10	8	10	15	5	13	12	12	8
Bedlington Terriers	8	2	-	-	7	7	9	11	19	17
Billingham Sythonia	-	-	-	1	-	-	-	-	-	-
Billingham Town	10	4	-	4	4	-	-	5	7	4
Brandon United	4	1	-	-	-	-	-	-	-	-
Chester-Le-Street Town	1	-	-	-	-	-	5	16	3	-
Consett	-	-	-	-	-	1	-	-	-	-
Crook Town	-	-	-	-	-	-	6	13	8	18
Darlington Cleveland Bridge	6	8	18	16	14	16	12	10	18	11
Darlington Reserves	11	16	15	-	-	-	-	-	-	-
Dunston Federation Breweries	-	-	-	-	-	-	-	-	5	1
Durham City	5	5	4	13	3	-	-	-	2	-
Easington Colliery	-	-	2	-	-	-	-	3	-	-
Eppleton Colliery Welfare	-	-	-	-	-	-	-	-	-	2
Esh Winning	9	11	20	17	5	15	20	7	11	13
Evenwood Town	-	15	17	14	16	17	7	6	17	6
Guisborough Town	-	-	3	2	-	-	-	-	-	-
Hartlepool United Reserves	7	3	-	-	-	-	-	-	-	-
Hebburn	-	-	-	-	-	-	15	4	4	-
Horden Colliery Welfare	-	-	13	18	11	8	16	19	15	19
Langley Park Welfare	13	9	12	19	12	13	4	2	-	20
Murton Colliery Welfare	-	-	-	-	-	11	1	-	-	-
Newcaslte Blue Star	-	-	1	-	-	-	-	-	-	-
Northallerton Town	12	12	16	12	9	9	2	-	-	-
Norton & Stockton Ancients	16	13	9	8	10	14	18	9	13	12
Peterlee Newtown	-	-	-	-	8	6	3	-	-	-
Prudhoe East End	-	-	-	-	-	4	8	8	6	5
Ryhope Community Assoc.	2	-	-	-	-	10	11	14	10	10
Seaham C.W. Red Star	3	6	6	9	2	-	-	-	-	-
Shildon	-	-	19	3	-	-	-	-	-	3
Shotton Comrades	15	18	14	15	18	20	17	15	14	14
Stockton	-	-	7	6	1	-	-	-	1	-
Washington	-	-	-	-	-	18	10	17	16	15
West Auckland Town	17	17	5	5	17	12	19	1	-	-
Whickham	-	-	-	-	-	3	-	-	-	7
Willington	18	7	11	11	13	19	14	18	20	16
No. of Clubs	**18**	**18**	**20**	**19**	**18**	**20**	**20**	**19**	**20**	**20**

BILLINGHAM SYNTHONIA

Chairman: Mr Harry Davies **Vice Chairman:** Mr Peter Lax **President:** Mr Dennis Rickards
Sec./Press Officer: Graham Craggs, 2 Ribble Close, Billingham, Cleveland TS22 5NT (0642 535856).
Manager: Stuart Coleby **Physio:** Tony Hetherington **Coach:** Lenny Gunn
Ground: The Stadium, Central Avenue, Billingham, Cleveland (0642 552358).
Directions: Turn off A19 onto A1027 signposted Billingham, Norton (this applies from either north or south),
continue straigh on along Central Avenue, ground on left opposite office block. By rail; ground 1 mile along
Cowpen Lane from Billingham (BR).
Seats: 370 **Cover:** 370 **Capacity:** 1,970 **Floodlights:** Yes **Founded:** 1923
Club colours: Green/white/green. **Change colours:** All blue **Club Shop:** No.
Midweek Matches: Wednesday **Previous League:** Teesside (1923-War).
Programme: 12 pages (+ads), 50p **Editor:** Harry Davies (0642 560445) **Souvenir Shop:** No.
Rec. Gate: 4,200 v Bishop Auck. 6/9/58. **Clubhouse:** 200yds across car park. Normal club hours.
Best F.A. Cup season: 1st Rd 48-49 51-52 56-57 57-58 87-88 89-90.
Prev. Ground: Belasis Lane 23-58 **Previous Name:** Billingham Synthonia Recreation
Players progressing to Football League: Peter Atkinson & Ken Harrison (Hull 1947), Ernie Wardle & John Murray
(M'boro 1948 & 49), Richard Mulvaney (Blackburn 1964), Mike Hodgson (Hartlepool 1964), David Hockaday
(Blackpool 1975), Terry Gaffney (Hartlepool 1977), Aidan Davidson (Notts County 1988).
Nickname: Synners **Club Sponsors:** Billingham Arms Hotel.
Captain 92-93: Stephen Corkain **Top Scorer 92-93:** Richard Allen **P.o.Y. 92-93:** Barney Malone.
Club record scorer: Tony Hetherington **Club record appearances:** Andy Harbron.
Honours: Northern Lg 56-57 88-89 89-90 (R-up 49-50 50-51*(No goals conceded at home; P 13, W 12, D 1, L 0; F
44, A 0)* 51-52, Lg Cup 51-52 87-88 89-90, Div 2 86-87), Teesside Lg 36-37 (Lg Cup 34-35 38-39), Durham
Challenge Cup 88-89 90-91, North Riding Snr Cup 66-67 71-72 78-79, North Riding Amateur Cup 38-39 56-57 62-
63 63-64, FA Amateur Cup 4th Rd 48-49, FA Tphy 1st Rd replay 90-91.

BLYTH SPARTANS

President: M Johnson **Manager:** Peter Freeman
Chairman: Andrew Fairholm-Little **Physio:** D Robertson.
Secretary: R Cotterill, 34 Solingen Estate, Blyth, Northumberland NE24 3ER (0670 361057).
Ground: Croft Park, Blyth, Northumberland. (0670) 354818
Directions: Through Tyne tunnel heading north on A19, take Cramlington turn, follow signs for Newsham/Blyth.
Right fork at railway gates in Newsham, down Plessey Rd, ground can be seen on left before Masons Arms. Buses
X24, X25, X26, X1 from Newcastle.
Seats: 300 **Cover:** 2,500 **Capacity:** 6,000 **Floodlights:** Yes **Founded:** 1899
Colours: Green & white stripes/black/green **Change colours:** All yellow or red
Previous leagues: Northumberland 01-07/ Northern Alliance 07-13/ 46-47/ North Eastern 13-14 19-39 47-58 62-
64/
Northern Combination 45-46/ Midland 58-60/ Northern Counties 60-62. **Sponsors:** Viz Magazine.
Programme: 20 pages, 20p **Programme Editor:** R R Clark **Souvenir Shop:** Yes
Clubhouse details: Open every night plus Saturday & Sunday lunch & matchdays.
Best F.A. Cup season: 5th Rd replay 77-78 (lost to Wrexham). Competition Proper on 25 occasions.
League Clubs defeated in F.A. Cup: Ashington, Gillingham 22-23/ Hartlepool United 71-72/ Crewe Alexandra,
Stockport County 71-72/ Chesterfield, Stoke City 77-78.
Players progressing to Football League: William McGlen (Manchester United 1946), Joe Roddom (Chesterfield
1948), Henry Mills (Huddersfield 1948), John Allison (Reading 1949), James Kelly (Watford 1949), Robert Millard
(Reading 1949), Jim Kerr (Lincoln 1952), James Milner (Burnley 1952), John Hogg (Portsmouth 1954), John
Allison (Chesterfield 1955), John Inglis (Gateshead 1957), John Longland (Hartlepool 1958).
Hons: Northern Lg(10) 72-73 74-76 79-84 86-88 (R-up 71-72 73-74 77-78 84-85, Lg Cup(5) 72-73 77-79 81-82 91-
92), Nth Eastern Lg 35-36 (R-up 22-23, Lg Cup 49-50 54-55), Northumberland Lg 03-04, Northern All. 08-09 12-13
(R-up 46-47), Northumberland Snr Cup(18) 13-15 31-32 33-37 51-52 54-55 58-59 62-63 71-72 73-75 77-78 80-82
84-85, FA Tphy QF rep. 79-80 82-83, FA Amtr Cup SF 71-72.
Local Newspapers: Newcastle Journal & Evening Chronicle. **Midweek Matches:** Tuesday

BRANDON UNITED

Chairman: Neil Scott **Vice Chairman:** N Green **President:** T Jacques
Sec./Press Off.: Brian Richardson, 108 Braunespath Estate, New Brancepeth, Durham DH7 7JF (091 373 1304).
Mgrs: Steve Dixon/Keith Brown **Asst Mgr:** John Carey **Physio:** Bev Dougherty
Ground: Welfare Ground, rear of Commercial Street, Brandon, Durham (091 378 2957).
Directions: A690 - 3 miles west of Durham City. Buses 49 & 49A from Durham.
Seats: 60 **Cover:** 300 **Capacity:** 4,060 **Floodlights:** Yes **Founded:** 1972.
Colours: All blue (white trim) **Change colours:** All red (white trim).
Previous Lges: Durham & Dist. Sunday 72-77/ Northern All. 77-80/ Northern Amtr 80-81/ Wearside 81-83.
Programme: 40 pages, 30p. **Editor:** Keith Nellis (091 378 0704) **Souvenir Shop:** No
Clubhouse: Open every day, lunch & evening. Pool & juke box. Entertainment at weekends.
Best F.A. Cup season: 1st Rd replay 88-89 (lost to Doncaster). Also 1st Rd 79-80.
League Clubs defeated in F.A. Cup: None.
Record Gate: 2,500, FA Sunday Cup SF. **Previous Name:** Rostrons 72-74.
Nickname: Blues or United **Club Sponsors:** Shildon Sawmills.
Players progressing to Football League: Bryan Liddle & Dean Gibbs & Dean Gibb (Hartlepool 1984 & 86 & 87),
Paul Dalton (Manchester Utd 1988).
Local Newspapers: Newcastle Journal, Northern Echo. **Midweek Matches:** Wednesday
Record win: 8-2 v West Auckland Town **Record defeat:** 0-9 v Murton (both Northern Lge).
Captain 92-93: David Martin **Top Scorer 92-93:** Steve Pidgeon **P.o.Y. 92-93:** TBA
Club record scorer: Tommy Holden **Club record appearances:** Unknown.
Hons: FA Sunday Cup 75-76, FA Vase QF 82-83 83-84, Northern Lg Div 2 84-85 (Lg Cup R-up 92-93), Northern
All.(2) 77-79 (R-up 79-80, Lg Cup 77-78 79-80 (R-up 78-79)), Sunderland Shipowners Cup 81-82, Durham Co.
Sunday Cup 73-74 75-76 76-77, FA Tphy 3rd Qual. Rd 87-88 89-90, Durham & Dist Sunday Lg(4) 73-77.

CHESTER-LE-STREET TOWN

Chairman: John Tomlinson   **Vice Chairman:** Jack Thornback   **President:** John Holden.
Secretary: John Watson, 30 Hadrian Avenue, Chester-le-Street, Co Durham DH3 3RS (091 3887307).
Manager: John Lang   **Asst Mgr/Coach:** Peter Stronach   **Physio:** Billy Jacobson.
Commercial Manager: Paul Days   **Press Officer:** Jack Thornback (091 3883554).
Ground: Moor Park, Chester Moor, Chester-le Street, County Durham (091 3883363).
Directions: Ground lies approx 2 miles south of town on A167 (C.-le-S. to Durham road). Regular buses from C.-le-S. and Durham pass ground. Railway station 2 miles distant in town centre.
Seats: 200   **Cover:** 500   **Capacity:** 2,000   **Floodlights:** Yes   **Founded:** 1972
Midweek Matches: Tuesday   **Shop:** No, but old programmes available from editor.
Cols: Blue & white hoops/white/white   **Change colours:** All yellow.
Programme: 32 pages, 30p   **Programme Editor:** Press Officer   **Nickname:** Cestrians
Clubhouse details: Open matchdays, Wed, Thurs & Sun. Wed/Thurs 7-10.30pm, Sun 12-2pm, midweek matches 6.30-10.30pm, Sat 12-10.30pm.
Previous Names: Garden Farm 1972-78.
Record win: 8-0 v Billingham T., FA Vase Preliminary Rd 6/10/84.
Record defeeat: 1-7 v Curzon Ashton, FA Vase Third Rd, 12/12/92.
Previous Leagues: Newcastle City Amtr 72-75/ Washington 75/ Wearside 77-83.
Previous Grounds: Ravensworth Welfare, Low Fell 72-73/ Riverside Pk 73-78/ Sacriston Welfare 78-79.
Record Gate: 473 v Barrow, FA Cup 83-84 (3,000 for Sunderland v Newcastle, Bradford appeal match 1985).
Players progressing to Football League: Dave Atkinson (Sunderland 1986), Peter Ward (Huddersfield 1987).
Captain & P.O.Y. 92-93: Steven Smith   **Top Scorer 92-93:** Jarrod Suddick, 30.
Club record scorer: Colin Howey, 50   **Club record appearances:** Brian Wray, 148.
Hons: Northern Lg Div 2 83-84, Wearside Lg 80-81 (R-up 82-83), Monkwearmouth Cup 80-81 81-82, FA Vase 4th Rd 91-92, Washington Lg, Durham Minor Cup, Washington AM Cup.

CONSETT

Chairman: F Lemon   **Vice Chairman:** I Hamilton.   **President:** D McVickers
Secretary: Peter McClean, 11 Cohort Close, Ebchester, Consett, Co. Durham DH8 0PG (0207 562712).
Manager: Colin Carr **Physio:** Joe Darroch   **Press Officer:** Colin French (0207 580899)
Ground: Belle Vue Park, Ashdale Road, Consett, County Durham (0207 503788)
Directions: Quarter of mile north of town centre - along Medomsley Rd, left down Ashdale Rd, ground 100m yards on left. Follow signs for Sports Centre and Baths. Buses 745, 711 & 772 from Newcastle, 719, 765 from Durham. w signs for Sports Centre and Baths, about 800 yds from town centre.
Seats: 400   **Cover:** 1,000   **Capacity:** 4,000   **Floodlights:** Yes   **Founded:** 1899
Colours: Red/black/red   **Change colours:** Sky blue/dark blue/sky blue
Previous Leagues: Northern Alliance 19-26 35-37/ North Eastern 26-35 37-58 62-64/ Midland 58-60/ Northern Counties 60-62/ Wearside 64-70.
Programme: 16 pages, 30p   **Programme Editor:** Colin French   **Souvenir Shop:** No
Record Gate: 7,000 v Sunderland Reserves, first match at Belle Vue, 1950.   **Nickname:** Steelmen
Clubhouse: Matchdays, and evenings on request. Darts & pool.
Best F.A. Cup season: 1st Rd 58-59 (lost 0-5 at Doncaster Rovers).
Previous Grounds: Vicarage Field (pre-1948)/ Leadgates Eden Colliery 48-50.
Players progressing to Football League: Tommy Lumley (Charlton), Alan Ellison (Reading), Laurie Cunningham (Barnsley), Jimmy Moir (Carlisle), Jackie Boyd (West Bromwich Albion).
Hons: North Eastern Lg 39-40 (Div 2 26-27, Lg Cup 50-51(jt) 53-54), Durham Challenge 47-48 49-50 58-59 60-61 68-69 (R-up 76-77 89-90), Northern Lg R-up 76-77 (Div 2 88-89, Lg Cup 78-79 and Wearside Lg R-up 68-69 69-70, FA Trophy 2nd Rd 78-79.
Local Newspapers: Journal, Northern Echo, Consett Advertiser.   **Midweek Matches:** Wednesday

DUNSTON FEDERATION BREWERY

Chairman: John Thompson   **Vice Chairman:** Malcolm James   **President:** Norman Rippon.
Secretary: Bill Montague, 12 Dundee Close, Chapel House, Newcastle-upon-Tyne NE5 1JJ (091 2672250).
Manager: Peter Quigley   **Asst Manager:** Steve Kendal   **Physio:** Alf Anderson.
Press Officer: Secretary   **Commercial Secretary:** Malcolm James.
Ground: Federation Park, Wellington Road, Dunston, Gateshead (091 493 2935).
Directions: Dunston/Whickham exit off A1(M), ground 400 yds north along Dunston Rd on left. 1 mile from Dunston or Metrocentre stations. Numerous buses from Gateshead & Metrocentre stop outside ground.
Seats: 80   **Cover:** 200   **Capacity:** 2,000   **Floodlights:** Yes   **Founded:** 1975
Colours: All blue (with trim)   **Change:** Racing green/white.   **Nickname:** The Fed
Programme: 28 pages, 30p   **Editor:** Tom McClements (091 261 4695)   **Souvenir Shop:** No
Previous Ground: Dunston public park 75-86
Previous Leagues: Northrn Amtr 75-80/ Northern Combination 80-87/ Wearside 87-91.
Record Attendance: 1,550 - Sunderland Shipowners Cup Final 1/4/88.
Previous Names: Whickham Sports/ Dunston Mechanics Sports.
Best F.A. Vase season: Quarter-Finals 92-93 (lost 0-2 at Gresley Rovers).
Best F.A. Cup season: 2nd Qualifying Rd 2nd replay 91-92 (lost 1-2 at Penrith).
Sponsors: Federation Brewery   **Clubhouse:** Matchdays only. Hot & cold snacks, darts, pool.
Midweek home matchday: Tuesday   **Reserve team:** None.
Record win: 11-0 v Willinghton (A), Northern League Division Two, 1992-93.
Record defeat: 2-5 v Blyth Spartans (A), Northern League Cup Quarter-Final, 1992-93.
Club record scorer: Paul King   **Club record appearances:** Paul Dixon.
Captain 92-93: Steve Kendal   **Top Scorer 92-93:** Ian Mulholland   **P.O.Y. 92-93:** Tommy Ditchburn.
Hons: Northern Lg Div 2 92-93, Northern Amtr Lg 77-78 (R-up 76-77 78-79, Lg Cup 77-78 78-79 (R-up 75-76), Lg Shield 78-79 79-80), Wearside Lg 88-89 89-90 (R-up 90-91, Lg Cup 90-91), Northern Comb. 86-87 (R-up 80-81 83-84 85-86, Lg Cup 83-84 86-87 (R-up 80-81 84-85 85-86)), Sunderland Shipowners Cup 87-88, Durham County Tphy 81-82 (R-up 83-84 85-86, Minor Cup 79-80 (R-up 78-79)), Gateshead Charity Cup 77-78 80-81, Heddon Homes Cup 80-81.

DURHAM CITY

Chairman: Dennis Kerry   **Vice Chairman:** A Thompson   **President:** G Newton.
Secretary/Press Off.: G R Lilley, 108 High Str., Carrville, Durham DH1 1BQ (091 384 5924).
Manager: B Cruddas   **Asst Manager/Coach:** T Harrison
Physio: Joanne Dowson   **Commercial Manager:** B Last.
Ground: 'Ferens Park', The Sands, Durham DH1 1JY (091 386 9616).
Directions: Down Post Office Bank, right at the bottom, 200 yds along The Sands.
Seats: 250   **Cover:** 500   **Capacity:** 6,000   **Floodlights:** Yes   **Founded:** 1918
Colours: All white   **Change colours:** Red/black/red.   **Nickname:** City   **Reformed:** 1949.
Programme: 30 pages   **Editor:** Dave Asberry (091 386 6469)   **Souvenir Shop:** No
Clubhouse details: Mon - Fri 7-11pm & Sat 12-6 & 7-11pm (closed Sunday).
Previous Leagues: Victory 18-19/ North Eastern 19-21 28-38/ Football League 21-28/ Wearside 38-39 50-51.
Previous Grounds: Garden House Park 18-21/ Holliday Park 21-38 *N.B. club disbanded in 1938.*
Record Attendance: 6,000 v Tranmere Rovers, FA Cup 2nd Rd 56-57.
Best F.A. Cup season: 2nd Rd 25-26 57-58 (Also 1st Rd 27-28 55-56).
Players progressing to Football League: Harry Houlahan (Newcastle 1951), Derek Clark (Lincoln 1951), Leo Dale & David Adamson (Doncaster 1954 & 70), Stan Johnstone (Gateshead 1954), Dennis Coughlan (Barnsley 1957), John Wile (Sunderland 1966), Brian Taylor (Coventry 1968), Paul Malcolm (Rochdale 1984).
Club Sponsors: Key Windsors   **Club record appearances:** Joe Raine, 552.
Captain 92-93 & P.o.Y.: John Reach   **Top Scorer 92-93:** Micky Taylor, 42.
Hons: Northern Lg R-up 70-71 (Div 2 R-up 30-31 91-92), FA Vase QF 87-88, Durham Benevolent Bowl 55-56, FA Amtr Cup 2nd Rd rep. 57-58, FA Tphy 1st Rd 83-84, Durham Challenge Cup R-up(2).
Local Newspapers: Northern Echo, Sunderland Echo, Evening Chronicle.
Midweek Matches: Wednesday.

Durham City 3, Ferryhill Athletic 2 - 9/4/93. City's Mark Ferguson evades a tackles but shoots narrowly wide in the Good Friday rain. Photo - Alan Watson.

Dunston Federation Brewery F.C. - Division Two champions 1992-93. Photo - Gavin Ellis-Neville.

EPPLETON COLLIERY WELFARE

Chairman: Ralph Lawson   **Vice Chairman:** Mr R D Tate   **President:** Mr A Robertson.
Secretary: Mr K Browell, 9 Willis Street, Hetton-le-Hole DH15 9AE (091 526 0080).
Manager: Stuart Sherwood   **Asst Manager:** Tony Heslop   **Physio:** Ted Collinson.
Commercial Mgr: David Gardner   **Press Officer:** John Tweddle (091 5262707).
Ground: Eppleton Welfare Park, Park View, Hetton-le-Hole, Tyne & Wear (091 5261048).
Directions: Situated behind Front Street Post Office & directly behind Hetton swimming baths, Hetton-le-Hole on A182. Buses 194, 535, 231, X5, X94 in Front Street. 8 miles from Durham BR statio; buses 154 and 254 from Durham.
Seats: 50   **Cover:** 500   **Capacity:** 2,500   **Floodlights:** Yes   **Founded:** 1929.
Colours: White (blue/black trim)/blue/blue   **Change:** Red & white hoops/red/red.
Record Attendance: 2,300 v Emlyn Hughes All-Stars, July 1992. Competitive: 1,250 - Monkwearmouth Charity Cup Final 1987-88.
Previous Grounds: None   **Previous Names:** None (merged with Natcobos, early 70's).
Previous Leagues: Wearside 51-65 74-92/ Houghton & District 65-74.
Programme: 16 pages, 20p   **Editor:** Fred Berry (091 584 2452)   **Nickname:** Welfare
Club Shop: Club sweaters, polo shirts, metal lapel badges available - contact David Gardiner (091 526 5543).
Club Sponsors: Citibank Life
Midweek home matchday: Wednesday   **Reserve team's League:** None.
Clubhouse: Bar & lounge on ground. Normal opening hours. Whitbread beers.
Top Scorer 92-93: Keith McNall   **Captain & P.o.Y 92-93:** Paul Bryson
Hons: Northern Lg Div 2 R-up 92-93, Wearside Lg 90-91 91-92 (Lg Cup 74-75 78-79 87-88, Sunderland Shipowners Cup 47-48 85-86 90-91 (R-up 91-92), Monkwearmouth Charity Charity Cup 89-90 90-91 91-92), Durham Challenge Cup 89-90.

FERRYHILL ATHLETIC

Chairman: B Campbell   **Vice Chairman:** W Walker   **President:** Forster.
Secretary: Ralph Carr, 23 Morrison Terrace, Ferryhill Station, Co. Durham DL17 9DQ (0740 652437).
Manager: P Mulcaster   **Asst Manager:** M Crowe   **Coach:** G Hartley.
Press Officer: Secretary   **Physio:** V Chapman/ M Mulcaster.
Ground: Darlington Road, Ferryhill, County Durham (0740 651937).
Directions: Ground on main A167 (old A1) Darlington-Durham road, on left coming from south. United buses 722 & 723 (Newcastle-Darlington) pass ground.
Seats: 400   **Cover:** 400   **Capacity:** 6,000   **Floodlights:** Yes   **Founded:** 1921.
Colours: Amber & black quarters   **Change colours:** Red & white stripes/white/white.
Midweek Matches: Tuesday   **Previous Leagues:** Palatine 21-23.   **Nickname:** Latics.
Record Attendance: 13,000 v Bishop Auckland, FA Amateur Cup.
Previous Name: Dean Bank Villa.   **Best F.A. Cup season:** 1st Rd 35-36 53-54.
Players progressing to Football League: William Marsh (Barsley 1947), Richard Steel (Bristol City 1953), Alex Greenwood (Chelsea 1953), John Edgar & John Peverell (Darlington 1954 & 59), Roland Horney (Blackburn 1963), John Pearson (Hartlepool 1967).
Programme: TBA   **Midweek home matchday:** Tuesday   **Club Shop:** No.
Clubhouse: Opens 7pm Mon-Fri, 7pm Sat (1pm matchdays), Sun 12-3 & 7pm Sundays.
Captain 92-93: K Pearson   **Top Scorer 92-93:** K Black.
Honours: Northern Lg 37-38 47-48 57-58 (R-up 23-24), Durham Challenge Cup 23-24 70-71, Durham Benevolent Cup 53-54 56-57 61-62, Durham Amateur Cup 21-22, FA Amateur Cup 4th Rd 25-26 63-64, FA Trophy 2nd Qualifying Rd replay 81-82 89-90 90-91.
Local Newspapers: Northern Echo

GUISBOROUGH TOWN

Chairman: John Newton   **Vice Chairman:** Keith Watson   **President:** J H Morgan, OBE.
Secretary: Keith Smeltzer, 55 Thame Ave., Guisborough, Cleveland TS14 8AR (0287 638993).
Manager: Mike Hodgson   **Asst Manager:** Bob Dewhirst   **Coach:** Alec Smith.
Physio: Bobby Veart   **Press Officer:** John Newton.
Ground: King George V Ground, Howlbeck Rd, Guisborough, Cleveland (0287 636925).
Directions: From west: bear left at 2nd set of lights, left into Howlbeck Rd after quarter mile, ground at end. Buses from Middlesbrough.
Seats: 20   **Cover:** 400   **Capacity:** 3,500   **Floodlights:** Yes   **Founded:** 1973.
Colours: Red & white   **Change colours:** Yellow   **Nickname:** Priorymen
Previous Leagues: Middlesbrough & District/ South Bank/ Northern Alliance 77-80/ Midland Counties 80-82/ Northern Counties (East) 82-85.
Programme: 32 pages, 30p   **Programme Editor:** Les Crossman (0642 473478).
Club Shop: Yes, selling clothing etc. Contact Bob & Gladys Hall (0287 635769).
Club Sponsors: Bells Stores.   **Midweek home matchday:** Wednesday
Record Gate: 3,112 v Hungerford, FA Vase SF, 1980 *(at Middlesbrough FC - 5,990 v Bury, FA Cup 1st Rd 1988).*
Best F.A. Cup season: First Round Proper 1988-89 (lost 0-1 to Bury).
Rec. win: 6-0 v Ferryhill & v Easington   **Record defeat:** 0-4 v Billingham Synthonia.
Clubhouse: Evenings & weekends. Darts & pool. Hot & cold snacks and drinks from kitchen on matchdays.
Players progressing to Football League: Frank Harrison (Middlesbrough 1982), Mark Foster (Leicester 1983).
Local Newspapers: Middlesbrough Evening Gazette, Northern Echo.
Captain & P.O.Y. 92-93: Trevor Smith   **Top Scorer 92-93:** Mark Davis
Club record scorer: Mark Davis   **Club record appearances:** Mark Davis.
Hons: F.A. Vase R-up 79-80, Northern Lg Cup 87-88 (Div 2 R-up 86-87), Northern Alliance 79-80 (R-up 78-79, Lg Cup 78-79), North Riding Senior Cup 90-91 92-93, F.A. Trophy 1st Rd replay 90-91, Newcastle Sunday Cup.

Eppleton Colliery Welfare, Division Two runners-up 1992-93. Photo - Dave West.

Dean Wilkinson fires a shot during the goalless draw at home to Darlington Cleveland Bridge. Photo - Dave West.

Guisborough Town, who were in contention for the title for most of the season. Photo - Gavin Ellis-Neville.

HEBBURN

Chairman: J Hunter **Vice Chairman:** B Errington
Secretary/Press Officer: R Hodgson, 23 Redhouse Road, Hebburn, Tyne & Wear (091 430 1098).
Manager/Coach: John Diamond **Commercial Manager:** V Pearson.
Ground: Hebburn Sports & Social, Club Ground, South Drive, Hebburn (091 483 5101).
Directions: On the main road through the town about 1 mile from railway station. Hebburn lies on the Metroline - excellent bus service from Heworth Metro.
Seats: 20 **Cover:** 200 **Capacity:** 2,000 **Floodlights:** Yes **Founded:** 1912
Colours: Yellow & black stripes/black/black **Change colours:** Red/red/blue
Programme: 16 pages with entry **Programme Editor:** John Diamond **Souvenir Shop:** No
Clubhouse details: Open 7-11pm weekdays, Sat 11am-1pm, Sun noon-2.30pm. Pool, darts etc.
Previous Grounds: None **Previos Names:** Reyrolles/ Hebburn Reyrolles (pre-1988).
Midweek Matches: Wednesday **Previous Lge:** Wearside 39-40 60-89 **Nickname:** Hornets.
Best F.A. Cup season: 2nd Qualifying Rd replay 89-90 (lost 0-3 at South Bank).
Record win: 10-1 **Record defeat:** 3-10.
Capt. 92-93: Les Tatum/ Ian Potts **Top Scorer 92-93 & Club record scorer:** S Wright
Hons: Shields Gazette Cup 91-92, FA Vase 2nd Rd 91-92, Wearside Lg 66-67 (Monkwearmouth Charity Cup 68-69), Durham Challenge Cup 42-43.

MURTON

Chairman: J T Pratt **Vice Chairman:** J Hudson **President:** John Hellens.
Secretary: J C Gardner, 74 Winds Lonnen, Murton, County Durham SR7 9TG (091 526 3449).
Manager: Jeff Cranson **Asst Mgr:** Brian Burlinson **Coach:** Richie Madden.
Physio: Vince Symmonds **Press Officer:** Willie Grogan **Commercial Mgr:** T Carr.
Ground: Recreation Park, Church Lane, Murton, County Durham (091 517 0814).
Directions: Exit A19 onto B1285 heading west into Murton - Church Lane on left opposite catholic church.
Seats: 100 **Cover:** 320 **Capacity:** 3,500 **Floodlights:** Yes **Founded:** 1904
Colours: White (red trim) **Change colours:** Red/black/red **Nickname:** Gnashers
Previous Grounds: Fatton Pasture 04-28.
Previous Names: Murton Red Star 04-28/ Murton Colliery Welfare 28-88.
Previous Leagues: Wearside 13-46 51-88/ North East Counties 46-51.
Past players progressing to Football League: Numerous.
Programme: 12 pages, 30p **Programme Editor:** Stuart Upperton **Club Shop:** No.
Club Sponsors: John Hellyns **Midweek home matchday:** Wednesday
Record Gate: 3,500 v Spennymoor Utd, Durham Challenge Cup 1951.
Record win: 17-1 v Thornley **Record defeat:** 0-14 v South Shields (H).
Clubhouse: 'The International' 300 yards from ground on B1285. Normal pub hours. Restaurant upstairs. Function room for 100. Open plan downstairs with horse shoe bar. Matchday snacks at ground.
Captain 92-93: David Nigel Stewart **Top Scorer 92-93:** David Laws, 24.
P.O.Y. 92-93: Lee Adamson. **Club record scorer:** David Campbell (66 in 70-71)
Club record appearances: Robert Welch 500 (1962-78).
Hons: Northern Lg Div 2 89-90, Wearside Lg 28-29 36-37 59-60 (Lg Cup 58-59 70-71), Sunderland Shipowners Cup 59-60 69-70 70-71, Monkwearmouth Charity Cup 21-22 28-29 34-35 35-36 63-64 70-71 87-88, Durham Chall. Cup 92-93, Durham Jnr Cup 50-51.

NEWCASTLE BLUE STAR

Chairman/Press Officer: Tom Derrick (091 469 6935) **Manager:** Rob Carney.
Secretary: Jim Anderson, 7 Whitbeck Rd, Statyford, Newcastle-upon-Tyne NE5 2XA (091 274 3941).
Ground: Wheatsheaf Sports Ground, Woolsington, Newcastle-upon-Tyne (091 286 0425).
Directions: From central station follow airport signs for 7 miles - ground next to Wheatsheaf Hotel on left, approximately 800yds before airport. Metro station 400yds from ground.
Seats: 300 **Cover:** 300 **Capacity:** 2,000 **Floodlights:** Yes **Founded:** 1930
Colours: Blue/blue/blue & white **Change colours:** Red/white/red **Nickname:** Gnashers
Previous Grounds: None **Previous Names:** Blue Star F.C. (pre-1986).
Previous Leagues: Newcastle Business Houses 32-38/ North East Amateur/ Tyneside Amateur/ Northern Combination/ Wearside 75-85.
Past players progressing to Football League: Ian Crumplin & Tony Robinson (Hartlepool 1976 & 1986), Barry Dunn (Darlington 1979), Ian McInerney (Huddersfield Town 1988).
Programme: 20 pages **Programme Editor:** T.B.A.
Club Shop: No, but club souvenirs are available in tea bar.
Midweek home matchday: Monday **Record Gate:** 1,800 v Almondsbury Greenway SF 77-78.
Clubhouse: Open matchdays only. **Best F.A. Cup season:** 1st Rd 84-85 (lost 0-2 at York C.).
Hons: FA Vase 77-78 (SF 81-82), FA Trophy QF 88-89, Northern Lg R-up 87-88 (Lg Cup 85-86 (R-up(1)), Div 2 85-86), Wearside Lg 73-74 75-76 82-83 83-84 84-85 (R-up 74-75 77-78 79-80, Lg Cup 76-77 79-80 80-81 82-83 83-84, Sunderland Shipowners Cup 82-83 84-85, Monkwearmouth Charity Cup 74-75 79-80 82-83 88-89, Northern Comb. 62-63 68-69 (Lg Cup 66-67 71-72), Northumberland Snr Cup 76-77 82-83 85-86 87-88 (R-up 74-75 78-79 80-81, Minor Cup 64-65), J R Cleator Cup 86-87.

Hebburn, who survived a difficult first season in the top flight. Photo - Gavin Ellis-Neville.

NORTHALLERTON TOWN

Chairman/Comm. Mgr: Les Hood **Vice Chairman:** Ian Bolland **President:** Dennis Cope
Secretary: Mr Ken Homer, 28 Aysgarth Grove, Romanby, North Yorks DL7 8HY (0609 779686).
Manager: Tony Lee **Asst Manager:** Trevor Arnold **Coach:** T.B.A.
Physio: John Murray **Press Officer:** Ian Bolland (0609 776900).
Ground: Ainderby Rd, Romanby, Northallerton, North Yorks (0609 772418).
Directions: Leave A1 at Leeming Motel, six miles on A167 to Northallerton, at 'Northallerton' sign take B1333 signed Romanby - ground 250yds on left. Three quarters of a mile from Northallerton BR station - local bus from town centre (one and a half miles) passes ground.
Seats: 125 **Cover:** 500 **Capacity:** 3,000 **Floodlights:** Yes **Founded:** 1893
Cols: Black & white stripes/black/black **Change colours:** Yellow/green/yellow. **Nickname:** Town
Previous Ground: Bluestone Ground (pre-1975).
Previous Leagues: Allertonshire (now defunct)/ Vale of Mowbray (defunct)/ Ripon & Dist./ Teesside/ North Yorks (defunct)/ Darlington & Dist./ Harrogate & Dist.
Programme: 16 pages, 50p **Programme Editor:** T.B.A.
Club Shop: Replica shirts, bobble hats, rosettes, progs, club lapel badges. Contact Mike Walker (0609 780835).
Club Sponsors: Calvert Carpet **Record Gate:** 671 v Farnborough, FA Tphy 3rd Rd 20/2/93.
Midweek home matchday: Wednesday **Best F.A. Cup year:** 4th Qual. Rd 92-93, lost 1-3 at Accrington
Record win: 7-0, away to Willington **Record defeat:** 2-7, away to Easington C.W.
Previous Name: Northallerton Alliance.
Clubhouse: Mon-Fri 7.30-11pm, Sat (matchdays only) 12-8pm, Sun 12-2 & 7.30-10.30pm.
Local Newspapers: Northern Echo, Darlington & Stockton Times, North Yorks News.
Captain 92-93: Lee Wasden **P.O.Y. 92-93:** T.B.A.
Top Scorer 92-93: John Woods (now Bridlington), Marty Hewitt (now Spennymoor) both fifteen.
Club record scorer: Jimmy Lagan **Club record appearances:** Lee Wasden.
Hons: Northern Lg Div 2 R-up 89-90, North Riding Snr Cup R-up 83-84, Harrogate & Dist. Lg, Richmond Cup, Bedale Cup, Milbank Cup, Orde Powlett Cup, Harrogate Invitation Cup, Alverton Trophy, F.A. Trophy 3rd Rd 92-93.

SEAHAM RED STAR

Chairman: Bryan C Mayhew **Vice Chairman:** Reg Atkinson **President:** Michael English.
Secretary: John McBeth, 29 Frederick Street, Seaham, County Durham SR7 7HX (091 581 5712).
Manager: Chris Copeland **Asst Manager:** Paul Walker.
Physio: Allan Jackson **Press Officer:** John Campbell (091 581 4308).
Ground: Seaham Town Park, Stockton Road, Seaham, County Durham (091 581 2540).
Directions: From Tyne Tunnel: A19 Teeside approx 8 miles; B1404 Seaham slip road, left at top of slip road. Right at traffic lights & first left past school into ground.
Seats: 60 **Cover:** 200 **Capacity:** 4,000 **Floodlights:** Yes **Year Formed:** 1973
Colours: Red & white/red/red **Change colours:** All blue **Nickname:** The Star
Previous Leagues: Sunday football/ Houghton & District 73-74/ Northern Alliance 74-79/ Wearside 79-83.
Programme: 20 pages **Editor:** David Copeland (091 581 8514) **Club Shop:** No.
Clubhouse details: New clubhouse. Mon-Sat 11am-11pm, Sun 12-2, 7-10.30pm. Large function room, snooker, pool, Restuarant & Bars.
Record Attendance: 1,500 v Guisborough, Wearside Lg/ v Sunderland, floodlight opener 1979.
Previous Name: Seaham Colliery Welfare Red Star 78-87.
Previous Grounds: Deneside Recreation Park 73-75/ Vane Tempest Welfare 75-78.
Players progressing to Football League: Bobby Davison (Huddersfield 1980), Nigel Gleghorn (Ipswich 1985), Billy Stubbs (Nottm Forest 1987), Paul Nixon (Bristol Rovers 1989), Mick Smith (Hartlepool).
Local Newspapers: Sunderland Echo, Journal, Northern Echo, Football Echo, Washington Times.
Midweek home matchday: Wednesday **Reserve team's League:** Banks Youth League.
Capt. 92-93: Phil Coxall **Top Scorer 92-93:** Gary McDonald **P.O.Y. 92-93:** Phil Coxall/ Paul Walker
Club record scorer: Tom Henderson **Club record appearances:** Michael Whitfield.
Hons: Northern Lg Cup 92-93, Phillips F'lit Tphy 78-79, Durham Chal. Cup 79-80, Wearside Lg 81-82 (Lg Cup 81-82, Div 2 R-up 87-88, Monkwearmouth Charity Cup R-up 79-80), FA Vase 5th Rd 78-79, FA Tphy 2nd Rd 89-90.

SHILDON

Chairman: Bill Aisbitt   **Vice Chairman:** George Elliott   **President:** John Atkinson.
Secretary: Mike Armitage, 22 Hambleton Ct, Byerley Park, Newton Aycliffe, Co. Durham DL5 7HR (0325 316322).
Manager: Ray Gowan   **Asst Manager:** Phil Owers   **Physio:** Doug Grant.
Press Officer: Secretary   **Ground:** Dean Street, Shildon, County Durham (0388 773877).
Directions: In the town centre one mile from BR station and 300yds from Darlington-Bishop Auckland bus stop (Hippodrome stop).
Seats: 400   **Cover:** 500   **Capacity:** 4,000   **Floodlights:** Yes   **Founded:** 1890
Club colours: All red   **Change colours:** Green & black.
Programme: 28 pages, 30p   **Editor:** Neil Bennett (0325 332310)   **Souvenir Shop:** No
Clubhouse details: Open every evening 7.30-11pm (open earlier on matchnights), 1pm onwards on Satrurday matchdays. Bar, pool & darts.
Previous Leagues: Auckland & District 1892-96/ Wearside 96-97/ North Eastern 07-32.
Record Attendance: 13,000 - Leeholme v Perkinsville, schoolboys game, 1920s. For Shildon game; 11,000 Shildon v Ferryhill Athletic, Durham Senior Cup 1922.
Previous Names: Shildon Town 1890-94/ Shildon Utd 94-1900/ Shildon Athletic 00-23.
Best F.A. Cup season: 2nd Rd 36-37. Also 1st Rd 27-28 29-30 34-35 36-37 55-56 59-60 61-62.
Players progressing to Football League: Ken Whitfield (Wolves 1947), James Smith (Chelsea 1951), Mike Peacock & Philip Shute (Darlington 1960 & 84), Kevin Stonehouse (Blackburn 1979).
Local Newspapers: Northern Echo   **Midweek Matches:** Wednesday
Club Sponsors: Atkinsons Stairs   **Club Nickname:** Railwaymen.
Reserve's League: Banks Group Northern Yth.
Club record scorer: Jack Downing, 61 (1936-37).
Captain & P.o.Y. 92-93: Bryan Liddle   **Top Scorer 92-93:** Nigel Bolton, 19.
Honours: Northern Lg 33-34 34-35 35-36 36-37 39-40 (R-up 32-33 38-39, Lg Cup 33-34 34-35 37-38 38-39 39-40 52-53), Durham Challenge Cup 07-08 25-26 71-72, Durham Amateur Cup 01-02 02-03, Durham Benevolement Bowl 24-25, FA Trophy 3rd Qualifying Rd 74-75, FA Amateur Cup 4th Rd 58-59, FA Vase 1st Rd 86-87.

STOCKTON

Chairman: A Ruddy   **President:** K Wren.
Secretary/Press Officer/Commercial Manager: John M Smith, 71 Rimswell Road, Fairfield, Stockton-on-Tees, Cleveland TS19 7LE (0642 584593).
Manager: Alan Robinson   **Asst Mgr/Coach:** Bryan Symons   **Physio:** Ken Pounder.
Ground: Teesdale Park, Acklam Road, Thornaby, Stockton-on-Tees TS19 8TZ (0642 606803).
Directions: A19 to Thornaby turn off, ground half mile on right. One mile from Thornaby BR station. Any Stockton-Middlesbrough bus - stop at Acklam Rd, Thornaby.
Seats: 20   **Cover:** 100   **Capacity:** 5,000   **Floodlights:** Yes   **Year Formed:** 1980
Club colours: Red & black stripes/black/red   **Change colours:** All sky.
Previous Leagues: Stockton & District 80-81/ Wearside 81-85.
Previous Names: Stockton Cricket Club 65-80.
Previous Grounds: Grangefield Community Centre, Fairfield 80-82/ Tilery Sports Centre 82-83.
Programme: 24 pages, 30p   **Editor:** Peter Morris (0642 760779)   **Souvenir Shop:** No.
Clubhouse: 200+ seater social club with concert room, pool/games room and bar. Open every night and weekend lunchtimes. Sandwiches available in bar, canteen in ground sells pies, burgers, soup, drinks etc.
Best F.A. Cup season: 4th Qual. Rd replay 92-93 (lost 1-2 at home to Blyth after 1-1 draw).
Record Attendance: 3,000 v Middlebrough, pre-season friendly August 1986.
Club Sponsors: Intertractor   **Record win:** 10-0 v Evenwood (H), Div 2 91-92.
Capt. 92-93: Michael Sell   **Top Scorer 92-93:** George Woodhouse **P.o.Y. 92-93:** Stephen Carter (keeper)
Hons: Northern Lg Div 2 87-88 91-92, Nth Riding Co. Cup 85-86, FA Vase 2nd Rd, FA Tphy 1st Rd.
Midweek Matches: Tuesday.   **Local Newspapers:** Northern Echo, Evening Gazette.

Stockton F.C. 1992-93, who enjoyed an excellent season.

TOW LAW TOWN

Chairman: Harry Hodgson   **Press Officer:** Secretary
Secretary: Bernard Fairbairn, 3 Coppice Walk, Mowden Park, Darlington, County Durham DL3 9DP (0325 350743).
Manager: Stuart Leeming   **Assistant Manager:** Michael Haley
Ground: Ironworks Road, Tow Law, Bishop Auckland (0388 731443).
Directions: Just of High Street in Tow Law town centre.
Seats: 200   **Capacity:** 6,000   **Floodlights:** Due   **Founded:** 1890
Colours: Black & white stripes/black/black & white   **Change colours:** Red & white
Previous leagues: None   **Programme:** None   **Club Shop:** Yes
Clubhouse: Every evening 8.30 -10.30.   **Record Gate:** 5,500 v Mansfield Town, FA Cup 1967.
Best F.A. Cup season: 2nd Rd replay 67-68. Also Competition Proper 68-69 84-85 89-90.
League Clubs defeated in F.A. Cup: Mansfield Town 67-68.   **Nickname:** Lawyers.
Players progressing to Football League: Reuben Cook & Ralph Guthrie (Arsenal 1951 & 53), Gordon Hughes & Terry Melling & Chris Waddle (Newcastle 1956 & 65 & 80), Eric Johnstone & Kevin Dixon (Carlisle 1963 & 83), Keith Adamson (Barnsley 1966), Tom Henderson (Bradford PA 1969), Vincent Chapman (Huddersfield 1988).
Hons: Rothmans National 1977, Northern Lg 23-24 24-25 (R-up 28-29 88-89, Lg Cup 73-74, Rothmans Overseas Cup 76-77), Durham Chal. Cup 1895-96, Durham Amtr Cup 1892-93, FA Amtr Cup 3rd Rd rep. 70-71, FA Tphy 2nd Rd rep. 82-83.
Local Newspapers: Northern Echo   **Midweek Matches:** Tuesday

WEST AUCKLAND

Chairman: Mr Norman Ayton   **Vice Chairman:** Mr L Nevison   **President:** Mr R H Tomlinson
Sec./Press Officer: Allen Bayles, 11 Edith Terrace, West Auckland, Co. Durham DL14 9JT (0388 833783).
Manager: Eddy Sharp   **Coach:** Peter Storey   **Commercial Mgr:** John Nicols.
Ground: Darlington Road, West Auckland, County Durham (0388 834403).
Directions: Leaving West Auckland take A68 - ground on right before leaving the village. On bus route via Bishop Auckland from Newcastle or Darlington.
Seats: 250   **Cover:** 250   **Capacity:** 3,000   **Floodlights:** Yes   **Founded:** 1892
Midweek Matches: Tuesday   **Prev. Names:** St Helens Utd (1919 only)/ West Auck. Town.
Colours: All white   **Change colours:** Tangerine/red/red.   **Nickname:** West.
Sponsors: Fenwick Transport/ Southfield Builders.   **Souvenir Shop:** No.
Previous League: Auckland & District.
Clubhouse: None - use local Working Men's Club five mins walk away (Thomas Lipton Trophy on display within). On ground reception room for visiting officials and snack bar selling teas, coffees, soup, pies, burgers etc.
Record Attendance: 6,000 v Dulwich Hamlet, F.A. Amateur Cup 58-59.
Best FA Cup season: 1st Rd 58-59 61-62**Players progressing to Football League:** None.
Record win: 11-0 in Durham Co. Cup   **Record defeat:** 0-10 v Stanley United.
Captain 92-93: Robin Gill   **Top Scorer 92-93:** Michael Spring   **P.O.Y. 92-93:** Ian Mohan
Club record scorer: George Brown   **Club record appearances:** Alan Porter, 10 seasons.
Hons: FA Amtr Cup R-up 60-61 (QF 59-60), Northern Lg 59-60 60-61 (Div 2 90-91, Lg Cup 59-60 62-63 (R-up 48-49 61-62 63-64)), Durham Challenge Cup 63-64, Durham Benevolent Cup 62-63, FA Trophy 3rd Rd 77-78, Sir Thomas Lipton Trophy (First World Cup!) 1909 1911.

WHITBY TOWN

Chairman: R Scaife   **President:** Don Dunwell.
Secretary: C T Woodward, 31 Castle Rd, Whitby (0947 602312).
Manager: R H 'Bob' Scaife   **Asst Manager:** L Scott   **Physio:** I Jackson.
Press Officer: Secretary   **Commercial Manager:** G Manser (0947 83382).
Ground: Turnbull Ground, Upgang Lane, Whitby, North Yorks (0947 604847).
Directions: Take A174 road from town centre. Ground on offside travelling towards Sandsend.
Seats: 200   **Cover:** 400   **Capacity:** 4,000   **Floodlights:** Yes   **Founded:** 1926
Colours: All royal blue   **Change colours:** All white   **Previous Lges:** None
Programme: 18 pages, 30p   **Editor:** G Manser (0947 83382)   **Souvenir Shop:** No.
Record Attendance: 4,000 v Scarborough, North Riding Snr Cup 18/4/65   **Nickname:** Seasiders.
Prev. Name: Whitby Utd (pre-1950)   **Best F.A. Cup season:** 2nd Rd 83-84 (0-1 at Wigan).
Football League Clubs defeated in F.A. Cup: Halifax Town 83-84.
Players progressing to Football League: Malcolm Poskett (Hartlepool, Brighton, Watford, Sammy Kemp (Huddersfield), Jimmy Mulvaney (Hartlepool, Barrow, Stockport), Bobby Veart (Hartlepool), Derek Hampton & Trevor Smith & John Linacre & Phil Linacre (Hartlepool), Mark Hine (Grimsby).
Midweek Matches: Wednesday   **Local Newspapers:** Whitby Gazette, Northern Echo.
Club Sponsors: Arnott Insurance   **Previous Grounds:** None.
Record win: 11-2 v Cargo Fleet Wks, 1950
Record defeat: 3-13 v Willington, 24/3/28.
Clubhouse: Mon-Fri 7-11pm, Sat 12-11pm, Sun 12-2 & 7-10.30.
Captain & Top Scorer & P.O.Y. 92-93: Paul Pitman, 45 goal (top scorer in League with 35).
Club record scorer: Paul Pitman   **Club record appearances:** Derek Hampton.
Honours: FA Amtr Cup R-up 64-65, FA Tphy QF 83-84, Northern Lg 92-93 (R-up 27-28 33-34 67-68 81-82 82-83, Lg Cup 28-29 63-64 69-70 76-77 84-85), Rothmans Overseas Cup 75-76 77-78), Nth Riding Snr Cup 83-84 84-85 87-88 90-91.

SECOND DIVISION CLUBS 1993-94

ALNWICK TOWN

Chairman: Judith Draycott   **Press Officer:** Secretary
Secretary: Cyril Cox, 19 Melness Road, Hazelrigg, Tyne & Wear NE13 7BN (091 236 6456).
Manager: Mick Dagless   **Assistant Manager:** Brian Penfold
Coach: Dave Clarke   **Physiotherapist:** Mac Belsize.
Ground: St James' Park, Alnwick, Northumberland (0665 603162).
Directions: 35 miles north of Newcastle on A1, take the slip road to Alnwick, then first left. At roundabout turn left, ground is then on your left.
Seats: 100   **Cover:** 200   **Capacity:** 2,500   **Floodlights:** Yes   **Founded:** 1879
Colours: Black & white stripes/black/black   **Change colours:** All yellow
Reserve Team's League: North Northumberland   **Sponsors:** Schat Davit.
Previous Leagues: North Northumberland/ East Northumberland/ Northern Alliance 36-39 46-64 65-82/ Durham Central 64-65.
Programme: 20 pages, 25p   **Programme Editor:**   **Souvenir Shop:**
Previous Leagues: Wearside 13-37 39-64 73-88.
Record Attendance: 600 v Bedlington Terriers, Northern Alliance 1971.
Previous Names: Alnwick United Services/ Alnwick United.
Best F.A. Cup season: 3rd Qual. Rd 51-52 (3-4 at Blyth), 57-58 (4-6 at Easington Colliery).
Players progressing to Football League: George Turnbull (Grimsby 1950), Brian Pringle (1973).
Honours: Northern Lg Div 2 R-up 88-89, Northern Alliance 37-38 62-63 63-64 65-66 67-68 68-69 69-70 70-71 71-72 (R-up 59-60 61-62 66-67 72-73, Lg Cup 61-62 65-66 67-68 68-69 70-71, Subsidiary Cup 80-81), Durham Central Lg Cup 64-65, Northumberland Benevolent Bowl 86-87, Northumberland SNR Cup R-up 61-62, Northumberland Amtr Cup 71-72, FA Trophy 3rd Qualifying Rd 90-91.
Midweek Matches: Tuesday   **Local Press:** Northumberland Gazette, Alnwick Advertiser.

ASHINGTON

Chairman: Ray Graham   **Press Officer:** Brian Bennett (0670 856606)
Secretary: Chris Sanderson, 10 Rydal Mount, Newbiggin-by-the-Sea, Northumberland NE64 6JT (0670 855271).
Ground: Portland Park, Ashington NE63 9XG. (0670) 812240
Directions: 200 yds north at traffic lights in centre of town.
Seats: 350   **Cover:** 2,200   **Capacity:** 4,000   **Floodlights:** Yes   **Year Formed:** 1883
Midweek Matches: Wednesday
Club colours: Black & white stripes/black/black   **Change colours:** All red
Programme: Yes, 20p   **Programme Editor:** C Sanderson
Clubhouse details: Open normal licensing hours.
Previous Leagues: Northern Alliance 1892-93 1902-14 69-70/ Tyneside Football League/ North Eastern 14-21 29-58 62-64/ Midland 58-60/ Northern Counties 60-62/ Wearside 64-65/ Northern Premier 68-69.
Record Attendance: 13,199 v Rochdale, FA Cup 2nd Rd 9/12/50.
Nickname: The Colliers.   **Best F.A. Cup season:** 3rd Rd 26-27.
League Clubs defeated in F.A. Cup: Halifax Town 50-51.
Past players progressing to Football League: Tony Lowery (Mansfield), Les Mutrie (Colchester), R Cummins (Aberdeen, Newcastle).
Hons: FA Amateur Cup SF 73-74, Northumberland Snr 20-21 32-33 38-39 49-50 55-56 56-57 61-62 66-67 79-80, Northumberland Challenge Bowl 12-13 21-22 22-23 23-24 25-26 33-34, Midland Lg 58-59, North Eastern Lg Cup 33-34 (jt with Sunderland Reserves) 39-40 (Div 2 26-27(Res)), Northern Alliance 13-14 24-25(Res) 39-40(Res) 55-56(Res) (R-up 05-06 10-11 11-12 22-23(Res) 54-55(Res) 56-57(Res), Lg Cup 47-48(Res)).

BEDLINGTON TERRIERS

Chairman: William Ward   **Press Officer:** Eric Young (0670 829196)
Secretary: Eric Young, 6 Millbank Place, Bedlington, Northumberland NE22 5AT (0670 829196).
Ground: Welfare Park, Park Rd., Bedlington, Northumberland (0670 825485).
Directions: Into Bedlington, turn left at 'Northumberland Arms' on Front St., then 2nd Right, ground on right 100 yds.
Seats: 40   **Cover:** Yes   **Capacity:** 600   **Floodlights:** No   **Year Formed:** 1949
Midweek Matches: Wednesday   **Previous Leagues:** Northern Alliance.
Colours: All red   **Change colours:** All blue   **Souvenir Shop:** No
Clubhouse: Open every evening, 11-11pm Sat. & Sun lunch. Pool, darts etc.
Record Attendance: 1,013 v Blyth Spartans, Northern Lg 85-86.
Previous Names: Bedlington Mechanics 49-53/ Colliery Welfare 53-56/ Mechanics 56-61/ Bedlington United 61-65/ Bedlington Colliery 65-68/ Bedlington Town 68-74.
Hons: Northern League Div 2 R-up 84-85, Northern Alliance 66-67 (R-up 67-68 69-70 71-72, Lg Cup 57-58 66-67 69-70 81-82).

BILLINGHAM TOWN

Chairman: Mr G A Maxwell   **President:** Mr F Cook, MP
Secretary: Thomas Donnelly, 36 Cumberland Crescent, Billingham, Cleveland TS23 1AY (0642 555332).
Manager: R Halliday   **Assistant Manager:** A Boynton   **Physio:** T Cushley
Ground: Bedford Terrace, Billingham, Cleveland. (0642 560043)
Directions: Leave A19 on A1027 (signed Billingham). Turn left at 3rd roundabout, over bridge 1st left, then 1st left again to ground.
Seats: 250   **Cover:** 250   **Capacity:** 3,000   **Floodlights:** Yes   **Founded:** 1967
Colours: All royal (white trim)   **Change colours:** All red
Programme: 28 pages, 30p.   **Programme Editor:** A Matthews   **Souvenir Shop:** No
Clubhouse: Matchdays only.   **Previous Lges:** Stockton & Dist. 68-74/ Teesside 74-82.
Record Attendance: 1,500 v Manchester City, FA Youth Cup 1985.
Midweek Matches: Tuesday   **Previous Ground:** Mill Lane (pre-1974).
Previous Name: Billingham Social Club (pre-1982).
Nickname: The Social.   **Best F.A. Cup season:** 1st Round Proper 1955-56.
Players progressing to Football League: Gary Pallister (Middlesbrough & Manchester Utd), Gerry Forrest (Southampton), Dave Robinson (Halifax), Tony Barratt (Hartlepool), Mark Hine (Grimsby & Darlington), Tony Hall (Middlesbrough).
Honours: Durham Amateur Cup 76-77 77-78, Teesside Lg 77-78 81-82, Nth Riding Snr Cup R-up 76-77 81-82, Stockton & Dist. Lg(3).

CROOK TOWN

Chairman: B M Humphreys   **Press Officer:** Secretary   **Manager:** Paul Adams.
Secretary: Eric Burton, 12 West End Villas, Crook, County Durham DL15 9PF (0388 762026).
Ground: Millfield Ground, West Road, Crook, County Durham (0388 762959).
Directions: 400 yds from town centre on Wolsingham Road.
Seats: 400   **Cover:** 1,150   **Capacity:** 9,500   **Floodlights:** Yes   **Year Formed:** 1889
Colours: Amber (black trim)/black/black   **Change colours:** All white
Clubhouse details: Open 7-11 each evening plus matchdays.
Previous Leagues: None.   **Record Attendance:** 17,500, FA Amateur Cup.
Nickname: Black Ambers   **Previous Name:** Crook Colliery Welfare (pre-1950).
Midweek Matches: Wednesday   **Best F.A. Cup season:** 3rd Rd (v Leicester) 31-32.
Honours: FA Amtr Cup 00-01 53-54 58-59 61-62 63-64 (SF 48-49 57-58 59-60), Northern Lg 14-15 26-27 52-53 58-59
62-63 (R-up 24-25 46-47 53-54 54-55 55-5663-64 64-65), Lg Cup 36-37 45-46 60-61), Durham Challenge Cup 26-27 31-
32 54-55 59-60, Durham Benevolent Bowl 13-14 19-20 20-21 21-22 25-26 54-55, FA Trophy 2nd Rd 76-77.

DARLINGTON CLEVELAND SOCIAL

Chairman: S Guy   **President:** D Morrison/ W Stephenson.
Secretary/Press Officer/Commercial Manager: Mr Lawrence Appleby, 49 Heaton Park Court, Newcastle-upon-
Tyne NE6 5PR (091 2766965).
Manager: Roger Wicks   **Coach:** Nick Day/ Steve Wright   **Physio:** Kevin Reece.
Ground: Neasham Road, Darlington (0325 469735).
Directions: From Darlington BR station turn left and follow Park Lane. At bottom turn left into Parkside, ground on left.
Leave A1 at A66, follow Darlington by-pass and turn right into Neasham Rd at 3rd island - follow to ground. Or, leave A1
on A167 and follow to town centre, turn left following signs for station, at 2nd r'bout turn left into Parkgate, right at next
r'bout following signs for Neasham, after 1 mile turn between social club and public house into Geneva Lane (ground).
Seats: None   **Cover:** 700   **Capacity:** 3,000   **Floodlights:** Yes   **Founded:** 1903
Colours: All yellow   **Change colours:** Black & white stripes
Programme: New for 93-94, 50p   **Programme Editor:** Secretary
Club Shop: Due 93-93, selling programmes, club badges (£2.50) and other souvenirs as they become available.
Contact secretary.
Midweek Matchday: Wednesday   **Club Sponsors:** To be determined by draw.
Clubhouse details: Normal social club hours. No food - canteen open matchdays in ground.
Previous Leagues: Local works league 03-62/ Darlington & Dist. 62-81/ Northern Alliance 81-83.
Nickname: The Bridge.   **Record Gate:** 2,500 v Darlington, friendly
Players progressing to Football League: Jeff Wealands (Birmingham City, Manchester United).
Previous Grounds: None   **Previous Name:** Darlington Cleveland Bridge 1903-1993.
Youth team's League: Banks Northern Yth.
Captain 92-93: F Jones   **Top Scorer 92-93:** M McCarthy
Honours: Northern Alliance 82-83, North Riding Challenge Cup 81-82, Northern Region County Cup 82-83,
Darlington & Dist. Lg (5) - over twenty local cups in Darlington & Dist.

EASINGTON COLLIERY

Chairman: F Wellburn
Sec./Press Off.: Tom Goodrum, 8 Oswald Terrace, Easington Colliery, Peterlee SR8 3LB (091 527 0737)
Manager: Lol Jones   **Asst Manager:** Kenny Charlton   **Physio:** Davy Smith.
Ground: Easington Colliery Welfare Ground, C.W. Park, Easington, Co Durham. (091-5273047)
Directions: A19 Easington turn-off, B1284 thru Easington till Black Diamond PH, turn right for ground.
Seats: 50   **Cover:** 400   **Capacity:** 2,000   **Floodlights:** Yes   **Founded:** 1913
Midweek Matches: Tuesday   **Nickname:** The Colliery.
Cols: White & green stripes/green/green   **Change colours:** Yellow/black/yellow
Programme: 20 pages, 20p   **Programme Editor:** Dave Elliot   **Club Shop:** No
Clubhouse details: Normal licensing hours. Pies, soup and sandwiches available.
Previous Leagues: Wearside 13-37 39-64 73-88.
Record Attendance: 4,500 v Tranmere Rovers, FA Cup 1st Round 1955.
Prev. Name: Easington Colliery Welfare.   **Best F.A. Cup season:** 1st Round Proper 1955-56.
Players progressing to Football League: Ron Greener (Newcastle 1951), Frank Wayman (Darlington 1957), John
Langridge (Hartlepool 1982).
Record win: 7-1 v Northallerton, 1986   **Record defeat:** 2-8 v Blyth Spartans, 1993.
Captain & P.o.Y.: 92-93: G Gofton   **Top Scorer 92-93:** T Garside
Club record scorer: D Howard   **Club record appearances:** D Howard.
Honours: Northern Lg Div 2 R-up 85-86, Wearside League 29-30 31-32 32-33 47-48 48-49 (R-up 28-29 46-47 73-74, Lg
Cup 32-33 45-46 61-62), Monkwearmouth Cup 30-31 47-48 75-76, Sunderland Shipowners Cup 74-75 79-80, FA
Trophy 2nd Qualifying Rd replay 88-89, FA Vase 4th Rd replay 82-83.

ESH WINNING

Chairman: Charles Allen Ryan   **Vice Chairman:** Anthony Clarney   **President:** Jack Lumsden
Secretary: Allan Morton, 20 Durham Road, Esh Winning, Durham DH7 9NP (091 373 3611).
Manager: Douglas Robson   **Physio:** Barry Wainwright.
Ground: West Terrace, Waterhouses, Durham (091 373 3872).
Directions: Durham to Ushaw Moor, to Esh Winning; ground 1 mile further at Waterhouses.
Seats: 160   **Cover:** 160   **Capacity:** 3,500   **Floodlights:** Yes   **Year Formed:** 1967
Midweek Matches: Tuesday   **Club Sponsors:** Lumsden & Carroll.
Colours: Green & yellow halves/green/green.   **Change colours:** All orange.
Programme: 20 pages, 50p   **Programme Editor:** Harold Wharton   **Souvenir Shop:** No
Previous Grounds: None   **Prev. Lges:** Durham & Dist Sunday/ Northern Alliance 81-82.
Nickname: 'Esh'   **Previous Names:** Esh Winning Pineapple (pre-1982).
Clubhouse: Open daily. Snacks served   **Record Gate:** 900 v Liverpool Fantail, FA Sunday Cup 1982.
Best F.A. Cup season: 2nd Qualifying Rd 90-91 (lost 1-3 at home to Spennymoor).
Record win: 9-0 v Langley Park   **Record defeat:** 0-8 v Dunston F.B. (A).
Record transfer fee paid: Nil   **Received:** £400 for Derek Middleton (Easington Colliery).
Capt. & P.o.Y. 92-93: Chris Harrison   **Top Scorer 92-93:** Tony Theales, Derek Parkin (both 14).
Club record scorer: Ray Pegg 27   **Club record appearances:** Paul Hewitson 40.
Honours: Durham & District Sunday Lg 78-79 79-80, Durham County Sunday Cup R-up 78-79, Staffieri Cup 74-75,
Guards Cup 72-73, FA Vase 2nd Rd 83-84.

EVENWOOD TOWN

Chairman: Gordon Nicholson   **Press Officer:** Secretary   **Manager:** Dr Graeme Forster.
Secretary: Jim Coates, 19 Wellgarth, Evenwood, Bishop Auckland, Co Durham DL14 9QU (0388 833035).
Ground: Welfare Ground, Stones End, Evenwood, County Durham (0388 832281).
Directions: In village centre by Sports & Social club in Stones Rd.
Seats: None   **Cover:** 200   **Capacity:** 3,500   **Floodlights:** No   **Founded:** 1890
Previous Leagues: None.   **Midweek Matches:** Wednesday   **Programme:** None
Club colours: All blue   **Change colours:** Green (yellow sleeves)/green/green
Nickname: None   **Clubhouse:** Open lunch & evening every day.
Best F.A. Cup season: 1st Rd 1936.   **Record Gate:** 9,000 v Bishop Auckland, FA Amtr Cup 1931.
Previous Names: None   **Players progressing to Football League:** None.
Hons: Northern Lg 48-49 69-70 70-71 (Lg Cup 35-36), Durham Challenge Cup 69-70.

HORDEN COLLIERY WELFARE

Chairman: J McCoy   **Press Officer:** Secretary
Secretary: Robert Wood, 29 Morpeth Str., Horden, Peterlee, County Durham SR8 4BE (091 586 8802).
Ground: Welfare Park Ground, Park Road, Horden, Peterlee, County Durham (091 518 0248)
Directions: A19 to Peterlee, signposted from there.
Seats: 300   **Cover:** 400   **Capacity:** 4,500   **Floodlights:** Yes   **Reformed:** 1980
Midweek Matches: Tuesday   **Programme:** 10 pages, 20p   **Nickname:** Colliers
Colours: Red (white trim)/red/red   **Change colours:** Blue/black/blue
Clubhouse: Normal licensing hours. Hot & cold snacks, darts, pool.
Previous Lges: Wearside 07-35 63-75/ N. Eastern 35-58 62-64/ Midland (Co's) 58-60/ Northern Co's 60-62.
Best FA Cup year: 2nd Rd 38-39 (2-3 at home to Newport Co.). Also 1st Rd 25-26 52-53 53-54 54-55 81-82.
Previous Names: Horden Athletic.   **Record Attendance:** 8,000 - FA Cup 1937.
Players progressing to Football League: Paul Dobson (Hartlepool United).
Hons: Durham Challenge Cup 35-36 63-64 80-81 81-82, Durham Benevolent Cup 33-34, Wearside Lg 11-12 12-13 13-14 33-34 64-65 67-68 69-70 70-71 71-72 72-73 (Lg Cup 33-34 49-50, Monkwearmouth Charity Cup 12-13 23-24 32-33 69-70 72-73, Sunderland Shipowners Cup 65-66 72-73), North Eastern Lg 37-38 63-64 ('Non-Reserve' Medal 50-51).

LANGLEY PARK S. & S. UNITED

Chairman: C Fairless   **President:** Bobby Robson.
Secretary: G M Freeman, 35 Kidd Ave., Sherburn Village, Durham DH6 1JR (091 372 1960).
Manager: Vic Hillier   **Press Officer:** Secretary
Ground: Welfare Ground, Low Moor Road, Langley Park, Durham (091 373 1526).
Directions: A691 Durham to Consett. First left after Witton Gilbert, signed Langley Park. Turn right in town centre, ground quarter of a mile on right. Frequent buses from Durham.
Seats: 30   **Cover:** 500   **Capacity:** 3,000   **Floodlights:** No   **Reformed:** 1973
Midweek Matches: Tuesday
Club colours: All blue   **Change colours:** White/navy/navy OR All yellow
Programme: 30+ pages, 20p.   **Programme Editor:** Jeff Dover   **Club Shop:** No
Clubhouse: Open every evening, plus Sat & Sun lunch & directly after match on matchdays.
Previous Leagues: Durham & District Sunday/ Durham City & District.
Previous Name: Rams Head (pre-1983) as Sunday side.
Best F.A. Cup season: 2nd Qualifying Rd replay 90-91 (lost 0-1 at home to Easington Colliery).
Hons: FA Sunday Cup 76-77, Northern Lg Div 2 R-up 90-91, Staffieri Cup 74-75 76-77 77-78 78-79 80-81, Durham & Dist Lg JW Morgan Mem. Cup 82-83, Durham & Dist. Sunday Lg 78-79 (Lg Cup 76-77 78-79 79-80), FA Vase 2nd Rd 85-86 90-91.

NORTON & STOCKTON ANCIENTS

Chairman: Richard Scott   **President:** Dennis Swales.
Secretary: Steve Clarkson, 4 South Way, Norton, Stockton-on-Tees, Cleveland TS20 2TQ (0642 534524)
Press Officer: Brian Symons (0642 585836).
Ground: Station Road, Norton, Stockton-on-Tees, Cleveland (0642 530203).
Directions: Norton village 2 miles from Stockton centre, turn into Station Road on outskirts of village.
Seats: 200   **Cover:** Yes   **Capacity:** 2,000   **Floodlights:** No   **Year Formed:** 1959
Midweek Matches: Wednesday
Cols: Amber (black trim)/black/amber   **Change colours:** White with amber trim
Nickname: Ancients   **Previous Name:** Norton & Stockton Cricket Club Trust.
Programme: 12 pages with entry   **Programme Editor:** Richard Scott
Clubhouse details: Full bar facilities, 150 yds from ground.
Previous Leagues: Teesside (pre-1982).
Record Attendance: 1,430 v Middlesbrough, Friendly 1988.
Best F.A. Cup season: First Qualifying Rd(4) 88-89 90-93.
Hons: Northern Lg Cup 81-82.

PETERLEE NEWTOWN

Chairman: Brian Hall   **Press Officer:** Secretary
Secretary: Danny Cassidy, 23 Melbury Street, Seaham, County Durham SR7 7NF (091 581 4591).
Manager: Bobby Huntington   **Assistant Manager:** Gordon Huntington
Ground: Eden Lane, Peterlee, County Durham (091 586 3004).
Directions: From town centre Fire Station, turn left into Edenhill Rd, then right into Robson Ave. Left at the next junction and ground is on the right.
Seats: 50   **Cover:** 200   **Capacity:** 6,000   **Floodlights:** Yes   **Year Formed:** 1976
Colours: Sky/white/sky   **Change colours:** Yellow/black/yellow
Previous leagues: Northern Alliance 76-79/ Wearside 79-82.
Clubhouse details: Open normal licensing hours
Record Attendance: 2,350 v Northern, Hillsborough Fund match 1989.
Nickame: Newtowners.
Best F.A. Cup season: 4th Qual. Rd replay 85-86 (lost 0-1 at home to Whitby after 2-2 draw).
Honours: Northern Lg Div 2 82-83, North Eastern F'lit League, 4th Qual Rd FA Cup
Local Newspapers: Hartlepool Mail, Sunderland Echo, Northern Echo.   **Midweek Matches:** Wednesday.

Crook Town F.C. 1992-93. Photo - Gavin Ellis-Neville.

Evenwood Town F.C. 1992-93. Photo - Gavin Ellis-Neville.

Peterlee Newtown F.C. 1992-93. Photo - Gavin Ellis-Neville.

PRUDHOE EAST END

Chairman: George Bell **Press Off./Sec.:** Brian Tulip, 12 Orchard Close, Prudhoe (0661 833169).
Ground: Kimberley Park, Broomhouse Road, Prudhoe, Northumberland (0661 35900).
Directions: Approach Prudhoe along A695, turn right at 'Falcon' Inn, 200 yds down Eastwood Rd., turn left into Broomhouse Rd., ground on right.
Seats: 150 **Cover:** Yes **Capacity:** 5,000 **Floodlights:** Yes **Founded:** 1959
Colours: Sky & navy stripes/navy/sky **Change:** All yellow **Prog:** 8 pages, 20p **Editor:** J Smith
Midweek Matches: Wednesday **Clubhouse:** Open every evening plus Sat/Sun lunchtimes
Prev. Lges: Hexham & Dist 59-69/ Newcastle & Dist 69-71/ Northern Comb./ Northern Amtr/ Northern All. 84-88.
Record Attendance: 2,500 v Blyth Spartans, Northumberland Senior Cup 1981. **Nickname:** Citizens
Previous Names: Ovington 1969-75. **Prev. Grounds:** Farm field, Ovington 59-68/ Mickley Welfare 68-69.
Hons: Hexham & Dist. Lg 68-69 (Lg Cup 68-69), Newcastle & Dist. Lg 69-70 70-71 (Lg Cup 69-70, Charity Shield 69-70 70-71), Northern Comb. 79-80, Northerm Amtr Lg 71-72, Clayton Charity Cup 68-69, Northumberland Minor Cup 78-79, Northumberland Benevolent Bowl 79-80, Heddon Homes Charity Cup 81-82.

RYHOPE COMMUNITY ASSOCIATION

Chairman: Mick Walker **Vice Chairman:** S B Mottram **President:** A Clarke.
Secretary: Eric Dryden, 3 Maclyn Close, Moorside, Sunderland, Tyne & Wear (091 528 8358).
Manager: Ron King **Asst Mgr/Coach:** Granville Mervyn **Physio:** 'Rod'.
Commercial Manager: D Lawson **Press Officer:** Mark Taylor (091 374 5423).
Ground: Meadow Park, Ryhope, Sunderland (091 523 6555).
Directions: From Sunderland follow signs for A19 south - ground adjacent to Cherry Knowle Hospitals in Ryhope.
Seats: 200 **Cover:** 200 **Capacity:** 5,000 **Floodlights:** Yes **Founded:** 1960
Midweek Matches: Wednesday **Record Gate:** 1,018 v Newcastle, friendly 1982.
Cols: Red & white stripes/black/red **Change colours:** All blue **Nickname:** Ryes.
Programme: 40 pages, 40p **Editor:** D Lawson (091 567 799) **Club Shop:** No.
Sponsors: Lawson Freight **Clubhouse:** Open matchdays only. Hot dogs etc available.
Previous Leagues: Seaham & District/ Houghton & District/ Northern Alliance 78-82.
Players progressing to Football League: Kevin Todd (now Berwick, to Newcastle for £20,000).
Record win: 15-0 **Record loss:** 0-8 **Club Record scorer:** Ian Lawson.
Record transfer received: £4,000 (from Newcastle for Mitchell, 1986).
Captain 92-93: Glenn Moan **Top Scorer & P.o.Y. 92-93:** Ian Lawson.
Hons: Northern Alliance Lg Cup 80-81, Northern Lg Div 2 R-up 83-84, Banks Yth League & Cup double 92-93.

SHOTTON COMRADES

Chairman: Mr E A Jones **Vice Chairman:** Mr M Taylor **President:** Mr G Taylor.
Secretary/Press Officer: Mr W Banks, 6 Syston Close, Chilton Moor, Fencehouses, Houghton-le-Spring, Tyne & Wear DH4 6TB (091 385 5361).
Mgr/Coach: J Maddison **Asst Manager:** W Constantine. **Physio:** K Price.
Commercial Manager: Mr T Robinson.
Ground: Shotton Recreational Ground, Station Road, Shotton Colliery, Co. Durham (091 526 2859).
Directions: A19 to Peterlee to Shotton, right at War Mem. t-junction, follow round 800yds, ground on right.
Seats: 80 **Cover:** 400 **Capacity:** 1,700 **Floodlights:** No **Year Formed:** 1973
Colours: Red & white stripes/black/red (white tops) **Change colours:** All orange.
Club Sponsors: T.B.A. **Midweek home matches:** Wednesday **Nickname:** Coms
Programme: 12 pages, 20p **Programme Editor:** Mr E A Jones **Club Shop:** No
Previous Leagues: Peterlee Sunday 74-76/ Houghton & District 76-80/ Northern Alliance 80-83.
Previous Grounds: None **Record Attendance:** 1,726 v Dennis Waterman XI.
Best F.A. Cup season: 2nd Qualifying Rd 85-86 (lost 0-2 at home to Wingate). **Clubhouse:** No.
Reserves' Lge: Banks u-19 Yth **Record transfer received:** £500 for G Gudlip (Shildon)
Rec. win: 8-0 v Bedlington Ter. (H), '92 **Rec. defeat:** 1-7 v Brandon Utd (A), F.A. Cup Prel. Rd 91-92.
Captain & P.o.Y. 92-93: G Gudlip **Top Scorer 92-93:** M Gilhooley 12.
Record scorer: Keith Willets 50 **Record appearances:** J Gudlip.
Hons: Houghton & District Lg 78-79 (Lg Cup(2)), Northern Alliance Lg Cup SF, Hetton Charity Cup 78-79, Peterlee Sunday Lg 75-76 (Div 2 74-75), FA Vase 1st Rd 86-87 90-91, Durham Challenge Cup QF 78-79 (Minor Cup QF 78-79).

WASHINGTON

Chairman: Billy Blevins **Press Officer:** John Hurst (091 438 4513).
Secretary: George Abbott, 14 Grosvenor Street, Southwick, Sunderland SR5 2DG (091 549 1384).
Ground: Albany Park, Spout Lane, Concord, Washington (091 417 7779).
Directions: Ground situated behind the cinema opposite bus station.
Seats: 25 **Cover:** Yes **Capacity:** 3,000 **Floodlights:** No **Founded:** 1949
Colours: All red **Change colours:** All blue **Midweek Matches:** Wednesday
Programme: 8 pages, 10p **Programme Editor:** Mr Bull (091 4164618) **Club Shop:** No
Clubhouse: Open normal licensing hours, with live entertainment, pool etc. **Nickname:** Mechanics
Previous Leagues: Washington Amateur/ Northern Alliance 67-68/ Wearside 68-88.
Previous Ground: Usworth Welfare Park **Record Gate:** 3,800 v Bradford Park Avenue, FA Cup 1970.

WHICKHAM

Chairman: Robert Ferriday **Manager:** Billy Hodgson **Press Officer:** Secretary
Secretary: Albert Hutchinson, 6 Fellside Ave., Sunniside, Newcastle upon Tyne NE16 5NL (091 488 7011).
Ground: Glebe Ground, Rectory Lane, Whickham (091 488 3054).
Directions: A692 (Consett) from A69. Left at r'bout signed Consett/Whickham. Up hill and right at mini-r'bout. Continue along & turn left into Rectory Lane (by Lloyds Bank) for about 500 yds, clubhouse on right.
Seats: 100 **Cover:** Yes **Capacity:** 4,000 **Floodlights:** Due **Founded:** 1944
Colours: Black & white stripes/black/black **Change colours:** All white
Previous Leagues: Derwent Valley -55/ Northern Comb. 55-57 59-74/ Tyneside Amtr 57-59/ Wearside 74-88.
Programme: 20p **Midweek Matches:** Wednesday **Souvenir Shop:** No
Clubhouse: Mon-Fri. 12-3 & 7-11, Sat.11-11, Sun. 12-2, 7.30-11
Record Gate: 3,165 v Windsor & Eton, F.A. Vase SF 1981.
Prev. Ground: Rectory Rec. Field **Best F.A. Cup season:** 1st Qual. 89-90 (0-1 at Nth Shields)
Players progressing to Football League: Nigel Walker (Newcastle 1977), David Norton (Hartlepool 1981), Mike Carroll (Chesterfield 1981).
Honours: FA Vase 80-81, Wearside Lg 77-78 87-88 (R-up 80-81 84-85, Lg Cup 86-87, Monkwearmouth Charity Cup 76-77, Sunderland Shipowners Cup 77-78 80-81), Northern Comb. 69-70 72-73 73-74 (Lg Cup 60-61 73-74).
Local Newspapers: Newcastle Journal, Sunday Sun, Evening Chronicle

WILLINGTON

Chairman: Mr Desmond Ayre **Vice Chairman:** Mr R H Nichols **President:** Mr D H Warner
Secretary/Press Officer: Mr R H Nichols, 34 Stephenson Cres., Willington, Co. Durham DH6 4JD.
Manager: Ian Gaunt **Asst Mgr/Coach:** Dave Brownson **Physio:** Ian Welch.
Ground: Hall Lane, Willington, County Durham (0388 746221).
Directions: Willington is on A690 seven miles west of Durham and 3 miles east of Crook. At 'The Black Horse
Tavern' corner turn into Commercial Street, left into Hall Lane after 50yds.
Seats: 400 **Cover:** 400 **Capacity:** 7,000 **Floodlights:** Yes **Founded:** 1906.
Colours: Blue & white stripes/blue/blue **Change colours:** Yellow/green/yellow.
Programme: 20 pages, 20p **Programme Editor:** Secretary
Club shop: No, but secretary can supply club badges, old progs and 'Northern Ventures' League magazine.
Clubhouse details: Usual food and beverages available on matchdays.
Midweek Matches: Wednesday **Previous Leagues:** Auckland & Dist. 1906-11.
Nickname: Blue & Whites
Record Attendance: 10,000 v Bromley, FA Amateur Cup 2nd Rd 24/1/53/
Best F.A. Cup season: 1st Rd replay 73-74 (lost 1-6 at Blackburn after 0-0 draw). Also 1st Rd 45-46 50-51.
Prev. Grnd: West End Ground 1906-11. **Previous Names:** Willington Temperance 1906-11.
Record win: 13-3 v Whitby (H), 1953 **Record defeat:** 0-11 v Dunston Feds (H), 1992.
Captain 92-93: Mark Blunt **Top Scorer & P.O.Y. 92-93:** Simon Andrews.
Club record scorer: Unknown **Club record appearances:** Stan Rutherford, 1947-61.
Hons: FA Amtr Cup 49-50 (R-up 38-39, SF 27-28), Northern Lg 13-14 25-26 29-30 (R-up 12-13 57-58 75-76, Lg Cup
24-25 25-26 27-28 56-57 30-31 31-32 48-49 74-75), FA Trophy 3rd Rd 75-76, Durham Benevolent Cup 48-49 50-51
57-58.

Willington 0, Alnwick Town 1 - 15/8/92. Alnwick's Darren Coxford shoots for goal. Photo - Alan Watson.

Shotton Comrades F.C. 1992-93. Photo - Gavin Ellis-Neville.

G.C. DEVELOPMENTS LTD
TEESSIDE LEAGUE

(Established 1891)

Hon. Secretary: R D Marsay, 12 Aislaby Court, Wilton Lane, Guisborough TS14 6TG.

	P	W	D	L	F	A	PTS
Rowntrees	32	25	2	5	86	35	77
Acklam Steelworks	32	22	5	5	79	38	71
Grangetown Y.C.C.	32	18	7	7	69	40	61
I.C.I. Wilton	32	14	10	8	69	44	52
Nunthorpe Athletic	32	15	7	10	71	47	52
Redcar Wks B.S.C.	32	15	5	12	63	50	50
Dormans Athletic	32	15	5	12	61	52	50
New Marske S.C.	32	14	7	11	65	66	49
Fishburn Park	32	13	6	13	62	63	45
Stokesley	32	11	7	14	62	68	40
Thornaby Y.C.	32	9	10	13	52	65	37
Hartlepool T. Res.	32	11	4	17	58	78	37
Tees Components	32	9	8	15	64	85	35
Richmond Town	32	9	8	15	49	56	35
Stockton Supporters	32	8	7	17	55	79	31
BEADS	32	7	3	22	42	73	24
Guisboro. Quoit	32	4	5	23	33	97	17

Rowntrees 3, Guisborough Quoit 1

Quarter Finals
Acklam Steelworks 0, Nunthorpe Athletic 0
r: Nunthorpe 1, Acklam 3
Redcar Works B.S.C. 0, Grangetown Y.C.C. 2
Thornaby Youth Club 1, Stokesley 3
Rowntrees 4, I.C.I. Wilton 2

Semi Finals
Rowntrees 2, Grangetown Y.C.C. 1
Acklam Steelworks 4, Stokesley 1

Final: Rowntrees 1, Acklam Steelworks 0

R.T. RAINE CUP
Preliminary Round
Guisborough uoit 2, Dormans Athletic 3

Quarter Finals
BEADS 0, Stockton Supporters 1
Fishburn Park 4, Hartlepool T. Res. 3
Rochmond Town 3, Tees Components 0
New Marske S.C. 1, Dorman Athletic 0

Semi Finals
New Marske S.C. 0, Fishburn Park 1
Richmond Town 3, Stockton Supporters 3
r: Stockton Supporters 1, Richmond T. 0

Final: Stockton Supporters 3, Fishburn Pk 1

J V MADDEN CUP
Final: Wingate Mall 2, Thornaby Y.C. 0

McMILLAN BOWL
Preliminary Round
Dormans Ath. 2 v Hartlepool T. Res. 3
Fishburn Park 3, BEADS 2

First Round
Redcar Wks B.S.C. 5, Hartlepool T. Res. 1
Thornaby Y.C. 4, Stockton Supporters 1
New Marske S.C. 0, Grangetown Y.C.C. 4
Nunthorpe Athletic 2, Richmond Town 0
Acklam S.W. *(w/o)* Darlington G.S.O.B. *(scr)*
Stokesley 2, Fisburn Park 0

RESULT CHART 1992-93

	1	2	3	4	5	6	7	8	9	10	11	12	13	14	15	16	17
1. Acklam Steel Works	*	2-1	4-2	1-0	1-0	4-1	2-1	2-2	3-1	2-0	3-3	3-2	1-2	7-0	4-2	5-0	2-0
2. B.E.A.D.S.	0-1	*	2-1	1-3	1-4	1-2	0-2	1-1	0-2	0-2	0-2	1-2	2-4	2-1	1-2	4-2	1-2
3. Dormans Athletic	3-1	4-0	*	2-1	2-1	4-1	1-1	2-2	3-1	3-2	1-2	1-2	2-3	1-0	2-1	2-2	2-1
4. Fishburn Park	3-1	4-0	1-4	*	1-1	7-0	6-1	2-0	0-1	0-7	0-4	1-0	0-4	5-0	2-1	1-2	1-1
5. Grangetown Y.C.C.	2-2	4-1	4-2	2-1	*	3-0	2-1	1-0	0-3	0-2	4-0	1-0	2-0	0-1	2-2	1-2	2-2
6. Guisborough Quoit	1-3	0-2	1-0	0-1	1-5	*	2-2	2-0	0-3	1-1	0-4	1-1	0-7	2-2	4-4	2-4	0-2
7. Hartlepool Town Reserves	1-2	4-4	3-2	1-2	2-3	6-1	*	0-2	4-3	2-4	0-6	1-0	1-2	1-4	1-2	1-1	1-2
8. I.C.I. Wilton	0-1	1-1	0-1	6-1	2-2	2-1	4-1	*	1-1	1-0	2-2	3-2	1-7	3-1	3-1	4-0	1-1
9. New Marske S.C.	1-4	3-2	2-2	6-3	1-1	2-1	6-1	0-5	*	2-2	2-1	2-2	1-2	3-2	1-3	1-7	2-2
10. Nunthorpe Athletic	1-0	1-3	5-2	2-2	2-1	1-2	2-4	1-0		*	1-1	3-1	0-1	4-3	2-1	8-1	6-1
11. Redcar Works B.S.C.	1-1	3-2	1-3	0-4	1-3	0-2	1-2	2-0	4-1	1-2	*	2-2	2-0	3-0	0-3	0-3	2-0
12. Richmond Town	0-2	0-2	1-0	5-1	3-3	2-1	1-2	0-2	0-1	1-0	3-4	*	1-1	2-2	1-3	3-0	3-1
13. Rowntrees	2-1	3-0	1-3	2-1	0-2	3-1	5-1	3-1	2-3	2-1	2-0	3-1	*	3-1	4-0	5-1	5-0
14. Stockton Supporters	1-4	2-3	0-1	2-5	0-4	3-2	0-2	2-1	4-0	3-3	2-1	6-2	2-2	*	3-3	1-2	2-4
15. Stokesley	1-4	5-1	3-1	2-1	0-1	4-0	1-3	0-0	2-4	4-3	1-2	0-2	2-3	1-1	*	5-3	0-2
16. Tees Components	2-2	3-2	2-1	1-3	2-3	10-1	2-5	0-2	1-5	0-0	2-3	3-3	0-1	2-3	2-2	*	2-0
17. Thornaby Youth Club	2-3	4-1	1-1	1-1	2-5	2-1	4-2	2-6	1-1	1-1	2-5	1-1	1-2	1-1	5-0	1-1	*

Darlington Cleveland Bridge F.C. 1992, who are now renamed Darlington Cleveland Social. Photo - Dave West.

WEARSIDE LEAGUE

President: J.C.Thomas

Chairman: P.J.Maguire

Hon Secretary & Treasurer: Bill Robson,
12 Deneside, Howden-le-Wear, Crook, Co.Durham DL15 8JR

Season 1992-93 proved to be virtually a repeat of the previous year with the championships of both divisions not being decided until the very last week of the season.

South Shields, under the management of former Newcastle favourite Bobby Elwell, came with a late surge to pip long time leaders Hartlepool Town for the title of Division One, while Hartlepool B.W.O.B. in Division Two exchanged the leadership of the division with North Shields before finally clinching the championship.

The question of South Shields being promoted to Division Two of the Northern League, via the Pyramid, hinged around the future of Whitby Town being accepted into the Northern Premier and as the question could not be resolved by the date of our A.G.M. it was agreed by the member clubs that the membership of the premier division should be increased to eighteen teams. As a result three sides gained promotion to Division One; champions Hartlepool B.W.O.B. being joined by North Shields and Jarrow, while Windscale although finishing in bottom place retained their senior division status.

On the domestic cup front teams from Division Two again had a good season with Wingate Mall taking pride of place in reaching the final of the Monkwearmouth Cup as well as qualifying for the last stage of the divisional cup. Annfield Plain, however proved to be too strong for the Mall winning the Monkwearmouth by two clear goals while in an all Cleveland final of the League Cup, Marske United crushed Wolviston 4-0.

The Sunderland Shipowners Cup featured the two leading clubs from Division One, South Shields and Hartlepool Town. In the Final, played before a crowd of almost 1,300 at Shield's Filtrona Park, the Mariners captured the trophy following a rousing tie with a 2-1 scoreline to round off a commendable season.

Wingate Mall's season, which saw them reaching two Finals as well as two semi-finals, ended in disappointment when Nissan took the Divisional Cup with a 4-3 win.

Clubs from the League again had a disappointing year in County Cup competitions with Windscale in the Cumbria Cup and Wingate Mall and Washington Glebe in the Durham Trophy all being defeated at the semi-final stage.

Next season will see five new clubs taking part in Division Two. South Shields County Kitchens join the League after being transferred from the Northern Alliance via the Pyramid with the election as Associate Members of Sunderland Tradelink, Newcastle City, North Ormesby and Guisborough Priory making up the new sides.

On the question of the Pyramid the member clubs at an Extraordinary Meeting in April committed themselves to membership of the North East Section of the Pyramid of Football. As a result the clubs currently in membership of Division One have been subject to inspections of their grounds and facilities with all sides now being fully aware of the improvements required if the League is to meet the stipulations of the Northern League for a system of automatic promotion and relegation to be in place for the end of season 1993-94. Clubs have accepted that should the League fail to meet the 50% minimum standard then a system of adjustment between Divisions One and Two will be implemented before the date of next year's A.G.M.

The question of the extension of the Pyramid below Division Two of the League has been put on hold for at least one season to enable the clubs in membership of the Teesside and Washington Leagues to consider their position with regard to the provision of enclosed and private grounds and facilities.

The League's Centenary Year saw a League side defeating a Northern League XI and being held to a draw by the Northern Alliance. It is now expected that these inter league fixtures will become a part of the domestic programme in future seasons.

Bill Robson

Division One	P	W	D	L	F	A	PTS
South Shields	28	20	5	3	84	36	65
Hartlepool Town	28	19	6	3	70	30	63
Silksworth	28	18	5	5	59	29	59
Jarrow Roofing	28	16	5	7	51	39	53
Marske United	28	12	11	5	55	37	47
Annfield Plain	28	11	7	10	57	58	49
Roker	28	12	3	13	54	32	39
Boldon C.A.	28	12	3	13	42	50	39
Cleadon S.C.	28	9	7	12	51	49	34
Wolviston	28	9	5	14	47	50	32
Ryhope C.W.	28	8	6	14	60	64	30
Newton Aycliffe	28	6	9	13	33	63	27
Cleator Moor C.	28	6	5	17	41	59	23
Herrington C.W.	28	5	6	17	37	78	21
Windscale	28	5	1	22	36	82	16

Division Two	P	W	D	L	F	A	PTS
Hartlepool B.W.O.B.	28	19	6	3	72	34	63
North Shields	28	18	5	5	79	36	59
Jarrow	28	16	5	7	73	41	53
Washington Glebe	28	16	4	8	65	41	52
Nissan	28	14	6	8	55	39	48
Wingate Mall	28	12	10	6	58	46	46
Hebburn Colliery	28	10	8	10	51	51	38
Esh Winning A.	28	11	4	13	47	73	37
Birtley	28	8	10	10	40	44	34
Stanley United	28	8	6	14	50	59	30
N'allerton T. Supp.	28	9	4	15	58	65	*28
Marchon	28	7	5	16	42	57	26
Usworth Village	28	4	10	14	17	47	22
Murton International	28	5	7	16	35	75	22
Flo-Gas Fulwell	28	5	6	17	36	70	21

* - 3 pts deducted

DIV. ONE RESULTS

	1	2	3	4	5	6	7	8	9	10	11	12	13	14	15
1. Annfield Plain	*	0-1	2-1	1-4	2-2	3-0	2-2	4-2	0-1	1-1	2-5	0-6	5-2	6-3	3-2
2. Bolden C.A.	2-5	*	2-1	0-6	1-0	0-0	2-0	4-1	0-3	0-0	3-4	0-1	2-1	3-1	0-3
3. Cleator Moor Celtic	0-0	2-5	*	1-2	2-3	4-1	1-1	3-4	2-1	2-5	2-5	1-2	2-1	1-2	2-2
4. Hartlepool Town	3-1	1-1	4-3	*	6-1	0-1	2-3	1-0	4-1	2-1	1-3	2-1	2-1	3-0	1-0
5. Herrington C.W.	0-2	3-2	0-0	3-3	*	1-2	1-1	2-1	1-2	1-3	0-4	2-4	2-4	2-1	0-1
6. Jarrow Roofing	3-2	2-1	1-0	0-2	3-0	*	0-0	3-1	1-0	2-1	3-3	2-1	4-1	7-0	4-1
7. Marske United	1-1	1-0	2-1	1-5	4-1	1-1	*	3-0	0-0	5-0	1-6	2-1	3-0	2-0	1-0
8. Newton Aycliffe	0-2	0-2	2-1	1-1	2-3	2-0	0-0	*	0-0	1-3	2-2	2-1	2-0	0-1	0-6
9. Roker	3-4	3-0	4-2	0-1	5-0	3-1	1-2	8-0	*	1-3	1-4	20	0-2	3-1	1-2
10. Silksworth	1-0	4-3	3-0	1-2	2-0	0-0	1-0	5-0	1-0	*	1-1	2-2	4-2	4-0	1-0
11. South Shields	4-0	2-1	1-0	0-5	6-0	3-0	4-3	1-0	6-0	0-2	*	2-0	2-3	4-1	4-2
12. S.S. Cleadon S.C.	2-2	0-1	3-3	1-3	3-3	3-4	3-3	2-3	2-1	0-2	2-2	*	1-1	2-0	2-4
13. Vaux Ryhope	0-0	4-2	0-2	2-2	5-1	4-1	1-5	2-2	1-1	3-1	0-3	2-1	*	2-3	2-4
14. Windscale	3-5	2-3	0-2	0-2	5-2	1-2	0-6	2-2	0-4	0-2	1-2	5-2	*		2-4
15. Wolviston	3-1	0-1	1-2	2-2	0-1	1-3	2-2	1-1	0-5	1-3	0-1	2-3	2-2	1-0	*

DIV. TWO RESULTS

	1	2	3	4	5	6	7	8	9	10	11	12	13	14	15
1. Birtley	*	5-2	1-1	4-2	1-0	1-1	0-2	5-0	3-1	1-2	0-2	0-1	3-4	2-2	
2. Esh Albion	2-3	*	3-2	3-1	2-1	3-1	6-2	0-2	2-1	4-1	1-1	2-1	1-3	5-1	3-2
3. Hartlepool BWOB	3-1	3-0	*	1-0	4-0	1-0	3-0	4-2	5-1	1-1	3-2	0-0	3-1	0-0	3-0
4. Hebburn Colliery	1-1	3-0	1-5	*	0-1	3-0	5-0	4-3	2-2	3-3	1-1	1-2	1-2	1-1	0-3
5. Jarrow	4-0	4-0	2-4	5-3	*	5-0	5-3	2-0	4-2	1-1	2-0	7-0	1-2	3-2	2-2
6. Marchon	0-1	1-1	2-3	1-3	3-3	*	6-2	2-3	1-2	4-3	4-1	1-0	1-2	4-2	1-3
7. Murton International	1-1	5-2	1-3	0-1	2-2	0-2	*	0-0	1-1	2-0	4-1	1-1	2-1	0-4	0-5
8. Nissan	0-0	5-1	2-2	2-2	1-0	2-1	2-0	*	6-0	2-0	5-0	1-0	3-1	2-1	0-1
9. Northallerton SC	2-1	7-0	1-5	2-3	0-3	5-0	8-0	0-3	*	1-4	1-2	3-1	2-2	4-4	1-3
10. Stanley United	0-2	3-1	2-3	6-3	1-3	2-2	1-1	3-0	2-1	*	7-2	0-2	1-5	0-1	2-2
11. S'land Flo-Gas	0-0	2-3	3-4	3-0	0-4	1-2	1-3	2-1	0-3	0-1	*	1-1	1-1	0-4	0-5
12. Usworth Village	1-1	0-0	0-0	0-2	1-4	0-0	1-0	2-2	0-5	0-1	0-0	*	1-4	0-2	0-1
13. Washington Glebe	1-1	1-1	0-1	3-0-1	3-0-1	1-0	3-2	2-1	1-0	4-0-0	6	4-0	*	1-1	3-0
14. Wingate Mall	2-1	3-1	2-2	2-2	1-1	2-1	3-0	3-3	1-3	3-2	3-2	0-0	3-1	*	0-0
15. North Shields	6-0	3-0	1-0	1-3	2-0	2-2	6-2	4-0	4-0	3-2	6-0	4-1	4-6	4-3	*

LEAGUE CUP 1992-93

Preliminary Round

Wingate Mall v Esh Winning Albion	5-3	Darlington Railway Ath. *(scr)* Boldon C.A. *(w/o)*	
Vaux Ryhope v Cleator Moor Celtic	3-0	Herrington C.W. v Northallerton Town S.C.	1-2
Hartlepool B.W.O.B. v Usworth Village	2-1	Stanley United *(bye)*	
Marske United v I.F.G. Roker	4-1	Hartlepool Town v Annfield Plain	3-4
Cleadon S.C. v Murton International	4-3	Silksworth v South Shields	2-1
Nissan v Marchon	1-0	Hebburn Colliery v Windscale	0-1
Jarrow v Newton Aycliffe	4-3	Washington Glebe *(bye)*	
Wolviston v Flo-Gas Fulwell	7-2	Birtley v Jarrow Roofing	1-3

First Round

Wingate Mall v Boldon Community Assn	2-1	Ryhope Colliery Welfare v Northallerton S.C.	2-0
Hartlepool B.W.O.B. v Stanley United	4-1	Marske United v Annfield Plain	2-0
Cleadon S.C. v Silksworth	4-5	Nissan v Windscale	1-0
Jarrow v Washington Glebe	0-5	Wolviston v Jarrow Roofing	3-2

Quarter Finals

Wingate Mall v Ryhope Colliery Welfare	0-4	Hartlepool B.W.O.B. v Marske United	1-2
Silksworth v Nissan	1-2	Washington Glebe v Wolviston	1-4

Semi-Finals

Nissan v Wolviston	4-5	Ryhope Colliery Welfare v Marske United	1-2

Final: Marske United 4, Wolviston 0

DIVISION TWO CUP 1992-93

First Round

Usworth Village v Stanley United	1-4	Wingate Mall v Flo-Gas Fulwell	5-4*(aet)*
Jarrow v Hartlepool B.W.O.B.	2-3	Washington Glebe v Marchon	3-1
Murton International v Esh Albion	2-2,2-3	Hebburn Colliery Welfare v Northallerton Town S.C.	2-1

Quarter-Finals

Stanley United v Wingate Mall	2-7*(aet)*	Hartlepool B.W.O.B. v Washington Glebe	0-0,1-4
Nissan v Birtley	4-0	Esh Winning Albion v Hebburn Colliery Welfare	2-4

Semi-Finals

Wingate Mall v Washington Glebe	3-2	Hebburn Colliery v Nissan	1-1,0-2

Final: Nissan 4, Wingate Mall 3

MONKWEARMOUTH CHARITY CUP 1992-93 Preliminary Round

Wingate Mall v Hebburn Colliery	5-1	Washington Glebe v Esh Winning Albion	0-1
Birtley v Newton Aycliffe	8-0	Jarrow Roofing v Boldon Community Association	0-2
Wolviston v Sunderland I.F.G. Roker	2-1	Darlington Railway Athletic (scr) Jarrow (w/o)	
Herrington C.W. v Cleator Moor Celtic	3-1	Windscale v Nissan	1-4
Ryhope v Usworth Village	4-0	Cleadon Social Club v Marske United	0-4
Murton International v Northallerton S.C.	1-0	Flo-Gas Fulwell (bye)	
Annfield Plain (bye)		South Shields v Marchon	1-0
Hartlepool Town v Silksworth	5-1	Hartlepool Boys Welfare v Stanley United	2-2,3-0

First Round

Wingate Mall v Esh Winning Albion	4-0	Boldon Community Association v Birtley	4-1
Roker v Jarrow	2-4	Herrington Colliery Welfare v Nissan	3-4
Ryhope C.W. v Marske United	2-3	Murton International v Flo-Gas Fulwell	2-2,5-0
Annfield Plain v South Shields	3-1	Hartlepool Town v Hartlepool Boys W.O.B.	1-1,0-3

Quarter-Finals

Marske United v Murton International	5-0	Wingate Mall v Boldon Community Association	4-2
Jarrow v Nissan	3-0	Hartlepool Boys Welfare O.B. v Annfield Plain	1-1,0-2

Semi-Finals

Marske United v Annfield Plain	0-1	Wingate Mall v Jarrow	3-2

Final: Annfield Plain 2, Wingate Mall 0

SUNDERLAND SHIPOWNERS' CUP 1992-93 Preliminary Round

Silksworth v Northallerton Supporters Club	2-1	Birtley (bye)	
South Shields v Annfield Plain	2-1	Vaux Ryhope v Marchon	3-1
Hebburn Colliery v Newton Aycliffe	2-3	Herrington Colliery Welfare v Cleator M.C.	3-3,1-4
Wolviston v Hartlepool Boys Welfare O.B.	4-3	Windscale v Sunderland I.F.G. Roker	0-6
Wingate Mall v Marske United	3-1	Nissan v Flo-Gas Fulwell	3-4
Jarrow (w/o) Darlington Railway Athletic (scr)		Usworth Village v Esh Winning Albion	1-1,1-6
Stanley United v Boldon Community Assn	4-1	Hartlepool Town v Jarrow Roofing	4-0
Cleadon Social Club (bye)		Washington Glebe v Murton International	4-3

First Round

Silksworth v Birtley	3-0	South Shields v Ryhope Colliery Welfare	3-1
Newton Aycliffe v Cleator Moor Celtic	5-2	Wolviston v Roker	3-1
Wingate Mall v Flo-Gas Fulwell	4-3	Jarrow v Esh Winning Albion	3-0
Stanley United v Hartlepool Town	1-2	Washington Glebe v Cleadon Social Club	2-2,0-3

Quarter-Finals

Silksworth v South Shields	0-1	Newton Aycliffe v Wolviston	2-1
Wingate Mall v Jarrow	3-2	Hartlepool Town v Cleadon Social Club	4-0

Semi-Finals

Wingate Mall v Hartlepool Town	0-1	South Shields v Newton Aycliffe	3-0

Final: South Shields 2, Hartlepool Town 1

VAUX WEARSIDE LEAGUE DIVISION ONE TEN YEAR RECORD

	83/4	84/5	85/6	86/7	87/8	88/9	89/0	90/1	91/2	92/3
Annfield Plain	7	9	4	1	18	13	7	3	5	6
Blackhall Colliery Welfare	-	-	-	-	12	17	-	-	-	-
Boldon Community Association	9	13	16	13	15	8	4	4	6	8
Clarke Champions	-	16	15	18	16	16	-	-	-	-
Cleadon Social Club	-	-	-	-	-	-	-	-	8	9
Cleator Moor Celtic	-	-	-	-	-	11	12	8	12	13
Coundon Three Tuns	2	3	1	8	2	15	6	14	-	-
Darlington Railway Athletic	-	-	-	-	-	-	-	-	14	-
Dawdon Colliery Welfare	12	18	17	10	8	14	13	10	-	-
Dunston Federation Brewery	-	-	-	-	9	1	1	2	-	-
Easington Colliery	3	8	-	-	-	-	-	-	-	-
Eppleton Colliery Welfare	10	5	10	6	3	2	2	1	1	-
Gateshead Reserves	15	14	8	20	-	-	-	-	-	-
Greatham Mayfair Centre					(See Hartlepool Town)					
Hartlepool Boys Welfare Old Boys	-	-	-	-	5	17	9	9	17	-
Hartlepool Town	-	-	-	-	-	-	-	12	2	2
Hebburn (formerly Reyrolles)	16	19	13	15	7	5	-	-	-	-
Herrington Colliery Welfare	-	-	-	17	19	10	14	16	13	14
Jarrow Roofing	-	-	-	-	-	-	-	-	-	4
Marske United	-	-	7	7	6	6	8	6	4	5
Murton Colliery Welfare	13	12	2	2	4	-	-	-	-	-
Newcastle Blue Star	1	1	-	-	-	-	-	-	-	-
Newcastle (ex-NEI) Bohemians	-	-	-	-	-	-	15	13	16	-
Newton Aycliffe	-	17	11	16	13	7	3	9	9	12
Nissan	-	-	-	-	-	-	-	18	-	-
Reyrolles					(See Hebburn)					
Roker					(See Sunderland IFG Roker)					
Ryhope Colliery Welfare	14	6	18	14	20	-	-	-	-	-
Sporting Club Vaux					(See Sunderland Vaux Ryhope)					
Silksworth	-	-	-	-	-	-	-	-	-	3
South Hetton	18	-	-	-	-	-	-	-	-	-
South Shields	6	4	12	9	5	4	5	5	3	1
Stockton E.D.C.	11	20	-	-	-	-	-	-	-	-
Sunderland I.F.G. Roker	17	15	14	12	14	12	10	7	11	7
Sunderland Vaux Ryhope	-	-	-	-	-	3	11	11	10	11
Usworth Village	-	-	-	-	-	-	-	-	15	-
Washington	8	10	6	11	11	-	-	-	-	-
Whickham	5	2	3	4	1	-	-	-	-	-
Windscale	-	-	-	-	-	-	-	-	-	15
Wingate	4	7	9	19	-	-	-	-	-	-
Wolviston	-	-	-	-	-	-	-	15	7	10
No. of clubs competing	**18**	**20**	**18**	**20**	**20**	**17**	**15**	**18**	**16**	**15**

DIVISION ONE CLUBS 1993-94

ANNFIELD PLAIN

Chairman: J H Barrett   **Press Officer:** F Ross, 15 Northgate, Annfield Plain.
Sec./Treasurer: Marshall Lawson, 24 Northgate, Anfield Plain, Stanley, Co. Durham DH9 7UY (0207 235879).
Manager: D Longstaff   **Ground:** Derwent Park, Annfield Plain.
Directions: On A693 road to Consett, 200 yds west of junction with A6067. Ground behind new housing estate. 6 miles from Durham (BR). Buses from Sunderland, Newcastle & Durham.
Seats: 20   **Cover:** 200   **Capacity:** 6,000   **Floodlights:** No   **Founded:** 1890.
Colours: Claret/white/claret   **Change colours:** All blue.
Programme: 16 pages, 20p
Previous Names: Annfield Plain Celtic.   **Local Press:** Newcastle Journal.
Record Attendance: 7,200 v Southport, FA Cup 28-29.
Previous Leagues: North Eastern 25-58 62-64/ Northern Alliance 02-25 58-60.
Past players progressing to Football League: A Graver (Lincoln), N Wilkinson (York), K Smith (Blackpool), J Hather (Aberdeen).
Honours: Wearside Lg 84-85 (Monkwearmouth Charity Cup 92-93), FA Cup 1st Rd 26-27 28-29 64-65, Durham Challenge Cup 52-53, Northern Alliance 19-20, Harelaw Snr Cup 35-36, North Eastern Lg Cup 46-47.

BOLDON COMMUNITY ASSOCIATION

Chairman: R A O Shepherd.   **Vice Chairman:** G Smith   **President:** A Brewster.
Sec./Press Off./Commercial Mgr: George Pollard, 126 Horsley Hill Road, South Shields (091 4546821).
Manager: Bill Newham   **Asst Manager:** P Quinn   **Coach:** Tommy Frazer.
Treasurer: A Bell   **Physio:** G Meston/ R Fenwick
Ground: Boldon Community Association, North Road, Boldon Colliery.
Directions: A19 to junction with A184 Sunderland/Newcastle. Follow signs to Boldon Asda stores, then to North Road Social Club (SHACK). Ground behind. 800 yds from East Boldon (BR). Buses 533, 531, 319, 528.
Seats: 100   **Cover:** 400   **Capacity:** 3,500   **Floodlights:** No   **Founded:** 1892.
Colours: Green & yellow halves   **Change:** Red (white sleeves)/black   **Programme:** No.
Record Attendance: 1,550 v Stockton, Durham Challenge Cup 1934.   **Nickname:** Villa.
Previous Names: Boldon Villa (reformed in 1946)/ Boldon Colliery Welfare 50-76.
Prev. Grnds: Station Rd/ Colliery Rd   **Prev. Lges:** None (Boldon Villa: Sth Tyne Alliance)
Clubhouse: Matchdays only. Bar snacks
Club Sponsors: Tyne Dock Engineering Co., South Shields.
Midweek home matchday: Mon or Wed   **Reserve team:** None.
Captain 92-93: Peter Quinn   **Top Scorer 92-93:** S Brewis   **P.O.Y. 92-93:** Ian Robson
Club record scorer: Darran Palmer   **Club record appearances:** Peter Quinn.
Hons: Wearside Lg 52-53 54-55 74-75 (Lg Cup 67-68 72-73 75-76), Monkwearmouth Charity Cup 57-58 71-72, Shipowners Cup 62-63 71-72 75-76 76-77 78-79 88-89).

CLEATOR MOOR CELTIC

Chairman: R Doyle   **Press Officer:** Secretary
Secretary: Pat McGrath, 105 Birks Road, Cleator Moor, Cumbria (0946 811488).
Ground: Birks Field, Birks Road, Cleator Moor, Cumbria (0946 812476).
Directions: A66 to Bridgefoot, A595 for Barrow at Hensingham, left to Cleator Moor after 2 miles, left approaching town centre to Birks Road, club 200 yds on left. 5 miles from Whitehaven (BR).
Seats: No   **Cover:** 500   **Capacity:** 2,000   **Floodlights:** No   **Founded:** 1908.
Colours: Green & white/white/white   **Change colours:** All green
Record Attendance: 3,100 v Penrith 1950 (12,212 v Tranmere at Workington, FA Cup 1st Rd 1950).
Previous Ground: The Celtic Field 08-59   **Prev. Lges:** West Cumberland/ Carlisle & Dist. (pre'88).
Past players progressing to Football League: Billy Elliott & Pat Fitzsimmons (Preston), Joe Kennedy (West Bromwich Albion), Charlie Woods & Paul Tynan (Ipswich Town)
Honours: FA Cup 1st Rd 50-51, West Cumberland Lg(51).

HARTLEPOOL BOYS WELFARE OLD BOYS

Chairman: Glen Thompson   **Press Officer/Treasurer:** George Lester (0429 275327).
Secretary: Tom Harvey, 59 Wansbeck Gdns, Hartlepool TS26 9JH (0429 264753).
Manager: Jimmy Costello   **Asst Manager:** Wilf Constantine   **Physio:** Tony Metcalfe.
Ground: Grayfields Enclosure, Jesmond Road, Hartlepool.
Directions: Leave A19 on A179 signed Hartlepool, right for Throston Grange at 1st r'bout, left at 1st lights into Jesmond Road, ground 400yds on left.
Seats: None   **Cover:** No   **Capacity:**   **Floodlights:** No   **Founded:** 1952.
Colours: All white   **Change colours:** All yellow.   **Nickname:** None.
Previous Grounds: None   **Prev. Lges:** Hartlepool Church/ Hartlepool & Dist./ Teesside.
Reserve team: None   **Local Press:** Hartlepool Mail.
Players progressing to Football League: A Walsh (Middlesbrough, Darlington, Bristol City).
Programme: 10 pages, 50p   **Programme Editor:** Secretary   **Club Shop:** No.
Midweek home matchday: Monday   **Clubhouse:** No.
Captain 92-93: David Pattison   **Top Scorer 92-93:** Andy McKenna   **P.O.Y. 92-93:** Scott Cartwright.
Hons: FA Vase 3rd Rd, Wearside Lg Div 2 92-93, Hartlepool Church Lg(2)(Lg Cup(3)), Hartlepool Mem. Shield, Durham Amateur Cup 64-65 73-74 (Minor Cup 60-61 (R-up 64-65)), Hartlepool & Dist. Lg(3)(Lg Cup(3)), Horden Aged Miners Cup, Wingate Aged Miners Cup, Teesside Lg 73-74 85-86(R-up(3)).

HARTLEPOOL TOWN

Chairman/Treasurer: Robert Lupton
Secretary/Press Officer: Gordon Thornton, 14 Regency Drive, Hartlepool TS25 1LX (0429 266527).
Ground & Directions: As Ferryhill Athletic F.C. (see page 992).
Colours: Red/white/red   **Change colours:** Blue & black/white/black.
Prev. Name: Greatham Mayfair (pre-1991)   **Previous Leagues:** Hartlepool/ Teesside (pre-1988).
Previous Ground: Mayfair Park, Mayfair Centre, Tees Road, Seaton Carew (pre-1993).
Honours: Wearside Lg R-up 91-92 92-93 (Shipowners Cup 91-92 (R-up 92-93)).

HERRINGTON COLLIERY WELFARE

Chairman: Paul Foster   **Treasurer:** W Oxenden.
Secretary/Press Officer: Mel Speding, 12 Lodore Court, Doxford Park, Sunderland (091 5200881).
Ground: Welfare Park, New Herrington.
Directions: Situated on B1286 between the Board Inn and Herrington Burn. Behind New Herrington W.M.C.
Colours: Black & white/black/black & white   **Change:** Grey & black/grey/grey.
Previous Leagues: Washington Amateur 76-89.   **Founded:** 1920   **Reformed:** 1976.
Hons: Monkwearmouth Charity Cup 09-10 10-11 31-32, Shipowners Cup R-up 89-90, NCB National 5-aside 1975.

JARROW

Chairman: Dave Wiscombe   **Treasurer:** Gavin Bainbridge.
Secretary/Press Officer: Calum McAuley, 109 Bamburgh Avenue, South Shields (091 4555924).
Ground: Perth Green Community Centre.
Directions: From A19 or A1(M) follow drections to South Shields, right onto John Reid Road. First slip road onto Brockley Whinns Estate, follow road past Red Hackle pub, third left left onto Inverness Road, then right into Perth Green Community Centre.
Colours: All yellow   **Change:** All green   **Founded:** 1980.
Prev. Names: Unionist FC/ Benson Perth Green.   **Prev. Lges:** Sth Tyne 80-87/ Washington 87-91.
Hons: Sth Tyne Lg & Lg Cup, Washington Lg R-up 89-90 (Lg Cup 90-91, Aged Peoples Tphy R-up 90-91), Gateshead Charity Cup 90-91, Durham Tphy R-up 90-91.

JARROW ROOFING BOLDON C.A.

Chairman: Brian Marshall   **Press Off.:** Rose McLoughlin.
Secretary/Manager/Coach: Richard McLoughlin, 8 Kitchener Terrace, Jarrow NE32 5PU (091 4899825).
Asst Manager: Dennis Melia   **Physio:** Fred Corner.
Ground: As Boldon C.A. (above).   **Previous Leagues:** Mid-Tyne/ Tyneside Amtr 88-91.
Colours: Blue & white   **Change colours:** Claret & blue   **Founded:** 1987.
Programme: 20 pages, free with entry   **Editor:** Brian Marshall (091 4551190)   **Club Shop:** No.
Sponsors: Jarrow Roofing Co.   **Record Gate:** 500 v South Shields   **Nickname:** Roofing.
Midweek home matchday: Mon/Wed   **Clubhouse:** Yes, matchdays.
Captain 92-93: Tom Owens   **Top Scorer 92-93:** Kevin McElwee
Club record scorer: Kevin McElwee   **Club record appearances:** Kevin McElwee.
Hons: Vaux Wearside Lg Div 2 R-up 91-92, Tyneside Amtr Lg R-up 90-91 (Chal. Shield 90-91 (R-up 89-90), Bill Dixon Cup 90-91), Mid-Tyne Lg 87-88, Fred Giles Cup R-up 87-88, Gateshead Charity Cup SF 90-91.

MARSKE UNITED

President: Raymond Jarvis   **Chairman/Press Off.:** John Hodgson   **Vice Chairman:** John Corner.
Secretary: Ian Rowe, 2 Cliff Cres., Loftus, Saltburn, Cleveland TS13 4RY (0287 644606).
Manager: Allan Marples   **Asst Manager:** Barry Sill   **Coach:** Charlie Bell
Physio: Barry Schollay   **Commercial Mgr:** Don Willan   **Treasurer:** Mrs Pat Hodgson.
Ground: Mount Pleasant, Mount Pleasant Ave., Marske-by-Sea, Redcar (0642 471091).
Directions: From A19 take A174 exit marked Yarm, Teesport, Redcar, Whitby and head east towards Teesport and Redcar, continue on A174 and enter Marske by A1040 or A1084. In town square right into Southfield Road, and right again to ground. 300 yds from Marske BR station - trains from Darlington via Middlesbrough.
Seats: 40   **Cover:** 50   **Capacity:** 2,000   **Floodlights:** No   **Founded:** 1956.
Colours: Yellow/blue/white   **Change:** Blue/white/blue.   **Nickname:** Codheads
Previous Ground: None.   **Record Gate:** 950 v Sunderland, friendly 1983.
Midweek home matchday: Wednesday   **Previous Lges:** Cleveland/ Sth Bank & Dist./ Teesside 76-85.
Past players progressing to Football League: Peter Beagrie (Middlesbrough, Stoke City, Sheffield United, Everton, England 'B'), Dave Logan (Mansfield Town, Scarborough), Tony Butles (Gillingham).
Programme: 32 pages with entry   **Programme Editor:** John Hodgson (0642 484006).
Club Shop: Club scarves, ties and sweaters available - contact Mrs P Hodgson (0642 484006).
Club Sponsors: Arnott Insurance   **Reserve team's League:** Teesside Alliance.
Record win: 16-0   **Record defeat:** 3-9.
Clubhouse: Open every night and weekend lunchtimes. Food served after all games.
Club record scorer: Chris Morgan   **Club record appearances:** John Hodgson.
Captain 92-93: Charlie Bell   **Top Scorer 92-93:** Steve Winn   **P.O.Y. 92-93:** Tony Robson
Local Press: Sunday Sun/ Northern Echo/ Middlesbrough Evening Gazette.
Honours: North Riding County Cup 84-85, Teesside BR 80-81 84-85, Wearside Lg Cup R-up 88-89 (Lg Cup 92-93).

Marske United F.C., League Challenge Cup winners 1992-93.

NEWTON AYCLIFFE

Chairman: Luke Raine   **Treasurer:** Andrew Coulthard.
Press Officer/Secretary: Luke Raine, 31 Bede Crescent, Newton Aycliffe (0325 314844).
Ground: Moore Lane Sports Club, Newton Aycliffe, County Durham (0325 300324).
Directions: Turn in at Approved School A167, then left at r'bout. Third left, first right, ground at bottom on right. 2 miles from Newton Aycliffe (BR), served by Durham-Darlington buses.
Seats: None   **Cover:** None   **Capacity:** 2,000   **Floodlights:** No   **Founded:** 1968.
Colours: White/blue/blue   **Change colours:** Red/white/red.
Record Attendance: 500 - Vaux Wearside League Cup Final 1987-88.
Previous Names: Newton Aycliffe Sports Club Rangers   **Nickname:** Acorns
Previous Leagues: Auckland District 68-80/ Teesside 80-84.
Players progressing to Football League: Eric Gates (Ipswich Town & England).
Honours: Auckland & District Lg 75-76 (Div 2 68-69, Lg Cup), Brancepeth Aged Miners Cup, Bishop Auckland Charity Cup, Weardale Cup, Wearside Lg Cup R-up 88-89 (Monkwearmouth Charity Cup R-up 86-87).

NORTH SHIELDS

Chairman: Richard P Slade   **Press Officer:** Raymond Laidlaw (091 257 3271).
Secretary: Robert D Wilkinson, 72 Albatross Way, The Links, Blyth NE24 3QH (0670 352237).
Ground: Swallow Sports Ground, Kings Road North, Rising Sun.
Directions: From Tyne Tunnel; A19 northbound, left at 1st r'bout onto A1058 coast road, 3rd exit, right at bottom of slip road, 1st left, right after 500yds where road bears left after next crossroads, ground 500yds on right. From west; Thru Newcastle onto A1052 coast road, 2nd exit to r'bout, 2nd exit and continue parallel to coast road, road bears left, when road bears right turn left (straight on), ground 500yds on right after next crossroads.
Colours: All red   **Change colours:** Sky/navy/navy   **Reformed:** 1992.
Previous Leagues: None   **Previous Ground:** Percy Main Amateurs F.C. 1992-93.
Hons: Wearside Lg Div 2 R-up 92-93.

SILKSWORTH

Chairman: Jeff Eltringham   **Press Officer:** Secretary
Secretary: John Cumiskey, 21 Symington Gdns, Silksworth (091 5283098).
Treasurer: Anthony Stubbs   **Ground:** Silksworth Welfare Park
Directions: Behind Lord Seaham Public House, Blind Lane, Silksworth. 3 miles from Sunderland (BR), bus 133 to Vicarage Court from Sunderland centre.
Seats: No   **Cover:** None   **Capacity:** 1,600   **Floodlights:** No   **Founded:**
Colours: All white   **Change colours:** All red.   **Reformed:** 1988.
Players progressing to Football League: Bobby Gurney (Sunderland).
Hons: Wearside Lg 26-27 57-58 (Div 2 91-92, Lg Cup 51-52 59-60, Monkwearmouth Charity Cup 19-20 51-52, Shipowners Cup 53-54, Div 2 Cup 91-92).

SOUTH SHIELDS

Chairman: John Rundle   **Vice Chairman:** George Scott   **President:** Dick Butler.
Secretary/Press Off.: David Fall, 50 Basil Way, Holder House Est., South Shields NE34 8UD (091 5366809).
Manager: Bob Elwell   **Asst Manager:** Kenny Parker   **Coach:** Malcolm Leask
Physio: Derek Williamson   **Treasurer:** Paul Honeyman.
Ground: Filtrona Park, Shaftesbury Avenue, Simonside Industrial Estate.
Directions: From A1(M) take A194(M) to South Shields, town centre road, ignore A1300 to coast and turn left at next lights beside Co-op store into Shaftesbury Ave., ground half mile on right.
Seats: None   **Cover:** 200   **Capacity:** 2,000   **Floodlights:** Yes   **Founded:** 1974
Colours: Claret/sky/sky   **Change:** Blue & white stripes   **Nickname:** Mariners
Prev. Lge: Northern Alliance 74-76.   **Prev. Ground:** Jack Clarke Park 74-92.
Record Attendance: 1,400 v Hartlepool Town, Sunderland Shipowners Cup final 3/5/93. *At previous ground:* *1,500 v Brigg Town, FA Vase 1975.*
Sponsors: Northumbria Windows, Consett   **Local Press:** Shields Gazette/ Newcastle Journal.
Programme: Yes   **Programme Editor:** Steve Leonard   **Club Shop:** No.
Midweek home matchday: Wednesday   **Reserve team:** None.
Clubhouse: Open all day. Function suite, bar (capacity 130). Canteen facilities available.
Captain 92-93: Paul Thompson   **Top Scorer 92-93:** Paul Thompson, 35.
P.O.Y. 92-93: Gary Davies   **Club record scorer:** Paul Thompson.
Honours: FA Vase QF 75-76, Northern Alliance 74-75 75-76, Wearside Lg 76-77 92-93 (Monkwearmouth Charity Cup 86-87, Lg Cup R-up 82-83 83-84, Shipowners Cup 92-93 (R-up 83-84)), Durham Chal. Cup 76-77.

SOUTH SHIELDS CLEADON SOCIAL CLUB

Chairman: John Morris   **Press Officer:** David Wood (091 4554607).
Secretary: Peter Spencer, 15 Longfield Close, South Shields NE34 0YJ (091 4559766).
Treasurer: Mrs Joan Wood   **Ground:** Jack Clarke Park, South Shields.
Directions: Enter South Shields on A194 to r'bout taking you onto John Reid Rd. 2nd left at 3rd r'bout into King George Rd, then Sunderland Road. Follow on right into Grosvenor Rd then then left into Horsly Hill Rd. Ground on right behind bowling alley. Three quarters of a mile from Chichester Metro station.
Colours: White stripes/black/black   **Change:** Claret & blue/white/claret   **Founded:** Early 60s
Previous Leagues: Shields & Dist./ Washington Amtr (pre'89).
Hons: Wearside Lg Div 2 90-91, Shields & Dist. Lg, Washington Amtr(2), Durham Cup.

SUNDERLAND KENNEK ROKER

Chairman: J Broadbent   **Press Officer:** Secretary   **Treasurer:** Les Dodd.
Secretary: Tom W Clark, 55 Vicarage Close, New Silksworth SR3 1BQ (091 5211242).
Ground: As Silksworth (see above).   **Record Attendance:** Unknown.   **Founded:** 1940.
Colours: Red & white stripes/black/black   **Change:** Sky/navy/navy.
Previous Names: Roker Methodists/ Roker/ Roker Zanussi/ Sunderland Roker/ Sunderland I.F.G. Roker.
Local Press: Sunderland Echo.
Players progressing to Football League: Paul Rutherford (Newcastle).
Hons: Wearside Lg Cup 91-92 (Shipowners Cup 89-90 (R-up 80-81), Monkwearmouth Charity Cup R-up 80-81).

SUNDERLAND RYHOPE COLLIERY WELFARE

Chairman: R E Forster **Press Officer:** Secretary **Treasurer:** I Mankin.
Secretary: Trevor Whitehead, 6 Byron Walk, Gateshead (091 477 2065).
Ground: Ryhope Recreation Park, Ryhope Street, Ryhope, Sunderland (091 521 2843).
Directions: Take A19 (3 miles south of Sunderland centre) to Ryhope village, at Village Green turn into Evelyn Terrace/Ryhope Street and carry on up bank past Presto's for 600 yds - ground appears on left. 3 miles from Sunderland Central (BR), bus every 10 minutes from Sunderland centre.
Seats: No **Cover:** No **Capacity:** 1,000 **Floodlights:** Yes **Founded:** 1988.
Colours: All blue **Change colours:** Red & white/black/red.
Previous Names: Ryhope Colliery Welfare (founded 1898, previously Ryhope Villa) merged with Sporting Club Vaux (founded in 1968 as Monkwearmouth, later Bishopwearmouth, South Hetton) in 1988/ Sunderland Vaux Ryhope Colliery Welfare 88-93.
Previous Grounds: Sporting Club Vaux: Glenesk Road (pre-1988).
Previous Leagues: Sporting Club Vaux: Tyne & Wear/ North Eastern Amateur.
Record Gate: 2,000; Ryhope Colliery Welfare v Workington, FA Cup 1967.
Players progressing to Football League: Alan Harding (Lincoln, Darlington, Hartlepool), Kenny Ellis (Hartlepool, Darlington, Belgian clubs), Kenny Mitchell (prof. Icelandic club), Robert Malt (Leeds), Brian Smiles (Chelsea), Ron Robinson (Ipswich, Leeds), Nigel Staddington (Doncaster, Sunderland).
Honours *(Sporting Club Vaux hons italicised)* Wearside Lg 61-62 62-63 63-64 65-66 (Lg Cup 63-64 77-78), Durham Challenge Cup 77-78, Monkwearmouth Charity Cup 09-10 65-66 66-67, Sunderland Shipowners Cup 61-62 *86-87*, FA Cup 1st Rd Proper 67-68, FA Vase 1st Rd 81-82.

WINDSCALE

Chairman: R Napier **Press Officer:** Secretary **Treasurer:** A Barwise
Secretary: Geoff Turrell, 65 Leathwaite, Loop Road South, Whitehaven, Cumbria CA28 7UG (0936 62229)
Ground: Falcon Field, Egremont. **Directions:** A66 to Bridgefoot. A595 for Barrow, at bottom of hill approaching Egremont take 3rd turn off island (signed) Smithfield/ Gillfoot, ground in centre of housing estate
Colours: White/black/black **Change:** Royal & white stripes/royal/white
Previous Lges: West Cumberland Snr/ Derwent Valley/ Furness Premier. **Founded:** 1950
Hons: Furness Snr Cup 85-86 **Previous Names:** Windscale Rovers/ Windscale United.

WOLVISTON

Chairman: Eddie Poole **Vice Chairman:** Derek Stockton **President:** Derek Hayton
Sec./Press Off./Physio: Keith Simpson, 14 Lodore Grove, Acklam, Middlesbrough TS5 8PB (0642 823734).
Manager: Colin Henderson **Asst Mgr/Coach:** Andrew McCreesh **Treasurer:** Brian Jones.
Ground: Metcalfe Way, Wynyard Road, Wolviston, Billingham, Cleveland TS22 5NE.
Directions: Situated on Wynyard Road between Thorpe Thewles and Wolviston. From A19 onto A689 into Wolviston village, take Wynyard Road heading towards Thorpe Thewles, ground on left before Sir John Halls Estate. Or, from A1(M) to Stockton direction, turn left at Thorpe Thewles along Wynyard Road, ground on right after Sir John Halls Estate. All public transport to Billingham town centre just under one mile from ground.
Seats: None **Cover:** 200 **Capacity:** 2,000 **Floodlights:** No **Founded:** 1910
Colours: Royal/white/royal **Change:** Scarlet/white/scarlet. **Nickname:** Wolves
Prev. Name: Wolviston St Peters 10-46 **Prev. Lges:** Stockton & Dist. 46-82/ Teesside 82-88.
Previous Grounds: Greenwood Rd, Billingham (5 years)/ Billingham Community Centre (10 years).
Programme: 8 pages, 20p **Editor:** Secretary or Ben Foreman (0642 550352).
Sponsors: R.C.I. Industrial Cleaners **Rec. Gate:** 500 v Middlesbrough 27/7/93 **Club Shop:** No.
Midweek home matchday: Wednesday **Reserve team's League:** Stockton & District.
Record win: 13-0 v Ministry of Defence F.C.
Record defeat: 1-8 v South Shields
Clubhouse: Licensed bar. Tea room. Lounge. Hot & cold meals, sandwiches, crisps, soft drinks. Open 11am-11pm on matchdays.
Players progressing to Football League: Peter (Pike) Atkinson (Grimsby), David Hockaday (Blackpool, Swindon), Ken McCue (Blackpool), Kenny Lowe (Hartlepool), Laurie Duff (Leicester).
Club record scorer: Bob Easby 54 **Club record appearances:** Bob Easby 300+.
Captain 92-93: Colin Stott **Top Scorer 92-93:** Chris Hayes 31 **P.o.Y. 92-93:** Martin Oakley.
Hons: Wearside Lg Div 2 89-90 (Lg Cup R-up 92-93), Teesside Lg R-up 84-85 (R.T. Raine Cup 86-87), Stockton & District Lg 73-74 75-76 76-77 (Lg Cup 72-73 74-75 77-78, Lg Charity Cup 79-80).

Wolviston's 1992-93 League Cup final squad.

DIVISION TWO CLUBS 1993-94

BIRTLEY TOWN

Chairman: J Heslington   **Press Officer:** Secretary
Secretary: Richard Barrett, 16 Coldstream, Ouston, Chester-le-Street DH2 1LQ (091 410 7395).
Treasurer: G Johnson   **Ground:** Birtley Welfare Ground.
Directions: (From Durham) Along Birtley High Street past Red Lion, Fire Station first left at junction on bottom of the bank, 1st left again through gates to childrens park, ground adjacent.
Colours: Green & white hoops/white/white   **Change:** White/grey/black.
Hons: Northern Alliance 23-24 (R-up 13-14).

ESH WINNING ALBION

Press Off./Secretary/Treasurer: Dennis R Fort, 8 Durham Rd, Esh Winning, Durham DH7 9NW (091 3734292).
Chairman: Keith Wardman   **Ground:** Esh Winning Welfare.
Directions: From Nevilles Cross take A690 (Crook) to bottom of Nevilles Cross Bank (Stone Bridge Inn). Right onto B6302 thru Broompark and Ushaw Moor, and on to Esh Winning. Ground at rear of South Terrace (first row of houses as you enter Esh).
Colours: Amber/black/black   **Change:** Green/white/white   **Founded:** 1986
Prev. Name: Esh Winning Pineapple 86-91 **Prev. League:** Crook & District 86-89.
Hons: Colin Waites Cup 88-89, Monkwearmouth Charity Cup R-up 91-92.

Esh Winning Albion F.C. 1992-93. Photo - Andrew Mollitt.

GUISBOROUGH PRIORY

Founded: 1993   *(all other details as per Guisborough Town F.C. (page 992))*

HEBBURN D.T.

Chairman: P Hedley   **Treasurer:** P Breeze.
Secretary/Press Officer: Mr J Haswell, 16 Troon Close, Washington NE37 2LN (091 415 3329).
Manager: T Manson   **Asst Manager:** D Tate   **Coach:** J Carney.
Physio: Moira Short   **Commercial Manager:** G McHugh (0091 483 7114).
Ground: Metupa Park, Monkton Stadium, Jarrow.
Directions: A1(M) to Newcastle, at White Mare Pool take A194 for South Shields, pass r'bout, after half mile take B1516 for Jarrow along Fork Avenue. At end of dual c'way turn left and follow signs to Monkton Stadium. From A19 take second slip road after Tescos onto A194 for Gateshead. Monkton Stadium signed.
Colours: White (navy stripe)/navy/white   **Change colours:** All royal
Seats: None   **Cover:** No   **Floodlights:** No   **Reformed:** 1990   **Nickname:** None
Previous Grounds: None.   **Prev. Names:** Victoria Park/ Hebburn Colliery (pre-1993).
Previous Leagues: Shields & Dist. 1899-1900/ Gateshead & Dist. 00-09/ Wallsend Amtr 09-13/ Newcastle & Dist. 13-18/ Northern Alliance 18-25/ Mid-Tyne 25-39/ Tyneside/ Business Houses/ Washington Amtr.
Players progressing to Football League: Ned Barkas (Huddersfield), John Wigham (Hartlepool), Jack McQuillam (Hull), David Wilson (Hamilton Academicals).
Prog: 20 pages, 50p with entry   **Editor:** G McHugh (091 483 7114)   **Club Shop:** No.
Sponsors: Dougies Tavern   **Record Gate:** Unknown.   **Clubhouse:** No.
Midweek home matchday: Wednesday   **Reserve team:** None.
Club record scorer: P Duggan   **Club record appearances:** J Donaghy.
Captain 92-93: B Kilford   **Top Scorer 92-93:** P Duggan   **P.o.Y. 92-93:** J Donaghy.
Hons: Tyneside Lg(3) 28-31, Mid-Tyne Lg(2) 25-27, Durham F.A. Trophy R-up 91-92.

MARCHON

Chairman: Neil Fennel   **Press Officer:** Secretary
Secretary: Harry Upton, 14 Foxhouses Road, Whitehaven CA28 8AF (0946 61750)
Treasurer: Steve Gibbons   **Ground:** Albright & Wilson, Whitehaven Works
Directions: From Cockermouth turn off A66 onto A595 and enter Whitehaven. Follow 'Town Centre' A5094 then zig zag through one way system following 'St Bees' B5345. Fork right up hill at junction signed 'Sandwith and Marchon Works'. Ground on right or main road beyond works at top of hill. Two miles from Bransty (BR).
Seats: None   **Cover:** 50   **Capacity:**   **Floodlights:** No   **Founded:**
Colours: Blue/black/blue   **Change colours:** White/blue/white
Previous Leagues: West Cumberland/ Carlisle & District/ Cumberland.
Previous Name: Haig Colliery   **Clubhouse:** Works Social Club. Normal hours.

MURTON INTERNATIONAL

Chairman: Mr T Pratt   **Manager:** Kevin Speight.
Sec./Press Off.: John Collings, 7 Station Rd South, Murton, Seaham, Co. Durham SR7 9RS (091 526 4906).
Founded: 1992   **Ground:** As Murton (see page 994).
Cols: All white   **Change colours:** All red   **Previous Leagues:** None.
Programme: No.   **Club Shop:** No.   **Previous Grounds:** None.   **Nickname:** The Nash
Captain & P.o.Y. 92-93: John Vine   **Top Scorer 92-93:** Jason Lennox
Club record scorer: Jason Lennox   **Club record appearances:** David Lowes. **Hons:** None.

NEWCASTLE CITY

Chairman: Kami Kundi   **Press Officer:** Tom McClements/ Shindi Dhugga.
Secretary: Satinder Dhugga, 15 Casteway, Dinnington, Newcastle-upon-Tyne NE13 7LS (091 661 821506).
Treasurer: Dav Mattu   **Ground:** Broadway East, Gosforth.
Directions: A1 turning off at Gosforth, Fawdon, follow signs for Fawdon leading to Kingston Park Rd, pass 1 set of lights, left at mini-r'bout, 1st left to ground. Through town over Tyne Bridge take Gosforth turn off, thru Gosforth High Street, pass ASDA (on right), main r'bout, left at Broadway West, ground 400yds on right.
Colours: Yellow/blue/yellow   **Change:** Blue/blue/yellow   **Founded:** 1993.

NORTHALLERTON TOWN SUPPORTERS

Secretary: Trevor Arnold, 55 Ullswater Drive, Acklam, Middlesbrough TS5 7DJ (0642 823923).
Ground: As Northallerton Town (see page 995).   **Founded:** 1992
Colours: Black & white stripes/black/black   **Change colours:** All yellow

NORTH ORMESBY SPORTS

Chairman: Geoffrey Cane   **Founded:** 1993.
Secretary: Simon Egan, 11 Lambourne Drive, Denepark, Marton, Middlesbrough (0642 313235).
Treasurer: Martin Gibb   **Ground:** Vicarage Playing Fields, Ormesby Rd (0609 772418).
Cols: Black & red halves/black/black   **Change:** Yellow & green halves/green/yellow.

SOUTH SHIELDS COUNTY KITCHENS BRINKBURN

Chairman: Barry Raper   **Press Officer:** Graham Carlton (091 456 2835).
Secretary: Martin Lynn, 261 Sunderland Rd, South Shields (091 455 5145)
Manager/Coach: G Charlton   **Treasurer:** Dean Apes.
Ground: Brinkburn Comprehensive School, Harton Lane, South Shields.
Directions: A19, left filter for South Shields, right at 1st r'bout onto A194, 200yds right onto John Reid Rd (A1300), 2 miles to 3rd r'bout, 1st left after r'bout into Temple Park Rd to Grey Hen pub, left into Harton Lane, ground 150yds on left - concealed entrance.
Colours: Red/navy/red   **Change colours:** All blue
Prev. Lge: Northern Alliance (pre-1993)   **Hons:** Northern Alliance Amateur Cup R-up 91-92.

STANLEY UNITED

President: W Westgarth   **Treasurer:** Secretary
Sec./Manager/Comm. Mgr/Press Off.: J V Kirkup, 71 Scripton Gill, Brandon, Durham DH7 8BQ (091 3780921)
Physio: J Burn.   **Asst Manager/Coach:** K Finnegan
Ground: High Road, Stanley, near Crook (nicknamed Hill Top Ground).
Directions: From Teeside on A689 to Bishop Auckland and onto Crook, turn left at Market Place then first right for Tow Law to Billy Row and Stanley, right at top of bank then first left, ground is 250 yards on left. From Tyneside and Sunderland; to Durham city onto A698 westbound thru Langley Moor, thru Brancepeth Village, turn right onto Oakenshaw/Tow Law road for approx. 3 miles, turn right at junction, right opposite Post Office in Stanley after half mile, ground is 250 yards on left
Seats: None   **Cover:** 300   **Capacity:** 3,000   **Floodlights:** No   **Founded:** 1890.
Colours: Red & white stripes/black/red   **Change colours:** Sky/navy/navy   **Nickname:** The Nops
Previous Name: Stanley Nops 1880-1890.   **Record Gate:** 5,000 v Leytonstone, FA Amateur Cup QF.
Previous Leagues: Mid-Durham/ Crook & District/ South Durham Alliance (all pre-1910)/ Northern 10-36 45-74/ Durham Central 36-45/ Durham City & Dist. 74-88.
Players progressing to Football League: Geoff Strong (Liverpool, Arsenal), Tommy Cummins (Burnley), Dickie Dale & Eli Ashurst (Birmingham), Jackie Brown & John Wilkinson (York), Gordon Bradley & Fred Batty (Bradford PA), Archie Brown (Sunderland), Jackie Howarth (Chelsea, Aldershot), John Birbeck (Norwich), Alan Ball (Queen of the South), Dickie Smart Exeter, Bill McKay (Bolton), Ed Holmes (Barnsley).
Programme: No   **Club Shop:** No, but club jerseys, polo shirts and training tops available from secretary.
Sponsors: Company Cars Direct   **Clubhouse:** Open matchdays. Fast food & light refreshments.
Midweek home matchday: Mon/Wed   **Reserve team:** None.
Record transfer fee paid: Nil   **Received:** Undisclosed for Geoff Strong (Arsenal, 1958).
Capt. 92-93: Stephen Thompson   **Top Scorer 92-93:** Alan Briggs   **P.o.Y. 92-93:** Gregory Thompson.
Hons: Northern Lg 45-46 61-62 63-64 (R-up 62-63, Lg Cup 46-47 57-58 61-62), FA Cup 1st Rd 53-54, FA Amtr Cup SF 19-20, Durham Challenge Cup 41-42 (Amtr Cup 00-01 05-06), Wearside Lg John McGrath Mem. Tphy (Fair-Play award) 92-93. *Club champions of all league entered except Wearside Lge.*

SUNDERLAND FULWELL MYERS

President: John V Holtan   **Chairman:** Rob Craggs   **Vice Chairman:** Colin Dagg.
Press Off./Sec./Comm. Mgr: Alan Harrison, 40 Castleview, Castle Town, Sunderland SR5 3EA (091 549 5404)
Manager: Ian Peary   **Coach:** Tom Middlemass   **Treasurer:** Billy Gibson.
Ground: Northumbria Centre, Washington, Tyne & Wear.
Directions: From A19 take A1231 to Washington, A195 for District 12, right at 3rd r'bout, ground on left.
Seats: No   **Cover:** No   **Floodlights:** No   **Clubhouse:** No   **Founded:** 1985.
Colours: All blue   **Change:** Red & white/red/red   **Nickname:** None.
Programme: 20 pages, 30p   **Editors:** Ian Peary/ Mark Harrison   **Club Shop:** No.
Sponsors: Myers Tools   **Previous Ground:** Monkwearmouth School 85-91.
Midweek home matchday: Wednesday   **Previous League:** Wearside Combination 87-91.
P.o.Y. 92-93: Barry Christie.   **Prev. Names:** R & J Carpets/ S'land Flo-Gas Fulwell (pre-'93)
Captain 92-93: Chris Holtan   **Top Scorer 92-93/ Club Record Scorer:** Robert Johnson.
Hons: Wearside Combination 90-91 (Div 2 R-up 89-90, Div 3 R-up 88-89), Jollies Cup 88-89, J S Pears Memorial Trophy 88-89 89-90, C.E.F.A.S. Div 2 88-89.

SUNDERLAND TRADELINK D.I.Y.

Chairman: Colin Prior   **Press Officer:** Robert Page (091 528 9409).
Secretary: William I Shepherd, 16 Fairmead Way, South Hylton, Sunderland SR4 0LY (091 534 4127)
Treasurer: Mark Richardson   **Ground:** Y.M.C.A., Herrington Burn.
Directions: On end of B1286 in Herrington Burn - 1st left off r'bout next to Y.M.C.A.
Colours: Blue & white/blue/blue   **Change colours:** Red & white/black/red
Previous League: Washington League (pre-1993).

USWORTH VILLAGE

Press Off./Treasurer/Sec.: Steven Cullen, 302 Leechmere Rd, Tunstall, Sunderland SR2 9DF (091 5226164).
Ground: Houghton Complex.
Directions: A690 for Durham from A19, A182 slip road for Washington town centre, 1st left at next r'bout, 1st right, 2nd left to Leyburn Grove.
Colours: Red/black/black   **Change colours:** All sky.
Previous Names: David Brown FC/ Mountain Daisy 85-87/ Castle View 87-90.
Previous Leagues: Wearside Apprentices/ Wearside Comb. 72-79/ North Eastern Amtr 79-88/ Washington 88-90.
Hons: Wearside Comb. R-up 78-79, GHB Eltringham Tphy 85-86, North Eastern Amtr Lg 87-88.

WASHINGTON GLEBE

Chairman: Frank Lanaghan   **Press Officer:** Secretary
Secretary: Robert Robson, 24 Talbot Close, Glebe, Washington NE38 7RH (091 4151893).
Treasurer: Graham Thirlaway   **Ground:** Washington Glebe Welfare.
Directions: A1 them A19, A1231 into Washington, 3rd exit road (signed Gateshead A195), turn for District 9 at r'bout, right for Washington Village at next r'bout, right at 1st T-jnct., pitch 200 yds on right.
Colours: Blue & white   **Change colours:** All red.

WASHINGTON NISSAN

Chairman: Colin Dodge   **Press Officer:** Secretary
Secretary: Harry English, 159 Alston Crescent, Seaburn Dene, Sunderland SR6 8NF (091 5487194)
Treasurer: Tom Dixon   **Ground:** Nissan Spts Complex.
Directions: Northwards along A1 (M) use A690 (sign post Sunderland) to connect with A19, travel north on A19, after passing the A1231 turn off the plant is on the left. Go past plant and follow signs for 'Nissan Offices'. Southwards along A19 and leave A19 at signpost for 'Nissan Offices'.
Colours: White/blue/white   **Change colours:** Red/red/blue
Founded: 1988   **Hons:** Wearside Lg Cup R-up 91-92 (Div 2 Cup 92-93), Nissan European Tphy 88-89.

WINGATE MALL

Chairman: Joe Bannister   **Press Officer:** Ray Morton
Secretary: Richard Hayes, 40 Tyrone Road, Fairfield, Stockton on Tees TS19 7JW (0642 588900).
Treasurer: John Malcolm   **Ground:** Welfare Park, Wingate
Directions: From North A19 to A181 junct. South A19 to A179 junct. From Durham A181; to B1280, Front Street, Wingate turn right at Queens Head Public House. Ground 400 yards ahead through Market Crescent.
Colours: Red/white/red   **Change colours:** Sky/navy/sky.
Previous Names: Wingate St Marys, Wingate Wanderers merged in 1967 to form Wingate FC. This club then merged with Billingham Cassel Mall in 1992.
Previous Leagues: Hartlepool & Dist. *(St Marys & Wanderers)*/ Wearside 67-87/ Auckland & Dist. 87-88. *Billingham Cassel Mall: Teesside (pre-1992).*
Hons: Wearside Lg R-up 78-79 (Lg Cup 69-70 (R-up 78-79), Div 2 Cup R-up 92-93), Monkwearmouth Charity Cup 77-78 83-84, Shipowners Cup R-up 67-68 78-79), Durham Chal. Cup R-up 73-74, J V Madden Cup 92-93, FA Cup 3rd Qual. Rd. *Cassel Mall: Teesside Lg 91-92.*

Stanley United F.C. 1992-93. Back Row (L/R): Kevin Bruce, Neil Wynd, Keith Burn, Graeme Dougherty, Graeme Ord, Darren Watson, Tony Ainley, Vince Kirkup (Secretary/Manager). Front: Phil Shaw, Mark Thompson, Gary Davison, Steve Thompson, Andrew Sugden, Graeme Priestley, Billy Reed.

'COURAGE' NORTHERN ALLIANCE

President: Sir John Hall (Newcastle United FC)
Chairman: R.M.Griffiths
Press Officer: Bill Gardner, 12 Coronation Road, Sunniside, Newcastle upon Tyne NE16 5NR
(091 4883422).

The Northern Alliance's 102nd season turned out to be one of the most competitive for many years. The Premier Division championship had to be settled by a play-off between old rivals Seaton Delaval and West Allotment Celtic with Celtic looking to complete a title hat-trick.

In the first shoot-out the sides fought out a 2-2 draw but, a week later Seaton Delaval claimed the championship with a 2-1 victory.

Longbenton clinched the Division One title and were chased home by Newbiggin who were only relegated from the top flight last year.

Amble Town enjoyed a brilliant spell in the Alliance in the decade from 1950 to 1960 and the club was recently resurrected. In only their second season back in the league's ranks the Town claimed the Division Two championship. The runners-up in the division were Gosforth Bohemians who are set to celebrate their centenary this year.

Premier Division outfit West Allotment Celtic enjoyed a successful campaign despite narrowly missing out on a third successive league championship. Celtic won the Northumberland Senior Bowl after six years of trying and also added the Northern Alliance League Cup to their trophy cupboard. The Premier Division Cup Final, traditionally staged on Newcastle United's ground, saw Seaton Delaval and Winlaton Hallgarth splash their way to a goal-less draw in monsoon conditions at St.James' Park. In the Benfield Park replay Delaval completed the first half of a notable cup and league double by winning 4-1 thanks mainly to a hat-trick by centre forward Rob Cross.

Division One champions Longbenton also managed the double by winning the division's Combination Cup but it took a replay of the final tie to settle the issue against North Shields St.Columbas.

County Kitchens Brinkburn were successful in the Division Two Amateur Cup Final where the beaten finalists were Swalwell Crowley. Brinkburn were near to adding the Durham FA Trophy to their cabinet but lost to Cockfield in the Ferens Park final. Alliance clubs north of the Tyne had better luck in County FA competitions. In addition to West Allotment's success in the Senior Bowl competition, Shankhouse turned on the style against league colleagues Wylam at Blue Star's Wheatsheaf Ground to lift the Northumberland FA Minor Cup.

Ponteland United, who enjoyed a tremendous run in the FA Vase, were disappointed by the decision of their 38-year-old top marksman Ian Crumplin to hang up his boots. After receiving an award from the North East's Sports writers at a dinner in Durham, Crumplin made his last appearance for United against West Allotment in the League Cup Final.

The league's officials and clubs were saddened by the sudden death during the season of their long-serving and dedicated President Stan Seymour. Sir John Hall accepted an invitation to be Stan's successor, continuing the tradition of friendly connections between the Northern Alliance and Newcastle United. **Bill Gardner (Press Officer).**

Seaton Delaval Amateurs - Division Premier Champions 1992-93. Photo: G.M.Ellis-Neville.

PREM. DIVISION

	P	W	D	L	F	A	PTS
Seaton Delaval	30	20	6	4	79	34	66
West Allotment	30	21	3	6	86	35	66
Carlisle	30	19	6	5	80	41	63
Morpeth	30	20	3	7	67	37	63
S.Terrace	30	18	1	11	74	46	55
Walker	30 .	15	5	10	75	52	50
Gillford Park	30	13	9	8	72	56	48
Ponteland	30	13	6	11	71	59	45
Haltwhistle	30	12	5	13	43	41	41
Winlaton	30	12	4	14	58	64	40
Spittal	30	12	3	15	55	54	39
Heaton	30	9	4	17	49	68	31
Wark	30	8	2	20	45	79	26
Blyth KB	30	7	5	18	50	100	26
Westerhope	30	5	7	18	36	66	22
Forest Hall	30	1	1	28	24	132	4

Championship Play-Off:
(at Benfield Park, Fri 21st & Mon 31st May)
Seaton Delaval 2, West Allotment Celtic 2
Seaton Delaval 2, West Allotment Celtic 1

DIVISION ONE

	P	W	D	L	F	A	PTS
Longbenton	30	21	4	5	105	38	67
Newbiggin C.W.	30	21	2	7	80	36	65
Benfield Park	30	19	3	8	84	42	60
St Columbas	30	16	6	8	63	50	54
NEI Reyrolle	30	14	7	9	76	60	49
Wylam	30	14	7	9	66	50	49
Swalwell	30	12	7	11	53	48	43
Procter & G.	30	11	8	11	61	59	41
Dudley	30	10	8	12	60	69	38
Percy Rovers	30	11	5	14	57	68	38
N. Counties	30	10	6	14	52	74	36
New York	30	8	8	14	49	62	32
Percy Main	30	9	5	16	52	70	32
Ryton	30	7	7	16	41	69	28
Hexham	30	5	6	19	36	94	21
N Electric	30	5	5	20	48	94	20

DIVISION TWO

	P	W	D	L	F	A	PTS
Amble	30	24	3	3	132	42	75
Bohemians	30	23	3	4	101	43	72
Ashington Hirst	30	23	3	4	104	52	72
Shankhouse	30	20	2	8	92	46	62
Co. K. Brinkburn	30	18	3	9	119	68	57
Marden	30	16	6	8	69	48	54
Highfield	30	13	3	14	73	76	42
KOSA *	30	12	7	11	58	69	40
Swalwell CC	30	12	3	15	70	74	39
D.H.S.S.	30	10	5	15	58	87	35
Newcastle University	30	9	6	15	58	57	33
Norgas	30	8	4	18	78	100	28
Stobswood	30	7	5	18	52	106	26
Heddon	30	6	7	17	43	74	25
New Winning	30	5	3	22	73	127	18
Wallsend	30	2	1	27	32	144	7

* - 3pts deducted.

PREMIER DIVISION RESULT CHART 1992-93

HOME TEAM	1	2	3	4	5	6	7	8	9	10	11	12	13	14	15	16
1. Blyth K. Brewster	*	1-5	2-1	3-2	0-2	2-4	1-2	2-6	1-6	2-3	0-3	2-2	2-0	1-2	4-2	6-3
2. Carlisle City	3-0	*	4-1	6-2	0-0	3-0	1-1	0-0	2-2	3-1	4-2	2-1	4-1	1-0	0-2	2-1
3. Gillford Park	10-2	2-2	*	6-0	1-0	5-2	1-1	2-0	0-0	3-2	4-2	0-3	3-1	1-1	3-1	2-0
4. Forest Hall	3-3	1-3	0-4	*	0-5	1-3	0-6	2-8	1-3	0-3	0-4	2-5	1-4	0-3	1-3	0-5
5. Haltwhistle C.P.	1-1	1-3	5-1	4-0	*	2-0	2-1	3-0	1-1	1-5	0-2	0-2	2-1	1-2	3-1	2-0
6. Heaton Stannington	3-4	0-4	4-5	4-1	3-0	*	0-0	1-4	1-4	1-5	2-3	4-0	0-1	0-2	2-2	1-0
7. Morpeth Town	7-1	4-2	3-1	6-1	1-0	2-1	*	2-0	1-3	1-0	4-0	3-2	3-0	1-1	2-0	2-1
8. Ponteland United	2-2	1-2	3-3	7-2	4-1	2-0	1-2	*	0-4	6-3	4-0	1-2	4-2	3-7	1-1	1-1
9. Seaton Delaval	2-1	1-4	2-2	5-0	2-2	1-2	2-1	2-1	*	4-0	3-2	3-0	1-1	2-3	2-0	4-2
10. Seaton Terrace	1-0	0-1	5-1	3-0	3-0	1-1	3-2	5-0	1-2	*	1-0	5-2	1-0	2-3	5-0	3-1
11. Spittal Rovers	0-1	1-4	1-1	3-0	0-0	2-1	1-3	4-1	0-2	3-0	*	2-4	6-2	2-2	2-1	0-1
12. Walker	11-1	3-7	1-0	6-0	1-0	3-0	2-3	1-1	2-3	4-3	0-3	*	9-1	1-2	3-2	1-1
13. Wark	3-1	3-2	2-2	4-2	0-1	2-3	1-3	1-3	1-5	1-4	2-0	0-2	*	3-4	1-0	2-3
14. West Allotment	5-1	3-1	1-2	8-0	4-0	4-2	0-1	0-1	2-1	1-2	2-0	0-1	5-0	*	0-0	5-3
15. Westerhope	1-1	3-3	2-2	0-1	2-1	3-4	0-1	0-1	1-3	2-4	1-1	0-2	1-5	*		1-0
16. Winlaton Hailgrath	5-2	3-2	4-3	5-1	0-3	0-0	2-1	2-5	0-2	2-1	3-1	2-2	3-2	0-4	5-3	*

DIVISION ONE RESULT CHART 1992-93

HOME TEAM	1	2	3	4	5	6	7	8	9	10	11	12	13	14	15	16
1. Benfield Park	*	2-3	7-3	1-6	1-0	0-2	2-1	7-1	2-0	0-1	3-1	2-1	3-0	4-1	1-2	2-2
2. Dudley Welfare	1-6	*	1-2	0-6	0-0	0-2	3-3	2-2	4-3	0-1	1-4	1-1	3-1	2-3	1-0	1-1
3. Hexham Swinton	0-3	1-0	*	0-4	1-0	1-3	2-2	1-3	2-3	0-2	0-1	1-2	0-4	1-2	0-3	0-3
4. Longbenton	1-5	0-1	12-0	*	2-2	4-1	0-0	4-2	4-3	4-2	2-0	7-0	0-0	1-1	3-1	5-3
5. NEI Reyrolle	2-2	2-5	9-2	2-3	*	3-2	2-1	3-3	5-0	3-0	6-3	2-5	3-1	1-1	2-3	0-5
6. Newbiggin C.W.	3-2	3-3	6-1	3-1	2-1	*	4-0	1-2	4-0	5-1	3-1	1-3	2-2	1-2	4-0	4-0
7. New York	0-3	3-4	1-1	0-3	2-2	1-3	*	3-1	3-1	4-0	5-0	1-1	1-1	0-4	1-4	0-4
8. Northern Counties	1-6	3-2	3-1	3-6	1-5	1-6	0-2	*	0-0	1-1	5-1	1-1	2-0	1-2	3-1	0-4
9. Northern Electric	0-3	1-5	2-2	0-3	2-2	0-2	1-4	3-7	*	6-1	1-0	1-2	2-2	3-1	2-2	0-3
10. Percy Main Amateurs	1-3	4-6	3-1	1-3	1-3	3-1	0-1	9-1	*		3-1	3-1	2-1	2-4	0-0	1-3
11. Percy Rovers	1-6	1-1	2-2	1-0	3-4	0-1	1-0	5-3	6-1	3-1	*	3-2	4-1	2-2	1-1	2-4
12. Procter & Gamble	4-2	1-1	1-2	0-4	1-4	0-2	5-0	4-1	5-2	1-1	1-4	*	5-0	0-1	5-3	1-1
13. Ryton	1-2	5-4	2-4	1-5	2-3	1-3	0-3	0-0	2-1	0-4	3-2	3-2	*	1-0	1-2	1-1
14. St. Columbas	0-3	3-1	2-6	2-3	2-1	2-2	2-0	4-1	2-2	5-0	1-1	4-2	*	3-1	1-2	
15. Swalwell	1-1	4-1	6-0	2-1	3-4	1-0	3-2	0-1	2-6	2-0	0-0	1-2	1-1	1-2	*	0-0
16. Wylam	2-0	1-3	2-2	1-3	2-0	2-3	2-3	1-0	3-2	5-2	1-4	3-3	1-2	4-2	0-3	*

DIVISION TWO RESULT CHART 1992-93

HOME TEAM	1	2	3	4	5	6	7	8	9	10	11	12	13	14	15	16
1. Amble Town	*	3-3	3-1	1-0	10-0	4-0	2-1	2-2	1-0	2-1	5-2	2-0	3-1	5-2	7-2	10-0
2. Ashington Hirst Progressive	3-1	*	3-1	3-3	5-3	1-3	2-3	3-2	3-0	3-1	7-2	2-5	0-1	5-3	6-4	5-0
3. Berwick Highfield	2-3	1-6	*	2-9	1-1	0-2	1-1	4-1	1-3	2-0	4-0	1-4	3-0	1-3	6-4	4-0
4. County Kitchen Brinkburn	3-6	2-4	10-4	*	2-3	4-2	5-0	2-5	1-3	5-4	5-2	2-1	4-1	3-1	6-4	3-1
5. Newcastle D.S.S.	0-3	2-4	2-1	2-2	*	2-6	2-0	1-5	1-1	1-1	3-7	3-6	6-0	1-2	2-2	4-3
6. Gosforth Bohemians	2-1	1-1	6-1	2-1	5-0	*	2-1	2-2	1-2	2-1	5-1	4-1	3-3	5-2	5-3	7-2
7. Heddon Institute	0-5	0-3	1-9	2-5	2-1	1-3	*	1-2	1-1	2-2	3-1	0-0	2-4	5-2	5-2	2-0
8. Marden Athletic	4-4	1-2	4-2	4-1	2-1	1-2	2-0	*	1-1	1-1	3-0	1-4	4-0	0-5	5-3	4-1
9. Monkseaton KOSA Robin Hood	2-8	2-3	0-4	1-5	4-3	0-5	2-2	0-3	*	1-1	2-1	1-2	6-3	3-1	2-1	4-4
10. Newcastle University	1-2	1-3	0-1	1-2	1-1	2-1	0-0	0-2		*	7-3	0-3	4-1	1-2	7-0	1-0
11. Norgas United	2-6	1-7	1-1	1-4	3-0	0-1	3-2	1-2	3-4	4-4	*	2-4	4-4	6-2	6-2	5-1
12. Shankhouse	3-4	0-2	5-0	2-2	6-3	5-0	2-1	0-1	3-0	2-0	3-0	*	0-2	3-4	6-1	9-1
13. Stobswood Welfare	0-9	2-3	0-3	0-6	0-2	0-1	1-1	1-0	2-5	2-4	0-11	1-3	*	4-4	4-2	8-0
14. Swalwell Crowley	2-0	2-3	1-2	0-5	0-2	1-3	1-1	3-2	2-0	1-3	5-0	0-1	1-1	*	4-3	8-1
15. Wallsend New Winning	3-7	2-4	2-3	1-11	1-2	0-5	3-1	1-2	3-3	1-0	2-3	2-5	12-5	2-5	*	3-2
16. Wallsend Rising Sun	0-13	0-5	1-7	1-6	2-3	1-10	3-1	0-3	0-3	0-4	2-4	3-4	0-2	3-1	0-1	*

LEAGUE CUP 1992-93

First Round (Premier clubs exempt)

Match	Score	Match	Score
Newcastle University v Hexham Swinton	7-1	Dudley Welfare v North Shields St Columbas	2-3
Northern Counties v Benfield Park	1-3	Ryton v Gosforth Bohemians	3-2
Northern Electric v Marden Athletic	5-3	Proctor & Gamble v Amble Town	0-5
Newcastle D.H.S.S. v Percy Main	2-3	Monkseaton KOSA v Wallsend R.S.	8-0
Swalwell v Wylam	1-2	Alnwick Percy Rovers v Shankhouse	0-5
Swalwell Crowley v Stobswood Welfare	6-0	Longbenton v Berwick Highfield	3-2
Newbiggin Central Welfare v Heddon Institute	6-0	Wallsend New Winning v New York	2-6
County Kitchens Brinkburn v N.E.I. Reyrolle	4-1	Norgas United v Ashington Hirst Progressive	2-4

Second Round

Match	Score	Match	Score
Walker v Northern Electric	3-2	North Shields St Columbas v Carlisle City	1-5
Heaton Stannington v Wylam	1-0	West Allotment Celtic v Percy Main Amateurs	4-1
Blyth Kitty Brewster v Winlaton Hallgarth	3-1	Longbenton v Ryton	4-2
Seaton Terrace v Benfield Park	3-0	New York v Morpeth Town	0-3
Shankhouse v Forest Hall	4-3	Wark v Gillford Park	6-7
Amble Town v Newcastle University	6-0	Ponteland United v Spittal Rovers	1-0
Haltwhistle Crown Paints v Newbiggin	1-0	Swalwell Crowley v Westerhope	0-4
County Kitchens Brinkburn v Seaton Delaval	1-4	Monkseaton KOSA v Ashington Hirst Progressive	2-6

Third Round

Match	Score	Match	Score
Ponteland United v Westerhope	3-2	Haltwhistle Crown Paints v Carlisle City	2-3
Amble Town v Seaton Delaval	2-3	Walker v Morpeth Town	0-1
Heaton Stannington v West Allotment Celtic	2-5	Gillford Park v Shankhouse	3-2
Blyth Kitty Brewster v Seaton Terrace	0-2	Ashington Hirst Progressive v Longbenton	5-1

Fourth Round

Match	Score	Match	Score
Morpeth Town v West Allotment Celtic	0-1	Ponteland United v Ashington Hirst Progressive	4-2
Gillford Park v Seaton Terrace	1-2	Carlisle City v Seaton Delaval Amateurs	1-0

Semi Finals

Match	Score	Match	Score
West Allotment Celtic v Seaton Terrace	8-1	Ponteland United v Carlisle City	2-1

Final: West Allotment Celtic 2, Ponteland United 0

PREMIER DIVISION CUP 1992-93

First Round

Match	Score	Match	Score
Seaton Terrace v Blyth Kitty Brewster	2-0	Forest Hall v Westerhope	1-0
Heaton Stannington v Walker	2-0	Wark v Winlaton Hallgarth	3-4
Ponteland United v Gillford Park	3-2	West Allotment Celtic v Haltwhistle Crown Paints	1-0
Spittal Rovers v Carlisle City	0-5	Seaton Delaval v Morpeth Town	4-0

Quarter Finals

Match	Score	Match	Score
Carlisle City v Ponteland United	0-1	Winlaton Hallgarth v Seaton Terrace	3-2
Forest Hall v Seaton Delaval	0-6	West Allotment Celtic v Heaton Stannington	4-2

Semi Finals

Match	Score	Match	Score
Seaton Delaval v West Allotment Celtic	2-0	Ponteland United v Winlaton Hallgarth	0-2

Final: Seaton Delaval 4, Winlaton Hallgarth 1 *(after 0-0 draw)*

DIVISION ONE COMBINATION CUP 1992-93

First Round

Match	Score	Match	Score
Benfield Park v New York	3-1	Hexham Swinton v North Shield St Columbas	0-6
Northern Electric v N.E.I. Reyrolle	0-5	Alnwick Percy Rovers v Swalwell	3-1
Ryton v Percy Main	1-5	Wylam v Northern Counties	2-1
Longbenton v Proctor & Gamble	2-0	Dudley Welfare v Newbiggin	1-5

Quarter Finals

Match	Score	Match	Score
Alnwick Percy Rovers v Longbenton	0-2	Benfield Park v North Shields St Columbas	2-5
Percy Main v Wylam	5-0	Newbiggin v N.E.I. Reyrolle	2-3

Semi Finals

Match	Score	Match	Score
Longbenton v Percy Main	2-0	North Shields St Columbas v N.E.I. Reyrolle	3-2

Final: Longbenton 4, North Shields St Columbas 1 *(after 1-1 draw)*

DIVISION TWO AMATEUR CUP 1992-93

First Round

Match	Score	Match	Score
Amble Town v Monkseaton KOSA	5-1	County Kitchens Brinkburn v Newcastle D.H.S.S.	2-1
Berwick Highfield v Norgas United	2-0	Ashington Hirst Progressive v Newcastle University	5-2
Wallsend New Winning v Gosforth Bohemians	5-4	Shankhouse v Marden Athletic	2-3
Swalwell Crowley v Stobswood Welfare	2-1	Heddon Institute v Wallsend Rising Sun	5-1

(continued overleaf)

(continued from page 1017) **Quarter Finals**

Amble Town v Ashington Hirst Progressive	1-3	Swalwell Crowley v Berwick Highfield	2-1
Marden Athletic v Heddon Institute	2-3	Wallsend New Winning v County Kitchens B.	4-13

Semi Finals

Heddon Institute v Swalwell Crowley	0-2	Ashington Hirst v County Kitchens Brinkburn	1-3

Final: County Kitchens Brinkburn 1, Swalwell Crowley 0

SEYMOUR CUP 1992-93

Final: Swalwell 1, N.E.I. Reyrolle 0
(Swalwell reached final by beating Stobswood Welfare 3-2 and Haltwhistle Crown Paints 2-1.

NORTHERN ALLIANCE PREMIER DIVISION TEN YEAR RECORD

	83/4	84/5	85/6	86/7	87/8	88/9	89/0	90/1	91/2	92/3
Blyth Kitty Brewster	-	-	-	-	-	-	-	-	11	14
Carlisle City	14	13	9	16	-	-	-	-	-	3
Carlisle Gillford Park	-	-	-	-	-	-	-	11	3	7
Dudley Welfare	2	1	11	12	6	12	15	-	-	-
Dunston Tyne Sports	-	-	1	2	15	4	13	-	-	-
Forest Hall	12	8	12	8	5	10	3	5	12	16
Gateshead Tyne					(see Dunston Tyne)					
Gorforth St Nicholas	-	14	14	4	3	-	-	-	-	-
Haltwhistle Crown Paints	11	15	-	-	-	-	12	13	9	9
Heaton Stannington	-	-	-	13	7	6	8	3	14	12
Morpeth Town	1	2	3	3	9	9	10	12	13	4
Newbiggin Colliery Welfare	-	-	-	-	12	5	4	8	16	-
Percy Main	13	12	13	11	11	13	6	15	-	-
Ponteland United	9	4	10	5	13	8	5	9	10	8
Prudhoe East End	6	3	2	7	2	-	-	-	-	-
Seaton Delaval Amateurs	8	5	8	15	8	3	1	4	4	1
Seaton Terrace	4	7	7	10	1	1	9	2	6	5
Spittal Rovers	-	-	-	-	-	-	-	-	5	11
Stobsood Welfare	3	10	16	-	-	15	-	-	-	-
Swalwell	-	-	-	14	14	7	11	6	15	-
Walker	-	-	-	-	-	-	-	7	2	6
Wallsend Town	10	9	15	-	-	-	-	-	-	-
Wark	-	-	-	-	-	11	14	14	8	13
West Allotment Celtic	5	6	5	1	4	2	2	1	1	2
Westerhope Hillheads	-	-	-	-	-	-	-	10	7	15
Wigton	7	11	6	9	10	14	7	-	-	-
Winlaton Hallgarth	-	-	-	-	-	-	-	-	-	10
Winlaton Queens Head	-	-	4	6	-	-	-	-	-	-
No. of clubs competing	14	15	16	16	15	15	15	15	16	16

Mick Bell of Seaton Delaval Amateurs bursts through the West Allotment defence. Seaton lost 1-2 away in this top-of-the-table clash on Easter Saturday, but ultimately took the title in a play-off. Photo - Gavin Ellis-Neville.

PREMIER DIVISION CLUBS 1993-94

BLYTH KITTY BREWSTER

Chairman: A Hall
Manager/Coach: T Lee
Secretary: J Norris, 28 Dene View Drive, Cowpen Estate, Blyth (0670 352940).
Press Off.: G Allon (0670 366079)
Ground: Tynedale High School, Blyth.
Directions: Comin north on Spine Rd take slip road signed Kitty Brewster Ind. Est., take right exit & follow signs, 1st left after mini-r'bout, school half mile on right.
Colours: Grey & maroon/maroon/maroon **Change colours:** Royal/white/royal.
Hons: Northern Alliance Div 1 90-91 (Div 2 88-89, Lg Cup R-up 90-91).

CARLISLE CITY

Chairman: G Walker
Manager: D Iveson
Coach: A Walker.
Secretary/Press Officer: J Ewbanks, 16 Lansdown Cres., Stanwix, Carlisle (0228 34623).
Ground: The Sheep Mount.
Directions: B6264 Brampton-Carlisle road (not A69) direst to Hardwick Circus, keep in righthand lane at r'bout and take far exit (Workington), dual c'way down hill (Carlisle Castle on right), where road intersects double back on yourself and take turning before castle, left and follow down hill, bear left as road divides, over to sports field.
Colours: All sky
Change colours: White/red
Hons: Northern All. R-up 75-76 76-77 77-78 79-80 (Div 1 91-92, Chal. Cup 75-76 (R-up 76-77), Comb. Cup 91-92).

CARLISLE GILLFORD PARK

Chairman: R Wilson
Manager/Press Officer: R Rutherford (0228 47476)
Secretary: J Carr, 7 Blackwell Rd, Currock, Carlisle CA2 4AB (0228 512030).
Coach: D Kenyon.
Ground: Gillford Park, Carlisle (0228 26649).
Directions: A69 to Rose Hill r'bout, straight over & 2nd left into Eastern Way, 1 mile to lights, left, 1st right Petrill Bank Rd, right at bridge, ground 200yds up this road.
Colours: All red
Change colours: White (black pin-stripe)/black.

HALTWHISTLE CROWN PAINTS

Chairman: J Jackson)
Manager/Coach: David Murray.
Secretary/Press Officer: R Skeet, 14 Westgate, Haltwhistle (0434 320703/ 321271).
Ground: South Tyne Park, Haltwhistle.
Directions: A69 to Haltwhistle, off Main Rd at sign for Hadrian Works, under rail bridge. Parking at Crown Paints car park.
Colours: All royal blue
Change colours: All yellow.

HEATON STANNINGTON

Chairman: W Pitt
Manager/Press Off./Coach: E Temple (091 270 0739).
Secretary: J R Groundsell, 73 Cleveland Gdns, High Heaton, Newcastle (091 266 7464).
Ground: Newton Park, Newton Rd, High Heaton, Newcastle.
Directions: From Newcastle; left at 'Corner House' pub lights into Newton Rd, left at r'bout for 30yds, ground on right behind shops. From South Gosforth; into Freeman Rd, pass Freeman Hosp., left at next r'bout, ground 250yds on left.
Colours: White/black/white
Change colours: Red/white
Hons: Northern Alliance Chal. Cup R-up 88-89.

LONGBENTON

Chairman: J Fawcett
Manager/Coach: A Bollado.
Press Officer/Secretary: G Minto, 43 Elizabeth Cres., Dudley, Cramlingham NE23 7AJ (091 250 1581).
Ground: Burradon Recreation Centre. **Directions:** From south: from r'bout at Sth Gosforth to r'bout at Killingworth on A189, left to Cramlingham, right at next r'bout, left at mini-r'bout into Burradon. From north: A189 to Annitsford, left to Burradon, ground behing houses.
Cols: Red & white stripes/white
Change colours: White/black.
Hons: Northern All. Div 1 92-93 (Div 2 R-up 89-90, Combination Cup 92-93).

MORPETH TOWN

Chairman: K B Beattle
Press Officer: R Griffiths (0670 516533).
Secretary: W Hollan, 7 North Leech, Lancaster Park, Morpeth (0670 511086).
Manager/Coach: B Penfold
Ground: Craik Park, Morpeth Common, Morpeth.
Directions: Morpeth signs off A1 onto A197, take B6524, right at Mitford sign, right after 1 mile into ground next to Morpeth Common.
Colours: Yellow/black
Change colours: Red (white trim)
Previous Ground: Storey Park, Morpeth (pre-1992).
Hons: Northern All. 83-84 (R-up 37-38 65-66 73-74 81-82 84-85, Chal. Cup 38-39 85-86 (R-up 36-37 62-63 73-74)).

PONTELAND UNITED

Chairman: F W Smith
Manager: P Lowery
Coach: W Charlton
Press Officer/Secretary: L McMahon, 1 Wardle Drive, Annitsford, Cramlingham (091 250 0463).
Ground: Ponteland Leisure Centre, Ponteland (0661 25441).
Directions: Left at lights entering Ponteland from Newcastle, ground 100m on left at Castle Ward Spts Centre.
Seats: None **Cover:** None **Capacity:** 3,500 **Floodlights:** No **Founded:** 1900.
Colours: Black & white stripes/black **Change colours:** Blue & red stripes.
Record Gate: 3,500 v Blyth Spartans, 1982-83.
Hons: Northern Alliance Lg Cup R-up 91-92 92-93 (Chal. Cup R-up 84-85 90-91).

SEATON DELAVAL AMATEURS

Chairman: R Westwood
Manager/Coach/Press Officer: K Scott (0670 714105)
Secretary: W Fellows, 52 Hastings Str., Klondyke, Cramlington (0670 731833).
Ground: Wheatridge Park, Seaton Delaval.
Directions: A189 from Newcastle, at Annitsford r'bout A190 to Seaton Delaval, left at r'bout entering village, ground 450yds on right next to Deal Garage and behind Market Garden. 3 miles from Cramlington BR station. Bus 363 from Newcastle passes ground.
Seats: None **Cover:** 200 **Capacity:** 6,000 **Floodlights:** No **Founded:**
Cols: White/red **Change colours:** All blue **Record Gate:** 6,000 on 1926.
Hons: Northern All. 89-90 92-93 (R-up 20-21, Chall. Cup 88-89 92-93).

SEATON DELAVAL SEATON TERRACE

Chairman: K Thompson **Manager/Coach:** I Watts
Secretary: J Mitchell, 7 Turnberry Way, Cramlington (0670 712577).
Press Officer: Secretary **Ground & Directions:** Bates Welfare, Seaton Delaval. Entering Seaton Delaval on A190 from Annitsford & Newcastle, turn right at roundabout. Ground approx 800 yds on right.
Club colours: Yellow/blue **Change colours:** Red/navy.
Hons: Northern All. 87-88 88-89 (Lg Cup 90-91, Chal. Cup 86-87 91-92).

SPITTAL ROVERS

Chairman: G Johnson **Manager/Coach:** W Young.
Secretary: D Burglass, 7-13 Wheatfield Place, Edingburgh EH11 3PE (031 3135235).
Press Officer: G Burn (0289 305835) **Ground:** Shieldfield Park, Berwick-on-Tweed.
Directions: A1 to r'bout signposting Berwick, follow to r'bout at Sports Centre, straight over, left immediately after after railway bridge up Shieldfield Terrace, ground 200yds on right.
Colours: Black & white stripes/black/red **Change colours:** Red/white/red.

WALKER

Chairman: R T McClellan **Manager/Coach/Press Off.:** R Mulroy (091 263 4237).
Secretary: Mrs S Gooding, 8 Stanmore Road, Heaton, Newcastle (091 276 0795).
Ground: Monkchester Recreation Ground. **Directions:** From City: Shields Rd to Union Rd, to Welbeck Rd, into Monkchester Rd, left into pitch (between houses) opposite Norbury Grove.
Club colours: White/black/black. **Change colours:** Green/green/black.
Hons: Northern Alliance Div 1 R-up 89-90.

WARK

Chairman: D Chrisholm **Manager:** K Glendinning **Coach:** J Wright
Secretary/Press Officer: J Armstrong, 12 St Michaels Mount, Wark, Hexham (0434 230382).
Ground: Wark Spts Field, Wark, Hexham (0434 230359).
Directions: Enter Wark, right at filling station over river bridge, turn right and ground is on right.
Club colours: Blue/white **Change colours:** Yellow/white.

WEST ALLOTMENT CELTIC

Chairman: J Mather **Manager/Coach:** D Taylor.
Secretary: J T Jackson, 4 Rosewood Crescent, Seaton Sluice, Whitley Bay (091 237 0416).
Press Officer: A Smailes (091 253 2172). **Ground:** Backworth Miners Welfare (091 268 1048).
Directions: From Newcastle, Old Coast Rd (A189) to Sth Gosforth, A191 to Holystone r'bout, A186 to mini r'bout at Shiremoor, left (B1322), ground 1 mile on left, entrance opp. Backworth Soc. Club. 2 miles Shiremoor Metro.
Seats: None **Cover:** None **Capacity:** 800 **Floodlights:** No **Founded:** 1928.
Club colours: All blue **Change colours:** All red.
Previous Ground: Farm Ground 1928-68. **Hons:** Northern Alliance 86-87 90-91 91-92 (R-up 88-89 89-90 92-93, Lg Cup 92-93, Challenge Cup 84-85 90-91), Northumberland Senior Bowl 92-93.

WESTERHOPE

Chairman/Press Off.: J Loan (091 267 9132) **Manager/Coach:** I Weatherburn
Secretary: B Patterson, 16 Burnstone, West Denton, Newcastle NE5 2EW (091 264 5211).
Ground: Cowgate Tavern Sports Ground, Ponteland Rd, Newcastle-upon-Tyne.
Directions: Kenton turn off A1, over Kenton r'bout & next 2 r'bouts, ground on right behind Co-op dairy.
Colours: White/white/blue **Change colours:** Sky & navy.
Hons: Northern All. Div 1 89-90. **Previous Ground:** Riverside Park, Newburn (pre-1993).

WINLATON HALLGARTH

Chairman: F Parker **Manager/Coach:** K Rides.
Secretary/Press Officer: G S Batey, 6 Wylam View, Winlaton (091 414 7970).
Ground: Shiblon Park, Blaydon. **Directions:** From north, over new A1 bridge to 1st slip road, take Swalwell and Consett road to r'bour, Blaydon Baths car park and ground 400yds on right.
Colours: White/navy/navy **Change colours:** All red.
Hons: Northern All. Lg Cup 91-92 (Div 1 R-up 91-92, Comb. Cup R-up 91-92).

FIRST DIVISION CLUBS 1993-94

AMBLE TOWN

Chairman: E Reymolds **Press Officer:** F Young (0665 712 820).
Secretary: R Falkous, 30 George Street, Amble, Morpeth, Northumberland NE65 0DW (0665 711041).
Manager/Coach: R Gibbard. **Ground:** Amble Welfare Park, Acklington Rd, Amble
Directions: From Ashington or Morpeth; north on A1068 entering Amble past industrial est. on right, over zebra crossing 100yds turn left before Masons Arms, follow as if you are going out of Amble. New Hassal Housing estate on right, turn left opp. Coquet High School car park. Pitch adjacent.
Colours: All tangerine **Change colours:** All blue.
Hons: Northern All.(5) 54-55 56-57 58-61 (Div 2 92-93, Chal. Cup 54-55 60-61 (R-up 37-38 59-60)).

DUDLEY WELFARE

Chairman: K Wake **Manager/Coach:** J Scragg
Secretary: C Hilliary, 68 Alexandra Way, Hall Cross Chase, Cramlingham NE23 6EB (0670 719604).
Press Off.: A Ord (091 250 2202) **Ground:** Dudley Welfare.
Directions: From Tyne Tunnel follow A1 to Moor Farm r'bout, A1 Morpeth road then 1st slip road, left at junction, ground on left opp. Owen Pugh. From Newcastle follow main Morpeth road as far as Seaton Burn flyover, take A1 in southerly direction (signed Tyne Tunnel), 1st slip road to r'bout then follow signs to Dudley and as above.
Colours: Green/white/green **Change colours:** Blue/white.
Hons: Northern Alliance 84-85 (R-up 83-84, Chal. Cup 83-84 (R-up 82-83)).

FOREST HALL

Chairman: G Vasey **Manager/Press Officer:** A Brannen (0670 590480).
Secretary: R Thompson, 57 Glebe Cres., Forest Hall, Newcastle (091 268 3753).
Coach: B Kipling **Ground:** Procter & Gamble Spts, Great Lime Rd, Forest Hall.
Directions: From West Moor, east along Great Lime Rd towards Whitley Bay, ground on north side 150yds past Musketeer pub. A1 (Morpeth road) from Tyne Tunnel, left towards next at r'bout with A191 Whitley Bay road, right onto Great Lime Rd, ground on north side just under a mile.
Colours: All red **Change colours:** Black & white stripes **Hons:** Northern All. Chal. Cup R-up 89-90.

GATESHEAD NORTHERN COUNTIES

Manager/Coach: J Ferry   **Press Officer:** G Greenup (091 4604011)
Secretary/Chairman: A Skelton, 101 Tebay Drive, Denton Burn, Newcastle-upon-Tyne NE5 2XH (091 275 0228).
Ground: Wardley Welfare, Felling.
Directions: From Gateshead International Stadium to Heworth r'bout, across, left at slip road at Wardley Black Bull after 1km. A194, left at top of slip road, second right after 250m, ground 800m on right.
Colours: All blue   **Change colours:** All white

GOSFORTH BOHEMIAN

Chairman/Press Officer: J Bell (091 268 3306)   **Manager/Coach:** P Rowntree.
Secretary: B Dale, 118 Newton Road, Newcastle (091 281 1403)
Ground: Benson Park, Brunton Park Estate, Gosforth
Directions: Turn off Great North Road after passing Gosforth Rugby Club into Polwarth Drive. 2nd left into Layfield Road then 1st right into South Ridge Ground 50 yards on left (concealed entrance between houses)
Colours: Red & white/black   **Change colours:** Blue/black   **Founded:** 1893.
Hons: Northern Alliance Div 2 R-up 92-93.

HEBBURN REYROLLE

Chairman: F Hopkins   **Manager/Coach:** G Taylor.
Secretary: G Taylor, 29 Crawley Ave., Hebburn NE31 2LT (091 483 4537).
Press Officer: A Graham.   **Ground:** Hebburn Sports Ground, Victoria Road West, Hebburn.
Alternative ground: South Tyneside College, Mill Lane, Hebburn.
Directions: From Newcastle along Felling by-pass, Heworth r'bout take Hebburn/Jarrow road, ground two and a half miles on left. College ground as above, but from Newcastle ground approx. 2 miles on right. From Tunnel ground approx. two and a half miles on left.
Colours: All royal blue   **Change colours:** Red/black/red.
Hons: Northern All. Seymour Cup R-up 92-93.
Previous Name: Hebburn N.E.I. Reyrolle (pre-1993).

HEXHAM SWINTON

Chairman: D Tiffin   **Press Officer:** P Rutherford (0434 606161 ex4288)
Secretary: D Tiffin, 8 Valebrook, Hexham, Northumberland NE46 2BQ (0434 604573).
Manager/Coach: D Soulsby   **Ground:** Wentworth Park, Hexham.
Directions: A69 to Hexham r'bout, left towards Hexham, follow to mini-r'bout, straight over and 1st left into car park. Ground opposite Hexham BR station (Carlisle-Newcastle line).
Colours: All red   **Change colours:** White/red/red.

NEWBIGGIN CENTRAL WELFARE

Chairman: H Callan   **Manager/Coach:** T F Charlton.
Press Officer/Secretary: W Cooper, 33 Spital Crescent, Newbiggin (0670 854941).
Ground: Newbiggin Central Welfare, Newbiggin.   **Directions:** Enter Newbiggin from Spine Road towards town centre. After 2nd zebra crossing ground on right after 200 yds just before school entrance.
Colours: White & blue/blue   **Change colours:** Red/black/black
Hons: Northern Alliance Chal. Cup R-up 46-47 88-89 (Div 1 R-up 92-93).

NEWCASTLE BENFIELD PARK

Chairman: J Rowe   **Manager/Coach:** D Thompson
Press Officer/Secretary: D Gates, 5 Winship Terrace, Byker, Newcastle (091 276 3049).
Ground: Benfield Park.
Directions: From Newcastle take 2nd exit after Corner House pub, right into Benfield Rd, ground on left in school grounds.
Colours: All white   **Change colours:** All blue.

NORTH SHIELDS ST COLUMBAS

Chairman: N Hooper   **Manager/Coach:** J Wall.
Secretary: A J Baird, 8 Beanley Crescent, Tynemouth (091 258 2375).
Press Off.: D Wall (091 253 0992)   **Ground:** Appletree Pk, Preston Ave., North Shields.
Directions: Coast road to Tynemouth swimming baths, right to North Shields, 2nd left after school into Preston Ave., ground on left after Rugby Club.
Colours: All white   **Change colours:** Green & yellow stripes/green.
Hons: Northern Alliance Combination Cup R-up 92-93.

PERCY MAIN AMATEURS

Chairman: E Beasley   **Mgr/Coach/Press Off.:** R McCullough (091 295 0017)
Secretary: A Purvis, 81 Elsdon Terrace, Percy Main, North Shields NE29 7AS (091 257 7150).
Ground: St John's Green, Percy Main.
Directions: Nth Shield road from Tyne Tunnel past Duke of Wellington, 2nd left after half mile, ground on right. From North and West turn off coast road at Formica factory, right down Norham Rd to Percy Main Social Club, road to Percy Main Village at r'bout, after half mile left at St John's Terrace. Ground on left past church.
Colours: Claret & blue/blue   **Change colours:** Red & white/black.
Hons: Northern Alliance 80-81 81-82 (R-up 82-83, Lg Cup 71-72, Chal. Cup R-up 79-80 86-87).

PERCY ROVERS

Chairman: P Davies   **Manager/Coach:** T Miller
Press Officer/Secretary: I Arkle, 5 Tanners Garth, Alnwick (0665 510105)
Ground: Duchess High School Cricket Field, Alwnside, Alnwick.
Colours: Black & blue stripes/black/black **Change colours:** White/black/black
Hons: Northern All. Div 2 R-up 91-92   **Previous Name:** Percy Roverrs Alnwick (pre-1993)

PROCTER & GAMBLE (NEWCASTLE)

Chairman: W J Darby   **Manager/Coach/Press Secretary:** B Hudson (091 2668239).
Secretary: T Gannie, 11 Barrass Mews, Segehill, Northumberland NE23 7NZ (091 237 5319).
Ground: Longbenton Community High School.
Directions: From Newcastle, Benton Rd to Four Lane Ends metro station, continue to 2nd r'bout, right into Goathland Ave., ground and school at end.
Colours: Red & blue/blue   **Change colours:** All red.
Hons: Northern Alliance Div 2 90-91.

RYTON

Chairman: H Taylor   **Manager/Coach:** A Patterson.
Press Off./Secretary: L Robson, 31 Park View Gdns, Runhead, Ryton (091 413 7628).
Ground: Clara Vale Recreation Ground.   **Directions:** Thru Ryton to Crawcock crossroads, right 50yds down
road, right at T-junction, entering Clara Vale ground is signposted.
Colours: Blue & black stripes/black   **Change colours:** Orange/black.

SWALWELL

Chairman: T Todd   **Manager/Coach:** M Falcus.
Secretary: S Sibbald, 33 Affleck Street, Gateshead NE8 1QR (091 477 0064).
Press Officer: S Boe (091 482 4824).   **Ground:** Avenue Ground, Hexham Road, Swalwell.
Directions: From Newcastle cross river by Redbeugh Bridge, take A69 (Western bypass) for 3 miles, 1st left after
Metro Centre. Right at r'bout, after half mile ground on right just past Fewsters and opposite Blaydon Rugby Club.
Colours: Red & white/red & black   **Change colours:** All blue
Hons: Northern Alliance Lg Seymour Cup 92-93.

WYLAM

Chairman: I Slowther   **Manager/Coach:** J Gordon.
Secretary: J Pearson, 12 Holeyn Hall Rd, Wylam, Northumberland NE41 8BB (0661 853353).
Press Officer: G Bowmer (0661 852035). **Ground:** Wylam Playing Fields.
Directions: From Newcastle, A69 Hexham road to Wylam turn, into village, left opp. bus shelter by Black Bull
heading towards Fox & Hounds. Pitch opposite.
Colours: Red & blue stripes   **Change colours:** Yellow/black/white.
Hons: Div 2 R-up 90-91.

SECOND DIVISION CLUBS 1993-1994

ASHINGTON HIRST PROGRESSIVE

Chairman: J S Evans   **Press Officer:** A Johnson (0670 816464).
Secretary: G Gibbons, 41 Hawthorn Road, Ashington (0670 815218).
Manager/Coach: G Gibbons/ O O'Neill.
Ground: Ashington High School, Green Lane, Ashington.
Directions: From Spine Rd, Ashington turn off at Woodhorn, A197 at next 2 r'bouts, left at next r'bout, at end turn
right, then left down Park Rd, school 500yds on right.
Cols: Yellow/green **Change colours:** Red/white   **Hons:** Northern Alliance Amateur Cup 91-92.

GATESHEAD DURHAM RANGERS

Chairman: K Wood   **Manager/Coach:** A Mahon
Press Officer/Secretary: M Thornton, 23 Wealcroft, Leam Lane Est., Gateshead NE10 8LJ (091 438 2704)
Cols: Black & silver/black   **Ground:** As Gateshead Northern Counties (page 1021).
Change colours: All blue   **Previous League:** South East Northumberland (pre-1993).

HEDDON INSTITUTE

Chairman: A Smith   **Press Officer/Mgr/Coach:** B Tailford (0661 853314).
Secretary: N A D Anderson, 14 Aquila Drive, Heddon on the Wall (0661 853136)
Ground: Throckley Welfare, Throckley
Directions: A69 Newcastle take Throckley exit, turn left at roundabout approx. quarter mile, right into Poplar
Street, ground at end. Bus No. X82 and X83 from Eldon Centre, Newcastle to Throckley.
Colours: Maroon & blue   **Change colours:** All blue.

HIGHFIELDS UNITED

Chairman: B Weatherburn   **Manager/Coach/Press Officer:** S Roughead (0289 308162).
Secretary: B Dytor, 43 Newfields, Berwick-on-Tweed (0289 305342).
Ground: Pier Field, Berwick-on-Tweed.
Directions: A1 to Berwick centre, right down High Str., keep right of Town Hall, right into Hide Hill, left at bottom
into Silver Str., straight over staggered crossroads, follow road along river bank to clifftops carpark.
Colours: Blue/white/red   **Change colours:** Red/white/red.

MARDEN ATHLETIC

Chairman: G Clark   **Manager/Coach:** D Williams.
Secretary: A Pattison, 74 Bamborough Terrace, North Shields (091 259 2389)
Ground: Valley Garden School, Monkseaton
Directions: From Coast Road follow signs for Whitley Bay, along Seatonville Road, turn right at Cannon Cinema
r'bout, left after Monkseaton Arms Pub into Rolton Terrace.
Colours: White/black/black   **Change colours:** Blue & white.
Previous Ground: Churchill Playing Fields, Whitley Bay (pre-1993).

MONKSEATON K.O.S.A. ROBIN HOOD

Chairman: J Graham   **Manager/Coach:** P McBride
Press Officer/Sec.: R A Woods, 15 Rayleigh Drive, Wideopen, Newcastle-upon-Tyne (091 236 2988).
Directions: From Newcastle Coast Road to Tynemouth Swimmming Baths, left at r'bout and proceed to r'bout at
Foxhunters Pub, turn right at this roundabout and left at next r'bout. School ground is 150 yards on left
Colours: Yellow/green/yellow   **Change colours:** Green/black/white.

NEWCASTLE D.H.S.S.

Chairman/Press Officer: R G Blenkinsopp (091 416 5469).
Secretary: L Procter, 4 Alcombe Crescent, Red House Farm Estate, Newcastle-upon-Tyne (091 285 3320).
Manager/Coach: S Lakey   **Ground:** Darsley Park, Longbenton.
Directions: Bus or Metro to Four Lane Ends, Benton. Grounds half mile along Old Whitley Rd towards coast.
Colours: All red   **Change colours:** Sky/navy.   **Previous Lge:** Tyneside Amateur (pre-1992).

NEWCASTLE NORGAS UNITED

Chairman: M Hopper   **Press Officer:** P Benson (091 268 5100).
Secretary: C R Hogg, 43 Falkirk, Highfields, Killingworth (091 268 3935)
Manager/Coach: M Granh   **Ground:** Whitley Park, Whitley Road, Benton.
Directions: Bus or Metro to Four Lane Ends, Benton, park half mile along Old Whitley Rd on right (towards coast).
Colours: White/black/black   **Change colours:** Green/white/white.

NEWCASTLE UNIVERSITY
Secretary/Press Officer: M Rutherford, 110 Brighton Grove, Fenham, Newcastle-upon-Tyne (091 226 0615).
Chairman/Manager: P J Say.
Ground: Cochrane Park, Newcastle-upon-Tyne.
Directions: From Newcastle, left off coast road at 1st slip road after Corner House pub, right at next r'bout into Etherstone Ave., ground 400yds on left.
Colours: Blue/black/blue   **Change colours:** Red/black/red.

NORTHERN ELECTRIC (WALLSEND)
Chairman: R Veale   **Manager/Coach:** T Cornfoot.
Press Off./Secretary: I Thompson, 3 Frenton Close, Chapel House, Newcastle-upon-Tyne (091 264 4855).
Ground: Kings Park, Kings Rd South, Wallsend.
Directions: Coast road from Newcastle, 1st exit past Wills factory, across bridge over motorway, left along slip road to Monitor Eng., right down Kings Rd South, ground 150 yds on left. From coast; Wallsend turn off, bear left to T-junction facing Monitor Eng., then as above.
Colours: Sky & navy   **Change colours:** Orange & black.

ORWIN NEW WINNING (WALLSEND)
Chairman: S Pattinson   **Manager/Coach:** D Prest.
Secretary: A Gilroy, 67 South Terrace, Wallsend (091 263 1123).
Press Off.: K Gilroy (091 2639555)   **Ground:** Wallsend Sports Centre.
Directions: A1058 Newcastle coast road, Station Rd exit and follow signs for Wallsend Golf Course & Spts Centre.
Colours: All green   **Previous Name:** New Winning (Wallsend)(pre-1993).
Change colours: Red/white   **Previous Lge:** South East Northumberland (pre-1992)

SHANKHOUSE
Chairman: F Dobson   **Manager/Coach:** K Schooling
Press Officer/Secretary: S Ramsey, 6 Brinkburn Avenue, Cramlington (0670 715943).
Ground: East Hartford Welfare
Directions: Take A189 out of Newcastle to 3rd slip road after Moor Farm r'bout marked Cramlington Ind. Est. Morpeth A192 turn 1st left at r'bout at the top of the slip road. Approx. 1/2 mile down road turn right into East Hartford. The ground is situated on the left.
Colours: Yellow/blue   **Change colours:** Red & blue/blue
Hons: Northern Alliance 1892-93 (R-up 95-96), Northumberland Snr Cup 1885-86(joint) 86-87 90-91 92-93 93-94 94-95 (Minor Cup 1992-93).

SHILBOTTLE COLLIERY WELFARE
Chairman: G Brown   **Manager/Coach:** I Ford.
Press Off./Secretary: P Andrucci, 7 Kiln Lonnen, Shilbottle, Alnwick NE66 2UR (0665 575488).
Ground: Shilbottle Welfare Ground.
Directions: A1 north, right turn 3 miles south of Alnwick and follow signs to Shilbottle.
Colours: Green/white/green   **Change colours:** White/black/black
Previous Leagues: Northern Alliance 46-54/ North Northumberland 54-93.
Hons: North Northumberland Lg 91-92 (R-up 92-93, Anderson Cup 92-93).

STOBSWOOD WELFARE
Chairman/Press Officer: J W Rutherford (0670 790110).
Secretary: I Service, 41 Elizabeth Street, Widdrington, Morpeth NE61 5NW (0670 790110 - messages).
Manager/Coach: N Gibbard   **Ground:** Stobswood Welfare (0670 790609).
Directions: A1 to Morpeth, turn right over bridge and follow road to Widdrington, left at Karva Woodcraft, right after 300 yds, ground at bottom.
Colours: Green/black   **Change colours:** Yellow/blue
Hons: Northern All. Div 2 R-up 88-89 (Chal. Cup 82-83 (R-up 83-84)).

WALLSEND RISING SUN
Chairman: T Russell MBE.   **Press Officer:** G Brand (091 262 1409).
Manager/Coach/Secretary: G Tubman, 43 Regent Court, Wallsend (091 263 1829).
Ground: Rising Sun Welfare, Wallsend.
Directions: At top of Kings Road North. Right Swallow Spts Club. Buses 308 306 309 to Rising Sun Hotel.
Colours: All red   **Change colours:** All yellow.
Hons: Northern Alliance Chal. Cup R-up 58-59.

WESTMORLAND LEAGUE

DIVISION ONE	P	W	D	L	F	A	PTS
Kendal United	26	23	0	3	120	20	46
Keswick	26	22	2	2	89	32	46
Ambleside	26	17	4	5	82	45	38
Kirkby Stephen	26	14	4	8	59	51	32
Coniston	26	13	5	8	69	60	31
Kendal County	26	13	2	11	55	48	28
Appleby	26	12	4	10	59	66	28
Wetheriggs	26	10	6	10	53	47	26
Burnside	26	8	6	12	53	60	22
Kirkoswald	26	7	4	15	40	83	18
Staveley	26	5	7	14	29	52	17
Netherfield Res.	26	7	2	17	34	61	16
Windermere	26	3	4	19	35	88	10
Greystoke	26	1	4	21	28	92	6

DIVISION TWO	P	W	D	L	F	A	PTS
Keswick Res.	30	24	3	3	123	47	51
Penrith United	30	22	4	4	153	46	48
Sedbergh	30	23	2	5	105	54	46
Shap	30	20	6	4	95	44	46
Lunesdale United	30	13	10	7	74	51	36
Victoria Sporting	30	16	3	11	59	50	35
Ambleside Res.	30	12	5	13	57	75	29
Kendal United Res.	30	8	10	12	65	72	26
Braithwaite	30	10	6	14	49	73	26
Wetheriggs Res.	30	10	4	16	53	77	24
Burnside Res.	30	10	2	18	40	62	22
Kendal County Res	30	7	6	17	38	74	20
Consiston Res.	30	8	4	18	55	106	20
Kirkby Stephen Res.	30	8	3	19	66	96	19
Ibis	30	7	5	18	45	88	19
Windermere Res.	30	4	3	23	33	95	11

TSB BANK HEXHAM & NORTH TYNE LEAGUE

BY DAVID WALTON

Clubs had a restricted programme in the TSB Bank Hexham & North Tyne league playing only 14 league games; the lowest since the league formation in 1971 on the amalgamation of the Hexham & District league (1946) and the North Tyne league (1909). Champions for the past two seasons, Otterburn, and near neighbours Bellingham Town left to join the North Eastern Amateur league leaving only eight members.

Hexham Town, formed only in 1989, were champions for the first time and also reached a hat-rick of cup finals, a fine achievement for player-manager Arnie White.

The Subsidiary Cup was played on a group basis and the league committee also decided on a new points system of three points for a win and one for each goal scored to encourage attacking football.

In the league cup first round matches were played on a home and away basis second leg ties between Haltwhistle Red Star v Corbridge United and Haydon Bridge v Hexham Town were ordered to be replayed due to an infringement of rules. The results remained unaltered. The Clayton Charity Cup (1904) went to form apart from a 2-1 win by Haydon Bridge over Haltwhistle Red Star.

Haltwhistle Red Star, under manager Colin Tancock, had their best season since joining the league in 1989, finishing runners-up although their robust type of football did not win them many friends. Haydon Bridge improved on past seasons and won the knockout cup after being beaten finalists last season. They also finished fourth in the league.

At the end of the previous season doubts were expressed about the future of Corbridge United and Hexhamshire. Corbridge found themselves a new manager in former player Mal Burke but their form was mixed and they ended the season without a Trophy for the first time in seven seasons. Hexhamshire were under new management in player boss David Nixon and a new chairman Roy Walker. They had a poor start but their form improved and they turned in some useful performances.

Rochester, the only side in the league from the old North Tyne league, had a rough time of it and on some occasions could not turn out a full team although they did make an appearance in the Knockout Cup final. Whitfield finished the season bottom their worst season in many years they were also on the end of Haltwhistle Red Star's record win of 10-1.

In the D & P Trophies Northumberland FA Minor Cup clubs had mixed fortunes. Hexham Town and Haydon Bridge both made it to the third round and both lost to McEwans Northern Alliance teams, Hexham Town losing 2-0 to Alnwick Percy Rovers and Haydon Bridge suffering a 9-0 defeat away to eventual winners Shankhouse.

FINAL TABLE

	P	W	D	L	F	A	PTS
Hexham Town	14	12	2	0	54	14	26
Haltwhistle R.S.	14	8	3	3	52	35	19
Haltwhistle C.P.	14	7	3	4	31	22	17
Haydon Bridge	14	6	3	5	33	26	15
Corbridge United	14	5	4	5	36	32	14
Hexhamshire	14	4	1	9	21	37	9
Rochester	14	4	0	10	25	56	8
Whitfield	14	1	2	11	16	46	4

RESULT GRID

Corbridge Utd	*	1-4	1-4	2-2	1-4	0-0	4-2	3-1
Haltwhistle C.P.	2-1	*	0-0	0-3	4-0	1-3	4-1	2-0
Haltwhistle R.S.	3-3	6-6	*	0-3	4-1	4-8	6-1	10-1
Haydon Bridge	4-4	1-3	1-2	*	2-1	2-4	6-0	1-1
Hexhamshire	1-3	1-4	3-4	0-3	*	1-1	2-1	1-4
Hexham Town	2-0	3-0	4-1	4-1	4-0	*	2-0	4-2
Rochester	2-8	1-0	2-5	5-2	2-5	1-9	*	5-2
Whitfield	1-5	1-1	1-3	0-2	0-1	1-6	1-2	*

MATTHEW CHARLTON & SONS LEAGUE CUP

1st Round	1st Leg	2nd Leg
Hexham Town v Haydon Bridge	7-2	4-1
Rochester v Haltwhistle C.P.	3-6	0-7
Whitfield v Hexhamshire	1-4	1-1
Corbridge Utd v Haltwhistle R.S.	1-1	3-4

Semi-Finals

Haltwhistle R.S. v Hexham Town	3-8
Hexhamshire v Haltwhistle C.P.	2-4

Final

Haltwhistle C.P. v Hexham T. 0-0(aet)	5-4(pens)

CLAYTON CHARITY CUP

1st Round

Hexham Town v Whitfield	8-1
Hexhamshire v Rochester	3-0
Haltwhistle C.P. v Corbridge	2-1
Haydon Bridge v Haltwhislte R.S.	2-1

Semi-Finals

Haltwhistle C.P. v Haydon Bridge	2-1
Hexhamshire v Hexham Town	0-5

Final

Haltwhistle C.P. v Hexham Town	2-4

TSB BANK HEXHAM & NORTH TYNE FOOTBALL LEAGUE SUBSIDIARY CUP

Semi-Finals

Hexham Town v Haltwhistle C.P.	2-0
Haltwhistle R.S. v Hexhamshire	7-1

Final

Haltwhistle R.S. v Hexham Town	2-1

CROWN BERGER KNOCKOUT CUP

Semi-Finals

Hexhamshire v Rochester	3-4
Whitfield v Haydon Bridge	2-3

Final

Haydon Bridge v Rochester	3-0

NORTH NORTHUMBERLAND LEAGUE

President: H S Lancaster
Hon. Secretary: N Laidler,
29 Greyfield Est., Embleton, Alnwick (Tel: Embleton 343).

DARK HORSES WIN TITLE RACE

The 92-93 championship race proved to be one of the most close fought for many seasons with three clubs staking a good claim come the final weeks of the season. As it was, dark horses Alnmouth kept their nerve to pip 1992 champions Shilbottle C.W. with Braeside finishing a close third five points behind the champions.

1991 champions Wooler faced the agony of relegation, their place being taken by Second Division champions Ashington Reserves who took the title nine points ahead of Belford who make a quick return to Division One having been relegated the previous season.

On the cup front, Springhill reached all three domestic finals and were to lose the first two virtue of a 3-2 reversal to Shilbottle in the Anderson Cup and 2-1 to Alnmouth in the Sanderson Cup, but were fortunate to avoid a demoralising hat-trick of final defeats when they defeated Braeside in the Bilclough Cup. Ashington Reserves capped a fine season to make a clean sweep of Second Division cups lifting both the Runciman Cup and Robson Cup with respective wins over Spittal Rovers 'A' and Belford. Rothbury were the toast of the league reaching the quarter-final of the Northumberland FA Minor Cup before bowing out gallantly to Gosforth Bohemians with Braeside, Hedgeley and Amble Vikings all reaching the Fifth Round, itself an achievement.

The 92-93 season saw the introduction of the Northumberland Gazette Leading Scorer award for both divisions. Shilbottle striker Bobby Pile edged out Robert Taylor of Alnmouth on the final day of the season, while the Second Division award went to Gary Caldow of Ashington Reserves with 29 goals, 13 ahead of nearest rival Marc Payne of Berwick Allan Brothers.

The forthcoming season sees the league welcome four new sides, although at the time of going to press it may well be that Shilbottle will will try their luck in the Northern Alliance after two highly successful seasons in the North Northumberland League. In an attempt to encourage good conduct, the N.N.L. are to introduce a fair play league for the new season, the scheme being sponsored by Alnwick Breweries.

Chris Sanderson, Fixture Secretary & Press Officer.

Division One	P	W	D	L	F	A	PTS
Alnmouth	24	18	1	5	74	37	55
Shilbottle C.W.	24	16	3	5	70	35	51
Braeside	24	16	2	6	73	30	50
Rothbury	24	13	3	6	50	44	44
Alnwick T. Res.	24	11	5	7	48	36	38
Amble Vikings	24	10	4	10	48	40	34
Springhill	24	9	5	10	46	51	32
North Sunderland	24	9	4	11	41	43	31
Lowick	24	9	3	12	55	58	30
Hedgeley	24	7	7	10	49	53	28
Wallington	24	5	5	14	47	70	20
Percy Rvrs Res.	24	6	5	13	39	64	*20
Wooler	24	0	5	19	17	94	5

* - 3 pts deducted

Bilclough Cup final: Springhill 2, Braeside 0
Sanderson Cup final: Alnmouth 2, Springhill 1
Anderson Cup final: Shilbottle 3, Springhill 2

Division Two	P	W	D	L	F	A	PTS
Ashington Res.	18	15	2	1	91	27	47
Belford	18	12	2	4	38	17	38
Spittal Rvrs 'A'	18	11	0	7	56	41	33
Berwick Allan Bros	18	10	2	6	42	38	32
Craster Rovers	18	9	2	7	48	42	29
Lowick Res.	18	8	4	6	54	37	28
Longhoughton	18	7	3	8	40	46	24
Embleton W.R.	18	6	2	10	48	56	20
Acklington Prison Res.	18	3	1	14	44	83	*7
Hedgeley Rovers	18	0	0	18	18	95	0

Runciman Cup final: Ashington Res 1, Spittal 'A' 0
Robson Cup final: Ashington Res 4, Belford 1

(all Cup finals played at Alnwick Town F.C.)

Div. One Top Scorer: Bobby Pile (Shilbottle) 25
Div. Two Top Scorer: Gary Caldow (Ashington) 29

TYNESIDE AMATEUR LEAGUE

	P	W	D	L	F	A	PTS
Walker Ledwood F.	22	21	1	0	105	23	64
S.S. Simonside SC	22	17	1	4	89	27	52
Pizzeria F. Jesmond	22	12	0	10	66	59	36
South Shields Res.	22	11	3	8	62	58	36
Jarrow Roofing Res.	22	9	3	10	44	51	30
Newc. N.Co's OB 'A'	22	9	3	10	41	54	30
Newc. DHSS Wdrs	22	9	2	11	45	54	29
South Tyneside	22	8	4	10	49	55	28
Newcastle Univ. 'A'	22	8	4	10	57	73	28
Wallsend Cooksons	22	8	2	12	51	58	26
Lindisfarne Ath.	22	5	2	15	36	61	17
Wallsend Athletic	22	1	3	18	18	90	6

LEAGUE CHALLENGE CUP FINAL
(at Gateshead F.C., Monday 26th April):
South Shields Simonside S.C. 2, South Tyneside 1

JACK BOWMAN TROPHY FINAL
(at Heaton Stannington F.C., Wed 28th April):
Newcastle D.H.S.S. Wdrs 1, Pizzeria Francasca Jesmond 0

BILL DIXON MEMORIAL CUP FINAL
(at Heaton Stannington F.C., Monday 10th May):
Walker Ledwood Fosse 5, Pizzeria Francesca Jesmond 0

TONY HESLOP TROPHY
(Player of the Year): Rob Moorhead (Newcastle Northern Counties Old Boys 'A')

MATT DOCHERTY TROPHY
(Leading Scorer): John Wilson (South Shields Simonside S.C.) 22 goals/

HARRY GIBSON SPORTSMANSHIP TROPHY
(Best disciplinary record): Newcastle University 'A'

NEWCASTLE DISTRICT WELFARE LEAGUE

DIVISION ONE	P	W	D	L	F	A	PTS
Hazlerigg C.W.	22	18	2	2	78	26	56
Blaydon Huntsman	22	16	4	2	72	24	52
Howdon Labour C.	22	14	3	5	66	37	45
Printers Pie 'A'	22	14	2	6	78	39	44
Lyndhurst Victoria	22	12	7	3	78	42	43
Throckley & Dist.	22	10	4	8	41	42	34
Vickers Sports	22	10	2	10	54	50	32
Interpon	22	6	2	14	41	75	20
Moorhouse 'A'	22	5	1	16	32	60	16
Winlaton	22	4	2	16	27	70	14
Newton Park	22	4	0	18	33	81	12
Newcastle City	22	2	5	15	25	79	11

Leading Scorers: Adrian Eddy (Lyndhurst Victoria) 22, Steve Thompson (Printers Pie 'A') 20, Michael Lowther (Blaydon Huntsman) 16, Neil Gascoigne (Vickers Sports) 15, Adrian Palmer (Blaydon Huntsman) 15.

DIVISION TWO	P	W	D	L	F	A	PTS
Highpoint	22	17	0	5	92	33	51
Coxlodge S.C.	22	15	4	3	83	38	49
Allendale	22	15	1	6	81	38	46
Kenton	22	14	1	7	77	41	43
N'land Co. Counc.	22	13	0	9	75	60	39
Nalgo Technics	22	10	3	9	57	55	33
L.D.S. Gateshead	22	9	5	8	63	63	32
Duke of C'berland	22	9	4	9	75	42	31
R.O. Birtley	22	7	2	13	47	74	23
Bakers Oven	22	5	2	15	44	109	17
Nat West Bank	22	3	5	14	39	81	14
Graham House	22	1	1	20	35	136	4

Leading Scorers: Michael Bell (L.D.S. Gateshead) 27, Alan Robson (Allendale) 24,, Frank McGhee (Allendale) 22, Jimmy Moore (Northumberland County Council) 20, Ronnie Leman (Coxlodge S.C.) 19.

HATHAWAY AUCKLAND & DISTRICT LEAGUE

	P	W	D	L	F	A	PTS
Cockfield	28	24	4	0	131	21	52
Witton Park	28	18	10	0	101	30	46
Shildon Railway	28	20	5	3	97	37	45
Rolling Mills	28	16	4	8	65	43	36
Coxhoe Athletic	28	14	4	10	58	46	32
Quinns Inn	28	13	4	11	63	47	30
Ferryhill Bk Bull	28	12	6	10	64	69	30
Trimdon Bk Bull	28	13	3	12	72	59	29
Black & Decker	28	11	2	15	58	59	24
Station Hotel	28	9	6	13	54	66	24
Eden Arms	28	10	4	14	59	75	24
Hurworth Grange SC	28	9	3	16	63	71	*19
Coundon T.T.	28	6	2	20	43	94	14
Springfield	28	3	2	23	35	126	8
Bowburn Hare/G'hnd	28	2	1	25	28	156	5

* - 2 pts deducted

Kevin Butters (stripes) gets in a telling tackle as Shotton Comrades win 1-0 at Crook Town in a Northern League Division Two fixture on Easter Sunday. Photo - Gavin Ellis-Neville.

AMATEUR FOOTBALL ALLIANCE
SEASON 1992-93

CUP COMPETITION FINALS

A.F.A. SENIOR
Nat West Bank 2*:3 v 2*:0 Old Hamptonians

GREENLAND MEMORIAL
Liverpool Victoria 4 v 2 Slaughter & May 2

A.F.A. ESSEX SENIOR
Duncombe Sports 1 v 3 Hale End Athletic

A.F.A. MIDDLESEX SENIOR
Old Cholmeleians 0 v 1 Winchmore Hill

A.F.A. SURREY SENIOR
Nat West Bank 5 v 0 Kew Association

A.F.A. INTERMEDIATE
Franklands Village Res. 1 v 4 Norseman Res.

A.F.A. ESSEX INTERMEDIATE
Duncombe Sports Res. 2 v 1 Old Parmiterians Res.

A.F.A. KENT INTERMEDIATE
Coutts & Co. 2 v 1 Midland Bank Res.

A.F.A. MIDDLESEX INTERMEDIATE
Latymer O.B. Res 2 v 3 Old Salvatorians Res.

A.F.A. JUNIOR
Nat West 'A' 3* v 1* Old Stationers 'A'

A.F.A. MINOR
Old Esthameians 'B' 0 v 3 Old Actonians Assoc. 'B'

SENIOR NOVETS
Midland Bank 'C' 1 v 3 Old Parmiterians 'C'

INTERMEDIATE NOVETS
Civil Service 'D' 0 v 1 Old Parmiterians 'D'

JUNIOR NOVETS
Old Salvatorians 9th 2 v 1 Old Salvatorians 7th

VETERANS'
Old Fairlopians Vets 0 v 2 Old Minchendenians Vets

OPEN VETERANS
Old Wulfrunians Vets 2 v 0 Toby Vets
(* = After extra-time)

National Westminster Bank, A.F.A. Senior Cup winners 1992-93. Photo - Eric Marsh.

Old Hamptonians, A.F.A. Senior Cup runners-up 1992-93. Photo - Eric Marsh.

AMATEUR FOOTBALL ALLIANCE SENIOR CUP 1992-93

1st Round Proper

West Wickham	1	Glyn Old Boys	2	Carshalton	1	Old Aloysians	2
Carshalton	5	Old Finchleians	1	Glyn Old Boys	2	Old Esthameians	0
Mill Hill Village	0	Old Tiffinian	4	Nottsborough	1	Old Bealonians	2
Old Chigwellians	6	Old Brentwoods	2	Crouch End Vamps	1*2	Sth Bank Poly	1*0
Old Esthameians	4	Old Grocers	3	Cardinal Manning OB	2	Old Tiffinian	1
Enfield O. Gram.	2	Civil Service	1	Broomfield	7	Tansley	1
O. Westminster Cit.	0	Old Meadonians	4	Winchmore Hill	2	Old Meadonians	1
Old Bealonians	2	Old Owens	1	Old Wilsonians	1	Old Hamptonians	3
Old Latymerians	3	Sth Bank Poly	4	Old Tollingtonians	2	Midland Bank	3
Midland Bank	1	Southgate Olympic	0	Old Parmiterians	4	Old Stationers	2
Wandsworth Boro.	1	Broomfield	2	Kew Association	3*:0	Nat West Bank	3*:2
Lloyds Bank	0	Cardinal Man. OB	1	Enfield Old Gram.	1	Old Ignations	2
Old Elizabethans	2	Old Wokingians	0				

Barclays Bank	2	Old Stationers	3
Hale End Ath.	2*	O Actonians Ass.	3*
Wake Green	0	Old Wilsonians	3
Kew Association	4	John Fisher O.B.	2
Old Manorians	2	Southgate County	0
Nottsborough	5	Old Danes	1
Leyton Co. O.B.	0	Old Aloysians	1
Old Parkonians	1	Old Isleworthians	2
Tansley	4	Old Southallians	3
Old Hamptonians	5	Old Malvernians	0
Old Monovians.	5	Old Cholmeleians	1
Old Grammarians	1	Old Ignatians	2
Crouch End Vamps	2	Lensbury	1
Hassocks (w/o)		Ibis (scr)	
Old Parmiterians	6	Parkfield	1
Old Tollingtonians	6	Old Buckwellians	1
Silhill	1	Winchmore Hill	2
Nat West Bank	5	Old Kingsburians	0
Old Minchendenians	2	Norsemen	3

3rd Round Proper

Winchmore Hill	3	Old Isleworthians	1
Nat West Bank	2	Old Ignatians	1
Old Meadonians	4	Broomfield	1
Old Bealonians	2	Crouch End Vamps	9
Old Actonians Ass.s	0*	Norsemen	2*
Old Hamptonians	1	Old Parmiterians	0
Old Aloysians	3	Glyn Old Boys	1
Cardinal Manning OB	1	Midland Bank	0

2nd Round Proper

Old Isleworthians	6	Old Monovians	1
Old Elizabethans	1	Old Meadonians	2
Old Actonians Ass.	6*	Ibis	0*
Norsemen	2	Old Chigwellians	0

4th Round Proper

Old Hamptonians	2	Old Aloysians	0
Nat West Bank	5	Winchmore Hill	3
Cardinal M.	0*:1	Old Meadonians	0*:2
Norsemen	1	Crouch End Vamps	0

Semi-Finals

Norsemen	2*	Old Hamptonians	3*
Nat West Bank	4	Old Meadonians	0

Final

Old Hamptonians	2*:0	Nat West Bank	2*:3

(* = After extra-time)

SOUTHERN AMATEUR LEAGUE

FIRST DIVISION	P	W	D	L	F	A	PTS
Nat West Bank	22	16	1	5	50	26	33
Crouch End Vamps	22	14	4	4	41	18	32
Old Actonians Assn	22	13	5	4	47	27	31
Old Esthameians	22	10	5	7	36	24	25
Norsemen	22	9	4	9	24	34	22
West Wickham	22	8	5	9	38	35	21
South Bank Poly	22	8	4	10	28	39	20
Civil Service	22	8	2	12	44	42	18
Midland Bank	22	7	3	12	28	42	17
Carshalton	22	5	7	10	28	45	17
Old Parkonians	22	6	3	13	25	39	15
Old Bromleians	22	5	3	14	23	41	13

SECOND DIVISION	P	W	D	L	F	A	PTS
Lensbury	22	16	5	1	59	20	37
Winchmore Hill	22	14	5	3	53	23	33
Broomfield	22	13	6	3	53	27	32
Alexandra Park	22	13	2	7	59	43	28
Polytechnic	22	11	4	7	44	33	26
Lloyds Bank	22	7	8	7	33	27	22
Southgate Olympic	22	7	5	10	45	44	19
Old Stationers	22	5	8	9	22	31	18
Ibis	22	6	4	12	30	51	16
Kew Association	22	5	3	14	33	58	13
Barclays Bank	22	4	5	13	30	56	13
Old Salesians	22	2	3	17	31	79	7

THIRD DIVISION	P	W	D	L	F	A	PTS
Old Latymerians	22	19	1	2	76	15	39
E. Barnet Old Gram.	22	16	4	2	72	25	36
Old Parmiterians	22	13	5	4	69	33	31
Cuaco	22	13	5	4	66	33	31
Old Lyonians	22	10	4	8	42	39	24
Ryl Bank of Scotl.	22	10	3	9	65	56	23
Brentham	22	7	9	6	41	45	23
Old Westminster C.	22	7	3	12	25	50	17
Bank of England	22	5	4	13	30	56	14
Merton	22	5	2	15	47	63	12
Alleyn Old Boys	22	4	2	16	27	63	10
Reigate Prory	22	1	2	19	18	100	4

Reserve Section
Div 1: 12 teams, won by Old Esthameians
Div 2: 12 teams, won by Nat Westminster Bank
Div 3: 12 teams, won by Old Parmiterians

3rd Teams Section
Div 1: 12 teams, won by Norsemen
Div 2: 12 teams, won by Civil Service
Div 3: 12 teams, won by Old Parmiterians

4th Teams Section
Div 1: 12 teams, won by Polytechnic
Div 2: 12 teams, won by Civil Service
Div 3: 12 teams, won by Old Parmiterians

5th Teams Section
Div 1: 12 teams, won by Midland Bank
Div 2: 11 teams, won by Old Esthameians
Div 3: 9 teams, won by Old Parmiterians

6th Teams Section
Div 1: 11 teams, won by Civil Service
Div 2: 10 teams, won by Old Actonians Assoc.
Div 3: 8 teams, won by Old Parmiterians

7th Teams Section
Div 1: 10 teams, won by Old Esthameians
Div 2: 9 teams, won by Old Parmiterians

8th & 9th Teams Sections
Div 1: 8 teams, won by Nat West Bank 8th
Div 2: 7 teams, won by Old Parmiterians 8th

ARTHURIAN LEAGUE

ARTHUR DUNN CUP FINAL: LANCING OLD BOYS 1, OLD REPTONIANS 0

PREM. DIVISION	P	W	D	L	F	A	PTS
Old Etonians	16	11	0	5	42	30	22
Lancing Old Boys	16	8	6	2	35	23	22
Old Reptonians	16	9	0	7	27	27	18
Old Chigwellians	16	7	5	4	43	30	*16
Old Carthusians	16	6	4	6	33	24	16
Old Malvernians	16	6	3	7	26	24	15
Old Cholmeleians	16	4	5	7	26	27	13
Old Wellingburians	16	5	2	9	25	33	12
Old Bradfieldians	16	2	3	11	19	58	7

DIVISION ONE	P	W	D	L	F	A	PTS
Old Salopians	18	15	2	1	63	23	32
Old Brentwoods	18	14	2	2	64	22	30
Old Foresters	18	12	4	2	79	31	28
Old Harrovians	18	10	1	7	61	37	21
Old Witleians	18	8	4	6	50	32	20
Old Aldehamians	18	9	1	8	54	43	19
Old Wykehamists	18	6	0	12	31	54	12
Old Westminsters	18	4	1	13	25	76	9
Old Ardinians	18	2	1	15	29	88	5
Old Haileyburians	18	1	2	15	35	85	4

DIVISION TWO	P	W	D	L	F	A	PTS
Old Etonians Res.	16	13	2	1	51	8	28
Old Cholmel. Res.	16	12	3	1	45	16	27
Old Carthus. Res.	16	9	1	6	47	28	19
Old Chigwel. Res.	16	7	3	6	42	33	*14
Old Foresters Res.	16	6	2	8	25	47	14
Old Repton. Res.	16	6	1	9	34	38	13
Old Chigwellians 'A'	16	4	6	6	32	39	*11
Old Aldenham. Res.	16	2	3	11	25	60	7
Old Harrov. Res.	16	2	1	13	11	43	5

Div. 3 - 9 teams, won by Old Salopian Res.
Div. 4 - 9 teams, won by Old Wellingburian Res.
Div. 5 - 8 teams, won by Old Foresters 'B'
Div. 6 - 20 140 160 180 200

Junior League Cup:
Old Etonians Res. 4, Old Carthusians Res. 1

Derrik Moore Veterans' Cup:
Old Carthusians 2, Lancing Old Boys 1

Jim Dixon 6-a-side Tournament: Not played

LONDON BANKS F.A.

DIVISION ONE	P	W	D	L	F	A	PTS
Hill Samuel I.M.	16	15	0	1	41	18	27
Coutts & Co.	16	10	2	4	48	26	22
Credit Suisse	16	7	4	5	34	30	18
Invesco M.I.M.	16	7	1	8	37	36	15
Kleinwort Benson	16	5	5	6	25	27	15
Salomon Brothers	16	5	5	6	29	38	15
Allied Irish Bank	16	4	5	7	26	41	13
Citibank	16	4	3	9	25	31	11
Bank of America	16	2	4	10	23	41	8

DIVISION TWO	P	W	D	L	F	A	PTS
Nikko Europe	18	15	0	3	84	33	30
Hong King Bank	18	13	1	4	71	37	27
Westpac Bkg Corp.	18	8	4	6	45	47	20
Chemical Bank	18	9	1	8	48	39	19
Union Bk of Switz.	18	8	2	8	40	46	18
Nat West Bank 'A'	18	4	7	7	28	41	15
Coutts & Co. Res	18	5	5	8	25	38	15
Polytechnic Res.	18	5	4	9	36	51	14
Morgan Stanley	18	6	1	11	40	53	13
Chase Manhattan	18	3	3	12	35	67	9

Challenge Cup: Midland Bank 0, Lensbury 3
Senior Cup: Coutts & Co. 0, Nat West Bank 3rd 3
Senior Plate: Bank of America 2, Morgan Stanley 0
Minor Cup: Westpac Banking Corp. 4, Nat West 5th 1
Junior Cup: Utd Bank of Switzerland 2, Morgan Guaranty 1
Veterans' Cup: Lensbury 3, Midland Bank 0

DIVISION THREE	P	W	D	L	F	A	PTS
Goldman Sachs	16	11	4	1	44	11	26
C. Hoare & Co.	16	8	5	3	35	29	21
Abbey National	16	6	6	4	30	22	18
Morgan Guaranty	16	5	6	5	29	27	16
U.C.B. Bank	16	5	5	6	20	26	15
Citibank Res.	16	4	6	6	21	29	14
Nat West Bk 'B'	16	4	4	8	23	32	12
Hill Samuel Bank	16	3	5	8	21	30	11
Bk of America Res.	16	3	5	8	19	36	11

DIVISION FOUR (9 teams, won Utd Bank of Kuwait)

Junior Plate: Swiss Bank Corporation 1, Goldmans Sachs 0
Sportsmans Cup: Hill Samual Investment Mgmt 3, Morgan Stanley 2

REPRESENTATIVE MATCHES

United Banks v. Stock Exchange (won 4-0)
Royal Marines (drew 4-4)
Southern Olympian Lge (won 1-0)
Old Boys Lge (lost 0-2)

London Banks v. Old Boys Lge 'B' (lost 0-2)
Royal Marines (won 4-1)
London Legal Lge (lost 1-4)
London Insurance (lost 2-3)

LONDON INSURANCE F.A.

DIVISION ONE	P	W	D	L	F	A	PTS
Temple Bar	14	12	2	0	75	16	26
Colonial Mutual	14	7	4	3	47	28	18
Liverpool Vict.	14	6	3	5	45	33	15
Sun Alliance	14	7	1	6	31	32	15
Granby	14	5	2	7	33	38	12
Bardhill	14	5	1	8	24	60	11
Noble Lowndes	14	4	0	10	27	40	8
Eagle Star	14	3	1	10	25	58	7

DIVISION TWO	P	W	D	L	F	A	PTS
Bowring	16	9	3	4	54	43	21
Temple Bar Res.	16	9	3	4	51	30	21
Temple Bar 'A'	16	9	3	4	46	31	21
Sedgwick	16	9	2	5	46	35	20
Liverpool V. Res.	16	8	1	7	50	49	17
Granby Res.	16	8	1	7	42	45	17
Gaflac	16	6	1	9	42	47	13
Sun Alliance Res.	16	5	1	10	40	49	11
Eagle Star Res.	16	1	1	14	25	77	3

Charity Cup: Cuaco 4, Granby 1
Challenge Cup: Cuaco Res. 3, Granby 1
Junior Cup: Liverpool V. Res. 2, Granby 1 (aet)
Minor Cup: Cannon Lincoln 2, Bowring Res. 1

DIVISION THREE	P	W	D	L	F	A	PTS
Cannon Lincoln	20	19	1	0	73	14	39
Temple Bar 'B'	20	15	1	4	67	26	31
Norw. Union London	20	10	5	5	63	42	25
Noble Lowndes Res.	20	11	2	7	56	34	24
Sun Alliance 'A'	20	11	2	7	53	31	24
Bowring Res.	20	7	4	9	48	53	18
Eagle Star 'A'	20	4	6	10	53	57	14
Guardian Ryl Ex.	20	5	4	11	30	45	14
L'pool Victoria 'A'	20	6	2	12	44	83	14
Gaflac Res.	20	4	3	13	37	75	11
Temple Bar 'C'	20	1	4	15	23	87	6

W A Jewell Mem. Trophy (5-aside): Temple Bar (runners-up: Noble Lowndes)
Sportsmanship Trophy: Noble Lowndes

REPRESENTATIVE MATCHES

London Ins FA v. Southern Olymp. Lge (lost 0-5)
Bristol Ins. Inst. (lost 1-5)
Southern Amateur Lge (lost 0-5)
Old Boys Lge (lost 3-5)
London Banks ('B' team won 3-2)

SOUTHERN OLYMPIAN LEAGUE

DIVISION ONE	P	W	D	L	F	A	PTS
Parkfield	18	13	4	1	45	22	30
Nottsborough	18	10	5	3	55	23	25
Old Owens	18	9	5	4	48	30	23
Old Finchleians	18	8	4	6	47	38	20
Witan	18	6	4	8	29	39	16
Old Grammarians	18	6	3	9	40	40	15
Mill Hill Village	18	5	4	9	32	41	14
Old Bealonians	18	5	4	9	26	42	14
Old Fairlopians	18	4	5	9	27	53	13
Southgate County	18	4	2	12	29	50	10

DIVISION TWO	P	W	D	L	F	A	PTS
St Marys College	20	13	3	4	52	26	29
Wandsworth Boro.	20	12	4	4	67	31	28
Duncombe Spts	20	8	8	4	56	32	24
Academicals	20	10	4	6	44	30	24
Albanian	20	9	6	5	39	32	24
Hadley	20	10	3	7	36	30	23
Ealing Assoc.	20	10	3	7	55	53	23
Pollygons	20	5	3	12	47	76	13
Old Monovians	20	6	1	13	26	65	13
City of London	20	5	2	13	33	48	12
H'stead Heathens	20	3	1	16	38	70	7

DIVISION THREE	P	W	D	L	F	A	PTS
Ulysses	20	15	3	2	60	18	33
Corinthian-C. 'A'	20	15	1	4	66	35	31
Hale End Athletic	20	13	2	5	68	27	28
Old Woodhousians	20	14	0	6	67	43	28
Old Colfeians	20	9	4	7	43	43	22
B.B.C.	20	9	3	8	46	46	21
Pegasus Inner-Tple	20	9	1	10	49	63	19
Westerns	20	6	4	10	34	49	16
Birkbeck College	20	4	1	15	29	55	9
Electrosport	20	3	3	14	34	75	9
Brent	20	1	2	17	19	61	4

Intermediate Section

Div 1: 10 teams, won by Albanian Res
Div 2: 10 teams, won by Parkfield Res
Div 3: 10 teams, won by B.B.C. Res
Div 4: 9 teams, won by Fulham Compton OB Res

DIVISION FOUR	P	W	D	L	F	A	PTS
Hon. Artillery Co.	20	17	1	2	70	28	35
Bourneside	20	15	2	3	85	25	32
London Welsh	20	14	2	4	50	35	30
Fulham Compt. OB	20	11	1	8	59	35	23
Centymca	20	8	4	8	34	40	20
Mayfield Athletic	20	8	2	10	48	49	18
Inland Revenue	20	8	2	10	39	40	18
London Airways	20	7	3	10	42	52	17
Economicals	20	4	2	14	38	64	10
Distillers	20	3	4	13	32	75	10
Tansley	20	3	1	16	37	91	7

Junior Section

Div 1: 10 teams, won by Albanian 'A'/ Witan 'A'
Div 2: 10 teams, won by Witan 'A'
Div 3: 8 teams, won by City of London 'C'
Div 4: 9 teams, won by Parkfield 'D'

Minor Section

Div A: 10 teams, won by Mayfield Ath. 'A'
Div B: 10 teams, won by Old Owens 'B'
Div C: 11 teams, won by B.B.C. 'B'
Div D: 10 teams, won by Duncombe Spts 'A'
Div E: 9 teams, won by Duncombe Spts 'B'
Div F: 9 teams, won by Witan 'D'
Veterans: 6 teams, won by Tansley Vets

Senior Challenge Bowl: Nottsborough
Senior Challenge Shield: Old Grammarians
Intermediate Chal. Cup: Fulham Compton OB Res
Intermediate Challenge Shield: Parkfield Res
Junior Challenge Cup: Mill Hill Village 'A'
Junior Challenge Shield: Ealing Assoc. 'A'
Mander Cup: Albanian 'B'
Mander Shield: Academicals 'B'
Burntwood Trophy: Parkfield 'C'
Burntwood Shield: City of London 'C'
Thomas Parmiter Cup: Parkfield 'D'
Thomas Parmiter Shield: O Finchleians 8th
Veterans' Challenge Cup: City of London Vets
Veterans' Chal. Shield: Corinthian-Casuals Vets

MIDLAND AMATEUR ALLIANCE

DIVISION ONE	P	W	D	L	F	A	PTS
Sherwood Amateurs	22	17	1	4	88	29	35
Magdala Amateurs	22	16	1	5	89	36	33
Old Elizabethans	22	12	4	6	54	31	28
Lady Bay	22	12	3	7	52	45	27
Peoples College	22	9	6	7	49	43	24
Bassingfield	22	10	3	9	59	53	23
Tibshelf O.B.	22	9	5	8	47	46	23
Brunts Old Boys	22	7	4	11	38	55	18
Kirton B.W.	22	5	5	12	23	51	15
Old Bemrosians	22	5	4	13	30	56	14
Nottinghamshire	22	5	4	13	28	66	14
Derbyshire Amtrs	22	2	6	14	30	76	10

DIVISION THREE	P	W	D	L	F	A	PTS
County Nalgo	20	15	3	2	59	27	33
Ilkeston Electric	20	12	4	4	61	35	28
Woodborough Utd	20	10	8	2	57	40	28
W Bridgford Cas.	20	11	5	4	60	46	27
Bassingfield Res	20	9	3	8	67	55	21
Ilkeston Rgrs	20	6	7	7	44	45	19
Monty Hind O.B.	20	5	6	9	48	64	16
Peoples Col. Res	20	5	5	10	41	44	15
Derbys Amtrs Res	20	5	4	11	49	71	14
O Elizabeth. 'A'	20	4	5	11	39	55	13
Old Bemrosians Res	20	2	2	16	30	73	6

Div. 4 - 10 teams, won by Keyworth A.F.C.

Senior Cup: Old Elizabethans
Intermediate Cup: Old Elizabethans Res
Minor Cup: Derbys Amateurs 'A'
Challenge Cup: Magdala Amateurs
Division Two Challenge Cup: Nottm Spartan
Division Three Challenge Cup: County Nalgo
Division Four Challenge Cup: Magdale Amtrs 'A'
Supplementary Cup: Ilkeston Rgrs Res.
H.B. Poole Trophy: Sherwood Amateurs

DIVISION TWO	P	W	D	L	F	A	PTS
Magdala Amtrs Res	22	18	1	3	75	28	37
O Elizabeth. Res	22	14	3	5	70	26	31
Nottm Spartan	22	14	3	5	80	41	31
Beeston OB Assn	22	10	3	9	55	42	23
Chilwell	22	9	5	8	41	38	23
Sherwood Am. Res	22	9	4	9	46	39	22
Tibshelf OB Res	22	7	7	8	34	43	21
Brunts O.B. Res.	22	8	5	9	41	51	21
Nottm Univ P'grads	22	8	4	10	44	42	20
F.C. Toton	22	7	3	12	36	60	17
Nottm'shire Res.	22	5	6	11	27	59	16
Lady Bay Res.	22	0	2	20	15	95	2

A.F.A. REPRESENTATIVE MATCHES 1992-93

v Cambridge University, won 6-5
v Army F.A., lost 2-3
v Royal Air Force, lost 1-3
v London University, won 1-0

v Oxford University, won 1-0
v Royal Navy F.A., lost 2-3
v Sussex County F.A., won 4-1

THE OLD BOYS LEAGUE

PREMIER DIVISION	P	W	D	L	F	A	PTS
Old Meadonians	20	15	3	2	51	25	33
Old Ignatians	20	13	3	4	54	21	29
Old Tenisonians	20	8	9	3	43	30	25
Old Aloysans	20	6	8	6	36	28	20
Old Tiffinians	20	8	4	8	35	38	20
Glyn Old Boys	20	7	5	8	40	29	19
Cardinal Mann. OB	20	6	6	8	40	46	18
Old Wilsonians	20	5	8	7	31	46	18
Old Danes	20	5	6	9	42	56	16
Chertsey O. Sales.	20	1	10	9	24	42	12
Enfield Old Gram.	20	3	4	13	31	66	10

SENIOR DIV. ONE	P	W	D	L	F	A	PTS
O Tenison. Res.	18	13	2	3	51	21	28
Old Hamptonians	18	10	6	2	42	20	26
Phoenix Old Boys	18	8	6	4	43	32	22
Old Suttonians	18	7	5	6	36	35	19
Old Wokingians	18	6	6	6	25	25	18
Old Salvatorians	18	6	6	6	29	35	18
O Isleworthians	18	5	4	9	32	42	14
Latymer Old Boys	18	5	4	9	29	39	14
O Minchendenians	18	4	5	9	32	41	13
Mill Hill Co. OB	18	2	4	12	22	51	8

SENIOR DIV. TWO	P	W	D	L	F	A	PTS
Clapham O Xaverians	22	13	5	4	62	29	31
Old Edmontonians	22	13	3	6	62	38	29
O Tollingtonians	22	10	7	5	50	39	27
Old Grocers	22	9	8	5	43	34	26
Old Southallians	22	10	4	8	38	39	24
Old Kingsburians	22	9	4	9	48	57	22
Old Meadon. Res.	22	8	5	9	48	40	21
Shene Old Gram.	22	9	2	11	37	39	20
John Fisher O.B.	22	8	3	11	43	48	19
Old Ignatians Res	22	7	2	13	35	52	16
Old Greenfordians	22	6	4	12	31	50	16
Old Alpertonians	22	5	3	14	37	69	13

SENIOR DIV. 3	P	W	D	L	F	A	PTS
Old Vaughanians	22	18	2	2	76	23	38
Leyton Co. O.B.	22	11	5	6	50	42	27
Old Wokingians Res	22	11	4	7	47	38	26
Old Highburians	22	12	1	9	48	40	25
Old Hampt. Res.	22	10	5	7	47	39	25
Old Manorians	22	11	2	9	56	38	24
Phoenix OB Res.	22	9	5	8	42	34	23
Old Aloysians Res	22	10	2	10	43	54	22
Ravenscroft OB	22	6	3	13	33	39	15
Old Buckwellians	22	6	3	13	34	55	15
Old Josephians	22	4	5	13	28	65	13
Enfield O.G. Res.	22	4	3	15	32	69	11

I'mediate Div Nth: 12 teams, won by O Camdenians
I'mediate Div Sth: 12 teams, won by O Addeyans
Div 1 Nth: 10 teams, won by O Edmontonians Res
Div 1 Sth: 11 teams, won by Glyn O.B. Res
Div 1 W: 11 teams, won by Old Manorians Res
Div 2 Nth: 11 teams, won by Old Camdenians 'A'
Div 2 Sth: 11 teams, won by Old Tiffinians Res
Div 2 W: 11 teams, won by Old Isleworthians 'A'
Div 3 Nth: 9 teams, won by O Grocers 'A'
Div 3 Sth: 11 teams, won by Clapham O Xaverians 'A'
Div 3 W: 10 teams, won by O Salvatorians 'B'
Div 4 Nth: 9 teams, won by O Edmontonians 'B'
Div 4 Sth: 11 teams, won by Chertsey O Salesians 'B'
Div 4 W: 11 teams, won by Old Paludians
Div 5 Nth: 9 teams, won by O Tollingtonians 'C'
Div 5 Sth: 10 teams, won by Clapham O Xaverians 'B'
Div 5 W: 11 teams, won by Old Salvatorians 'D'
Div 6 Nth: 12 teams, won by Latymer Old Boys 'C'
Div 6 Sth: 11 teams, won by Clapham O Xav. 'C'
Div 6 W: 11 teams, won by Cardinal Mainning OB 'B'
Div 7 Nth: 9 teams, won by O Egbertians 'B'
Div 7 Sth: 11 teams, won by Old Sinjuns 'C'
Div 7 W: 11 teams, won by Chorley Wd OB Res.
Div 8 Nth: 7 teams, won by Old Elysians 'C'
Div 8 Sth: 11 teams, won by Chertsey O Salesians 'F'
Div 8 W: 11 teams, won by Old Hamptonians 'E'

Senior Cup Second Round
O Esthameians 3, O Bromleians 0
O Salesians 2, O Parkonians 4
O Finchleians 2, Glyn Old Boys 3
O Owens 4, O Wilsonians 0
Semi Finals: O Parkonians 0, O Owens 3
O Esthameians 3, Glyn Old Boys 1
Final (at O Bromleians, Sat 24th April):
O Esthameians 3, O Owens 0

Junior Cup Second Round
O Esthameians 5, O Parkonians 1
E Barnet O.G. 4, O Owens 1
O Bromleians 2, O Finchleians 3
O Tenisonians 2, O Minchendenians 1
Semi Finals: O Esthameians 1, O Tenisonians 0
E Barnet O.G. 0, O Finchleians 2
Final (at O Parkonians, Sat 17th April):
O Esthameians 2, O Finchleians 1

Minor Cup Second Round
O Bromleians 5, O Salesians 4
O Lyonians 4, O Woodhousians 2
O Esthameians 1, O Latymerians 0
O Minchendenians 2, O Tenisonians 3
Semi Finals:
O Bromleians 1, O Esth. *(won on pens)* 1
O Lyonians 0, O Tenisonians 7
Final (at O Westminster Citizens, Sat 20th Mar):
O Esthameians 4, O Tenisonians 3

4th XI Cup Second Round
O Suttonians 1, O Minchendenians 0
O Parkonians 0, O Esthameians 2
O Stationers 2, O Finchleians 1
O Bromleians *(won on pens)* 1 , O Colfeians 1
Semi Finals: O Suttonians 1, O Stationers 4
O Esthameians 3, O Bromleians 2
Final (at O Stationers, Sat 1st May):
O Esthameians 2, O Stationers 0

5th XI Cup Second Round
O Esthameians 3, O Suttonians 2
O Latymerians 3, O Salesians 0
O Tenisonians 4, E Barnet O.G. 2
O Stationers 2, O Bromleians 1
Semi Finals: O Latymerians 4, O Tenisonians 1
O Esthameians 0, O Stationers 1
Final (at O Minchendenians, Sat 3rd April):
O Latymerians *(won on pens)* 0, O Stationers 0

6th XI Cup Second Round
O Esthameians 6, O Minchendenians 2
E Barnet O.G. 2, O Westminster Citizens 3
O Latymerians 3, O Parkonians 1
O Bromleians 5, Glyn Old Boys 0
Semi Finals
O Westminster Citizens 1, O Esthameians 2 *aet*
O Latymerians 2, O Bromleians 0
Final (at Alleyn Old Boys, Sat 27th March):
O Esthameians 2, O Latymerians 0

Senior Cup Second Round
O Esthameians 10, O Finchleians 3
Glyn Old Boys 7, O Parkonians 1
O Minchendenians 5, O Stationers 4
O Latymerians 4, O Bromleians 1
Semi Finals: Glyn Old Boys 0, O Latymerians 1
O Esthameians 3, O Minchendenians 0
Final (at O Minchendenians, Sat 3rd April):
O Esthameians 6, O Latymerians 0

Veterans Cup Second Round
Alleyn Old Boys 2, O Minchendenians 6
O Finchleians 1, O Tenisonians 6
O Westminster Citizens 2, O Stationers 4
O Wilsonians 2, O Lyonians 1
Semi Finals
O Minchendenians 3, O Stationers 4
O Tenisonians 8, O Wilsonians 0
Final (at O Wilsonians, Sun 18th April):
O Tenisonians 4, O Stationers 2

Esthameians notched a record six wins in the eight cup competitions. With Latymerians and Stationers reaching three finals each, it proved to be a strong year for Southern Amateur League clubs. Stationers head the list of Senior Cup winners with eleven successes, followed by Esthameians, Owens and Parkonians with six wins each. Stationers and Esthameians head the Junior and Minor Cups respectively, with eight wins each. Esthameians head the total winners with 37 cups, closely followed by Stationers with 36, while Westminster Citizens are a long way behind with 19 wins. Colfeians and Lyonians each have only one cup victory to their name, while Suttonians and Woodhouseians are still to break their duck.

BIRMINGHAM & DISTRICT A.F.A.

PREM. DIVISION	P	W	D	L	F	A	PTS
Dunlop Sports	26	21	2	3	80	31	44
Sutton United	26	19	3	4	66	29	41
Wake Green Amtrs	26	16	6	4	58	27	38
Walsall Phoenix	26	16	3	7	69	37	35
Smethwick Hall OB	26	14	4	8	61	36	32
Old Wulfrunians	26	14	3	9	68	43	31
Sihill	26	10	7	9	57	44	27
Richmond Amateurs	26	10	3	13	31	46	23
Colinthians	26	10	1	15	55	64	21
Handsworth GSOB	26	7	4	15	35	72	18
G.E.C. Avery	26	7	2	17	41	60	16
Parkfield Amateur	26	5	4	17	31	76	14
Univ. Barbarians	26	3	7	16	21	68	13
Shirley Athletic	26	2	7	17	22	62	11

DIV. ONE	P	W	D	L	F	A	PTS
Tamworth QEOB	26	19	3	4	86	48	41
Kynoch IMI	26	17	3	6	80	39	37
Penncroft	26	14	7	5	52	31	35
Village	26	14	6	6	68	47	34
Holly Lodge OB	26	13	5	8	52	40	31
Sutton Utd Res	26	9	9	8	58	50	27
Scammell	26	10	7	9	52	52	27
Wake Green Am. Res	26	8	9	9	49	43	25
Britannia O.B.	26	11	3	12	47	58	25
Causeway United	26	7	9	10	42	60	23
West Hagley	26	6	7	13	58	61	19
St Francis Xavier	26	6	6	14	35	63	18
Cresconians	26	4	3	19	46	82	11
H'sworth GSOB Res	26	2	7	17	37	88	11

DIV. TWO	P	W	D	L	F	A	PTS
Holly Lodge	26	20	4	2	105	37	44
Wake Green Am. 'A'	26	15	3	8	54	45	33
Tamworth QEOB Res	26	14	4	8	64	63	32
Collins	26	13	3	8	63	49	31
Ajax United	26	8	10	8	58	65	26
F.C. Milan	26	9	7	10	55	44	25
Midland Bank	26	10	5	11	41	42	25
Welwyn	26	9	5	12	51	58	23
Sutton Utd 'A'	26	8	7	11	47	56	23
Transaction	26	7	9	10	49	63	23
West Mids Travel	26	9	5	12	52	74	23
Old Wulfrunians Res	26	8	4	14	46	56	20
Lloyds Bank	26	7	4	15	39	51	18
Sihill Res	26	6	6	14	40	61	18

DIV. THREE	P	W	D	L	F	A	PTS
Old Nortonians	26	20	6	0	98	32	46
Elmdon Sports	26	21	4	1	94	30	46
Bartley Green O.B.	26	16	3	7	96	49	35
British Telecom	26	15	5	6	79	45	35
Digby Amateur	26	11	6	9	63	63	28
Barclays Bank	26	10	6	10	69	60	26
Britannic Assurance	26	10	5	11	41	52	25
Somers Sports	26	11	2	13	78	76	24
Colinthians Res	26	10	4	12	56	60	24
Arcadian	26	11	2	13	58	84	24
College	26	8	1	17	50	77	17
Cresconians Res	26	6	3	17	39	83	15
Handsworth GSOB 'A'	26	5	4	17	36	82	14
Parkfield Amtr Res	26	2	1	23	32	96	5

DIV. FOUR	P	W	D	L	F	A	PTS
New Fullbrook	26	23	3	0	93	21	49
Sparkbrook Elim	26	15	2	9	67	48	32
Walsall Phoenix Res	26	14	3	9	58	45	31
St Philips GSOB	26	13	3	10	58	47	29
Silhill 'A'	26	11	5	10	60	49	27
West Hagley Res	26	10	7	9	51	61	27
Handsworth Wood	26	11	5	10	49	63	27
Cradley Castings	26	12	1	13	59	55	25
Keaps	26	9	4	13	55	65	22
Old Nortonians Res	26	8	6	12	38	53	22
Welwyn Res	26	10	2	14	46	65	22
Yardley Grange	26	7	6	13	32	46	20
Sutton United 'B'	26	5	8	13	41	49	18
Wake Green Am. 'B'	26	4	5	17	32	72	13
Alcan plate resigned - record expunged							

DIV. FIVE	P	W	D	L	F	A	PTS
Selly Oak Ex-Service	28	23	3	2	135	41	49
Yardley Optical Snrs	28	23	2	3	129	41	48
Northfield Juniors	28	19	5	4	99	41	43
G.E.C. Avery Res	28	17	3	8	95	65	37
Old Wulfrunians 'A'	28	12	6	10	75	60	30
Britannia OB Res	28	10	8	10	55	47	28
Shirley Ath. Res	28	13	1	14	71	74	27
Sutton Utd 'C'	28	10	7	11	66	73	27
Tamworth QEOB 'A'	28	9	6	13	71	93	24
Severn Trent Water	28	9	5	14	66	85	23
Colinthians 'A'	28	10	3	15	53	79	23
Cresonians 'A'	28	10	1	17	61	91	21
Wood Wanderers	28	8	5	15	47	79	21
Rowley	28	3	4	21	28	95	10
Britannic Ass. Res	28	4	1	23	30	117	9

DIV. SIX	P	W	D	L	F	A	PTS
Village Res	26	20	1	5	80	32	41
Old Wulfrunians 'B'	26	19	3	4	68	35	41
Colmore Rovers	26	15	7	4	84	37	37
Holly Lodge Res	26	17	2	7	81	44	36
Sihill 'B'	26	16	4	6	76	54	36
Perryfields Lincoln	26	13	6	7	74	47	32
Holly Lodge OB 'A'	26	7	7	13	45	57	21
Manchester Wdrs	26	9	2	15	54	73	20
Walsall Phoenix 'A'	26	6	7	13	47	67	19
Solihull Gas	26	7	5	14	38	60	19
Handsworth GSOB 'B'	26	7	5	14	44	71	19
Settlement	26	5	8	13	44	68	18
Aston '76	26	5	4	17	48	78	14
Wake Green Am. 'C'	26	4	3	19	36	96	11

DIV. SEVEN	P	W	D	L	F	A	PTS
Handsworth Wd Res	24	17	3	4	79	32	37
Silhill 'C'	24	16	2	6	61	44	34
Brit. Telecom Res	24	13	6	5	54	32	32
Britannia OB 'A'	24	12	4	8	78	59	28
College Res	24	11	6	7	60	44	28
Dynamo Brandhall	24	10	5	9	60	66	25
Old Nortonians 'A'	24	11	2	11	54	45	24
Old Wulfrunians 'C'	24	9	4	11	44	60	22
Sutton United 'D'	24	6	8	10	45	62	20
Lloyds Bank Res	24	6	7	11	45	57	19
St Francis Xav. Res	24	8	3	13	55	69	*17
Colinthians 'B'	24	3	9	12	38	60	15
Wake Green Am. 'D'	24	4	1	19	39	82	9
* - 2 points deducted							

DIV. EIGHT	P	W	D	L	F	A	PTS
Selly Oak Ex-S. Res	24	17	4	3	85	35	38
Sparkbrook Elim Res	24	17	1	6	93	45	35
Village 'A'	24	14	3	7	82	44	31
Silhill 'D'	24	14	3	7	73	39	31
Walsall Phoenix 'B'	24	12	4	8	57	48	28
Holly Lodge 'B'	24	12	1	11	85	69	25
Keaps Res	24	10	3	11	64	62	23
Tamworth QEOB 'B'	24	9	4	11	65	76	22
Handsworth GSOB 'C'	24	8	4	12	73	85	20
Dy. Brandhall Res	24	9	1	14	42	89	19
Cresconians 'C'	24	8	0	16	54	100	16
Parkfield Amateur 'A'	24	7	1	16	51	81	15
Shirley Ath. 'A'	24	3	3	18	38	89	9

LONDON OLD BOYS CUPS

Senior Cup:
Glyn OB 1, O Westhamians 0

Intermediate:
O Meadonians Res 4, Chorleywood Danes OB 1
(aet)

Junior Cup:
O Salvat. 'A' 4, O Meadonians 'A' 1 *(after 1-1)*

Minor Cup:
O Tenisonians 'B' 5, Chertsey Old Salesians 0

Novets:
Old Sinjuns 'C' 1, City of London 0

Drummond Cup:
O Parmiterians 'D' 3, O Tollingtonians 'D' 1

Nemean Cup:
Old Salvatorians 7, Glyn Old Boys 7th 2

Veterans:
O Simmarians Vets 3, O Meadonians Vets 0

LONDON LEGAL LEAGUE

DIV. ONE	P	W	D	L	F	A	PTS
Slaughter & May	26	17	7	2	86	26	41
Grays Inn	26	17	6	3	100	47	40
Pegasus Inner-Tple	26	18	4	4	55	32	40
Clifford Chance	26	13	7	6	76	51	33
Allen Overy	26	13	6	7	91	54	32
Freshfields	26	14	3	9	82	60	31
Wilde Sapte	26	9	7	10	46	57	25
Herbert Smith	26	7	10	9	55	43	24
Linklaters & Paines	26	11	2	13	70	70	24
Cameron Markby H.	26	9	5	12	59	67	23
Lovell White Durrant	26	10	2	14	50	75	22
Norton Rose	26	6	2	18	24	82	14
Titmuss Sainer & W.	26	4	2	20	29	99	10
MacFarlanes	26	1	3	22	37	107	5

DIV. ONE	P	W	D	L	F	A	PTS
Nabarro Nathanson	24	19	1	4	94	34	39
Stephenson Harwood	24	15	3	6	63	42	33
Taylor Joynson Gar.	24	15	2	7	67	34	32
Gouldens	24	12	2	10	55	53	26
Simmons & Simmons	24	11	3	10	69	58	25
DJ Freeman & Co	24	10	3	11	57	53	23
Watson Farley & Will.	24	7	9	8	40	44	23
Baker & McKenzie	24	9	4	11	34	56	22
Denton Hall	24	8	4	12	39	62	20
B.H.T. Goddard	24	5	9	10	39	55	19
Beachcroft Stanleys	24	7	3	14	41	67	17
Rowe & Maw	24	4	7	13	37	54	15

League Cup Final: Grays Inn 3, Allen & Overy 0
Weavers Arms Cup: Freshfields 3, Taylor Joynson Garrett 1
Invitation Cup: Beachcroft Stanley 4, Titmuss Sainer & Webb 0

UNIVERSITY OF LONDON INTER-COLLEGIATE LEAGUE

PREM. DIV.	P	W	D	L	F	A	PTS
R Holl/New B'ford C.	12	9	0	3	39	15	18
King's College	12	8	1	3	35	16	17
Imperial College	12	5	5	2	27	22	15
University College	12	6	2	4	31	22	14
L'don Sch of Econ.	12	5	1	6	28	28	11
Goldsmiths College	12	3	2	7	16	26	8
St Georges H.M.S.	12	0	1	11	17	64	1

DIV. THREE	P	W	D	L	F	A	PTS
R London Med. Col.	12	6	4	2	53	36	16
University Coll. 'A'	12	6	4	2	38	30	16
King's College 'A'	12	7	0	5	39	34	14
R Sch of Mines (IC)	12	5	3	4	29	26	13
Imperial College 'A'	12	4	2	6	33	37	10
Goldsmiths Col. Res.	12	4	0	8	28	39	8
Qu. Mary W.C. 'A'	12	2	3	7	17	35	7

DIV. ONE	P	W	D	L	F	A	PTS
Qu. Mary W'field C.	12	11	1	0	39	7	*19
Imperial Col. Res.	12	8	1	3	32	20	17
R Holl/B'ford Res.	12	6	2	4	44	25	14
University Col. Res.	12	5	2	5	32	24	12
U.M.D.S.	12	3	2	7	17	28	8
St Marys Hos. M.S.	12	4	0	8	26	40	8
Sch. of Pharmacy	12	1	0	11	8	54	2

* - pts deducted

DIV. FOUR	P	W	D	L	F	A	PTS
R Hol/New B'ford 'A'	12	11	0	1	46	12	22
Sch Slav & E Euro.	12	8	2	2	28	15	18
L.S.E. 'A'	12	7	0	5	38	24	14
L.S.E. Res.	12	4	3	5	28	23	11
Ryl Free H.S.E. Res.	12	3	2	7	18	31	8
University Col. 'B'	12	4	0	8	23	39	8
U.M.D.S. Res.	12	0	3	9	5	42	*1

* - pts deducted.

DIV. TWO	P	W	D	L	F	A	PTS
Ryl Free Hos. S.M.	12	9	2	1	36	14	20
Middx/Uni Col. HMS	12	6	3	3	14	15	15
King's Col. H.M.S.	12	5	4	3	23	20	14
Ch. Cross & WHMS	12	3	6	3	15	14	12
St Bartholomews	12	3	5	4	15	18	11
King's College Res.	12	4	1	7	20	24	9
Qu. Mary W.C. Res.	12	0	3	9	13	31	3

Div 5: 7 teams, won by Imperial College 'B'
Div 6: 8 teams, won by Royal Holloway & Bedford New College 'B'
Div 7: 8 teams, won by London School of Economics 'B'
Div 8: 8 teams, won by School of Slavonic & Eastern European Studies Reserves.

The Army F.A. celebrate after winning the South West County championship. Photo - Eric Marsh.

SUBURBAN FOOTBALL LEAGUE

Hon. Secretary: M J Bidmead
55 Grange Road, Chessington, Surrey KT9 1EZ. (081-397 4834)

SOUTH DIV.	P	W	D	L	F	A	PTS
Carshalton Athletic	38	31	3	4	137	42	96
Sutton United	38	24	5	9	124	47	77
Dulwich Hamlet	38	24	5	9	115	55	77
Bromley	38	23	6	9	109	54	75
Tooting & Mitcham	38	21	8	9	117	58	71
Malden Vale	38	19	8	11	68	56	65
Kingstonian	38	20	5	13	94	85	65
Dorking	38	20	2	16	67	83	62
Met. Police	38	18	4	16	93	72	58
Crawley Town	38	18	4	16	72	66	58
Croydon	38	18	8	12	94	58	*56
Croydon Athletic	38	14	7	17	65	83	49
Leatherhead	38	14	7	17	51	82	49
Corinthian-Casuals	38	14	5	19	67	84	47
Whyteleafe	38	13	9	16	85	89	+45
Epsom & Ewell	38	11	8	19	58	78	41
Three Bridges	38	7	5	26	43	111	26
Banstead Athletic	38	8	4	26	49	107	+25
Redhill	38	4	4	30	39	129	16
Horsham	38	4	3	31	37	145	15

* - 6 points deducted
+ - 3 points deducted

Leading Scorers: (League, League Cup, Champions Cup): 29 - K Glavey (Carshalton). 26 - Z Newman (Sutton). 25 - D Tomlin (Dulwich). 22 - R Morgan (Tooting). 21 - R Seagroatt (Sutton. 20 - D Heath (Dorking). 19 - R Scott (Sutton). 18 - P Carew (Tooting), M Sestanovich (Whyteleafe). 17 - S Wheeler (Kingstonian), J Scola (Met Police), S Taylor (Whyteleafe). 16 - D Annon (Carshalton). 15 - T Stuart (Bromley), J Gass (Carshalton), N Willie (Crawley), J Kempster (Dulwich). 14 - C Hewitt (Bromley), S Tomlin (Carshalton), N Webb (Epsom). 13 - T Wright (Dorking), P Callingham (Kingstonian), T Hope (Tooting). 12 - N Mathew (Met Police), J Earp (Sutton).

'Double Figure' Scores: Leatherhead 0, Whyteleafe 13. Redhill 1, Sutton 10. Carshalton 10, Kingstonian 1. Croydon 10, Whyteleafe 2.

NORTH DIV.	P	W	D	L	F	A	PTS
Hendon	34	27	7	0	89	17	88
Hayes	34	21	4	9	93	41	67
Molesey	34	21	5	8	87	44	+67
Ruislip Manor	34	19	4	11	77	41	61
Wembley	34	18	5	11	73	62	59
Edgware Town	34	17	6	11	84	48	57
Northwood	34	18	3	13	75	60	57
Staines Town	34	16	8	10	76	42	56
Uxbridge	34	16	4	14	57	49	52
Yeading	34	14	7	13	72	63	49
Chalfont St Peter	34	14	5	15	55	53	47
Walton & Hersham	34	13	5	16	61	93	*41
Hampton	34	13	1	20	56	75	40
Hanwell Town	34	13	0	21	51	77	39
Chertsey Town	34	9	7	18	50	81	34
Kingsbury Town	34	7	5	22	48	94	26
Feltham & H.B.	34	7	2	25	55	114	23
Hillingdon Borough	34	2	4	28	28	133	10

* - 3 points deducted
+ - 1 point deducted

Leading Scorers: 20 - P Okoro (Hayes). 18 - D Morris (Edgware), M Rattue (Molesey). 17 - T Flaherty (Ruislip M.). 15 - V Murphy (Hayes). 14 - A Mills (Ruislip M.), K Phillips (Staines), P Antwi (Wembley). 13 - R Cobley (Molesey). 12 - J Quinn (Edgware inc. 5 for Kingsbury), A Sibanda (Hendon), S Johnson & H Pacquette (Northwood), B Inch (Staines), M Howard & N Whiting (Ruislip M.), B Smith (Walton & H.), J Williams (Yeading).

'Double Figure' Scores: Edgware 13, Hillingdon 0. Feltham & Hounslow 1, Ruislip Manor 10. Yeading 10, Walton & Hersham 2.

WEST DIV.	P	W	D	L	F	A	PTS
Woking	34	24	6	4	109	40	78
Thame United	34	22	10	2	103	46	76
Marlow	34	20	6	8	106	52	66
Cove	34	19	8	7	77	40	65
Abingdon Town	34	17	12	5	79	30	63
Slough Town	34	17	6	11	89	57	*54
Maidenhead United	34	16	6	12	81	62	54
Wokingham Town	34	13	8	13	52	50	47
Basingstoke Town	34	15	5	14	72	72	47
Newbury Town	34	13	4	17	73	86	43
Fleet Town	34	12	9	13	66	68	*42
Thatcham Town	34	11	6	17	70	76	39
Burnham	34	10	4	20	51	104	34
Camberley Town	34	8	7	19	64	108	31
Bracknell Town	34	7	10	17	44	96	+30
Windsor & Eton	34	8	5	21	63	89	29
Egham Town	34	7	6	21	48	98	+26
Hungerford Town	34	6	4	24	42	115	22

* - 3 points deducted
+ - 1 point deducted

Leading Scorers: 33 - G Roffe (Woking). **21 -** L Walker (Slough). **20 -** A Thomas (Thame). **19 -** D Goodliff (Slough). **17 -** R Jack & M Blunden (Marlow). **15 -** P Hall (Cove), S Doyle (Maidenhead (inc. 7 with Windsor)), B Chowns (Thame), S Milton (Woking), S Husband (Wokingham). **14 -** T Bax (Basingstoke). **13 -** J Varney (Abingdon), W Wylie (Hungerford (inc. 10 with Thatcham)), G Hutchinson & T Senior (Woking). **12 -** D Godfrey (Wokingham).

'Double Figure' Scores: Thame Utd 12, Burnham 1. Marlow 10, Bracknell 0. Slough 10, Hungerford 0.

Individual Scoring feats: 6 - S Taylor (Whyteleafe v Leatherhead), G Roffe (Woking v Bracknell).
5 - R Smith (Leatherhead v Redhill), D Goodliff (Slough v Windsor), W Alleyne (Uxbridge v Kingsbury).
4 - R Green (Abingdon v Egham), I Jopling (Cove v Burnham), S Warne (Croydon v Whyteleafe), C Nassim (Croydon Ath. v Horsham), D Tomlin (Dulwich v Epsom), D Morris (Edgware v Hillingdon), D Traylen (Egham v Basingstoke), P Okoro (Hayes v Kingsbury - Lge Cup), S Tull (Hungerford v Egham), P Wood (Kingstonian v Redhill), P Dadson (Maidenhead v Feltham - Lge Cup), E Payne (Maidenhead v Newbury), N Mathew (Met Police v Whyteleafe), M Rattue (Molesey v Kingsbury), G Friel (Slough v Egham), Z Newman (Sutton v Hillingdon - Lge Cup), G Roffe (Woking v Marlow & Woking v Maidenhead), T Senior (Woking v Windsor & Woking v Thame), S Milton (Woking v Horsham - Lge Cup), D Puckett (Woking v Thame).

LEAGUE CUP:
Winners: Woking
Runners-up: Ruislip Manor

'Double Figure' Scores: Hillingdon 1, Sutton 11. Woking 10, Horsham 2.

LEAGUE RECORDS BROKEN:
Hendon (North Division) - Unbeaten throughout season.
Carshalton Ath. (South Division) - 137 goals scored.
Sutton United (South Division) - 124 goals scored.
Horsham (South Division) - 145 goals conceded.

THE CAPITAL LEAGUE

Hon. Secretary: P B Braxton, 80 Woodlands Avenue, Eastcote, Ruislip, Middx. HA4 9RH. Tel: 081 866 8596. Fax: 081 429 1680.

	P	W	D	L	F	A	PTS
Barnet	20	13	2	5	57	34	41
Leyton Orient	20	12	3	5	54	32	39
Brentford	20	10	5	5	52	35	35
Cambridge United	20	10	4	6	44	29	34
Gillingham	20	9	4	7	35	27	31
Southend Manor	20	8	5	7	41	32	29
Crystal Palace	20	8	5	7	33	33	29
Sutton United	20	6	9	5	27	30	27
Reading	20	6	2	12	33	50	20
Wycombe Wanderers	20	3	6	11	27	49	15
Wokingham Town	20	1	3	16	19	71	6

* - Farnborough & Wealdstone's playing records expunged.

Proposed 93-94 Constitution
Barnet
Brentford
Cambridge United
Colchester United
Enfield
Gillingham
Leyton Orient
Southend United
St. Albans City
Sutton United
Woking
Wokingham Town
Wycombe Wanderers

HOME TEAM		1	2	3	4	5	6	7	8	9	10	11
1.	Barnet	*	5-2	1-0	2-3	2-1	5-0	3-2	4-1	4-1	7-0	3-3
2.	Brentford	1-3	*	2-5	1-1	2-0	5-4	3-0	3-1	2-1	2-0	2-3
3.	Cambridge Utd	3-1	4-3	*	2-2	1-2	3-1	2-4	3-1	0-1	3-2	2-0
4.	Crystal Palace	1-0	0-5	0-3	*	0-0	1-2	1-3	1-3	1-2	6-0	1-0
5.	Gillingham	0-3	2-2	1-0	1-2	*	1-2	4-1	1-0	1-1	6-0	2-2
6.	Leyton Orient	9-2	1-1	4-2	2-2	2-3	*	4-2	0-0	3-0	5-0	2-0
7.	Reading	1-3	0-5	0-4	1-3	0-2	3-1	*	1-0	1-2	5-4	5-1
8.	Southend United	3-1	1-2	2-2	3-2	3-1	1-3	3-1	*	1-1	5-2	6-1
9.	Sutton United	1-1	1-1	1-1	1-1	4-3	0-2	3-1	0-0	*	2-2	0-0
10.	Wokingham Town	1-4	0-5	1-1	0-1	0-3	1-4	1-1	1-5	1-2	*	2-0
11.	Wycombe Wanderers	1-3	3-3	0-3	2-4	0-1	0-3	1-1	2-2	4-3	4-1	*

PRESIDENT'S CUP 1992-93

First Round

Brentford v Crystal Palace	1-2	Cambridge United v Gillingham (A.E.T.)	0-1
Leyton Orient v Barnet	2-1	Reading v Wycombe Wanderers	1-0
Wokingham v Southend United	1-4	**Byes:** Farnborough, Sutton Utd & Wealdstone	

Second Round

Sutton United v Reading	2-2	Farnborough Town v Crystal Palace	3-4
(aet, Reading won 4-1 on pens)			
Southend united v Wealdstone	W/O	Gillingham v Leyton Orient	0-1

Semi Finals

Reading v Leyton Orient	1-4	Crystal Palace v Southend United	3-2

Final

Crystal Palace v Leyton Orient   1-3

Crystal Palace scorers: Niall Thompson 39.
Leyton Orient scorers: David Thompson 14, Simon Livett 59, Kenny Achampong 86.
Attendance: 227 (At Selhurst Park).

CAPITAL LEAGUE NINE YEAR RECORD (SINCE FORMATION)

	84/5	85/6	86/7	87/8	88/9	89/0	90/1	91/2	92/3
Aldershot	-	-	-	-	-	8	7	w/d	-
Aylesbury United	-	-	-	-	13	-	-	-	-
Barnet	6	10	6	9	1	5	6	2	1
Brentford	2	9	-	1	3	3	3	7	3
Cambridge United	-	-	-	-	4	4	2	1	4
Colchester United	-	-	-	-	6	6	5	10	-
Crystal Palace	-	-	-	-	-	-	-	6	7
Dagenham	3	4	2	8	-	-	-	-	-
Enfield	4	3	7	10	10	9	w/d	-	-
Gillingham	7	1	3	6	8	7	-	-	5
Leyton Orient	8	5	9	3	2	2	4	5	2
Reading	-	-	-	-	-	-	-	-	9
Slough Town	-	-	-	-	-	-	10	12	-
Southend United	-	8	8	-	5	1	1	4	6
Sutton United	-	-	-	-	-	-	12	8	8
Wealdstone	1	2	1	5	7	13	9	9	-
Welling United	-	-	-	7	11	12	-	-	-
Wimbledon	5	7	5	4	-	-	-	-	-
Wokingham Town	-	-	-	-	12	11	8	11	11
Wycombe Wanderers	-	6	4	2	9	10	11	3	10
No. of clubs	**8**	**10**	**9**	**10**	**13**	**13**	***13**	**+13**	**#13**

* - Enfield withdrew after 1 game.   + - Aldershot folded in mid-season.   # - Farnborough & Wealdstone both resigned during the season.

ESSEX THAMES-SIDE CHALLENGE TROPHY

FIRST ROUND

Walthamstow Pennant v Tilbury	1-8
Barkingside v Aveley	2-3
Canvey v Eton Manor	2-0

SECOND ROUND

Burnham Ramblers v Canvey Island	0-2
Aveley v Southend Manor	0-1
Purfleet v Ford United	4-1
Grays Athletic v Bailsdon United	2-1
Billericay Town v Chelmsford City	1-2
Tilbury	Bye
Rainham Town v Hornchurch	2-1
Leyton v Collier Row	2-0

THIRD ROUND

Tilbury v Purfleet 0-0 *(Tilbury won 5-4 on pens)*	
Southend Manor v Canvey Island	1-0
Grays Athletic v Leyton	1-3
Chelmsford City v Rainham Town	1-4

SEMI FINAL

Southend Manor v Leyton	1-2
Rainham Town v Tilbury	0-0
(Rainham won 3-1 on pens)	

FINAL

Rainham Town v Leyton	4-5

SOUTHERN COMBINATION CHALLENGE CUP

FIRST ROUND

Bracknell Town v Chipstead	3-4
Epsom & Ewell v Banstead Athletic	1-0
Malden Vale v Virginia Water	0-0
(Virginia won 3-2 on pens)	
Wokingham Town v Molesey	1-5
Dorking v Croydon Athletic	3-2
Frimley Green v Feltham & Hounslow Boro.	2-0
Walton & Hersham v Chertsey Town	4-1
Leatherhead v Cove	1-0

SECOND ROUND

Leatherhead v Dorking	1-2
Molesey v Frimley Green	4-0
Epsom & Ewell v Walton & Hersham	3-2 (aet)
Chipstead v Virginia Water	2-1

SEMI FINALS

Dorking v Molesey	1-0
Epsom & Ewell v Chipstead	1-0

FINAL

Dorking v Epsom & Ewell	1-0

THE EVANS HALSHAW FLOODLIT CUP

WESTERN GROUP

Belper Town v Leek Town	0-4
Belper Town v Matlock Town	0-3
Belper Town v Rocester	1-3
Leek Town v Belper Town	2-0
Leek Town v Matlock Town	6-1
Leek Town v Rocester	2-1
Matlock Town v Belper Town	3-3
Matlock Town v Leek Town	2-0
Matlock Town v Rocester	2-0
Rocester v Belper Town	3-1
Rocester v Leek Town	0-1
Rocester v Matlock Town	0-1

MIDLANDS GROUP

Alfreton Town v Ashfield United	3-2
Alfreton Town v Eastwood Town	4-3
Alfreton Town v Hucknall Town	1-2
Ashfield United v Alfreton Town	1-6
Ashfield United v Eastwood Town	1-3
Ashfield United v Hucknall Town	3-0
Eastwood Town v Alfreton Town	0-1
Eastwood Town v Ashfield United	6-0
Eastwood Town v Hucknall Town	3-1
Hucknall Town v Alfreton Town	1-4
Hucknall Town v Ashfield United	0-1
Hucknall Town v Eastwood Town	1-1

LINCOLNSHIRE GROUP

Holbeach United v Ilkeston Town	0-0
Holbeach United v Lincoln United	0-4
Ilkeston Town v Holbeach United	4-0
Ilkeston Town v Lincoln United	2-1
Lincoln United v Holbeach United	8-0
Lincoln United v Ilkeston Town	2-1

SEMI-FINAL

Alfreton Town v Leek Town	1-2

SOUTH-EAST GROUP

Bourne Town v Mirrlees Blackstone	0-0
Bourne Town v Stamford	2-3
Mirrlees Blackstone v Bourne Town	2-3
Mirrlees Blackstone v Stamford	1-4
Stamford v Bourne Town	0-2
Stamford v Mirrlees Blackstone	0-2

SEMI-FINAL

Lincoln United v Bourne Town	6-2

MIDLANDS GROUP

	P	W	D	L	F	A	Pts
Leek Town	6	5	0	1	15	4	15
Matlock Town	6	4	1	1	12	9	13
Rocester	6	2	0	4	7	8	6
Belper Town	6	0	1	5	5	18	1

MIDLANDS GROUP

	P	W	D	L	F	A	Pts
Alfreton Town	6	5	0	1	19	9	15
Eastwood Town	6	3	1	2	16	8	10
Ashfield United	6	2	0	4	8	18	6
Hucknall Town	6	1	1	4	5	13	4

LINCOLNSHIRE GROUP

	P	W	D	L	F	A	Pts
Lincoln United	4	3	0	1	15	3	9
Ilkeston Town	4	2	1	1	7	3	7
Holbeach United	4	0	1	3	0	16	1

SOUTH-EAST GROUP

	P	W	D	L	F	A	Pts
Bourne Town	4	2	1	1	7	5	7
Stamford	4	2	0	2	7	7	6
Mirrlees Blackstone	4	1	1	2	5	7	4

SUNDAY LEAGUES

"106 Sunday Leagues have been submitted from the 1992-93 season. The top divisions of all these leagues are published in full, together with the champions of lower divisions. The numbers in brackets for the lower divisions indicate the number of teams competing. Remember, if your league is not featured then send us final tables next year".

ANDOVER & DIST. SUNDAY LGE
COUNTY: HAMPSHIRE

SEN. DIV. 1	P	W	D	L	F	A	PTS
Ludgershall Spts	14	11	1	2	49	23	34
Southampton Arms	14	10	3	1	55	16	33
Wherwell	14	8	2	4	56	28	26
Nether Wallop	14	5	2	7	29	51	17
Fred Druce	14	4	4	6	36	32	16
Longmeadow	14	4	4	6	34	39	16
Andover Press	14	3	0	11	31	66	9
Whitchurch R.H.	14	2	2	10	20	55	8

Lower Division Champions:
Senior Div. 2 (8): Ducal
Junior Div. 1 (10): Borough Arms
Junior Div. 2 (10): Upper Clatford
Junior Div. 3 (11): Tesco
Junior Div. 4 (10): Mucky Duck

Cup Winners:
Jimmy Monro Mem. Open Chal. Cup: Southampton Arms
Presidents Cup: Ludgershall Sports
Div. 3 & 4 Challenge Cup: Tidworth Sports
Junior Challenge Cup: Tidworth Sports

BANGOR & DIST. SUNDAY LGE
COUNTY: GWYNEDD

I & H GRIFFITHS

DIVISION ONE	P	W	D	L	F	A	PTS
Bull Valley	12	11	0	1	62	16	33
Mona	12	9	1	2	58	26	28
Rhosnegir & Dist.	12	7	0	5	46	34	31
Waterloo	12	7	0	5	30	32	21
Bodedern	12	2	1	9	25	49	7
Caergeiliog	12	3	1	8	26	51	*7
UCNW	12	1	1	10	14	50	4

* - 3pts deducted.

Lower Division Champions:
Caprice - Div. 2 (8) Octel
My Scaffolding - Div. 3 (8) Mermaid

BARKING & DIST. SUNDAY LGE
COUNTY: ESSEX

PREM. DIV.	P	W	D	L	F	A	PTS
Byron Red Star	20	15	3	2	109	34	33
Blakehall	20	14	5	1	92	35	33
Mordfown	20	11	5	4	55	30	27
Hornchurch Wasps	20	10	5	5	68	31	25
Fairview	19	9	1	9	43	69	19
Southchurch	20	8	2	10	54	48	18
Valancia	20	8	2	10	48	54	18
London City	20	6	4	10	60	46	16
Newbury Park	20	7	2	11	44	48	16
Lippatarno	20	5	3	12	32	65	13
Keys	19	0	0	19	9	154	0

NB. Fairview v Keys not played.

Lower Division Champions:
Div. 1 (11): Nightingale
Div. 2 (12): Skytech
Div. 3 (12): Morsefield

Cup Winners:
League Cup: Morfdown
Premier Div. Cup: Blakehall
Div. 1 Cup: Morlando
Div. 2 Cup: Skytech
Div. 3 Cup: Morsefield

BARNET & DIST. SUNDAY LGE
COUNTY: HERTFORDSHIRE

PREM. DIV.	P	W	D	L	F	A	PTS
Elliott Star	18	15	3	0	63	16	33
Conyers Park	18	14	2	2	50	22	30
Leevale	18	12	2	4	34	19	26
Fairfield Griffin	18	8	4	6	33	32	20
Prince of Wales	18	8	3	7	45	29	19
Imperial	18	6	4	8	31	36	16
Ebogs	18	5	4	9	34	46	14
Hendon St Marys	18	5	3	10	38	41	13
Roving Reporters	18	3	0	15	23	61	6
Stanborough Sports	18	0	3	15	18	67	3

Lower Division Champions:
Div. 1 (10): Suffolk Punch
Div. 2 (9): Oakmere
Div. 3 (9): Wroxham Park Reserves
Div. 4 (11): Leevale Res. (won play-off v Green Man)

'TNT EXPRESS'
BATH & DIST. SUNDAY LGE
COUNTY: SOMERSET & AVON (SOUTH)

DIVISION ONE	P	W	D	L	F	A	PTS
Rosewarn	24	20	3	1	79	22	43
W Ex-Services	24	16	0	8	89	43	32
Shireway	24	12	7	5	59	35	31
Pucklechurch	24	12	5	7	57	39	29
Bath Police	24	11	4	9	77	51	26
Larkhall	24	8	7	9	55	55	23
Livingstone V.	24	8	6	10	45	42	22
Horseshoe	24	10	2	12	38	59	22
Kingsmead	24	9	4	11	33	57	22
Hinton Char.	24	9	2	13	59	56	20
Roman Sports	24	7	3	14	57	86	17
Odd Down Sunday	24	6	1	17	53	102	13
Moorfield	24	5	2	17	41	97	*10

* - 2pts deducted.

Lower Division Champions:
Div. 2 (14) Midland Bank
Div. 3 (13) Yate Praparts
Div. 4 (14) Shireway Reserves
Div. 5 (14) Brains

BEACON SUNDAY LGE
COUNTY: BIRMINGHAM

PREM. DIV.	P	W	D	L	F	A	PTS
Sedgley Red Lion	14	11	1	2	55	31	23
East Park Rangers	13	9	1	3	42	24	19
Beacon Athletic	14	6	5	3	41	26	17
Smethwick Rangers	13	6	3	4	33	26	15
W.H.T.F.C.	14	6	2	6	33	39	14
Woodcross Eagles	14	6	1	7	24	27	13
Sunners	14	3	2	9	27	48	8
Bescot United	14	0	1	13	15	49	1

N.B. East Park Rgrs v Smethwich Rgrs left unplayed.

Lower Division Champions:
Div. 1 (10): Claregate Wanderers
Div. 2 (12): Wrottersley Arms
Div. 3 (10): Staffs Steels
Div. 4 (11): Bentley Juniors

'MICHAEL R PETERS'
BEDFORD & DIST. SUNDAY LGE
COUNTY: BEDFORDSHIRE

'Craddocks Plastics' Prem. Div.

	P	W	D	L	F	A	PTS
Bedford W. Indians	22	18	2	2	78	34	38
Sandy Albion Sunday	22	15	2	5	76	38	32
Bedford Young Inds	22	15	1	6	69	38	31
Griffin	22	15	1	6	66	38	31
Biggleswade Libs	22	15	0	7	81	36	30
Meltis	22	11	1	10	63	57	23
Carlton & Pavenham	22	8	2	12	51	71	18
Fox & Duck Spts	22	8	1	13	62	63	17
Gamlingay Old Boys	22	7	3	12	41	58	17
Brickhill Tigers	22	6	2	14	39	61	14
Clapham Groomsmen	22	4	1	17	36	76	9
Sharnbrook Casuals	22	1	2	19	32	113	4

Lower Division Champions:
'The Bed Shop' Div. 1 (13): Queensmen
'Keyline' Div. 2 (11): Century Old Boys
'Lee Roofing' Div. 3 (11): Bluebell Casuals
'T.R. Metals' Div. 4 (12): Renhold Utd Sunday
'Modplan' Div. 5 (12): Harrows (Cotton End)
'Bedford Mobile Communications' Div. 6 (13): Dynamo Rgrs

Cup Winners:
League Cup: Meltis
'Harrison & Rowley' Snr Shield: Bedford West Indians

BIRMINGHAM SUNDAY ALLIANCE
COUNTY: BIRMINGHAM

PREM. DIV.	P	W	D	L	F	A	PTS
St Clements	22	15	4	3	77	33	34
Northwood Star	22	15	3	4	61	35	33
Woodsman Smiths W	22	15	2	5	59	28	32
Redwood Ben Johns.	22	11	6	5	56	38	28
Dovecote United	22	11	4	7	59	31	26
Oscott Liberals	22	11	4	7	40	31	26
Yardley Arms	22	7	5	10	46	58	19
Prince Hal	22	7	3	12	42	51	17
Selly Park	22	5	5	12	31	54	15
Watering Hole	22	3	7	12	39	75	13
Westbrook	22	3	6	13	25	56	12
Kings Norton RBL	22	3	3	16	28	72	9

Lower Division Champions:
Div. 1 (12): Brookhill
Div. 2 (11): Sparkhill & Greet RBL
Div. 3 (14): Ridgacre Rangers

BLACKBURN SUNDAY LGE
COUNTY: LANCASHIRE

DIV. ONE	P	W	D	L	F	A	PTS
Gibraltar	18	13	3	2	54	24	29
Woodlands	18	12	3	3	51	27	27
Clifton	18	9	4	5	39	27	22
Darwen Sun Leis.	18	9	3	6	33	17	21
Old Toll Bar	18	7	3	8	32	30	17
Gepal	18	7	3	8	28	30	17
Station	18	5	5	8	20	32	15
Foresters	18	4	6	8	24	32	14
Marwill	18	4	3	11	27	51	11
Cowies	18	2	3	13	22	60	7

Lower Division Champions:
Div. 2 (12): Arcade Bar
Div. 3 (11): Vauxhall (after play-off v Blackburn Aztecs)

Cup Winners:
Blue & White Rosebowl Cup: Gepal

'HAYWARD' BOURNEMOUTH SUNDAY LEAGUE
COUNTY: HAMPSHIRE/ DORSET

DIV. ONE	P	W	D	L	F	A	PTS
Sth Kinson Spts	22	16	4	2	73	22	52
Hamworthy Eng.	22	13	2	7	59	43	41
Bransome R. Hotel	22	12	3	7	63	42	39
E. Howe Wiltons	22	12	3	7	43	30	39
Gracelands	22	12	1	9	57	43	37
Hurn Rovers	22	10	1	11	53	63	31
B'mouth Electric	22	9	3	10	60	51	30
Ferndown Town Spts	22	8	6	8	57	56	30
P.S.C. Wareham	22	8	3	11	42	48	27
Oakmead Bearwood	22	6	4	12	37	75	22
Budeford Mens Cl.	22	5	3	14	39	67	18
Panbourne Sports	22	3	3	16	34	77	10

* - 2 points deducted

Lower Division Champions:
Div. 2 (11): Sovereign
Div. 3 (11): Royal Mail Bournemouth
Div. 4 (11): New Milton
Div. 5 (11): Lymington Starfish
Div. 6 (11): Wimborne Magpies
Div. 7 (11): C.B.B.
Div. 8 (11): St Ives & St Leonards
Div. 9 (11): Gas Tavern
Div. 10 (12): Astra
Div. 11 (12): Clockwork Rangers
Div. 12 (12): Steam House

BRADFORD SUNDAY ALLIANCE
COUNTY: WEST RIDING

PREM. DIV.	P	W	D	L	F	A	PTS
E. Bowling Unity	22	14	6	2	60	28	48
Ventus United	22	14	3	5	48	23	45
Oakenshaw	22	12	7	3	80	43	43
Bolton Woods	22	10	9	3	41	28	39
Albion Sports	22	9	2	11	45	51	29
Fiddlers Three	22	9	2	11	41	59	29
Green Man '88	22	7	6	9	35	39	27
White Horse	22	8	3	11	41	53	27
Market Tavern	22	7	5	10	46	50	26
Victoria Rangers	22	7	3	12	33	45	24
Hargreaves	22	5	6	11	39	39	21
Woodlands '84	22	2	4	16	26	77	10

Lower Division Champions:
1st Div. (11): Stanley Road
Div. 1A (12): Aire United
Div. 1B (12): Bolton Woods Socials
Div. 2A (12): Eccleshill United
Div. 2B (11): Calverley New Inn
Div. 3A (11): Dick Delaneys
Div. 3B (12): Fagley
Div. 4A (14): Microvitec
Div. 4B (13): Thornton

Cup Winners:
Senior Cup: Bolton Woods
Intermediate Cup: Eccleshill United
Amateur Cup: Queensbury

'SPALL' BRENTWOOD SUNDAY LGE
COUNTY: ESSEX

SENIOR DIV.	P	W	D	L	F	A	PTS
Cherry Tree	18	17	1	0	59	12	35
Prince Albert	18	13	2	3	49	26	28
Elm Park United	18	6	7	5	32	31	19
Delma	18	6	6	6	39	37	18
Havering Nalgo	18	6	6	6	37	37	18
Harold Hill	18	6	5	7	43	40	17
Blackmore	18	6	3	9	37	45	15
Brentwood Sports	18	4	5	9	31	50	13
King Harold	18	3	4	11	28	51	10
Mowbrays	18	2	3	13	29	55	7

Lower Division Champions:
Div. 1 (11): Wood United
Div. 2 (12): Oldchurch Park
Div. 3 (11): Warley Hospital
Div. 4 (13): Wickford Dynamoes

'DON BIDGOOD' BRIDGWATER & DISTRICT SUNDAY LEAGUE
COUNTY: SOMERSET & AVON (SOUTH)

DIV. ONE	P	W	D	L	F	A	PTS
Commercial	20	17	3	0	104	19	37
Cavaliers	20	13	5	2	59	34	31
Bridgwater YMCA	20	12	5	3	79	34	29
R.O. Phoenix	20	9	1	10	65	55	19
Woolavington	20	8	2	10	45	44	18
Hamp	20	7	3	10	47	51	17
Ashcott	20	7	2	11	42	71	16
Blake Old Boys	20	5	5	10	41	71	15
Berrow Athletic	20	5	4	11	61	64	14
Crown Inn	20	5	2	13	44	83	12
Withycutter	20	5	2	13	31	92	12

Lower Division Champions:
Div. 2 (14): Coasters
Div. 3 (15): Rosewood

Cup Winners:
Bill Brown K.O. Cup: Cavaliers
Dave Hobbs League K.O. Cup: Cavaliers
Danny Markall/ B'water Refs Cup: Chilton Wdrs
Geoff Ramsey K.O. Cup: Middlezoy Wanderers
Tom Bell Trophy: Castleford/ Cavaliers (shared)
Sportsmanship Shield: Blake Old Boys
Club Linesman award: Woolavington
Top Referee: Steve Richardson
Fair Play award: Blake Old Boys Reserves

BRIGHOUSE SUNDAY LGE
COUNTY: WEST RIDING

DIV. ONE	P	W	D	L	F	A	PTS
Star	18	14	2	2	64	15	30
Sun Inn (L)	18	14	2	2	64	19	30
Rastrick C.C.	18	13	3	2	61	28	29
Spring Gardens	18	8	4	6	46	40	20
Windmill	18	8	2	8	39	33	18
Triangle	18	5	5	8	26	44	15
Thornhill Briggs	18	5	3	10	38	54	13
Pond	18	5	3	10	36	64	13
A.F.C. Whitehall	18	2	3	13	31	55	7
Pop Inn	18	1	3	14	20	73	5

Lower Division Champions:
Div. 2 (11): Town Hall Tavern

'MICK McNEIL' CAMBRIDGE SUNDAY ALLIANCE

COUNTY: CAMBRIDGESHIRE

DIV. ONE	P	W	D	L	F	A	PTS
Rock Rovers	20	15	0	5	60	33	30
Elmdon	20	13	3	4	69	33	29
Oakington	20	10	4	6	73	49	24
Ickleton	20	11	2	7	56	45	24
Reed	20	10	3	7	61	52	23
IDA Darwin	20	7	4	9	59	55	18
Academicals	20	7	2	11	42	58	16
Chem. Labs.	20	6	3	11	41	56	15
Fen Ditton	20	6	3	11	32	67	15
Nokia	20	5	6	11	38	51	14
Sawston R.	20	5	2	13	34	66	12

Longstowe R. - withdrawn

Lower Division Champions:
Div. 2 (12): Chishill A.
Div. 3 (11): Museum Reserves

Cup Winners:
League Cup: Rock Rovers

CARLISLE CITY SUNDAY LGE

COUNTY: CUMBERLAND

DIV. ONE	P	W	D	L	F	A	PTS
Nenthead	22	21	1	0	103	27	43
Pirelli	22	18	2	2	105	33	38
Arroyo	22	16	2	4	95	32	34
Howard Arms	22	12	4	6	77	48	28
Border Rambler	22	8	3	11	52	67	19
N.B.S.	22	8	2	12	57	73	18
Morton	22	7	4	11	58	81	18
Eskdale Thistle	22	6	2	14	44	70	14
Wrestlers	22	6	2	12	47	86	14
Magpie	22	4	5	13	42	75	13
Belle Vue	22	5	3	14	32	81	13
Museum	22	5	2	15	38	77	12

Lower Division Champions:
Div. 2 (11): W.M. Club
Div. 3 (11): Museum Reserves

CARR & CARR SUNDAY LGE

COUNTY: LINCOLNSHIRE

	P	W	D	L	F	A	PTS
E.K.M. International	20	19	0	1	171	29	38
Albert Darnell	20	14	2	4	78	41	*28
Rock Youth Club	20	12	2	6	90	56	26
West Marsh Juniors	20	11	4	5	70	39	26
Wilton Cobley	20	10	1	9	43	71	21
Rock Yth Club Ath.	20	9	1	10	69	64	19
Top Town Market	20	6	3	11	53	71	15
A.C. Dental	20	6	2	12	50	90	14
New Market Wdrs	20	5	3	12	38	111	13
Lloyds Arms	20	3	3	14	39	69	9
Appollo Sports	20	3	2	15	26	83	8

* - 2 points deducted

Cup Winners:
Senior Challenge Cup: E.K.M. International
T G Blow Insurance Junior Cup: Top Town Market
Mayne Challenge Cup: Albert Darnell
Stallingborough Car Centre Shield: Wilton Cobley
Chairman's Shield: A.C. Dental

CENTRAL WARKS OVER 35'S LGE

COUNTY: BIRMINGHAM

DIVISION ONE	P	W	D	L	F	A	PTS
Baldwin & Williams	14	11	1	2	56	13	23
Co-op Tennis	14	11	1	2	47	12	23
Kings Heath Veterans	14	8	1	5	36	22	17
Farthings Old Boys	14	7	2	5	27	22	16
Folly Lane Old Boys	14	5	1	8	25	36	11
Sher Khan	14	4	1	9	19	47	9
Adler Insurance	14	3	2	9	21	44	8
Kynoch	14	2	1	11	22	57	5

Lower Division Champions:
Div.2 (8) Club Sporting

Cup Winners:
Open Cup: Club Sporting
W.H.Richards Memorial Cup: Silhill

'POPE & SMITH' CHELMSFORD SUNDAY FOOTBALL LEAGUE

COUNTY: ESSEX

PREM. DIV.	P	W	D	L	F	A	PTS
Ongar	18	11	4	3	36	20	26
Woodham Town	18	7	7	4	44	35	21
Templar	18	7	6	5	48	42	20
Melbourne United	18	7	4	7	30	30	18
Highfield Victoria	18	7	3	8	48	48	17
Redstones	18	6	5	7	40	43	17
Priory Sports	18	6	4	8	40	43	16
Writtle	18	6	4	8	30	36	16
Gt Baddow Kings Hd	18	6	4	8	34	42	16
Danbury	18	5	3	10	30	41	13

Lower Division Champions:
Div. 1 (12): Little Waltham
Div. 2 (12): Longmeads Manor
Div. 3 (10): Hutton
Div. 4 (11): New Barn
Div. 5 (10): Army & Navy
Div. 6 (11): Margaretting S.S.C.

Cup Winners:
John Coward Chal. Cup: Priory Sports
Peter Gillott Res. Cup: Cherry Tree Spts
Prem. Div. Cup: Highfield Victoria
Div. 1 Cup: Little Waltham
Div. 2 Cup: Star
Div. 3 Cup: Good Easter
Div. 4 Cup: Whitbread Sports
Div. 5 Cup: Army & Navy
Div. 6 Cup: Whitbread Spts Res.
Charity Shield: Redstones

'C. & G.' CHELTENHAM SUNDAY LGE

COUNTY: GLOUCESTERSHIRE

PREM. DIV.	P	W	D	L	F	A	PTS
Lokomotiv Bass	14	11	1	2	52	23	23
Cat and Fiddle	14	10	3	1	57	30	23
Endsleigh	14	9	1	4	43	25	19
Charlton Bass	14	6	3	5	42	33	15
Floormasters	14	5	3	6	30	32	13
Newton Wanderers	14	3	3	8	31	46	9
Old Patesians	14	1	3	10	17	44	5
Cheltenham Saras	14	2	1	11	27	66	5

Lower Division Champions:
Div. 1 (10): Whaddon Sunday
Div. 2 (12): Tewkesbury YMCA
Div. 3 (10): Grosvenor Batman
Div. 4 (10): Warden Hill United
Div. 5 (12): Whaddon Sunday Reserves

CHESHAM SUNDAY LGE

COUNTY: BERKS & BUCKS

PREM. DIVISION	P	W	D	L	F	A	PTS
Pioneer	16	12	3	1	50	11	36
Eldorado	16	9	4	3	58	26	31
Gatecrashes	16	9	3	4	53	30	30
Iyax 61	16	8	5	3	43	21	29
Missdenden	16	6	4	6	45	32	22
Oldens	16	5	7	4	47	39	22
Pheasant	16	4	3	8	30	48	15
C.S.G.	16	3	2	11	21	66	11
Chartridge	16	0	1	15	20	93	1

Lower Division Champions:
Div.1 (10) Iyax 61 Reserves
Div.2 (10) Martin Baker
Div.3 (10) Pheasant (Amersham)
Div.4 (8) Belmont

Cup Winners:
Junior Invitation Cup: Belmont
League Cup: Chesham Nomades
Subsidiary Cup: Ashley Green Eagles

Redstones F.C., Pope & Smith Chelmsford Sunday League Charity Shield winners. Back Row (L/R): Ron Bailey, Trevor Bailey, Graham Hart, Paul Cridland, Gary Meadows, Mick Warren, Alan Tregido, Gary Smith-Herzberg (Manager). Front: Audrey Smith-Herzberg (Secretary), Chris Hart, Gareth Howard, Nick Gonella, Mark Martin, Mick Headon, Mark Wakeham.

Staveley Miners Welfare - Chesterfield Sunday League champions 1992-93. Back Row (L/R): Ray Hill, Kevin Lee, David Pugh, Pete Kenworthy, Rob Langley, Darren Adams, Andy Walker, Phil Greaves, Tony Barnes, Darryn Evans. Front: Lee Vernon, Shane Turner, Steve Botchett, Steve Shipp, Shaun Oldfield, Paul Bicholls. Missing: Ady Wells, Andy Knowles, Avit Burton.

Woolley Moor - Chesterfield Sunday League runners-up 1992-93. Back Row (L/R): Keith Buckley, Gary Weighill, Eric Germany, Nigel Bailey, Andy McGurk, Adam Carline, Phil Boam, Carl Slinn, Don Carline, Ian Cooke, Dave Corcoran, Billy Auld, Dougie Newton. Front: Andy Buckley, Stuart Auld, Neil Ward, Mick Boam, Peter Maltby, Micky Anderson, Martin Riley. Missing: Graham Greaves.

'MANSFIELD BITTER' CHESTERFIELD & DIST. SUNDAY LGE

COUNTY: SHEFFIELD & HALLAMSHIRE

DIV. ONE	P	W	D	L	F	A	PTS
Staveley M.W.	26	17	7	2	81	28	41
Woolley Moor	26	15	8	3	55	38	38
Doe Lea	26	16	5	5	51	28	37
Eckington W. End	26	12	8	6	55	33	32
Brampton Rovers	26	12	5	9	69	51	29
Hasland Pk Rgrs	26	12	3	11	58	49	27
Killamarsh Jnrs	26	11	4	11	53	45	26
K.S.P.O.	26	9	7	10	41	49	25
Matlock Red Lion	26	7	8	11	43	47	22
Kelstedge	26	7	6	13	41	72	20
Wingerworth	22	8	3	15	45	38	19
Hepthorne Lane	26	8	2	16	37	61	18
Grassmoor WMC	26	7	3	16	42	69	17
Coal Aston	26	6	1	19	41	84	13

Cup Winners:
'Tarmac Homes' Alma Cup: Three Horseshoes Colts

CHICHESTER & DIST. SUNDAY LGE

COUNTY: SUSSEX

DIV. ONE	P	W	D	L	F	A	PTS
Whyke	17	12	5	0	49	26	*28
Wittering RBL	18	12	3	3	65	26	27
Gem Travel	18	10	4	4	39	36	24
Charta Furniture	18	11	1	6	46	41	23
East Preston YC	18	9	0	9	62	43	18
Pagham Social Cl.	17	7	4	6	46	50	18
Friary Arms	18	5	4	9	41	47	14
Selsey	18	5	0	13	38	57	10
Fishbourne	18	3	3	12	31	45	9
Bader	18	3	0	15	32	78	6

* - 1 point deducted
N.B. Whyke v Pagham Social Club not played

Lower Division Champions:
Div. 2 (10): Hunston Community Club
Div. 3 (11): Flansham Rangers
Div. 4 (13): True Blue
Div. 5 (11): Spotted Cow

CLACTON & DIST. SUNDAY LGE

COUNTY: ESSEX

PREM. DIVISION	P	W	D	L	F	A	PTS
FC Spartak	18	14	1	3	89	34	29
More Sports	18	13	1	4	52	33	27
Clacton Harlequins*	18	12	2	4	70	27	20
Gunfleet Old Boys	18	10	0	8	46	41	20
St.Osyth	18	9	2	7	46	47	20
West Wing	18	8	2	8	68	43	18
Crossways Sports	18	6	3	9	32	62	15
Napier Royals	18	5	2	11	39	42	12
United Services	18	3	2	13	25	71	8
Inter Hotspurs	18	2	1	15	37	104	5

* - 6pts deducted.

Lower Division Champions:
Div.1 (10) Cosmos Sporting
Div.2 (12) Merrydowners
Div.3 (12) Vista Park
Div.4 (11) Trafalgar

Cup Winners:
Cooley Cup: Clacton Harlequins
Vincent Cup: Clacton Harlequins
Pryke Cup: Gunfleet Old Boys Reserves
Hemsted Trophy: Arantez

CORONATION SUNDAY LGE

COUNTY: BIRMINGHAM

DIV. ONE	P	W	D	L	F	A	PTS
Bournville Warriors	22	15	2	5	58	28	32
Olton Royale	22	13	3	6	54	34	29
Leefal	22	10	8	4	57	37	28
Farthings	22	10	7	5	58	44	27
Kingshurst AVT	22	9	7	6	49	35	25
Bell Marston Green	22	9	6	7	46	44	24
Kenwick Dymano	22	8	6	8	37	37	22
Sheldon Hth Soc.	22	9	4	9	39	46	22
Jumbos XI	22	9	2	12	48	56	19
Bromford Colts	22	5	5	12	28	51	15
Capricorn	22	3	5	14	28	58	11
Wychall Sports	22	2	6	14	22	54	10

Lower Division Champions:
Premier Div. 1 (9): Bordesley Rovers
Div. 1 (10): C. Coach & Horses
Div. 2 (12): Mackadown Lane Spts & Soc.
Div. 3 (12): Fairfax United
Div. 4 (11): Merritts Brook
Alliance Div. 1 (12): Evode
Alliance Div. 2 (12): Rio Saints
Alliance Div. 3 (12): Greenlands Social
Alliance Div. 4 (12): Two Hands
Alliance Div. 5 (13): Crusaders 'B'

Cup Winners:
'First Personnel' Coronation Cup: Bournville Warriors
Keeley Cup: Farthings
George Tomlinson Cup: Fleet Athletic
'Sandells' Senior Cup: Merritts Brook
Jim Walsh Cup: Hillfield Stables 'A'
'J.P. Computers' Alliance Cup: Rio Saints
Delmar Cup: Evode
Sid Houlders Cup: Rio Saints
Trevor Thornton Cup: King of Bohemia
'Celebrations Disco' Shield: Crusaders 'B'

'MITCHELLS & BUTLERS SALES' COVENTRY & DIST. SUNDAY LGE

COUNTY: BIRMINGHAM

PREMIER ONE	P	W	D	L	F	A	PTS
J.F.Kennedy	22	16	4	2	61	28	36
Alvis S&S	22	16	1	5	59	22	33
Unipart	22	13	4	5	68	44	30
Golden Eagle	22	9	9	4	51	35	27
Poplat Athletic	22	10	5	7	52	35	25
Collycroft Rangers	22	10	4	8	41	31	24
Finham Park	22	8	2	12	34	44	18
Tile Hill Social	22	7	3	12	39	34	17
St.Finbarrs	22	6	5	11	44	43	17
Wheel Wanderers	22	6	5	11	60	54	17
Twenty Millpool	22	5	6	11	31	58	16
Coventry Jaguar	22	1	2	19	14	106	4

Lower Division Champions:
Premier 2 (11) Devon Wanderers
Senior 1 (11) Holbrooks Athletic
Senior 2 (11) Newman Old Boys
Senior 3 (11) Green Lane Social
Senior 4 (14) Long Lawford
Senior 5 (24) Barras Aces
Intermediate 1 (13) Coventry Apex
Intermediate 2 (12) Parkstone W.M.C. Reserves
Intermediate 3 (13) Boat Van Plas

'BROTHER' CRAMLINGTON SUNDAY LGE

COUNTY: NORTHUMBERLAND

PREMIER DIV.	P	W	D	L	F	A	PTS
Dudley & Weetslade	22	17	3	2	84	37	37
Shankhouse United	22	16	2	4	82	39	34
Trav. Rest Wideopen	22	14	4	4	58	32	32
W. Wideopen S.C.	22	13	4	5	58	27	30
Cram. Benedict. CSC	22	14	2	6	60	31	30
New Hartley	22	9	8	5	62	46	26
Blyth Tavern	22	6	4	12	55	67	16
Seghill S.C.	22	7	0	15	50	52	14
Bed'ton Bk Bull Terr.	22	6	2	14	38	72	14
New Fordley	22	6	1	15	50	79	13
Drift Inn Seaton Bn	22	6	1	15	36	74	13
Cram'ton Phoenix	22	2	1	19	23	101	5

Lower Division Champions:
Div. 1 (14): East Hartford S.C.
Div. 2 (13): Bridge Inn Annitsford
Div. 3 (15): Ponteland A.F.I.

CREWE REGIONAL SUNDAY LEAGUE
COUNTY: CHESHIRE

DIV. ONE	P	W	D	L	F	A	PTS
Malpas	18	14	4	0	97	14	32
Betley	18	12	3	3	70	26	27
Haslington Villa	18	10	4	4	60	21	24
Wybunbury	18	10	4	4	53	35	24
Alexandra	18	8	5	5	80	32	21
Willaston White Star	18	9	3	6	65	33	21
Verdin United	18	6	3	9	43	49	15
Faddiley	18	4	1	13	43	63	9
Weston	18	3	1	14	45	70	7
Permanent Way	18	0	0	18	13	229	0

Lower Division Champions:
Div. 2 (12): Cumberland Arms
Div. 3 (13): Cholmondeley

CROSBY & DIST. SUNDAY LGE
COUNTY: LIVERPOOL

DIV. ONE	P	W	D	L	F	A	PTS
Lion Hotel	20	18	2	0	91	15	38
Eden Vale	20	16	3	1	88	23	35
R.N.A. Kirkby	20	10	3	7	53	40	23
Lathom	20	9	6	5	52	46	*22
Strand Tavern	20	9	2	9	36	33	20
Dominion	20	9	2	9	54	57	20
Hawthorne	20	8	3	9	48	50	19
Chesterfield Park	20	4	7	9	28	43	15
Carisbrooke Hotel	20	6	2	12	47	73	14
Brownmoore Park	20	4	1	15	29	53	9
Toms Tavern	20	1	1	18	19	113	3

Lower Division Champions:
Div. 2 (13): St William of York
Div. 3 (14): Thornton Rangers

Cup Winners:
Lal Evans Memorial Trophy: Carisbrooke Hotel
Can Francis Cup: Eden Vale
League Challenge Cup: Alex
Lol Hunt Memorial Cup: Sunblest

CROYDON SUNDAY LGE
COUNTY: SURREY

PREM. DIV.	P	W	D	L	F	A	PTS
Holderness United	12	7	3	2	38	13	17
Stafford Athletic	12	5	4	3	30	19	14
Addington M'well	12	5	4	3	29	24	14
Lion Brewery	12	4	5	3	25	25	13
Newton	12	5	2	5	22	23	12
Glendale United	12	4	1	7	19	34	9
Kerria Sports	12	1	3	8	18	43	5

Lower Division Champions:
Div. 1 (9): Windmill Warriors
Div. 2 (9): Blackhorse
Div. 3 (9): Eversley Rangers
Div. 4 (10): Croydon Council
Div. 5 (10): Croydon Pitlake
Div. 6 (10): Croydon Corporation
Div. 7 (10): Vikings
Div. 8 (11): Kendall Athletic
Div. 9 (11): Tornadoes Reserves
Div. 10 (10): Grunwald Reserves

DAGENHAM & DIST. SUNDAY LGE
COUNTY: ESSEX

SENIOR DIVISION	P	W	D	L	F	A	PTS
Clapton Agyle	14	11	2	1	37	13	24
Rainham Rangers	14	9	4	1	52	19	22
Manor House	14	7	2	5	37	20	16
Dagenham T. H.	14	4	6	4	28	27	14
Station Garage 'A'	14	5	2	7	29	31	12
Church Elm	14	4	2	8	15	32	10
Thorbridge	14	2	3	9	15	35	7
Little Heath	14	3	1	10	19	55	7

Lower Division Champions:
Div. 1 (10) Manhattans   **Div. 2** (10) Gidea Park
Div. 3 (10) Cue Ball 'B'   **Div. 4** (10) Chandlers

Cup Winners:
Webb Cup: Hook End Rgrs
Palmer Cup: Tyndale Utd
Bellamy Cup: Heathlane
Senior Cup: Clapton Argyle
Stevens Cup: Rainham Rgrs

Carlowe Cup: Manhattans
Potter Cup: Hook End Rgrs
Nicholls Cup: Lessa Forest
Sweetlove Cup: Rialto   **Essex Cup:** Europa Spts
Ward Cup: Europa Spts   **Celtic Cup:** Chandlers
Girling Cup: Chester

DONCASTER & DISTRICT SUNDAY ALLIANCE
COUNTY: SHEFFIELD & HALLAMSHIRE

PREM. DIV.	P	W	D	L	F	A	PTS
Case Sports	18	15	1	2	78	14	31
Flying Childers	18	10	3	5	41	27	23
Clay Lane WMC	18	7	6	5	32	27	20
Broadway Celtic	18	9	2	7	44	49	20
Bullcroft S.P.A.	18	8	3	7	33	36	19
Railway Hotel	18	5	6	7	44	54	16
Adam & Eve	18	7	1	10	36	44	15
Wheatsheaf Hotel	18	5	4	9	26	36	14
Hatfield Woodhouse	18	6	2	10	25	43	14
Leger F.C.	18	3	2	13	31	60	8

Lower Division Champions:
Div. 1 (12): Scawthorpe
Div. 2 (12): Edlington Spartans
Div. 3 (12): Magdalen
Div. 4 (12): Balby Bridge
Div. 5 (12): South Kirkby
Div. 6 (11): The Maltings
Div. 7 (12): Hallcross

Cup Winners:
League Cup: Case Sports
Supplementary Cup: Edlington Spartans

DUDLEY & CRADLEY HEATH SUNDAY LEAGUE
COUNTY: BIRMINGHHAM

PREM. DIV.	P	W	D	L	F	A	PTS
Jolly Good	16	15	0	1	82	14	30
Labour	16	15	0	1	89	25	30
White Horse	16	9	1	6	39	44	19
Roebuck	16	7	2	7	33	41	16
Wren's	16	6	2	8	32	53	14
W. Villa	16	5	2	9	22	33	12
Plough	16	4	3	9	26	57	11
Homark	16	3	0	13	25	47	6
Albron	16	2	2	12	17	51	6

Lower Division Champions:
Div. 1 (11): Malt Shovel
Div. 2 (12): Tavern
Div. 3 (11): Caves
Div. 4 (11): Good Intent
Div. 5 (12): Sporting
Div. 6 (10): Red Lion

'JUSTSPORT' DURHAM & DISTRICT SUNDAY LEAGUE
COUNTY: DURHAM

PREM. DIV.	P	W	D	L	F	A	PTS
Sherburn Vill. WMC	22	17	5	0	102	29	56
Jasprint Biddick Inn	22	12	6	4	85	31	42
Peterlee Cath. Club	22	12	4	6	59	31	40
Fram'gate Moor WMC	22	12	3	7	74	46	39
Ferryhill WMC	22	11	5	6	51	41	38
Relton Terrace WMC	22	10	2	10	63	48	32
Byers Green WMC	22	8	4	10	58	52	28
Shinley Row	22	7	6	9	48	56	27
Belmont WMC	22	8	2	12	40	141	*23
W. Cornforth Vic.	22	5	4	13	41	52	19
Lumley WMC	22	4	2	16	36	83	14
Silksworth Cavalier	22	3	3	16	46	93	*9

* - points deducted

Lower Division Champions:
Div. 1 (11): Hetton WMC
Div. 2 (12): Lambton Arms

Cup Winners:
Russell Office Systems Cup: W.A. Systems
Durham City AFC Supporters Club Cup: Chester Bridge Hotel
'Moor Coachways' League Cup: Ferryhill WMC
Racing Promotions Cup: Sherburn Village WMC
Fair Play Award: Kimblesworth C.C.

ESSEX SUNDAY COMBINATION
COUNTY: ESSEX

SENIOR DIV.	P	W	D	L	F	A	PTS
Tow	19	14	3	2	45	25	45
Nacano	20	13	2	5	67	30	41
Collier Row Supp.	19	10	2	7	38	43	32
Scala	16	9	4	3	33	23	31
Star Albion	20	9	3	8	43	44	30
St Peters	17	7	4	6	23	24	25
Manor House	20	6	5	9	36	33	23
Coach & Horses	17	4	5	8	32	31	17
Lita Sports	17	4	2	11	16	50	14
Hornchurch	16	4	1	11	31	35	13
Ludlows	15	0	5	10	15	41	5

(several matches left unplayed)

Lower Division Champions:
Premier Div. (11): New Beckton
Div. 1 (9): Medhurst
Div. 2 (11): Gidea Park Rangers
Div. 3 (10): Cardinals
Div. 4 (9): L.T. Hornchurch

Cup Winners:
Premier Cup: Scala
McDougall Cup: Caterham
C White Senior Div. Cup: St Peters
Milton Premier Div. Cup: Campion Old Boys
Morfey Div. 1 Cup: Glenthorne United
J.L. Div. 2 Cup: Pretoria Seniors
Beitler Div. 3 Cup: Cardinals
T Evans Div. 4 Cup: Cottons Park
Endeavour Sportmanship Award: St Peters

FESTIVAL SUNDAY LGE
COUNTY: BIRMINGHAM

PREM. DIV.	P	W	D	L	F	A	PTS
Slade Celtic	22	15	5	2	59	25	35
Lodge Cottrell	22	15	3	3	52	19	35
Altone Steels	22	12	6	4	37	24	30
Dulwich	22	11	0	11	44	33	22
Birmingham Celtic	22	8	5	9	35	28	21
Regent	22	8	5	9	38	42	21
Travellers	22	7	6	9	33	44	20
Inter Volante	22	6	7	9	30	41	19
Brookvale Athletic	22	6	6	10	32	45	18
Cork & Bottle	22	6	5	11	36	46	17
Ansells Stockland Star	22	5	3	14	22	46	13
Hundred Acre	22	4	5	13	22	47	13

Lower Division Champions:
Premier Div. 1 (12): Erdington Cosmos
Premier Div. 2 (12): St Andrews Athletic
Festival Div. 1 (11): Kings Colts
Festival Div. 2 (12): Birchley
Festival Div. 3 (11): Old Horns
Festival Div. 4 (12): Delta
Comb. Div. 1 (12): Alba Vale
Comb. Div. 2 (12): Yenton Social
Comb. Div. 3 (12): Portway '74
Comb. Div. 4 (12): Flickers '83
Snr Amateur Div. 1 (9): Black Initiative Rovers
Snr Amateur Div. 2 (9): Oaklands Amateurs
Junior Div. 1 (10): Locomotive Saltley
Junior Div. 2 (10): Sorrento '86

'JEWSON' EVESHAM SUNDAY LGE
COUNTY: WORCESTERSHIRE

DIV. ONE	P	W	D	L	F	A	PTS
Moreton Youth	18	14	2	2	70	30	30
Bear	18	14	0	4	62	22	28
Evesham W.M.C.	18	12	0	6	52	40	24
Bretforton V.I.C.	18	9	1	8	25	31	19
Ashchurch	18	7	3	8	46	41	17
Tewkesbury	18	8	1	9	36	36	17
Red Horse	18	5	4	9	36	41	14
Pershore Dynamoes	18	6	0	12	37	53	12
Bidford Boys Club	18	4	3	11	35	68	11
Littleton	18	3	2	13	26	63	8

Lower Division Champions:
Div. 2 (11): Campden Town
Div. 3 (12): Bredon
Div. 4 (12): Ashchurch Reserves
Div. 5 (12): Bury

Cup Winners:
'Birdseye Sport' K.O. Cup: Bear
'Jewson' Subsidiary Cup: Tewkesbury Town
Bluck Cup: Evesham W.M.C. Reserves

'MARCH PRESS' FROME & DIST. SUNDAY LGE
COUNTY: SOMERSET & AVON (SOUTH)

PREM. DIVISION	P	W	D	L	F	A	PTS
Elm Tree Sports	20	15	3	2	86	35	33
Crown Sports	20	16	1	3	80	38	33
Knatchbull Arms	20	16	0	4	73	28	32
Guss & Crook	20	10	2	8	68	47	22
Railway Taveners	20	9	3	8	51	48	21
Dolphin Sports	20	8	4	8	55	48	19
Elm Tree Inn	20	6	7	7	36	52	19
Chapmanslade	20	6	3	11	45	55	15
Welton White Hart	20	5	2	13	45	50	12
Woolpack Wasps	20	3	2	15	39	101	8
R.E.M.E.	20	2	1	17	25	96	5

Lower Division Champions:
Div. 1 (11) Bradford Albion
Div. 2 (10) Legion Sports Reserves
Div. 3 (10) A.F.C. Prunells

Below: St Peters F.C., Essex Sunday Combination Senior Division Cup winners 1992-93. Photo - Gavin Ellis-Neville.

GLOUCESTER & DIST. SUNDAY LGE
COUNTY: GLOUCESTERSHIRE

PREM. DIV.	P	W	D	L	F	A	PTS
Brockworth Nomads	20	15	0	5	56	25	45
Pint Pot Bowmen	20	15	0	5	86	34	*44
Pikemen	20	12	0	8	55	51	36
Churchdown Parish	20	11	2	7	60	49	35
Jennings O.H.	20	10	2	8	52	50	32
Longford	20	10	1	9	72	61	31
Ermin Plant	20	8	2	10	42	72	26
Brockworth Parish	20	8	0	12	59	66	24
Year 2,000	20	6	2	12	45	68	20
Temco Sports	20	6	1	13	43	61	19
Woolpack	20	3	2	15	50	82	11

* - 1 point deducted

Lower Division Champions:
Div. 1 (12): Hardwicke
Div. 2 (12): Glos Tramways
Div. 3 (12): Customade
Div. 4 (12): Severn Sound
Div. 5 (12): Forest Police
Div. 6 (12): Westgate Harriers
Div. 7 (10): John Carr

GOSPORT & FAREHAM SUNDAY LGE
COUNTY: HAMPSHIRE

DIVISION ONE	P	W	D	L	F	A	PTS
Wheatsheaf	16	14	0	2	74	22	28
Cilvil Service Cross	16	11	1	4	46	34	23
Salterns W.M.C.	16	9	3	4	44	28	21
Hill Park W.M.C.	16	8	2	6	47	38	18
Junction	16	6	3	7	43	40	15
Wallington	16	5	3	8	28	43	13
AFC Castle	16	5	2	9	33	58	12
Lee R.B. Legion	16	4	3	9	38	39	11
Rowner Rec. Centre	16	1	1	14	22	73	3

Lower Division Champions:
Div. 2 (9) AFC Stubbington
Div. 3 (9) Queen's Head Crusaders
Div. 4 (10) Locksheath W.M.C.
Div. 5 (12) FC Sporting Eagles
Div. 6 (12) Pentas

GREAT YARMOUTH & DISTRICT SUNDAY LEAGUE
COUNTY: NORFOLK

DIV. ONE	P	W	D	L	F	A	PTS
Tudor Tavern	22	18	1	3	99	29	55
Schooners	22	17	2	3	74	23	53
Acle Rangers	22	14	2	6	79	43	44
Gorleston United	22	14	1	7	57	33	43
East Coast	22	11	2	9	83	56	35
Alley Cats	22	11	4	7	72	43	*34
Halvergate	22	10	4	8	62	43	34
Wheelwrights	22	11	1	10	62	46	34
Portofino	22	3	6	13	32	73	15
Ludham	22	3	4	15	32	99	13
St Cloud	22	2	4	16	30	94	10
G.C. Tigers	22	1	3	18	28	127	6

* - 3 points deducted

Lower Division Champions:
Div. 2 (12): Bure Cons
Div. 3 (11): Caister Athletic
Div. 4 (12): Caister United

GRIMSBY, CLEETHORPES & DISTRICT SUNDAY LEAGUE
COUNTY: LINCOLNSHIRE

DIV. ONE	P	W	D	L	F	A	PTS
Blossom Way Spts	20	16	1	3	64	22	33
Young Ross	20	13	4	3	62	24	30
Freetime Sports	20	13	3	4	49	23	29
Grimsby College	20	10	5	5	42	27	25
Athletico	20	8	6	6	48	27	22
Swigs	20	8	2	10	50	51	18
Seawave United	20	7	3	10	31	52	17
Bradley Amateurs	20	5	6	9	36	50	16
Healing	20	6	3	11	35	64	15
Imperial Ford	20	2	3	15	23	67	7
Kingsway Printers	20	2	4	14	23	56	6

Lower Division Champions:
Div. 2 (12): Humberston
Div. 3 (10): Freetime Sports Reserves
Div. 4 (12): Bridge
Div. 5 (13): Habrough H.H.
Div. 6 (12): Jazz
Div. 7 (13): Findus
Div. 8 (13): Cross Keys
Div. 9 (13): Newtons
Div. 10 (12): New Clee

HARINGEY, TOTTENHAM & DISTRICT SUNDAY LGE
COUNTY: LONDON

PREM. DIV.	P	W	D	L	F	A	PTS
Wood Green Labour	16	12	2	2	61	21	26
Criterion	16	12	1	3	52	19	25
S.T. Dutch House	16	10	2	4	45	25	22
Raggermuffins	16	9	2	5	43	32	20
Black Horse	16	5	3	8	30	37	13
Risley	16	6	0	10	23	36	12
Fountain	16	4	4	8	28	45	12
Gunners	16	3	2	11	18	54	8
Highbury Grove	16	2	2	12	19	50	6

Lower Division Champions:
Div. 1 (9): Seaton
Div. 2 (10): Belmont
Div. 3 (9): St Pauls

HARLOW & DIST. SUNDAY LGE
COUNTY: ESSEX

PREM. DIVISION	P	W	D	L	F	A	PTS
Marquis Sports	16	11	3	2	47	18	25
Maypole Athletic	16	11	1	4	59	21	23
United Glass Spts	16	9	4	3	52	18	22
Maypole Sports	16	9	4	3	53	31	22
Cossor Swifts	16	9	2	5	38	21	20
Pitney Bowes	16	4	5	7	28	37	13
Lindsay Street	16	4	4	8	23	59	12
Milwards	16	1	2	13	20	71	4
Northbrooks C.A.	16	1	1	14	21	65	3

Lower Division Champions:
Div. 1 Gilbeys
Div. 2 Bassett Rangers
Div. 3 RHM Computing
Div. 4 U.G.Sports Reserves
Div. 5 Highways
Div. 6 General Portfolio
Div. 7 Creative PPE

Cup Winners:
Premier Div. Cup: Cossor Swifts
Div. 1 Cup: Whalebone Rangers
Div. 2 Cup: Toot Hill
Div. 3 Cup: Hummingbird
Div. 4 Cup: Moot House
Div. 5 Cup: Memorial
Div. 6 Cup: Cascade United
Div. 7 Cup: Altham Grove

HASTINGS & EAST SUSSEX SUNDAY LGE
COUNTY: SUSSEX

DIV. ONE	P	W	D	L	F	A	PTS
Kings Head (Ore)	20	15	3	2	61	18	33
Oddfellows Arms	20	15	2	3	73	28	32
Hastings Postal	20	11	4	5	47	31	26
Vikings	20	9	5	6	48	33	23
Hastings Fishermen	20	10	1	9	63	39	21
Ellerhoop	20	8	5	7	42	36	21
Kings Head (Battle)	20	9	1	10	68	45	19
Comet	20	8	3	9	43	42	19
Harrow	20	4	6	10	49	61	14
Westfield Plough	20	3	2	15	26	88	8
Clarence	20	1	2	17	17	116	4

Lower Division Champions:
Div. 2 (11): Bexhill A.A.C.
Div. 3 (11): Kent Cricketer
Div. 4 (11): Hastings Postal Reserves
Div. 5 (12): Churchills Hotel

Cup Winners: *(see overleaf)*

Demarco Cup: Kings Head (Ore)
Peter Harris Mem. Trophy: Kings Head (Ore)
Observer Cup: Oddfellows Arms Reserves
'Roebuck Hire Centre' Lower Divs Cup: Hastings Postal Reserves
Oberver Sportsmanship Trophy: Saxons
Leading Scorer award: Steve Engelfield (47)

HAYES & DISTRICT SUNDAY LGE
COUNTY: MIDDLESEX

PREM. DIV.	P	W	D	L	F	A	PTS
Beavers	14	10	3	1	47	19	33
Hillingdon Pk Rgrs	14	9	2	3	50	16	29
Eastville (Liftco)	14	8	2	4	21	23	26
White Lodge Sun.	14	6	2	6	40	34	20
Eastcote United	14	6	1	7	46	40	19
Dawley Wanderers	14	6	1	7	28	27	19
Bourne Athletic	14	4	1	9	25	39	13
Sandersons	14	1	0	13	18	77	3

Technicolor Sunday and Isleworth both withdrawn

Lower Division Champions:
Div. 1 (8): Northolt United
Div. 2 (10): Drayton Wanderers
Div. 3 (8): Southall G.P.O.
Div. 4 (9): Beavers Reserves
Div. 5 (10): The Vine

HEAVY WOOLLEN GATE SUNDAY ALLIANCE LGE
COUNTY: WEST RIDING

PREM. DIVISION	P	W	D	L	F	A	PTS
Layezee	22	19	2	1	65	17	59
Overthorpe SC	22	17	4	1	70	18	55
Thornhill Lees	22	13	5	4	72	34	44
Battyeford BC	22	11	2	9	51	38	35
St.John Fisher OB	22	9	6	7	59	52	33
Pear Tree	22	8	3	11	45	51	27
Rose & Crown C.	22	8	2	12	56	68	26
Birkenshaw	22	4	8	10	37	55	20
Shaw Cross BC	22	5	5	12	45	80	20
Birstall St.Pats	22	4	6	12	44	65	18
Nelson Inn	22	4	6	12	36	63	18
Hanging Heaton	22	4	3	15	40	79	15

Lower Division Champions:
Div. 1 (12) Alma
Div. 2 (12) Cleckheaton Joiners
Div. 3 (12) Battyford BC Reserves
Div. 4 (12) White Lee
Div. 5 (13) New Albion
Div. 6 (13) Battyford BC 'A'

HENDON & DIST. SUNDAY LGE
COUNTY: MIDDLESEX/LONDON

PREM. DIVISION	P	W	D	L	F	A	PTS
Linton	16	14	1	1	51	15	29
West Hendon ESC	16	11	3	2	58	25	25
Kingsfisher Yth	16	10	2	4	39	24	22
Nissan Wembley	16	6	5	5	29	28	17
Belmont Seniors	16	5	3	8	52	41	13
Kenboro	16	6	1	9	47	38	13
Park Royals	16	2	6	8	26	53	10
Maccabi	16	1	6	9	22	42	8
Moberley	16	2	3	11	20	78	7

Lower Division Champions:
Intermediate Div. (9) Rossmore
Div. 1 (11) Espana
Div. 2 (11) All Saints Ken
Div. 3 (9) Eversfield
Div. 4 (12) Tara Ramblers
Div. 5 (11) Westcroft

Cup Winners:
Challenge Cup: Linton
Presidents Cup: Wealdstone ESC
Mulston Cup: Tara Ramblers
Wishing Well Final Senior: Cygen
Wishing Well Final Junior: Apex Corner

HITCHIN GAZETTE SUNDAY LGE
COUNTY: HERTFORDSHIRE

PREM. DIV.	P	W	D	L	F	A	PTS
Sportsman	22	16	4	2	86	31	36
Cricketers	22	15	4	3	70	25	34
Offley Social	22	14	3	5	79	46	31
Walsworth	22	14	3	5	70	48	31
Westbury C.A.	22	10	5	7	44	33	25
Nightingale Utd	22	10	3	9	61	37	23
Old White Horse	22	10	2	10	36	40	22
Bell	22	8	5	9	55	52	21
Angels	22	6	5	11	62	74	17
Wanderers	22	4	4	14	33	61	12
Westbury United	22	4	3	15	36	72	11
New Found Out	22	0	1	21	15	128	1

Lower Division Champions:
Div. 1 (11): Baldock '82
Div. 2 (12): Engineers Arms
Div. 3 (10): Letchworth G.C.
Div. 4 (11): Hitchin Social

Cup Winners:
Gazette Challenge Cup: Sportsman
George John Trophy: Westbury C.A.
Premier Div. Cup: Sportsman
Div. 1 Cup: Four Emblems
Div. 2 Cup: Engineers Arms
Div. 3 Cup: Letchworth Garden City
Div. 4 Cup: Grange
Reserve Team Cup: Sportsman

HUDDERSFIELD & DISTRICT SUNDAY LEAGUE
COUNTY: WEST RIDING

DIVISION ONE	P	W	D	L	F	A	PTS
Sikh Temple	18	14	2	2	62	23	44
Railway Inn	18	13	1	4	53	33	40
Wappy Springs	18	11	1	6	57	43	34
Bradley R.	18	9	3	6	49	22	30
Moldgreen Con.	18	8	5	5	30	31	29
Beaumont Arms	18	8	3	7	43	30	27
Junction	18	7	1	10	51	36	22
Clayton West	18	6	3	9	47	34	21
Black Bull Birkby	18	5	0	13	41	51	15
Stile Common	18	0	0	18	14	139	0

Lower Division Champions:
Div. 2 (11) Rowley Hill
Div. 3 (12) Burton R.
Div. 4 (11) Fleece Inn
Div. 5 (12) Town Hall

HYDE & DISTRICT SUNDAY LGE
COUNTY: MANCHESTER

PREM. DIV.	P	W	D	L	F	A	PTS
Haughton Villa	18	13	3	2	57	30	29
Crown & Cushion F.	18	10	6	2	54	20	26
Royal Oak Gorton	18	9	6	3	43	20	24
Carters Bridge	18	11	1	6	58	38	*19
Lamb Hotel	18	8	3	7	33	27	19
Sycamore	18	6	4	8	30	47	16
Tintwistle Villa	18	6	2	10	41	50	14
Woodley	18	5	3	10	41	49	13
Jolly Carter	18	3	3	12	25	58	9
White Horse	18	3	1	14	17	60	7

* - 4 points deducted

Lower Division Champions:
Div. 1 (13): Grapes
Div. 2 (11): Gee Cross Villa
Div. 3 (13): Crown
Div. 4 (14): New Inn Ashton
Div. 5 (12): Halfway House Ashton
Div. 6 (11): New Inn Dukinfield

Cup Winners:
Challenge Cup: Penny Farthing
Reporter Cup: Crown & Cushion Failsworth
John Wood Cup: Grapes
John Godley Cup: Gamesley
Dennis Mooney Mem. Trophy: Mechanics Arms
Kevin Furness Cup: Halfway House Ashton
Gledhill Cup: Acres Inn

ISLE OF WIGHT SUNDAY LGE
COUNTY: HAMPSHIRE

DIV. ONE	P	W	D	L	F	A	PTS
Plessey	20	18	0	2	101	20	54
W.A.S.S.	20	14	3	3	66	39	*44
Northwood United	20	10	4	6	51	38	34
Tavern	20	9	6	5	60	49	33
Wight City	20	10	2	8	55	54	32
East Cowes Libs	20	8	5	7	41	37	*28
Fleming Estates	20	7	4	9	43	55	25
Castle	20	7	3	10	40	46	24
Columbia	20	4	2	14	28	60	14
Nomads XI	20	4	2	14	45	83	14
Shide Rovers	20	2	3	15	26	72	9

* - 1 point deducted

Lower Division Champions:
Div. 2 (9): Plessey Reserves
Div. 3 (14): Cowes Social '92

KIDDERMINSTER & DISTRICT SUNDAY LGE
COUNTY: WORCESTERSHIRE

PREM. DIV.	P	W	D	L	F	A	PTS
London	26	16	7	3	75	36	55
Stourbridge United	26	16	5	5	70	43	53
Brickhouse	26	15	5	6	64	43	50
Burlish Olympic	26	13	7	6	53	35	46
Cradley Olympic	26	11	9	6	58	38	42
S.R.M.	26	12	6	8	65	58	42
William Stevens	26	11	8	7	35	29	41
Kingswinford	26	10	5	11	39	38	35
Preston '81	26	9	3	14	49	64	30
Wolverley Athletic	26	7	8	11	66	56	29
Norton	26	8	5	13	46	58	29
Swindon Greyhound	26	8	3	15	45	58	27
Grange Athletic	26	6	5	15	38	72	23
Longlands	26	0	4	22	22	93	4

Lower Division Champions:
Div. 1 (14): Brintons
Div. 2 (14): Alveley
Div. 3 (14): Gornal Social
Div. 4 (14): Pedmore
Div. 5 (16): Talbot Spa
Div. 6 (16): Grange United Reserves

'LINLEY HAULAGE' KINGSTON-UPON-HULL SUNDAY LGE
COUNTY: EAST RIDING

PREM. DIV.	P	W	D	L	F	A	PTS
New Inn	20	15	3	2	67	35	33
Brighams	20	14	3	3	49	25	31
Swanfield	20	12	2	6	55	29	26
B & A Scaffolding	20	8	8	4	28	21	24
Viking Malet	20	8	4	8	38	49	20
Keyingham	20	6	7	7	39	41	19
Chalk Lane	20	6	6	8	41	36	18
Northwood	20	7	3	10	31	36	17
Lord Nelson	20	6	4	10	22	42	16
St Peters	20	4	4	12	34	48	12
Dockers	20	1	2	17	27	69	4

Lower Division Champions:
Div. 1 (11): Settingdyke Youth Club
Div. 2 (12): Boothferry Tigers
Div. 3 (12): Fish Trades 'B'
Div. 4 (12): West Lee Youth Club
Div. 5 (11): Spreadeagle Driffield
Div. 6 (12): Malet Uni Flo
Div. 7 (12): Mill Lane United
Div. 8 (12): Falcon
Div. 9 (12): Charlton 'B'
Div. 10 (12): Wellington Inn
Div. 11 (12): Endyke 'B'
Div. 12 (12): Lambwath Juventus
Div. 13 (12): Holderness Casuals
Div. 14 (12): Cornmill
Div. 15 (11): Stadium Developments
Div. 16 (12): A.F.C. Lodge
Div. 17 (12): Cherokee S.C.
Div. 18 (11): A.F.C. Waggoners
Div. 19 (12): Royal British Legion
Div. 20 (11): Oddbottle

Cup Winners:
'Munro' Senior Cup: Chalk Lane
'Hostick' Intermediate Cup: Malet Uni-Flo
'Halford' Intermediate Cup: Eldons
'Linley Haulage' Junior Cup: Inglemire Rangers

'NORMAN STEPHENS UNLIMITED' LEAMINGTON & DIST. SUNDAY LGE
COUNTY: BRIMINGHAM

PREM. DIVISION	P	W	D	L	F	A	PTS
Leamington C.	18	14	1	3	57	12	29
Long Itchington	18	13	1	4	68	30	27
St.Patricks	18	10	5	3	47	25	25
Radford Newbold	18	9	2	7	39	31	20
Westlea Wanderers	18	7	3	8	36	31	17
Harbury Albion	18	5	5	8	27	45	15
Cubbington Albion	18	5	4	9	32	41	14
Whitnash	18	5	2	11	31	52	12
Kenilworth S.	18	5	1	12	20	40	11
Lighthorne Sports	18	4	2	12	17	57	10

Lower Division Champions:
Div. 1 Kenilworth Wardens
Div. 2 Radford Newbold Reserves
Div. 3 Kenilworth Gauntlet
Div. 4 Stockton
Div. 5 Bearley United Reserves

LEEDS SUNDAY COMBINATION
COUNTY: WEST RIDING

JUBILEE PREMIER	P	W	D	L	F	A	PTS
Beulah	22	13	5	4			31
Oldfield Hotel	22	8	10	4			26
Monkbridge	22	10	5	7			25
Prince Philip	22	8	8	6			24
Fforde Grene	22	8	7	7			23
Gildersome Tavs	22	8	6	8			22
Bird In Hand	22	6	8	8			20
Holbeck Boys C.	22	6	8	8			20
Horsforth Bridge	22	6	7	9			19
Main Line Social	22	7	5	10			19
Myrtle FC	22	7	4	11			18
White Hart	22	6	5	11			17

Lower Division Champions:
Prem. Div. Marksmen
Div. 1 Swillington Welfare
Div. 2 W. Leeds Railwaymen
Div. 3 Woodman Churwell
Div. 4 Bulls Head
Div. 5 Burmantofts Sports
Div. 6 Boars Head Athletic

'MANULIFE' LEATHERHEAD & DISTRICT SUNDAY LGE
COUNTY: SURREY

PREM. DIVISION	P	W	D	L	F	A	PTS
Bookham	16	12	2	2	40	15	26
West Ewell	16	12	1	3	46	23	25
Leatherhead Rgrs	16	9	4	3	37	22	22
Amstell United	16	7	4	5	34	35	18
O.Wimbledonians	16	7	2	7	37	38	16
Fetcham Ionians	16	4	7	5	34	23	15
Molesey Social	16	6	2	8	36	44	14
Beare Green	16	2	2	12	26	45	6
Rhodrons	16	1	0	15	25	71	2

Lower Division Champions:
Div. 1 S.C.R.
Div. 2 Sporting Wellington
Div. 3 A.F.C. Berrylands
Div. 4 Ashtead Park
Div. 5 Bookham Reserves
Div. 6 Surrey Electrics
Div. 7 Kingston Vale
Div. 8 Pelham Ashtead Reserves

Cup Winners
Senior Challenge Cup: Old Wimbledonians
Intermediate Challenge Cup: Europa
Junior Challenge Cup: Railway Arms

LEICESTER SUNDAY ALLIANCE
COUNTY: LEICESTERSHIRE & RUTLAND
'Leics Galvanising' Premier Division

	P	W	D	L	F	A	PTS
Westcotes United	14	12	1	1	53	19	25
Leicester Citybus	14	7	4	3	49	34	18
East Goscote	14	7	4	3	39	30	18
Demes Athletic	14	6	4	4	45	30	16
Sleath	14	4	3	7	34	38	11
Leicester Market	14	6	1	7	37	45	*11
Aylestone Pk Celtic	14	4	2	8	35	52	10
Mayflower Sunday	14	6	3	9	25	37	21

* - 2 points deducted

Lower Division Champions:
'Tebbutt Brown' Div. 1 (11): Saffron Dynamo Sunday
'Sonney James' Div. 2 (12): Anstey
'Nicks Travel' Div. 3 (12): Old Hare & Hounds Anstey
'Bells' Div. 4 (12): Saffron Park
Div. 5 (12): Dunton Plant
Div. 6 (12): Aylestone '91 Sunday
Div. 7 (12): Parva United

Cup Winners
'Bostik' Chairmans Cup: Cock Inn Arnesby
'Everards Brewery' League Cup: Westcotes Utd Res.
Presidents Cup: Serbia
Les King Mem. Invitation Tphy: Birstall Utd O.B.
Griffin Senior Cup: Westcotes United Reserves

LONDON COMMERCIAL SUNDAY LGE
COUNTY: MIDDLESEX/ LONDON

DIV. ONE	P	W	D	L	F	A	PTS
Evershed Social	18	12	4	2	47	23	40
British Airways	18	11	5	2	42	25	38
57 Club	18	11	5	2	38	21	38
Charing Cross	18	8	4	6	36	27	28
District Line	18	8	3	7	40	35	27
Meadhurst Sports	18	6	4	8	27	28	22
Royal Mail	18	6	3	9	40	40	21
Sudbury Court	18	6	3	9	25	37	21
Travaux (Dept of E.)	18	5	2	11	32	54	17
Priory	18	0	1	17	7	44	1

Division 2 Champions (10): Harrow Gas

LONG EATON SUNDAY LGE
COUNTY: DERBYSHIRE

PREM. DIVISION	P	W	D	L	F	A	PTS
Sandiacre Town	26	20	5	1	107	31	65
Sportsman	26	17	2	7	81	41	53
Stapleford C. Rgrs	26	15	4	7	68	49	49
Bracken Park	26	15	3	8	79	45	48
Grandstand 83	26	13	6	7	70	43	45
Railway	26	12	9	5	59	38	45
Squires United	26	13	4	9	62	69	43
Attenborough Spts	26	12	5	11	65	41	41
Ladywood	26	9	5	12	40	52	32
Jolly Potters	26	9	4	13	64	62	31
Wollaton Sunday	26	4	9	13	55	81	21
Greenwich Albion	26	2	7	17	29	82	10
Dovedale Long E.	26	3	4	19	29	109	10
Rutland Cottage	26	3	3	20	25	76	9

Lower Division Champions:
Div. 1 Athletica   **Div. 2** Beeston Rylands
Div. 3 Longmoor United
Div. 4 Jolly Potters Reserves

Cup Winners:
Snowball Cup: Sportsman
Premier Cup: Railway
Senior Cup: Carson Athletic
Junior Cup: Erewash Police

MANCHESTER AMATEUR SUNDAY LEAGUE
COUNTY: MANCHESTER

DIVISION ONE	P	W	D	L	F	A	PTS
E. Levenshulme	16	10	4	2	51	35	24
Kearsley	16	9	5	2	45	29	23
Moss Side	16	8	5	3	56	37	21
Mauldeth Parrswood	16	10	1	5	38	26	21
M'chester Maccabi	16	8	2	6	37	32	18
Burnage	16	6	3	7	38	34	15
Trafford Barons	16	4	2	10	34	28	10
Red Lion Withgton	16	2	3	11	22	54	7
Royce	16	1	1	14	29	75	3

Lower Division Champions:
Div. 2 (11): Orion Villa
Div. 3 (12): Alma Park
Div. 4 (14): Mile End Villa

Cup Winners:
J.A.Kennedy Cup: Mauldeth/Parrswood
John Old Cup: Fortland
Supplementary Cup:
Div. 1: Kearsley
Div. 2: Orion Villa
Div. 3: Leigh Boro
Div. 4: Portland

MEON VALLEY SUNDAY LGE
COUNTY: HAMPSHIRE

DIV. ONE	P	W	D	L	F	A	PTS
Hunters Inn	20	17	1	2	82	33	35
Wickham Dynamo	20	15	1	4	65	28	31
Denmead	20	14	1	5	67	38	29
Sir J Paxton	20	8	6	6	52	44	22
Good Sports	20	10	2	8	52	45	22
N. & P.	20	7	5	8	52	48	19
Kennett Bros.	20	8	3	9	54	56	19
Timberland	20	7	2	11	45	60	16
Hampshire Rose	20	6	2	12	44	68	14
New Casuals	20	6	1	13	34	65	13
Aztec Sports	20	0	0	20	25	87	0

Lower Division Champions:
Div. 2 (12): Seagull
Div. 3 (11): Crows Nest
Div. 4 (12): M.V. Hotel

METROPOLITAN SUNDAY
COUNTY: LONDON

PREM. DIVISION	P	W	D	L	F	A	PTS
London Thistle	16	9	4	3	51	22	22
Convoys	16	10	2	4	52	28	22
Fisher Elliotts	16	7	5	4	44	34	19
Brettell	16	8	3	5	42	33	19
Lambeth Sportsman	16	7	4	5	43	29	18
Woolwich Postal	16	8	1	7	45	59	17
Santogee 66	16	4	6	6	33	40	14
Oxford Road Social	16	4	2	10	23	39	10
Leeford	16	1	1	14	13	62	3

Lower Division Champions:
Sen. Div. 1 (10) Limestone
Sen. Div. 2 (9) Catford Invicta
Jun. Div. 1 (10) Lessa Albion
Jun. Div. 2 (9) Crown & Anchor
Jun. Div. 3 (11) Catford Invicta Reserves
Jun. Div. 4 (12) New Cross Catford
Jun. Div. 5 (12) Charlton Rangers Reserves

Cup Winners:
Bart Bowl: Convoys
Bart Cup: Catford Invicta
Junior Cup: Lessa Albion
Surrey Cup: Milton FC
Farlane Cup: Londoners
Evelina Cup: Charlton Rangers Reserves
Combination Cup: Charlton Rangers Reserves

MID-CHESHIRE SUNDAY LEAGUE
COUNTY: CHESHIRE

PREM. DIV.	P	W	D	L	F	A	PTS
Oaklands B.G.	20	17	1	2	57	18	35
Liverpool S.C.	20	11	5	4	49	28	27
Golden Lion	20	13	1	6	52	39	27
Greenbank	20	9	4	7	28	26	22
Lion Athletic	20	7	4	9	54	46	18
F.C. Salter	20	7	2	11	38	48	16
Pockets	20	6	4	10	27	37	16
Roebuck	20	5	5	10	31	41	15
Sandiway	20	6	3	11	29	46	15
F.C. Coachman	20	7	2	11	43	50	*14
Tesco	20	4	5	11	23	52	13

* - 2 points deducted

Lower Division Champions:
Div. 1 (12): Egerton B.C.
Div. 2 (11): Salter Cellar
Div. 3 (10): Little Budworth

MORDEN & DIST. SUNDAY LGE
COUNTY: SURREY

PREM. DIVISION	P	W	D	L	F	A	PTS
S.T.Merton	18	14	3	1	51	17	31
Hazelhurst	18	12	4	2	56	20	28
Puccinis	17	9	6	2	27	14	24
Morden Nomads	17	9	3	5	41	30	21
Spencer Park	17	8	3	6	31	27	18
Merton Admiral	15	7	3	5	27	24	17
Culvers Sunday	18	3	7	8	17	32	13
Chelsea Regents	18	4	2	12	27	51	10
QPR Supporters	18	1	4	13	18	52	6
Colliers Wood U.	18	1	3	14	18	46	5

Lower Division Champions:
Div. 1 (9) Manor Athletic
Div. 2 (10) Worcester Park Wandgas
Div. 3 (8) Woolpack
Div. 4 (10) Chessington Sports
Div. 5 (9) Beddington
Div. 6 (8) Everest
Div. 7 (10) Knollmead United
Div. 8 (10) Auriol Reserves
Div. 9 (9) Sherwood Achilles
Div. 10 (10) Cheam Village Warr Res.
Div. 11 (9) River Plate Reserves

Cup Winners:
Tom Lawson Premier Cup: S.T. Merton
Gordon Proctor Senior Cup: Beddington
Intermediate Cup: Auriol Reserves
Junior Cup: Cheam Village Warriors Reserves
Hemingway Cup: Morden Nomads
Arnold Cup: Kingston Rangers
Jones Cup: Ewell
Hickey Cup: Sons of the Desert

MEDWAY AREA SUNDAY LGE
COUNTY: Kent

FACIT SENIOR	P	W	D	L	F	A	PTS
Quested	24	19	1	4	92	33	39
Sheerness Steel	24	14	4	6	84	42	32
Sheerness East	24	15	2	7	66	28	32
St.Mary's	24	13	4	7	57	37	30
Bly Spartans	24	9	6	9	55	49	24
Gills Social	24	10	4	10	51	55	24
Cecil Arms	24	8	7	9	44	40	23
ABC Sports	24	9	4	11	43	49	22
Snodland Village	24	7	7	10	32	53	21
Earl Social	24	8	5	11	46	83	21
Cavaliers	24	7	5	12	46	62	19
Old Oak	24	5	6	13	41	59	16
Celtic Sports	24	4	1	19	32	99	9

Lower Division Champions:
Prem. Div. (14) Portland Arms
Div. 1 (14) Multi Trade Supplies
Div. 2 (12) Huntsman
Div. 3 (12) Red Dog
Div. 4 (14) Sherwood Dynamoes
Div. 5 (13) Waggon at Hale
Div. 6 (15) Burnt Oak
Comb. Div. (15) Sheerness East

MORECAMBE & LANCASTER SUNDAY LEAGUE
COUNTY: LANCASHIRE

DIV. ONE	P	W	D	L	F	A	PTS
Moorlands Hotel	14	10	3	1	55	19	33
Royal Oak Hotel	14	9	4	1	56	16	31
Slip Inn	14	6	4	4	39	30	22
Skerton Hotel	14	6	2	6	34	41	20
A.F.C. Hydeaway	14	5	4	5	32	25	19
Shrimp Inn	14	5	2	7	30	48	17
Greyhound Hotel	14	3	2	9	22	43	*8
Mayfield United	14	1	1	12	16	62	*1
* - points deducted							

Lower Division Champions:
Div. 2 (11): The Traveller
Div. 3 (12): Courtaulds

MORPETH SUNDAY LGE
COUNTY: NORTHUMBERLAND

DIV. ONE	P	W	D	L	F	A	PTS
Morpeth St George's	26	21	3	2	83	27	66
Lynemouth	26	21	3	2	72	24	66
Stobswood Welf. Res	26	21	1	4	96	39	64
Choppington Calbirch	26	15	0	11	60	32	45
Morpeth Comrades	26	14	3	9	80	69	45
Red Row Brick Club	26	12	3	11	72	66	39
Amble Dock Hotel	26	11	2	13	62	77	35
Pegswood Ex-Service	26	10	2	14	50	54	32
Bedlington Ex-Service	26	10	2	14	48	58	32
Morpeth Sour Grapes	26	9	3	14	63	84	30
Pegswood Social Club	26	9	1	16	45	82	28
Ashington Comrades	26	7	1	18	53	76	22
Morpeth Northern	26	7	1	18	54	68	*19
Bed'ton Gen. Havelock	26	1	3	22	30	111	6
* - 3 points deducted							

Lower Division Champions:
Div. 2 (14): Ellington Plough
Div. 3 (15): Ashington Northumbria

Cup Winners:
Challenge Cup: Morpeth St Georges
Subsidiary Cup: Amble Dock Hotel
Lewin (Div. 1) Cup: Lynemouth
Glaxochem (Div. 2) Cup: Morpeth Hearts
Welwyn (Div. 3) Cup: Morpeth Wansbeck
George Cave Mem. Cup: Morpeth St Georges
Rocky Stone Mem. Cup: Morpeth St Georges

NORTH EAST SUNDAY LGE
COUNTY: NORTHUMBERLAND

PREM. DIV.	P	W	D	L	F	A	PTS
Balloon	30	23	5	2	79	25	74
Wallsend Labour	30	23	5	2	73	24	74
Dunston Social	30	16	7	7	72	32	55
Burradon Social	30	16	6	8	64	37	54
Halls Elswick	30	14	8	8	60	50	50
Killingworth Arms	30	14	4	12	68	50	46
Teams Social	30	13	3	14	56	56	42
Whickham Rose & C.	30	11	9	10	59	63	42
Lonsdale	30	11	8	11	56	57	41
Crawcrook Albion	30	10	6	14	51	70	36
Dorset Sports	30	8	7	15	42	59	31
Scotswood Social	30	9	7	14	46	64	31
Queen Victoria	30	8	6	16	33	59	30
Bugle	30	8	5	17	46	64	29
Birds Nest	30	6	6	18	41	62	24
Fusilier	30	2	4	24	28	102	10
* - points deducted							

Lower Division Champions:
Div. B (16): Forest Hall R.B.L.
Div. C (15): Blakelaw Social
Div. D (15): South Gosforth Social
Div. E (13): Grainger Social
Div. F (13): Worswick Street

Cup Winners:
Justsport Centenary Cup: Balloon
Bob Younger Assoc. Cup: Lonsdale
Knock-Out Cup: Blakelaw Social
Harry Oxley Mem. Cup: Greenside
Gaskell Irons Cup: H.E.C. Compressors
Nick Porter Cup: South Benwell Institute
Sportsmanship Cup: Willows

NORTH KENT SUNDAY LGE
COUNTY: KENT

PREM. DIV.	P	W	D	L	F	A	PTS
Scott	18	14	1	3	60	24	43
Welsh Tavern	18	12	4	2	45	27	40
Sun	18	9	5	4	44	35	32
Springvale	18	9	3	6	51	53	30
Old Comrades	18	9	2	7	46	39	29
Guru Nanak	18	6	3	9	24	29	21
New Ash Green	18	5	5	8	31	33	20
Hollisters	18	5	3	10	28	49	18
Wellcombe Ath.	18	4	3	11	32	48	15
Meopham	18	2	1	15	24	53	7

Lower Division Champions:
Div. 1: Northfleet Scotts
Div. 2: Tonics Fitness Centre

(cont. over)

Div. 3: Northfleet Rangers   Div. 4: Fairfield
Combination Div.: Blue Circle Reserves

Cup Winners:
Reporter Cup: Northfleet Scotts
Senior Cup: Scott
League Cup 'A': Valley Rovers
League Cup 'B': The Terrace
Presidents Cup: Milton & Denton Reserves.

NORTH MIDDLESEX SUNDAY LGE
COUNTY: LONDON/ MIDDX

PREM. DIVISION	P	W	D	L	F	A	PTS
Middlesex Parke	16	13	1	2	55	32	27
Kuba	16	11	4	1	49	21	26
Royal Duchess	16	9	3	4	52	24	21
Wade	16	7	3	6	32	27	17
Sobell Elite	16	7	3	6	32	31	17
Foreigntina	16	5	0	11	27	33	10
Highgate	16	4	2	10	35	42	10
Stanton	16	3	4	9	15	57	10
New Stantos	16	3	0	13	24	54	6

Lower Division Champions:
Div. 1 (7) A.F.C. Samuda
Div. 2 (9) Clissold Athletic

Cup Winners:
C.Arnold Trophy: Kuba
Hackney Hospital Cup: Sobell Elite
St. John Ambulance Cup: Kingsgate

NORTH WEST ESSEX SUNDAY LGE
COUNTY: ESSEX

PREM. DIVISION	P	W	D	L	F	A	PTS
Barnston	18	13	4	1	69	19	30
Cleales	18	9	4	5	42	29	22
Mountfitchet	18	11	0	7	43	39	22
White Roding	18	10	1	7	37	34	21
Littlebury	18	9	2	7	24	23	20
Hargrave Wdrs	18	7	5	6	30	37	19
Northolt United	18	7	2	9	26	35	16
Sawbridgeworth Rgrs	18	5	5	8	33	32	15
Braughing	18	3	2	13	31	58	8
SC Birchanger	18	3	1	14	27	56	7

Lower Division Champions:
Div. 1 (9) The Swan
Div. 2 (10) Farnham Bury Green
Div. 3 (14) Silver Swifts

Cup Winners:
Prem. Cup: Barnston
Div. 1: Athletic 88
Div. 2: East Herts Nalgo
Div. 3: Grange Reserves
G.H.Wilson Senior Interdivisional Cup: Barnston
Bill Bruty Junion Interdivisional Cup Reserve Team
Trophy: Northolt United Reserves
H.A.B.Yabsley Trophy: Athletic 88

NORTHAMPTONSHIRE SUNDAY LGE
COUNTY: NORTHAMPTONSHIRE
F.G.WATTS & PARTNERS

PREM. DIVISION	P	W	D	L	F	A	PTS
Duke of York	22	15	4	3	67	22	34
Vaniad	22	15	3	4	81	29	33
Sun Kislingbury	22	12	7	3	72	35	31
Viking	22	12	5	5	64	32	29
White Lion	22	12	2	8	56	44	26
St.Margarets	22	10	3	9	66	60	23
Venturians	22	7	5	10	43	56	19
Hackleton United	22	8	2	12	56	54	18
Duston CA	22	7	4	11	48	49	18
Strollers	22	7	3	12	51	61	17
Wotton	22	5	6	11	39	76	16
Royals	22	0	0	22	20	145	0

Lower Division Champions:
Div. 1 (12) Duke of York Reserves
Div. 2 (12) Cobblers Mounties
Div. 3 (13) Sun Kislingbury Reserves
Div. 4 (13) Towcester Athletic
Div. 5 (13) Barretts Snooker Reserves

Cup Winners: Prem. Cup: White Lion
Div. 1: Senior Boys Club   Div. 2: Weedon
Div. 3: Sun Kislingbury Reserves
Div. 4: Towcester Athletic
Div. 5: Barretts Snooker Reserves
Ken Parker Cup: Duke of York
Derek Sutton Cup: Barretts Snooker Reserves

'WIMPEY HOMES' NORWICH & DISTRICT SUNDAY LEAGUE
COUNTY: NORFOLK

DIV. ONE	P	W	D	L	F	A	PTS
Poringland Wdrs	24	18	4	2	109	32	40
Norwich Busmen	24	18	1	5	100	36	37
Carrow Reserves	24	15	2	7	87	53	32
Saxlingham	24	11	7	6	54	45	29
Hellesdon Sunday	24	8	10	6	59	50	26
Costessey Sunday	24	11	4	9	58	55	26
Anglians	24	10	3	11	58	65	23
Hellesdon H.S.O.B.	24	9	4	11	63	72	22
New Inn	24	9	3	12	56	64	21
Unity Emeralds	24	7	6	11	63	65	20
Wymondham Sunday	24	7	4	13	46	65	18
Gibraltar Gardens	24	3	4	17	35	112	10
Florentina	24	3	2	19	37	111	8

Lower Division Champions:
Div. 2 (10): Bishopgate Lions
Div. 3 (13): King Edward Rangers
Div. 4 (14): Black Swan
Div. 5 (14): Hellesdon Hospital
Div. 6 (14): Sprowston S.C.
Div. 7 (13): Yeoman   Div. 8 (14): Brooks
Div. 9 (14): Aylsham Unicorns

Cup Winners:
League Cup: Poringland Wanderers
Charity Cup: Aylsham Sunday
Benevolent Cup: Harvey Bros.

NOTTINGHAMSHIRE SUNDAY LGE
COUNTY: NOTTINGHAMSHIRE

PREM. DIV.	P	W	D	L	F	A	PTS
Rolls Royce Celtic	18	16	2	0	68	12	34
A.D. Bulwell	18	14	2	2	51	20	30
Jolly Farmers	18	14	0	4	56	24	28
Cotgrave Welfare	18	10	2	6	59	45	32
Phoenix	18	7	2	9	42	30	16
Grange	18	5	3	10	36	47	13
Radford Park Rgrs	18	5	2	11	31	70	12
Bingham Town	18	4	3	11	24	47	11
Gedling United	18	3	4	11	21	49	10
The Carlton	18	3	2	13	17	59	8

Lower Division Champions:
Premier Div. 1 (12): Spot On
Premier Div. 2 (10): Three Crowns
Premier Div. 3 (12): Earl Decorators
Premier Div. 4 (11): Robin Hood & L.J.
Senior Div. 1 (12): Bayers Arms
Senior Div. 2 (12): New White Bull
Senior Div. 3 (12): Three Bs
Senior Div. 4 (11): Wellington Inn
Intermediate Div. 1 (12): Keyworth Tavern
Intermediate Div. 2 (12): Willoughby
Intermediate Div. 3 (12): Wasps
Intermediate Div. 4 (12): Arnold Ex-Service
Intermediate Div. 5 (12): Steam Engine Reserves
Junior Div. 1 (12): Highbury Vale
Junior Div. 2 (10): Max Steiner
Junior Div. 3 (12): Pork Farms L.V.A.
Junior Div. 4 (12): Brick & Tile
Junior Div. 5 (12): Bracken

MITCHELLS & BUTLERS NUNEATON & DIST. SUNDAY LGE
COUNTY: BIRMINGHAM

PREM. DIVISION	P	W	D	L	F	A	PTS
Frank Parker	18	11	3	4	52	27	36
Rose United	18	11	3	4	45	28	36
Ridge Lane	18	9	5	4	46	18	32
Bulkington WMC	18	9	3	6	36	36	30
Manor	18	7	4	7	41	30	25
Ansley Common	18	7	3	8	31	38	24
Drayton	18	7	3	8	27	40	24
Atherstone Bridge	18	5	4	9	41	46	19
Gaylors	18	2	8	8	30	46	14
Newdigate Arms	18	3	2	13	32	72	11

Lower Division Champions:
Div. 1 (11) Badgers FC
Div. 2 (12) Alderman Smith
Div. 3 (12) Abbey Social
Div. 4 (11) Nuneaton Shere
Div. 5 (12) Whitestone Reserves
Div. 6 (14) Coniston Tavern
Div. 7 (14) Hill Top & Caldwell

'MORRELLS' OXFORD SUNDAY LGE
COUNTY: OXFORDSHIRE

PREM. DIV.	P	W	D	L	F	A	PTS
Six Bells, Kidlington	20	15	2	3	64	29	32
Star Wanderers	20	11	4	5	67	40	26
Horspath Road	20	12	2	6	64	40	26
Cold Arbour	20	9	8	3	50	30	26
Star Royal	20	11	1	8	65	44	22
Saxon Warriors	20	7	5	8	55	56	19
Highfield	20	6	5	9	48	56	17
Rose Hill	20	7	3	10	37	50	17
Leafield Athletic	20	6	4	10	31	43	16
Oxford Libertas	20	6	4	10	35	66	16
Wol'cote	20	0	2	18	24	86	2

Lower Division Champions:
Div. 1 (13): New Wheatsheaf
Div. 2 (12): Marston Reserves
Div. 3 (12): Queens Athletic
Div. 4 (13): Masons
Div. 5 (14): Red Lion, Eynsham
Div. 6 (13): Evenlode

Cup Winners:
President's Cup: Star Royal
Jack Sadler Cup: Oxford United Social
Pete Faulkner Mem. Cup: Six Bells, Kidlington
Derek Parker Mem. Trophy: Oxford Utd Social
League Cup: Leafield Athletic
Sam Waters Cup: Horspath Road

PORTSMOUTH SUNDAY LGE
COUNTY: HAMPSHIRE

PREM. DIVISION	P	W	D	L	F	A	PTS
Civil Service	18	16	0	2	71	19	48
Portsbridge	18	12	2	4	55	31	37
Jolly Taxpayer	18	12	0	6	59	24	36
Cowplain Social	18	10	2	6	45	34	32
Beehive	18	9	5	4	33	31	32
Transfreight	18	6	5	7	36	45	23
Harvest Home	18	4	2	12	31	50	14
Drayton	18	3	4	11	30	59	13
Havant Rovers	18	3	4	11	21	62	13
Wicor Mill	18	2	2	14	32	55	8

Lower Division Champions:
Sen. Div. (12) Plover
Jun. 1 (13) Shearer
Jun. 2 (13) Eagles
Jun. 3 (13) Admiral
Jun. 4 (13) Queen Anne
Jun. 5 (13) Mayflower
Jun. 6 (13) Alan-Wright

READING SUNDAY LGE
COUNTY: BERKS & BUCKS

SEN. DIV.	P	W	D	L	F	A	PTS
Reading Borough	20	17	3	0	64	16	37
Theale	20	16	3	1	76	16	35
Caversham Park	20	10	3	7	48	28	23
Culham Rangers	20	7	6	7	38	39	20
Cavaliers	20	7	6	7	33	36	20
Quicksilver Ath.	20	7	5	8	38	33	19
Waingels Old Boys	20	5	7	8	31	37	17
Thorn Walk Tavern	20	7	3	10	37	63	17
Dee Road Rangers	20	7	2	11	34	43	16
Courage Imp.	20	2	7	11	30	55	11
Palmer Park	20	2	1	17	32	95	5

Lower Division Champions:
Premier Div. (12): Shiplake
Div. 1 (11): Alfred's Head
Div. 2 East (12): Earley Town
Div. 2 West (12): Norcot
Div. 3 East (12): Charvil Accs
Div. 3 West (10): A.F.C. Whitchurch
Div. 4 East (12): Trentonians
Div. 4 West (11): Burgfield Sports
Div. 5 East (12): Culham Reserves
Div. 5 West (12): Southcote Video
Div. 6 East (12): Woodley Hamm. Res.
Div. 6 West (11): Woolhampton Ex.

Cup Winners:
Ted Cambridge Cup: Reading Borough

REDDITCH & SOUTH WARKS SUNDAY COMBINATION
COUNTY: BIRMINGHAM

PREM. DIV.	P	W	D	L	F	A	PTS
Tudor Cross	18	13	3	2	46	16	29
Garringtons Sunday	18	11	3	4	51	23	25
High Duty Alloys	18	8	5	5	35	26	21
Wychbold R.B.L.	18	7	5	6	34	30	19
B.F.B. '83	18	8	2	8	25	44	18
Black Horse	18	7	3	8	31	33	17
Stoke Prior	18	6	4	8	26	31	16
Woodpecker	18	6	4	8	44	53	16
Alcester Rovers	18	5	1	12	20	39	11
Allendale	18	2	4	12	18	35	8

Lower Division Champions:
Div. 1 (11): Hymatic
Div. 2 (10): Kings Arms
Div. 3 (11): Hydrovane
Div. 4 (12): Cofton United
Div. 5 (11): Sherwood Rangers
Div. 6 (12): N.I. Sporting

Reading Borough F.C., undefeated champions of the Reading Sunday League. Photo - Eric Marsh.

REDHILL & DIST. SUNDAY LGE
COUNTY: SURREY

DIVISION ONE	P	W	D	L	F	A	PTS
Midday Sun	20	18	0	2	89	35	36
Woodhatch	20	17	1	2	93	27	35
Caterham Town	20	13	1	6	55	33	27
Iron Horse	20	12	2	6	60	50	26
Tudor Athletic	20	8	2	10	51	49	18
Nutfield	20	8	1	11	59	72	17
Meadvale Eagles	20	7	1	12	44	63	15
Horley Park Rgrs	20	3	6	11	34	60	12
Directors	20	5	2	13	38	66	12
Mickleham	20	5	2	13	31	67	12
Frenches	20	4	2	14	35	67	10

Lower Division Champions:
Div. 2 (10) Clarkson Hyde
Div. 3 (11) Grange Park Reserves
Div. 4 (10) Oxted

REVIEW SUNDAY LEAGUE
COUNTY: HERTFORDSHIRE

PREM. DIV.	P	W	D	L	F	A	PTS
Phoenix	18	16	1	1	57	14	33
Chequers	18	14	2	2	72	15	30
Wrestlers	18	9	2	7	56	39	20
Brookmans Park	18	8	2	8	33	40	18
Colney Heath Q.H.	18	8	1	9	44	35	17
Bricket Wood	18	6	5	7	42	43	17
Rats Castle Grange	18	7	3	8	37	41	17
Farriers Arms	18	5	4	9	42	58	14
Shenley Park	18	3	2	13	25	65	8
Parkwood	18	2	2	14	21	79	6

Lower Division Champions:
Div. 1 (11): Warriors
Div. 2 (10): Wine Ale
Div. 3 (12): Cotlandswick
Div. 4 (12): London Road
Div. 5 (13): Cell Barnes Reserves

Cup Winners:
K.O. Cup: Rothamsted
Challenge Cup: Bricket Wood
Intermediate Cup: Phoenix Reserves
Junior Cup: London Road
Reserve Cup: Bricket Wood Reserves

'DEE JAYS'
SCUNTHORPE SUNDAY LGE
COUNTY: LINCOLNSHIRE

DIVISION ONE	P	W	D	L	F	A	PTS
Poachers	20	16	2	2	100	27	34
Lions Head	20	15	1	4	84	25	31
Ashby Star	20	13	2	5	72	38	28
Keadby Cl.	20	11	4	5	47	39	26
Park West	20	9	2	9	47	47	20
Pied Piper	20	7	5	8	54	50	19
Cornet Wanderers	20	7	4	9	27	56	18
Dee Jays	20	7	3	10	51	61	17
Kypros	20	5	4	11	36	66	14
Duffs Dyn.	20	2	4	14	21	78	8
Burringham	20	1	3	16	34	86	5

Lower Division Champions:
Div. 2 (12) Old Br. Rovers
Div. 3 (12) Br'tn Clamart
Div. 4 (12) Mess Trinty Old Boys
Div. 5 (9) Blue Bell
Div. 6 (12) Beacon
Div. 7 (11) Blue Bell Reserves
Div. 8 (13) Br. Snooker

Cup Winners:
Intersport: Daimlers
H.(Nobby) Clark Memorial: Blue Bell
Geg McGowan Memorial: Crown (Messingham)
Ireson Memorial: Broughton Clamart
Ted Harrison Memorial: Old Brumby Rovers
Dave Ward Memorial: Ashby Star
Supplementary: Lions Head
Challenge: Ashby Star

'SHREWSBURY HOTEL'
SHREWSBURY & DIST. SUNDAY LGE
COUNTY: SHROPSHIRE

PREM. DIV.	P	W	D	L	F	A	PTS
Monkmoor	20	13	2	5	52	23	31
Ford	20	12	4	4	45	22	28
Bricklayers Sports	20	12	6	2	50	34	26
Belle Vue Sunday	20	9	6	5	49	33	23
Plough	20	7	6	7	45	28	21
Instones United	20	8	10	2	35	42	18
Cruckton Rovers	20	8	10	2	37	58	18
Bayston Hill C.	20	7	10	3	36	44	17
The Apprentice	20	6	9	5	25	36	17
All Stretton	20	3	11	6	36	56	12
Acorn	20	3	14	3	27	61	9

Lower Division Champions:
Div. 1 (13): Nalgo Sunday
Div. 2 (12): Duncan Dynamoes
Div. 3 (13): Welsh Harp
Div. 4 (14): Bridge '90

CITY OF SOUTHAMPTON
SUNDAY LEAGUE
COUNTY: HAMPSHIRE

PREM. DIVISION	P	W	D	L	F	A	PTS
Hamble Athletic	16	14	0	2	73	19	28
Soton Post Office	16	11	3	2	54	29	25
North Stoneham	16	11	1	4	47	27	23
M.J.Vosper	16	7	1	8	30	42	15
Newtown *	16	5	3	8	37	42	13
Tabburn	16	4	4	8	35	39	12
Eastleigh Police	16	4	4	8	21	45	12
Old Shirley	16	2	5	9	18	41	9
H.M.Customs	16	3	1	12	25	56	7

* - 2pts awarded.

Lower Division Champions:
Sen. Div. (12) Southern Sports
Jun. 1 (11) Barleycorn Hedge End
Jun. 2 (11) K & K Sports
Jun. 3 (11) Technicoil
Jun. 4 (11) Part Rangers

SOUTHAMPTON COMMERCIAL
HOUSES SUNDAY LGE
COUNTY: HAMPSHIRE

DIVISION ONE	P	W	D	L	F	A	PTS
Amplevine Holmes	14	13	0	1	64	12	26
Drummond	14	11	2	1	83	11	24
Ice House Sports	14	10	2	2	46	13	21
Sun Inn Romsey	14	5	2	7	34	43	12
Strickland Sports	14	5	1	8	29	66	11
Bishops Waltham Bl.	14	2	3	9	26	40	7
Obelisk	14	3	1	10	17	44	7
Trowtrinics	14	1	1	12	11	71	3

Lower Division Champions:
Div. 2 (11) Shirley Warren S.A.
Div. 3 (12) Postal Athletic
Div. 4 (11) Cricketers Arms

SOUTHPORT & DIST. SUNDAY LGE
COUNTY: LIVERPOOL

DIVISION ONE	P	W	D	L	F	A	PTS
Dell Rangers	22	19	1	2	76	27	39
Scarisbrick Hotel	21	17	2	2	89	17	36
Churchtown	22	15	2	5	76	29	32
Bedford Rangers*	21	13	3	5	55	33	31
Birkdale	22	12	3	7	46	36	27
Swan Athletic	21	7	4	10	46	48	18
Hacks United*	21	4	6	11	32	50	16
Sandgrounders	22	6	2	14	49	87	14
Ainsdale#	22	7	1	14	48	76	13
Wyke Cop Albion	22	5	2	15	33	57	12
Blowick	21	3	6	12	34	60	12
Smithy Vale*	21	3	4	14	33	99	12

* - 2pts awarded.
# - 2pts deducted.

Lower Division Champions:
Div. 2 (11) Packaging Dks.
Div. 3 (12) Metro
Div. 4 (7) Old Ship

STANLEY & DIST. SUNDAY LGE
COUNTY: DURHAM

DIV. ONE	P	W	D	L	F	A	PTS
Kings Head	24	20	2	2	103	21	62
Burnhope Ivy Leaf	24	19	0	5	97	46	57
Craghead Social	24	16	3	5	62	31	51
Ouston United	24	16	2	6	67	28	50
East Stanley	24	15	1	8	76	47	46
Honeysuckle	24	12	4	8	64	52	40
Coach & Horses	24	10	5	9	54	44	35
Quaking Houses	24	9	4	11	66	77	31
Stanley R.A.F.A.	24	6	3	15	38	78	21
British Legion	24	5	2	17	32	74	17
Pelton Fell	24	5	2	17	36	88	*14
Lintz Rangers	24	4	6	14	26	64	x9
Chopwell R.A.O.B.	24	1	2	21	30	101	5

* - 3 points deducted
x - 9 points deducted

Lower Division Champions:
Div. 2 (16): Newfield Inn

Cup Winners:
Moody Shield: Travellers Rest
Richardson Cup: Burnhope
Conroy Cup: Burnhope Ivy Leaf
Challenge Cup: Kings Head
Div. 2 Cup: Rams Head
Bev Haggett Cup: Ouston United

STEVENAGE SUNDAY LGE
COUNTY: HERTFORDSHIRE

PREM. DIV.	P	W	D	L	F	A	PTS
Singh Sabha	20	15	1	4	68	30	31
Waggon	20	15	1	4	59	26	31
Dynamics	20	13	2	5	63	42	28
Benington	20	12	0	8	51	28	24
Transpack	20	9	4	7	66	51	22
White Horse	20	10	2	8	61	49	22
Crooked Billet	20	9	3	8	46	40	21
Twin Foxes	20	8	2	10	42	49	18
Dellar Bros.	20	4	1	15	35	55	9
Shephall Ath. O.B.	20	4	0	16	24	75	8
Pig & Whistle (S)	20	3	0	17	30	100	6

Lower Division Champions:
Div. 1 (11): Manulife
Div. 2 (11): Stevenage Postels
Div. 3 (12): St Nicholas
Div. 4 (12): Dun Cow

Cup Winners:
K.L.M. Trophy: Twin Foxes
Prem. Div. Cup: Waggon
Div. 1 Cup: Pig & Whistle (A)
Div. 2 Cup: Stevenage Postels
Div. 3 Cup: Yorkshire Grey
Div. 4 Cup: A.V.C.

STOCKPORT DISTRICT SUNDAY LEAGUE
COUNTY: MANCHESTER

PREM. DIV.	P	W	D	L	F	A	PTS
Offerton United	22	17	4	1	79	15	38
Norris Albion	22	17	3	2	79	30	37
Rifle Volunteer	22	14	5	3	61	33	33
Carnforth	22	13	3	6	48	37	29
Hindley Street	22	7	5	10	50	51	19
Mount Villa	22	7	4	11	44	49	18
Millbrow	22	8	4	10	47	61	*18
Ludworth	22	6	6	10	40	58	*16
Dilke Celtic	22	6	4	12	35	64	16
Medoak	22	3	9	10	48	70	15
Bramhall Victoria	22	4	3	15	35	59	11
West Heaton	22	3	4	15	28	67	10

* - 2 points deducted

Lower Division Champions:
Div. 1 (12): Adswood Utd
Div. 2 (12): T.T. Academicals
Div. 3 (12): Offerton Green
Div. 2 (12): Bramhall Queensgate

Cup Winners:
Harold English Chal. Tphy: Offerton United
Paul Bailey/ Graham Wright Mem. Tphy: Offerton Green

SUSSEX SUNDAY LGE
COUNTY: Sussex

PREM. DIVISION	P	W	D	L	F	A	PTS
Preston Dynamos	20	14	4	2	49	15	32
South Ham United	20	13	5	2	46	20	31
Hangleton	20	13	3	4	63	39	29
Indesit U.K.	20	10	4	6	60	28	24
North Road Timber	20	10	4	6	38	32	24
Patcham North End	20	8	2	10	41	41	18
Henfield Mohawks	20	6	5	9	55	57	17
Newman	20	5	4	11	38	44	14
The St.George	20	6	2	12	27	47	14
Hove Dynamoes	20	5	3	12	31	53	13
Fratsom Rovers*	20	1	2	17	8	80	2

* - Indicates clubs with points adjustments.

Lower Division Champions:
Int. 1 (11) Bridge Boys
Int. 2 (11) James Lytle
Jun. 1 (12) Sussex Asphaltk
Jun. 2 (11) Brunswick Arms
Jun. 3 (11) Valley Social Centre
Jun. 4 (11) Old Boat Corner
Jun. 5 (11) Windmill Sports
Jun. 6 (12) Downs
Jun. 7 (12) Hangleton Manor
Jun. 8 (11) Ukrainians
Jun. 9 (11) Conway Colts
Jun. 10 (12) The Coach House (Rott)
Jun. 11 (11) Worthing Thistle
Jun. 12 (12) The Racehorse Inn

Cup Winners:
Sussex Sunday Senior Cup: James Lytle
Premier Office Bowl: Whitehorse Rottingdean
Vic Bettney Memorial Trophy: The Amsterdam
Skerritt Consultants Junior Cup: Southdown Rovers O.B.
Intermediate Invitaion Cup: Corals
Junior Inivitation Cup: Hangleton Manor
Lower Junior Invitation Cup: Colonnale

SUTTON & DIST. SUNDAY LGE
COUNTY: SURREY

PREM. DIVISION	P	W	D	L	F	A	PTS
Orion	18	14	3	1	71	19	31
Halfway	18	12	4	2	44	21	28
Grimstock	18	8	6	4	43	33	22
Tile Cross	18	7	4	7	48	49	18
Tame S & S	18	7	3	8	34	36	17
Springville W. Horse	18	7	2	9	41	45	16
Parklands	18	7	1	10	37	50	15
Calthorpe United	18	6	1	11	33	56	13
Crown Athletic	18	4	3	11	23	39	11
Kingshurst Labour	18	4	1	13	26	52	9

Lower Division Champions:
Div. 1 (11) Kingfisher
Div. 2 (12) Drayton Bassett
Div. 3 (12) Curdworth
Div. 4 (11) Farmer John
Div. 5 (24) Aldridge
Div. 6 (10) Cardinal New Inns

THE FEDERATION BREWERY TAMWORTH & DIST. SUNDAY LGE
COUNTY: BIRMINGHAM

LCL PREM. DIV	P	W	D	L	F	A	PTS
Foseco Sports & S.	22	17	2	3	94	31	53
Kingsbury United	22	16	5	1	84	27	53
Glascote Swifts	22	17	2	3	63	19	53
Fox Inn	22	12	5	5	64	39	41
Birch Coppice	22	10	2	10	42	46	32
Wilnecote W.M.C.	22	7	7	8	35	49	28
Mile Oak Hotel	22	6	7	9	34	40	28
Sacred Heart	22	5	6	11	35	61	21
Tamworth Prog.	22	5	4	13	31	52	19
Riftswood	22	4	5	13	35	62	17
Wood End W.Hart	22	5	1	16	30	61	16
Kettlebrook W.M.C.	22	4	2	16	31	91	14

Lower Division Champions:
Div. 1 (13) Edingale Swifts
Div. 2 (12) Denmark 90
Div. 3 (14) Polesworth W.M.C.
Div. 4 (12) Belgrave Sports & Social
Div. 5 (15) Hurley Daw Mill

TELFORD SUNDAY LGE
COUNTY: SHROPSHIRE

PREM. DIV.	P	W	D	L	F	A	PTS
B'north Shakespeare	22	17	4	1	74	26	38
Newport R.B.L.	22	14	3	5	52	29	31
St Georges S. & S.	22	13	3	6	68	42	29
Champion Jockey	22	12	5	5	44	27	29
Shifnal Juniors	22	10	4	8	54	35	24
Dun Cow Dynamos	22	10	4	8	54	40	24
Royal Oak	22	7	6	9	58	54	20
Red Lion Rovers	22	7	5	10	41	59	19
Shif. War Mem. Ath.	22	6	6	10	38	51	18
Granville Wood	22	5	4	13	34	48	14
Little Drayton Rgrs	22	3	5	14	39	74	11
Dawley	22	1	5	16	33	104	7

Lower Division Champions:
Div. 1 (11): Rose & Crown, Stirchley
Div. 2 (12): Hadley United Services
Div. 3 (12): Shrewsbury Arms
Div. 4 (12): Pigeon Box
Div. 5 (12): Ketley Nomads
Div. 6 (12): Coddon
Div. 7 (12): Nell Gwyn Reserves

VANGE & DIST. SUNDAY LGE
COUNTY: ESSEX

PREM. DIV.	P	W	D	L	F	A	PTS
C.Z. '81	18	13	2	3	65	26	41
East T. Dynamoes	18	13	1	4	46	25	40
Rettendon	18	8	5	5	38	28	24
Scotia	18	8	2	8	33	36	26
Winston	18	7	4	7	42	41	25
Mopsies Park	18	7	4	7	47	49	25
Greeves	18	6	5	7	29	43	23
Rackets	18	6	4	8	24	40	22
Crouch Nomads	18	3	6	9	35	44	15
Maycar Royals	18	1	3	14	24	51	6

Lower Division Champions:
Div. 1 (8): Watney Truman
Div. 2 (10): Sorata
Div. 3 (9): Golding United

Cup Winners:
Challenge Cup: Rettendon
Benevolent Cup: Rettendon
Premier Div. Cup: Rettendon
Div. 1 Cup: Tristar
Div. 2 Cup: Spar Town
Div. 3 Cup: Hodgson

WATFORD SUNDAY LEAGUE
COUNTY: HERTFORDSHIRE

PREM. DIV.	P	W	D	L	F	A	PTS
Evergreen	18	14	2	2	47	14	44
St Josephs	18	10	2	6	38	24	32
Hammer	18	9	3	6	49	36	30
Oxhey Labour	18	8	1	9	27	32	25
Mill End Rangers	18	7	4	7	36	44	25
Albion Rovers	18	7	3	8	28	39	24
Langleybury C.C.	18	6	3	9	33	45	21
Rolls Royce	18	5	4	9	26	28	19
Blues	18	5	3	10	26	37	18
Watford Labour Club	18	5	3	10	26	37	18

Lower Division Champions:
Div. 1 (9): Kendal Albion
Div. 2 (10): Microgen
Div. 3 (10): Loriner
Div. 4 (9): B.K. '91 Athletic Reserves
Div. 5 (12): Ocusta
Div. 6 (11): Rolls Royce Reserves

Cup Winners:
'Parry Trophy' Chal. Cup: Hammer
Industrial Finishers Cup: Croxley Guild of Sport
'Apple Press' Junior Cup: Elsums
Black Boy Reserve Cup: Rolls Royce Reserves

'C. & G.' WEST CORNWALL SUNDAY LEAGUE
COUNTY: CORNWALL

DIV. ONE	P	W	D	L	F	A	PTS
Redruth Rangers	16	13	1	2	67	17	40
Helston	16	11	1	4	78	34	34
F.C. Truro	16	9	1	6	56	31	28
Truro City	16	8	3	5	44	27	27
Ferrets	16	8	2	6	50	31	26
Penryn	16	6	3	7	75	48	21
Duke of Leeds	16	4	2	10	46	64	14
Safeways	16	4	1	11	49	61	13
Channel	16	1	0	15	7	157	3

Lower Division Champions:
Div. 2 (11): Copperhouse

WEST FULHAM SUNDAY LGE
COUNTY: MIDDX/ LONDON

PREM. DIV.	P	W	D	L	F	A	PTS
Mortlake	14	9	3	2	35	18	21
Horseferry	14	7	3	4	49	25	17
Hammersmith	14	6	5	3	47	29	17
Light Source	14	8	1	5	32	26	17
West Barnes	14	5	3	6	25	29	13
Westbourne P.V.	14	5	2	7	24	31	12
Heidelberg Green	14	5	1	8	26	47	11
Masons Arms	14	1	2	11	11	44	4

Lower Division Champions:
Div. 1 (7): Old Riordans
Div. 2 (10): Kings Arms
Div. 3 (10): Moorhead Park
Div. 4 (12): Mortlake 'B'

Cup Winners:
Alf Dear Challenge Cup: Westbourne Park Villa
Senior Cup: Hammersmith 6, Mortlake 2 (aet)
Intermediate Cup: Whitton Albion Reserves 3, Riverside 2
Margaret Gray Cup: Mortlake Reserves 1, West Barnes Reserves 0

WEST MIDDLESEX SUNDAY LGE
COUNTY: MIDDLESEX

DIV. ONE	P	W	D	L	F	A	PTS
A.F.C. Teddington	20	16	0	4	74	38	32
Kensington Argyll	20	14	3	3	49	23	31
Meadhurst	20	11	2	7	51	33	26
Bedfont Jays	20	11	3	6	69	33	25
Shirehorse	20	10	3	7	51	39	23
Hampton Villa	20	9	3	8	50	45	21
Isleworth Villa	20	7	5	8	38	28	18
Ashview Rangers	20	6	5	9	39	46	17
Redlees Rovers	20	6	2	12	32	39	14
Griffin Park	20	5	2	13	44	66	12
Watney Spts	20	0	0	20	15	122	0

Lower Division Champions:
Div. 2 (10): Manor
Div. 3 (10): Hayes End Wanderers
Div. 4 (9): Domine Athletic
Div. 5 (11): Inter Admin
Intermediate Div. (10): The Rising Sun
Junior Div. (10): Chiswick Albion

WESTON-SUPER-MARE SUNDAY LGE
COUNTY: SOMERSET & AVON (SOUTH)

DIVISION ONE	P	W	D	L	F	A	PTS
Slipway Bar	16	15	1	0	83	18	31
Brent House	15	10	1	4	56	38	21
AMS Sports	16	8	4	4	53	35	20
Nicks Bar	16	6	4	6	41	37	16
Old Kings Head	16	6	4	6	40	37	16
Bristol House*	15	7	1	7	49	48	13

* - 2pts deducted.

Lower Division Champions:
Div. 1 'A' (6): Moorland Rebels
Div. 2 (6): The Heron
Div. 2 'A' (6): AFC Nailsea

'REMBRANDT' WEYMOUTH PUBS FOOTBALL LEAGUE

COUNTY: DORSET

'LEGENDS' PREM.	P	W	D	L	F	A	PTS
Globe	18	15	0	3	77	29	30
Moorings	18	12	4	2	70	17	28
Duke of Albany	18	12	1	5	71	30	25
Mariners	18	11	1	6	76	44	23
Weatherbury	18	8	4	6	45	28	20
Chapelhay	18	9	2	7	34	27	20
Royal Exchange	18	6	4	8	53	33	16
Black Dog	18	6	1	11	50	62	13
Park	18	2	1	15	31	77	5
Market House	18	0	0	18	6	168	0

Lower Division Champions:
'Weymouth Sports' Div. 1 (11): White Hart Utd

WHARFEDALE SUNDAY LEAGUE

COUNTY: WEST RIDING

PREM. DIV.	P	W	D	L	F	A	PTS
Silsden	18	15	0	3	59	28	45
Druids Arms	18	13	3	2	52	35	42
Wrose Albion	18	13	2	3	56	22	41
Milestone	18	10	1	7	54	40	31
Owlet	18	7	2	9	38	36	23
Keighley Shamrocks	17	6	1	10	31	28	19
Thackley Shoulder	18	6	1	11	32	40	19
Ferrands Arms	16	6	1	9	31	55	19
Sandy Lane	17	4	1	12	34	47	13
New Inn Baildon	18	1	2	15	17	83	5

Keighley Shamrocks v Ferrands Arms and Sandy Lane v Ferrands Arms were not played!

Lower Division Champions:
Div. 1 (12): Windhill Cr. Cl.
Div. 2 (11): Keighley Shamrocks Reserves
Div. 3 (11): Branch

Cup Winners:
Russell Stone Senior Cup: Keighley Shamrocks
Ingham Sports Sunday Cup: Keighley Juniors
Cookson Memorial Trophy: Stanley Road

WHARFEDALE SUNDAY TRIANGLE LEAGUE

COUNTY: WEST RIDING

PREM. DIV.	P	W	D	L	F	A	PTS
Star Athletic	18	15	1	2	65	17	46
Regent Victoria	18	15	1	2	59	11	46
Keighley Star	18	15	0	3	67	21	45
Airedale Magnet	18	10	2	6	59	45	32
Wrose Bull	18	7	2	9	53	51	23
White Horse	18	7	2	9	34	35	23
Tarn Rangers	18	7	2	9	45	50	23
Horsforth Rangers	18	5	0	13	27	68	15
New Beacon	18	1	3	14	19	63	6
Ilkley Dynamo	18	1	1	16	20	87	4

Play-off: Star 3, Regent 3 - title shared

Lower Division Champions:
Div. 1 (12): Caroline Street
Div. 2 (12): Old Ball

Cup Winners:
League Cup: Star Athletic
Supplementary Cup: Farsley Wanderers

WIRRAL SUNDAY LEAGUE

COUNTY: LIVERPOOL

DIV. ONE	P	W	D	L	F	A	PTS
Stirrup	22	15	3	4	74	52	33
A.D.S. Graphics	22	15	2	5	72	39	32
Harp United	22	11	5	6	63	42	27
Great Eastern	22	12	2	8	64	33	26
Adaxia	22	13	0	9	79	61	26
Wirral Boxers	22	9	7	6	59	49	25
Caledonia	22	9	5	8	54	55	23
Nova	22	8	4	10	45	55	20
Queens Dixon	22	5	5	12	30	56	15
Horse & Oak	22	6	3	13	33	61	15
Lancelyn	22	6	2	14	48	78	14
Bluebell	22	4	0	18	40	80	8

Lower Division Champions:
Div. 1 (13): Richmond
Div. 2 (14): Naughty Edwardian

Cup Winners:
Pyke Cup: A.D.S. Graphics
Challenge Cup: St Marys
Premier Cup: A.D.S. Graphics
Snr Cup: Halfway Soc.   **Jnr Cup:** St Marys

WINCHESTER & DIST. SUNDAY LGE

COUNTY: HAMPSHIRE

PREM. DIV.	P	W	D	L	F	A	PTS
Rising Sun	16	12	3	1	75	25	27
Fryern Sports	16	12	2	2	69	32	26
Halfway Inn	16	10	1	5	66	21	21
Westgate	16	9	3	4	48	37	21
Worthies Sports	16	8	4	4	35	21	20
Warren Sports	16	4	3	9	39	55	11
Bitterne	16	4	1	11	26	45	9
St James Tavern	16	2	3	11	25	72	7
King Alfred	16	1	0	15	15	90	2

Lower Division Champions:
Div. 1 (11): March Hare
Div. 2 (11): Prince of Wales
Div. 3 (11): K.E.E.M.A.

WOLVERHAMPTON & DISTRICT SUNDAY LGE

COUNTY: BIRMINGHAM

PREM. DIV.	P	W	D	L	F	A	PTS
W'ton Electricity	22	15	3	4	56	19	33
Wednesfield Albion	22	13	6	3	52	27	32
Penn Old Boys	22	14	2	6	35	24	30
W'ton Retail Mart	22	13	3	6	52	29	29
Marston Sports	22	11	5	6	66	43	27
Bilston Jockey	22	7	8	7	40	37	22
Sheraton	22	8	4	10	37	43	20
Springfield WMC	22	7	5	10	36	47	19
Orton Vale	22	3	7	12	31	50	13
E. Pk Cleveland	22	5	3	14	33	60	13
Pendeford Dovecote	22	5	3	14	30	62	13
Essington St Johns	22	3	5	14	28	55	11

Lower Division Champions:
Div. 1 (13): Rovers Sports
Div. 2 (14): Bilston Community College
Div. 3 (14): Briton Lions
Div. 4 (14): Neachells
Div. 5 (14): Codsall Wheel
Div. 6 (14): Park Village
Div. 7 (10): Wolverhampton R.A.F.A.
Div. 8 (14): Victoria Old Boys

Cup Winners:
H.E. Bunch Cup: Victoria Old Boys
T. Bird Cup: Briton Lions
Corinthian Shield: Emerald Athletic
B.P. Roberts Cup: Rovers Sports
S.F. Skedgel Cup: Victoria Old Boys
G.A. Evans Cup: Wolverhampton Retail Market
Wolverhampton Charity Cup: Rovers Sports

WORCESTER & DIST. SUNDAY LGE

COUNTY: WORCESTERSHIRE

PREM. DIV.	P	W	D	L	F	A	PTS
Cooksons	21	18	2	1	73	18	38
Archdale '73	21	15	2	4	71	39	32
Newlakes	22	14	4	4	57	27	32
Warndon	22	12	3	7	44	41	27
Droitwich S.	22	11	4	7	46	41	26
Southside	22	8	4	10	58	50	20
Droitwich	22	8	4	10	39	49	20
Barbourne	22	8	2	12	36	56	18
Hallow	22	5	6	11	33	44	16
Kempsey	22	6	2	14	34	57	14
Cutnall G.	22	3	5	14	43	72	11
Albion	22	3	2	17	34	74	8

Cooksons v Archdales not played

Lower Division Champions:
Div. 1 (13): Upton Sunday
Div. 2 (12): Green Dragon
Div. 3 (14): Bewdley   **Div. 4 (14):** Drifters
Div. 5 (14): Worcester Juniors

WOMEN'S NATIONAL LEAGUE

Miss L Whitehead,
52 Middlebrook Drive, Lostock, Bolton, Lancs BL6 4RH.

Doncaster dominance gunned down!

The 1992/93 season saw the end of an era when Doncaster Belles were knocked off their perch, of top women's team in England, by Arsenal Ladies. Arsenal, in their first season in the Premier Division of the National League, not only took the League championship away from the Belles but also added the League Cup and WFA Cup to their honours list.

With a 2-0 victory over Arsenal, infront of a crowd of 350, it appeared that once again Doncaster had the upper hand, and retaining the title would be a formality. But then, as so often happens in the mens Premier League, Wimbledon turned up to spoil the Belle's party. With ten minutes to go and winning 2-1, Doncaster looked on course for yet another two points but, when the final whistle blew, it was Wimbledon Ladies who walked off with the two points and a place in history by being the first team to defeat Doncaster Belles in a National League match. This ineffect set up a title match between Arsenal and Doncaster. Played at Highbury infront of a crowd of 18,500, it was Arsenal who took the win, 2-1, and the title.

At the other end of the table, Maidstone Tigresses and Bronte failed to beat the drop to Division One South and North respectively. Bronte managed to salvage something from their season with an impressive run in the WFA Cup which saw them reach the semi-finals, only to lose 2-1 to Doncaster Belles.

In Divison One South there was only one winner all season with the excellent District Line topping the table, beating Hassocks by a clear five points. At the bottom it looked like Epsom & Ewell would finish bottom, but a late run of victories saw them climb out of the relegation zone leaving Bristol Backwell and Saltdean behind. It was Saltdean who had to play for their right to stay in the League against the impressive Bromley Borough, who not only won their league (South East Counties League) but also reached the semi-finals of the WFA Cup losing out to the mighty Arsenal. With a confident 3-0 victory Bromley Borough took their place in Division One South relegating Saltdean to the lower divisions.

In the Division One North Leasowe Pacific also strolled into the Premier League with a four point advantage over Nottingham Argyle. The impressive Liverpool side netting no fewer than 100 goals along the way. At the foot of the table Milton Keynes finished with a solitary point and elected not to compete in the play-offs, thus giving Kidderminster Harriers automatic promotion from the West Midland Region. With Kidderminster also lifting the WFA U16 Cup, with victory over Arsenal, they could be a team to look out for in the future. Another team to leave the league were Sunderland Ladies, whose place will be taken by the Eastern Region champions, Luton Ladies.

Dave West

Premier Division

	P	W	D	L	F	A	Pts
ARSENAL	18	17	0	1	66	8	34
DONCASTER BELLES	18	16	0	2	80	10	32
KNOWSLEY UNITED	18	11	1	6	37	33	23
WIMBLEDON	18	9	3	6	36	37	21
RS SOUTHAMPTON	18	7	3	8	37	41	17
IPSWICH TOWN	18	7	3	8	31	49	17
STANTON RANGERS	18	6	1	11	24	45	13
MILLWALL LIONESSES	18	3	2	13	16	41	8
MAIDSTONE T.	18	2	4	12	8	43	8
BRONTE	18	2	3	12	17	38	7

Division One North

	P	W	D	L	F	A	Pts
LEASOWE PACIFIC	18	16	1	1	100	21	33
NOTTINGHAM A.	18	14	1	3	73	23	29
ABBEYDALE	18	11	3	4	62	20	25
SHEFFIELD WED.	18	9	2	7	68	29	20
ST.HELENS	18	9	1	8	67	49	19
WOLVERHAMPTON	18	7	3	8	52	37	17
VILLA AZTECS	18	8	1	9	47	45	17
COWGATE KESTRALS	18	6	3	9	32	52	15
SUNDERLAND	18	2	0	16	19	103	4
MILTON KEYNES	18	0	1	17	8	150	1

Division One South

	P	W	D	L	F	A	Pts
DISTRICT LINE	18	15	1	2	93	28	31
HASSOCKS	18	12	2	4	53	38	26
TOWN & COUNTY	18	9	2	7	51	39	20
HEMEL HEMPSTEAD	18	8	4	6	38	37	20
BRIGHTON & H.	18	8	2	8	41	42	18
HORSHAM	18	6	5	7	34	42	17
OXFORD	18	5	5	8	20	34	15
EPSOM & EWELL	18	6	2	10	44	52	14
BRISTOL BACKWELL	18	4	3	11	31	50	11
SALTDEAN	18	3	2	13	30	70	8

NATIONAL LEAGUE CUP

Round 1

Oxford v Epsom & Ewell	1-2		Town & Co. v Saltdean	1-2
Nottingham A. v Bristol Backwell	3-0		Sheffield W. v Bronte	1-0
Milton Keynes v Sunderland	0-8		Wolves v Horsham	3-1
Distict Line v Villa Aztecs	4-1		Brighton v Leasowe P.	1-6
Arsenal v Hassocks	8-0			

Round 2

Epsom & E v Ipswich T	1-3		R.S. Southampton v Knowsley	0-1
Wimbledon v Nottingham A.	4-0		Maidstone T. v Stanton R. (6-5 pens)	2-2
Sunderland v District Line	0-5		Sheffield Wed v Wolves	0-2
Arsenal v Saltdean	9-0		Leasowe P. Millwall L.	7-0

Round 3

Ipswich T. v Wimbledon	1-2		Knowsley v Maidstone T.	2-0
District L. v Arsenal	1-5		Wolves v Leasowee P.	1-3

Semi-finals

Wimbledon v Arsenal	2-4		Knowsley v Leasowe P.	5-4

Final

Arsenal 3 - 0 Knowsley

WFA CUP

ARSENAL WIN BATTLE OF THE GIANTS

Arsenal Ladies began their quest for the Womens Football treble by beating current holders and five times winners Doncaster Belles 3-0, at the Manor Ground, home of Oxford United.

Belles started the match as if their whole lives depended on the result. Borman, Walker and Murray all going close with shots that found Arsenal's Lesley Shipp in superb form. Arsenal's first chance fell to Debbie Bampton who's shot was deflected for a corner after 14 minutes. This failed to deter the Belles who kept the pressure on Arsenal and forcing shipp to make more fine saves. Arsenal's next real chance came after 38 minutes, when Churchman latched on to a loose ball in the six yard box, which Ride cleared off the line. From that clearance Karen Walker, the Belles leading goalscorer, pounced on a loose ball in the Arsenal area, where, once again, Shipp was there to push a goal-bound shot around the post for a corner.

Right on the stroke of what should have been half-time, Arsenal got a corner on the Doncaster left. Michelle Curley floated the ball over the heads of everyone in the area and into the back of the net to put Arsenal 1-0 up.

Shortly afterwards Doncaster skipper Gillian Coultard and Arsenal's Debbie Bampton were involved in a collision, with Coultard eventually being carried off with a suspected broken collar bone. In the seventh minute of injury time Curley produced another great run down the left, the resultant cross finding Naz Ball at the far post, for her to head home her 39th goal of the season.

Doncaster started the second half the way they started the first. With Janice Murray causing the Arsenal defence all sorts of problems. Soon after though, Arsenals midfield began to get a grip on the game and Belles confidence was now beginning to waine. After 70 minutes Naz Ball won a free kick five yards outside the penalty area. Curley took the kick, picking out Chris Couling who failed to connect and Davidson saved with her legs. Soon after Belles broke free and substitute McQuiggan saw her shot go wide. This started a short period of dominance for Doncaster with Murray, Borman and Broadhurst going close. After 81 minutes Naz Ball set off on a run, had a shot from 20 yards out, Belles keeper Davidson blocked, Ball latched onto the rebound sending it high and towards the far post where Debbie Bampton headed home from close range. Final score: Arsenal 3 Doncaster 0

Brian Byles.

Arsenal Ladies celebrate after their WFA Cup victory over Doncaster. Photo: Dave West.

WFA Cup

The teams which won through to the fourth round were as follow:

Group One	Group Two	Group Three	Group Four
Epsom & Ewell	Bristol Backwell	Bromley Borough	Oxford United
Brighton	Swindon Spitfires	Leyton Orient	Abbeydale/Alvechurch
Horsham	Truro City	District Line	Wolverhampton

Group Five	Group Six	Group Seven	Group Eight
St.Helens	Sheffield Wednesday	Rainworth	Town & County
Wigan	Cowgate Kestrels	TNT	Luton Town
Leasowe Pacific	Middlesbrough		

Round 4

Brighton v Arsenal	1-5	Luton Town v Ipswich		0-9
Town & Co. v District Line	2-6	Stanton R. v Sheffield W.		4-2
Horsham v Epsom & Ewell	2-3	Abbeydale v Millwall		2-3
Wolves v RS Southampton	0-4	Doncaster Belles v Knowsley		W/O
Leasowe P. v Bristol Backwell	4-1	Maidstone T. v Swindon S.		0-4
Cowgate K. v Wimbledon	2-3	Middlesbrough v Truro C.		0-5
Rainworth v Oxford Utd	2-0	Wigan v Bronte		3-8
Bromley Borough v Leighton Orient	3-0	St.Helens v TNT	St.Helens	W/O

Round 5

Arsenal v District Line	4-1	Ipswich v Stanton Rangers	3-2
Epsom & Ewell v RS Southampton	0-1	Millwall v Doncaster	0-4
Leasowe P. v Wimbledon	2-5	Maidstone T. v Middlesbrough	2-0
Rainworth v Bromley Borough	1-4	Bronte v St.Helens	2-0

Quarter-finals

Arsenal v RS Southampton	5-1	Ipswich v Doncaster Belles	2-5
Wimbledon v Bromley Borough	2-1	Maidstone T. v Bronte	1-2

Semi-finals

Arsenal v Bromley Borough	2-0	Doncaster Belles v Bronte	2-1

Final
Arsenal 3 - 0 Doncaster Belles

PREVIOUS WFA CUP WINNERS

1970-71	Southampton	4-1	Stewart & Thistle
1971-72	Southampton	3-2	Leeds Ladies
1972-73	Southampton	2-0	Westhorn United
1973-74	Fodens	2-1	Southampton
1974-75	Southampton	4-2	Warminster
1975-76	Southampton	2-1	QPR
1976-77	QPR	1-0	Southampton
1977-78	Southampton	8-2	QPR
1978-79	Southampton	1-0	Lowestoft
1979-80	St.Helens	1-0	Preston North End
1980-81	Southampton	4-2	St.Helens
1981-82	Lowestoft	2-0	Cleveland Spartans
1982-83	Doncaster Belles	3-2	St.Helens
1983-84	Howbury Grange	4-2	Doncaster Belles
1984-85	Friends of Fulham	2-0	Doncaster Belles
1985-86	Norwich	4-3	Doncaster Belles
1986-87	Doncaster Belles	2-0	St.Helens
1987-88	Doncaster Belles	3-1	Leasowe Pacific
1988-89	Leasowe Pacific	3-2	Friends of Fulham
1989-90	Doncaster Belles	1-0	Friends of Fulham
1990-91	Millwall Lionesses	1-0	Doncaster Belles
1991-92	Doncaster Belles	4-0	RS Southampton

WFA International Scene

England Ladies - Back Row (L-R): G.Boreman, K.Walker, J.Murray, S.Hayward, T.Davidson, L.Shipp, M.Spacey, C.Taylor, M.Curley. Front: K.Davis, S.Williams, D.Bampton, G.Coultard, L.Waller, K.Burke, S.Law. Photo: Paul Dennis

EUROPEAN CUP QUARTER-FINAL v ITALY

England's hopes of European glory at Rotherham, floundered with a three-goal second-half blitz, led by the Italian captain and scoring machine Caroline Morace, after a 2-3 defeat for England in the first leg in Italy.

The first-half started brightly for England, with the Yorkshire crowd getting behind the girls. Marieanne Spacey (a scorer from the first leg) was the first to test the Italian defence with a long range effort which went just wide. While at the other end, stand-in central defender Kerry Davis (for the injured Jackie Sherrard, who was co-commentator with Martin Tyler, on a live transmission on Sky TV) kept Morace in her pocket. Doncaster Belles' Gail Borman almost got England on level terms, but her header looped over the bar. Then with only three minutes of the half remaining, the Italians had a chance to extend their aggregate lead, when Louise Waller handled a goal bound shot from A'Stolfo, and the referee, Mr Pratas from Portugal, had no option but to show the red card. However, the penalty, taken by Silvia Fiorini, was missed letting England back into the tie.

The second period was always going to be an uphill battle, and when Sue Law had the misfortune to clear a goal-bound shot into the back of the net, England's chances of reaching the next round looked all but over. This was confirmed two minutes later when Morace seized on a poor back-pass and shot for goal, with the unlucky Sue Law, once again, putting the ball in the back of the net.

England manager John Bilton then made a subisution with Arsenal's Sian Williams coming on for, the now dejected, Sue Law. England were forced into hurried shots by the well-drilled Italian defence, with Spacey, Williams and Walker all shooting wide.

With only a few minutes remaining England's eagerness to score was capitalised on as the Italians broke with Morace thumping the ball into the back of the net from the edge of the box.

Dave West.

Italy Ladies - Back Row (L-R): S.Antonini, R.Salmaso, F.D'Astocfo, A.Carta, C.Morace, D.Prestifilippo. Front Row: S.Fiorini, E.Iozzelli, A.Marsiletti, M.Cardenous, E.Bavagnoli. Photo: Dave West.

Regional Leagues

Eastern Region

PREM. DIVISION

	P	W	D	L	F	A	PTS
Luton town	14	13	1	0	75	14	27
Dunstable	14	12	0	2	75	16	24
Harlow Town	14	6	4	4	62	26	16
Racers	14	6	4	4	57	34	16
Suffolk B'birds	14	7	2	5	53	30	16
Ipswich Town R.	14	1	0	13	19	77	2
Breydon	14	1	0	13	13	130	2

DIVISION ONE

	P	W	D	L	F	A	PTS
Hemel Town	16	13	1	2	74	17	27
Stalham Seahawks	16	13	1	2	74	22	27
Pye	16	11	2	3	68	21	24
Bedford Town B.	16	9	2	5	52	21	20
Canary Rangers	16	8	4	4	56	26	20
Enfield Merryhills	16	5	2	9	40	35	12
Beccles	16	3	1	12	25	89	7
Norwich Reserves	16	2	1	13	11	66	5
Thetford	16	1	0	15	8	111	2

DIVISION TWO

	P	W	D	L	F	A	PTS
Colchester F.	16	14	2	0	98	15	30
Peterborough P.	16	14	1	1	111	11	29
Colchester E.	16	9	1	6	45	51	19
Stevenage	16	9	1	6	45	51	19
Woodham W.	16	6	0	10	44	44	12
Luton Town Res	16	7	0	9	40	57	14
Luton Jade Flyers	16	5	0	11	40	66	10
V.International	16	3	0	13	21	129	6
Abbey United	16	2	1	13	17	67	5

Greater London

PREM. DIVISION

	P	W	D	L	F	A	PTS
Leyton Orient	18	15	2	1	71	18	32
Arsenal Res.	18	14	2	2	72	25	30
Watford	18	10	4	4	43	25	24
Brentford	18	11	1	6	52	38	23
T.Hotspur	18	6	4	8	43	44	16
Tottenham	18	7	0	11	40	48	14
Wimbledon Res.	18	5	4	9	27	38	14
Millwall Res.	18	5	3	10	26	47	13
Romford	18	2	6	10	23	46	10
Hillingdon	18	0	4	14	7	75	4

DIVISION ONE

	P	W	D	L	F	A	PTS
Lambeth	18	13	4	1	51	17	30
Hackney A.	18	12	2	4	45	24	26
Yeading	18	12	2	4	37	28	26
Southend	18	10	4	4	45	27	24
Newham	18	8	2	8	45	29	18
Basildon	18	6	4	8	25	45	16
District Res.	18	6	1	11	35	47	13
Collier Row	18	5	0	13	39	45	10
Winchester	18	4	2	12	28	51	10
S.E.Rangers	18	3	1	14	24	61	7

DIVISION TWO

	P	W	D	L	F	A	PTS
Arsenal Third	18	16	1	1	78	26	33
Pinewood	18	11	2	5	65	47	24
Palace Eagles	18	11	1	6	51	42	23
Chelmsford	18	10	1	7	34	34	21
Walton Hersham	18	8	4	6	41	32	20
Chislehurst	18	6	5	7	18	25	17
Leyton O. Res	18	6	4	8	43	39	16
Wimbledon Third	18	4	4	10	24	45	12
Hampstead	18	3	2	13	32	64	8
Tottenham Res.	18	1	4	13	27	59	6

DIVISION THREE

	P	W	D	L	F	A	PTS
Barnet	16	14	0	2	87	20	28
Mill Hill Utd	16	10	3	3	55	21	23
Chelsea	16	11	0	5	51	25	22
West Ham Utd	16	8	3	5	36	40	19
Leyton O. 3rd	16	8	1	7	28	35	17
Newham Res.	16	6	2	8	29	36	14
Millwall 3rd	16	6	1	9	29	42	13
Hackney B.	16	3	1	12	28	62	7
Collier RW RS	16	0	1	15	12	74	1

DIVISION FOUR

	P	W	D	L	F	A	PTS
London Ladies	12	9	2	1	52	12	20
Abbey Rangers	12	8	1	3	38	15	17
Brentford Res.	12	8	0	4	54	20	16
Palace Eag. Rs	12	8	0	4	39	18	16
Camberwell	12	5	1	6	29	21	11
Lambeth Res.	12	1	0	11	7	64	2
West Ham Res.	12	1	0	11	13	82	2

Collier Row Ladies - Greater London League Division One.

Pilkingtons Ladies - North West Regional League. Photo: Dave West.

North West Region

DIVISION ONE

	P	W	D	L	F	A	PTS
Wigan	12	8	2	2	54	20	18
Man Belle Vue	12	8	2	2	49	16	18
Preston Rgrs*	12	7	2	3	33	28	12
Manchester Utd	12	4	2	6	30	25	10
Manchester City	12	4	1	7	26	49	9
Broadoak	12	2	4	6	25	42	8
Chorley	12	2	1	9	12	49	5

* - 4 points deducted.

DIVISION TWO

	P	W	D	L	F	A	PTS
Bury	18	16	2	0	97	26	34
Pilkingtons	18	15	2	1	80	39	32
Tranmere Rovers	18	12	0	6	65	44	24
Leek Town	18	10	2	6	38	36	22
Burnley	18	8	3	7	57	58	19
Vernon-Carus	18	5	5	8	36	42	15
Oldham Athletic	18	5	3	10	48	55	13
Clitheroe	18	4	3	11	38	67	11
Runcorn Town	18	2	3	13	16	65	7
Bolton	18	0	3	15	32	75	3

DIVISION THREE

	P	W	D	L	F	A	PTS
Blackpool	16	15	0	1	80	10	30
Blackburn Rov.	16	11	0	5	66	25	22
Rochdale	16	9	1	6	51	40	19
Bangor City	16	9	1	6	42	31	19
Colwyn Bay	16	8	1	7	61	52	17
Rossendale	16	7	2	7	41	48	16
Pilkingtons Res	16	5	2	9	42	49	12
Alsager College	16	1	2	13	22	103	4
Man Utd Res*	16	2	1	13	26	73	3

* - 2pts deducted.

DIVISION FOUR

	P	W	D	L	F	A	PTS
Liverpool Feds	18	15	2	1	72	22	32
Newsham Park	18	12	2	4	73	35	26
Lancs/Morecambe	18	11	2	5	54	41	24
Dry 201	18	10	3	5	50	29	23
Crewe Robins	18	10	1	7	71	43	21
Port Vale	18	8	2	8	41	42	18
Atherton Lab.	18	6	1	11	36	62	13
Sale United	18	3	2	13	44	75	8
Accrington Stan.	18	3	2	13	19	77	8
Northwich Vixens	18	3	1	14	32	66	7

Yorkshire & Humberside League

DIVISION ONE

	P	W	D	L	F	A	PTS
Doncaster Town	14	11	0	3	41	14	22
L.F.C. Haigh	14	10	1	3	53	23	21
Middlesborough	14	8	3	3	38	16	19
Huddersfield	14	6	3	5	32	24	15
Newcastle	14	7	1	6	32	27	15
Bradford City	14	4	4	6	19	24	12
Wakefield	14	1	3	10	22	54	5
Hull City	14	0	2	11	14	69	3

DIVISION TWO

	P	W	D	L	F	A	PTS
Barnsley	14	11	3	0	78	12	25
Bronte Bantams	14	11	2	1	86	14	24
Doncaster Belles R.	14	6	4	4	46	18	16
Oakland Rangers	14	5	3	6	23	31	13
Bransholme Astra	14	5	2	7	38	66	12
L.F.C.Haigh Res	14	4	2	8	45	76	10
Huddersfield Res	14	3	1	10	22	63	7
Grimsby Borough	14	2	1	11	15	73	5

DIVISION THREE

	P	W	D	L	F	A	PTS
Brighouse	14	14	0	0	83	20	28
Leeds United	14	10	0	4	79	30	20
Scunthorpe I.	14	10	0	4	81	34	20
City Roses	14	10	0	4	46	23	20
Selby Warriors	14	3	1	10	32	81	7
Grimsby L.F.C.	13	2	2	9	22	50	6
Leeds Poly*	13	3	0	10	30	65	6
Wiggington G.	14	1	1	12	9	80	3

* - nonfulfillment of fixtures.

English Schools'
Football Association 1992-93

Chief Executive: M R Berry, 4a, Eastgate Street, Stafford ST16 2NQ (0785) 51142

Contributor to Non-League Directory: Mike Simmonds, 19, The Spinney, Bulcote, Burton Joyce, Nottingham NG14 5GX (0602) 313299

The International Season - Under 18

1992-93 was another successful season for the England Schools' Under 18 squad. A run of eight games undefeated, starting in March 1992 only came to an end with the last match of 1992-93 when they went down 3-0 to the full Dutch Youth side. In the interim, England won the three-nation Centenary Shield held for the first time as a mini-tournament.

A 1-1 draw with the hosts, Wales was an unpromising start but a first ever victory over Switzerland, like the Dutch fielding their full Under 18 side, stands out as the season's best performance. Three goals in the first 25 minutes by Hardwick, Edgar and Smith gave England a flying start but they had to survive a gallant fight back by the Swiss before winning 3-2.

Under 18 Results

Eire	2 - 4	England	Dublin (Hardwick,Barham,Heffernan, Bass)	
Wales*	1 - 1	England	Merthyr (Chilton)	
Swizterland*	2 - 3	England	Cwmbran (Hardwick, Edgar,Smith)	
England	2 - 1	Austria	Middlesbrough (Hardwick,Smith)	
Holland	3 - 0	England	Heemskerk	

* Denotes Centenary Shield Match

THE CENTENARY SHIELD

	P	W	D	L	F	A	Pts
England	2	1	1	0	4	3	3
Switzerland	2	1	0	1	4	4	2
Wales	2	0	1	1	2	3	1

		Eire	Wales	Switzerland	Austria	Holland
1	Kelvin Arterton	1		1	1	1
2	Steven Brown	1(c)	1(c)		1(c)	1(c)
3	Neil Barham	1	1	1	1	1
4	Stephen Carberry	1	1	1	1	1
5	Jason Smith	1		1(c)	1	1
6	Jonathon Bass	1			1	1
7	Matthew Hardwick	1	S	1	1	
8	Ben Sedgemore	S	1	1	S	1
8	Richard Baker	1	1	S	S	S
9	Liam Heffernan	1	1	1	1	1
10	Paul O'Brien	1	S	1	1	1
11	Mark Pugh	S	1	1	1	1
12	Nicholas Edgar	S	1	1	1	1
13	Gary Chilton	1	1			
14	Paul Hughes	S	1	1	S	S
15	Michael Finch	S	1			S
16	Ben Shiers			1		S

Key: 1 = Played; S = Substitute

Scorers: Hardwick (3), Smith (2), Barham, Bass, Chilton, Edgar, Heffernan.

Under 15

A season of rather mixed fortunes for the Under 15 England Schools' international squad ended on a high note with two excellent performances against Germany, playing for the first time in this country as a unified team.

Although the match at Wembley ended as a 0-0 draw, the skills and commitment shown had raised the spirits of both the Wembley and television audience after the dismal showing of the senior international side the previous week. Only the bravery of goalkeepers, Dungey and Enke prevented the goals which would have climaxed an interesting game.

Two days later, at the Don Valley Stadium, Sheffield, England scored their best home victory over Germany for 12 years when goals from Cassidy, Clemence and a magnificent effort from Broomes brought a 3-0 victory. England could also afford to miss a penalty when Clemence's good strike was brilliantly saved by Miernik.

If games against Germany are always considered the bench mark against which the success or failure of an England Schools' season is judged, 1992-93 was another good year. There were, however, disappointments with the defeat by Scotland at Wembley wrestling the Victory Shield from England's control in a poor match while Austria won 1-0 at Walsall to mark their first ever visit to this country at schoolboy level.

Nevertheless, an overall record of five wins, a draw and two defeats maintained the view that the Under 15's remain one of the most successful of the many internatonal squads now fielded at different levels.

England		1 - 0	Eire	Reading (Cassidy)
England *		1 - 2	Scotland	Wembley (Cassidy)
Wales *		1 - 2	England	Swansea (Clemence, Fotiadis)
N.Ireland *		0 - 1	England	Newtownards (Fotiadis)
England		0 - 1	Austria	Walsall
Switzerland		2 - 3	England	Zurich (Hodges(2), Cassidy)
England		0 - 0	Germany	Wembley
England		3 - 0	Germany	Sheffield (Cassidy, Broomes, Clemence)

* Denotes Victory Shield Match

THE VICTORY SHIELD

	P	W	D	L	F	A	Pts
Scotland	3	2	1	0	5	1	5
England	3	2	0	1	4	3	4
N.Ireland	3	1	0	2	5	4	2
Wales	3	0	1	2	1	7	1

	Eire	Scot.	Wales	N.Ire.	Austria	Switz.	Germany	G'many
L.Bell			1	1	1	S	S	S
M.Broomes	1(c)	1(c)	1(c)	1(c)	1(c)	1(c)	1(c)	1(c)
J.Cassidy	1	1		S	S	1	1	1
J.Curtis	1	1	1	1	1	1	1	1
S.Clemence	S	S	1	1	1	1		1
A.Ducros	1	1						S
A.Duncan	S			1				S
J.Dungey	1	1	1			1		
A.Fotiadas		S	1	1	1	1		1
A.Futcher	1	1	1	1	1			
D.Hilton	1	1	1	1	1	1	1	
L.Hodges	1	1	1	1	S	1	1	1
J.Kyte			1	1	1	1		
M.Millett	1	1	1	1	1	1	1	
E.Omoyinmi	1	1	S	S	1	S	S	S
P.Teather						1	1	1
R.Wright				1	1			
J.Wynter	1	1						

Key: 1 = Played; S = Playing substitute; C = Captain

Goalscorers: Cassidy (4), Clemence, Fotiadas, Hodges (2), Broomes

The English Schools' F.A.
British Gas Trophy 1992-93

First Leg
29th April, Bramall Lane
Sheffield 2-2 Liverpool

Second Leg
10th May, Goddison Park
Liverpool 1-0 Sheffield

Liverpool won 3-2 on aggregate.

Liverpool ended a barren period of 17 years when they won the English Schools' Inter-Association Trophy for a record 13th time in the 84th year of the competition.

Sheffield making their third final appearance in four years, probably started as favourites, a position that appeared to be justified in the second minute of the first leg when Danny Hobson put them ahead. It was something of a surprise when they conceded an equaliser to Liverpool's Danny Webb but their immediate riposte, a Steve Thorpe header from an inswinging corner, gave them a deserved interval lead.

Although Liverpool had the better of the second half, Sheffield were coping adequately but 12 minutes from time, a goalkeeping mistake by Adam Wheeler gave Eddie Hussin the chance to head the equaliser which, in retrospect, decided the destination of the Trophy.

It was the defences which again took the eye in the second leg despite another early goal for the home side. After only 8 minutes, Sheffield half-cleared a Liverpool attack but Bart McHugh reacted quickly to drive the ball past an unsighted 'keeper. This put Liverpool in control especially as Kinsella, Prior, Webster and Brazier proved why the Merseysiders had conceded only eight goals in nine games up to the second leg. Sheffield were unable to breach the barrier they created and thus were defeated at the last hurdle for the second successive season.

Liverpool's route to the final				Sheffield's route to the final		
Round 1	Tameside	(A) 1-1		Round 1	Spen Valley	(A) 6-0
Replay		(H) 5-1		Round 2	Huddersfield	(A) 4-0
Round 2	South Ribble	(H) 4-2		Round 3	Sunderland	(A) 3-1
Round 3	Telford	(H) 2-0		Round 4	Walsall	(A) 2-0
Round 4	Chorley	(H) 4-1		Round 5	Kirkby/Knowsley	(A) 2-3
Round 5	South Notts	(A) 1-1		Round 6	Rotherham	(H) 3-2
Replay		(H) 3-1		S-Final	Leicester	(A) 2-0
Round 6	Vale of White H.	(H) 4-0				
S-Final	St. Albans	(A) 2-1				

Sheffield Schools' FA - Runners-up - Back Row (L-R): W.Thomas, C.Kelly, A.Wheeler, M.Kirkpatrick, D.O'Leary, T.Roberts, R.Humphreys, D.Hobson, R.Portman, J.Beachell, B.Holmes. Front: K.Kotylo, S.Gibbs, G.Hopson, A.Stevens, G.Smith, P.Parkin, D.Smith, S.Piletto, A.Ward, S.Thorpe.

The County Championships

Apart from the two international sides, the two national County Championships provide the highest level of schools' football for the best players in the country. Both are sponsored by Adidas and organised in a similar way with Regional winners meeting in the national stages. The only difference between the Under 19 and the Under 16 Championships is that the latter spreads over two seasons.

English Schools' Adidas Under 19 County Championship

South Yorkshire 4-1 Devon
Played at Bramall Lane, Sheffield, May 7th, 1993

These two sides were taking their first appearances in the final since they met in 1978 in the first ever championship. Although the score seems to indicate an easy win for South Yorkshire, it hides a second half recovery by Devon which deserved better than the two late goals scored by the home side, which gave them a flattering victory margin.

Individual hero of the night was England Schools' striker, Richard Barker, whose hat-trick was the difference between the two sides. His early goal put South Yorkshire ahead and when his quick reaction at the near post brought a second, Devon's long trip looked to have been in vain. If Lomas had added a third, as he ought to have done, the game would effectively have been over.

After the interval, however, a fine individual goal by Shane Powell made it 2-1 and for twenty minutes, an equaliser seemed inevitable. As Devon pressed forward, Barker's pace became an increasing threat and he completed his hat-trick seven minutes from time to end Devon's valiant fight-back. It was cruel on the visitors to concede a last minute fourth goal to Tunstall.
Semi-final results....**South Yorkshire** 1-0 **Suffolk**.....**Devon** 2-1 **W.Midlands**

South Yorkshire: Richard Barker,Rotherham; **Stephen Brown**,Sheffield; **Andrew Darby**,Barnsley; **Dean Fearon**,Barnsley; **Richard Fidler**,Sheffield; **Matthew Hardwick**,Sheffield; **Dean Henderson**,Rotherham; **Jack Lester**,Sheffield; **Andrew Little**,Sheffield; **Ian Matthews**,Sheffield; **Michael McVey**,Rotherham; **Matthew Sanderson**,Sheffield; **Neil Sykes**,Doncaster; **Andrew Thorpe**,Barnsley; **Jamie Tunstall**,Sheffield; **Alan Walker**,Barnsley; **Philip Waring**,Rotherham; Team Managers: A.Johnson, R.McVey, M.Sinclair.

Devon: Steve Lomas,S.Devon College; **Leigh Underhay**,Plymstock; **Lee Wadge**,Plymouth; **Andy David**,Plymstock; **Shane Powell**,Plymouth; **James Slomka**,King Edward VI; **Alan Chapman**,N.Devon College; **Neil Spittle**,Teignmouth; **Simon Wright**, N.Devon College; **Steve Murch**,Exeter; **Casey Grylls**,Exeter; **Kolvin Stone**,S.Devon College; **Zak Locke**,Clyst; **Matthew Taylor**,Exeter; **Mike Warburton**,Exeter; Team Managers: P.Hiller, B.Brewer.

English Schools' Adidas Under 16 County Championship

Essex 4-0 Avon
Played at Dagenham & Redbridge FC, 25th November 1992

After losing to Merseyside in 1990 and the following year to Cheshire, Essex were determined to make it third time lucky. It took them 26 minutes to open their account when McCann's skilful play set up a goal for Paul Scheider. The same player added a second after a fine run and shot from full back Taylor and in the final minute of the half, Darren Collins made it 3-0.

The second half was inevitably something of an anti-climax. Avon tried hard to get back into the game but Schneider turned provider in the 73rd minute, laying the ball off for the unmarked Daniel Shipp to complete the scoring.
Semi-final results.....**West Midlands** 1-3 **Avon**.....**Essex** 2-0 **South Yorkshire**

Essex: R.Bowman(Havering); **M.Trower**(Havering); **S.Blaney**(Basildon & Brentwood); **R.Taylor**(S.E.Essex); **K.Maher** (Redbridge); **S.Reynolds**(Basildon & Brentwood); - **D.Shipp**(Havering); **D.Collins**(Redbridge); **M.Black**(Harlow & W.Essex); **K.Dowson**(Basildon & Brentwood); **P.Schneider**(Barking & Dagenham); **C.McCann**(Newham); **S.Richardson**(Thurrock); **G.Eyles**(Havering); **M.Kent**(Newham); **G.Harris**(Chelmsford); **L.Blunden**(Havering); **W.Brown**(Barking & Dagenham).

Avon: M.Richards(Bath & Wansdyke); **C.Hamblin**(Bristol); **R.Weston**(Bristol); **M.Farrow**(Bristol); **S.Gitsham**(Bristol); **Ian Harvey**(Bath & Wansdyke); **R.Harding**(North Avon); **D.Haines**(North Avon); **D.Simmonds**(Bristol); **C.Woodman**(North Avon); **R.Crew**(N.Avon); **M.Parkinson**(S.W.Avon); **D.Dale**(Bristol); **J.Barton**(S.W.Avon); **K.Jacobs**(N.Avon); **P.Newberry**(Bristol); **D.Barclay**(Bristol); **S.Horne**(N.Avon).

E.S.F.A. Individual Schools' Competitions 1992-93

Individual schools competitions at local and county level provide the 'grass roots' football for an estimated 250,000 players involved in English Schools' FA activities throughout the season. Four of these are continued at national level to produce a national champion or, in the case of 1992/93, champions. Remarkably, three of the four national finals, ended in draws so the trophies in these were shared.

English Schools' Mars Under 19 Championship

Taunton's College (Southampton) 1-1 Longlands College (Middlesbrough)
Played at Aldershot Town FC, May 17th

Longlands College were drawn away in every round of the Mars Championship but this proved little handicap to them. They even took the lead in the final when David Goodchild flicked home a header but Taunton's equalised 12 minutes later when after strong play by Robert Harbut, Andy Whitehead coolly lobbed the 'keeper from over 25 yards.

ROUTES TO THE FINAL

Taunton's College			Longlands College		
Hampshire Final v Itchen College		1-1	Cleveland Final v Hartlepool SFC	(A)	4-1
Replay		2-0	Round 1 v York SFC	(A)	5-2
Round 1 v Charterhouse (Surrey)	(A)	2-1	Round 2 v Q.Elizabeth (Darlington)	(A)	6-3
Round 2 v New College (Swindon)	(A)	4-0	Round 3 v Wilmorton Coll. (Derby)	(A)	1-1
Round 3 v Millfield (Somerset)	(A)	2-1	Replay	(A)	2-1
Round 4 v Chichester (Sussex)	(H)	2-0	Round 4 v St.Cuthberts HS (N'castle)	(A)	3-0
Semi-final v Hewett HS (Norwich)	(H)	1-1	Semi-final v De La Salle School	(A)	4-1
Replay	(A)	2-1			

English Schools' Diamik Under 16 Championship

Farringdon School (Sunderland) 2-2 Dr.Challoner's Grammar S. (Amersham)
Played at Roker Park, Sunderland, May 12th

The last year of sponsorship by Leeds based educational furniture firm, Diamik, was marked with a thrilling final at Roker Park. Most of the support was for Farringdon and they were delighted by a goal in the 4th minute, Gray's corner being deflected in. They held the lead for three-quarters of the match but faced defeat in the face when goals from Wil Sterling and James Baker left them trailing 2-1 with only three minutes remaining. The spirit which typified both teams' performances was exemplified by Farringdon's immediate response through Mark Robinson's shot which brought the draw which all agreed was the right result.

Farringdon School			Dr.Challoner's School		
Round 1 v St.David's(Mid'boro)	(H)	1-0	Round 1 v Little Heath(Reading)	(A)	4-1
Round 2 v Priory (Barnsley)	(A)	1-1	Round 2 v Grange(Christchurch)	(A)	2-1
Replay	(H)	1-0	Round 3 v St.Thomas(London)	(H)	4-0
Round 3 v St.Cuthberts (N'castle)	(A)	1-1	Round 4 v Wooton Bassett(Swindon)	(A)	5-3
Replay	(H)	2-1	Semi-final v Bexleyheath	(A)	0-0
Round 4 v Cardinal H.(Liverpool)	(H)	3-2	Replay	(H)	3-0
Semi-final v Wolfreton(Hull)	(H)	2-1			

English Schools' McDonalds Under 12 5-a-sides

This competition was introduced to the English Schools calendar last season to reflect the growth of indoor football and to encourage the development of small-sided games. The sixteen survivors of local and regional events took part in the Finals Day at the Harvey Hadden Sports Centre (Nottingham) and after five hours of skilful football, yet another draw, this time goalless, meant that Pelton Roseberry School (Chester-le-Street) and St.Benedict's School from Upton in the Wirral shared the Trophy.
Semi-finals....**St.Benedict's** 2-0 **St.Paul's(Leicester)**
Pelton Roseberry 0-0 **Ixworth(Suffolk)** (Pelton went through because of superior results in the preliminary groups)

English Schools' Monster Munch Cup (6-a-side)

The last of the national individual schools' competitions to be completed produced a unique situation in the history of the English Schools' FA in which all four were shared. Played in front of a 30,000 crowd at Wembley prior to the Under 15 international against Germany. Beacon Rise School from Bristol and Ashtree School (Stevenage) drew 1-1 with the latter scoring a late equaliser.
The third place play-off between Heathlands Primary School (Birmingham) and East Bolden Junior School was also drawn (2-2) so all four schools left Wembley with some honour in this newly named event, reputed to be the largest schools' competition in the world.

An unusual save at the McDonalds' Under 12 Indoor 5-a-side finals at Nottingham.

The English Schools' Festivals

The English Schools' FA is proud of its festivals and the 1992-93 season saw nearly 3,000 pupils enjoy the opportunity of meeting new friends and opponents from different parts of their country in friendly contests with no cups or medals at stake. The football is no less competitive for that.

THE GILLETTE UNDER 19 FESTIVAL
Playing record 1992/93

	P	W	D	L	F	A
Cumbria	5	0	1	4	6	18
Durham	4	2	1	1	7	6
Northumberland	5	2	1	2	9	9
North Yorkshire	5	3	1	1	10	7
South Yorkshire	4	1	0	3	6	10
West Yorkshire	5	4	0	1	16	3
Isle of Man	5	1	0	4	7	19
Cheshire	5	3	2	0	16	5
Lancashire	5	1	0	4	8	16
Merseyside A	5	2	2	1	8	9
Merseyside B	5	2	2	1	9	8
Shropshire A	5	3	2	0	7	4
Shropshire B	5	2	1	2	9	10
West Midlands	5	4	0	1	16	12
Lincolnshire A	4	1	1	2	10	10
Lincolnshire B	4	1	0	3	7	15
Nottinghamshire	4	1	1	2	7	6
Northamptonshire	4	0	1	3	3	7
Hertfordshire	5	2	0	3	10	14
Essex A	5	1	1	3	6	15
Essex B	5	4	1	0	12	4
Middlesex	4	2	0	2	8	7
Kent A	4	3	0	1	8	3
Kent B	4	2	1	1	12	7
Kent C	4	1	1	2	4	7
Cornwall	5	2	0	3	11	8
Avon A	4	0	1	3	3	7
Avon B	5	2	0	3	6	9
Berkshire	5	2	0	3	4	10
Dorset A	5	3	1	1	10	6
Dorset B	4	1	1	2	6	7
Hampshire A	4	1	1	2	5	3
Hampshire B	5	1	2	2	4	5
Somerset A	5	3	0	2	11	10
Somerset B	5	2	1	2	12	8
Lanarkshire	5	2	1	2	13	12
Independent Schools	5	4	0	1	15	7
USA 1 (East)	5	2	0	3	12	16
USA 2 (North)	5	3	2	0	7	3
Greater Manchester	1	0	0	1	1	2
Morecambe Youth	2	2	0	0	8	3
Everton FC	1	0	0	1	2	3

THE SMITHS ISLE OF WIGHT UNDER 14 FESTIVAL

Tuesday 13th April

Blackheath	2	Coventry	1
Reading	0	Sheffield	3
Havant	0	Bradford	0
V.of W.Horse	2	Bury	2
East Berkshire	1	Peterborough	1
Bishop Auckland	0	Brierley Hill	0
Allerdale	0	Gravesham	6
Gateshead	2	Wellingborough	2
Leeds	2	Plymouth	0
E.Cornwall	2	Cambridge	3
Gosport & F.	2	Scunthorpe	0
Huntingdon	3	Salford	3
Oxford	2	Tameside	6
Isle of Wight	5	Doncaster	2
Manchester	8	Portsmouth	0

Wednesday 14th April

Cambridge	1	Oxford	2
Bishop Auckland	1	E.Cornwall	1
Plymouth	1	Manchester	1
V.of W.Horse	7	Allerdale	2
Gateshead	1	Portsmouth	0
Gosp. & Fareham	0	Sheffield	2
East Berkshire	1	Leeds	2
Reading	3	Scunthorpe	1
Bradford	0	Huntingdon	0
Blackheath	2	Doncaster	1
Brierley Hill	2	Salford	4
Bury	3	Havant	0
Gravesham	4	Wellingborough	0
Peterborough	2	Coventry	3
Isle of Wight	7	Tamside	5

Thursday 15th April

Brierley Hill	3	Portsmouth	0
Gosp & Fareham	3	Doncaster	2
Bradford	4	Scunthorpe	0
East Berkshire	0	Tameside	3
Havant	2	Leeds	1
Isle of Wight	0	Cambridge	5
Coventry	0	Salford	3
Allerdale	0	Wellingborough	2
Gateshead	1	Manchester	1
Bury	1	Reading	4
Bishop Auckland	1	Gravesham	0
Peterborough	4	Plymouth	1
V.of White H.	3	East Cornwall	1
Blackheath	3	Sheffield	1
Huntingdon	2	Oxford	1

Friday 16th April

Salford	1	Blackheath	1
Brierley Hill	2	Reading	4
Gosport & F.	1	Tameside	4
Coventry	0	Leeds	3
V.of White H.	6	Gravesham	1
Allerdale	1	E.Cornwall	6
Plymouth	1	Sheffield	4
Peterborough	1	Oxford	1
East Berkshire	2	Manchester	1
Isle of Wight	4	Scunthorpe	0
Havant	0	Wellingborough	0
Gateshead	3	Bury	2
Bishop Auckland	1	Huntingdon	0
Bradford	7	Portsmouth	0
Cambridge	1	Doncaster	0

Welsh Football

Major Honours 1992/93

COMPETITION	WINNERS	RUNNERS-UP
Allbrights Welsh Cup	Cardiff City	Rhyl
Intermediate Cup	Llansantffraid	Brecon Corinthians
Konica League of Wales	Cwmbran Town	Inter Cardiff
Konica League of Wales Cup	Afan Lido	Porthmadog
Manweb Cymru Alliance	Llansantffraid	Welshpool Town
Manweb Cymru Alliance Lge Cup	Rhyl	Gresford Athletic
Abacus League Division One	Ton Pentre	Brecon Corinthians
Abacus League Division Two	A.F.C. Porth	Caerau
Abacus League Division Three	Treowen Stars	Pontyclun
Sealink Welsh Alliance	Cemaes Bay	Llanfairpwll
R.Con. Welsh Nat.Lge (Wrexham)	Penley	Buckley
Richards The Builders M.Wales Lge	Machynlleth	Morda United
R.Con. Welsh National Lge Cup	Lex XI Reserves	Penley

KONICA LEAGUE OF WALES

	P	W	D	L	F	A	Pts
CWMBRAN	38	26	9	3	69	22	87
INTER CARDIFF	38	26	5	7	79	36	83
ABERYSTWYTH T.	38	25	3	10	85	49	78
EBBW VALE	38	19	9	10	76	61	66
BANGOR CITY	38	19	7	12	77	58	64
HOLLYWELL TOWN	38	17	8	13	65	48	59
CONWY UNITED	38	16	9	13	51	51	57
CONNAH'S QUAY N.	38	17	4	17	66	67	55
PORTHMADOG	38	14	11	13	61	49	53
HAVERFORDWEST C	38	16	5	17	66	66	53
CAERSWS	38	14	10	14	64	60	52
AFAN LIDO	38	14	10	14	64	65	52
*MOLD ALEXANDRA	38	16	4	18	63	69	48
LLANELLI	38	11	8	19	49	64	41
MAESTEG PK ATH	38	9	13	16	52	59	40
FLINT TOWN UTD	38	11	6	21	47	67	39
BRITON FERRY ATH	38	10	9	19	61	87	39
NEWTOWN	38	9	9	20	55	87	36
LLANIDLOES TOWN	38	7	9	22	48	93	30
ABERGAVENNY T.	38	7	7	24	36	76	28

* = 3pts deducted

ABACUS LEAGUE

DIVISION ONE	P	W	D	L	F	A	PTS
Ton Pentre	26	25	1	3	71	20	67
Brecon Corries	26	17	4	5	74	40	55
Pontypridd	26	14	9	3	53	24	51
Caldicot	26	12	4	5	50	31	46
Aberaman	26	13	3	10	54	47	42
Ammanford	26	11	7	8	38	44	40
Pembroke B.	26	11	3	12	46	51	36
Cardiff C.S.	26	11	2	13	40	36	35
Port Talbot	26	10	4	12	48	49	34
Morriston	26	9	5	12	46	66	32
Caerleon	26	8	2	16	37	54	26
Blaenrhondda	26	6	5	15	32	50	23
Bridgend T.	26	6	5	15	38	58	23
Ferndale	26	2	2	22	19	76	8

DIVISION TWO	P	W	D	L	F	A	PTS
AFC Porth	26	20	4	2	81	25	64
Caerau	26	16	5	5	61	30	53
Llanwern	26	15	6	5	43	22	51
Risca	26	13	4	7	44	29	49
Carmarthen	26	10	8	8	51	43	38
Taffs Well	26	11	5	10	48	42	38
Skewen	26	11	2	13	46	48	35
B.P.	26	9	8	9	35	41	35
Tonyrefail	26	7	9	10	38	42	30
Garw	26	6	8	12	40	55	26
Fields Park/Pon.	26	7	4	15	33	43	25
Cardiff Corries	26	7	7	12	33	69	25
Newport YMCA	26	6	3	17	37	64	21
Seven Sisters	26	4	3	19	24	61	15

DIVISION THREE	P	W	D	L	F	A	PTS
Treowen	26	21	4	1	61	14	67
Pontyclun	26	16	5	5	58	32	53
Milford	26	15	2	9	74	36	47
Penrhiwceiber	26	13	8	6	57	44	47
Cardiff Inst.	26	11	6	9	63	49	39
Panteg	26	10	8	8	44	39	38
Pontardawe	26	9	9	8	46	44	36
Goytre	26	11	3	12	48	49	36
Pontlottyn	26	7	9	10	35	44	30
Abercynon	26	7	8	11	35	47	29
AFC Tondu	26	6	8	12	43	60	26
Treharris	26	6	5	15	40	51	23
S.W.Constabulary	26	4	8	14	34	63	20
Trelewis	26	3	3	20	27	93	12

RICHARDS THE BUILDERS MID WALES LEAGUE

	P	W	D	L	F	A	PTS
Machynlleth	36	28	2	6	116	51	86
Morda United	36	26	4	6	85	36	82
Llandrindod	36	22	4	10	108	57	70
Talgarth	36	19	10	7	80	50	67
Waterloo Rovers	36	21	4	11	80	63	67
Caersws Reserves	36	21	2	13	82	57	65
Aberystwyth Res.	36	18	9	9	70	59	65
Vale of Arrow	36	18	10	8	77	49	64
Berriew	36	19	5	12	68	44	62
Newtown Res.	36	14	7	15	71	57	49
Penparcau	36	14	6	16	86	75	48
Kington	36	13	7	16	77	84	46
Clun Valley	36	8	11	17	31	58	35
Builth Wells	36	8	9	19	48	79	33
Presteigne S.A.	36	7	10	19	53	93	31
Knighton Res.	36	8	7	21	50	99	31
Penrhyncoch Res	36	5	8	23	38	107	23
U.C.W.	36	5	7	24	47	96	22
Llanidloes Res	36	3	7	26	44	97	16

MANWEB CYMRU ALLIANCE

	P	W	D	L	F	A	PTS
Llansantffraid	28	23	3	2	89	34	72
Welshpool Town	28	21	2	5	92	34	65
Rhyl	28	20	4	4	74	22	64
Wrexham	28	19	4	5	81	34	61
Lex XI	28	14	8	6	60	42	50
Carno	28	9	11	8	44	56	38
Cefn Druids	28	10	5	13	46	41	35
Penrhyncoch	28	10	5	13	56	71	35
Ruthin Town	28	9	7	12	43	58	34
Rhos Aelwyd	28	7	6	15	37	67	27
Knighton Town	28	7	6	15	48	82	27
Mostyn	28	7	3	18	35	64	24
Rhayader	28	6	5	17	32	66	23
Gresford Athletic	28	6	1	21	36	76	19
Brymbo	28	3	8	17	40	66	17

SEALINK STENA WELSH ALLIANCE LEAGUE

	P	W	D	L	F	A	PTS
Cemaes Bay	32	23	6	3	113	30	75
Llanfairpwll	32	22	4	6	73	42	70
Llangefni T.	32	21	6	5	97	45	69
Llandudno	32	21	4	7	86	41	67
Pilkingtons	32	18	6	8	78	57	60
Rhydymwyn	32	16	4	12	58	46	52
Nefyn United	32	13	8	11	61	64	47
Loco Llanberis	32	11	12	9	71	68	45
Bangor City	32	13	6	13	61	57	45
Nantle Vale	32	12	6	14	74	79	42
Llanrwst United	32	11	5	16	58	82	38
Llandyrnog Utd	32	9	7	16	50	71	34
Connahs Quay No.	32	9	6	17	47	84	33
Y Felinheli	32	7	10	15	52	64	31
Conwy United	32	6	5	21	49	78	23
Rhyl United	32	5	4	23	48	103	19
Penmaenmawr Ph	32	3	5	24	33	104	14

READ CONSTRUCTION WELSH NATIONAL LEAGUE (Wrexham Area)

PREM. DIVISION	P	W	D	L	F	A	PTS
Penley	26	15	7	4	63	36	52
Buckley	26	16	3	7	59	37	51
New Broughton	26	13	9	4	56	29	48
Llay Welfare	26	14	6	6	60	39	48
Marchweil	26	14	5	7	61	43	47
Lex XI Res.	26	12	5	9	46	40	41
Chirk A.A.A.	26	11	6	9	51	41	39
Pen-Y-Cae	26	10	7	9	60	54	37
Llay R.B.L.	26	8	6	12	49	46	30
Ruthin T. Res.	26	7	8	11	37	45	29
Overton	26	8	1	17	36	60	25
Corwen	26	6	6	14	41	66	24
Treuddyn	26	6	2	18	49	90	20
Castell A.C.	26	3	7	16	30	69	16

DIVISION ONE	P	W	D	L	F	A	PTS
Cefn/Druids Res.	30	23	4	3	107	41	73
New Brighton	30	20	6	4	84	28	66
R.O.Rockwell	30	19	5	6	87	60	62
Kelloggs	30	15	4	11	84	61	49
Bradley P.R.	30	17	4	9	79	58	55
British Aerospace	30	15	2	13	93	57	47
Johnstown *	30	16	4	10	68	66	47
New Broughton Res	30	13	4	13	65	57	43
Kinnerton	30	11	7	12	59	64	40
Rhos Aelwyd Res	30	9	6	15	56	71	33
Brymbo Res.*	30	13	3	14	64	84	36
Penley Res.	30	10	7	13	65	75	37
JCB	30	8	6	16	65	90	30
Gresford Res.	30	9	5	16	62	80	32
Marchwiel Res	30	4	2	24	52	117	14
Mynydd ISA	30	2	5	23	47	128	11

* - 3pts deducted.
** - 6pts deducted.

DIVISION TWO	P	W	D	L	F	A	PTS
Rhostyllen/Bers.	30	23	2	5	113	48	71
Ruthin Town Colts	30	18	9	3	86	34	63
Cefn/Druids Colts	30	17	7	6	89	55	58
Llangollen	30	18	4	8	78	50	58
Chirk A.A.A.Res	30	15	5	10	79	65	50
Bristish Aerospace R	30	14	7	9	107	82	49
Bala Town	30	11	11	8	64	55	44
O.C.Fiberglas	30	13	5	12	63	65	44
Llay Welfare Res.	30	11	7	12	57	49	40
Glynceiriog	30	11	6	13	65	73	39
Corwen Res.	30	11	5	14	60	79	38
Overton Res.*	30	10	3	17	59	91	30
Llanuwchllyn	30	8	3	19	65	100	27
Penycae Res.	30	6	4	20	58	98	22
Llay R.B.L. Res.	30	4	5	21	47	100	17
Castell A.C. R.**	30	7	3	20	45	95	15

* - 6pts deducted.
** - 9pts deucted.

KONICA LEAGUE OF WALES CLUBS 1993-94

ABERYSTWYTH TOWN

Chairman: Mr D Dawson　　**President:** Mrs D Richards　　**Vice Chairman:** M Nelson
Secretary: Arthur Griffiths, The Boars Head, Queens Rd, Aberystwyth, Dyfed SY23 2ET (0970 626106).
Manager: Tommy Morgan　　**Physio:** Terry Edwards　　**Press Officer:** Rhun Owens
Ground: Park Avenue, Aberystwyth, Dyfed (0970 612122).
Directions: From south: A487, 1st right at Trefachan Bridge to r'bout, 1st right with Park Avenue being 3rd right.
From north: A487 and follow one-way system to railway station, at r'bout 1st left with Park Avenue being 3rd right.
5 mins walk from Aberystwyth (BR) - follow as above.
Seats: 250　　**Cover:** 1,500　　**Capacity:** 6,000　　**Floodlights:** Yes　　**Founded:** 1884.
Colours: Green & black stripes/black/black　　**Change colours:** Yellow/blue/blue.
Previous League: Welsh 1896-97/ Nth Wales Comb. 99-1900/ Montgomeryshire & Dist. 04-20/ Central Wales 21-25 81-87/ Mid-Wales 26-32 51-81/ Cambrian Coast 32-51/ Welsh Lg South 51-63/ Abacus 87-92.
Programme: 36 pages, £1　　**Programme Editor:** Steve Moore　　**Club Shop:** No
Prev. Ground: Vicarage Field 06-07　　**Record Gate:** 4,500 v Hereford, Welsh Cup 1971.
Midweek matches: Wednesday　　**Local Press:** Cambrian News
Club Sponsors: Meiron Motors　　**Nickname:** Old Black & Green
Reserves' Lge: Mid-Wales　　**Clubhouse:** Nightly 7-11pm. Bar snacks. Hireable function room
Record win: 21-1 v Machynlleth, Cambrian Coast League 13/3/37.
Record defeat: 1-20 v Caerws, Mid-Wales League 8/9/62.
Captain 92-93: Tommy Morgan　　**Top Scorer 92-93:** Kevin Morrison 24　　**P.O.Y. 92-93:** David Morgan
Record scorer: Eddie Ellis, 67 in 42 games, 1948-49. Career: David Williams, 476 in 433 games 1966-83.
Record appearances: David P Whitney 572, 1962-81.
Hons: Welsh Cup 1899-1900, Welsh I'mediate Cup 85-86 87-88, Mid Wales Lg(11) 22-24 25-28 32-33 48-50 58-59 83-85 (Lg Cup(7) 26-28 31-32 38-39 47-48 84-86), Welsh Amtr Cup 30-31 32-33 69-70, Welsh Lg Div 2 Sth 51-52, Cambrian Coast Lg(8) 32-37 49-50 56-57 58-59 (Lg Cup 35-36 49-50 56-57), Central Wales Chal. Cup(6) 75-76 81-83 84-85 86-88.

AFAN LIDO

Chairman: Andrew Edwards　　**President:** Jim Mahoney　　**Manager:** Paul Evans.
Secretary: Mr P Robinson, 56 Abbeyville Avenue, Sandfields Est., Port Talbot SA12 6PY (0639 885638).
Physio: Glyn Thomas　　**Press Officer:** Robert Clement.
Ground: Afan Lido Sports Centre, Princess Margaret Way, Aberavon Beach, Port Talbot (0639 892960).
Directions: M4 to Port Talbot centre, follow signs to Aberavon Beach - ground at Afan Lido Leisure complex.
Seats: 150　　**Cover:** 150　　**Capacity:** 1,500　　**Floodlights:** Yes　　**Founded:** 1967.
Colours: Red/white/red　　**Change colours:** All blue.　　**Nickname:** The Lido
Previous Grounds: None　　**Previous Leagues:** Port Talbot/ Sth Wales Amtr/ Abacus
Sponsors: A & P Windows　　**Record Gate:** 1,250 v Wrexham, official ground opener 1990.
Programme: 24 pages with entry　　**Programme Editor:** Alun Evans.　　**Club Shop:** No
Midweek matches: Tuesday　　**Clubhouse:** No - use Grove Park Club.
Local Newspapers: Sth Wales Evening Post, Port Talbot Guardian, Port Talbot Tribune, Sth Wales Echo.
Reserves' Lge: Abacus Res.　　**Club Record Appearances:** David Rees.
P.O.Y. 92-93: Mitch Patton　　**Top Scorer 92-93:** Tim O'Connor 27.
Hons: Lg of Wales Cup 92-93, Abacus Lg Div 1(2) 87-89 (Yth Cup 91-92), Welsh I'mediate Cup 86-87.

BANGOR CITY

President: Lady Pennant　　**Chairman:** Gwyn Pierce Owen　　**Vice Chairman:** Keith Collier
Secretary: Alun Griffiths, 12 Lon-Y-Bryn, Menai Bridge, Anglesey, Gwynedd LL57 5NM (0248 712096).
Manager: Paul Rowlands　　**Comm. Manager:** G Thomas.　　**Press Off.:** Alun Griffiths
Ground: The Stadium, Farrar Road, Bangor, Gwynedd (0248 355852).
Directions: Old A5 into Bangor, 1st left before railway station, ground on left by garage.
Seats: 900　　**Cover:** 2,000　　**Capacity:** 10,000　　**Floodlights:** Yes　　**Founded:** 1876
Colours: All blue　　**Change colours:** All red.　　**Nickname:** Citizens
Prev. Lges: N. Wales Coast 1893-98 1911-12/ The Comb. 1898-1910/ N. Wales Comb. 30-33/ W. Mids (B'gham) 32-38/ Lancs. Comb. 38-39 46-50/ Ches. Co. 50-68/ NPL 68-79 81-82 84-92/ Alliance Prem. 79-81 82-84.
Midweek matches: Tuesday　　**Record Gate:** 10,000 v Wrexham, Welsh Cup final 78-79.
Programme: 24 pages, £1　　**Editor:** Alan Monument/John Jones　　**Club Shop:** No
Clubhouse: City of Bangor All Sports Club, open nightly and matchdays.
Local Press: Bangor Mail, Holyhead & Anglesey Mail, Nth Wales Weekly News, Nth Wales Chronicle, Liverpool Daily Post.
Sponsors: Pentraeth Motors　　**Reserve team's League:** Welsh Alliance.
P.O.Y. 92-93: Stuart Terry　　**Top Scorer 92-93:** Bob Colville/Stuart Terry, 14 each.
Hons: FA Tphy R-up 83-84, Northern Prem. Lg 81-82 (R-up 86-87), Lg Cup 68-69, Presidents Cup 88-89, Chal. Shield 81-82, Cheshire Co. Lg R-up 53-54 58-59, Lancs Comb. R-up 30-31, Welsh National Lg 27-28 (R-up 26-27), Nth Wales Coast Lg 1895-96, Welsh Cup 1888-89 95-96 1961-62 (R-up 27-28 60-61 63-64 72-73 77-78 84-85), Nth Wales Chal. Cup 26-27 35-36 36-37 37-38 46-47 51-52 57-58 64-65 67-68, Welsh Amtr Cup 1894-95 96-96 97-98 98-99 1900-01 02-03 04-05 05-06 11-12, Welsh Jnr Cup 1995-96 97-98 1919-20, Welsh All. Alves Cup 49-50 59-60 (Cookson Cup 61-62 68-69 84-85 86-87).

BRITON FERRY ATHLETIC

President: P D Langstone　　**Vice Chairman:** Len Thomas　　**Manager:** Carl Harris
Secretary/Chairman: Graham Jenkins, 262 Neath Rd, Briton Ferry, West Glamorgan SA11 2SL (0639 814762).
Ground: Old Road, Briton Ferry, West Glamorgan (0639 812458).　　**Directions:** M4 from Cardiff, onto A48 at r'bout (3rd exit) signed Briton Ferry, right at first traffic lights - ground half mile on right.
Seats: 100　　**Cover:** 350　　**Capacity:** 1,750　　**Floodlights:** Yes　　**Founded:** 1925.
Colours: Green & red quarters/white/white　　**Change colours:** All blue.
Previous Grounds: None　　**Previous League:** Abacus　　**Nickname:** The Athletic
Programme: 24 pages, 50p　　**Club Sponsors:** Graham Jenkins, Builders.
Record Gate: 1,090 v Abergavenny Thursdays, Abacus Welsh League National Division 1991.
Midweek home matchday: Tuesday　　**Reserve team's League:** Abacus Reserve Division.
Rec. win: 14-0 v Nantymoel, Welsh Lg 3/11/51.　　**Rec. loss:** 0-10 v Ebbw Vale, Lge of Wales 6/1/93.
Record transfer fee paid: Nil　　**Received:** £1,500 for Francis Ford (Cwmbran, 1993).
Top Scorer 92-93: Simon Dyer 22　　**Clubhouse:** Every evenings 7-11pm, and weekend lunchtimes.
Hons: Abacus Lg R-up 91-92 (Div 2 71-72), Welsh Lg Div 2 37-38 38-39 39-40 46-47.

CAERSWS

Chairman: Dilwyn Lewis   **Vice Chairman:** Wyn Jones   **President:** T M B Jones
Secretary: T M B Jones, 3 Hafren Terrace, Caersws, Powys SY17 5ES (0686 688103).
Manager: Mickey Evans   **Coach:** W Jones.
Physio: John Wilden   **Press Officer:** Ivor Williams (0686 420267).
Ground: The Recreation Ground, Caersws, Powys.
Directions: Entering Caersws (between Newtown & Llanidloes on A470) ground entrance on left by river bridge.
Seats: 150   **Cover:** 300   **Capacity:** 3,250   **Floodlights:** Yes   **Founded:** 1887.
Colours: Blue/white/blue   **Change colours:** All white.   **Nickname:** Bluebirds
Previous Grounds: None   **Previous Lges:** Mid-Wales (pre-1989)/Cymru Alliance 90-92.
Programme: 28 pages, £1   **Record Gate:** 2,795 v Swansea City, Welsh Cup 1990.
Midweek home matchday: Tuesday   **Reserve team's League:** Central Wales.
Club Shop: No.   **Record win:** 20-1 v Aberystwyth, Mid-Wales Lge 8/9/62.
Clubhouse: Not on ground, but in village centre. Normal licensing hours. Food served.
P.O.Y. 92-93: Mark Evans   **Top Scorer 92-93:** Paul Hughes 21.
Hons: Welsh Amtr Cup 60-61 (I'mediate Cup 88-89 (R-up 91-92)), Mid-Wales Lg(8) 59-61 62-63 77-78 82-83 85-86 88-90 (Lg Cup 79-80 82-83 87-88 89-90), Cent. Wales Chal. Cup 77-78 82-83 87-88 89-90 (Yth Cup 69-70 72-73), Montgom'shire Chal. Cup(16) 52-53 59-60 62-63 69-72 74-75 76-78 83-89 90-91, Montgom'shire Lg 77-78.

CONNAH'S QUAY NOMADS

Chairman: Mr R Morris   **President:**
Secretary: Bobby Hunter, 40 Brookdale Ave., Connah's Quay, Deeside, Clwyd CH5 4LU (0244 831212).
Manager: Neville Powell/Phil Evans   **Press Officer:** Geoff Thelwell (0244 815000).
Ground: Halfway Ground, Connah's Quay, Deeside, Clwyd.
Directions: On main coast road (A548) from Chester to Rhyl west end of Connah's Quay behind Halfway Hotel.
Seats: 105   **Cover:** 500   **Capacity:** 1,500   **Floodlights:** Yes   **Founded:** 1946
Colours: White/navy/white   **Change colours:** Maroon & blue stripes/blue/maroon.
Previous Grounds: None   **Prev. Lges:** Clwyd/ Welsh Alliance/ Cymru Alliance 90-92.
Midweek home matchday: Tuesday   **Record Gate:** 1,500 v Rhyl, Welsh Cup SF 29/3/93.
Programme: 26 pages, 50p   **Programme Editor:** Don Fowler.   **Club Shop:** No
Reserves' League: Clwyd   **Record win:** 16-0 v Rhydymwyn, 1949.
Nickname: Westenders   **Clubhouse:** No, but Halfway Hotel is adjacent
P.O.Y. 92-93: David O'Gorman   **Top Scorer 92-93:** David O'Gorman 28.
Local Newspapers: Evening Leader, Deeside Chronicle, Liverpool Daily Post.
Hons: Welsh Amtr Cup 52-53 54-55, Nth Wales F.A. Amtr Cup 52-53 54-55, Welsh Intermediate Cup 80-81, Welsh Alliance Cookson Cup 87-88, Welsh Youth Cup 47-48.

CONWY UNITED

Chairman: C R Jones   **Vice Chairman:** M T Fare   **President:** K Davies
Secretary: Mr Colin Jones, 'Iolyn', Iolyn Park, Conwy, Gwynedd LL32 8UX (0492 593496).
Manager: Mark Jones   **Press Officer:** Michael Fare (0492 596109).
Ground: Morfa Ground, Conwy, Gwynedd (0492 593860).
Directions: Leave A55 on 1st slip road after river tunnel and turn left towards Conwy. Sharp left immediately after overhead railway bridge - ground 400yds on left of Penmaen Rd.
Seats: 120   **Cover:** 400   **Capacity:** 1,500   **Floodlights:** Yes   **Founded:** 1977.
Colours: Tangerine/black/black   **Change colours:** All blue.   **N'kname:** Musselmen
Previous Leagues: Vale of Conwy/ Gwynedd/ Welsh Alliance/ Cymru Alliance.
Previous Grounds: None   **Record Gate:** 600 v Bangor City, Tyn Lyn Barritt Cup 1988.
Programme: 28 pages, 50p   **Editor:** Michael Fare (0492 596109)   **Club Shop:** No
Reserves' Lge: Welsh Alliance   **Midweek matches:** Tuesday.   **Clubhouse:** No
Club record scorer: Carl Dale   **Record win:** 11-1 v British Steel Shotton, Welsh Cup 1979-80.
Captain 92-93: Dave Wignall   **Top Scorer 92-93:** Paul Hughes 14.
Local Press: Liverpool Daily Post, Nth Wales Weekly News, Nth Wales Pioneer
Hons: Welsh Alliance 84-85 85-86, Barritt Cup 84-85, Welsh Intermediate Cup 81-82.

CWMBRAN TOWN

Chairman: George Thorneycroft   **Vice Chairman:** Clive Edwards   **President:** John Colley
Secretary: Mr R Langley, 2 Trafalgar Ct, Penylan Rd, Penylan, Cardiff CF2 5RL (0222 483341).
Manager: Tony Wilcox   **Press Officer:** Maurice Salway.
Ground: Cwmbran Stadium, Henllys Way, Cwmbran (0633 66192/3).
Directions: M4 jct 26, follow signns to Cwmbran on A4042 & A4051, bear right after 3rd r'bout on A4051 to stadium. One and a half miles from Cwmbran (BR).
Seats: 3,200   **Cover:** 4,700   **Capacity:** 13,200   **Floodlights:** Yes   **Founded:** 1955.
Colours: White/red/white   **Change colours:** Red/blue/red.   **Nickname:** The Town
Previous Leagues: Gwent Co./ Abacus   **Record Gate:** 3,000 v Hereford Utd, Welsh Cup 83-84.
Previous Ground: Cwmbran Park   **Record win:** 11-0 v Gwenai, Welsh Lg 21/9/68.
Programme: 28 pages, 50p   **Programme Editor:** Maurice Salway.   **Club Shop:** No.
Midweek matches: Wednesday.   **Clubhouse:** Pub hours, on ground. Catering facilities.
Sponsors: B.I.G. Batteries   **Local Press:** South Wales Argus, Cwmbran Free Press.
Reserves' League: Gwent County.   **Captain & P.O.Y. 92-93:** Jimmy Blackie
Top Scorer 92-93: Andrew Clissold 15   **Hons:** Lg of W. 92-93, Abacus Lg Div 1 66-67 (Lg Cup 85-86 90-91).

EBBW VALE

President: J S Harrison   **Vice Chairman:** M Carini   **Secretary:** T.B.A.
Manager: Steve Williams   **Assistant Manager:** Mick Martin.
Ground: Eugene Cross Park, Ebbw Vale, Gwent (0495 302995).
Directions: From A465 follow signs to Ebbw Vale, 1st left at next two r'bouts - ground on left.
Seats: 1,200   **Cover:** 1,200   **Capacity:** 10,000   **Floodlights:** Yes   **Founded:** 1950
Cols: Amber & black/black/black   **Change colours:** Sky/navy/grey.   **Nickname:** Cowboys
Previous League: Abacus   **Record Gate:** 1,762 v Wrexham, Welsh Cup 1989.
Programme: 25 pages, 50p   **Midweek matches:** Wednesday   **Club Shop:** No
Clubhouse: Pub hrs - shared with Rugby   **Record win:** 10-0 v Briton Ferry Ath., Lge of Wales 6/1/93.
Captain 92-93: Roger Mullen   **Top Scorer & P.O.Y. 92-93:** Steve Woods, 31 goals.
Hons: Abacus Lg 87-88 (Div 1 64-65, Southern Div 52-53, Div 2 East 60-61), Sth Wales Lg 03-04, Welsh Cup 25-26, South Wales Snr Cup 04-05, Gwent Snr Cup 24-25 26-27 28-29 32-33 45-46 50-51.

FLINT TOWN UNITED

President: David Hough.   **Vice Chairman:** Walter Francis
Secretary: Howard Greenhough, 9 Broadacre Close, Bagilt, Clwyd CH6 6EA (0352 735889).
Manager: Les Davies   **Commercial Manager:** Mrs V Hough.
Ground: Holywell Road, Flint (0352 733337) ***N.B. The Club will move during the 93-94 season ***
Directions: A548 from Chester thru Flint - ground on far side of town by gasworks. Half mile from Flint BR station.
Seats: 275   **Cover:** 450   **Capacity:** 2,500   **Floodlights:** Ys   **Founded:** 1886
Colours: Black & white stripes/black/red   **Change colours:** Yellow/black/black.
Previous Grounds: None   **Prev. Lges:** Clwyd/ Welsh Alliance/ Cymru Alliance 90-92.
Programme: 28 pages, 80p   **Club Sponsors:** Kimberley Clark   **Club Shop:** No.
Midweek home matchday: Tuesday   **Reserves' Lge:** Welsh Alliance   **Nickname:** The Town
Rec. win: 15-0 v Rhos Utd 1952   **Clubhouse:** Matchdays & training nights (Tue/Thurs) only.
Top Scorer 92-93: Carl Roberts 12.   **Hons:** Cymru Alliance 90-91, Welsh Cup 53-54, Welsh Amtr Cup 47-48, Welsh All.(4) 54-57 89-90 (Alves Cup 53-54 89-90, Cookson Cup 52-53 88-89), Welsh Championship Cup 90-91, N. Wales Coast Chal. Cup 90-91, Nth Wales Coast Amtr Cup(8) 09-10 30-36 68-69.

HAVERFORDWEST COUNTY

Chairman: Roger Cottrell   **Vice Chairman:** Ken Roberts   **President:** Jimmy Evans
Mgr: Ray Davies.   **Sec:** Mr C Sales, 46 Wesley Place, Trecwn, Haverfordwest, Dyfed (0348 840083).
Grnd: The Bridge Meadow, Hav'west SA61 2XE (0437 2082)   **Directions:** A40 from Carmarthen, under walkway, left at 3rd r'bout with Bridge Meadow facing. 5 mins walk from Haverfordwest (BR).
Seats: 1,180   **Cover:** 2,000   **Capacity:** 5,000   **Floodlights:** Due   **Founded:** Pre-1936.
Colours: Blue/white/white   **Change colours:** All white.   **Nickname:** Bluebirds
Previous Lges: Welsh/ Abacus   **Record Gate:** 3,000 v Milford Utd, 48-49.
Programme: 24 pages, 50p   **Programme Editor:** Cliff Sales.   **Club Shop:** No.
Midweek matches: Wednesday   **Local Newspapers:** Western Telegraph.
Club Sponsors: Welsh Water   **Reserves' League:** Pembrokeshire   **Prev. Grnds:** None
Record win: 14-3 v Tredomen 70-71   **Record fee received:** £150 for Ryan Preece (Maesteg, 1993)
Top Scorer 92-93: Neil Jones 20.   **Clubhouse:** Daily 2.30-11pm. Sat 2-11pm, Sun 12-2, 7-10.30pm.
Hons: Abacus Lg 56-57 80-81 89-90 (Div 1 55-56 79-80, Lg Cup 60-61 88-89), W. Wales Snr Cup 81-82 88-89 91-92.

HOLYWELL TOWN

Chairman: Emile Moore   **Vice Chairman:** Ian Ross   **President:** Charles Meredith
Secretary: G M Davies, 45 Bron-Y-Wern, Bigilt, Flint, Clwyd CH6 6BS (0352 763571).
Manager: Glyn Griffiths   **Asst Manager:** Mark Williams   **Coach:** Mike Thomas
Physio: Glyn Owen   **Press Officer:** Sean Elliott (0352 712833)
Ground: Halkyn Road, Holywell (0352 711411).   **Directions:** Coast road, signpost to Holywell past Hillcrest Garage, just past Stratford Gate Hotel turn right and ground is on the right.
Colours: Red & white stripes/red/red   **Change colours:** Blue & white stripes/blue/blue.
Previous Grounds: None   **Previous Lges:** Clwyd/ Welsh/ Cymru Alliance 90-92.
Programme: 24 pages, 50p   **Editor:** Sean Elliott (0352 712833)   **Club Shop:** No.
Club Sponsors: Rank Xerox   **Clubhouse:** No - use Beaufort Hotel, West St. Snack bar on ground
Midweek home matchday: Tuesday   **Reserve team's League:** Clwyd.   **Nickname:** Wellmen
Top Scorer 92-93: Ian Howat 21   **Hons:** Nth Wales Coast Amtr Cup 13-14 21-22 57-58, Nth Wales Coast Jnr Cup 76-77, Nth Wales Coast Chal. Cup 86-87, Nth Wales Coast Yth Cup 75-76.

INTER-CARDIFF

Chairman: Max James   **President:** Len Carroll.
Secretary: Paul Woollacott, 7 Lloyd Ave., Barry, South Glamorgan (0446 734389).
Manager: Lyn Jones   **Asst Manager:** Phil Hulme   **Physio:** Ron Swain
Press Officer: Max James   **Commercial Manager:** Terry Martin/ Dave Williams.
Ground: Ninian Park (Cardiff City F.C.), Sloper Rd, Cardiff (0222 398636).
Directions: M4 jct 33 towards Barry (A4232) onto link road - Ninian Park visible on left 5 miles past Culverhouse Cross. 5 mins walk from Ninian Park BR station.
Seats: 10,000   **Cover:** 14,000   **Capacity:** 18,000   **Floodlights:** Yes   **Founded:** 1990.
Colours: White/black/red   **Change colours:** Yellow/black/black.
Prev. Names: Lake Utd and Rumney Rgrs merged 1984 to form AFC Cardiff. This club merged with Sully in 1990.
Prev. Grnds: Cwrt-yr-Ala, Fairwater (pre-'92)/ Cardiff Ath. Stadium, Leckwith Rd 92-93. *Sully: Burnham Ave.*
Previous Leagues: Barry & District/ South Wales Amateur/ Abacus   **Nickname:** Seagulls
Sponsors: Brians Brewery   **Record Gate:** 1,500 v Cardiff City, Sth Wales Snr Cup 1974.
Programme: 24 pages, 50p   **Programme Editor:** Terry Martin.   **Club Shop:** No.
Midweek matches: Wednesday.   **Clubhouse:** Tues/Thurs/Sat 7-11pm at old ground (Cwrt-yr-Ala).
Rec. win: 11-1 v Abercynon 1990   **Top Scorer 92-93:** Chris Summers 27.
Local Press: Sth Wales Echo, Cardiff Post, Western Mail.   **Hons:** League Cup Wales R-up 92-93, Abacus Lg Div 1 86-87, Sth Wales Amtr Lg 84-85 85-86. *As Sully: Sth Wales Amtr Lg Coronation Cup 69-70, Corinthian Cup 78-79, Abacus Lg Div 1 83-84 85-86 89-90 (Div 2 80-81), Sth Wales Snr Cup 80-81 81-82.*

LLANELLI

Chairman: John James   **Vice Chairman:** Denley Mears.
Secretary: Roger Davies, 29 Pemberton Park, Llanelli, Dyfed SA14 8NH (0554 756176).
Manager: Gilbert Lloyd   **Physio:** Robert Grant.
Ground: Strebonheath Park, Llanelli, Dyfed (0554 772973).
Directions: M4 jct 48, link road to Llanelli for 4 miles, right at 1st lights, left after Esso garage (signed Strebonheath), ground 200yds on right. 2 miles from Llanelli (BR) station.
Seats: 700   **Cover:** 700   **Capacity:** 3,750   **Floodlights:** Yes   **Founded:** 1896.
Colours: All red   **Change:** White/black/black.   **Nickname:** Reds
Previous League: Southern/ Abacus   **Record Gate:** 20,000 (before redevelopment)
Previous Ground: Halfway Park   **Previous Name:** Llanelly FC.
Programme: 24 pages, 50p   **Programme Editor:** Neil Richards.   **Club Shop:** No
Midweek matches: Wednesday.   **Local Newspapers:** Llanelli Star, Llanelli Weekly.
Record win: 17-0 v Treharris 1914   **Club Sponsors:** Classic Home Improvements Ltd
Clubhouse: Evenings 7-11pm, weekend lunchtimes   **Top Scorer 92-93:** Martin Armstrong/ Viv Watkeys 12.
Hons: Abacus Lg 29-30 32-33 70-71 76-77 77-78 (Lg Cup 29-30 74-75), West Wales Snr Cup 30-31 47-48 50-51 52-53 63-64 67-68 70-71 76-77.

LLANSANTFFRAID

Chairman: Edgar Jones   **President:** Mike Hughes.
Secretary: Graham Ellis, Brodawel, Church Lane, Llansantffraid, Powys SY22 6AA (0691 828583).
Manager: Graham Breeze   **Asst Manager:** John Muldoon.
Ground: Recreation Park, Treflan, Llansantffraid (0691 828112).
Directions: A470 between Welshpool and Oswestry, left for Llansantffraid at Llnmyrdach, over bridge into village, left thru village opposite silos, ground on right signed Community Centre.
Seats: 105   **Cover:** 200   **Capacity:** 1,500   **Floodlights:** Yes   **Club Shop:** No
Colours: Green/black/black   **Change:** Red/black/black.   **Nickname:** None
Rec. Gate: 475 v Rhyl, Welsh Cup '93   **Previous League:** Mid-Wales/ Cymru Alliance (pre-1993)
Programme: 24 pages, 50p   **Club Sponsors:** J J Hughes Garages.
Midweek matches: Tuesday   **Clubhouse:** Normal licensing hours.
Top Scorer 92-93: Andy Oakley 32   **Reserves' Lge:** Mid-Wales.   **Hons:** Cymru Alliance 92-93.

MAESTEG PARK ATHLETIC

Chairman: Brian Carpenter   **Vice Chairman:** Michael O'Brien **President:** Anthony Richards.
Secretary: David Griffiths, 3 Padleys Close, Maesteg, Bridgend, Mid-Glamorgan CF34 0TX (0656 733000).
Manager: Mike Ellery   **Press Officer:** David Griffiths.
Ground: Tudor Park, St Davids Place, Maesteg, Mid-Glamorgan (0656 732092-ground, 732029-club).
Directions: M6 jct 36, A4063 to Maesteg, top road into town past Gills garage, turn left at Royal Oak. At Gran pub turn left up hill to Red Cow pub, then right - ground on left.
Seats: 100   **Cover:** 200   **Capacity:** 2,000   **Floodlights:** Yes   **Founded:** 1945.
Colours: Blue & white/blue/blue   **Change:** Yellow & green stripes/green/yellow.
Previous Ground: South Parade 65-70   **Record Gate:** 1,100 v Cardiff, f'light opener 1981
Previous Leagues: Bridgend & Dist./ Port Talbot & Dist./ Abacus.   **Nickname:** Park.
Programme: 24 pages, with entry   **Programme Editor:** David Griffiths.   **Club Shop:** No.
Local Press: South Wales Echo, Glamorgan Gazette, South Wales Eveing Post.
Midweek matches: Wed/tues   **Reserves' League:** Abacus Reserve Division.
Clubhouse: 1-4pm, 6-11pm daily (matchdays all day). Meals and snacks available always.
Top Scorer 92-93: Tony Bolton 13   **Record win:** 10-2 v Glyn Corrwg, 1967-68.
Hons: Welsh Cup SF 91-92, Sth Wales Snr Cup 78-79 90-91, Abacus Lg R-up 79-80 (Div 1 78-79), Sth Wales Cup 78-79 90-91.

MOLD ALEXANDRA

Secretary: T Wynne, 1 Grays Rd, Mynydd Isa, nr Mold, Clwyd (0352 754531).
Manager: Mickey O'Brien/ Dave Allen   **Ground:** Alyn Park, Maesydre, Mold (0352 4007).
Directions: Wrexham-Mold A541, follow signs to Flint, then Denbigh at Tescos r'bout, ground 200yds on right opposite Bryn Awel Hotel.
Seats: 100   **Cover:** 300   **Capacity:** 2,250   **Floodlights:** Yes   **Founded:** 1929.
Colours: Royal/white/royal   **Change colours:** All white   **Nickname:** The Alex
Previous Grounds: None.   **Previous Lges:** Welsh Nat. (Wrexham Area)/ Cymru Alliance
Midweek home matchday: Tuesday   **Club Sponsors:** Synthrite Ltd.
Programme: 24 pages, 50p   **Top Scorer 92-93:** Chris Davies 21.   **Clubhouse:** No.
Hons: Welsh National Lg (Wrexham Area) 89-90, Nth Wales Coast Chal. Cup 85-86 89-90, Barritt Cup 89-90, N.E. Wales Chal. Cup 89-90, Nth Wales Coast Jnr Cup 30-31.

NEWTOWN

President: Melvyn Foulkes   **Manager:** Brian Coyne   **Asst Manager:** Jake King.
Secretary/Press Officer: Keith Harding, 7 Tradyddon Terrace, Newtown, Powys SY16 2ER (0686 628523).
Ground & Directions: Raelbrook Latham Park, Newtown(0686 626159). A43 to Newtown, right at 1st lights into Back Lane & town centre - 400yds left into Park St., 500yds right (at Library) into Park Lane - grnd at end.
Seats: 200   **Cover:** 700   **Capacity:** 5,000   **Floodlights:** Yes   **Founded:** 1875.
Colours: Red/white/white   **Change colours:** Yellow/black/black   **Nickname:** Robins
Previous Leagues: The Combination/ Central Wales/ Northern Premier.
Previous Grounds: 24 Acres/ The Cummings/ Plantation Lane (pre-1950).
Previous Name: Newtown White Star.   **Record Gate:** 5,002 v Swansea City, Welsh Cup 1954.
Best F.A. Cup year: 2nd Rd 1884-85. Also 1st Rd 1885-86.   **Players progressing to Football League:** Clive Lloyd (Orient), John Lovent (C Palace & Exeter), Mike Bloor (Stoke & Lincoln), Ian Woan (Nottm Forest), Jonathan Hill (Rochdale), Ray Newlands (Plymouth), Mike Williams (Shrewsbury).
Programme: 36 pages, 50p   **Programme Editor:** Keith Harding.
Club Shop: Yes. Open matchdays selling programmes etc. Contact Nigel Bevan.
Clubhouse: Open every evening. Hot & cold snacks, pool, darts.
Midweek matches: Tuesday   **Local Press:** Shropshire Times, County Times & Express.
Reserves' Lge: Central Wales   **Top Scorer 92-93:** Colin Reynolds 12.
Hons: FA Tphy 3rd Qual. R 89-90, Welsh Cup 1878-79 94-95 (R-up 85-65 87-88 96-97), Welsh Amtr Cup 1954-55, Central Wales Lg 75-76 78-79 81-82 86-87 87-88 (R-up 51-52 52-53 55-56 56-57 74-75 82-83, Lg Cup 54-55 56-57 74-75 75-76 81-82 83-84), Arthur Barritt Cup 86-87, Central Wales Cup 74-75 80-81, Emrys Morgan Cup 80-81.

PORTHMADOG

Chairman: Iwan Jones   **President:** William Pike   **Manager:** Melir Owen
Secretary: Mr R I Griffiths, Llyn-yr-Eryr, Ynys, Cricieth, Gwynedd LL52 0PH (0766 810349).
Physio: Ifor Roberts   **Press Officer:** Dylan Ellis (0978 853008).
Ground & Directions: Y Traeth, Porthmadog (0766 514687). At town centre crossroads (by Woolworths) into Snowdon Str., pass RBL/Craft Centre onto unmade track, over railway line - ground on right.
Seats: 140   **Cover:** 400   **Capacity:** 4,000   **Floodlights:** Yes   **Founded:** 1884.
Colours: Red & black/black/black   **Change:** Yellow & green/sky/white.   **Nickname:** Porth.
Previous Grounds: None   **Reserve team's league:** Gwynedd.
Prev. Lges: N. Wales/ Gwynedd/ Bangor & Dist./ Lleyn & Dist./ Cambrian Coast/ Welsh Alliance/ Cymru Alliance
Midweek home matchday: Tuesday   **Record Gate:** 3,500 v Swansea, Welsh Cup 64-65.
Programme: 28 pages, 50p   **Programme Editor:** Dylan Ellis.   **Club Shop:** No.
Clubhouse: Not on ground (use Midland Hotel), but matchday refreshments available.
Local Newspapers: Caernarfon & Denbigh Herald/ Cambrian News/ Nth Wales Chronicle/ Y Wylan.
Captain 92-93: Joe Gaffey   **Top Scorer 92-93:** David Taylor 15.
Hons: Welsh Amtr Cup(3) 55-58, N. Wales Amtr Cup 37-38 56-57 58-59 62-63, Lge of Wales Cup R-up 92-93, N. Wales Coast Chal. Cup(5) 55-56 73-75 76-78, Welsh All.(8) 02-03 37-38 66-69 74-76 89-90 (Cookson Cup 75-76 89-90, Barritt Cup 77-78, Alves Cup 65-66 73-74 76-77).

TON PENTRE

Chairman: Jeff Orrells   **Vice Chairman:** Trevor Lowe   **President:** Allan Rogers MP
Secretary/Press Officer: Paul Willoughby, 37 Bailey Street, Ton Pentre, Rhondda CF41 7EN (0443 438281).
Manager: John Emmanuel
Ground: Ynys Park, Ton Row, Ton Pentre, Rhondda (0443 432413).
Directions: A4058 Pontypridd to Treorchy Plain road, left at Thames Rico Garage then first left again. Ton Pentre (BR) station 400yds from ground.
Seats: 400   **Cover:** 800   **Capacity:** 2,750   **Floodlights:** Yes   **Founded:** 1935
Colours: All red   **Change colours:** All blue   **Nickname:** Ton.
Previous Grounds: None.
Previous Leagues: Welsh (Abacus) pre-1993.
Programme: 28 pages, 50p   **Club Shop:** No.
Club Sponsors: **Record Gate:** 2,900 v Cardiff City, F.A. Cup 1st Rd 1986.
Midweek home matchday: Wednesday   **Reserve team:** None.
Clubhouse: Open normal licensing hours seven days a week. Food always available.
Captain 92-93: Brian Gullett.   **Top Scorer 92-93:** Richard Haig.
Hons: Welsh League 57-58 60-61 73-74 81-82 92-93, Welsh Amateur Cup 51-52, South Wales Senior Cup 47-48 60-61 61-62 63-64 83-84.

Ton Pentre F.C. - Abacus Welsh League champions 1992-93. Photo - James Wright.

Afan Lido F.C. - Konica League of Wales Cup winners 1992-93. Photo - James Wright.

ABACUS WELSH LEAGUE DIVISION ONE CLUBS 1993-94

ABERAMAN ATHLETIC

Secretary: Brian Fear, 28 Mostyn Street, Abercwmboi, Mid-Glamorgan (0443 472858).
Manager: John Herniman
Ground: Aberaman Park.
Colours: All royal blue.   **Change colours:** Yellow/blue/yellow.
Programme: Yes   **Floodlights:** No   **Cover:** Yes   **Seats:** No

ABERGAVENNY THURSDAYS

Secretary: David Morris, 48 Richmond Road, Abergavenny, Gwent, NP7 5RE (0873 854730).
Ground: Penypound Stadium, Penypond, Abergavenny, Gwent (0873 853906)
Colours: All white.   **Change colours:** Navy/sky stripe/sky/navy.
Programme: Yes   **Floodlights:** Yes   **Cover:** Yes   **Seats:** Yes

A.F.C. PORTH

Secretary: Robert Lewis, 11 Wyndham Street, Porth, Rhondda, Mid Glam. (0443) 687854).
Ground: Dinas Park, Dinas, Rhondda, Mid Glam.
Colours: Maroon & blue/blue/blue.   **Change colours:** Red/blue/blue.
Programme: Yes   **Floodlights:** 1994 scheduled.   **Cover:** Yes   **Seats:** No
Founded: 1987 (prev. Beatus Utd)

AMMANFORD

Secretary: John Thomas, 154 Hendre Rd, Capel Hendre, Ammanford, Dyfed SA18 3TE (0269 843712).
Player: Alan Walters
Ground: Betws Sports Club, Rice Road, Bettws, Ammanford, Dyfed (0269 592407).
Directions: From Quay Street Post Office head towards Bettws, cross railway line, left on sharp bend into Colonel
Road, ground down narrow lane opposite Gwalia Stores.
Seats: Yes   **Cover:** Yes   **Floodlights:** No   **Clubhouse:** Yes   **Programme:** Yes
Club colours: Blue & white stripes/blue/blue   **Change colours:** Black & white/white/black.
Founded: 1991 (Ammanford Town founded 1948 merged with Ammanford Athletic)

BARRY TOWN

Secretary: Alan Whelan, Jenner Park, Barry, South Glam. CF62 7HR (0446 737188).
Ground: Jenner Park, Barry. (0446 721171)
Colours: Red & white/white/white.   **Change colours:** Yellow & blue/blue/blue.
Programme: Yes   **Floodlights:** Yes   **Cover:** Yes   **Seats:** Yes

BLAENRHONDDA

Secretary: Gwynne Davies, 60 Elizabeth Street, Pentre, Rhondda, Mid Glamorgan (0443 433901).
Ground: Blaenrhondda Park (0443 774772).
Colours: All royal blue.   **Change colours:** All red.
Founded: 1934   **Programme:**   **Floodlights:** No   **Cover:** Yes   **Seats:** No

BRECON CORINTHIANS

Secretary: Terry Harley, 20 Charles Street, The Watton, Brecon, Powys LD3 7HF. (0874 624568)
Ground: The Rich Field, The Watton, Brecon. (0656 55097)
Directions: Head from town centre, turn at Rich Way Road. Hourly bus from Merthyr takes 40 minutes
Colours: All red.   **Change colours:** All yellow.   **Founded:** 1940
Programme: Yes   **Floodlights:** Yes   **Cover:** Yes   **Seats:** Yes   **Clubhouse:** In Town

BRIDGEND TOWN

Secretary: Ray Warner, 1 Heol Treharne, Coytrahen, Bridgend, Mid Glam. CF32 0DS (0656 720618).
Ground: Coychurch Rd, Bridgend. (0656 655097)
Directions: M4 to Pencoed, left at Waterton Cross. 2nd right under railway brige.
Cover: Yes   **Floodlights:** Yes   **Clubhouse:** Yes   **Programme:** Yes   **Founded:** 1954.
Colours: Sky/navy/sky   **Change colours:** All white

CAERAU

Secretary: David Lewis, 19a Hermon Rd, Caerau, Mid-Glamorgan (0656 734388).
Ground: Humphreys Terrace, Caerau, Mid. Glam. (0656 732471)
Colours: All red   **Change colours:** All blue   **Founded:** 1901
Programme: Yes   **Floodlights:** Yes   **Cover:** Yes   **Seats:** No

CAERLEON

Secretary: Ken Alden, 2 Conifer Close, Caerleon, Newport, gwent NP6 1RH (0633 **Ground:** Cold Bath Road,
Caerleon, Gwent (0633 420074).
Colours: All green   **Change colours:** Blue/white/blue
Programme: Yes   **Floodlights:**   **Cover:** Yes   **Seats:** Yes   **Founded:** 1889.

CALDICOT TOWN

Secretary: Gordon Lewis, "Talfan", 83 Newport Road, Caldicot, Newport NP6 4BS (0291) 422035).
Ground: Jubilee Way, Caldicot, Gwent (0291 423519)
Directions: M4 - take Jnt 22 signs to town centre. Ground behind town centre car park.
Seats: No   **Cover:** Yes   **Programme:** Yes   **Floodlights:** No   **Founded:** 1953
Colours: Yellow/black/black   **Club colours:** White/navy/navy

CARDIFF CIVIL SERVICE

Secretary: Bob Fry, 30 Flaxland Avenue, Heath, Cardiff CF4 3NT (0222 619192).
Ground: Civil Service Sports Ground, Santatorium Rd, Leckwith, Cardiff.
Directions: West side of Cardiff, near Cardiff City FC.
Seats: No   **Cover:** No   **Clubhouse:** Yes   **Floodlights:** No   **Programme:** Yes
Founded: 1963   **Colours:** Green & white hoops/white/white   **Change colours:** red/white/red

FERNDALE ATHLETIC

Secretary: Glyn Lewis, Dan-yr-allt, Brown Street, Ferndale, Rhondda CF43 4SF. (0443 730201)
Ground: Darran Park, Ferndale. (0443 731060)
Directions: From Rhondda Hotel in main street go up the hill to the ground
Seats: Yes   **Cover:** Yes   **Programme:** Yes   **Floodlights:** Yes   **Founded:** 1945.
Colours: Yellow/black/black   **Club colours:** Blue/black/black

LLANWERN

Secretary: John Fitzgerald, 3 Lansdowne Road, Gaer, Newport, Gwent (0633 257319).
Ground: British Steel Sports Club, Llanwern, Newport, Gwent (0633 273790).
Founded: 1962 (prev. Spencer Works)
Colours: Navy/white/navy   **Change colours:** White/white/navy
Programme: Yes   **Floodlights:** No   **Cover:** Yes   **Seats:** No

MORRISTON TOWN

Secretary: Lynford Owen, 33 Maes y gelynen, Morriston, Swansea SA6 6SD (0792 796640).
Ground: The Dingle, Morriston, Nr Swansea (0792 702033).
Directions: Through Morriston centre and bear right at foot of hill - ground quarter mile on left.
Seats: No   **Cover:** No   **Programme:** Yes   **Floodlights:** No   **Founded:** 1951.
Club colours: Red & black stripes/black/red.   **Change colours:** Yellow/black/white

PEMBROKE BOROUGH

Secretary: Phil Tallet, 6 Shropshire Rd, Pembroke Dock, Dyfed (0646 682234).
Ground: London Road, Pembroke Dock, Pembroke. (0636 682239)
Directions: Take A477 from St Clears to Pembroke Dock (not Pembroke). Straight on at roundabout, pass rugby ground on right and football ground is also on right.
Cover: Yes   **Programme:** Yes   **Clubhouse:** Yes   **Founded:** 1935.   **Floodlights:** No
Colours: Black, white & blue stripes/black/white   **Change colours:** Amber/black/black

PONTYPRIDD TOWN

Secretary: Peter Chalmers, 9 Silver Hill Close, Cilfynydd, Pontypridd, Mid. Glam. (0443 492354).
Ground: Ynysangharad Park, Pontypridd (0443 790204).
Colours: Black & white stripes/black/black   **Change colours:** All sky blue
Previous Ground: Ynysbwl Rec. (pre-1992).   **Previous Names:** Ynysbwl 1995-1991/ Pontypridd-Ynysbwl 91-92
Programme: Yes   **Floodlights:** No   **Cover:** Yes   **Seats:** Yes

PORT TALBOT ATHLETIC

Secretary: Alf Germaine, 1 Bordsfield Cottage, Graig, Pontypridd CF37 1LE (0443 407868).
Ground: Victoria Park, Aberavon, Port Talbot (0639 8832465).
Directions: On left of main road from Port Talbot to Aberavon. 20 mins walk from Port Talbot (BR).
Cover: Yes   **Programme:** Yes   **Floodlights:** No   **Clubhouse:** Yes   **Founded:** 1901
Colours: All blue   **Change colours:** Yellow/black/black

ABACUS LEAGUE DIVISION TWO CLUBS 1993-94

B.P. LLANDARCY

Secretary: David Maddock, 20 Brookfield, Neath Abbey, Neath SA10 7EG (0639 636327).
Ground: B.P. Sports Ground, Llandarcy (0792 812036)
Colours: White/white/yellow.   **Change colours:** All light blue.
Programme: Yes   **Floodlights:** No   **Cover:** No   **Seats:** No   **Founded:** 1922

CARDIFF CORINTHIANS

Secretary: G Thomas, 9 Palace Rd, Llandaff, Cardiff (0222 562624).
Ground: Riverside Ground, Radyr, Cardiff (0222 843407). **Directions:** Left out of Radyr station, under railway - ground through gate marked cricket club. **Colours:** Cardinal & Amber Quarters/Cardinal/Cardinal **Change:** All blue
Programme: Yes   **Floodlights:**   **Cover:** Yes(150)   **Seats:** No   **Founded:** 1897

CARMARTHEN TOWN

Secretary: Alan Latham, 3 Maes Dolau, Idole, Carmarthen SA32 8DQ (0267 232432).
Ground: Richmond Park, Priory Street, Carmarthen, Dyfed (0267 232101).
Colours: Gold/black/black   **Change colours:** Blue/white/blue
Programme: Yes   **Floodlights:** No   **Cover:** Yes (1,000)   **Seats:** Yes   **Founded:** 1953

FIELDS PARK/PONTLLANFRAITH

Secretary: Paul Chiplin, 1 William Street, Cwmfrlinfach, Ynysddu, Newport NP1 7GY (0495 200349).
Ground: Islwyn Park, Pontllanfraith, Blackwood, Gwent (0495 224512)
Colours: All royal blue   **Change colours:** Black & white stripes/black/black
Programme: Yes   **Floodlights:** No   **Cover:** No   **Seats:** Yes (200)   **Founded:** 1964

GARW

Secretary: Tecwyn Thomas, Drosglo, 5 Victoria Street, Pontycymmer, Nr. Bridgend (0656 870411).
Ground: Blandy Park, Pontycymmer (0656 720777)
Colours: Red/black/red   **Change colours:** Yellow/blue/blue
Programme: Yes   **Floodlights:** No   **Cover:** Yes (100)   **Seats:** No   **Founded:** 1945

MILFORD UNITED

Secretary: Ken Lowe, 17 Milton Crescent, Pill, Milford Haven SA73 2QS (0646 692194).
Ground: Marble Hall Road, Milford Haven, Dyfed (0646 693691)
Colours: Red/black/red   **Change colours:** All blue
Programme: Yes   **Floodlights:** No   **Cover:** Yes (400)   **Seats:** Yes (300)   **Founded:** 1885

NEWPORT Y.M.C.A.

Secretary: Roy Leonard, 14 St.David's Crescent, Park Avenue, Newport, Gwent, NP9 3AW (0633 810783)
Ground: Y.M.C.A. Ground, Mendalgief Road, Newport, Gwent (0633 263387)
Colours: White & navy/navy/navy   **Change colours:** All blue
Programme: Yes   **Floodlights:** No   **Cover:** No   **Seats:** No   **Founded:** 1971

PONTYCLUN

Secretary: Peter Shilton, 3 Lilac Drive, Chandlers Reach, Llantwit Fardre, Mid.Glam. (0443 831606).
Ground: Ivor Park, Cowbridge Road, Pontyclun, Mid.Glam (0443 222182)
Colours: Yellow/blue/blue   **Change colours:** Blue/yellow/yellow
Programme: Yes   **Floodlights:** No   **Cover:** No   **Seats:** No   **Founded:** 1896

RISCA UNITED

Secretary: Mrs Ann Luckwell, 137 Ty Isaf Park Ave., Pontyminster, Risca, Gwent (0633 613434).
Ground: Ty Asaf Park, Risca, Gwent (0633 615081).
Colours: Black & white stripes/black/black **Change colours:** Yellow/black/black
Programme: Yes   **Floodlights:** No   **Cover:** Yes (250)   **Seats:** No   **Founded:** 1946

SEVEN SISTERS

Secretary: Peter Warnes, 1 Mary Street, Seven Sisters, Neath, West Glam. (0639 700121).
Ground: Welfare Ground, Church Road, Seven Sisters, Neath (0639 700354).
Colours: Yellow/blue/yellow **Change colours:** Green/black/black
Programme: Yes **Floodlights:** No **Cover:** No **Seats:** No **Founded:** 1919

SKEWEN ATHLETIC

Secretary: Bob Smith, 50 Southall Avenue, Skewen, Neath, West Glam. SA10 6YW (0792 814518).
Ground: Tennant Park, Skewen, Neath, West Glam.
Colours: Blue/white/blue **Change colours:** Wine/white
Programme: Yes **Floodlights:** No **Cover:** Yes (100) **Seats:** No **Founded:** 1949

TAFF'S WELL

Secretary: Ray Toghill, 38 Heol Berry, Gwaelod-y-Garth CF4 8HB (0222 811356).
Ground: Rhiwddar, Parish Road, Taffs Well, Mid. Glam. (0222 811080)
Colours: Amber/black/black **Change colours:** All blue
Programme: Yes **Floodlights:** No **Cover:** No **Seats:** No **Founded:** 1947

TONYREFAIL WELFARE

Secretary: Peter Jones, 13 Rees Street, Treorchy, Rhondda, Mid Glam. (0443 773460).
Ground: Welfare Park, Tonyrefail, Porth, Mid. Glam.
Colours: Red & black stripes/black/red **Change colours:** Yellow/black/black
Programme: Yes **Floodlights:** No **Cover:** No **Seats:** Yes (100) **Founded:** 1926

TREOWEN STARS

Secretary: A.J.Davies, 19 Meredith Terrace, Newbridge, Gwent NP1 4FN (0495 245494).
Ground: Bush Park, Newbridge, Gwent (0495 248249).
Colours: Blue & white stripes/black/black **Change colours:** Grey & red/red/red
Programme: Yes **Floodlights:** No **Cover:** No **Seats:** No **Founded:** 1926

ABACUS LEAGUE DIVISION THREE CLUBS 1993-94

ABERCYNON ATHLETIC

Secretary: Jeffrey Dudley, 131 Abercynon Rd, Abercynon. Mid. Glam CF45 4NE (0443 741433).
Ground: Parc Abercynon, Abercynon, Mid. Glam. (0443 740238).
Colours: Black & white/black/black **Change colours:** Yellow & black/black/red
Programme: Yes **Floodlights:** No **Cover:** No **Seats:** No **Founded:** 1933

ALBION ROVERS

Secretary: Mr N.A.Cueto, 37 Gilbert Close, Newport, Gwent (0633 275 785).
Ground: Spetty Stadium, Spetty. **Colours:** All red **Change colours:** All blue
Programme: Yes **Floodlights:** Yes **Cover:** Yes (3,000) **Seats:** Yes (1,500)

CARDIFF INSTITUTE OF HIGHER EDUCATION

Secretary: Lee Morgan, 96 Cowbridge Road West, Ely, Cardiff (0222 757223).
Ground: Cyncoed College, Cyncoed Rd, Cardiff (0222 757223).
Colours: Blue & white/blue/white **Change colours:** Maroon & gold stripes/maroon/Maroon
Programme: Yes **Floodlights:** No **Cover:** No **Seats:** No **Founded:** 1957

GRANGE HARLEQUINS

Secretary: Mike Smith-Phillips, 48 Penlan Road, Llandough, Nr. Penarth, South Glam. (0222 700200).
Ground: Cardiff Athletic Stadium, Leckwith Road, Cardiff (0222 225345).
Colours: All red **Change colours:** All blue
Programme: Yes **Floodlights:** Yes **Cover:** Yes **Seats:** Yes (2,500) **Founded:** 1948

GOYTRE UNITED

Secretary: Boris Suhanski, 20 Goytre Cres., Port Talbot (0639 886826).
Ground: Glenhafod Park, Goytre, Port Talbot, West Glam. (0639 898983).
Colours: Blue & white stripes/blue/blue
Programme: Yes **Floodlights:** No **Cover:** No **Seats:** Yes (213) **Founded:** 1963

PANTEG

Secretary: Bob Small, 26 Laburnum Drive, New Inn, Pontypool (0495 756280).
Ground: Panteg House, Greenhill Rd, Griffithstown, Pontypool. (0495 763605).
Colours: White & black/black/black. **Change colours:** Yellow/black/red.
Programme: Yes **Floodlights:** No **Cover:** No **Seats:** No **Founded:** 1940

PENRHIWCEIBER RANGERS

Secretary: Chris Kerr, 8 Church Street, Penrhiwceiber, Mountain Ash, Mid. Glam. (0443 476134).
Ground: Glasbrook Field, Glasbrook Terrace, Penrhiwceiber (0443 473368).
Previous League: Sth Wales Amtr (champs 91-92). **Colours:** All red.
Programme: Yes **Floodlights:** No **Cover:** Yes (200) **Seats:** No **Founded:** 1945

PONTARDAWE ATHLETIC

Secretary: John Slater, 133 Lowe Road, Clydach, Swansea (0792 842530).
Ground: The Recreation Ground, Pontardawe Trading Estate, Pontardawe (0792 862228).
Colours: Black & white/black/black.
Programme: Yes **Floodlights:** No **Cover:** Yes (100) **Seats:** No **Founded:** 1947

PONTLOTTYN BLAST FURNACE

Secretary: Barry Horsman, Wordesley, Gwerthonor Road, Gilfach, Bargoed CF8 8JS (0443 831606).
Ground: Welfare Ground, Hill Road, Pontlottyn, Mid. Glam. (0685 841305).
Colours: Yellow/green/yellow. **Change colours:** White & red stripes/red/red.
Programme: Yes **Floodlights:** No **Cover:** Yes (100) **Seats:** No **Founded:** 1968

PORTH TYWYN SUBURBS

Secretary: Colin Jenkins, 25 St.Mary's Rise, Burry Port, Dyfed SA16 0SH (0554 832109).
Ground: Parc Tywyn, Woodbrook Terrace, Burry Port, Dyfed (0554 833991).
Colours: All green **Change colours:** All red
Programme: Yes **Floodlights:** No **Cover:** No **Seats:** No

SOUTH WALES CONSTABULARY

Secretary: Alan Davies, 147 Bwlch Road, Fairwater, Cardiff CF5 3EE (0222 569105).
Ground: Police Sports Ground, Waterton Cross, Bridgend (0656 65555x218).
Colours: Red/blue/blue. **Change colours:** Yellow/blue/yellow/blue
Programme: Yes **Floodlights:** No **Cover:** No **Seats:** No **Founded:** 1969

TONDU ROBINS

Secretary: Dennis Jones, 66 Sunnyside, Bridgend, Mid. Glam. CF31 4AF (0656 658108).
Ground: Pandy Park, Aberkenfig, Bridgend, Mid. Glam (0656 720045).
Colours: All red **Change colours:** Yellow/black/black
Programme: Yes **Floodlights:** No **Cover:** No **Seats:** No **Founded:** 1897

TREHARRIS ATHLETIC

Secretary: Mike Casey, 10 Windsor Rd, Edwardsville, Treharris (0443 411153).
Ground: Athletic Ground, Commercial Terrace, Treharris, Mid. Glam.
Colours: Blue & white stripes/blue/blue **Change colours:** Yellow/black/red
Programme: Yes **Floodlights:** No **Cover:** Yes (200) **Seats:** No **Founded:** 1889

TRELEWIS WELFARE

Secretary: Kyrien Thomas, 10 West Avenue, Maesycwmmer, Hengoed, Mid. Glam. CF8 7QN (0443 862876).
Ground: The Welfare Ground, Trelewis, Mid. Glam.
Directions: Through Trelewis village heading north and take sharp right after bridge - continue past houses to end of road, across wasteland to ground. **Colours:** Red & white/red/red **Change colours:** Blue/black/blue.
Programme: Yes **Floodlights:** No **Cover:** No **Seats:** No **Founded:** 1966

MANWEB CYMRU ALLIANCE CLUBS 1993-94

BRYMBO

Secretary: N.Jones, 29 Bryn Coed, Gwersyllt, Wrexham, Clwyd, LL11 4UE (00978 753250).
Ground: Brymbo Sports Club, Tanyfron, Wrexham, (0978 755886).
Colours: Yellow/black/black **Change colours:** Black & blue/black/black
Programme: Yes **Floodlights:** No **Cover:** Yes (100) **Seats:** No **Founded:** 1943

BUCKLEY

Secretary: M.Williams, 4 Hillany Grove, Western Park, Buckley, Clwyd (0244 546893).
Ground: Maes Y Dare, Denbigh Road, Mold.
Colours: Red & blue/blue/blue. **Change colours:** Amber/black/black.
Programme: Yes **Floodlights:** Yes **Cover:** Yes **Seats:** Yes (100)

CARNO

Secretary: John Griffiths, Llwyneuron, Carno, Powys, SY17 5LT (0686 420202).
Ground: Recreation Ground, Carno, Powys.
Colours: Green/black/black. **Change colours:** Red/black/black.
Programme: Yes **Floodlights:** No **Cover:** No **Seats:** Yes (105) **Founded:** 1960

CEFN DRUIDS

Secretary: Steve Williams, 9 Beacon Road, Pendine Park, Summerhill, Wrexham LL11 4UW (0978 752489).
Ground: Plaskynaston, Cefn Mawr (0978 820004).
Colours: White/black/black **Change colours:** Yellow & green/green/green
Programme: Yes **Floodlights:** No **Cover:** Yes (300) **Seats:** No
Founded: 1992 (Merger of Cefn Albion & Druids United).

CEMAES BAY

Secretary: Mrs N.Hughes, 12 Maes Garnedd, Tregele, Anglesey, Gwynedd LL67 0DR (0407 710297).
Ground: School Lane, Cemaes Bay, Anglesey.
Colours: All red **Change colours:** All blue
Programme: Yes **Floodlights:** No **Cover:** Yes (300) **Seats:** Yes (100)

GRESFORD ATHLETIC

Secretary: D.C.Rowlands, 26 Gorse Crescent, Marford, Wrexham, Clwyd LL12 8QZ (0978 855354)
Ground: Clappers Lane, Chester Road, Gresford, Wrexham, Clwyd.
Colours: Red/white/white **Change colours:** All green
Programme: Yes **Floodlights:** No **Cover:** Yes (75) **Seats:** No **Founded:** 1946

KNIGHTON TOWN

Secretary: W.J.Rollason, "Brynoffa", Conjour's Drive, Knighton, Powys LD7 1EP (0547 520356).
Ground: Bryn Y Castell, Knighton, Powys (0547 528339).
Colours: All red **Change colours:** Yellow/black/black
Programme: Yes **Floodlights:** Yes **Cover:** No **Seats:** Yes (100) **Founded:** 1881

LEX XI

Secretary: Phil Jones, 18 Mayflower Drive, Marford, Wrexham, Clwyd LL12 8LD (0978 854028).
Ground: Stansty Park, Mold Road, Wrexham (0978 261351).
Colours: Amber/black/black & amber **Change colours:** White/white/red
Programme: Yes **Floodlights:** No **Cover:** Yes (75) **Seats:** No **Founded:** 1965

LLANDUDNO

Secretary: E.B.Jarvis, 10 Howard Road, Llandudno, Gwynedd, LL30 1EA (0492 877113).
Ground: Maesdu Park, Maesdu Road, Llandudno.
Colours: White/navy blue/white **Change colours:** Red/navy/white
Programme: Yes **Floodlights:** No **Cover:** Yes (150) **Seats:** No

LLANIDLOES TOWN

Secretary: G.E.Parry, 22 Llysnant, Llanidloes, Powys, SY18 6BD (0551 225500).
Ground: Victoria Park, Victoria Avenue, Llanidloes (0551 222196).
Colours: Yellow/green/yellow **Change colours:** Green/white/white
Programme: Yes **Floodlights:** Yes **Cover:** Yes (100) **Seats:** Yes (240) **Founded:** 1875

MOSTYN

Secretary: Bryn Hughes, 11 Penrho Estate, Mostyn, Clwyd CH8 9QS (0745 560822).
Ground: Maes Pennant, Mostyn.
Colours: Red & black/black/black **Change colours:** Yellow & blue/blue/blue
Programme: Yes **Floodlights:** No **Cover:** Yes (100) **Seats:** No **Founded:** 1912

PENRHYNCOCH
Secretary: Rolant Ellis, 4 Maes Laura, Aberystwyth, Dyfed SY23 2AU (0970 617171).
Ground: Cae Baker, Penrhyncoch (0970 828992).
Colours: Yellow/blue/yellow   **Change colours:** Red/black/red
Programme: Yes   **Floodlights:** No   **Cover:** Yes (100)   **Seats:** No   **Founded:** 1965

RHAYADER TOWN
Secretary: Phil Woosman, 'Highlands', St.Harmon Road, Rhayader, Powys LD6 5PN (0597 811286).
Ground: The Weirglodd, Rhayader.
Colours: Red & white/white/red   **Change colours:** Claret & blue/blue/blue
Programme: Yes   **Floodlights:** Yes   **Cover:** Yes (250)   **Seats:** Yes (120)

RHOS AELWYD
Secretary: D.Parry, "Penrallt", Queen Street, Rhos, Wrexham LL14 1PY (0978 845148).
Ground: Ponciau Park, Clarke Street, Ponciau.
Colours: Blue & black stripes/black/black   **Change colours:** All green
Programme: Yes   **Floodlights:** No   **Cover:** No   **Seats:** No   **Founded:** 1948

RHYL
Secretary: A.R.Hayes, 83 Grange Road, Rhyl, Clwyd LL18 4BT (0745 330264)
Ground: Belle Vue, Grange Road, Rhyl (0745 338327).
Colours: All white   **Change colours:** red & black stripe/black/red
Programme: Yes   **Floodlights:** Yes   **Cover:** Yes (1,250)   **Seats:** Yes (200)   **Founded:** 1928

RUTHIN TOWN
Secretary: B.Lewis, 40 Maeshafod, Ruthin, Clwyd LL15 1LS (0824 702828).
Ground: Memorial Playing Fields, Parc-y-Dre, Ruthin (0824 702766).
Colours: Blue & white stripes/blue/blue   **Change colours:** All red
Programme: Yes   **Floodlights:** No   **Cover:** No   **Seats:** No   **Founded:** 1951

WELSHPOOL
Secretary: J.A.Bartley, 24 Bryn Glas, Welshpool, Powys SY21 7TL (0938 552131)
Ground: Maesydre, Welshpool, Powys.
Colours: White/black/white   **Change colours:** Red/navy/navy
Programme: Yes   **Floodlights:** No   **Cover:** Yes (100)   **Seats:** No   **Founded:** 1878

WREXHAM RES
Secretary: David Rhodes, The Racecourse Ground, Mold Road, Wrexham Clwyd LL11 2AN (0978 262129).
Ground: The Racecourse Ground, Mold Road, Wrexham (0978 262129).
Colours: Red/white/red   **Change colours:** Yellow & green/green/green
Programme: Yes   **Floodlights:** Yes   **Cover:** Yes (11,000)   **Seats:** Yes (6,000)   **Founded:** 1873

MISCELLANEOUS WELSH LEAGUES

SAIN CAERNARFON & DISTRICT LGE

	P	W	D	L	F	A	PTS
Caernarfon Ath.	30	28	1	1	117	20	85
Deiniolen	30	26	3	1	101	27	81
Talysdarn	30	17	3	10	60	37	54
Bethesda Ath.	30	14	7	9	65	51	49
Llanystumdwy	30	15	2	3	59	61	47
Nefyn United	30	13	6	11	74	73	45
Harlech Town	30	13	6	11	67	71	45
Nantlle Vale	30	12	4	14	59	55	40
Llanrug United	30	12	4	14	70	79	40
Loco Llanberis	30	10	8	12	62	64	38
Mountain Rgrs	30	9	7	14	61	77	34
Y Felinheli	30	7	9	14	45	68	30
Caernarfon Borough	30	8	5	17	61	86	29
Porthmadog Junior	30	7	3	20	52	85	24
Bangor University	30	4	7	19	42	96	19
P'draeth	30	6	3	21	46	91	*18

* - pt(s) deducted

MOORE SCOTT MID WALES LEAGUE

	P	W	D	L	F	A	PTS
Penybont	26	18	6	2	76	20	60
Hay St.Marys	26	17	6	3	94	42	57
Builth Wells Res	26	17	4	5	79	38	55
Crickhowell	26	16	5	5	86	41	53
Rhayader Res	26	12	9	5	54	33	45
Kington Res.	26	12	8	6	48	44	44
Radnor Valley	26	8	9	9	58	43	33
Newcastle	26	8	9	9	40	38	33
Clun Res.	26	10	1	15	39	82	31
Llandrindod Res.	26	8	4	14	45	65	28
Bucknell	26	8	3	15	42	62	27
Presteigne Res.	26	5	5	16	39	74	20
Newbridge	26	3	6	17	33	76	15
Vale of Arrow Res.	26	2	1	23	24	98	7

OCS CLWYD LEAGUE

	P	W	D	L	F	A	PTS
St.Asaph City	24	18	3	3	78	33	57
Prestatyn Town	24	14	9	1	99	30	51
Point of Ayr	24	15	3	6	85	48	48
Denbigh Town	24	13	7	4	68	41	46
Flint Town Utd	24	13	4	7	83	35	43
Colwyn Bay YMCA	24	11	8	5	69	38	41
Abbey Life	24	12	2	10	63	52	38
Holywell Town R.	24	9	6	9	53	45	33
Connahs Quay Alb*	24	8	2	14	68	66	23
Rhuddlan Town	24	5	7	12	43	52	22
Abergele Celts	24	4	4	16	33	62	16
Connahs Q.RAFA*	24	3	4	17	32	100	7
Trefnant Village	24	1	1	22	19	191	4

THE B & M ROOFING ANGLESEY LEAGUE

	P	W	D	L	F	A	PTS
Llangefni T. Res.	34	31	1	2	145	36	94
Gwalchmai	34	25	4	5	119	44	79
Holyhead Mt. Rgrs	34	25	3	6	122	42	78
Holyhead Hotspur	34	24	4	6	109	52	73
Llandegfan	34	23	3	8	115	47	72
Cemaes Bay Res.	34	17	4	13	88	70	55
Llanfairpwll	34	15	7	12	74	54	52
Amlwch	34	16	3	15	93	81	51
Treaddur Bay	34	15	5	14	63	61	50
Moelfre	34	15	3	16	67	70	48
Gaerwen	34	13	5	16	96	83	44
R.A.F. Valley	34	12	6	16	44	85	42
Holyhead Town	34	10	7	17	61	90	37
Bodedern	34	10	5	19	58	104	35
Llangoed	34	6	4	24	52	105	22
Bryngwran Bulls	34	4	5	25	55	123	19
Beaumaris Town	34	3	5	26	42	94	14
Glantreath Res.	34	4	1	29	48	207	13

SCOTTISH NON-LEAGUE FOOTBALL

HIGHLAND LEAGUE

	P	W	D	L	F	A	PTS
Elgin City	34	24	5	5	110	35	77
Cove Rangers	34	23	4	7	78	37	73
Lossiemouth	34	21	6	7	105	54	69
Caledonian	34	21	6	7	76	41	69
Ross County	34	19	7	8	87	49	64
Huntly	34	19	5	10	96	55	62
Clachnacuddin	34	17	7	10	47	34	58
Inverness Thistle	34	17	6	11	55	50	57
Buckie Thistle	34	17	4	13	62	55	55
Fraserburgh	34	15	7	12	63	52	52
Deveronvale	34	14	4	16	57	71	46
Keith	34	12	9	13	46	59	45
Brora Rangers	34	11	8	15	72	74	41
Peterhead	34	8	10	16	61	80	34
Rothes	34	4	8	22	42	104	20
Fort William	34	5	4	25	37	89	19
Forres Mechanics	34	4	6	24	40	94	18
Nairn County	34	1	2	31	26	126	5

League Championship withheld

SOUTH OF SCOTLAND

	P	W	D	L	F	A	PTS
Threave Rovers	22	15	3	4	76	32	33
Dalbeattie Star	22	15	2	5	74	29	32
Wigtown & B'noch	22	15	2	5	47	27	32
St.Cuthbert's W.	22	12	4	6	66	42	28
Blackwood D'moes	22	11	3	8	55	55	25
Queen of the S''A'	22	12	0	10	77	40	24
Maxwelltown H.S.FP	22	9	3	10	57	53	21
Newton Stewart	22	9	2	11	63	62	20
Girvan Amateurs	22	9	2	11	62	64	20
Annan Athletic 'A'	22	5	2	15	43	84	12
Tarff Rovers	22	3	4	15	29	82	10
Creetown	22	2	3	17	25	104	7

EAST OF SCOTLAND

PREM. DIVISION	P	W	D	L	F	A	PTS
Whitehall	18	10	7	1	46	23	27
Spartans	18	9	5	4	27	20	23
Gala F'dean	18	9	4	5	27	20	22
Vale of L'then	18	9	3	6	35	25	21
Edinburgh City	18	7	7	4	31	29	21
Easthouses L.	18	4	9	5	27	33	17
Craigroyston	18	6	4	8	30	27	16
Manor Thistle	18	4	7	7	29	33	15
Tollcross United	18	3	7	8	27	33	13
Goldstream	18	0	5	13	17	52	5

EAST OF SCOTLAND

DIVISION ONE	P	W	D	L	F	A	PTS
CS Strollers	18	11	4	3	46	21	26
Anna Athletic	18	12	2	4	38	27	26
Hawick RA	18	11	3	4	53	29	25
Kelso United	18	9	5	4	43	26	23
Edinburgh University	18	8	6	4	37	20	22
Pencaitland	18	7	7	4	29	20	21
Peebles Rovers	18	5	3	10	16	45	13
Selkirk	18	3	4	11	31	49	10
Heriot Watt Un.	18	3	3	12	26	44	9
Eyemouth United	18	1	3	14	25	63	5

SCOTTISH QUALIFYING CUP

NORTH
First Round

Cove Rangers v Nairn County	11-0
Fraserburgh v Buckie Thistle	2-2,4-3
Keith v Elgin City	0-3
Peterhead v Rothes	3-1

Second Round

Cove Rangers v Lossiemouth	2-1
Elgin City v Inverness Caley	1-2
Fort Williams v Clach	1-3
Fraserburgh v Ross County	0-1
Golspie S. v Inverness Thistle	0-4
Huntly v Deveronvale	1-0
Peterhead v Brora Rangers	2-1
Wick Academy v Forres Mechanics	2-3

Third Round

Forres Mechanics v Huntly	1-4
Inverness Thistle v Clach	1-0
Peterhead v Inverness Caley	1-0
Ross County v Cove Rangers	1-3

Semi-final

Inverness Thistle v Huntly	0-3
Peterhead v Cove Rangers	0-0, 2-3

Final

November 14th at Inverness Thistle.

Cove Rangers v Huntly	2-2, (3-5 pens)

SOUTH
First Round

Annan Athletic v Selkirk	4-0
St. Cuthbert W. v Coldstream	3-0
Taraff Rovers v Wigtown & B.	1-2

Second Round

Burntland S. v St. Cuthbert W.	6-1
Dalbeattie S. v C.S.Strollers	1-2
Gala F. v Glasgow University	2-1
Girvan Amateurs v Edinbrugh University	2-2, 4-1
Newton Stewart v Wigtown & B.	1-4
Threave Rovers v Hawick R.A.	3-1
Vale of Leithen v Annan Athletic	6-2
Whitehill W. v Spartans	0-1

Third Round

Burntisland S. v C.S.Strollers	2-5
Gala F. v Threave Rovers	6-1
Vale of Leithen v Girvan Amateurs	2-1
Wigtown & B. v Spartans	1-2

Semi final

Gala F. v C.S.Strollers	2-0
Vale of Leithen v Spartans	5-0

Final

November 28th at Gala F. FC

Gala f. v Vale of Leithen	0-4

SCOTTISH JUNIOR LEAGUES

'ROYAL LIFE' AYRSHIRE AMATEUR LEAGUE

NORTH DIVISION 1	P	W	D	L	F	A	PTS
Knockentiber	22	16	5	1	59	18	37
Ardrossan CR	22	16	0	6	51	31	32
Shortlees	22	14	3	5	69	37	31
Clark Drive	22	10	7	5	49	30	27
Beith Amateurs	22	10	6	6	44	46	26
Girdle Toll U.*	22	9	4	9	51	42	22
West Kilbride	22	6	7	9	32	49	19
Irvine Thistle	22	6	6	10	45	52	18
Johnnie Walker	22	7	3	12	36	48	17
Calderglen	22	6	4	12	35	51	16
Lochran Amateurs	22	2	6	14	43	78	10
Garnock Lab.Club	22	4	1	17	38	70	9

CENTRAL REGION

PREM. DIVISION	P	W	D	L	F	A	PTS
Petershill	22	18	1	3	44	22	37
Pollok	22	12	3	7	45	33	27
Lesmahagow	22	10	6	6	50	31	26
Shotts BA	22	9	7	6	37	34	25
Glencairn	22	8	7	7	43	33	23
Shettleston	22	7	9	6	41	35	23
Renfrew	22	7	8	7	33	33	22
Arthurlie	22	8	5	9	39	40	21
Cambuslang R.	22	6	7	9	24	39	19
Neilston	22	6	6	10	26	35	18
Vale of Clyde	22	4	6	12	22	48	14
Kilsyth Rangers	22	3	3	16	13	34	9

EAST REGION
JOHN WALKER LEAGUE

DIVISION ONE	P	W	D	L	F	A	PTS
Fauldhouse Utd	22	14	5	3	57	38	33
Whitburn	22	12	5	5	50	37	29
Newtongrange S.	22	11	6	5	48	25	28
Camelon	22	11	4	7	40	31	26
Bo'ness United	22	10	6	6	35	29	26
Linlithgow Rose	22	8	7	7	50	45	23
Livingston Utd	22	5	8	9	37	45	18
Armdale Thistle	22	5	8	9	33	41	18
Edinburgh Utd	22	7	4	11	30	39	18
Bonnyrigg Rose	22	5	7	10	38	47	17
Bathgate Thistle	22	5	6	11	31	38	16
Bonnybridge	22	4	4	14	23	57	12

FYFE REGION

	P	W	D	L	F	A	PTS
Kelty Hearts	26	22	3	1	82	32	47
Hill of Beath H.	26	19	4	3	73	33	42
St.Andrews Utd	26	14	6	6	44	25	34
Newburgh	26	13	6	7	61	45	32
Rosyth Recreation	26	10	9	7	49	48	29
Oakley United	26	11	4	11	57	56	26
Dundonald B'bell	26	10	5	11	53	48	25
Lochore Welfare	26	11	3	12	60	55	25
Thornton Hibs	26	10	5	11	51	50	25
Glenrothes	26	8	4	14	45	55	20
Lochgelly Albert	26	4	11	11	51	68	19
Crossgates P'rose	26	7	2	17	40	65	16
Clackmannan	26	4	4	18	32	71	12
Tulliallan Thistle	26	2	8	16	37	84	12

TAYSIDE REGION

DIVISION ONE	P	W	D	L	F	A	PTS
Tayport	26	21	4	1	79	18	46
Forfar West End	26	16	7	3	62	33	39
Downfield	26	16	5	5	65	24	37
Forfar Albion	26	13	7	6	49	35	33
Jeanfield Swifts	26	13	4	4	53	39	30
Arbroath SC	26	13	3	10	63	48	29
Kinnoull	26	11	7	8	46	48	29
North End	26	12	4	10	48	48	28
Carnoustie P'mure	26	7	8	11	50	53	22
Lochee Harp	26	7	5	14	38	53	19
Violet	26	6	4	16	38	77	16
Lochee United	26	5	5	16	37	71	15
East Cragie	26	4	3	19	30	74	11
Kirrie Thistle	26	2	6	18	41	78	10

METRIK OFFICE SUPPLIES
DUMFRIES & DISTRICT AMATEUR LEAGUE

DIVISION ONE	P	W	D	L	F	A	PTS
Dumfries YM	22	14	4	4	55	29	32
L'cluden Colt	22	15	1	6	62	41	31
Abbey Vale	22	12	6	4	66	31	30
Dumfries HSFP	22	9	6	7	63	39	24
Upper An'dale	22	10	4	8	46	48	24
Nithsdale	22	9	5	8	45	42	23
Dumf. Acad FP	22	9	5	8	63	65	23
Galloway Rovers	22	7	7	8	41	40	21
Kirkconnel	22	6	5	11	44	58	17
Lochmaben	22	6	3	13	43	70	15
Lochar Thistle	22	4	6	12	32	53	14
Hoddom Rangers	22	3	4	15	28	72	10

Name	No.
Capel	580
Capenhurst	907
Cardiff Civil Service	1076
Cardiff Corinthians	1077
Cardiff Inst. H.E.	1078
Caribbean Int. Sports	444
Carlisle City	1019
Carlisle Gillford Park	1019
Carlton Athletic	963
Carlton Athletic	971
Carmarthen Town	1077
Carnforth Rangers	916
Carno	1079
Carrow	642
Carshalton Athletic	291
Carterton Town	736
Castle	580
Castle Cary	777
Castleton Gabriels	897
Catford Wanderers	373
Catsfield	587
Cavalier Club	981
Caversham Park	425
Cefn Druids	wel
Cemaes Bay	wel
Centrax	793
Chadderton	890
Chagford	781
Chailey	593
Chalfont St Peter	319
Chalfont Wasps	421
Channings Wood	793
Chard Town	770
Charfield	752
Charlton United	744
Charlwood	415
Charnock Richard	916
Chasetown	679
Chatburn	918
Chatham Town	600
Chatteris Town	627
Cheadle Town	898
Cheam Village Warriors	415
Checkendon Sports	425
Cheddar	778
Chelmsford City	486
Chelmsley Town	699
Chelston	791
Cheltenham Saracens	737
Cheltenham Town	487
Chequers Fladbury	718
Chertsey Town	338
Chesham United	292
Cheshunt	353
Cheslyn Hay	687
Chessington & Hook U.	413
Chessington White Hart	415
Chester-le-Street Town	990
Chichester City	558
Chichester Hospital	580
Chingford Town Wdrs	373
Chinnor	421
Chippenham Borough	821
Chippenham Town	765
Chipperfield Corinthians	381
Chipping Norton Town	743
Chipping Sodbury	753
Chipstead	396
Chipstead 'A'	415
Chiseldon	820
Chobham	405
Chorley	841
Chorlton Town	911
Christchurch	808
Christleton	907
Chudleigh Athletic	792
Church Stretton Town	728
Churchill Club '70	778
Churston Ferrers	792
Ciba-Geigy	580
Cinderford Town	734
Circle	390
Cirencester Towm	734
Cirencester United	738
City & Sherwood Hosp.	963
Clacton Town	634
Clancey Dudley	724
Clandown	779
Clanfield	738
Clapton	353
Clapton Villa	373
Classic Inter	374
Claverham	586
Clavering	444
Clayton	594
Cleator Moor Celtic	1008
Clevedon Town	510
Clevedon United	777
Clifton All Whites	964
Clifton Athletic	918
Clipstone Welfare	962
Clitheroe	890
Clutton	779
Clymping	580
Clyst Rovers	770
Clyst Valley	788
Cobham	396
Cobham 'A'	415
Cockfosters	588
Cocking	580
Codicote	384
Cogenhoe United	658
Colden Common	824
Coleford United	751
Coleshill Town	699
Colets Green	706
Collier Row	340
Colliers Wood United	413
Colne British Legion	916
Colne United	918
Colney Heath	381
Coltishall H.V.	642
Colts '85	616
Column	728
Colwall Rangers	728
Colwyn Bay	842
Combined '89	792
Compton	425
Compton	828
Concord Rangers	432
Coney Hall	413
Congleton Hornets	721
Congleton Town	863
Congresbury	777
Connahs Quay Nomads	1072
Consett	990
Continental Star	712
Conwy United	1072
Cookham Dean	425
Cooksons	718
Corby Town	488
Corinthian	601
Corinthian Casuals	368
Corinthians	580
Cornard United	627
Corsham Town	820
Cotgrave Colliery Welfare	962
Cotmanhay	959
Cotswold	425
Cottesmore Amateurs	715
Cottingham	666
Cove	354
Covies	828
Cowes Sports	824
Cowfold	580
Cox Green	425
Cradley Town	680
Crag Road United	976
Cranbrook Town	586
Cranfield United	468
Cranleigh	397
Craven	373
Crawley Down Village	593
Crawley Town	489
Cray Valley	373
Cray Wanderers	601
Crediton United	765
Crescent Rovers	413
Cressing A.F.C.	444
Cricklade Town	822
Crockenhill	601
Crompton	921
Crook Town	999
Crosshills	918
Crowborough Athletic	558
Crowland Town	670
Crowthorne Sports	425
Croxley Guild	382
Croydon	320
Croydon Athletic	369
Croydon M.O.	405
Crusaders	745
Cuckfield	593
Cuffley	382
Cullompton Rangers	782
Curzon Ashton	864
Cwmbran Town	1072
D.C.A. Basingstoke	397
D.M.S. Cuckfield	594
D.R.G.	748
Dagenham & Redbridge	163
Danbury Trafford	443
Danehill	595
Danson Furness Utd	602
Darenth Heathside	602
Darlaston	680
Darlington C.S.	999
Dartford	602
Dartington Hall	794
Dartington United	791
Dartmouth United	791
Dartmouth Y.M.R.C.	791
Darwen	890
Daventry Town	453
Dawlish Town	770
De Havilland	469
Deal Town	602
Deanshangers Athletic	468
Dedham Old Boys	644
Deeping Rangers	670
Delco Products	469
Denaby & Cadeby M.W.	768
Denaby United	930
Denham United	425
Derby Arms	959
Derby C & W Reckitts	956
Derby Rolls Royce	956
Dereham Town	627
Desborough Town	660
Devizes Town	770
Devon & Cornwall Police	796
Dewsbury Moor Ath.	973
Didcot Town	738
Diss Town	627
Dittisham United	793
Ditton	398
Doddinghurst	443
Donnington Park	728
Donnington Wood	687
Dorcan	821
Dorchester Town	490
Dorking	293
Dormansland Rockets	595
Dover Athletic	169
Down Ampney	822
Downes Sports	715
Downham Town	634
Downton	808
Dowty Dynamos	748
Draycott	959
Drayton Park	826
Drayton Wanderers	421
Droitwich	718
Droylsden	843
Dudley Hill Athletic	978
Dudley Sports	706
Dudley Town	511
Dudley Welfare	1020
Dukinfield Town	920
Dulwich Hamlet	294
Dunbar Wills	821
Dundry Athletic	777
Dunkirk	962
Dunstable	537
Dunston Fed. Brewery	990
Durgates	588
Durham City	991
Dursley Town	751
Dynamics Stevenage	384
Dynamo C.E.F.	587
Dynamoes	979
Eagley	916
Earl Shilton Albion	716
Earlbourne	425
Earls Barton United	472
Earlswood Town	709
Easington Colliery	999
Easington Sports	738
Easington United	982
East Allington United	794
East Cowes Victoria Ath.	808
East Dean	581
East End Park W.M.C.	972
East End United	581
East Grinstead	560
East Grinstead Mariners	595
East Ham United	434
East Hoathley	587
East Manchester	920
East Preston	574
East Thurrock United	355
Eastbourne Fishermen	585
Eastbourne Rose & Cn	586
Eastbourne Town	560
Eastbourne United	566
Eastergate United	581
Eastleigh	808
Eastmoor Albion	978
Eastwood Hanley	890
Eastwood Town	865
Eaton Bray	469
Eaton United	472
Ebbw Vale	1072
Ecchinswell	826
Eccleshall	721
Eccleshill United	930
Edenstone	616
Edgware Town	340
Edwards Sports	574
Egham Town	341
Ekco Sports & Social	443
Elburton Villa	782
Ellesmere Port Town	898
Ellesmere Rangers	728
Elliott Star	382
Ellwood	748
Elmer Beach	581
Elmore	765
Ely City	635
Emberton	468
Emley	844
Emmbrook Sports Club	425
Emsworth	581
Endsleigh	748
Enfield	295
Englefield	425
Enville Athletic	709
Eppingsale	444
Eppleton C.W.	992
Epsom & Ewell	355
Erith & Belvedere	538
Esh Winning	999
Esh Winning Albion	1012
Essex Police	442
Esso Fawley	828
Eton Manor	434
Eton Wick	398
Ettingshall Holy Trinity	687
Evenwood Town	1000
Evergreen	384
Eversley Rangers	414
Evesham United	512
Ewyas Harold United	728
Ex-Blues	616
Exeter City 'A'	788
Exeter Civil Service	788
Exmouth Amateurs	788
Exmouth Town	765
Eye United	670
Eynesbury Rovers	660
Eynsham	743
Fairfield Villa	709
Fairford Town	734
Fairham	964
Fairwarp	594
Fakenham Town	627
Falmouth Town	796
Fareham Town	539
Farleigh Rovers	398
Farleigh Sports	779
Farnborough Town	491
Farnham Town	399
Farnley	976
Farsley Celtic	866
Faversham Town	604
Featherstone Colliery	972
Feckenham United	718
Felbridge	594
Felixstowe Town	627
Feltham & Hounslow	356
Feniscowles	916
Ferndale Ath. Wilts	820
Ferndale Ath. Wales	1076
Fernhurst Sports	581
Ferring	581
Ferrybridge Amateurs	976
Ferryhill Athletic	992
Fetcham	414
Field	976
Fields Pk Pontllanfraith	1077
Finchampstead	420
Firehills	588
Fisher '93	540
Fittleworth	581
Flackwell Heath	356
Flamstead	470
Fleet Spurs	826
Fleet Town	808
Fleetlands	824
Fleetwood Hesketh	916
Fleetwood Town	845
Flight Refuelling	817
Flint Town United	1073
Flixton	892
Folkestone Invicta	604
Ford Sports	666
Ford United - Essex	434
Ford United - Sussex	581
Forest	575
Forest Green Rovers	513
Forest Hall S.C.	1020
Forest Hill	745
Forest Old Boys	425
Forest Row	594
Formby	898
Fosse Imps	716
Fownhope	728
Foxhill	918
Foxhole Stars	801
Foxhole United	792
Framlingham Town	648
Frampton Athletic	753
Frampton United	751
Frank Ford	974
Franklands Village	575
Frant	587
Frecheville C.A.	968
Freckleton	916
Friar Lane Old Boys	715
Frickley Athletic	846
Friends' Provident	581
Frilsham & Yattendon	426
Frimley Green	399
Frinton Rovers	405
Fritwell	745
Frome Town	766
Fry Club	777
Fulwood Amateurs	916
G.D.S. Valmar	384
G.E.C. Stafford	724
G.N. Prince Phillips	972
G.P.T.	962
G.P.T. Coventry	709
Gainsborough Trinity	847
Gala Wilton	752
Galleywood	444
Galmpton United	792
Garforth Town	938
Garforth W.M.C.	974
Garsington	743
Garswood United	911
Garw	1077
Gas Recreation	644
Gascoigne United	972
Gateshead	175
Gateshead Durham R.	1022
Gateshead Northern C.	1021
Gedling Colliery Wel.	963